Revised Edition

THE ARBUTHNOT ANTHOLOGY

OF CHILDREN'S LITERATURE

This book is affectionately dedicated

to my niece

Margaret Elizabeth Hill

THE ARBUTHNOT ANTHOLOGY OF CHILDREN'S LITERATURE is composed principally
of three books: TIME FOR POETRY, Copyright © 1961, 1952 by Scott, Foresman
and Company; TIME FOR FAIRY TALES OLD AND NEW, Copyright © 1961, 1952 by Scott,
Foresman and Company; and TIME FOR TRUE TALES AND ALMOST TRUE, Copyright © 1961,
1953 by Scott, Foresman and Company.

PREFACE
TO THE REVISED EDITION

The Arbuthnot Anthology was planned as a source book for classes in children's literature and as a collection of materials to be enjoyed with children in homes, camps, and school-rooms. It has fulfilled these purposes so satisfactorily that a revision was undertaken only after long deliberation. As did the first edition, the revision presents a balanced offering of different types of literature for children of all ages and tastes. Here is a great variety of poems, folk tales, modern fairy tales, myth, epic, fables, realistic stories of many kinds, with nonsense and humor balanced by hero tales and biographies of noble and dedicated men.

Poetry

There are 95 new poems in this edition with 735 poems in all. These range from nonsense and light verse to ballads and fine lyric poetry. There are more selections for the older children than there were and more of the old favorites, as well as many new selections by modern poets that adults and children should enjoy together. The introduction, "Reading Poetry to Children," and the comments in the footnotes give many suggestions for presenting these poems and sharing them with children.

Choral speaking

Because of the increasing interest in and use of verse choirs or choral speaking, an entirely new section has been added on the techniques of launching and conducting verse choirs with children of different ages. In addition to the detailed step-by-step description of how to develop choral speaking, many patterns for presenting individual poems are provided. Often several ways of casting a specific poem are given, including an easy way for a young or inexperienced

group and a more complex and subtle form for an experienced or older choir. Children find the singing words of poetry tremendously exhilarating to speak together and thoroughly enjoy their verse choir experiences in Sunday schools, camps, and, of course, classrooms.

Fairy tales

The *Anthology* also contains a rich collection of fairy tales, the name children give to all stories of magic or make-believe, however lacking they may be in fairies. Oddly enough, in this mechanistic age, fantasy is enormously popular with children, who dream of space travel as their parents dreamed of a new bicycle. To satisfy our dream-hungry children, this section of the *Anthology* has been enlarged numerically and expanded geographically. The myths, fables, and epics are here as well as the old folk tales with their wish-fulfilling charm and their ideals of bravery, kindness, and beauty that is more than skin-deep. More countries are represented by folk tales and new and scholarly collections have been the sources for some of the additions. Distinguished examples of recent fantasies are also included.

Storytelling and reading aloud

Because the folk tales were created by anonymous storytellers and kept alive by oral tradition, a detailed discussion of storytelling and reading aloud has been included. Suggestions are given for the quickest method of learning a story, for telling or reading aloud most effectively, and for determining which stories should be told and which read. The four section introductions and the headnotes to the individual selections in *Fairy Tales* also provide suggestions for presenting the stories.

To cope with the triviality and violence of much of our mass media of entertainment today, children need to meet in their literature examples of a gay, courageous dealing with life's problems, gentleness that is strong, and selfless heroism. Such examples in biography or realistic stories make a tremendous impression on young readers; the characters in a story or a biography may become as real to the reader as members of his own family. So here are interesting and moving stories of the here and now, of other lands and other times, of hard-pressed animals and of men and women who lived and struggled gallantly. Such literature brings children ideals without preaching, and memorable characters as convincing and as varied as life itself. Nine new stories add distinction to this section of the *Anthology* and will have wide appeal to children.

A history of picture books

"The Development of the Modern Picture Book" is a completely new section. The child's picture book cannot be reproduced in its entirety in an anthology—text, pictures, and format. Yet for young children these books constitute an important introduction both to literature and to art. No anthology would be complete without a sampling of them, text and pictures, and their history provides a fascinating glimpse of periods, customs, countries, the children themselves, and adult attitudes toward them. So *The Arbuthnot Anthology* contains the entire text of a number of picture-stories as well as illustrations from a wide range of picture books, either in black and white or color. "The Development of the Modern Picture Book" traces the history of picture-book art from small, crude, early woodcuts to the lavish color illustrations of the picture books of the last half-century. Grownups will find much in this section to tell children about their favorite artists, and children of all ages will enjoy the pictures and want to see the books.

Milestones in children's books

"Milestones in Children's Books" is also a new section. It has been added to the *Anthology*

for the convenience of adults and to pique the curiosity of children, whose time sense develops slowly. The chronology of children's books is full of surprises. For instance, the fact that *Aesop's Fables* was printed in England before Columbus discovered America should startle older children and grownups into a new respect for these ancient moralities. Adults are generally amazed to discover that *Peter Rabbit* is over sixty years old. Yet children enjoy it today as wholeheartedly as they enjoy *Babar* or *The Happy Lion*. Chiefly, of course, this section is for students of children's literature. It furnishes not merely dates and a chronology of landmarks in children's books, but tantalizing clues to trends, relationships, and unpredictable innovations. Disagreements over precise dates are inevitable because some sources give the date of writing, others the date of copywriting or first publication or publication in the United States. When reliable references and even librarians disagree it is indeed "a puzzlement." These dates have been checked and double-checked, but apparently unanimity is impossible.

Here then, is an overall view of the revised *Arbuthnot Anthology*. Almost all of the poetry and stories in the original edition are retained and choice new or recent materials have been added. The result is a well-proportioned collection of poetry and prose old and new for children of all ages. There is a variety of information to help in using these materials with children. The introductions to sections will be of special help to students of children's literature and to any adult who would like to know something about the books, artists, and authors so beloved by children. The extensive annotated bibliography has been brought up to date. Finally, to the children themselves these stories and poems will bring magic and make-believe, people true as true, nonsense and heroism, laughter and nobility, in short, a look at life with goodness and beauty uppermost.

May Hill Arbuthnot

Cleveland, 1960

CONTENTS

The three books Time for Poetry, Time for Fairy Tales Old and New, *and* Time for True Tales and Almost True *have been combined to make up* The Arbuthnot Anthology of Children's Literature. *In the table of contents* Time for Poetry *is designated as Book One;* Time for Fairy Tales, *Book Two; and* Time for True Tales, *Book Three. Each book is numbered beginning with page 1. To help the reader find his way around in the text, there are brown divider pages indicating where Books Two and Three begin. At the bottom of each text page the title of the book is given beside the page number. In the Index (p. 444), the entries for Book One:* Time for Poetry *are designated by* P; *those for Book Two:* Time for Fairy Tales *by* FT; *and those for Book Three:* Time for True Tales *by* TT.

Book One: Time for Poetry

THE ANIMAL FAIR 44

Book Two: Time for Fairy Tales old and new

Book Three: Time for True Tales and almost true

The following titles were supplied by the compiler for untitled chapters or excerpts: A Collie Finds His Work, A Tramp and a Baby Skunk, Mr. Kildee Makes Friends with Old Grouch, First Adventures of a Young Raccoon, The Wild Rams Find a Friend, New Life on the Mountains, Tragedy, The Rescue, A New Act for the Circus, Hat Trouble, Going South, The Academy Versus the High School, Everything Is Different, A Hobo Adventure, School Troubles in Ancient Greece, Robin Turns Actor, The Play's the Thing, Captured by the Abenaki, A Calm Before the Storm, Boy into Man, "That a Man Can Stand Up," Lee at West Point

THE DEVELOPMENT OF THE MODERN PICTURE BOOK

No one can walk into a bookstore today and not be struck by the beauty of picture books for young children. Compared with these alluring books, the illustrated books for older children are tame indeed. Grownups entranced by the latest adventures of Ludwig Bemelmans' *Madeline* or some new edition of Mother Goose are likely to remark, "We never had such picture books when we were children"—a true statement if the speaker has passed the half-century mark. Indeed, the glorious illustrations we know today were nonexistent fifty years ago, although there were picture books long before that.

The development from small crude woodcuts in older books to handsome color prints in books of all sizes and varieties is a fascinating study, and an important one. Picture books may reflect the art and customs of a period or a country; certainly they reveal the attitudes of adults toward the needs and interests of young children. Since picture books cannot be reproduced as a whole in an anthology, it seems worth while to represent this important area of children's literature by a brief discussion of the varieties of picture books and the history of their development and the artists' unique contributions to this special field. The books discussed and the pictures reproduced here provide a fair sampling of the art and literature created for children over the years.

What is a picture book?

In her discriminating evaluation of the art of the picture book as it is found in the books of the Caldecott Medal winners, Esther Averill makes this distinction:

> In an illustrated book the pictures are, as the term "illustrated" implies, a mere extension—illumination—of the text. In a picture book, as the term also implies, the pictures play a livelier role, and are an integral part of the action of the book.[1]

The "livelier role" generally means more pictures and a more complete interdependence between pictures and text than is true in an illustrated book. Indeed one test of a true picture book is that, after a few hearing-and-looking experiences, the prereading child can "read" the book from the pictures. This happens in every nursery school and kindergarten with such books as Wanda Gág's *Millions of Cats* or Robert McCloskey's *Make Way for Ducklings*.

Obviously then, the picture book is limited in its age appeal; generally, it is for the prereaders from two to seven years old. Children who can read fluently still like the picture books secretly but don't like to admit it or to be seen enjoying one because, as they say, "It's baby stuff." Yet from the standpoint of the author or artist, the production of a lively, absorbing picture book is so difficult that many notable artists never attempt it. Hence in this discussion, a few major artists in the children's book field may be omitted simply because they have never tried their hand at a picture book for the youngest.

[1] Esther Averill, "What Is a Picture Book?" in *Caldecott Medal Books: 1938–1957*, ed. by Bertha Mahony Miller and Elinor Whitney Field, Horn Book Papers (Boston: Horn Book, 1957), II, 307.

Of the many varieties of picture books the picture-story is undoubtedly the children's favorite. It differs from a story with illustrations not only because it has a far greater number of pictures but also because the pictures are more important to meaning. For instance, all the little "Tale" books by Beatrix Potter are beautifully

Flowers.	XV.	Flores.

Amongst the Flowers the most noted,	Inter flores notissimi,
In the beginning of the Spring are the *Violet*, 1. the *Crow-toes*, 2. the *Daffodil*, 3.	Primo vere, *Viola*, 1. *Hyacinthus*, 2. *Narcissus*, 3.
Then the *Lillies*, 4. white and yellow and blew, 5. and the *Rose*, 6. and the *Clove gilliflowers*, 7. &c.	Tum *Lilia*, 4. alba & lutea, & cœrulea, 5. tandem *Rosa*, 6. & *Caryophillum*, 7. &c.
Of these *Garlands*, 8. and *Nosegays*, 9. are tyed round with twigs.	Ex his *Serta*, 8. & *Serviæ*, 9. vientur.
There are added also *sweet herbs*, 10. as *Marjoram*, *Flower gentle, Rue, Lavender, Rosemary*.	Adduntur etiam *Herbæ odoratæ*, 10. ut *Amaracus, Amaranthus, Ruta, Lavendula, Rosmarinus*, (Libanotis).

From Comenius' *Orbis Pictus*.

written, and yet they are diminished in significance without the enchanting water colors with which the author embellished her texts. *The Tale of Peter Rabbit* is a perfect example of the picture-story—that is, a story in which pictures and text are interdependent. The crude imitations of her pictures on the market today are as offensive to the eye as the banal corruptions of her vigorous prose are to the ear.

Picture-biographies and the modern "awareness" books for young children may be judged by the same criteria. They are picture books if the meaning is clear from the illustrations and if, page by page, text and pictures reinforce each other. Some ABC books are pure picture books, completely dependent on the illustrations for meaning. Others have texts as rich in meaning as the illustrations.

The books in this discussion will not be evaluated solely or even primarily from the standpoint of the artists' techniques or the printers' methods. Rather they will be judged first according to the texts—how much they contribute to the child's growing social, emotional, and intellectual capacities; second according to the pictures—how much they clarify or augment the text; and third according to the total effect —the meaning, humor, strength, and beauty produced by text and pictures working together.

Picture book beginnings

Antiquarians generally consider the *Orbis Pictus* (1657 or 1658), by Comenius (1592–1670), the first picture book for children. It is more accurately described as an illustrated primer, but, at any rate, it was the first book for children in which pictures were used to interpret the meaning of a word or phrase. Written in Latin by a learned Moravian bishop, it was translated into most European tongues and was a widely used textbook. The format was interesting. The word *Flores* appeared over a little woodcut showing flowers in a vase and flowers growing in a field and the picture was followed by a pleasant little commentary on spring flowers. *Terrae foetus*, "fruits of the earth," was illustrated by a picture of different crops and *Venator*, the "hunter," appeared over a picture of a man on a horse, armed with a spear, pursuing wild animals. In each case, word and picture led directly into the reading matter.

In Japan, long before the appearance of this seventeenth-century primer, picture-book art was getting underway unencumbered by any burden of teaching. There in the twelfth century, the artist Kakuyu, popularly known as Toba Sojo, produced a "Scroll of Animals" that must have delighted old and young. In 1954, Velma Varner,

The illustrations in this color section provide a sampling of picture-book art. The work of the seventeen artists represented here is discussed in detail in the text.

Illustration from Virginia Lee Burton's *Mike Mulligan and His Steam Shovel*, Houghton Mifflin. Copyright, 1939, by Virginia Lee Demetrios. (book 9¼ by 8½)

"THERE WAS AN OLD WOMAN LIVED UNDER A HILL."

1.

A IS FOR ANTELOPE

2.

3.

1. Illustration by Arthur Rackham for *Mother Goose: The Old Nursery Rhymes*, Century. Copyright 1913 by Arthur Rackham. Reproduced by permission of Appleton-Century-Crofts, Inc. (book 7 by 9½)

2. Illustration from C. B. Falls' *ABC Book*, Doubleday, 1923. Reproduced by permission of Doubleday and Co., Inc. (book 8¾ by 12)

3. Illustration by Leonard Weisgard for *The Little Island* by Golden MacDonald, Doubleday, 1946. Reproduced by permission of Doubleday and Co., Inc. (book 10 by 7¾)

4. Illustration by Helen Stone for *All Around the Town* by Phillis McGinley, Lippincott. Copyright, 1948, by Phyllis McGinley and Helen Stone. (book 7½ by 9½)

4.

S

S is the snorting Subway
  That slithers below the ground.
It's sort of a scaly dragon.
  It roars with a dragon sound.
And sometimes far
In the foremost car
  The motorman lets you stand
To see the place
Where the dragons race
  Through their dark and shivery land.

5. Illustration from Fritz Eichenberg's *Ape in a Cape*, Harcourt. Copyright, 1952, by Fritz Eichenberg. (book 7¾ by 10½)

Sheep in a leap

Under a tree in the garden stood a
strange looking box with red wheels.

The gate leading into the garden was wide open.

1.

"*Bonjour*, Mesdames," the happy lion said farther down the street
when he saw three ladies he had known at the zoo.
"Huuuuuuuuuuuhhhhhh . . . " cried the three ladies,
and ran away as if an ogre were after them.
"I can't think," said the happy lion, "what makes them do that.
They are always so polite at the zoo."

2.

THE LITTLE GIRL
WITH A CURL

POLLY AND SUKEY

There was a little girl
          and she had a little curl
Right in the middle of her forehead.
When she was good,
          she was very, very good,

But when she was bad she was horrid.

110

Polly, put the kettle on,
    Polly, put the kettle on,
Polly, put the kettle on,
    And let's have tea.

Sukey, take it off again,
    Sukey, take it off again,
Sukey, take it off again,
    They've all gone away.

111

3.

1. Illustration from Maud and Miska Petersham's *The Box with Red Wheels*, The Macmillan Company, 1949. Reproduced by permission. (book 8 by 10)

2. Illustration by Roger Duvoisin for *The Happy Lion* by Louise Fatio, Whittlesey House, a division of McGraw-Hill Book Co., Inc. Copyright, 1954, by Louise Fatio Duvoisin and Roger Duvoisin. (book 8 by 10)

3. Illustrations by Feodor Rojankovsky for *The Tall Book of Mother Goose*, Harper. Copyright 1942 by Artists and Writers Guild, Inc. (book 5 by 12)

4. Illustration by Barbara Cooney for *Chanticleer and the Fox* by Geoffrey Chaucer, Thomas Y. Crowell, 1958. Reproduced by permission. (book 7½ by 9¾)

5. Illustration by Marcia Brown for *Puss in Boots* by Charles Perrault, Charles Scribner's Sons. Copyright 1952 by Marcia Brown. (book 8½ by 10¾)

4.

A free translation
from the French
of Charles Perrault

PUSS
IN BOOTS

WITH PICTURES BY
Marcia Brown

CHARLES SCRIBNER'S SONS, NEW YORK

5.

1. Illustration from Bruno Munari's *ABC*, World Publishing Company. Copyright © 1960 by Bruno Munari. (book 8½ by 11¾)
2. Illustration by Maurice Sendak for *The Moon Jumpers* by Janice May Udry, Harper. Copyright © 1959 by Maurice Sendak. (book 7¼ by 10)
3. Illustration from Edward Ardizzone's *Tim and Lucy Go to Sea*, Walck and Oxford. © Edward Ardizzone 1958. (book 7¼ by 10)
4. Illustration by Barbara Neustadt for *The First Christmas*, Thomas Y. Crowell. Copyright © 1960 by Barbara Neustadt. (book 6½ by 9½)

a Rose
and a Red Ribbon

1.

2.

'Tim,' said the Captain, 'we must rescue them. Call the second mate, tell him to get a boat's crew together and order all hands on deck to lower away a boat.'

With great difficulty they managed to get a boat away.

In the meantime Mrs Smawley, hearing the noise and wondering what had happened, had hurried on deck.

3.

4.

1.

2.

1. Illustration by Felix Hoffmann for *The Sleeping Beauty*, Harcourt, 1960. Reproduced by permission. (book 8¼ by 11½)
2. Illustration by Nicolas Sidjakov for *Baboushka and the Three Kings* by Ruth Robbins, Parnassus. Copyright 1960 by Ruth Robbins and Nicolas Sidjakov. (book 6¾ by 6½)

an imaginative editor of children's books, published the Scroll in book form under the title *The Animal Frolic* (Putnam). The Scroll originally carried no text, but Miss Varner added an unobtrusive running commentary to each page. For American children, accustomed to the crude simplification of the comics, such aids to interpretation may be needed. Miss Varner wisely kept her text to a minimum, thus permitting children, enthralled by the pictures, to speculate and add their own details. And what a challenge to the imagination these pictures present! They show frogs, rabbits, and monkeys enjoying a gala picnic with swimming, feasting, a sword dance by two frogs, and athletic contests leading to the choosing and crowning of a king-for-a-day. A frog wins, but not entirely by fair means. And one mischievous monkey has to be chased off the grounds by the busy rabbit who is obviously chairman of the hospitality committee and master of ceremonies. The characterizations of these animals and their droll antics are as fascinating today as they must have been eight centuries ago. It is true that the "Scroll of Animals" could not have influenced later artists since it was not available in book form until 1954, but Japanese prints circulated widely and their lively records of birds and beasts have always appealed to artists and children. Here, in spite of the original scroll form, is a true picture book with pictures that tell the story, show the action, and reveal the character of the animals without benefit of text.

William Caxton, England's first printer, issued his famous edition of *Aesop's Fables* in 1484. Although it was undoubtedly intended for adults, children so enjoyed the fables, probably from hearing them read aloud, that illustrated editions began to appear for children. Percy Muir[2] vouches for the Ogilby translation in 1651 with "elegant pictures," and much later, 1818, Thomas Bewick made his dramatic and beautiful illustrations for the *Fables*. However, none of these early editions carried enough illustrations to be classed as picture books.

That is true also of the chapbooks, so popular with the children of the seventeenth century. These badly written, abbreviated versions of such tales as Jack the Giant-Killer, Tom Thumb, Valentine and Orson, and Dick Whittington were printed on cheap paper with a few crude illustrations and were sold by the chapmen for anything from a penny to a sixpence.

Then as now, children undoubtedly appropriated adult books they understood and enjoyed. Such books as *Gulliver's Travels, Robinson Crusoe,* and *Pilgrim's Progress* were taken over at least in part by children. But again these books were not in the picture book category. Facsimiles of the first editions of *Pilgrim's*

[2] *English Children's Books, 1600 to 1900* (New York: Frederick A. Praeger, Inc., 1954), p. 24.

Illustration by Toba Sojo for *The Animal Frolic* by Velma Varner, G. P. Putnam's Sons. Copyright © 1954 by the Temple of Kozanji, Kyoto, Japan. (book 9 by 7)

Progress and *Robinson Crusoe* show a few illustrations; *Gulliver's Travels* shows none. The content of these books, of course, goes well beyond that of picture books.

From the fifteenth and sixteenth centuries on, there have been superbly illustrated editions of both the Old and New Testaments, but these could not be classed as picture books either, although children undoubtedly pored over them as they have always done with any adult book which catches their imagination.

In their *Oxford Dictionary of Nursery Rhymes,* Iona and Peter Opie tell us that as early as 1671, a worthy English divine quoted that most familiar of all the ABC jingles, "*A* was an apple-pie;/*B* bit it,/*C* cut it,/*D* dealt it,"[3] et cetera. To have been so quoted this alphabet chant was probably already well known. Surely, then, some artist must have popularized it with pictures, as artists have been doing with the alphabet ever since. This particular ABC jingle was reprinted for generations before artists decided to take the alphabet out of the apple pie routine and have some fun with it textually and pictorially.

Also in England, John Newbery in the eighteenth century discovered a unique outlet for his publishing business. Grownups actually bought books for children, and the children loved them and demanded more. His first book published for children was the now famous *A Little Pretty Pocket-Book* (1744), gaily bound in flowery paper and generously illustrated with small woodcuts. It included letters to the young by no less a hero than Jack the Giant-Killer, games, riddles, fables, and a rhyming alphabet which had already left the pie sequence:

> Great A, B, and C,
> and tumbledown D,
> The cat's a blind Buff,
> And she cannot see.[4]

Even more famous than the *Pocket-Book* was Newbery's first edition of *Mother Goose's Melody or Sonnets for the Cradle,* published between 1760 and 1765. No copy of this important little

book exists, but to judge by a replica of the Isaiah Thomas pirated American edition, Newbery's book clearly was a real picture book with a picture for each verse, which is far more than many recent editions of Mother Goose supply. Perhaps many of these woodcuts were crude, but some of them provided amusing or spirited interpretations of the jingles they illustrated. This Newbery edition was unique in that it added sixteen of Shakespeare's songs to the fifty-two anonymous jingles.[5]

Newbery's list of juvenile publications also included *The History of Little Goody Two-Shoes* (1765). Although this small book is enriched with thirty-five woodcuts, it is more a story or novel with illustrations than a picture book.

The Public Library of Toronto, Canada, houses the unique Osborne Collection of Early Children's Books, over 3000 of them. To look at these small books is to feel a new respect for the printers, publishers, and artists who lavished so much care and good taste on these early experiments in a new book field.

In the collection is an astonishing manuscript book of *The Three Bears,* by Eleanor Mure (1831), made as a birthday present for her nephew Horace Brooke. This little book is interesting because the first telling of this old nursery tale has always been credited to the poet Southey, 1837. The Mure version, six years earlier, uses the same nosey Old Woman, but has three brother Bears instead of the usual mother-father-baby trio. On each left-hand page there are two neatly written verses relating the horrid behavior of the prying old woman, and on the opposite page a hand-drawn and hand-colored picture showing her destructive activities and the Bears' punishments. First they threw her into the fire, but she would not burn. Then they threw her into the water, "but drown there she wouldn't." So finally, they threw her over the church steeple where perhaps you may see her to this very day. This is a much livelier tale than our Goldilocks version with, you notice, proper punishment for prying persons at the end. Why was this little book never published? It is still not so good as Southey's tale, but with its gay, colorful illustrations the pre-

---

[3] (New York: Oxford, 1951), p. 47.

[4] Iona and Peter Opie, eds., *The Oxford Dictionary of Nursery Rhymes* (New York: Oxford, 1951), p. 51.

[5] For further details see May Hill Arbuthnot, *Children and Books,* Scott, Foresman, 1957, Chapter 4.

reading child could soon "read" the story from its pictures.[6]

Looking back, it is interesting to note that in these early picture books are to be found popular types that still persist: Mother Goose editions, ABC books, picture-stories about animals and people. We have, in fact, developed recently only two new types—the picture-biography (see p. L) and the curious little "awareness" narratives (see p. LII), which will be discussed later.

NINETEENTH-CENTURY PICTURE BOOKS

Two lively picture books

From Germany in 1846 came a genuinely comic picture book, *Struwwelpeter*, by Dr. Heinrich Hoffmann. It was translated and reissued in the United States under the title *Slovenly Peter*. The pictures are hilarious and the verses are tongue-in-cheek moralities. For instance, there is the boy who would not brush his hair or cut his nails and ends up with a head like a bush and nails a foot long. The boy who declares, "O take the nasty soup away! I won't have any soup to-day," pines away until "on the fifth day, he was—dead!" And snooty Johnny Head-in-Air steps overboard, goes down with the staring fishes, loses his writing book, and is well-nigh drowned for his silly airs. These absurd tales with the animated drawings make a picture book children still think very funny. Certainly its humorous exaggeration is superior nonsense to some of the comic strips and modern moralities that have followed it.

From Canada came *The Brownies: Their Book* (1887), the first of a series, by Palmer Cox. The rhymed stories were slight and rather tedious, but the pen-and-ink pictures spellbound the children. These showed hundreds of Brownies with individual characters, such as the Dude, the Chinaman, the Dutchman, and others. These favorites were hunted out in each picture and gleefully welcomed by the children.

[6] *Permission could not be secured to reproduce here any part of this manuscript, because the Osborne Collection hopes to reproduce the whole book in the near future.*

SLOVENLY PETER

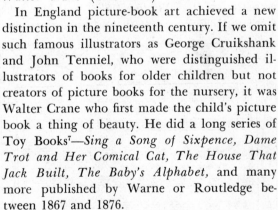

See Slovenly Peter! Here he stands,
With his dirty hair and hands.
See! his nails are never cut;
They are grim'd as black as soot;
No water for many weeks,
Has been near his cheeks;
And the sloven, I declare,
Not once this year has combed his **hair**!
Anything to me is sweeter
Than to see shock-headed Peter.

From Heinrich Hoffmann's *Slovenly Peter*, John C. Winston, n.d. (original in color, book 7 by 10)

Walter Crane (1845–1915) ✓

In England picture-book art achieved a new distinction in the nineteenth century. If we omit such famous illustrators as George Cruikshank and John Tenniel, who were distinguished illustrators of books for older children but not creators of picture books for the nursery, it was Walter Crane who first made the child's picture book a thing of beauty. He did a long series of Toy Books[7]—*Sing a Song of Sixpence, Dame Trot and Her Comical Cat, The House That Jack Built, The Baby's Alphabet,* and many more published by Warne or Routledge between 1867 and 1876.

Walter Crane's picture-book illustrations show a Japanese influence in their use of clear, flat colors, uncluttered design, and dramatic composition. They bear comparison with the best of our modern picture books in their restrained use of color and their beautiful design.

[7] The term "toy book" is used today to mean books with pop-ups or cut-outs that make them more toys than books. The Crane "toy books" were simply books intended for the nursery or prereading child.

Randolph Caldecott (1846–1886) ✓

The excellent qualities of the Crane books are found also in the numerous picture books made by Randolph Caldecott, in whose honor the Caldecott Medal is named. *The Diverting History of John Gilpin,* written by William Cowper (1731–1800) and illustrated by Caldecott in 1878, is still one of the funniest picture stories we have, enjoyed by both children and grown-ups. His wildly galloping horse, distressed rider, snapping and yapping dogs are characteristic of the action and humor in his pictures. Droll situations, characters, and mood, marvelously suggested and the whole picture beautifully drawn, make his books a delight to the eye. Caldecott picked up the challenge of the toy book launched by Crane and made some sixteen of them, often duplicating Crane's titles. These were later grouped together to reappear as several larger bound books.

His gentle, devastating sense of the absurd and his ability to record action with sure artistic craftsmanship are unexcelled.

Kate Greenaway (1846–1901)

After the pictures of Randolph Caldecott, the illustrations of Kate Greenaway for her own verses, *Under the Window* (1878) and *Marigold Garden* (1885), seem static and humorless. But what her pictures lack in action and humor is compensated for by the charming format and sheer grace of her compositions. The illustrations for her *Mother Goose* (n.d.) and *A Apple Pie* (n.d.), are exquisite indeed with small clusters of fruits or flowers decorating the wide margins or the corners or used as tailpieces, and with the gentle landscapes and the quaintly costumed figures all in pastel colors. In this age of violence such grace is needed.

The nineteenth century gave us other distinguished illustrators, but it was Walter Crane, Randolph Caldecott, and Kate Greenaway who elevated the child's picture book to a creation of good design and excellent composition with a restrained use of color that might well be respected today.

EARLY TWENTIETH-CENTURY PICTURE-BOOK ARTISTS

L. Leslie Brooke (1862–1940) ✓

Leslie Brooke began the twentieth century in the Crane-Caldecott-Greenaway tradition. In 1903 he published his inimitable *Johnny Crow's Garden* and in later years added two more books about Johnny Crow's decorous entertainment of his furred and feathered friends. Compared with the lively antics pictured in the

Illustration from Walter Crane's *Baby's Opera,* Warne, n.d. Reproduced by permission. (original in color, book 7 by 7)

Japanese *Animal Frolic,* Leslie Brooke's creatures seem comparatively static. Certainly, they are every inch proper Britons. The pen-and-ink sketches have a subtle drollery, sometimes adult and dependent on the text, as in the episode concerning the sow and the cow who sing a duet, "Squeal and Low." For his book of selections from Mother Goose called *Ring o' Roses* (n.d.), Brooke abandoned black and white and used the soft pastels of Caldecott and Greenaway. In this book the landscapes provide a veritable breath of the English countryside, and the pigs for "This little pig went to market" are the funniest and most endearing ever painted. Leslie Brooke launched the new century with beauty and verve.

Louis Maurice Boutet de Monvel (1850–1913)

In 1907 the text of a French picture book was translated into English, and the book made as profound an impression on young artists as it did on children and librarians. It was, of course, Boutet de Monvel's *Jeanne d'Arc,* published in France in 1897. Perhaps the nobility of the subject matter, the heroic character of Jeanne and her tragic story account in part for the book's distinction. But even without the story, the pictures will stand on their own, superb by every criterion of art. Although the text is well beyond the picture-book age, many a prereader has been completely spellbound by the illustrations. These begin gently and sweetly with the country girl and her visions, but they sweep into magnificent action with savage battle scenes and the colorful pomp of the coronation, and all through the book are the revealing and unforgettable faces of individual characters. The colors range from the delicate gray-greens of the French countryside to the glorious flamboyance of banners and robes. It is a pity that one of the finest and first of the picture-biographies should be allowed to go out of print.

Willebeek H. Le Mair (1889–   )

Another artist, whose lovely picture books of Mother Goose rhymes have also been allowed to go out of print, is Willebeek Le Mair. After working under the exacting tutelage of a Dutch artist, this talented young woman went to Paris to study with Boutet de Monvel. His influence

shows in her melting use of color, the action, and the storytelling quality of her illustrations for *Little Songs of Long Ago* and *Our Old Nursery Rhymes,* with music by A. E. Moffat, published around 1912. Garlands frame the

And the Pig Danced a Jig

From L. Leslie Brooke's *Johnny Crow's Garden,* Warne, 1903. Reproduced by permission. (book 6½ by 8)

oval of each of the pictures, which have dramatic, unforgettable composition. The misty blues-to-white of "Twinkle, twinkle, little star" center on the small, wistful figure of the child gazing out through the soft curtains to the night sky above. The comical, lonesome figure of the little boy wondering "Where, oh where has my little dog gone?" the bright details of interiors, the beautiful landscapes and formal gardens— these pictures give children a rare experience in beauty.

E. Boyd Smith (1860–1943)

Another artist who left his mark on the picture books of the first decade of the twentieth century was E. Boyd Smith. His *Chicken World* (1910) can hold its own with *The Animal Frolic,* or any recent picture book, both in beauty and significance. The border of each colorful page marks off the passing of a month of the year with appropriate flowers or leaves or scenes. Through this subtle suggestion of time, the cock struts grandly, his jewellike feathers all ashine. The hens, especially one black hen that appears in every picture, shepherd their fluffy broods to maturity, first showing them proudly to the other denizens of the farmyard and then guarding them from folly and danger. This may be a chicken's-eye view of the world, but it is a glowing, colorful world full of small activities, not without conflicts. His *Farm Book* (1910) is in softer colors but is equally beautiful although unfortunately more dated and less useful than *The Chicken World*. E. Boyd Smith used the colors appropriate to his subject matter. His pictures show a quiet sense of humor and his subject matter ranges from *The Seashore Book* (1912) to a very funny *Story of Noah's Ark* (1909) to a moving *Story of Pocahontas and Captain John Smith* (1906), another step toward the picture-biography (see p. ·L).

Boutet de Monvel, Willebeek Le Mair, and E. Boyd Smith set the pace for the new century. From these beginnings picture-book artists have increased in numbers to the point where no single article can do more than indicate a few outstanding artists who have contributed richly to picture-book art.

THE LAST FIFTY YEARS OF PICTURE-BOOK ART

Mother Goose, the artists' favorite author

Why do artists love to make a Mother Goose picture book? The answer is evident. Each verse is a unit with new characters, new scenes, and a great variety of situations and moods. Moreover, the good dame is public domain, so an artist is free to select and arrange the jingles as he pleases. He may pick a few choice verses that show his specialties or he may go in for a huge compilation and have a whirl at all sorts of pictures and decorations. Artists have done both to the continuing delight of children.

Iona and Peter Opie are two eminent authorities on the derivation of these anonymous jingles. Their *Oxford Dictionary of Nursery Rhymes* was published in 1951. Later they compiled their unique *Oxford Nursery Rhyme Book* (Oxford,

1955). The latter book is an important link with the past, and should be looked at first because of its contrast with modern editions of Mother Goose. Almost every one of its eight hundred verses has a little woodcut illustration. Most of them are reproduced from the old chapbooks or toy books, and when no old picture could be found, Joan Hassall, a distinguished artist, has drawn pictures in keeping with the old ones. Of course, the illustrations are uniformly black and white, but the fact that children enjoy them bears witness to their lack of dependence on color. This is a choice book and a wholesome antidote to the gaudy colors used today in mass-produced editions of Mother Goose. Action, humor, and a genuine interpretation of the text are to be found in most of the pictures. Probably what children like best is the perfect synchronizing of verse and illustration.

Arthur Rackham (1867–1939)

A great artist who gave us the outstanding *Mother Goose: The Old Nursery Rhymes* (Century, 1913) was Arthur Rackham. Both in text and format this is a superlative book, and the illustrations, whether in black and white or color, show an imaginative quality not common these days. Three types of pictures give variety to the pages: full color, pen-and-ink sketches, and silhouettes. Silhouettes are generally dull, but not Arthur Rackham's. Action is as visible in the silhouettes as in the other pictures, and all three types vary in mood. There are eerie, scary color pictures and tender, lovely ones. Elves and gnomes appear here and there, which is unusual in Mother Goose, and some of the color pictures, which range from delicate pastels to deep rich hues, are so beautiful you would like to take them out of the book for framing (see Color Plate 1, p. XXVI). To neglect the work of this gifted English artist is to miss a rare visual treat.

Tasha Tudor (1915–   )

The pictures Tasha Tudor made for her *Mother Goose* (Oxford, 1944) and for her alphabet book, *A Is for Annabelle* (Oxford, 1954), are in the Kate Greenaway tradition. Pastel colors, exquisite landscapes, pretty children, grownups, and dolls in old-fashioned clothes make the world of Tasha Tudor a picture-book land of great charm. Her choice of seventy-seven Mother Goose rhymes is good, and her picture interpretations are unusual.

Marguerite de Angeli (1889–   ) ✓

Already a well-known writer and illustrator and a winner of the Newbery Medal, Mrs. de Angeli with the arrival of grandchildren turned to the grateful task of making for them *Marguerite de Angeli's Book of Nursery and Mother Goose Rhymes* (Doubleday, 1954). This book was undoubtedly a labor of love. The 376 jingles are adorned with some 260 pictures and endless decorative touches of great beauty. Birds and flowers, nosegays and garlands adorn the corners of the pages or finish off a page delightfully. Beguiling children and animals frolic through the pictures, and the interiors are as fascinating as the landscapes. Warm colors, but not bright, make the pages glow, and if this is a too pretty world, why shouldn't it be? Mother Goose belongs to the springtime of life when the world is all ashine.

Harold Jones (1904–   )

By way of contrast, the illustrations Harold Jones made for Kathleen Lines' *Lavender's Blue* (Watts, 1954) have dignity, almost austerity, that suggests old engravings. This book will not make the immediate appeal either to children or grownups that prettier pictures do, but it will grow on anyone who is fortunate enough to possess it and thus be able to pore over the details in the pictures. The double-page spreads are beautiful in color and composition although the colors are, on the whole, somewhat somber. The figures are in action, the pages attractively bordered so that the picture appears in a frame. The central figures, whether animal or human, are so well characterized they tempt the beholder to speculation. Indeed the importance of this handsome book, over and above its excellent design, lies in the fact that no single glance suffices—details grow in significance with each fresh view and somehow or other the picture comes alive as a whole and is remembered. What is happening, of course, is that the child who possesses this book is unconsciously learning how to look at pictures.

Feodor Rojankovsky (1891–   ) ✓

None of these artists—Tasha Tudor, Marguerite de Angeli, or Harold Jones—is notable for his humor or use of strong colors. Feodor Rojankovsky excels in both. He and Roger Duvoisin have in their pictures caught the absurdities, the daft nonsense of the Mother Goose ditties, and both have used color gloriously.

Feodor Rojankovsky's *Tall Book of Mother Goose* (Harper, 1956) is unique in format. The long narrow book, 5 × 12, is surprisingly comfortable for small hands to hold. The pages lend themselves to wide, deep, double-page spreads that are effective both for landscapes and action. The colors are strong and rich, the texture of feathers, fur, and woolly mufflers so convincing you can almost feel them (see Color Plate 3, p. XXVIII). The children in these pictures are not pretty or graceful or picturesque. They are the sturdy, homely, beguiling children every one of us sees daily and loves. Somehow you find yourself smiling at these small, staunch beings.

Perhaps the most wonderful pictures Mr. Rojankovsky ever made are for that strange, haunting Russian story called *Treasure Trove of the Sun* by Mikhail M. Prishvin (Viking, 1952). It should be better known than it is. But the book and pictures that won him the Caldecott Medal are from Mother Goose—*Frog Went a-Courtin'* (Harcourt, 1955) with text and music adapted by John Langstaff. This is a delicious book that children study gravely and then chuckle over—absurd, pompous Mr. Frog, coy Miss Mousie, the lovely springtime colors of bog and meadow, and the hilarious wedding pictures that show even more confusion than most wedding scenes, but that manage to end happily.

Roger Duvoisin (1904–   ) ✓

The pictorial output of this gifted artist is so much more distinguished in fields other than Mother Goose that his contribution to the good dame has been almost forgotten. His *Mother Goose* (Heritage, 1936) is a huge book in bright primary colors that spill all over the printed text to the horror of the reading experts. The pictures are funny, the text extensive, including several alphabet and counting-out rhymes, and the action in the pictures is hilarious. (See also pp. XL, XLVIII and LIII.)

C. B. Falls (1874–   )

In 1923 a handsome ABC book appeared by C. B. Falls. It follows the simplest pattern of such books—"*A* is for Antelope," "*B* is for Bear,"— but the pictures are arresting (see Color Plate 2, p. XXVI) . The brief sentences are placed well down on the page; the black capital letters are set in bands of color to harmonize with the picture above. The animals are generally in action, the colors are deep, rich, or brilliant, and the whole composition of picture and page is extraordinarily striking. Jaguar, Rooster, Swan, Antelope are visually remembered over the years, and this book is as cherished by children and discriminating adults today as the latest ABC book on the market.

Wanda Gág (1893–1946) ✓

After the flowery, garlanded ABC books of Caldecott and Greenaway in the nineteenth century, *The ABC Bunny,* by Wanda Gág (Coward, 1933) , was an innovation. It remains one of the most striking and appealing books of its kind. Wanda Gág was already famous for her *Millions of Cats,* and *The ABC Bunny* (see *Time for Poetry,* p. 97) was no less original. The rhymed narrative has continuity and a surprise ending. The wide white margins and the single capital letter on each page in a striking scarlet, the powerful use of rhythmic line and massing of black-and-white areas, all these result in a page as lively as color could achieve. The delight young children take in this big, handsome book again refutes the idea that they like only pictures with bright colors (see also p. XLI) .

Fritz Eichenberg (1901–   ) ✓

Ape in a Cape (Harcourt, 1952) is another break with the old apple-pie sequence and mere prettiness. The idea of this alphabet book permits Fritz Eichenberg to have a wonderful time drawing all sorts of animals in all sorts of strange situations with rhymes to match the wildness of the illustrations (see Color Plate 5, p. XXVII) . There is no continuity either to text or pictures, but each combination of letter, picture, and rhymed caption makes a unit. After the sixes and sevens have chuckled over "*G* Goat in a boat" or

"*H* Hare at the Fair," they want to make their own alphabet rhymes. If they can resist the inevitable "Cat in a hat" they may come up with "Cub in a tub" and others to rival the originals. Here is a major artist having a frolic with words and pictures.

Roger Duvoisin ✓

A for the Ark (Lothrop, 1952) is for older children, seven, eight, and nine, because the text is sometimes a bit subtle. For instance, when Noah starts calling the animals by alphabet he gets into trouble. Some bears come for *B*, others hold out for *U*—Ursus. But the procession of the traveling beasts is comical, and, as always with Mr. Duvoisin's pictures, wonderfully decorative.

Helen Stone (1904–   )

There is one alphabet book no child should miss—*All Around the Town* (Lippincott, 1948) , by Phyllis McGinley, illustrated by Helen Stone. With their unique contributions these two women have lifted the humble ABC book to new levels of beauty both as literature and art (see Color Plate 4, p. XXVII) .

In her rhymed introduction the author proclaims her book a city alphabet full of "The gay things/The stray things/That city children see." Then they are off with Aeroplane, Bus, Circus, and such city oddities as Escalators, Jay-walkers, next-door Neighbors, the Subway, and all sorts of other surprises. The verses are so amusing and deftly written that they can stand by themselves without any alphabet. As for the illustrations, Helen Stone has never drawn or painted lovelier ones than these. Color pages alternate with black and white, and in both cases a double-page picture encircles a handsome big capital letter and the verse. The colors make a gorgeous splash across the two pages, the black and whites are equally strong in composition, and both kinds make of illustration, letter, and verse a perfect unit. Although the book is ostensibly about New York, it fits any sizable city or town, and children and grownups enjoy it equally.

Bruno Munari (1907–   ) ✓

In completely different style, with little text and many pictures, is Bruno Munari's *ABC*

(World, 1960). This Italian artist, with a flare for solving problems of design, space, color, and form in many different media, has made some children's books with little content but outstanding beauty. His ABC book is no exception. In modern style, with a striking use of space and color, every page is a surprise. "*F* a Fly a Flower a Feather more Flies and a Fish" launches a fly on its way and the miserable creature is "going *Zzzz*" on the last page. The clear, white paper and the generous size of the book make such a page as "*R* a Rose and a Red Ribbon" so beautiful that you hate to leave it to turn to the next (see Color Plate 1, p. XXX). Children enjoy the alliteration of "*S* a Sack of Stars and Snow for Santa Claus" and the clear, satisfying colors of "*L* a Long Leaf a Leaf a Little Leaf and a Lemon." Such an alphabet book with its sensory rather than ideational appeal is for the nursery-kindergarten ages, but it is wonderful eye-training for older boys and girls and will give deep satisfaction to their perhaps unconscious enjoyment of color and form.

Picture-Stories at the turn of the century

Undoubtedly, the most beloved type of picture book is the picture-story, which began in its modern form in 1899 with Helen Bannerman's *The Story of Little Black Sambo* (Chatto and Windus, n.d.; Lippincott, 1900) and was followed in 1901 or 1903 by Beatrix Potter's beloved *Tale of Peter Rabbit* (Warne). From these the picture-story has gone on to glory and in such numbers that only a few can be cited.

Helen Bannerman (1863–1946) ✓

The pictures of *Little Black Sambo* are stylized, undistinguished, but faithfully illustrative with one to every sentence or two of text. The story itself is an imaginative adventure with a triumphant ending that every child adores. Best of all, so perfectly are pictures and story synchronized that any four-year-old can soon "read" it from the illustrations. Unfortunately, in this day of racial tensions, the word "black" is used repetitively when each person is mentioned. To be sure, Sambo was an East Indian and an Aryan, but that adjective will probably ban the story from book lists and schools for years to

come. Historically, *Little Black Sambo* remains not only a good hero tale for the youngest but an admirable example of the true picture-story.

Beatrix Potter (1866–1943) ✓

Beatrix Potter's *Tale of Peter Rabbit* was written several years before it was published. Not only has it all the virtues of *Little Black Sambo* but Miss Potter's prose is as vigorous as her water colors are delicate and detailed. She was an artist in both words and paints, and manipulated both with meticulous care. In her "Tale" series—there are over thirty of the books—the stories unfold with fascinating themes, conflicts, action, suspense, near tragedy, and saved-at-the-last-moment conclusions that delight children. Always these plots are reinforced with pictures rich in fascinating details—lovely English landscapes and cozy interiors and small, foolish animals forever getting in and out of hot water. No wonder these picture-stories still stand as models of picture-story techniques.

Picture-Stories in the Golden Thirties

In the thirties, the picture book really came into its own. Indeed, this form became so important to artists that one of them, Lynd Ward, has said, ". . . the book work of the thirties that is most significant in itself, and in terms of what it contributes to the world at large, was done in the picture book form."[8] Just before the thirties a gifted and highly original artist-author produced a picture-story for young children which clearly demonstrated that this form of art was worthy of artists' best efforts.

Wanda Gág

The innovator was Wanda Gág and her book was *Millions of Cats* (Coward, 1928), a small masterpiece which has never worn out its popularity. Wanda Gág grew up in an artist family which took drawing and painting for granted. All during childhood she heard the European folk tales told by fine storytellers as

[8] Lynd Ward, "The Book Artist: Yesterday and Tomorrow," in *Illustrators of Children's Books, 1744–1945*, comp. by Bertha E. Mahony, Louise P. Latimer, and Beulah Folmsbee (Boston: Horn Book, 1947), p. 254.

they were meant to be told. So when she came to artistic maturity, she created original stories with all the rhythm and cadence of the oral tradition. And when she illustrated them, the flowing lines of her pictures reflected the rhythm of her text. No finer example can be found of the perfect synchronization of picture and text than *Millions of Cats*. Her later books are almost as good, and in these and in her illustrations for Grimm's tales you see the same sweeping lines, rhythmic use of black-and-white areas, a gift for details, and a homely warmth that pervades all of her work.

Marjorie Flack (1897–1958)

In 1930 *Angus and the Ducks* (Doubleday; see *Time for True Tales*, p. 4) became the darling of the fours and fives. The author was no great artist, but her clear, graphic illustrations matched precisely the words on the page. Moreover, her mastery of a simple storytelling style for the youngest children made her *Angus* series, *Ask Mr. Bear* (Macmillan, 1932; see *Time for Fairy Tales*, p. 279), and others, important and generally popular in nursery schools, kindergartens, and homes.

Kurt Wiese (1887–   )

In 1933 when *The Story about Ping* (Viking), another milestone in picture-stories, appeared, the artist, Kurt Wiese, was already established as an able illustrator of books for children and youth. But it took the rare storytelling art of Marjorie Flack together with Mr. Wiese's illustrations to produce a perfect story in text and pictures for the youngest children. Later, Kurt Wiese made an occasional picture-story of his own. They were amusing, especially the charming Chinese story, *Fish in the Air* (Viking, 1948), about a small boy and a huge kite. However, even this does not have the perfect balance of text and pictures that distinguishes *The Story about Ping*. For this book Mr. Wiese has suggested by way of his pictures the river life of China, which he knew so well. The story of the rebellious little duck who ran away from home and a spank only to discover that home is best even with a spank is full of reassurance for the runaway age. The illustrations are as dramatic as the text and the fours and fives still pore over them as tirelessly as the children did in 1933 when the book appeared.

Jean de Brunhoff (1899–1937)

The year 1933 was further enlivened by the arrival on our shores of a debonair French adventurer, Babar the elephant. That first book, *The Story of Babar* (translated by Merle Haas, Random, 1933), was a huge, bright affair with fetching end papers showing gray elephants against a red background. The story and pictures gave the world its first glimpse of Babar, fresh from the jungle, wide-eyed at the wonders of Paris, finding a kindly patron, being outfitted in smart new clothes, and enjoying Paris de luxe. Adults took to the book immediately and read it to small fry willingly, but wondered if it was too sophisticated for the very young. Whether it was or wasn't, Babar was accepted with so much enthusiasm that the big book was worn to shreds and each new adventure of the gentlemanly Babar was welcomed eagerly. Even when war and a paper shortage reduced these handsome big books to half their original size, their popularity never waned. Today librarians tell us the need for replacements is continuous and children do not seem to tire of tales about Babar, his Queen, his kingdom, and his children. Mr. de Brunhoff's bright, clear, detailed pictures match his slow, easy storytelling style. His son, Laurent, is continuing the series.

Ludwig Bemelmans (1898–   ) ✓

Ludwig Bemelmans made his first picture book for children in 1934, when *Hansi* (Viking) was published. It was the story of a small boy's Christmas holiday in the mountains, and the chief excitement was putting a dachshund on skis and sending him zipping down a couple of Alps. The humorous, colorful big pictures of people and places, of mountain scenery, and a small outraged dog are still very beautiful and very funny, but the story never quite went over. It was not until *Madeline* (Simon, 1939; see *Time for True Tales*, p. 217) made her bow that the children really took Bemelmans to their hearts. Yet the story and the pictures in the *Madeline* books are completely foreign to anything the average child knows. Apparently it is Madeline, the rugged individualist, they love.

The twelve little girls may walk and eat and brush their teeth "in two straight rows," but Madeline always manages to be different. She has her appendix out, she falls off a bridge, she brings a dog home, she tames the naughty son of the Spanish family next door. For, of course, *Madeline* had to have sequels, and *Madeline's Rescue* (1953) won the 1954 Caldecott Medal. Ludwig Bemelmans' entrancing use of color and the marvelous details in his huge pictures keep the children poring over them. They may not now recognize the Restaurant de Deux Magots or the cemetery of Père la Chaise, but they will when they see them fifteen years hence, and they will exclaim with delight, "Why, that was in *Madeline!*"

Marie Hall Ets (1895–   ) ✓

The year 1935 marked the advent of an artist who was to win the Caldecott Medal in 1960 for her *Nine Days to Christmas* (Viking, 1959). She is Marie Hall Ets, and the 1935 book is *Mister Penny* (Viking). The story is about a lot of lazy animals who reform and save their kind owner from ruin. The pictures are amusing black and whites, graphic and well-synchronized with the text. But neither this book nor the Caldecott winner is as charming as the artist's *Play With Me* (Viking, 1955), in which the delicate springtime pictures illumine the very heart of each episode. These pictures show the impetuous little girl, rushing at the shy woodland creatures, trying to make friends with them. But the final picture, which might so easily have been saccharine, is a restrained and gentle triumph for the child as well as the sensitive, perceptive artist who portrays so magically the joy of the little girl's new friendships.

Edward Ardizzone (1900–   )

The outsize picture-story of *Little Tim and the Brave Sea Captain,* by Edward Ardizzone (Oxford, 1936), came from England as a delightful surprise to American children. Later, *Tim All Alone* (Oxford, 1957; see *Time for True Tales,* p. 209) brought Mr. Ardizzone the honor of being the first winner of England's Kate Greenaway Medal. And there are several other adventures of the redoubtable Tim. He personifies the adventurer every child yearns to be. Ship-

wrecks, fires, lost parents—nothing daunts this up-and-doing hero, who comes through his great vicissitudes triumphant and nonchalant. Enthralling as these wish-fulfilling plots are, it is the author-artist's water-color seascapes, landscapes, and vistas of ships and port towns that are the glory of these books (see Color Plate 3, p. XXXI). The colors are often ominous grays to match Tim's stormy career, but there are also gay and cozy interiors and heartening glimpses of blue skies over harbors. The books have been reduced to little more than half their original size, but the water colors and the adventures are still powerful. Long may Tim flourish!

Clare Newberry (1903–   )

Clare Newberry's appealing picture-stories of kittens began with *Mittens* (Harper, 1936), which was followed by *Marshmallow* (Harper, 1942) and numerous others. Her drawings of cats, kittens, rabbits, and puppies are done with water colors, charcoal, crayon, pen and ink, and pastel. The furry textures look so soft and fluffy that small children invariably pat the pictures. The stories are slight, but the pictures tell the story and invoke a desirably tender response in young viewers.

Robert Lawson (1892–1957) ✓

This versatile artist won the Caldecott for his dullest book, *They Were Strong and Good* (Viking, 1940), but he will be long remembered for his illustration of *Pilgrim's Progress* (Stokes, 1939), *Adam of the Road* (Viking, 1942), *Rabbit Hill* (Viking, 1944), *The Tough Winter* (Viking, 1954) and, of course, that matchless picture-story, *The Story of Ferdinand* (Viking, 1936). Munro Leaf's tale of the hopelessly pacific young bull, stung into uncharacteristic and violent action by a bee, reads well all by itself. The episodes are funny and the conclusion a bucolic joy. But it is Robert Lawson's unforgettable pen-and-ink sketches that bring Ferdinand uniquely to life. Ferdinand languidly sniffing posies, Ferdinand listening to the advice of his mother "who was a cow," Ferdinand cavorting wildly after the bee sting or calmly ignoring those annoying men in the bull ring—all these gentle, careful drawings lend the final touch of hilarity to a droll character, and it is these pictures everyone remembers in detail. The late Robert Lawson was not only a master of neat, precise drawing, but he had a genius for characterization of both people and animals. *Ferdinand* is a beautiful example of his art and his humor.

Illustration by Robert Lawson for *The Story of Ferdinand* by Munro Leaf, Viking. Copyright 1936 by Munro Leaf and Robert Lawson. (book 7 by 8)

Dorothy Lathrop (1891–   ) ✓

The picture-story had a gala year in 1937. That year marked the appearance of the first Dr. Seuss book, and the first book to win the newly granted Caldecott Award for "the most distinguished picture book of the year." That first medal was given in 1938 to Dorothy Lathrop for her *Animals of the Bible* (Lippincott, originally Stokes, 1937). This book is hard to classify. It is not precisely a picture-story, although each picture illustrates a Bible animal, usually in a complete story as "The Story of the Creation," "The Animals of the Ark," "Peter's Cock." Occasionally, the picture illustrates only a verse or two, as the eagle in Psalm 103—"Who satisfieth thy mouth with good things; so that thy youth is renewed like the eagle's." It is an

exquisite book to study. The black-and-white drawings are true to every flower, costume, and creature of Bible times. Even the mythical leviathan conforms to Bible specification. The grace of lovely Eve, the power of Daniel, the tender scene of the Nativity are pictures to remember whenever the text is heard or read. This artist, so sensitive to the lithe movement, the furry, knowing faces of small animals, also produced two animal picture books of unmatched beauty, *Hide and Go Seek* (Macmillan, 1938) and *Who Goes There?* (Macmillan, 1935).

Dr. Seuss (1904–   ) ✓

No reviewer of children's books will ever forget the shock of delighted hilarity that attended the first reading of *And to Think That I Saw It on Mulberry Street* (Vanguard, 1937) by an unknown author with a built-in degree, "Dr. Seuss." Since then, Theodor Seuss Geisel has provided a fresh surprise or two yearly. His books are generally tall tales in rhyme, with lots of made-up nonsense words, and pictures in strong primary colors. It is a question which are wilder, the yarns or the illustrations, and the children love them both. Some say Dr. Seuss can't draw, hence the cartoonlike illustrations with lots of exaggerated heights and depths, bigness and littleness, and a kind of bedithered action. His pictures may not be art, but they have flowing rhythms to match the cadence of the words. From this first book about the comeuppance of an exaggerator, to *Horton Hatches the Egg* (Random, 1940)—(undoubtedly the funniest of all his books)—and on to his latest easy-to-read achievement, Theodor Seuss Geisel is always original and amazingly productive. Even though his recent illustrations may show less imagination and fewer hints of beauty, and may be more in the obvious grotesque style of the comic strip, his juvenile devotees forgive him and agree that he deserves the top degree of them all— D.D.C., Doctor of Delighted Children.

Thomas Handforth (1897–1948) ✓

The second Caldecott Medal was awarded in 1939 to Thomas Handforth for his *Mei Li* (Doubleday, 1938). The book was the result of the author-artist's years in China and his skilled artistry with pencil and brush. His acceptance paper[9] gives a vivid account of those years and the fun he had sketching camels, Mongol ponies, actors, dancers, acrobats, jugglers, and the children who came his way. They are all to be seen in *Mei Li*, and to look at those powerful black-and-white pictures is to see movement, energy, vitality, life in every line. Mei Li herself is a bundle of activity, reveling in the New Year's Day Fair, getting in and out of trouble, savoring every experience happily, and getting home just in time for the blessing of the Kitchen God. The story is not so vigorous as those bold, wonderful pictures that show brush and pencil work at their black-and-white best, but the story can be "read" from the illustrations.

James Daugherty (1889–   )

In the same year that *Mei Li* was awarded the Caldecott Medal there was another picture-story that might have won it—*Andy and the Lion* (Viking, 1938) by James Daugherty. Later this author-artist received the Newbery Medal for his *Daniel Boone* (Viking, 1939; see *Time for True Tales*, p. 303). Both books are as distinguished for their illustrations as for the text. Warm earthiness and a tender appreciation of people distinguish James Daugherty's pictures. *Andy and the Lion* is a good example. It tells the story of a boy who read about lions but never expected to meet one. Then he did, with astonishing results. The story is good, but the pictures are unforgettable. The rear view of young Andy reaching for a book on high library shelves, or Andy suddenly confronted with a lion-sized lion in full roar, or Andy toppling over backwards as he extracts the thorn—these and the other pictures in yellow and black have a gusto only Daugherty can impart to awkward, beautiful, absurd human beings. *Mei Li* has vigorous and stunning pictures, but so in a different style has Andy's story, and it is to the latter that the children would have given the Caldecott Medal.

Virginia Burton (1909–   ) ✓

The last year of this brilliant decade for the picture book marked the publication of Virginia Burton's *Mike Mulligan and His Steam*

[9] Bertha Mahony Miller and Elinor Whitney Field, eds., *Caldecott Medal Books: 1938–1957*, Horn Book Papers (Boston: Horn Book, 1957), II, 22–43.

Shovel (Houghton, 1939; see *Time for Fairy Tales*, p. 287), which ranks in popularity and distinction with her Caldecott winner, *The Little House* (Houghton, 1942). To be sure, *Choo Choo* (Houghton, 1937) had preceded both, and it is good, but it is *Mike Mulligan* and *The Little House* which have become household words and nursery favorites and which represent a style that is most distinctly Virginia Burton and no one else (see Color Plate on p. XXV). It was lucky for children that the artist once studied ballet because the swirling rhythms of her pictures fascinate all beholders. Even Mary Anne, the steam shovel, goes into dipping, digging,

This is the thrifty princess,
Whose house is always clean,
No dirt within her kingdom
Is ever to be seen.

Her food is fit
For a king to eat,
Her hair and clothes
Are always neat.

Illustration from Thomas Handforth's *Mei Li*, Doubleday. Copyright 1938 by Thomas Handforth. Reproduced by permission of Doubleday and Co., Inc. (book 9 by 12)

plunging rhythms, and the Little House is encircled by a dance of sun, moon, and stars, a cycle of seasons, and then the moving multiplicity of city beings and city towers. And under all these rhythmic lines and within the subtly cadenced texts, there are facts galore and meanings within meanings.[10] These are choice books which children never tire of because they are rich in visual details and beauty and rich with a significance which children may not analyze but which keeps them saying, "Read it again."

What a galaxy of distinguished artists this makes for one decade—Wanda Gág, Marjorie Flack, Kurt Wiese, Jean de Brunoff, Ludwig Bemelmans, Marie Hall Ets, Edward Ardizzone, Clare Newberry, Robert Lawson, Dorothy Lathrop, Dr. Seuss, Thomas Handforth, James Daugherty, and Virginia Burton! The thirties were indeed golden years for the picture-story, to say nothing of the picture-biography and the little "awareness" books, which also made a beginning in this decade. Nor do these picture books represent all the excellent ones made in that period, but they are, for the most part, the books of authors and artists who have continued to produce and who have turned the picture book into an art form that challenges and delights each new generation.

Picture books after the thirties

Picture books of single folk tales

One of the brightest areas of the picture-story today is the single folk or fairy tale brought vividly to life for children by gifted artists. Their generous use of pictures not only follows the action play by play but interprets both character and mood.

Marcia Brown (1918–   ) √

Marcia Brown has made a fine contribution to children's books in the folk tale field—*Stone Soup* (1947), now available also in French, *Dick Whittington and His Cat* (1950), *Puss in Boots* (1952), *Cinderella* (1954), and Andersen's *The Steadfast Tin Soldier* (1953) (all published by Scribner's), each one beloved by children. Each of these books is in a different style to match the mood or atmosphere of the tale. *Stone Soup* is gay, colorful, and earthy like the rogues who taught the miserly peasants a better way of

---

[10] *Read Virginia Burton's acceptance paper, "Making Picture Books," in Caldecott Medal Books: 1938–1957, ed. by Bertha Mahony Miller and Elinor Whitney Field, Horn Book Papers (Boston: Horn Book, 1957), II, 88–92.*

life. *Puss* is a flamboyant, gorgeous feline in shocking pinks, quite the handsomest Master Cat ever drawn (see Color Plate 5, p. XXIX). *Dick* is in browns and blacks as substantial as his career, and both the *Tin Soldier* and *Cinderella* are in misty blues and pinks grayed down to the gentle mood of the stories. *Cinderella* won the Caldecott Medal, but each book illumines the text "in spirit and in truth."

Barbara Cooney (1917–   ) √

Of the more than thirty books Barbara Cooney has illustrated, two of them are notable picture-stories. The first one, Lee Kingman's *Peter's Long Walk* (Doubleday, 1953), is a sensitive story of a little boy's search for some children to play with. The pictures interpret tenderly the child's long journey, the lovely New England countryside through which he trudges, his disappointment, and the sad homecoming which turns out cheerfully after all. The pictures in muted colors are understanding and appealing. Then, to everyone's delight her *Chanticleer and the Fox* (Crowell, 1958) won the Caldecott Medal. In this skillful adaptation of Chaucer's *Nun's Priest's Tale,* the artist took pains to see that every costume, every plant, and every flower were historically accurate. The pages are alive with bright, clear reds, greens, and blues. The people, the hens, the gorgeous cock, and, of course, old Reynard are in full color, and action runs riotously over every page (see Color Plate 4, p. XXIX). This is one of the gayest, most exuberant picture tales children have had, and the wit and wisdom of the old fable add richness to the book.

Hans Fischer (1909–1958)

Hans Fischer, a Swiss artist of rare talent, made some picture-stories of his own, notably *Pitschi* (Harcourt, 1953), but best of all his books is his picture edition of Grimm's *Traveling Musicians* (Harcourt, 1955). The pictures are in pen and ink with color. They are sketchily done in modern style, but every page is alive with droll details which the children relish.

Felix Hoffmann (1911–   )

Also Swiss, Felix Hoffmann followed the late Hans Fischer with delightful picture-book editions of *The Wolf and the Seven Little Kids* (Harcourt, 1959) and *The Sleeping Beauty* (Harcourt, 1960). His style is finished, realistic, and beautiful both in color and composition. The first book is in deep, glowing colors with enchanting details which the children check carefully. *The Sleeping Beauty* is in the grand manner of Howard Pyle. There are droll touches, such as the cat that stalks through the pages, but the beautiful landscapes, the glimpses of the castle through the wall of thorns, the medieval pageantry of the robed figures in the christening and the wedding scenes are sheer poetry (see Color Plate 1, p. XXXII). These are the loveliest pictures we have ever had for this romantic tale.

Adrienne Adams

Houses from the Sea (Scribner's, 1959) by Alice Goudey, illustrated by Adrienne Adams, was runner-up for the Caldecott Medal. The artist later made a delightful picture book edition of *The Shoemaker and the Elves* (Scribner's, 1960). The cozy details of the shoemaker's house and shop, the costumes of the customers, the cobbler, and his wife, the perky, naked little elves and their comical action once they don their new clothes, tell the story to perfection. The colors are warm, delicate, and beautifully combined, the details are realistic.

Erik Blegvad (1923–)

Erik Blegvad's small picture editions of Andersen's *The Swineherd* and *The Emperor's New Clothes* (Harcourt, 1958 and 1959) are choice introductions to these tales. His translations are lively and the pictures, sometimes in black and white and sometimes in bright clear colors, have humor and charm. It is to be hoped he will make a series of these exquisite picture editions of Andersen.

Miscellaneous picture books

Françoise, pseud. Françoise Seignobosc (1900–)

Preschool children take special delight in the mild little-girl-adventures of Jeanne-Marie by the French artist Françoise. Whether *Jeanne-Marie Counts Her Sheep* (Scribner's, 1951) or enjoys Paris or the springtime or goes to the fair,

the pictures are in clear delicate colors, in the naïve style of a child artist but decorative and beautifully composed as only a gifted artist can paint them. *Chouchou* (Scribner's, 1958) and

Illustration from Françoise's *Jeanne-Marie at the Fair.* Copyright © 1959, Charles Scribner's Sons, 1959. (original in color, book 7¾ by 10)

Things I Like (Scribner's, 1960) even minus Jeanne-Marie are equally appealing.

Nicolas, pseud. Nicolas Mordvinoff (1911–) ✓

The team of "Will and Nicolas" or William Lipkind and Nicolas Mordvinoff, the writer and the artist, won the Caldecott Medal for their *Finders Keepers* (Harcourt, 1951), which followed their equally original *The Two Reds* (Harcourt, 1950). Mr. Mordvinoff has also made a picture-story of his own, *Bear's Land* (Coward, 1955), but his pictures are stronger than his text. He is an avowed enemy of the pretty-pretty in art for children, and his own illustrations give them something stronger to grow on. Bold composition, sparing use of details, and tremendous storytelling power distinguish his pictures.

Roger Duvoisin

Sometimes called the artists' artist and certainly one of the most versatile of them all, Roger Duvoisin's work is worth special study. No illustrator can reveal mood, intention, and character more subtly than he. His *Petunia* (Knopf, 1950) was the first in an amusing picture-book series about a goose of a goose whose misadventures delight the children. But in his illustrations for Louise Fatio's series about *The Happy Lion* (Whittlesey, 1954) the artist is at his whimsical best. Beautifully drawn, in clear, warm colors, full of complex details and lively action, these pictures fascinate youngsters and delight the grownups who begin to know the nameless French town in the series as well as Main Street. Not as stylized as his pictures for the Alvin Tresselt books, these pictures for *The Happy Lion* match the stories in subtle humor (see Color Plate 2, p. XXVIII).

Lynd Ward (1905–) ✓

The Biggest Bear (Houghton, 1952) won the Caldecott Medal for Lynd Ward, who was already a well-known illustrator, and that book seems to have overshadowed the lovely pictures he made for Hildegarde Swift's *The Little Red Lighthouse and the Great Gray Bridge* (Harcourt, 1942). In spite of the long, awkward title this was an unusually significant picture-story that was made doubly moving by Mr. Ward's pictures. In both books—*The Biggest Bear,* in black and white, and *The Little Red Lighthouse,* in dark blues and grays with touches of red—it is the artist's sure sense of dramatic contrast that tells the stories and grips and holds the children's attention.

Conrad Buff (1886–)

Swiss-born but a Californian by adoption and devotion, Conrad Buff is a landscape painter who has received many awards, with paintings in the Metropolitan, the Boston, the British, and other art museums. For the books written by his wife, Mary Buff, he has made striking illustrations both in color and sepia. In their picture-stories *Dash and Dart* (Viking, 1942), which tells of a year in the lives of forest deer; *Hurry, Skurry and Flurry* (Viking, 1954), about forest squirrels; and *Elf Owl* (Viking, 1958), which

tells of desert creatures, the cadenced text and the sensitive sepia drawings are good science, good stories, and sheer poetry.

Their fur grows long and silky.
Their tails spread like gray plumes.
They are growing up.

Illustration from Mary and Conrad Buff's *Hurry, Skurry, and Flurry,* Viking. Copyright 1954 by Mary Marsh Buff and Conrad Buff. (book 6½ by 10)

Robert McCloskey (1914–) ✓

Make Way for Ducklings (Viking, 1941), by Robert McCloskey, is a perfect example of picture-story synchronization, but no more so than the artist's earlier piece of humorous Americana, *Lentil* (Viking, 1940). So popular is every one of this artist's picture-stories that it is not surprising to find he is the first artist to receive the Caldecott Medal twice, the first time for *Make Way for Ducklings* and the second time for *Time of Wonder* (Viking, 1957). With the exception of this last book, which is not a story but an "awareness" narrative, the pictures are in sepia or black and white. Whether it is *Lentil* or *Ducklings, Blueberries for Sal* (Viking, 1948), or *One Morning in Maine* (Viking, 1952), the pictures are strong in line, realistic but never prettified, humorous, with mood and character suggested in every picture—of policeman or ducks, a bear cub or a child, a patriotic statue or a harmonica-playing boy.

Virginia Kahl (1919–   )

The style of this prolific author-artist has been influenced, she tells us, by her devotion to the art of the Middle Ages. Her stories are invariably hilarious from the first one, *Away Went Wolfgang* (Scribner's, 1954), to the last rhymed tale about the Duchess, the Duke, and their thirteen children. The misadventures of that absurd family run along as gaily as their titles suggest. The series began with the still popular *The Duchess Bakes a Cake* (Scribner's, 1955) and is going strong. The pictures are handsome, colorful, and decoratively composed.

Berta and Elmer Hader (1889–   )

Among the dependable older favorites there are Berta and Elmer Hader, who won the Caldecott Medal for their pictorial record of *The Big Snow* (Macmillan, 1948) and what happened to the birds and small animals around their house during that blizzard. Their quaint, colorful edition of *Mother Goose* (Coward, 1944) has always been well liked.

Maud (1889–   ) and Miska Petersham (1888–   )

Maud and Miska Petersham won the Caldecott Medal for their American Mother Goose, *The Rooster Crows* (Macmillan, 1945), and celebrated the advent of a grandchild with the charming *The Box with Red Wheels* (Macmillan, 1949)—a book with bold bright colors, strong composition, and a slight story with a surprise ending which appeals to children four to seven (see Color Plate 1, p. XXVIII). However, it is their beautiful picture-story of the Nativity, *The Christ Child* (Doubleday, 1931), that has especially endeared them to parents, children, and teachers. A year in Palestine gave them the inspiration and background for this classic, for which they wisely used the texts from St. Matthew and St. Luke. Their exquisite pictures, historically authentic in scene, costumes, and other details, have successfully caught and interpreted for young children the tender majesty of that matchless narrative.

Looking back over the many varieties of art that adorn, interpret, and illumine children's picture books, we find they tend on the whole toward realistic representation. To be sure, there is today Nicolas Mordvinoff with his bold, vigorous style, and here and there an occasional book breaks out into a freer, more modern approach to picture-book art. Helen Sewell, a distinguished illustrator, did a completely unrealistic

Little Bear's mother turned around to see what on earth could make a noise like *kuplunk!*

"*Garumpf!*" she cried, choking on a mouthful of berries, "This is not my child! Where is Little Bear?" She took one good look and backed away. (She was old enough to be shy of people, even a very small person like Little Sal.) Then she turned around and walked off very fast to hunt for Little Bear.

From Robert McCloskey's *Blueberries for Sal*, Viking. Copyright 1948 by Robert McCloskey. (book 11 by 8½)

interpretation of Alf Evers' *The Three Kings of Saba* (Lippincott, 1955), which is the story of the three kings' journey to visit the Holy Child. This was an unusual and beautiful picture-story in modern idiom that deserved a warmer reception than it received. The Christmas story has inspired many artists, and curiously has seemed to free artists imaginatively. Two of the most strikingly illustrated books in the modern vein—*Baboushka and the Three Kings* and *The First Christmas*—appeared in 1960 and both have Christmas themes.

Nicolas Sidjakov

Nicolas Sidjakov has created two remarkable picture books in modern idiom. *The Friendly Beasts* (Parnassus, 1957) was selected by the *New York Times* as one of the ten best illustrated books of the year. The other book, *Baboushka and the Three Kings* (Parnassus, 1960), won the Caldecott Medal. It is a Russian folk tale of an old woman doomed to wander because of her refusal to leave her comfortable house and journey with the Three Kings. The story is beautifully told by Ruth Robbins and the format of the book, especially the typography and spacing of text and pictures, is completely satisfying. But the pictures are the book's crowning distinction. Strong blue, red-orange, black, and a green-yellow are used throughout the book. The figures are blocklike and completely stylized, but they reveal character and mood. The cozy interiors with the cat are in striking contrast to the interminable stretches of snowy countryside. Villages and streets look down frowningly on the wandering old woman, and every picture is an arresting composition (see Color Plate 2, p. XXXII). This book and Mr. Sidjakov's *The Friendly Beasts* are examples of modern art effectively used to give children a fresh look at the world.

Barbara Neustadt

Another arresting book in the modern style is *The First Christmas* (from the King James version of St. Luke and St. Matthew), illustrated by Barbara Neustadt (Crowell, 1960). Here is a superlative example of fine bookmaking. The clear blue binding with its one golden, trumpeting angel; the glowing jewellike colors of the etchings framed by wide, decorated margins; the clear typography—all together achieve a unity that is sheer beauty. The illustrations are striking in their simplicity, and Miss Neustadt has made dramatic use of the wide borders with their feathery blue, scroll-like decorations (see Color Plate 4, p. XXXI). These picture borders will delight the children with their unobtrusive but imaginative details which add to, never detract from, the story.

The authentic and tender realism of the Petershams' *Christ Child* is moving. To read Miss Neustadt's book is to see and feel the story in a new way, with equal reverence and appreciation for beauty of a different kind.

Picture-Biographies

E. Boyd Smith

The picture-biographies of the twentieth century began with E. Boyd Smith's *The Story of Pocahontas and Captain John Smith* (Houghton, 1906). Rereading this text and looking again at the pictures makes one regret that the book has gone out of print. The story is movingly told and the pictures have rare interpretative values although stronger colors would have helped the Indian scenes.

Yet this book and Boutet de Monvel's *Jeanne d'Arc* (see p. XXXVII) as well as Esther Averill's *Voyages of Jacques Cartier* (Viking, 1937), dramatically illustrated by Feodor Rojankovsky, have one characteristic in common which may account for their disappearance from the list of books in print. Their texts appeal to the reading child of ten to twelve years old, but that age group turns away from picture-book format which is suspect as babyish. Yet teachers of art or social studies, had they introduced these books to older children along with their history or their art appreciation for details of scene, costumes, and character, would have found the children enjoying both texts and illustrations.

Ingri (1904–) and Edgar d'Aulaire (1898–)

It was Ingri and Edgar d'Aulaire who really brought the picture-biography into its own. It seems especially interesting that the Norwegian-born wife and the French husband should have turned to the heroes of their adopted land for their subjects. Edgar d'Aulaire in his Caldecott Medal acceptance speech for their *Abraham Lincoln* (Doubleday, 1939) explains this. "We counted as our biggest asset just the fact that our conceptions of our American themes had never been shaped into school clichés."[11] And his wife adds that after they had studied Lincoln he became so real to them that he was like "a warm and kind and generous relative who had moved right into our studio with us." In striving for authenticity, these artists camped in three states to collect their Lincoln materials and tramped all over the George Washington country in Virginia for their first book. After their first sketches, the D'Aulaires work directly on the lithograph stone, which gives their pictures unusual strength and depth. These qualities were not so effectively used in their first picture-biography, *George Washington* (Doubleday, 1936), in which the pictures seem wooden. But by the time they wrote and made the pictures for their Caldecott Medal book, *Abraham Lincoln*, they were using this difficult medium superbly. The colors in this book are deep and rich, the lines and composition have a sort of primitive simplicity that suggests folk art, and the pictures are full of authentic factual details. Their *Benjamin Franklin* (1950) is equally rich in the storytelling qualities of the illustrations. *Leif the Lucky* (1951) and *Columbus* (1955) are the most colorful, *Pocahontas* (1946) and *Buffalo Bill* (1952), the most picturesque. All their biographies are appealing and deservedly popular.

Leo Politi (1908–   ) ✓

Leo Politi's pictures for Alice Dalgliesh's *The Columbus Story* (Scribner's, 1955) are lovely in color, but his style seems a shade too gentle for so stern and dedicated a hero. On the other hand, the colorful, almost primitive style of the artist seems admirably suited to his own book, *The Mission Bell* (Scribner's, 1953), which is about Father Junípero Serra, who built the missions of California. The brown hills of his beloved California, the mountains and valleys, the little mission enclosures, and the humble strength of the

[11] Bertha Mahony Miller and Elinor Whitney Field, eds., *Caldecott Medal Books: 1938–1957* (Boston: Horn Book, 1957), II, 45 and 50.

Illustration from Ingri and Edgar Parin d'Aulaire's *Abraham Lincoln,* Doubleday, 1957. Reproduced by permission of Doubleday and Co., Inc. (book 8¾ by 12½)

good Father himself are all revealed in these charming pictures.

Georges Schreiber (1904–   )

Ride on the Wind (Scribner's, 1956), adapted from Charles Lindbergh's *Spirit of St. Louis* by Alice Dalgliesh and illustrated by Georges Schreiber, is thrilling both in text and pictures. The artist has succeeded in suggesting the youthful daring of the hero, the loneliness of the flight, and the exuberant triumph of the landing. In this space age when the significance of this one-engine, one-man flight is in danger of being forgotten or underestimated, this is a great story. When the modern child looks at the pictures of that flimsy little machine, when he sees the blue night sky, the stormy sea beneath, with just that one small plane cleaving the immensity of the heavens, pitting its puny strength against the elements, he will realize that this man's achievement was an early step toward modern space exploration.

Wesley Dennis (1903–   )

Marguerite Henry's *Benjamin West and His Cat Grimalkin* (Bobbs, 1947; see *Time for True Tales,* p. 324), illustrated by Wesley Dennis, is not strictly speaking a picture-biography, but it comes close to it. This delightful story of America's first major artist is so illumined by Mr. Dennis' amusing pen-and-ink sketches that you can't think of text without pictures, or vice versa. Mr. Dennis is forever associated with the splendid horse pictures he has made for Mrs. Henry's books, but lively, ingenious Benjamin, struggling with his Quaker family, and poor Grimalkin, the cat, whose tail yielded hairs for paint brushes, are convincingly alive and will delight children as young as five or six years old.

Compared with the endless list that might be made of good picture-stories, the list of picture-biographies is short indeed. Yet the D'Aulaires have demonstrated the successful possibilities of such books. Perhaps more will follow.

"Awareness" books and other nonfiction

No one seems to know who gave the label "awareness" to a baffling group of picture books for the youngest children about such a variety of things as friendship, love, an island, a tree, aloneness, noises, wetness ("plink, plink goes the water in the sink"). They are all alike in one respect. They are earnestly trying to make the young child aware of the things of this world, such as trees, weather, seasons, or of sensory experiences or of meaning. They are innocent of plot but they do have a theme, generally stated in the title. Nine times out of ten the texts cannot stand alone but are completely dependent upon the interpretations and embellishments of the illustrations. Here, over and over again, the writers have been fortunate in their collaboration with some of the most gifted artists in the field of children's books.

Who started these awareness books? Where did they come from? Perhaps they sprang from Lucy Sprague Mitchell's *Here and Now Story Book* (Dutton, 1921), which emphasized the importance to the young child of understanding the world around him, and substituted sensory stimuli for plot, and cadence for action. The emphasis on the "here and now" was a wholesome revolt from an overdose of folk tales, prevalent at that time. Mrs. Mitchell had many devoted followers and may be said to have established a new school of writing for the nursery. How much of this writing will survive remains to be seen.

Lois Lenski (1893–   )

The success of the purely factual was first demonstrated by Lois Lenski's famous explanatory series beginning with *The Little Auto* (Oxford, 1934) and followed by *The Little Sail Boat* (Oxford, 1937), *The Little Train* (Oxford, 1940), and others. Uncomplicated pen-and-ink sketches showed children how the impeccable Mr. Small drove his car safely and surely throughout the day, likewise his train or his boat or his airplane. The pictures and text were so simple and objective that children apparently experienced the vicarious thrill of sitting in the driver's seat, master of the machine.

Norman Bate (1916–   )

With more significant text and pictures than those in Lois Lenski's series, Norman Bate's picture books are based, he says, "on a small child's interest in the power and excitement of big machines."[12] *Who Built the Bridge?* (Scribner's, 1954) shows the enormous pile drivers, cranes, derricks, and the hero-sized men who swing the great steel beams into place and dominate machines and materials as easily as a child rides his bicycle. The text is clear and factual but almost poetic in its cadenced narration of the dramatic battle between the river and the workers. The splendid pictures in cloudy yellows, grays, and blacks reinforce the words and together make a picture book boys enjoy, respect, and go back to again and again. *Who Built the Highway?* (Scribner's, 1953) describes and shows the machines that tear up the modern landscape and put it together again. *Who Built the Dam?* (Scribner's, 1958) becomes more complex and difficult, too much so for a picture-book format.

[12] Ruth Hill Viguers, Marcia Dalphin, and Bertha Mahony Miller, comps., *Illustrators of Children's Books, 1946–1956* (Boston: Horn Book, 1958), p. 70.

These books are quite different from the sulky fire engine, the big-eyed auto, and the playboy tugboat school of writing. Mr. Bate's books give facts the glorification of fine style and pictures, and leave young children with an awed respect for machines and the workers who command them.

Leonard Weisgard (1916–   )

There is little doubt that the late Margaret Wise Brown (pseudonym Golden MacDonald) was one of the chief creators of the awareness books. She was the gifted student and follower of Lucy Sprague Mitchell, but she differed from Mrs. Mitchell in an important way: she was not afraid of fantasy and she was as imaginative as she was creative. At the peak of her productivity it was said she turned out over fifty small books in two years. *The Noisy Book* (W. R. Scott, 1939) and *The City Noisy Book* (W. R. Scott, 1946) were illustrated by Leonard Weisgard and are the beginnings of a remarkably successful collaboration. The intent of these books is obvious —to make children aware of the sources and significance of the noises that are the background of their everyday living. In these Noisy books Mr. Weisgard was limited in his use of colors, although the deprivation is not obvious. Not until the author and artist did *The Little Island* together (Doubleday, 1946) did they really come into their own. This Caldecott Medal winner glows with color. The gently cadenced text falls pleasantly on the ear and has obvious meanings for the child and less obvious overtones.

> There was a little Island in the ocean.
> Around it the winds blew
> And the birds flew
> And the tides rose and fell on the shore.
> . . . .
> And a little kitten came to the Island.
> . . . .
> "Maybe I am a little Island too."
> said the kitten—
> "a little fur Island in the air."
> And he left the ground
> And jumped in the air.

The pictures that accompany this rhythmic text are strong and colorful. The seascapes are in deep greens and blues and the Island is sometimes lost in mist. The land scenes are in lush yellow-greens and flashing blues. Brilliant kingfishers and gulls lend sharp clear contrasts (see Color Plate 3, p. XXVI). Then comes a lone little cat, a dramatic and mysterious figure, a small island of furry life. Of course, the idea of each one of us being an island is a concept entirely foreign to children, but Mr. Weisgard's kitty is understandable—kitty in her little sailboat, kitty jumping straight up in the air in kitten fashion, kitty a gay, courageous explorer of the unknown such as every child would like to be. This book lifted the awareness books to a new level of beauty, but has never been a children's favorite. The collaboration of these two creative artists also gave young children *The Golden Egg Book* (Simon & Schuster, 1947) and *The Little Lost Lamb* (Doubleday, 1945), two superb picture books that, together with *The Little Island,* represent Leonard Weisgard's finest work.

Margaret Wise Brown, with her incredible output, used many other artists but never achieved with them the distinction of these three books in which the pictures of Leonard Weisgard not only interpret but illumine her text.

Roger Duvoisin

Another collaboration that has won praise and popularity is to be found in the weather and season books written by Alvin Tresselt and illustrated by the versatile Roger Duvoisin. *White Snow, Bright Snow* (1947) won the Caldecott Medal. Many more books followed, with *Sun Up* (1949), *Follow the Wind* (1950), and *Autumn Harvest* (1951), all published by Lothrop, among the best. The texts are pleasantly rhythmic and make the child aware of the dramatic changes in weather or season, not as something to fear but to watch, be a part of, and enjoy. Mr. Duvoisin's illustrations for these books are simple and almost posterlike when compared with the intricate details of his Happy Lion illustrations. But these weather and season pictures are also full of action and interpret mood and a feeling for nature's little dramas.

Marc Simont (1915–   )

Another awareness book that won the Caldecott Medal for its illustrator, Marc Simont, is *A*

Tree Is Nice, by Janice May Udry (Harper, 1956). Here is Awareness with a capital *A,* and it reminds some oldsters of such grade-school afflictions as being asked to write a theme on Trees. "Some trees have nuts," wrote the country child. "Trees make it shady," scribbled the city child, and then both resorted to intensive pencil-chewing for further inspiration. Of course, Miss Udry

In bed you can have your own little house for a little while— under the blankets.

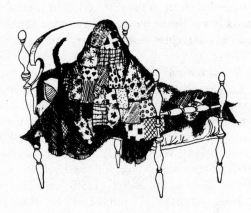

Just you and the pussy cat.

Illustration by Irene Haas for *A Little House of Your Own* by Beatrice Schenk de Regniers, Harcourt. Copyright 1954 by Beatrice Schenk de Regniers and Irene Haas. (book 4½ by 9)

does better and Mr. Simont does better still. At least "We can climb a tree" is a child's point of view about nature—what you can do *with* it, *to* it or *in* it, so Marc Simont shows them climbing adventurously. "In the fall leaves come down and we play in them." Here the brilliant reds and orange of autumn are the background for the children's activities in the fallen leaves. If these pictures lack the usual humor which is one of Mr. Simont's strongest characteristics, it is because the expository text does not lend itself to the jocular. Brilliant color and the strong composition of these pictures are some compensation. This book pleases teachers because of the seasonal activities it records, but ask librarians how many children ever take the book out on their own.

Irene Haas (1929–   )

Like many other young artists, Irene Haas had tried her hand at various kinds of art work before she had the good fortune to encounter Margaret McElderry, a gifted editor of children's books. It was she who helped Miss Haas find "The work I love best"—making pictures for children's books. Certainly her discovery was a happy event for children because this talented artist gives them pictures that are full of lively details and humor and that provide a penetrating interpretation of the text. Her pictures for Beatrice Schenk de Regniers' *A Little House of Your Own* (Harcourt, 1954) give a sensitive interpretation of the child's desire to be alone sometimes, and to have his privacy respected. The mood is one of quietness and withdrawal. On the other hand, Miss Haas' sketches for *Was It a Good Trade?* (Harcourt, 1956), written by Mrs. de Regniers, are in a vein of humorous exaggeration as giddy as the text. Her illustrations for Paul Kapp's *A Cat Came Fiddling* (Harcourt, 1956) and Sesyle Joslin's *There is a Dragon in My Bed* (Harcourt, 1961) are among her humorous best.

Joan Walsh Anglund

One type of awareness book attempts to objectify abstractions for children despite the fact that the young are hopeless realists, addicted to action and more action, with precious little introspection along the way. One of the successful creators of these abstractions-made-concrete is Joan Walsh Anglund, whose books are so pretty in format and sentiment adults buy them for valentines. *Look Out the Window* (Harcourt, 1959) may have a double meaning for adults but is pleasantly objective in calling children's attention to the everyday world. *A Friend Is Someone Who Likes You* (Harcourt, 1958) deals with a more abstract idea and *Love Is a Special Way of Feeling* (Harcourt, 1960) with one still more abstract. To be sure, in both books the author-artist tries with simplicity and sincerity to explain friendship or love in terms of a child's activities, but what has fishing to do with love? Consider the poor fish. And does or can a child feel love when he watches a bird "soar against a pale blue sky . . ." or will reading these pages make him feel love the next time he watches a bird? Feeding a lost cat or helping someone who needs help are objective, understandable acts, but sharing thoughts and feelings is far removed from the consciousness of a child. These concepts appeal to grownups who fondly remember the charm and the evanescence of childhood and hope with these little books to catch and hold the child's attention with the significance of the experiences he is bouncing through so heedlessly.

Maurice Sendak (1928–) ✓

Another type of awareness book, one dealing humorously with the meaning of words from a child's point of view, brought the artist Maurice Sendak into well-deserved prominence. The book was *A Hole Is to Dig* (Harper, 1952), by Ruth Krauss. It is made up of children's definitions which are undeniably funny to adults and to children old enough to see the joke. Typical is "mud is to jump in and slide in and yell doodlee-doodleedoo." For these definitions Mr. Sendak's pen-and-ink drawings of small, homely, cavorting children are irresistible. Just to look at them is to chuckle and feel a fearful desire to kick up your heels and stand on your head also. Equally comic are his pictures for Beatrice Schenk de Regniers' *What Can You Do With a Shoe?* (Harper, 1955). Here Mr. Sendak's gift for humorous exaggeration comes into full play. A poker-faced boy in his father's coat teases a dressed-up little girl by suggesting the most out-

landish things to do with a shoe or a chair or what have you. Then when she reaches the boiling point or tears, he fiendishly capitulates and a chair, after all, is to sit on! Equally amusing are

Illustration by Maurice Sendak for *What Do You Say, Dear?* by Sesyle Joslin, Young Scott Books. Copyright 1958 by Sesyle Joslin. (book 8¼ by 7)

his pictures for that astonishing "Book of Manners for All Occasions"—*What Do You Say, Dear?* by Sesyle Joslin (W. R. Scott, 1958). The same boy in the outsized coat is on hand and the same little girl but in various garbs, as a nurse, for instance, bandaging a patient who has been bitten by a dinosaur, and when he thanks her the book prompts in long-suffering parental style—

What do you say, dear?

You're welcome. However, humorous exaggeration does not represent Maurice Sendak's only style. In his own picture-story, *Kenny's Window* (Harper, 1956), he shows a sensitive perception of the lonely, imaginative quality of childhood, and in his pictures for Janice Udry's *Moon Jumpers* (Harper, 1959) he interprets the occasional ecstasies of childhood. In that book, a runner-up for the Caldecott Medal, text and pictures make a lyric whole (see Color Plate 2, p. XXX). This is awareness with beauty. Its appeal to children is doubtful.

What is the future of these awareness books? Anyone who risks a prophecy in the field of juvenile publications is courting disaster. After all, grownups are the buyers of books for children, and grownups in every generation lean toward didacticism of one kind or another. Besides, ours is a self-conscious generation. Adults talk about the subconscious, their complexes, their frustrations, and they worry about the same things in their children. At least these awareness picture books try to increase the children's happy, wholesome sensitivities. Leonard Weisgard and Maurice Sendak have been either fortunate or perspicacious in choosing some of the better texts to illustrate because there are dozens of these books not comparable to the few mentioned in this sampling. Will their adult appeal keep them alive or will artists find some of their best work falling into the limbo of the out of print?

SUMMARY

Looking back over this development of the child's picture book, we realize that it has obviously come a long way from the Latin *Orbis Pictus* of the seventeenth century and the English *A Little Pretty Pocket-Book* of the eighteenth century. But interestingly enough, there is nothing livelier nor better drawn today than those frolicking animals from the Japanese "Scroll of Animals" of the twelfth century.

With only a few new trends, certain types of picture books have persisted over the years. For instance, every generation of children loves the animal picture book whether it is that proper Briton *Johnny Crow* or the French *Happy Lion* or the Bostonian *Ducklings*. ABC books also persist in great variety. "*A* apple pie" has given way to every sort of beast known to ark and zoo, while the modern city provides an alphabet. Mother Goose continues to be the artists' favorite author, and it is probably safe to say that a new picture edition of the good dame's jingles turns up yearly. Picture-stories, whether about *Peter Rabbit* of over half a century ago or the last adventure of *Little Tim* or *Madeline,* are the most numerous, varied, and popular of all the picture books. Of the many kinds of picture-stories, picture-book editions of single fairy tales have been one of the brightest developments in recent years. These have added greatly to children's understanding and enjoyment of the old tales.

Two new types of picture books have evolved recently—the picture-biography and the awareness book. There are still not very many picture-biographies, but they may well develop richly in the future since the D'Aulaires have shown the way. For the awareness books no prophecy is safe, but the comical or the beautiful seem to stand a better chance with children unless adult enthusiasm for the abstract and philosophical carries the day.

With such artists as Roger Duvoisin, Feodor Rojankovsky, Lynd Ward, Fritz Eichenberg, Nicolas Sidjakov, Maurice Sendak, Barbara Neustadt, Bruno Munari, Barbara Cooney, and Marcia Brown working in the field of picture books, the future is bright. And for the child not yet able to read, these books are sources of new ideas, new understandings, and new delights. A child poring over a picture book is a young explorer, discovering in his book adventure or fun or new ideas. More than this he is also unconsciously learning to be aware of line, color, and composition, as great artists have used them in their pictures for meaning and beauty.

BIBLIOGRAPHY

COLBY, JEAN POINDEXTER, *The Children's Book Field,* Pellegrini, 1952.

DARTON, F. J. H., *Children's Books in England: Five Centuries of Social Life,* Macmillan, 1932.

FERRIS, HELEN, ed., *Writing Books for Boys and Girls,* Doubleday, 1952.

HUDSON, DEREK, *Arthur Rackham, His Life and Work,* Scribner, 1960.

KIEFER, MONICA, *American Children Through Their Books, 1700–1835,* foreword by Dorothy Canfield Fisher, Univ. of Pennsylvania Press, 1948.

MAHONY, BERTHA E., LOUISE P. LATIMER, and BEULAH FOLMSBEE, comps., *Illustrators of Children's Books, 1744–1945,* Horn Book, 1947.

MILLER, BERTHA MAHONY and ELINOR WHITNEY FIELD, eds., *Caldecott Medal Books: 1938–1957,* Horn Book, 1957. *Newbery Medal Books: 1922–1955,* Horn Book, 1955.

MUIR, PERCY, *English Children's Books, 1600 to 1900,* Praeger, 1954.

OPIE, IONA and PETER, eds., *The Oxford Dictionary of Nursery Rhymes,* Oxford, 1951.

SMITH, IRENE, *A History of the Newbery and Caldecott Medals,* Viking, 1957.

VIGUERS, RUTH HILL, MARCIA DALPHIN, and BERTHA MAHONY MILLER, comps., *Illustrators of Children's Books, 1946–1956,* Horn Book, 1958.

MILESTONES IN CHILDREN'S BOOKS

From 1484 to 1928

1484 Aesop's Fables, translated and printed by William Caxton

Illustration by William Caxton for *Aesop's Fables*.

These fables were originally intended for adult reading, but the children probably heard them read aloud and took them over. Later, in 1692, Sir Roger l'Estrange put out a special children's edition.

1646 Spiritual Milk for Boston Babes, John Cotton

This tedious theological treatise in catechism form was designed, alas, for the edification of the young; it is important only because it was one of the earliest children's books to be imported from England.

1657 or 1658 Orbis Pictus, Comenius (original in Latin)

Generally considered to be the earliest picture book for children, *Orbis Pictus* was certainly the first book we know to use explanatory pictures to amplify a word's meaning, much as the modern primer does.

1691 The New England Primer

Almost as depressing as the *Spiritual Milk,* this little primer inducted New England children into the joys of reading.

1697 Contes de ma Mère l'Oye, Perrault

In France appeared *Histoires ou Contes du Temps Passé avec des Moralités,* popularly called *Contes de ma Mère l'Oye.* These eight famous folk tales—The Sleeping Beauty, Cinderella, Puss in Boots, Little Red Riding Hood, Bluebeard, Riquet with the Tuft, Little Thumb, Diamonds and Toads—are still beloved by children.

1715 Divine and Moral Songs for Children, Isaac Watts

Realizing that poetry makes words easily remembered, Watts fashioned moralistic verses and wonderful hymns, the former for children, the latter for all ages. *Divine and Moral Songs* was originally titled *Divine Songs Attempted in Easy Language for the Use of Children.*

1719 Robinson Crusoe, Daniel Defoe

Adventure at last! Defoe, pamphleteer and satirist, in trouble politically and religiously most of his life, turned out the memorable story of a lone man, marooned on an island, creating and controlling a savage world.

1726 Gulliver's Travels, Jonathan Swift

A political satire by the famous Dean of the Dublin Cathedral, *Gulliver's Travels* was not intended for children, but was appropriated by them, in part at least. The miniature world of the Lilliputians is their favorite section and the double meanings do not trouble them.

1729 Tales of Mother Goose, Perrault (first English translation)

Perhaps it was from this pioneer translation of the popular folk tales that John Newbery got the idea for the title of his nursery rhyme book.

1744 A Little Pretty Pocket-Book

John Newbery's famous first venture into the field of book publishing for children was highly successful. This little miscellany included games, proverbs, fables, a rhymed alphabet, and two moral letters to children signed by Jack the Giant-Killer.

1765 Mother Goose's Melody or Sonnets for the Cradle

The publication date of this work has been open to question, but the Opies (*Oxford Dictionary of Nursery Rhymes*) place it as 1765. However, no copy earlier than T. Carmen's edition of 1780 survives.

1765 The History of Little Goody Two-Shoes

Almost as famous as *A Little Pretty Pocket-Book* and *Mother Goose* is this little novel of the life, sufferings, and successes of the enterprising Margery Meanwell.

1785 Mother Goose's Melodies (Isaiah Thomas edition)

Publisher W. H. Whitmore vouches for the fact that this was the first American edition of Mother Goose, pirated from Newbery. The 1899 Whitmore edition was titled *The Original Mother Goose's Melody.*

1789 Songs of Innocence, William Blake

Authentic poetry began for children with William Blake's remarkable book. It was followed by *Songs of Experience* in 1794.

1804 Original Poems for Infant Minds, Ann and Jane Taylor

In the gently moralistic vein of Isaac Watts, these sisters wrote children's verses that were much-loved in their day. In 1806 *Rhymes for the Nursery* appeared.

1807 The Butterfly's Ball, William Roscoe

Enormously popular in its day, this long picture-poem has no story but is full of amusing descriptions of dressy insects, pictured with human faces.

1822 A Visit from St. Nicholas, Clement C. Moore

This lively narrative poem has attracted many major artists whose imaginative illustrations have proved as spellbinding as the spirited verse. It was written in 1822, but not published until 1823.

1823 Grimm's Popular Stories (translated into English by Edgar Taylor)

Published in two volumes between the years 1823 and 1826, these unforgettable old tales caught the imagination of English children and of adults as well.

1843 A Christmas Carol, Charles Dickens

Perhaps this classic was intended for adults, but how wise children are when they appropriate books that speak to them.

1846 Book of Nonsense, Edward Lear

Illustration from Edward Lear's *Book of Nonsense.*

Hilarious jingles with equally absurd pictures constituted England's first contribution to laughter in the evolution of children's books.

1846 Fairy Tales, Hans Christian Andersen (first English translation)

These beautiful stories, sometimes adaptations of folk themes, sometimes completely original, mark the beginning of the modern fanciful tale.

1846 Struwwelpeter, Heinrich Hoffmann

Translated from the German in 1848, *Slovenly Peter* added its humorous exaggerations both in picture and verse to the child's sense of the comic. Here was tongue-in-cheek moralizing about untidiness or fussiness or haughtiness that set both children and grownups chuckling.

1852 A Wonder-Book for Girls and Boys, Nathaniel Hawthorne

Hawthorne's famous retelling of the Greek myths, popular for a long time because of its imaginative and storytelling qualities, is now little used, perhaps because the author reduced the Olympians to child size, sacrificing the stern adult meanings.

1865 Alice's Adventures in Wonderland, Lewis Carroll (Charles Lutwidge Dodgson)

Illustration by Sir John Tenniel for *Through the Looking-Glass* by Lewis Carroll.

One of the world's great fantasies came from an Oxford don, a lecturer in logic and mathematics. The nonsensical adventures of Alice in her mad world have a curious logic that is not wholly childlike.

1865 Hans Brinker, or the Silver Skates, Mary Mapes Dodge

Written by an American who had never been to Holland, this story of Dutch life and adventure is still good reading and has enjoyed long popularity.

1867-1876 Sing a Song of Sixpence, illustrated by Walter Crane

Since Crane's Toy Books were never dated, 1867–1876 is only an approximation of the years in which his picture books appeared. His work marked the beginning of modern color printing and fine design applied to children's books.

1868-1869 Little Women, Louisa M. Alcott

This notably realistic classic of family life has been read, reread, laughed and cried over by girls for generations. Issued originally in two parts.

1872 Sing-Song, Christina Rossetti

A gifted poet wrote these tender and lovely lyrics for children, their first collection of lyric verse since William Blake.

1876 The Adventures of Tom Sawyer, Mark Twain (Samuel Clemens)

Here is realism and Americana for young readers, written in the vernacular by a great humorist who, in Tom, remembered his own boyhood.

1877 Black Beauty, Anna Sewell

Although the horse is overly humanized, this famous book marks the beginning of the popularity of stories about the vicissitudes of animals, both pets and wild creatures.

1878 Under the Window, Kate Greenaway

Undistinguished verses about children's play activities are recorded on pages that are pictorial lyrics. The quaint costumes of the characters influenced children's clothes over much of the world.

1878 The House That Jack Built and The Diverting History of John Gilpin, illustrated by Randolph Caldecott

Illustration from *Randolph Caldecott's Picture Book.*

Continuing in the tradition of Walter Crane, Randolph Caldecott brought the picture book new distinction with his humorous, lively illustrations.

1880 The Peterkin Papers, Lucretia Hale

Told with a straight face, these "moron stories" are as fantastic as any of the "Clever Elsies" or sillies of the folk tales.

1883 Treasure Island, Robert Louis Stevenson

Mystery, unforgettable characters, and hair-raising action make this absorbing story by a great storyteller as spellbinding today as ever.

1883 Nights with Uncle Remus, Joel Chandler Harris

Illustration by A. B. Frost for *Uncle Remus: His Songs and His Sayings* by Joel Chandler Harris. Copyright, 1908, 1920 by Esther La Rose Harris. Reproduced by permission of Appleton-Century-Crofts, publishers.

These Negro folk tales, recorded by a man with a keen ear for dialect and the cadence of Negro speech, are the first great collection of folk tales passed on by oral tradition in our United States.

1883 The Merry Adventures of Robin Hood, Howard Pyle

Illustration by Howard Pyle for *The Merry Adventures of Robin Hood* by Howard Pyle, Charles Scribner's Sons. Reproduced by permission.

For years this was the favorite version of these enchanting hero tales. Pyle's meticulous and beautiful illustrations greatly enhanced the book.

1884 Heidi, Johanna Spyri (date of English translation)

The story of the little Swiss girl, her grandfather, and her goats has become a classic. Heidi's great love for the peace and beauty of her mountains speaks to every young reader.

1884 **The Adventures of Huckleberry Finn, Mark Twain (Samuel Clemens)**

This work is considered by many critics to be the greatest of all Twain's books, but *Tom Sawyer* still holds first place with most young readers.

1885 **A Child's Garden of Verses, Robert Louis Stevenson**

Said to have been inspired by one of Kate Greenaway's little books, *A Child's Garden of Verses* contains poems as fresh today as ever. Their singing quality and the subject matter make the book a real treasure.

1886 **Little Lord Fauntleroy, Frances Hodgson Burnett**

Though this book seems saccharine today, it did not seem so to the children of the time.

1889 **The Blue Fairy Book, Andrew Lang**

This was the first of Andrew Lang's long series of folk tale collections, named for various colors. His excellent versions popularized the tales.

1894 **The Jungle Book, Rudyard Kipling**

Children were fascinated by this tale of a boy raised by wolves, knowing the languages and laws of the jungle.

1899 **The Story of the Treasure-Seekers, E. Nesbit**

This was the first of the much-loved series of stories about the Bastable children, forever intent on restoring the fortune of the family.

1900 **Little Black Sambo, Helen Bannerman**

Helen Bannerman's book is a perfect example of the picture-story in which text and illustrations are a complete unit.

1901 **The Tale of Peter Rabbit, Beatrix Potter**

Because this book was written and circulated before the idea of publication occurred to the author there is a conflict about the dates. Percy Muir (*English Children's Books*) insists that the author's own date, 1900, is wrong and 1901 is correct. We know at least that this small picture-story is written and illustrated with consummate skill.

1903 **Johnny Crow's Garden, L. Leslie Brooke**

Leslie Brooke is known for this and for *Ring o' Roses,* a delightful Mother Goose book. Sly humor, excellent drawing, and good use of color mark his picture books.

1908 **Wind in the Willows, Kenneth Grahame**

Written by a master of prose style, *Wind in the Willows* is pure enchantment. It is rich in sensory appeal, peopled with unforgettable characters, full of humor, kindliness, and warmth.

1921 **The Story of Mankind, Hendrik Willem van Loon**

Illustration from Hendrik Willem van Loon's *The Story of Mankind,* Black and Gold Library. Reproduced by permission of Liveright, publishers.

The first book to receive the Newbery Medal tells the history of man's slow march toward civilization.

1924 **When We Were Very Young, A. A. Milne**

With these deft verses, Christopher Robin joined the juvenile immortals and went gaily on through *Now We Are Six* (1927).

1926 **Winnie-the-Pooh, A. A. Milne**

Illustration by E. H. Shepard for *The House at Pooh Corner* by A. A. Milne. Copyright, 1928, by E. P. Dutton & Co., Inc. Renewal, 1956, by A. A. Milne. Reproduced by publisher's permission. Illus. copyright, E. H. Shepard.

After the first book of verse, Christopher Robin and Pooh Bear set off on a series of prose adventures that are the essence of straight-faced humor. *The House at Pooh Corner* followed in 1928.

1926 **Smoky, the Cow Horse, Will James**

Written in cowboy vernacular, this is a genuinely moving story of the vulnerability of animals at the hands of unscrupulous men.

1928 **Millions of Cats, Wanda Gág**

Told and illustrated by an artist steeped in folk tales, *Millions of Cats* paved the way for the "golden years" of the thirties when picture books achieved a new importance. Which of today's books will become the classics of tomorrow?

BOOK 1: TIME FOR POETRY

READING POETRY TO CHILDREN

With the child's world overflowing with brightly illustrated books about everything from puppies to atoms, fairy tales to biography, and here-and-now adventures to adventures on Mars, it is reassuring to hear teachers and parents ask, "What about children and poetry? When and how should it begin? Is it possible today to develop in children a permanent liking for poetry when other books, radio, television, and moving pictures all seem to crowd it out?"

The oral approach to poetry

Young children make it possible to answer these questions optimistically because in the years before they learn to read, they get their poetry as men first got it—through their ears. And, like their unread ancestors, children respond to verse with every evidence of enjoyment and almost immediate participation. When a grownup reads *Mother Goose* to small children their frequent response is "Sing it again," which the willing slave does until presently the children join in and chant with him. They may mark time with their heads or hands, or jounce gaily with their small bodies, or begin to chant the words for themselves. These responses are precisely the responses children make to that other aural art, music, because poetry is like music. It tickles their ears with its tunefulness and rhythm, and promotes a joining-in response just as music does.

This is a first clue for the happy introduction of poetry to children and young people—it should be spoken and heard in order to be wholly understood and enjoyed. The Irish poet William Butler Yeats wrote:

I have just heard a poem spoken with so delicate a sense of its rhythm, with so perfect a respect for its meaning, that if I were a wise man and could persuade a few people to learn the art I would never open a book of verse again.[1]

By this he implies that reading a poem silently from the printed page is to miss its music and perhaps even its meaning. If this is true for grownups, it is doubly true for children, who encounter so many reading difficulties in the printed form of poetry that they come to suspect it as queer and hazardous. But when they hear it read with sincerity and vigor, they enjoy its swing and readily catch its meaning. If children are to develop a genuine liking for poetry, they must hear quantities of it read aloud from their earliest years, and, simultaneously, begin to speak it, and, later, read it aloud for themselves.

This places the responsibility for the development of a growing taste for poetry upon the grownups who guide children's literary experiences. It is the grownups who must choose and read poetry to children in the years before they can read it for themselves. And, since adults are sometimes as afraid of poetry as children are, a few first aids to reading it aloud may be in order.

When the small child commands "Sing it again," it shows that he recognizes music when he hears it, whether it is made with an instrument or with words. For the first appeal of poetry is through its melody and movement, and when it is read, these must be preserved and even emphasized. Walter de la Mare calls these qualities "tune and runningness" and they are the qualities which distinguish poetry from prose. Nor are they merely ear-tickling devices. They serve a

[1] William Butler Yeats, *Ideas of Good and Evil* (New York: Macmillan, 1907), p. 16.

variety of purposes. The melody and movement of a poem sometimes suggest the action the poet is describing. Sometimes they help to establish a mood or feeling. And sometimes they underscore or clarify the meaning. Since this is true, it is well to know what is meant by melody and movement in poetry or "tune and runningness" or music and rhythm, however you wish to designate these qualities.

The melody or tune of poetry

Let's consider the tune of poetry first. This refers in part to the sound of the words. That is, a poet chooses words not only for their precise shades of meaning but also for their peculiar vowel or consonant sounds, which actually reinforce the mood or meaning he is trying to express. Melody in poetry may stem from rhyming words at the conclusion or within the lines, but rhyme is only a part of the music. Vowel or consonant combinations, the explosiveness or smoothness of the lines, the clipped brevity or sonority of the words, these are also involved. For instance, half the fun of Laura Richards'

> Riddle cum diddle cum dido,
> My little dog's name is Fido,

turns upon the ear-tickling sounds of those explosive consonants. And, by the way, it is interesting to notice how often nonsense verse depends for its effects upon the staccato beat of consonants. "One misty moisty morning," "Husky hi, husky hi," "Godfrey Gordon Gustavus Gore," "The Pirate Don Durk of Dowdee" are all funnier because of their absurd sounds. And you know something humorous is under way the moment you read the titles of T. S. Eliot's poems about his nonsensical cats—"The Rum Tum Tugger" and "Macavity: the Mystery Cat." So, when you have nonsense verse to read, watch for the funny-sounding consonants and make the most of them.

Lovely vowel combinations produce subtler and more beautiful melodies.

> Oh, fair to see
> Bloom-laden cherry tree,
> Arrayed in sunny white;

> An April day's delight,
> Oh, fair to see!

is like a clear, sweet tune because of the beauty of its vowel sounds. *Mother Goose,* with her "Blow, wind, blow" and many others, develops early the child's sensitivity to the melody of words. Eleanor Farjeon has two poems, "Boys' Names" and "Girls' Names," whose charm lies in the unique tone color produced by the vowel sounds of certain first names. These vowels must be given full value, not only to bring out the music of the lines but to enhance the humor of the surprise endings, which turn upon a sharp contrast in sound.

Perhaps these examples suffice to illustrate the principle that to read poetry aloud effectively and meaningfully, the reader must give careful thought to the sound values of words. Ignore this melody of verse, whether it is sonorous or clipped, harsh or sweet, staccato or flowing, and you lessen the impact of the poem on yourself and your listeners. Give the vowels and consonants their full values in roundness or crispness and you enhance both the melody and the meaning of the poem.

Rhythm and movement in poetry

Mother Goose is a good first source of "runningness" for children. Her pages are full of bouncy rhythms that hop, skip, jump, gallop, walk, or swing as gently as a lullaby. "Ride a cock horse" is as unmistakably a gallop as "Hippety hop to the barber shop" is a skip, and "To market to market" an everyday, off-to-the-grocery sort of a walk. Movement in verse is its swing and lilt, its sledge-hammer beat, or its soporific softness. These are the result of meter and the rhythmic patterns of words and lines. Like melody, they differentiate verse from prose.

Small children usually like their rhythms well marked and contagiously gay, in poetry as well as in music. When a small boy in Utah heard Dorothy Baruch's "Merry-Go-Round" for the first time, he immediately responded by waving one arm in a big arc, going faster and faster as the carrousel gained momentum, and slowing down until he and the poem came to a full stop together. Some little girls thought Kate Greenaway's children were jumping rope in her "Jump—jump—jump," so they tried it themselves. And the children soon discover that the words in Mr. Milne's "Hoppity" hop right along with Christopher Robin.

Presently, the grownup who reads many poems to children discovers subtler movements in poetry than the obvious examples just cited. For instance, in Stevenson's "Where Go the Boats" there is a flowing-water movement throughout the lines, for all the world like the surge of the river in the music of Smetana's "River Moldau." Or in Walter de la Mare's "The Cupboard" there is a gay, tripping rhythm, almost syncopated, that is like the jubilant prancing of the small boy who is about to receive some "Banbury Cakes and Lollipops." To read this poem heavily with a singsong emphasis on the metrical beat is to destroy completely its gaiety and fun.

Meter and rhythm

This brings up a ticklish problem in reading verse aloud. Because of the nature of poetry and the exciting effect of its movement, it is agreed that this quality of rhythm must be preserved and emphasized. Yet that very emphasis may result, both with children and adults, in singsong which can reduce a poem to meaningless patter. To avoid this, the reader must recognize the difference between rhythm and the metric beat of poetry. Meter is the precise number of syllables or the organization of feet to a line, while rhythm is the larger flow of cadences, the rise and fall of sound. It might be said that the metric beat of poetry is like the beat of the metronome in music. If you play a musical composition with the precise beat of a metronome, you have music as mechanical as a hurdy-gurdy. So, if you read poetry with a precise marking of the metric beat, the results will be singsong and meaningless patter. To avoid this, think carefully of the meaning the words must convey and speak them in the rhythms of natural speech while respecting the larger flow of the lines as well. The metric beat often obscures meaning where the natural rhythm will clarify it. Take the first two lines of "The Cupboard." The metric beat would make it read:

I knoẃ a little ́ cup board ́
With a ́ tee ny ́ tiny ́ key,

But such reading is nonsense. No one tells an interesting bit of news in any such singsong patter. The rhythms of natural speech would find the child telling his exciting news like this:

I know a little *cupboard*
With a teeny tiny *key,*

Those last words are not overstressed, but they do stand out as the very center and focus of a delightful secret. And the metric pattern is not upset by this reading. There is a due regard for lines and rhymes, but the mechanical tick tick tick of the metronome gives way to the natural rhythms of storytelling in verse form.

Functions of melody and movement

Actually, melody and movement in poetry are not two separate qualities but inseparables, one an integral part of the other. That is, the vowel and consonant sounds of words help to make the swing and movement of the lines, and these, in turn, are a part of the melody or tune of the poem. Together, these essential characteristics of poetry serve three purposes: melody and movement may suggest the very action the poet is describing; they may help to establish the mood of the poem; or they may even clarify or emphasize the idea—what the poem is about.

For example, in the words and short lines of Eleanor Farjeon's "Mrs. Peck Pigeon," there is actually the bobbing, teetering motion of a pigeon "picking for bread." In Herbert Asquith's "Skating," the lines swing and swoop with the skater. The galloping rhythm of Stevenson's "Windy Nights" goes on and on like the mysterious wind-rider galloping farther and farther away and then coming back again. "Texas Trains and Trails" gives the "chuck-a-luck, chuck-a-luck" movement of trains to perfection, ending with a burst of speed and a "whoop," which the children love. These are only a few of innumerable examples wherein the music of poetry suggests the action being described.

The power of poetry to evoke a mood is evident as you speak or read it aloud. The quiet sound of "This Happy Day" induces a mood of gentle serenity. "Where's Mary?" is an amusing study in mounting irritability. The words and lines pile up with an accumulative, staccato beat that makes the reader feel like the peevish woman who is speaking. In contrast, there are quiet and peace in the plain words of "Evening Hymn." This poem has no patter, no swinging rhythm, but it uses simple words, rich in associative values, and its melody is like plain song, almost monotonous in its austere simplicity and its power to comfort and reassure. There is a mood of hushed mystery in "Some One," sheer gaiety in "The Little Whistler" and "Jill Came from the Fair," sober reflection in "House Blessing," and fun and nonsense in "Timothy Boon." These are only a few examples of the power of melody and movement in poetry to evoke a mood.

Even more surprising is the discovery that when you speak or read poetry aloud, the unique music of a particular poem may help to emphasize or clarify the meaning. For instance, if you understood no English and heard someone read "Firefly," you would know that it had to do with something small and frail because the words are little with no sonorities, and as vanishing in sound as the "little bug all lit" is in sight. Or, if you heard "The sea gull curves his wings" without understanding the words, you would still catch the feeling of contrasting ideas in each verse. The first couplets in each are smooth, slow, and melodious. The second couplets are harsh, staccato, like a cry of warning, which they really are. Understanding the words of these two poems, you are likely to forget how much the effectiveness and even the clarity of the idea in each is due to the tone patterns in which they are expressed. These examples can be multiplied. The sledge-hammer beat of T. S. Eliot's "The world turns and the world changes" actually serves to hammer in the grave importance of his message. And all through James Stephens' "The Snare" there is a sense of hurry and pressure which is the very essence of the idea or significance of that poem.

It is true that in order to read poetry aloud or to speak it effectively the reader must understand its meaning. And it is also true that the process of aloudness forces the reader to know what he is saying. If his words are not making sense as he reads aloud, he quickly becomes aware of it. But there is an additional point—namely, that as he reads a poem aloud, its tune and movement will, over and over again, supply the reader with clues to meaning which are entirely lacking when the poem is read silently.

Here lies the chief reason for the oral (and aural) approach to poetry. If it is read silently, the reader may miss its unique musical pattern and he may also be blandly unaware of how little of its meaning he is getting. This is driven home the moment he tries it aloud and he is forced to go back, to find out what he is really saying. This means that every unfamiliar poem, of any degree of complexity, must be explored orally so that its music may have a chance to supply clues to meaning and increased enjoyment. It also means that the child's taste for poetry will develop in proportion to the amount of good and suitable verse which he hears vigorously spoken, has a chance to speak for himself, and, later, as his reading skill matures, to read from the printed page also.

Sensory and emotional response to poetry

When you read poetry aloud to children and catch its tempo, tone color, and cadence, you discover that these qualities evoke other reactions which are also essential to understanding and appreciation. These reactions are sensory imagery and emotional response. Sometimes the interpretation of a poem depends upon visual imagery—a picture of trees bowing down their heads as the wind passes by. Sometimes it demands auditory imagery—the rain playing "a little sleep-song on our roof at night." Kinesthetic imagery is especially prominent in poems for small children—the feel of going "Hippity hop to bed," or galloping to "Husky Hi." Even smell, touch, and taste sensations are evoked in the varied poetry offering for children. For instance, the galloping rhythm of "Windy Nights" helps to rouse a feeling of eerie excitement over that galloping wind-rider who comes and goes so mysteriously. This example suggests the close relationship between sensory imagery and emotional response. It might be said that the more vivid the sensory imagery aroused by the lines of a poem, the deeper the emotional reaction to that poem will be. And it might be added that without sensory imagery and emotional reaction there can be no real understanding or appreciation of a poem.

This point is so basic to the whole literature program, both poetry and prose, that it will bear amplification. When, for instance, a child hears a story or a poem for which there are no illustrations, it is quite possible that he will enjoy it only in proportion to his ability to create his own mental pictures of the characters, action, or situation. Hilda Conkling's "Little Snail" will have slight reality for the child who has never seen a snail. That child needs the help of experience or pictures or both before "his house on his back" means anything to him or before there is any humor in the concluding lines of that poem. Walter de la Mare's simple little jingle "The Huntsmen" never says in so many words that it is about three little boys riding their hobbyhorses up to bed. But if children do not understand this and do not see the picture clearly in their minds, then the "clitter clatter" of those wooden sticks on the stairs, and indeed the whole meaning of the poem, will be obscure. If the American child translates "Banbury Cakes and Lollipops" into his favorite chocolate cakes and popsicles, then his sensory imagery of luscious-tasting sweets will illumine the words, and he will share the delight of the boy in the poem.

The grownup's responsibility for interpretation

This is where the grownup comes in. It is his function to help the child translate a poem into his own experience until he shares the vivid sensory imagery and feels a lively emotional response to the selection. This can be done either by preparing for any possible obscurities in a poem before reading it or by talking it over afterwards and taking time to savor its charm. Nowadays, so many children are urban and so much of our poetry is rural that the combination invariably calls for first aids to understanding and enjoyment. Think, for instance, of the peculiar picture a city child must visualize when he hears how Chanticleer "shakes his comb." This is sheer nonsense unless he knows both Chanti-

cleer and his topknot. And, for city children, you may be sure that "the strong withered horse" evokes the peculiar picture of a wrinkled old horse unless the meaning of this expression is cleared up in advance. The ballads are, of course, full of strange words that must be defined before understanding is possible.

But all of these are fairly obvious examples of first aids to meaning. The preparation of a poem may call for something more subtle than attention to unfamiliar words or situations. The adult who has prepared a poem by reading it aloud before she presents it to the children knows the varying moods of poetry for which preparation is often needed. Over and over, the poetry of Walter de la Mare demands some word of explanation in advance. For example, she might say: "This poem 'Some One' is a mystery. Who came knocking? I don't know. See what you think." Or, "Before I read you this poem about 'Tillie' I must tell you something queer. Fern seeds are supposed to work magic on people. Something awful happened to poor old Tillie after she swallowed some." It would be fun, by the way, to follow this poem with "Midsummer Magic" by Ivy Eastwick, where fern (bracken) seed also works its spell. Or, in Elizabeth Coatsworth's " 'Who are you?' asked the cat of the bear," children are much more ready to catch the fun of that poem if you furnish them with one clue in advance—"This poem is a conversation between a cat and a bear. The bear is boasting of his size and his strength, but notice the way the little cat manages to take him down." The condensation in the ballads, together with unfamiliar words, makes it almost necessary to tell the story in advance or at least to furnish the children with definite clues to the main points of the narrative. Then these poems will grow in richness with each rereading.

With many poems, it is better to read them first and then mull them over informally, and reread them. For small children, "Minnie and Mattie" is easy enough to follow but they usually miss the rather amusing detail that one of the old mother hens is guarding a brood of ducklings instead of chickens. That can be brought out casually in the discussion of the poem, and then it is more interesting to them when the poem is reread. "Falling Star" invariably elicits a burst of personal experiences with falling stars and wishes. At an older level, "To Beachey, 1912" calls for amplification until the children sense the wonder and admiration we should all feel when, lying snug in our beds, we hear planes overhead and think of those unknown pilots winging their way through storms and darkness. The ballad stories need to be talked over and speculated about. Why did the wife in the "The Raggle, Taggle Gypsies" run away from her fine hall and husband? Could she have been a gypsy too? What about the maid in "The Wife of Usher's Well?" What has she to do with the story? Certainly, the poems in the last section of the book, "Wisdom and Beauty," call for quiet discussion. These poems are obviously for older children, but, even so, they will often need to be translated into terms of the children's own lives to be really understood. By the way, these should never be used as a group, but slipped in occasionally, one at a time, along with other poetry.

Such preparations for the meaning and mood of a poem and such honest, simple, informal discussions at its conclusion should heighten both understanding and appreciation. Needless to say, the atmosphere of poetry time, whether by the fireside, at bedtime, around a campfire, or in a schoolroom, should be kept informal, happy, and completely comfortable. Not all children will like all of the poems you select, and that is to be expected and is quite all right. Start where your children are, with nonsense verse, probably, and story poems, and you may be sure they will want many of both. But help them at the same time to explore a wide variety of poems. Their enjoyment will increase as they begin to say their favorites with you and learn them in the process. Choral speech or verse choirs may add enormously to their zest for speaking verse and they will learn an astonishing amount of it. A detailed discussion of verse choirs follows this introduction on page xxiv.[2]

How to use this book

Time for Poetry is a collection of poems to be read aloud in schoolrooms, on vacations, by campfires, and in homes. The verses are grouped

[2] *See also May Hill Arbuthnot,* Children and Books *(Scott, Foresman, 1957), Chapter 9. This whole chapter deals with verse choir techniques*

under large subject matter heads with subdivisions under each. For instance, "The Animal Fair" begins with dogs and cats, progresses to birds and beasts of all varieties, and includes the animals of the forest, the farm, the circus, and the zoo. "Animals" is a good group to illustrate the organization. In general, the poems progress, under each topic, from easy to hard, or for young children 4 to 6 to older children 12 to 14. But such a plan means that at the conclusion of a mature poem about a *dog,* suitable for a twelve-year-old child, the unwary reader may find himself confronting a *Mother Goose* jingle about *cats,* suitable for a five-year-old. Even so, it seems best to keep this easy-to-hard plan of organization for the convenience of the teacher or mother who wants a group of cat or rabbit poems all together, so that she can scan them at a glance and choose the ones simple enough or mature enough for her children. There are poems here to fit the seasons, the festivals, and most of the units of the school year. But there are many others which are included just for fun, for variety, or for sheer beauty. These are quite as important as the poems which "correlate" with school subjects, and they will do much to promote the child's emotional and literary growth.

In reading these poems to children, you may wish to begin with the subject that is uppermost in your school activities or in the child's interests, and find a group of verses to fit. The child may love pets or wild animals, or you may be working with community helpers, or modes of travel, or Indians, or colonial heroes. Autumn may be splashing the hillsides with color, or spring working her heady enchantment. Poems may be found to add beauty and fresh meaning to all of these subjects or experiences. But sometimes, when you and the children are bogged down with routine or a general dullness, and such days do occur now and then, why not take a fling at nonsense verse, or a blood and thunder ballad, or a curious whimsey like "Sam" or "Macavity: the Mystery Cat," or end the day with "Evening Hymn" for quiet beauty? Poems may be found which fit the subjects and interests of school and home, but look also for poems in contrast to these, poems which breathe a new breath of life into the everyday world.

With a book that has as wide an age-range appeal as this one and as great a variety of poetry types, it would seem essential that you know in advance what you are going to read. Explore the unfamiliar poems by reading them aloud, of course, in order that you may interpret their melody adequately, know their sensory and emotional appeal, and discover what you wish to clear up in advance or talk over afterwards. Actually, this preparation should not be too onerous. The reading aloud is the one essential. With the children, you can feel your way. If you watch them, it is easy to sense their blankness, and you can amplify, reread, or translate the poem into their own everyday experiences. You can also sense their delight when they chuckle, or their eyes shine, or they sit hushed and breathless, or they ask you to read it again. That is your triumph and your goal—a continuous, day-after-day growth in their liking poetry and wanting to hear more.

For help in reading these poems to children occasional footnotes have been placed at the bottom of the page to be out of your way when you are reading but they are italicized in the hope that they will catch your eye before you read. These footnotes accomplish several purposes. Sometimes they throw additional light on the meaning of the poem. Sometimes they afford first aid to good oral reading or interpretation. Frequently they call attention to the unique musical pattern of a poem or suggest its possibilities for choral speaking. In addition to these footnotes you will find in May Hill Arbuthnot's *Children and Books* (Scott, Foresman and Company, 1957), seven chapters on poetry in Part 2: Sing It Again. These chapters are "Mother Goose," "Ballads and Story-Poems," "Verses in the Gay Tradition," "Poetry of the Child's World," "Singing Words," "Using Poetry with Children," and "Verse Choirs." You will gain much help from using *Poetry Time* (Scott, Foresman and Company, 1951), an album of records in which Mrs. Arbuthnot demonstrates with her own readings her theory and methods of using poetry with small children.

The miracle of the poems in this book is that they take many of the experiences of the child's everyday world and give them a new importance, a kind of glory that they did not have when they were just experiences. "Not the rose, but the scent of the rose" says Eleanor Farjeon about this curious distillation of experience to its essence, which is poetry. And so, because it heightens, deepens, and enriches experience, it becomes a shining armor against vulgarity and brutality. Here are the small animals that the child loves— puppies, kittens, snails, fireflies, butterflies, rabbits that

> ". . . dance hungry and wild
> Under a winter's moon."

In these poems a child goes "Skipping Along Alone" by the sea, or he watches "Boats of mine a-boating" and wonders "Where will all come home?" He finds it pleasant to say "Good morning to the sun" and not unusual to converse with fairies or to hear a goblin arguing with a nymph. These poems carry him from skips and gallops to dreams and aspirations. *Time for Poetry* should be a time to lift young spirits and give them something to grow on, for poetry lovers do grow in grace and in reverence for life because

> "Loveliness that dies when I forget
> Comes alive when I remember."

And children remember poetry.

USING POETRY IN VERSE CHOIRS

A verse choir or choral speaking group is composed of children or adults who speak literature together. A choir usually has three sections of blended voices that may be combined or not as the selection seems to require. Ordinarily such groups speak poetry, but sometimes they use prose when the prose selections are effective spoken in choral form. As a matter of fact, there is such a variety of selections suitable for choral speaking that the choice becomes a matter of choir skills and the individual taste of the leader.

BACKGROUND FOR CHOIR WORK

Launching a verse choir sounds like a formidable undertaking, but actually, in the schoolroom, choral speaking almost starts itself. Wherever there is a teacher who knows and loves poetry, there will be children who love it, too. When the teacher reads aloud to her class, there are always favorite poems the children demand over and over. An observant teacher will presently remark, "I believe you almost know that poem. You are saying it to yourselves right along with me. Let's see if you really know it. I'll read it slowly and softly and you say it with me." Two or three repetitions on two or three consecutive days, and the children will know the poem by heart. They learn poetry as readily as they learn songs, and in no time at all they will have memorized a lot of poetry in just this casual, effortless way. A most desirable outcome!

If the class is a big one, let half the group speak a poem while the other half listens. Then reverse the process, but to keep the listening half on the alert, see if it can come in right on the beat when the first half finishes. Mark the time with your hand or finger as you do when the children sing together, and be sure to keep the

voices light and pleasant to hear. Stop them at once if they become loud or harsh or if they are sing-songing or racing along without thinking. Any of these undesirable things may happen when children or even adults begin to speak together. But when half the group listens, it begins to develop an ear for clear, understandable speech, good timing, and agreeable voices.

A dialogue or a narrative poem with one or more choruses gives the children another chance to listen critically to each other and you begin to get such comments as these: "That was too fast," the listening group says, or, "That was just right. We could understand every word." "That sounded real nice," refers vaguely to both voices and diction. "They kept together," means good timing and unison. Such comments show that the children are unconsciously acquiring good ear training and a feeling for timing, diction, and unison speech.

They should also be developing a sense of speaking for meaning. For instance, in "Oh, Susan Blue" (p. 11) are there one or two persons speaking? The group must decide whether a friend greets Susan Blue and Susan replies hesitatingly, or whether one person speaks the whole six lines. The answer to this decides the way the lines will be spoken. The first interpretation is almost inevitable once the poem is read aloud. "Pussy-cat, pussy-cat" (p. 48) is simple enough for the four-year-olds to speak glibly, but the sixes are capable of deciding whether Cat is telling a tall tale as an excuse or whether he really did see the Queen. Does Cat's Owner believe the runaway? On the answer to these questions depends the way in which those cryptic lines, by Cat and by Owner, will be spoken.

In this preliminary stage, it is just as well to choose practice verses that are not too easily spoiled—Mother Goose for the youngest and nonsense verse for the older children. Here are a few suggestions for this beginning work:

PRELIMINARY SPEAKING TOGETHER
[UNISON]

Children 4–8
THE GRAND OLD DUKE OF YORK (p. 94), a brisk marching rhyme, when repeated may grow louder and nearer and then fade gradually away.
ROCKABYE BABY, a lullaby as peaceful and quieting as "The Grand Old Duke of York" is martial.
HOPPITY (p. 94), a genuine hop with staccato words from the diaphragm.
HOW MANY DAYS HAS MY BABY TO PLAY? (p. 173), a jig if ever there was one.
JONATHAN (p. 127).

Children 9–12
MASTER I HAVE, AND I AM HIS MAN (p. 95), a tremendous gallop requiring lots of breath control to carry that old dun horse through to the end.
HUSKY HI (p. 95), guaranteed to wake up everyone; another gallop, pure nonsense, but wonderful staccato from the diaphragm.
JOG ON, JOG ON, THE FOOT-PATH WAY (p. 78), a regular Boy Scout sort of walking tune.
BELL HORSES, BELL HORSES, WHAT TIME OF DAY? (p. 164), refers to a clock tower where horses prance out.
GRIZZLY BEAR (p. 121).

[DIALOGUE]

Children 4–8
PUSSY-CAT, PUSSY-CAT (p. 48), a subtle conversation between Cat and Owner.
BOW, WOW, WOW! (p. 44), big bully of a dog and little new dog.

Children 9–12
OH, SUSAN BLUE (p. 11), two little girls, over the gate asking, what shall we do?
OLD WOMAN, OLD WOMAN, SHALL WE GO A-SHEARING? (p. 126), not too subtle and good fun.

[CHORUS]

Children 4–8
MY DONKEY (p. 117), the way the chorus is spoken indicates the faking quality of the donkey's ailments.

Children 9–12
A FARMER WENT TROTTING UPON HIS GRAY MARE (p. 116). Each chorus heightens the pleasant or disastrous or laughing events described.

By second or third grades—if the children have heard a variety of poems, can think what they speak, can read dialogue with spirit and understanding, and can distinguish between clear and muddled speech, they are ready to begin work on choral speaking in organized form. It is challenging, it is exhilarating, and it is fun. Let's begin.

GROUPING FOR A VERSE CHOIR

Simply speaking a poem in unison is not verse choir, nor does saying dialogue poems with two groups, or a narrative poem with a single voice reading the story and the group coming in on the chorus constitute true choral speaking. A speaking choir, like a singing choir, requires a tonal grouping of like voices. Instead of having the soprano, contralto, tenor, and bass of a singing choir, a speaking group generally has the three divisions—high, medium, and low voices (H, M, L). With children the range is not so great as with adults, but there *is* a range and the divisions are not too difficult to make. Any teacher who listens to her children talking and reading day after day knows some of the extremely high voices and the surprisingly low voices in the group. Explain to the children that they have been speaking their poems so well that it seems a good time to begin a verse choir. For such a choir they will need high voices, low voices, and some in-between voices to blend the two.

Start by finding some of the high, sweet voices and some of the low, rich voices. Take two or three children at the high range and have them speak some Mother Goose jingle together—"Jack and Jill" or "Little Miss Muffet" or "Jack be nimble"—any ditty that can't be spoiled by repetition. When you have four or five voices that blend nicely in the high range, repeat the process with the low voices. Then try the remaining children for the medium choir, adding as you go to both the high and low groups. There will be a range within each division, but curiously enough there comes to be a blending of voices with a like timbre that the children themselves can recognize. Often they will say, "Oh, Mary belongs in the low choir," or, "John should move up to the high choir."

There is, by the way, no grouping by sex. There is the whole range of high to low among boys as well as girls. Be sure to stress the desirability of having a voice in any of these groups—high, sweet, and light; low, deep, and rich; or medium and pleasant to hear. Children are extremely sensitive to anything in themselves that is out of the ordinary and so there must be sincere praise for each kind of voice. And as for that occasional problem voice that is harsh or nasal, place it in the back of its group and you may need to say now and then, "You have such a strong, carrying voice, Virginia, you can speak just a bit more softly than the others and still be heard." Console yourself with the knowledge that choir work may help that voice.

The moment you have your three groups, let them try—in divided choir form—some poem they already know so that they can hear themselves and sample the curiously exciting effect of the three different choruses. The usual arrangement of the three choirs is shown in the diagram below.

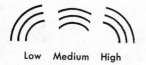

Low   Medium   High

The children stand for both practice sessions and actual performances. As a start take something easy and familiar, perhaps "Chanticleer" by John Farrar (p. 68), for the young children. Have the low voices speak the first two lines, medium voices lines 3 and 4, high voices lines 5 and 6, and conclude lines 7 and 8 with the low voices. And by the way, you will have to transcribe these markings to the poem itself. For the older children, you might use Langston Hughes' "April Rain Song" (p. 160)—line 1 M, 2 H, 3 L—line 4 M, 5 L, 6 H, and the concluding line 7, which is almost like a sigh, may be spoken by the low choir or the whole group of three choirs, speaking together as softly as a breath. When the children first hear the three choirs and the entirely different effect each one gives to a line, they are astonished and delighted. Invari-

ably they want to try more, so be ready with poems that will lend themselves to a variety of choral speaking forms.

CASTING A POEM FOR VERSE CHOIRS

Casting means not only assigning lines to certain choirs but also deciding whether to do a poem in antiphonal style or in unison or perhaps line-a-child. The question of which is the best way to cast a poem cannot be answered conclusively. Probably no two leaders of verse choirs would cast a poem in precisely the same way. Indeed, teachers say that using the same poem a second year with another group of children often leads to a change in the assignment of lines.

However, there are a few general principles which may help a new director. Usually high voices ask a question, unless the questioner is male or definitely on the gruff side. High voices also give a lift to lines and speak the little tripping words or the gay singing words that are bright and clear. Low voices generally answer a question, unless the answer is spoken by a woman. Low voices also take the lines with sonorous, big-sounding words, the grave or ominous lines, or those in the minor key. The medium choir blends the high and low and is most effective for narrative portions of a poem or for opening lines or lines that state an idea. Look back now at "Chanticleer" and "April Rain Song" and, as you read them aloud, see if you can feel why the lines were assigned as they were.

One other general principle: the younger or less experienced the choirs are, the more difficult it is for them to break off or come in briskly at the end of one line. A two- or three-line assignment is safer for beginners than a single line because the choir that picks up the next line must come in precisely on the metric beat. Older children with experience can do this but never the youngest or the beginners. The teacher who is starting this work with her class should read and reread a poem aloud before she decides on the form. Her own interpretation of the lines, her feeling for the quality of the words—grave or gay, brisk, small words or sonorous, big words—these are her clues to casting the poem.

Unison speech

In the British handbooks for choral speaking, unison speech is pointed up as the crowning achievement of well-trained choral groups. But in this country, as we suggested earlier, unison speech is used informally as a starting point. It is unfortunate that many groups never go any further, since there is nothing more monotonous than a whole program of poems spoken in unison. In such programs, the children generally over-enunciate to make up for the mob, or use extremes of high and low voices, or over-dramatize their material. It is natural and desirable to let children speak some of their favorite poems together and in so doing learn to keep their voices light and sweet and to follow the time beat of their leader. So used, unison speech is a good background for choir work until the children are old enough to accept the practice and careful discipline of the latter.

After this preliminary work, when the children have achieved some degree of precision and beauty in their choirs, short poems are often enhanced by fine unison speech. In addition to the verses suggested for "Preliminary Speaking Together," here are other verses that require disciplined practice. All of those listed for the younger children are also acceptable for the older groups.

UNISON

Children 4–8

SINGING-TIME, Rose Fyleman, p. 165
GOOD NIGHT, Victor Hugo, p. 170. For analysis see *Children and Books*, pp. 221–222
GRIZZLY BEAR, Mary Austin, p. 121
WEATHER, Hilda Conkling, p. 152
WATER, Hilda Conkling, p. 152
THE TIDE IN THE RIVER, Eleanor Farjeon, p. 162
Any of the Ogden Nash nonsense verses
THIS HAPPY DAY, Harry Behn, p. 166
AND TIMID, FUNNY, BRISK LITTLE BUNNY, Christina Rossetti
WHO HAS SEEN THE WIND? C. Rossetti, p. 153

Children 9–14

HE WHO HAS NEVER KNOWN HUNGER, Elizabeth Coatsworth, p. 199
FINIS, Sir Henry Newbolt, p. 171

BUFFALO DUSK, Carl Sandburg, p. 33
DUST OF SNOW, Robert Frost, p. 202
FOR, LO, THE WINTER IS PAST, Bible, p. 191
SEAL LULLABY, Rudyard Kipling, p. 76
OH, FAIR TO SEE, Christina Rossetti, p. 194
THE RAINS OF SPRING, Lady Ise, p. 160
DAFFODILS, Kikurio, p. 191
BE LIKE THE BIRD, Victor Hugo, p. 202
THE NOISE OF WATERS, James Joyce, p. 163

Except for "Good Night" and "This Happy Day," the poems for the younger children offer no particular difficulties. The latter may be spoken in unison, but if the group of children is large, let half speak the first verse and the other half the second verse. The higher voices speak the first verse cheerfully and, if you like, a solo voice may speak the last line "Good morning Sun!" The lower voices will speak the second verse with a serene, smooth, sustained tone that is as peaceful as twilight. The last two lines should be spoken quietly and reverently. It is a little prayer of thanksgiving, child-size.

"Who has seen the wind" may also be divided between two groups, each speaking one verse in unison. It calls for sweet, light voices and a slow even, sustained tone throughout.

Be sure the children get the hop into the words when they speak this all-staccato, Christina Rossetti poem:

> And timid, funny, brisk little bunny,
> Winks his nose and sits all sunny.

The suggested poems for older children are a challenge and will reveal that unison speech, if it is to be a finished performance, is far from easy. Take Rossetti's "Oh, fair to see"—it calls for a sustained, even tone and sweet, light quality. When the children first speak it, they may not notice the important contrasting words in the two verses—"bloom-laden" and "fruit-laden." In each case, a lovely description follows. These contrasted verbal pictures need not be unduly emphasized but must come through clearly, and the final "Oh, fair to see!" sings with a special warmth. It is a Gloria!

Kipling's "Seal Lullaby" requires perfect timing. The slow tempo and rocking movement that run throughout the poem must be maintained unbroken to the end. To avoid monotony, there is a light, tender touch in the two lines beginning "Where billow meets billow" and climaxing in the charming "Ah, weary wee flipperling, curl at thy ease!" Then, the slow, even, rocking movement resumes with the wonderful reassurance of the last line that comes out warmly.

One of the most beautiful poems to speak in unison with an experienced choir is "The Noise of Waters." It calls for predominantly low, rich voices speaking slowly, gravely, almost in a monotone. Notice in the first verse the long *o* sounds with *m* or *n* which, by prolonging the nasals ever so slightly, give almost the effect of a moaning wind. In the second verse, the words *blowing, flowing, go, below, fro* bring a rich, round, melody that is beautiful to speak and to hear. The children should make the most of these sounds which give contrast to the two verses and the whole melodic pattern of the poem. But don't let them mouth their words unnaturally.

To console the high voices who were left out of the last poem, let them say lightly "The Rains of Spring" and "Daffodils." In the first poem the lines move along in conversational style, building up to the charming climax of the last line. In "Daffodils" there is a similar pattern, except that the last line is in distinct contrast to the dismal first line and should be spoken as a happy surprise.

The chief problems in unison speaking are to keep the timing exact, to avoid monotony, a heavy tone, or a heavy metric beat, and above all to so interpret meaning that the poem is enhanced by such choral work. It is wonderful training for the children, and these selections are well worth memorizing. Remember always, however, that in a program of choral speaking, unison selections are scattered among other types of choir work.

Dialogue or antiphonal choir work

Like unison speech, dialogue or antiphonal choir work may be a natural starting point and it may also culminate in subtle and disciplined interpretation of poetry. A dialogue poem is, of course, a conversation. A poem that falls into two parts—the two parts often contrasting—is read antiphonally. For example, for the youngest, "Oh, Susan Blue" is dialogue. The friend speaks

the first three lines and Susan answers, somewhat hesitatingly, with the last three lines. On the other hand, the contrasting effects in "Blow wind, blow, and go mill, go" (p. 153), make it a good example of an antiphonal poem, with half the children speaking the sonorous first two lines, and the other half coming in briskly and trippingly on the other three lines. Here are some suggested poems for the two age groups.

DIALOGUE OR ANTIPHONAL

Children 4–8

WHAT DOES THE BEE DO? Christina Rossetti, p. 4

OH, SUSAN BLUE, Kate Greenaway, p. 11

BLOW WIND, BLOW, AND GO MILL, GO, Mother Goose, p. 153

MOON-COME-OUT, Eleanor Farjeon, p. 169

"TALENTS DIFFER," Laura E. Richards, p. 51

OPEN THE DOOR, Marion Edey and Dorothy Grider, p. 172

CONVERSATION BETWEEN MR. AND MRS. SANTA CLAUS, Rowena Bennett (also enjoyed by older group)

PUPPY AND I, A. A. Milne, p. 45

Children 9–14

MOMOTARA, Rose Fyleman, p. 129

OVERHEARD ON A SALTMARSH, Harold Monro, p. 143

HALLOWEEN, Marie Lawson

"WHO ARE YOU?" ASKED THE CAT OF THE BEAR, Elizabeth Coatsworth, p. 50

IT IS RAINING, Lucy Sprague Mitchell, p. 160

GYPSY JANE, William Brighty Rands, p. 14

HOLIDAY, Ella Young, p. 154

COLD WINTER NOW IS IN THE WOOD, Elizabeth Coatsworth, p. 188

THE SEA GULL CURVES HIS WINGS, Elizabeth Coatsworth, p. 54

The first group for the younger children offers no particular difficulties. "Moon-Come-Out" might well be thought of as a unison poem, but the nice little contrast in the two verses suggests the antiphonal form: the first verse for the low voices, a bit slow and sleepy; the second verse brisk, bright, and gay with high voices.

"Talents Differ" goes along in a regular pattern, high voices asking the question, lower voices answering, until the last verse where the tables are turned and the high voices come out triumphantly.

"Open the Door" is delightful dialogue with all sorts of variations possible. The high choir certainly asks the question each time. For the answers, it is fun to use not more than five children, a different group for each verse, or the answers spoken by different solo voices if you prefer.

This poem by Rowena Bennett is a delightful dialogue poem for the youngest:

CONVERSATION BETWEEN
MR. AND MRS. SANTA CLAUS
(*Overheard at the North Pole
Early Christmas Morning*)

"Are the reindeer in the rain, dear?"	**High**
Asked Mrs. Santa Claus.	
"No. I put them in the barn, dear,	**Low**
To dry their little paws."	
"Is the sleigh, sir, put away, sir,	**High**
In the barn beside the deer?"	
"Yes, I'm going to get it ready	**Low**
To use again next year."	
"And the pack, dear, is it back, dear?"	**High**
"Yes. It's empty of its toys,	**Low**
And tomorrow I'll start filling it,	
For next year's girls and boys."	

The selections for the older children range from the simple "Momotara" and "Gypsy Jane" to some rather subtle and beautiful poetry. Marie Lawson's "Halloween" is an eerie dialogue, almost scary until the last two lines in which the child admits—*what?* That she was fooling all along, or that strange, eerie things *do* appear on Halloween? Let the children discuss this and upon their decision will rest the interpretation of those last two lines. The child's lines belong to the high choir. Granny is matter-of-fact, a complete skeptic, and her lines belong to the low voices. The poem may also be spoken by only two children.

"Conversation Between Mr. and Mrs. Santa Claus" by Rowena Bastin Bennett in *Jack and Jill*, December 1947. Copyright 1947 by the Curtis Publishing Company, Philadelphia. By permission of the author.

HALLOWEEN

"Granny, I saw a witch go by,	**High**
I saw two, I saw three!	
I heard their skirts go swish, swish, swish——"	
"Child, 'twas leaves against the sky,	**Low**
And the autumn wind in the tree."	
"Granny, broomsticks they bestrode,	**High**
Their hats were black as tar,	
And buckles twinkled on their shoes——"	
"You saw but shadows on the road,	**Low**
The sparkle of a star."	
"Granny, all their heels were red,	**High**
Their cats were big as sheep.	
I heard a bat say to an owl——"	
"Child, you must go straight to bed,	**Low**
'Tis time you were asleep."	
"Granny, I saw men in green,	**High**
Their eyes shone fiery red,	
Their heads were yellow pumpkins——"	
"Now you've told me what you've seen,	**Low**
WILL you go to bed?"	
"Granny?"	**High**
"Well?"	**Low**
"Don't you believe——?"	**High**
"What?"	**Low**
"What I've seen?	**High**
Don't you know it's Halloween?"	

"Overheard in a Saltmarsh" is a dramatic dialogue that children from second grade to high school speak well. The goblin's lines are spoken by low-medium voices. Keep the "No" down to conversational level until the last; let that come out decisively with emphasis.

"The sea gull curves his wings" is also subtle antiphonal work for older children. The first two lines of both verses are smooth and easy, suggesting the sailing flight of the gull. The second two lines of each verse are a sharp cry of warning.

"Halloween" by Marie A. Lawson in *Child Life*, October 1936. Copyright 1936 by Rand McNally & Company, Chicago. Reprinted by permission of the Estate of Marie A. Lawson.

THE SILENT SNAKE
Author unknown

High	The birds go fluttering in the air,
	The rabbits run and skip,
	Brown squirrels race along the bough,
	The May-flies rise and dip;
	But, whilst these creatures play and leap,
Low (at creeping pace, in creepy tone)	The silent snake goes *creepy-creep!*
High	The birdies sing and whistle loud,
	The busy insects hum,
	The squirrels chat, the frogs say "Croak!"
	But the snake is always dumb.
	With not a sound through grasses deep
(at creeping pace, in creepy tone)	The silent snake goes *creepy-creep!*

RING OUT, WILD BELLS
Alfred, Lord Tennyson

High (slowly, exultantly; "sky" not "sky-ee")	Ring out, wild bells, to the wild sky,
Medium	The flying cloud, the frosty light;
	The year is dying in the night;
High	Ring out, wild bells, and let him die.
Medium	Ring out the old, ring in the new,
Low	Ring, happy bells, across the snow;
Medium (or all choirs) slowly, gravely, but not loudly	The year is going, let him go;
	Ring out the false, ring in the true.

For both dialogue and antiphonal speech it is well to divide your three choirs into two groups in this way:

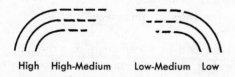

High   High-Medium   Low-Medium   Low

Narrative poems with a chorus

Narrative poems with a chorus are a third possibility for beginning choral work and, like unison and dialogue, may be simple and easy or may require rather subtle interpretations. For instance, "The Christmas Pudding" (p. 182) is simple enough to swing the four-year-old along with gusto. Half of the children speak narrative lines and the other half come in with a vigorous "Stirabout, stirabout, stirabout." Although "A farmer went trotting upon his gray mare"

(p. 116) is equally simple, it calls for a more subtle performance. The two choruses may be spoken by two different groups or one choir may speak both. In either case, the chorus underscores the change of mood—in the first verse all is serene, in the second all is catastrophic, and in the third the villainous crow is laughing and the chorus is spoken just on the edge of laughter.

Here are a few possibilities:

NARRATIVE POEMS WITH CHORUS

Children 4–8

A FARMER WENT TROTTING UPON HIS GRAY MARE, Mother Goose, p. 116

MY DONKEY, Rose Fyleman, p. 117

THE BABY GOES TO BOSTON, Laura E. Richards, p. 78

KINDNESS TO ANIMALS, Laura E. Richards, p. 116

WHAT TO DO, William Wise

WAKING TIME, Ivy O. Eastwick

In "The Baby Goes to Boston" there are two choruses which, as in "A farmer went trotting upon his gray mare," may be spoken by one or by two choirs. These also reinforce the mood or the tempo of the narrative: slowly and easily in the first verse, more briskly in the second, really fast in the third, more slowly in the fourth, and slowing to a stop in the last verse. The poem has two choruses that are amusing tongue-twisters the young children enjoy saying.

"What to Do" may be cast in various ways. It may, of course, be spoken antiphonally. The first and fourth lines of each verse may be spoken by a narrative group made up of a blend of voices, or by a solo voice each time, a different voice for each verse. The chorus to each verse is almost like an echo and may well be carried all the way through by the medium choir. The poem ends jubilantly. Here is "What to Do" by William Wise.

WHAT TO DO

What to do on a rainy day;
What to do
What to do.
There must be a new kind of game to play;
I wish I knew
I wish I knew.

Sister is dressing her dolls again;
They're fine for her
They're fine for her.
Cat and Kitten are washing themselves,
Cleaning their fur
Cleaning their fur.

What to do while it rains outside;
Where to go
Where to go.
I've already eaten, I've already napped;
And the time goes slow
The time goes slow.

But now I see some blue in the sky;
I see some blue
I see some blue.
The clouds are parting, the wind has changed;
And the rain is through
The rain is through!

And soon I'll be out of the house again;
I'll run and shout
I'll run and shout.
I can think of a dozen things to do,
When the sun is out
When the sun is out.

"Waking Time," by Ivy O. Eastwick, might be cast in this way:

WAKING TIME

At four o'clock in the morning,	Medium
The cockerels wake, they do,	
With a "Cocker-doo-dle,	High
Cocker-doo-dle,	
Cocker-doo-dle-doo!"	
At five o'clock in the morning,	Medium
The thrushes wake, they do,	
With a "Pretty-sweet!	High
Oh, pretty-sweet!	
The sky is rose-and-blue!"	
At six o'clock in the morning,	Medium
The blackbirds wake, they do,	
With a 'What's to eat?	High
Oh, what's to eat?	
I'd like a worm or two!"	
At seven o'clock in the morning,	Medium
The mothers wake, they do,	
With a "Here's the honey,	Low
And here's the bread,	
And milk all sweet and new!"	

At eight o'clock in the morning,	Medium
The children wake, they do,	
With a "Where's my sock?"	Low
And "Where's my smock?"	
And "I can't find my left shoe!"	

For the older children, the poems are more difficult.

"I Will Go with My Father A-Ploughing" is a beautiful poem that should be spoken with complete simplicity and sincerity. The first two and last two lines of each verse constitute a chorus of great importance. High voices may speak the first two lines, low voices the last two in each verse, while the medium choir carries the narrative throughout. This poem requires care both in the interpretation and in the diction.

"Cottonwood Leaves" is even more difficult. Let the high voices carry the narrative of the first two verses, with the medium choir speaking the choruses, lines 2 and 5. On the third verse, have the medium choir speak the narrative and the high choir the choruses, lines 2 and 5. Low voices will speak the narrative of the last two verses and the medium choir will resume the choruses. This poem is so rich in onomatopoetic words that it requires much practice and drill. The "clap, clap" almost *is* the sound of cottonwood leaves, and every verse is full of words whose sound, as well as meaning, conjures up the picture the words are describing. This is a thriller recited beside a camp fire—even a stage campfire. The last verse is ghostly and ends in a wail.

Line-a-child or line-a-choir

Line-a-child or line-a-choir interpretation of a poem marks a more advanced form of choral speaking, but one that is challenging and greatly enjoyed. Speaking a couplet instead of a single line is about as fast as beginners are able to pick up on the beat and keep both the rhythm and the meaning. With the youngest groups try "Little wind, blow on the hill-top" (p. 152) in couplets until they catch the idea of coming in on the beat and then try it with one child speaking the first line, another the second line, a third the third line, and all three speaking the last line together. Or try it a couplet-a-choir and then a line-a-choir with all three groups speaking the

last line joyously. Here are some other interesting possibilities (some of the poems have appeared in earlier lists):

LINE-A-CHILD OR LINE-A-CHOIR

Children 4–8
EIGHT O'CLOCK, Christina Rossetti, p. 10
THE LITTLE RED SLED, Jocelyn Bush, p. 101
JUMP OR JIGGLE, Evelyn Beyer, p. 96 (by couplets)
FOR, LO, THE WINTER IS PAST, Bible, p. 191
TRAINS, James S. Tippett, p. 80 (by couplets)
FINIS, Sir Henry Hewbolt, p. 171 (by couplets)

Children 9–14
AMY ELIZABETH ERMYNTRUDE ANNIE, Queenie Scott Hopper, p. 8
GIRLS' NAMES, Eleanor Farjeon, p. 6
BOYS' NAMES, Eleanor Farjeon, p. 6
BUNCHES OF GRAPES, Walter de la Mare, p. 7
THE FALLING STAR, Sara Teasdale, p. 169
WRITTEN IN MARCH, William Wordsworth, p. 192
LEISURE, William Henry Davies, p. 203 (by couplets)
SPRING, Harry Behn, p. 191
HIE AWAY, HIE AWAY, Sir Walter Scott, p. 89

The words "by couplets" following the poems in the list above mean that it is safer to have younger children and beginners speak two lines rather than one, until they have mastered the art of coming in right on the beat.

In "The Little Red Sled" the first two lines should be spoken by one child or choir, but the other lines singly. In this poem, it seems desirable to end by repeating the first line.

The children enjoy the exciting movement of "Trains," but they will run away with it unless you mark time for them. Don't let them begin to gain momentum until the last verse, when all may come in on the final line.

For the older children there are so many possibilities it is hard to select a few. "Amy Elizabeth Ermyntrude Annie" is great fun for them, either with choirs or with single children speaking the lines individually. Again, it may be well to speak couplets to begin with and then single lines. For that poem, let all the voices speak the first and last couplets together, the first simply, introducing the idea, the last on a note of happy triumph.

Two of the loveliest poems for line-a-choir and for subtle tone color in the voices are Eleanor Farjeon's "Boys' Names" and "Girls' Names." These are equally possible for both primary and upper-grade choirs and are superlatively effective.[1]

Scott's "Hie Away, hie away" is also delightful to speak chorally. This is definitely smoother in couplets, either by single children or by choirs. All voices speak the first and last two lines, H choir speaks lines 3 and 4; M, lines 5 and 6; H, lines 7 and 8; L, lines 9 and 10.

Group work

Group work using three or more choirs is the major part of choral speaking because inducting all the children into the pleasure of speaking poetry is, of course, the goal. So many poems lend themselves to this work that it is possible to suggest only a few to represent the range and variety.

GROUP WORK

Children 4–8
THE LITTLE KITTENS, Elisa Lee Follen, p. 113
TAKING OFF, Unknown, p. 81
HAVE YOU WATCHED THE FAIRIES? Rose Fyleman, p. 136
MERRY-GO-ROUND, Dorothy Baruch, p. 109
SONG, Eugene Field, p. 185
JONATHAN BING, Beatrice Curtis Brown, p. 132
APRIL RAIN SONG, Langston Hughes, p. 160
JUMP OR JIGGLE, Evelyn Beyer, p. 96
VALENTINE FOR EARTH, Frances M. Frost

Children 9–14
SONG FOR A BLUE ROADSTER, Rachel Field, p. 86
DOGS AND WEATHER, Winifred Welles, p. 47
HALLOWE'EN, Harry Behn, p. 176
TO BEACHEY, Carl Sandburg, p. 82
THE LITTLE FOX, Marion Edey and Dorothy Grider, p. 60
SKATING, Herbert Asquith, p. 93
UNTIL WE BUILT A CABIN, Aileen Fisher, p. 169
HALLOWEEN, John Ciardi
THE RIVER IS A PIECE OF THE SKY, John Ciardi

[1] See *Children and Books*, pp. 217–218

Frances M. Frost's "Valentine for Earth" is a delightful and easy poem for beginning choirs. Let the children speak the verses choir by choir until the last verse when all of the children will speak the final two lines gently but fervently. The order of assigning the verses may vary—this form is only a suggestion. Notice that in verses 3 and 4 the questions carry over to the following verses.

VALENTINE FOR EARTH

Oh, it will be fine	Medium
To rocket through space	
And see the reverse	
Of the moon's dark face,	
To travel to Saturn	Low
Or Venus or Mars,	
Or maybe discover	
Some uncharted stars.	
But do they have anything	High
Better than we?	
Do you think, for instance,	
They have a blue sea	
For sailing and swimming?	
Do planets have hills	Medium
With raspberry thickets	
Where a song sparrow fills	
The summer with music?	
And do they have snow	Low
To silver the roads	
Where the school buses go?	
Oh, I'm all for rockets	High
And worlds cold or hot,	
But I'm wild in love	All
With the planet we've got!	

"Merry-Go-Round," "Taking Off," "Song," "Jonathan Bing," and "April Rain Song" are thoroughly enjoyed by older children. But with the possible exception of "The Little Fox," the poems listed for older children are far too difficult for the younger ones.

choirs	HALLOWEEN	line-a-child
Low	Ruth says apples have learned to bob.	1st child
Medium	Bob says pumpkins have a job.	2nd
Low	Here's the man from the Witching Tree	3rd
	Ask *him* since you won't ask me:	
High	Do you think Ruth is telling the truth?	1st
Low	"Man from the Tree your skin is green.	4th
Low/High	What night is this?" "It's Halloween."	4th/5th
Low	Ruth, Ruth, you told the truth.	1st
	The man says Apples *have* learned to bob.	
Medium	The man says Pumpkins *do* have a job.	2nd
	The man come down from the Witching Tree	
Medium/High	Says he wants someone. No, not me.	2nd/3rd
High	Says he wants someone good and true—	3rd
All	YOU	All
High	Mother, Mother, Ruth's gone flying!	High (three children)
Medium and Low	*Hush, children, stop that crying.*	One low voice (mother)
High	Mother, Mother, she's up in The Tree!	High (three children)
Medium and Low	*Climb up and tell me what you see.*	One low voice (mother)
High	Mother, she's higher than I can climb!	High (three children)
Medium and Low	*She'll be back by breakfast time.*	One low voice (mother)
High	Mother, what if she's gone for good?	High (three children)
Medium and Low	*She'll have to make do with witches' food.*	One low voice (mother)
High	Mother, what do witches eat?	High (three children)
Medium and Low	*Milk and potatoes and YOU, my sweet.*	One low voice (mother)

Dorothy Baruch's "Merry-Go-Round" is as melodic as carousel music. Let the medium choir introduce the idea in the first four lines. Then the movement of the merry-go-round begins with low voices speaking the next four lines, very low and slowly at first, gradually going higher and faster, until the high choir picks up on the ninth line going with increasing speed and excitement through line 12. Line 13, spoken by medium voices, slows down markedly. Low speaks 14, still more slowly and brings the poem haltingly to a stop just as the old merry-go-round runs down. This poem demands graduation in tone for each choir as well as acceleration and deceleration.

"Taking Off" and "Song" will be analyzed later because both are better with a solo voice.

"Dogs and Weather" (p. 47) is very effectively done in choral form. The words in this poem are lovely but require careful diction, especially the last three lines with all those *s*'s. It will require practice. Let all speak the first 2 lines slowly, reflectively; M, line 3; L, lines 4–7, making the most of lines 5 and 7; H, lines 8–10; and M, lines 11–14. Those last lines are a challenge. If one choir has better enunciation than another give it the last four lines and change the order of the others.

Another fine poem that is most effective in choral form is Harry Behn's "Hallowe'en" (p. 176). Number the 22 lines and try it in this form: L, lines 1 and 2, mysteriously; M, lines 3 and 4 (don't hiss *s*'s but bite off *tch*'s); H, lines 5–7, eerily; M, lines 8 and 9, hushed; L, lines 10 and 11 (stress long *o*'s); H, lines 12–14; L, lines 15 and 16; M, lines 17 and 18; H, lines 19–21; and 22, all voices in a high squeal. Or try the final verse in this alternate form: L, lines 15–18; M, lines 19–21; H, line 22, in a squeal.

Another Halloween poem—this by John Ciardi—lends itself to many ways of casting for choral speaking. Two possibilities are suggested here. This poem is a conversation, but the speakers are not indicated until the exchange between children and mother in the last five couplets.

Before you cast this poem, read it to the children two or three times. Before you repeat it the third time, say to the children, "What do you think about that last dialogue between the mother and children? If they are youngsters speaking, they are working themselves up to a good scare. Do you think the mother, in that last line, really wants them to be scared, or do you think she might feel this scare-game has gone far enough and so would speak the last line with a smile, almost laughing?" Read it to the children both ways and see what they think.

In the line-a-child interpretation, choose the highest voices in the group for the three children, and let their voices crescendo on their first four lines. But when it comes to the last question, their voices drop to a scared half-whisper. On the other hand, the mother (a low voice) has spoken casually until the last line; then she either intends to scare them or she thinks it's time to let them know this is all a joke. Let the children decide.

Whether this poem is spoken by groups or line-a-child, the interpretation is the thing. The green-skinned man from the Witching Tree evidently speaks the words, "It's Halloween," so choose a high voice that can say those words eerily, hanging on to the "eennnnn" almost like a high wailing wind. Beginning with "Ruth, Ruth," the couplets are spoken light-heartedly, almost chanted. When all the voices say "You!" it should come with a scary little shout (not too loud), and a step forward with everyone pointing to someone in the audience. The last dialogue is really fun. The whole poem requires a thoughtful interpretation of every line.

An easier poem of Mr. Ciardi's to speak is "The River Is a Piece of the Sky." The conclusion offers triumphant proof that sky is sky, not river. For children who know a river in city or country and have looked at it from the middle of a bridge, this poem will mean something. Actually, this poem speaks so simply, that the casting does not really matter so long as small groups of children speak together until the middle five lines. These can be line-a-child for variety and prompt pick up.

THE RIVER IS A PIECE OF THE SKY

From the top of a bridge	Medium
The river below	
Is a piece of the sky—	
Until you throw	
A penny in	
Or a cockleshell	Line-a-child 1
Or a pebble or two	Line-a-child 2
Or a bicycle bell	Line-a-child 3
Or a cobblestone	Line-a-child 4
Or a fat man's cane—	Line-a-child 5
And then you can see	High
It's a river again.	
	Low
The difference you'll see	
When you drop your penny:	
The river has splashes,	All
The sky hasn't any.	

A solo voice with the choir

Sometimes a solo voice with the choir is startlingly effective. Try that little airplane poem, popular with any age group, "Taking Off" (p. 81)—L choir, lines 1 and 2; M choir, lines 3 and 4; H choir, lines 5 and 6; a clear, distinct, single voice, line 7; and all the voices speaking softly line 8. The three choirs should take their couplets in an ascending scale; the solo voice should mark the climax with a high, clear voice, and then the drop to the soft, regretful last line should come in a lower pitch.

Eugene Field's "Song" (p. 185) beginning "Why do bells for Christmas ring?" is much lovelier when a beautiful solo voice asks the questions in the first two lines; the M choir takes lines 3–6; the L choir, lines 7 and 8; the H choir, lines 9 and 10; and then the solo voice takes the quiet conclusion. In this case the single voice may be chosen from any of the three choirs, just so it has a clear, lovely quality. Some prefer to close the poem with all the choirs speaking the concluding couplet softly. Try it and see which way you prefer. The soloist may speak from his place in the group or may step out and stand a little apart.

How well your children speak any or all of these poems will depend upon your own interpretation of them in the first place. After the choirs have spoken them, take out a number of children and let them listen, then another group and another, so the children have a chance to hear the effect of different voices. When the children are up speaking such poems individually, the listening group is also important—not to criticize, but to appreciate.[2]

THE CHOIR LEADER

The leader of a verse choir must in the beginning be an adult. If a few children develop sufficient skill to lead, now and then it is desirable to let them lead, but children should not lead in the beginning, and not during the learning of a new poem or during the practice periods that must follow if any degree of precision is to be attained. In a verse choir, as in a singing choir, beautiful effects and good teamwork do not happen—they are the result of careful and repeated practice. The leader must have read a poem aloud a number of times, marked it for casting, and studied it for meaning and interpretation before she reads it to the children. When they begin to speak it with her, she will mark the time just as she would for singing, and the tempo and the light, sweet voices must be maintained evenly during the learning process. The leader may gesture with her hand or finger—never a baton—for starting and stopping, for marking the time, and for going from choir to choir. Make this work as natural as possible and develop precision in your directing gestures so that the choirs know what is expected of them. In the beginning the gestures may have to be larger and a little more vehement than is desirable later. As the choirs become more proficient, the gestures should be toned down to the point of being completely unobtrusive and barely visi-

[2] Other suggestions for verse choir work are made in the footnotes accompanying these poems: The Raggle Taggle Gypsies (p. 15), The Crafty Farmer (p. 16), Get Up and Bar the Door (p. 17), Stop—Go (p. 85), Momotara (p. 129), Holiday (p. 154), Open the Door (p. 172), Psalms 24, 100, 103, 147, and 150 (p. 178), Here We Come A-Caroling (p. 184), In the Week When Christmas Comes (p. 184), For Christmas Day (p. 185), Song (p. 185), A Christmas Carol (p. 186).

ble to an audience. Indeed, for a finished performance the leader can sit for her directing if she likes and she may limit her gestures to a signal to begin, a signal for the entrance of each choir, and occasionally a gesture to increase or diminish tone.

PROGRAMS BY VERSE CHOIRS

Programs of choral speaking by children should be easy, natural outgrowths of what they have been doing in class. Special costumes are neither necessary nor desirable, and colored lights and dramatic gestures are both anathema. Light, pleasant voices; intelligent interpretation of the poems; and a quiet enjoyment of what they are speaking—these are the essentials of a good performance, whether it is for the class next door or the PTA or visiting celebrities. Anything that smacks of the theatrical is out of place. Poetry is precious because of its melodies, its meaning, its beauty, or its laughter and these rather than choir vestments or elaborate staging are valuable both to the children and to their hearers.

Program selections as in music should represent a pleasant variety, a story poem perhaps, some humorous selections—some charming lyrics, and a serious poem or two. The various ways of casting the poems will also add interest and prevent monotony. On the whole, poems that have marked melodic values lend themselves especially well to choral speaking, but this is not necessarily true. Occasionally a prose selection may be effectively spoken by experienced choirs. Speaking of story poems, "The Pied Piper of Hamelin" (p. 24) has been superbly spoken by solo voices, choirs, and choruses, and in a great variety of ways. Certainly the rhyme, rhythms, and dramatic contrasts in this famous poem make it exciting both to speak and to hear. "The Pirate Don Durk of Dowdee" (p. 133) is also amusing in choir form. One class was divided for that colorful jingle on the basis of sex and made a very funny performance of it. The boys spoke of his wickedness, and the girls replied exuberantly or simperingly, "But oh, he was perfectly gorgeous to see!/The Pirate Don Durk of Dowdee."

VALUES IN CHORAL SPEAKING

Obviously, successful choral speaking requires considerable preparation on the part of a teacher and practice on the part of the children. Is it worth while? Interestingly enough, the first testimonial of anyone who has worked with choral speaking groups, whether young children, preadolescents, youths, or adults, is that the work is tremendously exhilarating. "It's fun!" the children say. Poetry is therapeutic just as music is. When you are tired, speaking it with others can give you a lift and a sense of renewed energy. If you are keyed up, it can rest you, and if you are dull or stale or just plain discouraged, it can take you out of yourself and make you over. For the children, some remarkable personal changes are often noticeable. The over-aggressive child who monopolizes class discussions or activities is suddenly dropped into the background. If he is an intelligent child, he listens and becomes sensitive to the beauty of group voices speaking together quietly in pleasant harmony. This is a corrective for his exhibitionism. He adds his good voice to the others and the result is pleasing. The over-timid, self-conscious child really comes into his own. As one of a group, he speaks confidently, perhaps aggressively, and is not even surprised at himself. One of these days, the teacher gives him a solo line and he speaks it without thinking twice. A milestone for him! Children who have been roughly treated at home, who have heard coarse, harsh speech and use it themselves, speak gently and quietly in a verse choir, in pleasant voices they hardly knew they possessed. To see and hear rough boys speak richly and longingly "I must go down to the seas again, to the lonely sea and the sky," is to feel the power of words and ideas penetrating the hard crust of youthful bravado to the spirit of youth that somehow or other holds fast its dreams.

Poetry will do much for children's voices and for their speech as well. There is no question that experience in a verse choir is one of the most pleasant ways there is of improving speech.

The leader says, "You know speaking together this way magnifies every sound. The *s*'s hiss and the *r*'s bur-r-r as they don't when we speak individually; so we must soften them a bit. Consonants," she tells the children, "give vigor and crispness to words. Whatever we do, we must be sure the consonants come through with distinctness—especially *t*'s, *ng*'s and all the others except the troublesome *s*'s and *r*'s." Even these are important if not overstressed. Work for pure, clear vowels and strive for the best, the most understandable, and cultured speech of your particular area of the country. New England should not strive for Southern speech, nor the South for a New England accent, nor the West for either—and, of course, Americans should not ape British English. The goal is clear, crisp, vigorous speech with neither affectations nor impurities. Verse choir practice is as painless a method of improving diction as anything we know.

And finally as these children develop personally, and improve their voice quality and diction, they also develop in their range of experience with poetry. Over and over again, children have confided, "Until we started choral speaking, I always skipped poetry in a book. I would never have thought of opening a book that was all poems. Now I read poetry—I even asked for a book of poems for a Christmas present!" This last is, of course, the ultimate tribute. If children begin to read and explore poetry on their own, if their taste has broadened so that they enjoy not merely light verse or nonsense, but fine lyric verse as well, then indeed they have grown. And if they speak it or read it unselfconsciously, trying to bring out its music and its meaning, then they are on the way to being poetry-lovers for life.

One word of caution in conclusion: Be sure you don't endanger these achievements by excessive drill. Choral speaking should be exhilarating and joyous. By way of it, children should grow in their appreciation of good literature and in their sensitivity to beauty and to the power of the spoken word.

THE PEOPLE

Elizabeth Madox Roberts

The ants are walking under the ground,
And the pigeons are flying over the steeple,
And in between are the people.

NEIGHBORLY

Violet Alleyn Storey

My Mother sends our neighbors things
    On fancy little plates.
One day she sent them custard pie
    And they sent back stuffed dates.

And once she sent them angel food
    And they returned ice cream;
Another time for purple plums
    They gave us devil's dream.

She always keeps enough for us
    No matter what she sends.
Our goodies seem much better
    When we share them with our friends.

And even if they didn't, why,
    It's surely lots of fun,
'Cause that way we get two desserts
    Instead of only one!

ALL SORTS OF PEOPLE

Christina Georgina Rossetti

Mother shake the cherry-tree,
    Susan catch a cherry;
Oh how funny that will be,
    Let's be merry!

One for brother, one for sister,
  Two for mother more,
Six for father, hot and tired,
  Knocking at the door.

"SH"

James S. Tippett

"Sh!" says mother,
"Sh!" says father.
"Running in the hall
Is a very great bother."

"Mrs. Grumpy Grundy,
Who lives down below,
Will come right up
First thing you know."

"Sh!" says father,
"Sh!" says mother.
"Can't you play a quiet game
Of some kind or other?"

SHOP WINDOWS

Rose Fyleman

Mother likes the frocks and hats
And pretty stuffs and coloured mats.

Daddy never, never looks
At anything but pipes and books.

Auntie's fond of chains and rings
And all the sparkly diamond things.

Richard likes machines the best;
He doesn't care about the rest.

Nannie always loves to stop
In front of every single shop.

But I don't want to wait for a minute
Till we get to the one with the puppy dogs in it.

SMELLS (JUNIOR)

Christopher Morley

My Daddy smells like tobacco and books,
  Mother, like lavender and listerine;
Uncle John carries a whiff of cigars,
  Nannie smells starchy and soapy and clean.

Shandy, my dog, has a smell of his own
  (When he's been out in the rain he smells
    most) ;
But Katie, the cook, is more splendid than all—
  She smells exactly like hot buttered toast!

SHOES

Tom Robinson

  My father has a pair of shoes
  So beautiful to see!
  I want to wear my father's shoes,
  They are too big for me.

  My baby brother has a pair,
  As cunning as can be!
  My feet won't go into that pair,
  They are too small for me.

  There's only one thing I can do
  Till I get small or grown.
  If I want to have a fitting shoe,
  I'll have to wear my own.

FATHER

Frances Frost

My father's face is brown with sun,
His body is tall and limber.
His hands are gentle with beast or child
And strong as hardwood timber.

My father's eyes are the colors of sky,
Clear blue or gray as rain:

They change with the swinging change of days
While he watches the weather vane.

That galleon, golden upon our barn,
Veers with the world's four winds.
My father, his eyes on the vane, knows when
To fill our barley bins,

To stack our wood and pile our mows
With redtop and sweet tossed clover.
He captains our farm that rides the winds,
A keen-eyed brown earth-lover.

AUTOMOBILE MECHANICS

Dorothy Baruch

Sometimes
  I help my dad
  Work on our automobile.
    We unscrew
    The radiator cap
      And we let some water run—
      Swish—from a hose
      Into the tank.

And then we open up the hood
And feed in oil
From a can with a long spout.
And then we take a lot of rags
And clean all about.
    We clean the top
    And the doors
    And the fenders and the wheels
    And the windows and floors. . . .
      We work *hard*
      My dad
      And I.

Christina Georgina Rossetti

What does the bee do?
  Bring home honey.
And what does Father do?
  Bring home money.

And what does Mother do?
  Lay out the money.
And what does baby do?
  Eat up the honey.

SONG FOR MY MOTHER

Anna Hempstead Branch

My mother has the prettiest tricks
  Of words and words and words.
Her talk comes out as smooth and sleek
  As breasts of singing birds.

She shapes her speech all silver fine
  Because she loves it so.
And her own eyes begin to shine
  To hear her stories grow.

And if she goes to make a call
  Or out to take a walk,
We leave our work when she returns
  And run to hear her talk.

We had not dreamed these things were so
  Of sorrow and of mirth.
Her speech is as a thousand eyes
  Through which we see the earth.

God wove a web of loveliness,
  Of clouds and stars and birds,
But made not anything at all
  So beautiful as words.

They shine around our simple earth
  With golden shadowings,
And every common thing they touch
  Is exquisite with wings.

There's nothing poor and nothing small
  But is made fair with them.
They are the hands of living faith
  That touch the garment's hem.

They are as fair as bloom or air,
  They shine like any star,
And I am rich who learned from her
  How beautiful they are.

"Automobile Mechanics." From *I Like Machinery* by Dorothy Baruch. Harper & Brothers, New York, 1933. Used by permission of the author
  "What does the bee do?" From *Sing-Song* by Christina Georgina Rossetti
  "Song for My Mother." Anna Hempstead Branch. From

The Shoes That Danced and Other Poems. Published by Houghton Mifflin Company, Boston, 1905
  "Andre." From *Bronzeville Boys and Girls* by Gwendolyn Brooks. Copyright © 1956 by Gwendolyn Brooks Blakely. Published by Harper & Brothers, New York
  "Slippery." From *Smoke and Steel* by Carl Sandburg,

ANDRE

Gwendolyn Brooks

I had a dream last night. I dreamed
I had to pick a Mother out.
I had to choose a Father too.
At first, I wondered what to do,
There were so many there, it seemed,
Short and tall and thin and stout.

But just before I sprang awake,
I knew what parents I would take.

And *this* surprised and made me glad:
They were the ones I always had!

SLIPPERY

Carl Sandburg

The six month child
Fresh from the tub
Wriggles in our hands.
This is our fish child.
Give her a nickname: Slippery.

INFANT JOY

William Blake

"I have no name;
I am but two days old."
What shall I call thee?
"I happy am,
Joy is my name."
Sweet joy befall thee!

Pretty joy!
Sweet joy, but two days old.
Sweet joy I call thee;
Thou dost smile,
I sing the while;
Sweet joy befall thee!

Kate Greenaway

Little Blue Shoes
Mustn't go
Very far alone, you know.
Else she'll fall down,
Or, lose her way.
Fancy—what
Would mamma say?
Better put her little hand
Under sister's wise command.
When she's a little older grown
Blue Shoes may go quite alone.

LITTLE

Dorothy Aldis

I am the sister of him
And he is my brother.
He is too little for us
To talk to each other.

So every morning I show him
My doll and my book;
But every morning he still is
Too little to look.

TWO IN BED

Abram Bunn Ross

When my brother Tommy
Sleeps in bed with me,
He doubles up
And makes
himself
exactly
like
a
V

And 'cause the bed is not so wide,
A part of him is on my side.

copyright, 1920, by Harcourt, Brace and Company, Inc.
"Infant Joy." *This is an imaginary dialogue between an adult and a tiny baby, with the child saying lines 1, 2, 4, and 5.*
"Little Blue Shoes." From *Marigold Garden* by Kate Greenaway. Frederick Warne and Company, New York and London, 1910
"Little." From *Everything and Anything* by Dorothy Aldis. Minton, Balch and Company, New York, 1927. Copyright 1925, 1926, 1927 by Dorothy Aldis
"Two in Bed." By permission of Mrs. A. B. Ross, Philadelphia

LITTLE BROTHER'S SECRET

Katherine Mansfield

When my birthday was coming
Little Brother had a secret:
He kept it for days and days
And just hummed a little tune when I asked
    him.
But one night it rained
And I woke up and heard him crying:
Then he told me.
"I planted two lumps of sugar in your garden
Because you love it so frightfully.
I thought there would be a whole sugar tree for
    your birthday.
And now it will all be melted."
O the darling!

GIRLS' NAMES

Eleanor Farjeon

What lovely names for girls there are!
There's Stella like the Evening Star,
And Sylvia like a rustling tree,
And Lola like a melody,
And Flora like a flowery morn,
And Sheila like a field of corn,
And Melusina like the moan
Of water. And there's Joan, like Joan.

BOYS' NAMES

Eleanor Farjeon

What splendid names for boys there are!
There's Carol like a rolling car,
And Martin like a flying bird,
And Adam like the Lord's First Word,

And Raymond like the Harvest Moon,
And Peter like a piper's tune,
And Alan like the flowing on
Of water. And there's John, like John.

THE TWINS

Elizabeth Madox Roberts

The two-ones is the name for it,
And that is what it ought to be,
But when you say it very fast
It makes your lips say *twins,* you see.

When I was just a little thing,
About the year before the last,
I called it two-ones all the time,
But now I always say it fast.

TIRED TIM

Walter de la Mare

Poor tired Tim! It's sad for him.
He lags the long bright morning through,
Ever so tired of nothing to do;
He moons and mopes the livelong day,
Nothing to think about, nothing to say;
Up to bed with his candle to creep,
Too tired to yawn, too tired to sleep:
Poor tired Tim! It's sad for him.

BUNCHES OF GRAPES
Walter de la Mare

"Bunches of grapes," says Timothy;
"Pomegranates pink," says Elaine;
"A junket of cream and a cranberry tart
    For me," says Jane.

"Love-in-a-mist," says Timothy;
"Primroses pale," says Elaine;
"A nosegay of pinks and mignonette
    For me," says Jane.

"Chariots of gold," says Timothy;
"Silvery wings," says Elaine;
"A bumpity ride in a wagon of hay
    For me," says Jane.

THE CUPBOARD
Walter de la Mare

I know a little cupboard,
With a teeny tiny key,
And there's a jar of Lollipops
    For me, me, me.

It has a little shelf, my dear,
As dark as dark can be,
And there's a dish of Banbury Cakes
    For me, me, me.

I have a small fat grandmamma,
With a very slippery knee,
And she's Keeper of the Cupboard,
    With the key, key, key.

And when I'm very good, my dear,
As good as good can be,

There's Banbury Cakes, and Lollipops
    For me, me, me.

AMY ELIZABETH ERMYNTRUDE ANNIE
Queenie Scott Hopper

Amy Elizabeth Ermyntrude Annie
Went to the country to visit her Grannie,

Learnt to churn butter and learnt to make
    cheese,
Learnt to milk cows and take honey from bees,

Learnt to spice rose-leaves and learnt to cure
    ham,
Learnt to make cider and black currant jam.

When she came home she could not settle down,
Said there was nothing to do in the town.

Nothing to do there and nothing to see:
Life was all shopping and afternoon tea!

Amy Elizabeth Ermyntrude Annie
Ran away back to the country and Grannie.

WHERE'S MARY?
Ivy O. Eastwick

Is Mary in the dairy?
Is Mary on the stair?
What? Mary's in the garden?
What is she doing there?
Has she made the butter yet?
Has she made the beds?
Has she topped the gooseberries
And taken off their heads?
Has she the potatoes peeled?
Has she done the grate?
Are the new green peas all shelled?

It is getting late!
What? She hasn't done a thing?
Here's a nice to-do!
Mary has a dozen jobs
And hasn't finished two.
Well! here IS a nice to-do!
Well! upon my word!
She's sitting on the garden bench
Listening to a bird!

PORTRAIT BY A NEIGHBOR

Edna St. Vincent Millay

Before she has her floor swept
  Or her dishes done,
Any day you'll find her
  A-sunning in the sun!

It's long after midnight
  Her key's in the lock,
And you never see her chimney smoke
  Till past ten o'clock!

She digs in her garden
  With a shovel and a spoon,
She weeds her lazy lettuce
  By the light of the moon.

She walks up the walk
  Like a woman in a dream,
She forgets she borrowed butter
  And pays you back cream!

Her lawn looks like a meadow,
  And if she mows the place
She leaves the clover standing
  And the Queen Anne's lace!

GRANDFATHER WATTS'S PRIVATE FOURTH

H. C. Bunner

Grandfather Watts used to tell us boys
That a Fourth wa'n't a Fourth without any noise.
He would say, with a thump of his hickory stick,
That it made an American right down sick
To see his sons on the Nation's Day
Sit round in a sort of a listless way,

With no oration and no trained band,
No firework show and no root-beer stand;
While his grandsons, before they were out of
    bibs,
Were ashamed—Great Scott!—to fire off Squibs.

And so, each Independence morn,
Grandfather Watts took his powder horn,
And the flintlock shotgun *his* father had
When he fought under Schuyler, a country lad.
And Grandfather Watts would start and tramp
Ten miles to the woods at Beaver Camp;
For Grandfather Watts used to say—and scowl—
That a decent chipmunk, or woodchuck, or owl
Was better company, friendly or shy,
Than folks who didn't keep Fourth of July.
And so he would pull his hat down on his brow,
And march for the woods, sou'east by sou'.

But once—ah! long, long years ago;
For Grandfather's gone where good men go—
One hot, hot Fourth, by ways of our own
(Such short cuts as boys have always known),
We hurried, and followed the dear old man
Beyond where the wilderness began—
To the deep black woods at the foot of the
    dump;
And there was a clearing and a stump—

A stump in the heart of a great wide wood;
And there on that stump our grandfather stood,
Talking and shouting out there in the sun,
And firing that funny old flintlock gun
Once in a minute, his head all bare,
Having his Fourth of July out there—
The Fourth of July that he used to know,
Back in eighteen-and-twenty, or so.

First, with his face to the heaven's blue,
He read the "Declaration" through;
And then, with gestures to left and right,
He made an oration erudite,
Full of words six syllables long;
And then our grandfather burst into song!
And, scaring the squirrels in the trees,
Gave "Hail, Columbia!" to the breeze.

"Portrait by a Neighbor." From *A Few Figs from Thistles*, published by Harper & Brothers. Copyright, 1920, 1948, by Edna St. Vincent Millay

"Grandfather Watts's Private Fourth." H. C. Bunner, *Delsarte Recitation Book*

And I tell you the old man never heard
When we joined in the chorus, word for word!
But he sang out strong to the bright blue sky;
And if voices joined in his Fourth of July,
He heard them as echoes from days gone by.

And when he had done, we all slipped back,
As still as we came, on our twisting track,
While words more clear that the flintlock shots
Rang in our ears. And Grandfather Watts?
He shouldered the gun his father bore,
And marched off home, nor'west by nor'.

THE RAGGEDY MAN
James Whitcomb Riley

O The Raggedy Man! He works fer Pa;
An' he's the goodest man ever you saw!
He comes to our house every day,
An' waters the horses, an' feeds 'em hay;
An' he opens the shed—an' we all ist laugh
When he drives out our little old wobble-ly calf;
An' nen—ef our hired girl says he can—
He milks the cow fer 'Lizabuth Ann.—
  Ain't he a' awful good Raggedy Man?
    Raggedy! Raggedy! Raggedy Man!

W'y, The Raggedy Man—he's ist so good
He splits the kindlin' an' chops the wood;
An' nen he spades in our garden, too,
An' does most things 'at boys can't do.—
He clumbed clean up in our big tree
An' shooked a' apple down fer me—
An' nother'n', too, fer 'Lizabuth Ann—
An' nother'n', too, fer The Raggedy Man.—
  Ain't he a' awful kind Raggedy Man?
    Raggedy! Raggedy! Raggedy Man!

An' The Raggedy Man, he knows most rhymes
An' tells 'em, ef I be good, sometimes:
Knows 'bout Giunts, an' Griffuns, an' Elves,
An' the Squidgicum-Squees 'at swallers ther-
    selves!
An', wite by the pump in our pasture-lot,
He showed me the hole 'at the Wunks is got,
'At lives 'way deep in the ground, an' can
Turn into me, er 'Lizabuth Ann!
  Ain't he a funny old Raggedy Man?
    Raggedy! Raggedy! Raggedy Man!

The Raggedy Man—one time when he
Was makin' a little bow-'n'-orry fer me,
Says, "When *you're* big like your Pa is,
Air you go' to keep a fine store like his—
An' be a rich merchunt—an' wear fine clothes?—
Er what *air* you go' to be, goodness knows!"
An' nen he laughed at 'Lizabuth Ann,
An' I says " 'M go' to be a Raggedy Man!"
  I'm ist go' to be a nice Raggedy Man!"
    Raggedy! Raggedy! Raggedy Man!

DOORBELLS

Rachel Field

You never know with a doorbell
  Who may be ringing it—
It may be Great-Aunt Cynthia
  To spend the day and knit;
It may be a peddler with things to sell
  (I'll buy some when I'm older),
Or the grocer's boy with his apron on
  And a basket on his shoulder;

"Doorbells." From *The Pointed People* by Rachel Field. The Macmillan Company, New York, 1930. Used by per- mission of Arthur S. Pederson, Trustee, Estate of Rachel Field Pederson

It may be the old umbrella-man
  Giving his queer, cracked call,
Or a lady dressed in rustly silk,
  With a card-case and parasol.
Doorbells are like a magic game,
  Or the grab-bag at a fair—
You never know when you hear one ring
  Who may be waiting there!

THE SCISSOR-MAN

Madeline Nightingale

Sing a song of Scissor-men,
"Mend a broken plate,
Bring your knives and garden shears,
I'll do them while you wait.
Buzz-a-wuzz! Buzz-a-wuzz!
Fast the wheel or slow,
Ticker Tacker! Ticker Tack!
Rivets in a row."

Sing a song of Scissor-men,
Sitting in the sun,
Sing it when the day begins,
Sing it when it's done.
Be it hard or be it soft,
Here's a jolly plan;
Sing to make the work go well,
Like the Scissor-man.

THE POSTMAN

Laura E. Richards

Hey! the little postman,
  And his little dog,
Here he comes a-hopping
  Like a little frog;
Bringing me a letter,
  Bringing me a note,
In the little pocket
  Of his little coat.

Hey! the little postman,
  And his little bag,
Here he comes a-trotting
  Like a little nag;
Bringing me a paper,
  Bringing me a bill,
From the little grocer
  On the little hill.

Hey! the little postman,
  And his little hat,
Here he comes a-creeping
  Like a little cat.
What is that he's saying?
  "Naught for you to-day!"
Horrid little postman!
  I wish you'd go away!

Christina Georgina Rossetti

Eight o'clock;
The postman's knock!
Five letters for Papa;
  One for Lou,
  And none for you,
And three for dear Mamma.

THE NEW NEIGHBOR

Rose Fyleman

Have you had your tonsils out?
  Do you go to school?
Do you know that there are frogs
  Down by Willow Pool?

Are you good at cricket?
  Have you got a bat?
Do you know the proper way
  To feed a white rat?

Are there any apples
  On your apple tree?

"The Scissor-Man." From *Nursery Lays for Nursery Days* by Madeline Nightingale. By permission of Basil Blackwell & Mott, Ltd., Oxford

"The Postman." From *Tirra Lirra* by Laura E. Richards. Little, Brown & Company, Boston, 1932

"Eight o'clock." From *Sing-Song* by Christina Georgina Rossetti

"The New Neighbor." From *Gay Go Up* by Rose Fyleman. Copyright 1929, 1930 by Doubleday & Company, Inc. By permission also of Miss Fyleman, The Society of Authors, and Messrs. Methuen & Co.

"Oh, Susan Blue." *Here is a conversation over the garden gate. First the friend speaks, then Susan has the last three lines. This poem is read by May Hill Arbuthnot in the record album* Poetry Time, Scott, Foresman. *From* Marigold Garden *by Kate Greenaway. Frederick Warne*

Do you think your mother
    Will ask me in to tea?

                    Kate Greenaway

Oh, Susan Blue,
    How do you do?
Please may I go for a walk with you?
    Where shall we go?
Oh, I know—
Down in the meadow where the cowslips grow!

AT MRS. APPLEBY'S
Elizabeth Upham McWebb

When frost is shining on the trees,
    It's spring at Mrs. Appleby's.
You smell it in the air before
    You step inside the kitchen door.

Rows of scarlet flowers bloom
    From every window in the room.
And funny little speckled fish
    Are swimming in a china dish.

A tiny bird with yellow wings
    Just sits and sings and sings and SINGS!
Outside when frost is on the trees,
    It's spring at Mrs. Appleby's!

A. A. Milne

Diana Fitzpatrick Mauleverer James
Was lucky to have the most beautiful names.
How awful for Fathers and Mothers to call
Their children Jemima!—or nothing at all!
But *hers* were much wiser and kinder and clev-
        erer,
They called her Diana Fitzpatrick Mauleverer
        James.

MISS T.
Walter de la Mare

It's a very odd thing—
    As odd as can be—
That whatever Miss T. eats
    Turns into Miss T.;
Porridge and apples,
    Mince, muffins and mutton,
Jam, junket, jumbles—
    Not a rap, not a button
It matters; the moment
    They're out of her plate,
Though shared by Miss Butcher
    And sour Mr. Bate;
Tiny and cheerful,
    And neat as can be,
Whatever Miss T. eats
    Turns into Miss T.

from ALL AROUND THE TOWN
Phyllis McGinley

P's the proud Policeman
    With buttons polished neat.
He's pleased to put his hand up
    When you want to cross the street.
By daylight he protects you;
    He protects you through the dark,
And he points the way politely
    To the playground or the park.

and Company, New York and London, 1910.
    "At Mrs. Appleby's." From *Child Life*, February 1945.
Child Life, Inc., Boston. Used by permission of the author
    "Diana Fitzpatrick Mauleverer James." From *A Gallery of Children* by A. A. Milne. David McKay Company, Inc., New York, 1925
    "Miss T." *If you really bite your consonants off distinctly when you speak this poem, you'll discover prim, prissy*

Miss T. *in the very sound of the words.* From *Collected Poems, 1901–1918,* by Walter de la Mare. Copyright, 1920, by Henry Holt and Company, Inc. Copyright, 1948, by Walter de la Mare. Reprinted by permission of the publishers
    "P's the proud Policeman." From *All Around the Town.* Copyright 1948 by Phyllis McGinley. Reprinted by permission of J. B. Lippincott Company

THE POLICEMAN

Marjorie Seymour Watts

He never used to notice me
When I went by, and stared at him.
And then he smiled especially,
And now he says, "Hello there, Jim."

If he becomes a friend of mine,
And I learn all I ought to know,
Perhaps he'll let me turn the sign
And make the people Stop! and Go!

He and I are friends, you see,
And he always smiles at me.

Once I wasn't very good
Rather near to where he stood,
But he never said a word
Though I'm sure he must have heard.

Nurse has a policeman too
(Hers has brown eyes, mine has blue),
Hers is sometimes on a horse,
But I like mine best of course.

MY POLICEMAN

Rose Fyleman

He is always standing there
At the corner of the Square;
He is very big and fine
And his silver buttons shine.

All the carts and taxis do
Everything he tells them to,
And the little errand boys
When they pass him make no noise.

Though I seem so very small
I am not afraid at all;

THE BALLOON MAN

Dorothy Aldis

Our balloon man has balloons.
He holds them on a string.
He blows his horn and walks about
Through puddles, in the spring.

He stands on corners while they bob
And tug above his head—
Green balloons and blue balloons
And yellow ones, and red.

He takes our pennies and unties
The two we choose; and then
He turns around, and waves his hand,
And blows his horn again.

THE DENTIST

Rose Fyleman

I'd like to be a dentist with a plate upon the door
And a little bubbling fountain in the middle of
   the floor;
With lots of tiny bottles all arranged in coloured
   rows
And a page-boy with a line of silver buttons
   down his clothes.

I'd love to polish up the things and put them
    every day
Inside the darling chests of drawers all tidily
    away;
And every Sunday afternoon when nobody was
    there
I should go riding up and down upon the velvet
    chair.

THE COBBLER
Eleanor Alletta Chaffee

Crooked heels
   And scuffy toes
Are all the kinds
   Of shoes he knows.

He patches up
   The broken places,
Sews the seams
   And shines their faces.

MANUAL SYSTEM
Carl Sandburg

Mary has a thingamajig clamped on her ears
And sits all day taking plugs out and sticking
    plugs in.
Flashes and flashes—voices and voices calling for
    ears to pour words in
Faces at the ends of wires asking for other faces
    at the ends of other wires:
All day taking plugs out and sticking plugs in,
Mary has a thingamajig clamped on her ears.

MELONS
Mary Mapes Dodge

Melons! melons!
   All day long
Joe's mother sits
   Selling melons.

"Ho! ripe and rich!"
   Is her song,
All day long
   Selling melons.

Melons! melons!
   All day long
Joe walks the street
   Selling melons.
"Ho! ripe and sweet!"
   Is his song,
All day long
   Selling melons.

THE SHEPHERD
William Blake

How sweet is the shepherd's sweet lot!
From the morn to the evening he strays;
He shall follow his sheep all the day,
And his tongue shall be filléd with praise.

For he hears the lambs' innocent call,
And he hears the ewes' tender reply;
He is watchful while they are in peace,
For they know when their shepherd is nigh.

A PIPER
Seumas O'Sullivan

A piper in the streets to-day
Set up, and tuned, and started to play,
And away, away, away on the tide
Of his music we started; on every side
Doors and windows were opened wide,
And men left down their work and came,
And women with petticoats coloured like flame.
And little bare feet that were blue with cold,
Went dancing back to the age of gold,
And all the world went gay, went gay,
For half an hour in the street to-day.

"Manual System." *This is an amusing picture of a tele-phone switchboard operator. From* Early Moon *by Carl Sandburg, copyright, 1930, by Harcourt, Brace and Company, Inc.*

"Melons." *From* Rhymes and Jingles *by Mary Mapes Dodge, Charles Scribner's Sons, 1874*

"The Shepherd." From *Songs of Innocence* by William Blake.

"A Piper." From *Collected Poems* by Seumas O'Sullivan. Orwell Press, Dublin, 1940. Used by permission of the author

GYPSY JANE

William Brighty Rands

She had corn flowers in her hair
  As she came up the lane;
"What may be your name, my dear?"
  "O, sir, Gypsy Jane."

"You are berry-brown, my dear."
  "That, sir, well may be,
For I live more than half the year,
  Under tent or tree."

Shine, Sun! Blow, Wind!
  Fall gently, Rain!
The year's declined, be soft and kind.
  Kind to Gypsy Jane.

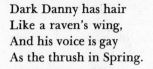

BEING GYPSY

Barbara Young

A gypsy, a gypsy,
Is what I'd like to be,
If ever I could find one who
Would change his place with me.

Rings on my fingers,
Earrings in my ears,
Rough shoes to roam the world
For years and years and years!

I'd listen to the stars,
I'd listen to the dawn,
I'd learn the tunes of wind and rain,
The talk of fox and faun.

A gypsy, a gypsy!
To ramble and to roam
For maybe—oh,
A week or so—
And then I'd hie me home!

DARK DANNY

Ivy O. Eastwick

Dark Danny has eyes
As black as the sloe,
And his freckles tell
Where the sunbeams go!

Dark Danny has hair
Like a raven's wing,
And his voice is gay
As the thrush in Spring.

Dark Danny will show
You the first wild rose;
Where the earliest violet
Blooms—he knows!

Where the red fox hides,
Why the nightingale sings . . .
Dark Danny knows all
These lovely things.

MEG MERRILIES

John Keats

Old Meg she was a Gipsy,
  And liv'd upon the Moors:
Her bed it was the brown heath turf,
  And her house was out of doors.

Her apples were swart blackberries,
  Her currants pods o' broom;
Her wine was dew of the wild white rose,
  Her book a churchyard tomb.

Her Brothers were the craggy hills,
  Her Sisters larchen trees—
Alone with her great family
  She liv'd as she did please.

No breakfast had she many a morn,
  No dinner many a noon,
And 'stead of supper she would stare
  Full hard against the Moon.

But every morn of woodbine fresh
  She made her garlanding,
And every night the dark glen Yew
  She wove, and she would sing.

And with her fingers old and brown
  She plaited Mats o' Rushes,

"Being Gypsy." From *Christopher O!* by Barbara Young.
David McKay Company, Inc., New York, 1947
"Dark Danny." Taken from *Fairies and Suchlike*, by Ivy
O. Eastwick, published and copyright, 1946, by E. P. Dutton & Co., Inc., New York

And gave them to the Cottagers
  She met among the Bushes.

Old Meg was brave as Margaret Queen
  And tall as Amazon:
An old red blanket cloak she wore;
  A chip hat had she on.
God rest her aged bones somewhere—
  She died full long agone!

THE FIDDLER OF DOONEY

William Butler Yeats

When I play on my fiddle in Dooney,
Folk dance like a wave of the sea;
My cousin is priest in Kilvarnet,
My brother in Moharabuiee.

I passed my brother and cousin:
They read in their books of prayer;
I read in my book of songs
I bought at the Sligo fair.

When we come at the end of time
To Peter sitting in state,
He will smile on the three old spirits,
But call me first through the gate;

For the good are always the merry,
Save by an evil chance,
And the merry love the fiddle
And the merry love to dance:

And when the folk there spy me,
They will all come up to me,
With 'Here is the fiddler of Dooney!'
And dance like a wave of the sea.

THE RAGGLE, TAGGLE GYPSIES

(Old Folk Song)

There were three gypsies a-come to my door,
  And downstairs ran this lady, O.

One sang high and another sang low,
  And the other sang "Bonnie, Bonnie Bis-
    kay, O."

Then she pulled off her silken gown,
  And put on hose of leather, O.
With the ragged, ragged rags about her door
  She's off with the Raggle, Taggle Gypsies, O.

'Twas late last night when my lord came home,
  Inquiring for his lady, O.
The servants said on every hand,
  "She's gone with the Raggle, Taggle Gyp-
    sies, O."

"Oh, saddle for me my milk-white steed,
  Oh, saddle for me my pony, O,
That I may ride and seek my bride
  Who's gone with the Raggle, Taggle Gyp-
    sies, O."

Oh, he rode high and he rode low,
  He rode through woods and copses, O,
Until he came to an open field,
  And there he espied his lady, O.

"What makes you leave your house and lands?
  What makes you leave your money, O?
What makes you leave your new-wedded lord
  To go with the Raggle, Taggle Gypsies, O?"

"What care I for my house and lands?
  What care I for my money, O?
What care I for my new-wedded lord?
  I'm off with the Raggle, Taggle Gypsies, O."

"Last night you slept on a goose-feather bed,
  With the sheet turned down so bravely, O.
Tonight you will sleep in the cold, open field,
  Along with the Raggle, Taggle Gypsies, O."

"What care I for your goose-feather bed,
  With the sheet turned down so bravely, O?
For tonight I shall sleep in a cold, open field,
  Along with the Raggle, Taggle Gypsies, O."

"The Fiddler of Dooney." From *Poetical Works* by William Butler Yeats. Copyright 1906, 1934 by The Macmillan Company and used with their permission. By permission also of Mrs. William Butler Yeats and The Macmillan Company of Canada

"The Raggle, Taggle Gypsies." *Why did the lady run away? Could she have been a gypsy herself? This is exciting to speak with one group of voices for the narrative, another group for the frightened servants, and single voices for the lord and the lady.*

THE CRAFTY FARMER

(*Ballad*)

The song that I'm going to sing,
   I hope it will give you content,
Concerning a silly old man,
   That was going to pay his rent.

As he was riding along,
   Along all on the highway,
A gentleman-thief overtook him,
   And thus to him did say.

"Well overtaken!" said the thief,
   "Well overtaken!" said he;
And "Well overtaken!" said the old man,
   "If thou be good company."

"How far are you going this way?"
   Which made the old man for to smile;
"By my faith," said the old man,
   "I'm just going two mile.

"I am a poor farmer," he said,
   "And I farm a piece of ground,
And my half-year's rent, kind sir,
   Just comes to forty pound.

"And my landlord has not been at home;
   I've not seen him this twelvemonth or more,
Which makes my rent be large;
   I've to pay him just fourscore."

"Thou shouldst not have told any body,
   For thieves there's ganging many;
If any should light on thee,
   They'll rob thee of thy money."

"O never mind," said the old man,
   "Thieves I fear on no side,
For the money is safe in my bags,
   On the saddle on which I ride."

As they were riding along,
   The old man was thinking no ill,
The thief he pulled out a pistol
   And bid the old man stand still.

"The Crafty Farmer." *This lends itself to speaking with a group of voices for the story and solo voices for farmer, robber, and wife.*

But the old man provd crafty,
   As in the world there's many;
He threw his saddle oer the hedge,
   Saying, Fetch it, if thou'lt have any.

The thief got off his horse,
   With courage stout and bold,
To search for the old man's bag,
   And gave him his horse to hold.

The old man put's foot i the stirrup
   And he got on astride;
To its side he clapt his spur up,
   You need not bid the old man ride.

"O stay!" said the thief, "O stay!
   And half the share thou shalt have;"
"Nay, by my faith," said the old man,
   "For once I have bitten a knave."

The thief he was not content,
   But he thought there must be bags;
He out with his rusty old sword
   And chopt the old saddle in rags.

When he came to the landlord's house,
   This old man he was almost spent;
Saying, "Come, show me a private room
   And I'll pay you a whole year's rent.

"I've met a fond fool by the way,
   I swapt horses and gave him no boot;
But never mind," said the old man,
   "For I got the fond fool by the foot."

He opend this rogue's portmantle,
   It was glorious to behold;
There were three hundred pounds in silver,
   And three hundred pounds in gold.

And as he was riding home,
   And down a narrow lane,
He espied his mare tied to a hedge,
   Saying, "Prithee, Tib, wilt thou gang hame?"

When he got home to his wife
   And told her what he had done,
Up she rose and put on her clothes,
   And about the house did run.

She sung, and she sung, and she sung,
  She sung with a merry devotion,
Saying, If ever our daughter gets wed,
  It will help to enlarge her portion.

GET UP AND BAR THE DOOR

(Ballad)

It fell about the Martinmas time,
  And a gay time it was then,
When our goodwife got puddings to make,
  And she's boild them in the pan.

The wind sae cauld blew south and north,
  And blew into the floor;
Quoth our goodman to our goodwife,
  "Gae out and bar the door."

"My hand is in my hussyfskap,
  Goodman, as ye may see:
An it shoud nae be barrd this hundred year,
  It's no be barrd for me."

They made a paction tween them twa,
  They made it firm and sure,
That the first word whaeer shoud speak,
  Shoud rise and bar the door.

Then by there came two gentlemen,
  At twelve o clock at night,
And they could neither see house nor hall,
  Nor coal nor candle-light.

"Now whether is this a rich man's house,
  Or whether is it a poor?"
But neer a word wad ane o them speak,
  For barring of the door.

And first they ate the white puddings,
  And then they ate the black;
Tho muckle thought the goodwife to hersel,
  Yet neer a word she spake.

Then said the one unto the other,
  "Here, man, tak ye my knife;
Do ye tak aff the auld man's beard,
  And I'll kiss the goodwife."

"But there's nae water in the house,
  And what shall we do than?"
"What ails ye at the pudding-broo,
  That boils into the pan?"

O up then started our goodman,
  An angry man was he:
"Will ye kiss my wife before my een,
  And scad me wi pudding-bree?"

Then up and started our goodwife,
  Gied three skips on the floor:
"Goodman, you've spoken the foremost word,
  Get up and bar the door."

ROBIN HOOD RESCUING THE WIDOW'S THREE SONS

(Ballad)

There are twelve months in all the year,
  As I hear many say,
But the merriest month in all the year
  Is the merry month of May.

Now Robin Hood is to Nottingham gone,
  With a link and a down, and a day,
And there he met a silly old woman,
  Was weeping on the way.

"What news? what news? thou silly old woman,
  What news hast thou for me?"
Said she, "There's my three sons in Nottingham
    town
  Today condemned to die."

"O, have they parishes burnt?" he said,
  "Or have they ministers slain?
Or have they robbèd any virgin?
  Or other men's wives have ta'en?"

"Get Up and Bar the Door." *Hussyfscap means housewifery, kitchen chores, perhaps. It is such a funny word, it's too bad it's gone. Puddingbree is the hot water in which the pudding is cooking. This poem suggests crude dramatization with lots of exaggeration and fun. Let a* group speak the story, and solo voices speak and act the absurd roles of husband, wife, and two robbers.
  "Robin Hood Rescuing the Widow's Three Sons." *The old English words of this ballad have been translated into modern English.*

"They have no parishes burnt, good sir,
  Nor yet have ministers slain,
Nor have they robbèd any virgin,
  Nor other men's wives have ta'en."

"O, what have they done?" said Robin Hood,
  "I pray thee tell to me."
"It's for slaying of the king's fallow deer,
  Bearing their long bows with thee."

"Dost thou not mind, old woman," he said,
  "How thou madest me sup and dine?
By the truth of my body," quoth Robin Hood,
  "You could not tell it in better time."

Now Robin Hood is to Nottingham gone,
  With a link and a down, and a day,
And there he met with a silly old palmer,
  Was walking along the highway.

"What news? what news? thou silly old man,
  What news, I do thee pray?"
Said he, "Three squires in Nottingham town
  Are condemned to die this day."

"Come change thy apparel with me, old man,
  Come change thy apparel for mine;
Here is ten shillings in good silver,
  Go drink it in beer or wine."

"O, thine apparel is good," he said,
  "And mine is ragged and torn;
Wherever you go, wherever you ride,
  Laugh not an old man to scorn."

"Come change thy apparel with me, old churl,
  Come change thy apparel with mine;
Here is a piece of good broad gold,
  Go feast thy brethren with wine."

Then he put on the old man's hat,
  It stood full high in the crown:
"The first good bargain that I come at,
  It shall make thee come down."

Then he put on the old man's cloak,
  Was patch'd black, blue and red;
He thought it no shame all the day long,
  To wear the bags of bread.

Then he put on the old man's breeks,
  Was patch'd from leg to side;
"By the truth of my body," bold Robin gan say,
  "This man loved little pride."

Then he put on the old man's hose,
  Were patched from knee to wrist;
"By the truth of my body," said bold Robin Hood,
  "I'd laugh if I had any list."

Then he put on the old man's shoes,
  Were patch'd both beneath and aboon;
Then Robin Hood swore a solemn oath,
  "It's good habit that makes a man."

Now Robin Hood is to Nottingham gone,
  With a link a down, and a down,
And there he met with the proud sheriff,
  Was walking along the town.

"Save you, save you, sheriff!" he said,
  "Now heaven you save and see!
And what will you give to a silly old man
  Today will your hangman be?"

"Some suits, some suits," the sheriff he said,
  "Some suits I'll give to thee;
Some suits, some suits, and pence thirteen,
  Today's a hangman's fee."

Then Robin he turns him round about,
  And jumps from stock to stone;
"By the truth of my body," the sheriff he said,
  "That's well jumpt, thou nimble old man."

"I was ne'er a hangman in all my life,
  Nor yet intends to trade;
But curst be he," said bold Robin,
  "That first a hangman was made."

"I've a bag for meal, and a bag for malt,
  And a bag for barley and corn;
A bag for bread, and a bag for beef,
  And a bag for my little small horn."

"I have a horn in my pocket,
  I got it from Robin Hood,
And still when I set it to my mouth,
  For thee it blows little good."

"O, wind thy horn, thou proud fellow!
  Of thee I have no doubt.
I wish that thou give such a blast,
  Till both thy eyes fall out."

The first loud blast that he did blow,
  He blew both loud and shrill;
A hundred and fifty of Robin Hood's men
  Came riding over the hill.

The next loud blast that he did give,
  He blew both loud and amain,
And quickly sixty of Robin Hood's men
  Came shining over the plain.

"O, who are those," the sheriff he said,
  "Come tripping over the lee?"
"They're my attendants," brave Robin did say;
  "They'll pay a visit to thee."

They took the gallows from the slack,
  They set it in the glen,
They hangèd the proud sheriff on that,
  Released their own three men.

SIR PATRICK SPENCE

(Ballad)

The king sits in Dumferling town,
  Drinking the blood-red wine:
"O where will I get a good sailor,
  To sail this ship of mine?"

*"Sir Patrick Spence." This is a close translation of old
English words into modern. Even so, like all the traditional
ballads, it leaves much unsaid. It is possible that this ballad refers to the shipwreck and drowning of a number of
Scottish nobles who in 1281 were returning from accompanying Margaret, daughter of the king of Scotland, to
Norway, where she was to be married to King Eric.*

Up and spoke an elderly knight,
  (Sat at the king's right knee),
"Sir Patrick Spence is the best sailor
  That sails upon the sea."

The king has written a broad letter,
  And signed it with his hand,
And sent it to Sir Patrick Spence,
  Was walking on the sand.

The first line that Sir Patrick read,
  A loud laugh laughed he;
The next line that Sir Patrick read,
  A tear blinded his eye.

"O who is this has done this deed,
  This ill deed done to me,
To send me out this time of year,
  To sail upon the sea!

"Make haste, make haste, my merry men all,
  Our good ship sails the morn:"
"O say not so, my master dear,
  For I fear a deadly storm.

"Late late yestereven I saw the new moon
  With the old moon in her arm,
And I fear, I fear, my master dear,
  That we will come to harm."

O our Scotch nobles were right loathe
  To wet their cork-heeled shoes;
But long after the play was played
  Their hats floated into view.

O long, long may their ladies sit,
  With their fans within their hand,
Or ever they see Sir Patrick Spence
  Come sailing to the land.

O long, long may their ladies stand,
  With their gold combs in their hair,
Waiting for their own dear lords,
  For they'll see them never more.

Half o'er, half o'er to Aberdour,
  It's fifty fathoms deep,
And there lies good Sir Patrick Spence,
  With the Scotch lords at his feet.

THE WIFE OF USHER'S WELL

(Ballad)

There lived a wife at Usher's well,
  And a wealthy wife was she;
She had three stout and stalwart sons,
  And sent them o'er the sea.

They had not been a week from her,
  A week but barely one,
When word came to the carline wife
  That her three sons were gone.

They had not been a week from her,
  A week but barely three,
When word came to the carline wife
  That her sons she'd never see.

"I wish the wind may never cease,
  Nor fishes in the flood,
Till my three sons come home to me
  In earthly flesh and blood!"

It fell about the Martinmas,
  When nights are long and dark,
The carline wife's three sons came home,
  And their hats were of birch bark.

It neither grew in trench nor ditch,
  Nor yet in any furrow;
But at the gates of Paradise
  That birch grew fair enough.

"Blow up the fire, my maidens!
  Bring water from the well!
For all my house shall feast this night,
  Since my three sons are well."

And she has made for them a bed,
  She's made it large and wide;
And she's put her mantle about her,
  And sat at their bedside.

Up then crowed the red, red cock,
  And up and crowed the gray;

The eldest son to the youngest said,
  " 'Tis time we were away."

The cock he had not crowed but once,
  And clapped his wings at all,
When the youngest to the eldest said,
  "Brother, we must awa'."

"The cock doth crow, the day doth dawn,
  The fretting worm doth chide;
When we are out of our place,
  A sore pain we must bide."

"Lie still, lie still but a little wee while,
  Lie still but if we may;
When my mother misses us when she wakes
  She'll go mad before it's day."

"Fare ye well, my mother dear!
  Farewell to barn and byre!
And fare ye well, the bonny lass
  That kindles my mother's fire."

A SONG OF SHERWOOD

Alfred Noyes

Sherwood in the twilight, is Robin Hood awake?
Grey and ghostly shadows are gliding through
  the brake,
Shadows of the dappled deer, dreaming of the
  morn,
Dreaming of a shadowy man that winds a shadowy horn.

Robin Hood is here again: all his merry thieves
Hear a ghostly bugle-note shivering through the
  leaves,
Calling as he used to call, faint and far away,
In Sherwood, in Sherwood, about the break of
  day.

"The Wife of Usher's Well." *The old English words of this ballad have been translated into modern English. This is a ghost story that is unusually moving. When this wealthy woman (carline wife) learns that her sons have been lost at sea, she curses the sea and wishes her sons home. They appear, and after she has feasted them, she evidently falls asleep at their bedside. As ghosts must al-* *ways leave before dawn, these three depart reluctantly shortly after cock's crow. The last two lines suggest that one of them leaves a sweetheart behind him.*

"A Song of Sherwood." From *Collected Poems*, Volume I. Copyright 1913, 1941 by Alfred Noyes. Published by J. B. Lippincott Co., Philadelphia and William Blackwood & Sons, London.

Merry, merry England has kissed the lips of
    June:
All the wings of fairyland were here beneath the
    moon,
Like a flight of rose-leaves fluttering in a mist
Of opal and ruby and pearl and amethyst.

Merry, merry England is waking as of old,
With eyes of blither hazel and hair of brighter
    gold:
For Robin Hood is here again beneath the burst-
    ing spray
In Sherwood, in Sherwood, about the break of
    day.

Love is in the greenwood building him a house
Of wild rose and hawthorn and honeysuckle
    boughs:
Love is in the greenwood, dawn is in the skies,
And Marian is waiting with a glory in her eyes.

Hark! The dazzled laverock climbs the golden
    steep!
Marian is waiting: is Robin Hood asleep?
Round the fairy grass-rings frolic elf and fay,
In Sherwood, in Sherwood, about the break of
    day.

Oberon, Oberon, rake away the gold,
Rake away the red leaves, roll away the mould,
Rake away the gold leaves, roll away the red,
And wake Will Scarlett from his leafy forest bed.

Friar Tuck and Little John are riding down to-
    gether
With quarter-staff and drinking-can and grey
    goose-feather.
The dead are coming back again, the years are
    rolled away
In Sherwood, in Sherwood, about the break of
    day.

Softly over Sherwood the south wind blows.
All the heart of England hid in every rose

Hears across the greenwood the sunny whisper
    leap,
Sherwood in the red dawn, is Robin Hood
    asleep?

Hark, the voice of England wakes him as of old
And, shattering the silence with a cry of brighter
    gold,

Bugles in the greenwood echo from the steep,
*Sherwood in the red dawn, is Robin Hood
    asleep?*

Where the deer are gliding down the shadowy
    glen
All across the glades of fern he calls his merry
    men—
Doublets of the Lincoln green glancing through
    the May
In Sherwood, in Sherwood, about the break of
    day—

Calls them and they answer: from aisles of oak
    and ash
Rings the *Follow! Follow!* and the boughs begin
    to crash,
The ferns begin to flutter and the flowers begin
    to fly,
And through the crimson dawning the robber
    band goes by.

Robin! Robin! Robin! All his merry thieves
Answer as the bugle-note shivers through the
    leaves,
Calling as he used to call, faint and far away,
In Sherwood, in Sherwood, about the break of
    day.

THE ADMIRAL'S GHOST

Alfred Noyes

I tell you a tale to-night
　　Which a seaman told to me,
With eyes that gleamed in the lanthorn light
　　And a voice as low as the sea.

You could almost hear the stars
　　Twinkling up in the sky,
And the old wind woke and moaned in the
　　　spars
And the same old waves went by,

Singing the same old song
　　As ages and ages ago,
While he froze my blood in that deep-sea night
　　With the things that he seemed to know.

A bare foot pattered on deck;
　　Ropes creaked; then—all grew still,
And he pointed his finger straight in my face
　　And growled, as a sea-dog will.

"Do 'ee know who Nelson was?
　　That pore little shrivelled form
With the patch on his eye and the pinned-up
　　　sleeve
　　And a soul like a North Sea storm?

"Ask of the Devonshire men!
　　They know, and they'll tell you true;
He wasn't the pore little chawed-up chap
　　That Hardy thought he knew.

"He wasn't the man you think!
　　His patch was a dern disguise!
For he knew that they'd find him out, d'you
　　　see,
　　If they looked him in both his eyes.

"He was twice as big as he seemed;
　　But his clothes were cunningly made.
He'd both of his hairy arms all right!
　　The sleeve was a trick of the trade.

"You've heard of sperrits, no doubt;
　　Well, there's more in the matter than that!
But he wasn't the patch and he wasn't the
　　　sleeve,
　　And he wasn't the laced cocked-hat.

"Nelson was just—a Ghost!
　　You may laugh! But the Devonshire men
They knew that he'd come when England
　　　called,
　　And they know that he'll come again.

"I'll tell you the way it was
　　(For none of the landsmen know),
And to tell it you right, you must go a-starn
　　Two hundred years or so.

． 　． 　． 　． 　． 　．

"The waves were lapping and slapping
　　The same as they are to-day;
And Drake lay dying aboard his ship
　　In Nombre Dios Bay.

"The scent of the foreign flowers
　　Came floating all around;
'But I'd give my soul for the smell o' the pitch,'
　　Says he, 'in Plymouth sound.

" 'What shall I do,' he says,
　　'When the guns begin to roar,
An' England wants me, and me not there
　　To shatter 'er fores once more?'

"(You've heard what he said, maybe,
　　But I'll mark you the p'ints again;
For I want you to box your compass right
　　And get my story plain.)

"The Admiral's Ghost." *Here is a hero tale, a ghost story, and a famous English legend. But it is difficult to understand in one reading, unless you know something of the background of the story.*

England, a small island, has pulled through war after war because of the strength of her navy and her naval heroes. Of all of these, the two who are probably most honored are Sir Francis Drake and Lord Nelson.

In this poem, a story within a story, an old sailor tells
a strange tale. He begins by assuring the listener that there was more to Nelson than met the eye. Nelson may have looked small and "chawed up," with an eye patch and an empty sleeve, but he was far more than he looked. These merely disguised the real man, and the old sailor proposes to explain why the real Nelson was so mighty.

So, he goes back 200 years before Nelson to that other sea hero, Drake, who saved England from the Spanish Armada. The old sailor describes Drake dying on ship-

"'You must take my drum,' he says,
  'To the old sea-wall at home;
And if ever you strike that drum,' he says,
  'Why, strike me blind, I'll come!

"'If England needs me, dead
  Or living, I'll rise that day!
I'll rise from the darkness under the sea
  Ten thousand miles away.'

"That's what he said; and he died;
  An' his pirates, listenin' roun'
With their crimson doublets and jewelled
    swords
  That flashed as the sun went down.

"They sewed him up in his shroud
  With a round-shot top and toe,
To sink him under the salt sharp sea
  Where all good seamen go.

"They lowered him down in the deep,
  And there in the sunset light
They boomed a broadside over his grave,
  As meanin' to say 'Good-night.'

"They sailed away in the dark
  To the dear little isle they knew;
And they hung his drum by the old sea-wall
  The same as he told them to.

          .   .   .   .

"Two hundred years went by,
  And the guns began to roar,
And England was fighting hard for her life,
  As ever she fought of yore.

"'It's only my dead that count,'
  She said, as she says to-day;
'It isn't the ships and it isn't the guns
  'Ull sweep Trafalgar's Bay.'

"D'you guess who Nelson was?
  You may laugh, but it's true as true!
There was more in that pore little chawed-up
    chap
  Than ever his best friend knew.

"The foe was creepin' close,
  In the dark, to our white-cliffed isle;
They were ready to leap at England's throat,
  When—O, you may smile, you may smile;

"But—ask of the Devonshire men;
  For they heard in the dead of night
The roll of a drum, and they saw him pass
  On a ship all shining white.

"He stretched out his dead cold face
  And he sailed in the grand old way!
The fishes had taken an eye and his arm,
  But he swept Trafalgar's Bay.

"Nelson—was Francis Drake!
  O, what matters the uniform,
Or the patch on your eye or your pinned-up
    sleeve,
  If your soul's like a North Sea storm?"

board and worrying about what will happen to England when he is gone. He gives his men, from Devonshire like himself, a drum and promises that if Devon men ever strike that drum in time of peril, he will return and fight again for England.

Then, two hundred years later, in Nelson's day the moment of peril came with the foe "creepin' close." In the night the Devonshire men heard Drake's drum and saw a ship pass by with Drake's cold dead face aboard. And Nelson won the battle because, the old sailor thinks, he was more than Nelson, he was Francis Drake too. No patch over the eye, no pinned-up sleeve could disguise his greatness. Drake lived again in Nelson and England was saved.

THE PIED PIPER OF HAMELIN

Robert Browning

Hamelin Town's in Brunswick
By famous Hanover city;
  The river Weser, deep and wide,
  Washes its wall on the southern side;
  A pleasanter spot you never spied;
But, when begins my ditty,
  Almost five hundred years ago,
  To see the townsfolk suffer so
    From vermin was a pity.

                          Rats!

They fought the dogs, and killed the cats,
  And bit the babies in the cradles,
And ate the cheeses out of the vats,
  And licked the soup from the cook's own
    ladles,
Split open the kegs of salted sprats,
Made nests inside men's Sunday hats,
And even spoiled the women's chats,
  By drowning their speaking
  With shrieking and squeaking
In fifty different sharps and flats.

  At last the people in a body
  To the Town Hall came flocking:
  " 'Tis clear," cried they, "our Mayor's a noddy;
  And as for our Corporation—shocking
  To think that we buy gowns lined with ermine
  For dolts that can't or won't determine
  What's best to rid us of our vermin!
  You hope, because you're old and obese,
  To find in the furry civic robe ease?
  Rouse up, sirs! Give your brain a racking
  To find the remedy we're lacking,
  Or, sure as fate, we'll send you packing!"
At this the Mayor and Corporation
Quaked with a mighty consternation.

An hour they sat in council,
  At length the Mayor broke silence:
"For a guilder I'd my ermine gown sell;
  I wish I were a mile hence!
It's easy to bid one rack one's brain—
I'm sure my poor head aches again
I've scratched it so, and all in vain,
  Oh for a trap, a trap, a trap!"
Just as he said this, what should hap
At the chamber door but a gentle tap?
  "Bless us," cried the Mayor, "what's that?"
  (With the Corporation as he sat,
  Looking little though wondrous fat;
  Nor brighter was his eye, nor moister,
  Than a too-long-opened oyster,
  Save when at noon his paunch grew mutinous
  For a plate of turtle green and glutinous),
  "Only a scraping of shoes on the mat?
  Anything like the sound of a rat
  Makes my heart go pit-a-pat!"

  "Come in!"—the Mayor cried, looking bigger:
  And in did come the strangest figure.
  His queer long coat from heel to head
  Was half of yellow and half of red;
  And he himself was tall and thin,
  With sharp blue eyes, each like a pin,
  And light loose hair, yet swarthy skin,
  No tuft on cheek nor beard on chin,
  But lips where smiles went out and in—
  There was no guessing his kith and kin!
  And nobody could enough admire
  The tall man and his quaint attire.
  Quoth one: "It's as my great grandsire,
  Starting up at the Trump of Doom's tone,
  Had walked this way from his painted tomb-
    stone."

He advanced to the council-table:
And, "Please, your honours," said he, "I'm able,

By means of a secret charm, to draw
All creatures living beneath the sun,
That creep, or swim, or fly, or run,
After me so as you never saw!
And I chiefly use my charm
On creatures that do people harm,
The mole, and toad, and newt, and viper;
And people call me the Pied Piper."
(And here they noticed round his neck
A scarf of red and yellow stripe,
To match with his coat of the selfsame cheque;
And at the scarf's end hung a pipe;
And his fingers, they noticed, were ever straying
As if impatient to be playing
Upon this pipe, as low it dangled
Over his vesture so old-fangled.)
"Yet," said he, "poor piper as I am,
In Tartary I freed the Cham,
Last June, from his huge swarms of gnats;
I eased in Asia the Nizam
Of a monstrous brood of vampire bats:
And, as for what your brain bewilders,
If I can rid your town of rats
Will you give me a thousand guilders?"
"One? fifty thousand!"—was the exclamation
Of the astonished Mayor and Corporation.

Into the street the Piper stept,
  Smiling first a little smile,
As if he knew what magic slept
  In his quiet pipe the while;
Then, like a musical adept,
To blow the pipe his lips he wrinkled,
And green and blue his sharp eyes twinkled
Like a candle-flame where salt is sprinkled;
And ere three shrill notes the pipe uttered,
You heard as if an army muttered;
And the muttering grew to a grumbling;
And the grumbling grew to a mighty rum-
  bling;
And out of the house the rats came tumbling.
Great rats, small rats, lean rats, brawny rats,
Brown rats, black rats, gray rats, tawny rats,
Grave old plodders, gay young friskers,
  Fathers, mothers, uncles, cousins,
Cocking tails and pricking whiskers,
  Families by tens and dozens,
Brothers, sisters, husbands, wives—
Followed the Piper for their lives.
From street to street he piped advancing,

And step by step they followed dancing,
Until they came to the river Weser
Wherein all plunged and perished
—Save one, who, stout as Julius Caesar,
Swam across and lived to carry
(As he the manuscript he cherished)
To Rat-land home his commentary,
Which was, "At the first shrill notes of the
  pipe,
I heard a sound as of scraping tripe,
And putting apples, wondrous ripe,
Into a cider press's gripe;
And a moving away of pickle-tub boards,
And a drawing the corks of train-oil flasks,
And a breaking the hoops of butter casks;
And it seemed as if a voice
(Sweeter far than by harp or by psaltery
Is breathed) called out, Oh, rats! rejoice!
The world is grown to one vast drysaltery!
To munch on, crunch on, take your nuncheon,
Breakfast, supper, dinner, luncheon!
And just as a bulky sugar puncheon,
All ready staved, like a great sun shone
Glorious scarce an inch before me,
Just as methought it said, come, bore me!
—I found the Weser rolling o'er me."

You should have heard the Hamelin people
Ringing the bells till they rocked the steeple.
  "Go," cried the Mayor, "and get long poles!
  Poke out the nests and block up the holes!
  Consult with carpenters and builders,
  And leave in our town not even a trace
  Of the rats!"—when suddenly up the face
  Of the Piper perked in the market-place,
With a, "First, if you please, my thousand
  guilders!"

A thousand guilders! The Mayor looked blue;
So did the Corporation too.
For council dinners made rare havoc
With Claret, Moselle, Vin-de-Grave, Hock;
And half the money would replenish
Their cellar's biggest butt with Rhenish.
To pay this sum to a wandering fellow
With a gipsy coat of red and yellow!
  "Beside," quoth the Mayor, with a knowing
  wink,
  "Our business was done at the river's brink;

We saw with our eyes the vermin sink,
And what's dead can't come to life, I think.
So, friend, we're not the folks to shrink
From the duty of giving you something to
    drink,
And a matter of money to put in your poke,
But, as for the guilders, what we spoke
Of them, as you very well know, was in joke.
Besides, our losses have made us thrifty;
A thousand guilders! Come, take fifty!"

The piper's face fell, and he cried,
"No trifling! I can't wait, beside!
I've promised to visit by dinnertime
Bagdad, and accepted the prime
Of the Head Cook's pottage, all he's rich in,
For having left the Caliph's kitchen,
Of a nest of scorpions no survivor—
With him I proved no bargain-driver,
With you, don't think I'll bate a stiver!
And folks who put me in a passion
May find me pipe to another fashion."

"How?" cried the Mayor, "d'ye think I'll brook
Being worse treated than a Cook?
Insulted by a lazy ribald
With idle pipe and vesture piebald?
You threaten us, fellow? Do your worst,
Blow your pipe there till you burst!"

Once more he stept into the street;
  And to his lips again
Laid his long pipe of smooth straight cane;
  And ere he blew three notes (such sweet
Soft notes as yet musicians cunning
  Never gave the enraptured air),
There was a rustling, that seemed like a bustling
Of merry crowds justling, at pitching and hus-
    tling,
Small feet were pattering, wooden shoes clatter-
    ing,
Little hands clapping, and little tongues chatter-
    ing,
And, like fowls in a farmyard when barley is
    scattering,
Out came the children running.
All the little boys and girls,
With rosy cheeks and flaxen curls,
And sparkling eyes and teeth like pearls,

Tripping and skipping, ran merrily after
The wonderful music with shouting and laugh-
    ter.

The Mayor was dumb, and the Council stood
As if they were changed into blocks of wood,
Unable to move a step, or cry
To the children merrily skipping by—
And could only follow with the eye
That joyous crowd at the Piper's back.
But how the Mayor was on the rack,
And the wretched Council's bosoms beat,
As the piper turned from the High Street
To where the Weser rolled its waters
Right in the way of their sons and daughters!
However, he turned from South to West,
And to Koppelberg Hill his steps addressed,
And after him the children pressed;
Great was the joy in every breast.
  "He never can cross that mighty top!
  He's forced to let the piping drop
  And we shall see our children stop!"
When lo! As they reached the mountain's side,
A wondrous portal opened wide,
As if a cavern was suddenly hollowed;
And the Piper advanced and the children fol-
    lowed,
And when all were in to the very last,
The door in the mountain-side shut fast.
Did I say all? No! one was lame,
And could not dance the whole of the way;
And in after years, if you would blame
His sadness, he was used to say:
  "It's dull in our town since my playmates left!
  I can't forget that I'm bereft
  Of all the pleasant sights they see,
  Which the Piper also promised me;
  For he led us, he said, to a joyous land,
  Joining the town and just at hand,
Where waters gushed and fruit trees grew,
And flowers put forth a fairer hue,
And everything was strange and new.
The sparrows were brighter than peacocks here,
And their dogs outran our fallow deer,
And honey-bees had lost their stings;
And horses were born with eagle's wings;
And just as I became assured
My lame foot would be speedily cured,
The music stopped, and I stood still,

And found myself outside the Hill,
Left alone against my will,
To go now limping as before,
And never hear of that country more!"

Alas, alas for Hamelin!
  There came into many a burger's pate
  A text which says, that Heaven's Gate
Opes to the Rich at as easy rate
As the needle's eye takes a camel in!
The Mayor sent East, West, North and South,
To offer the Piper by word of mouth,
  Wherever it was men's lot to find him,
Silver and gold to his heart's content,
If he'd only return the way he went,
  And bring the children all behind him.
But when they saw 'twas a lost endeavour,
And Piper and dancers were gone forever
They made a decree that lawyers never
  Should think their records dated duly
If, after the day of the month and year,
These words did not as well appear,
  "And so long after what happened here
  On the twenty-second of July,
  Thirteen hundred and seventy-six:"
And the better in memory to fix
The place of the Children's last retreat,
They called it, the Pied Piper's street—
Where anyone playing on pipe or tabor,
Was sure for the future to lose his labour.
Nor suffered they hostelry or tavern
To shock with mirth a street so solemn;
But opposite the place of the cavern
  They wrote the story on a column,
And on the great church window painted
The same, to make the world acquainted
How their children were stolen away;
And there it stands to this very day.
And I must not omit to say
That in Transylvania there's a tribe
Of alien people that ascribe
The outlandish ways and dress,
On which their neighbours lay such stress,
To their fathers and mothers having risen
Out of some subterraneous prison,
Into which they were trepanned
Long time ago in a mighty band
Out of Hamelin town in Brunswick land,
But how or why they don't understand.

"HOW THEY BROUGHT THE GOOD NEWS FROM GHENT TO AIX"

Robert Browning

I sprang to the stirrup, and Joris, and he;
I galloped, Dirck galloped, we galloped all three;
"Good speed!" cried the watch, as the gatebolts
    undrew;
"Speed!" echoed the wall to us galloping
    through;
Behind shut the postern, the lights sank to rest,
And into the midnight we galloped abreast.

Not a word to each other; we kept the great pace
Neck by neck, stride by stride, never changing
    our place;
I turned in my saddle and made its girths tight,
Then shortened each stirrup, and set the pique
    right,
Rebuckled the cheek-strap, chained slacker the
    bit,
Nor galloped less steadily Roland a whit.

'Twas moonset at starting; but while we drew
    near
Lokeren, the cocks crew and twilight dawned
    clear;
At Boom, a great yellow star came out to see;
At Düffeld, 'twas morning as plain as could be;
And from Mecheln church-steeple we heard the
    half-chime,
So Joris broke silence with, "Yet there is time!"

At Aershot, up leaped of a sudden the sun,
And against him the cattle stood black every one,
To stare through the mist at us galloping past,
And I saw my stout galloper Roland at last,
With resolute shoulders, each butting away
The haze, as some bluff river headland its spray;

And his low head and crest, just one sharp ear
    bent back
For my voice, and the other pricked out on his
    track;

  "How They Brought the Good News from Ghent to
Aix." *A good rider, a great horse, and an exciting story
told with a galloping rhythm that sets the reader galloping
too—inside himself!*

And one eye's black intelligence—ever that
    glance
O'er its white edge at me, his own master,
    askance!
And the thick heavy spume-flakes which aye and
    anon
His fierce lips shook upwards in galloping on.

By Hasselt, Dirck groaned; and cried Joris, "Stay
    spur!
Your Roos galloped bravely, the fault's not in
    her,
We'll remember at Aix"—for one heard the
    quick wheeze
Of her chest, saw the stretched neck and stagger-
    ing knees,
And sunk tail, and horrible heave of the flank,
As down on her haunches she shuddered and
    sank.

So we were left galloping, Joris and I,
Past Looz and past Tongres, no cloud in the sky;
The broad sun above laughed a pitiless laugh,
'Neath our feet broke the brittle bright stubble
    like chaff;
Till over by Dalhem a dome-spire sprang white,
And "Gallop," gasped Joris, "for Aix is in sight!"

"How they'll greet us!"—and all in a moment his
    roan
Rolled neck and croup over, lay dead as a stone;
And there was my Roland to bear the whole
    weight
Of the news which alone could save Aix from her
    fate,
With his nostrils like pits full of blood to the
    brim,
And with circles of red for his eye-sockets' rim.

Then I cast loose my buffcoat, each holster let
    fall,
Shook off both my jack-boots, let go belt and all,
Stood up in the stirrup, leaned, patted his ear,
Called my Roland his pet-name, my horse with-
    out peer;
Clapped my hands, laughed and sang, any noise,
    bad or good,
Till at length into Aix Roland galloped and
    stood.

And all I remember is—friends flocking round
As I sat with his head 'twixt my knees on the
    ground;
And no voice but was praising this Roland of
    mine,
As I poured down his throat our last measure of
    wine,
Which (the burgesses voted by common consent)
Was no more than his due who brought good
    news from Ghent.

A LADY COMES TO AN INN
Elizabeth Coatsworth

Three strange men came to the Inn.
One was a black man, pocked and thin,
one was brown with a silver knife,
and one brought with him a beautiful wife.

That lovely woman had hair as pale
as French champagne or finest ale,
that lovely woman was long and slim
as a young white birch or a maple limb.

Her face was like cream, her mouth was a rose,
what language she spoke nobody knows,
but sometimes she'd scream like a cockatoo
and swear wonderful oaths that nobody knew.

Her great silk skirts like a silver bell
down to her little bronze slippers fell,
and her low-cut gown showed a dove on its nest
in blue tattooing across her breast.

Nobody learned the lady's name,
nor the marvelous land from which they came,
but still they tell through the countryside
the tale of those men and that beautiful bride.

THE GOATHERD
Grace Hazard Conkling

One day there reached me from the street
The sound of little trampling feet:
And through the dust and sunlight, I
Saw 'most a thousand goats go by.

The goatherd followed close behind:
He looked quite undisturbed and kind,
And Pablo said he knew him well,
And called him Señor Manuel.

His jacket was a shaggy skin,
And scarlet figures woven in
His blue zarape, made it gay
As though for a fiesta day.

His black eyes twinkled in the shade
That his broad-brimmed sombrero made:
And all his teeth were shiny bright
Like Mother's porcelain, and as white.

Before he went he took a drink
Of something very good, I think,
For he held up the gourd he wore
To Pablo's lips—then drank some more.

I told him there had seemed to be
At least a thousand goats, and he
Just laughed and said—to make a guess—
There *were* a thousand, more or less!

NEW MEXICO

Polly Chase Boyden

Out West is windy
And Out West is wide.
I pass villages of prairie dogs
On every horseback ride.

    I pass jack rabbits and sunsets
    And pueblo Indians,
    And Mexicans in great big hats,
    And they are all my friends.

But when the moon comes sliding
And sagebrush turns to foam,
Then outdoors is Out West,
But indoors is Home.

NOONDAY SUN

Kathryn and Byron Jackson

    Oh, I've ridden plenty of horses
        And I've broken a score in my time,
    But there never was one
        Like the colt Noonday Sun—
    Now there was a horse that was prime!
        Oh, yippi ippi ai—Oh, yippi ippi ay,
    Now there was a horse that was prime!

    She'd run up the side of a mountain
        Or she'd tackle a wildcat alone.
    Oh, she stood twelve hands high
        And her proud shining eye
    Would soften the heart of a stone.
        Oh, yippi ippi ai—Oh, yippi ippi ay,
    Would soften the heart of a stone.

    She'd splash through a treach'rous river,
        Or she'd tease for an apple or sweet,
    She'd buck and she'd prance,
        Or she'd do a square dance
    On her four little white little feet.
        Oh, yippi ippi ai—Oh, yippi ippi ay,
    On her four little white little feet.

    But one night the rustlers stole her,
        They stole her and took her away.
    Now the sun never shines,
        And the wind in the pines
    Says, "You've lost your colt, lack-a-day!"
        Oh, yippi ippi ai—Oh, yippi ippi ay,
    Says, "You've lost your colt, lack-a-day!"

    Someday I'll ride through the prairie.
        Someday I'll pull out my gun,
    And I'll plug him—bang-bang!—
        And I may even hang—
    The outlaw who stole Noonday Sun.
        Oh, yippi ippi ai—Oh, yippi ippi ay,
    The outlaw that stole Noonday Sun.

Oh, I still have her bridle and saddle,
 And I still have her bare empty stall.
But there'll never be one
 Like the colt Noonday Sun,
And she'll never more come to my call!
 Oh, yippi ippi ai—Oh, yippi ippi ay,
And she'll never more come to my call!

WHOOPEE TI YI YO, GIT ALONG LITTLE DOGIES

(Unknown)

As I walked out one morning for pleasure,
I spied a cow-puncher all riding alone;
His hat was throwed back and his spurs was a-
 jingling,
And he approached me a-singin' this song,

 Whoopee ti yi yo, git along little dogies,
 It's your misfortune, and none of my own.
 Whoopee ti yi yo, git along little dogies,
 For you know Wyoming will be your new
  home.

Early in the spring we round up the dogies,
Mark and brand and bob off their tails;
Round up our horses, load up the chuck-wagon,
Then throw the dogies upon the trail.

It's whooping and yelling and driving the dogies;
Oh how I wish you would go on;
It's whooping and punching and go on little
 dogies,
For you know Wyoming will be your new home.

Some boys goes up the trail for pleasure,
But that's where you get it most awfully wrong:
For you haven't any idea the trouble they give us
While we go driving them along.

When the night comes on and we hold them on
 the bedground,
These little dogies that roll on so slow;
Roll up the herd and cut out the strays,
And roll the little dogies that never rolled before.

Your mother she was raised way down in Texas,
Where the jimson weed and sand-burrs grow;
Now we'll fill you up on prickly pear and cholla
Till you are ready for the trail to Idaho.

Oh, you'll be soup for Uncle Sam's Injuns;
"It's beef, heap beef," I hear them cry.
Git along, git along, git along little dogies,
You're going to be beef steers by and by.

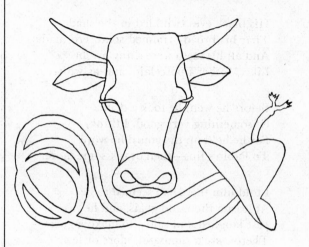

OPEN RANGE

Kathryn and Byron Jackson

 Prairie goes to the mountain,
  Mountain goes to the sky.
 The sky sweeps across to the distant hills
 And here, in the middle,
  Am I.

 Hills crowd down to the river,
  River runs by the tree.
 Tree throws its shadow on sunburnt grass
 And here, in the shadow,
  Is me.

 Shadows creep up the mountain,
  Mountain goes black on the sky,
 The sky bursts out with a million stars
 And here, by the campfire,
  Am I.

THE COWBOY'S LIFE

Attributed to James Barton Adams

The bawl of a steer,
To a cowboy's ear,
Is music of sweetest strain;
And the yelping notes
Of the gay coyotes
To him are a glad refrain.

For a kingly crown
In the noisy town
His saddle he wouldn't change;
No life so free
As the life we see
Way out on the Yaso range.

The rapid beat
Of his broncho's feet
On the sod as he speeds along,
Keeps living time
To the ringing rhyme
Of his rollicking cowboy song.

The winds may blow
And the thunder growl
Or the breezes may safely moan;—
A cowboy's life
Is a royal life,
His saddle his kingly throne.

A SONG OF GREATNESS

Mary Austin

When I hear the old men
Telling of heroes,
Telling of great deeds
Of ancient days,

When I hear that telling
Then I think within me
I too am one of these.

When I hear the people
Praising great ones,
Then I know that I too
Shall be esteemed,
I too when my time comes
Shall do mightily.

INDIAN CHILDREN

Annette Wynne

Where we walk to school each day
Indian children used to play—
All about our native land,
Where the shops and houses stand.

And the trees were very tall,
And there were no streets at all,
Not a church and not a steeple—
Only woods and Indian people.

Only wigwams on the ground,
And at night bears prowling round—
What a different place to-day
Where we live and work and play!

COTTONWOOD LEAVES

Badger Clark

Red firelight on the Sioux tepees,
  (Oh, the camp-smoke down the wind!)
Red firelight on the cottonwood trees
That clap, clap, clap in the dry night breeze.
  (Oh, the camp-smoke down the wind!)

Red-skinned braves in the circling dance;
  (Oh, the bright sparks toward the stars!)
The moccasined feet that stamp and prance
And the brandished knife and the lifted lance.
  (Oh, the bright sparks toward the stars!)

"A Song of Greatness." Mary Austin, *The Children Sing in the Far West*. Reprinted by permission of and arrangement with Houghton Mifflin Company, the authorized publishers
"Indian Children." From *For Days and Days* by Annette Wynne. Copyright 1919 by J. B. Lippincott Company
"Cottonwood Leaves." From *Sky Lines and Wood Smoke* by Badger Clark. The Chronicle Shop, Custer, S. D., 1947. Copyright 1935 by Francis Case. By permission of the author

Eagle plumes in the swirling troop,
  (Oh, the wild flame leaping high!)
And the painted bodies ramp and stoop
To the drum's hot thump and the vaunting
    whoop.
  (Oh, the wild flame leaping high!)

Back where the darkness drops its veil
  (Oh, the sad smoke drifting low!)
The far wolves howl and the widows wail
For the graveless dead on the grim war trail.
  (Oh, the sad smoke drifting low!)

Night on the plains, and the dreams it weaves,
  (Oh, the embers black and cold!)
Where painted ghosts with the step of thieves
Dance to the clap of the cottonwood leaves.
  (Oh, the embers black and cold!)

HIAWATHA'S CHILDHOOD

Henry Wadsworth Longfellow

By the shores of Gitche Gumee,
By the shining Big-Sea-Water,
Stood the wigwam of Nokomis,
Daughter of the Moon, Nokomis.
Dark behind it rose the forest,
Rose the black and gloomy pine-trees,
Rose the firs with cones upon them;
Bright before it beat the water,
Beat the clear and sunny water,
Beat the shining Big-Sea-Water.
  There the wrinkled, old Nokomis
Nursed the little Hiawatha,
Rocked him in his linden cradle,
Bedded soft in moss and rushes,
Safely bound with reindeer sinews;
Stilled his fretful wail by saying,
"Hush! the Naked Bear will hear thee!"
Lulled him into slumber, singing,
"Ewa-yea! my little owlet!
Who is this, that lights the wigwam?
With his great eyes lights the wigwam?
Ewa-yea! my little owlet!"
  Many things Nokomis taught him
Of the stars that shine in heaven;
Showed him Ishkoodah, the comet,
Ishkoodah, with fiery tresses;

Showed the Death-Dance of the spirits,
Warriors with their plumes and war-clubs,
Flaring far away to northward
In the frosty nights of Winter;
Showed the broad, white road in heaven,
Pathway of the ghosts, the shadows,
Running straight across the heavens,
Crowded with the ghosts, the shadows.
  At the door on summer evenings
Sat the little Hiawatha;
Heard the whispering of the pine-trees,
Heard the lapping of the water,
Sounds of music, words of wonder;
"Minne-wawa!" said the pine-trees,
"Mudway-aushka!" said the water.
  Saw the fire-fly, Wah-wah-taysee,
Flitting through the dusk of evening,
With the twinkle of its candle
Lighting up the brakes and bushes,
And he sang the song of children,
Sang the song Nokomis taught him:
"Wah-wah-taysee, little fire-fly,
Little, flitting, white-fire insect,
Little, dancing, white-fire creature,
Light me with your little candle,
Ere upon my bed I lay me,
Ere in sleep I close my eyelids!"
  Saw the moon rise from the water,
Rippling, rounding from the water,
Saw the flecks and shadows on it,
Whispered, "What is that, Nokomis?"
And the good Nokomis answered:
  "Once a warrior, very angry,
Seized his grandmother, and threw her
Up into the sky at midnight;
Right against the moon he threw her;
'T is her body that you see there."
  Saw the rainbow in the heaven,
In the eastern sky, the rainbow,
Whispered, "What is that, Nokomis?"
And the good Nokomis answered:
  " 'T is the heaven of flowers you see there;
All the wild flowers of the forest,
All the lilies of the prairie,
When on earth they fade and perish,
Blossom in that heaven above us."
  When he heard the owls at midnight,
Hooting, laughing in the forest,
"What is that?" he cried in terror;
"What is that?" he said, "Nokomis?"

And the good Nokomis answered:
"That is but the owl and owlet,
Talking in their native language,
Talking, scolding at each other."
    Then the little Hiawatha
Learned of every bird its language,
Learned their names and all their secrets,
How they built their nests in Summer,
Where they hid themselves in Winter,
Talked with them whene'er he met them,
Called them "Hiawatha's Chickens."
    Of all beasts he learned the language,
Learned their names and all their secrets,
How the beavers built their lodges,
Where the squirrels hid their acorns,
How the reindeer ran so swiftly,
Why the rabbit was so timid,
Talked with them whene'er he met them,
Called them "Hiawatha's Brothers."

THE PIONEER

Arthur Guiterman

Long years ago I blazed a trail
    Through lovely woods unknown till then
And marked with cairns of splintered shale
    A mountain way for other men;

For other men who came and came:
    They trod the path more plain to see,
They gave my trail another's name
    And no one speaks or knows of me.

The trail runs high, the trail runs low
    Where windflowers dance or columbine;
The scars are healed that long ago
    My ax cut deep on birch and pine.

Another's name my trail may bear,
    But still I keep, in waste and wood,
My joy because the trail is there,
    My peace because the trail is good.

BUFFALO DUSK

Carl Sandburg

The buffaloes are gone.
And those who saw the buffaloes are gone.
Those who saw the buffaloes by thousands and
    how they pawed the prairie sod into dust
    with their hoofs, their great heads down
    pawing on in a great pageant of dusk,
Those who saw the buffaloes are gone.
And the buffaloes are gone.

THE GOOD JOAN

Lizette Woodworth Reese

Along the thousand roads of France,
Now there, now here, swift as a glance,
A cloud, a mist blown down the sky,
Good Joan of Arc goes riding by.

In Domremy at candlelight,
The orchards blowing rose and white
About the shadowy houses lie;
And Joan of Arc goes riding by.

On Avignon there falls a hush,
Brief as the singing of a thrush
Across old gardens April-high;
And Joan of Arc goes riding by.

The women bring the apples in,
Round Arles when the long gusts begin,

Then sit them down to sob and cry;
And Joan of Arc goes riding by.

Dim fall the hoofs down old Calais;
In Tours a flash of silver-gray,
Like flaw of rain in a clear sky;
And Joan of Arc goes riding by.

Who saith that ancient France shall fail,
A rotting leaf driv'n down the gale?
Then her sons knew not how to die;
Then good God dwells no more on high,

Tours, Arles, and Domremy reply!
For Joan of Arc goes riding by.

COLUMBUS

Annette Wynne

An Italian boy that liked to play
In Genoa about the ships all day,
With curly head and dark, dark eyes,
That gazed at earth in child surprise;
And dreamed of distant stranger skies.

He watched the ships that came crowding in
With cargo of riches; he loved the din
Of the glad rush out and the spreading sails
And the echo of far-off windy gales.

He studied the books of the olden day;
He studied but knew far more than they;
He talked to the learned men of the school—
So wise he was they thought him a fool,
A fool with the dark, dark, dreamful eyes,
A child he was—grown wonder-wise.

Youth and dreams are over past
And out, far out he is sailing fast
Toward the seas he dreamed;—strange lands
    arise—
The world is made rich by his great emprise—
And the wisest know he was more than wise.

COLUMBUS

Joaquin Miller

Behind him lay the gray Azores,
    Behind the Gates of Hercules;
Before him not the ghost of shores,
    Before him only shoreless seas.
The good mate said: "Now must we pray,
    For lo! the very stars are gone.
Brave Admiral, speak, what shall I say?"
    "Why, say 'Sail on! sail on! and on!'"

"My men grow mutinous day by day;
    My men grow ghastly wan and weak."
The stout mate thought of home; a spray
    Of salt wave washed his swarthy cheek.
"What shall I say, brave Admiral, say,
    If we sight naught but seas at dawn?"
"Why, you shall say at break of day,
    'Sail on! sail on! sail on! and on!'"

They sailed and sailed, as winds might blow,
    Until at last the blanched mate said,
"Why, now not even God would know
    Should I and all my men fall dead.
These very winds forget their way,
    For God from these dread seas is gone.
Now speak, brave Admiral, speak and say"—
    He said: "Sail on! sail on! and on!"

They sailed. They sailed. Then spake the
    mate:
    "This mad sea shows his teeth tonight.
He curls his lip, he lies in wait,
    With lifted teeth, as if to bite!
Brave Admiral, say but one good word:
    What shall we do when hope is gone?"
The words leapt like a leaping sword:
    "Sail on! sail on! sail on! and on!"

Then, pale and worn, he kept his deck,
    And peered through darkness. Ah, that
    night
Of all dark nights! And then a speck—
    A light! a light! a light! a light!

It grew, a starlit flag unfurled!
    It grew to be Time's burst of dawn.
He gained a world; he gave that world
    Its grandest lesson: "On! sail on!"

ATLANTIC CHARTER, A.D. 1620–1942

Francis Brett Young

What are you carrying Pilgrims, Pilgrims?
What did you carry beyond the sea?
    We carried the Book, we carried the Sword,
    A steadfast heart in the fear of the Lord,
    And a living faith in His plighted word
    That all men should be free.

What were your memories, Pilgrims, Pilgrims?
What of the dreams you bore away?
    We carried the songs our fathers sung
    By the hearths of home when they were young,
    And the comely words of the mother-tongue
    In which they learnt to pray.

What did you find there, Pilgrims, Pilgrims?
What did you find beyond the waves?
    A stubborn land and a barren shore,
    Hunger and want and sickness sore:
    All these we found and gladly bore
    Rather than be slaves.

How did you fare there, Pilgrims, Pilgrims?
What did you build in that stubborn land?
    We felled the forest and tilled the sod
    Of a continent no man had trod
    And we established there, in the Grace of God,
    The rights whereby we stand.

What are you bringing us, Pilgrims, Pilgrims?
Bringing us back in this bitter day?
    The selfsame things we carried away:
    The Book, the Sword,
    The fear of the Lord,
    And the boons our fathers dearly bought:
    Freedom of Worship, Speech and Thought,
    Freedom from Want, Freedom from Fear,
    The liberties we hold most dear,
    And who shall say us Nay?

THE LANDING OF THE PILGRIM FATHERS

(NOVEMBER 19, 1620)

Felicia Dorothea Hemans

The breaking waves dashed high
    On a stern and rock-bound coast,
And the woods, against a stormy sky,
    Their giant branches tossed;

And the heavy night hung dark
    The hills and waters o'er,
When a band of exiles moored their bark
    On the wild New England shore.

Not as the conquerer comes,
    They, the true-hearted came:
Not with the roll of the stirring drums,
    And the trumpet that sings of fame;

Not as the flying come,
    In silence and in fear,—
They shook the depths of the desert's gloom
    With their hymns of lofty cheer.

Amidst the storm they sang,
    And the stars heard, and the sea;
And the sounding aisles of the dim woods rang
    To the anthem of the free!

The ocean-eagle soared
    From his nest by the white waves' foam,
And the rocking pines of the forest roared;
    This was their welcome home!

There were men with hoary hair
    Amidst that pilgrim-band;
Why had they come to wither there,
    Away from their childhood's land?

There was woman's fearless eye,
    Lit by her deep love's truth;
There was manhood's brow, serenely high,
    And the fiery heart of youth.

What sought they thus afar?
    Bright jewels of the mine?
The wealth of seas, the spoils of war?—
    They sought a faith's pure shrine!

Aye, call it holy ground,
    The soil where first they trod!
They have left unstained what there they
        found—
    Freedom to worship God!

PAUL REVERE'S RIDE

Henry Wadsworth Longfellow

Listen, my children, and you shall hear
Of the midnight ride of Paul Revere,
On the eighteenth of April, in seventy-five;
Hardly a man is now alive
Who remembers that famous day and year.
He said to his friend, "If the British march
By land or sea from the town tonight,
Hang a lantern aloft in the belfry arch
Of the North Church tower as a signal light,—
One, if by land, and two, if by sea;
And I on the opposite shore will be,
Ready to ride and spread the alarm
Through every Middlesex village and farm,
For the country folk to be up and to arm."

Then he said, "Good Night!" and with muffled
        oar
Silently rowed to the Charleston shore,
Just as the moon rose over the bay,
Where swinging wide at her moorings lay
The *Somerset,* British man-of-war;
A phantom ship, with each mast and spar
Across the moon like a prison bar,
And a huge black hulk, that was magnified
By its own reflection in the tide.

Meanwhile, his friend, through alley and street,
Wanders and watches with eager ears,
Till in the silence around him he hears
The muster of men at the barrack door,
The sound of arms, and the tramp of feet,
And the measured tread of the grenadiers,
Marching down to their boats on the shore.

Then he climbed the tower of the Old North
        Church
By the wooden stairs, with stealthy tread,
To the belfry-chamber overhead,
And startled the pigeons from their perch
On the somber rafters, that round him made
Masses and moving shapes of shade,—
By the trembling ladder, steep and tall,
To the highest window in the wall,
Where he paused to listen and look down
A moment on the roofs of the town,
And the moonlight flowing over all.

Beneath in the churchyard, lay the dead,
In their night-encampment on the hill,
Wrapped in silence so deep and still
That he could hear, like a sentinel's tread,
The watchful night-wind, as it went
Creeping along from tent to tent,
And seeming to whisper, "All is Well!"
A moment only he feels the spell
Of the place and the hour, and the secret dread
Of the lonely belfry and the dead;
For suddenly all his thoughts are bent
On a shadowy something far away,
Where the river widens to meet the bay,—
A line of black that bends and floats
On the rising tide, like a bridge of boats.

Meanwhile, impatient to mount and ride,
Booted and spurred, with a heavy stride
On the opposite shore walked Paul Revere.
Now he patted his horse's side,
Now gazed at the landscape far and near,
Then, impetuous, stamped the earth,
And turned and tightened his saddle-girth;
But mostly he watched with eager search
The belfry-tower of the Old North Church,
As it rose above the graves on the hill,
Lonely and spectral and somber and still.
And lo! as he looks, on the belfry's height
A glimmer, and then a gleam of light!
He springs to the saddle, the bridle he turns,
But lingers and gazes, till full on his sight
A second lamp in the belfry burns!

A hurry of hoofs in a village street,
A shape in the moonlight, a bulk in the dark,
And beneath, from the pebbles, in passing, a
        spark
Struck out by a steed flying fearless and fleet:
That was all! And yet, through the gloom and
        the light,
The fate of a nation was riding that night;
And the spark struck out by that steed, in his
        flight
Kindled the land into flame with its heat.
He has left the village and mounted the steep,
And beneath him, tranquil and broad and deep,
Is the Mystic, meeting the ocean tides;
And under the alders that skirt its edge,
Now soft on the sand, now loud on the ledge,
Is heard the tramp of his steed as he rides.

It was twelve by the village clock,
When he crossed the bridge into Medford town.
He heard the crowing of the cock,
And the barking of the farmer's dog,
And felt the damp of the river fog,
That rises after the sun goes down.
It was one by the village clock,
When he galloped into Lexington.
He saw the gilded weathercock
Swim in the moonlight as he passed.
And the meeting-house windows, blank and bare,
Gaze at him with a spectral glare,
As if they already stood aghast
At the bloody work they would look upon.

It was two by the village clock,
When he came to the bridge in Concord town.
He heard the bleating of the flock,
And the twitter of birds among the trees,
And felt the breath of the morning breeze
Blowing over the meadows brown.
And one was safe and asleep in his bed
Who at the bridge would be first to fall,
Who that day would be lying dead,
Pierced by a British musket-ball.

You know the rest. In the books you have read,
How the British Regulars fired and fled,—
How the farmers gave them ball for ball,
From behind each fence and farmyard wall,
Chasing the red-coats down the lane,
Then crossing the fields to emerge again
Under the trees at the turn of the road,
And only pausing to fire and load.

So through the night rode Paul Revere;
And so through the night went his cry of alarm
To every Middlesex village and farm,—
A cry of defiance and not of fear,
A voice in the darkness, a knock at the door,
And a word that shall echo forevermore!
For, borne on the night-wind of the Past,
Through all our history, to the last,
In the hour of darkness and peril and need,
The people will waken and listen to hear
The hurrying hoof-beats of that steed,
And the midnight message of Paul Revere.

BALLAD OF JOHNNY APPLESEED
Helmer O. Oleson

Through the Appalachian valleys, with his kit
    a buckskin bag,
Johnny Appleseed went plodding past high peak
    and mountain crag.
Oh, his stockings were of leather, and his moc-
    casins were tough;
He was set upon a journey where the going
    would be rough.
        See him coming in the springtime,
        Passing violets in the glade.
        Many apple trees are needed,
        And the pioneers want shade.
Johnny carried many orchards in the bag upon
    his back,
And the scent of apple blossoms always lingered
    in his track.
Over half a fertile continent he planted shiny
    seed;
He would toss them in the clearings where the
    fawn and yearling feed.
        In the summer see him tramping
        Through the windings of the wood.
        Big red apples in the oven
        Make the venison taste good.
He would wander over mountain; he would
    brave a raging stream,
For his eyes were filled with visions like an an-
    cient prophet's dream.
He would travel after nightfall, start again at
    early morn;
He was planting seeds of apples for the children
    yet unborn.
    Where the autumn leaves turned crimson,
    He was eager to explore.
    Apple dumplings never blossomed
    On a shady sycamore.
Johnny traveled where the war whoop of the
    painted tribes rang loud;
And he walked among grim chieftains and their
    hot-eyed warrior crowd.
He told them of his vision, of his dream that
    would not die,
So he never was molested, and the settlers had
    their pie.
        Bitter winter found him trudging,
        Not for glory or applause,
        Only happy for the winesaps
        In tomorrow's applesauce!

WASHINGTON

Nancy Byrd Turner

He played by the river when he was young,
He raced with rabbits along the hills,
He fished for minnows, and climbed and swung,
And hooted back at the whippoorwills.
Strong and slender and tall he grew—
And then, one morning, the bugles blew.

Over the hills the summons came,
Over the river's shining rim.
He said that the bugles called his name,
He knew that his country needed him,
And he answered, "Coming!" and marched away
For many a night and many a day.

Perhaps when the marches were hot and long
He'd think of the river flowing by
Or, camping under the winter sky,
Would hear the whippoorwill's far-off song.
Working or playing, in peace or strife,
He loved America all his life!

THOMAS JEFFERSON
1743–1826

*Rosemary Carr and
Stephen Vincent Benét*

Thomas Jefferson,
What do you say
Under the gravestone
Hidden away?

"I was a giver,
I was a molder,
I was a builder
With a strong shoulder."

Six feet and over,
Large-boned and ruddy,
The eyes grey-hazel
But bright with study.

The big hands clever
With pen and fiddle
And ready, ever,
For any riddle.

From buying empires
To planting 'taters,
From Declarations
To trick dumb-waiters.

"I liked the people,
The sweat and crowd of them,
Trusted them always
And spoke aloud of them.

"I liked all learning
And wished to share it
Abroad like pollen
For all who merit.

"I liked fine houses
With Greek pilasters,
And built them surely,
My touch a master's.

"I liked queer gadgets
And secret shelves,
And helping nations
To rule themselves.

"Jealous of others?
Not always candid?

But huge of vision
And open-handed.

"A wild-goose-chaser?
Now and again,
Build Monticello,
You little men!

"Design my plow, sirs,
They use it still,
Or found my college
At Charlottesville.

"And still go questing
New things and thinkers,
And keep as busy
As twenty tinkers.

"While always guarding
The people's freedom—
You need more hands, sir?
I didn't need 'em.

"They call you rascal?
They called me worse,
You'd do grand things, sir,
But lack the purse?

"I got no riches.
I died a debtor.
I died free-hearted
And that was better.

"For life was freakish
But life was fervent,
And I was always
Life's willing servant.

"Life, life's too weighty?
Too long a haul, sir?
I lived past eighty.
I liked it all, sir."

"Benjamin Franklin 1706–1790." From *A Book of Americans,* published by Rinehart & Company, Inc. Copyright, 1933, by Rosemary Carr and Stephen Vincent Benét

BENJAMIN FRANKLIN 1706–1790

*Rosemary Carr and
Stephen Vincent Benét*

Ben Franklin munched a loaf of bread while
    walking down the street
And all the Philadelphia girls tee-heed to see
    him eat,
A country boy come up to town with eyes as big
    as saucers
At the ladies in their furbelows, the gempmum
    on their horses.

Ben Franklin wrote an almanac, a smile upon
    his lip,
It told you when to plant your corn and how to
    cure the pip,
But he salted it and seasoned it with proverbs sly
    and sage,
And people read "Poor Richard" till Poor Rich-
    ard was the rage.

Ben Franklin made a pretty kite and flew it in
    the air
To call upon a thunderstorm that happened to
    be there,
—And all our humming dynamos and our electric
    light
Go back to what Ben Franklin found the day he
    flew his kite.

Ben Franklin was the sort of man that people
    like to see,
For he was very clever but as human as could be.
He had an eye for pretty girls, a palate for good
    wine,
And all the court of France were glad to ask him
    in to dine.

But it didn't make him stuffy and he wasn't
    spoiled by fame
But stayed Ben Franklin to the end, as Yankee as
    his name.

"Nancy Hanks 1784–1818." From *A Book of Americans,* published by Rinehart & Company, Inc. Copyright, 1933, by Rosemary Carr and Stephen Vincent Benét

"He wrenched their might from tyrants and its
    lightning from the sky."
And oh, when he saw pretty girls, he had a tak-
    ing eye!

NANCY HANKS
1784-1818

Rosemary Carr and
Stephen Vincent Benét

If Nancy Hanks
Came back as a ghost,
Seeking news
Of what she loved most,
She'd ask first
"Where's my son?
What's happened to Abe?
What's he done?"

"Poor little Abe,
Left all alone
Except for Tom,
Who's a rolling stone;
He was only nine
The year I died.
I remember still
How hard he cried.

"Scraping along
In a little shack,
With hardly a shirt
To cover his back,
And a prairie wind
To blow him down,
Or pinching times
If he went to town.

"You wouldn't know
About my son?
Did he grow tall?
Did he have fun?
Did he learn to read?
Did he get to town?
Do you know his name?
Did he get on?"

"A Reply to Nancy Hanks." From *Children and Books.*
Scott, Foresman and Company, Chicago, 1957
    "I Saw a Ghost." From *Children and Books.* Scott,

A REPLY TO NANCY HANKS

Julius Silberger

Yes, Nancy Hanks,
The news we will tell
Of your Abe
Whom you loved so well.
You asked first,
"Where's my son?"
He lives in the heart
Of everyone.

I SAW A GHOST

Joan Boilleau

As twilight fell
O'er the river's banks,
I saw the ghost
Of Nancy Hanks
Floating in mist
O'er the river's banks.

I told the ghost
Of Nancy Hanks
Floating in mist
O'er the river's banks,
How Abe saved our nation
And kept it one,
How slaves were made free
By a great man; her son.

As moonlight fell
O'er the river's banks,
The smiling ghost
Of Nancy Hanks
Faded in mist
O'er the river's banks.

LINCOLN

Nancy Byrd Turner

There was a boy of other days,
A quiet, awkward, earnest lad,
Who trudged long weary miles to get
A book on which his heart was set—
And then no candle had!

Foresman and Company, Chicago, 1957
    "Lincoln." From *Child Life,* February 1929. Child Life,
Inc., Boston. Used by permission of the author

He was too poor to buy a lamp
But very wise in woodmen's ways.
He gathered seasoned bough and stem,
And crisping leaf, and kindled them
Into a ruddy blaze.

Then as he lay full length and read,
The firelight flickered on his face,
And etched his shadow on the gloom.
And made a picture in the room,
In that most humble place.

The hard years came, the hard years went,
But, gentle, brave, and strong of will,
He met them all. And when to-day
We see his pictured face, we say,
"There's light upon it still."

ABRAHAM LINCOLN

Mildred Plew Meigs

Remember he was poor and country-bred;
    His face was lined; he walked with awkward
        gait.
Smart people laughed at him sometimes and
        said,
    "How can so very plain a man be great?"

Remember he was humble, used to toil.
    Strong arms he had to build a shack, a fence,
Long legs to tramp the woods, to plow the soil,
    A head chuck full of backwoods common
        sense.

Remember all he ever had he earned.
    He walked in time through stately White
        House doors;
But all he knew of men and life he learned
    In little backwoods cabins, country stores.

Remember that his eyes could light with fun;
    That wisdom, courage, set his name apart;
But when the rest is duly said and done,
    Remember that men loved him for his heart.

"Abraham Lincoln." From *Child Life,* February 1936. Child Life, Inc., Boston. By permission of Marion Plew Ruckel

ABRAHAM LINCOLN
1809–1865

Rosemary Carr and
Stephen Vincent Benét

Lincoln was a long man.
He liked out of doors.
He liked the wind blowing
And the talk in country stores.

He liked telling stories,
He liked telling jokes.
"Abe's quite a character,"
Said quite a lot of folks.

Lots of folks in Springfield
Saw him every day,
Walking down the street
In his gaunt, long way.

Shawl around his shoulders,
Letters in his hat.
"That's Abe Lincoln."
They thought no more than that.

Knew that he was honest,
Guessed that he was odd,

"Abraham Lincoln 1809–1865." From *A Book of Americans,* published by Rinehart & Company, Inc. Copyright, 1933, by Rosemary Carr and Stephen Vincent Benét

Knew he had a cross wife
Though she was a Todd.

Knew he had three little boys
Who liked to shout and play,
Knew he had a lot of debts
It took him years to pay.

Knew his clothes and knew his house.
"That's his office, here.
Blame good lawyer, on the whole,
Though he's sort of queer.

"Sure, he went to Congress, once,
But he didn't stay.
Can't expect us all to be
Smart as Henry Clay.

"Need a man for troubled times?
Well, I guess we do.
Wonder who we'll ever find?
Yes—I wonder who."

That is how they met and talked,
Knowing and unknowing.
Lincoln was the green pine.
Lincoln kept on growing.

AND YET FOOLS SAY
George S. Holmes

He captured light and caged it in a glass,
Then harnessed it forever to a wire;
He gave men robots with no backs to tire
In bearing burdens for the toiling mass.

He freed the tongue in wood and wax and brass,
Imbued dull images with motions' fire,
Transmuted metal into human choir—
These man-made miracles he brought to pass.

Bulbs banish night along the Great White Way,
Thin threads of copper throb with might un-
    seen;
On silver curtains shadow-actors play
That walk and talk from magic-mouthed ma-
    chine,

While continents converse through skies o'er-
    head—
And yet fools say that Edison is dead!

ALEXANDER GRAHAM BELL DID NOT INVENT THE TELEPHONE
Robert P. Tristram Coffin

Alexander Graham Bell
Did not invent the telephone,
No good thing was ever yet
The work of any man alone.

My old Grandmother Sarah Bates,
Halfway out from coast to sky,
On Bates's Island, had a fine
Hand in that electric pie.

Grandma Bates with a small child
On her lap with quick hot breath

Willed the telephone to be
As she sat and stood off death.

Another grandmother I had,
Her head all over gimlet curls,
Ran that road of whispers to
Three other merry little girls.

Your Grandmother Fisher with her man
Down with fever of the lung
Willed that wiry line of life
Through the woodlands to be hung.

Your other Grandma Mary Snow,
Miles from your tall father's sire,
Sent out her love so stout, so straight,
It turned into a singing wire.

Little lonely barefoot boys
Aching for their freckled kind,
Old farmers through long nights of snow
Unrolled that wire from their mind.

Alexander Graham Bell
Had lots of help at his strange labor,
Maybe an arm down through the clouds
Helped him make the whole world neighbor.

*"I Hear America Singing." You may wish to end this
poem with the line, "Each sings what belongs to him or
her and to none else." Its emphasis on the importance of*

I HEAR AMERICA SINGING
Walt Whitman

I hear America singing, the varied carols I hear,
Those of the mechanics, each singing his as it
    should be blithe and strong,
The carpenter singing his as he measures his
    plank or beam,
The mason singing his as he makes ready for
    work or leaves off work,
The boatman singing what belongs to him in his
    boat, the deck hand singing on the steam-
    boat deck,
The shoemaker singing as he sits on his bench,
    the hatter singing as he stands,
The wood-cutter's song, the ploughboy's on his
    way in the morning, or at noon intermission
    or at sundown,
The delicious singing of the mother, or the
    young wife at work, or the girl sewing or
    washing,
Each sings what belongs to him or her and to
    none else,
The day what belongs to the day—at night the
    party of young fellows, robust, friendly,
Singing with open mouths their strong melodi-
    ous songs.

*each person's unique contribution is a thought worth
discussing.*

(Mother Goose)

> Bow, wow, wow!
> Whose dog art thou?
> Little Tommy Tinker's dog.
> Bow, wow, wow!

Christina Georgina Rossetti

> Pussy has a whiskered face,
> Kitty has such pretty ways;
> Doggie scampers when I call,
> And has a heart to love us all.

THE ANIMAL FAIR

THE EXTRAORDINARY DOG

Nancy Byrd Turner

> When Mother takes me calling
> I say, "Oh, please and please
> Let's visit with the folks who own
> The funny Pekinese!"
>
> I walk around him softly
> Upon my tipsy-toes;
> He sits so queer and solemn there,
> So scornful in the nose.

I wonder very often:
Suppose I gave a sneeze,
A loud "Kerchoo!"—what would he do,
The pompous Pekinese?

THE ORDINARY DOG

Nancy Byrd Turner

When Brother takes me walking
I cry, "Oh, hip, hooray!
We're sure to see the jolly pup
That joins us every day!"

His ears are raggy-shaggy;
His coat's a dusty brown;
He meets me like a cannon ball
And nearly knocks me down.

He tells me all his secrets,
With joyful jumpings-up.
I wish the pompous Pekinese
Could know the Jolly Pup!

JIPPY AND JIMMY

Laura E. Richards

Jippy and Jimmy were two little dogs.
They went to sail on some floating logs;
The logs rolled over, the dogs rolled in,
And they got very wet, for their clothes were
    thin.

Jippy and Jimmy crept out again.
They said, "The river is full of rain!"
They said, "The water is far from dry!
Ki-hi! ki-hi! ki-*hi*-yi! ki-hi!"

Jippy and Jimmy went shivering home.
They said, "On the river no more we'll roam;
And we won't go to sail until we learn how,
Bow-wow! bow-wow! bow-*wow*-wow! bow-wow!"

"Bow, wow, wow." *See record album* Poetry Time
"Pussy has a whiskered face." From *Sing-Song* by Christina Georgina Rossetti
"The Extraordinary Dog" and "The Ordinary Dog." From *Magpie Lane* by Nancy Byrd Turner, copyright 1927 by Harcourt, Brace and Company, Inc.; renewed 1955 by Nancy Byrd Turner. Reprinted by permission of the publishers.
"Jippy and Jimmy." From *Tirra Lirra* by Laura E. Richards. Little, Brown & Company, Boston, 1932

PUPPY AND I

A. A. Milne

I met a man as I went walking;
We got talking,
Man and I.
"Where are you going to, Man?" I said
    (I said to the Man as he went by).
"Down to the village, to get some bread.
    Will you come with me?" "No, not I."

I met a Horse as I went walking;
We got talking,
Horse and I.
"Where are you going to, Horse, to-day?"
    (I said to the Horse as he went by).
"Down to the village to get some hay.
    Will you come with me?" "No, not I."

I met a Woman as I went walking;
We got talking,
Woman and I.
"Where are you going to, Woman, so early?"
    (I said to the Woman as she went by).
"Down to the village to get some barley.
    Will you come with me?" "No, not I."

I met some Rabbits as I went walking;
We got talking,
Rabbits and I.
"Where are you going in your brown fur coats?"
    (I said to the Rabbits as they went by).
"Down to the village to get some oats.
    Will you come with us?" "No, not I."

I met a Puppy as I went walking;
We got talking,
Puppy and I.
"Where are you going this nice fine day?"
    (I said to the Puppy as he went by).
"Up in the hills to roll and play."
    "*I'll* come with you, Puppy," said I.

"Puppy and I." *Whenever you find a poem with a repetitional refrain it is apt to be monotonous unless you can get a little variety into your speaking of the refrain. Listen when you say the "We got talking" part and if you sing-song it, stop and experiment. And you see Milne uses italics in the last line to make sure you notice the change from the other verses. Taken from* When We Were Very Young, *by A. A. Milne, published and copyright, 1924, by E. P. Dutton & Co., Inc., New York*

VERN

Gwendolyn Brooks

When walking in a tiny rain
Across the vacant lot,
A pup's a good companion—
If a pup you've got.

And when you've had a scold,
And no one loves you very,
And you cannot be merry,
A pup will let you look at him,
And even let you hold
His little wiggly warmness—

And let you snuggle down beside.
Nor mock the tears you have to hide.

A MALTESE DOG

(*Greek,* second century B.C.)

Trans. by Edmund Blunden

He came from Malta; and Eumêlus says
He had no better dog in all his days.
We called him Bull; he went into the dark.
Along those roads we cannot hear him bark.

THE BUCCANEER

Nancy Byrd Turner

Danny was a rascal,
    Danny was a scamp;
He carried off a lady doll
    And left her in the damp.

He took her off on Monday;
    On Wednesday in he came
And dumped her gayly on the floor
    Without a bit of shame.

He was not sad or humble,
    He begged nobody's pardon;
He merely barked: "A lady doll
    I found out in the garden!"

MY DOG

Marchette Chute

His nose is short and scrubby;
    His ears hang rather low;
And he always brings the stick back,
    No matter how far you throw.

He gets spanked rather often
    For things he shouldn't do,
Like lying-on-beds, and barking,
    And eating up shoes when they're new.

He always wants to be going
    Where he isn't supposed to go.
He tracks up the house when it's snowing—
    Oh, puppy, I love you so.

TOM'S LITTLE DOG

Walter de la Mare

Tom told his dog called Tim to beg,
    And up at once he sat,
His two clear amber eyes fixed fast,
    His haunches on his mat.

Tom poised a lump of sugar on
    His nose; then, "Trust!" says he;
Stiff as a guardsman sat his Tim;
    Never a hair stirred he.

"Paid for!" says Tom; and in a trice
    Up jerked that moist black nose;
A snap of teeth, a crunch, a munch,
    And down the sugar goes!

"Vern." From *Bronzeville Boys and Girls* by Gwendolyn Brooks. Copyright © 1956 by Gwendolyn Brooks Blakely. Published by Harper & Brothers, New York
"A Maltese Dog." Translated by Edmund Blunden. From *The Oxford Book of Greek Verse in Translation.* New York: Oxford University Press, 1943
"The Buccaneer." From *Magpie Lane* by Nancy Byrd Turner, copyright 1927 by Harcourt, Brace and Company, Inc.; renewed 1955 by Nancy Byrd Turner. Reprinted by permission of the publishers

"My Dog." From *Rhymes About Ourselves* by Marchette Chute. The Macmillan Company. New York, 1932. By permission of the author
"Tom's Little Dog." From *Bells and Grass* by Walter de la Mare. Copyright 1942 by Walter de la Mare. Reprinted by permission of The Viking Press, Inc., New York. By permission of the author and by Faber and Faber, Limited
"The Hairy Dog." From *Pillicock Hill* by Herbert Asquith. Used with the permission of The Macmillan

THE HAIRY DOG

Herbert Asquith

My dog's so furry I've not seen
His face for years and years:
His eyes are buried out of sight,
I only guess his ears.

When people ask me for his breed,
I do not know or care:
He has the beauty of them all
Hidden beneath his hair.

SUNNING

James S. Tippett

Old Dog lay in the summer sun
Much too lazy to rise and run.
He flapped an ear
At a buzzing fly.
He winked a half opened
Sleepy eye.
He scratched himself
On an itching spot,
As he dozed on the porch
Where the sun was hot.
He whimpered a bit
From force of habit
While he lazily dreamed
Of chasing a rabbit.
But Old Dog happily lay in the sun
Much too lazy to rise and run.

THE BANDOG

Walter de la Mare

Has anybody seen my Mopser?—
   A comely dog is he,
With hair of the colour of a Charles the Fifth.
   And teeth like ships at sea,

His tail it curls straight upwards,
   His ears stand two abreast,
And he answers to the simple name of Mopser,
   When civilly addressed.

DOGS AND WEATHER

Winifred Welles

I'd like a different dog
   For every kind of weather—
A narrow greyhound for a fog,
   A wolfhound strange and white,
   With a tail like a silver feather
      To run with in the night,
      When snow is still, and winter stars are
      bright.

In the fall I'd like to see
   In answer to my whistle,
A golden spaniel look at me.
   But best of all for rain
   A terrier, hairy as a thistle,
      To trot with fine disdain
      Beside me down the soaked, sweet-smelling
      lane.

LONE DOG

Irene Rutherford McLeod

I'm a lean dog, a keen dog, a wild dog, and lone;
I'm a rough dog, a tough dog, hunting on my
   own;
I'm a bad dog, a mad dog, teasing silly sheep;
I love to sit and bay the moon, to keep fat souls
   from sleep.

I'll never be a lap dog, licking dirty feet,
A sleek dog, a meek dog, cringing for my meat,
Not for me the fireside, the well-filled plate,
But shut door, and sharp stone, and cuff, and
   kick, and hate.

Company. By permission also of William Heinemann, Ltd.
   "Sunning." From *A World to Know* by James S. Tippett.
Copyright, 1933, Harper & Brothers
   "The Bandog." *A bandog is a dog that is kept on a
chain or rope. A Charles the Fifth is a small black and tan
spaniel.* From *Collected Poems, 1901–1918*, by Walter de
la Mare. Copyright, 1920, by Henry Holt and Company,
Inc. Copyright, 1948, by Walter de la Mare. Reprinted by

permission of the publishers
   "Dogs and Weather." *The wire-haired terrier doesn't
mind how wet it is because his coat sheds rain as well as
any raincoat.* From *Skipping Along Alone* by Winifred
Welles. The Macmillan Company, New York, 1931. Used
by permission of James Welles Shearer
   "Lone Dog." From *Songs to Save a Soul* by Irene Rutherford McLeod. Chatto & Windus, London, 1915

Not for me the other dogs, running by my side,
Some have run a short while, but none of them
    would bide.
O mine is still the lone trail, the hard trail, the
    best,
Wide wind, and wild stars, and hunger of the
    quest!

THE ANIMAL STORE
Rachel Field

If I had a hundred dollars to spend,
  Or maybe a little more,
I'd hurry as fast as my legs would go
  Straight to the animal store.

I wouldn't say, "How much for this or that?"—
  "What kind of a dog is he?"
I'd buy as many as rolled an eye,
  Or wagged a tail at me!

I'd take the hound with the drooping ears
  That sits by himself alone;
Cockers and Cairns and wobbly pups
  For to be my very own.

I might buy a parrot all red and green,
  And the monkey I saw before,
If I had a hundred dollars to spend,
  Or maybe a little more.

I LOVE LITTLE PUSSY
Jane Taylor

I love little Pussy,
  Her coat is so warm,
And if I don't hurt her,
  She'll do me no harm;
So I'll not pull her tail,
  Nor drive her away,
But Pussy and I
  Very gently will play.

(Mother Goose)

"Pussy-cat, pussy-cat,
  Where have you been?"
"I've been to London
  To visit the Queen."
"Pussy-cat, pussy-cat,
  What did you there?"
"I frightened a little mouse
  Under the chair."

A KITTEN
Eleanor Farjeon

He's nothing much but fur
And two round eyes of blue,
He has a giant purr
And a midget mew.

He darts and pats the air,
He starts and cocks his ear,
When there is nothing there
For him to see and hear.

He runs around in rings,
But why we cannot tell;
With sideways leaps he springs
At things invisible—

Then half-way through a leap
His startled eyeballs close,
And he drops off to sleep
With one paw on his nose.

TIGER-CAT TIM
Edith H. Newlin

Timothy Tim was a very small cat
Who looked like a tiger the size of a rat.
There were little black stripes running all over
  him,
With just enough white on his feet for a trim
On Tiger-Cat Tim.

Timothy Tim had a little pink tongue
That was spoon, comb and washcloth all made
    into one.
He lapped up his milk, washed and combed all
    his fur,
And then he sat down in the sunshine to purr,
Full little Tim.

Timothy Tim had a queer little way
Of always pretending at things in his play.
He caught pretend mice in the grass and the
    sand,
And fought pretend cats when he played with
    your hand,
Fierce little Tim!

He drank all his milk, and he grew and he grew.
He ate all his meat and his vegetables, too.
He grew very big and he grew very fat,
And now he's a lazy old, sleepy old cat,
Timothy Tim!

CAT
Dorothy Baruch

My cat
Is quiet.
She moves without a sound.
Sometimes she stretches herself curving
On tiptoe.
Sometimes she crouches low
And creeping.

Sometimes she rubs herself against a chair,
And there
    With a *miew* and a *miew*
    And a purrrr   purrrr   purrrr
    She curls up
    And goes to sleep.

My cat
Lives through a black hole
Under the house.

So one day I
Crawled in after her.
And it was dark
And I sat
And didn't know
Where to go.
And then—

Two yellow-white
Round little lights
Came moving . . . moving . . . toward me.
And there
With a *miew* and a *miew*
    And a purrrr   purrrr   purrrr
My cat
Rubbed, soft, against me.

    And I knew
    The lights
    Were MY CAT'S EYES
    In the dark.

IN HONOUR OF TAFFY TOPAZ
Christopher Morley

    Taffy, the topaz-coloured cat,
    Thinks now of this and now of that,
    But chiefly of his meals.
    Asparagus, and cream, and fish,
    Are objects of his Freudian wish;
    What you don't give, he steals.

    His gallant heart is strongly stirred
    By clink of plate or flight of bird,
    He has a plumy tail;
    At night he treads on stealthy pad
    As merry as Sir Galahad
    A-seeking of the Grail.

    His amiable amber eyes
    Are very friendly, very wise;
    Like Buddha, grave and fat,
    He sits, regardless of applause,
    And thinking, as he kneads his paws,
    What fun to be a cat!

THE MYSTERIOUS CAT

Vachel Lindsay

I saw a proud, mysterious cat,
I saw a proud, mysterious cat
Too proud to catch a mouse or rat—
Mew, mew, mew.

But catnip she would eat, and purr,
But catnip she would eat, and purr.
And goldfish she did much prefer—
Mew, mew, mew.

I saw a cat—'twas but a dream,
I saw a cat—'twas but a dream,
Who scorned the slave that brought her cream—
Mew, mew, mew.

Unless the slave were dressed in style,
Unless the slave were dressed in style
And knelt before her all the while—
Mew, mew, mew.

Did you ever hear of a thing like that?
Did you ever hear of a thing like that?
Did you ever hear of a thing like that?
Oh, what a proud mysterious cat.
Oh, what a proud mysterious cat.
Oh, what a proud mysterious cat.
Mew . . . Mew . . . Mew.

CAT

Mary Britton Miller

The black cat yawns,
Opens her jaws,
Stretches her legs,
And shows her claws.

Then she gets up
And stands on four
Long stiff legs
And yawns some more.

She shows her sharp teeth,
She stretches her lip,
Her slice of a tongue
Turns up at the tip.

Lifting herself
On her delicate toes,
She arches her back
As high as it goes.

She lets herself down
With particular care,
And pads away
With her tail in the air.

Elizabeth Coatsworth

"Who are *you?*" asked the cat of the bear.
"I am a child of the wood,
I am strong with rain-shedding hair,
I hunt without fear for my food,
The others behold me and quail."
Said the cat, "You are lacking a tail."

"What can you *do?*" asked the cat.
"I can climb for the honey I crave.
In the fall when I'm merry and fat
I seek out a suitable cave
And sleep till I feel the spring light."
Said the cat, "Can you see in the night?"

Said the cat, "*I* sit by man's fire,
But I am much wilder than you.
I do the thing I desire
And do nothing I don't want to do.
I am small, but then, what is that?
My spirit is great," said the cat.

LITTLE LADY WREN

Tom Robinson

Little Lady Wren,
Hopping from bough to bough,
Bob your tail for me,
Bob it now!

You carry it so straight
Up in the air and when
You hop from bough to bough
You bob it now and then.

Why do you bob your tail,
Hopping from bough to bough,
And will not bob it when I say,
"Bob it now!"?

Christina Georgina Rossetti

Wrens and robins in the hedge,
  Wrens and robins here and there;
Building, perching, pecking, fluttering,
  Everywhere!

THE SECRET

(Unknown)

We have a secret, just we three,
The robin, and I, and the sweet cherry-tree;
The bird told the tree, and the tree told me,
And nobody knows it but just us three.

But of course the robin knows it best,
Because he built the—I shan't tell the rest;
And laid the four little—something in it—
I'm afraid I shall tell it every minute.

But if the tree and the robin don't peep,
I'll try my best the secret to keep;
Though I know when the little birds fly about
Then the whole secret will be out.

"Little Lady Wren." From *In and Out* by Tom Robinson. Copyright, 1943, by Tom Robinson. Reprinted by permission of The Viking Press, Inc., New York
"Wrens and robins in the hedge." From *Sing-Song* by

WHAT ROBIN TOLD

George Cooper

How do robins build their nests?
  Robin Redbreast told me—
First a wisp of yellow hay
In a pretty round they lay;

Then some shreds of downy floss,
Feathers, too, and bits of moss,
Woven with a sweet, sweet song,
This way, that way, and across;
  That's what Robin told me.

Where do robins hide their nests?
  Robin Redbreast told me—
Up among the leaves so deep,
Where the sunbeams rarely creep,
Long before the winds are cold,
Long before the leaves are gold,
Bright-eyed stars will peep and see
Baby robins—one, two, three;
  That's what Robin told me.

"TALENTS DIFFER"

Laura E. Richards

"What are you doing there, Robin a Bobbin,
  Under my window, out in the blue?"
"Building my nest, O Little One, Pretty One,
  Doing the thing that you cannot do!"

"What are you doing now, Robin a Bobbin,
  Under my window, out in the blue?"
"Brooding my eggs, O Little One, Pretty One,
  Doing the thing that you cannot do!"

Christina Georgina Rossetti
"Talents Differ." From *Tirra Lirra* by Laura E. Richards, by permission of Little, Brown & Co. Copyright 1918, 1930, 1932 by Laura E. Richards

"What are you doing there, Robin a Bobbin,
    Under my window, out in the blue?"
"Feeding my nestlings, Little One, Pretty One,
    Doing the thing that you cannot do.

"And what are *you* doing, pray, Little One,
    Pretty One,
    What are you doing, tell me now true?"
"Sewing my patchwork, Robin a Bobbin,
    Doing the thing that *you* cannot do!"

CROWS

David McCord

I like to walk
And hear the black crows talk.

I like to lie
And watch crows sail the sky.

I like the crow
That wants the wind to blow:

I like the one
That thinks the wind is fun.

I like to see
Crows spilling from a tree,

And try to find
The top crow left behind.

I like to hear
Crows caw that spring is near.

I like the great
Wild clamor of crow hate

Three farms away
When owls are out by day.

I like the slow
Tired homeward-flying crow;

I like the sight
Of crows for my good night.

MRS. PECK-PIGEON

Eleanor Farjeon

Mrs. Peck-Pigeon
Is picking for bread,
Bob-bob-bob
Goes her little round head.
Tame as a pussy-cat
In the street,
Step-step-step
Go her little red feet.
With her little red feet
And her little round head,
Mrs. Peck-Pigeon
Goes picking for bread.

CHICKADEE

Hilda Conkling

The chickadee in the appletree
Talks all the time very gently.
He makes me sleepy.
I rock away to the sea-lights.
Far off I hear him talking
The way smooth bright pebbles
Drop into water . . .
Chick-a-*dee-dee-dee* . . .

THE WOODPECKER

Elizabeth Madox Roberts

The woodpecker pecked out a little round hole
And made him a house in the telephone pole.

One day when I watched he poked out his head,
And he had on a hood and a collar of red.

When the streams of rain pour out of the sky,
And the sparkles of lightning go flashing by,

And the big, big wheels of thunder roll,
He can snuggle back in the telephone pole.

THE SNOW-BIRD

Frank Dempster Sherman

When all the ground with snow is white,
  The merry snow-bird comes,
And hops about with great delight
  To find the scattered crumbs.

How glad he seems to get to eat
  A piece of cake or bread!
He wears no shoes upon his feet,
  Nor hat upon his head.

But happiest is he, I know,
  Because no cage with bars
Keeps him from walking on the snow
  And printing it with stars.

WILD GEESE

Elinor Chipp

I heard the wild geese flying
  In the dead of the night,
With beat of wings and crying
I heard the wild geese flying,
And dreams in my heart sighing
  Followed their northward flight.
I heard the wild geese flying
  In the dead of the night.

THE SANDHILL CRANE

Mary Austin

Whenever the days are cool and clear
The sandhill crane goes walking
Across the field by the flashing weir
Slowly, solemnly stalking.
The little frogs in the tules hear
And jump for their lives when he comes near,
The minnows scuttle away in fear,
When the sandhill crane goes walking.

THE BLACKBIRD

Humbert Wolfe

In the far corner
close by the swings,
every morning
a blackbird sings.

His bill's so yellow,
his coat's so black,
that he makes a fellow
whistle back.

Ann, my daughter,
thinks that he
sings for us two
especially.

Emily Dickinson

A bird came down the walk:
He did not know I saw;
He bit an angle-worm in halves
And ate the fellow, raw.

And then he drank a dew
From a convenient grass,
And then hopped sidewise to the wall
To let a beetle pass.

pany, Inc. By permission also of Miss Ann Wolfe

"A bird came down the walk." From *The Poems of Emily Dickinson*. Little, Brown & Company, Boston, 1939

"Wild Geese." From *The City and Other Poems* by Elinor Chipp. Copyright, 1923, by The Four Seas Co. Reprinted by permission of Bruce Humphries, Inc.

"The Sandhill Crane." *There is a significant contrast in the movement of these lines. The first four lines of each* verse have the slow movement of the crane's long legs, "solemnly stalking." The next three lines in each verse are full of hurry and fear. And then the concluding line of each resumes the slow, nonchalant rhythm of the walking crane. From *The Children Sing in the Far West* by Mary Austin. Reprinted by permission of and arrangement with Houghton Mifflin Company, the authorized publishers

The field folk know if he comes that way,
Slowly, solemnly stalking,
There is danger and death in the least delay
When the sandhill crane goes walking.
The chipmunks stop in the midst of their play,
The gophers hide in their holes away
And hush, oh, hush! the field mice say,
When the sandhill crane goes walking.

THE PHEASANT
Robert P. Tristram Coffin

A pheasant cock sprang into view,
A living jewel, up he flew.

His wings laid hold on empty space,
Scorn bulged his eyeballs out with grace.

He was a hymn from tail to beak
With not a tender note or meek.

Then the gun let out its thunder,
The bird descended struck with wonder.

He ran a little, then, amazed,
Settled with his head upraised.

The fierceness flowed out of his eyes
And left them meek and large and wise.

Gentleness relaxed his head,
He lay in jewelled feathers, dead.

GULL
William Jay Smith

Life is seldom if ever dull
For the lazy long-winged white Sea Gull.
    It is as interesting as can be;
He lies on the wind, a slender reed,
And wheels and dips for hours to feed
On scruffy fish and pickleweed
    And to smell the smell of the sea.

He wheels and dips: beneath his wings
The pirate grins, the sailor sings,
    As they ply the China Sea.
While cold winds grip a schooner's sail
And water spouts from a great White Whale,
Perched on a mast, he rides the gale—
    What a wonderful life has he!

Elizabeth Coatsworth

The sea gull curves his wings,
The sea gull turns his eyes.
Get down into the water, fish!
(If you are wise.)

The sea gull slants his wings,
The sea gull turns his head.
Get down into the water, fish!
(Or you'll be dead.)

THE EAGLE

Alfred, Lord Tennyson

He clasps the crag with crooked hands;
Close to the sun in lonely lands,
Ringed with the azure world, he stands.

The wrinkled sea beneath him crawls;
He watches from his mountain walls,
And like a thunderbolt he falls.

MOUSE

Hilda Conkling

Little Mouse in gray velvet,
Have you had a cheese-breakfast?
There are no crumbs on your coat,
Did you use a napkin?
I wonder what you had to eat,
And who dresses you in gray velvet?

"The Pheasant." From *Strange Holiness* by Robert P. Tristram Coffin. Copyright 1935 by The Macmillan Company and used with their permission
"Gull." From *Boy Blue's Book of Beasts*. Copyright © 1956, 1957 by William Jay Smith. By permission of the author and publisher, Little, Brown & Company, Boston
"The sea gull curves his wings." *This is a wonderful example of the music of words and rhythm actually suggesting the idea the poem is presenting. The first couplet of each verse has the smooth, flowing rhythm of the gulls'*

MICE
Rose Fyleman

I think mice
Are rather nice.

Their tails are long,
Their faces small,
They haven't any
Chins at all.
Their ears are pink,
Their teeth are white,
They run about
The house at night.
They nibble things
They shouldn't touch
And no one seems
To like them much.

But *I* think mice
Are nice.

THE HOUSE OF THE MOUSE
Lucy Sprague Mitchell

The house of the mouse
is a wee little house,
a green little house in the grass,
which big clumsy folk
may hunt and may poke
and still never see as they pass
this sweet little, neat little,
wee little, green little,
cuddle-down hide-away
house in the grass.

Christina Georgina Rossetti

The city mouse lives in a house;—
The garden mouse lives in a bower,
He's friendly with the frogs and toads,
And sees the pretty plants in flower.

The city mouse eats bread and cheese;—
The garden mouse eats what he can;
We will not grudge him seeds and stalks,
Poor little timid furry man.

THE MOUSE
Elizabeth Coatsworth

I heard a mouse
Bitterly complaining
In a crack of moonlight
Aslant on the floor—

"Little I ask
And that little is not granted.
There are few crumbs
In this world any more.

"The bread-box is tin
And I cannot get in.

"The jam's in a jar
My teeth cannot mar.

"The cheese sits by itself
On the pantry shelf—

"All night I run
Searching and seeking,
All night I run
About on the floor,

"Moonlight is there
And a bare place for dancing,
But no little feast
Is spread any more."

soaring flight. They are all beauty and grace. The concluding couplets are in startling contrast. They come like a cry of warning, which, of course, they are. From *Plum Daffy Adventure* by Elizabeth Coatsworth. Copyright 1947 by The Macmillan Company and used with their permission

"Mouse." From *Poems by a Little Girl* by Hilda Conkling. Copyright 1920 by J. B. Lippincott Company

"Mice." From *Fifty-One New Nursery Rhymes* by Rose Fyleman. Copyright 1931, 1932 by Doubleday & Company, Inc. By permission also of Miss Rose Fyleman, The Society of Authors, and Messrs. Methuen & Co.

"The House of the Mouse." Taken from *Another Here and Now Story Book*, edited by Lucy Sprague Mitchell, published and copyright, 1937, by E. P. Dutton & Co., Inc., New York

"The city mouse lives in a house." From *Sing-Song* by Christina Georgina Rossetti

"The Mouse." From *Compass Rose* by Elizabeth Coatsworth. Copyright, 1929, by Coward-McCann

A LITTLE SQUIRREL

Child in Winnetka Nursery

I saw a little squirrel,
Sitting in a tree;
He was eating a nut
And wouldn't look at me.

THE STORY
OF THE BABY SQUIRREL

Dorothy Aldis

He ran right out of the woods to me,
Little and furry and panting with fright;
I offered a finger just to see—
And both of his paws held on to it tight.

Was it dogs that had scared him? A crashing
     limb?
I waited a while but there wasn't a sign
Of his mother coming to rescue him.
So then I decided he was mine.

I lifted him up and he wasn't afraid
To ride along in the crook of my arm.
"A very fine place," he thought, "just made
For keeping me comfortable, safe and warm."

At home he seemed happy to guzzle his milk
Out of an eye dropper six times a day.
We gave him a pillow of damask silk
On which he very royally lay.

He frisked on the carpets, he whisked up the
     stairs
(Where he played with some soap till it made
     him sneeze).
He loved it exploring the tables and chairs,
And he climbed up the curtains exactly like
     trees.

He watched his fuzzy gray stomach swell.
He grew until he could leave a dent
In the pillow on which he'd slept so well—
And then . . . Oh, then one morning he went.

Perhaps a squirrel around the place
Adopted him: oh, we're certain it's true
For once a little looking down face
Seemed to be saying: "How do you do?"

THE SQUIRREL

(Unknown)

Whisky, frisky,
Hippity hop.
Up he goes
To the tree top!

Whirly, twirly,
Round and round,
Down he scampers
To the ground.

Furly, curly,
What a tail!
Tall as a feather,
Broad as a sail!

Where's his supper?
In the shell,
Snappity, crackity,
Out it fell!

JOE

David McCord

We feed the birds in winter,
And outside in the snow
We have a tray of many seeds
For many birds of many breeds
And one gray squirrel named Joe.
     But Joe comes early,
     Joe comes late,
     And all the birds
     Must stand and wait.
And waiting there for Joe to go
Is pretty cold work in the snow.

"A Little Squirrel." Reprinted from *Very Young Verses* published by Houghton Mifflin Company. The editors of this book searched diligently to find the source and to obtain permission to use this poem, but without success
"The Story of the Baby Squirrel." From *Before Things Happen* by Dorothy Aldis. G. P. Putnam's Sons, New York, 1939. Copyright 1939 by Dorothy Aldis
"Joe" and "Fred." From *Far and Few* by David McCord. Copyright 1929, 1931, 1952 by David McCord. By permission of Little, Brown & Company, Boston
"Little Charlie Chipmunk." From *Animal Etiquette Book* by Helen Cowles LeCron. Frederick A. Stokes Co.,

FRED

David McCord

Speaking of Joe, I should have said
Our flying squirrel's name is Fred.

Fred is no flyer, but a glider.
His skin is loose and soft as eider.

But Fred himself is no softy:
He likes tough trees, and likes them lofty.

Fred is not around much at noon;
But at night, and under a bright full moon,

He sails from tree to tree like a circus performer;
And once last summer he sailed right into the
     dormer

Window of the empty house next door.
But that's Fred all over. Need I say more?

LITTLE CHARLIE CHIPMUNK

Helen Cowles LeCron

Little Charlie Chipmunk was a *talker*. Mercy me!
He chattered after breakfast and he chattered
     after tea!
He chattered to his father and he chattered to
     his mother!
He chattered to his sister and he chattered to his
     brother!
He chattered till his family was almost driven
     wild!
Oh, little Charlie Chipmunk was a *very* tiresome
     child!

RABBITS

Dorothy Baruch

My two white rabbits
Chase each other
With humping, bumping backs.
     They go hopping, hopping,
     And their long ears
          Go flopping, flopping.

1926. Used by permission of the author
   "Rabbits." From *I Like Animals* by Dorothy Baruch.
Harper & Brothers, New York, 1933. Used by permission
of the author

And they
Make faces
With their noses
Up and down.

Today
I went inside their fence
To play rabbit with them.
And in one corner
Under a loose bush
I saw something shivering the leaves.
     And I pushed
     And I looked.
     And I found—
     There
     In a hole
     In the ground—
     Three baby rabbits
     Hidden away.
          And *they*
          Made faces
          with their noses
          Up and down.

THE RABBIT

Elizabeth Madox Roberts

When they said the time to hide was mine,
I hid back under a thick grapevine.

And while I was still for the time to pass,
A little gray thing came out of the grass.

He hopped his way through the melon bed
And sat down close by a cabbage head.

He sat down close where I could see,
And his big still eyes looked hard at me,

His big eyes bursting out of the rim,
And I looked back very hard at him.

"The Rabbit." From *Under the Tree* by Elizabeth
Madox Roberts. Copyright 1922 by B. W. Huebsch, Inc.,
1950 by Ivor S. Roberts. Reprinted by permission of The
Viking Press, Inc., New York

WHITE SEASON

Frances M. Frost

In the winter the rabbits match their pelts to the
    earth.
With ears laid back, they go
Blown through the silver hollow, the silver
    thicket,
Like puffs of snow.

A STORY IN THE SNOW

Pearl Riggs Crouch

This morning, as I walked to school
    Across the fluffy snow,
I came upon a bunny's tracks—
    A jumping, zigzag row.

He must have hurried very fast,
    For here and there I saw
Along his jerky, winding trail
    The print of Rover's paw!

I set my lunch pail on the snow
    And stood there very still,
For only Rover's clumsy tracks
    Led down the little hill.

Then suddenly I thought I heard
    A rustling sound close by;
And there within a grassy clump
    Shone Bunny's twinkling eye!

THE HARE

Walter de la Mare

In the black furrow of a field
I saw an old witch-hare this night;
And she cocked a lissome ear,
And she eyed the moon so bright,

And she nibbled of the green;
And I whispered "Whsst! witch-hare,"
Away like a ghostie o'er the field
She fled, and left the moonlight there.

THE SNARE

James Stephens

I hear a sudden cry of pain!
There is a rabbit in a snare:
Now I hear the cry again,
But I cannot tell from where.

But I cannot tell from where
He is calling out for aid!
Crying on the frightened air,
Making everything afraid!

Making everything afraid!
Wrinkling up his little face!
As he cries again for aid;
—And I cannot find the place!

And I cannot find the place
Where his paw is in the snare!
Little One! Oh, Little One!
I am searching everywhere!

THE RABBITS' SONG OUTSIDE THE TAVERN

Elizabeth Coatsworth

We, who play under the pines,
We, who dance in the snow
That shines blue in the light of the moon,
Sometimes halt as we go—
Stand with our ears erect,
Our noses testing the air,
To gaze at the golden world
Behind the windows there.

"White Season." From *Pool in the Meadow* by Frances M. Frost. Reprinted by permission of and arrangement with Houghton Mifflin Company, the authorized publishers

"A Story in the Snow." From *Wee Wisdom*, January 1931. Unity School of Christianity, Lee's Summit, Mo. Used by permission of the author

"The Hare." From *Collected Poems, 1901–1918*, by Walter de la Mare. Copyright, 1920, by Henry Holt and Company, Inc. Copyright, 1948, by Walter de la Mare. Reprinted by permission of the publishers

"The Snare." *Notice how reading this poem aloud gives you a sense of hurry. You almost want to run.* From *Songs from the Clay* by James Stephens. Copyright, 1915, by The Macmillan Company and used with their permission. From *Collected Poems* by James Stephens. Used by permission of Mrs. James Stephens and Macmillan & Co., Ltd., London

Suns they have in a cave,
Stars, each on a tall white stem,
And the thought of a fox or an owl
Seems never to trouble them.
They laugh and eat and are warm,
Their food is ready at hand,
While hungry out in the cold
We little rabbits stand.

But they never dance as we dance!
They haven't the speed nor the grace.
We scorn both the dog and the cat
Who lie by their fireplace.
We scorn them licking their paws,
Their eyes on an upraised spoon—
We who dance hungry and wild
Under a winter's moon.

THE SKUNK
Robert P. Tristram Coffin

When the sun has slipped away
And the dew is on the day,
Then the creature comes to call
Men malign the most of all.

The little skunk is very neat,
With his sensitive, plush feet
And a dainty, slim head set
With diamonds on bands of jet.

He walks upon his evening's duty
Of declaring how that beauty
With her patterns is not done
At the setting of the sun.

He undulates across the lawn,
He asks nobody to fawn
On his graces. All that he
Asks is that men let him be.

He knows that he is very fine
In every clean and rippling line,
He is a conscious black and white
Little symphony of night.

THE JOLLY WOODCHUCK
Marion Edey and Dorothy Grider

The woodchuck's very very fat
But doesn't care a pin for that.

When nights are long and the snow is deep,
Down in his hole he lies asleep.

Under the earth is a warm little room
The drowsy woodchuck calls his home.

Rolls of fat and fur surround him,
With all his children curled around him,

Snout to snout and tail to tail.
He never awakes in the wildest gale;

When icicles snap and the north wind blows
He snores in his sleep and rubs his nose.

PRAIRIE-DOG TOWN
Mary Austin

Old Peter Prairie-Dog
Builds him a house
In Prairie-Dog Town,
With a door that goes down
And down and down,
And a hall that goes under
And under and under,
Where you can't see the lightning,
You can't hear the thunder,
For they don't *like* thunder
In Prairie-Dog Town.

Old Peter Prairie-Dog
Digs him a cellar
In Prairie-Dog Town,
With a ceiling that is arched
And a wall that is round,
And the earth he takes out he makes into a
    mound.
And the hall and the cellar
Are dark as dark,
And you can't see a spark,
Not a single spark;
And the way to them cannot be found.

Old Peter Prairie-Dog
Knows a very clever trick
Of behaving like a stick
When he hears a sudden sound,
Like an old dead stick;
And when you turn your head
He'll jump quick, quick,
And be another stick
When you look around.
It *is* a clever trick,
And it keeps him safe and sound
In the cellar and the halls
That are under the mound
In Prairie-Dog Town.

THE LITTLE FOX

Marion Edey and Dorothy Grider

Who came in the quiet night,
Trotting so lightly?
It was the russet fox who came
And with his shadow played a game;
Where the snow lay whitely
And the moon shone brightly
There he wrote his name.

Who spoke in the winter night,
A cold sound and lonely?
The clock-faced owl, so round and hunchy,
The yellow-eyed owl, in a voice so crunchy:

"Who-oo-oo-oo, are you?
I *like* to be only
Squat and bunchy—
Do you-oo-oo-oo, too?"

NIGHT OF WIND
Frances M. Frost

How lost is the little fox at the borders of night,
Poised in the forest of fern, in the trample of
    wind!
Caught by the blowing cold of the mountain
    darkness,
He shivers and runs under tall trees, whimper-
    ing,
Brushing the tangles of dew. Pausing and run-
    ning,
He searches the warm and shadowy hollow, the
    deep
Home on the mountain's side where the nuz-
    zling, soft
Bodies of little foxes may hide and sleep.

FOUR LITTLE FOXES
Lew Sarett

Speak gently, Spring, and make no sudden sound;
For in my windy valley, yesterday I found
New-born foxes squirming on the ground—
        Speak gently.

Walk softly, March, forbear the bitter blow;
Her feet within a trap, her blood upon the snow,
The four little foxes saw their mother go—
        Walk softly.

Go lightly, Spring, oh, give them no alarm;
When I covered them with boughs to shelter
    them from harm,
The thin blue foxes suckled at my arm—
        Go lightly.

Step softly, March, with your rampant hurricane;
Nuzzling one another, and whimpering with
    pain,
The new little foxes are shivering in the rain—
        Step softly.

"The Little Fox." Reprinted from *Open the Door* by Marion Edey and Dorothy Grider. Copyright 1949 by Marion Edey and Dorothy Grider. Used by permission of the publishers, Charles Scribner's Sons

"Night of Wind." From *Pool in the Meadow* by Frances M. Frost. Reprinted by permission of and arrangement with Houghton Mifflin Company, the authorized publishers

"Four Little Foxes." From *Covenant with Earth*, by Lew Sarett. Edited and copyrighted, 1956, by Alma Johnson Sarett. Gainesville: University of Florida Press, 1956. Reprinted by permission of Mrs. Sarett

THE WOLF

Georgia R. Durston

When the pale moon hides and the wild wind
  wails,
And over the treetops the nighthawk sails,
The gray wolf sits on the world's far rim,
And howls: and it seems to comfort him.

The wolf is a lonely soul, you see,
No beast in the wood, nor bird in the tree,
But shuns his path; in the windy gloom
They give him plenty, and plenty of room.

So he sits with his long, lean face to the sky
Watching the ragged clouds go by.
There in the night, alone, apart,
Singing the song of his lone, wild heart.

Far away, on the world's dark rim
He howls, and it seems to comfort him.

LITTLE THINGS

James Stephens

Little things, that run, and quail,
And die, in silence and despair!

Little things, that fight, and fail,
And fall, on sea, and earth, and air!

All trapped and frightened little things,
The mouse, the coney, hear our prayer!

As we forgive those done to us,
—The lamb, the linnet, and the hare—

Forgive us all our trespasses,
Little creatures, everywhere!

FEATHER OR FUR

John Becker

When you watch for
Feather or fur
Feather or fur
Do not stir
Do not stir.

Feather or fur
Come crawling
Creeping
Some come peeping
Some by night
And some by day.
Most come gently
All come softly
Do not scare
A friend away.

When you watch for
Feather or fur
Feather or fur
Do not stir
Do not stir.

FIREFLY

Elizabeth Madox Roberts

A little light is going by,
Is going up to see the sky,
A little light with wings.

I never could have thought of it,
To have a little bug all lit
And made to go on wings.

Lillian Schulz Vanada

Fuzzy wuzzy, creepy crawly
  Caterpillar funny,
You will be a butterfly
  When the days are sunny.

"The Wolf" by Georgia R. Durston, reprinted by permission of the Child Training Association, Inc.
"Little Things" from *Collected Poems* by James Stephens. Copyright 1941 by James Stephens. Reprinted by permission of The Macmillan Company, New York, Macmillan & Company, Ltd., London, and Mrs. James Stephens
"Feather or Fur" from *New Feathers for the Old Goose* by John Becker. New York: Pantheon Books, Inc., 1956
"Firefly." *See the introduction, p. xviii.* From *Under the Tree* by Elizabeth Madox Roberts. Copyright 1922 by B. W. Huebsch, Inc., 1950 by Ivor S. Roberts. Reprinted by permission of The Viking Press, Inc., New York
"Fuzzy Wuzzy, creepy crawly." From *Sung under the Silver Umbrella*. The Macmillan Company, New York, 1935. Used by permission of the author

Winging, flinging, dancing, springing
  Butterfly so yellow,
You were once a caterpillar,
  Wriggly, wiggly fellow.

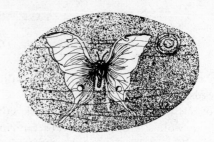

BUTTERFLY

Hilda Conkling

As I walked through my garden
I saw a butterfly light on a flower.
His wings were pink and purple:
He spoke a small word . . .
It was *Follow!*
"I cannot follow"
I told him,
"I have to go the opposite way."

BUTTERFLY

William Jay Smith

Of living creatures most I prize
Black-spotted yellow Butterflies
Sailing softly through the skies,

Whisking light from each sunbeam,
Gliding over field and stream—
Like fans unfolding in a dream,

Like fans of gold lace flickering
Before a drowsy elfin king
For whom the thrush and linnet sing—

Soft and beautiful and bright
As hands that move to touch the light
When Mother leans to say good night.

GREEN MOTH

Winifred Welles

The night the green moth came for me,
  A creamy moon poured down the hill,

The meadow seemed a silver sea,
Small pearls were hung in every tree,
  And all so still, so still—

He floated in on my white bed,
  A strange and soundless fellow.
I saw the horns wave on his head,
  He stepped across my pillow
In tiny ermine boots, and spread
  His cape of green and yellow.

He came so close that I could see
  His golden eyes, and sweet and chill,
His faint breath wavered over me.
"Come Child, my Beautiful," said he,
  And all so still, so still—

LITTLE SNAIL

Hilda Conkling

I saw a little snail
Come down the garden walk.
He wagged his head this way . . . that
    way . . .
Like a clown in a circus.
He looked from side to side
As though he were from a different country.
I have always said he carries his house on his
    back . . .
To-day in the rain
I saw that it was his umbrella!

"Butterfly." From *Poems by a Little Girl* by Hilda Conkling. Copyright 1920 by J. B. Lippincott Company

"Butterfly," from *Boy Blue's Book of Beasts* by William Jay Smith. Copyright © 1956, 1957 by William Jay Smith. Reprinted by permission of the author and publisher, Little, Brown & Company, Boston

"Green Moth." *In this poem the luna moth is accurately described and yet it all sounds like a dream. Notice how* the use of the word "still" *produces and enhances the feeling of hushed mystery.* From *Skipping Along Alone* by Winifred Welles. The Macmillan Company, New York, 1931. Used by permission of James Welles Shearer

"Little Snail." *See the introduction, p. xix.* From *Poems by a Little Girl* by Hilda Conkling. Copyright 1920 by J. B. Lippincott Company

SNAIL

Langston Hughes

Little snail,
Dreaming you go.
Weather and rose
Is all you know.

Weather and rose
Is all you see,
Drinking
The dewdrop's
Mystery.

THE LITTLE TURTLE

Vachel Lindsay

There was a little turtle.
He lived in a box.
He swam in a puddle.
He climbed on the rocks.

He snapped at a mosquito.
He snapped at a flea.
He snapped at a minnow.
And he snapped at me.

He caught the mosquito.
He caught the flea.
He caught the minnow.
But he didn't catch me.

GRANDFATHER FROG

Louise Seaman Bechtel

Fat green frog sits by the pond,
Big frog, bull frog, grandfather frog.
Croak—croak—croak.
Shuts his eye, opens his eye,
Rolls his eye, winks his eye,
Waiting for
A little fat fly.

Croak, croak.
I go walking down by the pond,
I want to see the big green frog,
I want to stare right into his eye,
Rolling, winking, funny old eye.
But oh! he hears me coming by.
Croak—croak—
SPLASH!

OUR MR. TOAD

David McCord

Our Mr. Toad
Has a nice abode
Under the first front step.
When it rains he's cool
In a secret pool
Where the water goes
    drip
    drop
    drep.

Our Mr. Toad
Will avoid the road:
He's a private-cellar man.
And it's not much fun
In the broiling sun
When you *have* a good
    ten
    tone
    tan.

Our Mr. Toad
Has a kind of code
That tells him the coast is clear.
Then away he'll hop
With a stop, stop, stop
When the dusk draws
    nigh
    no
    near.

THE NEWT
David McCord

The little newt
Is not a brute,
A fish or fowl,
A kind of owl:
He doesn't prowl
Or run or dig
Or grow too big.
He doesn't fly
Or laugh or cry—
He doesn't try.

The little newt
Is mostly mute,
And grave and wise,
And has two eyes.
He lives inside,
Or likes to hide;
But after rain
He's out again
And rather red,
I should have said.

The little newt
Of great repute
Has legs, a tail,
A spotted veil.
He walks alone
From stone to stone,
From log to log,
From bog to bog,
From tree to tree,
From you to me.

The little newt
By grass or root
Is very kind
But hard to find.
His hands and feet
Are always neat:
They move across
The mildest moss.
He's very shy,
He's never spry—
Don't ask me why.

SNAKE
D. H. Lawrence

A snake came to my water-trough
On a hot, hot day, and I in pyjamas for the
    heat,
To drink there.

In the deep, strange-scented shade of the great
    dark carob-tree
I came down the steps with my pitcher
And must wait, must stand and wait, for there
    he was at the trough before me.

He reached down from a fissure in the earth-wall
    in the gloom
And trailed his yellow-brown slackness soft-
    bellied down, over the edge of the stone
    trough
And rested his throat upon the stone bottom,
And where the water had dripped from the tap,
    in a small clearness,
He sipped with his straight mouth,
Softly drank through his straight gums, into his
    slack long body,
Silently.

Someone was before me at my water-trough,
And I, like a second comer, waiting.

He lifted his head from this drinking, as cattle do,
And looked at me vaguely, as drinking cattle do,
And flickered his two-forked tongue from his lips,
    and mused a moment,
And stooped and drank a little more,
Being earth brown, earth golden from the burn-
    ing burning bowels of the earth
On the day of Sicilian July, with Etna smoking.

The voice of my education said to me
He must be killed,
For in Sicily the black, black snakes are innocent,
    the gold are venomous.

And voices in me said, If you were a man
You would take a stick and break him now, and
    finish him off.

But I must confess how I liked him,
How glad I was he had come like a guest in
    quiet, to drink at my water-trough
And depart peaceful, pacified, and thankless,
Into the burning bowels of this earth.

Was it cowardice, that I dared not kill him?
Was it perversity, that I longed to talk to him?
Was it humility, to feel so honoured?
I felt so honoured.

And yet those voices:
If you were not afraid, you would kill him!

And truly I was afraid, I was most afraid,
But even so, honoured still more
That he should seek my hospitality
From out the dark door of the secret earth.

He drank enough
And lifted his head, dreamily, as one who has
    drunken,
And flickered his tongue like a forked night on
    the air, so black,
Seeming to lick his lips,
And looked around like a god, unseeing, into
    the air,
And slowly turned his head,
And slowly, very slowly, as if thrice adream,
Proceeded to draw his slow length curving round
And climb again the broken bank of my wall-
    face.

And as he put his head into that dreadful hole,
And as he slowly drew up, snake-easing his
    shoulders, and entered farther,

A sort of horror, a sort of protest against his
    withdrawing into that horrid black hole,
Deliberately going into the blackness, and slowly
    drawing himself after,
Overcame me now his back was turned.

I looked round, I put down my pitcher,
I picked up a clumsy log
And threw it at the water-trough with a clatter.

I think it did not hit him,
But suddenly that part of him that was left be-
    hind convulsed in undignified haste,
Writhed like lightning, and was gone
Into the black hole, the earth-lipped fissure in
    the wall-front,
At which, in the intense still noon, I stared with
    fascination.

And immediately I regretted it.
I thought how paltry, how vulgar, what a mean
    act!
I despised myself and the voices of my accursed
    human education.

And I thought of the albatross,
And I wished he would come back, my snake.

For he seemed to me again like a king,
Like a king in exile, uncrowned in the under-
    world,
Now due to be crowned again.
And so, I missed my chance with one of the
    lords
Of life.
And I have something to expiate;
A pettiness.

THE ANT VILLAGE

Marion Edey and Dorothy Grider

Somebody up in the rocky pasture
    Heaved the stone over.
Here are the cells and a network of furrows
    In the roots of the clover.

Hundreds of eggs lie fitted in patterns,
    Waxy and yellow.
Hundreds of ants are racing and struggling.
    One little fellow

Shoulders an egg as big as his body,
    Ready for hatching.
Darkness is best, so everyone's rushing,
    Hastily snatching

Egg after egg to the lowest tunnels.
    And suddenly, where
Confusion had been, there now is nothing.
    Ants gone. Cells bare.

Mary Britton Miller

A son just born
To a duck is a drake,
And the child of a goose
Is called gosling,
And the moment when
The little chick steps
From the egg of a hen
A chicken is born.
But who knows the name
Of the new-born son
Of the beautiful swan?

(Cygnet)

GOOD MORNING

Muriel Sipe (Mrs. David Ross)

One day I saw a downy duck,
With feathers on his back;
I said, "Good morning, downy duck,"
And he said, "Quack, quack, quack."

One day I saw a timid mouse,
He was so shy and meek;
I said, "Good morning, timid mouse,"
And he said, "Squeak, squeak, squeak."

One day I saw a curly dog,
I met him with a bow;
I said, "Good morning, curly dog,"
And he said, "Bow-wow-wow."

One day I saw a scarlet bird,
He woke me from my sleep;
I said, "Good morning, scarlet bird,"
And he said, "Cheep, cheep, cheep."

THE BARNYARD

Maude Burnham

When the Farmer's day is done,
In the barnyard, ev'ry one,
Beast and bird politely say,
"Thank you for my food to-day."
The cow says, "Moo!"
The pigeon, "Coo!"
The sheep says, "Baa!"
The lamb says, "Maa!"
The hen, "Cluck! Cluck!"

"The Ant Village." Reprinted from *Open the Door* by Marion Edey and Dorothy Grider. Copyright 1949 by Marion Edey and Dorothy Grider. Used by permission of the publishers, Charles Scribner's Sons
"A son just born to a duck." From *Give a Guess* by Mary Britton Miller. New York: Pantheon Books, Inc., 1957
"Good Morning." From *Sung under the Silver Umbrella*. The Macmillan Company, New York, 1935. Used by permission of the author

"Quack!" says the duck;
The dog, "Bow Wow!"
The cat, "Meow!"
The horse says, "Neigh!
I love sweet hay!"
The pig near by,
Grunts in his sty.

When the barn is locked up tight,
Then the Farmer says, "Good night!";
Thanks his animals, ev'ry one,
For the work that has been done.

Christina Georgina Rossetti

Minnie and Mattie
    And fat little May,
Out in the country,
    Spending a day.

Such a bright day,
    With the sun glowing,
And the trees half in leaf,
    And the grass growing.

Pinky white pigling
    Squeals through his snout,
Woolly white lambkin
    Frisks all about.

Cluck! cluck! the nursing hen
    Summons her folk,—
Ducklings all downy soft,
    Yellow as yolk.

Cluck! cluck! the mother hen
    Summons her chickens
To peck the dainty bits
    Found in her pickings.

Minnie and Mattie
    And May carry posies,
Half of sweet violets,
    Half of primroses.

THE CHICKENS
(German)
Rose Fyleman

What a fearful battle,
What a dreadful storm!
Five little chickens
Fighting for a worm.

When the worm had vanished
They all said—Peep—and then
The five little chickens
Were all good friends again.

THE EGG

Laura E. Richards

Oh! how shall I get it, how shall I get it,—
A nice little new-laid egg?
My grandmamma told me to run to the barn-
    yard,
And see if just one I could beg.

"Moolly-cow, Moolly-cow, down in the meadow,
Have you any eggs, I pray?"
The Moolly-cow stares as if I were crazy,
And solemnly stalks away.

"Oh! Doggie, Doggie, perhaps you may have it,
That nice little egg for me."
But Doggie just wags his tail and capers,
And never an egg has he.

"Now, Dobbin, Dobbin, I'm sure you must have
    one,
Hid down in your manger there."
But Dobbin lays back his ears and whinnies,
With "Come and look, if you dare!"

"Piggywig, Piggywig, grunting and squealing,
Are you crying 'Fresh eggs for sale'?"
No! Piggy, you're very cold and unfeeling,
With that impudent quirk in your tail.

"Minnie and Mattie." *Did you discover that of the two hens mentioned in this barnyard poem, one has a brood of chicks, but the other has a flock of ducklings? See analysis on the record album,* Poetry Time. *From* Sing-Song *by Christina Georgina Rossetti*

"The Chickens." From *Picture Rhymes from Foreign Lands.* Copyright 1935 by Rose Fyleman. Reprinted by permission of J. B. Lippincott Company

"The Egg." From *Tirra Lirra* by Laura E. Richards. Little, Brown & Company, Boston, 1932

"You wise old Gobbler, you look so knowing,
I'm sure you can find me an egg.
You stupid old thing! just to say 'Gobble-gobble!'
And balance yourself on one leg."

Oh! how shall I get it, how shall I get it,—
That little white egg so small?
I've asked every animal here in the barn-yard,
And they won't give me any at all.

But after I'd hunted until I was tired,
I found—not one egg, but ten!
And you *never* could guess where they all were
        hidden,—
Right under our old speckled hen!

CHICKEN

Walter de la Mare

Clapping her platter stood plump Bess,
    And all across the green
Came scampering in, on wing and claw,
    Chicken fat and lean:—
Dorking, Spaniard, Cochin China,
    Bantams sleek and small,
Like feathers blown in a great wind,
    They came at Bessie's call.

CHANTICLEER

John Farrar

High and proud on the barnyard fence
Walks rooster in the morning.
He shakes his comb, he shakes his tail
And gives his daily warning.

"Chicken." *See record album* Poetry Time. From *Collected Poems, 1901–1918,* by Walter de la Mare. Copyright, 1920, by Henry Holt and Company, Inc. Copyright, 1948, by Walter de la Mare. Reprinted by permission of the publishers
"Chanticleer." From *Songs for Parents* by John Farrar.

"Get up, you lazy boys and girls,
It's time you should be dressing!"
I wonder if he keeps a clock,
Or if he's only guessing.

CHANTICLEER

Katherine Tynan

Of all the birds from East to West
    That tuneful are and dear,
I love that farmyard bird the best,
    They call him Chanticleer.

Gold plume and copper plume,
    Comb of scarlet gay;
'Tis he that scatters night and gloom,
    And summons back the day!

He is the sun's brave herald
    Who, ringing his blithe horn,
Calls round a world dew-pearled
    The heavenly airs of morn.

Oh, clear gold, shrill and bold,
    He calls through creeping mist
The mountains from the night and cold
    To rose and amethyst.

He sets the birds to singing,
    And calls the flowers to rise;
The morning cometh, bringing
    Sweet sleep to heavy eyes.

Gold plume and silver plume,
    Comb of coral gay;
'Tis he packs off the night and gloom,
    And summons home the day.

Black fear he sends it flying,
    Black care he drives afar;
And creeping shadows sighing
    Before the morning star.

The birds of all the forest
    Have dear and pleasant cheer,

Yale University Press, New Haven, 1921
"Chanticleer." From *Collected Poems* by Katherine Tynan. Used with the permission of The Macmillan Company. By permission also of Miss Pamela Hinkson and The Society of Authors
"The Hens." From *Under the Tree* by Elizabeth Madox

But yet I hold the rarest
    The farmyard Chanticleer.

Red cock and black cock,
    Gold cock or white,
The flower of all the feathered flock,
    He summons back the light!

THE HENS

Elizabeth Madox Roberts

The night was coming very fast;
It reached the gate as I ran past.

The pigeons had gone to the tower of the church
And all the hens were on their perch,

Up in the barn, and I thought I heard
A piece of a little purring word.

I stopped inside, waiting and staying,
To try to hear what the hens were saying.

They were asking something, that was plain,
Asking it over and over again.

One of them moved and turned around,
Her feathers made a ruffled sound,

A ruffled sound, like a bushful of birds,
And she said her little asking words.

She pushed her head close into her wing,
But nothing answered anything.

THE DUCKS

Alice Wilkins

When our ducks waddle to the pond,
They're awkward as awkward can be—
But when they get in the water and swim,
They glide most gracefully.

DUCKS AT DAWN

James S. Tippett

"Quack! Quack!"
Said seven ducks at dawn
While night dew
Glimmered on the lawn.

"Quack! Quack!" they said.
"It's time to eat.
We'll go hunt mushrooms
For a treat."

And in the light
Of early dawn
I saw them chasing
On the lawn.

They sought their treat
With hungry quacks
And marked the dew
With criss-cross tracks.

They ate the mushrooms
One by one
And quacked to greet
The rising sun.

But in my bed
I settled back
And slept to tunes
Of "Quack! Quack! Quack!"

DUCKS' DITTY

Kenneth Grahame

All along the backwater,
Through the rushes tall,
Ducks are a-dabbling,
Up tails all!

Ducks' tails, drakes' tails,
Yellow feet a-quiver,

Yellow bills all out of sight
Busy in the river!

Slushy green undergrowth
Where the roach swim—
Here we keep our larder,
Cool and full and dim.

Everyone for what he likes!
We like to be
Heads down, tails up,
Dabbling free!

High in the blue above
Swifts whirl and call—
We are down a-dabbling
Up tails all!

QUACK!

Walter de la Mare

The duck is whiter than whey is,
His tail tips up over his back,
The eye in his head is as round as a button,
And he says, *Quack! Quack!*

He swims on his bright blue mill-pond,
By the willow tree under the shack;
Then stands on his head to see down to the bottom,
And says, *Quack! Quack!*

When Mollie steps out of the kitchen,
For apron—pinned round with a sack;
He squints at her round face, her dish, and what's in it,
And says, *Quack! Quack!*

He preens the pure snow of his feathers
In the sun by the wheat-straw stack;
At dusk waddles home with his brothers and sisters,
And says, *Quack! Quack!*

"Quack!" From *Bells and Grass* by Walter de la Mare. Copyright 1942 by Walter de la Mare. Reprinted by permission of The Viking Press, Inc., New York. By permission of the author and by Faber and Faber Limited
"The Cow." From *A Child's Garden of Verses* by Robert

(Mother Goose)

Baa, baa, black sheep,
Have you any wool?
Yes, marry, have I,
Three bags full;

One for my master,
One for my dame,
But none for the little boy
Who cries in the lane.

THE COW

Robert Louis Stevenson

The friendly cow all red and white,
I love with all my heart:
She gives me cream, with all her might,
To eat with apple-tart.

She wanders lowing here and there,
And yet she cannot stray,
All in the pleasant open air,
The pleasant light of day;

And blown by all the winds that pass
And wet with all the showers,
She walks among the meadow grass
And eats the meadow flowers.

GREEN GRASS AND WHITE MILK

Winifred Welles

Teeney and Weeney together are going
Down to the dairy to fetch the milk,
Down through the meadow as shiny as silk,
Where grass bends over and daisies are blowing.

With never a word yet somehow hobnobbing,
Teeney and Weeney, like tots in a dream,
Trudge solemnly down to bring back the cream,
Their bright yellow heads like buttercups bobbing.

Louis Stevenson
"Green Grass and White Milk." From *Skipping Along Alone* by Winifred Welles. The Macmillan Company, New York, 1931. Used by permission of James Welles Shearer
"Buttercup Cow." Elizabeth Rendall from "Here We

Up through the field that the sun makes glossy,
  Tossing their tails and taking their time,
  Tinkling their bells in a rusty chime,
Cropping and crunching, come Bossy and Bossy.

They stoop to the ground or they stand unblink-
    ing,
  Munching and munching, making green grass
  Into white milk to pour into a glass
For Teeney and Weeney to have for drinking.

BUTTERCUP COW

Elizabeth Rendall

Buttercup Cow has milk for me
I drink in my silver cup at tea.
Buttercup Cow is speckled and white,
She lives in the meadow from morning till night.

Buttercup Cow hasn't got any bed,
But the moon and the stars look in at her shed.
Buttercup Cow, I'm glad to be me,
Drinking your pretty white milk for my tea.

THE NEW BABY CALF

Edith H. Newlin

Buttercup, the cow, had a new baby calf,
          a fine baby calf,
          a strong baby calf,

Not strong like his mother
But strong for a calf,
For *this* baby calf was so *new!*

Buttercup licked him with her strong warm
    tongue,
Buttercup washed him with her strong warm
    tongue,
Buttercup brushed him with her strong warm
    tongue,
And the new baby calf *liked that!*

Come A' Piping," Book I (by Rose Fyleman). By permission of Basil Blackwell & Mott, Ltd., Oxford
  "The New Baby Calf." From *Very Young Verses*. Houghton Mifflin Company, Boston, 1945. Used by permission of the author

The new baby calf took a very little walk,
          a tiny little walk,
          a teeny little walk,

But his long legs wobbled
When he took a little walk,
  And the new baby calf fell down.

Buttercup told him with a low soft "Moo-oo!"
That he was doing very well for one so very new
And she talked very gently, as mother cows do,
  And the new baby calf *liked that!*

The new baby calf took another little walk,
          a little longer walk,
          a little stronger walk,
He walked around his mother and he found the
    place to drink.
  And the new baby calf liked *that!*

Buttercup told him with another low moo
That drinking milk from mother was a fine thing
    to do,
That she had lots of milk for him and for the
    farmer too,
  And the new baby calf liked *that!*

The new baby calf drank milk every day,
His legs grew so strong that he could run and
    play,
He learned to eat grass and then grain and hay,
  And the big baby calf grew fat!

THE PASTURE

Robert Frost

I'm going out to clean the pasture spring;
I'll only stop to rake the leaves away
(And wait to watch the water clear, I may):
I sha'n't be gone long.—You come too.

I'm going out to fetch the little calf
That's standing by the mother. It's so young
It totters when she licks it with her tongue.
I sha'n't be gone long.—You come too.

"The Pasture." From *Collected Poems of Robert Frost*. Copyright, 1930, 1939, by Henry Holt and Company, Inc. Copyright, 1939, by Robert Frost. Reprinted by permission of Henry Holt and Company, Inc.

THE YOUNG CALVES

Robert P. Tristram Coffin

A hush had fallen on the birds,
 And it was almost night,
When I came round a turn and saw
 A whole year's loveliest sight.

Two calves that thought their month of life
 Meant June through all the year
Were coming down the grassy road
 As slender as young deer.

They stopped amazed and took me in,
 Putting their ears out far,
And in each of four round eyes
 There was an evening star.

They did not breathe, they stared so hard,
 Brother close to brother,
Then their legs awoke, and they
 Turned flank to flank for mother.

A small boy in torn knickers came
 And caught them as they fled,
He put a slender arm around
 Each slender, startled head.

He never looked at me at all,
 I was not in his mind;
The three of them went down the road
 And never glanced behind.

GREEN AFTERNOON

Frances M. Frost

The mother cow looked up and great surprise
Darkened her soft eyes
To see a spotted fawn come out to play
With her young calf that day.

The young ones both were tan with narrow
 shanks.
The puzzled cow gave thanks

Hers wasn't crazy-spotted like the other:
It must have a careless mother

If she would let it leave the wood's soft shadow
For this wide clover meadow.
Fawn danced on air toward calf, and calf half-
 stumbled,
Bawled as it nearly tumbled.

The mother cow grew nervous and said so—
With a soft commanding low—
And then she saw the tawny doe keen-watching
From a hemlock's thatching.

Both mothers watched their young—the tame,
 the free—
Rub foreheads awkwardly.
The calf pushed fawn, the slender fawn pushed
 calf.
Both mothers had to laugh.

Then suddenly the wind changed: in a breath
The fawn was gone beneath
Green boughs; the cow beside the meadow's rail
Scrubbed her calf from nose to tail.

GREEN HILL NEIGHBORS

Frances M. Frost

When I look at our green hill,
I think of all the wild
Small hearts that live inside it:
The woodchuck's chubby child,

Rabbits with busy whiskered faces
Peering out of rocks,
The big-eared meadow mouse, the dainty
Gold-eyed baby fox.

When I look at our green hill
Beneath the sunny sky,
I'm pleased to have such friends inside—
And glad I live nearby!

This is the way the ladies ride,
  Tri, tre, tre, tree,
  Tri, tre, tre, tree!
This is the way the ladies ride,
  Tri, tre, tre, tre, tri-tre-tre-tree!

This is the way the gentlemen ride,
  Gallop-a-trot,
  Gallop-a-trot!
This is the way the gentlemen ride,
  Gallop-a-gallop-a-trot!

This is the way the farmers ride,
  Hobbledy-hoy,
  Hobbledy-hoy!
This is the way the farmers ride,
  Hobbledy-hobbledy-hoy!

FOAL

Mary Britton Miller

Come trotting up
Beside your mother,
Little skinny.

Lay your neck across
Her back, and whinny,
Little foal.

You think you're a horse
Because you can trot—
But you're not.

Your eyes are so wild,
And each leg is as tall
As a pole;

And you're only a skittish
Child, after all,
Little foal.

TROT ALONG, PONY

Marion Edey and Dorothy Grider

Trot along, pony.
  Late in the day,
Down by the meadow
  Is the loveliest way.

The apples are rosy
  And ready to fall.
The branches hang over
  By Grandfather's wall.

But the red sun is sinking
  Away out of sight.
The chickens are settling
  Themselves for the night.

Your stable is waiting
  And supper will come.
So turn again, pony,
  Turn again home.

THE RUNAWAY

Robert Frost

Once, when the snow of the year was beginning
  to fall,
We stopped by a mountain pasture to say,
  "Whose colt?"
A little Morgan had one forefoot on the wall,
The other curled at his breast. He dipped his
  head
And snorted to us. And then he had to bolt.
We heard the miniature thunder where he fled
And we saw him or thought we saw him dim
  and gray,

"Foal." From *Menagerie* by Mary Britton Miller, published by The Macmillan Company, 1928. By permission of the author

"Trot Along, Pony." Reprinted from *Open the Door* by Marion Edey and Dorothy Grider. Copyright 1949 by

Marion Edey and Dorothy Grider. Used by permission of the publishers, Charles Scribner's Sons

"The Runaway." *Morgan horses are Vermont horses and their story has been well told by Marguerite Henry in* Justin Morgan Had a Horse. From *New Hampshire* by

Like a shadow against the curtain of falling
    flakes.
"I think the little fellow's afraid of the snow.
He isn't winter-broken. It isn't play
With the little fellow at all. He's running away.
I doubt if even his mother could tell him, 'Sakes,
It's only weather.' He'd think she didn't know!
Where is his mother? He can't be out alone."
And now he comes again with a clatter of stone,
And mounts the wall again with whited eyes
And all his tail that isn't hair up straight.
He shudders his coat as if to throw off flies.
"Whoever it is that leaves him out so late,
When other creatures have gone to stall and bin,
Ought to be told to come and take him in."

EXCUSE US, ANIMALS IN THE ZOO
Annette Wynne

Excuse us, Animals in the Zoo,
I'm sure we're very rude to you;
Into your private house we stare
And never ask you if you care;
And never ask you if you mind.
Perhaps we really are not kind;
I think it must be hard to stay
And have folks looking in all day,
I wouldn't like my house that way.

Excuse us, Animals in the Zoo,
I'm sure we're very rude to you;
Suppose you all to our house came
And stared at us and called our name.

I hardly think we'd like it at all
In a house that didn't have a wall.
No wonder you pace up and down the floor
And growl a little or even roar—
I'm sure if 'twere we, we'd growl much more.

Excuse us, Animals in the Zoo,
I'm sure we're very rude to you.

THE ELEPHANT'S TRUNK
Alice Wilkins

The elephant always carries his trunk.
I couldn't do that with my own.
His trunk is a part of himself, you see—
It's part of his head—it's grown!

HOLDING HANDS
Lenore M. Link

Elephants walking
Along the trails

Are holding hands
By holding tails.

Trunks and tails
Are handy things

When elephants walk
In Circus rings.

Elephants work
And elephants play

And elephants walk
And feel so gay.

And when they walk—
It never fails

They're holding hands
By holding tails.

THE ELEPHANT

Hilaire Belloc

When people call this beast to mind,
  They marvel more and more
At such a *little* tail behind,
  So LARGE a trunk before.

THE ELEPHANT

Herbert Asquith

Here comes the elephant
Swaying along
With his cargo of children
All singing a song:
To the tinkle of laughter
He goes on his way,
And his cargo of children
Have crowned him with may.
His legs are in leather
And padded his toes:
He can root up an oak
With a whisk of his nose:
With a wave of his trunk
And a turn of his chin
He can pull down a house,
Or pick up a pin.
Beneath his gray forehead
A little eye peers;
Of what is he thinking
Between those wide ears?
Of what does he think?
If he wished to tease,
He could twirl his keeper
Over the trees:
If he were not kind,
He could play cup and ball
With Robert and Helen,
And Uncle Paul:
But that gray forehead,
Those crinkled ears,
Have learned to be kind
In a hundred years:

And so with the children
He goes on his way
To the tinkle of laughter
And crowned with the may.

THE MONKEYS

Edith Osborne Thompson

Sing a song of monkeys,
A jolly bunch of monkeys!
Leaping, swinging in their cages
Looking wise as ancient sages,
Nonchalant and carefree manner,
Nibbling peanut or banana,
Every day is just another
To a monkey or his brother.

Sing a song of monkeys,
Happy, merry monkeys,
If you're ever tired or blue
I can tell you what to do!
Let the monkeys at the Zoo
Make a monkey out of you!

THE HIPPOPOTAMUS

Georgia Roberts Durston

In the squdgy river,
  Down the oozely bank,
Where the ripples shiver,
  And the reeds are rank.

Where the purple Kippo
  Makes an awful fuss,
Lives the hip-hip-hippo
  Hippo-pot-a-mus!

Broad his back and steady;
  Broad and flat his nose;
Sharp and keen and ready
  Little eyes are those.

You would think him dreaming
  Where the mud is deep.

"The Elephant." Reprinted from *Cautionary Verses* by Hilaire Belloc. By permission of Alfred A. Knopf, Inc. Copyright 1931 by Hilaire Belloc

"The Elephant." From *Pillicock Hill* by Herbert Asquith. Used with the permission of The Macmillan Company. By permission also of the author and William Heinemann, Ltd.

"The Monkeys." From *St. Nicholas*, February 1936. Used with the kind permission of Juliet Lit Stern

"The Hippopotamus." From *Junior Home Magazine*. Used by permission of Child Training Association, Incorporated, publishers of *Children's Activities*

It is only seeming—
He is not asleep.

Better not disturb him,
  There'd be an awful fuss
If you touched the Hippo,
  Hippo-pot-a-mus.

THE SEALS
Dorothy Aldis

The seals all flap
Their shining flips
And bounce balls on
Their nosey tips,
And beat a drum,
And catch a bar,
And wriggle with
How pleased they are.

SEAL LULLABY
Rudyard Kipling

Oh! hush thee, my baby, the night is behind us,
  And black are the waters that sparkled so
    green.
The moon, o'er the combers, looks downward
    to find us
  At rest in the hollows that rustle between.
Where billow meets billow, then soft be thy pil-
    low,
  Ah, weary wee flipperling, curl at thy ease!
The storm shall not wake thee, nor shark over-
    take thee,
  Asleep in the arms of the slow-swinging seas!

"The Seals." From *Hop, Skip and Jump* by Dorothy
Aldis. Minton, Balch and Company, New York, 1934.
Copyright 1934 by Dorothy Aldis
"Seal Lullaby." From *The Jungle Book* by Rudyard
Kipling. Reprinted by permission of Mrs. George Bam-

THE KANGAROO
Elizabeth Coatsworth

It is a curious thing that you
don't wish to be a kangaroo,
  to hop hop hop
  and never stop
the whole day long and the whole night, too!

to hop across Australian plains
with tails that sweep behind like trains
  and small front paws
  and pointed jaws
and pale neat coats to shed the rains.

If skies be blue, if skies be gray,
they bound in the same graceful way
  into dim space
  at such a pace
that where they go there's none to say!

HERE SHE IS
Mary Britton Miller

Jungle necklaces are hung
Around her tiger throat
And on her tiger arms are slung
Bracelets black and brown;
She shows off when she lies down
All her tiger strength and grace,
You can see the tiger blaze
In her tiger eyes, her tiger face.

THE TIGER
William Blake

Tiger! Tiger! burning bright
In the forests of the night,
What immortal hand or eye
Could frame thy fearful symmetry?

In what distant deeps or skies
Burnt the fire of thine eyes?
On what wings dare he aspire?
What the hand dare seize the fire?

bridge, The Macmillan Company of Canada, Ltd., and
Macmillan & Company, Ltd., London
"The Kangaroo." From *Summer Green* by Elizabeth
Coatsworth. Copyright 1948 by The Macmillan Company
and used with their permission

And what shoulder, and what art,
Could twist the sinews of thy heart?
And when thy heart began to beat,
What dread hand? and what dread feet?

What the hammer? what the chain?
In what furnace was thy brain?
What the anvil? what dread grasp
Dare its deadly terrors clasp?

When the stars threw down their spears,
And watered heaven with their tears,
Did He smile His work to see?
Did He who made the Lamb make thee?

Tiger! Tiger! burning bright
In the forests of the night,
What immortal hand or eye
Dare frame thy fearful symmetry?

FRANCIS JAMMES: A PRAYER TO GO TO PARADISE WITH THE DONKEYS

Richard Wilbur

When I must come to you, O my God, I pray
It be some dusty-roaded holiday,
And even as in my travels here below,
I beg to choose by what road I shall go
To Paradise, where the clear stars shine by day.
I'll take my walking-stick and go my way,
And to my friends the donkeys I shall say,
"I am Francis Jammes, and I'm going to Paradise,
For there is no hell in the land of the loving God."
And I'll say to them: "Come, sweet friends of the blue skies,
Poor creatures who with a flap of the ears or a nod
Of the head shake off the buffets, the bees, the flies . . ."

Let me come with these donkeys, Lord, into your land,
These beasts who bow their heads so gently, and stand
With their small feet joined together in a fashion
Utterly gentle, asking your compassion.
I shall arrive, followed by their thousands of ears,
Followed by those with baskets at their flanks,
By those who lug the carts of mountebanks
Or loads of feather-dusters and kitchen-wares,
By those with humps of battered water-cans,
By bottle-shaped she-asses who halt and stumble,
By those tricked out in little pantaloons
To cover their wet, blue galls where flies assemble
In whirling swarms, making a drunken hum.
Dear God, let it be with these donkeys that I come,
And let it be that angels lead us in peace
To leafy streams where cherries tremble in air,
Sleek as the laughing flesh of girls; and there
In that haven of souls let it be that, leaning above
Your divine waters, I shall resemble these donkeys,
Whose humble and sweet poverty will appear
Clear in the clearness of your eternal love.

THE FLOWER-FED BUFFALOES

Vachel Lindsay

The flower-fed buffaloes of the spring
In the days of long ago,
Ranged where the locomotives sing
And the prairie flowers lie low:—
The tossing, blooming, perfumed grass
Is swept away by the wheat,
Wheels and wheels and wheels spin by
In the spring that still is sweet.
But the flower-fed buffaloes of the spring
Left us, long ago.
They gore no more, they bellow no more,
They trundle around the hills no more:—
With the Blackfeet, lying low.
With the Pawnees, lying low,
Lying low.

William Shakespeare

Jog on, jog on, the foot-path way,
    And merrily hent the stile-a:
A merry heart goes all the day,
    Your sad tires in a mile-a.

A MODERN DRAGON

Rowena Bastin Bennett

A train is a dragon that roars through the dark.
He wriggles his tail as he sends up a spark.
He pierces the night with his one yellow eye,
And all the earth trembles when he rushes by.

TRAVELING WE GO

THE BABY GOES TO BOSTON

Laura E. Richards

What does the train say?
    Jiggle joggle, jiggle joggle!
What does the train say?
    Jiggle joggle jee!
Will the little baby go
Riding with the locomo?
Loky moky poky stoky
    Smoky choky chee!

Ting! ting! the bells ring,
  Jiggle joggle, jiggle joggle!
Ting! ting! the bells ring,
  Jiggle joggle jee!
Ring for joy because we go
Riding with the locomo,
Loky moky poky stoky
  Smoky choky chee!

Look! how the trees run,
  Jiggle joggle, jiggle joggle!
Each chasing t' other one,
  Jiggle joggle jee!
Are they running for to go
Riding with the locomo?
Loky moky poky stoky
  Smoky choky chee!

Over the hills now,
  Jiggle joggle, jiggle joggle!
Down through the vale below,
  Jiggle joggle jee!
All the cows and horses run,
Crying, "Won't you take us on,
Loky moky poky stoky
  Smoky choky chee?"

So, so, the miles go,
  Jiggle joggle, jiggle joggle!
Now it's fast and now it's slow,
  Jiggle joggle jee!
When we're at our journey's end,
Say good-by to snorting friend,
Loky moky poky stoky
  Smoky choky chee!

TEXAS TRAINS AND TRAILS

Mary Austin

Whenever I ride on the Texas plains
I never hear the couplings cluck,

I never hear the trains
Go chuck-a-luck, chuck-a-luck, chuck-a-luck,
I never hear the engine snort and snuffle,
I never see the smoke plume, I never watch the
    rails,
But I see the moving dust where the beef herds
    shuffle,
And I think I am a cowboy,
A rope and tie 'em cowboy,
Punching Texas longhorns
On the Texas trails.

And the engine goes *Whoop!*
Whoopee, whoopala!
And the cars go *Ki-yi,*
Ki-yi, ki-yi, coma-la ky-yi,
          Whoopala,
Ki-yi!
          Whoop!

No, I never hear the bell, nor the brakeman call
When I ride on the Texas trains;
But I hear the steers bellow and the yearlings
    bawl,
And the lone wolf howl on the wire grass plains.
And I never play I'm fireman, nor anything like
    that,
For I'm playing I'm a cowboy,
A bronco-bustin' cowboy,
Riding Texas longhorns
In a ten-gallon hat.

And the trains go *Youpi-ya,*
Get a-long, dogies,
Get a-long, get a-long
Youpi-yi, youpi-ya,
Youpi-youpi-youpi-ya
Get a-long, get a-long,
Youpi-ya,
          Yo-o-u-up!

"Jog on, jog on, the foot-path way." *See May Hill Arbuthnot*, Children and Books, *p. 181.* From *The Winter's Tale,* Act IV, Sc. 3

"A Modern Dragon." From *Around a Toadstool Table* by Rowena Bastin Bennett. Follett Publishing Company, Chicago, 1930

"The Baby Goes to Boston." *This poem jiggles along like the Toonerville Trolley. See record album* Poetry Time. *From* Tirra Lirra *by Laura E. Richards. Little, Brown & Company, Boston, 1932*

"Texas Trains and Trails." *This poem sounds for all the world like a train in motion but it is not easy to read. You will just have to try it aloud repeatedly till you get it. In the first refrain, there seems to be a silent beat after the line, "Whoopee, whoopala!" In each refrain the train seems to start slowly, gain momentum, and end with a grand "whoop" for full speed ahead! From* The Children Sing in the Far West *by Mary Austin. Reprinted by permission of and arrangement with Houghton Mifflin Company, the authorized publishers*

FROM A RAILWAY CARRIAGE

Robert Louis Stevenson

Faster than fairies, faster than witches,
Bridges and houses, hedges and ditches;
And charging along like troops in a battle
All through the meadows the horses and cattle:
All of the sights of the hill and the plain
Fly as thick as driving rain;
And ever again, in the wink of an eye,
Painted stations whistle by.

Here is a child who clambers and scrambles,
All by himself and gathering brambles;
Here is a tramp who stands and gazes;
And there is the green for stringing the daisies!
Here is a cart run away in the road
Lumping along with man and load;
And here is a mill, and there is a river:
Each a glimpse and gone for ever!

TRAINS AT NIGHT

Frances M. Frost

I like the whistle of trains at night,
The fast trains thundering by so proud!
They rush and rumble across the world,
They ring wild bells and they toot so loud!

But I love better the slower trains.
They take their time through the world instead,
And whistle softly and stop to tuck
Each sleepy blinking town in bed!

TRAINS

James S. Tippett

Over the mountains,
Over the plains,
Over the rivers,
Here come the trains.

Carrying passengers,
Carrying mail,
Bringing their precious loads
In without fail.

Thousands of freight cars
All rushing on
Through day and darkness,
Through dusk and dawn.

Over the mountains,
Over the plains,
Over the rivers,
Here come the trains.

THE WAYS OF TRAINS

Elizabeth Coatsworth

I hear the engine pounding
in triumph down the track—
trains take away the ones you love
and then they bring them back!

trains take away the ones you love
to worlds both strange and new
and then, with care and courtesy,
they bring them back to you.

The engine halts and snuffs and snorts,
it breathes forth smoke and fire,
then snatches crowded strangers on—
but leaves what you desire!

TRAVEL

Edna St. Vincent Millay

The railroad track is miles away,
   And the day is loud with voices speaking,
Yet there isn't a train goes by all day
   But I hear its whistle shrieking.

All night there isn't a train goes by,
   Though the night is still for sleep and dream-
      ing
But I see its cinders red on the sky,
   And hear its engine steaming.

My heart is warm with the friends I make,
   And better friends I'll not be knowing,
Yet there isn't a train I wouldn't take,
   No matter where it's going.

TAKING OFF

Unknown

The airplane taxis down the field
And heads into the breeze,
It lifts its wheels above the ground,
It skims above the trees,
It rises high and higher
Away up toward the sun,
It's just a speck against the sky
—And now it's gone!

UP IN THE AIR

James S. Tippett

Zooming across the sky
Like a great bird you fly,
   Airplane,
   Silvery white
   In the light.

Turning and twisting in air,
When shall I ever be there,

   Airplane,
   Piloting you
   Far in the blue?

AEROPLANE

Mary McB. Green

There's a humming in the sky
There's a shining in the sky
Silver wings are flashing by
Silver wings are shining by
   Aeroplane
   Aeroplane
   Flying—high

Silver wings are shining
As it goes gliding by
First it zooms
And it booms
Then it buzzes in the sky
Then its song is just a drumming
A soft little humming
   Strumming
   Strumming

The wings are very little things
The silver shine is gone
Just a little black speck
Away down the sky
With a soft little strumming
And a far-away humming
   Aeroplane
   Aeroplane
   Gone—by.

SILVER SHIPS

Mildred Plew Meigs

There are trails that a lad may follow
   When the years of his boyhood slip,
But I shall soar like a swallow
   On the wings of a silver ship,

"Taking Off." Reprinted from *Very Young Verses* published by Houghton Mifflin Company. The editors of this book searched diligently to find the source and to obtain permission to use this poem, but without success
"Up in the Air." From *I Go A-Traveling* by James S. Tippett. Copyright, 1929, Harper & Brothers

"Aeroplane." Taken from *Another Here and Now Story Book*, edited by Lucy Sprague Mitchell, published and copyright, 1937, by E. P. Dutton & Co., Inc., New York
"Silver Ships." From *Child Life*, May 1930. Child Life, Inc., Boston. By permission of Marion Plew Ruckel

Guiding my bird of metal,
　One with her throbbing frame,
Floating down like a petal,
　Roaring up like a flame;

Winding the wind that scatters
　Smoke from the chimney's lip,
Tearing the clouds to tatters
　With the wings of a silver ship;

Grazing the broad blue sky light
　Up where the falcons fare,
Riding the realms of twilight,
　Brushed by a comet's hair;

Snug in my coat of leather,
　Watching the skyline swing,
Shedding the world like a feather
　From the tip of a tilted wing.

There are trails that a lad may travel
　When the years of his boyhood wane,
But I'll let a rainbow ravel
　Through the wings of my silver plane.

COCKPIT IN THE CLOUDS
Dick Dorrance

Two thousand feet beneath our wheels
The city sprawls across the land
Like heaps of children's blocks outflung,
In tantrums, by a giant hand.
To east a silver spire soars
And seeks to pierce our lower wing.
Above its grasp we drift along,
A tiny, droning, shiny thing.

The noon crowds pack the narrow streets.
The el trains move so slow, so slow.
Amidst their traffic, chaos, life,
The city's busy millions go.
Up here, aloof, we watch them crawl.
In crystal air we seem to poise
Behind our motor's throaty roar—
Down there, we're just another noise.

NIGHT PLANE
Frances M. Frost

The midnight plane with its riding lights
looks like a footloose star
wandering west through the blue-black night
to where the mountains are,

a star that's journeyed nearer earth
to tell each quiet farm
and little town, "Put out your lights,
children of earth. Sleep warm."

TO BEACHEY, 1912
Carl Sandburg

　Riding against the east,
　A veering, steady shadow
　Purrs the motor-call
　Of the man-bird
　Ready with the death-laughter
　In his throat
　And in his heart always
　The love of the big blue beyond.

　Only a man,
　A far fleck of shadow on the east
　Sitting at ease
　With his hands on a wheel
　And around him the large gray wings.
　Hold him, great soft wings,
　Keep and deal kindly, O wings,
　With the cool, calm shadow at the wheel.

BOATS
Rowena Bastin Bennett

　The steamboat is a slow poke,
　　You simply cannot rush him.

"Cockpit in the Clouds." From *The* (New York) *Sun.*
Used by permission of the *New York World Telegram*
and *The Sun.* By permission also of the author
"Night Plane." From the *New York Herald Tribune,*
May 1956. Reprinted by permission of the author

"To Beachey, 1912." *See the introduction, p. xx.* From
Chicago Poems by Carl Sandburg. Copyright, 1916, by
Henry Holt and Company, Inc. Copyright, 1944, by Carl
Sandburg. Used by permission of the publishers
"Boats." From *Around a Toadstool Table* by Rowena

The sailboat will not move at all
  Without a wind to push him;

But the speed boat, with his sharp red nose,
  Is quite a different kind;
He tosses high the spray and leaves
  The other boats behind.

FERRY-BOATS

James S. Tippett

Over the river,
Over the bay,
Ferry-boats travel
Every day.

Most of the people
Crowd to the side
Just to enjoy
Their ferry-boat ride.

Watching the seagulls,
Laughing with friends,
I'm always sorry
When the ride ends.

WHISTLES

Rachel Field

I never even hear
The boats that pass by day;
By night they seem so near,
A-whistling down the bay,
That I can almost understand
The things their whistles say.

I've waked sometimes all warm
In my bed, when eerily
I have heard them out of the dark
A-whistling cheerily
To tell the sleepy folk on land
All's well at sea.

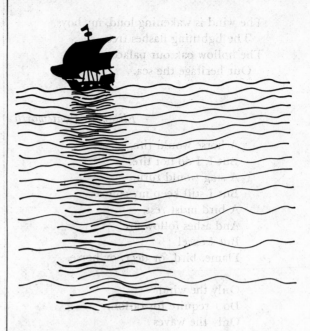

A WET SHEET AND A FLOWING SEA

Allan Cunningham

A wet sheet and a flowing sea,
  A wind that follows fast
And fills the white and rustling sail,
  And bends the gallant mast!
And bends the gallant mast, my boys,
  While, like the eagle free,
Away the good ship flies, and leaves
  Old England on the lee.

O for a soft and gentle wind!
  I heard a fair one cry;
But give to me the swelling breeze,
  And white waves heaving high:
The white waves heaving high, my lads,
  The good ship tight and free;
The world of waters is our home,
  And merry men are we.

There's tempest in yon horned moon,
  And lightning in yon cloud;
And hark the music, mariners!
  The wind is wakening loud.

Bastin Bennett. Follett Publishing Company, Chicago, 1930.
"Ferry-Boats." From *I Go A-Traveling* by James S. Tippett. Copyright, 1929, Harper & Brothers

"Whistles." From *The Pointed People* by Rachel Field. The Macmillan Company, New York, 1930. Used by permission of Arthur S. Pederson, Trustee, Estate of Rachel Field Pederson

The wind is wakening loud, my boys,
  The lightning flashes free—
The hollow oak our palace is,
  Our heritage the sea.

Elizabeth Coatsworth

A horse would tire,
But I, I do not tire.
A stag would turn,
But I still keep my course.
A bird must rest,
And ashes follow fire,
But I excel
Flame, bird, or deer, or horse.

Only the wind
Do I require for ration,
Only the waves
Beneath my forefoot curled.
Eager I run
From nation unto nation
And seek my harbor
Halfway round the world.

SEA-FEVER

John Masefield

I must go down to the seas again, to the lonely
  sea and the sky,
And all I ask is a tall ship and a star to steer
  her by,
And the wheel's kick and the wind's song and the
  white sail's shaking
And a gray mist on the sea's face and a gray dawn
  breaking.

I must go down to the seas again, for the call of
  the running tide
Is a wild call and a clear call that may not be
  denied;

And all I ask is a windy day with the white
  clouds flying,
And the flung spray and the blown spume, and
  the sea-gulls crying.

I must go down to the seas again to the vagrant
  gypsy life,
To the gull's way and the whale's way where the
  wind's like a whetted knife;
And all I ask is a merry yarn from a laughing
  fellow-rover,
And quiet sleep and a sweet dream when the
  long trick's over.

CARGOES

John Masefield

Quinquireme of Nineveh from distant Ophir
Rowing home to haven in sunny Palestine,
With a cargo of ivory,
And apes and peacocks,
Sandalwood, cedarwood, and sweet white wine.

Stately Spanish galleon coming from the Isth-
  mus,
Dipping through the Tropics by the palm-green
  shores,
With a cargo of diamonds,
Emeralds, amethysts,
Topazes, and cinnamon, and gold moidores.

Dirty British coaster with a salt-caked smoke-
  stack
Butting through the Channel in the mad March
  days,
With a cargo of Tyne coal,
Road-rails, pig-lead,
Firewood, iron-ware, and cheap tin trays.

"A horse would tire." *This might be used as a riddle.
Certainly, it is a remarkable description of a ship and its
power.* From *The Fair American* by Elizabeth Coatsworth.
Copyright 1940 by The Macmillan Company and used
with their permission
"Sea-Fever." *"Trick" in the last line of this poem is the
spell or time a sailor spends at the pilot's wheel steering
the ship.* From *Story of a Round House* by John Masefield.

Copyright 1912, 1940 by The Macmillan Company and
used with their permission. Permission granted also by Dr.
John Masefield, O.M., and The Society of Authors
"Cargoes." *Ships may be romantic or as utilitarian as
trucks. Masefield contrasts the cargoes of the ancient
quinquiremes and galleons with the dirty, useful, modern
freighters. The sound of the words and lines in these three
verses emphasizes the contrasts.* From *Story of a Round*

RED IRON ORE

Come all you bold sailors that follow the Lakes
On an iron ore vessel your living to make.
I shipped in Chicago, bid adieu to the shore,
Bound away to Escanaba for red iron ore.
    Derry down, down, down derry down.

The wind from the south'ard sprang up a fresh
    breeze,
And away through Lake Michigan the *Roberts*
    did sneeze.
Down through Lake Michigan the *Roberts* did
    roar,
And on Friday morning we passed through
    death's door.
    Derry down, down, down derry down.

This packet she howled across the mouth of
    Green Bay,
And before her cutwater she dashed the white
    spray.
We rounded the sand point, our anchor let go,
We furled in our canvas and the watch went
    below.
    Derry down, down, down derry down.

Next morning we hove alongside the *Exile*,
And soon was made fast to an iron ore pile,
They lowered their chutes and like thunder did
    roar,
They spouted into us that red iron ore.
    Derry down, down, down derry down.

Some sailors took shovels while others got spades,
And some took wheelbarrows, each man to his
    trade.
We looked like red devils, our fingers got sore,
We cursed Escanaba and damned iron ore.
    Derry down, down, down derry down.

The tug *Escanaba* she towed out the *Minch,*
The *Roberts* she thought she had left in a pinch,
And as she passed by us she bid us good-bye,
Saying, "We'll meet you in Cleveland next
    Fourth of July!"
    Derry down, down, down derry down.

STOP—GO
Dorothy Baruch

    Automobiles
    In
       a
         row
    Wait to go
    While the signal says:
                    STOP

    Bells ring
    Tingaling
    Red light's gone!
    Green light's on!
    Horns blow!
    And the row
    Starts
        to
               GO

House by John Masefield. Copyright 1912, 1940 by The
Macmillan Company and used with their permission. Per-
mission granted also by Dr. John Masefield, O.M., and The
Society of Authors
"Red Iron Ore." *Stanzas 2 and 8–12 are omitted. See
May Hill Arbuthnot,* Children and Books, *p. 95. From* The
American Songbag *compiled by Carl Sandburg. Harcourt,*
Brace and Company, Inc., New York, 1927
"Stop-Go." *A study in slow and fast like this one is fun
to say with two people or two groups of children, one
speaking the first and one the second verse, with slow and
fast tempos. From* I Like Automobiles *by Dorothy Baruch.
The John Day Company, New York, 1931. Copyright, 1931,
by Dorothy Walter Baruch*

MOTOR CARS

Rowena Bastin Bennett

From a city window, 'way up high,
I like to watch the cars go by.
They look like burnished beetles, black,
That leave a little muddy track
Behind them as they slowly crawl.
Sometimes they do not move at all
But huddle close with hum and drone
As though they feared to be alone.
They grope their way through fog and night
With the golden feelers of their light.

SONG FOR A BLUE ROADSTER

Rachel Field

Fly, Roadster, fly!
  The sun is high,
Gold are the fields
  We hurry by,
Green are the woods
  As we slide through,
Past harbor and headland,
  Blue on blue.

Fly, Roadster, fly!
  The hay smells sweet,
And the flowers fringing
  Each village street,
Where carts are blue,
  And barns are red,
And the road unwinds
  Like a twist of thread.

Fly, Roadster, fly!
  Leave Time behind;
Out of sight
  Shall be out of mind.
Shine and shadow,
  Blue sea, green bough,
Nothing is real
  But Here and Now.

from ALL AROUND THE TOWN

Phyllis McGinley

  J's the jumping Jay-walker,
    A sort of human jeep.
  He crosses where the lights are red.
    Before he looks, he'll leap!
  Then many a wheel
  Begins to squeal,
    And many a brake to slam.
  He turns your knees to jelly
    And the traffic into jam.

TAXIS

Rachel Field

Ho, for taxis green or blue,
  Hi, for taxis red,
They roll along the Avenue
  Like spools of colored thread!

  Jack-o'-Lantern yellow,
  Orange as the moon,
  Greener than the greenest grass
  Ever grew in June.
  Gayly striped or checked in squares,
  Wheels that twinkle bright,
  Don't you think that taxis make
  A very pleasant sight?
  Taxis shiny in the rain,
  Scudding through the snow,
  Taxis flashing back the sun
  Waiting in a row.

Ho, for taxis red and green,
  Hi, for taxis blue,
I wouldn't be a private car
  In sober black, would you?

from ALL AROUND THE TOWN

Phyllis McGinley

  B's the Bus,
  The bouncing Bus,
    That bears a shopper store-ward.

"Motor Cars." From *Around a Toadstool Table* by Rowena Bastin Bennett. Follett Publishing Company, Chicago, 1930
"Song for a Blue Roadster." From *Poems* by Rachel Field. Copyright © 1957 by The Macmillan Company,

New York, and used with their permission
"J's the jumping Jay-walker," "B's the Bus," "E is the Escalator," and "R is for the Restaurant." From *All Around the Town* by Phyllis McGinley. Copyright © 1948 by Phyllis McGinley. Published by J. B. Lippincott Com-

It's fun to sit
In back of it
    But seats are better forward.
Although it's big as buildings are
    And looks both bold and grand,
It has to stop obligingly
    If you but raise your hand.

from ALL AROUND THE TOWN

Phyllis McGinley

E is the Escalator
    That gives an elegant ride.
You step on the stair
With an easy air
    And up and up you glide.
It's nicer than scaling ladders
    Or scrambling 'round a hill,
For you climb and climb
But all the time
    You're really standing still.

from ALL AROUND THE TOWN

Phyllis McGinley

R is for the Restaurant—
    A really special treat.
(We do respect the relative
    Who takes us there to eat.)
The waiters rush with plates of rolls,
    They run to hold one's chair,
And always seem
To read ice-cream
    Upon the bill-of-fare.

MOVING

Eunice Tietjens

I like to move. There's such a feeling
Of hurrying
    and scurrying,
And such a feeling
Of men with trunks and packing cases,
Of kitchen clocks and mother's laces,
Dusters, dishes, books and vases,
Toys and pans and candles.

I always find things I'd forgotten,
An old brown Teddy stuffed with cotton,
Some croquet mallets without handles,
A marble and my worn-out sandals,
A half an engine and a hat . . .
And I like that.

I like to watch the big vans backing,
And the lumbering
    and the cumbering,
And the hammering and the tacking.
I even like the packing!

And that will prove
I like to move!

COUNTRY TRUCKS

Monica Shannon

Big trucks with apples
    And big trucks with grapes
Thundering through the mountains
    While every wild thing gapes.

Thundering through the valley,
    Like something just let loose,
Big trucks with oranges
    For city children's juice.

Big trucks with peaches,
    And big trucks with pears,
Frightening all the rabbits
    And giving squirrels gray hairs.

Yet, when city children
    Sit down to plum or prune,
They know more trucks are coming
    As surely as the moon.

CITY STREETS AND COUNTRY ROADS

Eleanor Farjeon

    The city has streets—
        But the country has roads.

In the country one meets
    Blue carts with their loads
Of sweet-smelling hay,
    And mangolds, and grain:
Oh, take me away
    To the country again!

In the city one sees,
    Big trams rattle by,
And the breath of the chimneys
    That blot out the sky,
And all down the pavements
    Stiff lamp-posts one sees—
But the country has hedgerows,
    The country has trees.

As sweet as the sun
    In the country is rain:
Oh, take me away
    To the country again!

ROADS GO EVER EVER ON

J. R. R. Tolkien

Roads go ever ever on,
    Over rock and under tree,
By caves where never sun has shone,
    By streams that never find the sea;
Over snow by winter sown,
    And through the merry flowers of June,
Over grass and over stone,
    And under mountains in the moon.

T. S. Eliot

And now you live dispersed on ribbon roads,
And no man knows or cares who is his neighbour
Unless his neighbour makes too much disturb-
ance,
But all dash to and fro in motor cars,
Familiar with the roads and settled nowhere.

"Roads Go Ever Ever On." From *The Hobbitt* by J. R. R. Tolkien. London: George Allen and Unwin, Ltd., 1936, and Boston: Houghton Mifflin Company, 1938

"And now you live dispersed on ribbon roads." From "The Rock" in *Collected Poems 1909–1935* by T. S. Eliot, copyright, 1936, by Harcourt, Brace and Company, Inc. Reprinted by permission of Harcourt, Brace and Com-

Edna St. Vincent Millay

Wonder where this horseshoe went.
Up and down, up and down,
Up and past the monument,
Maybe into town.

Wait a minute. "Horseshoe,
How far have you been?"
*Says it's been to Salem
And halfway to Lynn.*

Wonder who was in the team.
Wonder what they saw.
Wonder if they passed a bridge—
Bridge with a draw.

*Says it went from one bridge
Straight upon another.
Says it took a little girl
Driving with her mother.*

FAREWELL TO THE FARM

Robert Louis Stevenson

The coach is at the door at last;
The eager children, mounting fast
And kissing hands, in chorus sing:
Good-bye, good-bye, to everything!

To house and garden, field and lawn,
The meadow-gates we swung upon,
To pump and stable, tree and swing,
Good-bye, good-bye, to everything!

And fare you well for evermore,
O ladder at the hayloft door,
O hayloft where the cobwebs cling,
Good-bye, good-bye, to everything!

Crack goes the whip, and off we go;
The trees and houses smaller grow;
Last, round the woody turn we swing:
Good-bye, good-bye, to everything!

pany, Inc., and Faber and Faber, Limited

"Wonder where this horseshoe went." From "A Very Little Sphinx" in *Poems Selected for Young People*, published by Harper & Brothers. Copyright, 1923, by Edna St. Vincent Millay

"Farewell to the Farm." From *A Child's Garden of Verses* by Robert Louis Stevenson

JOHNNY FIFE AND JOHNNY'S WIFE

Mildred Plew Meigs

Oh, Johnny Fife and Johnny's wife,
   To save their toes and heels,
They built themselves a little house
   That ran on rolling wheels.

They hung their parrot at the door
   Upon a painted ring,
And round and round the world they went
   And never missed a thing;

And when they wished to eat they ate,
   And after they had fed,
They crawled beneath a crazy quilt
   And gayly went to bed;

And what they cared to keep they kept,
   And what they both did not,
They poked beneath a picket fence
   And quietly forgot.

Oh, Johnny Fife and Johnny's wife,
   They took their brush and comb,
And round and round the world they went
   And also stayed at home.

ADVENTURE

Harry Behn

It's not very far to the edge of town
Where trees look up and hills look down,
We go there almost every day
To climb and swing and paddle and play.

It's not very far to the edge of town,
Just up one little hill and down,
And through one gate, and over two stiles—
But coming home it's miles and miles.

Sir Walter Scott

Hie away, hie away,
Over bank and over brae,
Where the copsewood is the greenest,
Where the fountains glisten sheenest,
Where the lady fern grows strongest,
Where the morning dew lies longest,
Where the black-cock sweetest sips it,
Where the fairy latest trips it.
Hie to haunts right seldom seen,
Lovely, lonesome, cool, and green,
Over bank and over brae,
Hie away, hie away.

RING AROUND THE WORLD

Annette Wynne

Ring around the world
Taking hands together
All across the temperate
And the torrid weather.
Past the royal palm-trees
By the ocean sand
Make a ring around the world
Taking each other's hand;
In the valleys, on the hill,
Over the prairie spaces,
There's a ring around the world
Made of children's friendly faces.

"Johnny Fife and Johnny's Wife." From *Child Life,* May 1929. Child Life, Inc., Boston. By permission of Marion Plew Ruckel

"Adventure." From *The Little Hill* by Harry Behn. Copyright 1949 by Harry Behn. Reprinted by permission of Harcourt, Brace and Company, Inc., New York

"Hie away, hie away." *This is fun to do with verse* choirs. See May Hill Arbuthnot, Children and Books, *p. 218*

"Ring Around the World." *A pleasant picture of what the world might be with friendly faces all round it.* From *All Through the Year.* Copyright 1932 by Annette Wynne. Reprinted by permission of J. B. Lippincott Company

TRAVEL

Robert Louis Stevenson

I should like to rise and go
Where the golden apples grow;—
Where below another sky
Parrot islands anchored lie,
And, watched by cockatoos and goats,
Lonely Crusoes building boats;—
Where in sunshine reaching out
Eastern cities, miles about,
Are with mosque and minaret
Among sandy gardens set,
And the rich goods from near and far
Hang for sale in the bazaar;—
Where the Great Wall round China goes,
And on one side the desert blows,
And with bell and voice and drum,
Cities on the other hum;—
Where are forests, hot as fire,
Wide as England, tall as a spire,
Full of apes and cocoa-nuts
And the Negro hunters' huts;—
Where the knotty crocodile
Lies and blinks in the Nile,
And the red flamingo flies
Hunting fish before his eyes;—
Where in jungles, near and far,
Man-devouring tigers are,
Lying close and giving ear
Lest the hunt be drawing near,
Or a comer-by be seen
Swinging in a palanquin;—
Where among the desert sands
Some deserted city stands,
All its children, sweep and prince,
Grown to manhood ages since,
Not a foot in street or house,
Not a stir of child or mouse,
And when kindly falls the night,
In all the town no spark of light.
There I'll come when I'm a man

With a camel caravan;
Light a fire in the gloom
Of some dusty dining-room;
See the pictures on the walls,
Heroes, fights, and festivals;
And in a corner find the toys
Of the old Egyptian boys.

WANDER-THIRST

Gerald Gould

Beyond the East the sunrise, beyond the West the
    sea,
And East and West the wander-thirst that will
    not let me be;
It works in me like madness, dear, to bid me say
    good-bye;
For the seas call and the stars call, and oh! the
    call of the sky!

I know not where the white road runs, nor what
    the blue hills are,
But a man can have the sun for friend, and for
    his guide a star;
And there's no end of voyaging when once the
    voice is heard,
For the rivers call and the roads call, and oh! the
    call of a bird!

Yonder the long horizon lies, and there by night
    and day
The old ships draw to home again, the young
    ships sail away;
And come I may, but go I must, and if men ask
    you why,
You may put the blame on the stars and the sun
    and the white road and the sky.

"Travel." From *A Child's Garden of Verses* by Robert
Louis Stevenson
"Wander-Thirst." From *The Collected Poems of Gerald
Gould.* Used by permission of Michael Ayrton

Walt Whitman

Afoot and light-hearted, I take to the open road,
Healthy, free, the world before me,
The long brown path before me, leading wher-
    ever I choose.

Henceforth I ask not good-fortune, I myself am
    good-fortune,
Henceforth I whimper no more, postpone no
    more, need nothing,
Done with indoor complaints, libraries, queru-
    lous criticisms,
Strong and content, I travel the open road.

MAPS

Dorothy Brown Thompson

High adventure
    And bright dream—
Maps are mightier
    Than they seem:

Ships that follow
    Leaning stars—
Red and gold of
    Strange bazaars—

Ice floes hid
    Beyond all knowing—
Planes that ride where
    Winds are blowing!

Train maps, maps of
    Wind and weather,
Road maps—taken
    Altogether

Maps are really
    Magic wands
For home-staying
    Vagabonds!

"Maps." From *Bridled with Rainbows* by Dorothy
Brown Thompson. The Macmillan Company, New York,
1949. Used by the permission of the author

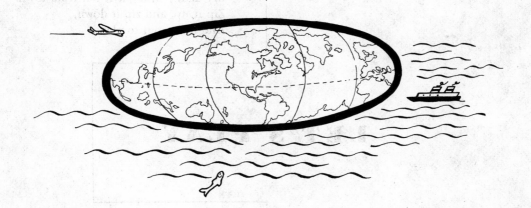

(*Mother Goose*)

Girls and boys, come out to play,
The moon doth shine as bright as day;
Leave your supper, and leave your sleep,
And come with your playfellows into the street.
Come with a whoop, come with a call,
Come with a good will or not at all.
Up the ladder and down the wall,
A half-penny roll will serve us all.
You find milk, and I'll find flour,
And we'll have a pudding in half an hour.

MY ZIPPER SUIT

Marie Louise Allen

My zipper suit is bunny-brown—
The top zips up, the legs zip down.
I wear it every day.
My daddy brought it out from town.
Zip it up, and zip it down,
And hurry out to play!

LET'S PLAY

Kate Greenaway

School is over,
  Oh, what fun!
Lessons finished,
  Play begun.
Who'll run fastest,
  You or I?
Who'll laugh loudest?
  Let us try.

RIDDLES FROM MOTHER GOOSE

As round as an apple, as deep as a cup,
And all the king's horses can't fill it up.
(*A Well*)

A riddle, a riddle, as I suppose,
A hundred eyes and never a nose!
(*A Sieve*)

Higher than a house,
Higher than a tree,
Oh! whatever can that be?
(*A Star*)

Lives in winter,
Dies in summer,
And grows with its roots upward!
(*An Icicle*)

A hill full, a hole full,
Yet you cannot catch a bowl full.
(*The Mist*)

Thirty white horses upon a red hill,
Now they tramp, now they champ,
Now they stand still.
(*The Teeth and Gums*)

Hick-a-more, Hack-a-more,
On the King's kitchen door;
All the King's horses,
And all the King's men,
Couldn't drive Hick-a-more,
Hack-a-more,
Off the King's kitchen door.
(*Sunshine*)

Old Mother Twitchett had but one eye,
And a long tail which she let fly;
And every time she went through a gap,
A bit of her tail she left in a trap.
(*A Needle and Thread*)

Little Nanny Etticoat
In a white petticoat,
And a red nose;
The longer she stands
The shorter she grows.
(*A Candle*)

Runs all day and never walks,
Often murmurs, never talks.
It has a bed but never sleeps,
It has a mouth, but never eats.
(*A River*)

I have a little sister they call her "Peep-peep,"
She wades in the ocean deep, deep, deep.
She climbs up the mountain high, high, high,
The poor little thing hasn't got but one eye.
(*A Star*)

RHYMING RIDDLES

Mary Austin

I come more softly than a bird,
And lovely as a flower;
I sometimes last from year to year
And sometimes but an hour.

I stop the swiftest railroad train
Or break the stoutest tree.
And yet I am afraid of fire
And children play with me.
(*Snow*)

I have no wings, but yet I fly,
I'm slender as a snake and straight as rain,
Who takes me in must die,
Who lets me quickly go will surest gain.
(*Arrow*)

"My Zipper Suit." From *Sung under the Silver Umbrella*. The Macmillan Company, New York, 1935. Used by permission of the author

"School is over." From *Under the Window* by Kate Greenaway. Frederick Warne and Company, New York and London, 1910

"Riddles from Mother Goose." *These old, old riddles may suggest making rhymed riddles of our own.*

"Runs all day and never walks." From *The American Mother Goose* compiled by Ray Wood. Copyright 1940 by J. B. Lippincott Company

"I have a little sister they call her 'Peep-peep.'" From *The American Mother Goose* compiled by Ray Wood. Copyright 1940 by J. B. Lippincott Company

"Rhyming Riddles." From "Seven Rhyming Riddles" in *The Children Sing in the Far West* by Mary Austin. Reprinted by permission of and arrangement with Houghton Mifflin Company, the authorized publishers

I never speak a word
But when my voice is heard
Even the mountains shake,
No hands I have
And yet great rocks I break.
        (*Thunder and Lightning*)

First I am frosted,
Second, I am beaten,
Third, I am roasted,
Fourth, I am eaten.
        (*Chestnut*)

        (*Mother Goose*)

To market, to market, to buy a fat pig,
Home again, home again, jiggety jig.

To market, to market, to buy a fat hog,
Home again, home again, jiggety jog.

To market, to market, to buy a plum bun,
Home again, home again, market is done.

        (*Mother Goose*)

The grand Old Duke of York
    He had ten thousand men,
He marched them up a very high hill
    And he marched them down again.
And when he was up he was up
    And when he was down he was down
And when he was only halfway up
    He was neither up nor down.

        (*Mother Goose*)

Hippety hop to the barber shop,
    To get a stick of candy,
One for you and one for me,
    And one for Sister Mandy.

"To market, to market, to buy a fat pig." *This jingle
and "The grand Old Duke of York" are as good to march
to as music. This one is an everydayish walk to the store
and "The Duke" is very martial, military, and snappy.*
    "Hippety hop to the barber shop." *See introduction, p.
xviii.*
    "Hoppity." *The words in this poem go hopping exactly
as Christopher hops, ending with a big one, on one foot,
perhaps. See record album* Poetry Time. *Taken from*

HOPPITY

A. A. Milne

Christopher Robin goes
Hoppity, hoppity,
Hoppity, hoppity, hop.
Whenever I tell him
Politely to stop it, he
Says he can't possibly stop.

If he stopped hopping, he couldn't go anywhere,
Poor little Christopher
Couldn't go anywhere . . .
That's why he *always* goes
Hoppity, hoppity,
Hoppity,
Hoppity,
Hop.

HIPPITY HOP TO BED

Leroy F. Jackson

        O it's hippity hop to bed!
        I'd rather sit up instead.
        But when father says "must,"
        There's nothing but just
        Go hippity hop to bed.

(*Mother Goose*)

    Dance to your daddie,
      My bonnie laddie;
Dance to your daddie, my bonnie lamb;
    You shall get a fishy,
      On a little dishy;
You shall get a fishy, when the boat comes home.

(*Mother Goose*)

        Ride a cock horse
        To Banbury Cross
        To see a fair lady upon a white horse;

When We Were Very Young, by A. A. Milne, published
and copyright, 1924, by E. P. Dutton & Co., Inc., New York
    "Hippity Hop to Bed." *See the introduction, p. xx, and
record album* Poetry Time. *From The Peter Patter Book
by Leroy F. Jackson. Rand McNally & Company, Chicago,
1918. Used by permission of the author*
    "Dance to your daddie." *You can jounce your baby on
your knee to this little jig or you can take hands with*

With rings on her fingers,
And bells on her toes,
She shall have music wherever she goes.

(*Mother Goose*)

Ride away, ride away,
  Johnny shall ride,
And he shall have pussy-cat
  Tied to one side;
And he shall have little dog
  Tied to the other,
And Johnny shall ride
  To see his grandmother.

HUSKY HI
(*Norwegian*)

Rose Fyleman

Husky hi, husky hi,
Here comes Keery galloping by.
She carries her husband tied in a sack,
She carries him home on her horse's back.
Husky hi, husky hi,
Here comes Keery galloping by!

(*Mother Goose*)

Master I have, and I am his man,
  Gallop a dreary dun;
Master I have, and I am his man,
  And I'll get a wife as fast as I can;
With a heighly gaily gamberally,
  Higgledy, piggledy, niggledy, niggledy,
  Gallop a dreary dun.

(*Mother Goose*)

Jack be nimble,
  Jack be quick,
Jack jump over
  The candlestick.

Jump it lively,
  Jump it quick,
But don't knock over
  The candlestick.

LITTLE JUMPING JOAN
(*Mother Goose*)

Here am I, little jumping Joan,
  When nobody's with me
  I'm always alone.

Kate Greenaway

Jump—jump—jump—
  Jump away
From this town into
  The next, to-day.

Jump—jump—jump—
  Jump over the moon;
Jump all the morning,
  And all the noon.

Jump—jump—jump—
  Jump all night;
Won't our mothers
  Be in a fright?

Jump—jump—jump—
  Over the sea;
What wonderful wonders
  We shall see.

Jump—jump—jump—
  Jump far away;
And all come home
  Some other day.

your friend and really jig to it while all the other children say it. See record album Poetry Time.

"Ride a cock horse." *This and the next three jingles are good gallops. Part of the children might say them while the others hold their imaginary reins and cluck to their horses. See record album* Poetry Time.

"Husky Hi." *See the introduction, p. xviii, and record album* Poetry Time. *From* Picture Rhymes from Foreign Lands. *Copyright 1935 by Rose Fyleman. Reprinted by permission of J. B. Lippincott Company*

"Master I have, and I am his man." *This is the song sung by a lad as he gallops along on his master's errands, riding a dreary old dun colored horse.*

"Jump—jump—jump." *From* Marigold Garden *by Kate Greenaway. Frederick Warne and Company, New York and London, 1910*

JUMP OR JIGGLE

Evelyn Beyer

Frogs jump
Caterpillars hump

Worms wiggle
Bugs jiggle

Rabbits hop
Horses clop

Snakes slide
Sea gulls glide

Mice creep
Deer leap

Puppies bounce
Kittens pounce

Lions stalk—
But—
I walk!

David McCord

Every time I climb a tree
Every time I climb a tree
Every time I climb a tree
I scrape a leg
Or skin a knee
And every time I climb a tree
I find some ants
Or dodge a bee
And get the ants
All over me

And every time I climb a tree
Where have you been?
They say to me
But don't they know that I am free,
Every time I climb a tree?
I like it best
To spot a nest
That has an egg
Or maybe three

And then I skin
The other leg
But every time I climb a tree
I see a lot of things to see
Swallows rooftops and TV
And all the fields and farms there be
Every time I climb a tree
Though climbing may be good for ants
It isn't awfully good for pants
But still it's pretty good for me
Every time I climb a tree

(Mother Goose)

Pease porridge hot,
Pease porridge cold,
Pease porridge in the pot,
Nine days old.
Some like it hot,
Some like it cold,
Some like it in the pot,
Nine days old.

(Mother Goose)

Higgledy, piggledy, my black hen,
She lays eggs for gentlemen;
Sometimes nine, and sometimes ten,
Higgledy, piggledy, my black hen.

(Mother Goose)

Intery, mintery, cutery corn,
Apple seed and apple thorn;
Wine, brier, limber lock,
Three geese in a flock,
One flew east, one flew west,
And one flew over the goose's nest.

(Mother Goose)

1, 2, 3, 4, 5!
I caught a hare alive;
6, 7, 8, 9, 10!
I let her go again.

One, two,
Buckle my shoe;
Three, four,
Knock at the door;
Five, six,
Pick up sticks;
Seven, eight,
Lay them straight;
Nine, ten,
A good, fat hen;
Eleven, twelve,
Dig and delve;
Thirteen, fourteen,
Maids a-courting;
Fifteen, sixteen,
Maids in the kitchen;
Seventeen, eighteen,
Maids a-waiting;
Nineteen, twenty,
My plate's empty.

THE A B C BUNNY
Wanda Gág

A for Apple, big and red
B for Bunny snug a-bed
C for Crash!
D for Dash!
E for Elsewhere in a flash
F for Frog—he's fat and funny
"Looks like rain," says he to Bunny
G for Gale!
H for Hail!
Hippy-hop goes Bunny's tail
I for Insects here and there
J for Jay with jaunty air
K for Kitten, catnip-crazy
L for Lizard—look how lazy
M for Mealtime—munch, munch, munch!
M-m-m these greens are good for lunch
N for Napping in a Nook
O for Owl with bookish look
P for prickly Porcupine
Pins and needles on his spine

Q for Quail
R for Rail
S for Squirrel Swishy-tail
T for Tripping back to Town
U for Up and Up-side-down
V for View
Valley too
W—"We welcome you!"
X for eXit—off, away!
That's enough for us today
Y for You, take one last look
Z for Zero—close the book!

Edward Lear

A was once an apple-pie,
  Pidy,
  Widy,
  Tidy,
  Pidy,
Nice insidy,
Applie-pie!

B was once a little bear,
  Beary,
  Wary,
  Hairy,
  Beary,
Taky cary,
Little bear!

C was once a little cake,
  Caky,
  Baky,
  Maky,
  Caky,
Taky caky,
Little cake!

D was once a little doll,
  Dolly,
  Molly,
  Polly,
  Nolly,
Nursy dolly,
Little doll!

"Higgledy, piggledy, my black hen." *See record album Poetry Time.*
"The A B C Bunny." *Alphabet books are useful for teaching the names of the letters. The rhymes usually are fun to say and the pictures are amusing to look at. "The*

A B C Bunny" is an especially good alphabet book and so is Phyllis McGinley's All Around the Town. *From The A B C Bunny by Wanda Gág. Copyright, 1933, by Wanda Gág. Reprinted by permission of Coward-McCann, Inc.*

E was once a little eel,
  Eely,
  Weely,
  Peely,
  Eely,
Twirly, tweely,
Little eel!

F was once a little fish,
  Fishy,
  Wishy,
  Squishy,
  Fishy,
In a dishy,
Little fish!

G was once a little goose,
  Goosy,
  Moosy,
  Boosey,
  Goosey,
Waddly-woosy,
Little goose!

H was once a little hen,
  Henny,
  Chenny,
  Tenny,
  Henny,
Eggsy-any,
Little hen?

I was once a bottle of ink,
  Inky,
  Dinky,
  Thinky,
  Inky,
Blacky minky,
Bottle of ink!

J was once a jar of jam,
  Jammy,
  Mammy,
  Clammy,
  Jammy,
Sweety, swammy,
Jar of jam!

K was once a little kite,
  Kity,
  Whity,
  Flighty,
  Kity,
Out of sighty,
Little kite!

L was once a little lark,
  Larky,
  Marky,
  Harky,
  Larky,
In the parky,
Little lark!

M was once a little mouse,
  Mousy,
  Bousy,
  Sousy,
  Mousy,
In the housy,
Little mouse!

N was once a little needle,
  Needly,
  Tweedly,
  Threedly,
  Needly,
Wisky, wheedly,
Little needle!

O was once a little owl,
  Owly,
  Prowly,
  Howly,
  Owly,
Browny fowly,
Little owl!

P was once a little pump,
  Pumpy,
  Slumpy,
  Flumpy,
  Pumpy,
Dumpy, thumpy,
Little pump!

Q was once a little quail,
  Quaily,
  Faily,
  Daily,
  Quaily,
  Stumpy-taily,
  Little quail!

R was once a little rose,
  Rosy,
  Posy,
  Nosy,
  Rosy,
  Blows-y, grows-y,
  Little rose!

S was once a little shrimp,
  Shrimpy,
  Nimpy,
  Flimpy,
  Shrimpy,
  Jumpy, jimpy,
  Little shrimp!

T was once a little thrush,
  Thrushy,
  Hushy,
  Bushy,
  Thrushy,
  Flitty, flushy,
  Little thrush!

U was once a little urn,
  Urny,
  Burny,
  Turny,
  Urny,
  Bubbly, burny,
  Little urn!

V was once a little vine,
  Viny,
  Winy,
  Twiny,
  Viny,
  Twisty-twiny,
  Little vine!

W was once a whale,
  Whaly,
  Scaly,
  Shaly,
  Whaly,
  Tumbly-taily,
  Mighty whale!

X was once a great king Xerxes,
  Xerxy,
  Perxy,
  Turxy,
  Xerxy,
  Linxy, lurxy,
  Great King Xerxes!

Y was once a little yew,
  Yewdy,
  Fewdy,
  Crudy,
  Yewdy,
  Growdy, grewdy,
  Little yew!

Z was once a piece of zinc,
  Tinky,
  Winky,
  Blinky,
  Tinky,
  Tinky minky,
  Piece of zinc!

CHOOSING

Eleanor Farjeon

Which will you have, a ball or a cake?
A cake is so nice, yes, that's what I'll take.

Which will you have, a cake or a cat?
A cat is so soft, I think I'll take that.

Which will you have, a cat or a rose?
A rose is so sweet, I'll have that, I suppose.

Which will you have, a rose or a book?
A book full of pictures?—oh, do let me look!

"Choosing." From *Over the Garden Wall*. Copyright 1933 by Eleanor Farjeon. Reprinted by permission of J. B. Lippincott Company

Which will you have, a book or a ball?
Oh, a ball! No, a book! No, a—
                There! have them all!

WHAT THE TOYS ARE THINKING

Ffrida Wolfe

In the jolly, jolly Spring
When we long to leave the shop,
It's the most exciting thing
When any of you stop
And stare and ask the price
Of a Teddy or a top,
Or a baby-doll or Bunny,
Or a little speckled horse.
O, we think it's very nice
When you stand behind the nurses
Counting out what's in your purses;
We are watching you, of course,
Wond'ring what you mean to do,
Hoping, hoping you've the money
And can take us back with you.
But supposing you have not
Quite enough (we cost a lot),
Shake a paw then, stroke a head,
Pat a wistful nose instead,
Whisper in a furry ear,
Comfort us for what we're missing—
Nursery tea and bedtime kissing—
All that never happens here.
You would find it slow yourselves
Sitting still all day on shelves.
Well, next time you're passing through
You'll remember what to do.

TELEGRAM

William Wise

I never got a telegram before;
But I went to the big front door,
And here was a man
Who wanted to see

Master Jonathan Blake!
So I said, "That's me."
And to make things clear,
He said, "Please sign here."
I never got a telegram before,
But I'd like to get at least a million more.

I never got a "wire" in my life;
So I sliced this one open with a knife.
Mother said most men
Prefer to use a cutter,
Since the knife I found
Was designed for butter.
But I never got a "wire" in my life!
So *naturally* I sliced it with a knife.

I never got a telegram before;
And when I went to the big front door,
It said: "Congratulations
On being six today
Every one of us loves you
That's all we can say."
I never got a telegram before,
But I'd like to get at least a *million* more!

US TWO

A. A. Milne

Wherever I am, there's always Pooh,
There's always Pooh and Me.
Whatever I do, he wants to do,
"Where are you going to-day?" says Pooh:
"Well, that's very odd 'cos I was too.
Let's go together," says Pooh, says he.
"Let's go together," says Pooh.

"What's twice eleven?" I said to Pooh.
("Twice what?" said Pooh to Me.)
"I *think* it ought to be twenty-two."
"Just what I think myself," said Pooh.
"It wasn't an easy sum to do,
But that's what it is," said Pooh, said he.
"That's what it is," said Pooh.

"What the Toys Are Thinking." Ffrida Wolfe in *Merry-Go-Round*, December, 1924. By permission of Basil Blackwell & Mott, Ltd., Oxford
"Telegram." From *Jonathan Blake* by William Wise. Copyright © 1956 by William Wise. Reprinted by permission of Alfred A. Knopf, Inc., New York
"Us Two." *Though Pooh was only Christopher Robin's toy teddy bear, this poem gives you the feeling of how alive he seemed to Christopher.* Taken from *Now We Are Six*, by A. A. Milne, published and copyright, 1927,

"Let's look for dragons," I said to Pooh.
"Yes, let's," said Pooh to Me.
We crossed the river and found a few—
"Yes, those are dragons all right," said Pooh.
"As soon as I saw their beaks I knew.
That's what they are," said Pooh, said he.
"That's what they are," said Pooh.

"Let's frighten the dragons," I said to Pooh.
"That's right," said Pooh to Me.
"*I'm* not afraid," I said to Pooh,
And I held his paw and I shouted "Shoo!
Silly old dragons!"—and off they flew.
"I wasn't afraid," said Pooh, said he,
"I'm *never* afraid with you."

So wherever I am, there's always Pooh,
There's always Pooh and Me.
"What would I do?" I said to Pooh,
"If it wasn't for you," and Pooh said: "True,
It isn't much fun for One, but Two
Can stick together," says Pooh, says he.
"That's how it is," says Pooh.

MERRY ARE THE BELLS

Anonymous

Merry are the bells, and merry would they ring,
Merry was myself, and merry could I sing;
With a merry ding-dong, happy, gay, and free,
And a merry sing-song, happy let us be!

Merry have we met, and merry have we been;
Merry let us part, and merry meet again;
With our merry sing-song, happy, gay, and free,
With a merry ding-dong, happy let us be!

Christina Georgina Rossetti

All the bells were ringing
And all the birds were singing,
When Molly sat down crying
    For her broken doll:
    O you silly Moll!

Sobbing and sighing
    For a broken doll,
When all the bells are ringing,
And all the birds are singing.

THE LITTLE RED SLED

Jocelyn Bush

"Come out with me!" cried the little red sled.
"I'll give you the wings of a bird," it said.
"The ground is all snowy;
The wind is all blowy!
We'll go like a fairy,
So light and so airy!"

SKATING

Herbert Asquith

When I try to skate,
My feet are so wary
They grit and they grate:
And then I watch Mary
Easily gliding,
Like an ice-fairy;
Skimming and curving,
Out and in,
With a turn of her head,
And a lift of her chin,
And a gleam of her eye,
And a twirl and a spin;
Sailing under
The breathless hush
Of the willows, and back
To the frozen rush;
Out to the island
And round the edge,

by E. P. Dutton & Co., Inc., New York
  "All the bells were ringing." From *Sing-Song* by Christina Georgina Rossetti
  "Skating." *This is a good example of the rhythm of words suggesting the activity the poet is describing. It* lends itself to choral speaking. See May Hill Arbuthnot, Children and Books, *p. 219*. From *Pillicock Hill* by Herbert Asquith. Used with the permission of The Macmillan Company. By permission also of William Heinemann, Ltd.

Skirting the rim
Of the crackling sedge,
Swerving close
To the poplar root,
And round the lake
On a single foot,
With a three, and an eight,
And a loop and a ring;
Where Mary glides,
The lake will sing!
Out in the mist
I hear her now
Under the frost
Of the willow-bough
Easily sailing,
Light and fleet,
With the song of the lake
Beneath her feet.

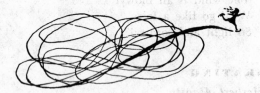

WINGS AND WHEELS
Nancy Byrd Turner

Ahoy and ahoy, birds!
We cannot have wings
And feathers and things,
But dashing on wheels
With the wind at our heels
Is almost like flying—
Such joy, birds!

Oho and oho, birds!
Of course we can't rise
Up and up to the skies;
But skimming and sliding
On rollers, and gliding,
Is almost as jolly,
You know, birds!

DIFFERENT BICYCLES
Dorothy Baruch

When I ride my bicycle
I pedal and pedal
Knees up, knees down.
Knees up, knees down.

But when the boy next door
Rides his,
It's whizz—
A chuck   a chuck—

And away
He's gone
With his
Knees steady-straight
In one place . . .
Because—
    His bicycle has
    A motor fastened on.

THE SWING
Robert Louis Stevenson

How do you like to go up in a swing,
    Up in the air so blue?
Oh, I do think it the pleasantest thing
    Ever a child can do!

Up in the air and over the wall,
    Till I can see so wide,
Rivers and trees and cattle and all
    Over the countryside—

Till I look down on the garden green,
    Down on the roof so brown—
Up in the air I go flying again,
    Up in the air and down!

Robert Louis Stevenson

PICNIC DAY
Rachel Field

Sing a song of picnics,
  Bread and butter spread,
Greenery all around about,
  And cherries overhead!

THE PICNIC
Dorothy Aldis

We brought a rug for sitting on,
Our lunch was in a box.
The sand was warm. We didn't wear
Hats or Shoes or Socks.

Waves came curling up the beach.
We waded. It was fun.
Our sandwiches were different kinds.
I dropped my jelly one.

THE HUNTSMEN
Walter de la Mare

Three jolly gentlemen,
  In coats of red,
Rode their horses
  Up to bed.

Three jolly gentlemen
  Snored till morn,
Their horses champing
  The golden corn.

Three jolly gentlemen,
  At break of day,
Came clitter-clatter down the stairs
  And galloped away.

UPON THE BEACH
Ilo Orleans

Upon the beach
  With pail and spade,
My sandy pies and wells I made.

And people passed
  On every hand
And left their footprints on the sand.

Then came a wave
  With the rushing tide—
And everything was washed aside.

AT THE SEA-SIDE
Robert Louis Stevenson

When I was down beside the sea
A wooden spade they gave to me
  To dig the sandy shore.

My holes were empty like a cup.
In every hole the sea came up,
  Till it could come no more.

ter de la Mare. Reprinted by permission of the publishers
  "At the Sea-Side." From *A Child's Garden of Verses* by Robert Louis Stevenson
  "Picnic Day." From *A Little Book of Days* by Rachel Field. Copyright 1927 by Doubleday & Company, Inc.

  "The Picnic." From *Hop, Skip and Jump* by Dorothy Aldis. Minton, Balch and Company, New York, 1934. Copyright, 1934, by Dorothy Aldis
  "Upon the Beach." From *Funday* by Ilo Orleans. Used with the kind permission of Ilo Orleans.

SKIPPING ALONG ALONE

Winifred Welles

Oh, how I love to skip alone
  Along the beach in moisty weather;
The whole world seems my very own,
Each fluted shell and glistening stone,
  Each wave that twirls a silver feather.

I skip along so brave and big
  Behind the sand-birds gray and tiny,
I love to see their quick feet jig,
Each leaves a mark, neat as a twig,
  Stamped in the sand so clear and shiny.

And fine and faint as drops of spray
  I hear their little voices calling,
"Sweet, sweet! Sweet, sweet!" I hear them say—
I love to skip alone and play
  Along the sand when mist is falling.

SHORE

Mary Britton Miller

Play on the seashore
And gather up shells,
Kneel in the damp sands
Digging wells.

Run on the rocks
Where the seaweed slips,
Watch the waves
And the beautiful ships.

BEACH FIRE

Frances M. Frost

When the picnic was over,
We sat by the tide
And watched the white-winged
Sea gulls slide

Down the evening wind.
The stars came out
Above the sea,
And Dad gave a shout:

"Oh, wish on that little
Brand-new moon!
Let's build up the fire
With wood from the dune!"

We wished on the moon,
We built up the fire,
We sang, while the sparks
Flew higher, higher,

Like stars of our own
Above the foam,
Till, sleepy, we
And the birds went home.

WHERE GO THE BOATS?

Robert Louis Stevenson

Dark brown is the river,
  Golden is the sand.
It flows along forever,
  With trees on either hand.

Green leaves a-floating,
  Castles of the foam,
Boats of mine a-boating—
  Where will all come home?

On goes the river
  And out past the mill,
Away down the valley,
  Away down the hill.

Away down the river,
  A hundred miles or more,
Other little children
  Shall bring my boats ashore.

"Skipping Along Alone." *Say the title over and over and feel its gay skipping rhythm! The whole poem skips.* From *Skipping Along Alone* by Winifred Welles. The Macmillan Company, New York, 1931. Used by permission of James Welles Shearer

"Shore." From *Menagerie* by Mary Britton Miller. Copyright 1928 by The Macmillan Company and used with their permission

"Beach Fire." From *The Little Whistler* by Frances M. Frost. Whittlesey House, McGraw-Hill Book Company, Inc., New York, 1949

"Where Go the Boats?" *These words and lines have the smooth, flowing movement of a quiet river. Notice from the beginning of the third verse, the lines flow on and on and never really come to a rest until the last line.* From *A Child's Garden of Verses* by Robert Louis Stevenson

Zhenya Gay

The world is full of wonderful smells,
And you have a nose that always tells
Of bread in the oven, hot and nice,
Of cake being baked with lots of spice,
Of a barn with fresh-cut hay in the mows,
Of horses and pigs and cats and cows,
Of a dog when he's warm and lies in the sun,
Of applesauce and chocolate and a sugar bun.
Wouldn't it be dreadful if you'd no nose to tell
Of every wonderful, wonderful smell?

THE LITTLE WHISTLER

Frances M. Frost

My mother whistled softly,
My father whistled bravely,
My brother whistled merrily,
And I tried all day long!
I blew my breath inwards,
I blew my breath outwards,
But all you heard was breath blowing
And not a bit of song!

But today I heard a bluebird,
A happy, young, and new bird,
Whistling in the apple tree—
He'd just discovered how!
Then quick I blew my breath in,
And gay I blew my breath out,
And sudden I blew three wild notes—
And I can whistle now!

NEW SHOES

Alice Wilkins

I have new shoes in the Fall-time
And new ones in the Spring.
Whenever I wear my new shoes
I always have to sing!

HAPPINESS

A. A. Milne

John had
Great Big
Waterproof
Boots on;
John had a
Great Big
Waterproof
Hat;
John had a
Great Big
Waterproof
Mackintosh—
And that
(Said John)
Is
That.

CHOOSING SHOES

Ffrida Wolfe

New shoes, new shoes,
 Red and pink and blue shoes.
Tell me, what would *you* choose,
 If they'd let us buy?

Buckle shoes, bow shoes,
 Pretty pointy-toe shoes,
Strappy, cappy low shoes;
 Let's have some to try.

Bright shoes, white shoes,
 Dandy-dance-by-night shoes,
Perhaps-a-little-tight shoes,
 Like some? So would I.

But

Flat shoes, fat shoes,
 Stump-along-like-that shoes,
Wipe-them-on-the-mat shoes,
 That's the sort they'll buy.

"The world is full of wonderful smells." From *Jingle Jangle* by Zhenya Gay. Copyright 1953 by Zhenya Gay. Reprinted by permission of The Viking Press, Inc., New York
"The Little Whistler." *See record album* Poetry Time. From *The Little Whistler* by Frances M. Frost. Whittlesey House, McGraw-Hill Book Company, Inc., New York, 1949
"New Shoes." From *The Golden Flute* compiled by Alice Hubbard. The John Day Company, Inc., New York, 1932

"Happiness." *These words go clumping along for all the world like John's rubber boots. See record album* Poetry Time. Taken from *When We Were Very Young*, by A. A. Milne, published and copyright, 1924, by E. P. Dutton & Co., Inc., New York
"Choosing Shoes." From *The Very Thing* by Ffrida Wolfe. Sidgwick and Jackson, Ltd., London, 1928

MARCHING SONG

Robert Louis Stevenson

Bring the comb and play upon it!
   Marching, here we come!
Willie cocks his highland bonnet,
   Johnnie beats the drum.

Mary Jane commands the party,
   Peter leads the rear;
Feet in time, alert and hearty,
   Each a Grenadier!

All in the most martial manner
   Marching double-quick;
While the napkin, like a banner,
   Waves upon the stick!

Here's enough of fame and pillage,
   Great commander Jane!
Now that we've been round the village,
   Let's go home again.

MY SHADOW

Robert Louis Stevenson

I have a little shadow that goes in and out
   with me,
And what can be the use of him is more than I
   can see.
He is very, very like me from the heels up to the
   head;
And I see him jump before me, when I jump into
   my bed.

The funniest thing about him is the way he likes
   to grow—
Not at all like proper children, which is always
   very slow;
For he sometimes shoots up taller like an India-
   rubber ball,
And he sometimes gets so little that there's none
   of him at all.

He hasn't got a notion of how children ought to
   play,
And can only make a fool of me in every sort of
   way.
He stays so close beside me, he's a coward you
   can see;
I'd think shame to stick to nursie as that shadow
   sticks to me!

One morning, very early, before the sun was up,
I rose and found the shining dew on every buttercup;
But my lazy little shadow, like an arrant sleepyhead,
Had stayed at home behind me and was fast
   asleep in bed.

SHADOW DANCE

Ivy O. Eastwick

O Shadow,
Dear Shadow,
Come, Shadow,
And dance!
On the wall
In the firelight
Let both of
Us prance!
I raise my
Arms, thus!
And you raise
Your arms, so!
And dancing
And leaping
And laughing
We go!
From the wall
To the ceiling,
From ceiling
To wall,
Just you and
I, Shadow,
And none else
At all.

"Marching Song." From *A Child's Garden of Verses* by Robert Louis Stevenson

"My Shadow." *It is easy to singsong this poem. Think of the story it is telling and keep it alive in natural story-telling style.* From *A Child's Garden of Verses* by Robert Louis Stevenson

"Shadow Dance." Taken from *Fairies and Suchlike*, by Ivy O. Eastwick, published and copyright, 1946, by E. P. Dutton & Co., Inc., New York

"Sniff." By Frances M. Frost. From *American Junior Red Cross News*. Copyright 1944 by the American National Red Cross

SNIFF

Frances M. Frost

When school is out, we love to follow
our noses over hill and hollow,
smelling jewelweed and vetch,
sniffing fern and milkweed patch.

The airy fifth of our five senses
leads us under, over, fences.
We run like rabbits through bright hours
and poke our noses into flowers!

THE TOASTER

William Jay Smith

A silver-scaled Dragon with jaws flaming red
Sits at my elbow and toasts my bread.
I hand him fat slices, and then, one by one,
He hands them back when he sees they are done.

HIDING

Dorothy Aldis

I'm hiding, I'm hiding,
And no one knows where;
For all they can see is my
Toes and my hair.

And I just heard my father
Say to my mother—
"But, darling, he must be
Somewhere or other;

"Have you looked in the ink well?"
And Mother said, "Where?"
"In the INK WELL," said Father. But
I was not there.

Then "Wait!" cried my mother—
"I think that I see
Him under the carpet." But
It was not me.

"Inside the mirror's
A pretty good place,"
Said Father and looked, but saw
Only his face.

"We've hunted," sighed Mother,
"As hard as we could
And I AM so afraid that we've
Lost him for good."

Then I laughed out aloud
And I wiggled my toes
And Father said—"Look, dear,
I wonder if those

Toes could be Benny's.
There are ten of them. See?"
And they WERE so surprised to find
Out it was me!

FUN IN A GARRET
Emma C. Dowd

"We're having a lovely time to-day!
We're all of us up in the garret at play!
We have three houses under the eaves—
Not real, you know, but make-believes;
Two we live in, and one is a store,
Where a little old screen makes a truly door.
Warren keeps store, and Joe is his clerk,
And Betty and I stay at home and work.
Joe comes around and knocks or rings,
And we order potatoes and steaks and things;
And sometimes we go to the store and buy,
Or send the children for ribbons or pie.
It's lots of fun—just try it some day
When it rains too hard to go out and play.

A GOOD PLAY
Robert Louis Stevenson

We built a ship upon the stairs
All made of the back-bedroom chairs,
And filled it full of sofa pillows
To go a-sailing on the billows.

We took a saw and several nails,
And water in the nursery pails;
And Tom said, "Let us also take
An apple and a slice of cake;"—
Which was enough for Tom and me
To go a-sailing on, till tea.

We sailed along for days and days,
And had the very best of plays;
But Tom fell out and hurt his knee,
So there was no one left but me.

PIRATE STORY

Robert Louis Stevenson

Three of us afloat in the meadow by the swing,
  Three of us aboard in the basket on the lea.
Winds are in the air, they are blowing in the
    spring,
  And waves are on the meadow like the waves
    there are at sea.

Where shall we adventure, to-day that we're
    afloat,
  Wary of the weather and steering by a star?
Shall it be to Africa, a-steering of the boat,
  To Providence, or Babylon, or off to Malabar?

Hi! but here's a squadron a-rowing on the sea—
  Cattle on the meadow a-charging with a roar!
Quick, and we'll escape them, they're as mad as
    they can be,
  The wicket is the harbour and the garden is
    the shore.

THE LAND OF STORY-BOOKS

Robert Louis Stevenson

At evening when the lamp is lit,
Around the fire my parents sit;
They sit at home and talk and sing,
And do not play at anything.

Now, with my little gun, I crawl
All in the dark along the wall,
And follow round the forest track
Away behind the sofa back.

There, in the night, where none can spy,
All in my hunter's camp I lie,
And play at books that I have read
Till it is time to go to bed.

These are the hills, these are the woods,
These are my starry solitudes;
And there the river by whose brink
The roaring lions come to drink.

I see the others far away
As if in firelit camp they lay,
And I, like to an Indian scout,
Around their party prowled about.

So, when my nurse comes in for me,
Home I return across the sea,
And go to bed with backward looks
At my dear Land of Story-books.

BEDTIME

Eleanor Farjeon

Five minutes, five minutes more, please!
  Let me stay five minutes more!
Can't I just finish the castle
  I'm building here on the floor?
Can't I just finish the story
  I'm reading here in my book?
Can't I just finish this bead-chain—
  It *almost* is finished, look!
Can't I just finish this game, please?
  When a game's once begun
It's a pity never to find out
  Whether you've lost or won.
Can't I just stay five minutes?
  Well, can't I stay just four?
Three minutes, then? two minutes?
  Can't I stay *one* minute more?

"Pirate Story." From *A Child's Garden of Verses* by Robert Louis Stevenson
"The Land of Story-books." From *A Child's Garden of Verses* by Robert Louis Stevenson
"Bedtime." From *Over the Garden Wall*. Copyright 1933 by Eleanor Farjeon. Reprinted by permission of J. B. Lippincott Company

"Mrs. Brown." From *The Fairy Green* by Rose Fyleman. Copyright 1923 by Doubleday & Company, Inc. By permission also of Miss Rose Fyleman, The Society of Authors, and Messrs. Methuen & Co.
"Merry-Go-Round." *The words and lines of this poem go round and round like the carrousel itself. From the fifth line on, the merry-go-round and words seem to move*

MRS. BROWN

Rose Fyleman

As soon as I'm in bed at night
And snugly settled down,
The little girl I am by day
Goes very suddenly away,
And then I'm Mrs. Brown.

I have a family of six,
And all of them have names,
The girls are Joyce and Nancy Maud,
The boys are Marmaduke and Claude
And Percival and James.

We have a house with twenty rooms
A mile away from town;
I think it's good for girls and boys
To be allowed to make a noise—
And so does Mr. Brown.

We do the most exciting things,
Enough to make you creep;
And on and on and on we go—
I sometimes wonder if I know
When I have gone to sleep.

MERRY-GO-ROUND

Dorothy Baruch

I climbed up on the merry-go-round,
And it went round and round.
I climbed up on a big brown horse
And it went up and down.
  Around and round
  And up and down,
  Around and round
  And up and down,
  I sat high up
  On a big brown horse
  And rode around
  On the merry-go-round

And rode around
On the merry-go-round
I rode around
On the merry-go-round
  Around
  And round
  And
  Round.

from ALL AROUND THE TOWN

Phyllis McGinley

C is for the Circus
  Which springtime brings to town.
(The country has its crocus,
  But we much prefer the clown.)
C's for canes and cracker-jack
  And curious camels, too.
I wouldn't trade a Circus
  For some crocuses. Would you?

THE CIRCUS PARADE

Olive Beaupré Miller

O Goody, it's coming, the circus parade
  And all the way up the street,
What crowds of people in gay-colored clothes,
  With popcorn and peanuts to eat!

The children have red, blue, and yellow bal-
    loons,
  As up by the curbing they stand,
And now, in the distance, we suddenly hear
  The circus's big brass band!

faster and faster until shortly after the "big brown horse" they run down, slower and slower, until they stop with the last word. From *I Like Machinery* by Dorothy Baruch. Harper & Brothers, New York, 1933. Used by permission of the author

"C is for the Circus." From *All Around the Town.* Copy-

right 1948 by Phyllis McGinley. Reprinted by permission of J. B. Lippincott Company.

"The Circus Parade." From *My Book House.* Used by permission of the author, Olive Beaupré Miller, and the publishers, The Book House for Children, Chicago, Illinois

Behind the crash-bang! of the music they play,
  Come riders in red velvet gowns,
And after them doing the funniest things,
  A silly procession of clowns.

Then lions and tigers that pace up and down,
  In wagons all painted with gold,
And monkeys a-playing just all kinds of tricks,
  As they grimace and chatter and scold.

O, next there come camels and elephants, too,
  High on their backs men ride;
There are queer little ponies, no bigger than
    dogs,
  With a clown on a donkey, beside!

And then there come chariots rumbling by
  With horses all four in a row;
And the wheezing, old, piping calliope is
  The very tail end of the show!

OUR CIRCUS
Laura Lee Randall

We had a circus in our shed
(Admission, three new pins a head)
And every girl and boy I know
Is talking yet about our show.

They laughed so hard at Fatty Brown
When he came out to be the clown,
That all the neighbors ran to see
Whatever such a noise could be.

Our tin-pan and mouth-organ band
Played tunes that sounded simply grand;
We had a truly sawdust ring,
Pink lemonade, 'n everything.

The big menagerie was nice:
Three cats, one dog, and five white mice,
A parrot that Bill's uncle lent;
All underneath a bedspread tent.

Then Ned and Buster took a sheet
That covered them from head to feet
And made a horse that kicked and pranced
And when it heard the band, it danced.

And Sally Ann was "Bareback Queen"!
No finer rider could be seen;
She stood right up, and looked so proud,
But kissed her hand to all the crowd.

We took some chalk—blue, green, and red—
And made a "Tattooed Man" of Fred;
Jim juggled lighted cigarettes,
And Tom turned double somersets.

We had tall stilts—and flying rings—
And lots and lots of other things—
And every boy and girl I know
Said yes, it was a *dandy* show!

Richard LeGallienne

I meant to do my work to-day—
  But a brown bird sang in the apple-tree,
And a butterfly flitted across the field,
  And all the leaves were calling me.

And the wind went sighing over the land,
  Tossing the grasses to and fro,
And a rainbow held out its shining hand—
  So what could I do but laugh and go?

JILL CAME FROM THE FAIR
Eleanor Farjeon

    Jill came from the Fair
    With her pennies all spent.
    She had had her full share
    Of delight and content;

"Our Circus." From *Child Life*, September 1924. Child
Life, Inc., Boston. By permission of the author
"I meant to do my work to-day." From *The Lonely Dan-
cer* by Richard LeGallienne. Reprinted by permission of
Dodd, Mead & Company

"Jill Came from the Fair." *This poem is as full of hurry
and confusion as the fair! And the excitement seems to
grow until, like Jill, you reach the end a bit dazed and
breathless. See the introduction, p. xx.* From *Over the
Garden Wall.* Copyright 1933 by Eleanor Farjeon. Re-

She had ridden the ring
To a wonderful tune,
She had flown in a swing
Half as high as the moon,
In a boat that was drawn
By an ivory swan
Beside a green lawn
On a lake she had gone,
She had bought a gold packet
That held her desire,
She had touched the red jacket
Of one who ate fire,
She had stood at the butt,
And although she was small
She had won a rough nut
With the throw of a ball,
And across the broad back
Of a donkey a-straddle,
She had jolted like Jack-
In-the-Box on a saddle—
Till mid frolic and shout
And tinsel and litter,
The lights started out
Making everything glitter,
And dazed by the noise
And the blare and the flare,
With her toys and her joys
Jill came from the Fair.

AFTER ALL AND AFTER ALL

Mary Carolyn Davies

Dreaming of a prince,
Cinderella sat among the ashes long ago;
Dreaming of a prince,
She scoured the pots and kettles till they shone;
and so,
After all and after all,
Gaily at the castle ball
Cinderella met her prince long and long ago!

printed by permission of J. B. Lippincott Company
"After All and After All." From *The Century*. The Century Company, New York, June 1917. Used by permission of A. H. Davies

Dreaming of a prince,
Sleeping Beauty lay in happy slumber, white and
still;
Dreaming of a prince,
She waited for a hundred years, and then his
bugles shrill,
After all and after all,
Woke the castle, bower, and hall,
And he found her waiting him long and long
ago!

Dreaming of a prince,
I polish bowl and tea-pot and the spoons, each
one;
Dreaming of a prince,
I hang the new-washed clothes to wave a-drying
in the sun;
After all and after all,
Great adventures may befall
Like to those that happened once long and long
ago!

LAUGHING SONG

William Blake

When the green woods laugh with the voice of
joy,
And the dimpling stream runs laughing by;
When the air does laugh with our merry wit,
And the green hill laughs with the noise of it;

When the meadows laugh with lively green,
And the grasshopper laughs in the merry scene;
When Mary and Susan and Emily
With their sweet round mouths sing, "Ha ha he!"

When the painted birds laugh in the shade,
When our table with cherries and nuts is spread;
Come live, and be merry, and join with me,
To sing the sweet chorus of "Ha ha he!"

"Laughing Song." *This charming poem about laughter is as gay as a sunny day. You may not visualize all of the pictures because they pass by so quickly. See May Hill Arbuthnot,* Children and Books, *p. 166*

(*Mother Goose*)

Hey, diddle, diddle!
The cat and the fiddle,
The cow jumped over the moon;
The little dog laughed
To see such sport,
And the dish ran away with the spoon.

HOW RIDICULOUS

(*Mother Goose*)

Tom he was a piper's son,
He learned to play when he was young,
But all the tunes that he could play,
Was "Over the hills and far away."

Now Tom with his pipe made such a noise,
That he pleased both girls and boys,
And they stopped to hear him play
"Over the hills and far away."

Tom with his pipe did play with such skill,
That those who heard him could never keep
    still;
Whenever they heard they began for to dance,
Even pigs on their hind legs would after him
    prance.

THE LITTLE KITTENS

Eliza Lee Follen

"Where are you going, my little kittens?"
"We are going to town to get us some mittens."
  "What! Mittens for kittens!
  Do kittens wear mittens?
Who ever saw little kittens with mittens?"

"Where are you going, my little cat?"
"I am going to town to get me a hat."
  "What! A hat for a cat!
  A cat get a hat!
Who ever saw a cat with a hat?"

"Where are you going, my little pig?"
"I am going to town to get me a wig."
  "What! A wig for a pig!
  A pig in a wig!
Who ever saw a pig in a wig?"

THE CATS' TEA-PARTY

Frederick E. Weatherly

Five little pussy-cats, invited out to tea,
Cried: "Mother, let us go—Oh do! for good we'll
    surely be.
We'll wear our bibs and hold our things as you
    have shown us how—
Spoons in right paws, cups in left—and make a
    pretty bow;
We'll always say 'Yes, if you please,' and 'Only
    half of that.' "
"Then go, my darling children," said the happy
    Mother Cat.
The five little pussy-cats went out that night to
    tea.
Their heads were smooth and glossy, their tails
    were swinging free;
They held their things as they had learned, and
    tried to be polite;—
With snowy bibs beneath their chins they were a
    pretty sight.
But, alas, for manners beautiful, and coats as soft
    as silk!
The moment that the little kits were asked to
    take some milk,
They dropped their spoons, forgot to bow, and—
    oh, what do you think?

They put their noses in the cups and all began
    to drink!
Yes, every naughty little kit set up a mew for
    more,
Then knocked their tea-cups over, and scampered
    through the door.

THE DUEL

Eugene Field

The gingham dog and the calico cat
Side by side on the table sat;
'T was half-past twelve, and (what do you think!)
Nor one nor t' other had slept a wink!
    The old Dutch clock and the Chinese plate
    Appeared to know as sure as fate
There was going to be a terrible spat.
    *(I wasn't there; I simply state
    What was told to me by the Chinese plate!)*

The gingham dog went, "bow-wow-wow!"
And the calico cat replied, "mee-ow!"
The air was littered, an hour or so,
With bits of gingham and calico,
    While the old Dutch clock in the chimney-
        place
    Up with its hands before its face,
For it always dreaded a family row!
    *(Now mind: I'm only telling you
    What the old Dutch clock declares is true!)*

The Chinese plate looked very blue,
And wailed, "Oh, dear! what shall we do!"
But the gingham dog and the calico cat
Wallowed this way and tumbled that,
    Employing every tooth and claw
    In the awfullest way you ever saw—
And, oh! how the gingham and calico flew!
    *(Don't fancy I exaggerate—
    I got my news from the Chinese plate!)*

Next morning, where the two had sat
They found no trace of dog or cat;
And some folks think unto this day
That burglars stole that pair away!
    But the truth about the cat and pup

"The Duel." From *Poems of Childhood* by Eugene Field.
Charles Scribner's Sons, New York, 1904

Is this: they ate each other up!
Now what do you really think of that!
(*The old Dutch clock it told me so,*
And that is how I came to know.)

THE OWL AND THE PUSSY-CAT

Edward Lear

The Owl and the Pussy-Cat went to sea
   In a beautiful pea-green boat,
They took some honey, and plenty of money
   Wrapped up in a five-pound note.
The Owl looked up to the stars above,
   And sang to a small guitar,
"O lovely Pussy, O Pussy, my love,
   What a beautiful Pussy you are,
          You are,
          You are!
What a beautiful Pussy you are!"

Pussy said to the Owl, "You elegant fowl,
   How charmingly sweet you sing!
Oh! let us be married, too long we have tarried:
   But what shall we do for a ring?"
They sailed away, for a year and a day,
   To the land where the Bong-tree grows;
And there in a wood a Piggy-wig stood,
   With a ring at the end of his nose,
          His nose,
          His nose,
   With a ring at the end of his nose.

"Dear Pig, are you willing to sell for one shilling
   Your ring?" Said the Piggy, "I will."
So they took it away, and were married next day
   By the Turkey who lives on the hill.
They dined on mince and slices of quince,
   Which they ate with a runcible spoon;
And hand in hand, on the edge of the sand,
   They danced by the light of the moon,
          The moon,
          The moon,
They danced by the light of the moon.

"The Rum Tum Tugger." From *Old Possum's Book of Practical Cats,* copyright, 1939, by T. S. Eliot. Reprinted by permission of Harcourt, Brace and Company, Inc., and Faber and Faber Limited

THE RUM TUM TUGGER

T. S. Eliot

The Rum Tum Tugger is a Curious Cat:
If you offer him pheasant he would rather have
   grouse.
If you put him in a house he would much prefer
   a flat,
If you put him in a flat then he'd rather have a
   house.
If you set him on a mouse then he only wants a
   rat,
If you set him on a rat then he'd rather chase a
   mouse.
Yes the Rum Tum Tugger is a Curious Cat—
   And there isn't any call for me to shout it:
      For he will do
      As he do do
         And there's no doing anything about it!

The Rum Tum Tugger is a terrible bore:
When you let him in, then he wants to be out;
He's always on the wrong side of every door,
As soon as he's at home, then he'd like to get
   about.
He likes to lie in the bureau drawer,
But he makes such a fuss if he can't get out.
Yes the Rum Tum Tugger is a Curious Cat—
   And it isn't any use for you to doubt it:
      For he will do
      As he do do
         And there's no doing anything about it!

The Rum Tum Tugger is a curious beast:
His disobliging ways are a matter of habit.
If you offer him fish then he always wants a
   feast;
When there isn't any fish then he won't eat
   rabbit.
If you offer him cream then he sniffs and sneers,
For he only likes what he finds for himself;
So you'll catch him in it right up to the ears,
If you put it away on the larder shelf.
The Rum Tum Tugger is artful and knowing,
The Rum Tum Tugger doesn't care for a cud-
   dle;
But he'll leap on your lap in the middle of your
   sewing,
For there's nothing he enjoys like a horrible
   muddle.

Yes the Rum Tum Tugger is a Curious Cat—
    And there isn't any need for me to spout it:
    For he will do
    As he do do
        And there's no doing anything about it!

MACAVITY: THE MYSTERY CAT
T. S. Eliot

Macavity's a Mystery Cat: he's called the Hidden
    Paw—
For he's the master criminal who can defy the
    Law.
He's the bafflement of Scotland Yard, the Flying
    Squad's despair:
For when they reach the scene of crime—*Macavity's not there!*

Macavity, Macavity, there's no one like Macavity,
He's broken every human law, he breaks the law
    of gravity.
His powers of levitation would make a fakir
    stare,
And when you reach the scene of crime—*Macavity's not there!*
You may seek him in the basement, you may
    look up in the air—
But I tell you once and once again, *Macavity's not there!*

Macavity's a ginger cat, he's very tall and thin;
You would know him if you saw him, for his eyes
    are sunken in.
His brow is deeply lined with thought, his head
    is highly domed;
His coat is dusty from neglect, his whiskers are
    uncombed.
He sways his head from side to side, with move-
    ments like a snake;
And when you think he's half asleep, he's always
    wide awake.

Macavity, Macavity, there's no one like Macavity,
For he's a fiend in feline shape, a monster of
    depravity.

"Macavity: The Mystery Cat." *Doesn't Mr. Eliot have
wonderful names for his cats?* From *Old Possum's Book of
Practical Cats,* copyright, 1939, by T. S. Eliot. Reprinted
by permission of Harcourt, Brace & Company, Inc., and
Faber and Faber Limited

You may meet him in a by-street, you may see
    him in the square—
But when a crime's discovered, then *Macavity's not there!*

He's outwardly respectable. (They say he cheats
    at cards.)
And his footprints are not found in any file of
    Scotland Yard's.
And when the larder's looted, or the jewel-case is
    rifled,
Or when the milk is missing, or another Peke's
    been stifled,
Or the greenhouse glass is broken, and the trellis
    past repair—
Ay, there's the wonder of the thing! *Macavity's not there!*

And when the Foreign Office find a Treaty's gone
    astray,
Or the Admiralty lose some plans and drawings
    by the way,
There may be a scrap of paper in the hall or on
    the stair—
But it's useless to investigate—*Macavity's not there!*
And when the loss has been disclosed, the Secret
    Service say:
"It *must* have been Macavity!"—but he's a mile
    away.
You'll be sure to find him resting, or a-licking of
    his thumbs,
Or engaged in doing complicated long division
    sums.

Macavity, Macavity, there's no one like Macavity,
There never was a Cat of such deceitfulness and
    suavity.
He always has an alibi, and one or two to spare:
At whatever time the deed took place—MACAV-
ITY WASN'T THERE!
And they say that all the Cats whose wicked
    deeds are widely known,
(I might mention Mungojerrie, I might mention
    Griddlebone)
Are nothing more than agents for the Cat who
    all the time
Just controls their operations: the Napoleon of
    Crime!

Sing a song of sixpence,
　A pocket full of rye;
Four-and-twenty blackbirds
　Baked in a pie!

When the pie was opened
　The birds began to sing;
Was not that a dainty dish
　To set before the king?

The king was in his counting-house
　Counting out his money;
The queen was in the parlor,
　Eating bread and honey.

The maid was in the garden,
　Hanging out the clothes;
When down came a blackbird
　And snapped off her nose.

(Mother Goose)

Hickory, dickory, dock!
The mouse ran up the clock;
　The clock struck one,
　And down he run,
Hickory, dickory, dock!

(Mother Goose)

A farmer went trotting upon his gray mare;
　Bumpety, bumpety, bump!
With his daughter behind him so rosy and fair;
　Lumpety, lumpety, lump!

A raven cried "Croak!" and they all tumbled
　down,
　Bumpety, bumpety, bump!
The mare broke her knees, and the farmer his
　crown,
　Lumpety, lumpety, lump!

The mischievous raven flew laughing away,
　Bumpety, bumpety, bump!
And vowed he would serve them the same the
　next day,
　Lumpety, lumpety, lump!

(Mother Goose)

I saw a ship a-sailing,
　A-sailing on the sea;
And, oh! it was all laden
　With pretty things for thee!

There were comfits in the cabin,
　And apples in the hold;
The sails were made of silk,
　And the masts were made of gold.

The four-and-twenty sailors
　That stood between the decks,
Were four-and-twenty white mice
　With chains about their necks.

The captain was a duck,
　With a packet on his back;
And when the ship began to move,
　The captain said, "Quack! Quack!"

KINDNESS TO ANIMALS
Laura E. Richards

Riddle cum diddle cum dido,
My little dog's name is Fido;
　I bought him a wagon,
　And hitched up a dragon,
And off we both went for a ride, oh!

Riddle cum riddle cum doodle,
My little cat's name is Toodle;
　I curled up her hair,
　But she only said, "There!
You have made me look *just* like a poodle!"

"A farmer went trotting upon his gray mare." *This is fun to do with either two or three speaking choirs. See May Hill Arbuthnot,* Children and Books, *p. 215, and also record album* Poetry Time.

"Kindness to Animals." From *Tirra Lirra* by Laura E. Richards. Copyright 1918, 1930, 1932 by Laura E. Rich-

ards. By permission of Little, Brown & Co.

"Higgledy, piggledy! see how they run!" From *Under the Window* by Kate Greenaway. Frederick Warne and Company, New York and London, 1910

"My Donkey." *Could this wise little donkey be faking his pains to win sympathy and presents? Charming for*

Riddle cum diddle cum dinky,
My little pig's name is Winkie;
  I keep him quite clean
  With the washing machine,
And I rinse him all off in the sinkie.

Kate Greenaway

Higgledy, piggledy! see how they run!
Hopperty, popperty! what is the fun?
Has the sun or the moon tumbled into the sea?
What is the matter, now? Pray tell it me!

Higgledy, piggledy! how can I tell?
Hopperty, popperty! hark to the bell!
The rats and the mice even scamper away;
Who can say what may not happen to-day?

MY DONKEY

(French)

Rose Fyleman

My donkey, my dear,
Had a pain in his head;
A kind lady gave him
A bonnet of red,
And little shoes of lavender,
Lav—lav—lavender,
And little shoes of lavender
To keep him from the cold.

My donkey, my dear,
Had a pain in his throat;
A kind lady gave him
A button-up coat,
And little shoes of lavender,
Lav—lav—lavender,
And little shoes of lavender
To keep him from the cold.

My donkey, my dear,
Had a pain in his chest;
A kind lady gave him
A thick woolly vest,
And little shoes of lavender,
Lav—lav—lavender,
And little shoes of lavender,
To keep him from the cold.

ALL WOOL

Abbie Farwell Brown

I've noticed how the woolly lamb
  Dislikes the rain and dew.
I wonder if he fears to damp
  His little garments through?

How very horrid it would be
  If they should shrink when wet!
He cannot take his woollies off
  And wear another set.

His legs would be so bare and cold,
  An ugly sight to see!
The flock would bleat, "Bah! Bah!" at him.
  How sheepish he would be!

THE PURPLE COW

Gelett Burgess

I never saw a Purple Cow,
  I never hope to see one;
But I can tell you, anyhow,
  I'd rather see than be one.

(American Mother Goose)

How much wood would a wood-chuck chuck
If a wood-chuck could chuck wood?
He would chuck as much wood as a wood-chuck
  would chuck,
If a wood-chuck could chuck wood.

choral speaking. From *Picture Rhymes from Foreign Lands.* Copyright 1935 by Rose Fyleman. Reprinted by permission of J. B. Lippincott Company

"All Wool." From *Songs of Sixpence* by Abbie Farwell Brown. Reprinted by permission of and arrangement with Houghton Mifflin Company, the authorized publishers

"The Purple Cow." From *The Burgess Nonsense Book* by Gelett Burgess. J. B. Lippincott Company, New York, 1901. Used by permission of the author

"How much wood would a wood-chuck chuck." From *The American Mother Goose* compiled by Ray Wood. Copyright 1940 by J. B. Lippincott Company

THE TREE TOAD

Monica Shannon

The Tree Toad is a creature neat,
With tidy rubbers on his feet.
Embarrassment is all he knows—
His color comes, his color goes.

The Tree Toad is quite small, at least,
Unless his girth has just increased.
The truth is always hard to seek,
For things are changing every week.

ONLY MY OPINION

Monica Shannon

Is a caterpillar ticklish?
    Well, it's always my belief
That he giggles, as he wiggles
    Across a hairy leaf.

THE BUMBLEBEAVER

Kenyon Cox

A cheerful and industrious beast,
    He's always humming as he goes
To make mud-houses with his tail
    Or gather honey with his nose.

Although he flits from flower to flower
    He's not at all a gay deceiver.
We might take lessons by the hour
    From busy, buzzy Bumblebeaver.

ALAS, ALACK

Walter de la Mare

Ann, Ann!
    Come! Quick as you can!
There's a fish that *talks*
    In the frying-pan.

Out of the fat,
    As clear as glass,
He put up his mouth
    And moaned "Alas!"
Oh, most mournful,
    "Alas, alack!"
Then turned to his sizzling,
    And sank him back.

SOME FISHY NONSENSE

Laura E. Richards

Timothy Tiggs and Tomothy Toggs,
They both went a-fishing for pollothywogs;
    They both went a-fishing
    Because they were wishing
To see how the creatures would turn into frogs.

Timothy Tiggs and Tomothy Toggs,
They both got stuck in the bogothybogs;
    They caught a small minnow,
    And said 't was a sin oh!
That things with no legs should pretend to be
    frogs.

THERE ONCE WAS A PUFFIN

Florence Page Jaques

Oh, there once was a Puffin
Just the shape of a muffin,
And he lived on an island
In the
    bright
        blue
            sea!

He ate little fishes,
That were most delicious,
And he had them for supper
And he
    had
        them
            for tea.

But this poor little Puffin,
He couldn't play nothin',
For he hadn't anybody
To
  play
    with
      at all.

So he sat on his island,
And he cried for awhile, and
He felt very lonely,
And he
  felt
    very
      small.

Then along came the fishes,
And they said, "If you wishes,
You can have us for playmates,
Instead
  of
    for
      tea!"

So they now play together,
In all sorts of weather,
And the puffin eats pancakes,
Like you
  and
    like
      me.

THREE LITTLE PUFFINS

Eleanor Farjeon

Three little puffins
Were partial to muffins,
As partial as partial can be.
    They wouldn't eat nuffin
    But hot buttered muffin
For breakfast and dinner and tea.

Pantin' and puffin'
  And chewin' and chuffin'
They just went on stuffin', dear me!
  Till the three little puffins
  Were chockful of muffins
And puffy as puffy can be,
            All three
  Were puffy as puffy can be.

THE OCTOPUS

Ogden Nash

Tell me, O Octopus, I begs,
Is those things arms, or is they legs?
I marvel at thee, Octopus;
If I were thou, I'd call me Us.

THE OCTOPUSSYCAT

Kenyon Cox

I love Octopussy, his arms are so long;
There's nothing in nature so sweet as his song.
'Tis true I'd not touch him—no, not for a farm!
If I keep at a distance he'll do me no harm.

Lewis Carroll

How doth the little crocodile
  Improve his shining tail,
And pour the waters of the Nile
  On every golden scale!

How cheerfully he seems to grin,
  How neatly spreads his claws,
And welcomes little fishes in,
  With gently smiling jaws!

Lewis Carroll

"The time has come," the Walrus said,
"To talk of many things:
Of shoes—and ships—and sealing-wax—
Of cabbages—and kings—
And why the sea is boiling hot—
And whether pigs have wings."

THE MONKEYS AND THE CROCODILE

Laura E. Richards

Five little monkeys
  Swinging from a tree;
Teasing Uncle Crocodile,
  Merry as can be.
Swinging high, swinging low,
  Swinging left and right:
"Dear Uncle Crocodile,
  Come and take a bite!"

Five little monkeys
  Swinging in the air;
Heads up, tails up,
  Little do they care.
Swinging up, swinging down,
  Swinging far and near:
"Poor Uncle Crocodile,
  Aren't you hungry, dear?"

Four little monkeys
  Sitting in the tree;
Heads down, tails down,
  Dreary as can be.
Weeping loud, weeping low,
  Crying to each other:
"Wicked Uncle Crocodile,
  To gobble up our brother!"

SO MANY MONKEYS

Marion Edey and Dorothy Grider

Monkey Monkey Moo!
Shall we buy a few?
Yellow monkeys,
Purple monkeys,
Monkeys red and blue.

Be a monkey, do!
Who's a monkey, *who?*
He's a monkey,
She's a monkey,
You're a monkey, too!

THE SHIP OF RIO

Walter de la Mare

There was a ship of Rio
  Sailed out into the blue,
And nine and ninety monkeys
  Were all her jovial crew.
From bo'sun to the cabin boy,
  From quarter to caboose,
There weren't a stitch of calico
  To breech 'em—tight or loose;
From spar to deck, from deck to keel,
  From barnacle to shroud,
There weren't one pair of reach-me-downs
  To all that jabbering crowd.
But wasn't it a gladsome sight,
  When roared the deep-sea gales,
To see them reef her fore and aft,
  A-swinging by their tails!
Oh, wasn't it a gladsome sight,
  When glassy calm did come,
To see them squatting tailor-wise
  Around a keg of rum!
Oh, wasn't it a gladsome sight,
  When in she sailed to land,

To see them all a-scampering skip
    For nuts across the sand!

HABITS OF THE HIPPOPOTAMUS

Arthur Guiterman

The hippopotamus is strong
    And huge of head and broad of bustle;
The limbs on which he rolls along
    Are big with hippopotomuscle.

He does not greatly care for sweets
    Like ice cream, apple pie, or custard,
But takes to flavor what he eats
    A little hippopotomustard.

The hippopotamus is true
    To all his principles, and just;
He always tries his best to do
    The things one hippopotomust.

He never rides in trucks or trams,
    In taxicabs or omnibuses,
And so keeps out of traffic jams
    And other hippopotomusses.

THE KANGAROOSTER

Kenyon Cox

His tail is remarkably long
And his legs are remarkably strong;
    But the strength and the length of his legs and
        his tail
Are as naught to the strength of his song.

He picks up his food with his bill;
He bounds over valley and hill;
    But the height of his bounds can't compare
        with the sounds
He lets out when he crows with a will.

Zhenya Gay

    When a goose meets a moose
    At the house of a mouse
    I wonder if all three
    Sit down and drink tea.

GRIZZLY BEAR

Mary Austin

    If you ever, ever, ever meet a grizzly bear,
    You must never, never, never ask him *where*
    He is going,
    Or *what* he is doing;
    For if you ever, ever, dare
    To stop a grizzly bear,
    You will never meet *another* grizzly bear.

RACCOON

William Jay Smith

One summer night a little Raccoon,
Above his left shoulder, looked at the new moon.
    He made a wish;
    He said: "I wish
    I were a Catfish,
    A Blowfish, a Squid,
    A Katydid,
    A Beetle, a Skink,
    An Ostrich, a pink
    Flamingo, a Gander,
    A Salamander,
    A Hippopotamus,
    A Duck-billed Platypus,
    A Gecko, a Slug,
    A Water Bug,
    A pug-nosed Beaver,
    Anything whatever
Except what I am, a little Raccoon!"

Above his left shoulder, the Evening Star
Listened and heard the little Raccoon
      Who wished on the moon;
      And she said: "Why wish
      You were a Catfish,
      A Blowfish, a Squid,
      A Katydid,
      A Beetle, a Skink,
      An Ostrich, a pink
      Flamingo, a Gander,
      A Salamander,
      A Hippopotamus,
      A Duck-billed Platypus,
      A Gecko, a Slug,
      A Water Bug,
      A pug-nosed Beaver,
      Anything whatever?
Why must you change?" said the Evening Star,
"When you are perfect as you are?
I know a boy who wished on the moon
That *he* might be a little Raccoon!"

HOW TO TELL THE WILD ANIMALS

Carolyn Wells

If ever you should go by chance
   To jungles in the East;
And if there should to you advance
   A large and tawny beast,
If he roars at you as you're dyin'
You'll know it is the Asian Lion.

Or if some time when roaming round,
   A noble wild beast greets you,
With black stripes on a yellow ground,
   Just notice if he eats you.
This simple rule may help you learn
The Bengal Tiger to discern.

If strolling forth, a beast you view,
   Whose hide with spots is peppered,
As soon as he has lept on you,

You'll know it is the Leopard.
'Twill do no good to roar with pain,
He'll only lep and lep again.

If when you're walking round your yard,
   You meet a creature there,
Who hugs you very, very hard,
   Be sure it is the Bear.
If you have any doubt, I guess
He'll give you just one more caress.

Though to distinguish beasts of prey
   A novice might nonplus,
The Crocodiles you always may
   Tell from Hyenas thus:
Hyenas come with merry smiles;
But if they weep, they're Crocodiles.

The true Chameleon is small,
   A lizard sort of thing;
He hasn't any ears at all,
   And not a single wing.
If there is nothing on the tree,
'Tis the Chameleon you see.

(American Mother Goose)

I asked my mother for fifteen cents
To see the elephant jump the fence,
He jumped so high that he touched the sky
And never came back 'till the Fourth of July.

ELETELEPHONY

Laura E. Richards

Once there was an elephant,
Who tried to use the telephant—
No! no! I mean an elephone
Who tried to use the telephone—
(Dear me! I am not certain quite
That even now I've got it right.)

"How to Tell the Wild Animals." From *Baubles* by Carolyn Wells. Reprinted by permission of Dodd, Mead & Company

"I asked my mother for fifteen cents." From *The American Mother Goose* compiled by Ray Wood. Copyright 1940 by J. B. Lippincott Company

Howe'er it was, he got his trunk
Entangled in the telephunk;
The more he tried to get it free,
The louder buzzed the telephee—
(I fear I'd better drop the song
Of elephop and telephong!)

JABBERWOCKY

Lewis Carroll

'Twas brillig, and the slithy toves
   Did gyre and gimble in the wabe:
All mimsy were the borogoves,
    And the mome raths outgrabe.

"Beware the Jabberwock, my son!
   The jaws that bite, the claws that catch!
Beware the Jubjub bird, and shun
    The frumious Bandersnatch!"

He took his vorpal sword in hand:
   Long time the manxome foe he sought—
So rested he by the Tumtum tree,
    And stood awhile in thought.

And, as in uffish thought he stood,
   The Jabberwock, with eyes of flame,
Came whiffling through the tulgey wood,
    And burbled as it came!

One, two! One, two! And through and through
   The vorpal blade went snicker-snack!
He left it dead, and with its head
    He went galumphing back.

"And hast thou slain the Jabberwock?
   Come to my arms, my beamish boy!

O frabjous day! Callooh! Callay!"
   He chortled in his joy.

'Twas brillig, and the slithy toves
   Did gyre and gimble in the wabe:
All mimsy were the borogoves,
    And the mome raths outgrabe.

THE SPANGLED PANDEMONIUM

Palmer Brown

The Spangled Pandemonium
Is missing from the zoo.
He bent the bars the barest bit,
And slithered glibly through.

He crawled across the moated wall,
He climbed the mango tree,
And when his keeper scrambled up,
He nipped him in the knee.

To all of you, a warning
Not to wander after dark,
Or if you must, make very sure
You stay out of the park.

For the Spangled Pandemonium
Is missing from the zoo,
And since he nipped his keeper,
He would just as soon nip you!

A CENTIPEDE

Unknown

A centipede was happy quite,
Until a frog in fun
Said, "Pray, which leg comes after which?"
This raised her mind to such a pitch,
She lay distracted in a ditch,
Considering how to run.

"Eletelephony." From *Tirra Lirra* by Laura E. Richards. Copyright 1918, 1930, 1932 by Laura E. Richards. By permission of Little, Brown & Co.
"Jabberwocky." *This sounds as convincing as if it made sense and it is wonderful to roll under your tongue.*
"The Spangled Pandemonium." From *Beyond the Paw Paw Trees* by Palmer Brown. Copyright 1954 by Palmer Brown. Published by Harper & Brothers, New York

ANTONIO
Laura E. Richards

Antonio, Antonio,
Was tired of living alonio.
    He thought he would woo
    Miss Lissamy Lou,
Miss Lissamy Lucy Molonio.

Antonio, Antonio,
Rode off on his polo-ponio.
    He found the fair maid
    In a bowery shade,
A-sitting and knitting alonio.

Antonio, Antonio,
Said, "If you will be my ownio,
    I'll love you true,
    And I'll buy for you,
An icery creamery conio!"

"Oh, nonio, Antonio!
You're far too bleak and bonio!
    And all that I wish,
    You singular fish,
Is that you will quickly begonio."

Antonio, Antonio,
He uttered a dismal moanio;
    Then ran off and hid
    (Or I'm told that he did)
In the Antarctical Zonio.

STATELY VERSE
Unknown

If Mary goes far out to sea,
    By wayward breezes fanned,
I'd like to know—can you tell me?—
    Just where would Maryland?

If Tenny went high up in air
    And looked o'er land and lea,
Looked here and there and everywhere,
    Pray what would Tennessee?

I looked out of the window and
    Saw Orry on the lawn;
He's not there now, and who can tell
    Just where has Oregon?

Two girls were quarrelling one day
    With garden tools, and so
I said, "My dears, let Mary rake
    And just let Idaho."

A friend of mine lived in a flat
    With half a dozen boys;
When he fell ill I asked him why.
    He said: "I'm Illinois."

An English lady had a steed.
    She called him 'Ighland Bay.
She rode for exercise, and thus
    Rhode Island every day.

DIAMOND CUT DIAMOND
Ewart Milne

Two cats
One up a tree
One under the tree
The cat up a tree is he
The cat under the tree is she
The tree is witch elm, just incidentally.
He takes no notice of she, she takes no notice of he.
He stares at the woolly clouds passing, she stares at the tree.
There's been a lot written about cats, by Old Possum, Yeats and Company
But not Alfred de Musset or Lord Tennyson or Poe or anybody
Wrote about one cat under, and one cat up, a tree.
God knows why this should be left for me
Except I like cats as cats be
Especially one cat up
And one cat under
A witch elm
Tree.

THE OSTRICH IS A SILLY BIRD

Mary E. Wilkins Freeman

The ostrich is a silly bird,
  With scarcely any mind.
He often runs so very fast,
  He leaves himself behind.

And when he gets there, has to stand
  And hang about till night,
Without a blessed thing to do
  Until he comes in sight.

RELATIVITY

Anonymous

There was a young lady named Bright,
Who traveled much faster than light.
  She started one day
  In the relative way,
And returned on the previous night.

(Mother Goose)

Mary, Mary, quite contrary,
  How does your garden grow?
Silver bells and cockle-shells,
  And pretty maids all in a row.

(Mother Goose)

Little Boy Blue, come blow your horn;
The sheep's in the meadow, the cow's in the corn.
Where's the little boy that looks after the sheep?
He's under the haystack, fast asleep.

(Mother Goose)

Wee Willie Winkie runs through the town,
Upstairs and downstairs, in his nightgown;
Rapping at the window, crying through the lock,
  "Are the children in their beds?
  Now it's eight o'clock."

(Mother Goose)

Jack and Jill went up the hill
  To fetch a pail of water.
Jack fell down and broke his crown
  And Jill came tumbling after.

Up Jack got and home he did trot
  As fast as he could caper.
He went to bed to mend his head
  In vinegar and brown paper.

(Mother Goose)

  Little Miss Muffet
  Sat on a tuffet,
Eating of curds and whey;
  There came a big spider,
  And sat down beside her,
And frightened Miss Muffet away.

(Mother Goose)

Little Bo-Peep has lost her sheep,
And can't tell where to find them;
Leave them alone, and they'll come home,
And bring their tails behind them.

Little Bo-Peep fell fast asleep,
And dreamt she heard them bleating;
But when she awoke, she found it a joke,
For still they all were fleeting.

Then up she took her little crook,
Determined for to find them;
She found them indeed, but it made her heart
    bleed,
For they'd left all their tails behind 'em!

It happened one day, as Bo-Peep did stray
Unto a meadow hard by—
There she espied their tails, side by side,
All hung on a tree to dry.

She heaved a sigh and wiped her eye,
And over the hillocks she raced;
And tried what she could, as a shepherdess
    should,
That each tail should be properly placed.

"Antonio." By Laura E. Richards. By permission of Trustee u/w Laura E. Richards
"Diamond Cut Diamond" is reproduced from a volume of verse by Ewart Milne published under the title *Dia-mond Cut Diamond* by The Bodley Head, Ltd.
"The Ostrich is a Silly Bird." By Mary E. Wilkins Freeman. From *Harper's Magazine*, August 1905. Reprinted by permission of the publishers

THE BONNIE CRAVAT

(Mother Goose)

Jennie, come tie my,
Jennie, come tie my,
Jennie, come tie my bonnie cravat;
    I've tied it behind,
    I've tied it before,
I've tied it so often, I'll tie it no more.

(Mother Goose)

Ding, dong, bell!
Pussy's in the well!
    Who put her in?
Little Johnny Green.
    Who pulled her out?
Little Johnny Stout.

What a naughty boy was that
To try to drown poor pussy cat
    Which never did him any harm,
But killed the mice in his father's barn!

(Mother Goose)

A diller, a dollar, a ten o'clock scholar!
    What makes you come so soon?
You used to come at ten o'clock,
    But now you come at noon.

(Mother Goose)

    Bye, baby bunting,
    Father's gone a-hunting,
    Mother's gone a-milking,
        Sister's gone a-silking,
    And brother's gone to buy a skin
    To wrap the baby bunting in.

(Mother Goose)

There was an old woman who lived in a shoe;
She had so many children she didn't know what
    to do;
She gave them some broth without any bread;
She whipped them all soundly and put them to
    bed.

(Mother Goose)

"Old woman, old woman, shall we go a-shear-
    ing?"
"Speak a little louder, sir, I am very thick of
    hearing."
"Old woman, old woman, shall I kiss you
    dearly?"
"Thank you, kind sir, I hear you very clearly."

(Mother Goose)

    Hark, hark! the dogs do bark!
        Beggars are coming to town:
    Some in jags, and some in rags,
        And some in velvet gown.

(American Mother Goose)

There was an old man named Michael Finnegan,
He grew a long beard right on his chinnigan,
Along came a wind and blew it in again—
Poor old Michael Finnegan.

(Mother Goose)

There was an old woman, as I've heard tell,
She went to market her eggs to sell;
She went to market all on a market-day,
And she fell asleep on the king's highway.

There came by a peddler whose name was Stout;
He cut her petticoats all round about;
He cut her petticoats up to the knees,
Which made the old woman to shiver and freeze.

When this little woman first did wake,
She began to shiver and she began to shake;
She began to wonder and she began to cry,
"Oh! deary, deary me, this is none of I!

"But if it be I, as I do hope it be,
I've a little dog at home, and he'll know me;
If it be I, he'll wag his little tail,
And if it be not I, he'll loudly bark and wail."

"The Bonnie Cravat." *This seems to demand a duet performance—either by one boy and one girl or by two verse choirs.*

"There was an old man named Michael Finnegan." From *The American Mother Goose* compiled by Ray Wood. Copyright 1940 by J. B. Lippincott Company

"There was a Young Lady whose chin." *These are only*

Home went the little woman all in the dark;
Up got the little dog, and he began to bark;
He began to bark, so she began to cry,
"Oh! deary, deary me, this is none of I!"

Edward Lear

There was a Young Lady whose chin
Resembled the point of a pin;
So she had it made sharp, and purchased a harp,
And played several tunes with her chin.

Edward Lear

There was an Old Man in a tree,
Who was horribly bored by a Bee;
When they said, "Does it buzz?"
    he replied, "Yes, it does!
It's a regular brute of a Bee."

Edward Lear

There was an Old Man with a beard,
Who said, "It is just as I feared!—
Two Owls and a Hen, four Larks and a Wren,
Have all built their nests in my beard."

Edward Lear

There was a Young Lady of Norway,
Who casually sat in a doorway;
When the door squeezed her flat,
    she exclaimed, "What of that?"
This courageous Young Lady of Norway.

JONATHAN

(Dutch)
Rose Fyleman

Jonathan Gee
Went out with his cow;
He climbed up a tree

And sat on a bough.
He sat on a bough
And it broke in half,
And John's old cow
Did nothing but laugh.

Kate Greenaway

Tommy was a silly boy,
"I can fly," he said;
He started off, but very soon,
He tumbled on his head.

His little sister Prue was there,
To see how he would do it;
She knew that, after all his boast,
Full dearly Tom would rue it!

TIMOTHY BOON

Ivy O. Eastwick

Timothy Boon
Bought a balloon
Blue as the sky,
Round as the moon.
"Now I will try
To make it fly
Up to the moon,
Higher than high!"
Timothy said,
Nodding his head.

Timothy Boon
Sent his balloon
Up through the skies,
Up to the moon.
But a strong breeze
Stirred in the trees,
Rocked the bright moon,
Tossed the great seas,
And, with its mirth,
Shook the whole earth.

a few of Lear's many limericks. Look at his The Complete Nonsense Book *and you may feel inspired to try writing some limericks of your own.*
"Jonathan." From *Picture Rhymes from Foreign Lands.* Copyright 1935 by Rose Fyleman. Reprinted by permission of J. B. Lippincott Company

"Tommy was a silly boy." From *Under the Window* by Kate Greenaway. Frederick Warne and Company, New York and London, 1910
"Timothy Boon." Taken from *Fairies and Suchlike,* by Ivy O. Eastwick, published and copyright, 1946, by E. P. Dutton & Co., Inc., New York

Timothy Boon,
And his balloon,
Caught by the breeze
Flew to the moon;
Up past the trees,
Over the seas,
Up to the moon—
Swift as you please!—
And, ere I forget,
They have not come down yet!

THE STORY OF JOHNNY
HEAD-IN-AIR

Heinrich Hoffman

As he trudg'd along to school,
It was always Johnny's rule
To be looking at the sky
And the clouds that floated by;
But what just before him lay,
In his way,
Johnny never thought about;
So that every one cried out—
"Look at little Johnny there,
Little Johnny Head-in-Air!"

Running just in Johnny's way,
Came a little dog one day;
Johnny's eyes were still astray
Up on high,
In the sky;
And he never heard them cry—
"Johnny, mind, the dog is nigh!"
Bump!
Dump!
Down they fell, with such a thump,
Dog and Johnny in a lump!

Once, with head as high as ever,
Johnny walk'd beside the river.
Johnny watch'd the swallows trying
Which was cleverest at flying.
Oh! what fun!
Johnny watch'd the bright round sun
Going in and coming out;
This was all he thought about.
So he strode on, only think!
To the river's very brink,
Where the bank was high and steep,
And the water very deep;

And the fishes, in a row,
Stared to see him coming so.

One step more! Oh! sad to tell!
Headlong in Poor Johnny fell.
And the fishes, in dismay,
Wagg'd their tails and ran away.

There lay Johnny on his face,
With his nice red writing-case;
But, as they were passing by,
Two strong men had heard him cry;
And, with sticks, these two strong men
Hook'd poor Johnny out again.
Oh! you should have seen him shiver
When they pull'd him from the river.
He was in a sorry plight!
Dripping wet, and such a fright!
Wet all over, everywhere,
Clothes, and arms, and face, and hair;
Johnny never will forget
What it is to be so wet.

And the fishes, one, two, three,
Are come back again, you see,
Up they came the moment after,
To enjoy the fun and laughter.
Each popp'd out his little head,
And, to tease poor Johnny, said,
"Silly little Johnny, look,
You have lost your writing-book!"

THE STORY OF AUGUSTUS

Heinrich Hoffmann

Augustus was a chubby lad;
Fat ruddy cheeks Augustus had;
And every body saw with joy
The plump and hearty healthy boy.
He ate and drank as he was told,
And never let his soup get cold.
But one day, one cold winter's day,
He scream'd out—"Take the soup away!
O take the nasty soup away!
I won't have any soup to-day."

"The Story of Johnny Head-in-Air" and *"The Story of
Augustus."* These two selections from the famous old
book *Slovenly Peter* are fun to illustrate verse by verse.
They make lively comic strips.
"Godfrey Gordon Gustavus Gore." Did you ever notice
how often nonsense verse turns upon a humorous-sound-

Next day, now look, the picture shows
How lank and lean Augustus grows!
Yet, though he feels so weak and ill,
The naughty fellow cries out still—
"Not any soup for me, I say:
O take the nasty soup away!
I won't have any soup to-day."

The third day comes; Oh what a sin!
To make himself so pale and thin.
Yet, when the soup is put on table,
He screams, as loud as he is able,—
"Not any soup for me, I say:
O take the nasty soup away!
I won't have any soup to-day."

Look at him, now the fourth day's come!
He scarcely weighs a sugar-plum;
He's like a little bit of thread,
And on the fifth day, he was—dead!

GODFREY GORDON GUSTAVUS GORE

William Brighty Rands

Godfrey Gordon Gustavus Gore—
No doubt you have heard the name before—
Was a boy who never would shut a door!

The wind might whistle, the wind might roar,
And teeth be aching and throats be sore,
But still he never would shut the door.

His father would beg, his mother implore,
"Godfrey Gordon Gustavus Gore,
We really *do* wish you would shut the door!"

Their hands they wrung, their hair they tore;
But Godfrey Gordon Gustavus Gore
Was deaf as the buoy out at the Nore.

When he walked forth the folks would roar,
"Godfrey Gordon Gustavus Gore,
Why don't you think to shut the door?"

They rigged out a Shutter with sail and oar,
And threatened to pack off Gustavus Gore
On a voyage of penance to Singapore.

But he begged for mercy, and said, "No more!
Pray do not send me to Singapore
On a Shutter, and then I will shut the door!"

"You will?" said his parents; "then keep on
    shore!
But mind you do! For the plague is sore
Of a fellow that never will shut the door,
Godfrey Gordon Gustavus Gore!"

MOMOTARA

(Japanese)

Rose Fyleman

Where did Momotara go,
With a hoity-toity-tighty?
He went to lay the giants low,
The wicked ones and mighty.

What did Momotara take?
His monkey, dog and pheasant,
Some dumplings and an almond cake,
Which made the journey pleasant.

How did Momotara fare
Upon the fearful meeting?
He seized the giants by the hair
And gave them all a beating.

ing combination of consonants? *You can't say this mouth-filling name in a hurry.*

"Momotara." *This is about a famous Japanese folk tale. It lends itself to choral speaking with two choirs, one for the question and one for the answer. But note the changing atmosphere of the stanzas or the poem will become monotonous. Stanzas one and three are "fearful" indeed. Stanza two is pleasant enough, stanza four full of beautiful things, and the last stanza a gay, brisk conclusion.* From *Picture Rhymes from Foreign Lands.* Copyright 1935 by Rose Fyleman. Reprinted by permission of J. B. Lippincott Company

What did Momotara bring?
Oh, more than you could measure:
A silver coat, a golden ring
And a waggon-load of treasure.

What did Momotara do?
He sat himself astride it;
The monkey pushed, the pheasant drew
And the little dog ran beside it.

AMBITION

Edith Agnew

When I am grown an *hombre*
I shall have another *nombre,*
They won't call me "Ramonito" any more;
But they'll call me *"caballero,"*
And I'll wave my wide *sombrero*
At all the señoritas I adore.

I've extravagant ideas:
Butter on all my *tortillas,*
And as much chokeberry jelly as I dare!
I will buy red combs for Mother—
She shall wear them, and no other—
With shiny stones to lie against her hair.

There will not be any, any,
That can use the words so many,
Or make speech so long as mine when I am big;
And for my songs I'll borrow
Uncle Pablo's good *guitarra.*—
But now I have to go and feed the pig.

CURIOUS SOMETHING

Winifred Welles

If I could smell smells with my ears,
    If sounds came buzzing in my nose,
If in my lips were looks and tears,
    Tongues in my eyes, do you suppose
        That I should have this kind of face,
        Or something curious in its place?

PHIZZOG

Carl Sandburg

This face you got,
This here phizzog you carry around,
You never picked it out for yourself, at all, at all
        —did you?
This here phizzog—somebody handed it to you
        —am I right?
Somebody said, "Here's yours, now go see what
        you can do with it."
Somebody slipped it to you and it was like a
        package marked:
"No goods exchanged after being taken away"—
This face you got.

THE TWINS

Henry Sambrooke Leigh

In form and feature, face and limb,
    I grew so like my brother
That folks got taking me for him
    And each for one another.
It puzzled all our kith and kin,
    It reach'd an awful pitch;
For one of us was born a twin
    And not a soul knew which.

One day (to make the matter worse),
    Before our names were fix'd,
As we were being wash'd by nurse,
    We got completely mix'd.
And thus, you see, by Fate's decree,
    (Or rather nurse's whim),
My brother John got christen'd *me,*
    And I got christen'd *him.*

This fatal likeness even dogg'd
    My footsteps when at school,
And I was always getting flogg'd—
    For John turn'd out a fool.
I put this question hopelessly
    To every one I knew,—

"Ambition." From *The Songs of Marcelino* by Edith Agnew. Ward Anderson Printing Company, Albuquerque, New Mexico, 1940. Used by permission of the author
"Curious Something." From *Skipping Along Alone* by Winifred Welles. The Macmillan Company, New York,
1931. Used by permission of James Welles Shearer
"Phizzog." From *Early Moon* by Carl Sandburg, copyright, 1930, by Harcourt, Brace and Company, Inc.
"Felicia Ropps." *Have you met her? And have you any other candidates for Goopdom? Maybe people who won't*

What *would* you do, if you were me,
  To prove that you were *you?*

Our close resemblance turn'd the tide
  Of my domestic life;
For somehow my intended bride
  Became my brother's wife.
In short, year after year the same
  Absurd mistake went on;
And when I died—the neighbors came
  And buried brother John!

FELICIA ROPPS
Gelett Burgess

Funny, how Felicia Ropps
Always handles things in shops!
Always pinching, always poking,
Always feeling, always stroking
Things she has no right to touch!
Goops like that annoy me much!

MRS. SNIPKIN AND MRS. WOBBLECHIN
Laura E. Richards

Skinny Mrs. Snipkin,
  With her little pipkin,
Sat by the fireside a-warming of her toes.
Fat Mrs. Wobblechin,
  With her little doublechin,
Sat by the window a-cooling of her nose.

Says this one to that one,
  "Oh! you silly fat one,
Will you shut the window down? You're freezing
  me to death!"

Says that one to t' other one,
  "Good gracious, how you bother one!
There isn't air enough for me to draw my pre-
  cious breath!"

Skinny Mrs. Snipkin,
  Took her little pipkin,
Threw it straight across the room as hard as she
  could throw;
  Hit Mrs. Wobblechin
  On her little doublechin,
And out of the window a-tumble she did go.

GOING TOO FAR
Mildred Howells

A woman who lived in Holland, of old,
Polished her brass till it shone like gold.
She washed her pig after all his meals
In spite of his energetic squeals.
She scrubbed her doorstep into the ground,
And the children's faces, pink and round,
She washed so hard that in several cases
She polished their features off their faces—
Which gave them an odd appearance, though
She thought they were really neater so!
Then her passion for cleaning quickly grew,
And she scrubbed and polished the village
  through,
Until, to the rage of all the people,
She cleaned the weather-vane off the steeple.
As she looked at the sky one summer's night
She thought that the stars shone out less bright;
And she said with a sigh, "If I were there,
I'd rub them up till the world should stare."
That night a storm began to brew,
And a wind from the ocean blew and blew
Till, when she came to her door next day
It whisked her up, and blew her away—
Up and up in the air so high
That she vanished, at last, in the stormy sky.
Since then it's said that each twinkling star
And the big white moon, shine brighter far.
But the neighbors shake their heads in fear
She may rub so hard they will disappear!

*wait in line or who talk during a movie or—well, you
name some.* From *Goop Directory* by Gelett Burgess. J. B.
Lippincott, New York, 1913. Used by permission of the
author
  "Mrs. Snipkin and Mrs. Wobblechin." From *Tirra Lirra*
by Laura E. Richards. Little, Brown & Company, Boston,
1932
  "Going Too Far." From *St. Nicholas.* Copyright, 1898,
Century Co. Reprinted by permission of Appleton-Century-Crofts, Inc.

MR. PYME

Harry Behn

Once upon a time
Old Mr. Pyme
Lived all alone
Under a stone.

When the rain fell
He rang a bell,
When the sun shined
He laughed and dined

And floated to town
On thistledown,
And what a nice time
Had Mr. Pyme!

JONATHAN BING

Beatrice Curtis Brown

Poor old Jonathan Bing
Went out in his carriage to visit the King,
But everyone pointed and said, "Look at that!
Jonathan Bing has forgotten his hat!"
(He'd forgotten his hat!)

Poor old Jonathan Bing
Went home and put on a new hat for the King,
But up by the palace a soldier said, "Hi!
You can't see the King; you've forgotten your
 tie!"
(He'd forgotten his tie!)

Poor old Jonathan Bing,
He put on a *beautiful* tie for the King,
But when he arrived an Archbishop said, "Ho!
You can't come to court in pyjamas, you know!"

Poor old Jonathan Bing
Went home and addressed a short note to the
 King:

If you please will excuse me
I won't come to tea;
For home's the best place for
All people like me!

OLD QUIN QUEERIBUS

Nancy Byrd Turner

Old Quin Queeribus—
  He loved his garden so,
He wouldn't have a rake around,
  A shovel or a hoe.

For each potato's eyes he bought
  Fine spectacles of gold,
And mufflers for the corn, to keep
  Its ears from getting cold.

On every head of lettuce green—
  What do you think of that?—
And every head of cabbage, too,
  He tied a garden hat.

Old Quin Queeribus—
  He loved his garden so,
He couldn't eat his growing things,
  He only let them grow!

Lewis Carroll

"You are old, Father William," the young man
 said,
  "And your hair has become very white;
And yet you incessantly stand on your head—
  Do you think, at your age, it is right?"

"In my youth," Father William replied to his
 son,
  "I feared it might injure the brain;

"Mr. Pyme." From *The Little Hill*, copyright, 1949, by Harry Behn. Reprinted by permission of Harcourt, Brace and Company, Inc.

"Jonathan Bing." From *Jonathan Bing and Other Verses*

by Beatrice Curtis Brown. Oxford University Press, New York, 1936. Copyright 1936 by Beatrice Curtis Brown. Reprinted by permission of the author

"Old Quin Queeribus." From *Zodiac Town* by Nancy

But, now that I'm perfectly sure I have none,
　　Why, I do it again and again."

"You are old," said the youth, "as I mentioned
　　before.
　　And have grown most uncommonly fat;
Yet you turned a back-somersault in at the
　　door—
　　Pray, what is the reason of that?"

"In my youth," said the sage, as he shook his
　　grey locks,
　　"I kept all my limbs very supple
By the use of this ointment—one shilling the
　　box—
　　Allow me to sell you a couple?"

"You are old," said the youth, "and your jaws are
　　too weak
　　For anything tougher than suet;
Yet you finished the goose, with the bones and
　　the beak—
　　Pray, how did you manage to do it?"

"In my youth," said his father, "I took to the law,
　　And argued each case with my wife;
And the muscular strength, which it gave to my
　　jaw
　　Has lasted the rest of my life."

"You are old," said the youth, "one would hardly
　　suppose
　　That your eye was as steady as ever;
Yet you balanced an eel on the end of your
　　nose—
　　What made you so awfully clever?"

"I have answered three questions, and that is
　　enough,"
　　Said his father. "Don't give yourself airs!
Do you think I can listen all day to such stuff?
　　Be off, or I'll kick you down-stairs!"

Byrd Turner. By permission of Little, Brown & Co.
　"The Pirate Don Durk of Dowdee." *Here is another
name concocted out of a delightful combination of con-*

THE PIRATE DON DURK OF DOWDEE

Mildred Plew Meigs

Ho, for the Pirate Don Durk of Dowdee!
He was as wicked as wicked could be,
But oh, he was perfectly gorgeous to see!
　　The Pirate Don Durk of Dowdee.

His conscience, of course, was as black as a bat,
But he had a floppety plume on his hat
And when he went walking it jiggled—like that!
　　The plume of the Pirate Dowdee.

His coat it was crimson and cut with a slash,
And often as ever he twirled his mustache
Deep down in the ocean the mermaids went
　　splash,
　　Because of Don Durk of Dowdee.

Moreover, Dowdee had a purple tattoo,
And stuck in his belt where he buckled it through
Were a dagger, a dirk and a squizzamaroo,
　　For fierce was the Pirate Dowdee.

So fearful he was he would shoot at a puff,
And always at sea when the weather grew rough
He drank from a bottle and wrote on his cuff,
　　Did Pirate Don Durk of Dowdee.

sonants. Do you think of any others? From *Child Life,*
March 1923. Child Life, Inc., Boston. By permission of
Marion Plew Ruckel

Oh, he had a cutlass that swung at his thigh
And he had a parrot called Pepperkin Pye,
And a zigzaggy scar at the end of his eye
   Had Pirate Don Durk of Dowdee.

He kept in a cavern, this buccaneer bold,
A curious chest that was covered with mould,
And all of his pockets were jingly with gold!
   Oh jing! went the gold of Dowdee.

His conscience, of course, it was crook'd like a
   squash,
But both of his boots made a slickery slosh,
And he went through the world with a wonder-
   ful swash,
   Did Pirate Don Durk of Dowdee.

It's true he was wicked as wicked could be,
His sins they outnumbered a hundred and three,
But oh, he was perfectly gorgeous to see,
   The Pirate Don Durk of Dowdee.

THE JUMBLIES

Edward Lear

They went to sea in a sieve, they did;
   In a sieve they went to sea:
In spite of all their friends could say,
On a winter's morn, on a stormy day,
   In a sieve they went to sea.
And when the sieve turned round and round,
And every one cried, "You'll all be drowned!"
They called aloud, "Our sieve ain't big;
But we don't care a button, we don't care a fig:
   In a sieve we'll go to sea!"
    Far and few, far and few,
      Are the lands where the Jumblies live:
    Their heads are green, and their hands are
      blue;
    And they went to sea in a sieve.

They sailed away in a sieve, they did,
   In a sieve they sailed so fast,
With only a beautiful pea-green veil
Tied with a ribbon, by way of a sail,

"The Jumblies." *These outrageous Jumblies are annoying because they do things they shouldn't do and come
through all right.*

To a small tobacco-pipe mast.
And every one said who saw them go,
"Oh! won't they be soon upset, you know?
For the sky is dark, and the voyage is long;
And, happen what may, it's extremely wrong
   In a sieve to sail so fast."
    Far and few, far and few,
      Are the lands where the Jumblies live:
    Their heads are green, and their hands are
      blue;
    And they went to sea in a sieve.

The water it soon came in, it did;
   The water it soon came in:
So, to keep them dry, they wrapped their feet
In a pinky paper all folded neat;
   And they fastened it down with a pin.
And they passed the night in a crockery-jar;
And each of them said, "How wise we are!
Though the sky be dark, and the voyage be long,
Yet we never can think we were rash or wrong,
   While round in our sieve we spin."
    Far and few, far and few,
      Are the lands where the Jumblies live:
    Their heads are green, and their hands are
      blue;
    And they went to sea in a sieve.

And all night long they sailed away;
   And when the sun went down,
They whistled and warbled a moony song,
To the echoing sound of a coppery gong,
   In the shade of the mountains brown.
"O Timballoo! How happy we are
When we live in a sieve and a crockery-jar!
And all night long, in the moonlight pale,
We sail away with a pea-green sail
   In the shade of the mountains brown."
    Far and few, far and few,
      Are the lands where the Jumblies live:
    Their heads are green, and their hands are
      blue;
    And they went to sea in a sieve.

They sailed to the Western Sea, they did,—
   To a land all covered with trees:
And they bought an owl, and a useful cart,
And a pound of rice, and a cranberry-tart,
   And a hive of silvery bees;

And they bought a pig, and some green jackdaws,
And a lovely monkey with lollipop paws,
And forty bottles of ring-bo-ree,
    And no end of Stilton cheese.
      Far and few, far and few,
        Are the lands where the Jumblies live:
        Their heads are green, and their hands are
          blue;
          And they went to sea in a sieve.

And in twenty years they all came back,—
   In twenty years or more;
And every one said, "How tall they've grown!

For they've been to the Lakes, and the Torrible
    Zone,
    And the hills of the Chankly Bore."
And they drank their health, and gave them a
    feast
Of dumplings made of beautiful yeast;
And every one said, "If we only live,
We, too, will go to sea in a sieve,
    To the hills of the Chankly Bore."
      Far and few, far and few,
        Are the lands where the Jumblies live:
        Their heads are green, and their hands are
          blue;
          And they went to sea in a sieve.

FAIRIES

Hilda Conkling

I cannot see fairies.
I dream them.
There is no fairy can hide from me;
I keep on dreaming till I find him:
There you are, Primrose! I see you, Black Wing!

HAVE YOU WATCHED THE FAIRIES?

Rose Fyleman

Have you watched the fairies when the rain is
    done
Spreading out their little wings to dry them in
    the sun?
  I have, I have! Isn't it fun?

Have you heard the fairies all among the limes
Singing little fairy tunes to little fairy rhymes?
  I have, I have, lots and lots of times!

Have you seen the fairies dancing in the air,
And dashing off behind the stars to tidy up their
    hair?
  I have, I have; I've been there!

MAGIC AND MAKE BELIEVE

I KEEP THREE WISHES READY

Annette Wynne

I keep three wishes ready,
Lest I should chance to meet,
Any day a fairy
Coming down the street.

I'd hate to have to stammer,
Or have to think them out,
For it's very hard to think things up
When a fairy is about.

And I'd hate to lose my wishes,
For fairies fly away,
And perhaps I'd never have a chance
On any other day.

So I keep three wishes ready,
Lest I should chance to meet,
Any day a fairy
Coming down the street.

COULD IT HAVE BEEN A SHADOW?

Monica Shannon

What ran under the rosebush?
    What ran under the stone?
Could it have been a shadow,
    Running away alone?
Maybe a fairy's shadow,
    Slipping away at dawn
To guard a gleaming pot of gold
    For a busy leprechaun.

THE BEST GAME THE FAIRIES PLAY

Rose Fyleman

The best game the fairies play,
    The best game of all,
Is sliding down steeples—
    (You know they're very tall.)
You fly to the weathercock,
    And when you hear it crow
You fold your wings and clutch your things
    And then let go!

They have a million other games—
    Cloud-catching's one,
And mud-mixing after rain
    Is heaps and heaps of fun;
But when you go and stay with them
    Never mind the rest,
Take my advice—they're very nice,
    But steeple-sliding's best!

YESTERDAY IN OXFORD STREET

Rose Fyleman

Yesterday in Oxford Street, oh, what d'you think,
    my dears?
I had the most exciting time I've had for years
    and years;
The buildings looked so straight and tall, the sky
    was blue between,
And, riding on a motor-bus, I saw the fairy
    queen!

Sitting there upon the rail and bobbing up and
    down,
The sun was shining on her wings and on her
    golden crown;
And looking at the shops she was, the pretty silks
    and lace—
She seemed to think that Oxford Street was quite
    a lovely place.

And once she turned and looked at me, and
    waved her little hand;
But I could only stare and stare—oh, would she
    understand?
I simply couldn't speak at all, I simply couldn't
    stir,
And all the rest of Oxford Street was just a shin-
    ing blur.

Then suddenly she shook her wings—a bird had
    fluttered by—
And down into the street she looked and up into
    the sky;
And perching on the railing on a tiny fairy
    toe,
She flashed away so quickly that I hardly saw
    her go.

I never saw her any more, altho' I looked all
    day;
Perhaps she only came to peep, and never meant
    to stay:
But oh, my dears, just think of it, just think what
    luck for me,
That she should come to Oxford Street, and I be
    there to see!

FOR A MOCKING VOICE

Eleanor Farjeon

Who   calls?   Who   calls?   Who?
Did you call?   Did you?—
I call!   I call!   I!
Follow where I fly.—
Where?   O where?   O where?
On Earth or in the Air?—
Where you come, I'm gone!
Where you fly, I've flown!—
Stay! ah, stay! ah, stay,
Pretty Elf, and play!
Tell me where you are—
Ha, ha, ha, ha, ha!

"For a Mocking Voice." From *Collection of Poems* by
Eleanor Farjeon. Copyright 1929, 1957 by Eleanor Farjeon.
Published by J. B. Lippincott Company, Philadelphia
  "When a Ring's Around the Moon." From *Top of the*

WHEN A RING'S AROUND THE MOON

Mary Jane Carr

The wee folk will be tripping,
   In their silver dancing shoon,
Ring-around-the-meadow,
   When a ring's around the moon:

Curtsy to the right and left,
   And curtsy to the middle—
The fiddler will be fiddling
   On his tiny fairy fiddle;

In and out and round about,
   A magic circle making;
The pipers will be piping
   Till their tiny throats are aching.

Oh, few may watch the wee ones dance,
   For fairy guards are spying,
And down beneath the grasses
   All the dancers will be hieing;

But hearken well, what time you see
   A ring around the moon;
And you will hear the music
   Of the wee folks' dancing tune.

MIDSUMMER MAGIC

Ivy O. Eastwick

Midsummer Eve, a year ago, my mother she com-
    manded,
"Now don't you go a'running down to Ragwort
    Meadow!
And don't you go a'plucking of the bracken-seed
    or nightshade;
Stay out of the moonlight, mind! and keep out of
    the shadow,
   For they say that the Ragtag,
                  Bobtail,
                   Merry-derry
                   Fairy-men
Tonight will go a'dancing down in Ragwort
    Meadow!"

Morning by Mary Jane Carr. Copyright 1941, by Mary
Jane Carr
  "Midsummer Magic." *When this child forgot her moth-
er's commands and went to find the fairies, she heard*

Midsummer Eve, a year ago, my mother she com-
    manded,
"Now don't you go a'playing down in Ragwort
    Meadow!
Keep away from thorn-tree, from adders' tongue
    and henbane!
Keep away from moonlight and don't venture in
    the shadow,
    For they say that the Ragtag,
                Bobtail,
                Merry-derry
                Fairy-men
Are out a'snaring mortals down in Ragwort
    Meadow."

I wouldn't heed my mother's words! I wouldn't
    heed her warning!
I ran through the moonlight, through the star-
    light and the shadow!
And I never stopped a'running though my
    breath came quick and gasping,
Till I reached the very middle of Ragwort
    Meadow,
    And there I heard the Ragtag,
                Bobtail,
                Merry-derry
                Fairy-men
A'laughing fit to kill themselves in Ragwort
    Meadow.

I heard 'em! But I couldn't see, no! not a little
    sight of 'em!
I pulled a curly bracken-leaf a'growing in the
    meadow,
I scratched out all the bracken-seeds and rubbed
    them on my eyelids—
The moon gave brilliant sunlight! There wasn't
    any shadow!
    And there I saw the Ragtag,
                Bobtail,
                Merry-derry
                Fairy-men
A'dancing round me in a ring in Ragwort
    Meadow.

*their laughter but could not see them until she rubbed her
eyes with "bracken" seed. That is fern seed and is supposed to have magic power like the other flowers and trees
the mother mentions. Taken from Fairies and Suchlike, by*

Half-a-hundred fairy-men and half-a-score of rab-
    bits;
Half-a-dozen squirrels down in Ragwort Meadow,
Dancing round me in a ring—you never saw the
    like of it!—
Underneath the daylight which the bright moon
    shed! Oh!
    A blessing on the Ragtag,
                Bobtail,
                Merry-derry
                Fairy-men
Who showed themselves to me down in Ragwort
    Meadow.

CRAB-APPLE
Ethel Talbot

I dreamed the Fairies wanted me
    To spend my birth-night with them all;
And I said, "Oh, but you're so wee
    And I am so tremendous tall,
What could we do?"
    "Crab-apple stem!"
Said they, and I was just like them.

And then, when we were all the same,
    The party and the fun began;
They said they'd teach me a new game
    Of "Dew-ponds." "I don't think I can
Play that," I said.
    "Crab-apple blue!"
Said they, and I could play it too.

And then, when we had played and played,
    The Fairies said that we would dance;
And I said, "Oh, but I'm afraid
    That I've no shoes." I gave a glance
At my bare toes.
    "Crab-apple sweet!"
Said they, and shoes were on my feet.

And then we danced away, away,
    Until my birth-night all was done;

Ivy O. Eastwick, published and copyright, 1946, by E. P.
Dutton & Co., Inc., New York
    "Crab-Apple." *Oh, what a dream!* From *Punch*. Repro-
duced by permission of the Proprietors of *Punch*

And I said, "I'll go home to-day;
    And thank you for my lovely fun,
I'll come again."
    "Crab-apple red!"
Said they, and I woke up in bed.

STOCKING FAIRY

Winifred Welles

In a hole of the heel of an old brown stocking,
A little old Fairy sits rocking and rocking,
And scolding and pointing and squeaking and
    squinting,
Brown as a nut, a bright eye glinting,
She tugs at a thread, she drags up a needle,
She stamps and she shrills, she commences to
    wheedle,
To whine of the cold, in a fine gust of temper
She beats on my thumb, and then with a whim-
    per
She sulks in her shawl, she says I've forgotten
I promised to make her a lattice of cotton,
A soft, woven window, cozy yet airy,
Where she could sit rocking and peeking—Hush,
    Fairy,
Tush, Fairy, sit gently, look sweetly,
I'll do what I said, now, and close you in neatly.

THE PLUMPUPPETS

Christopher Morley

When little heads weary have gone to their bed,
When all the good nights and the prayers have
    been said,
Of all the good fairies that send bairns to rest
The little Plumpuppets are those I love best.

"Stocking Fairy." *The staccato thud of these words creates the picture of this cross, crabby old fairy as much as
the words themselves. After all her scolding, notice the
quiet, soothing ending.* From *Skipping Along Alone* by
Winifred Welles. The Macmillan Company, New York,
1931. Used by permission of James Welles Shearer

If your pillow is lumpy, or hot, thin and flat,
The little Plumpuppets know just what
    they're at;
They plump up the pillow, all soft, cool and
    fat—
    The little Plumpuppets plump-up it!

The little Plumpuppets are fairies of beds:
They have nothing to do but to watch sleepy
    heads;
They turn down the sheets and they tuck you in
    tight,
And they dance on your pillow to wish you good
    night!

No matter what troubles have bothered the day,
Though your doll broke her arm or the pup ran
    away;
Though your handies are black with the ink that
    was spilt—
Plumpuppets are waiting in blanket and quilt.

If your pillow is lumpy, or hot, thin and flat,
The little Plumpuppets know just what
    they're at;
They plump up the pillow, all soft, cool and
    fat—
    The little Plumpuppets plump-up it!

THE ROCK-A-BY LADY

Eugene Field

The Rock-a-By Lady from Hushaby street
    Comes stealing; comes creeping;
The poppies they hang from her head to her feet,
And each hath a dream that is tiny and fleet—
She bringeth her poppies to you, my sweet,
    When she findeth you sleeping!

There is one little dream of a beautiful drum—
    "Rub-a-dub!" it goeth;
There is one little dream of a big sugar-plum,
And lo! thick and fast the other dreams come

"The Plumpuppets." From *The Rocking Horse*. Copy-
right 1918, 1946 by Christopher Morley. Published by J. B.
Lippincott Company
"The Rock-a-By Lady." From *Poems of Childhood* by
Eugene Field. Charles Scribner's Sons, New York, 1904

Of popguns that bang, and tin tops that hum,
    And a trumpet that bloweth!

And dollies peep out of those wee little dreams
    With laughter and singing;
And boats go a-floating on silvery streams,
And the stars peek-a-boo with their own misty
        gleams,
And up, up, and up, where the Mother Moon
        beams,
    The fairies go winging!

Would you dream all these dreams that are tiny
        and fleet?
    They'll come to you sleeping;
So shut the two eyes that are weary, my sweet,
For the Rock-a-By Lady from Hushaby street,
With poppies that hang from her head to her
        feet,
    Comes stealing; comes creeping.

THE HORSEMAN
Walter de la Mare

I heard a horseman
    Ride over the hill;
The moon shone clear,
    The night was still;
His helm was silver,
    And pale was he;
And the horse he rode
    Was of ivory.

KIPH
Walter de la Mare

My Uncle Ben, who's been
To Bisk, Bhir, Biak—
Been, and come back:
To Tab, Tau, Tze, and Tomsk,
And home, by Teneriffe:
Who, brown as desert sand,
Gaunt, staring, slow and stiff,
Has chased the Unicorn
And Hippogriff,
Gave me a smooth, small, shining stone,
Called *Kiph*.

"The Horseman" and "Kiph." From *Rhymes and Verses* by Walter de la Mare. Published by Henry Holt & Company, Inc., New York, 1947. By permission of the literary trustees of Walter de la Mare and The Society of

"Look'ee, now, Nevvy mine,"
He told me—"*If*
You'd wish a wish,
Just rub this smooth, small, shining stone,
Called *Kiph*."

Hide it did I,
In a safe, secret spot;
Slept, and the place
In dreams forgot.

One wish *alone*
Now's mine: Oh, if
I could but find again
That stone called *Kiph!*

THE GNOME
Harry Behn

I saw a gnome
As plain as plain
Sitting on top
Of a weathervane.

He was dressed like a crow
In silky black feathers,
And there he sat watching
All kinds of weathers.

He talked like a crow too,
Caw caw caw,
When he told me exactly
What he saw,

Snow to the north of him
Sun to the south,
And he spoke with a beaky
Kind of a mouth.

But he wasn't a crow,
That was plain as plain
'Cause crows never sit
On a weathervane.

What I saw was simply
A usual gnome
Looking things over
On his way home.

Authors, London, as their representatives
"The Gnome." From *Windy Morning* by Harry Behn. Copyright 1953 by Harry Behn. Reprinted by permission of Harcourt, Brace and Company, Inc., New York

THE GOBLIN

(French)

Rose Fyleman

A goblin lives in *our* house, in *our* house, in *our*
  house,
A goblin lives in *our* house all the year round.
He bumps
And he jumps
And he thumps
And he stumps.
He knocks
And he rocks
And he rattles at the locks.
A goblin lives in *our* house, in *our* house, in *our*
  house,
A goblin lives in *our* house all the year round.

A GOBLINADE

Florence Page Jaques

A green hobgoblin,
  Small but quick,
Went out walking
  With a black thorn stick.

He was full of mischief,
  Full of glee.
He frightened all
  That he could see.

He saw a little maiden
  In a wood.
He looked as fierce as
  A goblin should.

He crept by the hedge row,
  He said, "Boo!"
"Boo!" laughed the little girl,
  "How are you?"

"What!" said the goblin,
  "Aren't you afraid?"
"I think you're funny,"
  Said the maid.

"Ha!" said the goblin,
  Sitting down flat.
"You think I'm funny?
  I don't like that.

"I'm very frightening.
  You should flee!"
"You're cunning," she said,
  "As you can be!"

Then she laughed again, and
  Went away.
But the goblin stood there
  All that day.

A beetle came by, and
  "Well?" it said.
But the goblin only
  Shook his head.

"For I am funny,"
  He said to it.
"I thought I was alarming,
  And I'm not a bit.

"If I'm amusing,"
  He said to himself,
"I won't be a goblin,
  I'll be an elf!

"For a goblin must be goblin
  All the day,
But an elf need only
  Dance and play."

So the little green goblin
  Became an elf.
And he dances all day, and
  He likes himself.

"The Goblin." *The words suggest in their sound the awkward, thumping movements of the goblin. For verse choir see May Hill Arbuthnot,* Children and Books, *p. 215.* From Picture Rhymes from Foreign Lands. Copyright 1935 by Rose Fyleman. Reprinted by permission of J. B. Lippincott Company

"A Goblinade." From Child Life, October 1927. Child Life, Inc., Boston. By permission of the author

"Overheard on a Saltmarsh." *Here is a long conversation between a nymph and a goblin with never a "he said" or*

OVERHEARD ON A SALTMARSH

Harold Monro

Nymph, nymph, what are your beads?

Green glass, goblin. Why do you stare at them?

Give them me.

> No.

Give them me. Give them me.

> No.

Then I will howl all night in the reeds,
Lie in the mud and howl for them.

Goblin, why do you love them so?

They are better than stars or water,
Better than voices of winds that sing,
Better than any man's fair daughter,
Your green glass beads on a silver ring.

Hush, I stole them out of the moon.

Give me your beads, I desire them.

> No.

I will howl in a deep lagoon
For your green glass beads, I love them so.
Give them me. Give them.

> No.

THE LITTLE ELFMAN

John Kendrick Bangs

I met a little Elfman once,
 Down where the lilies blow.
I asked him why he was so small,
 And why he didn't grow.

He slightly frowned, and with his eye
 He looked me through and through—
"I'm just as big for me," said he,
 "As you are big for you!"

THE ELF AND THE DORMOUSE

Oliver Herford

Under a toadstool
 Crept a wee Elf,
Out of the rain
 To shelter himself.

Under the toadstool,
 Sound asleep,
Sat a big Dormouse
 All in a heap.

Trembled the wee Elf,
 Frightened, and yet
Fearing to fly away
 Lest he get wet.

To the next shelter—
 Maybe a mile!
Sudden the wee Elf
 Smiled a wee smile,

"she said" to tell you who is speaking. Yet if you read it aloud it is perfectly clear and a delightful poem for verse choirs or individual reading. From Children of Love by Harold Monro. The Poetry Bookshop, London, 1913. Used by permission of Alida Monro

"The Little Elfman." By permission of Mary Gray Bangs for the Estate of John Kendrick Bangs
"The Elf and the Dormouse." From *Artful Anticks* by Oliver Herford. Reprinted by permission of Appleton-Century-Crofts, Inc.

Tugged till the toadstool
   Toppled in two.
Holding it over him
   Gaily he flew.

Soon he was safe home
   Dry as could be.
Soon woke the Dormouse—
   "Good gracious me!

Where is my toadstool?"
   Loud he lamented.
—And that's how umbrellas
   First were invented.

HOW TO TELL GOBLINS FROM ELVES

Monica Shannon

The Goblin has a wider mouth
   Than any wondering elf.
The saddest part of this is that
   He brings it on himself.
For hanging in a willow clump
   In baskets made of sheaves,
You may see the baby goblins
   Under coverlets of leaves.

They suck a pink and podgy foot,
   (As human babies do),
And then they suck the other one,
   Until they're sucking two.
And so it is that goblins' mouths
   Keep growing very round.
So you can't mistake a goblin,
   When a goblin you have found.

THE MAN WHO HID HIS OWN FRONT DOOR

Elizabeth MacKinstry

There was a little, Elvish man
   Who lived beside a moor,

A shy, secretive, furtive soul
   Who hid his own front door.

He went and hid his door beneath
   A pink laburnum bush:
The neighbors saw the curtains blow,
   They heard a singing thrush.

The Banker came and jingled gold,
   It did not serve him there;
The honey-colored walls uprose
   Unbroken and foresquare.

The Mayor called, the Misses Pitt
   With cordials and game pie;
There was not any door at all,
   They had to pass him by!

But ah! my little sister.
   Her eyes were wild and sweet,
She wore blue faded calico,
   And no shoes on her feet.

She found the wandering door in place
   And easily went through
Into a strange and mossy Hall
   Where bowls of old Delft blue

Held feasts of blackberries, like gems
   In webs of shining dew—
There stood that little Elvish man
   And smiled to see her, too!

(*Mother Goose*)

I had a little nut tree, nothing would it bear
   But a silver nutmeg and a golden pear;
   The king of Spain's daughter came to visit me,
And all for the sake of my little nut tree.
   I skipped over water, I danced over sea,
   And all the birds in the air couldn't catch me.

SLEEPYHEAD

Walter de la Mare

As I lay awake in the white moonlight,
I heard a faint singing in the wood,
  "Out of bed,
  Sleepyhead,
  Put your white foot now,
  Here are we,
  Neath the tree
  Singing round the root now!"

I looked out of window, in the white moonlight,
The trees were like snow in the wood—
  "Come away,
  Child, and play
  Light with the gnomies;
  In a mound,
  Green and round,
  That's where their home is.

  "Honey sweet,
  Curds to eat,
  Cream and fruménty,
  Shells and beads,
  Poppy seeds,
  You shall have plenty."

But soon as I stooped in the dim moonlight
To put on my stocking and my shoe,
The sweet, sweet singing died sadly away,
And the light of the morning peeped through:
Then instead of the gnomies there came a red
  robin
To sing of the buttercups and dew.

SOME ONE

Walter de la Mare

  Some one came knocking
    At my wee, small door;
  Some one came knocking,
    I'm sure—sure—sure;

"Some One." *This is as hushed as the mystery it describes. And who or what was it, do you think?* From *Collected Poems, 1901–1918,* by Walter de la Mare. Copyright, 1920, by Henry Holt and Company, Inc. Copyright, 1948, by Walter de la Mare. Reprinted by permission of the publishers

  I listened, I opened,
    I looked to left and right,
  But nought there was a-stirring
    In the still dark night;
  Only the busy beetle
    Tap-tapping in the wall,
  Only from the forest
    The screech-owl's call,
  Only the cricket whistling
    While the dew drops fall,
  So I know not who came knocking,
    At all, at all, at all.

William Shakespeare

  Where the bee sucks, there suck I:
  In a cowslip's bell I lie;
  There I couch when owls do cry.
  On the bat's back I do fly
  After summer merrily.
 Merrily, merrily, shall I live now
 Under the blossom that hangs on the bough.

THE BAGPIPE MAN

Nancy Byrd Turner

The bagpipe man came over our hill
  When no one knew he was anywhere round,
With a whirl and a skirl, a toot and a trill;
  And we all went scampering after the sound.
We cried, "Oh, tell us, what do you play?
  What do you play so queer, so queer?"
And he skipped a couple of notes to say,
  "But tell me, what do ye hear?"
Then one of us heard a trumpet sweet,
  And the tramp, tramp, tramp of marching
    men;
And one of us heard the dancing feet
  Of fairies down in a dusky glen;
And one of us called it a bird in June,
  And one, a river that ran and ran.
But he never would tell us the name of his tune,
  The funny old bagpipe man!

"Where the bee sucks, there suck I." From *The Tempest,* Act V, Sc. 1

"The Bagpipe Man." From *Magpie Lane* by Nancy Byrd Turner, copyright, 1927, by Harcourt, Brace and Company, Inc.

THE BALLAD OF
THE HARP-WEAVER

Edna St. Vincent Millay

"Son," said my mother,
  When I was knee-high,
"You've need of clothes to cover you,
  And not a rag have I.

"There's nothing in the house
  To make a boy breeches,
Nor shears to cut a cloth with
  Nor thread to take stitches.

"There's nothing in the house
  But a loaf-end of rye,
And a harp with a woman's head
  Nobody will buy,"
  And she began to cry.

That was in the early fall.
  When came the late fall,
"Son," she said, "the sight of you
  Makes your mother's blood crawl,—

"Little skinny shoulder-blades
  Sticking through your clothes!
And where you'll get a jacket from
  God above knows.

"It's lucky for me, lad,
  Your daddy's in the ground,
And can't see the way I let
  His son go around!"
  And she made a queer sound.

That was in the late fall.
  When the winter came,
I'd not a pair of breeches
  Nor a shirt to my name.

I couldn't go to school,
  Or out of doors to play.
And all the other little boys
  Passed our way.

"Son," said my mother,
  "Come, climb into my lap,
And I'll chafe your little bones
  While you take a nap."

And, oh, but we were silly
  For half an hour or more,
Me with my long legs
  Dragging on the floor,

A-rock-rock-rocking
  To a mother-goose rhyme!
Oh, but we were happy
  For half an hour's time!

But there was I, a great boy,
  And what would folks say
To hear my mother singing me
  To sleep all day,
  In such a daft way?

Men say the winter
  Was bad that year;
Fuel was scarce,
  And food was dear.

A wind with a wolf's head
  Howled about our door,
And we burned up the chairs
  And sat upon the floor.

All that was left us
  Was a chair we couldn't break,
And the harp with a woman's head
  Nobody would take,
  For song or pity's sake.

The night before Christmas
  I cried with the cold,
I cried myself to sleep
  Like a two-year-old.

And in the deep night
  I felt my mother rise,
And stare down upon me
  With love in her eyes.

I saw my mother sitting
  On the one good chair,
A light falling on her
  From I couldn't tell where,

Looking nineteen,
   And not a day older,
And the harp with a woman's head
   Leaned against her shoulder.

Her thin fingers, moving
   In the thin, tall strings,
Were weav-weav-weaving
   Wonderful things.

Many bright threads,
   From where I couldn't see,
Were running through the harp-strings
   Rapidly,

And gold threads whistling
   Through my mother's hand.
I saw the web grow,
   And the pattern expand.

She wove a child's jacket,
   And when it was done
She laid it on the floor
   And wove another one.

She wove a red cloak
   So regal to see,
"She's made it for a king's son,"
   I said, "and not for me."
But I knew it was for me.

She wove a pair of breeches
   Quicker than that!
She wove a pair of boots
   And a little cocked hat.

She wove a pair of mittens,
   She wove a little blouse,
She wove all night
   In the still, cold house.

She sang as she worked,
   And the harp-strings spoke;
Her voice never faltered,
   And the thread never broke.
   And when I awoke,—

There sat my mother
   With the harp against her shoulder,
Looking nineteen
   And not a day older,

A smile about her lips,
   And a light about her head,
And her hands in the harp-strings
   Frozen dead.

And piled up beside her
   And toppling to the skies,
Were the clothes of a king's son,
   Just my size.

TILLIE

Walter de la Mare

Old Tillie Turveycombe
Sat to sew,
Just where a patch of fern did grow;
There, as she yawned,
And yawn wide did she,
Floated some seed
Down her gull-e-t;
And look you once,
And look you twice,
Poor old Tillie
Was gone in a trice.
But oh, when the wind
Do a-moaning come,
'Tis poor old Tillie
Sick for home;
And oh, when a voice
In the mist do sigh,
Old Tillie Turveycombe's
Floating by.

BERRIES

Walter de la Mare

There was an old woman
   Went blackberry picking
Along the hedges
   From Weep to Wicking.
Half a pottle—
   No more she had got,
When out steps a Fairy
   From her green grot;

And says, "Well, Jill,
   Would 'ee pick 'ee mo?"
And Jill, she curtseys,
   And looks just so.
"Be off," says the Fairy,
   "As quick as you can,
Over the meadows
   To the little green lane,
That dips to the hayfields
   Of Farmer Grimes:
I've berried those hedges
   A score of times;
Bushel on bushel
   I'll promise 'ee, Jill,
This side of supper
   If 'ee pick with a will."
She glints very bright,
   And speaks her fair;
Then lo, and behold!
   She had faded in air.

Be sure Old Goodie
   She trots betimes
Over the meadows
   To Farmer Grimes.
And never was queen
   With jewellery rich
As those same hedges
   From twig to ditch;
Like Dutchmen's coffers,
   Fruit, thorn, and flower—

They shone like William
   And Mary's bower.
And be sure Old Goodie
   Went back to Weep
So tired with her basket
   She scarce could creep.

When she comes in the dusk
   To her cottage door,
There's Towser wagging
   As never before,
To see his Missus
   So glad to be
Come from her fruit-picking
   Back to he.
As soon as next morning
   Dawn was grey,
The pot on the hob
   Was simmering away;
And all in a stew
   And a hugger-mugger
Towser and Jill
   A-boiling of sugar,
And the dark clear fruit
   That from Faërie came,
For syrup and jelly
   And blackberry jam.

Twelve jolly gallipots
   Jill put by;
And one little teeny one,
   One inch high;
And that she's hidden
   A good thumb deep,
Halfway over
   From Wicking to Weep.

"Berries." From *Collected Poems, 1901–1918*, by Walter de la Mare. Copyright, 1920, by Henry Holt and Company, Inc. Copyright, 1948, by Walter de la Mare. Reprinted by permission of the publishers
"Behind the Waterfall." From *Skipping Along Alone* by Winifred Welles. The Macmillan Company, New York, 1931. Used by permission of James Welles Shearer

BEHIND THE WATERFALL
Winifred Welles

A little old woman
   In a thin white shawl,
Stepped straight through the column
   Of the silver waterfall,
As if the fall of water
   Were not anything at all.
I saw her crook her finger,
   I heard her sweetly call.
Over stones all green and glossy
   I fled and did not fall;
I ran along the river
   And through the waterfall,
And that heavy curve of water
   Never hindered me at all.
The little old woman
   In the thin white shawl
Took my hand and laughed and led me
   Down a cool, still hall,
Between two rows of pillars
   That were glistening and tall.
At her finger's tap swung open
   A wide door in the wall,
And I saw the crystal city
   That's behind the waterfall.

THE LITTLE GREEN ORCHARD
Walter de la Mare

Some one is always sitting there,
   In the little green orchard;
Even when the sun is high,
In noon's unclouded sky,
And faintly droning goes
The bee from rose to rose,
Some one in shadow is sitting there,
   In the little green orchard.

Yes, and when twilight's falling softly
   On the little green orchard;

When the grey dew distils
And every flower-cup fills;
When the last blackbird says,
   "What—what!" and goes her way—ssh!
I have heard voices calling softly
   In the little green orchard.

Not that I am afraid of being there,
   In the little green orchard;
Why, when the moon's been bright,
Shedding her lonesome light,
And moths like ghosties come,
And the horned snail leaves home:
I've sat there, whispering and listening there,
   In the little green orchard;

Only it's strange to be feeling there,
   In the little green orchard;
Whether you paint or draw,
Dig, hammer, chop, or saw;
When you are most alone.
All but the silence gone . . .
Some one is waiting and watching there,
   In the little green orchard.

SAM

Walter de la Mare

When Sam goes back in memory,
   It is to where the sea
Breaks on the shingle, emerald-green
   In white foam, endlessly;
He says—with small brown eye on mine—
   "I used to keep awake,
And lean from my window in the moon,

Watching those billows break.
And half a million tiny hands,
   And eyes, like sparks of frost,
Would dance and come tumbling into the moon,
   On every breaker tossed.
And all across from star to star,
   I've seen the watery sea,
With not a single ship in sight,
   Just ocean there, and me;
And heard my father snore . . . And once,
   As sure as I'm alive,
Out of those wallowing, moon-flecked waves
   I saw a mermaid dive;
Head and shoulders above the wave,
   Plain as I now see you,
Combing her hair, now back, now front,
   Her two eyes peeping through;
Calling me, 'Sam!'—quietlike—'Sam!' . . .
   But me . . . I never went,
Making believe I kind of thought
   'Twas someone else she meant . . .
Wonderful lovely there she sat,
   Singing the night away,
All in the solitudinous sea
   Of that there lonely bay.
P'raps," and he'd smooth his hairless mouth,
   "P'raps, if 'twere *now*, my son,
P'raps, if I heard a voice say, 'Sam!' . . .
   Morning would find me gone."

FAITH, I WISH I WERE A LEPRECHAUN

Margaret Ritter

Faith, I wish I were a leprechaun
Beneath a hawthorn tree,
A-cobblin' of wee, magic boots,
A-eatin' luscious, lovely fruits;
Oh, fiddle-dum, oh, fiddle-dee,
I wish I were a leprechaun
Beneath a hawthorn tree!

"Faith, I Wish I Were a Leprechaun." *Do you know the fairy shoemaker, the leprechaun, who has to give you his pot of gold if you can keep your eyes on him? From Mirrors by Margaret Ritter. Copyright 1925 by The Macmillan Company and used with their permission*

Faith, I wish I were a leprechaun
Beneath a hawthorn tree,
A-throwin' snuff into the eyes
Of young and old and dull and wise;
Oh, fiddle-dum, oh, fiddle-dee,
I wish I were a leprechaun
Beneath a hawthorn tree!

Faith, I wish I were a leprechaun
Beneath a hawthorn tree,
With no more irksome thing to do
Than sew a small, bewitchin' shoe;
Oh, fiddle-dum, oh, fiddle-dee,
I wish I were a leprechaun
Beneath a hawthorn tree!

THE UNICORN

Ella Young

While yet the Morning Star
Flamed in the sky
A Unicorn went mincing by,
Whiter by far than blossom of the thorn:
His silver horn
Glittered as he danced and pranced
Silver-pale in the silver-pale morn.

The folk that saw him, ran away.

"The Unicorn." *This poem is sheer music. The picture of the strange, bright fairy creature is beautiful but it is the melody of the lines that will haunt you. From The Horn Book March–April, 1939. The Horn Book Inc., Boston.*

Where he went, so gay, so fleet,
Star-like lilies at his feet
Flowered all day,
Lilies, lilies in a throng,
And the wind made for him a song:

But he dared not stay
Over-long!

INTRODUCTION
to SONGS OF INNOCENCE
William Blake

Piping down the valleys wild,
  Piping songs of pleasant glee,
On a cloud I saw a child,
  And he laughing said to me:

"Pipe a song about a Lamb!"
  So I piped with merry cheer.
"Piper, pipe that song again;"
  So I piped; he wept to hear.

"Drop thy pipe, thy happy pipe;
  Sing thy songs of happy cheer!"
So I sang the same again,
  While he wept with joy to hear.

"Piper, sit thee down and write
  In a book, that all may read."
So he vanished from my sight;
  And I plucked a hollow reed,

And I made a rural pen,
  And I stained the water clear,

And I wrote my happy songs
  Every child may joy to hear.

THE SONG OF
WANDERING AENGUS
William Butler Yeats

I went out to the hazel wood,
Because a fire was in my head,
And cut and peeled a hazel wand,
And hooked a berry to a thread;
And when white moths were on the wing,
And moth-like stars were flickering out,
I dropped a berry in a stream
And caught a little silver trout.

When I had laid it on the floor
I went to blow the fire aflame,
But something rustled on the floor,
And some one called me by my name:
It had become a glimmering girl
With apple blossom in her hair
Who called me by my name and ran
And faded through the brightening air.

Though I am old with wandering
Through hollow lands and hilly lands,
I will find out where she has gone,
And kiss her lips and take her hands;
And walk among long dappled grass,
And pluck till time and times are done
The silver apples of the moon,
The golden apples of the sun.

"Introduction" to Songs of Innocence. *This is Blake's account of how he came to write his poems. His cloud child commanded and he obeyed. It makes a lovely picture to read or to draw.*
  "The Song of Wandering Aengus." From *Poetical Works*

by William Butler Yeats. Copyright 1906, 1934 by The Macmillan Company and used with their permission. By permission also of Mrs. William Butler Yeats and The Macmillan Company of Canada

William Shakespeare

> With hey, ho, the wind and the rain,—
> For the rain—it raineth every day.

WEATHER

Hilda Conkling

> Weather is the answer
> When I can't go out into flowery places;
> Weather is my wonder
> About the kind of morning
> Hidden behind the hills of sky.

WATER

Hilda Conkling

> The world turns softly
> Not to spill its lakes and rivers.
> The water is held in its arms
> And the sky is held in the water.
> What is water,
> That pours silver,
> And can hold the sky?

WIND AND WATER

Kate Greenaway

> Little wind, blow on the hill-top,
> Little wind, blow down the plain;
> Little wind, blow up the sunshine,
> Little wind, blow off the rain.

Blow wind, blow, and go mill, go,
That the miller may grind his corn;
That the baker may take it,
And into bread bake it,
And bring us a loaf in the morn.

WINDY WASH DAY

Dorothy Aldis

The wash is hanging on the line
And the wind's blowing—
Dresses all so clean and fine,
Beckoning
And bowing.

Stockings twisting in a dance,
Pajamas very tripping,
And every little pair of pants
Upside down
And skipping.

A KITE

Unknown

I often sit and wish that I
Could be a kite up in the sky,
And ride upon the breeze and go
Whichever way I chanced to blow.

Christina Georgina Rossetti

Who has seen the wind?
  Neither I nor you:
But when the leaves hang trembling
  The wind is passing thro'.

Who has seen the wind?
  Neither you nor I:
But when the trees bow down their heads
  The wind is passing by.

THE WIND

Robert Louis Stevenson

I saw you toss the kites on high
And blow the birds about the sky;
And all around I heard you pass,
Like ladies' skirts across the grass—
  O wind, a-blowing all day long,
  O wind, that sings so loud a song!

I saw the different things you did,
But always you yourself you hid.
I felt you push, I heard you call,
I could not see yourself at all—
  O wind, a-blowing all day long,
  O wind, that sings so loud a song!

O you that are so strong and cold,
O blower, are you young or old?
Are you a beast of field and tree,
Or just a stronger child than me?
  O wind, a-blowing all day long,
  O wind, that sings so loud a song!

THE KITE

Harry Behn

How bright on the blue
Is a kite when it's new!

With a dive and a dip
It snaps its tail

"With hey, ho, the wind and the rain." From *King Lear*, Act III, Sc. 2
"Weather." From *Poems by a Little Girl* by Hilda Conkling. Copyright 1920 by J. B. Lippincott Company
"Water." From *Poems by a Little Girl* by Hilda Conkling. Copyright 1920 by J. B. Lippincott Company
"Little wind, blow on the hill-top." From *Under the Window* by Kate Greenaway. Frederick Warne and Company, New York and London, 1910
"Blow wind, blow, and go mill, go." *Notice the change in tempo when you come to the third line. The first two are slow and sonorous. The last three trip along briskly because of those staccato consonants. See the introduction, p. xvi, and record album* Poetry Time.

"Windy Wash Day." From *Hop, Skip and Jump* by Dorothy Aldis. Minton, Balch and Company, New York, 1934. Copyright 1934 by Dorothy Aldis
"Who has seen the wind?" From *Sing-Song* by Christina Georgina Rossetti
"The Wind." *This is a favorite wind poem and lends itself to several possible arrangements for choral speaking. See May Hill Arbuthnot,* Children and Books, *p. 215.* From *A Child's Garden of Verses* by Robert Louis Stevenson
"The Kite." From *Windy Morning* by Harry Behn. Copyright 1953 by Harry Behn. Reprinted by permission of Harcourt Brace and Company, Inc., New York

Then soars like a ship
With only a sail

As over tides
Of wind it rides,

Climbs to the crest
Of a gust and pulls,

Then seems to rest
As wind falls.

When string goes slack
You wind it back

And run until
A new breeze blows

And its wings fill
And up it goes!

How bright on the blue
Is a kite when it's new!

But a raggeder thing
You never will see

When it flaps on a string
In the top of a tree.

Unknown

When the winds blow and the seas flow?
Hey, nonny no!

T. Sturge Moore

But hark to the wind how it blows!
None comes, none goes,
None reaps or mows,
No friends turn foes,
No hedge bears sloes,
And no cock crows,
But the wind knows!

WINDY MORNING

Harry Behn

Who minds if the wind whistles and howls
    When sun makes a wall of pleasant light,
Who minds if beyond the wind owls
    Are hooting as if it still were night!

I know the night is somewhere stalking
    Singing birds, and high in tall
Far away air owls are talking,
    But I don't care if they do at all.

Inside a wall of pleasant sun,
    Inside a wall of the wind's noise
My room is still, and there's much to be done
    With paper and paste and trains and toys.

HOLIDAY

Ella Young

Where are you going
Little wind of May-time?

*To the silver-branched wood
For an hour's playtime.*

"But hark to the wind how it blows. . . ." From *Poems* by T. Sturge Moore, Macmillan & Company Ltd., 1931

"Windy Morning." From *Windy Morning* by Harry Behn. Copyright 1953 by Harry Behn. Reprinted by permission of Harcourt, Brace and Company, Inc., New York

"Holiday." *A delightful conversation to be read by two voices perhaps, or two choirs, or just read for sheer pleasure.* Used by permission of the author

O, who'll be in the naked wood
To keep you company?

Ruby-branched and silver-thorned
I'll find a wild rose-tree.

What games will you play,
Little wind?

Any game that chance sends:
I'll run in the tall tree-tops,
And dance at the branch-ends.

Whom will you take for comrade,
Little wind so gaily going?

Anyone who finds the path,
Without my showing.

WINDY NIGHTS

Robert Louis Stevenson

Whenever the moon and stars are set,
  Whenever the wind is high,
All night long in the dark and wet,
  A man goes riding by.
Late in the night when the fires are out,
Why does he gallop and gallop about?

Whenever the trees are crying aloud,
  And ships are tossed at sea,
By, on the highway, low and loud,
  By at the gallop goes he:
By at the gallop he goes, and then
By he comes back at the gallop again.

Christina Georgina Rossetti

The wind has such a rainy sound
  Moaning through the town,
The sea has such a windy sound,—
  Will the ships go down?

The apples in the orchard
  Tumble from their tree.—
Oh, will the ships go down, go down,
  In the windy sea?

WIND-WOLVES

William D. Sargent

Do you hear the cry as the pack goes by,
The wind-wolves hunting across the sky?
Hear them tongue it, keen and clear,
Hot on the flanks of the flying deer!

Across the forest, mere, and plain,
Their hunting howl goes up again!
All night they'll follow the ghostly trail,
All night we'll hear their phantom wail,

For tonight the wind-wolf pack holds sway
From Pegasus Square to the Milky Way,
And the frightened bands of cloud-deer flee
In scattered groups of two and three.

DO YOU FEAR THE WIND?

Hamlin Garland

Do you fear the force of the wind,
The slash of the rain?
Go face them and fight them,
Be savage again.
Go hungry and cold like the wolf,
Go wade like the crane:
The palms of your hands will thicken,
The skin of your cheek will tan,
You'll grow ragged and weary and swarthy,
But you'll walk like a man!

"Windy Nights." *The galloping rhythm of these lines heightens the sense of mystery and adds to the excitement as a galloping rhythm always does whether in poetry or music. If you mark the time as you say these lines, you will discover the silent beat at the end of lines 2, 4, 6, 8, 10, 12. This is like the rest in music and must be observed in reading.* From *A Child's Garden of Verses* by Robert Louis Stevenson

"The wind has such a rainy sound." From *Sing-Song* by Christina Georgina Rossetti
"Wind-Wolves." *This figure of speech may need to be talked over until the picture or idea is clear.* Reprinted from *Scholastic Magazine.* Copyright 1926, by permission of the editors
"Do You Fear the Wind?" From *Silver Pennies* compiled by Blanche Jennings Thompson. The Macmillan

STORM

Hilda Doolittle Aldington

You crash over the trees,
you crack the live branch—
the branch is white,
the green crushed,
each leaf is rent like split wood.

You burden the trees
with black drops,
you swirl and crash—
you have broken off a weighted leaf
in the wind,
it is hurled out,
whirls up and sinks,
a green stone.

Christina Georgina Rossetti

O wind, why do you never rest,
　Wandering, whistling to and fro,
Bringing rain out of the west,
　From the dim north bringing snow?

(Unknown)

White sheep, white sheep,
On a blue hill,
When the wind stops
You all stand still.
When the wind blows
You walk away slow.
White sheep, white sheep,
Where do you go?

(Mother Goose)

Rain, rain, go away,
Come again another day;
Little Johnny wants to play.

(Mother Goose)

One misty moisty morning,
　When cloudy was the weather,
I chanced to meet an old man,
　Clothed all in leather.
He began to compliment
　And I began to grin.
How do you do? And how do you do?
　And how do you do again?

A SHOWER

Izembō (Arranged by Olive Beaupré Miller)

Shower came;
In I came;
Blue sky came!

THE RAIN

(Unknown)

Rain on the green grass,
　And rain on the tree,
And rain on the house-top,
　But not upon me!

RAIN

Robert Louis Stevenson

The rain is raining all around,
　It falls on field and tree,
It rains on the umbrellas here,
　And on the ships at sea.

Company, New York, 1925. Used by permission of Constance Garland Doyle

"Storm." From *Sea Garden* by Hilda Doolittle Aldington. Jonathan Cape Limited, London, 1924

"O wind, why do you never rest." From *Sing-Song* by Christina Georgina Rossetti

"One misty moisty morning." *See the introduction, p. xviii, and record album* Poetry Time

"A Shower." From *Little Pictures of Japan.* Used by permission of the author, Olive Beaupré Miller, and the publishers, The Book House for Children, Chicago, Illinois

"The Rain." From *Romney Gay's Picture Book of Poems.* Copyright, 1940, by Phyllis I. Britcher. Grosset and Dunlap, New York, 1940. By permission of Phyllis I. Britcher

"Rain." From *A Child's Garden of Verses* by Robert Louis Stevenson

MUD

Polly Chase Boyden

Mud is very nice to feel
All squishy-squash between the toes!
I'd rather wade in wiggly mud
Than smell a yellow rose.

Nobody else but the rosebush knows
How nice mud feels
Between the toes.

WHO LIKES THE RAIN?

Clara Doty Bates

"I," said the duck, "I call it fun,
For I have my little red rubbers on;
They make a cunning three-toed track
In the soft, cool mud. Quack! Quack! Quack!"

SPRING RAIN

Marchette Chute

The storm came up so very quick
    It couldn't have been quicker.
I should have brought my hat along,
    I should have brought my slicker.

My hair is wet, my feet are wet,
    I couldn't be much wetter.
I fell into a river once
    But this is even better.

THE REASON

Dorothy Aldis

Rabbits and squirrels
Are furry and fat,
And all of the chickens
Have feathers and that

Is why when it's raining
They need not stay in
The way children do who have
Only their skin.

GALOSHES

Rhoda W. Bacmeister

Susie's galoshes
Makes splishes and sploshes
And slooshes and sloshes,
As Susie steps slowly
Along in the slush.

They stamp and they tramp
On the ice and concrete,
They get stuck in the muck and the mud;
But Susie likes much best to hear

The slippery slush
As it slooshes and sloshes,
And splishes and sploshes,
All round her galoshes!

from ALL AROUND THE TOWN

Phyllis McGinley

U is for Umbrellas
    That bloom in rainy weather,
Like many-colored mushrooms,
    Sprouting upward altogether.
How useful an umbrella is!
    But still I often wonder
If a roof on stormy evenings
    Isn't nicer to be under.

VERY LOVELY

Rose Fyleman

Wouldn't it be lovely if the rain came down
Till the water was quite high over all the town?
If the cabs and buses all were set afloat,
And we had to go to school in a little boat?

Wouldn't it be lovely if it still should pour
And we all went up to live on the second floor?
If we saw the butcher sailing up the hill,
And we took the letters in at the window sill?

It's been raining, raining, all the afternoon;
All these things might happen really very soon.
If we woke to-morrow and found they had be-
    gun,
Wouldn't it be **glorious**? *Wouldn't* it be fun?

RAIN IN THE NIGHT

Amelia Josephine Burr

Raining, raining,
All night long;
Sometimes loud, sometimes soft,
Just like a song.

There'll be rivers in the gutters
And lakes along the street.
It will make our lazy kitty
Wash his little dirty feet.

The roses will wear diamonds
Like kings and queens at court;
But the pansies all get muddy
Because they are so short.

I'll sail my boat tomorrow
In wonderful new places,
But first I'll take my watering-pot
And wash the pansies' faces.

THE UMBRELLA BRIGADE

Laura E. Richards

"Pitter patter!" falls the rain
On the school-room window-pane.
Such a plashing! such a dashing!
Will it e'er be dry again?
Down the gutter rolls a flood,
And the crossing's deep in mud;
And the puddles! oh, the puddles
Are a sight to stir one's blood!

Chorus.   But let it rain
        Tree-toads and frogs,
        Muskets and pitchforks,
        Kittens and dogs!
        Dash away! plash away!
        Who is afraid?
        Here we go,
        The Umbrella Brigade!

Pull the boots up to the knee!
Tie the hoods on merrily!
Such a hustling! such a jostling!
Out of breath with fun are we.
Clatter, clatter, down the street,
Greeting every one we meet,
With our laughing and our chaffing,
Which the laughing drops repeat.

Chorus.   So let it rain
        Tree-toads and frogs,
        Muskets and pitchforks,
        Kittens and dogs!
        Dash away! plash away!
        Who is afraid?
        Here we go,
        The Umbrella Brigade!

LITTLE RAIN

Elizabeth Madox Roberts

When I was making myself a game
Up in the garden, a little rain came.

It fell down quick in a sort of rush,
And I crawled back under the snowball bush.

I could hear the big drops hit the ground
And see little puddles of dust fly round.

A chicken came till the rain was gone;
He had just a very few feathers on.

He shivered a little under his skin,
And then he shut his eyeballs in.

Even after the rain had begun to hush
It kept on raining up in the bush.

One big flat drop came sliding down,
And a ladybug that was red and brown

Was up on a little stem waiting there
And I got some rain in my hair.

SPRING RAIN

Harry Behn

Leaves make a slow
Whispering sound
As down the drops go
Drip to the ground
   Peace, peace, says the tree.

Good wet rain!
Shout happy frogs,
Peepers and big green
Bulls in bogs,
   Lucky, lucky are we!

On a bough above,
Head under wing,
A mourning dove
Waits time to sing.
   Ah me, she sighs, ah me!

CITY RAIN

Rachel Field

Rain in the city!
  I love to see it fall
Slantwise where the buildings crowd
  Red brick and all.
Streets of shiny wetness
  Where the taxis go,
With people and umbrellas all
  Bobbing to and fro.

Rain in the city!
  I love to hear it drip
When I am cosy in my room
  Snug as any ship,
With toys spread on the table,
  With a picture book or two,
And the rain like a rumbling tune that sings
  Through everything I do.

THE RAINS OF SPRING

Lady Ise (Arranged by Olive Beaupré Miller)

The rains of spring
Which hang to the branches
Of the green willow,
Look like pearls upon a string.

IT IS RAINING

Lucy Sprague Mitchell

It is raining.

Where would you like to be in the rain?
Where would you like to be?

I'd like to be on a city street,
where the rain comes down in a driving sheet,
where it wets the houses—roof and wall—
the wagons and horses and autos and all.
That's where I'd like to be in the rain,
that's where I'd like to be.

It is raining.

Where would you like to be in the rain?
Where would you like to be?

I'd like to be in a tall tree top,
where the rain comes dripping, drop, drop, drop,
around on every side:
where it wets the farmer, the barn, the pig,
the cows, the chickens both little and big;
where it batters and beats on a field of wheat
and makes the little birds hide.

It is raining.

Where would you like to be in the rain?
Where would you like to be?

I'd like to be on a ship at sea,
where everything's wet as wet can be

and the waves are rolling high,
where sailors are pulling the ropes and singing,
and wind's in the rigging and salt spray's stinging,
and round us sea gulls cry.
On a dipping skimming ship at sea—
that's where I'd like to be in the rain;
that's where I'd like to be!

APRIL RAIN SONG

Langston Hughes

Let the rain kiss you.
Let the rain beat upon your head with silver
liquid drops.
Let the rain sing you a lullaby.

The rain makes still pools on the sidewalk.
The rain makes running pools in the gutter.
The rain plays a little sleep-song on our roof at
night—

And I love the rain.

RAIN

Ella Young

Dancing dancing down the street
Comes the rain on silver feet:
O hush, O hush,
For the wind is fluting a song.

Little flute of the wind,
Little flute of the wind,
Little flute of the wind
Play on.

Silver feet of the rain
Come again, come again,
Come with a fluting song.

and the publishers, The Book House for Children, Chi-
cago, Illinois
"It Is Raining." Taken from *Another Here and Now
Story Book*, edited by Lucy Sprague Mitchell, published
and copyright, 1937, by E. P. Dutton & Co., Inc., New
York

"April Rain Song." *The music of these words is as quiet
and peaceful as a gentle rain on the roof. See the intro-
duction, p. xx.* Reprinted from *The Dream Keeper* by
Langston Hughes. By permission of Alfred A. Knopf, Inc.
Copyright 1932 by Alfred A. Knopf, Inc.
"Rain." Reprinted by permission of the author

RAIN RIDERS

Clinton Scollard

Last night I heard a *rat-tat-too;*
  'Twas not a drum-beat, that was plain;
I listened long, and then I knew
  It was the Riders of the Rain.

But with the rising of the dawn
  There was no sound of any hoofs;
The Riders of the Rain had gone
  To tramp on other children's roofs.

IN TIME OF SILVER RAIN

Langston Hughes

In time of silver rain
The earth
Puts forth new life again,
Green grasses grow
And flowers lift their heads,
And over all the plain
The wonder spreads
    Of life,
    Of life,
    Of life!

In time of silver rain
The butterflies
Lift silken wings
To catch a rainbow cry,
And trees put forth
New leaves to sing
In joy beneath the sky
As down the roadway
Passing boys and girls
Go singing, too,
In time of silver rain
    When spring
    And life
    Are new.

THE RAIN

William Henry Davies

I hear leaves drinking rain;
  I hear rich leaves on top
Giving the poor beneath
  Drop after drop;
'Tis a sweet noise to hear
These green leaves drinking near.

And when the Sun comes out,
  After this rain shall stop,
A wondrous light will fill
  Each dark, round drop;
I hope the Sun shines bright;
'Twill be a lovely sight.

FOG

Carl Sandburg

The fog comes
on little cat feet.

It sits looking
over harbor and city
on silent haunches
and then moves on.

THE FOG

William Henry Davies

I saw the fog grow thick,
  Which soon made blind my ken;
It made tall men of boys,
  And giants of tall men.

It clutched my throat, I coughed;
  Nothing was in my head
Except two heavy eyes
  Like balls of burning lead.

And when it grew so black
  That I could know no place,
I lost all judgment then,
  Of distance and of space.

The street lamps, and the lights
  Upon the halted cars,
Could either be on earth
  Or be the heavenly stars.

A man passed by me close,
  I asked my way, he said,
'Come, follow me, my friend'—
  I followed where he led.

He rapped the stones in front,
  'Trust me' he said 'and come';
I followed like a child—
  A blind man led me home.

Christina Georgina Rossetti

Boats sail on the rivers,
  And ships sail on the seas;
But clouds that sail across the sky
  Are prettier far than these.

There are bridges on the rivers,
  As pretty as you please;
But the bow that bridges heaven,

And overtops the trees,
And builds a road from earth to sky,
  Is prettier far than these.

THE RAINBOW

Walter de la Mare

I saw the lovely arch
Of Rainbow span the sky,
The gold sun burning
As the rain swept by.

In bright-ringed solitude
The showery foliage shone
One lovely moment,
And the Bow was gone.

William Wordsworth

My heart leaps up when I behold
  A rainbow in the sky:
So was it when my life began;
So is it now I am a man;
So be it when I shall grow old,
  Or let me die!

Eleanor Farjeon

The tide in the river,
The tide in the river,

"The Fog." From *The Collected Poems of W. H. Davies.* London: Jonathan Cape, Ltd., 1929. Reprinted by permission of the publishers and Mrs. H. M. Davies.
"Boats sail on the rivers." *In the last stanza, there is an accumulative pattern that keeps the reader from dropping to a conclusion until the final line. From Sing-Song by*

Christina Georgina Rossetti
"The Rainbow." From *Collected Poems, 1901–1918,* by Walter de la Mare. Copyright, 1920, by Henry Holt and Company, Inc. Copyright, 1948, by Walter de la Mare. Reprinted by permission of the publishers
"The tide in the river." From *Gypsy and Ginger.* Copyright 1920, 1948 by Eleanor Farjeon

The tide in the river runs deep.
　I saw a shiver
　Pass over the river
As the tide turned in its sleep.

THE NOISE OF WATERS

James Joyce

All day I hear the noise of waters
　Making moan,
Sad as the sea-bird is, when going
　Forth alone,
He hears the winds cry to the waters'
　Monotone.

The grey winds, the cold winds are blowing
　Where I go.
I hear the noise of many waters
　Far below.
All day, all night, I hear them flowing
　To and fro.

T. S. Eliot

I do not know much about gods; but I think that
　the river
Is a strong brown god—sullen, untamed and in-
　tractable,
Patient to some degree, at first recognised as a
　frontier;
Useful, untrustworthy, as a conveyor of com-
　merce;
Then only a problem confronting the builder of
　bridges.
The problem once solved, the brown god is al-
　most forgotten
By the dwellers in cities—ever, however, impla-
　cable,
Keeping his seasons and rages, destroyer, re-
　minder

Of what men choose to forget. Unhonoured,
　unpropitiated
By worshippers of the machine, but waiting,
　watching and waiting.

COMPOSED UPON WESTMINSTER BRIDGE

William Wordsworth

Earth has not anything to show more fair:
Dull would he be of soul who could pass by
A sight so touching in its majesty:
This City now doth like a garment wear
The beauty of the morning; silent, bare,
Ships, towers, domes, theaters, and temples lie
Open unto the fields, and to the sky;
All bright and glittering in the smokeless air.
Never did sun more beautifully steep
In his first splendor valley, rock, or hill;
Ne'er saw I, never felt, a calm so deep!
The river glideth at his own sweet will:
Dear God! the very houses seem asleep;
And all that mighty heart is lying still!

BROOKLYN BRIDGE AT DAWN

Richard Le Gallienne

Out of the cleansing night of stars and tides,
Building itself anew in the slow dawn,
The long sea-city rises: night is gone,
Day is not yet; still merciful, she hides
Her summoning brow, and still the night-car
　glides
Empty of faces; the night-watchmen yawn
One to the other, and shiver and pass on,
Nor yet a soul over the great bridge rides.

Frail as a gossamer, a thing of air,
A bow of shadow o'er the river flung,
Its sleepy masts and lonely lapping flood;
Who, seeing thus the bridge a-slumber there,
Would dream such softness, like a picture hung,
Is wrought of human thunder, iron and blood?

THE BIG CLOCK

(*Unknown*)

Slowly ticks the big clock;
Tick-tock, tick-tock!
But Cuckoo clock ticks double quick;
Tick-a-tock-a, tick-a-tock-a,
Tick-a-tock-a, tick!

(*Mother Goose*)

Bell horses, bell horses, what time of day?
One o'clock, two o'clock, three and away.

(*Mother Goose*)

The cock doth crow
To let you know,
If you be wise,
'Tis time to rise.

ROUND THE CLOCK

(*Mother Goose*)

Cocks crow in the morn
To tell us to rise,
And he who lies late
Will never be wise;

For early to bed
And early to rise,
Is the way to be healthy
And wealthy and wise.

A CHILD'S DAY, PART II

Walter de la Mare

Softly, drowsily,
Out of sleep;
Into the world again
Ann's eyes peep;
Over the pictures
Across the walls
One little quivering
Sunbeam falls.
A thrush in the garden
Seems to say,
Wake, little Ann,
'Tis day, 'tis day!
Faint sweet breezes
The casement stir,
Breathing of pinks
And lavender.
At last from her pillow,
With cheeks bright red,
Up comes her round little
Tousled head;
And out she tumbles
From her warm bed.

SINGING-TIME

Rose Fyleman

I wake in the morning early
And always, the very first thing,
I poke out my head and I sit up in bed
And I sing and I sing and I sing.

A SUMMER MORNING

Rachel Field

I saw dawn creep across the sky,
And all the gulls go flying by.
I saw the sea put on its dress
Of blue mid-summer loveliness,
And heard the trees begin to stir
Green arms of pine and juniper.
I heard the wind call out and say:
"Get up, my dear, it is to-day!"

THE SUN

John Drinkwater

I told the Sun that I was glad,
    I'm sure I don't know why;
Somehow the pleasant way he had
    Of shining in the sky,
Just put a notion in my head
    That wouldn't it be fun
If, walking on the hill, I said
    "I'm happy" to the Sun.

AFTERNOON ON A HILL

Edna St. Vincent Millay

I will be the gladdest thing
    Under the sun!
I will touch a hundred flowers
    And not pick one.

I will look at cliffs and clouds
    With quiet eyes,
Watch the wind bow down the grass,
    And the grass rise.

And when lights begin to show
    Up from the town,
I will mark which must be mine,
    And then start down!

"The Big Clock." *See record album* Poetry Time. Every effort has been made to locate the copyright owner of this poem but without success

"A Child's Day, Part II." From *A Child's Day* by Walter de la Mare. Used by permission of Henry Holt and Company, Inc. By permission also of the author and by Faber and Faber Limited

"Singing-Time." From *The Fairy Green* by Rose Fyleman. Copyright 1923 by Doubleday & Company, Inc. By permission also of Miss Rose Fyleman, The Society of Authors, and Messrs. Methuen & Co.

"A Summer Morning." From *The Pointed People* by Rachel Field. The Macmillan Company, New York, 1930. Used by permission of Arthur S. Pederson, Trustee, Estate of Rachel Field Pederson

"The Sun." From *All About Me* by John Drinkwater. Reprinted by permission of and arrangement with Houghton Mifflin Company, the authorized publishers

"Afternoon on a Hill." From *Renascence and Other Poems*, published by Harper & Brothers. Copyright 1917, 1945 by Edna St. Vincent Millay

Kate Greenaway

In the pleasant green Garden
   We sat down to tea;
"Do you take sugar?" and
   "Do you take milk?"
She'd got a new gown on—
   A smart one of silk.
We all were as happy
   As happy could be,
On that bright Summer's day
   When she asked us to tea.

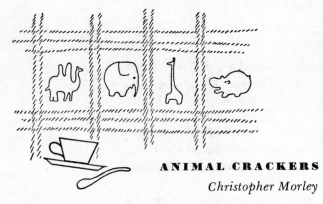

ANIMAL CRACKERS

Christopher Morley

Animal crackers, and cocoa to drink,
That is the finest of suppers, I think;
When I'm grown up and can have what I please
I think I shall always insist upon these.
What do *you* choose when you're offered a treat?
When Mother says, "What would you like best
   to eat?"
Is it waffles and syrup, or cinnamon toast?
It's cocoa and animals that *I* love most!

The kitchen's the cosiest place that I know:
The kettle is singing, the stove is aglow,
And there in the twilight, how jolly to see
The cocoa and animals waiting for me.

Daddy and Mother dine later in state,
With Mary to cook for them, Susan to wait;

But they don't have nearly as much fun as I
Who eat in the kitchen with Nurse standing by;
And Daddy once said, he would like to be me
Having cocoa and animals once more for tea!

THIS HAPPY DAY

Harry Behn

Every morning when the sun
Comes smiling up on everyone,
It's lots of fun
To say good morning to the sun.
   Good morning, Sun!

Every evening after play
When the sunshine goes away,
It's nice to say,
Thank you for this happy day,
   This happy day!

from ALL AROUND THE TOWN

Phyllis McGinley

W's for Windows.
   Watch them welcome in the night.
How they twinkle, twinkle, twinkle
   With the waning of the light!
There's nothing half so wonderful
   In all the wond'rous town
As a million winking Windows
   When the dusk is coming down.

THE PARK

James S. Tippett

I'm glad that I
   Live near a park

For in the winter
   After dark

The park lights shine
As bright and still

As dandelions
On a hill.

Elizabeth Coatsworth

Hard from the southeast blows the wind
  Promising rain.
The clouds are gathering, and dry leaves
  Tap at the pane.

Early the cows come wandering home
  To shadowy bars,
Early the candles are alight
  And a few stars.

Now is the hour that lies between
  Bright day and night,
When in the dusk the fire blooms
  In tongues of light,

And the cat comes to bask herself
  In the soft heat,
And Madame Peace draws up her chair
  To warm her feet.

SETTING THE TABLE
Dorothy Aldis

Evenings
When the house is quiet
I delight
To spread the white
Smooth cloth and put the flowers on the table.

I place the knives and forks around
Without a sound.
I light the candles.

I love to see
Their small reflected torches shine
Against the greenness of the vine
And garden.

Is that the mignonette, I wonder,
Smells so sweet?

And then I call them in to eat.

EVENING HYMN
Elizabeth Madox Roberts

The day is done;
The lamps are lit;
Woods-ward the birds are flown.
Shadows draw close,—
Peace be unto this house.

The cloth is fair;
The food is set.
God's night draw near.
Quiet and love and peace
Be to this, our rest, our place.

PRELUDE I
T. S. Eliot

The winter evening settles down
With smell of steaks in passageways.
Six o'clock.
The burnt-out ends of smoky days.
And now a gusty shower wraps
The grimy scraps
Of withered leaves about your feet
And newspapers from vacant lots;
The showers beat
On broken blinds and chimney-pots,
And at the corner of the street
A lonely cab-horse steams and stamps.
And then the lighting of the lamps.

up by an open fire is a picture of peace; so the poet says, "Madame Peace draws up her chair." From *Away Goes Sally* by Elizabeth Coatsworth. Copyright 1934 by The Macmillan Company and used with their permission

"Setting the Table." From *Any Spring* by Dorothy Aldis. Minton, Balch and Company, New York, 1933. Copyright 1933 by Dorothy Aldis

"Evening Hymn." *Read this slowly and softly and feel its peace. See the introduction, p. xix.* From *Song in the*

Meadow by Elizabeth Madox Roberts. Copyright 1940 by Elizabeth Madox Roberts. Reprinted by permission of The Viking Press, Inc., New York

"Prelude I." *This might be called "Nocturne," or "Day's End in a City," or—you name it.* From *Collected Poems 1909–1935* by T. S. Eliot, copyright, 1936, by Harcourt, Brace and Company, Inc. Reprinted by permission of Harcourt, Brace and Company, Inc., and Faber and Faber Limited

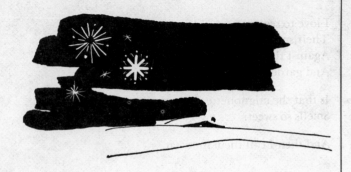

SNOW TOWARD EVENING

Melville Cane

Suddenly the sky turned gray,
The day,
Which had been bitter and chill,
Grew intensely soft and still.
Quietly
From some invisible blossoming tree
Millions of petals cool and white
Drifted and blew,
Lifted and flew,
Fell with the falling night.

CHECK

James Stephens

The Night was creeping on the ground!
She crept and did not make a sound,

Until she reached the tree: And then
She covered it, and stole again

Along the grass beside the wall!
—I heard the rustling of her shawl

As she threw blackness everywhere
Along the sky, the ground, the air,

And in the room where I was hid!
But, no matter what she did

To everything that was without,
She could not put my candle out!

So I stared at the Night! And she
Stared back solemnly at me!

(*American Mother Goose*)

Star-light, star-bright
First star I've seen tonight;
I wish I may, I wish I might
Get the wish I wish tonight.

THE STAR

Jane Taylor

Twinkle, twinkle, little star,
How I wonder what you are!
Up above the world so high,
Like a diamond in the sky.

ESCAPE AT BEDTIME

Robert Louis Stevenson

The lights from the parlour and kitchen shone
out
Through the blinds and the windows and
bars;
And high overhead and all moving about,
There were thousands of millions of stars.

There ne'er were such thousands of leaves on a
tree,
Nor of people in church or the Park,
As the crowds of the stars that looked down
upon me,
And that glittered and winked in the dark.

The Dog, and the Plough, and the Hunter, and
all,
And the Star of the Sailor, and Mars,

These shone in the sky, and the pail by the wall
    Would be half full of water and stars.

They saw me at last, and they chased me with
      cries,
    And they soon had me packed into bed;
But the glory kept shining and bright in my
      eyes,
    And the stars going round in my head.

UNTIL WE BUILT A CABIN

Aileen L. Fisher

When we lived in a city
(three flights up and down)
I never dreamed how many stars
could show above a town.

    When we moved to a village
    where lighted streets were few,
    I thought I could see ALL the stars,
    but, oh, I never knew—

        Until we built a cabin
        where hills are high and far,
        I never knew how many
            many
                stars there really are!

THE FALLING STAR

Sara Teasdale

I saw a star slide down the sky,
Blinding the north as it went by,
Too burning and too quick to hold,
Too lovely to be bought or sold,
Good only to make wishes on
And then forever to be gone.

STARS

Sara Teasdale

    Alone in the night
    On a dark hill

    With pines around me
      Spicy and still,

    And a heaven full of stars
      Over my head,
    White and topaz
      And misty red;

    Myriads with beating
      Hearts of fire
    That aeons
      Cannot vex or tire;

    Up the dome of heaven
      Like a great hill,
    I watch them marching
      Stately and still,

    And I know that I
      Am honored to be
    Witness
      Of so much majesty.

MOON-COME-OUT

Eleanor Farjeon

    Moon-Come-Out
    And Sun-Go-In,
    Here's a soft blanket
    To cuddle your chin.

Moon-Go-In
And Sun-Come-Out,
Throw off the blanket
And bustle about.

GOOD NIGHT

Dorothy Mason Pierce

On tip-toe comes the gentle dark
To help the children sleep
And silently, in silver paths,
The slumber fairies creep.

Then overhead, God sees that all
His candles are a-light,
And reaching loving arms to us
He bids His world Good Night.

(Unknown)

I see the moon,
And the moon sees me;
God bless the moon,
And God bless me.

CRESCENT MOON

Elizabeth Madox Roberts

And Dick said, "Look what I have found!"
And when we saw we danced around,
And made our feet just tip the ground.

We skipped our toes and sang, "Oh-lo.
Oh-who, oh-who, oh what do you know!
Oh-who, oh-hi, oh-loo, kee-lo!"

We clapped our hands and sang, "Oh-ee!"
It made us jump and laugh to see
The little new moon above the tree.

THE WHITE WINDOW

James Stephens

The Moon comes every night to peep
  Through the window where I lie,
And I pretend to be asleep;
  But I watch the Moon as it goes by,
And it never makes a sound.

It stands and stares, and then it goes
  To the house that's next to me,
Stealing on its tippy-toes,
  To peep at folk asleep maybe;
And it never makes a sound.

FULL MOON

Walter de la Mare

One night as Dick lay fast asleep,
  Into his drowsy eyes
A great still light began to creep
  From out the silent skies.
It was the lovely moon's, for when
  He raised his dreamy head,

Her surge of silver filled the pane
And streamed across his bed.
So, for awhile, each gazed at each—
Dick and the solemn moon—
Till, climbing slowly on her way,
She vanished, and was gone.

SILVER

Walter de la Mare

Slowly, silently, now the moon
Walks the night in her silver shoon;
This way, and that, she peers, and sees
Silver fruit upon silver trees;
One by one the casements catch
Her beams beneath the silvery thatch;
Couched in his kennel, like a log,
With paws of silver sleeps the dog;
From their shadowy cote the white breasts peep
Of doves in a silver-feathered sleep;
A harvest mouse goes scampering by,
With silver claws, and silver eye;
And moveless fish in the water gleam,
By silver reeds in a silver stream.

LAST SONG

James Guthrie

To the Sun
Who has shone
    All day,
To the Moon
Who has gone
    Away,
To the milk-white,
Silk-white,
Lily-white Star
A fond goodnight
Wherever you are.

FINIS

Sir Henry Newbolt

Night is come,
    Owls are out;
Beetles hum
    Round about.

Children snore
    Safe in bed,
Nothing more
    Need be said.

(*Mother Goose*)

Spring is showery, flowery, bowery;
Summer: hoppy, croppy, poppy;
Autumn: wheezy, sneezy, freezy;
Winter: slippy, drippy, nippy.

ROUND THE CALENDAR

OPEN THE DOOR
Marion Edey and Dorothy Grider

Open the door and who'll come in?
  Who'll come in?
  Who'll come in?
Open the door and who'll come in,
  So early Monday morning?

My little pussycat, she'll come in,
Rubbing her fur against my shin.
She'll arch her back and she'll step right in,
  So early Monday morning.

Open the door and who'll come in?
  Who'll come in?
  Who'll come in?
Open the door and who'll come in,
  So early Tuesday morning?

My little puppy dog, he'll come in,
Mud on his paws and mud on his chin.
He'll bounce and he'll pounce as he dashes in,
   So early Tuesday morning.

Open the door and who'll come in?
   Who'll come in?
   Who'll come in?
Open the door and who'll come in,
   So early Wednesday morning?

My little Dicky bird, he'll come in,
His eyes so black and his legs so thin.
He'll fly to his cage and he'll pop right in,
   So early Wednesday morning.

Open the door and who do you see?
   Who do you see?
   Who do you see?
Open the door and who do you see,
   So early Thursday morning?

Beulah the pony is visiting me,
Nuzzling her nose against my knee,
Asking for sugar, as plain as can be,
   So early Thursday morning.

Open the door and who'll be there?
   Who'll be there?
   Who'll be there?
Open the door and who'll be there,
   So early Friday morning?

The Skillipot turtles, a tiny pair,
Their shells so hard and their heads so bare.
It takes them an hour to get anywhere
   So early Friday morning.

Open the door and what do you know?
   What do you know?
   What do you know?
Open the door and what do you know,
   So early Saturday morning?

My beautiful bunnies are white as snow,
And their pink little noses wiggle so.
Three pretty hops, and in they go,
   So early Saturday morning.

(*Mother Goose*)

   How many days has my baby to play?
     Saturday, Sunday, Monday,
   Tuesday, Wednesday, Thursday, Friday,
     Saturday, Sunday, Monday.

(*Mother Goose*)

   January brings the snow,
     Makes our feet and fingers glow.
   February brings the rain,
     Thaws the frozen lake again.
   March brings breezes loud and shrill,
     Stirs the dancing daffodil.

   April brings the primrose sweet,
     Scatters daisies at our feet.
   May brings flocks of pretty lambs,
     Skipping by their fleecy dams.
   June brings tulips, lilies, roses,
     Fills the children's hands with posies.

   Hot July brings cooling showers,
     Apricots and gillyflowers.
   August brings the sheaves of corn,
     Then the harvest home is borne.
   Warm September brings the fruit,
     Sportsmen then begin to shoot.

   Fresh October brings the pheasant,
     Then to gather nuts is pleasant.
   Dull November brings the blast,
     Then the leaves are whirling fast.
   Chill December brings the sleet,
     Blazing fire and Christmas treat.

"Open the Door." *This is charming to do with a verse choir. Let a chorus of light voices carry the "Open the door" refrain, and then let individual children say the answers.* Reprinted from *Open the Door* by Marion Edey and Dorothy Grider. Copyright 1949 by Marion Edey and

Dorothy Grider. Used by permission of the publishers, Charles Scribner's Sons
   "How many days has my baby to play?" *See record album* Poetry Time.

O DEAR ME!

Walter de la Mare

Here are crocuses, white, gold, grey!
    "O dear me!" says Marjorie May;
Flat as a platter the blackberry blows:
    "O dear me!" says Madeleine Rose;
The leaves are fallen, the swallows flown:
    "O dear me!" says Humphrey John;
Snow lies thick where all night it fell:
    "O dear me!" says Emmanuel.

SEPTEMBER

Edwina Fallis

A road like brown ribbon,
A sky that is blue,
A forest of green
With that sky peeping through.

Asters, deep purple,
A grasshopper's call,
Today it is summer,
Tomorrow is fall.

AUTUMN FIRES

Robert Louis Stevenson

In the other gardens
    And all up the vale,
From the autumn bonfires
    See the smoke trail!

Pleasant summer over
    And all the summer flowers.
The red fire blazes,
    The gray smoke towers.

Sing a song of seasons!
    Something bright in all!
Flowers in the summer,
    Fires in the fall!

DOWN! DOWN!

Eleanor Farjeon

    Down, down!
    Yellow and brown
The leaves are falling over the town.

AUTUMN WOODS

James S. Tippett

    I like the woods
        In autumn
    When dry leaves hide the ground,
    When the trees are bare
    And the wind sweeps by
    With a lonesome rushing sound.

    I can rustle the leaves
        In autumn
    And I can make a bed
    In the thick dry leaves
    That have fallen
    From the bare trees
    Overhead.

THE CITY OF FALLING LEAVES

Amy Lowell

    Leaves fall,
    Brown leaves,
    Yellow leaves streaked with brown.
    They fall,
    Flutter,
    Fall again.

"O Dear Me!" *You might read this once or twice and never stop to think that each couplet has to do with one of the four seasons, beginning with spring.* From *Collected Poems, 1901–1918,* by Walter de la Mare. Copyright, 1920, by Henry Holt and Company, Inc. Copyright, 1948, by Walter de la Mare. Reprinted by permission of the publishers

"September." From *Sung under the Silver Umbrella.* The Macmillan Company, New York, 1935. Used by permission

of the author

"Autumn Fires." From *A Child's Garden of Verses* by Robert Louis Stevenson

"Down! Down!" From *Joan's Door* by Eleanor Farjeon. Copyright 1926 by J. B. Lippincott Company

"Autumn Woods." From *A World to Know* by James S. Tippett. Copyright, 1933, Harper & Brothers

"The City of Falling Leaves." From "1777" in *Men,*

The brown leaves,
And the streaked yellow leaves,
Loosen on their branches
And drift slowly downwards.
One,
One, two, three,
One, two, five.
All Venice is a falling of Autumn leaves—
Brown,
And yellow streaked with brown.

Emily Dickinson

The morns are meeker than they were,
The nuts are getting brown;
The berry's cheek is plumper,
The rose is out of town.

The maple wears a gayer scarf,
The field a scarlet gown.
Lest I should be old-fashioned,
I'll put a trinket on.

FALL

Aileen L. Fisher

The last of October
We lock the garden gate.
(The flowers have all withered
That used to stand straight.)

The last of October
We put the swings away
And the porch looks deserted
Where we liked to play.

The last of October
The birds have all flown,
The screens are in the attic,
The sandpile's alone:

Everything is put away
Before it starts to snow—
I wonder if the ladybugs
Have any place to go!

SPLINTER

Carl Sandburg

The voice of the last cricket
across the first frost
is one kind of good-by.
It is so thin a splinter of singing.

MY BROTHER

Dorothy Aldis

My brother is inside the sheet
That gave that awful shout.
I know because those are his feet
So brown and sticking out.

And that's his head that waggles there
And his eyes peeking through—
So I can laugh, so I don't care:
"Ha!" I say. "It's you."

BLACK AND GOLD

Nancy Byrd Turner

Everything is black and gold,
    Black and gold, tonight:
Yellow pumpkins, yellow moon,
    Yellow candlelight;

Jet-black cat with golden eyes,
    Shadows black as ink,
Firelight blinking in the dark
    With a yellow blink.

Women and Ghosts by Amy Lowell. Reprinted by permission of and arrangement with Houghton Mifflin Company, the authorized publishers
"The morns are meeker than they were." From *The Poems of Emily Dickinson*. Little, Brown & Company, Boston, 1939
"Fall." From *The Coffee-Pot Face* by Aileen L. Fisher. Robert M. McBride & Company, New York, 1933

"Splinter." From *Good Morning, America*, copyright, 1928, by Carl Sandburg. Reprinted by permission of Harcourt, Brace and Company, Inc.
"My Brother." From *Hop, Skip and Jump* by Dorothy Aldis. Minton, Balch and Company, New York, 1934. Copyright 1934 by Dorothy Aldis
"Black and Gold." From *Child Life*. Child Life, Inc., Boston, October 1929. Used by permission of the author

Black and gold, black and gold,
  Nothing in between—
When the world turns black and gold,
  Then it's Halloween!

THEME IN YELLOW
Carl Sandburg

I spot the hills
With yellow balls in autumn.
I light the prairie cornfields
Orange and tawny gold clusters
And I am called pumpkins.
On the last of October
When dusk is fallen
Children join hands
And circle round me
Singing ghost songs
And love to the harvest moon;
I am a jack-o'-lantern
With terrible teeth
And the children know
I am fooling.

HALLOWE'EN
Harry Behn

Tonight is the night
When dead leaves fly
Like witches on switches
Across the sky,
When elf and sprite
Flit through the night
On a moony sheen.

Tonight is the night
When leaves make a sound
Like a gnome in his home
Under the ground,
When spooks and trolls
Creep out of holes
Mossy and green.

Tonight is the night
When pumpkins stare
Through sheaves and leaves
Everywhere,
When ghoul and ghost
And goblin host
Dance round their queen.
It's Hallowe'en!

THIS IS HALLOWEEN
Dorothy Brown Thompson

Goblins on the doorstep,
  Phantoms in the air,
Owls on witches' gateposts
  Giving stare for stare,
Cats on flying broomsticks,
  Bats against the moon,
Stirrings round of fate-cakes
  With a solemn spoon,
Whirling apple parings,
  Figures draped in sheets
Dodging, disappearing,
  Up and down the streets,
Jack-o'-lanterns grinning,
  Shadows on a screen,
Shrieks and starts and laughter—
  This is Halloween!

THE RIDE-BY-NIGHTS
Walter de la Mare

Up on their brooms the Witches stream,
Crooked and black in the crescent's gleam,
One foot high, and one foot low,
Bearded, cloaked, and cowled, they go.
'Neath Charlie's Wane they twitter and tweet,
And away they swarm 'neath the Dragon's feet,
With a whoop and a flutter they swing and sway,
And surge pell-mell down the Milky Way.
Between the legs of the glittering Chair

They hover and squeak in the empty air.
Then round they swoop past the glimmering
    Lion
To where Sirius barks behind huge Orion;
Up, then, and over to wheel amain
Under the silver, and home again.

THE LAST WORD OF A BLUEBIRD
(As Told to a Child)

Robert Frost

As I went out a Crow
In a low voice said 'Oh,
I was looking for you.
How do you do?
I just came to tell you
To tell Lesley (will you?)
That her little Bluebird
Wanted me to bring word
That the north wind last night
That made the stars bright
And made ice on the trough
Almost made him cough
His tail feathers off.
He just had to fly!
But he sent her Good-by,
And said to be good,
And wear her red hood,
And look for skunk tracks
In the snow with an ax—
And do everything!
And perhaps in the spring
He would come back and sing.'

SOMETHING TOLD THE WILD GEESE

Rachel Field

Something told the wild geese
    It was time to go.
Though the fields lay golden
    Something whispered, "Snow."
Leaves were green and stirring,
    Berries, luster-glossed,
But beneath warm feathers
    Something cautioned, "Frost."
All the sagging orchards
    Steamed with amber spice,
But each wild breast stiffened
    At remembered ice.
Something told the wild geese
    It was time to fly—
Summer sun was on their wings,
    Winter in their cry.

THANKSGIVING MAGIC

Rowena Bastin Bennett

Thanksgiving Day I like to see
Our cook perform her witchery.
She turns a pumpkin into pie
As easily as you or I
Can wave a hand or wink an eye.
She takes leftover bread and muffin
And changes them to turkey stuffin'.
She changes cranberries to sauce
And meats to stews and stews to broths,
And when she mixes gingerbread
It turns into a man instead
With frosting collar 'round his throat
And raisin buttons down his coat.
Oh, some like magic made by wands,
    And some read magic out of books,
And some like fairy spells and charms
    But I like magic made by cooks!

SELECTIONS FROM THE PSALMS

(Psalm 150)

Praise ye the Lord.
Praise God in his sanctuary:
Praise him in the firmament of his power.
Praise him for his mighty acts:
Praise him according to his excellent greatness.
Praise him with the sound of the trumpet:
Praise him with the psaltery and harp.
Praise him with the timbrel and dance:
Praise him with stringed instruments and organs.
Praise him upon the loud cymbals:
Praise him upon the high sounding cymbals.
Let every thing that hath breath praise the
    Lord.
Praise ye the Lord.

(Psalm 100)

Make a joyful noise unto the Lord, all ye lands.
Serve the Lord with gladness:
Come before his presence with singing.
Know ye that the Lord he is God:
It is he that hath made us, and not we ourselves;
We are his people, and the sheep of his pasture.
Enter into his gates with thanksgiving,
And into his courts with praise:
Be thankful unto him, and bless his name.
For the Lord is good; his mercy is everlasting;
And his truth endureth to all generations.

(Psalm 103)

Bless the Lord, O my soul:
And all that is within me, bless his holy name.
Bless the Lord, O my soul,
And forget not all his benefits:

Who forgiveth all thine iniquities;
Who healeth all thy diseases;
Who redeemeth thy life from destruction;
Who crowneth thee with loving-kindness and
    tender mercies;
Who satisfieth thy mouth with good things;
So that thy youth is renewed like the eagle's.
Bless the Lord, O my soul:
And all that is within me, bless his holy name.

(Psalm 147)

Praise ye the Lord:
For it is good to sing praises unto our God;
For it is pleasant; and praise is comely.
Great is our Lord, and of great power:
Who covereth the heaven with clouds,
Who prepareth rain for the earth,
Who maketh grass to grow upon the mountains.
He giveth to the beast his food,
And to the young ravens which cry.
He giveth snow like wool:
He scattereth the hoarfrost like ashes.
He casteth forth his ice like morsels:
Who can stand before his cold?
He sendeth out his word, and melteth them:
He causeth his wind to blow, and the waters flow.
Sing unto the Lord with thanksgiving;
Praise ye the Lord.

(Psalm 24)

The earth *is* the Lord's, and the fulness
    thereof;
The world, and they that dwell therein.
For he hath founded it upon the seas,
And established it upon the floods.
Who shall ascend into the hill of the Lord?
Or who shall stand in his holy place?

"Praise ye the Lord." Psalm 150. *When we think of the day and its name—Thanksgiving—we are immediately reminded of those matchless songs of praise and thanksgiving, the Psalms. Here are a few memorable selections, many of which are especially beautiful to speak in verse choirs. Some suggestions for casting them in this form are indicated, although there is usually more than one way of arranging them.*
A discussion of choral speaking is found on page xxiv of this book. In these notes H, M, and L indicate the high, medium, and low choirs. (Also see Chapter 10, Verse Choirs, in Children and Books *by May Hill Arbuthnot.)*

For Psalm 150 number the lines and mark for speaking in the following groups: All three choirs: line 1; M: 2, 3; H: 4, 5; M: 6, 7; L: 8, 9; H: 10, 11; L: 12; all choirs: the last line.
"Make a joyful noise unto the Lord." Psalm 100. *Number lines; cast for these groups: all choirs: line 1; H: 2, 3; L: 4, 5, 6; M: 7, 8, 9; all choirs: 10, 11*
"Bless the Lord, O my soul." Psalm 103: 1-5. *Number lines; cast for these groups: M: 1, 2; H: 3, 4; L: 5, 6; M: 7, 8; H and M: 9, 10; All: 12. Notice that after line 2 there is no conclusion until line 10. Then, lines 11 and 12 repeat the beginning and are a great swelling chorus*

He that hath clean hands, and a pure heart;
Who hath not lifted up his soul unto vanity,
Nor sworn deceitfully.
He shall receive the blessing from the Lord,
And righteousness from the God of his salvation.
This is the generation of them that seek him,
That seek thy face, O Jacob.
Lift up your heads, O ye gates;
And be ye lifted up, ye everlasting doors;
And the King of glory shall come in.
Who is this King of glory?
The Lord strong and mighty,
The Lord mighty in battle.
Lift up your heads, O ye gates;
Even lift them up, ye everlasting doors;
And the King of glory shall come in.
Who is this King of glory?
The Lord of hosts,
He *is* the King of glory.

(Psalm 23)

The Lord is my shepherd; I shall not want.
He maketh me to lie down in green pastures:
He leadeth me beside the still waters.
He restoreth my soul:
He leadeth me in the paths of righteousness for
     his name's sake.
Yea, though I walk through the valley of the
     shadow of death,
I will fear no evil: for thou art with me;
Thy rod and thy staff they comfort me.
Thou preparest a table before me in the presence
     of mine enemies:
Thou anointest my head with oil; my cup run-
     neth over.
Surely goodness and mercy shall follow me all
     the days of my life:
And I will dwell in the house of the Lord for
     ever.

of thanksgiving.
"Praise ye the Lord." Psalm 147: 1, 5, 8, 9, 16, 17, 18, 7,
20. *All choirs speak line 1; H: 2, 3; M: 4, 5, 6, 7; H: 8, 9;
M: 10, 11, 12, 13; L: 14, 15, 16.*
"The earth is the Lord's." Psalm 24. *All choirs speak
lines 1, 2; M: 3, 4; H: 5, 6; M: 7, 8, 9; L: 10, 11, 12, 13;
M: 14, 15, 16; H: 17; L: 18, 19; M: 20, 21, 22; H: 23. This
is an especially dramatic selection for choirs to speak. The
question may come from the high voices or ring out clearly
from one solo voice, if preferred. In that case, use two
choirs for the other lines, one choir M to H and the other
M to L.*

THE MITTEN SONG
Marie Louise Allen

"Thumbs in the thumb-place,
Fingers all together!"
This is the song
We sing in mitten-weather.
When it is cold,
It doesn't matter whether
Mittens are wool,
Or made of finest leather.
This is the song
We sing in mitten-weather:
"Thumbs in the thumb-place,
Fingers all together!"

ICE
Dorothy Aldis

When it is the winter time
I run up the street
And I make the ice laugh
With my little feet—
"Crickle, crackle, crickle
Crrreeet, crrreeet, crrreeet."

FIRST SNOW
Marie Louise Allen

Snow makes whiteness where it falls.
The bushes look like popcorn-balls.
And places where I always play,
Look like somewhere else today.

"The Lord is my shepherd." Psalm 23. *It seems best to
let the sheer perfection of the Twenty-Third Psalm stand
alone without verse choir arrangement.*
"The Mitten Song." From *Sung under the Silver Umbrella.* The Macmillan Company, New York, 1935. Used
by permission of the author
"Ice." From *Everything and Anything* by Dorothy Aldis.
Minton, Balch and Company, New York, 1927. Copyright
1925, 1926, 1927 by Dorothy Aldis
"First Snow." From *A Pocketful of Rhymes.* Harper &
Brothers, New York, 1939. Used by permission of the
author

FIRST SNOW

Ivy O. Eastwick

Lighter than thistledown
  Blown by a fairy,
Fine flakes of snow fall through
  Space grey and airy.

Whiter than lily that
  Blows sweet in summer,
This first snow of winter,
  This gentle newcomer.

To dim each glaring light
With star-shaped feathers
  Of frosty white.
And not the tallest building
  Halfway up the sky;
Or all the trains and busses,
  And taxis scudding by;
And not a million people,
  Not one of them at all,
Can do a thing about the snow
  But let it fall!

SNOW

Dorothy Aldis

The fenceposts wear marshmallow hats
On a snowy day;
Bushes in their night gowns
Are kneeling down to pray—
And all the trees have silver skirts
And want to dance away.

CYNTHIA IN THE SNOW

Gwendolyn Brooks

It SUSHES.
It hushes
The loudness in the road.
It flitter-twitters,
And laughs away from me.
It laughs a lovely whiteness,
And whitely whirs away,
To be
Some otherwhere,
Still white as milk or shirts.
So beautiful it hurts.

SNOW

Alice Wilkins

The snow fell softly all the night.
It made a blanket soft and white.
It covered houses, flowers and ground,
But did not make a single sound!

FALLING SNOW

(Unknown)

See the pretty snowflakes
  Falling from the sky;
On the walk and housetop
  Soft and thick they lie.

SNOW IN THE CITY

Rachel Field

Snow is out of fashion,
  But it still comes down,
To whiten all the buildings
  In our town;
To dull the noise of traffic;

On the window-ledges
  On the branches bare;
Now how fast they gather,
  Filling all the air.

"First Snow." Taken from *Fairies and Suchlike*, by Ivy O. Eastwick, published and copyright, 1946, by E. P. Dutton & Co., Inc., New York

"Snow." From *Everything and Anything* by Dorothy Aldis. Minton, Balch and Company, New York, 1927. Copyright 1925, 1926, 1927 by Dorothy Aldis

"Snow." From *The Golden Flute* compiled by Alice Hubbard. The John Day Company, Inc., New York, 1932

"Snow in the City." From *Branches Green* by Rachel Field. Copyright 1934 by The Macmillan Company and used with their permission

"Cynthia in the Snow." From *Bronzeville Boys and Girls*, copyright © 1956 by Gwendolyn Brooks Blakely. Published by Harper & Brothers, N. Y., and used with permission

Look into the garden,
  Where the grass was green;
Covered by the snowflakes,
  Not a blade is seen.

Now the bare black bushes
  All look soft and white,
Every twig is laden—
  What a pretty sight!

Ralph Waldo Emerson

he trumpets of the sky,

n,

eet
it

AH

ialik

Uncle had a present for me,
  An old penny for my own.
In whose honor, for whose glory?
  For Hanukkah alone.

DREIDEL SONG

Efraim Rosenzweig

Twirl about, dance about,
  Spin, spin, spin!
Turn, Dreidel, turn—
  Time to begin!

Soon it is Hanukkah—
  Fast Dreidel, fast!
For you will lie still
  When Hanukkah's past.

A SONG OF ALWAYS

Efraim Rosenzweig

The Temple is clean
  The lamp burns bright;
Judah the leader,
  Has started the light.

The sun shines by days,
  And dark is the night;
But always and always
  The lamp burns bright.

BLESSINGS FOR CHANUKAH

Jessie E. Sampter

Blessed art Thou, O God our Lord,
Who made us holy with his word,
And told us on this feast of light
To light one candle more each night.

by H. N.
of Ameri-
1939
"Dreidel Song. rian J. and
Efraim M. Rosenzweig. Union of American Hebrew Congregations, Cincinnati, Ohio, 1937

"A Song of Always." From *Now We Begin* by Marian J.
and Efraim M. Rosenzweig. Union of American Hebrew
Congregations, Cincinnati, Ohio, 1937

"Blessings for Chanukah." From *Around the Year in
Rhymes for the Jewish Child* by Jessie E. Sampter. Bloch
Publishing Company, New York, 1920

(Because when foes about us pressed
  To crush us all with death or shame,
The Lord his priests with courage blest
To strike and give his people rest
And in the House that he loved best
  Relight our everlasting flame.)

Blest are Thou, the whole world's King,
Who did so wonderful a thing
For our own fathers true and gold
At this same time in days of old!

AN OLD CHRISTMAS GREETING

(Unknown)

Sing hey! Sing hey!
For Christmas Day;
Twine mistletoe and holly,
For friendship glows
In winter snows,
And so let's all be jolly.

CHRISTMAS

(Mother Goose)

Christmas is coming, the geese are
  getting fat,
Please to put a penny in an old
  man's hat;
If you haven't got a penny a
  ha'penny will do,
If you haven't got a ha'penny, God
  bless you.

THE CHRISTMAS PUDDING

(Unknown)

Into the basin put the plums,
Stirabout, stirabout, stirabout!

Next the good white flour comes,
Stirabout, stirabout, stirabout!

Sugar and peel and eggs and spice,
Stirabout, stirabout, stirabout!

Mix them and fix them and cook them twice,
Stirabout, stirabout, stirabout!

CAROL, BROTHERS, CAROL

William Muhlenberg

Carol, brothers, carol,
Carol joyfully,
Carol the good tidings,
Carol merrily!
And pray a gladsome Christmas
For all good Christian men,
Carol, brothers, carol,
Christmas comes again.

Sir Walter Scott

Heap on more wood!—the wind is chill;
But let it whistle as it will,
We'll keep our Christmas merry still.

Christina Georgina Rossetti

But give me holly, bold and jolly,
Honest, prickly, shining holly;
Pluck me holly leaf and berry
For the day when I make merry.

BUNDLES

John Farrar

A bundle is a funny thing,
It always sets me wondering;
For whether it is thin or wide
You never know just what's inside.

Especially on Christmas week,
Temptation is so great to peek!
Now wouldn't it be much more fun
If shoppers carried things undone?

"Christmas." From *The Real Mother Goose*. Rand
McNally & Company, Chicago, 1916
"The Christmas Pudding." *Five- and six-year-olds enjoy
saying this in two groups, one for the narrative and the*
other for the "stirabout" chorus. The latter will get more
vigor into their part if they suit the action to the words.
"But give me holly, bold and jolly." From *Sing-Song* by
Christina Georgina Rossetti

A VISIT FROM ST. NICHOLAS

Clement C. Moore

"Twas the night before Christmas, when all
    through the house
Not a creature was stirring, not even a mouse;
The stockings were hung by the chimney with
    care,
In hopes that St. Nicholas soon would be there;
The children were nestled all snug in their beds
While visions of sugar-plums danced in their
    heads;
And Mamma in her 'kerchief, and I in my cap,
Had just settled our brains for a long winter's
    nap,
When out on the lawn there arose such a clatter,
I sprang from my bed to see what was the matter.
Away to the window I flew like a flash,
Tore open the shutters and threw up the sash.
The moon on the breast of the new-fallen snow
Gave a lustre of midday to objects below,
When, what to my wondering eyes did appear,
But a miniature sleigh and eight tiny reindeer,
With a little old driver, so lively and quick,
I knew in a moment it must be St. Nick.
More rapid than eagles his coursers they came,
And he whistled, and shouted, and called them
    by name:
"Now, Dasher! now, Dancer! now, Prancer and
    Vixen!
On, Comet! on, Cupid! on, Donder and Blitzen!
To the top of the porch! to the top of the wall!
Now dash away! dash away! dash away, all!"
As dry leaves that before the wild hurricane fly,
When they meet with an obstacle, mount to the
    sky,
So up to the housetop the coursers they flew,
With the sleigh full of toys, and St. Nicholas too.

And then, in a twinkling, I heard on the roof
The prancing and pawing of each little hoof.
As I drew in my head, and was turning around,
Down the chimney St. Nicholas came with a
    bound.
He was dressed all in fur, from his head to his
    foot,
And his clothes were all tarnished with ashes and
    soot;
A bundle of toys he had flung on his back,
And he looked like a peddler just opening his
    pack.
His eyes—how they twinkled! his dimples, how
    merry!
His cheeks were like roses, his nose like a cherry!
His droll little mouth was drawn up like a bow,
And the beard on his chin was as white as the
    snow;
The stump of a pipe he held tight in his teeth,
And the smoke, it encircled his head like a
    wreath;
He had a broad face and a little round belly
That shook, when he laughed, like a bowl full of
    jelly.
He was chubby and plump, a right jolly old elf,
And I laughed when I saw him, in spite of my-
    self;
A wink of his eye and a twist of his head,
Soon gave me to know I had nothing to dread;
He spoke not a word, but went straight to his
    work,
And filled all the stockings; then turned with a
    jerk,
And laying his finger aside of his nose,
And giving a nod, up the chimney he rose.
He sprang to his sleigh, to his team gave a
    whistle,
And away they all flew like the down of a thistle.
But I heard him exclaim, ere he drove out of
    sight,
"HAPPY CHRISTMAS TO ALL,
AND TO ALL A GOOD-NIGHT!"

"Bundles." From *Songs for Parents* by John Farrar. Yale
University Press, New Haven, 1921
"A Visit from St. Nicholas." *See* Children and Books,
pp. 96–97, for the history of this famous poem.

HERE WE COME A-CAROLING

(An Old Christmas Carol)

Here we come a-caroling
    Among the leaves so green;
Here we come a-wand'ring
    So fair to be seen.

Love and joy come to you
And a joyful Christmas, too;
And God bless you and send
You a Happy New Year—
And God send you a Happy New Year.

We are not daily beggars
    That beg from door to door;
But we are neighbors' children
    That you have seen before.

Love and joy come to you
And a joyful Christmas, too;
And God bless you and send
You a Happy New Year—
And God send you a Happy New Year.

God bless the master of the house
    Likewise the mistress, too;
And all the little children
    That round the table go.

Love and joy come to you
And a joyful Christmas, too;
And God bless you and send
You a Happy New Year—
And God send you a Happy New Year.

CEREMONIES FOR CHRISTMAS

Robert Herrick

Come, bring with a noise,
    My merry, merry boys,
The Christmas log to the firing;

While my good dame, she
    Bids ye all be free;
And drinks to your hearts' desiring.

With the last year's brand
    Light the new block, and
For good success in his spending,
    On your psaltries play,
    That sweet luck may
Come while the log is a-tending.

Drink now the strong beer,
    Cut the white loaf here,
The while the meat is a-shredding;
    For the rare mince-pie
    And the plums stand by
To fill the paste that's a-kneading.

IN THE WEEK WHEN CHRISTMAS COMES

Eleanor Farjeon

This is the week when Christmas comes.

Let every pudding burst with plums,
And every tree bear dolls and drums,
    In the week when Christmas comes.

Let every hall have boughs of green,
With berries glowing in between,
    In the week when Christmas comes.

Let every doorstep have a song
Sounding the dark street along,
    In the week when Christmas comes.

Let every steeple ring a bell
With a joyful tale to tell,
    In the week when Christmas comes.

"Here We Come A-Caroling." *The carols are beautiful for individual reading or for choral speaking. Although arrangements for the latter are suggested, please remember that the quiet individual reading of these songs is always desirable.*

"Here We Come A-Caroling" *is a familiar carol for singing but it also reads well. For choral speaking, half the children may speak the narrative and half the chorus. Or three solo voices may be used for the three verses while the* whole group speaks the chorus softly; or three different groups may take one chorus each.

"In the Week When Christmas Comes." *Easy and delightful for verse choirs! All the children speak the first and last lines; M, verses 1 and 6; H, verses 2 and 4; L, verses 3 and 5.* Reprinted by permission of the publishers, J. B. Lippincott Company from *Come Christmas* by Eleanor Farjeon. Copyright 1927 by J. B. Lippincott Company

Let every night put forth a star
To show us where the heavens are,
  In the week when Christmas comes.

Let every stable have a lamb
Sleeping warm beside its dam,
  In the week when Christmas comes.

This is the week when Christmas comes.

FOR CHRISTMAS DAY
Eleanor Farjeon

A carol round the ruddy hearth,
  A song outside the door—
Let Christmas Day make sure its lay
  Sounds sweetly to the poor.

A turkey in the baking-tin,
  A pudding in the pot—
Let Christmas Day the hunger stay
  In them that have not got.

Red berries on the picture-frame,
  White berries in the hall—
Let Christmas Day look twice as gay
  With evergreens for all.

A stocking on the chimneypiece,
  A present on the chair—
Let Christmas Day not pass away
  Till those who have do share.

A star upon the midnight sky,
  A shepherd looking East—
On Christmas Day let all men pray,
  And not till after feast.

SONG
Eugene Field

Why do bells for Christmas ring?
Why do little children sing?

Once a lovely, shining star,
Seen by shepherds from afar,
Gently moved until its light
Made a manger's cradle bright.

There a darling baby lay,
Pillowed soft upon the hay;
And its mother sang and smiled,
"This is Christ, the holy child!"

Therefore bells for Christmas ring,
Therefore little children sing.

CRADLE HYMN
Martin Luther

Away in a manger,
No crib for a bed,
The little Lord Jesus
Lay down his sweet head;
The stars in the heavens
Looked down where he lay,
The little Lord Jesus
Asleep in the hay.

The cattle are lowing,
The poor baby wakes,
But little Lord Jesus
No crying he makes.
I love thee, Lord Jesus,
Look down from the sky,
And stay by my cradle
Till morning is nigh.

"For Christmas Day." *The second couplet of each verse is in the nature of a warning or reminder, but speak it gravely and gently, or it will sound too moralistic and lugubrious. The low choir might carry the second couplet in verses 1, 2, 3, and 4; H: the first couplet in verses 2 and 4; M: the first couplet in verses 1, 3, and 5; and everyone the last couplet. Reprinted by permission of the publishers, J. B. Lippincott Company, from Eleanor Farjeon's Poems for Children.* Copyright, 1951, by Eleanor Farjeon

"Song." *A solo voice, light and clear, asks the question in the first two lines; M to L: verse 2; M to H: verse 3; the last couplet may be spoken by all or by a low, warm solo voice. Reprinted from Sharps and Flats by Eugene Field; copyright 1900, 1928 by Julia Sutherland Field; used by permission of the publishers, Charles Scribner's Sons*

LONG, LONG AGO

(Unknown)

Winds through the olive trees
  Softly did blow,
Round little Bethlehem
  Long, long ago.

Sheep on the hillside lay
  Whiter than snow;
Shepherds were watching them,
  Long, long ago.

Then from the happy sky,
  Angels bent low,
Singing their songs of joy,
  Long, long ago.

For in a manger bed,
  Cradled we know,
Christ came to Bethlehem,
  Long, long ago.

A CHRISTMAS FOLK-SONG

Lizette Woodworth Reese

The little Jesus came to town;
The wind blew up, the wind blew down;
Out in the street the wind was bold;
Now who would house Him from the cold?

Then opened wide the stable door,
Fair were the rushes on the floor;
The Ox put forth a hornèd head:
"Come, little Lord, here make Thy bed."

Up rose the Sheep were folded near:
"Thou Lamb of God, come, enter here."
He entered there to rush and reed,
Who was the Lamb of God indeed.

The little Jesus came to town;
With ox and sheep He laid Him down;

Peace to the byre, peace to the fold,
For that they housed Him from the cold!

A CHRISTMAS CAROL

Gilbert K. Chesterton

The Christ-child lay on Mary's lap,
  His hair was like a light.
(O weary, weary were the world,
  But here is all aright.)

The Christ-child lay on Mary's breast,
  His hair was like a star.
(O stern and cunning are the kings,
  But here the true hearts are.)

The Christ-child lay on Mary's heart,
  His hair was like a fire.
(O weary, weary is the world,
  But here the world's desire.)

The Christ-child stood at Mary's knee,
  His hair was like a crown,
And all the flowers looked up at Him
And all the stars looked down.

THE SHEPHERD AND THE KING

Eleanor Farjeon

The Shepherd and the King,
The Angel and the Ass,
They heard Sweet Mary sing
When her joy was come to pass;
They heard Sweet Mary sing
To the Baby on her knee;
Sing again, Sweet Mary,
And we will sing with thee!
  Earth, bear a berry!
  Heaven, bear a light!
  Man, make you merry
  On Christmas Night.

"A Christmas Folk Song." From *The Selected Poems of Lizette Woodworth Reese*. Copyright 1926 by Lizette Woodworth Reese, and reprinted by permission of Rinehart & Company, Inc., Publishers

"A Christmas Carol." *Each verse has a refrain and a nar-rative. These may be variously distributed: Verse 1: High, refrain: Medium; verse 2: High, refrain: Low; verse 3: High, refrain: Low, verse 4: Medium, refrain: High; or all may speak the refrain softly and tenderly. Taken from The Wild Knight and Other Poems, by G. K. Chesterton,*

The Oxen in the stall,
The Sheep upon the hill,
They are waking all
To hear Sweet Mary still.
The Baby is a Child,
And the Child is running free;
Sing again, Sweet Mary,
And we will sing with thee!
    Earth, bear a berry!
    Heaven, bear a light!
    Man, make you merry
    On Christmas night.

The People in the land,
So many million strong,
All silently do stand
To hear Sweet Mary's song.
The Child He is a Man,
And the Man hangs on a tree.
Sing again, Sweet Mary,
And we will sing with thee!
    Earth, bear a berry!
    Heaven, bear a light!
    Man, make you merry
    On Christmas night.

The Stars that are so old,
The Grass that is so young,
They listen in the cold
To hear Sweet Mary's tongue.
The Man's the Son of God,
And in Heaven walketh He.
Sing again, Sweet Mary,
And we will sing with thee!
    Earth, bear a berry!
    Heaven, bear a light!
    Man, make you merry
    On Christmas night.

                William Shakespeare

Some say, that ever 'gainst that season comes
Wherein our Savior's birth is celebrated,
The bird of dawning singeth all night long:
So hallow'd and so gracious is the time.

published by E. P. Dutton & Co., Inc. Reprinted by
permission of the publishers and Miss Collins, Executrix.
"The Shepherd and the King." Reprinted by permission
of the publishers, J. B. Lippincott Company from *Eleanor
Farjeon's Poems for Children*. Copyright, 1951, by Eleanor
Farjeon

CHRISTMAS IN THE WOODS

Frances M. Frost

Tonight when the hoar frost falls on the wood,
And the rabbit cowers, and the squirrel is cold,
And the horned owl huddles against a star,
And the drifts are deep, and the year is old,
All shy creatures will think of Him.
The shivering mouse, the hare, the wild young
        fox,
The doe with the startled fawn,
Will dream of gentleness and a Child:

The buck with budding horns will turn
His starry eyes to a silver hill tonight,
The chipmunk will awake and stir
And leave his burrow for the chill, dark mid-
        night,
And all timid things will pause and sigh, and
        sighing, bless
That Child who loves the trembling hearts,
The shy hearts of the wilderness.

GLADDE THINGS

(Unknown)

    Of gladde things there be four, ay four:
    A Larke above ye olde nest blithely singing,
    A wild Rose clinging
    In safety to a rock, a Shepherd bringing
    A Lambe found in his arms,
    And Christmasse Bells a-ringing.

CHRISTMAS CAROL

(Unknown)

    God bless the master of this house,
        The mistress also,
    And all the little children,
        That round the table go,
    And all your kin and kinsmen
        That dwell both far and near;
    I wish you a Merry Christmas
        And a Happy New Year.

"Some say, that ever 'gainst that season comes." From
Hamlet, Act I, Sc. 1
"Christmas in the Woods." From *Christmas in the
Woods* by Frances M. Frost. Copyright, 1942, by Frances
M. Frost

NEW YEAR'S DAY
Rachel Field

Last night, while we were fast asleep,
  The old year went away.
It can't come back again because
  A new one's come to stay.

Elizabeth Coatsworth

Cold winter now is in the wood,
The moon wades deep in snow.
Pile balsam boughs about the sills,
  And let the fires glow!

The cows must stand in the dark barn,
The horses stamp all day.
Now shall the housewife bake her pies
And keep her kitchen gay.

The cat sleeps warm beneath the stove,
The dog on paws outspread;
But the brown deer with flinching hide
Seeks for a sheltered bed.

The fox steps hungry through the brush,
The lean hawk coasts the sky.
"Winter is in the wood!" the winds
In the warm chimney cry.

WINTER NIGHT
Mary Frances Butts

Blow, wind, blow!
  Drift the flying snow!
Send it twirling, whirling overhead!
  There's a bedroom in a tree
  Where, snug as snug can be,
The squirrel nests in his cozy bed.

Shriek, wind, shriek!
  Make the branches creak!
Battle with the boughs till break o' day!

In a snow-cave warm and tight,
  Through the icy winter night
The rabbit sleeps the peaceful hours away.

Call, wind, call,
  In entry and in hall,
Straight from off the mountain white and wild!
  Soft purrs the pussy-cat,
  On her little fluffy mat,
And beside her nestles close her furry child.

Scold, wind, scold,
  So bitter and so bold!
Shake the windows with your tap, tap, tap!
  With half-shut dreamy eyes
  The drowsy baby lies
Cuddled closely in his mother's lap.

STOPPING BY WOODS ON A SNOWY EVENING
Robert Frost

Whose woods these are I think I know.
His house is in the village though;
He will not see me stopping here
To watch his woods fill up with snow.

My little horse must think it queer
To stop without a farmhouse near
Between the woods and frozen lake
The darkest evening of the year.

He gives his harness bells a shake
To ask if there is some mistake.
The only other sound's the sweep
Of easy wind and downy flake.

The woods are lovely, dark and deep.
But I have promises to keep,
And miles to go before I sleep,
And miles to go before I sleep.

VELVET SHOES
Elinor Wylie

Let us walk in the white snow
   In a soundless space;
With footsteps quiet and slow,
   At a tranquil pace,
   Under veils of white lace.

I shall go shod in silk,
   And you in wool,
White as a white cow's milk,
   More beautiful
   Than the breast of a gull.

We shall walk through the still town
   In a windless peace;
We shall step upon white down,
   Upon silver fleece,
   Upon softer than these.

We shall walk in velvet shoes:
   Wherever we go
Silence will fall like dews
   On white silence below.
   We shall walk in the snow.

WINTER NIGHT
Collister Hutchison

A tree may be laughter in the spring
Or a promise
Or conceit.

In the summer it may be anything
Lazy and warm with life,
Complete.

In the fall
It is the answer
To a long-forgotten call.

But on a lonely winter night
In still air
When it takes the shape of a candle flame
Springing dark from a hill all white,
It is a dare.

WAITING
Harry Behn

Dreaming of honeycombs to share
With her small cubs, a mother bear
Sleeps in a snug and snowy lair.

Bees in their drowsy, drifted hive
Sip hoarded honey to survive
Until the flowers come alive.

Sleeping beneath the deep snow
Seeds of honeyed flowers know
When it is time to wake and grow.

A SURE SIGN
Nancy Byrd Turner

Here's the mail, sort it quick—
Papers, letters, notes,
Postcard scenes,
Magazines;
Our hearts are in our throats.
Something there,
White and square,
Sealed with wax, and bumpy—
At the edges flat and thin,
In the middle lumpy.

When you feel the envelope,
Do your fingers trace
Something narrow,
Like an arrow?
Or a part
Of a heart?
Or a Cupid's face?
Is your name across the back
In a crooked line?
Hurry, then; that's a sign
Someone's sent a valentine!

A VALENTINE

Eleanor Hammond

Frost flowers on the window glass,
Hopping chickadees that pass,
Bare old elms that bend and sway,
Pussy willows, soft and gray,

Silver clouds across the sky,
Lacy snowflakes flitting by,
Icicles like fringe in line—
That is Outdoor's valentine!

MY VALENTINE

Mary Catherine Parsons

I have a little valentine
    That some one sent to me.
It's pink and white and red and blue,
    And pretty as can be.

Forget-me-nots are round the edge,
    And tiny roses, too;
And such a lovely piece of lace—
    The very palest blue.

And in the center there's a heart,
    As red as red can be!

And on it's written all in gold,
    "To You, with Love from Me."

HEARTS WERE MADE TO GIVE AWAY

Annette Wynne

Hearts were made to give away
    On Valentine's good day;
Wrap them up in dainty white,
Send them off the thirteenth night,
Any kind of heart that's handy—
    Hearts of lace, and hearts of candy,
    Hearts all trimmed with ribbands fine
    Send for good St. Valentine.
Hearts were made to give away
On Valentine's dear day.

I'LL WEAR A SHAMROCK

Mary Carolyn Davies

St. Patrick's Day is with us,
    The day when all that's seen
To right and left and everywhere
    Is green, green, green!

And Irish tunes they whistle
    And Irish songs they sing,
To-day each Irish lad walks out
    As proud as any king.

I'll wear a four-leaf shamrock
    In my coat, the glad day through,
For my father and mother are Irish
    And I am Irish, too!

WISE JOHNNY

Edwina Fallis

Little Johnny-jump-up said,
    "It must be spring,

"A Valentine." From *Child Life*, February 1927. Child Life, Inc., Boston. By permission of Eleanor H. Doar
"My Valentine." From *Youth's Companion*. By permission of the author
"Hearts Were Made to Give Away." From *For Days and Days* by Annette Wynne. Copyright 1919, 1947 by Annette Wynne. By permission of J. B. Lippincott Company
"I'll Wear a Shamrock." From *Child Life*, March 1926.

Child Life, Inc., Boston. Used by permission of A. H. Davies
"Wise Johnny." From *Sung under the Silver Umbrella*. The Macmillan Company, New York, 1935. Used by permission of the author
"Daffodils." From *A Year of Japanese Epigrams* compiled by W. N. Porter. Used by permission of Oxford University Press, London

I just saw a lady-bug
And heard a robin sing."

(*Mother Goose*)

Daffadowndilly
    Has come up to town,
In a yellow petticoat
And a green gown.

DAFFODILS

Kikuriō

In spite of cold and chills
That usher in the early spring
We have the daffodils.

Christina Georgina Rossetti

Growing in the vale
    By the uplands hilly,
Growing straight and frail,
    Lady Daffadowndilly.

In a golden crown,
And a scant green gown
    While the spring blows chilly,
Lady Daffadown,
    Sweet Daffadowndilly.

E. Wyndham Tennant

I saw green banks of daffodil,
    Slim poplars in the breeze,
Great tan-brown hares in gusty March
    A-courting on the leas;
And meadows with their glittering
        streams, and silver scurrying dace,
Home—what a perfect place!

William Shakespeare

            . . . daffodils,
That come before the swallow dares, and take
The winds of March with beauty . . .

SPRING

Harry Behn

The last snow is going,
Brooks are overflowing,
And a sunny wind is blowing
    Swiftly along.

Through the sky birds are blowing,
On earth green is showing,
You can feel earth growing
    So quiet and strong.

A sunny wind is blowing,
Farmer's busy sowing,
Apple trees are snowing,
    And shadows grow long.

Now the wind is slowing,
Cows begin lowing,
Evening clouds are glowing
    And dusk is full of song.

from THE SONG OF SONGS

For, lo, the winter is past,
The rain is over and gone;
The flowers appear on the earth;
The time of the singing of birds is come,
And the voice of the turtle is heard in our land.

ROBIN'S SONG

E. L. M. King

Robin's song is crystal clear
Cold as an icicle,

"Growing in the vale." From *Sing-Song* by Christina Georgina Rossetti
"I saw green banks of daffodil. . . ." From *Home Thoughts in Laventi* by E. Wyndham Tennant. London: Oxford University Press. By permission of the Estate of the Author
"Spring." From *The Little Hill*, copyright, 1949, by Harry Behn. Reprinted by permission of Harcourt, Brace and Company, Inc.
"For, lo, the winter is past." The Song of Songs, 2:11, 12. *"The voice of the turtle"* refers to the bird, the turtle dove.
"Robin's Song." From *Fifty Country Rhymes for Children* by E. L. M. King. Copyright, 1926, by D. Appleton and Company. Reprinted by permission of Appleton-Century-Crofts, Inc.

Sharp as a spear.
I have seen Spring lift her head,
Snowdrops a-shivering,
Winter dead.

CROCUSES

Jōsa

The sunrise tints the dew;
The yellow crocuses are out,
And I must pick a few.

WRITTEN IN MARCH

William Wordsworth

The Cock is crowing,
The stream is flowing,
The small birds twitter,
The lake doth glitter,
The green field sleeps in the sun;
The oldest and youngest
Are at work with the strongest;
The cattle are grazing,
Their heads never raising;
There are forty feeding like one!

Like an army defeated
The snow hath retreated,
And now doth fare ill
On the top of the bare hill;
The ploughboy is whooping—anon—anon:
There's joy in the mountains;
There's life in the fountains;
Small clouds are sailing,
Blue sky prevailing;
The rain is over and gone!

I WILL GO WITH MY FATHER A-PLOUGHING

Joseph Campbell

I will go with my Father a-ploughing
To the Green Field by the sea,

And the rooks and crows and seagulls
Will come flocking after me.
I will sing to the patient horses
With the lark in the shine of the air,
And my Father will sing the Plough-Song
That blesses the cleaving share.

I will go with my Father a-sowing
To the Red Field by the sea,
And blackbirds and robins and thrushes
Will come flocking after me.
I will sing to the striding sowers
With the finch on the flowering sloe,
And my Father will sing the Seed-Song
That only the wise men know.

I will go with my Father a-reaping
To the Brown Field by the sea,
And the geese and pigeons and sparrows
Will come flocking after me.
I will sing to the weary reapers
With the wren in the heat of the sun,
And my Father will sing the Scythe-Song
That joys for the harvest done.

SEEDS

Walter de la Mare

The seeds I sowed—
For weeks unseen—
Have pushed up pygmy
Shoots of green;
So frail you'd think
The tiniest stone
Would never let
A glimpse be shown.

But no; a pebble
Near them lies,
At least a cherry-stone
In size,
Which that mere sprout
Has heaved away,
To bask in sun,
And see the day.

"Crocuses." From *A Year of Japanese Epigrams* compiled by W. N. Porter. Oxford University Press, London, 1911

"I Will Go With My Father A-Ploughing." From *The Mountainy Singer* by Joseph Campbell. Boston: The Four Seas Company, 1919

"Seeds." From *Rhymes and Verses* by Walter de la Mare. Published by Henry Holt & Company, Inc., New York, 1947. By permission of the literary trustees of Walter de la Mare and The Society of Authors, London, as their representatives

"Meeting the Easter Bunny." From *Around a Toadstool*

SPRING
William Blake

Sound the flute!
Now it's mute;
Birds delight,
Day and night,
Nightingale
In the dale,
Lark in sky,—
Merrily,
Merrily, merrily, to welcome in the year.

Little Boy,
Full of joy;
Little Girl,
Sweet and small;
Cock does crow,
So do you;
Merry voice,
Infant noise,
Merrily, merrily, to welcome in the year.

Little Lamb,
Here I am;
Come and lick
My white neck;
Let me pull
Your soft Wool;
Let me kiss
Your soft face;
Merrily, merrily, we welcome in the year.

MEETING THE EASTER BUNNY
Rowena Bastin Bennett

On Easter morn at early dawn
  before the cocks were crowing,
I met a bob-tail bunnykin
  and asked where he was going,
" 'Tis in the house and out the house
  a-tipsy, tipsy-toeing,
'Tis round the house and 'bout the house
  a-lightly I am going."

Table by Rowena Bastin Bennett. Follett Publishing Company, Chicago, 1930
  "The Day Before April." From *Youth Riding* by Mary Carolyn Davies. The Macmillan Company, New York, 1919.

"But what is that of every hue
  you carry in your basket?"
" 'Tis eggs of gold and eggs of blue;
  I wonder that you ask it.
'Tis chocolate eggs and bonbon eggs
  and eggs of red and gray,
For every child in every house
  on bonny Easter Day."
He perked his ears and winked his eye
  and twitched his little nose;
He shook his tail—what tail he had—
  and stood up on his toes.
"I must be gone before the sun;
  the east is growing gray;
'Tis almost time for bells to chime."—
  So he hippety-hopped away.

THE DAY BEFORE APRIL
Mary Carolyn Davies

The day before April
  Alone, alone,
I walked in the woods
  And I sat on a stone.

I sat on a broad stone
  And sang to the birds.
The tune was God's making
  But I made the words.

APRIL
Sara Teasdale

The roofs are shining from the rain,
  The sparrows twitter as they fly,
And with a windy April grace
  The little clouds go by.

Yet the back-yards are bare and brown
  With only one unchanging tree—
I could not be so sure of Spring
  Save that it sings in me.

Used by permission of A. H. Davies
  "April." From *Rivers to the Sea* by Sara Teasdale. Copyright 1915, 1943 by The Macmillan Company and used with their permission

EASTER

Hilda Conkling

On Easter morn
Up the faint cloudy sky
I hear the Easter bell,
 Ding dong . . . ding dong . . .
Easter morning scatters lilies
On every doorstep;
Easter morning says a glad thing
Over and over.
Poor people, beggars, old women
Are hearing the Easter bell . . .
 Ding dong . . . ding dong . . .

EASTER

Joyce Kilmer

The air is like a butterfly
 With frail blue wings.
The happy earth looks at the sky
 And sings.

LILIES

Shikō (Arranged by Olive Beaupré Miller)

I thought I saw white clouds, but no!—
 Bending across the fence,
 White lilies in a row!

THE FALL OF
THE PLUM BLOSSOMS

Rankō

I came to look, and lo!
The plum tree petals scatter down,
 A fall of purest snow.

Christina Georgina Rossetti

Oh, fair to see
Bloom-laden cherry tree,

Arrayed in sunny white:
An April day's delight,
Oh, fair to see!

Oh, fair to see
Fruit-laden cherry tree,
 With balls of shining red
 Decking a leafy head,
Oh, fair to see!

THE IRIS

Gasetsu

 Ere yet the sun is high,
All blue the iris blossoms wave,
 The colour of the sky.

William Shakespeare

Under the greenwood tree
Who loves to lie with me,
And turn his merry note
Unto the sweet bird's throat,
Come hither, come hither, come hither:
Here shall he see
No enemy
But winter and rough weather.

TREES

Harry Behn

Trees are the kindest things I know,
They do no harm, they simply grow

And spread a shade for sleepy cows,
And gather birds among their boughs.

They give us fruit in leaves above,
And wood to make our houses of,

And leaves to burn on Hallowe'en,
And in the Spring new buds of green.

They are the first when day's begun
To touch the beams of morning sun,

They are the last to hold the light
When evening changes into night,

And when a moon floats on the sky
They hum a drowsy lullaby

Of sleepy children long ago . . .
Trees are the kindest things I know.

WHAT DO WE PLANT?

Henry Abbey

What do we plant when we plant the tree?
We plant the ship, which will cross the sea.
We plant the mast to carry the sails;
We plant the planks to withstand the gales—
The keel, the keelson, and beam and knee;
We plant the ship when we plant the tree.

What do we plant when we plant the tree?
We plant the houses for you and me.
We plant the rafters, the shingles, the floors,
We plant the studding, the lath, the doors,
The beams and siding, all parts that be;
We plant the house when we plant the tree.

What do we plant when we plant the tree?
A thousand things that we daily see;
We plant the spire that out-towers the crag,
We plant the staff for our country's flag,
We plant the shade, from the hot sun free;
We plant all these when we plant the tree.

THE FLAG GOES BY

Henry Holcomb Bennett

Hats off!
Along the street there comes
A blare of bugles, a ruffle of drums,
A flash of color beneath the sky:

Hats off!
The flag is passing by!

Blue and crimson and white it shines,
Over the steel-tipped, ordered lines.
Hats off!
The colors before us fly;
But more than the flag is passing by.

Sea-fights and land-fights, grim and great,
Fought to make and to save the State:
Weary marches and sinking ships;
Cheers of victory on dying lips;

Days of plenty and years of peace;
March of a strong land's swift increase;
Equal justice, right and law,
Stately honor and reverend awe;

Sign of a nation, great and strong
To ward her people from foreign wrong:
Pride and glory and honor,—all
Live in the colors to stand or fall.

Hats off!
Along the street there comes
A blare of bugles, a ruffle of drums;
And loyal hearts are beating high:
Hats off!
The flag is passing by!

Christina Georgina Rossetti

The days are clear,
  Day after day,
When April's here,
  That leads to May,
And June
Must follow soon:
  Stay, June, stay!—
If only we could stop the moon
And June!

by W. N. Porter. By permission of Oxford University Press, London
"Under the greenwood tree." *This song always suggests Robin Hood and his merry men.* From *As You Like It*, Act II, Sc. 5
"Trees." From *The Little Hill*, copyright, 1949, by Harry Behn. Reprinted by permission of Harcourt, Brace and Company, Inc.
"What Do We Plant?" From *The Poems of Henry Abbey*. D. Appleton and Company, New York, 1904
"The Flag Goes By." Used with the kind permission of Martha Trimble Bennett
"The days are clear." From *Sing-Song* by Christina Georgina Rossetti

Christina Georgina Rossetti

There is but one May in the year,
   And sometimes May is wet and cold;
There is but one May in the year
   Before the year grows old.

Yet though it be the chilliest May,
   With least of sun and most of showers,
Its wind and dew, its night and day,
   Bring up the flowers.

DANDELION

Hilda Conkling

O little soldier with the golden helmet,
What are you guarding on my lawn?
You with your green gun
And your yellow beard,
Why do you stand so stiff?
There is only the grass to fight!

DANDELIONS

Frances M. Frost

Over the climbing meadows
Where swallow-shadows float,
These are the small gold buttons
On earth's green, windy coat.

MILLIONS OF STRAWBERRIES

Genevieve Taggard

Marcia and I went over the curve,
Eating our way down
Jewels of strawberries we didn't deserve,
Eating our way down.
Till our hands were sticky, and our lips painted,
And over us the hot day fainted,

And we saw snakes,
And got scratched,
And a lust overcame us for the red unmatched
Small buds of berries,
Till we lay down—
Eating our way down—
And rolled in the berries like two little dogs,
Rolled
In the late gold.
And gnats hummed,
And it was cold,
And home we went, home without a berry,
Painted red and brown,
Eating our way down.

SPRINKLING

Dorothy Mason Pierce

Sometimes in the summer
When the day is hot
Daddy takes the garden hose
And finds a shady spot;
Then he calls me over,
Looks at my bare toes
And says, "Why, you need sprinkling,
You thirsty little rose!"

THE LITTLE ROSE TREE

Rachel Field

Every rose on the little tree
Is making a different face at me!

Some look surprised when I pass by,
And others droop—but they are shy.

These two whose heads together press
Tell secrets I could never guess.

"There is but one May in the year." From *Sing-Song* by Christina Georgina Rossetti

"Dandelion." From *Poems by a Little Girl* by Hilda Conkling. Copyright 1920 by J. B. Lippincott Company

"Dandelions." From *Pool in the Meadow* by Frances M. Frost. Reprinted by permission of and arrangement with Houghton Mifflin Company, the authorized publishers

"Millions of Strawberries." From *The New Yorker*. The New Yorker Magazine, Inc., New York, June 8, 1929. Used by permission of Kenneth Durant, Executor, Estate of Genevieve Taggard

"Sprinkling." From *Sung under the Silver Umbrella*. The Macmillan Company, New York, 1935. Used by permission of the author

"The Little Rose Tree." From *The Pointed People* by Rachel Field. The Macmillan Company, New York, 1930. Used by permission of Arthur S. Pederson, Trustee, Estate of Rachel Field Pederson

Some have their heads thrown back to sing,
And all the buds are listening.

I wonder if the gardener knows,
Or if he calls each just a rose?

FOURTH OF JULY NIGHT

Dorothy Aldis

Pin wheels whirling round
Spit sparks upon the ground,
And rockets shoot up high
And blossom in the sky—
Blue and yellow, green and red
Flowers falling on my head,
And I don't ever have to go
To bed, to bed, to bed!

"Fourth of July Night." From *Hop, Skip and Jump* by Dorothy Aldis. Minton, Balch and Company, New York, 1934. Copyright 1934 by Dorothy Aldis.

Christina Georgina Rossetti

What is pink? a rose is pink
By the fountain's brink.
What is red? a poppy's red
In its barley bed.
What is blue? the sky is blue
Where the clouds float thro'.
What is white? a swan is white
Sailing in the light.
What is yellow? pears are yellow,
Rich and ripe and mellow.
What is green? the grass is green,
With small flowers between.
What is violet? clouds are violet
In the summer twilight.
What is orange? why, an orange,
Just an orange!

"What is pink? a rose is pink." From *Sing-Song* by Christina Georgina Rossetti

HAPPY THOUGHT

Robert Louis Stevenson

The world is so full of a number of things,
I'm sure we should all be as happy as kings.

I AM

Hilda Conkling

I am willowy boughs
For coolness;
I am gold-finch wings
For darkness;
I am a little grape
Thinking of September,
I am a very small violet
Thinking of May.

LESSON FROM A SUN-DIAL

(from the German adapted by Louis Untermeyer)

Ignore dull days; forget the showers;
Keep count of only shining hours.

OF QUARRELS

Arthur Guiterman

No Quarrel ever Stirred
Before the Second Word.

WISDOM AND BEAUTY

OF GIVING

Arthur Guiterman

Not what you Get, but what you Give
Is that which proves your Right to Live.

SHORT SERMON

(from the German adapted by Louis Untermeyer)

To give—and forgive—
Is a good way to live.

OF COURTESY

Arthur Guiterman

Good Manners may in Seven Words be found:
Forget Yourself and think of Those Around.

GOOD ADVICE

(from the German adapted by Louis Untermeyer)

Don't shirk
Your work
For the sake of a dream;
A fish
In the dish
Is worth ten in the stream.

MOTTO

(from the German adapted by Louis Untermeyer)

However they talk, whatever they say,
Look straight at the task without dismay—
And if you can do it, do it today.

DAY-DREAMER

(from the German adapted by Louis Untermeyer)

Too much thought:
Too little wrought.

Elizabeth Coatsworth

He who has never known hunger
Has never known how good
The taste of bread may be,
The kindliness of food.

COLLECTION OF PROVERBS

(Proverbs 16:32)

He that is slow to anger is better than the
    mighty;
And he that ruleth his spirit than he that taketh
    a city.

(Proverbs 15:1)

A soft answer turneth away wrath:
But grievous words stir up anger.

(Ecclesiastes 11:1)

Cast thy bread upon the waters:
For thou shalt find it after many days.

(II Timothy 1:7)

For God hath not given us the spirit of fear;
But of power, and of love, and of a sound mind.

(Isaiah 40:31)

But they that wait upon the Lord shall renew
    their strength;
They shall mount up with wings as eagles;

The poems in this section have to be thought about, talked about, or tucked away in memory to reread or say again. Here are manners, morals, and dreams to be savored thoughtfully. These poems are for children old enough to wonder about life and to be touched by beauty.

"Happy Thought." From *A Child's Garden of Verses* by Robert Louis Stevenson

"I Am." From *Poems by a Little Girl* by Hilda Conkling. Copyright 1920 by J. B. Lippincott Company

"Lesson from a Sun-Dial." From *Rainbow in the Sky* edited by Louis Untermeyer, copyright, 1935, by Harcourt, Brace and Company, Inc.

"Of Quarrels." Taken from *A Poet's Proverbs*, by Arthur Guiterman, published and copyright, 1924, by E. P. Dutton & Co., Inc., New York

"Of Giving." Taken from *A Poet's Proverbs*, by Arthur Guiterman, published and copyright, 1924, by E. P. Dutton & Co., Inc., New York

"Short Sermon." From *Rainbow in the Sky* edited by Louis Untermeyer, copyright, 1935, by Harcourt, Brace and Company, Inc.

"Of Courtesy." Taken from *A Poet's Proverbs*, by Arthur Guiterman, published and copyright, 1924, by E. P. Dutton & Co., Inc., New York

"Good Advice." From *Rainbow in the Sky* edited by Louis Untermeyer, copyright, 1935, by Harcourt, Brace and Company, Inc.

"Motto." From *Rainbow in the Sky* edited by Louis Untermeyer, copyright, 1935, by Harcourt, Brace and Company, Inc.

"Day-Dreamer." From *Rainbow in the Sky* edited by Louis Untermeyer, copyright, 1935, by Harcourt, Brace and Company, Inc.

"He who has never known hunger." From *The Fair American* by Elizabeth Coatsworth. Copyright 1940 by The Macmillan Company and used with their permission

They shall run, and not be weary;
And they shall walk, and not faint.

(Philippians 4:8)

Whatsoever things are true,
Whatsoever things are honest,
Whatsoever things are just,
Whatsoever things are pure,
Whatsoever things are lovely,
Whatsoever things are of good report;
If there be any virtue,
And if there be any praise,
I will think on these things.

FRET NOT THYSELF BECAUSE OF EVILDOERS

(Psalm 37)

Fret not thyself because of evildoers,
Neither be thou envious against the workers of
    iniquity.
For they shall soon be cut down like the grass,
And wither as the green herb.
I have seen the wicked in great power,
And spreading himself like a green bay tree.
Yet he passed away, and, lo, he was not:
Yea, I sought him, but he could not be found.
Trust in the Lord, and do good;
So shalt thou dwell in the land,
And verily thou shalt be fed.

T. S. Eliot

The world turns and the world changes,
But one thing does not change.
In all of my years, one thing does not change.
However you disguise it, this thing does not
    change:
The perpetual struggle of Good and Evil.

"Fret not thyself because of evildoers." Psalm 37 : 1, 2,
35, 36, 3

"The world turns and the world changes." *See the in-*
troduction, p. xx. From "The Rock" in *Collected Poems*
1909–1935 by T. S. Eliot, copyright, 1936, by Harcourt,

Christina Georgina Rossetti

An emerald is as green as grass;
    A ruby red as blood;
A sapphire shines as blue as heaven;
    A flint lies in the mud.

A diamond is a brilliant stone,
    To catch the world's desire;
An opal holds a fiery spark;
    But a flint holds fire.

THE LITTLE BOY LOST

William Blake

"Father, father, where are you going?
    Oh, do not walk so fast!
Speak, father, speak to your little boy,
    Or else I shall be lost."

The night was dark, no father was there,
    The child was wet with dew;
The mire was deep, and the child did weep,
    And away the vapour flew.

THE LITTLE BOY FOUND

William Blake

The little boy lost in the lonely fen,
    Led by the wandering light,
Began to cry, but God, ever nigh,
    Appeared like his father, in white.

He kissed the child, and by the hand led,
    And to his mother brought,
Who in sorrow pale, through the lonely dale,
    The little boy weeping sought.

Brace and Company, Inc. Reprinted by permission of
Harcourt, Brace and Company, Inc., and Faber and Faber,
Limited

"An emerald is as green as grass." From *Sing-Song* by
Christina Georgina Rossetti

THE PILGRIM

John Bunyan

Who would true valour see,
  Let him come hither!
One here will constant be,
  Come wind, come weather;
There's no discouragement
Shall make him once relent
His firm-avowed intent
  To be a Pilgrim.

Whoso beset him round
  With dismal stories,
Do but themselves confound;
  His strength the more is.
No lion can him fright;
He'll with a giant fight;
But he will have a right
  To be a Pilgrim.

Nor enemy, nor friend,
  Can daunt his spirit;
He knows he at the end
  Shall Life inherit:—
Then, fancies, fly away;
He'll not fear what men say:
He'll labour, night and day,
  To be a Pilgrim.

Elizabeth Coatsworth

Violets, daffodils,
Roses and thorn
Were all in the garden
Before you were born.

Daffodils, violets,
Green thorn and roses
Your grandchildren's children
Will hold to their noses.

A CHARM FOR SPRING FLOWERS

Rachel Field

Who sees the first marsh marigold
Shall count more wealth than hands can hold.

Who bends a knee where violets grow
A hundred secret things shall know.

Who finds hepatica's dim blue
Shall have his dearest wish come true.

Who spies on lady-slippers fair
Shall keep a heart as light as air.

But whosoever toucheth not
One petal, sets no root in pot,

He shall be blessed of earth and sky
Till under them he, too, shall lie.

Emily Dickinson

I'm nobody! Who are you?
Are you nobody too?
Then there's a pair of us—don't tell!
They'd banish us, you know.

How dreary to be somebody!
How public, like a frog
To tell your name the livelong day
To an admiring bog.

NIGHT

Sara Teasdale

Stars over snow,
  And in the west a planet
Swinging below a star—
  Look for a lovely thing and you will
    find it,
It is not far—
  It never will be far.

LOVELINESS

Hilda Conkling

Loveliness that dies when I forget
Comes alive when I remember.

BE LIKE THE BIRD

Victor Hugo

Be like the bird, who
Halting in his flight
On limb too slight
Feels it give way beneath him,
Yet sings
Knowing he hath wings.

I NEVER SAW A MOOR

Emily Dickinson

I never saw a moor,
I never saw the sea;
Yet know I how the heather looks,
And what a wave must be.

I never spoke with God,
Nor visited in heaven;
Yet certain am I of the spot
As if the chart were given.

A BLACKBIRD SUDDENLY

Joseph Auslander

Heaven is in my hand, and I
Touch a heart-beat of the sky,
Hearing a blackbird's cry.

Strange, beautiful, unquiet thing,
Lone flute of God, how can you sing
Winter to spring?

You have outdistanced every voice and word,
And given my spirit wings until it stirred
Like you—a bird!

DUST OF SNOW

Robert Frost

The way a crow
Shook down on me
The dust of snow
From a hemlock tree

Has given my heart
A change of mood
And saved some part
Of a day I had rued.

I HEARD A BIRD SING

Oliver Herford

I heard a bird sing
In the dark of December
A magical thing
And sweet to remember.

"We are nearer to Spring
Than we were in September,"
I heard a bird sing
In the dark of December.

DAYS

Karle Wilson Baker

Some days my thoughts are just cocoons—all
    cold, and dull and blind,
They hang from dripping branches in the grey
    woods of my mind;
And other days they drift and shine—such free
    and flying things!
I find the gold-dust in my hair, left by their
    brushing wings.

THE COIN

Sara Teasdale

Into my heart's treasury
    I slipped a coin
That time cannot take
    Nor a thief purloin,—
Oh, better than the minting
    Of a gold-crowned king
Is the safe-kept memory
    Of a lovely thing.

LEISURE

William Henry Davies

What is this life if, full of care,
We have no time to stand and stare.

No time to stand beneath the boughs
And stare as long as sheep or cows.

No time to see, when woods we pass,
Where squirrels hide their nuts in grass.

No time to see, in broad daylight,
Streams full of stars, like stars at night.

No time to turn at Beauty's glance,
And watch her feet, how they can dance.

No time to wait till her mouth can
Enrich that smile her eyes began.

A poor life this if, full of care,
We have no time to stand and stare.

BEAUTY

E-Yeh-Shure'

Beauty is seen
In the sunlight,
The trees, the birds,
Corn growing and people working
Or dancing for their harvest.

Beauty is heard
In the night,
Wind sighing, rain falling,
Or a singer chanting
Anything in earnest.

Beauty is in yourself.
Good deeds, happy thoughts
That repeat themselves
In your dreams,
In your work,
And even in your rest.

Elizabeth Coatsworth

Swift things are beautiful:
Swallows and deer,
And lightning that falls
Bright-veined and clear,
Rivers and meteors,

Wind in the wheat,
The strong-withered horse,
The runner's sure feet.

And slow things are beautiful:
The closing of day,
The pause of the wave
That curves downward to spray,
The ember that crumbles,
The opening flower,
And the ox that moves on
In the quiet of power.

HOLD FAST YOUR DREAMS

Louise Driscoll

Within your heart
Keep one still, secret spot
Where dreams may go,
And sheltered so,
May thrive and grow—
Where doubt and fear are not.
Oh, keep a place apart
Within your heart,
For little dreams to go.

HEAVEN

Langston Hughes

Heaven is
The place where
Happiness is
Everywhere.

T. S. Eliot

If humility and purity be not in the heart, they
  are not in the home: and if they are not
  in the home, they are not in the City.

THE CREATION

James Weldon Johnson

And God stepped out on space,
And he looked around and said:
I'm lonely—
I'll make me a world.

And as far as the eye of God could see
Darkness covered everything,
Blacker than a hundred midnights
Down in a cypress swamp.

Then God smiled,
And the light broke,
And the darkness rolled up on one side,
And the light stood shining on the other,
And God said: That's good!

Then God reached out and took the light in his
     hands,
And God rolled the light in his hands
Until he made the sun;
And he set that sun a-blazing in the heavens.
And the light that was left from making the sun
God gathered it up in a shining ball
And flung it against the darkness,
Spangling the night with the moon and stars.
Then down between
The darkness and the light

He hurled the world;
And God said: That's good!

Then God himself stepped down—
And the sun was on his right hand,
And the moon was on his left;
The stars were clustered about his head,
And the earth was under his feet.
And God walked, and where he trod
His footsteps hollowed the valleys out
And bulged the mountains up.

Then he stopped and saw
That the earth was hot and barren.
So God stepped over to the edge of the world
And he spat out the seven seas—
He batted his eyes, and the lightnings flashed—
He clapped his hands, and the thunders rolled—
And the waters above the earth came down,
The cooling waters came down.

Then the green grass sprouted,
And the little red flowers blossomed,
The pine tree pointed his finger to the sky,
And the oak spread out his arms,
The lakes cuddled down in the hollows of the
     ground,
And the rivers ran down to the sea;
And God smiled again,
And the rainbow appeared,
And curled itself around his shoulder.

Then God raised his arm and waved his hand,
Over the sea and over the land,
And he said: Bring forth! Bring forth!
And quicker than God could drop his hand,
Fishes and fowls
And beasts and birds
Swam the rivers and the seas,
Roamed the forests and the woods,

And split the air with their wings.
And God said: That's good!

Then God walked around,
And God looked around
On all that he had made.
He looked at his sun,
And he looked at his moon,
And he looked at his little stars;
He looked on his world
With all its living things,
And God said: I'm lonely still.

Then God sat down—
On the side of a hill where he could think;
By a deep, wide river he sat down;
With his head in his hands,
God thought and thought,
Till he thought: I'll make me a man!

Up from the bed of the river
God scooped the clay;
And by the bank of the river
He kneeled him down;
And there the great God Almighty
Who lit the sun and fixed it in the sky,
Who flung the stars to the most far corner of the
     night,
Who rounded the earth in the middle of his
     hand;
This great God,
Like a mammy bending over her baby,
Kneeled down in the dust
Toiling over a lump of clay
Till he shaped it in his own image;

Then into it he blew the breath of life,
And man became a living soul.
Amen. Amen.

WISDOM
Langston Hughes

I stand most humbly
Before man's wisdom,
Knowing we are not
Really wise:

If we were
We'd open up the kingdom
And make earth happy
As the dreamed of skies.

Walt Whitman

I believe a leaf of grass is no less than the jour-
ney-work of the stars,
And the pismire is equally perfect, and a grain of
sand, and the egg of the wren,
And the tree-toad is a chef-d'oeuvre for the highest,
And the running blackberry would adorn the
parlors of heaven,
And the narrowest hinge in my hand puts to
scorn all machinery,
And the cow crunching with depress'd head sur-
passes any statue,
And a mouse is miracle enough to stagger sextil-
lions of infidels.

Elizabeth Coatsworth

How gray the rain
And gray the world
And gray the rain clouds overhead,
When suddenly
Some cloud is furled
And there is gleaming sun instead!

The raindrops drip
Prismatic light,
And trees and meadows burn in green,
And arched in air
Serene and bright
The rainbow all at once is seen.

Serene and bright
The rainbow stands
That was not anywhere before,
And so may joy
Fill empty hands
When someone enters through a door.

Elizabeth Coatsworth

The warm of heart shall never lack a fire
However far he roam.
Although he live forever among strangers
He cannot lack a home.

For strangers are not strangers to his spirit,
And each house seems his own,
And by the fire of his loving-kindness
He cannot sit alone.

HOUSE BLESSING
Arthur Guiterman

Bless the four corners of this house,
    And be the lintel blest;
And bless the heart and bless the board
    And bless each place of rest;
And bless the door that opens wide
    To stranger as to kin;
And bless each crystal window-pane
    That lets the starlight in;
And bless the rooftree overhead
    And every sturdy wall.
The peace of man, the peace of God,
    The peace of Love on all!

WHO HATH A BOOK
Wilbur D. Nesbit

Who hath a book
    Hath friends at hand,
And gold and gear
    At his command;
And rich estates,
    If he but look,

Are held by him
Who hath a book.

Who hath a book
Hath but to read
And he may be
A king, indeed.
His kingdom is
His inglenook—
All this is his
Who hath a book.

TO THE WAYFARER

Unknown

A Poem Fastened to Trees in the Portuguese Forests

Ye who pass by and would raise your hand against me, hearken ere you harm me.

I am the heat of your hearth on the cold winter nights, the friendly shade screening you from summer sun, and my fruits are refreshing draughts, quenching your thirst as you journey on.

I am the beam that holds your house, the board of your table, the bed on which you lie, the timber that builds your boat.

I am the handle of your hoe, the door of your homestead, the wood of your cradle, and the shell of your coffin.

I am the bread of kindness and the flower of beauty.
Ye who pass by, listen to my prayer: harm me not.

THE SPLENDOR FALLS
ON CASTLE WALLS

Alfred, Lord Tennyson

The splendor falls on castle walls
    And snowy summits old in story;
The long light shakes across the lakes,
    And the wild cataract leaps in glory.
Blow, bugle, blow, set the wild echoes flying,
Blow, bugle; answer, echoes, dying, dying, dying.

O hark, O hear! how thin and clear,
    And thinner, clearer, farther going!
O sweet and far from cliff and scar
    The horns of Elfland faintly blowing!
Blow, let us hear the purple glens replying,
Blow, bugle; answer, echoes, dying, dying, dying.

O love, they die in yon rich sky,
    They faint on hill or field or river;
Our echoes roll from soul to soul,
    And grow forever and forever.
Blow, bugle, blow, set the wild echoes flying,
And answer, echoes, answer, dying, dying, dying.

Emily Dickinson

Hope is the thing with feathers
That perches in the soul,
And sings the tune without the words,
And never stops at all,

And sweetest in the gale is heard;
And sore must be the storm
That could abash the little bird
That kept so many warm.

I've heard it in the chillest land,
And on the strangest sea;
Yet, never, in extremity,
It asked a crumb of me.

A WORD

Emily Dickinson

A word is dead
When it is said,
    Some say.

I say it just
Begins to live
    That day.

THE WONDERFUL WORLD

William Brighty Rands

Great, wide, beautiful, wonderful World,
With the wonderful water round you curled,

And the wonderful grass upon your breast,
World, you are beautifully dressed.

MY LAND IS FAIR
FOR ANY EYES TO SEE

Jesse Stuart

My land is fair for any eyes to see—
Now look, my friends—look to the east and west!
You see the purple hills far in the west—
Hills lined with pine and gum and black-oak
　　　tree—
Now to the east you see the fertile valley!
This land is mine, I sing of it to you—
My land beneath the skies of white and blue.
This land is mine, for I am part of it.
I am the land, for it is part of me—
We are akin and thus our kinship be!
It would make me a brother to the tree!
And far as eyes can see this land is mine.
Not for one foot of it I have a deed—
To own this land I do not need a deed—
They all belong to me—gum, oak, and pine.

THE DAY WILL BRING SOME
LOVELY THING

Grace Noll Crowell

"The day will bring some lovely thing,"
I say it over each new dawn:
"Some gay, adventurous thing to hold
Against my heart when it is gone."

And so I rise and go to meet
The day with wings upon my feet.

I come upon it unaware—
Some sudden beauty without name:
A snatch of song—a breath of pine—
A poem lit with golden flame;
High tangled bird notes—keenly thinned—
Like flying color on the wind.

No day has ever failed me quite—
Before the grayest day is done,
I come upon some misty bloom
Or a late line of crimson sun.
Each night I pause—remembering
Some gay, adventurous, lovely thing.

GOOD NIGHT

Victor Hugo

　　　Good night! good night!
　　　Far flies the light;
　　　But still God's love
　　　Shall flame above,
　　　Making all bright.
　　　Good night! Good night!

"My Land is Fair for Any Eyes to See." From *Man with a Bull-Tongue Plough* by Jesse Stuart. New York: E. P. Dutton & Co., Inc., 1934. By permission of the author
"The Day Will Bring Some Lovely Thing." From *Silver in the Sun* by Grace Noll Crowell. Harper & Brothers, New York

BOOK 2: TIME FOR FAIRY TALES
old and new

TELLING STORIES AND
READING ALOUD TO CHILDREN

The principal of an elementary school paused in the hall, as a burst of contagious laughter rang out suddenly from the children in a second-grade room. Smiling involuntarily, the principal stepped into the room to see what had occasioned the merriment. The teacher was comfortably seated, reading aloud to her children, who were sitting, not with folded hands, but in a variety of relaxed positions. Their eyes were shining, their faces alive with interest as they anticipated the next ludicrous mishap that would overtake "Sonny-Boy Sim" in the forest. The principal remained to hear the hilarious conclusion of the story and the children's chuckles and comments. Then she went on her way thoughtfully. The children in that second-grade room were good readers. Why was the teacher spending time reading aloud? But come to think of it, that teacher always read aloud to her children and told stories, too. And whether she had a bright group or dull, her children were invariably interested in books and tackled their own reading activities with enthusiasm. Was there any connection between the children's interest in reading and the teacher's policy of telling stories and reading aloud? Perhaps so, but what could it be?

Why tell stories and read aloud to children?

There are many reasons why a program of telling stories and reading aloud to children is favorable to their own learning-to-read program. First, all normal children, bright or dull, good readers or poor, *need to have their reading interests expanded.* They get into a rut. Some children demand fairy tales and more fairy tales or horse stories and more horse stories. A grownup can

introduce them to better examples of their favorite sort of reading and gradually lead them into other fields and other subjects. One teacher whose children were sure they disliked biography began to tell them exciting or poignant episodes from some of the new biographies. She soon had her children reading that form of literature avidly. Many a mother has made poetry lovers of her children because she liked to read it aloud and shared her pleasure with her children. It is the business of adults in homes as well as schools to expand children's reading interests by exposing them to a variety of literature.

This sounds like a dangerous reduction of effort the child should make for himself. And it is dangerous if it is used to the point where it becomes a substitute for the child's own reading. But if storytelling and reading aloud are used now and then, as special treats, they serve as incomparable baits to an expanded experience with books.

The second reason why reading aloud and telling stories to children are desirable practices is that *they help reduce the lag between the child's ability to read for himself and his capacity to understand and enjoy literature.* Such a lag exists for all except a few older children who are superior readers. For most children there is a difference of from one to three years (and even more in exceptional cases) between their reading skill and their level of appreciation. This becomes evident to the most casual observer if he follows the stories the child enjoys in the moving pictures and on radio or television and compares them with the necessarily limited content of the materials with which the child is learning to read. Until a child acquires an easy fluency in reading, this discrepancy is bound to exist. An eight-year-old may enjoy listening to a story which he will not be able to read independently for another year or two. And the poorer or more limited the child's reading skill, the more irksome this difference is apt to be. So, to keep the child's reading limitations from discouraging him and to keep him interested in making an effort to learn to read, it is highly desirable to read to him poetry and stories which captivate him although they are beyond his reading ability at present.

There is an amusing by-product of the adult's fluent, effortless reading aloud. *It makes reading seem easy.* The child unconsciously gets the impression that if dad or teacher or mother can read like that, and have so much fun doing it, it can't be so hard after all. Reading begins to seem a simple and an enviable skill.

A fourth virtue of storytelling and reading aloud is that the listening children *develop a growing power of aural comprehension.* Their ears and minds are focused on the spoken word, without any extraneous aids to understanding. In this age, when there are immensely expanded opportunities for listening, the ability to hear, comprehend, and react intelligently to the spoken word is of great importance. But it is not easy. In a university nursery school it was found that the children were so used to stories with copious illustrations that they could not attend to or readily comprehend a story which was told without benefit of pictures. This is a serious limitation in learning a language. The ear must be trained, not merely to hear sound, but to make those appropriate connections within the brain which result in understanding. Picture clues are invaluable first aids to reading in the early years. But parallel with the use of pictures to aid word meaning, children should have practice in hearing poetry and stories which are not illustrated in picture-story style. With such practice, their vocabularies will grow and so will their ability to understand and react intelligently to the spoken word.

Incidentally, *a word which has been heard and understood is easier to recognize in print.* So, actually, this reading aloud policy, used in moderation, is just one more useful device for promoting word recognition on the printed page. It widens children's familiarity with words. It may increase their speaking vocabularies. It should train their ears for the music of language and their feeling for the beauty and power of words.

Finally, *storytelling and reading aloud make it easier for children to understand and enjoy certain types of literature which they might never try to read for themselves.* Probably no average American child will read *The Wind in the Willows* for himself. Does that mean that it should be removed from lists of books recommended for children's reading? The answer is No, and the justification for this answer is to be found in the example of the music groups in our schools. If they find most of their children are in the tin-pan-alley level of music enjoyment, do they say, "Ah, this means that there is no use in trying to give them Chopin, Schubert, and Beethoven. They could not understand them"? Indeed, they say nothing of the kind. Instead, they may begin where the child is, but they lead him to better music by daily and continuous exposure to it. Over and over, he hears simple, melodious selections from the classics until his ear is trained to these and he enjoys them. Then, he is ready to hear the themes of great symphonies in all their variations. Selections are discussed, replayed, and discussed again. The result of this music program in our schools is that young America today is listening to and enjoying better music than ever before.

Have we done as well for literature? Probably not, but we can if we go at it as systematically as the music people have. Such a program is immensely aided by teachers and parents who are themselves lovers of good literature. Books of quality and variety should be available to children both in their schools and their homes. And children should have a daily exposure to stories and poetry read aloud by adults who enjoy them and like to talk them over, informally, just for fun, as they read. A child who has grown up in a school or a home where someone reads aloud well and discusses as he reads is a lucky child because he acquires a homey approach to reading. He laughs or weeps or protests as the book progresses. He is used to talking books as some people talk baseball, with ardor and bias, because the people and situations in books seem as real as his baseball heroes. And children should, of course, develop their own point of view about their favorite and their not-so-favorite stories and characters.

When is there school time for reading aloud?

Teachers rightly raise the question about the time element in their already overcrowded curriculum. How can they possibly take a period to tell stories or read poetry and stories to the children? The general answer is that where there is a will to do it there will be time, but practically, it takes a little planning. Sometimes, stories in the children's readers suggest another story similar to or with a different slant on the same theme. Let the children conclude their reading period with a good stretch, and then read them the related story or poems. Good reader manuals list such materials and their sources. Sometimes, a social studies period finishes sooner than planned, or the nurse or the doctor keeps the children waiting. For such times have a book of stories on hand to read from. These are the casual, on-the-spur-of-the-moment periods which occur almost daily and may be utilized if you are prepared for them. But a planned period for reading aloud and storytelling, some three or four times a week, is also highly desirable. The last period either in the morning or the afternoon is particularly effective. A fascinating story, well read or told at the end of a school day, can unite teacher and children in a common interest. Small frictions and anxieties are forgotten in the pleasure of a shared interest. Children and teacher go home relaxed, buoyant, and secure in the feeling that school is a good place to be.

Camp councilors know the values of story hours round the campfire just before bedtime. Playground directors like to quiet the children down after strenuous activities by a story hour. In the home, the hour before dinner is ideal for stories if mother does not have to be too strenuously engaged in the kitchen. When she does, then just before bedtime for the children seems to be the favored period for reading or storytelling, and either mother or father may be pressed into service. This period has one disadvantage. Too much excitement is fatal to falling asleep; so, it means picking out poetry and stories of a quiet nature or at least tapering off with them.

If you know stories and poems to tell or say without benefit of books, your children are really in luck. A walk, a picnic, an ironing job, a too long automobile ride are all good occasions for the gentle arts of telling stories or saying poetry together.

You, who have children on playgrounds, in schools, camps, or your own homes, remember that the stories which you tell or read to your children you make memorable. They will associate those periods of enjoyment with you. Try, then, to conclude each day with the beauty, the fun, the thrill, and the nobility of fine literature.

Telling stories to children

Storytelling is the oldest, the least formal, and one of the most effective of the arts. It is the art not of the stage but of the fireside. When "peevish, won't-be-comforted, little bairns" have to wait for their suppers, or to have their curls brushed, or their playtime ended, mothers and nurses have always known the efficacy of storytelling. Many a father has discovered how close it brings him to his child to take him on his lap and tell him a tale, half remembered, half improvised, but wholly intimate and entertaining. Camp councilors can testify to the magic of storytelling around the glowing embers of a campfire. And both playground directors and teachers have seen a well-told story transform a group of belligerent young pugilists, at war with each other and the world, into a serene and united group. It is the intimate, personal quality of storytelling as well as the power of the story itself that accomplishes these minor miracles. Yet in order to work this spell, a story must be learned, remembered, and so delightfully told that it catches and holds the attention of the most inveterate wrigglers. And because this process of mastering a story requires laborious preparation and self-discipline, busy people ask quite reasonably, "But why not read a story? Why isn't reading just as effective as storytelling?"

The first answer to this question is that storytelling is more direct than reading. There is no book between you and your children. You can watch their faces and sense their reactions much more quickly than you can when you are cribbed and confined by an author's exact words and the physical presence of the book. The children watch your face and respond to the twinkle in your eye. They share with you anticipation of the joke that is just ahead. They also get the story plus your enjoyment of it. On your side, you watch the children, and their enjoyment heightens your own. Or you see Tommy begin to yawn or to tweak his neighbor's braid, and you call him back, not by speaking his name, but by intensifying the drama of the story. This close rapport between the storyteller and his audience makes it easier to see the blank look that an unfamiliar word or situation arouses. Immediately, the narrator paraphrases the strange word or amplifies the baffling situation until he sees comprehension replace confusion on the faces of his audience. In short, storytelling is direct communication between a grownup and children, almost as intimate as conversation. It creates a kind of homey "just-between-ourselves" atmosphere that makes it easy for children to accept and understand.

When to tell and when to read a story

The younger children are, the more they need the informal approach to literature that the storyteller brings. But even big boys and girls who read well are charmed by a storyteller who can relate, in folksy style, a tall tale, a folk story of wit and maturity, or an epic of heroic proportions. Folk tales were created orally and told over the years with many variations. They are infinitely more convincing to children today if they are told rather than read. Of course, it is better to read a story than to mangle it by poor storytelling. But anyone with any gift for spontaneous narration should tell and not read the folk tales. There is a unique satisfaction in making them come vividly to life for the children, just as the ancient storytellers made them live for their audiences long ago.

Stories which are better read, with book in hand, are of two varieties—the picture-stories for the youngest children and any story where the charm of the tale depends upon the exact words of the author. By picture-stories are meant such books as Marjorie Flack's *Angus* books or Beatrix Potter's *Tale of Peter Rabbit,* in which the pictures are an integral part of the text. Such stories lose much of their charm when they are used without their pictures. They should be read to the children and the pictures shown along with the text. Stories that are distinguished for their literary style or ones in which the text would suffer from any alterations in the wording should be read and not told. Kipling's *Just So Stories* (see "The Elephant's Child," p. 336) is a good example of both. To tell one of these stories, taking any liberties with the text, destroys the quality of the story which depends for its subtle humor upon the author's play with words. When someone elects to "tell" these stories, it is not really storytelling but pure recitation. The two are vastly different. The recitation is a memorized performance; storytelling is intimate and partially spontaneous communication. Kenneth Grahame's *Wind in the Willows* and Andersen's *Fairy Tales* may be cut, here and there, but not otherwise altered. Both demand reading rather than telling if the children are to catch their unusual beauty of style and spirit. Even Wanda Gág's little picture-stories, in which the illustrations are often too small for a whole group of children to see as they are read, have a precise wording that suffers from telling and should, therefore, be read. In general, it is safe to say that folk tales should be told, in so far as it is possible, and picture-stories and all stories which demand the precise words of the author, should be read.

How to tell stories

For a decade or so, storytelling seemed to be a lost art, but a new interest in the folklore of our own United States has brought with it a renewed appreciation of this ancient art. It is good to hear men's voices again among the storytellers today, for fathers and grandfathers and now brothers returned from the wars have always been able to enthrall children with their tales. One of the virtues of masculine storytelling is the lack of expurgation. Men are less afraid of gory or violent action or the colorful language of stories than women are; so their tales have a robust quality that has sometimes been lacking in feminine storytelling. However, if you listen to a number of good storytellers, you discover that their styles are as individual as their personalities and only certain general qualities are common to all of them.

The first of these qualities is basic. *The storyteller must enjoy his story and the telling of it.* He must have fallen in love with its sly humor, its beauty, or its exciting action to the point where he wants to share it with others. Its style must have captivated him so that he wants to get the hang of it and be able to use it as easily as if its vernacular were his own native language. To hear Richard Chase tell a "Jack" tale, in the laconic drawl of the mountain man, or Mrs. Gudrun Thorne-Thomsen tell "Gudbrand on the Hill-Side," with tender sympathy for the folly and the loyalty of the old couple, is to feel at once the storyteller's love for his tale and his complete identification with its characters and its style. These are essential. No one can tell a story without a genuine unforced delight in the story and emotional identification with its characters and situations.

It is desirable also to have *an agreeable voice and pure diction.* No story can survive slovenly, obscure speech nor a voice that fades away or is unpleasantly harsh, loud, or nasal. But certainly no special voice is needed for storytelling. The saccharine voices and unctuous tones of some of the radio storytellers should be a warning to all who essay the art. Children can sense the artificial in a flash, and there is nothing they resent more than the tone of patronage, the "dee-ah children" approach. Speak naturally, but be sure that your natural voice is pleasing. Don't over-articulate, but use your everyday diction if that is crisp, good diction. It will improve both your voice and diction to read poetry aloud or practice your storytelling orally, listening critically to yourself as you do so. Is your voice pleasant to hear and varied? Can you suggest in the dialogue of a story the cockiness of the Pancake, the sorrow of the Goose Girl, the sternness of the princess' royal father in "The Frog-King"? It will help you to hear yourself objectively, if you can obtain a tape recorder. Or have someone with a good ear listen to you and evaluate your voice and diction. Speak naturally, but be sure that your speech is the best there is for your locale. The West does not speak like New England nor New England like the South. Every part of this broad country of ours has its impure and its good speech. Try for the best diction indigenous to your part of the country.

The language of a story must be characteristic of the particular type of tale you are telling and it must be understood by your audience. This is easier said than done. Folk tales, because they grew up in certain countries and were told chiefly by rural people of long ago, have a distinct vocabulary and style. An Irish folk tale differs from a Norwegian, and both have a vocabulary and phrasing that would be completely foreign to an English folk tale, an East Indian story, or an American tall tale. A good storyteller must absorb this unique style of the story and he must also make it understandable to his audience. In spite of this latter requirement, a sensitivity to words should prevent you from interjecting any modern phrases or colloquialisms. "Boots got real mad" does not belong to a Norwegian folk tale, although it might fit a "Jack" tale. "Cinderella had a swell time at the dance" may be clear to the children, but it breaks the spell of the courtly French tale and turns Cinderella into a bobbysoxer out for "a good time." Read your story aloud until you catch its word patterns, and then, as you practice it orally, listen to yourself and see that the words fit the story.

To make the unfamiliar words clear to children is not always easy. Obsolete, rural, or little used words and phrases are common in folk tales. What, for instance, does a child get from such words as "lassie," "lad," "noodle," "goody," "steed," "mare," "foal," "tapers," or such phrases as "put the spade in his wallet," "laced her stays," "threw his tinder over the steed"? And these are just a few of the baffling words and phrases children hear in these folk tales. Don't drop the old words. They are part of the flavor of the story, but paraphrase them as briefly and unobtrusively as possible, "And the goody, the good wife, said—" or "So, he threw his tinder over the steed because he knew there was magic in his tinder." Such interjections clarify meaning without interrupting the flow of the story. But this practice can be carried to extremes. For instance, Sleeping Beauty's "spindle" does not call for an elaborate dissertation on spinning. It is merely a magic object (like the "tinder") which the fairy said would cause the spell to fall on Beauty. And it did. Sometimes, if a strange word is essential to knowing what the story is about, clear it up before you tell the tale. Sometimes talk about the spindle or tinder after the story is finished. Actually, these queer magic objects seldom bother the children. If they accept a fairy godmother or a magic horse, what is a spindle or a tinder more or less? In short, be clear but don't feel that you must turn lecturer in the middle of a story.

Your appearance while you tell a story is important in general, but the particulars of your style of beauty or plainness are of no consequence. What children look for are the twinkle in your eye and the relaxed air of leisure that promise a good time ahead. Sit down to tell your story, if possible, but if there is no corner in your classroom where you and your children can sit together, then stand, as comfortably as possible, and get on with the story. Perhaps you tell stories sitting in front of a fire with your child on your lap or on the ground by a campfire with children around you or by your child's bed or in a shady corner of a hot playground. It does not matter where you sit or stand just so that you create an atmosphere of easy enjoyment which storytelling should always carry with it.

Keep your hands free of handkerchiefs, pencils, or any other impedimenta which may cramp some of the small, natural gestures most storytellers use. But even to this rule there may be exceptions. A mother used to pacify her children, waiting impatiently for their supper, by telling them some of their favorite stories. It was funny to see her gesticulating like the goody in "The Pancake" with "the frying-pan in one hand and the ladle in the other." But she was satisfactorily dramatic and the children loved it, even if her "frying pan" was more hygienically the lid of a double boiler.

Practice your storytelling in front of a mirror to begin with, and watch your posture. Informality and ease do not mean sitting or standing sloppily. Watch yourself until you know how you should look, sitting or standing, so that you make an alert but an easy and agreeable picture. If you are telling to large groups, your clothes should be the kind the audience forgets the moment the tale begins. If you are a woman, don't wear a hat; it will give you a formal air. Beware of chains or dangles, which you may be tempted to finger

or, if you are a man, the inevitable pockets from which a hand can seldom be recalled once it has disappeared therein. These are all details of the general admonition—present to your audience an agreeable picture of relaxed enjoyment and the audience will relax too.

Finally, there is the matter of *learning to tell a story,* about which no two people are ever in complete agreement. Some visualize the characters and scenes in a story in considerable detail. They see the long bleak road down which the Lad travels to the North Wind's house. They see Tattercoats, advancing bravely to meet her handsome prince across the ballroom floor, with the geese hissing and waddling absurdly beside her to the tune of the herd boy's piping. When a narrator sees his story unfolding before his inner eye, he feels a great urgency to make his audience see it too and he relates it with conviction. But other storytellers are not conscious of this visualizing process, or feel that it comes only in flashes. The action of the story, the dramatic dialogue, the flow and cadence of word patterns, catch their imagination and remain in their memories.

Whatever your approach to a story may be, one thing is essential. *A story must be learned to the point where forgetting is impossible.* To learn a story to this degree would seem to imply exact memorizing and reciting, but that is not storytelling. The form of the folk tale was always fluid and varied with the teller. Even today, when words are learned from the printed page and not from the lips of another storyteller, no two students in a class in children's literature will tell a story alike. It becomes uniquely the story of each one who tells it. Exact memorizing of the printed text is not only out of key with folk tale tradition, but it is dangerous. A single slip of the memory will throw the teller completely off her narrative so that she has to start over, repeat phrases, or stop entirely while she racks her brain for the missing words. This is fatal to storytelling. If, instead of precise memorizing of every word, the story is thoroughly learned, in flexible form, it will remain in the memory for years.

The learning process goes something like this. Read your story carefully enough to know that you like it and would enjoy telling it. Then, read it aloud at a leisurely pace, noting the special vocabulary, the unusual turn of a phrase, the dialogue, and any repetitional refrains there may be. Then, begin to tell the story aloud, book in hand, from the beginning to the end. It will be a slow process, with constant reference to the book, but never mind, keep at it. Polish the beginning and the end until they are smooth and sure. Repeat dialogue over and over until you speak it fluently and are able to characterize the bully or the modest lad or the haughty sisters as you speak their words. Repeat the rough spots until you are sure of them but go through the whole story every time. Then, begin to live with your story. Tell it in bed, just before you fall asleep and in the morning, when you are getting dressed. Tell it on the bus or street car or while you are walking. When you reach the point where interruptions and distractions may stop your story but never cause you to forget it, when the language is flexible, fluent, and in character, when the whole creation seems to be a part of you, then you are ready to tell your story and you will be able to tell it years hence.

Storytelling is the art of the fireside, the campfire, the classroom, and the cribside but never the stage. It should remain as natural and sometimes as dramatic as everyday talk, but it is not drama. Small children like action and it is natural when you are telling them stories to make some of the large gestures that suggest the action of the tale, as making a big circular motion with the arm when the pancake rolls out of the door "like a wheel." But these imitative action-gestures should diminish to the vanishing point in stories for older children. With them, only the small gestures of everyday talk remain. Do not dramatize in storytelling. "The lassie made a low bow" is not accompanied by a bow. Instead, when you speak these words, your voice suggests the humility or fear of the lassie. Mockery, impudence, a tossing head or a hanging head are never acted literally, but merely suggested in voice and manner. The moment such restraint is forgotten, something stagy and foreign to the forthright simplicity of the folk tale creeps in.

How to read aloud

Most of the suggestions for telling stories apply to reading them aloud. A good voice and diction, sincerity, simplicity, a contagious enjoyment of the tale—these are as essential to reading as to telling a story. Reading may seem much easier than telling a story, but actually, with the exception of gaining complete independence of the text, the preparation is similar and it offers certain complications not found in storytelling. You have, for instance, the handicap of a book between you and your children. You look more at the book and less at the children. If there are pictures with the text, as in picture-stories, you have the added complication of showing the illustrations and satisfying the children's clamor to see them better. All this means that it is actually easier to lose your children when you are reading to them than it is when you tell them a story. To guard against this, be so familiar with the story you are going to read that you know just how and when to show the pictures and you can anticipate the suspense and build up to the climax most effectively.

Content and purpose of this book

This collection of stories has been assembled for grownups to tell or to read to children. It is designed for use in the home, around the campfire, with playground groups, and in the classroom, and its content will appeal to children from four-years-old to fourteen. Ideally, such a collection should contain only short stories, each one a complete unit in itself. But, unfortunately, some worth-while authors write only books and no short stories. It is possible that if a child encounters a portion of a fine book, presented with the contagious enthusiasm and prestige of grownup enjoyment, he may wish to read the whole book. It is, for instance, hard to imagine a child listening to the excerpt from *Robin Hood* or *Elmer and the Dragon* or *Pinocchio* without demanding the rest of the story. For this reason a few excerpts from books are included in this collection. They are in the minority, but they do occur with the hope that the adult who reads them will so spellbind the children that they will promptly demand the whole book.

This particular volume is devoted to tales of magic, old and new, grave and hilarious, fantastic nonsense and pseudoscientific. If a child does not like one story, he will probably be enthusiastic about another one. But it is well to be warned in advance that in the field of imaginative fiction there is a greater difference in children's tastes than in any other field. All you can do is to expose children to a variety of stories and be prepared to abide by their preferences.

Of course, you won't give children an unadulterated dose of these folk and fairy tales but will intersperse them with poetry, realistic fiction, and biography. Folk tales and myths may be used in connection with the study of a people; or you may just slip them in now and then for their entertainment values. The modern fanciful stories, in all their fascinating variety, can be used almost anytime as a special treat or as a change from a too intensive pursuit of the factual. All these imaginative stories are a wholesome antidote for the necessarily heavy emphasis upon facts which school and, indeed, our whole modern world entails. These tales, old and new, are imaginative play. They are dreams of a daft world where two and two may sometimes make five, or a tender world where a plain little princess becomes beautiful, but in any case, a world of wish fulfillment and fun.

Most of the stories in this collection will bear repetition, and the younger the children, the more they need such repetition. Perhaps the older children will come to love some of these stories to the point where they wish to take the book and read for themselves. This is greatly to be desired. But essentially, the collection is planned for grownups to use with children. What stories they are, sometimes full of beauty or sly humor, sometimes with a hint of tragedy or a burst of sheer nonsense. One quality they have in common, and that is imagination. They stretch the mind and spirit with their dreams. It is this quality of wonder and speculation that makes them worth using with children.

It is curious in an age as realistic and mechanized as ours that the magic of the folk tales still casts its spell on modern children. Witches and dragons, talking beasts and rebellious pancakes, flying carpets and cloaks of darkness, fairies and wise women, spells and enchantments are accepted as casually by children as airplanes and television.

It is true that the modern child becomes interested in fairy tales later than people used to think, and perhaps he wears them out a little sooner. Except for a few of the simplest nursery tales of "The Little Red Hen" and "The Story of the Three Little Pigs" variety, the peak of

OLD MAGIC: THE FOLK TALES

children's interest in tales of magic seems to fall somewhere around eight- or nine-years-old and not earlier. After nine there is a continued but steadily diminishing interest in such stories through the ages of ten, eleven, and twelve years. There are many reasons why the modern child still enjoys these tales, as we shall see, and why it is well to delay his exposure to any great number of them until sometime after the six-year-old period.

In the first place, most of these old stories were created by adults for the entertainment of other adults. Only a small fraction of them were composed for and told to children. A majority of the tales mirrors the mature lives, customs, beliefs, and emotions of peoples all over the world, and their adult themes make large numbers of them totally unsuited to children. There still remain, however, enough stories with lively plots, plenty of action, and conclusions which satisfy children's liking for justice and successful achievement, to account for their continued popularity with young people.

Origins of the folk tales[1]

The problem of why and how the folk tales originated has given rise to many conflicting theories. Some of these are now completely discredited, others are considered partially applicable, and new explanations have developed from the studies which psychologists and anthropologists have made of peoples all over the world, their motives and drives, customs and beliefs.

One of the earliest theories of folk tale origin stemmed from the belief that a language-group known as Aryan was a pure racial strain and that all of the folk tales sprang from this one source. This theory of *single origin* or *monogenesis* is now discredited because we know that there is no such thing as a pure racial strain, and that the Aryan group consisted of many strains.

The theory of *many origins* or *polygenesis* grew out of the belief that human beings are basically alike in their reactions, and would therefore make up the same kind of stories. This would seem to account for the 345 variants of "Cinderella" which have been discovered. But anthropological studies of different peoples show that human beings differ too widely in their customs and emotional reactions to explain such story similarities. Although stepmothers may be a problem in one group, they may not be in another.

The "Aryan myth" gave rise to another theory, namely, that the folk tales preserved *remnants of the nature myths* of that single racial strain. Perhaps Red Riding Hood may have symbolized the setting sun swallowed up by the darkness of the night, the wolf. But certainly no large number of the stories could be accounted for in this way. Nor could masses of them be explained on the grounds that they preserved *remnants of religious beliefs and rituals*. It is true that some evidence of early religions, charms, and incantations is to be found in a number of the tales, but the bulk of them contain no such traces.

Some of the recent psychological explanations of folk tale origins are interesting speculations. The idea that the tales were all *symbols of emotional fantasy*, unconscious sexual love for the parent, for example, has been refuted by anthropology's discovery that peoples differ in their emotional reactions and would also differ in their symbols. More plausible is the suggestion that the tales grew out of the *dreams and nightmares* of the storytellers. When the night turns cold, or the blanket slips off, we sometimes dream of being abroad with few or no clothes on. So, perhaps, tales developed of poor lassies out in the snow, clad only in paper dresses. And, perhaps, the descriptions of fine foods and rich feasts, so common in the fairy tales, may have grown from the hunger of the dreamer.

This theory suggests still another psychological interpretation of folk tale origin, namely that the old storytellers created in these tales a *satisfaction for their own unconscious frustrations and drives*. This is a fertile suggestion. The poor, the obscure, or the oppressed dream of riches, achievement, and power; so, they make up tales about the goose-girl who marries a prince and a cat that turns his master into the Lord Mayor of London—splendid dreams which symbolize *wish fulfillment* for each succeeding generation.

The most conclusive explanation of folk tale origin has grown out of the findings of social anthropology. In the light of their studies of modern folk societies, many anthropologists conclude that folk tales were the *cement of society*, the carriers of the moral code. The folk tales taught kindness, industry, and courage by dramatic stories revealing the rewards of these virtues. They showed meanness, laziness, and deceit exposed at last, and well punished. By creating these dramatic examples of good and bad behavior, properly rewarded or punished, they helped to cement society together with a common body of social and moral standards.

Modern children learn from these old tales

[1] For an expanded discussion of origins see May Hill Arbuthnot, *Children and Books*, pp. 231–234.

something about their own behavior in relation to other people. They learn that it's well to use your head. Henny Penny was punished for her gullibility, but the third little pig prospered because he had courage and used his wits. Children learn that you must look beyond appearances which do not always reveal character. The prince discovered this to his sorrow when he accepted the false maid as his princess, in "The Goose-Girl." Beauty found her true love because she looked beyond the ugliness of the poor beast to his kindness. And Boots accomplished the impossible because he had the courage to wonder, to investigate, and to tackle things for himself. To the sophisticated, such philosophy may not seem to be borne out by the hard facts of modern life. But actually, gangsters and dictators are still coming to bad ends. Children are going to inherit plenty of dragons, ogres, and giants to be exterminated. They need some of the cement of society to be found in the folk tales, a belief in the moral code of decency, courage, and goodness.

Wide diffusion of the folk tales

Folk tales are a legacy from anonymous artists of the past, the old wives and grannies as well as the professional storytellers. They were first created orally and passed on by word of mouth for generations before the printing press caught up with them. Soldiers, sailors, slaves, traders, monks, and scholars carried these stories from one country to another and, of course, the stories were changed in the process. A story passed on orally, from memory, is bound to vary with each new telling. This collecting of stories from the oral tradition of old storytellers is still going on today. Missionaries, marines, teachers, and scholars are still finding and preserving the old tales.

Written versions of some of the folk tales began to circulate in Europe in the twelfth century. Merchants and crusaders brought the talking beast tales from India, in Arabic or Persian translations, and these were soon turned into Latin. The great Celtic manuscripts introduced stories of witchcraft and enchantment that are said to go back to 400 B.C. The world of fairy which these remarkable vellum manuscripts recorded brought to the folk tales many of those elements which make the children call them "fairy tales." In the sixteenth century, Caxton's fine translations of Aesop's fables, the King Arthur legends, and the Homeric epics appeared. Although these are not folk tales, they are, like the ballads, a part of the rich stream of literature we know as folklore. In France, in the seventeenth century, Charles Perrault lent his name to a collection of eight famous folk tales which delighted the French court in Perrault's time.

Perrault's eight tales marked the beginning of a great interest in folklore collecting which has gone on ever since. The eighteenth century saw the appearance of some of the major collections. The Grimm brothers made scrupulous records of German tales from the lips of old storytellers, not for children's entertainment but as a serious study of the German language. Children soon appropriated them, however. In Norway, Peter Christian Asbjörnsen, a zoologist, and Jörgen E. Moe, a theologian and poet, collected the Norwegian folk tales. Since Sir George Webbe Dasent translated these into English, under the title *East o' the Sun and West o' the Moon,* they have become almost as familiar to American children as Grimm's "Hansel and Gretel." The English tales were edited by Joseph Jacobs, who was himself an authority on folklore. However, Jacobs had children definitely in mind in his collection and said frankly that he omitted episodes which were unduly coarse or brutal and made some changes in the language. However, when you study his changes they are not too heinous even to folklore scholars, and the full flavor of ancient storytelling is still there. Since Jacobs' time, printed collections of folk tales have multiplied until now there are collections from all the major countries of the world.[2]

Of special interest to the children of the United States is a newly inspired enthusiasm for American folk tales. Joel Chandler Harris' *Uncle Remus* tales of the American Negro have long delighted children and grownups. The so-called "tall tales" are favorites. Stories from the various tribes of the American Indian have been known but have never been popular, because they are not, on the whole, well constructed. But the new

[2] For further discussion of national collections see May Hill Arbuthnot, *Children and Books,* pp. 235–254.

enthusiasm is for the American variants of the old European folk tales which are now appearing in large numbers and which show a fresh turn of phrase and a humor that is characteristically American. Richard Chase is an enthusiastic collector of these tales, and his storytelling is doing much to popularize them all over the country.

Predominant types of folk tales

The stories in this collection are a sampling from important national and racial collections and from most of the types of stories which occur in folklore in general. Not all children will like every story, but most children will like a goodly number of them.

Accumulative or repetitional stories appeal to children four- to six-years-old or even seven. In these stories, plot is at a minimum and action takes its place. The episodes follow each other in logical order and are related in a repetitional cadence that is almost like a patter-song. It swings the listener along until the spiral action ends abruptly or runs backwards to its beginning. "The Old Woman and Her Pig" is an example of running up the spiral and back, but "Henny Penny" and "The Pancake" come to a sudden and surprising end at the top of the spiral. These stories grow imperceptibly, from mere chants to such plot stories as "The Four Musicians."

Talking beast stories are usually prime favorites. Sometimes the animals talk with human beings, as in "Puss in Boots" or "The Fox and His Travels," and sometimes they just converse with other animals. Their talk betrays their folly or wisdom even as human talk betrays it. Children feel superior when they sense the absurdity of Henny Penny's ruminations, and they identify themselves with the wise and witty remarks of Padre Porko. Occasionally there is a talking beast who is no beast at all but an unhappy prince or princess under a wicked spell. That is, of course, quite a different matter. But the talk of the three Billy Goats Gruff, Brer Rabbit, the clever jackal, and all the pigs, bears, and foxes of the folk tales is quite as understandable and perhaps a shade more reasonable to the child than much of the talking-to he receives from grownups.

The drolls or humorous stories were obviously told for sheer entertainment. Stories of the sillies

and the numskulls are ancestors of *The Peterkin Papers* and the modern moron tales. Fortunately, the humor of the folk tales is not confined to such foolish ones as "Clever Elsie" but progresses to the gaieties of "King O'Toole and His Goose," and "Tom Tit Tot," and the subtle humor of "Clever Manka" and "The Most Obedient Wife." The last two stories should always be used as a pair, with the elevens and twelves. Read them "The Most Obedient Wife" and hear the boys chuckle and the girls fume over the ignominious taming of the Wife. Then, the next day perhaps, read them "Clever Manka" and turn the tables, to the delight of the girls.

Realistic stories, wherein everything that happens might conceivably be so, are few and far between in the folk tales. The old storytellers seemed to have little use for the here-and-now stuff of everyday living. Even when they told a story that was possible, it was likely to be fabulous. "Clever Elsie" is the extreme of silliness. Dick Whittington, on the other hand, is a very possible hero of flesh-and-blood proportions and Manka and the obedient wife are possible, too. Perhaps the prettiest of the realistic stories is "Gudbrand on the Hill-Side," which is a tender version of "Mr. Vinegar," with a loving wife instead of a shrew. But, on the whole, folk tales pay scant attention to the laws of probability and are far happier and more numerous in the field of the impossible.

Some *religious tales* of long ago have been appropriated by the children. In the Middle Ages the stories which grew out of the morality plays often included the devil, the saints, or occasionally the Virgin or the Christ Child. The devil stories were invariably humorous with the devil getting the worst of it at the hands of resourceful human beings, especially scolding wives. The stories of the saints were generally grave, although this collection includes one that is broadly comic, "King O'Toole and His Goose."

Tales of magic are the heart of the folk tales. Fairies and fairy godmothers, giants, water nixies, lads who ride up glass hills, impossible tasks which are nonchalantly performed, three wishes, three trials, enchanted men or maidens, these are just a suggestion of fairy tale motifs and atmosphere. These give the tales an unearthly quality, often so beautiful that it comes close to poetry.

Fairies and magic

Actually, fairy folk are a remarkably varied lot as you will discover even in this selection of tales. Wise women, witches, and wizards may be either helpful or ruthless. Sometimes they serve as fairy godmothers and sometimes they lure children with gingerbread houses, for wicked reasons of their own. There are trooping fairies, with a queen, who live in underground halls of great magnificence. They sometimes steal children or bewitch handsome young men, but generally they are gay and kindly.

The Norse hill folk and the German dwarfs live underground also, but they are the humble workers of the fairy world. There are pixies who ride across moors on fairy steeds, water sprites and nixies who haunt wells and rivers, elves or brownies who sometimes abide in a house and make themselves useful, and an occasional imp, like Tom Tit Tot, who bobs up unexpectedly and invariably yearns for a human child to cheer his old age. Giants and ogres may be good or bad. Some are bloodthirsty and cruel and feast on their enemies. But others swallow oceans or stride over mountains in their seven-league boots on behalf of some cinderlad who shared his crust of bread with them.

Fairy animals not only aid discouraged heroes but, like Puss in Boots or the Horse of Power, are actually the brains of the enterprise. What a picturesque and unforgettable lot are these fairy beasts—Dapplegrim, sly old Lishka, the Flounder, the Three Bears, and the Three Pigs. And picturesque, too, are the magic objects in the tales—Aladdin's lamp, Boots' ram that coins money, and Freddy's merry fiddle.

Enchanted people are often a piteous group—the poor frog-king so rudely treated by the princess, Beauty's Beast, Little Burnt-Face, and the great White Bear, all waiting for someone to break their unhappy spells. And it can't be just anyone, either, because fairies and fairy spells work by definite laws. No magic ever ultimately succeeds for the mean or cowardly or cruel. But for kind souls, who are also courageous, help comes in time of need, and magic is always waiting for him who knows how to use it. Dark spells can only be broken by love and self-sacrifice and it takes a brave lassie to save her prince from the hags and witches who have ensnared him. The youngest son must first brave lions before magic reveals to him the water of life. Through all this fairy world the child hears over and over again that grace and strength are bestowed upon those who strive mightily and keep an honest, kindly heart.

Using the tales with children

On the whole the selections in this book are the simpler, merrier tales from the great collections. Each of the large groups begins with easier stories, most of them with nursery tales for the youngest children. They progress through tales of magic for the sevens, eights, and nines to the more mature stories which will command the respect of the elevens and twelves. Grownups will discover likenesses in some of the stories from the different national and racial groups, and these likenesses sometimes interest children. See "Tom Tit Tot" and "Rumpelstiltskin," "Mr. Vinegar" and "Gudbrand," "Cinderella," "Tattercoats," and "Little Burnt-Face," "Beauty and the Beast" and "East o' the Sun and West o' the Moon," "Sadko" and "Urashimo Taro and the Princess of the Sea." Remember that the folk tales were created and kept alive by the oral tradition of gifted storytellers. Read them aloud if you must, but tell them if you can, for in the spontaneity of good storytelling, these tales come most vividly to life for you and your children.

Finally, tales of magic should never be used exclusively or in too great numbers, but in balanced proportion to realistic fiction and informational reading. Use the folk tales in connection with the study of a people—the Chinese, English, or East Indian, for example. Use them to stimulate the children's creative urge to paint or dramatize or write. The tall tales have often set children to creating their own "whoppers." Above all, use these stories for sheer delight. They have humor, nonsense, romance, and poetic beauty. They will help to break up the tight literalness that overtakes some children. They also reiterate moral truths that are important for children to know. "Be of good cheer," these stories seem to say. "Use your head, keep a kindly heart, a civil tongue, and a fearless spirit and you will surely find the water of life and your heart's desire."

British folk tales

Joseph Jacobs, the folklorist, collected many of the English tales. He
had a child audience in mind and intended, he said, "to write as a good old nurse
will speak when she tells Fairy Tales." And he succeeded. Here in the
British collections, you find the favorites of the nursery—the accumulative, the
humorous, and the simple talking beast stories. What fun to share with
small children—"The Three Little Pigs," "Henny-Penny," "The Three Bears"
and all the others! The British folk tales are also notable for their
giant-killers, which are not included in this book, for their humor, and for
the songs and cadenced repetition that swing the stories along with a
contagious rhythm. Of the stories included here, only "The Black Bull of Norroway" and "Whippety Stourie" are for the oldest children—the elevens
and twelves. The others will be loved from four-years-old to ten or more.

THE OLD WOMAN AND HER PIG

*This accumulative tale falls naturally into a
kind of humorous chant, which the children like
to try with you. It is funnier if you speed up the
returning sequence a bit.*

An old woman was sweeping her house, and
she found a little crooked sixpence. "What," said
she, "shall I do with this little sixpence? I will go
to market, and buy a little pig."

As she was coming home, she came to a stile:
but the piggy wouldn't go over the stile.

She went a little further, and she met a dog. So
she said to him: "Dog! dog! bite pig; piggy won't
go over the stile; and I shan't get home to-night."
But the dog wouldn't.

She went a little further, and she met a stick.
So she said: "Stick! stick! beat dog! dog won't
bite pig; piggy won't get over the stile; and I
shan't get home to-night." But the stick wouldn't.

She went a little further, and she met a fire.
So she said: "Fire! fire! burn stick; stick won't
beat dog; dog won't bite pig; piggy won't get

over the stile; and I shan't get home to-night."
But the fire wouldn't.

She went a little further, and she met some
water. So she said: "Water! water! quench fire;
fire won't burn stick; stick won't beat dog; dog
won't bite pig; piggy won't get over the stile;
and I shan't get home to-night." But the water
wouldn't.

She went a little further, and she met an ox.
So she said: "Ox! ox! drink water; water won't
quench fire; fire won't burn stick; stick won't
beat dog; dog won't bite pig; piggy won't get
over the stile; and I shan't get home to-night."
But the ox wouldn't.

She went a little further, and she met a
butcher. So she said: "Butcher! butcher! kill ox;
ox won't drink water; water won't quench fire;
fire won't burn stick; stick won't beat dog; dog
won't bite pig; piggy won't get over the stile;
and I shan't get home to-night." But the
butcher wouldn't.

She went a little further, and she met a rope.
So she said: "Rope! rope! hang butcher; butcher
won't kill ox; ox won't drink water; water won't
quench fire; fire won't burn stick; stick won't
beat dog; dog won't bite pig; piggy won't get
over the stile; and I shan't get home to-night."
But the rope wouldn't.

She went a little further, and she met a rat. So
she said: "Rat! rat! gnaw rope; rope won't hang
butcher; butcher won't kill ox; ox won't drink

"The Old Woman and Her Pig." From *English Fairy
Tales*, edited by Joseph Jacobs. Selections from *English
Fairy Tales* are used by permission of G. P. Putnam's Sons
and Frederick Muller Ltd., London

water; water won't quench fire; fire won't burn stick; stick won't beat dog; dog won't bite pig; piggy won't get over the stile; and I shan't get home to-night." But the rat wouldn't.

She went a little further, and she met a cat. So she said: "Cat! cat! kill rat; rat won't gnaw rope; rope won't hang butcher; butcher won't kill ox; ox won't drink water; water won't quench fire; fire won't burn stick; stick won't beat dog; dog won't bite pig; piggy won't get over the stile; and I shan't get home to-night." But the cat said to her, "If you will go to yonder cow, and fetch me a saucer of milk, I will kill the rat." So away went the old woman to the cow.

But the cow said to her: "If you will go to yonder hay-stack, and fetch me a handful of hay, I'll give you the milk." So away went the old woman to the hay-stack; and she brought the hay to the cow.

As soon as the cow had eaten the hay, she gave the old woman the milk; and away she went with it in a saucer to the cat.

As soon as the cat had lapped up the milk, the cat began to kill the rat; the rat began to gnaw the rope; the rope began to hang the butcher; the butcher began to kill the ox; the ox began to drink the water; the water began to quench the fire; the fire began to burn the stick; the stick began to beat the dog; the dog began to bite the pig; the little pig in a fright jumped over the stile; and so the old woman got home that night.

THE STORY
OF THE THREE BEARS

This is the version of "The Three Bears" that the children like best. They will expect the traditional variations in the voices of the bears, from the deep, gruff voice of the Big Bear to the high, squeaky voice of the Little Wee Bear.

Once upon a time there were three Bears, who lived together in a house of their own, in a wood. One of them was a Little Wee Bear, and one was

"The Story of the Three Bears." From *English Fairy Tales* retold by Flora Annie Steel. By permission of The Macmillan Company, New York and Macmillan & Co. Ltd., London

a Middle-sized Bear, and the other was a Great Big Bear. They had each a bowl for their porridge: a little bowl for the Little Wee Bear; and a middle-sized bowl for the Middle-sized Bear; and a great bowl for the Great Big Bear. And they had each a chair to sit in: a little chair for the Little Wee Bear; and a middle-sized chair for the Middle-sized Bear; and a great chair for the Great Big Bear. And they had each a bed to sleep in: a little bed for the Little Wee Bear; and a middle-sized bed for the Middle-sized Bear; and a great bed for the Great Big Bear.

One day, after they had made the porridge for their breakfast, and poured it into their porridge-bowls, they walked out into the wood while the porridge was cooling, that they might not burn their mouths by beginning too soon, for they were polite, well-brought-up Bears.

And while they were away a little girl called Goldilocks, who lived at the other side of the wood and had been sent on an errand by her mother, passed by the house, and looked in at the window. And then she peeped in at the keyhole, for she was not at all a well-brought-up little girl. Then seeing nobody in the house she lifted the latch. The door was not fastened, because the Bears were good Bears, who did nobody any harm, and never suspected that anybody would harm them. So Goldilocks opened the door and went in; and well pleased was she when she saw the porridge on the table. If she had been a well-brought-up little girl she would have waited till the Bears came home, and then, perhaps, they would have asked her to breakfast; for they were good Bears—a little rough or so, as the manner of Bears is, but for all that very good-natured and hospitable. But she was an impudent, rude little girl and so she set about helping herself.

First she tasted the porridge of the Great Big Bear, and that was too hot for her. Next she tasted the porridge of the Middle-sized Bear, but that was too cold for her. And then she went to the porridge of the Little Wee Bear, and tasted it, and that was neither too hot nor too cold, but just right, and she liked it so well, that she ate it all up, every bit!

Then Goldilocks, who was tired, for she had been catching butterflies instead of running on her errand, sat down in the chair of the Great Big Bear, but that was too hard for her. And then she sat down in the chair of the Middle-sized Bear, and that was too soft for her. But when she sat down in the chair of the Little Wee Bear, that was neither too hard, nor too soft, but just right. So she seated herself in it, and there she sat till the bottom of the chair came out, and down she came, plump upon the ground; and that made her very cross, for she was a bad-tempered little girl.

Now, being determined to rest, Goldilocks went upstairs into the bedchamber in which the Three Bears slept. And first she lay down upon the bed of the Great Big Bear, but that was too high at the head for her. And next she lay down upon the bed of the Middle-sized Bear, and that was too high at the foot for her. And then she lay down upon the bed of the Little Wee Bear, and that was neither too high at the head, nor at the foot, but just right. So she covered herself up comfortably, and lay there till she fell fast asleep.

By this time the Three Bears thought their porridge would be cool enough for them to eat it properly; so they came home to breakfast. Now careless Goldilocks had left the spoon of the Great Big Bear standing in his porridge.

"SOMEBODY HAS BEEN AT MY PORRIDGE!" said the Great Big Bear in his great, rough, gruff voice.

Then the Middle-sized Bear looked at his porridge and saw the spoon was standing in it too.

"SOMEBODY HAS BEEN AT MY PORRIDGE!" said the Middle-sized Bear in his middle-sized voice.

Then the Little Wee Bear looked at his, and there was the spoon in the porridge-bowl, but the porridge was all gone!

"SOMEBODY HAS BEEN AT MY PORRIDGE, AND HAS EATEN IT ALL UP!" said the Little Wee Bear in his little wee voice.

Upon this the Three Bears, seeing that someone had entered their house, and eaten up the Little Wee Bear's breakfast, began to look about them. Now the careless Goldilocks had not put the hard cushion straight when she rose from the chair of the Great Big Bear.

"SOMEBODY HAS BEEN SITTING IN MY CHAIR!" said the Great Big Bear in his great, rough, gruff voice.

And the careless Goldilocks had squatted down the soft cushion of the Middle-sized Bear.

"SOMEBODY HAS BEEN SITTING IN MY CHAIR!"

said the Middle-sized Bear in his middle-sized voice.

"SOMEBODY HAS BEEN SITTING IN MY CHAIR, AND HAS SAT THE BOTTOM THROUGH!" said the Little Wee Bear in his little wee voice.

Then the Three Bears thought they had better make further search in case it was a burglar, so they went upstairs into their bedchamber. Now Goldilocks had pulled the pillow of the Great Big Bear out of its place.

"SOMEBODY HAS BEEN LYING IN MY BED!" said the Great Big Bear in his great, rough, gruff voice.

And Goldilocks had pulled the bolster of the Middle-sized Bear out of its place.

"SOMEBODY HAS BEEN LYING IN MY BED!" said the Middle-sized Bear in his middle-sized voice.

But when the Little Wee Bear came to look at his bed, there was the bolster in its place!

And the pillow was in its place upon the bolster!

And upon the pillow——? There was Goldilocks' yellow head—which was not in its place, for she had no business there.

"SOMEBODY HAS BEEN LYING IN MY BED—AND HERE SHE IS STILL!" said the Little Wee Bear in his little wee voice.

Now Goldilocks had heard in her sleep the great, rough, gruff voice of the Great Big Bear; but she was so fast asleep that it was no more to her than the roaring of wind, or the rumbling of thunder. And she had heard the middle-sized voice of the Middle-sized Bear, but it was only as if she had heard someone speaking in a dream. But when she heard the little wee voice of the Little Wee Bear, it was so sharp and so shrill, that it awakened her at once. Up she started, and when she saw the Three Bears on one side of the bed, she tumbled herself out at the other, and ran to the window. Now the window was open, because the Bears, like good, tidy Bears, as they were, always opened their bedchamber window when they got up in the morning. So naughty, frightened little Goldilocks jumped; and whether she broke her neck in the fall, or ran into the wood and was lost there, or found her way out of the wood and got whipped for being a bad girl and playing truant, no one can say. But the Three Bears never saw anything more of her.

THE STORY

OF THE THREE LITTLE PIGS

It is likely that this story is the top favorite of all five-year-olds who know it.

Once upon a time when pigs spoke rhyme,
And monkeys chewed tobacco,
And hens took snuff to make them tough,
And ducks went quack, quack, quack, O!

There was an old sow with three little pigs, and as she had not enough to keep them, she sent them out to seek their fortune. The first that went off met a man with a bundle of straw, and said to him:

"Please, man, give me that straw to build me a house."

Which the man did, and the little pig built a house with it. Presently came along a wolf, and knocked at the door, and said:

"Little pig, little pig, let me come in."

To which the pig answered:

"No, no, by the hair of my chinny chin chin."

The wolf then answered to that:

"Then I'll huff, and I'll puff, and I'll blow your house in."

So he huffed, and he puffed, and he blew his house in, and ate up the little pig.

The second little pig met a man with a bundle of furze and said:

"Please, man, give me that furze to build a house."

Which the man did, and the pig built his house. Then along came the wolf, and said:

"Little pig, little pig, let me come in."

"No, no, by the hair of my chinny chin chin."

"Then I'll puff, and I'll huff, and I'll blow your house in."

So he huffed, and he puffed, and he puffed and he huffed, and at last he blew the house down, and he ate up the little pig.

The third little pig met a man with a load of bricks, and said:

"Please, man, give me those bricks to build a house with."

So the man gave him the bricks, and he built his house with them. So the wolf came, as he did to the other little pigs, and said:

"Little pig, little pig, let me come in."

"No, no, by the hair of my chinny chin chin."

"Then I'll huff, and I'll puff, and I'll blow your house in."

"The Story of the Three Little Pigs." From *English Fairy Tales*, edited by Joseph Jacobs. Used by permission of G. P. Putnam's Sons and Frederick Muller Ltd., London

Well, he huffed, and he puffed, and he huffed and he puffed, and he puffed and huffed; but he could *not* get the house down. When he found that he could not, with all his huffing and puffing, blow the house down, he said:

"Little pig, I know where there is a nice field of turnips."

"Where?" said the little pig.

"Oh, in Mr. Smith's home-field, and if you will be ready to-morrow morning I will call for you, and we will go together, and get some for dinner."

"Very well," said the little pig, "I will be ready. What time do you mean to go?"

"Oh, at six o'clock."

Well, the little pig got up at five and got the turnips before the wolf came (which he did about six), who said:

"Little pig, are you ready?"

The little pig said, "Ready! I have been and come back again and got a nice potful for dinner."

The wolf felt very angry at this, but thought that he would be up to the little pig somehow or other, so he said:

"Little pig, I know where there is a nice apple-tree."

"Where?" said the pig.

"Down at Merry-Garden," replied the wolf, "and if you will not deceive me, I will come for you at five o'clock to-morrow and get some apples."

Well, the little pig bustled up the next morning at four o'clock, and went off for the apples, hoping to get back before the wolf came; but he had further to go and had to climb the tree, so that just as he was coming down from it, he saw the wolf coming, which, as you may suppose,

frightened him very much. When the wolf came up he said:

"Little pig, what! are you here before me? Are they nice apples?"

"Yes, very," said the little pig. "I will throw you down one."

And he threw it so far, that, while the wolf was gone to pick it up, the little pig jumped down and ran home. The next day the wolf came again and said to the little pig:

"Little pig, there is a fair at Shanklin this afternoon; will you go?"

"Oh, yes," said the pig, "I will go; what time shall you be ready?"

"At three," said the wolf. So the little pig went off before the time as usual and got to the fair and bought a butter-churn, which he was going home with, when he saw the wolf coming. Then he could not tell what to do. So he got into the churn to hide, and by so doing turned it round, and it rolled down the hill with the pig in it, which frightened the wolf so much, that he ran home without going to the fair. He went to the little pig's house and told him how frightened he had been by a great round thing which came down the hill past him. Then the little pig said:

"Hah, I frightened you then. I had been to the fair and bought a butter-churn; and when I saw you, I got into it, and rolled down the hill."

Then the wolf was very angry indeed and declared he *would* eat up the little pig, and that he would get down the chimney after him. When the little pig saw what he was about, he hung on the pot full of water and made up a blazing fire, and, just as the wolf was coming down, took off the cover, and in fell the wolf; so the little pig put on the cover again in an instant, boiled him up, and ate him for supper and lived happy ever afterwards.

HENNY-PENNY

Perhaps the East Indian "The Hare That Ran Away" is the ancestor of this story, "The Pancake," "The Gingerbread Boy," and all the other runaways.

One day Henny-Penny was picking up corn in the cornyard when—whack!—something hit her upon the head. "Goodness gracious me!" said Henny-Penny; "the sky's a-going to fall; I must go and tell the king."

So she went along, and she went along, and she went along till she met Cocky-Locky. "Where are you going, Henny-Penny?" says Cocky-Locky. "Oh! I'm going to tell the king the sky's a-falling," says Henny-Penny. "May I come with you?" says Cocky-Locky. "Certainly," says Henny-Penny. So Henny-Penny and Cocky-Locky went to tell the king the sky was falling.

They went along, and they went along, and they went along till they met Ducky-Daddles. "Where are you going to, Henny-Penny and Cocky-Locky?" says Ducky-Daddles. "Oh! we're going to tell the king the sky's a-falling," said Henny-Penny and Cocky-Locky. "May I come with you?" says Ducky-Daddles. "Certainly," said Henny-Penny and Cocky-Locky. So Henny-Penny, Cocky-Locky, and Ducky-Daddles went to tell the king the sky was a-falling.

So they went along, and they went along, and they went along, till they met Goosey-Poosey. "Where are you going to, Henny-Penny, Cocky-Locky, and Ducky-Daddles?" said Goosey-Poosey. "Oh! we're going to tell the king the sky's a-falling," said Henny-Penny and Cocky-Locky and Ducky-Daddles. "May I come with you?" said Goosey-Poosey. "Certainly," said Henny-Penny, Cocky-Locky, and Ducky-Daddles. So Henny-Penny, Cocky-Locky, Ducky-Daddles, and Goosey-Poosey went to tell the king the sky was a-falling.

So they went along, and they went along, and they went along, till they met Turkey-Lurkey. "Where are you going, Henny-Penny, Cocky-Locky, Ducky-Daddles, and Goosey-Poosey?" says Turkey-Lurkey. "Oh! we're going to tell the king

"Henny-Penny." From *English Fairy Tales*, edited by Joseph Jacobs. Used by permission of G. P. Putnam's Sons and Frederick Muller Ltd., London

the sky's a-falling," said Henny-Penny, Cocky-Locky, Ducky-Daddles, and Goosey-Poosey. "May I come with you, Henny-Penny, Cocky-Locky, Ducky-Daddles, and Goosey-Poosey?" said Turkey-Lurkey. "Oh, certainly, Turkey-Lurkey," said Henny-Penny, Cocky-Locky, Ducky-Daddles, and Goosey-Poosey. So Henny-Penny, Cocky-Locky, Ducky-Daddles, Goosey-Poosey, and Turkey-Lurkey all went to tell the king the sky was a-falling.

So they went along, and they went along, and they went along, till they met Foxy-Woxy, and Foxy-Woxy said to Henny-Penny, Cocky-Locky, Ducky-Daddles, Goosey-Poosey, and Turkey-Lurkey: "Where are you going, Henny-Penny, Cocky-Locky, Ducky-Daddles, Goosey-Poosey, and Turkey-Lurkey?" And Henny-Penny, Cocky-Locky, Ducky-Daddles, Goosey-Poosey, and Turkey-Lurkey said to Foxy-Woxy: "We're going to tell the king the sky's a-falling." "Oh! but this is not the way to the king, Henny-Penny, Cocky-Locky, Ducky-Daddles, Goosey-Poosey, and Turkey-Lurkey," says Foxy-Woxy; "I know the proper way; shall I show it you?" "Oh, certainly, Foxy-Woxy," said Henny-Penny, Cocky-Locky, Ducky-Daddles, Goosey-Poosey, and Turkey-Lurkey. So Henny-Penny, Cocky-Locky, Ducky-Daddles, Goosey-Poosey, Turkey-Lurkey, and Foxy-Woxy all went to tell the king the sky was a-falling. So they went along, and they went along, and they went along, till they came to a narrow and dark hole. Now this was the door of Foxy-Woxy's cave. But Foxy-Woxy said to Henny-Penny, Cocky-Locky, Ducky-Daddles, Goosey-Poosey, and Turkey-Lurkey: "This is the short way to the king's palace; you'll soon get there if you follow me. I will go first and you come after, Henny-Penny, Cocky-Locky, Ducky-Daddles, Goosey-Poosey, and Turkey-Lurkey." "Why of course, certainly, without doubt, why not?" said Henny-Penny, Cocky-Locky, Ducky-Daddles, Goosey-Poosey, and Turkey-Lurkey.

So Foxy-Woxy went into his cave, and he didn't go very far, but turned round to wait for Henny-Penny, Cocky-Locky, Ducky-Daddles, Goosey-Poosey, and Turkey-Lurkey. So at last at first Turkey-Lurkey went through the dark hole into the cave. He hadn't got far when "Hrumph," Foxy-Woxy snapped off Turkey-Lurkey's head and threw his body over his left shoulder. Then Goosey-Poosey went in, and "Hrumph," off went her head and Goosey-Poosey was thrown beside Turkey-Lurkey. Then Ducky-Daddles waddled down, and "Hrumph," snapped Foxy-Woxy, and Ducky-Daddles' head was off and Ducky-Daddles was thrown alongside Turkey-Lurkey and Goosey-Poosey. Then Cocky-Locky strutted down into the cave, and he hadn't gone far when "Snap, Hrumph!" went Foxy-Woxy and Cocky-Locky was thrown alongside of Turkey-Lurkey, Goosey-Poosey, and Ducky-Daddles.

But Foxy-Woxy had made two bites at Cocky-Locky; and when the first snap only hurt Cocky-Locky, but didn't kill him, he called out to Henny-Penny. But she turned tail and off she ran home; so she never told the king the sky was a-falling.

THE COCK, THE MOUSE, AND THE LITTLE RED HEN

Once upon a time there was a hill, and on the hill there was a pretty little house.

It had one little green door, and four little windows with green shutters, and in it there lived A COCK, and A MOUSE, and A LITTLE RED HEN. On another hill close by, there was another little house. It was very ugly. It had a door that wouldn't shut, and two broken windows, and all the paint was off the shutters. And in this house there lived A BOLD BAD FOX and FOUR BAD LITTLE FOXES.

One morning these four bad little foxes came to the big bad Fox and said:

"Oh, Father, we're so hungry!"

"We had nothing to eat yesterday," said one.

"And scarcely anything the day before," said another.

The big bad Fox shook his head, for he was thinking. At last he said in a big gruff voice:

"On the hill over there I see a house. And in that house there lives a Cock."

"And a Mouse!" screamed two of the little foxes.

"The Cock, the Mouse, and the Little Red Hen." By Félicité LeFèvre

"And a little Red Hen," screamed the other two.

"And they are nice and fat," went on the big bad Fox. "This very day I'll take my sack and I will go up that hill and in at that door, and into my sack I will put the Cock, and the Mouse, and the little Red Hen."

So the four little foxes jumped for joy, and the big bad Fox went to get his sack ready to start upon his journey.

But what was happening to the Cock, and the Mouse, and the little Red Hen, all this time?

Well, sad to say, the Cock and the Mouse had both got out of bed on the wrong side that morning. The Cock said the day was too hot, and the Mouse grumbled because it was too cold.

They came grumbling down to the kitchen, where the good little Red Hen, looking as bright as a sunbeam, was bustling about.

"Who'll get some sticks to light the fire with?" she asked.

"I shan't," said the Cock.

"I shan't," said the Mouse.

"Then I'll do it myself," said the little Red Hen.

So off she ran to get the sticks. "And now, who'll fill the kettle from the spring?" she asked.

"I shan't," said the Cock.

"I shan't," said the Mouse.

"Then I'll do it myself," said the little Red Hen.

And off she ran to fill the kettle.

"And who'll get the breakfast ready?" she asked, as she put the kettle on to boil.

"I shan't," said the Cock.

"I shan't," said the Mouse.

"I'll do it myself," said the little Red Hen.

All breakfast time the Cock and the Mouse quarrelled and grumbled. The Cock upset the milk jug, and the Mouse scattered crumbs upon the floor.

"Who'll clear away the breakfast?" asked the poor little Red Hen, hoping they would soon leave off being cross.

"I shan't," said the Cock.

"I shan't," said the Mouse.

"Then I'll do it myself," said the little Red Hen.

So she cleared everything away, swept up the crumbs and brushed up the fireplace.

"And now, who'll help me to make the beds?"
"I shan't," said the Cock.
"I shan't," said the Mouse.
"Then I'll do it myself," said the little Red Hen.

And she tripped away upstairs.

But the lazy Cock and Mouse each sat down in a comfortable arm-chair by the fire, and soon fell fast asleep.

Now the bad Fox had crept up the hill and into the garden, and if the Cock and Mouse hadn't been asleep, they would have seen his sharp eyes peeping in at the window.

"Rat tat tat! Rat tat tat!" the Fox knocked at the door.

"Who can that be?" said the Mouse, half opening his eyes.

"Go and look for yourself, if you want to know," said the rude Cock.

"It's the postman perhaps," thought the Mouse to himself, "and he may have a letter for me." So without waiting to see who it was, he lifted the latch and opened the door.

As soon as he opened it, in jumped the big Fox.

"Oh! oh! oh!" squeaked the Mouse, as he tried to run up the chimney.

"Doodle doodle do!" screamed the Cock, as he jumped on the back of the biggest arm-chair.

But the Fox only laughed, and without more ado he took the little Mouse by the tail, and popped him into the sack, and seized the Cock by the neck and popped him in too.

Then the poor little Red Hen came running downstairs to see what all the noise was about, and the Fox caught her and put her into the sack with the others.

Then he took a long piece of string out of his pocket, wound it round, and round, and round the mouth of the sack, and tied it very tight indeed. After that he threw the sack over his back, and off he set down the hill, chuckling to himself.

"Oh, I wish I hadn't been so cross," said the Cock, as they went bumping about.

"Oh! I wish I hadn't been so lazy," said the Mouse, wiping his eyes with the tip of his tail.

"It's never too late to mend," said the little Red Hen. "And don't be too sad. See, here I have my little work-bag, and in it there is a pair of scissors, and a little thimble, and a needle and

thread. Very soon you will see what I am going to do."

Now the sun was very hot, and soon Mr. Fox began to feel his sack was heavy, and at last he thought he would lie down under a tree and go to sleep for a little while. So he threw the sack down with a big bump, and very soon fell fast asleep.

Snore, snore, snore, went the Fox.

As soon as the little Red Hen heard this, she took out her scissors, and began to snip a hole in the sack just large enough for the Mouse to creep through.

"Quick," she whispered to the Mouse, "run as fast as you can and bring back a stone just as large as yourself."

Out scampered the Mouse, and soon came back, dragging the stone after him.

"Push it in here," said the little Red Hen, and he pushed it in, in a twinkling.

Then the little Red Hen snipped away at the hole, till it was large enough for the Cock to get through.

"Quick," she said, "run and get a stone as big as yourself."

Out flew the Cock, and soon came back quite out of breath, with a big stone, which he pushed into the sack too.

Then the little Red Hen popped out, got a stone as big as herself, and pushed it in. Next she put on her thimble, took out her needle and thread, and sewed up the hole as quickly as ever she could.

When it was done, the Cock, and the Mouse and the little Red Hen ran home very fast, shut the door after them, drew the bolts, shut the shutters, and drew down the blinds and felt quite safe.

The bad Fox lay fast asleep under the tree for some time, but at last he awoke.

"Dear, dear," he said, rubbing his eyes and then looking at the long shadows on the grass, "how late it is getting. I must hurry home."

So the bad Fox went grumbling and groaning down the hill, till he came to the stream. Splash! In went one foot. Splash! In went the other, but the stones in the sack were so heavy that at the very next step, down tumbled Mr. Fox into a deep pool. And then the fishes carried him off to their fairy caves and kept him a prisoner there, so he was never seen again. And the four greedy little foxes had to go to bed without any supper.

But the Cock and the Mouse never grumbled again. They lit the fire, filled the kettle, laid the breakfast, and did all the work, while the good little Red Hen had a holiday, and sat resting in the big arm-chair.

No foxes ever troubled them again, and for all I know they are still living happily in the little house with the green door and green shutters, which stands on the hill.

THE TRAVELS OF A FOX

There are some amusing phrases in this story which you must make the most of—"while I go to Squintum's," for example. The children like to roll that one under their tongues.

One day a fox was digging behind a stump and he found a bumblebee; and the fox put the bumblebee in a bag and took the bag over his shoulder and travelled.

At the first house he came to, he went in and said to the mistress of the house, "Can I leave my bag here while I go to Squintum's?"

"Yes," said the woman.

"Then be careful not to open the bag," said the fox.

But as soon as he was out of sight the woman said to herself, "Well, I wonder what the fellow has in his bag that he is so careful about. I will look and see. It can't do any harm, for I shall tie the bag right up again."

However, the moment she unloosed the string, out flew the bumblebee, and the rooster caught him and ate him all up.

After a while the fox came back. He took up his bag and knew at once that his bumblebee was gone, and he said to the woman, "Where is my bumblebee?"

And the woman said, "I untied the string just to take a little peep to find out what was in your bag, and the bumblebee flew out and the rooster ate him."

"The Travels of a Fox." From *The Oak Tree Fairy Book,* edited by Clifton Johnson, copyright 1933. With the kind permission of Mrs. Clifton Johnson

"Very well," said the fox; "I must have the rooster, then."

So he caught the rooster and put him in his bag and travelled.

At the next house he came to, he went in and said to the mistress of the house, "Can I leave my bag here while I go to Squintum's?"

"Yes," said the woman.

"Then be careful not to open the bag," said the fox.

But as soon as he was out of sight the woman said to herself, "Well, I wonder what the fellow has in his bag that he is so careful about. I will look and see. It can't do any harm, for I shall tie the bag right up again."

However, the moment she unloosed the string the rooster flew out and the pig caught him and ate him all up.

After a while the fox came back. He took up his bag and knew at once that his rooster was gone, and he said to the woman, "Where is my rooster?"

And the woman said, "I untied the string just to take a little peep to find out what was in your bag, and the rooster flew out and the pig ate him."

"Very well," said the fox, "I must have the pig, then."

So he caught the pig and put him in his bag and travelled.

At the next house he came to, he went in and said to the mistress of the house, "Can I leave my bag here while I go to Squintum's?"

"Yes," said the woman.

"Then be careful not to open the bag," said the fox.

But as soon as he was out of sight the woman said to herself, "Well, I wonder what the fellow has in his bag that he is so careful about. I will look and see. It can't do any harm, for I shall tie the bag right up again."

However, the moment she unloosed the string, the pig jumped out and the ox gored him.

After a while the fox came back. He took up his bag and knew at once that his pig was gone, and he said to the woman, "Where is my pig?"

And the woman said, "I untied the string just to take a little peep to find out what was in your bag, and the pig jumped out and the ox gored him."

And the woman said, "I untied the string just to take a little peep to find out what was in your bag, and the ox got out and my little boy chased him out of the house and across a meadow and over a hill, clear out of sight."

"Very well," said the fox, "I must have the little boy, then."

So he caught the little boy and put him in his bag and travelled.

At the next house he came to, he went in and said to the mistress of the house, "Can I leave my bag here while I go to Squintum's?"

"Yes," said the woman.

"Then be careful not to open the bag," said the fox.

The woman had been making cake, and when it was baked she took it from the oven, and her children gathered around her teasing for some of it.

"Oh, ma, give me a piece!" said one, and "Oh, ma, give me a piece!" said each of the others.

And the smell of the cake came to the little boy in the bag, and he heard the children beg for the cake, and he said, "Oh, mammy, give me a piece!"

"Very well," said the fox, "I must have the ox, then."

So he caught the ox and put him in his bag and travelled.

At the next house he came to, he went in and said to the mistress of the house, "Can I leave my bag here while I go to Squintum's?"

"Yes," said the woman.

"Then be careful not to open the bag," said the fox.

But as soon as he was out of sight the woman said to herself, "Well, I wonder what the fellow has in his bag that he is so careful about. I will look and see. It can't do any harm, for I shall tie the bag right up again."

However, the moment she unloosed the string, the ox got out, and the woman's little boy chased the ox out of the house and across a meadow and over a hill, clear out of sight.

After a while the fox came back. He took up his bag and knew at once that his ox was gone, and he said to the woman, "Where is my ox?"

Then the woman opened the bag and took the little boy out; and she put the house-dog in the bag in the little boy's place, and the little boy joined the other children.

After a while the fox came back. He took up his bag and he saw that it was tied fast and he thought that the little boy was safe inside. "I have been all day on the road," said he, "without a thing to eat, and I am getting hungry. I will just step off into the woods now and see how this little boy I have in my bag tastes."

So he put the bag on his back and travelled deep into the woods. Then he sat down and untied the bag, and if the little boy had been in there things would have gone badly with him.

But the little boy was at the house of the woman who made the cake, and when the fox untied the bag the house-dog jumped out and killed him.

MASTER OF ALL MASTERS

A girl once went to the fair to hire herself for servant. At last a funny-looking old gentleman engaged her, and took her home to his house. When she got there, he told her that he had something to teach her, for that in his house he had his own names for things.

He said to her: "What will you call me?"

"Master or mister, or whatever you please, sir," says she.

He said: "You must call me 'master of all masters.' And what would you call this?" pointing to his bed.

"Bed or couch, or whatever you please, sir."

"No, that's my 'barnacle.' And what do you call these?" said he pointing to his pantaloons.

"Breeches or trousers, or whatever you please, sir."

"You must call them 'squibs and crackers.' And what would you call her?" pointing to the cat.

"Cat or kit, or whatever you please, sir."

"You must call her 'white-faced simminy.' And this now," showing the fire, "what would you call this?"

"Fire or flame, or whatever you please, sir."

"You must call it 'hot cockalorum,' and what this?" he went on, pointing to the water.

"Water or wet, or whatever you please, sir."

"No, 'pondalorum' is its name. And what do you call all this?" asked he as he pointed to the house.

"House or cottage, or whatever you please, sir."

"You must call it 'high topper mountain.' "

That very night the servant woke her master up in a fright and said: "Master of all masters, get out of your barnacle and put on your squibs and crackers. For white-faced simminy has got a spark of hot cockalorum on its tail, and unless you get some pondalorum, high topper mountain will be all on hot cockalorum". . . .
. . . . That's all.

MR. VINEGAR

Gudbrand in the Scandinavian version of this tale was a luckier man than Mr. Vinegar, for in spite of Gudbrand's follies his wife remained loyal and loving and his foolish adventures had a happy conclusion.

Mr. and Mrs. Vinegar were very poor, and they lived in a shabby little house that they had built with their own hands. It was made of old boards and other rubbish which they had picked up, and it rattled and shook in every high wind. One morning, Mrs. Vinegar, who was a very good housewife, was busily sweeping her kitchen floor when an unlucky thump of the broom against the walls brought down the whole house, clitter-clatter about her ears. Mr. Vinegar had gone to a neighboring thicket to gather some fagots, and she hurried off with much weeping and wailing to tell him of the disaster.

When she found him she exclaimed, "Oh, Mr. Vinegar! Mr. Vinegar! we are ruined, we are ruined! I have knocked the house down and it is all to pieces!"

"My dear," said Mr. Vinegar, "pray do not

"Master of All Masters." From *English Fairy Tales*, edited by Joseph Jacobs. Used by permission of G. P. Putnam's Sons and Frederick Muller Ltd., London

"Mr. Vinegar." From *The Oak Tree Fairy Book*, edited by Clifton Johnson, copyright 1933. With the kind permission of Mrs. Clifton Johnson

weep any more. I will go back with you and see what can be done."

So they returned, and Mr. Vinegar said, "Yes, wife, the house is all in bits and we can never live in it again; but here is the door. I will take that on my back and we will go forth to seek our fortune."

With his wife's help he got the door on his back, and off they started. They walked all that day, and by nightfall they were both very tired. They had now come to a thick forest and Mr. Vinegar said, "My love, I will climb up into a tree with this door and you shall follow after."

So he climbed up among the branches of a great tree, and when he had adjusted the door at a level Mrs. Vinegar climbed up also, and they stretched their weary limbs on it and were soon fast asleep.

But in the middle of the night Mr. Vinegar was awakened by the sound of voices directly below him. He looked down and, to his dismay, saw that a party of robbers were met under the tree to divide some money they had stolen.

"Jack," said one, "here's five pounds for you; and Bill, here's ten pounds for you; and Bob, here's three pounds for you."

Mr. Vinegar was so frightened he could listen no longer, and he trembled so violently that he shook the door off the branches on which it lay, and he and Mrs. Vinegar had to cling to the tree to save themselves from a bad tumble. When the door began to drop, the noise it made startled the robbers and they looked up to learn the cause, but no sooner did they do this than the door came down on their heads and they all ran away greatly terrified.

Mr. and Mrs. Vinegar, however, dared not quit their tree till broad daylight. Then Mr. Vinegar scrambled down.

"I hope the door was not broken by its fall," said he as he lifted it.

Just then he espied a number of golden guineas that had been beneath the door where they had been dropped on the ground by the robbers in their haste to get away.

"Come down, Mrs. Vinegar!" he cried, "come down, I say! Our fortune is made! Come down, I say!"

Mrs. Vinegar came down as quickly as she could and saw the money with great delight, and when they counted it they found they were the possessors of forty guineas. "Now, my dear," said she, "I'll tell you what you shall do. You must take these forty guineas and go to the nearest town and buy a cow. I can make butter and cheese which you shall sell at market, and we shall then be able to live very comfortably."

"I will do as you say," replied Mr. Vinegar, "and you can stay here till I return."

So he took the money and went off to the nearest town; and there was a fair in the town, and crowds of people. When he arrived he walked about until he saw a beautiful red cow that he thought would just suit him.

"Oh, if I only had that cow," said Mr. Vinegar, "I should be the happiest man alive."

Then he offered the forty guineas for the cow and the owner was quite ready to part with it at that price, and the bargain was made. Mr. Vinegar was proud of his purchase, and he led the cow backwards and forwards to show it. But by and by he saw a man playing some bagpipes— tweedledum, tweedledee. The children followed after the bagpipe man, and he appeared to be pocketing a great deal of money.

"What a pleasant and profitable life that musician must lead," said Mr. Vinegar. "If I had that instrument I should be the happiest man alive, and I could earn far more than with this cow."

So he went up to the man and said, "Friend, what a charming instrument that is, and what a deal of money you must make!"

"Why, yes," said the man; "I make a great deal of money, to be sure, and it is a wonderful instrument."

"Oh!" cried Mr. Vinegar, "how I should like to possess it!"

"Well," said the man, "I will exchange it for your red cow."

"Done!" said the delighted Mr. Vinegar.

So the beautiful red cow was given for the bagpipes. Mr. Vinegar walked up and down with his purchase, but in vain he attempted to play a tune, and the children, instead of giving him pennies, hooted and laughed at him. The day was chilly and poor Mr. Vinegar's fingers grew very cold. At last, heartily ashamed and mortified, he was leaving the town when he met a man wearing a fine, thick pair of gloves.

"Oh, my fingers are so very cold!" said Mr.

Vinegar to himself. "If I had those warm gloves I should be the happiest man alive."

Then he went up to the man and said to him, "Friend, you seem to have a capital pair of gloves there."

"Yes, truly," replied the man, "these are excellent gloves."

"Well," said Mr. Vinegar, "I should like to have them. I will give you these bagpipes for them."

"All right," said the man, and he took the bagpipes and Mr. Vinegar put on the gloves and felt entirely contented as he trudged along toward the forest.

But the farther he walked the more tired he became, until presently he saw a man coming toward him with a good stout cane in his hand. "Oh!" said Mr. Vinegar, "if I had that cane I should be the happiest man alive."

Then he said to the man, "Friend, what a rare good cane you have."

"Yes," the man responded, "I have used it for many a mile and it has been a great help."

"How would it suit you to give it to me in exchange for these gloves?" asked Mr. Vinegar.

"I will do so willingly," replied the man.

"My hands had become perfectly warm," said Mr. Vinegar as he went on with his cane, "and my legs were very weary. I could not have done better."

As he drew near to the forest where he had left his wife he heard an owl on a tree laughing, "Hoo, hoo, hoo!" Then it called out his name and he stopped to ask what it wanted.

"Mr. Vinegar," said the owl, "you foolish man, you blockhead, you simpleton! you went to the fair and laid out all your money in buying a cow. Not content with that, you changed the cow for some bagpipes on which you could not play and which were not worth one tenth as much as the cow. Ah, foolish, foolish man! Then you no sooner had the bagpipes than you changed them for the gloves that were worth not one quarter as much as the bagpipes; and when you got the gloves you exchanged them for a cane, and now for your forty guineas you have nothing to show but that poor miserable stick which you might have cut in any hedge. Hoo, hoo, hoo, hoo, hoo!"

The bird laughed loud and long, and Mr. Vinegar became very angry and threw his cane at its head. The cane lodged in the tree, and Mr. Vinegar returned to his wife without money, cow, bagpipes, gloves, or stick, and she said things to him that he liked even less than what the bird had said.

TATTERCOATS

This is one of the prettiest of the 345 variants of the "Cinderella" theme.

In a great Palace by the sea there once dwelt a very rich old lord, who had neither wife nor children living, only one little granddaughter, whose face he had never seen in all her life. He hated her bitterly, because at her birth his favourite daughter died; and when the old nurse brought him the baby, he swore that it might live or die as it liked, but he would never look on its face as long as it lived.

So he turned his back, and sat by his window looking out over the sea, and weeping great tears for his lost daughter, till his white hair and beard grew down over his shoulders and twined round his chair and crept into the chinks of the floor, and his tears, dropping on to the window-ledge, wore a channel through the stone, and ran away in a little river to the great sea. And, meanwhile, his granddaughter grew up with no one to care for her, or clothe her; only the old nurse, when no one was by, would sometimes give her a dish of scraps from the kitchen, or a torn petticoat from the rag-bag; while the other servants of the Palace would drive her from the house with blows and mocking words, calling her "Tattercoats," and pointing at her bare feet and shoulders, till she ran away crying, to hide among the bushes.

And so she grew up, with little to eat or wear, spending her days in the fields and lanes, with only the gooseherd for a companion, who would play to her so merrily on his little pipe, when she was hungry, or cold, or tired, that she forgot all her troubles, and fell to dancing, with his flock of noisy geese for partners.

"Tattercoats." From *More English Fairy Tales*, edited by Joseph Jacobs. By permission of G. P. Putnam's Sons and Frederick Muller Ltd., London

But, one day, people told each other that the King was travelling through the land, and in the town near by was to give a great ball to all the lords and ladies of the country, when the Prince, his only son, was to choose a wife.

One of the royal invitations was brought to the Palace by the sea, and the servants carried it up to the old lord who still sat by his window, wrapped in his long white hair and weeping into the little river that was fed by his tears.

But when he heard the King's command, he dried his eyes and bade them bring shears to cut him loose, for his hair had bound him a fast prisoner and he could not move. And then he sent them for rich clothes, and jewels, which he put on; and he ordered them to saddle the white horse, with gold and silk, that he might ride to meet the King.

Meanwhile Tattercoats had heard of the great doings in the town, and she sat by the kitchen-door weeping because she could not go to see them. And when the old nurse heard her crying she went to the Lord of the Palace, and begged him to take his granddaughter with him to the King's ball.

But he only frowned and told her to be silent, while the servants laughed and said: "Tatter-coats is happy in her rags, playing with the gooseherd, let her be—it is all she is fit for."

A second, and then a third time, the old nurse begged him to let the girl go with him, but she was answered only by black looks and fierce words, till she was driven from the room by the jeering servants, with blows and mocking words.

Weeping over her ill-success, the old nurse went to look for Tattercoats; but the girl had been turned from the door by the cook, and had run away to tell her friend the gooseherd how unhappy she was because she could not go to the King's ball.

But when the gooseherd had listened to her story, he bade her cheer up, and proposed that they should go together into the town to see the King, and all the fine things; and when she looked sorrowfully down at her rags and bare feet, he played a note or two upon his pipe, so gay and merry, that she forgot all about her tears and her troubles, and before she well knew, the herdboy had taken her by the hand, and she, and he, and the geese before them, were dancing down the road towards the town.

Before they had gone very far, a handsome young man, splendidly dressed, rode up and stopped to ask the way to the castle where the King was staying; and when he found that they too were going thither, he got off his horse and walked beside them along the road.

The herdboy pulled out his pipe and played a low sweet tune, and the stranger looked again and again at Tattercoats' lovely face till he fell deeply in love with her, and begged her to marry him.

But she only laughed, and shook her golden head.

"You would be finely put to shame if you had a goosegirl for your wife!" said she; "go and ask one of the great ladies you will see to-night at the King's ball, and do not flout poor Tattercoats."

But the more she refused him the sweeter the pipe played, and the deeper the young man fell in love; till at last he begged her, as a proof of his sincerity, to come that night at twelve to the King's ball, just as she was, with the herdboy and his geese, and in her torn petticoat and bare feet, and he would dance with her before the King and the lords and ladies, and present her to them all, as his dear and honoured bride.

So when night came, and the hall in the castle was full of light and music, and the lords and ladies were dancing before the King, just as the clock struck twelve, Tattercoats and the herdboy, followed by his flock of noisy geese, entered at the great doors, and walked straight up the ballroom, while on either side the ladies whispered, the lords laughed, and the King seated at the far end stared in amazement.

But as they came in front of the throne, Tattercoats' lover rose from beside the King, and came to meet her. Taking her by the hand, he kissed her thrice before them all, and turned to the King.

"Father!" he said, for it was the Prince himself, "I have made my choice, and here is my bride, the loveliest girl in all the land, and the sweetest as well!"

Before he had finished speaking, the herdboy put his pipe to his lips and played a few low notes that sounded like a bird singing far off in the woods; and as he played, Tattercoats' rags were changed to shining robes sewn with glittering jewels, a golden crown lay upon her golden hair, and the flock of geese behind her became a crowd of dainty pages, bearing her long train.

And as the King rose to greet her as his daughter, the trumpets sounded loudly in honour of the new Princess, and the people outside in the street said to each other:

"Ah! now the Prince has chosen for his wife the loveliest girl in all the land!"

But the gooseherd was never seen again, and no one knew what became of him; while the old lord went home once more to his Palace by the sea, for he could not stay at Court, when he had sworn never to look on his granddaughter's face.

So there he still sits by his window, if you could only see him, as you some day may, weeping more bitterly than ever, as he looks out over the sea.

TOM TIT TOT

This is a humorous variant of the German "Rumpelstiltskin." No one knows which came first.

Once upon a time there was a woman, and she baked five pies. And when they came out of the oven, they were that overbaked the crusts were too hard to eat. So she says to her daughter:

"Darter," says she, "put you them there pies on the shelf, and leave 'em there a little, and they'll come again."—She meant, you know, the crust would get soft.

But the girl, she says to herself: "Well, if they'll come again, I'll eat 'em now." And she set to work and ate 'em all, first and last.

Well, come supper-time the woman said: "Go you, and get one o' them there pies. I dare say they've come again now."

The girl went and she looked, and there was nothing but the dishes. So back she came and says she:

"Noo, they ain't come again."

"Not one of 'em?" says the mother.

"Not one of 'em," says she.

"Well, come again, or not come again," said the woman, "I'll have one for supper."

"But you can't, if they ain't come," said the girl.

"But I can," says she. "Go you, and bring the best of 'em."

"Best or worst," says the girl, "I've ate 'em all, and you can't have one till that's come again."

Well, the woman she was done, and she took her spinning to the door to spin, and as she span she sang:

"Tom Tit Tot." From *English Fairy Tales,* edited by Joseph Jacobs. Used by permission of G. P. Putnam's Sons and Frederick Muller Ltd., London

"My darter ha' ate five, five pies to-day.
My darter ha' ate five, five pies to-day."

The king was coming down the street, and he heard her sing, but what she sang he couldn't hear, so he stopped and said:

"What was that you were singing, my good woman?"

The woman was ashamed to let him hear what her daughter had been doing, so she sang, instead of that:

"My darter ha' spun five, five skeins to-day.
My darter ha' spun five, five skeins to-day."

"Stars o' mine!" said the king. "I never heard tell of any one that could do that."

Then he said: "Look you here, I want a wife, and I'll marry your daughter. But look you here," says he, "eleven months out of the year she shall have all she likes to eat, and all the gowns she likes to get, and all the company she likes to keep; but the last month of the year she'll have to spin five skeins every day, and if she don't, I shall kill her."

"All right," says the woman; for she thought what a grand marriage that was. And as for the five skeins, when the time came, there'd be plenty of ways of getting out of it, and likeliest, he'd have forgotten all about it.

Well, so they were married. And for eleven months the girl had all she liked to eat, and all the gowns she liked to get, and all the company she liked to keep.

But when the time was getting over, she began to think about the skeins and to wonder if he had 'em in mind. But not one word did he say about 'em, and she thought he's wholly forgotten 'em.

However, the last day of the last month he takes her to a room she'd never set eyes on before. There was nothing in it but a spinning-wheel and a stool. And says he:

"Now, my dear, here you'll be shut in to-morrow with some victuals and some flax, and if you haven't spun five skeins by night, your head'll go off."

And away he went about his business.

Well, she was that frightened, she'd always been such a gatless girl, that she didn't so much

as know how to spin, and what was she to do to-morrow with no one to come nigh her to help her? She sat down on a stool in the kitchen, and law! how she did cry!

However, all of a sudden she heard a sort of a knocking low down on the door. She upped and oped it, and what should she see but a small little black thing with a long tail. That looked up at her right curious, and that said:

"What are you a-crying for?"

"What's that to you?" says she.

"Never you mind," that said, "but tell me what you're a-crying for."

"That won't do me no good if I do," says she.

"You don't know that," that said, and twirled that's tail round.

"Well," says she, "that won't do no harm, if that don't do no good," and she upped and told about the pies, and the skeins, and everything.

"This is what I'll do," says the little black thing, "I'll come to your window every morning and take the flax and bring it spun at night."

"What's your pay?" says she.

That looked out of the corner of that's eyes, and that said: "I'll give you three guesses every night to guess my name, and if you haven't guessed it before the month's up you shall be mine."

Well, she thought she'd be sure to guess that's name before the month was up. "All right," says she, "I agree."

"All right," that says, and law! how that twirled that's tail.

Well, the next day, her husband took her into the room, and there was the flax and the day's food.

"Now, there's the flax," says he, "and if that ain't spun up this night, off goes your head." then he went out and locked the door.

He'd hardly gone, when there was a knocking against the window.

She upped and she oped it, and there sure enough was the little old thing sitting on the ledge.

"Where's the flax?" says he.

"Here it be," says she. And she gave it to him.

Well, come the evening a knocking came again to the window. She upped and she oped it, and there was the little old thing with five skeins of flax on his arm.

"Here it be," says he, and he gave it to her.

"Now, what's my name?" says he.

"What, is that Bill?" says she.

"Noo, that ain't," says he, and he twirled his tail.

"Is that Ned?" says she.

"Noo, that ain't," says he, and he twirled his tail.

"Well, is that Mark?" says she.

"Noo, that ain't," says he, and he twirled his tail harder, and away he flew.

Well, when her husband came in, there were the five skeins ready for him. "I see I shan't have to kill you to-night, my dear," says he; "you'll have your food and your flax in the morning," says he, and away he goes.

Well, every day the flax and the food were brought, and every day that there little black impet used to come mornings and evenings. And all the day the girl sat trying to think of names to say to it when it came at night. But she never hit on the right one.

And as it got toward the end of the month, the impet began to look so maliceful, and that twirled that's tail faster and faster each time she gave a guess.

At last it came to the last day but one. The impet came at night along with the five skeins, and that said:

"What, ain't you got my name yet?"

"Is that Nicodemus?" says she.

"Noo, 't ain't," that says.

"Is that Sammle?" says she.

"Noo, 't ain't," that says.

"A-well, is that Methusalem?" says she.

"Noo, 't ain't that neither," that says.

Then that looks at her with that's eyes like a coal o' fire, and that says: "Woman, there's only to-morrow night, and then you'll be mine!" And away it flew.

Well, she felt that horrid. However, she heard the king coming along the passage.

In he came, and when he sees the five skeins, he says, says he:

"Well, my dear," says he. "I don't see but what you'll have your skeins ready to-morrow night as well, and as I reckon I shan't have to kill you, I'll have supper in here to-night." So they brought supper, and another stool for him, and down the two sat.

Well, he hadn't eaten but a mouthful or so, when he stops and begins to laugh.

"What is it?" says she.

"A-why," says he, "I was out a-hunting today, and I got away to a place in the wood I'd never seen before. And there was an old chalk-pit. And I heard a kind of a sort of humming. So I got off my hobby, and I went right quiet to the pit, and I looked down. Well, what should there be but the funniest little black thing you ever set eyes on. And what was that doing, but that had a little spinning-wheel, and that was spinning wonderful fast, and twirling that's tail. And as that span that sang:

"Nimmy nimmy not
My name's Tom Tit Tot."

Well, when the girl heard this, she felt as if she could have jumped out of her skin for joy, but she didn't say a word.

Next day that there little thing looked so maliceful when he came for the flax. And when the night came she heard that knocking against the window panes. She oped the window, and that come right in on the ledge. That was grinning from ear to ear, and Oo! that's tail was twirling round so fast.

"What's my name?" that says, as that gave her the skeins.

"Is that Solomon?" she says, pretending to be afeard.

"Noo, 't ain't," that says, and that came further into the room.

"Well, is that Zebedee?" says she again.

"Noo, 't ain't," says the impet. And then that laughed and twirled that's tail till you couldn't hardly see it.

"Take time, woman," that says; "next guess, and you're mine." And that stretched out that's black hands at her.

Well, she backed a step or two, and she looked at it, and then she laughed out, and says she, pointing her finger at it:

"Nimmy nimmy not
Your name's Tom Tit Tot."

Well, when that heard her, that gave an awful shriek and away that flew into the dark, and she never saw it any more.

THE BLACK
BULL OF NORROWAY

Here is a somber and beautiful story of a black spell which is broken at last by the faithful love of a girl. The rhymes add much to its charm.

Long ago in Norroway there lived a lady who had three daughters. Now they were all pretty, and one night they fell a-talking of whom they meant to marry.

And the eldest said, "I will have no one lower than an Earl."

And the second said, "I will have no one lower than a Lord."

But the third, the prettiest and the merriest, tossed her head and said, with a twinkle in her eye, "Why so proud? As for me I would be content with the Black Bull of Norroway."

At that the other sisters bade her be silent and not talk lightly of such a monster. For, see you, is it not written:

> To wilder measures now they turn,
> The black black Bull of Norroway;
> Sudden the tapers cease to burn,
> The minstrels cease to play.

So, no doubt, the Black Bull of Norroway was held to be a horrid monster.

But the youngest daughter would have her laugh, so she said three times that she would be content with the Black Bull of Norroway.

Well! It so happened that the very next morning a coach-and-six came swinging along the road, and in it sat an Earl who had come to ask the hand of the eldest daughter in marriage. So there were great rejoicings over the wedding, and the bride and bridegroom drove away in the coach-and-six.

Then the next thing that happened was that a coach-and-four with a Lord in it came swinging along the road; and he wanted to marry the second daughter. So they were wed, and there were great rejoicings, and the bride and bridegroom drove away in the coach-and-four.

"The Black Bull of Norroway." From *English Fairy Tales* retold by Flora Annie Steel. By permission of The Macmillan Company, New York and Macmillan & Co. Ltd., London

Now after this there was only the youngest, the prettiest and the merriest, of the sisters left, and she became the apple of her mother's eye. So you may imagine how the mother felt when one morning a terrible bellowing was heard at the door, and there was a great big Black Bull waiting for his bride.

She wept and she wailed, and at first the girl ran away and hid herself in the cellar for fear, but there the Bull stood waiting, and at last the girl came up and said:

"I promised I would be content with the Black Bull of Norroway, and I must keep my word. Farewell, mother, you will not see me again."

Then she mounted on the Black Bull's back, and it walked away with her quite quietly. And ever it chose the smoothest paths and the easiest roads, so that at last the girl grew less afraid. But she became very hungry and was nigh to faint when the Black Bull said to her, in quite a soft voice that wasn't a bellow at all:

> "Eat out of my left ear,
>   Drink out of my right,
> And set by what you leave
>   To serve the morrow's night."

So she did as she was bid, and, lo and behold! the left ear was full of delicious things to eat, and the right was full of the most delicious drinks, and there was plenty left over for several days.

Thus they journeyed on, and they journeyed on, through many dreadful forests and many lonely wastes, and the Black Bull never paused for bite or sup, but ever the girl he carried ate out of his left ear and drank out of his right, and set by what she left to serve the morrow's night. And she slept soft and warm on his broad back.

Now at last they reached a noble castle where a large company of lords and ladies were assembled, and greatly the company wondered at the sight of these strange companions. And they invited the girl to supper, but the Black Bull they turned into the field, and left to spend the night after his kind.

But when the next morning came, there he was ready for his burden again. Now, though the girl was loth to leave her pleasant companions, she remembered her promise, and mounted on his back, so they journeyed on, and journeyed on, and journeyed on, through many tangled woods and over many high mountains. And ever the Black Bull chose the smoothest paths for her and set aside the briars and brambles, while she ate out of his left ear and drank out of his right.

So at last they came to a magnificent mansion where Dukes and Duchesses and Earls and Countesses were enjoying themselves. Now the company, though much surprised at the strange companions, asked the girl in to supper; and the Black Bull they would have turned into the park for the night, but that the girl, remembering how well he had cared for her, asked them to put him into the stable and give him a good feed.

So this was done, and the next morning he was waiting before the hall-door for his burden; and she, though somewhat loth at leaving the fine company, mounted him cheerfully enough, and they rode away, and they rode away, and they rode away, through thick briar brakes and up fearsome cliffs. But ever the Black Bull trod the brambles underfoot and chose the easiest paths, while she ate out of his left ear and drank out of his right, and wanted for nothing, though he had neither bite nor sup. So it came to pass that he grew tired and was limping with one foot when, just as the sun was setting, they came to a beautiful palace where Princes and Princesses were disporting themselves with ball on the green grass. Now, though the company greatly wondered at the strange companions, they asked the girl to join them, and ordered the grooms to lead away the Black Bull to a field.

But she, remembering all he had done for her, said, "Not so! He will stay with me!" Then seeing a large thorn in the foot with which he had been limping, she stooped down and pulled it out.

And, lo and behold! in an instant, to every one's surprise, there appeared, not a frightful monstrous bull, but one of the most beautiful Princes ever beheld, who fell at his deliverer's feet, thanking her for having broken his cruel enchantment.

A wicked witch-woman who wanted to marry him had, he said, spelled him until a beautiful maiden of her own free will should do him a favour.

"But," he said, "the danger is not all over. You have broken the enchantment by night; that by day has yet to be overcome."

So the next morning the Prince had to resume the form of a bull, and they set out together; and they rode, and they rode, and they rode, till they came to a dark and ugsome glen. And here he bade her dismount and sit on a great rock.

"Here you must stay," he said, "while I go yonder and fight the Old One. And mind! move neither hand nor foot whilst I am away, else I shall never find you again. If everything around you turns blue, I shall have beaten the Old One; but if everything turns red, he will have conquered me."

And with that, and a tremendous roaring bellow, he set off to find his foe.

Well, she sat as still as a mouse, moving neither hand nor foot, nor even her eyes, and waited, and waited, and waited. Then at last everything turned blue. But she was so overcome with joy to think that her lover was victorious that she forgot to keep still, and lifting one of her feet, crossed it over the other!

So she waited, and waited, and waited. Long she sat, and aye she wearied; and all the time he was seeking for her, but he never found her.

At last she rose and went she knew not whither, determined to seek for her lover through the whole wide world. So she journeyed on, and she journeyed on, and she journeyed on, until one day in a dark wood she came to a little hut where lived an old, old woman who gave her food and shelter, and bid her Godspeed on her errand, giving her three nuts, a walnut, a filbert, and a hazel nut, with these words:

"When your heart is like to break,
  And once again is like to break,
Crack a nut and in its shell
  That will be that suits you well."

After this she felt heartened up, and wandered on till her road was blocked by a great hill of glass; and though she tried all she could to climb it, she could not; for aye she slipped back, and slipped back, and slipped back; for it was like ice.

Then she sought a passage elsewhere, and round and about the foot of the hill she went sobbing and wailing, but ne'er a foothold could she find. At last she came to a smithy; and the smith promised if she would serve him faithfully for seven years and seven days, that he would make her iron shoon wherewith to climb the hill of glass.

So for seven long years and seven short days she toiled, and span, and swept, and washed in the smith's house. And for wage he gave her a pair of iron shoon, and with them she clomb the glassy hill and went on her way.

Now she had not gone far before a company of fine lords and ladies rode past her talking of all the grand doings that were to be done at the young Duke of Norroway's wedding. Then she passed a number of people carrying all sorts of good things which they told her were for the Duke's wedding. And at last she came to a palace castle where the courtyards were full of cooks and bakers, some running this way, some running that, and all so busy that they did not know what to do first.

Then she heard the horns of hunters and cries of "Room! Room for the Duke of Norroway and his bride!"

And who should ride past but the beautiful Prince she had but half unspelled, and by his side was the witch-woman who was determined to marry him that very day.

Well! at the sight she felt that her heart was indeed like to break, and over again was like to break, so that the time had come for her to crack one of the nuts. So she broke the walnut, as it was the biggest, and out of it came a wonderful wee woman carding wool as fast as ever she could card.

Now when the witch-woman saw this wonderful thing she offered the girl her choice of anything in the castle for it.

"If you will put off your wedding with the Duke for a day, and let me watch in his room tonight," said the girl, "you shall have it."

Now, like all witch-women, the bride wanted everything her own way, and she was so sure she had her groom safe, that she consented; but before the Duke went to rest she gave him, with her own hands, a posset so made that any one who drank it would sleep till morning.

Thus, though the girl was allowed alone into the Duke's chamber, and though she spent the livelong night sighing and singing:

"Far have I sought for thee,
Long have I wrought for thee,
Near am I brought to thee,
Dear Duke o' Norroway;
Wilt thou say naught to me?"

The Duke never wakened, but slept on. So when day came the girl had to leave him without his ever knowing she had been there.

Then once again her heart was like to break, and over and over again like to break, and she cracked the filbert nut, because it was the next biggest. And out of it came a wonderful wee, wee woman spinning away as fast as ever she could spin. Now when the witch-bride saw this wonderful thing she once again put off her wedding so that she might possess it. And once again the girl spent the livelong night in the Duke's chamber sighing and singing:

"Far have I sought for thee,
Long have I wrought for thee,
Near am I brought to thee,
Dear Duke o' Norroway;
Wilt thou say naught to me?"

But the Duke, who had drunk the sleeping-draught from the hands of his witch-bride, never stirred, and when dawn came the girl had to leave him without his ever knowing she had been there.

Then, indeed, the girl's heart was like to break, and over and over and over again like to break, so she cracked the last nut—the hazel nut —and out of it came the most wonderful wee, wee, wee-est woman reeling away at yarn as fast as she could reel.

And this marvel so delighted the witch-bride that once again she consented to put off her wedding for a day, and allow the girl to watch in the Duke's chamber the night through, in order to possess it.

Now it so happened that when the Duke was dressing that morning he heard his pages talking amongst themselves of the strange sighing and singing they had heard in the night; and he said to his faithful old valet, "What do the pages mean?"

And the old valet, who hated the witch-bride, said:

"If the master will take no sleeping-draught to-night, mayhap he may also hear what for two nights has kept me awake."

At this the Duke marvelled greatly, and when the witch-bride brought him his evening posset, he made excuse it was not sweet enough, and while she went away to get honey to sweeten it withal, he poured away the posset and made believe he had swallowed it.

So that night when dark had come, and the girl stole in to his chamber with a heavy heart thinking it would be the very last time she would ever see him, the Duke was really broad awake. And when she sat down by his bedside and began to sing:

"Far have I sought for thee,"

he knew her voice at once, and clasped her in his arms.

Then he told her how he had been in the power of the witch-woman and had forgotten everything, but that now he remembered all and that the spell was broken for ever and aye.

So the wedding feast served for their marriage, since the witch-bride, seeing her power was gone, quickly fled the country and was never heard of again.

WHITTINGTON AND HIS CAT

The story of Dick Whittington is a popular legend, a hero tale and a success story! It is overlong and will be improved by a free telling of the main incidents, cutting the details. The children will enjoy Marcia Brown's picture-story of Dick.

In the reign of the famous King Edward III there was a little boy called Dick Whittington, whose father and mother died when he was very young. As poor Dick was not old enough to work, he was very badly off; he got but little for his dinner, and sometimes nothing at all for his breakfast; for the people who lived in the village

"Whittington and His Cat." From *English Fairy Tales*, edited by Joseph Jacobs. Used by permission of G. P. Putnam's Sons and Frederick Muller Ltd., London

were very poor indeed, and could not spare him much more than the parings of potatoes, and now and then a hard crust of bread.

Now Dick had heard many, many very strange things about the great city called London; for the country people at that time thought that folks in London were all fine gentlemen and ladies; and that there was singing and music there all day long; and that the streets were all paved with gold.

One day a large waggon and eight horses, all with bells at their heads, drove through the village while Dick was standing by the sign-post. He thought that this waggon must be going to the fine town of London; so he took courage, and asked the waggoner to let him walk with him by the side of the waggon. As soon as the waggoner heard that poor Dick had no father or mother, and saw by his ragged clothes that he could not be worse off than he was, he told him he might go if he would, so off they set together.

So Dick got safe to London, and was in such a hurry to see the fine streets paved all over with gold, that he did not even stay to thank the kind waggoner; but ran off as fast as his legs would carry him, through many of the streets, thinking every moment to come to those that were paved with gold; for Dick had seen a guinea three times in his own little village, and remembered what a deal of money it brought in change; so he thought he had nothing to do but to take up some little bits of the pavement, and should then have as much money as he could wish for.

Poor Dick ran till he was tired, and had quite forgot his friend the waggoner; but at last, finding it grow dark, and that every way he turned he saw nothing but dirt instead of gold, he sat down in a dark corner and cried himself to sleep.

Little Dick was all night in the streets; and next morning, being very hungry, he got up and walked about, and asked everybody he met to give him a halfpenny to keep him from starving; but nobody stayed to answer him, and only two or three gave him a halfpenny; so that the poor boy was soon quite weak and faint for the want of victuals.

In this distress he asked charity of several people and one of them said crossly: "Go to work for an idle rogue." "That I will," said Dick, "I will go to work for you, if you will let me." But the man only cursed at him and went on.

At last a good-natured looking gentleman saw how hungry he looked. "Why don't you go to work, my lad?" said he to Dick. "That I would, but I do not know how to get any," answered Dick. "If you are willing, come along with me," said the gentleman, and took him to a hay-field, where Dick worked briskly, and lived merrily till the hay was made.

After this he found himself as badly off as before; and being almost starved again, he laid himself down at the door of Mr. Fitzwarren, a rich merchant. Here he was soon seen by the cook-maid, who was an ill-tempered creature, and happened just then to be very busy dressing dinner for her master and mistress; so she called out to poor Dick: "What business have you there, you lazy rogue? there is nothing else but beggars; if you do not take yourself away, we will see how you will like a sousing of some dishwater; I have some here hot enough to make you jump."

Just at that time Mr. Fitzwarren himself came home to dinner; and when he saw a dirty ragged boy lying at the door, he said to him: "Why do you lie there, my boy? You seem old enough to work; I am afraid you are inclined to be lazy."

"No, indeed, sir," said Dick to him, "that is not the case, for I would work with all my heart, but I do not know anybody, and I believe I am very sick for the want of food."

"Poor fellow, get up; let me see what ails you."

Dick now tried to rise, but was obliged to lie down again, being too weak to stand, for he had not eaten any food for three days, and was no longer able to run about and beg a halfpenny of people in the street. So the kind merchant ordered him to be taken into the house, and have a good dinner given him, and be kept to do what work he was able to do for the cook.

Little Dick would have lived very happy in this good family if it had not been for the ill-natured cook. She used to say: "You are under me, so look sharp; clean the spit and the dripping-pan, make the fires, wind up the jack, and do all the scullery work nimbly, or——" and she would shake the ladle at him. Besides, she was so fond of basting, that when she had no meat to baste, she would baste poor Dick's head and shoulders with a broom, or anything else that happened to fall in her way. At last her ill-usage of him was told to Alice, Mr. Fitzwarren's daughter, who told the cook she should be turned away if she did not treat him kinder.

The behaviour of the cook was now a little better; but besides this, Dick had another hardship to get over. His bed stood in a garret, where there were so many holes in the floor and the walls that every night he was tormented with rats and mice. A gentleman having given Dick a penny for cleaning his shoes, he thought he would buy a cat with it. The next day he saw a girl with a cat, and asked her, "Will you let me have that cat for a penny?" The girl said: "Yes, that I will, master, though she is an excellent mouser."

Dick hid his cat in the garret, and always took care to carry a part of his dinner to her; and in a short time he had no more trouble with the rats and mice, but slept quite sound every night.

Soon after this, his master had a ship ready to sail; and as it was the custom that all his servants should have some chance for good fortune as well as himself, he called them all into the parlour and asked them what they would send out.

They all had something that they were willing to venture except poor Dick, who had neither money nor goods, and therefore could send nothing. For this reason he did not come into the parlour with the rest; but Miss Alice guessed what was the matter and ordered him to be called in. She then said: "I will lay down some money for him, from my own purse"; but her father told her: "This will not do, for it must be something of his own."

When poor Dick heard this, he said: "I have nothing but a cat which I bought for a penny some time since of a little girl."

"Fetch your cat then, my lad," said Mr. Fitzwarren, "and let her go."

Dick went upstairs and brought down poor puss, with tears in his eyes, and gave her to the captain; "For," he said, "I shall now be kept awake all night by the rats and mice." All the company laughed at Dick's odd venture; and Miss Alice, who felt pity for him, gave him some money to buy another cat.

This, and many other marks of kindness shown him by Miss Alice, made the ill-tempered cook jealous of poor Dick, and she began to use him more cruelly than ever, and always made game of him for sending his cat to sea. She asked him. "Do you think your cat will sell for as much money as would buy a stick to beat you?"

At last poor Dick could not bear this usage any longer, and he thought he would run away from his place; so he packed up his few things, and started very early in the morning, on All-hallows Day, the first of November. He walked as far as Halloway, and there sat down on a stone, which to this day is called "Whittington's Stone," and began to think to himself which road he should take.

While he was thinking what he should do, the Bells of Bow Church, which at that time were only six, began to ring, and at their sound seemed to say to him:

"Turn again, Whittington,
    Thrice Lord Mayor of London."

"Lord Mayor of London!" said he to himself. "Why, to be sure, I would put up with almost anything now, to be Lord Mayor of London, and ride in a fine coach, when I grow to be a man! Well, I will go back, and think nothing of the cuffing and scolding of the old cook, if I am to be Lord Mayor of London at last."

Dick went back, and was lucky enough to get into the house, and set about his work, before the old cook came downstairs.

We must now follow Miss Puss to the coast of Africa. The ship with the cat on board was a long time at sea; and was at last driven by the winds on a part of the coast of Barbary, where the only people were the Moors, unknown to the English. The people came in great numbers to see the sailors, because they were of different colour to themselves, and treated them civilly; and, when they became better acquainted, were very eager to buy the fine things that the ship was loaded with.

When the captain saw this, he sent patterns of the best things he had to the king of the country; who was so much pleased with them, that he sent for the captain to the palace. Here they were placed, as it is the custom of the country, on rich carpets flowered with gold and silver. The king and queen were seated at the upper end of the room; and a number of dishes were brought in for dinner. They had not sat long, when a vast number of rats and mice rushed in, and devoured all the meat in an instant. The captain wondered at this, and asked if these vermin were not unpleasant.

"Oh yes," said they, "very offensive; and the king would give half his treasure to be freed of them, for they not only destroy his dinner, as you see, but they assault him in his chamber, and even in bed, so that he is obliged to be watched while he is sleeping, for fear of them."

The captain jumped for joy; he remembered poor Whittington and his cat, and told the king he had a creature on board the ship that would despatch all these vermin immediately. The king jumped so high at the joy which the news gave him, that his turban dropped off his head. "Bring this creature to me," says he; "vermin are dreadful in a court, and if she will perform what you say, I will load your ship with gold and jewels in exchange for her."

The captain, who knew his business, took this opportunity to set forth the merits of Mrs. Puss. He told his majesty: "It is not very convenient to part with her, as, when she is gone, the rats and mice may destroy the goods in the ship—but to oblige your majesty, I will fetch her."

"Run, run!" said the queen; "I am impatient to see the dear creature."

Away went the captain to the ship, while another dinner was got ready. He put Puss under his arm, and arrived at the place just in time to see the table full of rats. When the cat saw them,

rats, bargained with the captain for the whole ship's cargo, and then gave him ten times as much for the cat as all the rest amounted to.

The captain then took leave of the royal party, and set sail with a fair wind for England, and after a happy voyage arrived safe in London.

One morning, early, Mr. Fitzwarren had just come to his counting-house and seated himself at the desk to count over the cash, and settle the business for the day, when somebody came tap, tap, at the door. "Who's there?" said Mr. Fitzwarren. "A friend," answered the other; "I come to bring you good news of your ship *Unicorn*." The merchant, bustling up in such a hurry that he forgot his gout, opened the door, and who should he see waiting but the captain and factor, with a cabinet of jewels and a bill of lading; when he looked at this the merchant lifted up his eyes and thanked Heaven for sending him such a prosperous voyage.

They then told the story of the cat, and showed the rich present that the king and queen had sent for her to poor Dick. As soon as the merchant heard this, he called out to his servants:

> "Go send him in, and tell him of
> his fame;
> Pray call him Mr. Whittington
> by name."

Mr. Fitzwarren now showed himself to be a good man; for when some of his servants said so great a treasure was too much for him, he answered: "God forbid I should deprive him of the value of a single penny; it is his own, and he shall have it to a farthing."

He then sent for Dick, who at that time was scouring pots for the cook, and was quite dirty. He would have excused himself from coming into the counting-house, saying, "The room is swept, and my shoes are

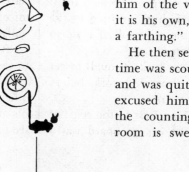

she did not wait for bidding, but jumped out of the captain's arms, and in a few minutes laid almost all the rats and mice dead at her feet. The rest of them in their fright scampered away to their holes.

The king was quite charmed to get rid so easily of such plagues, and the queen desired that the creature who had done them so great a kindness might be brought to her, that she might look at her. Upon which the captain called: "Pussy, pussy, pussy!" and she came to him. He then presented her to the queen, who started back, and was afraid to touch a creature who had made such a havoc among the rats and mice. However, when the captain stroked the cat and called: "Pussy, pussy," the queen also touched her and cried: "Putty, putty," for she had not learned English. He then put her down on the queen's lap, where she purred and played with her majesty's hand, and then purred herself to sleep.

The king, having seen the exploits of Mrs. Puss, and being informed that her kittens would stock the whole country, and keep it free from

dirty and full of hobnails." But the merchant ordered him to come in.

Mr. Fitzwarren ordered a chair to be set for him, and so he began to think they were making game of him, and at the same time said to them: "Do not play tricks with a poor simple boy, but let me go down again, if you please, to my work."

"Indeed, Mr. Whittington," said the merchant, "we are all quite in earnest with you, and I most heartily rejoice in the news that these gentlemen have brought you; for the captain has sold your cat to the King of Barbary, and brought you in return for her more riches than I possess in the whole world; and I wish you may long enjoy them!"

Mr. Fitzwarren then told the men to open the great treasure they had brought with them, and said: "Mr. Whittington has nothing to do but to put it in some place of safety."

Poor Dick hardly knew how to behave himself for joy. He begged his master to take what part of it he pleased, since he owed it all to his kindness. "No, no," answered Mr. Fitzwarren, "this is all your own; and I have no doubt but you will use it well."

Dick next asked his mistress, and then Miss Alice, to accept a part of his good fortune; but they would not, and at the same time told him they felt great joy at his good success. But this poor fellow was too kind-hearted to keep it all to himself; so he made a present to the captain, the mate, and the rest of Mr. Fitzwarren's servants; and even to the ill-natured old cook.

After this Mr. Fitzwarren advised him to send for a proper tailor, and get himself dressed like a gentleman; and told him he was welcome to live in his house till he could provide himself with a better.

When Whittington's face was washed, his hair curled, his hat cocked, and he was dressed in a nice suit of clothes, he was as handsome and genteel as any young man who visited at Mr. Fitzwarren's; so that Miss Alice, who had once been so kind to him, and thought of him with pity, now looked upon him as fit to be her sweetheart; and the more so, no doubt, because Whittington was now always thinking what he could do to oblige her, and making her the prettiest presents that could be.

Mr. Fitzwarren soon saw their love for each

other, and proposed to join them in marriage; and to this they both readily agreed. A day for the wedding was soon fixed; and they were attended to church by the Lord Mayor, the court of aldermen, the sheriffs, and a great number of the richest merchants in London, whom they afterwards treated with a very rich feast.

History tells us that Mr. Whittington and his lady lived in great splendour, and were very happy. They had several children. He was Sheriff of London, thrice Lord Mayor, and received the honour of knighthood by Henry V.

He entertained his king and his queen at dinner, after his conquest of France, so grandly, that the king said: "Never had prince such a subject"; when Sir Richard heard this, he said: "Never had subject such a prince."

The figure of Sir Richard Whittington with his cat in his arms, carved in stone, was to be seen till the year 1780 over the archway of the old prison at Newgate, which he built for criminals.

WHIPPETY STOURIE

This queer Scottish tale of the wee ladies with the lopsided mouths begins like a variant of "Tom Tit Tot," but the conclusion is amusingly different.

On a day long ago, when the bracken sprang green and tender on the hills, a fine gentleman rode over the braeside to woo a fair lady. As the summer passed the lady came to love her suitor very dearly; and by the time that the bracken

"Whippety Stourie." From *Scottish Folk-Tales and Legends* by Barbara Ker Wilson. Reprinted by permission of Henry Z. Walck, Inc.

hung crisp and golden on the hills they were married with great rejoicing, and he took her away from her father's home to live in his own house.

The lady thought she had never been happier in all her life, for she had all that her heart desired: a great house, rich velvet gowns, and beautiful jewels. But one day her husband came to her and said:

"Now, wife, it is time you put your fair hand to the spinning-wheel; for a home is no home without the clack of a shuttle within its walls; and a wife is no wife unless she can spin fine thread for her husband's shirts."

The lady looked downcast at these words, and she displayed her hands imploringly.

"Alas," she said, "I have never spun a single thread in all my life, husband, for in my father's house it was not thought fitting that a maid of high degree should learn such a lowly occupation."

Then her husband's face grew dark and he replied:

"To sit by the spinning-wheel and spin fine thread is a womanly task that all good wives should perform. From now on you must spin me twelve hanks of thread each day—or, dear as you are to my heart, it will be the worse for you."

"Truly, husband," his lady wept, "I am not too proud to do your bidding, for I would willingly obey your slightest wish. But I fear I shall never be able to spin one good hank of thread, let alone twelve. For how shall I set about my spinning, with no one to show me the way it should be done?"

But her husband would not listen to her pleading, and only replied that she must find out for herself how to spin. Then he ordered the servants to bring a spinning-wheel to his lady's room, and to provide her each day with sufficient flax to spin twelve hanks of thread.

During the week that followed, the lady rose early each morning and sat herself down before the spinning-wheel, with a heap of shining flax by her side. But though she turned the wheel from the time the sunlight first struck the heather on the hills until it grew dusk, she did not spin one good hank of thread. Every night when her husband came to her room, he would find her resting wearily on her stool and weeping bitterly. Then he would pick up the shuttle and see perhaps half a hank of ravelled and knotted thread.

"This is not the fine thread I want," he said, "but coarse stuff, fit for a crofter's garments. You must do better than this, wife—or, dear as you are to my heart, it will be the worse for you."

On the last night of the week he came to her and announced that he was going away on a journey.

"And when I come back," he said, "you must have spun a hundred hanks of fine thread. If you have not, then, dear as you are to my heart, I must surely cast you aside and find a new wife to spin for me."

(For you must know that in those days if a man was not satisfied with his first wife, he could cast her aside just so and get himself another instead.)

And he kissed his wife farewell and rode away.

"Alas, alas," the lady grieved, "what shall I do now? For I well know that I shall never manage to spin a hundred hanks of fine thread before my husband returns; and he will surely cast me aside and find a new wife."

She left her room and went out to the braeside to wander among the bracken and the heather, full of sorrowful thoughts. She had not gone far when she felt weary, and sat down on a flat grey stone in the shade of a scarlet-berried rowan-tree. By and by she heard a faint sound of music; and to her amazement it seemed to be coming from underneath the very stone where she sat.

"Now surely it is faery music I can hear," she thought. "For I never heard a mortal piper play such a bonny tune."

And plucking a twig of the rowan-tree to protect herself, she jumped up and rolled away the stone, to find that it had concealed the entrance to a green cave in the hill-side. Peering inside the cave, she was surprised to see six wee ladies in green gowns, all sitting round in a circle. One of them had a little spinning-wheel before her, and as the shuttle clacked busily to and fro she sang:

"*Little kens my dame at hame*
That Whippety Stourie is my name."

Without taking a second thought, the lady stepped into the cave and greeted the Little Folk pleasantly. They nodded to her in reply; and she noticed that all their six mouths were as lop-sided as a fir-tree leaning against the wind. Now as soon as she saw the fine, fine thread that the wee lady called Whippety Stourie was spinning, the lady was reminded of all her troubles, and she could not stop the tears from trickling down her cheeks.

"Why do you weep?" one of the Little Folk asked her out of the side of her mouth. "For you seem a fine lady in your rich velvet gown and beautiful jewels, and should have nothing to weep for."

"Alas, good folk, my husband has gone away on a journey, and when he comes back I must have spun for him a hundred hanks of fine thread—or, dear as I am to his heart, he will surely kill me and find another wife. And I weep because I am not able to spin one good hank of thread, let alone a hundred; and so I cannot do his bidding."

Then the six wee ladies looked at one another out of their sharp bright eyes, and they all burst into lop-sided laughter.

"Och, is that all your trouble?" said Whippety Stourie. "You can forget your sorrow, fair lady, for we will help you. If you ask us to take supper with you in your fine house on the day appointed for your husband's return, you will find that you will have nothing more to worry about."

The lady looked at the six wee folk in their gowns of green, and she felt an upspringing of hope.

"Indeed, you are welcome to take supper in our house on the day that my husband returns," she said. "And if only you can help me, I will be grateful to you as long as I live."

Then she took her leave of them and rolled back the flat grey stone so that it once more concealed the entrance to their green cave in the hill-side. When she returned to her house, she sat no more at her spinning-wheel, and left untouched the heap of shining flax that lay in her room—for she knew that the Little Folk would keep their word and come to help her.

Her husband came riding home in the evening of the day appointed for his return. He greeted his wife fondly and seemed to have left his grouchy humour behind him on his travels. At every moment his lady was expecting him to ask her about her spinning; but he did not have time to do so before the servants announced that supper was ready.

"Why are there six more places made ready at the table, and six wee stools drawn up beside them?" her husband asked as they sat down.

"Och, I asked six wee ladies to come and take supper with us tonight, for I thought the company would cheer you on your return," the lady replied.

She had no sooner spoken than there was a scuttering of feet in the passage outside, and in came the six wee ladies in their gowns of green. The husband greeted them courteously, and bade them be seated. During the meal he talked and joked with them in high good humour, and his wife was pleased to see how well they agreed. Then there was a pause in their talk, and the husband looked at the six wee ladies curiously.

"Would you mind telling me," he asked them, "why it is that your mouths are all as lop-sided as a fir-tree leaning against the wind?"

Then the six wee ladies burst into loud, lop-sided laughter, and Whippety Stourie herself replied:

"Och, it's with our constant spin-spin-spinning. For we're all of us great ones for the spinning, and there's no surer way to a lop-sided mouth."

At these words the husband grew pale. He looked at his fair wife, and he glanced at the wee ladies, and his alarm was plain to see.

And when their six wee guests had taken their leave and departed, he put his arm round his lady's shoulders and called the servants to him.

"Burn the spinning-wheel that is in my wife's room," he told them, "and see that it perishes on a bright flame. I would not have my fair lady spin one more inch of thread, for fear she should spoil her bonny face. For there's no surer way to a lop-sided mouth than a constant spin-spin-spinning."

The lady's heart leapt for joy at her husband's words; and from that day onwards the two of them lived contentedly for the rest of their days, with never the clack of a shuttle to disturb their happiness.

German folk tales

*The German folk tales were known to English children in translation
long before their own stories were collected. Since their first translation into English, the* Grimm Fairy Tales *have been translated into most of the languages of the civilized world and are the beloved heritage of children everywhere.
Because Jacob and Wilhelm Grimm were students of the German language,
they collected their stories from the lips of old storytellers and recorded them
faithfully. The result is that these German stories, even in translation,
have the authentic spellbinding quality of great storytelling. The plots range from
stories for the nursery to mature themes for older children and even
adults. The tales are dramatic, exciting, full of suspense and smashing climaxes
that make children eager to hear more of them. "Snow-White and
the Seven Dwarfs," "Mother Holle," and a lot of others are still among the best
known and the most continuously popular fairy tales ever told to children.*

THE WOLF AND
THE SEVEN LITTLE KIDS

*"The Story of the Three Little Pigs" can be
used with five-year-olds but this similar tale is a
bit more alarming and is better for the sevens.
The joyful conclusion makes everything all right.*

There was once on a time an old goat who
had seven little kids and loved them with all
the love of a mother for her children. One day
she wanted to go into the forest and fetch some
food. So she called all seven to her and said,
"Dear children, I have to go into the forest; be
on your guard against the wolf; if he comes in,
he will devour you all—skin, hair, and all. The
wretch often disguises himself, but you will know
him at once by his rough voice and his black
feet." The kids said, "Dear mother, we will take
good care of ourselves; you may go away without
any anxiety." Then the old one bleated, and
went on her way with an easy mind.

It was not long before some one knocked at
the house-door and cried, "Open the door, dear
children; your mother is here, and has brought
something back with her for each of you." But
the little kids knew that it was the wolf, by the
rough voice. "We will not open the door," cried

"The Wolf and the Seven Little Kids." From *Grimm's
Household Tales*, translated by Margaret Hunt

they, "You are not our mother. She has a soft,
pleasant voice, but your voice is rough; you are
the wolf!" Then the wolf went away to a shop-
keeper and bought himself a great lump of chalk,
ate this and made his voice soft with it. Then he
came back, knocked at the door of the house,
and cried, "Open the door, dear children, your
mother is here and has brought something back
with her for each of you." But the wolf had
laid his black paws against the window, and
the children saw them and cried, "We will not
open the door; our mother has not black feet
like you: you are the wolf!" Then the wolf ran
to a baker and said, "I have hurt my feet, rub
some dough over them for me." And when the
baker had rubbed his feet over, he ran to the
miller and said, "Strew some white meal over
my feet for me." The miller thought to himself,
"The wolf wants to deceive some one," and refused; but the wolf said, "If you will not do it,
I will devour you." Then the miller was afraid
and made his paws white for him. Truly men are
like that.

So now the wretch went for the third time to
the house-door, knocked at it, and said, "Open
the door for me, children, your dear little mother
has come home and has brought every one of you
something back from the forest with her." The
little kids cried, "First show us your paws that we
may know if you are our dear little mother."
Then he put his paws in through the window,
and when the kids saw that they were white,

they believed that all he said was true, and opened the door. But who should come in but the wolf! They were terrified and wanted to hide themselves. One sprang under the table, the second into the bed, the third into the stove, the fourth into the kitchen, the fifth into the cupboard, the sixth under the washing-bowl, and the seventh into the clock-case. But the wolf found them all and used no great ceremony; one after the other he swallowed them down his throat. The youngest in the clock-case was the only one he did not find. When the wolf had satisfied his appetite, he took himself off, laid himself down under a tree in the green meadow outside, and began to sleep. Soon afterwards the old goat came home again from the forest. Ah! what a sight she saw there! The house-door stood wide open. The table, chairs, and benches were thrown down, the washing-bowl lay broken to pieces, and the quilts and pillows were pulled off the bed. She sought her children, but they were nowhere to be found. She called them one after another by name, but no one answered. At last, when she came to the youngest, a soft voice cried, "Dear mother, I am in the clock-case." She took the kid out, and it told her that the wolf had come and had eaten all the others. Then you may imagine how she wept over her poor children.

At length in her grief she went out, and the youngest kid ran with her. When they came to the meadow, there lay the wolf by the tree and snored so loud that the branches shook. She looked at him on every side and saw that something was moving and struggling in his gorged body. "Ah, heavens," said she, "is it possible that my poor children whom he has swallowed down for his supper can be still alive?" Then the kid had to run home and fetch scissors, and a needle and thread, and the goat cut open the monster's stomach, and hardly had she made one cut, than one little kid thrust its head out, and when she had cut farther, all six sprang out one after another, and were all still alive, and had suffered no injury whatever, for in his greediness the monster had swallowed them down whole. What rejoicing there was! Then they embraced their dear mother, and jumped like a tailor at his wedding. The mother, however, said, "Now go and look for some big stones, and we will fill the wicked beast's stomach with them while he is still asleep." Then the seven kids dragged the stones thither with all speed, and put as many of them into his stomach as they could get in; and the mother sewed him up again in the greatest haste, so that he was not aware of anything and never once stirred.

When the wolf at length had had his sleep out, he got on his legs, and as the stones in his stomach made him very thirsty, he wanted to go to a well to drink. But when he began to walk and to move about, the stones in his stomach knocked against each other and rattled. Then cried he,

> "What rumbles and tumbles
> Against my poor bones?
> I thought 'twas six kids,
> But it's naught but big stones."

And when he got to the well and stooped over the water and was just about to drink, the heavy stones made him fall in and there was no help, but he had to drown miserably. When the seven kids saw that, they came running to the spot and cried aloud, "The wolf is dead! The wolf is dead!" and danced for joy round about the well with their mother.

THE ELVES

AND THE SHOEMAKER

This story has an excellent plot but dull style. Try turning the narrative into direct conversation here and there; for example, let the shoemaker say, "Good wife, good wife, see what has happened this night. Someone has stitched my leather into shoes." Then have the good wife reply, "And they are perfectly made. They should sell for a good price."

There was once a shoemaker who worked very hard and was very honest; but still he could not earn enough to live upon, and at last all he had in the world was gone, except just leather enough to make one pair of shoes.

"The Elves and the Shoemaker." From *Grimm's Popular Stories*, translated by Edgar Taylor

Then he cut them all ready to make up the next day, meaning to get up early in the morning to work. His conscience was clear and his heart light amidst all his troubles; so he went peaceably to bed, left all his cares to heaven, and fell asleep.

In the morning, after he had said his prayers, he set himself down to his work, when to his great wonder, there stood the shoes, all ready made, upon the table. The good man knew not what to say or think of this strange event. He looked at the workmanship; there was not one false stitch in the whole job, and all was so neat and true that it was a complete masterpiece.

That same day a customer came in, and the shoes pleased him so well that he willingly paid a price higher than usual for them; and the poor shoemaker with the money bought leather enough to make two pairs more. In the evening he cut out the work, and went to bed early that he might get up and begin betimes next day. But he was saved all the trouble, for when he got up in the morning the work was finished ready to his hand.

Presently in came buyers, who paid him handsomely for his goods, so that he bought leather enough for four pairs more. He cut out the work again over night, and found it finished in the morning as before; and so it went on for some time; what was got ready in the evening was always done by daybreak, and the good man soon became thriving and prosperous again.

One evening about Christmas time, as he and his wife were sitting over the fire chatting together, he said to her, "I should like to sit up and watch to-night, that we may see who it is that comes and does my work for me." The wife liked the thought; so they left a light burning, and hid themselves in the corner of the room behind a curtain and watched to see what would happen.

As soon as it was midnight, there came two little naked dwarfs; and they sat themselves upon the shoemaker's bench, took up all the work that was cut out, and began to ply with their little fingers, stitching and rapping and tapping away at such a rate that the shoemaker was all amazement, and could not take his eyes off for a moment. And on they went till the job was quite finished, and the shoes stood ready for use upon the table. This was long before daybreak; and then they bustled away as quick as lightning.

The next day the wife said to the shoemaker, "These little wights have made us rich, and we ought to be thankful to them, and do them a good office in return. I am quite vexed to see them run about as they do; they have nothing upon their backs to keep off the cold. I'll tell you what, I will make each of them a shirt, and a coat and waistcoat, and a pair of pantaloons into the bargain; do you make each of them a little pair of shoes."

The thought pleased the good shoemaker very much; and one evening, when all the things were ready, they laid them on the table instead of the work that they used to cut out, and then went and hid themselves to watch what the little elves would do.

About midnight the elves came in and were going to sit down to their work as usual; but when they saw the clothes lying for them, they laughed and were greatly delighted. Then they dressed themselves in the twinkling of an eye, and danced and capered and sprang about as merry as could be, till at last they danced out at the door and over the green; and the shoemaker saw them no more; but everything went well with him from that time forward, as long as he lived.

THE FOUR MUSICIANS

*This story is wonderful to tell, to illustrate,
and to dramatize! In another amusing version of
the rhyme the cock crows, "Cuck, cuck, cuck,
cucdoo-oo!" and the robber thinks a fellow is
calling, "Cut the man in two-oo!" The story
lends itself to simple dramatization by six- or
seven-year-olds in a classroom, playroom, or yard.
A few bandannas will make the robbers and the
animals may be costumed or not depending
upon the formality or spontaneity of the occasion.*

There was once a donkey who had worked for
his master faithfully many years, but his strength
at last began to fail, and every day he became
more and more unfit for work. Finally his master
concluded it was no longer worth while to keep
him and was thinking of putting an end to him.
But the donkey saw that mischief was brewing
and he ran away.

"I will go to the city," said he, "and like
enough I can get an engagement there as a musician; for though my body has grown weak, my
voice is as strong as ever."

So the donkey hobbled along toward the city,
but he had not gone far when he spied a dog
lying by the roadside and panting as if he had
run a long way. "What makes you pant so, my
friend?" asked the donkey.

"Alas!" replied the dog, "my master was going
to knock me on the head because I am old and
weak and can no longer make myself useful to
him in hunting. So I ran away; but how am I
to gain a living now, I wonder?"

"Hark ye!" said the donkey. "I am going to the
city to be a musician. You may as well keep
company with me and try what you can do in
the same line."

The dog said he was willing, and they went on
together. Pretty soon they came to a cat sitting
in the middle of the road and looking as dismal
as three wet days. "Pray, my good lady," said the
donkey, "what is the matter with you, for you
seem quite out of spirits?"

"Ah me!" responded the cat, "how can I be

"The Four Musicians." From *The Oak Tree Fairy Book*,
edited by Clifton Johnson, copyright 1933. With the kind
permission of Mrs. Clifton Johnson

cheerful when my life is in danger? I am getting
old, my teeth are blunt, and I like sitting by the
fire and purring better than chasing the mice
about. So this morning my mistress laid hold of
me and was going to drown me. I was lucky
enough to get away from her; but I do not know
what is to become of me, and I'm likely to
starve."

"Come with us to the city," said the donkey,
"and be a musician. You understand serenading,
and with your talent for that you ought to be
able to make a very good living."

The cat was pleased with the idea and went
along with the donkey and the dog. Soon afterward, as they were passing a farmyard, a rooster
flew up on the gate and screamed out with all
his might, "Cock-a-doodle-doo!"

"Bravo!" said the donkey, "upon my word you
make a famous noise; what is it all about?"

"Oh," replied the rooster, "I was only fore-
telling fine weather for our washing-day; and
that I do every week. But would you believe it!
My mistress doesn't thank me for my pains, and
she has told the cook that I must be made into
broth for the guests that are coming next Sunday."

"Heaven forbid!" exclaimed the donkey;
"come with us, Master Chanticleer. It will be
better, at any rate, than staying here to have your
head cut off. We are going to the city to be
musicians; and—who knows?—perhaps the four
of us can get up some kind of a concert. You
have a good voice, and if we all make music
together, it will be something striking. So come
along."

"With all my heart," said the cock; and the
four went on together.

The city was, however, too far away for them
to reach it on the first day of their travelling, and
when, toward night, they came to a thick woods,
they decided to turn aside from the highway and
pass the night among the trees. So they found
a dry, sheltered spot at the foot of a great oak
and the donkey and dog lay down on the ground
beneath it; but the cat climbed up among the
branches, and the rooster, thinking the higher he
sat the safer he would be, flew up to the very
top. Before he went to sleep the rooster looked
around him to the four points of the compass
to make sure that everything was all right. In

so doing he saw in the distance a little light shining, and he called out to his companions, "There must be a house no great way off, for I can see a light."

"If that be the case," said the donkey, "let us get up and go there. Our lodging here is not what I am used to, and the sooner we change it for better the more pleased I shall be."

"Yes," said the dog, "and perhaps I might be able to get a few bones with a little meat on them at that house."

"And very likely I might get some milk," said the cat.

"And there ought to be some scraps of food for me," said the rooster.

So the cat and the rooster came down out of the tree and they all walked off with Chanticleer in the lead toward the spot where he had seen the light.

At length they drew near the house, and the donkey, being the tallest of the company, went up to the lighted window and looked in.

"Well, what do you see?" asked the dog.

"What do I see?" answered the donkey. "I see that this is a robber's house. There are swords and pistols and blunderbusses on the walls, and there are chests of money on the floor, and all sorts of other plunder lying about. The robbers are sitting at a table that is loaded with the best of eatables and drinkables, and they are making themselves very comfortable and merry."

"Those eatables and drinkables would just suit us," declared the rooster.

"Yes, indeed they would," said the donkey, "if we could only get at them; but that will never be, unless we can contrive to drive away the robbers first."

Then they consulted together and at last hit on a plan. The donkey stood on his hind legs with his forefeet on the window-sill, the dog got on the donkey's shoulders, the cat mounted the back of the dog, and the rooster flew up and perched on the back of the cat. When all was ready they began their music.

"Hehaw! hehaw! hehaw!" brayed the donkey.

"Bow-wow! bow-wow!" barked the dog.

"Meow! meow!" said the cat.

"Cock-a-doodle-doo!" crowed the rooster.

Then they all burst through the window into the room, breaking the glass with a frightful clatter. The robbers, not doubting that some hideous hobgoblin was about to devour them, fled to the woods in great terror.

The donkey and his comrades now sat down at the table and made free with the food the robbers had left, and feasted as if they had been hungry for a month. When they had finished they put out the lights and each sought a sleeping-place to his own liking. The donkey laid himself down on some straw in the yard, the dog stretched himself on a mat just inside the door, the cat curled up on the hearth near the warm ashes, and the rooster flew up on the roof and settled himself on the ridge beside the chimney. They were all tired and soon fell fast asleep.

About midnight the robbers came creeping back to the house. They saw that no lights were burning and everything seemed quiet. "Well, well," said the robber captain, "we need not have been so hasty. I think we ran away without reason. But we will be cautious. The rest of you stay here while I go and find out if we are likely to have any more trouble."

So he stepped softly along to the house and entered the kitchen. There he groped about until he found a candle and some matches on the mantel over the fireplace. The cat had now waked up and stood on the hearth watching the robber with shining eyes. He mistook those eyes for two live coals and reached down to get a light by touching a match to them. The cat did not fancy that sort of thing and flew into his face, spitting and scratching. Then he cried out in fright and ran toward the door, and the dog, who was lying there, bit the robber's leg. He managed, however, to get out in the yard, and there the donkey struck out with a hind foot and gave him a kick that knocked him down, and Chanticleer who had been roused by the noise, cried out "Cock-a-doodle-doo! Cock-a-doodle-doo!"

The robber captain had barely strength to crawl away to the other robbers. "We cannot live at that house any more," said he. "In the kitchen is a grewsome witch, and I felt her hot breath and her long nails on my face, and by the door there stood a man who stabbed me in the leg, and in the yard is a black giant who beat me with a club, and on the roof is a little fellow who kept shouting, 'Chuck him up to me! Chuck him up to me!' "

So the robbers went away and never came back, and the four musicians found themselves so well pleased with their new quarters that they did not go to the city, but stayed where they were; and I dare say you would find them there at this very day.

MOTHER HOLLE

One little girl approved the justice of the conclusion of this tale by remarking sternly, "It served that girl right to get pitch on her. She was a real mean girl."

There was once a widow who had two daughters—one of whom was pretty and industrious, whilst the other was ugly and idle. But she was much fonder of the ugly and idle one, because she was her own daughter; and the other, who was a step-daughter, was obliged to do all the work, and be the Cinderella of the house. Every day the poor girl had to sit by a well, in the highway, and spin and spin till her fingers bled.

Now it happened that one day the shuttle was marked with her blood, so she dipped it in the well, to wash the mark off; but it dropped out of her hand and fell to the bottom. She began to weep, and ran to her step-mother and told her of the mishap. But she scolded her sharply, and was so merciless as to say, "Since you have let the shuttle fall in, you must fetch it out again."

So the girl went back to the well, and did not know what to do; and in the sorrow of her heart she jumped into the well to get the shuttle. She lost her senses; and when she awoke and came to herself again, she was in a lovely meadow where the sun was shining and many thousands of flowers were growing. Across this meadow she went, and at last came to a baker's oven full of bread, and the bread cried out, "Oh, take me out! take me out! or I shall burn; I have been baked a long time!" So she went up to it, and took out all the loaves one after another with the bread-shovel. After that she went on till she

came to a tree covered with apples, which called out to her, "Oh, shake me! shake me! we apples are all ripe!" So she shook the tree till the apples fell like rain, and went on shaking till they were all down, and when she had gathered them into a heap, she went on her way.

At last she came to a little house, out of which an old woman peeped; but she had such large teeth that the girl was frightened, and was about to run away. But the old woman called out to her, "What are you afraid of, dear child? Stay with me; if you will do all the work in the house properly, you shall be the better for it. Only you must take care to make my bed well, and to shake it thoroughly till the feathers fly—for then there is snow on the earth. I am Mother Holle."

As the old woman spoke so kindly to her, the girl took courage and agreed to enter her service. She attended to everything to the satisfaction of her mistress, and always shook her bed so vigorously that the feathers flew about like snowflakes. So she had a pleasant life with her; never an angry word; and to eat she had boiled or roast meat every day.

She stayed some time with Mother Holle, before she became sad. At first she did not know what was the matter with her, but found at length that it was home-sickness: although she was many thousand times better off here than at home, still she had a longing to be there. At last she said to the old woman: "I have a longing

"Mother Holle." From *Grimm's Household Tales*, translated by Margaret Hunt for home; and however well off I am down here, I cannot stay any longer; I must go up again to my own people." Mother Holle said, "I am pleased that you long for your home again, and as you have served me so truly, I myself will take you up again." Thereupon she took her by the hand, and led her to a large door. The door was opened, and just as the maiden was standing beneath the doorway, a heavy shower of golden rain fell, and all the gold remained sticking to her, so that she was completely covered over with it.

"You shall have that because you have been so industrious," said Mother Holle; and at the same time she gave her back the shuttle which she had let fall into the well. Thereupon the door closed, and the maiden found herself up above upon the earth, not far from her mother's house.

And as she went into the yard the cock was sitting on the well, and cried——

"Cock-a-doodle-doo!
   Your golden girl's come back to you!"

So she went in to her mother, and as she arrived thus covered with gold, she was well received, both by her and her sister.

The girl told all that had happened to her; and as soon as the mother heard how she had come by so much wealth, she was very anxious to obtain the same good luck for the ugly and lazy daughter. She had to seat herself by the well and spin; and in order that her shuttle might be stained with blood, she stuck her hand into a thorn bush and pricked her finger. Then she threw her shuttle into the well, and jumped in after it.

She came, like the other, to the beautiful meadow and walked along the very same path. When she got to the oven the bread again cried, "Oh, take me out! take me out! or I shall burn; I have been baked a long time!" But the lazy thing answered, "As if I had any wish to make myself dirty!" and on she went. Soon she came to the apple-tree, which cried, "Oh, shake me! shake me! we apples are all ripe!" But she answered, "I like that! one of you might fall on my head," and so went on.

When she came to Mother Holle's house she was not afraid, for she had already heard of her

big teeth, and she hired herself to her immediately.

The first day she forced herself to work diligently, and obeyed Mother Holle when she told her to do anything, for she was thinking of all the gold that she would give her. But on the second day she began to be lazy, and on the third day still more so, and then she would not get up in the morning at all. Neither did she make Mother Holle's bed as she ought, and did not shake it so as to make the feathers fly up. Mother Holle was soon tired of this, and gave her notice to leave. The lazy girl was willing enough to go, and thought that now the golden rain would come. Mother Holle led her also to the great door; but while she was standing beneath it, instead of the gold a big kettleful of pitch was emptied over her. "That is the reward for your service," said Mother Holle, and shut the door.

So the lazy girl went home; but she was quite covered with pitch, and the cock by the well-side, as soon as he saw her, cried out——

"Cock-a-doodle-doo!
   Your pitchy girl's come back to you!"

But the pitch stuck fast to her, and could not be got off as long as she lived.

THE HUT IN THE FOREST

A poor wood-cutter lived with his wife and three daughters in a little hut on the edge of a lonely forest. One morning as he was about to go to his work, he said to his wife, "Let my dinner be brought into the forest to me by my eldest daughter, or I shall never get my work done, and in order that she may not miss her way," he added, "I will take a bag of millet with me and strew the seeds on the path." When, therefore, the sun was just above the centre of the forest, the girl set out on her way with a bowl of soup, but the field-sparrows, and wood-sparrows, larks and finches, blackbirds and siskins had picked up the millet long before, and the girl could not find the track. Then trusting to

"The Hut in the Forest." From *Grimm's Household Tales,* translated by Margaret Hunt

chance, she went on and on, until the sun sank and night began to fall. The trees rustled in the darkness, the owls hooted, and she began to be afraid. Then in the distance she perceived a light which glimmered between the trees. "There ought to be some people living there, who can take me in for the night," thought she, and went up to the light. It was not long before she came to a house the windows of which were all lighted up. She knocked, and a rough voice from the inside cried, "Come in." The girl stepped into the dark entrance and knocked at the door of the room. "Just come in," cried the voice, and when she opened the door, an old grey-haired man was sitting at the table, supporting his face with both hands, and his white beard fell down over the table almost as far as the ground. By the stove lay three animals, a hen, a cock, and a brindled cow. The girl told her story to the old man, and begged for shelter for the night. The man said,

"Pretty little hen,
    Pretty little cock,
    And pretty brindled cow,
    What say ye to that?"

"Duks," answered the animals, and that must have meant, "We are willing," for the old man said, "Here you shall have shelter and food; go to the fire, and cook us our supper." The girl found in the kitchen abundance of everything, and cooked a good supper, but had no thought of the animals. She carried the full dishes to the table, seated herself by the grey-haired man, ate and satisfied her hunger. When she had had enough, she said, "But now I am tired, where is there a bed in which I can lie down, and sleep?" The animals replied,

"Thou hast eaten with him,
    Thou hast drunk with him,
    Thou hast had no thought for us,
    So find out for thyself where thou canst pass the
        night."

Then said the old man, "Just go upstairs, and thou wilt find a room with two beds; shake them up, and put white linen on them, and then I, too, will come and lie down to sleep." The girl went up, and when she had shaken the beds and

put clean sheets on, she lay down in one of them without waiting any longer for the old man. After some time, however, the grey-haired man came, took his candle, looked at the girl and shook his head. When he saw that she had fallen into a sound sleep, he opened a trap-door, and let her down into the cellar.

Late at night the wood-cutter came home and reproached his wife for leaving him to hunger all day. "It is not my fault," she replied, "the girl went out with your dinner, and must have lost herself, but she is sure to come back to-morrow." The wood-cutter, however, arose before dawn to go into the forest, and requested that the second daughter should take him his dinner that day. "I will take a bag with lentils," said he; "the seeds are larger than millet; the girl will see them better, and can't lose her way." At dinner-time, therefore, the girl took out the food, but the lentils had disappeared. The birds of the forest had picked them up as they had done the day before, and had left none. The girl wandered about in the forest until night, and then she too reached the house of the old man, was told to go in, and begged for food and a bed. The man with the white beard again asked the animals,

"Pretty little hen,
    Pretty little cock,
    And pretty brindled cow,
    What say ye to that?"

The animals again replied "Duks," and everything happened just as it had happened the day before. The girl cooked a good meal, ate and drank with the old man, and did not concern herself about the animals, and when she inquired about her bed they answered,

"Thou hast eaten with him,
    Thou hast drunk with him,
    Thou hast had no thought for us,
    So find out for thyself where thou canst pass the
        night."

When she was asleep the old man came, looked at her, shook his head, and let her down into the cellar.

On the third morning the wood-cutter said

to his wife, "Send our youngest child out with my dinner today, she has always been good and obedient, and will stay in the right path, and not run about after every wild humble-bee, as her sisters did." The mother did not want to do it, and said, "Am I to lose my dearest child, as well?"

"Have no fear," he replied, "the girl will not go astray; she is too prudent and sensible; besides I will take some peas with me, and strew them about. They are still larger than lentils, and will show her the way." But when the girl went out with her basket on her arm, the wood-pigeons had already got all the peas in their crops, and she did not know which way she was to turn. She was full of sorrow and never ceased to think how hungry her father would be, and how her good mother would grieve, if she did not go home.

At length when it grew dark, she saw the light and came to the house in the forest. She begged quite prettily to be allowed to spend the night there, and the man with the white beard once more asked his animals,

> "Pretty little hen,
> Pretty little cock,
> And beautiful brindled cow,
> What say ye to that?"

"Duks," said they. Then the girl went to the stove where the animals were lying, and petted the cock and hen, and stroked their smooth feathers with her hand, and caressed the brindled cow between her horns; and when, in obedience to the old man's orders, she had made ready some good soup, and the bowl was placed upon the table, she said, "Am I to eat as much as I want, and the good animals to have nothing? Outside is food in plenty, I will look after them first."

So she went and brought some barley and strewed it for the cock and hen, and a whole armful of sweet-smelling hay for the cow. "I hope you will like it, dear animals," said she, "and you shall have a refreshing draught in case you are thirsty." Then she fetched in a bucketful of water, and the cock and hen jumped on to the edge of it and dipped their beaks in, and then held up their heads as the birds do when they

drink, and the brindled cow also took a hearty draught. When the animals were fed, the girl seated herself at the table by the old man and ate what he had left. It was not long before the cock and the hen began to thrust their heads beneath their wings, and the eyes of the cow likewise began to blink. Then said the girl, "Ought we not to go to bed?"

> "Pretty little hen,
> Pretty little cock,
> And pretty brindled cow,
> What say ye to that?"

The animals answered "Duks,"

> "Thou hast eaten with us,
> Thou hast drunk with us,
> Thou hast had kind thought for all of us,
> We wish thee good-night."

Then the maiden went upstairs, shook the feather-beds, and laid clean sheets on them, and when she had done it the old man came and lay down on one of the beds, and his white beard reached down to his feet. The girl lay down on the other, said her prayers, and fell asleep.

She slept quietly till midnight, and then there was such a noise in the house that she awoke. There was a sound of cracking and splitting in every corner, and the doors sprang open, and beat against the walls. The beams groaned as if they were being torn out of their joints, it seemed as if the staircase were falling down, and at length there was a crash as if the entire roof had fallen in. As, however, all grew quiet once more, and the girl was not hurt, she stayed quietly lying where she was, and fell asleep again.

But when she woke up in the morning with the brilliancy of the sunshine, what did her eyes behold? She was lying in a vast hall, and everything around her shone with royal splendour; on the walls, golden flowers grew up on a ground of green silk, the bed was of ivory, and the canopy of red velvet, and on a chair close by, was a pair of shoes embroidered with pearls. The girl believed that she was in a dream, but three richly clad attendants came in, and asked what orders she would like to give? "If you will go," she replied, "I will get up at once and make ready some soup for the old man, and then I will feed the pretty little hen, and the cock, and the beautiful brindled cow." She thought the old man was up already, and looked round at his bed; he, however, was not lying in it, but a stranger.

And while she was looking at him, and becoming aware that he was young and handsome, he awoke, sat up in bed, and said, "I am a King's son, and was bewitched by a wicked witch, and made to live in this forest, as an old grey-haired man; no one was allowed to be with me but my three attendants in the form of a cock, a hen, and a brindled cow. The spell was not to be broken until a girl came to us whose heart was so good that she showed herself full of love, not only towards mankind, but towards animals—and that you have done, and by you at midnight we were set free, and the old hut in the forest was changed back again into my royal palace."

And when they had arisen, the king's son ordered the three attendants to set out and fetch the father and mother of the girl to the marriage feast. "But where are my two sisters?" inquired the maiden. "I have locked them in the cellar, and to-morrow they shall be led into the forest, and shall live as servants to a charcoal-burner, until they have grown kinder, and do not leave poor animals to suffer hunger."

THE FROG-KING

Here is an enchantment not broken by the love of the princess but by the king's stern insistence that what she has promised she must perform. Faithful Henry is a curious addition to the story which really ends with the transformation of the Frog into a prince.

In olden times when wishing still helped one, there lived a king whose daughters were all beautiful, but the youngest was so beautiful that the sun itself, which has seen so much, was astonished whenever it shone in her face. Close by the King's castle lay a great dark forest, and

"The Frog-King." From *Grimm's Household Tales*, translated by Margaret Hunt

under an old lime-tree in the forest was a well, and when the day was very warm, the King's child went out into the forest and sat down by the side of the cool fountain; and when she was bored she took a golden ball, and threw it up on high and caught it; and this ball was her favourite plaything.

Now it so happened that on one occasion the princess's golden ball did not fall into the little hand which she was holding up for it, but on to the ground beyond, and rolled straight into the water. The King's daughter followed it with her eyes, but it vanished, and the well was deep, so deep that the bottom could not be seen. At this she began to cry, and cried louder and louder, and could not be comforted. And as she thus lamented, some one said to her, "What ails you, King's daughter? You weep so that even a stone would show pity." She looked round to the side from whence the voice came, and saw a frog stretching forth its thick, ugly head from the water. "Ah! old water-splasher, is it you?" said she; "I am weeping for my golden ball, which has fallen into the well."

"Be quiet, and do not weep," answered the frog, "I can help you, but what will you give me if I bring your plaything up again?" "Whatever you will have, dear frog," said she—"my clothes, my pearls and jewels, and even the golden crown which I am wearing."

The frog answered: "I do not care for your clothes, your pearls and jewels, nor for your golden crown; but if you will love me and let me be your companion and play-fellow, and sit by you at your little table, and eat off your little golden plate, and drink out of your little cup, and sleep in your little bed—if you will promise me this I will go down below, and bring your golden ball up again."

"Oh, yes," said she, "I promise you all you wish, if you will but bring me my ball back again." But she thought: "How the silly frog does talk! He lives in the water with the other frogs, and croaks, and can be no companion to any human being!"

But the frog when he had received this promise, put his head into the water and sank down, and in a short while came swimming up again with the ball in his mouth, and threw it on the grass. The King's daughter was delighted to see her pretty plaything once more, and picked it up, and ran away with it. "Wait, wait," said the frog. "Take me with you. I can't run as you can." But what did it avail him to scream his croak, croak, after her, as loudly as he could? She did not listen to it, but ran home and soon forgot the poor frog, who was forced to go back into his well again.

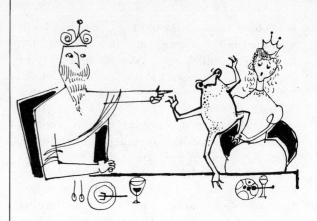

The next day when she had seated herself at table with the King and all the courtiers, and was eating from her little golden plate, something came creeping splish splash, splish splash, up the marble staircase, and when it had got to the top, it knocked at the door and cried, "Princess, youngest princess, open the door for me." She ran to see who was outside, but when she opened the door, there sat the frog in front of it. Then she slammed the door to, in great haste, sat down to dinner again, and was quite frightened. The King saw plainly that her heart was beating violently, and said, "My child, what are you so afraid of? Is there perchance a giant outside who wants to carry you away?" "Ah, no," replied she, "it is no giant, but a disgusting frog."

"What does the frog want with you?" "Ah, dear father, yesterday when I was in the forest sitting by the well, playing, my golden ball fell into the water. And because I cried so, the frog brought it out again for me; and because he insisted so on it, I promised him he should be my companion, but I never thought he would be able to come out of his water! And now he is outside there, and wants to come in to me."

In the meantime it knocked a second time, and cried:

"Princess! youngest princess!
Open the door for me!
Do you not know what you said to me
Yesterday by the cool waters of the fountain?
Princess, youngest princess!
Open the door for me!"

Then said the King, "That which you have promised must you perform. Go and let him in." She went and opened the door, and the frog hopped in and followed her, step by step, to her chair. There he sat still and cried: "Lift me up beside you." She delayed, until at last the King commanded her to do it. Once the frog was on the chair he wanted to be on the table, and when he was on the table he said: "Now, push your little golden plate nearer to me that we may eat together." She did this, but it was easy to see that she did not do it willingly. The frog enjoyed what he ate, but almost every mouthful she took choked her. At length he said, "I have eaten and am satisfied; now I am tired, carry me into your little room and make your little silken bed ready, and we will both lie down and go to sleep."

The King's daughter began to cry, for she was afraid of the cold frog which she did not like to touch, and which was now to sleep in her pretty, clean little bed. But the King grew angry and said, "He who helped you when you were in trouble ought not afterwards to be despised by you." So she took hold of the frog with two fingers, carried him upstairs, and put him in a corner.

But when she was in bed he crept to her and said: "I am tired, I want to sleep as well as you, lift me up or I will tell your father." Then she was terribly angry, and took him up and threw him with all her might against the wall. "Now, you will be quiet, odious frog," said she. But when he fell down he was no frog but a king's son with kind and beautiful eyes. He by her father's will was now her dear companion and husband. Then he told her how he had been bewitched by a wicked witch, and how no one could have delivered him from the well but herself, and that to-morrow they would go together into his kingdom.

Then they went to sleep, and next morning when the sun awoke them, a carriage came driving up with eight white horses, which had white ostrich feathers on their heads, and were harnessed with golden chains, and behind stood the young King's servant, faithful Henry. Faithful Henry had been so unhappy when his master was changed into a frog, that he had caused three iron bands to be laid round his heart, lest it should burst with grief and sadness. The carriage was to conduct the young King into his kingdom. Faithful Henry helped them both in, and placed himself behind again, and was full of joy because of this deliverance. And when they had driven a part of the way, the King's son heard a cracking behind him as if something had broken. So he turned round and cried: "Henry, the carriage is breaking."

"No, master, it is not the carriage. It is a band from my heart, which was put there in my great pain when you were a frog and imprisoned in the well." Again and once again while they were on their way something cracked, and each time the King's son thought the carriage was breaking; but it was only the bands which were springing from the heart of faithful Henry because his master was set free and was happy.

HANSEL AND GRETEL

This is a favorite story to illustrate and dramatize. Humperdinck added a fence of gingerbread children which came joyously to life when the wicked witch was dead.

Near a great forest there lived a poor woodcutter and his wife, and his two children; the boy's name was Hansel and the girl's, Gretel. They had very little to bite or to sup, and once, when there was great dearth in the land, the man could not even gain the daily bread.

As he lay in bed one night thinking of this, and turning and tossing, he sighed heavily, and said to his wife, who was the children's stepmother,

"What will become of us? We cannot even

"Hansel and Gretel." From *Household Stories from the Brothers Grimm*, translated by Lucy Crane. By permission of The Macmillan Company, publishers

feed our children; there is nothing left for ourselves."

"I will tell you what, husband," answered the wife; "we will take the children early in the morning into the forest, where it is thickest; we will make them a fire, and we will give each of them a piece of bread, then we will go to our work and leave them alone; they will never find the way home again, and we shall be quit of them."

"No, wife," said the man, "I cannot do that; I cannot find it in my heart to take my children into the forest and to leave them there alone; the wild animals would soon come and devour them."

"O you fool," said she, "then we will all four starve; you had better get the coffins ready," and she left him no peace until he consented.

The two children had not been able to sleep for hunger, and had heard what their stepmother had said to their father. Gretel wept bitterly, and said to Hansel,

"It is all over with us."

"Do be quiet, Gretel," said Hansel, "and do not fret; I will manage something." When the parents had gone to sleep, Hansel got up, put on his little coat, opened the back door, and slipped out. The moon was shining brightly, and the white pebbles that lay in front of the house glistened like pieces of silver. Hansel stooped and filled the little pocket of his coat as full as it would hold. Then he went back again, and said to Gretel,

"Be easy, dear little sister, and go to sleep quietly; God will not forsake us," and laid himself down again in his bed.

When the day was breaking, and before the sun had risen, the wife came and awakened the two children, saying,

"Get up, you lazy bones! We are going into the forest to cut wood."

Then she gave each of them a piece of bread, and said,

"That is for dinner, and you must not eat it before then, for you will get no more."

Gretel carried the bread under her apron, for Hansel had his pockets full of pebbles. Then they set off all together on their way to the forest. When they had gone a little way Hansel stood still and looked back towards the house, and this he did again and again, till his father said to him,

"Hansel, what are you looking at? Take care not to forget your legs."

"O father," said Hansel, "I am looking at my little white kitten, who is sitting up on the roof to bid me good-bye."

"You foolish boy," said the woman, "that is not your kitten, but the sunshine on the chimney pot."

Of course Hansel had not been looking at his kitten, but had been taking every now and then a pebble from his pocket and dropping it on the road.

When they reached the middle of the forest the father told the children to collect wood to make a fire to keep them warm; and Hansel and Gretel gathered brushwood enough for a little mountain; and it was set on fire, and when the flame was burning quite high the wife said,

"Now lie down by the fire and rest yourselves, you children, and we will go and cut wood; and when we are ready we will come and fetch you."

So Hansel and Gretel sat by the fire, and at noon they each ate their pieces of bread. They thought their father was in the wood all the time, as they seemed to hear the strokes of the axe, but really it was only a dry branch hanging to a withered tree that the wind moved to and fro.

So when they had stayed there a long time their eyelids closed with weariness, and they fell fast asleep. When at last they woke it was night, and Gretel began to cry, and said,

"How shall we ever get out of this wood?" But Hansel comforted her, saying,

"Wait a little while longer, until the moon rises, and then we can easily find the way home."

And when the full moon came up, Hansel took his little sister by the hand, and followed the way where the pebbles shone like silver, and showed them the road. They walked on the whole night through, and at the break of day they came to their father's house. They knocked at the door, and when their stepmother opened it and saw that it was Hansel and Gretel she said,

"You naughty children, why did you sleep so long in the wood? We thought you were never coming home again!"

But the father was glad, for it had gone to his heart to leave them both in the woods alone.

Not very long after that there was again great scarcity in those parts, and the children heard their stepmother say to their father,

"Everything is finished up; we have only half a loaf, and after that the tale comes to an end. The children must be off; we will take them farther into the wood this time, so that they shall not be able to find the way back again; there is no other way to manage."

The man felt sad at heart, and he thought,

"It would be better to share one's last morsel with one's children."

But the wife would listen to nothing that he said, but scolded and reproached him.

But the children were not asleep, and had heard all the talk. When the parents had gone to sleep, Hansel got up to go out and get more pebbles as he did before, but the stepmother had locked the door, and Hansel could not get out; but he comforted his little sister, and said,

"Don't cry, Gretel, and go to sleep quietly, and God will help us."

Early the next morning the wife came and pulled the children out of bed. She gave them each a little piece of bread—less than before; and on the way to the wood Hansel crumbled the bread in his pocket, and often stopped to throw a crumb on the ground.

"Hansel, what are you stopping behind and staring for?" said the father.

"I am looking at my little pigeon sitting on the roof, to say good-bye to me," answered Hansel.

"You foolish boy," said the wife, "that is no pigeon, but the morning sun shining on the chimney pots."

Hansel went on as before, and strewed bread crumbs all along the road.

The woman led the children far into the wood, where they had never been before in all their lives. And again there was a large fire made, and the stepmother said,

"Sit still there, you children, and when you are tired you can go to sleep; we are going into the forest to cut wood, and in the evening, when we are ready to go home we will come and fetch you."

So when noon came Gretel shared her bread with Hansel, who had strewed his along the road.

Then they went to sleep, and the evening passed, and no one came for the poor children. When they awoke it was dark night, and Hansel comforted his little sister, and said,

"Wait a little, Gretel, until the moon gets up, then we shall be able to see our way home by the crumbs of bread that I have scattered along the road."

So when the moon rose they got up, but they could find no crumbs of bread, for the birds of the woods and of the fields had come and picked them up. Hansel thought they might find the way all the same, but they could not.

They went on all that night, and the next day from the morning until the evening, but they could not find the way out of the wood, and they were very hungry, for they had nothing to eat but the few berries they could pick up. And when they were so tired that they could no longer drag themselves along, they lay down under a tree and fell asleep.

It was now the third morning since they had left their father's house. They were always trying to get back to it, but instead of that they only found themselves farther in the wood, and if help had not soon come they would have been starved. About noon they saw a pretty snow-white bird sitting on a bough, and singing so sweetly that they stopped to listen. And when he had finished, the bird spread his wings and flew before them, and they followed after him until they came to a little house, and the bird perched on the roof, and when they came nearer they saw that the house was built of gingerbread, and roofed with cakes; and the window was of transparent sugar.

"We will have some of this," said Hansel, "and make a fine meal. I will eat a piece of the roof, Gretel, and you can have some of the window—that will taste sweet."

So Hansel reached up and broke off a bit of the roof, just to see how it tasted, and Gretel stood by the window and gnawed at it. Then they heard a thin voice call out from inside,

"Nibble, nibble, like a mouse,
Who is nibbling at my house?"

And the children answered,

"Never mind,
It is the wind."

And they went on eating, never disturbing themselves. Hansel, who found that the roof tasted very nice, took down a great piece of it, and Gretel pulled out a large round window-pane, and sat her down and began upon it. Then the door opened, and an aged woman came out, leaning upon a crutch. Hansel and Gretel felt very frightened, and let fall what they had in their hands. The old woman, however, nodded her head, and said,

"Ah, my dear children, how come you here? You must come indoors and stay with me, you will be no trouble."

So she took them each by the hand, and led them into her little house. And there they found a good meal laid out, of milk and pancakes, with sugar, apples, and nuts. After that she showed them two little white beds, and Hansel and Gretel laid themselves down on them, and thought they were in heaven.

The old woman, although her behavior was so kind, was a wicked witch, who lay in wait for children, and had built the little house on purpose to entice them. When they were once inside she used to kill them, cook them, and eat them, and then it was a feast-day with her. The witch's eyes were red, and she could not see very far, but she had a keen scent, like the beasts, and knew very well when human creatures were near. When she knew that Hansel and Gretel were coming, she gave a spiteful laugh, and said triumphantly,

"I have them, and they shall not escape me!"

Early in the morning, before the children were awake, she got up to look at them, and as they lay sleeping so peacefully with round rosy cheeks, she said to herself,

"What a fine feast I shall have!"

She grasped Hansel with her withered hand, and led him into a little stable, and shut him up behind a grating; and call and scream as he might, it was no good. Then she went back to Gretel and shook her, crying,

"Get up, lazy bones! Fetch water, and cook something nice for your brother; he is outside in the stable, and must be fattened up. And when he is fat enough, I will eat him."

Gretel began to weep bitterly, but it was of no use, she had to do what the wicked witch bade her.

And so the best kind of victuals was cooked for poor Hansel, while Gretel got nothing but crab-shells. Each morning the old woman visited the little stable, and cried,

"Hansel, stretch out your finger, that I may tell if you will soon be fat enough."

Hansel, however, held out a little bone, and the old woman, who had weak eyes, could not see what it was, and supposing it to be Hansel's finger, wondered very much that it was not getting fatter. When four weeks had passed and Hansel seemed to remain so thin, she lost patience and could wait no longer.

"Now then, Gretel," cried she to the little girl, "be quick and draw water. Be Hansel fat or be he lean, to-morrow I must kill and cook him."

Oh, what a grief for the poor little sister to have to fetch water, and how the tears flowed down over her cheeks!

"Dear God, pray help us!" cried she. "If we had been devoured by wild beasts in the wood, at least we should have died together."

"Spare me your lamentations," said the old woman. "They are of no avail."

Early next morning Gretel had to get up, make the fire, and fill the kettle.

"First we will do the baking," said the old woman. "I have heated the oven already, and kneaded the dough."

She pushed poor Gretel towards the oven, out of which the flames were already shining.

"Creep in," said the witch, "and see if it is properly hot so that the bread may be baked."

And Gretel once in, she meant to shut the door upon her and let her be baked, and then she would have eaten her. But Gretel perceived her intention, and said,

"I don't know how to do it. How shall I get in?"

"Stupid goose," said the old woman, "the opening is big enough, do you see? I could get in myself!" and she stooped down and put her head in the oven's mouth. Then Gretel gave her a push, so that she went in farther, and she shut the iron door upon her, and put up the bar. Oh, how frightfully she howled! But Gretel ran away, and left her in the oven. Then Gretel went straight to Hansel, opened the stable door and cried,

"Hansel, we are free! The old witch is dead!"

Then out flew Hansel like a bird from its cage as soon as the door is opened. How rejoiced they both were! How they fell each on the other's neck! And danced about, and kissed each other! And as they had nothing more to fear, they went over all the old witch's house, and in every corner there stood chests of pearls and precious stones.

"This is something better than pebbles," said Hansel, as he filled his pockets. And Gretel, thinking she also would like to carry something home with her, filled her apron full.

"Now, away we go," said Hansel, "if we only can get out of the witch's wood!"

When they had journeyed a few hours they came to a great piece of water.

"We can never get across this," said Hansel. "I see no stepping-stones and no bridge."

"And there is no boat either," said Gretel. "But here comes a white duck; if I ask her, she will help us over." So she cried,

"Duck, duck, here we stand,
 Hansel and Gretel, on the land,
 Stepping-stones and bridge we lack,
 Carry us over on your nice white back."

And the duck came accordingly, and Hansel got upon her and told his sister to come too.

"No," answered Gretel, "that would be too hard upon the duck; we can go separately, one after the other."

And that was how it was managed, and after that they went on happily, until they came to the wood, and the way grew more and more familiar, till at last they saw in the distance their father's house. Then they ran till they came up to it, rushed in at the door, and fell on their father's neck. The man had not had a quiet hour since he left his children in the wood; but his wife was dead. And when Gretel opened her apron, the pearls and precious stones were scattered all over the room, and Hansel took one handful after another out of his pocket. Then was all care at an end, and they lived in great joy together.

SNOW-WHITE AND ROSE-RED

There was once a poor widow who lived in a lonely cottage. In front of the cottage was a garden wherein stood two rose-trees, one of which bore white and the other red roses. She had two children who were like the two rose-trees, and one was called Snow-White, and the other Rose-Red. They were as good and happy, as busy and cheerful as ever two children in the world were, only Snow-White was more quiet and gentle than Rose-Red. Rose-Red liked better to run about in the meadows and fields seeking flowers and catching butterflies; but Snow-White sat at home with her mother, and· helped her with her house-work, or read to her when there was nothing to do.

The two children were so fond of each other that they always held each other by the hand when they went out together, and when Snow-White said, "We will not leave each other," Rose-Red answered, "Never so long as we live," and their mother would add, "What one has she must share with the other."

They often ran about the forest alone and gathered red berries, and no beasts did them any harm, but came close to them trustfully. The little hare would eat a cabbage-leaf out of their hands, the roe grazed by their side, the stag leapt merrily by them, and the birds sat still upon the boughs, and sang whatever they knew.

No mishap overtook them; if they had stayed too late in the forest, and night came on, they laid themselves down near one another upon the moss, and slept until morning came, and their mother knew this and had no distress on their account.

Once when they had spent the night in the wood and the dawn had roused them, they saw a beautiful child in a shining white dress sitting near their bed. He got up and looked quite kindly at them, but said nothing and went away into the forest. And when they looked round they found that they had been sleeping quite close to a precipice, and would certainly have fallen into it in the darkness if they had gone only a few paces further. And their mother told

"Snow-White and Rose-Red." From *Grimm's Household Tales,* translated by Margaret Hunt

them that it must have been the angel who watches over good children.

Snow-White and Rose-Red kept their mother's little cottage so neat that it was a pleasure to look inside it. In the summer Rose-Red took care of the house, and every morning laid a wreath of flowers by her mother's bed before she awoke, in which was a rose from each tree. In the winter Snow-White lit the fire and hung the kettle on the wrekin. The kettle was of copper and shone like gold, so brightly was it polished. In the evening, when the snowflakes fell, the mother said, "Go, Snow-White, and bolt the door," and then they sat round the hearth, and the mother took her spectacles and read aloud out of a large book, and the two girls listened as they sat and span. And close by them lay a lamb upon the floor, and behind them upon a perch sat a white dove with its head hidden beneath its wings.

One evening, as they were thus sitting comfortably together, some one knocked at the door as if he wished to be let in. The mother said, "Quick, Rose-Red, open the door, it must be a traveller who is seeking shelter." Rose-Red went and pushed back the bolt, thinking that it was a poor man, but it was not; it was a bear that stretched his broad, black head within the door.

Rose-Red screamed and sprang back, the lamb bleated, the dove fluttered, and Snow-White hid herself behind her mother's bed. But the bear began to speak and said, "Do not be afraid, I will do you no harm! I am half-frozen, and only want to warm myself a little beside you."

"Poor bear," said the mother, "lie down by the fire, only take care that you do not burn your coat." Then she cried, "Snow-White, Rose-Red, come out, the bear will do you no harm, he means well." So they both came out, and by-and-by the lamb and dove came nearer, and were not afraid of him. The bear said, "Here, children, knock the snow out of my coat a little;" so they brought the broom and swept the bear's hide clean; and he stretched himself by the fire and growled contentedly and comfortably. It was not long before they grew quite at home, and played tricks with their clumsy guest. They tugged his hair with their hands, put their feet upon his back and rolled him about, or they took a hazel-switch and beat him, and when he growled they laughed. But the bear took it all in good part, only when they were too rough he called out, "Leave me alive, children,

"Snowy-White, Rosy-Red,
Will you beat your lover dead?"

When it was bed-time, and the others went to bed, the mother said to the bear, "You can lie there by the hearth, and then you will be safe from the cold and the bad weather." As soon as day dawned the two children let him out, and he trotted across the snow into the forest.

Henceforth the bear came every evening at the same time, laid himself down by the hearth, and let the children amuse themselves with him as much as they liked; and they got so used to him that the doors were never fastened until their black friend had arrived.

When spring had come and all outside was green, the bear said one morning to Snow-White, "Now I must go away, and cannot come back for the whole summer." "Where are you going, then, dear bear?" asked Snow-White. "I must go into the forest and guard my treasures from the wicked dwarfs. In the winter, when the earth is frozen hard, they are obliged to stay below and cannot work their way through; but now, when the sun has thawed and warmed the earth, they break through it, and come out to pry and steal; and what once gets into their hands, and in their caves, does not easily see daylight again."

Snow-White was quite sorry for his going away, and as she unbolted the door for him, and the bear was hurrying out, he caught against the bolt and a piece of his hairy coat was torn off, and it seemed to Snow-White as if she had seen gold shining through it, but she was not sure about it. The bear ran away quickly, and was soon out of sight behind the trees.

A short time afterwards the mother sent her children into the forest to get fire-wood. There they found a big tree which lay felled on the ground, and close by the trunk something was jumping backwards and forwards in the grass, but they could not make out what it was. When they came nearer they saw a dwarf with an old withered face and a snow-white beard a yard long. The end of the beard was caught in a crevice of the tree, and the little fellow was jumping backwards and forwards like a dog tied to a rope, and did not know what to do.

He glared at the girls with his fiery red eyes and cried, "Why do you stand there? Can you not come here and help me?" "What are you about there, little man?" asked Rose-Red. "You stupid, prying goose!" answered the dwarf; "I was going to split the tree to get a little wood for cooking. The little bit of food that one of us wants gets burnt up directly with thick logs; we do not swallow so much as you coarse, greedy folk. I had just driven the wedge safely in, and everything was going as I wished; but the wretched wood was too smooth and suddenly sprang asunder, and the tree closed so quickly that I could not pull out my beautiful white beard; so now it is tight in and I cannot get away, and the silly, sleek, milk-faced things laugh! Ugh! how odious you are!"

The children tried very hard, but they could not pull the beard out, it was caught too fast. "I will run and fetch some one," said Rose-Red. "You senseless goose!" snarled the dwarf; "why should you fetch some one? You are already two too many for me; can you not think of something better?" "Don't be impatient," said Snow-White, "I will help you," and she pulled her scissors out of her pocket, and cut off the end of the beard.

As soon as the dwarf felt himself free he laid hold of a bag which lay amongst the roots of the tree, and which was full of gold, and lifted it up, grumbling to himself, "Uncouth people, to cut off a piece of my fine beard. Bad luck to you!" and then he swung the bag upon his back, and went off without even once looking at the children.

Some time after that Snow-White and Rose-Red went to catch a dish of fish. As they came near the brook they saw something like a large grasshopper jumping towards the water, as if it were going to leap in. They ran to it and found it was the dwarf. "Where are you going?" said Rose-Red; "you surely don't want to go into the water?" "I am not such a fool!" cried the dwarf; "don't you see that the accursed fish wants to pull me in?" The little man had been sitting there fishing, and unluckily the wind had twisted his beard with the fishing-line; just then a big fish bit, and the feeble creature had not strength to pull it out; the fish kept the upper hand and pulled the dwarf towards him. He held on to all the reeds and rushes, but it was of little good, he was forced to follow the movements of the fish, and was in urgent danger of being dragged into the water.

The girls came just in time; they held him fast and tried to free his beard from the line, but all in vain, beard and line were entangled fast together. Nothing was left but to bring out the scissors and cut the beard, whereby a small part of it was lost. When the dwarf saw that he screamed out, "Is that civil, you toad-stool, to disfigure one's face? Was it not enough to clip off the end of my beard? Now you have cut off the best part of it. I cannot let myself be seen by my people. I wish you had been made to run the soles off your shoes!" Then he took out a sack of pearls which lay in the rushes, and without saying a word more he dragged it away and disappeared behind a stone.

It happened that soon afterwards the mother sent the two children to the town to buy needles and thread, and laces and ribbons. The road led them across a heath upon which huge pieces of rock lay strewn here and there. Now they noticed a large bird hovering in the air, flying slowly round and round above them; it sank lower and lower, and at last settled near a rock not far off. Directly afterwards they heard a loud, piteous cry. They ran up and saw with horror that the eagle had seized their old acquaintance the dwarf, and was going to carry him off.

The children, full of pity, at once took tight hold of the little man, and pulled against the eagle so long that at last he let his booty go. As soon as the dwarf had recovered from his first fright he cried with his shrill voice, "Could you not have done it more carefully! You dragged at my brown coat so that it is all torn and full of holes, you helpless clumsy creatures!" Then he took up a sack full of precious stones, and slipped away again under the rock into his hole. The girls, who by this time were used to his thanklessness, went on their way and did their business in the town.

As they crossed the heath again on their way home they surprised the dwarf, who had emptied out his bag of precious stones in a clean spot, and had not thought that any one would come there so late. The evening sun shone upon the brilliant stones; they glittered and sparkled with all colours so beautifully that the children stood still and looked at them. "Why do you stand gaping there?" cried the dwarf, and his ashen-grey face became copper-red with rage. He was going on with his bad words when a loud growling was heard, and a black bear came trotting towards them out of the forest. The dwarf sprang up in a fright, but he could not get to his cave, for the bear was already close. Then in the dread of his heart he cried, "Dear Mr. Bear, spare me, I will give you all my treasures; look, the beautiful jewels lying there! Grant me my life; what do you want with such a slender little fellow as I? You would not feel me between your teeth. Come, take these two wicked girls, they are tender morsels for you, fat as young quails; for mercy's sake eat them!" The bear took no heed of his words, but gave the wicked creature a single blow with his paw, and he did not move again.

The girls had run away, but the bear called to them, "Snow-White and Rose-Red, do not be afraid; wait, I will come with you." Then they knew his voice and waited, and when he came up to them suddenly his bearskin fell off, and he stood there a handsome man, clothed all in gold. "I am a King's son," he said, "and I was bewitched by that wicked dwarf, who had stolen my treasures; I have had to run about the forest as a savage bear until I was freed by his death. Now he has got his well-deserved punishment."

Snow-White was married to him, and Rose-Red to his brother, and they divided between them the great treasure which the dwarf had gathered together in his cave. The old mother lived peacefully and happily with her children for many years. She took the two rose-trees with her, and they stood before her window, and every year bore the most beautiful roses, white and red.

CLEVER ELSIE

There was once a man who had a daughter who was called Clever Elsie. And when she had grown up her father said, "We will get her

"Clever Elsie." From *Grimm's Household Tales,* translated by Margaret Hunt married." "Yes," said the mother, "if only any one would come who would have her." At length a man came from a distance and wooed her, who was called Hans; but he stipulated that Clever Elsie should be really wise. "Oh," said the father, "she's sharp enough"; and the mother said, "Oh, she can see the wind coming up the street, and hear the flies coughing." "Well," said Hans, "if she is not really wise, I won't have her." When they were sitting at dinner and had eaten, the mother said, "Elsie, go into the cellar and fetch some beer."

Then Clever Elsie took the pitcher from the wall, went into the cellar, and tapped the lid briskly as she went, so that the time might not appear long. When she was below she fetched herself a chair, and set it before the barrel so that she had no need to stoop, and did not hurt her back or do herself any unexpected injury. Then she placed the can before her, and turned the tap, and while the beer was running she would not let her eyes be idle, but looked up at the wall, and after much peering here and there, saw a pick-axe exactly above her, which the masons had accidently left there.

Then Clever Elsie began to weep and said, "If I get Hans, and we have a child, and he grows big, and we send him into the cellar here to draw beer, then the pick-axe will fall on his head and kill him." Then she sat and wept and screamed with all the strength of her body, over the misfortune which lay before her. Those upstairs waited for the drink, but Clever Elsie still did not come. Then the woman said to the servant, "Just go down into the cellar and see where Elsie is." The maid went and found her sitting in front of the barrel, screaming loudly. "Elsie, why do you weep?" asked the maid. "Ah," she answered, "have I not reason to weep? If I get Hans, and we have a child, and he grows big, and has to draw beer here, the pick-axe will perhaps fall on his head, and kill him." Then said the maid, "What a clever Elsie we have!" and sat down beside her and began loudly to weep over the misfortune.

After a while, as the maid did not come back, and those upstairs were thirsty for the beer, the man said to the boy, "Just go down into the cellar and see where Elsie and the girl are." The boy went down, and there sat Clever Elsie and the girl both weeping together. Then he asked, "Why are you weeping?" "Ah," said Elsie, "have I not reason to weep? If I get Hans, and we have a child, and he grows big, and has to draw beer here, the pick-axe will fall on his head and kill him." Then said the boy, "What a clever Elsie we have!" and sat down by her, and likewise began to howl loudly.

Upstairs they waited for the boy, but as he still did not return, the man said to the woman, "Just go down into the cellar and see where Elsie is!" The woman went down, and found all three in the midst of their lamentations, and inquired what was the cause; then Elsie told her also that her future child was to be killed by the pick-axe, when it grew big and had to draw beer, and the pick-axe fell down. Then said the mother likewise, "What a clever Elsie we have!" and sat down and wept with them.

The man upstairs waited a short time, but as his wife did not come back and his thirst grew ever greater, he said, "I must go into the cellar myself and see where Elsie is." But when he got into the cellar, and they were all sitting together crying, and he heard the reason, and that Elsie's child was the cause, and that Elsie might perhaps bring one into the world some day, and that he might be killed by the pick-axe, if he should happen to be sitting beneath it, drawing beer just at the very time when it fell down, he cried, "Oh, what a clever Elsie!" and sat down, and likewise wept with them.

The bridegroom stayed upstairs alone for a long time; then as no one would come back he thought, "They must be waiting for me below: I too must go there and see what they are about." When he got down, the five of them were sitting screaming and lamenting quite piteously, each out-doing the other. "What misfortune has happened then?" asked he. "Ah, dear Hans," said Elsie, "if we marry each other and have a child, and he is big, and we perhaps send him here to draw something to drink, then the pick-axe which has been left up there might dash his brains out if it were to fall down, so have we not reason to weep?" "Come," said Hans, "more understanding than that is not needed for my household, as you are such a clever Elsie, I will have you," and he seized her hand, took her upstairs with him, and married her.

After Hans had had her some time, he said, "Wife, I am going out to work and earn some money for us; go into the field and cut the corn that we may have some bread." "Yes, dear Hans, I will do that." After Hans had gone away, she cooked herself some good broth and took it into the field with her. When she came to the field she said to herself, "What shall I do; shall I cut first, or shall I eat first? Oh, I will eat first." Then she drank her cup of broth, and when she was fully satisfied, she once more said, "What shall I do? Shall I cut first, or shall I sleep first? I will sleep first." Then she lay down among the corn and fell asleep. Hans had been at home for a long time, but Elsie did not come; then said he, "What a clever Elsie I have; she is so industrious that she does not even come home to eat."

But when evening came and she still stayed away, Hans went out to see what she had cut, but nothing was cut, and she was lying among the corn asleep. Then Hans hastened home and brought a fowler's net with little bells and hung it round about her, and she still went on sleeping. Then he ran home, shut the house-door, and sat down in his chair and worked.

At length, when it was quite dark, Clever Elsie awoke and when she got up there was a jingling all round about her, and the bells rang at each

step which she took. Then she was alarmed, and became uncertain whether she really was Clever Elsie or not, and said, "Is it I, or is it not I?" But she knew not what answer to make to this, and stood for a time in doubt; at length she thought: "I will go home and ask if it be I, or if it be not I, they will be sure to know." She ran to the door of her own house, but it was shut; then she knocked at the window and cried, "Hans, is Elsie within?" "Yes," answered Hans, "she is within." Hereupon she was terrified, and said, "Ah, heavens! Then it is not I," and went to another door; but when the people heard the jingling of the bells they would not open it, and she could get in nowhere. Then she ran out of the village, and no one has seen her since.

SNOW-WHITE AND
THE SEVEN DWARFS

It was in the middle of winter, when the broad flakes of snow were falling around, that a certain queen sat working at a window, the frame of which was made of fine black ebony; and as she was looking out upon the snow, she pricked her finger, and three drops of blood fell upon it. Then she gazed thoughtfully upon the red drops which sprinkled the white snow, and said, "Would that my little daughter may be as white as that snow, as red as the blood, and as black as the ebony window-frame!"

And so the little girl grew up. Her skin was as white as snow, her cheeks as rosy as blood, and her hair as black as ebony; and she was called Snow-White.

But this queen died; and the king soon married another wife, who was very beautiful, but so proud that she could not bear to think that any one could surpass her. She had a magical mirror, to which she used to go and gaze upon herself in it, and say,

> "Mirror, Mirror on the wall
> Who is fairest of us all?"

"Snow-White and the Seven Dwarfs." From *Grimm's Popular Stories*, translated by Edgar Taylor (slightly adapted)

And the glass answered,

"Thou, queen, art fairest of them all."

But Snow-White grew more and more beautiful; and when she was seven years old, she was as bright as the day, and fairer than the queen herself. Then the glass one day answered the queen, when she went to consult it as usual,

"Queen, you are full fair, 'tis true,
But Snow-White fairer is than you."

When the queen heard this she turned pale with rage and envy; and called to one of her servants and said, "Take Snow-White away into the wide wood, that I may never see her more." Then the servant led Snow-White away; but his heart melted when she begged him to spare her life, and he said, "I will not hurt thee, thou pretty child." So he left her by herself, and though he thought it most likely that the wild beasts would tear her in pieces, he felt as if a great weight were taken off his heart when he had made up his mind not to kill her, but leave her to her fate.

Then poor Snow-White wandered along through the wood in great fear; and the wild beasts roared about her, but none did her any harm. In the evening she came to a little cottage, and went in there to rest herself, for her little feet would carry her no further. Every thing was spruce and neat in the cottage. On the table was spread a white cloth, and there were seven little plates with seven little loaves, and seven little glasses, and knives and forks laid in order; and by the wall stood seven little beds. Then, as she was very hungry, she picked a little piece off each loaf, and drank a very little from each glass; and after that she thought she would lie down and rest. So she tried all the little beds; and one was too long, and another was too short, till at last the seventh suited her; and there she laid herself down, and went to sleep.

Presently in came the masters of the cottage, who were seven little dwarfs that lived among the mountains, and dug and searched about for gold. They lighted up their seven lamps, and saw directly that all was not right. The first said, "Who has been sitting on my stool?" The second, "Who has been eating off my plate?" The third, "Who has been picking my bread?" The fourth, "Who has been meddling with my spoon?" The fifth, "Who has been handling my fork?" The sixth, "Who has been cutting with my knife?" The seventh, "Who has been drinking from my glass?" Then the first looked round and said, "Who has been lying on my bed?" And the rest came running to him, and every one cried out that somebody had been upon his bed. But the seventh saw Snow-White, and called all his brethren to come and see her; and they cried out with wonder and astonishment, and brought their lamps to look at her, and said, "Oh, what a lovely child she is!" And they were delighted to see her, and took care not to wake her; and the seventh dwarf slept an hour with each of the other dwarfs in turn, till the night was gone.

In the morning Snow-White told them all her story; and they pitied her, and said if she would keep all things in order, and cook and wash, and knit and spin for them, she might stay where she was, and they would take good care of her. Then they went out all day long to their work, seeking for gold and silver in the mountains; and Snow-White remained at home; and they warned her, and said, "The queen will soon find out where you are, so take care and let no one in."

But the queen, now that she thought Snow-White was dead, believed that she was certainly the handsomest lady in the land; and she went to her mirror and said,

> "Mirror, Mirror on the wall
> Who is fairest of us all?"

And the mirror answered,

> "Queen, thou art of beauty rare,
> But Snow-White living in the glen
> With the seven little men,
> Is a thousand times more fair."

Then the queen was very much alarmed; for she knew that the glass always spoke the truth, and was sure that the servant had betrayed her. And she could not bear to think that any one lived who was more beautiful than she was; so she disguised herself as an old pedlar and went her way over the hills to the place where the dwarfs dwelt. Then she knocked at the door, and cried, "Fine wares to sell!" Snow-White looked out at the window, and said, "Good-day, good-woman; what have you to sell?" "Good wares, fine wares," said she; "laces and bobbins of all colors." "I will let the old lady in; she seems to be a very good sort of body," thought Snow-White; so she ran down, and unbolted the door. "Bless me!" said the old woman, "how badly your stays are laced! Let me lace them up with one of my nice new laces." Snow-White did not dream of any mischief; so she stood up before the old woman, who set to work so nimbly, and pulled the lace so tight, that Snow-White lost her breath, and fell down as if she were dead. "There's an end of all thy beauty," said the spiteful queen, and went away home.

In the evening the seven dwarfs returned; and I need not say how grieved they were to see their faithful Snow-White stretched upon the ground motionless, as if she were quite dead. However, they lifted her up, and when they found what was the matter, they cut the lace; and in a little time she began to breathe, and soon came to life again. Then they said, "The old woman was the queen herself; take care another time, and let no one in when we are away."

When the queen got home, she went straight to her glass, and spoke to it as usual; but to her great surprise it still said,

> "Queen, thou art of beauty rare,
> But Snow-White living in the glen
> With the seven little men,
> Is a thousand times more fair."

Then the blood ran cold in her heart with spite and malice to see that Snow-White still lived; and she dressed herself up again in a disguise, but very different from the one she wore before, and took with her a poisoned comb. When she reached the dwarfs' cottage, she knocked at the door, and cried, "Fine wares to sell!" But Snow-White said, "I dare not let any one in." Then the queen said, "Only look at my beautiful combs"; and gave her the poisoned one. And it looked so pretty that Snow-White took it up and put it into her hair to try it. But the moment it touched her head the poison was so powerful that she fell down senseless. "There you may lie," said the queen, and went her way. But by good luck the dwarfs returned very early that evening, and when they saw Snow-White lying on the ground, they guessed what had happened, and soon found the poisoned comb. When they took it away, she recovered, and told them all that had passed; and they warned her once more not to open the door to any one.

Meantime the queen went home to her glass, and trembled with rage when she received exactly the same answer as before; and she said, "Snow-White shall die, if it costs me my life." So she went secretly into a chamber, and prepared a poisoned apple. The outside looked very rosy and tempting, but whoever tasted it was sure to die. Then she dressed herself up as a peasant's wife, and travelled over the hills to the dwarfs' cottage, and knocked at the door; but Snow-White put her head out of the window and said, "I dare not let any one in, for the dwarfs have told me not." "Do as you please," said the old woman, "but at any rate take this pretty apple; I will make you a present of it." "No," said Snow-White, "I dare not take it." "You silly girl!" answered the other, "what are you afraid of? Do you think it is poisoned? Come! Do you eat one part, and I will eat the other." Now the apple was so prepared that one side was good, though the other side was poisoned. Then Snow-White was very much tempted to taste, for the apple looked exceedingly nice; and when she saw the old woman eat, she could refrain no longer. But she had scarcely put the piece into her mouth, when she fell down dead upon the ground. "This time nothing will save you," said the queen; and she went home to her glass and at last it said,

> "Thou, queen, art the fairest of them all."

And then her envious heart was glad, and as happy as such a heart could be.

When evening came, and the dwarfs returned home, they found Snow-White lying on the ground. No breath passed her lips, and they were afraid that she was quite dead. They lifted her up, and combed her hair, and washed her face with water; but all was in vain, for the little girl seemed quite dead. So they laid her down upon a bier, and all seven watched and bewailed her three whole days; and then they proposed to bury her; but her cheeks were still rosy, and her face looked just as it did while she was alive; so they said, "We will never bury her in the cold ground." And they made a coffin of glass, so that they might still look at her, and wrote her name upon it, in golden letters, and that she was a king's daughter. And the coffin was placed upon the hill, and one of the dwarfs always sat by it and watched. And the birds of the air came too, and bemoaned Snow-White; first of all came an owl, and then a raven, but at last came a dove.

And thus Snow-White lay for a long, long time, and still looked as though she were only asleep; for she was even now as white as snow, and as red as blood, and as black as ebony. At last a prince came and called at the dwarfs' house; and he saw Snow-White, and read what was written in golden letters. Then he offered the dwarfs money, and earnestly prayed them to let him take her away; but they said, "We will not part with her for all the gold in the world." At last, however, they had pity on him, and gave him the coffin; but the moment he lifted it up to carry it home with him, the piece of apple fell

from between her lips, and Snow-White awoke, and said, "Where am I?" And the prince answered, "Thou art safe with me." Then he told her all that had happened, and said, "I love you better than all the world. Come with me to my father's palace, and you shall be my wife." And Snow-White consented, and went home with the prince; and every thing was prepared with great pomp and splendour for their wedding.

To the feast was invited, among the rest, Snow-White's old enemy, the queen; and as she was dressing herself in fine rich clothes, she looked in the glass, and said,

> "Mirror, Mirror on the wall,
> Who is fairest of us all?"

And the glass answered,

> "O Queen, although you are of beauty rare
> The young queen is a thousand times more
> fair."

When she heard this, she started with rage; but her envy and curiosity were so great, that she could not help setting out to see the bride. And when she arrived, and saw that it was no other than Snow-White, who, as she thought, had been dead a long while, she choked with passion, and fell ill and died. But Snow-White and the prince lived and reigned happily over that land many, many years.

THE FISHERMAN AND HIS WIFE

There is another version of the rhyme that goes, "Oh, fish of the sea,/Come listen to me,/ For, Isabel, my wife,/The plague of my life,/ Has sent me to beg a boon of thee." Because this story is unduly long, it is wise to cut one or two of the episodes.

There was once upon a time a Fisherman who lived with his wife in a miserable hovel close by the sea, and every day he went out fishing. And once as he was sitting with his rod, looking at the clear water, his line suddenly went down, far

"The Fisherman and His Wife." From *Grimm's Household Tales*, translated by Margaret Hunt

down below, and when he drew it up again, he brought out a large Flounder. Then the Flounder said to him, "Hark, you Fisherman, I pray you, let me live, I am no Flounder really, but an enchanted prince. What good will it do you to kill me? I should not be good to eat, put me in the water again, and let me go." "Come," said the Fisherman, "there is no need for so many words about it—a fish that can talk I should certainly let go, anyhow," with that he put him back again into the clear water, and the Flounder went to the bottom, leaving a long streak of blood behind him. Then the Fisherman got up and went home to his wife in the hovel.

"Husband," said the woman, "have you caught nothing to-day?" "No," said the man, "I did catch a Flounder, who said he was an enchanted prince, so I let him go again." "Did you not wish for anything first?" said the woman. "No," said the man; "what should I wish for?" "Ah," said the woman, "it is surely hard to have to live always in this dirty hovel; you might have wished for a small cottage for us. Go back and call him. Tell him we want to have a small cottage, he will certainly give us that." "Ah," said the man, "why should I go there again?" "Why," said the woman, "you did catch him, and you let him go again; he is sure to do it. Go at once." The man still did not quite like to go, but did not like to oppose his wife either, and went to the sea.

When he got there the sea was all green and yellow, and no longer so smooth; so he stood and said,

"Flounder, flounder in the sea,
Come, I pray thee, here to me;
For my wife, good Ilsabil,
Wills not as I'd have her will."

Then the Flounder came swimming to him and said: "Well, what does she want then?" "Ah," said the man, "I did catch you, and my wife says I really ought to have wished for something. She does not like to live in a wretched hovel any longer; she would like to have a cottage." "Go, then," said the Flounder, "she has it already."

When the man went home, his wife was no longer in the hovel, but instead of it there stood a small cottage, and she was sitting on a bench before the door. Then she took him by the hand and said to him, "Just come inside. Look, now isn't this a great deal better?" So they went in, and there was a small porch, and a pretty little parlour and bedroom, and a kitchen and pantry, with the best of furniture, and fitted up with the most beautiful things made of tin and brass, whatsoever was wanted. And behind the cottage there was a small yard, with hens and ducks, and a little garden with flowers and fruit. "Look," said the wife, "is not that nice!" "Yes," said the husband, "and so we must always think it—now we will live quite contented." "We will think about that," said the wife. With that they ate something and went to bed.

Everything went well for a week or a fortnight, and then the woman said, "Hark you, husband, this cottage is far too small for us, and the garden and yard are little; the Flounder might just as well have given us a larger house. I should like to live in a great stone castle; go to the Flounder, and tell him to give us a castle." "Ah, wife," said the man, "the cottage is quite good enough; why should we live in a castle?" "What!" said the woman; "just go there, the Flounder can always do that." "No, wife," said the man, "the Flounder has just given us the cottage, I do not like to go back so soon, it might make him angry." "Go," said the woman, "he can do it quite easily, and will be glad to do it; just you go to him."

The man's heart grew heavy, and he would not go. He said to himself, "It is not right," and yet he went. And when he came to the sea the water was quite purple and dark-blue, and grey and thick, and no longer so green and yellow, but it was still quiet. And he stood there and said,

"Flounder, flounder in the sea,
Come, I pray thee, here to me;
For my wife, good Ilsabil,
Wills not as I'd have her will."

"Well, what does she want, then?" said the Flounder. "Alas," said the man, half scared, "she wants to live in a great stone castle." "Go to it, then, she is standing before the door," said the Flounder.

Then the man went away, intending to go home, but when he got there, he found a great stone palace, and his wife was just standing on the steps going in, and she took him by the hand and said: "Come in." So he went in with her, and in the castle was a great hall paved with marble, and many servants, who flung wide the doors; and the walls were all bright with beautiful hangings, and in the rooms were chairs and tables of pure gold, and crystal chandeliers hung from the ceiling, and all the rooms and bedrooms had carpets, and food and wine of the very best were standing on all the tables, so that they nearly broke down beneath it. Behind the house, too, there was a great court-yard, with stables for horses and cows, and the very best of carriages; there was a magnificent large garden, too, with the most beautiful flowers and fruit-trees, and a park quite half a mile long, in which were stags, deer, and hares, and everything that could be desired. "Come," said the woman, "isn't that beautiful?" "Yes, indeed," said the man, "now let it be; and we will live in this beautiful castle and be content." "We will consider about that," said the woman, "and sleep upon it"; thereupon they went to bed.

Next morning the wife awoke first, and it was just daybreak, and from her bed she saw the beautiful country lying before her. Her husband was still stretching himself, so she poked him in the side with her elbow, and said, "Get up, husband, and just peep out of the window. Look you, couldn't we be the King over all that land? Go to the Flounder, we will be the King." "Ah, wife," said the man, "why should we be King? I do not want to be King." "Well," said the wife, "if you won't be King, I will; go to the Flounder, for I will be King." "Ah, wife," said the man, "why do you want to be King? I do not like to say that to him." "Why not?" said the woman; "go to him this instant; I must be King!" So the man went, and was quite unhappy because his wife wished to be King. "It is not right; it is not right," thought he. He did not wish to go, but yet he went.

And when he came to the sea, it was quite dark-grey, and the water heaved up from below, and smelt putrid. Then he went and stood by it, and said,

"Flounder, flounder in the sea,
Come, I pray thee, here to me;

For my wife, good Ilsabil,
Wills not as I'd have her will."

"Well, what does she want, then?" said the Flounder. "Alas," said the man, "she wants to be King." "Go to her; she is King already."

So the man went, and when he came to the palace, the castle had become much larger, and had a great tower and magnificent ornaments, and the sentinel was standing before the door, and there were numbers of soldiers with kettle-drums and trumpets. And when he went inside the house, everything was of real marble and gold, with velvet covers and great golden tassels. Then the doors of the hall were opened, and there was the court in all its splendour, and his wife was sitting on a high throne of gold and diamonds, with a great crown of gold on her head, and a sceptre of pure gold and jewels in her hand, and on both sides of her stood her maids-in-waiting in a row, each of them always one head shorter than the last.

Then he went and stood before her, and said: "Ah, wife, and now you are King." "Yes," said the woman, "now I am King." So he stood and looked at her, and when he had looked at her thus for some time, he said, "And now that you are King, let all else be, now we will wish for nothing more." "No, husband," said the woman, quite anxiously, "I find time passes very heavily, I can bear it no longer, go to the Flounder—I am King, but I must be Emperor, too." "Oh, wife, why do you wish to be Emperor?" "Husband," said she, "go to the Flounder. I will be Emperor." "Alas, wife," said the man, "he cannot make you Emperor; I may not say that to the fish. There is only one Emperor in the land. An Emperor the Flounder cannot make you! I assure you he cannot."

"What!" said the woman, "I am the King, and you are nothing but my husband; will you go this moment? go at once! If he can make a king he can make an emperor. I will be Emperor; go instantly." So he was forced to go. As the man went, however, he was troubled in mind, and thought to himself: "It will not end well; it will not end well! Emperor is too shameless! The Flounder will at last be tired out."

With that he reached the sea, and the sea was quite black and thick, and began to boil up from below, so that it threw up bubbles, and such a sharp wind blew over it that it curdled, and the man was afraid. Then he went and stood by it, and said,

> "Flounder, flounder in the sea,
> Come, I pray thee, here to me;
> For my wife, good Ilsabil,
> Wills not as I'd have her will."

"Well, what does she want, then?" said the Flounder. "Alas, Flounder," said he, "my wife wants to be Emperor." "Go to her," said the Flounder; "she is Emperor already."

So the man went, and when he got there the whole palace was made of polished marble with alabaster figures and golden ornaments, and soldiers were marching before the door blowing trumpets, and beating cymbals and drums; and in the house, barons, and counts, and dukes were going about as servants. Then they opened the doors to him, which were of pure gold. And when he entered, there sat his wife on a throne, which was made of one piece of gold, and was quite two miles high; and she wore a great golden crown that was three yards high, and set with diamonds and carbuncles, and in one hand she had the sceptre, and in the other the imperial orb; and on both sides of her stood the yeomen of the guard in two rows, each being smaller than the one before him, from the biggest giant, who was two miles high, to the very smallest dwarf, just as big as my little finger. And before it stood a number of princes and dukes.

Then the man went and stood among them, and said, "Wife, are you Emperor now?" "Yes," said she, "now I am Emperor." Then he stood and looked at her well, and when he had looked at her thus for some time, he said, "Ah, wife, be content, now that you are Emperor." "Husband," said she, "why are you standing there? Now, I am Emperor, but I will be Pope too; go to the Flounder." "Oh, wife," said the man, "what will you not wish for? You cannot be Pope; there is but one in Christendom; he cannot make you Pope." "Husband," said she, "I will be Pope, go immediately, I must be Pope this very day." "No, wife," said the man, "I do not like to say that to him; that would not do, it is too much; the Flounder can't make you Pope." "Husband," said she, "what nonsense! if

he can make an emperor he can make a pope. Go to him directly. I am Emperor, and you are nothing but my husband; will you go at once?"

Then he was afraid and went; but he was quite faint, and shivered and shook, and his knees and legs trembled. And a high wind blew over the land, and the clouds flew, and towards evening all grew dark, and the leaves fell from the trees, and the water rose and roared as if it were boiling, and splashed upon the shore; and in the distance he saw ships which were firing guns in their sore need, pitching and tossing on the waves. And yet in the midst of the sky there was still a small bit of blue, though on every side it was as red as in a heavy storm. So, full of despair, he went and stood in much fear and said,

> "Flounder, flounder in the sea,
> Come, I pray thee, here to me;
> For my wife, good Ilsabil,
> Wills not as I'd have her will."

"Well, what does she want, now?" said the Flounder. "Alas," said the man, "she wants to be Pope." "Go to her then," said the Flounder; "she is Pope already."

So he went, and when he got there, he saw what seemed to be a large church surrounded by palaces. He pushed his way through the crowd. Inside, however, everything was lighted up with thousands and thousands of candles, and his wife was clad in gold, and she was sitting on a much higher throne, and had three great golden crowns on, and round about her there was much ecclesiastical splendour; and on both sides of her was a row of candles the largest of which was as tall as the very tallest tower, down to the very smallest kitchen candle, and all the emperors and kings were on their knees before her, kissing her shoe. "Wife," said the man, and looked attentively at her, "are you now Pope?" "Yes," said she, "I am Pope." So he stood and looked at her, and it was just as if he was looking at the bright sun. When he had stood looking at her thus for a short time, he said: "Ah, wife, if you are Pope, do let well alone!" But she looked as stiff as a post, and did not move or show any signs of life. Then said he, "Wife, now that you are Pope, be satisfied, you cannot become anything greater now." "I will consider about that," said the woman. Thereupon they both went to bed, but she was not satisfied, and greediness let her have no sleep, for she was continually thinking what there was left for her to be.

The man slept well and soundly, for he had run about a great deal during the day; but the woman could not fall asleep at all, and flung herself from one side to the other the whole night through, thinking always what more was left for her to be, but unable to call to mind anything else. At length the sun began to rise, and when the woman saw the red of dawn, she sat up in bed and looked at it. And when, through the window, she saw the sun thus rising, she said, "Cannot I, too, order the sun and moon to rise?" "Husband," she said, poking him in the ribs with her elbows, "wake up! go to the Flounder, for I wish to be even as God is." The man was still half asleep, but he was so horrified that he fell out of bed. He thought he must have heard amiss, and rubbed his eyes, and said, "Alas, wife, what are you saying?" "Husband," said she, "if I can't order the sun and moon to rise, and have to look on and see the sun and moon rising, I can't bear it. I shall not know what it is to have another happy hour, unless I can make them rise myself." Then she looked at him so terribly that a shudder ran over him, and said, "Go at once; I wish to be like unto God." "Alas, wife," said the man, falling on his knees before her, "the Flounder cannot do that; he can make an emperor and a pope; I beseech you, go on as you are, and be Pope." Then she fell into a rage, and her hair flew wildly about her head, and she cried, "I will not endure this, I'll not bear it any longer; will you go this instant?" Then he put on his trousers and ran away like a madman. But outside a great storm was raging, and blowing so hard that he could scarcely keep his feet; houses and trees toppled over, the mountains trembled, rocks rolled into the sea, the sky was pitch black, and it thundered and lightened, and the sea came in with black waves as high as church-towers and mountains, and all with crests of white foam at the top. Then he cried, but could not hear his own words,

> "Flounder, flounder in the sea,
> Come, I pray thee, here to me;
> For my wife, good Ilsabil,
> Wills not as I'd have her will."

"Well, what does she want, then?" said the Flounder. "Alas," said he, "she wants to be like unto God." "Go to her, and you will find her back again in the dirty hovel." And there they are still living to this day.

RUMPELSTILTSKIN

This makes a splendid story for dramatization with puppets, either string puppets or hand. The children can cast the story into acts, line up their characters, and as they make the puppets, try out the dialogue with them. With children under ten-years-old hand puppets are easier to make and the dialogue is usually kept fluid. Children over ten may want to write parts of their dialogue or all of it.

There was once a miller who was poor, but he had one beautiful daughter. It happened one day that he came to speak with the king, and to give himself consequence, he told him that he had a daughter who could spin gold out of straw. The king said to the miller,

"That is an art that pleases me well; if your daughter is as clever as you say, bring her to my castle tomorrow, that I may put her to the proof."

When the girl was brought to him, he led her into a room that was quite full of straw, and gave her a wheel and spindle, and said,

"Now set to work, and if by the early morning you have not spun this straw to gold you shall die." And he shut the door himself, and left her there alone.

And so the poor miller's daughter was left there sitting, and could not think what to do for her life; she had no notion how to set to work to spin gold from straw, and her distress grew so great that she began to weep. Then all at once the door opened, and in came a little man, who said,

"Good evening, miller's daughter; why are you crying?"

"Oh!" answered the girl, "I have got to spin

"Rumpelstiltskin." From *Household Stories from the Brothers Grimm,* translated by Lucy Crane. By permission of The Macmillan Company, publishers

gold out of straw, and I don't understand the business."

Then the little man said,

"What will you give me if I spin it for you?"

"My necklace," said the girl.

The little man took the necklace, seated himself before the wheel, and whirr, whirr, whirr! three times round and the bobbin was full; then he took up another, and whirr, whirr, whirr! three times round, and that was full; and so he went on till the morning, when all the straw had been spun, and all the bobbins were full of gold. At sunrise came the king, and when he saw the gold he was astonished and very much rejoiced, for he was very avaricious. He had the miller's daughter taken into another room filled with straw, much bigger than the last, and told her that as she valued her life she must spin it all in one night. The girl did not know what to do, so she began to cry, and then the door opened, and the little man appeared and said,

"What will you give me if I spin all this straw into gold?"

"The ring from my finger," answered the girl.

So the little man took the ring, and began again to send the wheel whirring round, and by the next morning all the straw was spun into glistening gold. The king was rejoiced beyond measure at the sight, but as he could never have enough of gold, he had the miller's daughter taken into a still larger room full of straw, and said,

"This, too, must be spun in one night, and if you accomplish it you shall be my wife." For he thought, "Although she is but a miller's daugh-

ter, I am not likely to find any one richer in the whole world."

As soon as the girl was left alone, the little man appeared for the third time and said,

"What will you give me if I spin the straw for you this time?"

"I have nothing left to give," answered the girl.

"Then you must promise me the first child you have after you are queen," said the little man.

"But who knows whether that will happen?" thought the girl; but as she did not know what else to do in her necessity, she promised the little man what he desired, upon which he began to spin, until all the straw was gold. And when in the morning the king came and found all done according to his wish, he caused the wedding to be held at once, and the miller's pretty daughter became a queen.

In a year's time she brought a fine child into the world, and thought no more of the little man; but one day he came suddenly into her room, and said,

"Now give me what you promised me."

The queen was terrified greatly, and offered the little man all the riches of the kingdom if he would only leave the child; but the little man said, "No, I would rather have something living than all the treasures of the world."

Then the queen began to lament and to weep, so that the little man had pity upon her.

"I will give you three days," said he, "and if at the end of that time you cannot tell my name, you must give up the child to me."

Then the queen spent the whole night in thinking over all the names that she had ever heard, and sent a messenger through the land to ask far and wide for all the names that could be found. And when the little man came next day, (beginning with Caspar, Melchior, Balthazar) she repeated all she knew, and went through the whole list, but after each the little man said,

"That is not my name."

The second day the queen sent to inquire of all the neighbours what the servants were called, and told the little man all the most unusual and singular names, saying,

"Perhaps you are called Roast-ribs, or Sheep-shanks, or Spindleshanks?" But he answered nothing but

"That is not my name."

The third day the messenger came back again, and said,

"I have not been able to find one single new name; but as I passed through the woods I came to a high hill, and near it a little house, and before the house burned a fire, and round the fire danced a comical little man, and he hopped on one leg and cried,

"To-day do I bake, to-morrow I brew,
  The day after that the queen's child comes in;
And oh! I am glad that nobody knew
  That the name I am called is Rumpelstiltskin!"

You cannot think how pleased the queen was to hear that name, and soon afterwards, when the little man walked in and said,

"Now, Mrs. Queen, what is my name?" she said at first,

"Are you called Jack?"

"No," he answered.

"Are you called Harry?" she asked again.

"No," answered he. And then she said,

"Then perhaps your name is Rumpelstiltskin!"

"The devil told you that! the devil told you that!" cried the little man, and in his anger he stamped with his right foot so hard that it went into the ground above his knee; then he seized his left foot with both his hands in such a fury that he split in two, and there was an end of him.

ONE-EYE, TWO-EYES, AND THREE-EYES

The little rhymes of this story suggest ancient charms or incantations.

There was once a woman who had three daughters, the eldest of whom was called One-Eye, because she had only one eye in the middle of her forehead, and the second, Two-Eyes, because she had two eyes like other folks, and the youngest, Three-Eyes, because she had three eyes; and her third eye was also in the centre of her forehead. However, as Two-Eyes saw just as other human beings did, her sisters and her mother could not endure her. They said to her, "You, with your two eyes, are no better than the common people; you do not belong to us!" They pushed her about, and threw old clothes to her, and gave her nothing to eat but what they left, and did everything that they could to make her unhappy. It came to pass that Two-Eyes had to go out into the fields and tend the goat, but she was still quite hungry, because her sisters had given her so little to eat. So she sat down on a ridge and began to weep, and so bitterly that two streams ran down from her eyes. And once when she looked up in her grief, a woman was standing beside her, who said, "Why are you weeping, little Two-Eyes?" Two-Eyes answered, "Have I not reason to weep, when I have two eyes like other people, and my sisters and mother hate me for it, and push me from one corner to another, throw old clothes at me, and give me nothing to eat but the scraps they leave? To-day they have given me so little that I am still quite hungry." Then the wise woman said, "Wipe away your tears, Two-Eyes, and I will tell you something to stop you ever suffering from hunger again; just say to your goat,

'Bleat, my little goat, bleat,
  Cover the table with something to eat,'

and then a clean well-spread little table will stand before you, with the most delicious food

"One-Eye, Two-Eyes, and Three-Eyes." From *Grimm's Household Tales,* translated by Margaret Hunt upon it of which you may eat as much as you are inclined for; and when you have had enough, and have no more need of the little table, just say,

'Bleat, bleat, my little goat, I pray,
And take the table quite away,'

and then it will vanish again from your sight." Hereupon the wise woman departed. But Two-Eyes thought, "I must instantly make a trial, and see if what she said is true, for I am far too hungry," and she said,

"Bleat, my little goat, bleat,
Cover the table with something to eat,"

and scarcely had she spoken the words than a little table, covered with a white cloth, was standing there, and on it was a plate with a knife and fork, and a silver spoon; and the most delicious food was there also, warm and smoking as if it had just come out of the kitchen. Then Two-Eyes said the shortest prayer she knew, "Lord God, be with us always, Amen," and helped herself to some food, and enjoyed it. And when she was satisfied, she said, as the wise woman had taught her,

"Bleat, bleat, my little goat, I pray,
And take the table quite away,"

and immediately the little table and everything on it was gone again. "That is a delightful way of keeping house!" thought Two-Eyes, and was quite glad and happy.

In the evening, when she went home with her goat, she found a small earthenware dish with some food, which her sisters had set ready for her, but she did not touch it. Next day she again went out with her goat, and left the few bits of broken bread which had been handed to her, lying untouched. The first and second time that she did this, her sisters did not remark it at all, but as it happened every time, they did observe it, and said, "There is something wrong about Two-Eyes; she always leaves her food untasted, and she used to eat up everything that was given her; she must have discovered other ways of getting food." In order that they might learn the

truth, they resolved to send One-Eye with Two-Eyes when she went to drive her goat to the pasture, to observe what Two-Eyes did when she was there, and whether any one brought her anything to eat and drink. So when Two-Eyes set out the next time, One-Eye went to her and said, "I will go with you to the pasture, and see that the goat is well taken care of, and driven where there is food." But Two-Eyes knew what was in One-Eye's mind, and drove the goat into high grass and said, "Come, One-Eye, we will sit down, and I will sing something to you." One-Eye sat down and was tired with the unaccustomed walk and the heat of the sun, and Two-Eyes sang constantly,

"One eye, wakest thou?
One eye, sleepest thou?"

until One-Eye shut her one eye, and fell asleep, and as soon as Two-Eyes saw that One-Eye was fast asleep, and could discover nothing, she said,

"Bleat, my little goat, bleat,
Cover the table with something to eat,"

and seated herself at her table and ate and drank until she was satisfied, and then she again cried,

"Bleat, bleat, my little goat, I pray,
And take the table quite away,"

and in an instant all was gone. Two-Eyes now awakened One-Eye, and said, "One-Eye, you want to take care of the goat, and go to sleep while you are doing it, and in the meantime the goat might run all over the world. Come, let us go home again." So they went home, and again Two-Eyes let her little dish stand untouched, and One-Eye could not tell her mother why she would not eat it, and to excuse herself said, "I fell asleep when I was out."

Next day the mother said to Three-Eyes, "This time you shall go and observe if Two-Eyes eats anything when she is out, and if any one fetches her food and drink, for she must eat and drink in secret." So Three-Eyes went to Two-Eyes, and said, "I will go with you and see if the goat is taken proper care of, and driven where there is food." But Two-Eyes knew what was in Three-

Eyes' mind, and drove the goat into high grass and said, "We will sit down, and I will sing something to you, Three-Eyes." Three-Eyes sat down and was tired with the walk and with the heat of the sun, and Two-Eyes began the same song as before, and sang,

"Three eyes, are you waking?"

but then, instead of singing,

"Three eyes, are you sleeping?"

as she ought to have done, she thoughtlessly sang,

"Two eyes, are you sleeping?"

and sang all the time,

"Three eyes, are you waking?
Two eyes, are you sleeping?"

Then two of the eyes which Three-Eyes had, shut and fell asleep, but the third, as it had not been named in the song, did not sleep. It is true that Three-Eyes shut it, but only in her cunning, to pretend it was asleep too, but it blinked, and could see everything very well. And when Two-Eyes thought that Three-Eyes was fast asleep, she used her little charm,

"Bleat, my little goat, bleat,
Cover the table with something to eat,"

and ate and drank as much as her heart desired, and then ordered the table to go away again,

"Bleat, bleat, my little goat, I pray,
And take the table quite away,"

and Three-Eyes had seen everything. Then Two-Eyes came to her, waked her and said, "Have you been asleep, Three-Eyes? You are a good care-taker! Come, we will go home."

And when they got home, Two-Eyes again did not eat, and Three-Eyes said to the mother, "Now, I know why that high-minded thing there does not eat. When she is out, she says to the goat,

'Bleat, my little goat, bleat,
Cover the table with something to eat,'

and then a little table appears before her covered with the best of food, much better than any we have here, and when she has eaten all she wants, she says,

'Bleat, bleat, my little goat, I pray,
And take the table quite away,'

and all disappears. I watched everything closely. She put two of my eyes to sleep by using a certain form of words, but luckily the one in my forehead kept awake." Then the envious mother cried, "Dost thou want to fare better than we do? The desire shall pass away," and she fetched a butcher's knife, and thrust it into the heart of the goat, which fell down dead.

When Two-Eyes saw that, she went out full of trouble, seated herself on the ridge of grass at the edge of the field, and wept bitter tears. Suddenly the wise woman once more stood by her side, and said, "Two-Eyes, why are you weeping?" "Have I not reason to weep?" she answered. "The goat which covered the table for me every day when I spoke your charm has been killed by my mother, and now I shall again have to bear hunger and want." The wise woman said, "Two-Eyes, I will give you a piece of good advice; ask your sisters to give you the entrails of the slaughtered goat, and bury them in the ground in front of the house, and your fortune will be made." Then she vanished, and Two-Eyes went home and said to her sisters, "Dear sisters, do give me some part of my goat; I don't wish for what is good, but give me the entrails." Then they laughed and said, "If that's all you want, you can have it." So Two-Eyes took the entrails and buried them quietly in the evening, in front of the house-door, as the wise woman had counseled her to do.

Next morning, when they all awoke, and went to the house-door, there stood a strangely magnificent tree with leaves of silver, and fruit of gold hanging among them, so that in all the wide world there was nothing more beautiful or precious. They did not know how the tree could have come there during the night, but Two-Eyes saw that it had grown up out of the entrails of the goat, for it was standing on the exact spot where she had buried them. Then the mother said to One-Eye, "Climb up, my child, and gather some of the fruit of the tree for us." One-Eye climbed up, but when she was about to get hold of one of the golden apples, the branch escaped from her hands, and that happened each time, so that she could not pluck a single apple, let her do what she might. Then said the mother, "Three-Eyes, do you climb up; you with your three eyes can look about you better than One-Eye." One-Eye slipped down, and Three-Eyes climbed up. Three-Eyes was not more skilful, and might search as she liked, but the golden apples always escaped her. At length the mother grew impatient, and climbed up herself, but could get hold of the fruit no better than One-Eye and Three-Eyes, for she always clutched empty air.

Then said Two-Eyes, "I will just go up, perhaps I may succeed better." The sisters cried, "You indeed, with your two eyes, what can you do?" But Two-Eyes climbed up, and the golden apples did not get out of her way, but came into her hand of their own accord, so that she could pluck them one after the other, and brought a whole apronful down with her. The mother took them away from her, and instead of treating poor Two-Eyes any better for this, she and One-Eye and Three-Eyes were only envious, because Two-Eyes alone had been able to get the fruit, and they treated her still more cruelly.

It so befell that once when they were all standing together by the tree, a young knight came up. "Quick, Two-Eyes," cried the two sisters, "creep under this, and don't disgrace us!" and with all speed they turned an empty barrel which was standing close by the tree over poor Two-Eyes, and they pushed the golden apples, which she had been gathering, under it too. When the knight came nearer he was a handsome lord, who stopped and admired the magnificent gold and silver tree, and said to the two sisters, "To whom does this fine tree belong? Any one who would bestow one branch of it on me might in return for it ask whatsoever he desired." Then One-Eye and Three-Eyes replied that the tree belonged to them, and that they would give him a branch. They both took great trouble, but they were not able to do it, for the branches and fruit both moved away from them every time. Then

said the knight. "It is very strange that the tree should belong to you, and that you should still not be able to break a piece off." They again asserted that the tree was their property.

Whilst they were saying so, Two-Eyes rolled out a couple of golden apples from under the barrel to the feet of the knight, for she was vexed with One-Eye and Three-Eyes for not speaking the truth. When the knight saw the apples, he was astonished, and asked where they came from. One-Eye and Three-Eyes answered that they had another sister, who was not allowed to show herself, for she had only two eyes like any common person. The knight, however, desired to see her, and cried, "Two-Eyes, come forth." Then Two-Eyes, quite comforted, came from beneath the barrel, and the knight was surprised at her great beauty, and said, "Thou, Two-Eyes, canst certainly break off a branch from the tree for me." "Yes," replied Two-Eyes, "that I certainly shall be able to do, for the tree belongs to me." And she climbed up, and with the greatest ease, broke off a branch with beautiful silver leaves and golden fruit, and gave it to the knight. Then said the knight, "Two-Eyes, what shall I give thee for it?" "Alas!" answered Two-Eyes, "I suffer from hunger and thirst, grief and want, from early morning till late night; if you would take me with you, and deliver me from these things, I should be happy."

So the knight lifted Two-Eyes on to his horse and took her home with him to his father's castle, and there he gave her beautiful clothes, and meat and drink to her heart's content; and as he loved her so much he married her, and the wedding was solemnized with great rejoicing. When Two-Eyes was thus carried away by the handsome knight, her two sisters grudged her good fortune in downright earnest. "The wonderful tree, however, still remains with us," thought they, "and even if we can gather no fruit from it, still every one will stand still and look at it, and come to us and admire it. Who knows what good things may be in store for us?" But next morning, the tree had vanished, and all their hopes were at an end. When Two-Eyes looked out of the window of her own little room, to her great delight it was standing in front of it, and so it had followed her.

Two-Eyes lived a long time in happiness. Once

two poor women came to her in her castle, and begged for alms. She looked in their faces, and recognized her sisters, One-Eye and Three-Eyes, who had fallen into such poverty that they had to wander about and beg their bread from door to door. Two-Eyes, however, made them welcome, and was kind to them, and took care of them, so that they both with all their hearts repented the evil that they had done their sister in their youth.

THE GOOSE-GIRL

This is a somber romance in spite of the happy ending. The little rhyme the goose-girl says over Conrad's hat is certainly a powerful charm!

There was once upon a time an old Queen whose husband had been dead for many years, and she had a beautiful daughter. When the princess grew up she was betrothed to a prince who lived at a great distance. When the time came for her to be married, and she had to journey forth into the distant kingdom, the aged Queen packed up for her many costly vessels of silver and gold, and trinkets also of gold and silver; and cups and jewels, in short, everything which appertained to a royal dowry, for she loved her child with all her heart. She likewise sent her maid in waiting, who was to ride with her, and hand her over to the bridegroom, and each had a horse for the journey, but the horse of the King's daughter was called Falada, and could speak. So when the hour of parting had come, the aged mother went into her bedroom, took a small knife and cut her finger with it until it bled. Then she held a white handkerchief to it into which she let three drops of blood fall, gave it to her daughter and said, "Dear child, preserve this carefully, it will be of service to you on your way."

So they took a sorrowful leave of each other; the princess put the piece of cloth in her bosom, mounted her horse, and then went away to her bridegroom. After she had ridden for a while she felt a burning thirst, and said to her waiting-maid, "Dismount, and take my cup which you

"The Goose-Girl." From *Grimm's Household Tales,* translated by Margaret Hunt

have brought with you for me, and get me some water from the stream, for I should like to drink." "If you are thirsty," said the waiting-maid, "get off your horse yourself, and lie down and drink out of the water, I don't choose to be your servant." So in her great thirst the princess alighted, bent down over the water in the stream and drank, and was not allowed to drink out of the golden cup. Then she said: "Ah, Heaven!" and the three drops of blood answered: "If this your mother knew, her heart would break in two." But the King's daughter was humble, said nothing, and mounted her horse again. She rode some miles further, but the day was warm, the sun scorched her, and she was thirsty once more, and when they came to a stream of water, she again cried to her waiting-maid, "Dismount, and give me some water in my golden cup," for she had long ago forgotten the girl's ill words. But the waiting-maid said still more haughtily: "If you wish to drink, drink as you can, I don't choose to be your maid." Then in her great thirst the King's daughter alighted, bent over the flowing stream, wept and said, "Ah, Heaven!" and the drops of blood again replied, "If this your mother knew, her heart would break in two."

And as she was thus drinking and leaning right over the stream, the handkerchief with the three drops of blood fell out of her bosom, and floated away with the water without her observing it, so great was her trouble. The waiting-maid however, had seen it, and she rejoiced to think that she had now power over the bride, for since the princess had lost the drops of blood, she had become weak and powerless. So now when she wanted to mount her horse again, the one that was called Falada, the waiting-maid said, "Falada is more suitable for me, and my nag will do for you," and the princess had to be content with that. Then the waiting-maid, with many hard words, bade the princess exchange her royal apparel for her own shabby clothes; and at length she was compelled to swear by the clear sky above her, that she would not say one word of this to anyone at the royal court, and if she had not taken this oath she would have been killed on the spot. But Falada saw all this, and observed it well.

The waiting-maid now mounted Falada, and the true bride the bad horse, and thus they traveled onwards, until at length they entered the royal palace. There were great rejoicings over her arrival, and the prince sprang forward to meet her, lifted the waiting-maid from her horse, and thought she was his consort. She was conducted upstairs, but the real princess was left standing below.

Then the old King looked out of the window and saw her standing in the courtyard, and noticed how dainty and delicate and beautiful she was, and instantly went to the royal apartment, and asked the bride about the girl she had with her who was standing down below in the courtyard, and who she was. "I picked her up on my way for a companion; give the girl something to work at, that she may not stand idle." But the old King had no work for her, and knew of none, so he said, "I have a little boy who tends the geese, she may help him." The boy was called Conrad, and the true bride had to help him to tend the geese.

Soon afterwards the false bride said to the young King, "Dearest husband, I beg you to do me a favour." He answered, "I will do so most willingly." "Then send for the knacker, and have the head of the horse on which I rode here cut off, for it vexed me on the way." In reality, she was afraid that the horse might tell how she had behaved to the King's daughter. Then she succeeded in making the King promise that it should be done, and the faithful Falada was to die; this came to the ears of the real princess, and she secretly promised to pay the knacker a piece of gold if he would perform a small service for her. There was a great dark-looking gateway in the town, through which morning and evening she had to pass with the geese: would he be so good as to nail up Falada's head on it, so that she might see him again, more than once. The knacker's man promised to do that, and cut off the head, and nailed it fast beneath the dark gateway.

Early in the morning, when she and Conrad drove out their flock beneath this gateway, she said in passing,

"Alas, Falada, hanging there!"

Then the head answered,

"Alas, young Queen, how ill you fare!

If this your tender mother knew,
Her heart would surely break in two."

Then they went still further out of the town, and drove their geese into the country. And when they had come to the meadow, she sat down and unbound her hair which was like pure gold, and Conrad saw it and delighted in its brightness, and wanted to pluck out a few hairs. Then she said,

"Blow, blow, thou gentle wind, I say,
Blow Conrad's little hat away,
And make him chase it here and there,
Until I have braided all my hair,
And bound it up again."

And there came such a violent wind that it blew Conrad's hat far away across country, and he was forced to run after it. When he came back she had finished combing her hair and was putting it up again, and he could not get any of it. Then Conrad was angry, and would not speak to her, and thus they watched the geese until the evening, and then they went home.

Next day when they were driving the geese out through the dark gateway, the maiden said,

"Alas, Falada, hanging there!"

Falada answered,

"Alas, young Queen, how ill you fare!
If this your tender mother knew,
Her heart would surely break in two."

And she sat down again in the field and began to comb out her hair, and Conrad ran and tried to clutch it, so she said in haste,

"Blow, blow, thou gentle wind, I say,
Blow Conrad's little hat away,
And make him chase it here and there,
Until I have braided all my hair,
And bound it up again."

Then the wind blew, and blew his little hat off his head and far away, and Conrad was forced to run after it, and when he came back, her hair had been put up a long time, and he could get none of it, and so they looked after the geese till evening came.

But in the evening after they had got home,

Conrad went to the old King, and said, "I won't tend the geese with that girl any longer!" "Why not?" inquired the aged King. "Oh, because she vexes me the whole day long." Then the aged King commanded him to relate what it was that she did to him. And Conrad said, "In the morning when we pass beneath the dark gateway with the flock, there is a sorry horse's head on the wall, and she says to it,

'Alas, Falada, hanging there!'

And the head replies,

'Alas, young Queen, how ill you fare!
If this your tender mother knew,
Her heart would surely break in two.' "

And Conrad went on to relate what happened on the goose pasture and how when there he had to chase his hat.

The aged King commanded him to drive his flock out again next day, and as soon as morning came, he placed himself behind the dark gateway, and heard how the maiden spoke to the head of Falada, and then he too went into the country, and hid himself in the thicket in the meadow. There he soon saw with his own eyes the goose-girl and the goose-boy bringing their flock, and how after a while she sat down and unplaited her hair, which shone with radiance. And soon she said,

"Blow, blow, thou gentle wind, I say,
Blow Conrad's little hat away,
And make him chase it here and there,
Until I have braided all my hair,
And bound it up again."

Then came a blast of wind and carried off Conrad's hat, so that he had to run far away, while the maiden quietly went on combing and plaiting her hair, all of which the King observed. Then, quite unseen, he went away, and when the goose-girl came home in the evening, he called her aside, and asked why she did all these things. "I may not tell that, and I dare not lament my sorrows to any human being, for I have sworn not to do so by the heaven which is above me; if I had not done that, I should have lost my

life." He urged her and left her no peace, but he could draw nothing from her. Then said he, "If you will not tell me anything, tell your sorrows to the iron-stove there," and he went away. Then she crept into the iron-stove, and began to weep and lament, and emptied her whole heart, and said, "Here am I deserted by the whole world, and yet I am a King's daughter, and a false waiting-maid has by force brought me to such a pass that I have been compelled to put off my royal apparel, and she has taken my place with my bridegroom, and I have to perform menial service as a goose-girl. If my mother did but know that, her heart would break."

The aged King, however, was standing outside by the pipe of the stove, and was listening to what she said, and heard it. Then he came back again, and bade her come out of the stove. And royal garments were placed on her, and it was marvellous how beautiful she was! The aged King summoned his son, and revealed to him that he had got the false bride who was only a waiting-maid, but that the true one was standing there, as the sometime goose-girl. The young King rejoiced with all his heart when he saw her beauty and youth, and a great feast was made ready to which all the people and all good friends were invited. At the head of the table sat the bridegroom with the King's daughter at one side of him, and the waiting-maid on the other, but the waiting-maid was blinded, and did not recognize the princess in her dazzling array. When they had eaten and drunk, and were merry, the aged King asked the waiting-maid as a riddle, what punishment a person deserved who had behaved in such and such a way to her master, and at the same time related the whole story, and asked what sentence such a person merited. Then the false bride said, "She deserves no better fate than to be stripped entirely naked, and put in a barrel which is studded inside with pointed nails, and two white horses should be harnessed to it, which will drag her along through one street after another, till she is dead." "It is you," said the aged King, "and you have pronounced your own sentence, and thus shall it be done unto you." And when the sentence had been carried out, the young King married his true bride, and both of them reigned over their kingdom in peace and happiness.

THE WATER OF LIFE

The last three stories in this German group are for children of eleven or twelve. They are all complex and somber. In "The Water of Life" we see a clear example of the folk tales as carriers of the moral code. The youngest son must be courteous and brave to prove himself worthy of finding the water of life.

There was once a King who had an illness, and no one believed that he would come out of it with his life. He had three sons who were much distressed about it, and went down into the palace-garden and wept. There they met an old man who inquired as to the cause of their grief. They told him that their father was so ill that he would most certainly die, for nothing seemed to cure him. Then the old man said, "I know of one more remedy, and that is the water of life; if he drinks of it, he will become well again; but it is hard to find." The eldest said, "I will manage to find it," and went to the sick King, and begged to be allowed to go forth in search of the water of life, for that alone could save him. "No," said the King, "the danger of it is too great. I would rather die." But he begged so long that the King consented. The prince thought in his heart, "If I bring the water, then I shall be best beloved of my father, and shall inherit the kingdom."

So he set out, and when he had ridden forth a little distance, a dwarf stood there in the road who called to him and said, "Whither away so fast?" "Silly shrimp," said the prince, very haughtily, "it is nothing to you," and rode on. But the little dwarf had grown angry, and had wished an evil wish. Soon after this the prince entered a ravine, and the further he rode the closer the mountains drew together, and at last the road became so narrow that he could not advance a step further; it was impossible either to turn his horse or to dismount from the saddle, and he was shut in there as if in prison. The sick King waited long for him, but he came not.

Then the second son said, "Father, let me go forth to seek the water," and thought to himself,

"The Water of Life." From *Grimm's Household Tales,* translated by Margaret Hunt

"If my brother is dead, then the kingdom will fall to me." At first the King would not allow him to go either, but at last he yielded, so the prince set out on the same road that his brother had taken, and he too met the dwarf, who stopped him to ask whither he was going in such haste. "Little shrimp," said the prince, "that is nothing to you," and rode on without giving him another look. But the dwarf bewitched him, and he, like the other, rode into a ravine and could neither go forwards nor backwards. So fare haughty people.

As the second son also remained away, the youngest begged to be allowed to go forth to fetch the water, and at last the King was obliged to let him go. When he met the dwarf and the latter asked him whither he was going in such haste, he stopped, gave him an explanation, and said, "I am seeking the water of life, for my father is sick unto death." "Do you know, then, where that is to be found?" "No," said the prince. "As you have borne yourself as is seemly, and not haughtily like your false brothers, I will give you the information and tell you how you may obtain the water of life. It springs from a fountain in the courtyard of an enchanted castle, but you will not be able to make your way to it, if I do not give you an iron wand and two small loaves of bread. Strike thrice with the wand on the iron door of the castle, and it will spring open; inside lie two lions with gaping jaws, but if you throw a loaf to each of them, they will be quieted. Then hasten to fetch some of the water of life before the clock strikes twelve, else the door will shut again, and you will be imprisoned."

The prince thanked him, took the wand and the bread, and set out on his way. When he arrived, everything was as the dwarf had said. The door sprang open at the third stroke of the wand, and when he had appeased the lions with the bread, he entered the castle, and came to a large and splendid hall, wherein sat some enchanted princes whose rings he drew off their fingers. A sword and a loaf of bread were lying there, which he carried away. After this, he entered a chamber, in which was a beautiful maiden who rejoiced when she saw him, kissed him, and told him that he had set her free, and should have the whole of her kingdom, and that

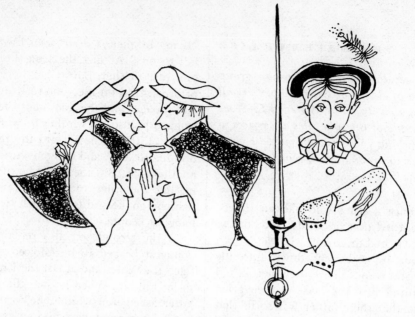

if he would return in a year their wedding should be celebrated; likewise she told him where the spring of the water of life was, and that he was to hasten and draw some of it before the clock struck twelve.

Then he went onwards, and at last entered a room where there was a beautiful newly-made bed, and as he was very weary, he felt inclined to rest a little. So he lay down and fell asleep. When he awoke, it was striking a quarter to twelve. He sprang up in a fright, ran to the spring, drew some water in a cup which stood near, and hastened away. But just as he was passing through the iron door, the clock struck twelve, and the door fell to with such violence that it carried away a piece of his heel. He, however, rejoicing at having obtained the water of life, went homewards, and again passed the dwarf. When the latter saw the sword and the loaf, he said, "With these you have won great wealth; with the sword you can slay whole armies, and the bread will never come to an end."

But the prince would not go home to his father without his brothers, and said, "Dear dwarf, can you not tell me where my two brothers are? They went out before I did in search of the water of life, and have not returned." "They are imprisoned between two mountains," said the dwarf. "I have condemned them to stay there, because they were so haughty." Then the prince begged until the dwarf released them; he warned him, however, and said, "Beware of them, for they have

bad hearts." When his brothers came, he rejoiced, and told them how things had gone with him, that he had found the water of life, and had brought a cupful away with him, and had rescued a beautiful princess, who was willing to wait a year for him, and then their wedding was to be celebrated, and he would obtain a great kingdom.

After that they rode on together, and chanced upon a land where war and famine reigned, and the King already thought he must perish, for the scarcity was so great. Then the prince went to him and gave him the loaf, wherewith he fed and satisfied the whole of his kingdom, and then the prince gave him the sword also, wherewith he slew the hosts of his enemies, and could now live in rest and peace. The prince then took back his loaf and his sword, and the three brothers rode on. But after this they entered two more countries where war and famine reigned, and each time the prince gave his loaf and his sword to the Kings, and had now delivered three kingdoms, and after that they went on board a ship and sailed over the sea. During the passage, the two eldest conversed apart and said, "The youngest has found the water of life and not we, for that our father will give him the kingdom,—the kingdom which belongs to us, and he will rob us of all our fortune." They then began to seek revenge, and plotted with each other to destroy him. They waited until once when they found him fast asleep, then they poured the water of life out of the cup, and took it for themselves, but into the cup they poured salt sea-water. Now therefore, when they arrived home, the youngest took his cup to the sick King in order that he might drink out of it, and be cured. But scarcely had he drunk a very little of the salt sea-water than he became still worse than before. And as he was lamenting over this, the two eldest brothers came, and accused the youngest of having intended to poison him, and said that they had brought him the true water of life, and handed it to him. He had scarcely tasted it, when he felt his sickness departing, and became strong and healthy as in the days of his youth. After that they both went to the youngest, mocked him, and said, "You certainly found the water of life, but you have had the pain, and we the gain; you should have been sharper, and should have kept your eyes open. We took it from you whilst you were asleep at sea, and when a year is over, one of us will go and fetch the beautiful princess. But beware that you do not disclose aught of this to our father; indeed he does not trust you, and if you say a single word, you shall lose your life into the bargain, but if you keep silent, you shall have it as a gift."

The old King was angry with his youngest son, and thought he had plotted against his life. So he summoned the court together, and had sentence pronounced upon his son, that he should be secretly shot. And once when the prince was riding forth to the chase, suspecting no evil, the King's huntsman was told to go with him, and when they were quite alone in the forest, the huntsman looked so sorrowful that the prince said to him, "Dear huntsman, what ails you?" The huntsman said, "I cannot tell you, and yet I ought." Then the prince said, "Say openly what it is, I will pardon you." "Alas!" said the huntsman, "I am to shoot you dead, the King has ordered me to do it." Then the prince was shocked, and said, "Dear huntsman, let me live; there, I give you my royal garments; give me your common ones in their stead." The huntsman said, "I will willingly do that, indeed I would not have been able to shoot you." Then they exchanged clothes, and the huntsman returned home; the prince, however, went further into the forest. After a time

three waggons of gold and precious stones came to the King for his youngest son, which were sent by the three Kings who had slain their enemies with the prince's sword, and maintained their people with his bread, and who wished to show their gratitude for it. The old King then thought, "Can my son have been innocent?" and said to his people, "Would that he were still alive, how it grieves me that I have suffered him to be killed!" "He still lives," said the huntsman, "I could not find it in my heart to carry out your command," and told the King how it had happened. Then a stone fell from the King's heart, and he had it proclaimed in every country that his son might return and be taken into favour again.

The princess, however, had a road made up to her palace which was quite bright and golden, and told her people that whosoever came riding straight along it to her, would be the right one and was to be admitted, and whoever rode by the side of it, was not the right one, and was not to be admitted. As the time was now close at hand, the eldest thought he would hasten to go to the King's daughter, and give himself out as her deliverer, and thus win her for his bride, and the kingdom to boot. Therefore he rode forth, and when he arrived in front of the palace, and saw the splendid golden road, he thought it would be a sin and a shame if he were to ride over that and turned aside, and rode on the right side of it. But when he came to the door, the servants told him he was not the right one, and was to go away again.

Soon after this the second prince set out, and when he came to the golden road, and his horse had put one foot on it, he thought it would be a sin and a shame to tread a piece of it off, and he turned aside and rode on the left side of it, and when he reached the door, the attendants told him he was not the right one, and he was to go away again. When at last the year had entirely expired, the third son likewise wished to ride out of the forest to his beloved, and with her forget his sorrows. So he set out and thought of her so incessantly, and wished to be with her so much, that he never noticed the golden road at all. So his horse rode onwards up the middle of it, and when he came to the door, it was opened and the princess received him with joy, and said he was her deliverer, and lord of the kingdom, and their wedding was celebrated with great rejoicing. When it was over she told him that his father invited him to come to him, and had forgiven him. So he rode thither, and told him everything; how his brothers had betrayed him, and how he had nevertheless kept silence. The old King wished to punish them, but they had put to sea, and never came back as long as they lived.

Scandinavian folk tales

Although the temper of the Scandinavian folk tales is, in the main, serious, they have also a drollery that equals the English tales. Peter Christian Asbjörnsen and Jörgen Moe, like the Grimm brothers, collected their stories from the lips of old storytellers and the stories have a dramatic and forthright quality that invariably characterizes such spontaneous narration. These tales were also fortunate in their translator, Sir George Webbe Dasent, who put them into such clear, vigorous English that their folk flavor and even the feeling of spontaneity are preserved. These qualities make them easy to tell and they should not be read if it is possible to learn them for telling. Since Dasent's day, Gudrun Thorne-Thomsen and Ingri d'Aulaire, both Norwegians, have retold these stories in even simpler style. Their books are fine sources for telling.

THE THREE BILLY GOATS GRUFF

This is a matchless little tale to tell, admirable in plot and economy of words. You will probably want to substitute for the Big Billy Goat Gruff's gruesome verse, the simpler, "Well, come along. I've two big spears to fight you with," and explain to the children, "By spears, of course, he meant his horns." This is fun for the five-year-olds to dramatize informally without any special costuming.

Once on a time there were three Billy Goats who were to go up to the hill-side to make themselves fat, and the name of all three was "Gruff."

On the way up was a bridge over a stream they had to cross; and under the bridge lived a great ugly Troll, with eyes as big as saucers and a nose as long as a poker.

So first of all came the youngest Billy Goat Gruff to cross the bridge.

"TRIP, TRAP! TRIP, TRAP!" went the bridge.

"WHO'S THAT tripping over my bridge?" roared the Troll.

"Oh! it is only I, the tiniest Billy Goat Gruff; and I'm going up to the hill-side to make myself fat," said the Billy Goat, with such a small voice.

"Now, I'm coming to gobble you up," said the Troll.

"Oh, no! pray don't take me. I'm too little, that I am," said the Billy Goat. "Wait a bit till the second Billy Goat Gruff comes; he's much bigger."

"Well! be off with you," said the Troll.

A little while after, came the second Billy Goat Gruff to cross the bridge.

"TRIP, TRAP! TRIP, TRAP! TRIP, TRAP!" went the bridge.

"WHO'S THAT tripping over my bridge?" roared the Troll.

"Oh! it's the second Billy Goat Gruff, and I'm going up to the hill-side to make myself fat," said the Billy Goat, who hadn't such a small voice.

"Now, I'm coming to gobble you up," said the Troll.

"Oh, no! don't take me. Wait a little till the big Billy Goat Gruff comes; he's much bigger."

"Very well! be off with you," said the Troll.

"The Three Billy Goats Gruff." From *Popular Tales from the Norse* by Peter Christian Asbjörnsen and Jörgen Moe, translated by Sir George Webbe Dasent. G. P. Putnam's Sons

But just then up came the big Billy Goat Gruff.

"TRIP, TRAP! TRIP, TRAP! TRIP, TRAP! TRIP, TRAP!" went the bridge, for the Billy Goat was so heavy that the bridge creaked and groaned under him.

"WHO'S THAT tramping over my bridge?" roared the Troll.

"IT'S I! THE BIG BILLY GOAT GRUFF," said the Billy Goat, who had an ugly hoarse voice of his own.

"Now, I'm coming to gobble you up," roared the Troll.

"Well, come along! I've got two spears,
And I'll poke your eyeballs out at your ears;
I've got besides two curling-stones,
And I'll crush you to bits, body and bones."

That was what the big Billy Goat said; and so he flew at the Troll, and poked him and knocked him, and crushed him to bits, body and bones, and tossed him out into the burn, and after that he went up to the hill-side. There the Billy Goats got so fat that they were scarce able to walk home again; and if the fat hasn't fallen off them, why they're still fat; and so—

"Snip, snap, snout,
This tale's told out."

THE PANCAKE

A simpler beginning is, "Once there was a mother who had seven hungry children." If you paraphrase "the goody, the good wife" two or three times, the children will have it.

Once on a time there was a goody who had seven hungry bairns, and she was frying a pancake for them. It was a sweet-milk pancake, and there it lay in the pan bubbling and frizzling so thick and good, it was a sight for sore eyes to look at. And the bairns stood round about, and the goodman sat by and looked on.

"Oh, give me a bit of pancake, mother, dear; I am so hungry," said one bairn.

"Oh, darling mother," said the second.

"Oh, darling, good mother," said the third.

"Oh, darling, good, nice mother," said the fourth.

"Oh, darling, pretty, good, nice mother," said the fifth.

"Oh, darling, pretty, good, nice, clever mother," said the sixth.

"Oh, darling, pretty, good, nice, clever, sweet mother," said the seventh.

So they begged for the pancake all round, the one more prettily than the other; for they were so hungry and so good.

"Yes, yes, bairns, only bide a bit till it turns itself,"—she ought to have said, "till I can get it turned,"—"and then you shall all have some—a lovely sweet-milk pancake; only look how fat and happy it lies there."

When the pancake heard that it got afraid, and in a trice it turned itself all of itself, and tried to jump out of the pan; but it fell back into it again t'other side up, and so when it had been fried a little on the other side too, till it got firmer in its flesh, it sprang out on the floor, and rolled off like a wheel through the door and down the hill.

"Holloa! Stop, pancake!" and away went the goody after it, with the frying-pan in one hand and the ladle in the other, as fast as she could, and her bairns behind her, while the goodman limped after them last of all.

"The Pancake." From *Tales from the Fjeld* by Peter Christian Asbjörnsen and Jörgen Moe, translated by Sir George Webbe Dasent. G. P. Putnam's Sons

"Hi! won't you stop? Seize it. Stop, pancake," they all screamed out, one after the other, and tried to catch it on the run and hold it; but the pancake rolled on and on, and in the twinkling of an eye it was so far ahead that they couldn't see it, for the pancake was faster on its feet than any of them.

So when it had rolled awhile it met a man.

"Good day, pancake," said the man.

"God bless you, Manny Panny!" said the pancake.

"Dear pancake," said the man, "don't roll so fast; stop a little and let me eat you."

"When I have given the slip to Goody Poody, and the goodman, and seven squalling children, I may well slip through your fingers, Manny Panny," said the pancake, and rolled on and on till it met a hen.

"Good day, pancake," said the hen.

"The same to you, Henny Penny," said the pancake.

"Pancake, dear, don't roll so fast; bide a bit and let me eat you up," said the hen.

"When I have given the slip to Goody Poody, and the goodman, and seven squalling children, and Manny Panny, I may well slip through your claws, Henny Penny," said the pancake, and so it rolled on like a wheel down the road.

Just then it met a cock.

"Good day, pancake," said the cock.

"The same to you, Cocky Locky," said the pancake.

"Pancake, dear, don't roll so fast, but bide a bit and let me eat you up."

"When I have given the slip to Goody Poody, and the goodman, and seven squalling children, and to Manny Panny, and Henny Penny, I may well slip through your claws, Cocky Locky," said the pancake, and off it set rolling away as fast as it could; and when it had rolled a long way it met a duck.

"Good day, pancake," said the duck.

"The same to you, Ducky Lucky."

"Pancake, dear, don't roll away so fast; bide a bit and let me eat you up."

"When I have given the slip to Goody Poody, and the goodman, and seven squalling children, and Manny Panny, and Henny Penny, and Cocky Locky, I may well slip through your fingers, Ducky Lucky," said the pancake, and with that it took to rolling and rolling faster than ever; and when it had rolled a long, long while, it met a goose.

"Good day, pancake," said the goose.

"The same to you, Goosey Poosey."

"Pancake, dear, don't roll so fast; bide a bit and let me eat you up."

"When I have given the slip to Goody Poody, and the goodman, and seven squalling children, and Manny Panny, and Henny Penny, and Cocky Locky, and Ducky Lucky, I can well slip through your feet, Goosey Poosey," said the pancake, and off it rolled.

So when it had rolled a long, long way farther, it met a gander.

"Good day, pancake," said the gander.

"The same to you, Gander Pander," said the pancake.

"Pancake, dear, don't roll so fast; bide a bit and let me eat you up."

"When I have given the slip to Goody Poody, and the goodman, and seven squalling children, and Manny Panny, and Henny Penny, and Cocky Locky, and Ducky Lucky, and Goosey Poosey, I may well slip through your feet, Gander Pander," said the pancake, which rolled off as fast as ever.

So when it had rolled a long, long time, it met a pig.

"Good day, pancake," said the pig.

"The same to you, Piggy Wiggy," said the pancake, which, without a word more, began to roll and roll like mad.

"Nay, nay," said the pig, "you needn't be in such a hurry; we two can then go side by side and see one another over the wood; they say it is not too safe in there."

The pancake thought there might be something in that, and so they kept company. But when they had gone awhile, they came to a brook. As for Piggy, he was so fat he swam safe across, it was nothing to him; but the poor pancake couldn't get over.

"Seat yourself on my snout," said the pig, "and I'll carry you over."

So the pancake did that.

"Ouf, ouf," said the pig, and swallowed the pancake at one gulp; and then, as the poor pancake could go no farther, why—this story can go no farther either.

WHY THE BEAR IS
STUMPY-TAILED

It has been said that all over the world, wherever there are bears, this story occurs. The folk tales are always warning the unwary against the folly of credulity.

One day the Bear met the Fox, who came slinking along with a string of fish he had stolen. "Whence did you get those from?" asked the Bear.

"Oh!, my Lord Bruin, I've been out fishing and caught them," said the Fox.

So the Bear had a mind to learn to fish too, and bade the Fox tell him how he was to set about it.

"Oh! it's an easy craft for you," answered the Fox, "and soon learnt. You've only got to go upon the ice, and cut a hole and stick your tail down into it; and so you must go on holding it there as long as you can. You're not to mind if

"Why the Bear Is Stumpy-Tailed." From *Popular Tales from the Norse*

your tail smarts a little; that's when the fish bite. The longer you hold it there the more fish you'll get; and then all at once out with it, with a cross pull sideways, and with a strong pull too."

Yes; the Bear did as the Fox had said, and held his tail a long, long time down in the hole, till it was fast frozen in. Then he pulled it out with a cross pull, and it snapped short off. That's why Bruin goes about with a stumpy tail this very day.

THE LAD WHO WENT
TO THE NORTH WIND

Here is a story that becomes more dramatic if you visualize the scenes and the characters. Children love the humor and the justice of the landlord's punishment.

Once on a time there was an old widow who had one son, and as she was poorly and weak, her son had to go up into the storehouse to fetch meal for cooking; but when he got outside the storehouse, and was just going down the steps, there came the North Wind, puffing and blowing, caught up the meal, and so away with it through the air. Then the Lad went back into the storehouse for more; but when he came out again on the steps, if the North Wind didn't come again and carry off the meal with a puff; and, more than that, he did so the third time. At this the Lad got very angry; and as he thought it hard that the North Wind should behave so, he decided he'd just look him up, and ask him to give back his meal.

So off he went, but the way was long, and he walked and walked; but at last he came to the North Wind's house.

"Good day!" said the Lad, "and thank you for coming to see us yesterday."

"GOOD DAY!" answered the North Wind, for his voice was loud and gruff, "AND THANKS FOR COMING TO SEE ME. WHAT DO YOU WANT?"

"Oh!" answered the Lad, "I only wished to

"The Lad Who Went to the North Wind." From *Popular Tales from the Norse*

ask you to be so good as to let me have back that meal you took from me on the storehouse steps, for we haven't much to live on; and if you're to go on snapping up the morsel we have, there'll be nothing for it but to starve."

"I haven't got your meal," said the North Wind; "but if you are in such need, I'll give you a cloth which will get you everything you want, if you only say, 'Cloth, spread yourself, and serve up all kinds of good dishes!'"

With this the Lad was well content. But, as the way was so long, he couldn't get home in one day, so he turned into an inn on the way; and when they were going to sit down to supper, he laid the cloth on a table which stood in the corner, and said,

"Cloth, spread yourself, and serve up all kinds of good dishes."

He had scarce said so before the cloth did as it was bid; and all who stood by thought it a fine thing, but most of all the landlord. So, when all were fast asleep, at dead of night, he took the Lad's cloth, and put another in its stead, just like the one he had got from the North Wind, but which couldn't so much as serve up a bit of dry bread.

So, when the Lad woke, he took his cloth and went off with it, and that day he got home to his mother.

"Now," said he, "I've been to the North Wind's house, and a good fellow he is, for he gave me this cloth, and when I only say to it, 'Cloth, spread yourself, and serve up all kind of good dishes,' I get any sort of food I please."

"All very true, I daresay," said his mother; "but seeing is believing, and I shan't believe it till I see it."

So the Lad made haste, drew out a table, laid the cloth on it, and said,

"Cloth, spread yourself, and serve up all kind of good dishes!"

But never a bit of dry bread did the cloth serve up.

"Well," said the Lad, "there's no help for it but to go to the North Wind again;" and away he went.

So he came to where the North Wind lived late in the afternoon.

"Good evening!" said the Lad.

"Good evening!" said the North Wind.

"I want my rights for that meal of ours which you took," said the Lad. "As for that cloth I got, it isn't worth a penny."

"I've got no meal," said the North Wind; "but yonder you have a ram which coins nothing but golden dollars as soon as you say to it, 'Ram, ram, make money!'"

So the lad thought this a fine thing; but as it was too far to get home that day, he turned in for the night at the same inn where he had slept before.

Before he called for anything, he tried the truth of what the North Wind had said of the ram, and found it all right; but, when the landlord saw that, he thought it was a famous ram, and, when the Lad had fallen asleep, he took another which couldn't coin gold dollars, and changed the two.

Next morning off went the Lad; and when he got home to his mother, he said,

"After all, the North Wind is a jolly fellow; for now he has given me a ram which can coin golden dollars if I only say, 'Ram, ram, make money!'"

"All very true, I daresay," said his mother; "but I shan't believe any such stuff until I see the dollars made."

"Ram, ram, make money!" said the Lad; but if the ram made anything it wasn't money.

So the Lad went back again to the North Wind, and blew him up and said the ram was worth nothing, and he must have his rights for the meal.

"Well!" said the North Wind; "I've nothing else to give you but that old stick in the corner yonder; but it's a stick of that kind that if you say,

'Stick, stick! lay on!' it lays on till you say,

'Stick, stick! now stop!'"

So as the way was long, the Lad turned in this night too to the landlord; but as he could pretty well guess how things stood as to the cloth and the ram, he lay down at once on the bench and began to snore, as if he were asleep.

Now the landlord, who easily saw that the stick must be worth something, hunted up one which was like it, and when he heard the Lad snore, was going to change the two; but just as the landlord was about to take it, the Lad bawled out:

"Stick, stick! lay on!"

So the stick began to beat the landlord, till he jumped over chairs, and tables, and benches, and yelled and roared,

"Oh my! oh my! bid the stick be still, else it will beat me to death, and you shall have back both your cloth and your ram."

When the Lad thought the landlord had got enough, he said,

"Stick, stick! now stop!"

Then he took the cloth and put it into his pocket, and went home with his stick in his hand, leading the ram by a cord round its horns; and so he got his rights for the meal he had lost.

BOOTS AND HIS BROTHERS

The name "Boots" came into the Norwegian tales by way of the distinguished British translator, Sir George Webbe Dasent. "Boots" is the English name for a boy who blacks the boots and does odds and ends of work. Perhaps it is enough to say to the children the first time you tell the story, "There was a poor man who had three sons, Peter, Paul, and John. And because John was the youngest son and had to black the boots, the shoes, of the others, he was called Boots." The d'Aulaires translate the name Espen Cinderlad, so take your choice. The children accept either one as a nickname.

Once on a time there was a man who had three sons, Peter, Paul, and John. John was Boots, of course, because he was the youngest. I can't say the man had anything more than these three sons, for he hadn't one penny to rub against another; and so he told his sons over and over again that they must go out into the world and try to earn their bread, for there at home there was nothing to be looked for but starving to death.

Now, a bit off from the man's cottage was the King's palace, and you must know, just against the King's windows a great oak had sprung up which was so stout and big that it took away all the light from the King's palace. The King had

"Boots and His Brothers." From *Popular Tales from the Norse* (slightly adapted)

said that he would give many, many dollars to the man who could fell the oak, but no one was man enough for that, for as soon as ever one chip of the oak's trunk flew off, two grew in its stead.

A well, too, the King wanted dug, that would hold water for the whole year; for all his neighbors had such wells, but he had none, and that he thought a shame. So the King said he would give any man who could dig him such a well as would hold water for the whole year round, both money and goods; but no one could do it, for the King's palace lay high, high up on a hill, and they hadn't dug a few inches before they came upon the living rock.

But as the King had set his heart on having these two things done, he had it given out far and wide, in all the churches of his kingdom, that he who could fell the big oak in the King's courtyard, and get him a well that would hold water the whole year round, should have the Princess and half the kingdom.

Well, you may easily know there was many a man who came to try his luck; but for all their hacking and hewing, and all their digging and delving, it was no good. The oak got bigger and stouter at every stroke, and the rock didn't get softer either. So one day those three brothers thought they'd set off and try too, and their father hadn't a word against it; for even if they didn't get the Princess and half the kingdom, it might happen they would get a place somewhere with a good master; and that was all he wanted. So when the brothers said they thought of going to the palace, their father said "yes" at once. So Peter, Paul, and Boots went off from their home.

Well, they hadn't gone far before they came to a firwood, and up along one side of it rose a steep hill-side, and as they went, they heard something hewing and hacking away up on the hill among the trees.

"I wonder now what it is that is hewing away up yonder," said Boots.

"You're always so clever with your wonderings," said Peter and Paul both at once. "What wonder is it, pray, that a woodcutter should stand and hack up on a hill-side?"

"Still, I'd like to see what it is, after all," said Boots, and up he went.

"Oh, if you're such a child, 'twill do you good to go and take a lesson," bawled out his brothers after him.

But Boots didn't care for what they said; he climbed the steep hill-side towards where the noise came, and when he reached the place, what do you think he saw? Why, an axe that stood there hacking and hewing, all of itself, at the trunk of a fir.

"Good day!" said Boots. "So you stand here all alone and hew, do you?"

"Yes; here I've stood and hewed and hacked a long, long time, waiting for you," said the Axe.

"Well, here I am at last," said Boots, as he took the axe, pulled it off its haft, and stuffed both head and haft into his wallet.

So when he got down again to his brothers, they began to jeer and laugh at him.

"And now, what funny thing was it you saw up yonder upon the hill-side?" they said.

"Oh, it was only an axe we heard," said Boots.

So when they had gone a bit farther, they came under a steep spur of rock, and up there they heard something digging and shovelling.

"I wonder now," said Boots, "what it is digging and shovelling up yonder at the top of the rock."

"Ah, you're always so clever with your wonderings," said Peter and Paul again, "as if you'd never heard a woodpecker hacking and pecking at a hollow tree."

"Well, well," said Boots, "I think it would be a piece of fun just to see what it really is."

And so off he set to climb the rock, while the others laughed and made game of him. But he didn't care a bit for that; up he climbed, and when he got near the top, what do you think he saw? Why, a spade that stood there digging and delving.

"Good day!" said Boots. "So you stand here all alone, and dig and delve!"

"Yes, that's what I do," said the Spade, "and that's what I've done this many a long day, waiting for you."

"Well, here I am," said Boots again, as he took the spade and knocked it off its handle, and put it into his wallet, and then went down again to his brothers.

"Well, what was it, so rare and strange," said

Peter and Paul, "that you saw up there at the top of the rock?"

"Oh," said Boots, "nothing more than a spade; that was what we heard."

So they went on again a good bit, till they came to a brook. They were thirsty, all three, after their long walk, and so they lay down beside the brook to have a drink.

"I wonder now," said Boots, "where all this water comes from."

"I wonder if you're right in your head," said Peter and Paul in one breath. "If you're not mad already, you'll go mad very soon, with your wonderings. Where the brook comes from, indeed! Have you never heard how water rises from a spring in the earth?"

"Yes; but still I've a great fancy to see where this brook comes from," said Boots.

So up alongside the brook he went, in spite of all that his brothers bawled after him. Nothing could stop him. On he went. So, as he went up and up, the brook got smaller and smaller, and at last, a little way farther on, what do you think he saw? Why, a great walnut, and out of that the water trickled.

"Good day!" said Boots again. "So you lie here, and trickle and run down all alone?"

"Yes, I do," said the Walnut; "and here have I trickled and run this many a long day, waiting for you."

"Well, here I am," said Boots, as he took up a lump of moss, and plugged up the hole, that the water mightn't run out. Then he put the walnut into his wallet and ran down to his brothers.

"Well, now," said Peter and Paul, "have you found out where the water comes from? A rare sight it must have been!"

"Oh, after all it was only a hole it ran out of," said Boots; and so the others laughed and made game of him again; but Boots didn't mind that a bit.

"After all, I had the fun of seeing it," said he.

So when they had gone a bit farther, they came to the King's palace; but as every one in the kingdom had heard how they might win the Princess and half the realm, if they could only fell the big oak and dig the King's well, so many had come to try their luck that the oak was now twice as stout and big as it had been at first, for

two chips grew for every one they hewed out with their axes, as I daresay you all bear in mind. So the King had now laid it down as a punishment, that if any one tried and couldn't fell the oak, he should be put on a barren island. But the two brothers didn't let themselves be scared by that; they were quite sure they could fell the oak, and Peter, as he was the eldest, was to try his hand first; but it went with him as with all the rest who had hewn at the oak; for every chip he cut out, two grew in its place. So the King's men seized him, and put him out on the island.

Now Paul, he was to try his luck, but he fared just the same; when he had hewn two or three strokes, they began to see the oak grow, and so the King's men seized him too, and put him out on the island.

So now Boots was to try.

"If your brothers could not cut down the tree, it is not likely that you can, Boots. You had better give up," said the King.

"Well, I'd like just to try," said Boots, and so he got leave. Then he took his axe out of his wallet and fitted it to its haft.

"Hew away!" said he to his axe; and away it hewed, making the chips fly again, so that it wasn't long before down came the oak.

When that was done Boots pulled out his spade, and fitted it to its handle.

"Dig away!" said he to the spade; and so the spade began to dig and delve till the earth and rock flew out in splinters, and so he had the well soon dug.

And when he had got it as big and deep as he chose, Boots took out his walnut and laid it in one corner of the well, and pulled the plug of moss out.

"Trickle and run," said Boots; and so the nut trickled and ran, till the water gushed out of the hole in a stream, and in a short time the well was brimfull.

Thus Boots had felled the oak which shaded the King's palace, and dug a well in the palace-yard, and so he got the Princess and half the kingdom, as the King had said; but it was lucky for Peter and Paul that they were off on the island, else they would have heard each hour and day how every one said, "Well, something came of Boots' wondering after all."

THE PRINCESS ON
THE GLASS HILL

If this story seems overly long, let Boots find only the Golden Horse and ride up the hill only once.

Once on a time there was a man who had a meadow which lay high up on the hill-side, and in the meadow was a barn, which he had built to keep his hay in. Now, I must tell you, there hadn't been much in the barn for the last year or two, for every St. John's night, when the grass stood greenest and deepest, the meadow was eaten down to the very ground the next morning, just as if a whole drove of sheep had been there feeding on it overnight. This happened once, and it happened twice; so at last the man grew weary of losing his crop of hay, and said to his sons—for he had three of them, and the youngest was nicknamed Boots, of course—that now one of them must just go and sleep in the barn in the outlying field when St. John's night came, for it was too good a joke that his grass should be eaten, root and blade, this year, as it had been the last two years. So whichever of them went must keep a sharp look-out; that was what their father said.

Well, the eldest son was ready to go and watch the meadow; trust him for looking after the grass! It shouldn't be his fault if man or beast, or the fiend himself got a blade of grass. So, when evening came, he set off to the barn, and lay down to sleep; but a little on in the night came such a clatter, and such an earthquake that walls and roof shook, and groaned, and creaked; then up jumped the lad, and took to his heels as fast as ever he could; nor dared he once look round till he reached home; and as for the hay, why it was eaten up this year just as it had been twice before.

The next St. John's night, the man said again it would never do to lose all the grass in the outlying field year after year in this way, so one of his sons must just trudge off to watch it, and watch it well too. Well, the next oldest son was ready to try his luck, so he set off, and lay down to sleep in the barn as his brother had done be-

"The Princess on the Glass Hill." From *Popular Tales from the Norse*

fore him; but as the night wore on, there came on a rumbling and quaking of the earth, worse even than on the last St. John's night, and when the lad heard it, he got frightened, and took to his heels as though he were running a race.

Next year the turn came to Boots; but when he made ready to go, the other two began to laugh, and to make game of him, saying,

"You're just the man to watch the hay, that you are; you, who have done nothing all your life but sit in the ashes and toast yourself by the fire."

But Boots did not care a pin for their chattering, and stumped away as evening drew on, up the hill-side to the outlying field. There he went inside the barn and lay down; but in about an hour's time the barn began to groan and creak, so that it was dreadful to hear.

"Well," said Boots to himself, "if it isn't worse than this, I can stand it well enough."

A little while after there came another creak and an earthquake, so that the litter in the barn flew about the lad's ears.

"Oh," said Boots to himself, "if it isn't worse than this, I daresay I can stand it out."

But just then came a third rumbling, and a third earthquake, so that the lad thought walls and roof were coming down on his head; but it passed off, and all was still as death about him.

"It'll come again, I'll be bound," thought Boots; but no, it did not come again; still it was and still it stayed; but after he had lain a little while he heard a noise as if a horse were standing just outside the barn-door, and cropping the grass. He stole to the door, and peeped through a chink, and there stood a horse feeding away. So big and fat and grand a horse, Boots had never set eyes on; by his side on the grass lay a saddle and bridle, and a full set of armour for a knight, all of brass, so bright that the light gleamed from it.

"Ho, ho!" thought the lad; "it's you, is it, that eats up our hay? I'll soon put a spoke in your wheel; just see if I don't."

So he lost no time, but took the steel out of his tinder-box, and threw it over the horse; then it had no power to stir from the spot, and became so tame that the lad could do what he liked with it. So he got on its back and rode off with it to a place which no one knew of, and there he put up the horse. When he got home his brothers laughed, and asked how he fared.

"You didn't lie long in the barn, even if you had the heart to go as far as the field."

"Well," said Boots, "all I can say is, I lay in the barn till the sun rose, and neither saw nor heard anything; I can't think what there was in the barn to make you both so afraid."

"A pretty story!" said his brothers; "but we'll soon see how you have watched the meadow." So they set off, but when they reached it, there stood the grass as deep and thick as it had been the night before.

Well, the next St. John's eve it was the same story over again; neither of the elder brothers dared to go out to the outlying field to watch the crop; but Boots, he had the heart to go, and everything happened just as it had happened the year before. First a clatter and an earthquake, then a greater clatter and another earthquake, and so on a third time; only this year the earthquakes were far worse than the year before. Then all at once everything was as still as death, and the lad heard how something was cropping the grass outside the barn-door, so he stole to the door, and peeped through a chink; and what do you think he saw? Why, another horse standing right up against the wall, and chewing and champing with might and main. It was far finer and fatter than the one which came the year before, and it had a saddle on its back and a bridle on its neck and a full suit of mail for a knight lay by its side, all of silver, and as grand as you would wish to see.

"Ho, ho!" said Boots to himself; "it's you that gobbles up our hay, is it? I'll soon put a spoke in your wheel"; and with that he took the steel out of his tinder-box, and threw it over the horse's crest, which stood as still as a lamb. Well, the lad rode this horse, too, to the hiding-place where he kept the other one, and after that he went home.

"I suppose you'll tell us," said one of his brothers, "there's a fine crop this year too, up in the hayfield."

"Well, so there is," said Boots; and off ran the others to see, and there stood the grass thick and deep, as it was the year before; but they didn't give Boots softer words for all that.

Now, when the third St. John's eve came,
the two elder still hadn't the heart to lie out in the barn and watch the grass, for they had got so scared at heart the night they lay there before, that they couldn't get over the fright; but Boots, he dared to go; and, to make a long story short, the very same thing happened this time as had happened twice before. Three earthquakes came, one after the other, each worse than the one which went before; and when the last came, the lad danced about with the shock from one barn wall to the other; and after that, all at once, it was as still as death. Now when he had lain a little while he heard something tugging away at the grass outside the barn; so he stole again to the door-chink, and peeped out, and there stood a horse close outside—far, far bigger and fatter than the two he had taken before.

"Ho, ho!" said the lad to himself, "it's you, is it, that comes here eating up our hay? I'll soon stop that—I'll soon put a spoke in your wheel." So he caught up his steel and threw it over the horse's neck, and in a trice it stood as if it were nailed to the ground, and Boots could do as he pleased with it. Then he rode off with it to the hiding-place where he kept the other two, and then went home. When he got home his two brothers made game of him as they had done before, saying they could see he had watched the grass well, for he looked for all the world as if he were walking in his sleep, and many other spiteful things they said; but Boots gave no heed to them, only asking them to go and see for themselves; and when they went, there stood the grass as fine and deep this time as it had been twice before.

Now, you must know that the king of the country where Boots lived had a daughter, whom he would give only to the man who could ride up over the hill of glass, for there was a high, high hill, all of glass, as smooth and slippery as ice, close by the king's palace. Upon the tip-top of the hill the king's daughter was to sit, with three golden apples in her lap, and the man who could ride up and carry off the three golden apples was to have half the kingdom and the Princess to wife. This the king had stuck up on all the church-doors in his realm, and had given it out in many other kingdoms besides. Now, this Princess was so lovely that all who set eyes on her fell over head and ears in love with her whether they would or no. So I needn't tell you how all the princes and knights who heard of her were eager to win her to wife, and half the kingdom beside; and how they came riding from all parts of the world on high prancing horses, and clad in the grandest clothes, for there wasn't one of them who hadn't made up his mind that he, and he alone, was to win the Princess.

So when the day of trial came, which the king had fixed, there was such a crowd of princes and knights under the glass hill, that it made one's head to whirl to look at them; and everyone in the country who could even crawl along was off to the hill, for they were all eager to see the man who was to win the Princess.

So the two elder brothers set off with the rest; but as for Boots, they said outright he shouldn't go with them, for if they were seen with such a dirty changeling, all begrimed with smut from cleaning their shoes and sifting cinders in the dusthole, they said folk would make game of them.

"Very well," said Boots, "it's all one to me. I can go alone, and stand or fall by myself."

Now when the two brothers came to the hill of glass, the knights and princes were all hard at it, riding their horses till they were all in a foam; but it was no good, by my troth; for as soon as ever the horses set foot on the hill, down they slipped, and there wasn't one who could get a yard or two up; and no wonder, for the hill was as smooth as a sheet of glass and as steep as a house-wall. But all were eager to have the Princess and half the kingdom. So they rode and slipped, and slipped and rode, and still it was the same story over again. At last all their horses were so weary that they could scarce lift a leg, and in such a sweat that the lather dripped from them, and so the knights had to give up trying any more. So the king was just thinking that he would proclaim a new trial for the next day, to see if they would have better luck, when all at once a knight came riding up on so brave a steed that no one had ever seen the like of it in his born days, and the knight had mail of brass, and the horse, a brass bit in his mouth, so bright that the sunbeams shone from it. Then all the others called out to him he might just as well spare himself the trouble of riding at the hill, for it would lead to no good; but he gave no heed to

them, and put his horse at the hill, and went up it like nothing for a good way, about a third of the height; and when he had got so far, he turned his horse and rode down again. So lovely a knight the Princess thought she had never yet seen; and while he was riding, she sat and thought to herself—"Would to heaven he might only come up, and down the other side."

And when she saw him turning back, she threw down one of the golden apples after him, and it rolled down into his shoe. But when he got to the bottom of the hill he rode off so fast that no one could tell what had become of him. That evening all the knights and princes were to go before the king, that he who had ridden so far up the hill might show the apple the princess had thrown; but there was no one who had anything to show. One after the other they all came, but not a man of them could show the apple.

At even, the brothers of Boots came home too, and had such a long story to tell about the riding up the hill.

"First of all," they said, "there was not one of the whole lot who could get so much as a stride up; but at last came one who had a suit of brass mail, and a brass bridle and saddle, all so bright that the sun shone from them a mile off. He was a chap to ride, just! He rode a third of the way up the hill of glass and he could easily have ridden the whole way up, if he chose; but he turned round and rode down thinking, maybe, that was enough for once."

"Oh! I should so like to have seen him, that I should," said Boots, who sat by the fireside, and stuck his feet into the cinders as was his wont.

"Oh!" said his brothers, "you would, would you? You look fit to keep company with such high lords, nasty beast that you are, sitting there amongst the ashes."

Next day the brothers were all for setting off again; and Boots begged them this time, too, to let him go with them and see the riding; but no, they wouldn't have him at any price, he was too ugly and nasty, they said.

"Well, well," said Boots; "if I go at all, I must go by myself. I'm not afraid."

So when the brothers got to the hill of glass, all the princes and knights began to ride again, and you may fancy they had taken care to shoe their horses sharp; but it was no good—they rode and slipped, and slipped and rode, just as they had done the day before, and there was not one who could get so far as a yard up the hill. And when they had worn out their horses, so that they could not stir a leg, they were all forced to give it up as a bad job. So the king thought he might as well proclaim that the riding should take place the day after for the last time, just to give them one chance more; but all at once it came across his mind that he might as well wait a little longer to see if the knight in brass mail would come this day too. Well, they saw nothing of him; but all at once came one riding on a steed far, far braver and finer than that on which the knight of brass had ridden, and he had silver mail, and a silver saddle and bridle, all so bright that the sunbeams gleamed and glanced from them far away. Then the others shouted out to him again, saying he might as well hold hard and not try to ride up the hill, for all his trouble would be thrown away; but the knight paid no heed to them, and rode straight at the hill and right up it, till he had gone two-thirds of the way, and then he wheeled his horse round and rode down again. To tell the truth, the Princess liked him still better than the knight in brass, and she sat and wished he might only be able to come right up to the top, and down the other side; but when she saw him turning back, she threw the second apple after him, and it rolled down and fell into his shoe. But as soon as ever he had come down from the hill of glass, he rode off so fast that no one could see what became of him.

At even, when all were to go in before the king and the Princess, that he who had the golden apple might show it, in they went, one after the other; but there was no one who had any apple to show. The two brothers, as they had done on the former day, went home and told how things had gone, and how all had ridden at the hill and none got up.

"But, last of all," they said, "came one in a silver suit, and his horse had a silver saddle and a silver bridle. He was just a chap to ride; and he got two-thirds up the hill, and then turned back. He was a fine fellow and no mistake; and the Princess threw the second gold apple to him."

"Oh!" said Boots, "I should so like to have seen him too, that I should."

"A pretty story," they said. "Perhaps you think his coat of mail was as bright as the ashes you are always poking about and sifting, you nasty, dirty beast."

The third day everything happened as it had happened the two days before. Boots begged to go and see the sight, but the two wouldn't hear of his going with them. When they got to the hill there was no one who could get so much as a yard up it; and now all waited for the knight in silver mail, but they neither saw nor heard of him. At last came one riding on a steed, so brave that no one had ever seen his match; and the knight had a suit of golden mail, and a golden saddle and bridle, so wondrous bright that the sunbeams gleamed from them a mile off. The other knights and princes could not find time to call out to him not to try his luck, for they were amazed to see how grand he was. So he rode right at the hill, and tore up it like nothing, so that the Princess hadn't even time to wish that he might get up the whole way. As soon as ever he reached the top, he took the third golden apple from the Princess' lap, and then turned his horse and rode down again. As soon as he got down, he rode off at full speed, and out of sight in no time.

Now, when the brothers got home at even, you may fancy what long stories they told, how the riding had gone off that day; and amongst other things, they had a deal to say about the knight in golden mail.

"He was just a chap to ride!" they said; "so grand a knight isn't to be found in the wide world."

"Oh!" said Boots, "I should so like to have seen him, that I should."

"Ah!" said his brothers, "his mail shone a deal brighter than the glowing coals which you are always poking and digging at; nasty, dirty beast that you are."

Next day all the knights and princes were to pass before the king and the Princess—it was too late to do so the night before, I suppose—that he who had the gold apple might bring it forth; but one came after another, first the princes, and then the knights, and still no one could show the gold apple.

"Well," said the king, "someone must have it, for it was something that we all saw with our own eyes, how a man came and rode up and bore it off."

So he commanded that everyone who was in the kingdom should come up to the palace and see if he could show the apple. Well, they all came, one after another, but no one had the golden apple, and after a long time the two brothers of Boots came. They were the last of all, so the king asked them if there was no one else in the kingdom who hadn't come.

"Oh, yes," said they; "we have a brother, but he never carried off the golden apple. He hasn't stirred out of the dusthole on any of the three days."

"Never mind that," said the king; "he may as well come up to the palace like the rest."

So Boots had to go up to the palace.

"How, now," said the king; "have you got the golden apple? Speak out!"

"Yes, I have," said Boots; "here is the first, and here is the second, and here is the third too"; and with that he pulled all three golden apples out of his pocket, and at the same time threw off his sooty rags, and stood before them in his gleaming golden mail.

"Yes!" said the king; "you shall have my daughter and half my kingdom, for you well deserve both her and it."

So they got ready for the wedding, and Boots got the Princess to wife, and there was great merry-making at the bridal-feast, you may fancy, for they could all be merry though they couldn't ride up the hill of glass; and all I can say is, that if they haven't left off their merry-making yet, why, they're still at it.

GUDBRAND ON THE HILL-SIDE

The sly humor and tenderness of "Gudbrand on the Hill-side" are beautifully interpreted by Mrs. Gudrun Thorne-Thomsen in her record of this name, which she made for the American Library Association.

Once on a time there was a man whose name was Gudbrand; he had a farm which lay far, far away, upon a hill-side, and so they called him Gudbrand on the Hill-side.

Now, you must know this man and his good-wife lived so happily together, and understood one another so well, that all the husband did the wife thought so well done, there was nothing like it in the world, and she was always glad whatever he turned his hand to. The farm was their own land, and they had a hundred dollars lying at the bottom of their chest, and two cows tethered up in a stall in their farmyard.

So one day his wife said to Gudbrand,

"Do you know, dear, I think we ought to take one of our cows into town and sell it; that's what I think; for then we shall have some money in hand, and such well-to-do people as we ought to have ready money like the rest of the world. As for the hundred dollars at the bottom of the chest yonder, we can't make a hole in them, and I'm sure I don't know what we want with more than one cow. Besides, we shall gain a little in another way, for then I shall get off with only looking after one cow, instead of having, as now, to feed and litter and water two."

Well, Gudbrand thought his wife talked right good sense, so he set off at once with the cow on

"Gudbrand on the Hill-side." From *Popular Tales from the Norse*

his way to town to sell her; but when he got to the town, there was no one who would buy his cow.

"Well! well! never mind," said Gudbrand, "at the worst, I can only go back home again with my cow. I've both stable and tether for her, I should think, and the road is no farther out than in"; and with that he began to toddle home with his cow.

But when he had gone a bit of the way, a man met him who had a horse to sell, so Gudbrand thought 'twas better to have a horse than a cow, so he swopped with the man. A little farther on, he met a man walking along, and driving a fat pig before him, and he thought it better to have a fat pig than a horse, so he swopped with the man. After that he went a little farther, and a man met him with a goat; so he thought it better to have a goat than a pig, and he swopped with the man that owned the goat. Then he went on a good bit till he met a man who had a sheep, and he swopped with him too, for he thought it always better to have a sheep than a goat. After a while he met a man with a goose, and he swopped away the sheep for the goose; and when he had walked a long, long time, he met a man with a cock, and he swopped with him, for he thought in this wise, " 'Tis surely better to have a cock than a goose." Then he went on till the day was far spent, and he began to get very hungry, so he sold the cock for a shilling, and bought food with the money, for, thought Gudbrand on the Hill-side, " 'Tis always better to save one's life than to have a cock."

After that he went on home till he reached his nearest neighbour's house, where he turned in.

"Well," said the owner of the house, "how did things go with you in town?"

"Rather so so," said Gudbrand. "I can't praise my luck, nor do I blame it either"; and with that he told the whole story from first to last.

"Ah!" said his friend, "you'll get nicely hauled over the coals, that one can see, when you get home to your wife. Heaven help you, I wouldn't stand in your shoes for something."

"Well!" said Gudbrand on the Hill-side, "I think things might have gone worse with me; but now, whether I have done wrong or not, I have so kind a goodwife, she never has a word to say against anything that I do."

"Oh!" answered his neighbour, "I hear what you say, but I don't believe it for all that."

"Shall we lay a bet upon it?" asked Gudbrand on the Hill-side. "I have a hundred dollars at the bottom of my chest at home; will you lay as many against them?"

Yes, the friend was ready to bet; so Gudbrand stayed there till evening, when it began to get dark, and then they went together to his house, and the neighbour was to stand outside the door and listen, while the man went in to see his wife.

"Good evening!" said Gudbrand.

"Good evening!" said the goodwife. "Oh! is that you? Now, God be praised!"

Yes, it was he. So the wife asked how things had gone with him in town.

"Oh! only so so," answered Gudbrand; "not much to brag of. When I got to the town there was no one who would buy the cow, so you must know I swopped it away for a horse."

"For a horse!" said his wife; "well, that is good of you; thanks with all my heart. We are so well-to-do that we may drive to church, just as well as other people; and if we choose to keep a horse we have a right to get one, I should think. So run out, child, and put up the horse."

"Ah!" said Gudbrand, "but you see I've not got the horse after all; for when I got a bit farther on the road, I swopped it away for a pig."

"Think of that, now!" said the wife; "you did just as I should have done myself; a thousand thanks! Now I can have a bit of bacon in the house to set before people when they come to see me, that I can. What do we want with a horse? People would only say we had got so proud that we couldn't walk to church. Go out, child, and put up the pig in the stye."

"But I've not got the pig either," said Gudbrand; "for when I got a little farther on, I swopped it away for a milch goat."

"Bless us!" cried his wife, "how well you manage everything! Now I think it over, what should I do with a pig? People would only point at us and say, 'Yonder they eat up all they have got.' No! now I have got a goat, and I shall have milk and cheese, and keep the goat too. Run out, child, and put up the goat."

"Nay, but I haven't got the goat either," said Gudbrand, "for a little farther on I swopped it away, and got a fine sheep instead."

"You don't say so!" cried his wife; "why you do everything to please me, just as if I had been with you; what do we want with a goat? If I had it I should lose half my time in climbing up the hills to get it down. No! if I have a sheep, I shall have both wool and clothing, and fresh meat in the house. Run out, child, and put up the sheep."

"But I haven't got the sheep any more than the rest," said Gudbrand, "for when I had gone a bit farther, I swopped it away for a goose."

"Thank you! thank you! with all my heart!" cried his wife; "what should I do with a sheep? I have no spinning-wheel, nor carding-comb, nor should I care to worry myself with cutting, and shaping, and sewing clothes. We can buy clothes now, as we have always done; and now I shall have roast goose, which I have longed for so often; and, besides, down to stuff my little pillow with. Run out, child, and put up the goose."

"Ah!" said Gudbrand, "but I haven't the goose either; for when I had gone a bit farther I swopped it away for a cock."

"Dear me!" cried his wife, "how you think of everything! just as I should have done myself! A cock! think of that! why, it's as good as an eight-day clock, for every morning the cock crows at four o'clock, and we shall be able to stir our stumps in good time. What should we do with a goose? I don't know how to cook it; and as for my pillow, I can stuff it with cotton-grass. Run out, child, and put up the cock."

"But, after all, I haven't got the cock," said Gudbrand; "for when I had gone a bit farther, I got as hungry as a hunter, so I was forced to sell the cock for a shilling, for fear I should starve."

"Now, God be praised that you did so!" cried his wife; "whatever you do, you do it always just after my own heart. What should we do with a cock? We are our own masters, I should think, and can lie a-bed in the morning as long as we like. Heaven be thanked that I have got you safe back again! you do everything so well that I want neither cock nor goose; neither pigs nor kine."

Then Gudbrand opened the door and said,

"Well, what do you say now? Have I won the hundred dollars?" and his neighbour was forced to allow that he had.

THE HUSBAND WHO WAS TO MIND THE HOUSE

Wanda Gág made a delightful little book of this story and called it Gone Is Gone.

Once upon a time there was a man so surly and cross, he never thought his wife did anything right in the house. So, one evening in hay-making time, he came home, scolding and swearing, and showing his teeth and making a dust.

"Dear love, don't be so angry; there's a good man," said his goody; "to-morrow let's change our work. I'll go out with the mowers and mow, and you shall mind the house at home."

Yes, the husband thought that would do very well. He was quite willing, he said.

So, early next morning his goody took a scythe over her neck, and went out into the hay-field with the mowers and began to mow; but the man was to mind the house, and do the work at home.

First of all he wanted to churn the butter; but when he had churned a while, he got thirsty, and went down to the cellar to tap a barrel of ale. So, just when he had knocked in the bung, and was putting the tap into the cask, he heard over-head the pig come into the kitchen. Then off he ran up the cellar steps, with the tap in his hand, as fast as he could, to look after the pig, lest it should upset the churn; but when he got up, and saw that the pig had already knocked the churn over, and stood there, routing and grunting amongst the cream which was running all over the floor, he got so wild with rage that he quite forgot the ale-barrel, and ran at the pig as hard as he could. He caught it, too, just as it ran out of doors, and gave it such a kick that piggy lay for dead on the spot. Then all at once he remembered he had the tap in his hand; but when he got down to the cellar, every drop of ale had run out of the cask.

Then he went into the dairy and found enough cream left to fill the churn again, and so he began to churn, for butter they must have at dinner. When he had churned a bit, he remembered that their milking cow was still shut up in the byre, and hadn't had a bit to eat or a

"The Husband Who Was to Mind the House." From *Popular Tales from the Norse* drop to drink all the morning, though the sun was high. Then all at once he thought 'twas too far to take her down to the meadow, so he'd just get her up on the housetop—for the house, you must know, was thatched with sods, and a fine crop of grass was growing there. Now their house lay close up against a steep down, and he thought if he laid a plank across to the thatch at the back he'd easily get the cow up.

But still he couldn't leave the churn, for there was his little babe crawling about on the floor, and "if I leave it," he thought, "the child is sure to upset it." So he took the churn on his back, and went out with it; but then he thought he'd better first water the cow before he turned her out on the thatch; so he took up a bucket to draw water out of the well; but, as he stooped down at the well's brink, all the cream ran out of the churn over his shoulders, and so down into the well.

Now it was near dinner-time, and he hadn't even got the butter yet; so he thought he'd best boil the porridge, and filled the pot with water, and hung it over the fire. When he had done that, he thought the cow might perhaps fall off the thatch and break her legs or her neck. So he got up on the house to tie her up. One end of the rope he made fast to the cow's neck, and the other he slipped down the chimney and tied round his own thigh; and he had to make haste, for the water now began to boil in the pot, and he had still to grind the oatmeal.

So he began to grind away; but while he was hard at it, down fell the cow off the housetop after all, and as she fell, she dragged the man up the chimney by the rope. There he stuck fast; and as for the cow, she hung halfway down the wall, swinging between heaven and earth, for she could neither get down nor up.

And now the goody had waited seven lengths and seven breadths for her husband to come and call them home to dinner; but never a call they had. At last she thought she'd waited long enough, and went home. But when she got there and saw the cow hanging in such an ugly place, she ran up and cut the rope in two with her scythe. But as she did this, down came her husband out of the chimney; and so when his old dame came inside the kitchen, there she found him standing on his head in the porridge-pot.

LITTLE FREDDY
WITH HIS FIDDLE

The Scandinavian tales are full of magic objects which assist those resourceful persons who learn how to use them. Freddy's fiddle is one of the gayest of these.

Once on a time there was a cottager who had an only son, and this lad was weakly, and hadn't much health to speak of; so he couldn't go out to work in the field.

His name was Freddy, and undersized he was too; and so they called him Little Freddy. At home there was little either to bite or sup, and so his father went about the country trying to bind him over as a cow-herd or an errand-boy; but there was no one who would take his son till he came to the sheriff, and he was ready to take him, for he had just packed off his errand-boy, and there was no one who would fill his place, for the story went that he was a skinflint.

But the cottager thought it was better there than nowhere; he would get his food, for all the pay he was to get was his board—there was nothing said about wages or clothes. So when the lad had served three years he wanted to leave, and then the sheriff gave him all his wages at one time. He was to have a penny a year. "It couldn't well be less," said the sheriff. And so he got threepence in all.

As for little Freddy, he thought it was a great sum, for he had never owned so much; but for all that, he asked if he wasn't to have something more.

"You have already had more than you ought to have," said the sheriff.

"Shan't I have anything, then, for clothes?" asked little Freddy; "for those I had on when I came here are worn to rags, and I have had no new ones."

And, to tell the truth, he was so ragged that the tatters hung and flapped about him.

"When you have got what we agreed on," said the sheriff, "and three whole pennies beside, I have nothing more to do with you. Be off!"

But for all that, he got leave just to go into the

"Little Freddy with His Fiddle." From *Tales from the Fjeld*

kitchen and get a little food to put in his script; and after that he set off on the road to buy himself more clothes. He was both merry and glad, for he had never seen a penny before; and every now and then he felt in his pockets as he went along to see if he had them all three. So when he had gone far and farther than far, he got into a narrow dale, with high fells on all sides, so that he couldn't tell if there were any way to pass out; and he began to wonder what there could be on the other side of those fells, and how he ever should get over them.

But up and up he had to go, and on he strode; he was not strong on his legs, and had to rest every now and then—and then he counted and counted how many pennies he had got. So when he had got quite up to the very top, there was nothing but a great plain overgrown with moss. There he sat him down, and began to see if his money was all right; and before he was aware of him a beggar-man came up to him, and he was so tall and big that the lad began to scream and screech when he got a good look of him, and saw his height and length.

"Don't you be afraid," said the beggar-man; "I'll do you no harm. I only beg for a penny, in God's name."

"Heaven help me!" said the lad. "I have only three pennies, and with them I was going to the town to buy clothes."

"It is worse for me than for you," said the beggar-man. "I have got no penny, and I am still more ragged than you."

"Well, then, you shall have it," said the lad.

So when he had walked on awhile he got weary, and sat down to rest again. But when he looked up there he saw another beggar-man, and he was still taller and uglier than the first; and so when the lad saw how very tall and ugly and long he was, he fell a-screeching.

"Now, don't you be afraid of me," said the beggar; "I'll not do you any harm. I only beg for a penny, in God's name."

"Now, may Heaven help me!" said the lad. "I've only got two pence, and with them I was going to the town to buy clothes. If I had only met you sooner, then—"

"It's worse for me than for you," said the beggar-man. "I have no penny, and a bigger body and less clothing."

"Well, you may have it," said the lad.

So he went awhile farther, till he got weary, and then he sat down to rest; but he had scarce sat down than a third beggar-man came to him. He was so tall and ugly and long, that the lad had to look up and up, right up to the sky. And when he took him all in with his eyes, and saw how very, very tall and ugly and ragged he was, he fell a-screeching and screaming again.

"Now, don't you be afraid of me, my lad," said the beggar-man; "I'll do you no harm; for I am only a beggar-man, who begs for a penny in God's name."

"May Heaven help me!" said the lad. "I have only one penny left, and with it I was going to the town to buy clothes. If I had only met you sooner, then—"

"As for that," said the beggar-man, "I have no penny at all, that I haven't, and a bigger body and less clothes, so it is worse for me than for you."

"Yes," said little Freddy, he must have the penny then—there was no help for it; for so each would have what belonged to him, and he would have nothing.

"Well," said the beggar-man, "since you have such a good heart that you gave away all that you had in the world, I will give you a wish for each penny." For you must know it was the same beggar-man who had got them all three; he had only changed his shape each time, that the lad might not know him again.

"I have always had such a longing to hear a fiddle go, and see folk so glad and merry that they couldn't help dancing," said the lad; "and so, if I may wish what I choose, I will wish myself such a fiddle, that everything that has life must dance to its tune."

"That he might have," said the beggar-man; but it was a sorry wish. "You must wish something better for the other two pennies."

"I have always had such a love for hunting and shooting," said little Freddy; "so if I may wish what I choose, I will wish myself such a gun that I shall hit everything I aim at, were it ever so far off."

"That he might have," said the beggar-man; but it was a sorry wish. "You must wish better for the last penny."

"I have always had a longing to be in company

with folk who were kind and good," said little Freddy; "and so, if I could get what I wish, I would wish it to be so that no one can say 'Nay' to the first thing I ask."

"That wish was not so sorry," said the beggarman; and off he strode between the hills, and he saw him no more. And so the lad lay down to sleep, and the next day he came down from the fell with his fiddle and his gun.

First he went to the storekeeper and asked for clothes, and at one farm he asked for a horse, and at another for a sledge; and at this place he asked for a fur coat, and no one said him "Nay" —even the stingiest folk, they were all forced to give him what he asked for. At last he went through the country as a fine gentleman, and had his horse and his sledge; and so when he had gone a bit he met the sheriff with whom he had served.

"Good day, master," said little Freddy, as he pulled up and took off his hat.

"Good day," said the sheriff. And then he went on, "When was I ever your master?"

"Oh, yes," said little Freddy. "Don't you remember how I served you three years for three pence?"

"Heaven help us!" said the sheriff. "How you have got on all of a hurry! And pray, how was it that you got to be such a fine gentleman?"

"Oh, that's telling," said little Freddy.

"And are you full of fun, that you carry a fiddle about with you?" asked the sheriff.

"Yes, yes," said Freddy. "I have always had such a longing to get folk to dance; but the funniest thing of all is this gun, for it brings down almost anything that I aim at, however far it may be off. Do you see that magpie yonder, sitting in the spruce fir? What'll you bet I don't bag it as we stand here?"

On that the sheriff was ready to stake horse and groom, and a hundred dollars beside, that he couldn't do it; but as it was, he would bet all the money he had about him; and he would go to fetch it when it fell—for he never thought it possible for any gun to carry so far.

But as the gun went off down fell the magpie, and into a great bramble thicket; and away went the sheriff up into the brambles after it, and he picked it up and showed it to the lad. But in a trice little Freddy began to scrape his fiddle, and

the sheriff began to dance, and the thorns to tear him; but still the lad played on, and the sheriff danced, and cried, and begged till his clothes flew to tatters, and he scarce had a thread to his back.

"Yes," said little Freddy, "now I think you're about as ragged as I was when I left your service; so now you may get off with what you have got."

But first of all, the sheriff had to pay him what he had wagered that he could not hit the magpie.

So when the lad came to the town he turned aside into an inn, and he began to play, and all who came danced, and he lived merrily and well. He had no care, for no one would say him "Nay" to anything he asked.

But just as they were all in the midst of their fun, up came the watchmen to drag the lad off to the townhall; for the sheriff had laid a charge against him, and said he had waylaid him and robbed him, and nearly taken his life. And now he was to be hanged—they would not hear of anything else. But little Freddy had a cure for all trouble, and that was his fiddle. He began to play on it, and the watchmen fell a-dancing, till they lay down and gasped for breath.

So they sent soldiers and the guard on their way; but it was no better with them than with the watchmen. As soon as ever little Freddy scraped his fiddle, they were all bound to dance, so long as he could lift a finger to play a tune; but they were half dead long before he was tired. At last they stole a march on him, and took him while he lay asleep by night; and when they had caught him, he was doomed to be hanged on the spot, and away they hurried him to the gallows-tree.

There a great crowd of people flocked together to see this wonder, and the sheriff, he too was there; and he was so glad at last at getting amends for the money and the skin he had lost, and that he might see him hanged with his own eyes. But they did not get him to the gallows very fast, for little Freddy was always weak on his legs, and now he made himself weaker still. His fiddle and his gun he had with him also—it was hard to part him from them; and so, when he came to the gallows, and had to mount the steps, he halted on each step; and when he got to the top he sat down, and asked if they could deny him a wish, and if he might have leave to do one thing? He had such a longing, he said, to scrape a tune and play a bar on his fiddle before they hanged him.

"No, no," they said; "it were sin and shame to deny him that." For, you know, no one could gainsay what he asked.

But the sheriff he begged them, for God's sake, not to let him have leave to touch a string, else, it was all over with them altogether; and if the lad got leave, he begged them to bind him to the birch that stood there.

So little Freddy was not slow in getting his fiddle to speak, and all that were there fell a-dancing at once, those who went on two legs, and those who went on four; both the dean and the parson, and the lawyer, and the bailiff, and the sheriff, masters and men, dogs and swine— they all danced and laughed and screeched at one another. Some danced till they lay for dead; some danced till they fell into a swoon. It went badly with all of them, but worst of all with the sheriff; for there he stood bound to the birch, and he danced and scraped great bits off his back against the trunk. There was not one of them who thought of doing anything to little Freddy, and away he went with his fiddle and his gun, just as he chose; and he lived merrily and happily all his days, for there was no one who could say him "Nay" to the first thing he asked for.

EAST O' THE SUN

AND WEST O' THE MOON

This story might well be a fragment of an ancient myth, with the polar bear an obvious symbol of winter in a northern country. The tale is also pure romance and fulfills all the usual desires for food, warmth, luxury, security, and love. Omit three of the winds, if you wish.

Once on a time there was a poor husbandman who had so many children that he hadn't much of either food or clothing to give them. Pretty children they all were, but the prettiest was the youngest daughter, who was so lovely there was no end to her loveliness.

"East o' the Sun and West o' the Moon." From *Popular Tales from the Norse* (slightly adapted)

So one day, 'twas on a Thursday evening late at the fall of the year, the weather was so wild and rough outside, and it was so cruelly dark, and rain fell and wind blew, till the walls of the cottage shook again and again. There they all sat round the fire, busy with this thing and that. But just then, all at once, something gave three taps on the window-pane. Then the father went out to see what was the matter; and, when he got out of doors, what should he see but a great big White Bear.

"Good evening to you," said the White Bear.

"The same to you," said the man.

"Will you give me your youngest daughter? If you will, I'll make you as rich as you are now poor," said the Bear.

Well, the man would not be at all sorry to be so rich; but still he thought he must have a bit of a talk with his daughter first; so he went in and told them how there was a great White Bear waiting outside, who had given his word to make them so rich if he could only have the youngest daughter.

The lassie said "No!" outright. Nothing could get her to say anything else; so the man went out and settled it with the White Bear, that he should come again the next Thursday evening and get an answer. Meantime he talked his daughter over, and kept on telling her of all the riches they would get, and how well off she would be herself; and so at last she thought better of it, and washed and mended her rags, made herself as smart as she could, and was ready to start. I can't say her packing gave her much trouble.

Next Thursday evening came the White Bear to fetch her, and she got upon his back with her bundle, and off they went. So, when they had gone a bit of the way, the White Bear said,

"Are you afraid?"

No, she wasn't.

"Well, mind and hold tight by my shaggy coat, and then there's nothing to fear," said the Bear.

So she rode a long, long way, till they came to a great steep hill. There, on the face of it, the White Bear gave a knock, and a door opened, and they came into a castle, where there were many rooms all lit up; rooms gleaming with silver and gold; and there too was a table ready laid, and it was all as grand as grand could be.

Then the White Bear gave her a silver bell; and when she wanted anything, she was only to ring it, and she would get it at once.

Well, after she had eaten and drunk, and evening wore on, she got sleepy after her journey, and thought she would like to go to bed, so she rang the bell; and she had scarce taken hold of it before she came into a chamber, where there was a bed made, as fair and white as anyone would wish to sleep in, with silken pillows and curtains, and gold fringe. All that was in the room was gold or silver; but when she had gone to bed, and put out the light, she heard someone come into the next room. That was the White Bear, who threw off his beast shape at night; but she never saw him, for he always came after she put out the light, and before the day dawned he was up and off again. So things went on happily for a while; but at last she began to get silent and sorrowful; for there she went about all day alone, and she longed to go home to see her father and mother, and brothers and sisters, and that was why she was so sad and sorrowful, because she couldn't get to them.

"Well, well!" said the Bear, "perhaps there's a cure for all this; but you must promise me one thing, not to talk alone with your mother, but only when the rest are by to hear; for she'll take you by the hand and try to lead you into a room alone to talk; but you must mind and not do that, else you'll bring bad luck on both of us."

So one Sunday, the White Bear came and said now they could set off to see her father and mother. Well, off they started, she sitting on his back; and they went far and long. At last they came to a grand house, and there her brothers and sisters were running about out of doors at play, and everything was so pretty, 'twas a joy to see.

"This is where your father and mother live now," said the White Bear; "but don't forget what I told you, else you'll make us both unlucky."

No, bless you, she'd not forget, and when she had reached the house, the White Bear turned right about and left her.

Then she went in to see her father and mother, and there was such joy, there was no end to it. None of them thought they could thank her enough for all she had done for them. Now, they had everything they wished, as good as good could be, and they all wanted to know how she got on where she lived.

Well, she said, it was very good to live where she did; she had all she wished. What she said beside I don't know; but I don't think any of them had the right end of the stick, or that they got much out of her. But so in the afternoon, after they had done dinner, all happened as the White Bear had said. Her mother wanted to talk with her alone in her bed-room; but she minded what the White Bear had said, and wouldn't go up stairs.

"Oh, what we have to talk about will keep," she said, and put her mother off. But somehow or other, her mother got around her at last, and she had to tell her the whole story. So she said, how every night, when she had gone to a bed, someone came into the next room as soon as she had put out the light, and how she never saw him, because he was always up and away before the morning dawned; and how she went about woeful and sorrowing, for she thought she should so like to see him, and how all day long she walked about there alone, and how dull, and dreary, and lonesome it was.

"My!" said her mother; "perhaps it is a Troll. But now I'll teach you a lesson how to set eyes on him. I'll give you a bit of candle, which you can carry in your bosom. Just light that while he is asleep; but take care not to drop the tallow on him."

Yes, she took the candle, and hid it in her bosom, and as night drew on, the White Bear came and fetched her away.

But when they had gone a bit of the way, the White Bear asked if all hadn't happened as he had said.

Well, she couldn't say it hadn't.

"Now mind," said he, "if you have listened to your mother's advice, you have brought bad luck on us both, and then, all that has passed between us will be as nothing."

"No," she said, "I haven't listened to my mother's advice."

So when she reached home, and had gone to bed, it was the old story over again. There came someone into the next room. So at dead of night, she got up and struck a light, lit the candle, and went into the other room to see for herself who it was. She let the light shine on him, and so she saw that he was the loveliest Prince she had ever set eyes on, and she fell so deep in love with him on the spot, that she thought she couldn't live if she didn't give him a kiss there and then. And so she did; but as she kissed him, she dropped three hot drops of tallow on his shirt, and he woke up.

"What have you done?" he cried; "now you have made us both unlucky, for had you held out only this one year, I had been freed. For I have a stepmother who has bewitched me, so that I am a White Bear by day, and a Man by night. But now all ties are snapt between us; now I must set off from you to her. She lives in a castle which stands EAST O' THE SUN AND WEST O' THE MOON, and there, too, is a Princess, with a nose three ells long, and she's the wife I must have now."

She wept and took it ill, but there was no help for it; go he must.

Then she asked him if she mightn't go with him.

No, she mightn't.

"Tell me the way, then," she said, "and I'll search you out; that surely I may get leave to do."

"Yes," she might do that, he said; but there was no way to that place. It lay EAST O' THE SUN AND WEST O' THE MOON, and thither she'd never find her way.

Next morning when she woke up, both Prince and castle were gone, and there she lay on a little green patch, in the midst of the gloomy thick wood, and by her side lay the same bundle of rags she had brought with her from her old home.

So when she had rubbed the sleep out of her eyes, and wept till she was tired, she set out on her way, and walked many, many days, till she came to a lofty crag. Under it sat an old hag, and played with a gold apple which she tossed about. Her the lassie asked if she knew the way to the Prince, who lived with his stepmother in the castle that lay EAST O' THE SUN AND WEST O' THE MOON, and who was to marry the Princess with a nose three ells long.

"How did you come to know about him?" asked the old hag; "but maybe you are the lassie who ought to have had him?"

Yes, she was.

"So, so; it's you, is it?" said the old hag. "Well, all I know about him is that he lives in the castle that lies EAST O' THE SUN AND WEST O' THE MOON, and thither you'll come late or never; but still you may have the loan of my horse, and on him you may ride to my next neighbour. Maybe she'll be able to tell you; and when you get there, just give the horse a switch under the left ear, and beg him to be off home; and, stay, this gold apple you may take with you."

So she got upon the horse and rode a long, long time, till she came to another crag, under which sat another old hag, with a gold carding-comb. Her the lassie asked if she knew the way to the castle that lay EAST O' THE SUN AND WEST O' THE MOON, and she answered, like the first old hag, that she knew nothing about it, except it was east o' the sun and west o' the moon.

"And thither you'll come, late or never; but you shall have the loan of my horse to my next neighbour; maybe she'll tell you all about it; and when you get there, just switch the horse under the left ear and beg him to be off home."

And this old hag gave her the golden carding-comb; it might be she'd find some use for it, she said. So the lassie got up on the horse, and rode a far, far way, and a weary time; and so at last she came to another great crag, under which sat another hag, spinning with a golden spinning-wheel. Her, too, the lassie asked if she knew the way to the Prince, and where the castle was that lay EAST O' THE SUN AND WEST O' THE MOON. So it was the same thing over again.

"Maybe it's you who ought to have had the Prince?" said the old hag.

Yes, it was.

But she, too, didn't know the way a bit better than the other two. "East o' the sun and west o' the moon it was," she knew—that was all.

"And thither you'll come, late or never; but I'll lend you my horse, and then I think you'd best ride to the East Wind and ask him; maybe he knows those parts, and can blow you thither. But when you get to him, you need only give the horse a switch under the left ear, and he'll trot home of himself."

And so, too, she gave her the gold spinning-wheel. "Maybe you'll find use for it," said the old hag.

Then on she rode many, many days, a weary time, before she got to the East Wind's house; but at last she did reach it, and then she asked the East Wind if he could tell her the way to the Prince who dwelt east o' the sun and west o' the moon. Yes, the East Wind had often heard tell of it, the Prince and the castle, but he couldn't tell the way, for he had never blown so far.

"But, if you will, I'll go to my brother, the West Wind; maybe he knows, for he's much stronger. So, if you will just get on my back, I'll carry you thither."

Yes, she got on his back, and I should just think they went briskly along.

So when they got there, they went into the West Wind's house; and the East Wind said the lassie he had brought was the one who ought to have had the Prince who lived in the castle EAST O' THE SUN AND WEST O' THE MOON; and so she had set out to seek him, and how he had come with her, and would be glad to know if the West Wind knew how to get to the castle.

"Nay," said the West Wind, "so far I've never blown; but if you will, I'll go with you to our brother the South Wind, for he's much stronger than either of us, and he has flapped his wings far and wide. Maybe he'll tell you. You can get on my back, and I'll carry you to him."

Yes, she got on his back, and so they travelled to the South Wind, and were not so very long on the way, I should think.

When they got there, the West Wind asked him if he could tell the lassie the way to the castle that lay EAST O' THE SUN AND WEST O' THE MOON, for it was she who ought to have had the Prince who lived there.

"You don't say so! That's she, is it?" said the South Wind.

"Well, I have blustered about in most places in my time, but so far have I never blown; but if you will, I'll take you to my brother the North Wind; he is the oldest and strongest of the whole lot of us, and if he doesn't know where it is, you'll never find any one in the world to tell you. You can get on my back, and I'll carry you thither."

Yes! she got on his back and away he went from his house at a fine rate. And this time, too, she wasn't long on her way.

When they got to the North Wind's house, he

was so wild and cross, cold puffs came from him a long way off.

"BLAST YOU BOTH, WHAT DO YOU WANT?" he roared out to them ever so far off, so that it struck them with an icy shiver.

"Well," said the South Wind, "you needn't be so foul-mouthed, for here I am, your brother, the South Wind, and here is the lassie who ought to have had the Prince who dwells in the castle that lies EAST O' THE SUN AND WEST O' THE MOON; and now she wants to ask you if you ever were there, and can tell her the way, for she would be so glad to find him again."

"YES, I KNOW WELL ENOUGH WHERE IT IS," said the North Wind; "once in my life I blew an aspen-leaf thither, but I was so tired I couldn't blow a puff for ever so many days after. But if you really wish to go thither, and aren't afraid to come along with me, I'll take you on my back and see if I can blow you thither."

Yes! with all her heart; she must and would get thither if it were possible in any way; and as for fear, however madly he went, she wouldn't be at all afraid.

"Very well, then," said the North Wind, "but you must sleep here to-night, for we must have the whole day before us, if we're to get thither at all."

Early the next morning the North Wind woke her, and puffed himself up, and blew himself out, and made himself so stout and big, 'twas gruesome to look at him; and so off they went high up through the air as if they would never stop till they got to the world's end.

Down below there was such a storm; it threw down long tracts of wood and many houses, and when it swept over the great sea, ships foundered by hundreds.

So they tore on and on—no one can believe how far they went—and all the while they still went over the sea, and the North Wind got more and more weary, and so out of breath he could scarce bring out a puff; and his wings drooped and drooped, till at last he sank so low that the crests of the waves dashed over his heels.

"Are you afraid?" said the North Wind.

No, she wasn't.

But they weren't very far from land; and the North Wind had still enough strength left in him that he managed to throw her up on the

shore under the windows of the castle which lay EAST o' THE SUN AND WEST o' THE MOON; but then he was so weak and worn out, he had to stay there and rest many days before he could get home again.

Next morning the lassie sat down under the castle window and began to play with the gold apple; and the first person she saw was the Long-nose who was to have the Prince.

"What do you want for your gold apple, you lassie?" said the Long-nose, and threw up the window.

"It's not for sale, for gold or money," said the lassie.

"If it's not for sale for gold or money, what is it that you will sell it for? You may name your own price," said the Princess.

"Well! if I may get to the Prince who lives here and be with him to-night, you shall have it," said the lassie whom the North Wind had brought.

Yes! she might; that could be done. So the Princess got the gold apple; but when the lassie came up to the Prince's bed-room at night he was fast asleep; she called him and shook him, and

between whiles she wept sore; but all she could do wouldn't wake him up. Next morning as soon as day broke, came the Princess with the long nose, and drove her out again.

So in the day-time she sat down under the castle windows and began to card with her golden carding-comb, and the same thing happened. The Princess asked what she wanted for it; and she said it wasn't for sale for gold or money, but if she might get leave to go to the Prince and be with him that night, the Princess should have it. But when she went up, she found him asleep again, and all she called, and all she shook, and wept, and prayed, she couldn't get life into him; and as soon as the first gray peep of day came, then came the Princess with the long nose, and chased her out again.

So in the day-time, the lassie sat down outside under the castle window, and began to spin with her golden spinning-wheel, and that, too, the Princess with the long nose wanted to have. So she threw up the window and asked what she wanted for it. The lassie said, as she had said twice before, it wasn't for sale for gold or money; but if she might go up to the Prince who was there, and be with him alone that night, she might have it.

Yes! she might do that and welcome. But now you must know there were some Christian folk who had been carried off thither, and as they sat in their room, which was next the Prince, they had heard how a girl had been in there, and wept and prayed, and called to him two nights running, and they told that to the Prince.

That evening when the Princess came with her sleeping potion, the Prince made as if he drank, but threw it over his shoulder for he could guess it was a sleeping potion. So, when the lassie came in, she found the Prince wide awake; and then she told him the whole story of how she had come thither.

"Ah," said the Prince, "you've just come in the very nick of time, for to-morrow is to be our wedding-day; and now I won't have the Long-nose, for you are the only lassie in the world who can set me free. I'll say I want to see what my wife is fit for, and beg her to wash the shirt which has the three spots of tallow on it; she'll say yes, for she doesn't know 'tis you who put them there; but that's a work only for Christian folk, and not for a pack of Trolls; and so I'll say that I won't have any other for my bride than the woman who can wash them out, and ask you to do it."

The next day, when the wedding was to be, the Prince said,

"First of all, I'd like to see what my bride is fit for."

"Yes," said the step-mother with all her heart.

"Well," said the Prince, "I've got a fine shirt which I'd like for my wedding shirt; but somehow or other it has got three spots of tallow on it, which I must have washed out; and I have sworn never to take any other bride than the woman who's able to do that. If she can't, she's not worth having."

Well, that was no great thing, they said; so they agreed, and she with the long nose began to wash away as hard as she could, but the more she rubbed and scrubbed, the bigger the spots grew.

"Ah!" said the old hag, her mother, "you can't wash; let me try."

But she hadn't long taken the shirt in hand before it got far worse than ever, and with all her rubbing, and wringing, and scrubbing, the spots grew bigger and blacker, and the darker and uglier was the shirt.

Then all the Trolls began to wash, but the longer they washed, the blacker and uglier the shirt grew, till at last it was as black all over as if it had been up the chimney.

"Ah!" said the Prince, "you're none of you worth a straw; you can't wash. Why there, outside, sits a beggar lassie; I'll be bound she knows how to wash better than the whole lot of you. COME IN, LASSIE!" he shouted.

Well, in she came.

"Can you wash this shirt, lassie, you?" said he.

"I don't know," she said, "but I think I can."

And almost before she had taken it and dipped it in the water, it was as white as driven snow, and whiter still.

"Yes; you are the lassie for me," said the Prince.

At that the old hag flew into such a rage, she burst on the spot, and the Princess with the long nose after her, and the whole pack of Trolls after her—at least I have never heard a word about them since.

As for the Prince and the lassie, they took with them all the silver and gold, and flitted away as far as they could from the castle that lay East o' the Sun and West o' the Moon.

THE MOST OBEDIENT WIFE

The other stories in this group have all been Norwegian. This one is Danish and certainly a most amusing variant of "The Taming of the Shrew" theme. For the sake of the girls, be sure to follow it with the Czech "Clever Manka."

Long ago there was a rich farmer who had three daughters, all grown up and marriageable, and all three very pretty. The eldest of them was the prettiest, and she was also the cleverest, but she was so quarrelsome and obstinate, that there was never any peace in the house. She constantly contradicted her father, who was a kind, peace-loving man, and she quarrelled with her sisters, although they were very good-natured girls.

Many wooers came to the farm, and one of them wished to marry the eldest daughter. The farmer said that he had no objection to him as a son-in-law, but at the same time he thought it his duty to tell the suitor the truth. Accordingly he warned him that his eldest daughter was so violent and strong-minded that no one could live in peace with her. As some compensation for these faults, she would receive three hundred pounds more in her dowry than would her two sisters. That was, of course, very attractive, but the young man thought over the matter and, after he had been visiting the house for some time, he altered his mind and asked for the hand of the second daughter. The daughter accepted him, and, as her father was willing, the two became man and wife and lived very happily together.

Then came another wooer, from another part of the country, and he also wanted to marry the eldest daughter. The father warned him, as he had cautioned the first wooer; telling him that she would receive three hundred pounds more than her youngest sister, but that he must be careful, for she was so stubborn and quarrelsome that nobody could live in peace with her. So the

"The Most Obedient Wife." From *Danish Fairy Tales* by Svend Grundtvig. Thomas Y. Crowell Company, New York. Reprinted by permission of the publisher

second wooer changed his mind and asked for the hand of the youngest daughter. They married shortly after and lived happily and peacefully together.

The eldest sister was now alone with her father, but she did not treat him any better than before, and grew even more ill-humoured because her two sisters had found favour in the eyes of the first two wooers. She was obstinate and quarrelsome, violent and bad-tempered, and she grew more so from day to day.

At last another wooer came, and he was neither from their own district nor even from their country, but from a distant land. He went to the farmer and asked for the hand of his eldest daughter. "I do not want her to marry at all," said the father, "it would be a shame to allow her to do so; she is so ill-tempered and violent that no human being could live in peace with her and I do not want to be the cause of such unhappiness." But the wooer remained firm; he wanted her, he said, whatever her faults might be. At length the father yielded, provided that his daughter were willing to marry the young man, for, after all, he would be glad to get rid of her, and as he had told the suitor the whole truth about her, his conscience was clear. Accordingly, the young man wooed the girl, and she did not hesitate long, but accepted the offer, for she was tired of sitting at home a despised and spurned spinster.

The wooer said that he had no time to remain with them just then, as he must return home at once, and, as soon as the wedding day was fixed, he rode away. He also told them not to wait for him at the farm on the day of the wedding, he would appear in good time at the church. When the day came the farmer drove with his daughter to the church, where a great company of wedding guests had assembled; the bride's sisters and brothers-in-law were there, and all the village people arrived in their Sunday clothes. The bridegroom was there also, but in ordinary travelling garments; and so the couple walked up to the altar and were married.

As soon as the ceremony was over, the bridegroom took his young wife by the hand and led her out of the church. He sent a message to his father-in-law asking him to excuse their absence from the marriage feast, as they had no time to waste. He had not driven in a coach, as is the custom at weddings, but travelled on horseback, on a fine big grey horse, with an ordinary saddle, and a couple of pistols in the saddlebags. He had brought no friends or relations with him, only a big dog, that lay beside the horse during the ceremony. The bridegroom lifted his bride on to the pommel, as if she had been a feather, jumped into the saddle, put the spurs to his horse and rode off with the dog trotting behind. The marriage party standing at the church door looked after them, and shook their heads in amazement. Then they got into their carriages, drove back to the house, and partook of the marriage feast without bride or bridegroom.

The bride did not like this at all, but as she did not want to quarrel with her bridegroom so soon, she held her tongue for a time; but as he did not speak either, she at last broke the ice and said that it was a very fine horse they were riding. "Yes," he replied; "I have seven other horses at home in my stables, but this is my favourite; it is the most valuable of all, and I like it best." Then she remarked that she liked the beautiful dog also. "It is indeed a jewel of a dog," he said, "and has cost me a lot of money."

After a while they came to a forest, where the bridegroom sprang from his horse and cut a thin switch from a willow-tree. This he wound three times round his finger, then tied it with a thread and gave it to his bride, saying: "This is my wedding gift to you. Take good care of it, and carry it about with you always! You will not repent it." She thought it a strange wedding gift, but put it in her pocket, and they rode on again. Presently the bride dropped her glove, and the bridegroom said to the dog: "Pick it up, Fido!" But the dog took no notice, and left the glove on the ground. Then his master drew his pistol from the holster, shot the dog, and rode on, leaving it lying dead. "How could you be so cruel?" said his bride. "I never say a thing twice," was the reply, and they journeyed on in silence.

After some time they came to a running stream that they had to cross. There being only a ford, and no bridge, the man said to his horse: "Take good care! Not a drop must soil my bride's dress!" When they had crossed, however, the dress was badly soiled, and the husband lifted his bride from the horse, drew out the other pistol and shot the horse, so that it fell dead to the ground. "Oh, the poor horse!" cried the bride. "Yes, but I never say a thing twice," answered her husband. Then he took saddle, bridle, and cover from the horse; bridle and cover he carried himself, but the saddle he gave to his young wife, and said: "You can carry that; we shall soon be home." He walked on in silence, and the bride quickly put the saddle on her back and followed him; she had no desire to make him say it twice.

Soon they arrived at his dwelling place, a very fine farm. The menservants and maidservants rushed to the door and received them, and the husband said to them: "See, this is my wife and your mistress. Whatever she tells you, you are to do, just as if I had ordered it." Then he led her indoors and showed her everything—living-rooms and bedrooms, kitchen and cellar, brew-house and dairy—and said to her: "You will look after everything indoors, I attend to everything out-of-doors," and then they sat down to supper, and soon after went to bed.

Days, weeks and months passed; the young wife attended to all household matters while her husband looked after the farm, and not a single angry word passed between them. The servants had been accustomed to obey their master implicitly, and now they obeyed their mistress likewise, and so six months passed without there having arisen any necessity for the husband to say the same thing twice to his wife. He was always kind and polite to her, and she was always gentle and obedient.

One day he said to her: "Would you not like to visit your relations?" "Yes, dear husband, I should like to do so very much, if it is convenient," she replied. "It is quite convenient," he said, "but you have never mentioned it. It shall be done at once; get ready, while I have the horses put to the carriage." He went to the stable and saw to everything, while his wife ran upstairs to dress as quickly as possible for the journey. The husband drove up, cracked his whip and asked: "Are you ready?" "Yes, dear," came the reply, and she came running out and entered the carriage. She had not quite finished dressing and carried some of her things in her hand, and these she put on in the carriage.

Then they started. When they had driven nearly half the distance, they saw a great flock of ravens flying across the road. "What beautiful white birds!" said the husband. "No, they are black, dear!" said his wife. "I think it is going to rain," he said, turned the horses, and drove home again. She understood perfectly why he had done so; it was the first time that she had contradicted him, but she showed no resentment, and the two conversed in quite a friendly fashion all the way home. The horses were put into the stable—and it did not rain.

When a month had passed, the husband said one morning: "I believe it is going to be fine to-day. Would you not like to visit your relations?" She wished to do so very much indeed, and she hastened a little more than the last time, so that when her husband drove up and cracked his whip, she was quite ready and mounted the carriage beside him. They had driven considerably more than half the distance, when they met a large flock of sheep and lambs. "What a fine pack of wolves!" said the husband. "You mean sheep, dear!" said the wife. "I think it will rain before evening," said the husband, looking up at the sky. "It will be better for us to drive home again." With these words he turned the horses and drove back home. They conversed in a friendly manner until they reached home; but it did not rain.

When another month had passed, the husband said one morning to his wife: "We really must see whether we cannot manage to visit your relations. What do you say to our driving across to-day? It looks as though the day would be fine." His wife thought so too; she was ready very soon and they set out. They had not travelled far when they saw a great flock of swans flying along over their heads. "That was a fine flock of storks," said the husband. "Yes, so it was, dear," said his wife, and they drove on; there was no change in the weather that day, so that they reached her father's farm in due course. He received them joyfully and sent at once for his two other daughters and their husbands, and a very merry family meeting it was.

The three married sisters went into the kitchen together, because they could talk more freely there, and they had a great deal to tell each other; the two younger ones in particular had many questions to ask their elder sister, because they had not seen her for a very long time. Then they helped to prepare the dinner; it goes without saying that nothing was too good for this festive occasion.

The three brothers-in-law sat meanwhile with their father-in-law in the sitting-room and they, too, had much to tell and ask each other. Then said the old farmer: "This is the first time that you have all three been gathered together under my roof, and I should like to ask you frankly how you are pleased with your wives." The husbands who had married the two younger, good-tempered sisters said at once that they were perfectly satisfied and lived very happily. "But how do you get on with yours?" the father-in-law asked the husband of the eldest sister. "Nobody ever married a better wife than I did," was the reply. "Well, I should like to see which of you has the most obedient wife," said the father-in-law, and then he fetched a heavy silver jug and filled it to the top with gold and silver coins. This he placed in the middle of the table before the three men, and said that he would give it to him who had the most obedient wife.

They put the matter to the test at once. The husband who had married the youngest sister went to the kitchen door and called: "Will you come here a moment, Gerda, please; as quickly as possible!" "All right, I am coming," she answered, but it was some time before she came, because as she explained, she had first to talk about something with one of her sisters. "What do you want with me?" she asked. The husband made some excuse, and she went out again.

Now it was the turn of the man who had married the middle sister. "Please come here a moment, Margaret!" he called. She also answered: "Yes, I am coming at once," but it was a good while before she came; she had had something in her hands and was compelled to put it down first. The husband invented some excuse, and she went out again.

Then the third husband went to the kitchen door, opened it slightly and just said: "Christine!"—"Yes!" she answered, as she stood there with a large dish of food in her hands. "Take this from me!" she said quickly to her sisters, but they looked at her in amazement and did not take the dish. Bang! she dropped it right on the middle of the kitchen floor, rushed into the room and asked: "What do you wish, dear?" —"Oh, I only wanted to see you," he said, "but since you are here, you may as well take that jug standing on the table; it is yours, with all that is in it.—You might also show us what you got from me as a marriage gift on your wedding day."—"Yes, dear, here it is," she said, and drew the willow ring from her bosom, where she had kept it ever since. The husband handed it to his father-in-law and asked: "Can you put that ring straight?"—No, that was impossible without breaking it. "Well, you see now," said the husband, "if I had not bent the twig when it was green, I could not have made it into this shape."

After that they sat down to a merry meal, then the husband of the oldest sister returned home with her, and they lived for many years very happily together.

French folk tales

"Sleeping Beauty," "Cinderella," and "The Master Cat" are taken from Perrault's versions of eight French folk tales. "Beauty and the Beast" and "The White Cat" are by two well-known French women and mark the beginning of the modern fanciful tale, although both suggest folk origin. Mme. de Beaumont wisely kept her "Beauty and the Beast" close to the simplicity of the traditional tale. "The White Cat" by Mme. d'Aulony is more elaborate and sophisticated but still retains much of the magic formula of folk tale construction. "The Mouse-Princess" and "The Grey Palfrey" are taken from Barbara Picard's recent collection of traditional French legends and stories. These two stories and "The White Cat" are for the oldest children, twelve to fourteen, while the others belong to the usual fairy tale age—eight to ten.

THE SLEEPING BEAUTY
IN THE WOOD

This version omits the second episode in which the ogress (Night) eats up Beauty's children (Dawn and Day) and threatens Beauty (the Sun), since that section is not suitable for telling to children. However, students of folklore will be interested in the omitted section, which is a clear evidence of myth origin.

There were formerly a king and a queen, who were sorry they had no children; so sorry that it cannot be expressed. They went to all the waters in the world; vows, pilgrimages, all ways were tried, and all to no purpose.

At last, however, the queen had a daughter. There was a very fine christening; and the princess had for her godmothers all the fairies they could find in the whole kingdom—they found seven. By this means the princess had all the perfections imaginable.

After the christening, all the company returned to the king's palace, where was prepared a great feast for the fairies. There was placed before every one of them a magnificent cover with a case of massive gold, wherein were a spoon, knife and fork, all of pure gold set with diamonds and rubies. But as they were sitting down at table they saw come into the hall a very old fairy, who had not been invited. It was above fifty years since she had been seen, and she was believed to be either dead or enchanted.

The king ordered her a cover, but could not furnish her with a case of gold because seven only had been made for the seven fairies. The old fairy fancied she was slighted and muttered some threats between her teeth. One of the young fairies, who sat by her, overheard how she grumbled. Judging that she might give the little princess some unlucky gift the young fairy went, as soon as they rose from the table, and hid herself behind the hangings, that she might speak last and repair, as much as she could, any evil which the old fairy intended.

"The Sleeping Beauty in the Wood." From *The Blue Fairy Book* edited by Andrew Lang. Used by permission of Longmans, Green and Company, Inc.

Meanwhile all the fairies began to give their gifts to the princess. The youngest for her gift said that the princess should be the most beautiful person in the world; the next, that she should have the wit of an angel; the third, that she should have wonderful grace in everything she did; the fourth, that she should dance perfectly; the fifth, that she should sing like a nightingale; and the sixth, that she should play all kinds of music to perfection.

The old fairy's turn coming next, with her head shaking more with spite than age, she said that the princess should have her hand pierced with a spindle and die of the wound. This terrible gift made the whole company tremble, and everybody fell a-crying.

At this very instant the young fairy came out from behind the hangings, and spoke these words aloud:

"Assure yourselves, O King and Queen, that your daughter shall not die. It is true, I have no power to undo entirely what my elder has done. The princess shall indeed pierce her hand with a spindle. But instead of dying, she shall only fall into a profound sleep, which shall last a hundred years. After a hundred years a king's son shall come and wake her."

The king, to avoid misfortune, immediately forbade spinning with a distaff and spindle, or to have so much as a spindle in the house. About fifteen or sixteen years after, the king and queen being gone to one of their pleasure houses, the young princess was diverting herself by running up and down the palace. She came into a little room at the top of the tower, where a good old woman was spinning with her spindle. This good woman had never heard of the king's proclamation against spindles.

"What are you doing there, goody?" said the princess.

"I am spinning, my pretty child," said the old woman.

"Ha," said the princess, "this is very pretty. How do you do it? Give it to me so I may see."

She had no sooner taken the spindle than it ran into her hand, and she fell down in a swoon.

The good old woman cried out for help. People came and threw water upon the princess' face, unlaced her, struck her on the palms of her hands, and rubbed her temples with Hungary water. But nothing would bring her to herself.

And now the king, who came up at the noise, bethought himself of the prediction of the fairies and, judging very well that this must necessarily come to pass since the fairies had said it, caused the princess to be carried into the finest apartment in his palace and laid upon a bed all embroidered with gold and silver.

One would have taken her for a little angel, she was so very beautiful, for her swooning had not dimmed her complexion: her cheeks were carnation and her lips were coral. Indeed her eyes were shut, but she was heard to breathe softly, which satisfied those about her she was not dead. The king commanded them not to disturb her, but let her sleep quietly till her hour of awakening was come.

The good fairy, who had saved the life of the princess by condemning her to sleep a hundred years, was in the kingdom of Matakin, twelve thousand leagues off, when this accident befell the princess. But she was instantly informed of it by a little dwarf, who had boots with which he could go seven leagues in one stride. The fairy came immediately, in a fiery chariot drawn by dragons.

The king handed her out of the chariot, and she approved everything he had done. But she touched with her wand everything in the palace —except the king and queen—governesses, maids of honor, ladies of the bed-chamber, gentlemen, officers, stewards, cooks, undercooks, scullions, guards with their beefeaters, pages, footmen. She likewise touched all the horses in the stables, the great dogs in the outward court and pretty little Mopsey too, the princess' little spaniel, which lay by her on the bed.

Immediately upon her touching them they all fell asleep that they might not awake before their mistress and might be ready to wait upon her when she wanted them. The very spits at the fire, as full as they could hold of partridges and pheasants, fell asleep also. All this was done in a moment. Fairies are not long in doing their magic.

And now the king and the queen, having kissed their dear child without waking her, went out of the palace, and in a quarter of an hour's time there grew up all round about the park such a vast number of trees, great and small, bushes and brambles, twining one with another, that neither man nor beast could pass through. Nothing could be seen but the very tops of the towers, and those only from a great distance.

When a hundred years were gone and passed the son of the king then reigning, who was of another family, being gone a-hunting, asked what those towers were which he saw in the middle of a great thick wood?

All answered according to the story they had heard. Some said it was a ruinous old castle, haunted by spirits; others, that all the sorcerers and witches of the country kept their night meetings there. The common opinion was that an ogre lived there, who carried thither all the little children he could catch.

The prince was at a loss, not knowing what to believe, when a very aged countryman spoke to him:

"May it please Your Royal Highness, it is now about fifty years since I heard from my father, who heard my grandfather say, there was in this castle a princess, who must sleep there a hundred years, and should be awakened by a king's son."

The young prince was all on fire at these words. Believing in this rare adventure, and pushed on by love and honor, he resolved that moment to look into it. Scarce had he advanced toward the wood when all the great trees, the bushes and brambles gave way of themselves to let him pass. He walked up a long avenue to the castle. What surprised him a little was that he saw none of his people could follow him. The trees closed behind him again as soon as he had passed through. However, he did not cease from continuing his way; a young prince is always valiant.

He came into a spacious outward court, where everything he saw might have frozen the most fearless person with horror. There was a frightful silence, and there was nothing to be seen but stretched-out bodies of men and animals, all seeming to be dead. He knew, however, by the ruby faces of the beefeaters, that they were only asleep; and their goblets, wherein still remained some drops of wine, showed plainly that they fell asleep in their cups.

The prince then crossed a court paved with marble, went up the stairs, and came into the guard chamber, where guards were standing in their ranks, with their muskets upon their shoulders, and snoring as loud as they could. After that he went through several rooms full of gentlemen and ladies, all asleep, some standing, others sitting. At last he came into a chamber all gilded with gold, where he saw upon a bed, the curtains of which were open, the finest sight a young prince ever beheld—a princess, who appeared to be about fifteen or sixteen years of age, and whose bright and resplendent beauty had somewhat in it divine. He approached with trembling and admiration and fell down before her upon his knees.

And now, as the enchantment was at an end, the princess awoke, and looking on him with eyes more tender than the first view might seem to admit, "Is it you, my Prince?" said she. "I have waited a long while."

The prince, charmed with these words, and much more with the manner in which they were spoken, knew not how to show his joy and gratitude. He assured her he loved her better than he did himself. Their discourse was not well connected, they did weep more than talk—little eloquence, a great deal of love. He was more at a loss than she, and we need not wonder at it: she had time to think on what to say to him; for it is very probable—though history mentions nothing of it—that the good fairy, during so long a sleep, had given her very agreeable dreams. In short, they talked four hours together, and yet they said not half what they had to say.

Meanwhile all the palace awoke; everyone thought upon their particular business, and as all of them were not in love they were ready to die for hunger. The chief lady of honor, being as sharp set as other folks, grew very impatient and told the princess loudly that supper was served. The prince helped the princess to rise. She was dressed magnificently, but his royal highness took care not to tell her she was dressed like his great-grandmother and had a point band peeping over a high collar. She looked not a bit the less charming and beautiful for all that.

They went into the great hall of looking glasses, where they supped, and were served by the princess' officers. The violins and hautboys played old tunes, very excellent, even though it was now above a hundred years since they had been played. After they had feasted, the whole court assembled in the chapel of the castle where the lord almoner married Beauty to the prince. In due time, the prince carried his bride away to his own kingdom where they lived in great happiness ever after.

CINDERELLA or
THE LITTLE GLASS SLIPPER

Here is the favorite theme of fiction writers of every age—the misunderstood, lowly maiden who finally comes into her own. No wonder folk tales record 345 variants of this story. Popular magazines, soap operas, and moving pictures are still overworking this theme. This French version is probably the first one recorded in European countries and remains the favorite.

Once there was a gentleman who married, for his second wife, the proudest and most haughty woman that was ever seen. She had, by a former husband, two daughters of her own humor, who were, indeed, exactly like her in all things. He had likewise a young daughter but of unparalleled goodness and sweetness of temper, which she took from her mother, who was the best creature in the world.

No sooner were the ceremonies of the wedding over but the mother began to show herself in her true colors. She could not bear the good qualities of this pretty girl, and all the less because they made her own daughters appear the more odious. She employed her in the meanest work of the house: scouring the dishes and tables and scrubbing madam's room, also those of her daughters. The girl slept in a sorry garret, upon a wretched straw bed, while her sisters lay in fine rooms, with floors all inlaid, upon beds of the very newest fashion, and where they had looking glasses so large they might see themselves at full length from head to foot.

The poor girl bore all patiently and dared not

"Cinderella or The Little Glass Slipper." From *The Blue Fairy Book* edited by Andrew Lang. Used by permission of Longmans, Green and Company, Inc.

tell her father who would have rattled her off, for his wife governed him entirely. When she had done her work, she used to go into the chimney corner and sit down among cinders and ashes, which caused her to be called Cinderwench. But the younger, who was not so rude and uncivil as the elder, called her Cinderella. However, Cinderella, notwithstanding her mean apparel, was a hundred times handsomer than her sisters, though they were always dressed very richly.

It happened that the king's son gave a ball and invited all persons of fashion to it. The two sisters were also invited, for they cut a very grand figure among the quality. They were delighted at this invitation and wonderfully busy in choosing such gowns, petticoats and headdresses as might become them. This was a new trouble to Cinderella, for it was she who ironed her sisters' linen and plaited their ruffles, while they talked all day long of nothing but how they should be dressed.

"For my part," said the elder, "I will wear my red-velvet suit with French trimming."

"And I," said the younger, "shall have my usual petticoat. But then, to make amends for that, I will put on my gold-flowered manteau, and my diamond stomacher, which is far from being the most ordinary one in the world."

They sent for the best tirewoman they could get to make up their headdresses and adjust their double pinners, and they had their red brushes and patches from Mademoiselle de la Poche.

Cinderella was likewise consulted in all these matters, for she had excellent notions, and advised them always for the best and offered her services to dress their hair, which they were very willing she should do. As she was doing this, they said to her:

"Cinderella, would you not like to go to the ball?"

"Alas," she said, "you only jeer at me. It is not for such as I to go thither."

"You are in the right of it," replied they. "It would certainly make people laugh to see a cinderwench at a palace ball."

Anyone but Cinderella would have dressed their heads awry, but she was very good and dressed them perfectly. They were almost two days without eating, so much were they transported with joy. They broke above a dozen of

laces in trying to be laced up close, that they might have a fine slender shape, and they were continually at their looking glass. At last the happy day came. They went to court, and Cinderella followed them with her eyes as long as she could, and when she had lost sight of them, she fell a-crying.

Her godmother, who saw her all in tears, asked her what was the matter.

"I wish I could—I wish I could—" She was not able to speak the rest, being interrupted by her tears and sobbing.

This godmother of hers, who was a fairy, said to her, "You wish to go to the ball. Is it not so?"

"Yes," cried Cinderella, with a great sigh.

"Well," said her godmother, "be a good girl, and I will contrive that you shall go." Then she said to her, "Run into the garden and bring me a pumpkin."

Cinderella went immediately to gather the finest one and brought it to her godmother, not being able to imagine how this pumpkin could make her go to the ball. Her godmother scooped out all the inside of it, leaving nothing but the rind; which done, she struck it with her wand, and the pumpkin was instantly turned into a fine coach, gilded all over with gold.

She then went to look into her mousetrap, where she found six mice, all alive. She told Cinderella to lift up the little trap door, when, giving each mouse, as it went out, a little tap with her wand, the mouse was at that moment turned into a fine horse. Altogether they made a very fine set of six horses of a beautiful mouse-colored gray.

Being at a loss for a coachman, Cinderella said, "I will go and see if there is a rat in the rat-trap—we may make a coachman of him."

"You are in the right," replied her godmother. "Go and look."

Cinderella brought the trap to her, and in it there were three huge rats. The fairy made choice of the one which had the largest beard, and having touched him with her wand, he was turned into a fat, jolly coachman, who had the smartest whiskers eyes ever beheld. After that, she said to her:

"Go again into the garden, and you will find six lizards behind the watering pot; bring them to me."

Cinderella had no sooner done so than her godmother turned them into six footmen, who skipped up immediately behind the coach, with their liveries all covered with gold and silver. They clung as close behind each other as if they had done nothing else their whole lives. The fairy then said to Cinderella:

"Well, you see here an equipage fit to take you to the ball. Are you not pleased with it?"

"Oh, yes," cried Cinderella, "but must I go thither as I am, in these old rags?"

Her godmother just touched her with her wand, and at the same instant her clothes were turned into cloth of gold and silver, all beset with jewels. This done, she gave her a pair of glass slippers, the prettiest in the whole world. Being thus decked out, Cinderella climbed into her coach, but her godmother, above all things, commanded her not to stay till after midnight, telling her, at the same time, that if she stayed one moment longer, the coach would be a pumpkin again, her horses mice, her coachman a rat, her footmen lizards, and her clothes would become just as they were before.

Cinderella promised her godmother she would not fail to leave the ball before midnight. And then away she drove, scarce able to contain herself for joy. The king's son, who was told that a great princess, whom nobody knew, had come, ran out to receive her. He gave her his hand as she alighted from the coach and led her into the hall, among all the company. There was immediately a profound silence. They left off dancing, and the violins ceased to play, so attentive was everyone to contemplate the singular beauties of the unknown newcomer. Nothing was then heard but the confused noise of:

"Ha! How handsome she is! Ha! How handsome she is!"

The king himself, old as he was, could not help watching her and telling the queen softly that it was a long time since he had seen so beautiful and lovely a creature. All the ladies were busied in considering her clothes and headdress, that they might have some made next day after the same pattern, provided they could meet with such fine materials and find able hands to make them.

The king's son conducted her to the most honorable seat, and afterward took her out to dance with him, and she danced so gracefully that all more and more admired her. A fine collation was served, whereof the young prince ate not a morsel, so intently was he busied in gazing on Cinderella.

She sat down by her sisters, showing them a thousand civilities, giving them part of the oranges and citrons with which the prince had presented her, which very much surprised them, for they did not know her. While Cinderella was thus amusing her sisters, she heard the clock strike eleven and three-quarters, whereupon she immediately made a curtsy to the company and hastened away as fast as she could.

Reaching home, she ran to seek out her godmother and, after having thanked her, said she could not but heartily wish she might go the next day to the ball, because the king's son had asked her. As she was eagerly telling her godmother whatever had passed at the ball, her two sisters knocked at the door, which Cinderella ran and opened.

"How long you have stayed!" cried she, rubbing her eyes and stretching herself as if she had been just waked out of her sleep. She had not, however, had any inclination to sleep since they went from home.

"If you had been at the ball," said one of her sisters, "you would not have been tired with it. There came thither the finest princess, the most beautiful ever seen with mortal eyes; she showed us a thousand civilities and gave us oranges and citrons."

Cinderella seemed very indifferent in the matter but asked them the name of that princess. They told her they did not know it and that the king's son would give all the world to know who she was. At this Cinderella, smiling, replied:

"She must, then, be very beautiful indeed. How happy you have been! Could not I see her? Ah, dear Miss Charlotte, do lend me your yellow clothes which you wear every day."

"Ay, to be sure," cried Miss Charlotte, "lend my clothes to a dirty cinderwench! I should be a fool."

Cinderella, indeed, expected such an answer and was very glad of the refusal, for she would have been sadly put to it if her sister had done what she asked for jestingly.

The next day the two sisters were at the ball,

and so was Cinderella, but dressed more magnificently than before. The king's son was always by her and never ceased his compliments and kind speeches to her. All this was so far from being tiresome that she quite forgot what her godmother had commanded her. At last, she counted the clock striking twelve when she took it to be no more than eleven. She then rose up and fled, as nimble as a deer. The prince followed but could not overtake her. She left behind one of her glass slippers which the prince took up most carefully. Cinderella reached home, quite out of breath, and in her old clothes, having nothing left of all her finery but one of the little slippers, fellow to the one she had dropped.

The guards at the palace gate were asked if they had not seen a princess go out. They had seen nobody but a young girl, very meanly dressed, and who had more the air of a poor country wench than a gentlewoman.

When the two sisters returned from the ball Cinderella asked them if they had been well diverted, and if the fine lady had been there. They told her, yes, but that she hurried away immediately when it struck twelve and with so much haste that she dropped one of her little glass slippers, the prettiest in the world. The king's son had taken it up. He had done nothing but look at her all the time at the ball, and most certainly he was very much in love with the beautiful girl who owned the glass slipper.

What they said was very true, for a few days afterward the king's son caused it to be proclaimed, by sound of trumpet, that he would marry her whose foot this slipper fit. They whom he employed began to try it upon the princesses, then the duchesses, and all the court, but in vain. It was brought to the two sisters, who each did all she possibly could to thrust her foot into the slipper. But they could not effect it. Cinderella, who saw all this, and knew her slipper, said to them, laughing:

"Let me see if it will not fit me."

Her sisters burst out laughing and began to banter her. The gentleman who was sent to try the slipper looked earnestly at Cinderella and, finding her very handsome, said it was but just she should try, and that he had orders to let everyone make trial.

He obliged Cinderella to sit down, and putting the slipper to her foot, he found it went on easily and fitted her as if it had been made of wax. The astonishment of her two sisters was great, but still greater when Cinderella pulled out of her pocket the other slipper and put it on her foot. Thereupon, in came her godmother who, having touched Cinderella's clothes with her wand, made them richer and more magnificent than any she had worn before.

And now her two sisters found her to be that fine, beautiful lady they had seen at the ball. They threw themselves at her feet to beg pardon for all the ill-treatment they had made her undergo. Cinderella raised them up and, as she embraced them, cried that she forgave them with all her heart and desired them always to love her.

She was conducted to the young prince. He thought her more charming than ever and, a few days after, married her. Cinderella, who was no less good than beautiful, gave her two sisters lodgings in the palace, and that very same day matched them with two great lords of the court.

THE MASTER CAT

Of all the wise and resourceful fairy animals of the folk tales, Puss in Boots is the cleverest. It will be interesting to compare Gustave Doré's romantic illustration of Puss with a modern artist's interpretation of the Master Cat as a saucy, impudent rascal, shown on page 105.

There was a miller who left no more estate to the three sons he had than his mill, his donkey and his cat. The division was soon made. Neither scrivener nor attorney was sent for; they would soon have eaten up all the poor patrimony. The eldest had the mill, the second the donkey, and the youngest nothing but the cat. The poor young fellow was quite comfortless at having so poor a lot.

"My brothers," said he, "may get their living handsomely enough by joining their stocks together. But for my part, when I have eaten my cat, and made me a muff of his skin, I must die of hunger."

"The Master Cat." From *The Blue Fairy Book* edited by Andrew Lang. Used by permission of Longmans, Green and Company, Inc.

The cat, who heard all this, said to him with a grave and serious air, "Do not thus afflict yourself, my good master. You need only give me a bag, and have a pair of boots made for me that I may scamper through the brambles. You shall see you have not so bad a portion with me as you imagine."

The cat's master had often seen him play a great many cunning tricks to catch rats and mice; he used to hide himself in the meal, and make as if he were dead; so he did not altogether despair. When the cat had what he asked for, he booted himself very gallantly, and putting his bag about his neck he held the strings of it in his two forepaws and went into a warren where was a great abundance of rabbits. He put bran and lettuce into his bag and, stretching out at length as if he were dead, he waited for some young rabbits, not yet acquainted with the deceits of the world, to come and rummage for what he had put into his bag.

Scarce had he lain down but he had what he wanted: a rash and foolish young rabbit jumped into his bag. Monsieur Puss, immediately drawing close the strings, killed him without pity. Proud of his prey, he went with it to the palace, and asked to speak with his majesty. He was shown into the king's apartment and making a low reverence, said to him:

"I have brought you, sir, a rabbit from the warren, which my noble lord, the Master of Carabas"—for that was the title Puss was pleased to give his master—"has commanded me to present to Your Majesty from him."

"Tell your master," said the king, "that I thank him, and that he gives me a great deal of pleasure."

Another time the cat hid himself among some standing corn, holding his bag open. When a brace of partridges ran into it, he drew the strings and so caught them both. He made a present of these to the king as he had the rabbit. The king, in like manner, received the partridges with great pleasure, and ordered some money to be given to him.

The cat continued thus for two or three months to carry to his majesty, from time to time, game of his master's taking. One day in particular, when he knew for certain that the king was to take the air along the riverside with his daughter, the most beautiful princess in the world, he said to his master:

"If you will follow my advice your fortune is made. You have nothing to do but wash yourself in the river, where I shall show you, and leave the rest to me."

The Marquis of Carabas did what the cat advised him to do, without knowing why or wherefore. While he was washing, the king passed by, and the cat began to cry out:

"Help! Help! My Lord Marquis of Carabas is going to be drowned."

At this the king put his head out of the coach window, and finding it was the cat who had so often brought him such good game, he commanded his guards to run immediately to the assistance of his lordship the Marquis of Carabas. While they were drawing him out of the river, the cat came up to the coach and told the king that, while his master was washing, there came by some rogues, who went off with his clothes, though he had cried out, 'Thieves! Thieves!' several times, as loud as he could.

This cunning cat had hidden them under a great stone. The king immediately commanded the officers of his wardrobe to run and fetch one of his best suits for the Marquis of Carabas.

The fine clothes set off his good mien, for he was well made and very handsome in his person.

The king's daughter took a secret inclination to him, and the Marquis of Carabas had no sooner cast two or three respectful and tender glances upon her than she fell in love with him to distraction. The king would needs have him come into the coach and take the air with them. The cat, quite overjoyed to see his project begin to succeed, marched on before, and meeting with some countrymen, who were mowing a meadow, he said to them:

"Good people, you who are mowing, if you do not tell the king that the meadow you mow belongs to my Lord Marquis of Carabas, you shall be chopped as small as herbs for the pot."

The king did not fail to ask the mowers to whom the meadow belonged.

"To my Lord Marquis of Carabas," they answered altogether, for the cat's threat had made them terribly afraid.

"You see, sir," said the marquis, "this is a meadow which never fails to yield a plentiful harvest every year."

The Master Cat, who still went on before, met with some reapers, and said to them, "Good people, you who are reaping, if you do not tell the king that all this corn belongs to the Marquis of Carabas you shall be chopped as small as herbs for the pot."

The king, who passed by a moment after, wished to know to whom all that corn belonged.

"To my Lord Marquis of Carabas," replied the reapers, and the king was very well pleased with it, as well as with the marquis, whom he congratulated thereupon. The Master Cat, who went always before, said the same words to all he met, and the king was astonished at the vast estates of the Marquis of Carabas.

Monsieur Puss came at last to a stately castle, the master of which was an ogre, the richest ever known. All the lands which the king had then gone over belonged to this ogre. The cat, who had taken care to inform himself who this ogre was and what he could do, asked to speak with him, saying he could not pass so near his castle without paying his respects to him.

The ogre received him as civilly as an ogre could and made him sit down.

"I have been assured," said the cat, "that you have the gift of being able to change yourself into any sort of creature. You can, for example,

transform yourself into a lion or elephant and the like."

"That is true," answered the ogre briskly, "and to convince you, you shall see me now become a lion."

Puss was so badly terrified at the sight of a lion so near him that he immediately got into the rain gutter, not without abundance of trouble and danger, because of his boots. They were of no use walking upon the tiles. A little while after, when Puss saw that the ogre had resumed his natural form, he came down and owned he had been very much frightened.

"I have been moreover informed," said the cat, "but I know not how to believe it, that you have also the power to take on the shape of the smallest animal; for example, to change yourself into a rat or a mouse; but I must own to you I take this to be impossible."

"Impossible!" cried the ogre. "You shall see that presently."

At the same time he changed himself into a mouse and began to run about the floor. Puss no sooner perceived this than he fell upon him and ate him up.

Meanwhile the king, who saw, as he passed, this fine castle of the ogre's, had a mind to go into it. Puss, who heard the noise of his majesty's coach running over the drawbridge, ran out, and said to the king:

"Your Majesty is welcome to this castle of my Lord Marquis of Carabas."

"What, my Lord Marquis!" cried the king. "And does this castle also belong to you? There can be nothing finer than this court and all the stately buildings which surround it. Let us go in, if you please."

The marquis gave his hand to the princess and followed the king, who went first. They passed into a spacious hall, where they found a magnificent collation, which the ogre had prepared for his friends, who were that very day to visit him, but dared not enter, knowing the king was there. His majesty was charmed with the good qualities of the Lord Marquis of Carabas, as was his daughter, and seeing the vast estate he possessed, said to him:

"It will be owing to yourself only, my Lord Marquis, if you are not my son-in-law."

The marquis, making several low bows, accepted the honor which his majesty conferred upon him, and forthwith, that very same day, married the princess.

Puss became a great lord, and never ran after mice any more.

BEAUTY AND THE BEAST

This story, like the Norse "East o' the Sun" and the Greek "Cupid and Psyche," has a unique charm of its own. Perhaps its appeal lies in Beauty's compassion for her poor Beast and her ability to see beyond his ugly exterior to his goodness and his pitiableness.

Once upon a time, in a far-off country, there lived a merchant who was enormously rich. As he had six sons and six daughters, however, who were accustomed to having everything they fancied, he did not find he had a penny too much. But misfortunes befell them. One day their house caught fire and speedily burned to the ground, with all the splendid furniture, books, pictures, gold, silver and precious goods it contained. The father suddenly lost every ship he had upon the sea, either by dint of pirates, shipwreck or fire. Then he heard that his clerks in distant countries, whom he had trusted entirely, had proved unfaithful. And at last from great wealth he fell into the direst poverty.

All that he had left was a little house in a desolate place at least a hundred leagues from the town. The daughters at first hoped their friends, who had been so numerous while they were rich, would insist on their staying in their houses, but they soon found they were left alone. Their former friends even attributed their misfortunes to their own extravagance and showed no intention of offering them any help.

So nothing was left for them but to take their departure to the cottage, which stood in the midst of a dark forest. As they were too poor to have any servants, the girls had to work hard, and the sons, for their part, cultivated the fields to earn their living. Roughly clothed, and living in the simplest way, the girls regretted unceasingly the luxuries and amusements of their for-

"Beauty and the Beast." From *The Blue Fairy Book* edited by Andrew Lang. Used by permission of Longmans, Green and Company, Inc.

mer life. Only the youngest daughter tried to be brave and cheerful.

She had been as sad as anyone when misfortune first overtook her father, but soon recovering her natural gaiety, she set to work to make the best of things, to amuse her father and brothers as well as she could, and to persuade her sisters to join her in dancing and singing. But they would do nothing of the sort, and because she was not as doleful as themselves, they declared this miserable life was all she was fit for. But she was really far prettier and cleverer than they were. Indeed, she was so lovely she was always called Beauty.

After two years, their father received news that one of his ships, which he had believed lost, had come safely into port with a rich cargo. All the sons and daughters at once thought that their poverty was at an end and wanted to set out directly for the town; but their father, who was more prudent, begged them to wait a little, and though it was harvest time, and he could ill be spared, determined to go himself to make inquiries.

Only the youngest daughter had any doubt but that they would soon again be as rich as they were before. They all loaded their father with commissions for jewels and dresses which it would have taken a fortune to buy; only Beauty did not ask for anything. Her father, noticing her silence, said:

"And what shall I bring for you, Beauty?"

"The only thing I wish for is to see you come home safely," she answered.

But this reply vexed her sisters, who fancied she was blaming them for having asked for such costly things. Her father, however, was pleased, but as he thought she certainly ought to like pretty presents, he told her to choose something.

"Well, dear Father," she said, "as you insist upon it, I beg that you will bring me a rose. I have not seen one since we came here, and I love them so much."

The merchant set out, only to find that his former companions, believing him to be dead, had divided his cargo between them. After six months of trouble and expense he found himself as poor as when he started on his journey. To make matters worse, he was obliged to return in the most terrible weather. By the time he was within a few leagues of his home he was almost exhausted with cold and fatigue. Though he knew it would take some hours to get through the forest, he resolved to go on. But night overtook him, and the deep snow and bitter frost made it impossible for his horse to carry him any farther. The only shelter he could get was the hollow trunk of a great tree, and there he crouched all the night, which seemed to him the longest he had ever known. The howling of the wolves kept him awake, and when at last day broke the falling snow had covered up every path, and he did not know which way to turn.

At length he made out some sort of path, but it was so rough and slippery that he fell down more than once. Presently it led him into an avenue of trees which ended in a splendid castle. It seemed to the merchant very strange that no snow had fallen in the avenue of orange trees, covered with flowers and fruit. When he reached the first court of the castle he saw before him a flight of agate steps. He went up them and passed through several splendidly furnished rooms.

The pleasant warmth of the air revived him, and he felt very hungry; but there seemed to be nobody in all this vast and splendid palace. Deep silence reigned everywhere, and at last, tired of roaming through empty rooms and galleries, he stopped in a room smaller than the rest, where a clear fire was burning and a couch was drawn up cosily before it. Thinking this must be prepared for someone who was expected, he sat down to wait till he should come and very soon fell into a sweet sleep.

When his extreme hunger wakened him after several hours, he was still alone; but a little table, with a good dinner on it, had been drawn up close to him. He lost no time in beginning his meal, hoping he might soon thank his considerate host, whoever it might be. But no one appeared, and even after another long sleep, from which he awoke completely refreshed, there was no sign of anybody, though a fresh meal of dainty cakes and fruit was prepared upon the little table at his elbow.

Being naturally timid, the silence began to terrify him, and he resolved to search once more through all the rooms; but it was of no use, there was no sign of life in the palace! Then he went down into the garden, and though it was winter everywhere else, here the sun shone, the birds sang, the flowers bloomed, and the air was soft and sweet. The merchant, in ecstasies with all he saw and heard, said to himself:

"All this must be meant for me. I will go this minute and bring my children to share all these delights."

In spite of being so cold and weary when he reached the castle, he had taken his horse to the stable and fed it. Now he thought he would saddle it for his homeward journey, and he turned down the path which led to the stable. This path had a hedge of roses on each side of it, and the merchant thought he had never seen such exquisite flowers. They reminded him of his promise to Beauty, and he stopped and had just gathered one to take to her when he was startled by a strange noise behind him. Turning round, he saw a frightful Beast, which seemed to be very angry and said in a terrible voice:

"Who told you you might gather my roses? Was it not enough that I sheltered you in my palace and was kind to you? This is the way you show your gratitude, by stealing my flowers! But your insolence shall not go unpunished."

The merchant, terrified by these furious words, dropped the fatal rose, and, throwing himself on his knees, cried, "Pardon me, noble sir. I am truly grateful for your hospitality, which was so magnificent I could not imagine you would be offended by my taking such a little thing as a rose."

But the Beast's anger was not lessened by his speech.

"You are very ready with excuses and flattery," he cried. "But that will not save you from the death you deserve."

Alas, thought the merchant, if my daughter Beauty could only know into what danger her rose has brought me! And in despair he began to tell the Beast all his misfortunes and the reason of his journey, not forgetting to mention Beauty's request.

"A king's ransom would hardly have procured all that my other daughters asked for," he said. "But I thought I might at least take Beauty her rose. I beg you to forgive me, for you see I meant no harm."

The Beast said, in a less furious tone, "I will

forgive you on one condition—that you will give me one of your daughters."

"Ah," cried the merchant, "If I were cruel enough to buy my own life at the expense of one of my children's, what excuse could I invent to bring her here?"

"None," answered the Beast. "If she comes at all she must come willingly. On no other condition will I have her. See if any one of them is courageous enough, and loves you enough, to come and save your life. You seem to be an honest man so I will trust you to go home. I give you a month to see if any of your daughters will come back with you and stay here, to let you go free. If none of them is willing, you must come alone, after bidding them good-bye forever, for then you will belong to me. And do not imagine that you can hide from me, for if you fail to keep your word I will come and fetch you!" added the Beast grimly.

The merchant accepted this proposal. He promised to return at the time appointed, and then, anxious to escape from the presence of the Beast, he asked permission to set off at once. But the Beast answered that he could not go until the next day.

"Then you will find a horse ready for you," he said. "Now go and eat your supper and await my orders."

The poor merchant, more dead than alive, went back to his room, where the most delicious supper was already served on the little table drawn up before a blazing fire. But he was too terrified to eat and only tasted a few of the dishes, for fear the Beast should be angry if he did not obey his orders. When he had finished, the Beast warned him to remember their agreement and to prepare his daughter exactly for what she had to expect.

"Do not get up tomorrow," he added, "until you see the sun and hear a golden bell ring. Then you will find your breakfast waiting for you, and the horse you are to ride will be ready in the courtyard. He will also bring you back again when you come with your daughter a month hence. Farewell. Take a rose to Beauty, and remember your promise!"

The merchant lay down until the sun rose. Then, after breakfast, he went to gather Beauty's rose and mounted his horse, which carried him off so swiftly that in an instant he had lost sight of the palace. He was still wrapped in gloomy thoughts when it stopped before the door of his cottage.

His sons and daughters, who had been uneasy at his long absence, rushed to meet him, eager to know the result of his journey which, seeing him mounted upon a splendid horse and wrapped in a rich mantle, they supposed to be favorable. But he hid the truth from them at first, only saying sadly to Beauty as he gave her the rose:

"Here is what you asked me to bring you. Little you know what it has cost."

Presently he told them his adventures from beginning to end, and then they were all very unhappy. The girls lamented loudly over their lost hopes, and the sons declared their father should not return to the terrible castle. But he reminded them he had promised to go back. Then the girls were very angry with Beauty and said it was all her fault. If she had asked for something sensible this would never have happened.

Poor Beauty, much distressed, said to them, "I have indeed caused this misfortune, but who could have guessed that to ask for a rose in the middle of summer would cause so much misery? But as I did the mischief it is only just that I should suffer for it. I will therefore go back with my father to keep his promise."

At first nobody would hear of it. Her father and brothers, who loved her dearly, declared nothing should make them let her go. But Beauty was firm. As the time drew near she divided her little possessions between her sisters, and said good-bye to everything she loved. When the fatal day came she encouraged and cheered her father as they mounted together the horse which had brought him back. It seemed to fly rather than gallop but so smoothly that Beauty was not frightened. Indeed, she would have enjoyed the journey if she had not feared what might happen at the end of it. Her father still tried to persuade her to go back, but in vain.

While they were talking the night fell. Then, to their great surprise, wonderful colored lights began to shine in all directions, and splendid fireworks blazed out before them; all the forest was illuminated. They even felt pleasantly warm,

though it had been bitterly cold before. They reached the avenue of orange trees and saw that the palace was brilliantly lighted from roof to ground, and music sounded softly from the courtyard.

"The Beast must be very hungry," said Beauty, trying to laugh, "if he makes all this rejoicing over the arrival of his prey." But, in spite of her anxiety, she admired all the wonderful things she saw.

When they had dismounted, her father led her to the little room. Here they found a splendid fire burning, and the table daintily spread with a delicious supper.

Beauty, who was less frightened now that she had passed through so many rooms and seen nothing of the Beast, was quite willing to begin, for her long ride had made her very hungry. But they had hardly finished their meal when the noise of the Beast's footsteps was heard approaching, and Beauty clung to her father in terror, which became all the greater when she saw how frightened he was. But when the Beast really appeared, though she trembled at the sight of him, she made a great effort to hide her horror, and saluted him respectfully.

This evidently pleased the Beast. After looking at her he said, in a tone that might have struck terror into the boldest heart, though he did not seem to be angry:

"Good evening, old man. Good evening, Beauty."

The merchant was too terrified to reply, but Beauty answered sweetly, "Good evening, Beast."

"Have you come willingly?" asked the Beast. "Will you be content to stay here when your father goes away?"

Beauty answered bravely that she was quite prepared to stay.

"I am pleased with you," said the Beast. "As you have come of your own accord, you may remain. As for you, old man," he added, turning to the merchant, "at sunrise tomorrow take your departure. When the bell rings, get up quickly and eat your breakfast, and you will find the same horse waiting to take you home."

Then turning to Beauty, he said, "Take your father into the next room, and help him choose gifts for your brothers and sisters. You will find two traveling trunks there; fill them as full as you can. It is only just that you should send them something very precious as a remembrance."

Then he went away, after saying, "Good-bye, Beauty; good-bye, old man." Beauty was beginning to think with great dismay of her father's departure, but they went into the next room, which had shelves and cupboards all around it. They were greatly surprised at the riches it contained. There were splendid dresses fit for a queen, with all the ornaments to be worn with them, and when Beauty opened the cupboards she was dazzled by the gorgeous jewels lying in heaps upon every shelf. After choosing a vast quantity, which she divided between her sisters —for she had made a heap of the wonderful dresses for each of them—she opened the last chest, which was full of gold.

"I think, Father," she said, "that, as the gold will be more useful to you, we had better take out the other things again, and fill the trunks with it."

So they did this, but the more they put in, the more room there seemed to be, and at last they put back all the jewels and dresses they had taken out, and Beauty even added as many more of the jewels as she could carry at once. Even then the trunks were not too full, but they were so heavy an elephant could not have carried them!

"The Beast was mocking us!" cried the merchant. "He pretended to give us all these things, knowing that I could not carry them away."

"Let us wait and see," answered Beauty. "I cannot believe he meant to deceive us. All we can do is to fasten them up and have them ready."

So they did this and returned to the little room where they found breakfast ready. The merchant ate his with a good appetite, as the Beast's generosity made him believe he might perhaps venture to come back soon and see Beauty. But she felt sure her father was leaving her forever, so she was very sad when the bell rang sharply.

They went down into the courtyard, where two horses were waiting, one loaded with the two trunks, the other for him to ride. They were pawing the ground in their impatience to start, and the merchant bade Beauty a hasty farewell. As soon as he was mounted he went off at such a pace she lost sight of him in an instant. Then Beauty began to cry and wandered sadly back to her own room. But she soon found she was very sleepy, and as she had nothing better to do she lay down and instantly fell asleep. And then she dreamed she was walking by a brook bordered with trees, and lamenting her sad fate, when a young prince, handsomer than anyone she had ever seen, and with a voice that went straight to her heart, came and said to her:

"Ah, Beauty, you are not so unfortunate as you suppose. Here you will be rewarded for all you have suffered elsewhere. Your every wish shall be gratified. Only try to find me out, no matter how I may be disguised, for I love you dearly, and in making me happy you will find your own happiness. Be as true-hearted as you are beautiful, and we shall have nothing left to wish for."

"What can I do, Prince, to make you happy?" said Beauty.

"Only be grateful," he answered, "and do not trust too much to your eyes. Above all, do not desert me until you have saved me from my cruel misery."

After this she thought she found herself in a room with a stately and beautiful lady, who said to her, "Dear Beauty, try not to regret all you have left behind you; you are destined for a better fate. Only do not let yourself be deceived by appearances."

Beauty found her dreams so interesting that she was in no hurry to awake, but presently the clock roused her by calling her name softly twelve times. Then she arose and found her dressing-table set out with everything she could possibly want, and when her toilet was finished, she found dinner waiting in the room next to hers. But dinner does not take very long when one is alone, and very soon she sat down cosily in the corner of a sofa, and began to think about the charming prince she had seen in her dream.

"He said I could make him happy," said Beauty to herself. "It seems, then, that this horrible Beast keeps him a prisoner. How can I set him free? I wonder why they both told me not to trust to appearances? But, after all, it was only a dream, so why should I trouble myself about it? I had better find something to do to amuse myself."

So she began to explore some of the many rooms of the palace. The first she entered was lined with mirrors. Beauty saw herself reflected on every side and thought she had never seen such a charming room. Then a bracelet which was hanging from a chandelier caught her eye, and on taking it down she was greatly surprised to find that it held a portrait of her unknown admirer, just as she had seen him in her dream. With great delight she slipped the bracelet on her arm and went on into a gallery of pictures, where she soon found a portrait of the same handsome prince, as large as life, and so well painted that as she studied it he seemed to smile kindly at her.

Tearing herself away from the portrait at last, she passed into a room which contained every musical instrument under the sun, and here she amused herself for a long while in trying them and singing. The next room was a library, and she saw everything she had ever wanted to read as well as everything she had read. By this time it was growing dusk, and wax candles in diamond and ruby candlesticks lit themselves in every room.

Beauty found her supper served just at the time she preferred to have it, but she did not see anyone or hear a sound, and though her father had warned her she would be alone, she began to find it rather dull.

Presently she heard the Beast coming and wondered tremblingly if he meant to eat her now. However, he did not seem at all ferocious, and only said gruffly:

"Good evening, Beauty."

She answered cheerfully and managed to conceal her terror. The Beast asked how she had been amusing herself, and she told him all the rooms she had seen. Then he asked if she thought she could be happy in his palace; and Beauty answered that everything was so beautiful she would be very hard to please if she could not be happy. After about an hour's talk Beauty began to think the Beast was not nearly so terrible as she had supposed at first. Then he rose to leave her, and said in his gruff voice:

"Do you love me, Beauty? Will you marry me?"

"Oh, what shall I say?" cried Beauty, for she was afraid to make the Beast angry by refusing.

"Say yes or no without fear," he replied.

"Oh, no, Beast," said Beauty hastily.

"Since you will not, good night, Beauty," he said.

And she answered, "Good night, Beast," very glad to find her refusal had not provoked him. After he was gone she was very soon in bed and dreaming of her unknown prince.

She thought he came and said, "Ah, Beauty! Why are you so unkind to me? I fear I am fated to be unhappy for many a long day still."

Then her dreams changed, but the charming prince figured in them all. When morning came her first thought was to look at the portrait and see if it was really like him, and she found it certainly was.

She decided to amuse herself in the garden, for the sun shone, and all the fountains were playing. She was astonished to find that every place was familiar to her, and presently she came to the very brook and the myrtle trees where she had first met the prince in her dream. That made her think more than ever he must be kept a prisoner by the Beast.

When she was tired she went back to the palace and found a new room full of materials for every kind of work—ribbons to make into bows and silks to work into flowers. There was an aviary full of rare birds, which were so tame they flew to Beauty as soon as they saw her and perched upon her shoulders and her head.

"Pretty little creatures," she said, "how I wish your cage was nearer my room that I might often hear you sing!" So saying she opened a door and found to her delight that it led into her own room, though she had thought it was on the other side of the palace.

There were more birds in a room farther on, parrots and cockatoos that could talk, and they greeted Beauty by name. Indeed, she found them so entertaining that she took one or two back to her room, and they talked to her while she was at supper. The Beast paid her his usual visit and asked the same questions as before, and then with a gruff good night he took his departure, and Beauty went to bed to dream of her mysterious prince.

The days passed swiftly in different amusements, and after a while Beauty found another strange thing in the palace, which often pleased her when she was tired of being alone. There was one room which she had not noticed particularly; it was empty, except that under each of the windows stood a very comfortable chair. The first time she had looked out of the window it seemed a black curtain prevented her from seeing anything outside. But the second time she went into the room, happening to be tired, she sat down in one of the chairs, when instantly the curtain was rolled aside, and a most amusing pantomime was acted before her. There were dances and colored lights, music and pretty dresses, and it was all so gay that Beauty was in ecstasies. After that she tried the other seven windows in turn, and there was some new and surprising entertainment to be seen from each of them so Beauty never could feel lonely any more. Every evening after supper the Beast came to see her, and always before saying good night asked her in his terrible voice:

"Beauty, will you marry me?"

And it seemed to Beauty, now she understood him better, that when she said, "No, Beast," he went away quite sad. Her happy dreams of the handsome young prince soon made her forget the poor Beast, and the only thing that disturbed her was being told to distrust appearances, to let her heart guide her, and not her eyes. Consider as she would, she could not understand.

So everything went on for a long time, until at last, happy as she was, Beauty began to long for the sight of her father and her brothers and sisters. One night, seeing her look very sad, the Beast asked her what was the matter. Beauty had quite ceased to be afraid of him. Now she knew he was really gentle in spite of his ferocious looks and his dreadful voice. So she answered that she wished to see her home once more. Upon hearing this the Beast seemed sadly distressed, and cried miserably:

"Ah, Beauty, have you the heart to desert an unhappy Beast like this? What more do you want to make you happy? Is it because you hate me that you want to escape?"

"No, dear Beast," answered Beauty softly, "I do not hate you, and I should be very sorry never to see you any more, but I long to see my father again. Only let me go for two months, and I promise to come back to you and stay for the rest of my life."

The Beast, who had been sighing dolefully while she spoke, now replied, "I cannot refuse you anything you ask, even though it should cost me my life. Take the four boxes you will find in the room next to your own and fill them with everything you wish to take with you. But remember your promise and come back when the two months are over, for if you do not come in good time you will find your faithful Beast dead. You will not need any chariot to bring you back. Only say good-bye to all your brothers and sisters the night before you come away and, when you have gone to bed, turn this ring round upon your finger, and say firmly, 'I wish to go back to my palace and see my Beast again.' Good night, Beauty. Fear nothing, sleep peacefully, and before long you shall see your father once more."

As soon as Beauty was alone she hastened to fill the boxes with all the rare and precious things she saw about her, and only when she was tired of heaping things into them did they seem to be full. Then she went to bed, but could hardly sleep, for joy. When at last she began to dream of her beloved prince she was grieved to see him stretched upon a grassy bank, sad and weary, and hardly like himself.

"What is the matter?" she cried.

But he looked at her reproachfully, and said, "How can you ask me, cruel one? Are you not leaving me to my death perhaps?"

"Ah, don't be so sorrowful!" cried Beauty. "I am only going to assure my father that I am safe and happy. I have promised the Beast faithfully I will come back, and he would die of grief if I did not keep my word!"

"What would that matter to you?" asked the prince. "Surely you would not care?"

"Indeed I should be ungrateful if I did not care for such a kind Beast," cried Beauty indignantly. "I would die to save him from pain. I assure you it is not his fault he is so ugly."

Just then a strange sound woke her—someone was speaking not very far away; and opening her eyes she found herself in a room she had never seen before, which was certainly not as splendid as those she had seen in the Beast's palace. Where could she be? She rose and dressed hastily and then saw that the boxes she had packed the night before were all in the room. Suddenly she heard her father's voice and rushed out to greet him joyfully. Her brothers and sisters were astonished at her appearance, for they had never expected to see her again. Beauty asked her father what he thought her strange dreams meant and why the prince constantly begged her not to trust to appearances. After much consideration he answered:

"You tell me yourself that the Beast, frightful as he is, loves you dearly and deserves your love and gratitude for his gentleness and kindness. I think the prince must mean you to understand you ought to reward him by doing as he wishes, in spite of his ugliness."

Beauty could not help seeing that this seemed probable; still when she thought of her dear prince who was so handsome, she did not feel at all inclined to marry the Beast. At any rate, for two months she need not decide but could enjoy herself with her sisters. Though they were rich now, and lived in a town again and had plenty of acquaintances, Beauty found that nothing amused her very much. She often thought of the palace, where she was so happy, especially as at home she never once dreamed of her dear prince, and she felt quite sad without him.

Then her sisters seemed quite used to being without her, and even found her rather in the way, so she would not have been sorry when the two months were over but for her father and brothers. She had not the courage to say good-bye to them. Every day when she rose she meant to say it at night, and when night came she put it off again, until at last she had a dismal dream which helped her to make up her mind.

She thought she was wandering in a lonely path in the palace gardens, when she heard groans. Running quickly to see what could be the matter, she found the Beast stretched out upon his side, apparently dying. He reproached her faintly with being the cause of his distress, and at the same moment a stately lady appeared, and said very gravely:

"Ah, Beauty, see what happens when people do not keep their promises! If you had delayed one day more, you would have found him dead."

Beauty was so terrified by this dream that the very next evening she said good-bye to her father and her brothers and sisters, and as soon as she was in bed she turned her ring round upon her finger, and said firmly:

"I wish to go back to my palace and see my Beast again."

Then she fell asleep instantly, and only woke up to hear the clock saying, "Beauty, Beauty," twelve times in its musical voice, which told her she was really in the palace once more. Everything was just as before, and her birds were so glad to see her, but Beauty thought she had never known such a long day. She was so anxious to see the Beast again that she felt as if suppertime would never come.

But when it came no Beast appeared. After listening and waiting for a long time, she ran down into the garden to search for him. Up and down the paths and avenues ran poor Beauty, calling him. No one answered, and not a trace of him could she find. At last, she saw that she was standing opposite the shady path she had seen in her dream. She rushed down it, and sure enough, there was the cave, and in it lay the Beast—asleep, so Beauty thought. Quite glad to have found him, she ran up and stroked his head, but to her horror he did not move or open his eyes.

"Oh, he is dead, and it is all my fault!" cried Beauty, crying bitterly.

But then, looking at him again, she fancied he still breathed. Hastily fetching some water from the nearest fountain, she sprinkled it over his face, and to her great delight he began to revive.

"Oh, Beast, how you frightened me!" she cried. "I never knew how much I loved you until just now, when I feared I was too late to save your life."

"Can you really love such an ugly creature as I am?" asked the Beast faintly. "Ah, Beauty, you came only just in time. I was dying because I thought you had forgotten your promise. But go back now and rest, I shall see you again by-and-by."

Beauty, who had half expected he would be angry with her, was reassured by his gentle voice and went back to the palace, where supper was awaiting her.

And afterward the Beast came in as usual and talked about the time she had spent with her father, asking if she had enjoyed herself and if they had all been glad to see her.

Beauty quite enjoyed telling him all that had happened to her. When at last the time came for him to go, he asked, as he had so often asked before:

"Beauty, will you marry me?"

She answered softly, "Yes, dear Beast."

As she spoke a blaze of light sprang up before the windows of the palace; fireworks crackled and guns banged, and across the avenue of orange trees, in letters all made of fireflies, was written: *Long live the prince and his bride.*

Turning to ask the Beast what it could all mean, Beauty found he had disappeared, and in its place stood her long-loved prince! At the same moment the wheels of a chariot were heard upon the terrace, and two ladies entered the room. One of them Beauty recognized as the stately lady she had seen in her dreams; the other was so queenly that Beauty hardly knew which to greet first. But the one she already knew said to her companion:

"Well, Queen, this is Beauty, who has had the courage to rescue your son from the terrible enchantment. They love each other, and only your consent to their marriage is wanting to make them perfectly happy."

"I consent with all my heart," cried the queen. "How can I ever thank you enough, charming girl, for having restored my dear son to his natural form?" And then she tenderly embraced Beauty and the prince, who had meanwhile been greeting the fairy and receiving her congratulations.

"Now," said the fairy to Beauty, "I suppose you would like me to send for all your brothers and sisters to dance at your wedding?"

And so she did, and the marriage was celebrated the very next day with the utmost splendor, and Beauty and the prince lived happily ever after.

THE WHITE CAT

Once upon a time there was a King who had three sons. The day came when they were grown so big and strong that he began to fear they would be planning to rule in his place. This would cause trouble among themselves and his

"The White Cat." From *The White Cat and Other French Fairy Tales* by Comtesse d'Aulnoy, arranged by Rachel Field. Copyright, 1928, by The Macmillan Company and used with their permission

subjects. Now the King was not so young as he once had been but nevertheless he had no notion of giving up his kingdom then and there. So after much thought he hit upon a scheme which should keep them too busily occupied to interfere in the affairs of state. Accordingly he called the three into his private apartments where he spoke to them with great kindliness and concern of his plans for the future.

"I am planning to retire from the affairs of state. But I do not wish my subjects to suffer from this change. Therefore, while I am still alive, I shall transfer my crown to one of you. I shall not follow the usual custom of leaving the crown to my eldest son, but whichever one of you shall bring me the handsomest and most intelligent little dog shall become my heir."

The Princes were greatly surprised by this strange request, but they could not very well refuse to humor their father's whim; and since there was luck in it for the two younger sons and the elder of the three was a timid, rather spiritless fellow, they agreed readily enough. The King then bade them farewell after first distributing jewels and money among them and adding that a year from that day at the same place and hour they should return to him with their little dogs.

Within sight of the city gates stood a castle where the three often spent many days in company with their young companions. Here they agreed to part and to meet again in a year before proceeding with their trophies to the King; and so having pledged their good faith, and changing their names that they might not be known, each set off upon a different road.

It would take far too long to recount the adventures of all three Princes so I shall tell only of those that befell the youngest, for a more gay and well-mannered Prince never lived, nor one so handsome and accomplished.

Scarcely a day passed that he did not buy a dog or two, greyhounds, mastiffs, bloodhounds, pointers, spaniels, water dogs, lapdogs; but the instant he found a handsomer one he let the first go and kept the new purchase, since it would have been impossible for him to carry them all on his journeyings. He went without fixed plan or purpose and so he continued for many days until at last darkness and a terrible storm overtook him at nightfall in a lonely forest. Thunder and lightning rumbled and flashed; rain fell in torrents; the trees seemed to close more densely about him until at last he could no longer find his way. When he had wandered thus for some time he suddenly saw a glint of light between the tree trunks. Feeling certain that this must mean a shelter of some sort he pressed on till he found himself approaching the most magnificent castle he had ever seen. The gate was of gold and covered with jewels of such brilliance that it was their light which had guided him to the spot. In spite of the rain and storm he caught glimpses of walls of finest porcelain decorated with pictures of the most famous fairies from the beginning of the world up to that very day: Cinderella, Graciosa, Sleeping Beauty, and a hundred others. As he admired all this magnificence he noticed a rabbit's foot fastened to the golden gates by a chain of diamonds. Marveling greatly at such a lavish display of precious gems, the young Prince pulled at the rabbit's foot and straightway an unseen bell of wonderful sweetness rang; the gate was opened by hundreds of tiny hands and others pushed him forward while he hesitated amazed upon the threshold. He moved on wonderingly, his hand on the hilt of his sword until he was reassured by two voices singing a welcome. Again he felt himself being pushed, this time toward a gate of coral opening upon an apartment of mother-of-pearl from which he passed into others still more richly decorated and alight with wax candles and great chandeliers sparkling with a thousand rainbows.

He had passed through perhaps sixty such rooms when the hands that guided him made a sign for him to stop. He saw a large armchair moving by itself toward a fireplace at the same moment that the fire began to blaze and the hands, which he now observed to be very small and white, carefully drew off his wet clothes and handed him others so fine and richly embroidered they seemed fit for a wedding day. The hands continued to dress him, until at last, powdered and attired more handsomely than he had ever been in his life before, the Prince was led into a banquet hall. Here the four walls were decorated solely with paintings representing famous cats, Puss-in-Boots and others whom he

was quick to recognize. Even more astonishing than this was the table set for two with its gold service and crystal cups.

There was an orchestra composed entirely of cats. One held a music book with the strangest notes imaginable; another beat time with a little baton; and all the rest strummed tiny guitars.

While the Prince stared in amazement, each cat suddenly began to mew in a different key and to claw at the guitar strings. It was the strangest music ever heard! The Prince would have thought himself in bedlam had not the palace itself been so marvelously beautiful. So he stopped his ears and laughed heartily at the various poses and grimaces of these strange musicians. He was meditating upon the extraordinary sights he had already seen in the castle, when he beheld a little figure entering the hall. It was scarcely more than two feet in height and wrapped in a long gold crêpe veil. Before it walked two cats dressed in deep mourning and wearing cloaks and swords, while still others followed, some carrying rat-traps full of rats and mice in cages.

By this time the Prince was too astonished to think. But presently the tiny pink figure approached him and lifted its veil. He now beheld the most beautiful little white cat that ever was or ever will be. She had such a very youthful and melancholy air and a mewing so soft and sweet that it went straight to the young Prince's heart.

"Son of a King," she said to him, "thou art welcome; my mewing Majesty beholds thee with pleasure.

"Madam," responded the Prince, bowing as low as possible before her, "it is very gracious of you to receive me with so much attention, but you do not appear to me to be an ordinary little cat. The gift of speech which you have and this superb castle you inhabit are certainly evidence to the contrary."

"Son of a King," rejoined the White Cat, "I pray that you will cease to pay me compliments. I am plain in my speech and manners, but I have a kind heart. Come," she added, to her attendants, "let them serve supper and bid the concert cease, for the Prince does not understand what they are singing."

"And are they singing words, madam?" he asked incredulously.

"Certainly," she answered, "we have very gifted poets here, as you will see if you remain long enough."

Supper was then served to them by the same hands that had guided him there, and a very strange meal it was. There were two dishes of each course—one soup, for instance, being of savory pigeons while the other had been made of nicely fattened mice. The sight of this rather took away the Prince's appetite until his hostess, who seemed to guess what was passing in his mind, assured him that his own dishes had been specially prepared and contained no rats and mice of any kind. Her charming manners convinced the Prince that the little Cat had no wish to deceive him, so he began to eat and drink with great enjoyment. During their meal he happened to observe that on one paw she wore a tiny miniature set in a bracelet. This surprised him so that he begged her to let him examine it more closely. He had supposed it would be the picture of Master Puss, but what was his astonishment to find it the portrait of a handsome young man who bore a strange resemblance to himself! As he stared at it, the White Cat was heard to sigh so deeply and with such profound sadness that the Prince became even more curious; but he dared not question one so affected. Instead he entertained her with tales of court life, with which, to his surprise, he found her well acquainted.

After supper the White Cat led her guest into another Hall, where upon a little stage twelve cats and twelve monkeys danced in the most fantastic costumes. So the evening ended in great merriment; and after the Cat had bade the Prince a gracious good night the same strange hands conducted him to his own apartment, where in spite of the softness of his bed he spent half the night trying to solve the mystery of the castle and his extraordinary little hostess.

But when morning came he was no nearer to an answer to his questionings, so he allowed the pair of hands to help him dress and lead him into the palace courtyard. Here a vast company of cats in hunting costume were gathering to the sound of the horn. A fête day indeed! The White Cat was going to hunt and wished the Prince to accompany her. Now the mysterious hands presented him with a wooden horse. He made some objection to mounting it, but it proved to be an excellent charger, and a tireless galloper. The White Cat rode beside him on a monkey, the handsomest and proudest that ever was seen. She had thrown off her long veil and wore a military cap which made her look so bold that she frightened all the mice in the neighborhood. Never was there a more successful hunt. The cats outran all the rabbits and hares and a thousand skillful feats were performed to the gratification of the entire company. Tiring of the hunt at last the White Cat took up a horn no bigger than the Prince's little finger and blew upon it with so loud and clear a tone it could be heard ten leagues away. Scarcely had she sounded two or three flourishes when all the cats in the countryside seemed to appear. By land and sea and through the air they all came flocking to her call, dressed in every conceivable costume. So, followed by this extraordinary train, the Prince rode back with his hostess to the castle.

That night the White Cat put on her gold veil again and they dined together as before. Being very hungry the Prince ate and drank heartily, and this time the food had a strange effect upon him. All recollection of his father and the little dog he was to find for him slipped from his mind. He no longer thought of anything but of gossiping with the White Cat and enjoying her kind and gracious companionship. So the days passed in pleasant sport and amusement and the night in feasting and conversation. There was scarcely one in which he did not discover some new charm of the little White Cat. Now he had forgotten even the land of his birth. The hands continued to wait upon him and supply every want till he began to regret that he could not become a cat himself to live forever in such pleasant company.

"Alas," he confessed to the White Cat at last, "how wretched it makes me even to think of leaving you! I have come to love you so dearly. Could you not become a woman or else make me a cat?"

But though she smiled at his wish, the look she turned upon him was very strange.

A year passes away quickly when one has neither pain nor care, when one is merry and in good health. The Prince took no thought of time, but the White Cat was not so forgetful.

"There are only three days left to look for the little dog you were to bring to the King, your father," she reminded him. "Your two brothers have already found several very beautiful ones."

At her words the Prince's memory returned to him and he marveled at his strange forgetfulness.

"What spell would have made me forget what was most important to me in the whole world?" he cried in despair. "My honor and my fortune are lost unless I can find a dog that will win a kingdom for me and a horse swift enough to carry me home again in this short time!"

So, believing this to be impossible, he grew very sorrowful. Then the White Cat spoke to him with great reassurance.

"Son of a King," she said, "do not distress yourself so. I am your friend. Remain here another day, and though it is five hundred leagues from here to your country the good wooden horse will carry you there in less than twelve hours' time."

"But it is not enough for me to return to my father, dear Cat," said the Prince. "I must take him a little dog as well."

"And so you shall," replied she. "Here is a walnut which contains one more beautiful than the Dog Star."

"Your Majesty jests with me," he protested.

"Put the walnut to your ear then," insisted the Cat, "and you will hear it bark."

He obeyed her, and as he held the walnut to his ear a faint "Bow-wow" came from within, more tiny and shrill than a cricket on a winter night. The Prince could scarcely believe his ears or contain his curiosity to see so diminutive a creature. But he was wise enough to follow the White Cat's advice not to open the walnut till he should reach his father's presence.

It was a sad leave-taking between the Prince and the White Cat. A thousand times he thanked her, but though he urged her to return to court with him, she only shook her head and sighed deeply as upon the night of his arrival. So he galloped away at last on the wooden horse, which bore him more swiftly than the wind to the appointed place.

He reached the castle even before his two brothers and enjoyed the sight of their surprise at seeing a wooden horse champing at the bit in the courtyard. The two brothers were so busy telling of their various adventures that they took little note of their younger brother's silence concerning his, but when the time came to show one another their dogs the two were vastly amused at sight of an ugly cur which the young Prince had brought along, pretending to consider it a marvel of beauty. Needless to say the elder Princes smiled with secret satisfaction to think how far superior were their own dogs, for though they wished their brother no ill luck, they had no wish to see him ruling over the kingdom.

Next morning the three set out together in the same coach. The two eldest brothers carried baskets filled with little dogs too delicate and beautiful to be touched, while the youngest carried the poor cur as if it also was precious. By no outward sign did he betray the presence of the walnut with its precious occupant which was safely hidden in his pocket. No sooner did the three set foot in the palace than all the court crowded around to welcome the returned travelers and see the results of their journeyings. The King received them with great joy, professing delight over the little dogs his two elder sons brought out for his inspection. But the more he studied their merits, the more puzzled he became, so nearly were they alike in beauty and grace. The two brothers were already beginning to dispute with one another as to which deserved the crown when the younger brother stepped forward, holding upon the palm of his hand the walnut so lately presented to him by the White Cat. Opening it without more ado, he revealed a tiny dog lying upon cotton. So perfectly formed was it and so small that it could pass through a little finger ring without touching any part of it. It was more delicate than thistledown and its coat shone with colors of the rainbow. Nor was this all; immediately it was released from its kennel, the little creature arose on its hind legs and began to go through the steps of a tarantella, with tiny castanets and all the airs and graces of a Spanish dancer!

The King was dumbfounded and even the two brothers were forced to acknowledge that such a beautiful and gifted dog had never been seen before. But their father was in no mood to give up his kingdom, so he announced that he had decided upon another test of their skill. This time he would give them a year to travel over land and sea in search of a piece of cloth so fine it would pass through the eye of the finest Venetian-point lace needle.

So the Prince remounted his wooden horse and set off at full speed, for now he knew exactly where he wanted to go. So great was his eagerness to see the beautiful White Cat once more that he could scarcely contain himself until her castle came into view. This time every window was alight to welcome him and the faithful pair of hands which had waited on him so well before were ready to take the bridle of the wooden horse and lead it back to the stable while the Prince hurried to the White Cat's private apartments.

He found her lying on a little couch of blue satin with many pillows. Her expression was sad until she caught sight of him. Then she sprang up and began to caper about him delightedly.

"Oh, dear Prince," cried she, "I had scarcely dared to hope for your return. I am generally so unfortunate in matters that concern me."

A thousand times must the grateful Prince caress her and recount his adventures, which perhaps she knew more about than he guessed. And now he told her of his father's latest whim—how he had set his heart upon having a piece of cloth that could pass through the eye of the finest needle. For his own part he did not believe it was possible to find such a thing, but he believed that if any one could help him in this quest it would be his dear White Cat. She listened attentively to all he told her and finally explained with a thoughtful air that this was a matter demanding careful consideration. There were, it seemed, some cats in her castle who could spin with extraordinary skill, and she added that she would also put a paw to the work herself so that he need not trouble himself to search farther.

The Prince was only too delighted to accept this offer and he and his charming hostess sat down to supper together, after which a magnificent display of fireworks was set off in his honor. And once more the days passed in enchanted succession. The ingenious White Cat knew a thousand different ways of entertaining her guest, so that he never once thought of missing human society. Indeed, he was probably the first person in the world to spend a whole year of complete contentment with only cats for company.

The second year slipped away as pleasantly as the first. The Prince could scarcely think of anything that the tireless hands did not instantly supply, whether books, jewels, pictures, old things or new. In short, he had but to say, "I want a certain gem that is in the cabinet of the Great Mogul, or the King of Persia, or such and such a statue in Corinth or any part of Greece," and he saw it instantly before him, without knowing how it came or who brought it. It is not unpleasant at all to find oneself able to possess any treasure in the world. No wonder our Prince was happy!

But the White Cat who was ever watchful of his welfare, warned him that the hour of departure was approaching and that he might make himself easy in his mind about the piece of cloth, for she had a most wonderful one for him. She added that it was her intention this time to furnish him with an equipage worthy of his high birth, and without waiting for his reply, beckoned him to the window overlooking the castle courtyard. Here he saw an open coach of gold and flame-color with a thousand gallant devices to please the mind and eye. It was drawn by twelve horses as white as snow, four-and-four abreast, with harnesses of flaming velvet embroidered with diamonds and gold. A hundred other coaches, each with eight horses and filled with superbly attired noblemen followed, escorted by a thousand bodyguards whose uniforms were so richly embroidered you could not see the material beneath. But the most remarkable part of this cavalcade was that a portrait of the White Cat was to be seen everywhere, in coach device, uniform, or worn as a decoration on the doublets of those who rode in the train, as if it were some newly created order that had been conferred upon them.

"Go now," said the White Cat to the Prince. "Appear at the court of the King, your father, in such magnificence that he cannot fail to be impressed and to bestow upon you the crown which you deserve. Here is another walnut. Crack it in his presence and you will find the piece of cloth you asked of me."

"Oh, dear White Cat," he answered tenderly,

"I am so overcome by your goodness that I would gladly give up my hopes of power and future grandeur to stay here with you the rest of life."

"Son of a King," she answered, "I am convinced of your kindness of heart. A kind heart is a rare thing among princes who would be loved by all, yet not love any one themselves. But you are the proof that there is an exception to this rule. I give you credit for the affection you have shown to a little white cat that after all is good for nothing but to catch mice."

So the Prince kissed her paw and departed.

This time the two brothers arrived at their father's palace before him, congratulating themselves that their young brother must be dead or gone for good. They lost no time in displaying the cloths they had brought, which were indeed so fine that they could pass through the eye of a large needle but not through the small eye of the needle the King had already selected. At this there arose a great murmuring at court. The friends of the two Princes took sides among themselves as to which had fulfilled the bargain better. But this was interrupted by a flourish of trumpets announcing the arrival of their younger brother.

The magnificence of his train fairly took away the breath of the King and his court, but their astonishment grew even greater when, after saluting his father, the young Prince brought out the walnut. This he cracked with great ceremony only to find, instead of the promised piece of cloth, a cherry stone. At sight of this the King and the court exchanged sly smiles. Nothing daunted, the Prince cracked the cherry stone, only to find a kernel inside. Jeers and murmurs ran through the great apartment. The Prince must be a fool indeed! He made no answer to them, but even he began to doubt the White Cat's words as he found next a grain of wheat and within that the smallest millet seed. "Oh, White Cat, White Cat! Have you betrayed me?" he muttered between his teeth. Even as he spoke he felt a little scratch upon his hand, so sharp that it drew blood. Taking this to be some sort of sign, the Prince proceeded to open the millet seed. Before the incredulous eyes of the whole court he drew out of it a piece of cloth four hundred yards long and marvelously embroidered with colored birds and beasts, with trees and fruits and flowers, with shells and jewels and even with suns and moons and countless stars. There were also portraits of Kings and Queens of the past upon it and of their children and children's children, not forgetting the smallest child, and each dressed perfectly in the habit of his century.

The sight of this was almost too much for the King. He could scarcely find the needle. Through its eye the wonderful piece of cloth was able to pass not only once, but six times, before the jealous gaze of the two older Princes. But the King was still far from ready to give up his kingdom. Once more he turned to his children.

"I am going to put your obedience to a new and final test," he told them. "Go and travel for another year and whichever one of you brings back with him the most beautiful Princess shall marry her and be crowned King on his wedding day. I pledge my honor that after this I shall ask no further favors of you."

So off the three went again, the youngest Prince still in a good humor although he had the least cause to be since he had twice been the acknowledged winner of the wager. But he was not one to dispute his father's will, so soon he and all his train were taking the road back to his dear White Cat. She knew the very day and hour of his arrival, and all along the way flowers had been strewn and perfume made the air sweet. Once more the castle gate was opened to him and the strange hands took him in charge while all the cats climbed into the trees to welcome their returning visitor.

"So, my Prince," said the White Cat when he reached her side at last, "once more you have returned without the crown. But no matter," she added as he opened his lips to explain. "I know that you are bound to take back the most beautiful Princess to court and I will find one for you, never fear. Meantime, let us amuse ourselves and be merry."

The third year passed for the young Prince as had the two others, and since nothing runs away faster than time passed without trouble or care, it is certain that he would have completely forgotten the day of his return to court had not the White Cat reminded him of it. This time, however, she told him that upon him alone depended his fate. He must promise to do whatever she asked of him. The Prince agreed readily enough until he heard her command him to cut off her head and tail and fling them into the fire.

"I!" cried the Prince, aghast, "I be so barbarous as to kill my dear White Cat? This is some trick to try my heart, but you should be sure of its gratitude."

"No, no, Son of a King," she answered, "I know your heart too well for that. But fate is stronger than either of us, and you must do as I bid you. It is the only way; and you must believe me, for I swear it on the honor of a Cat."

Tears came into the eyes of the Prince at the mere thought of cutting off the head of so amiable and pretty a creature. He tried to say all the most tender things he could think of, hoping to distract her. But she persisted that she wished to die by his hand because it was the only means of preventing his brothers from winning the crown. So piteously did she beg him that at last, all of a tremble, he drew his sword. With faltering hand he cut off the head and tail of his dear White Cat.

Next moment the most remarkable transformation took place before his very eyes. The body of the little White Cat suddenly changed into that of a young girl, the most graceful ever seen. But this was as nothing compared to the beauty and sweetness of her face, where only the shining brightness of the eyes gave any hint of the cat she had so recently been. The Prince was struck dumb with surprise and delight. He opened his eyes wider still to look at her, and what was his amazement to behold a troop of lords and ladies entering the apartment, each with a cat's skin flung over an arm. They advanced, and throwing themselves at the feet of their Queen, expressed their joy at seeing her once more restored to her natural form. She received them with great affection, but presently she desired them to leave her alone with the Prince.

"Behold, my dear Prince," she said as soon as they had done so, "I am released of a terrible enchantment, too long a tale to tell you now. Suffice it to say that this portrait which you saw upon my paw when I was a cat, was given to me by my guardian fairies during the time of my trial. I supposed it was of my first, unhappy love

who was so cruelly taken from me and whose resemblance to you is so striking. Conceive my joy then, to find that it is of the Prince who has my entire heart and who was destined to rescue me from my enchantment."

And she bowed low before our Prince, who was so filled with joy and wonder that he would have remained there forever telling her of his love, had she not reminded him that the hour for his return to his father's court was almost upon them. Taking him by the hands, she led him into the courtyard to a chariot even more magnificent than the one she had provided before. The rest were equally gorgeous, the horses shod with emeralds held in place by diamond nails, with such gold and jeweled trappings as were never seen before or since. But the young Prince had eyes for nothing beyond the beauty of his companion.

Just before they reached the outskirts of the city, they sighted the Prince's two brothers with their trains driving toward them from opposite directions. At this the Princess hid herself in a small throne of rock crystal and precious gems while the Prince remained alone in the coach. His two brothers, each accompanied by a charming lady, greeted him warmly but expressed surprise and curiosity that he should be alone. To these questions he replied that he had been so unfortunate as not to have met with any lady of sufficient beauty to bring with him to court. He added, however, that he had instead a very rare and gifted White Cat. At this the brothers laughed loudly and exchanged pleased glances, for now they were convinced that he was indeed a simpleton and they need have no fears of his outwitting them a third time.

Through the streets of the city the two elder Princes rode with their ladies in open carriages, while the youngest Prince came last. Behind him was borne the great rock crystal, at which every one gazed in wonder.

The two Princes eagerly charged up the palace stairs with their Princesses, so anxious were they for their father's approval. The King received them graciously, but once more had difficulty in deciding which should have the prize. So he turned to his youngest son, who stood alone before him. "Have you returned empty-handed this time?" he asked.

"In this rock your Majesty will find a little White Cat," he answered, "one which mews so sweetly and has such velvet paws that you cannot but be delighted with it."

But before the surprised King could reach the crystal, the Princess touched an inner spring. It flew open revealing her in all her beauty, more dazzling than the sun itself. Her hair fell in golden ringlets; she was crowned with flowers and she moved with incomparable grace in her gown of white and rose-colored gauze. Even the King himself could not resist such loveliness, but hastened to acknowledge her undisputed right to wear the crown.

"But I have not come to deprive your Majesty of a throne which you fill so admirably," she said, bowing before him graciously. "I was born the heiress to six kingdoms of my own, so permit me to offer one to you and to each of your elder sons. I ask no other favors of you than your friendship and that your youngest son shall be my husband. Three kingdoms will be quite enough for us."

And so in truth they found them.

THE GREY PALFREY

Kind beasts often come to the aid of the struggling heroes or heroines of folk tales, but never more romantically than in this tale.

In the county of Champagne there once lived a knight. He was young and handsome and brave, and indeed he was all things that a good knight should be; but he was poor, owning little land and only one small manor set in a forest, among the trees and away from the road.

This young knight went much to the tourneying, often going many miles from his home to where tournaments were being held, not only for the sake of the honour he would gain by his courage and skill, but for the prizes and for the ransoms he might ask from those he overthrew, for it was by these ransoms that he lived and bought all that was needed for himself and for

"The Grey Palfrey." From *French Legends, Tales and Fairy Stories* by Barbara Leonie Picard. Reprinted by permission of Henry A. Walck, Inc.

his servants and his few followers. Though his garments were always neat and his helmet and his hauberk polished bright, his clothes were plain and his armour none of the best, and the food he ate, though there was enough of it, was no rich fare.

But one thing this knight owned that would not have shamed the wealthiest lord, and that was a grey palfrey, the favourite among his few horses, with sleek and glossy hide and a mane and a tail like flowing silver, so that no one, seeing it, did not stop to admire. Very fleet was this palfrey, and it had not its match in all Champagne. It was the envy of the countryside, and many were the rich lords who sought to buy it from the knight. Yet poor as he was, not for all the wealth in the world would he have parted with his palfrey, for he counted it his friend; and so indeed it proved to be.

Some two miles from this knight's manor, beside the road which ran through the forest, stood the castle of a duke. Old he was, and rich, and very miserly, forever seeking to add wealth to wealth. He had one daughter, the only young and gracious thing in all his castle, and it was this maiden whom the poor knight loved, and she loved him in return. But because he was poor, though of good repute, her father would never have considered him as a suitor; and since the maiden was never permitted to leave the castle, they might only speak together secretly, through a crack in the castle wall.

Every day at the same hour, when he was not at the tourneying, the knight would ride on the grey palfrey from his manor to the castle of the Duke, by a secret path through the forest which he alone used. And every day when she might, the maiden would await his coming at the castle wall, and they would talk of their love for a few happy moments. But not every day could she leave her father's side, or steal away unobserved, so on many days the knight would wait in vain to see her before riding sadly home along the secret path. Yet this made the times when they met all the sweeter.

One day the knight could bear it no longer, and since he knew the maiden cared nothing for riches, and would have been content as his wife had he been a peasant and lived in a hovel, he went to the castle and asked to speak with her father. The old Duke welcomed him courteously, since fair words cost nothing, and the young knight said, "Lord, there is a favour I would ask of you."

"And what might it be?" said the Duke.

"I am poor," said the knight, "but I am nobly born, and my honour is unquestioned, and no man has ever been able to speak ill of me. I love your daughter and I know that she loves me. I am here to ask for her hand in marriage."

The old Duke went as pale as his white beard in his anger. "There is not a lord in all France, nor a prince in all Christendom, whom I could not buy for my daughter, if I wished her to marry. She is not for a poor knight such as you. Now begone from my castle and never speak to me of such matters again."

Heavy at heart, the knight rode home, but since the maiden loved him he did not lose all hope, and a day or two later he rode to a distant town where a great tournament was to be held, thinking that there he might win a small measure of those riches, which, if carefully saved, might cause the old Duke to relent.

At that time a lord, wealthy and old as the Duke himself, came to visit him, and after they had talked long together of the things they had done when young and the memories they had in common, the lord said, "We are both rich, but were our riches combined, they would be even greater. Were you to give me your daughter as a wife, I would ask no dowry with her, but you and I, thus linked by a marriage, might share our wealth for the rest of our days. What say you to this, my old friend?"

The Duke was glad and rubbed his hands together and nodded many times. "You have spoken well, it shall be as you say. In all France there will be none richer than we two."

The Duke set about preparations for the marriage and cared nothing for his daughter's tears, inviting some score or more guests for the wedding, old friends of his and the bridegroom's, greybeards all. And because of his avarice, he sent to his neighbours in the countryside, asking the loan of a horse or two from each, that there might be mounts enough to carry the guests and their squires along the road through the forest to the church. And so little shame he had, that he sent to the young knight to borrow his grey palfrey, that his daughter might ride to her wedding on the finest horse in all Champagne.

The young knight had returned from the tourneying, well pleased enough with life, for he had easily been the best of all the knights gathered there, and every prize he had carried home to his little manor in the forest; so that it seemed to him he was perhaps a step nearer that which he had set his heart upon. When he heard the Duke's message, he asked, "Why does your master wish to borrow my horse?"

And the Duke's servant answered, "So that my master's daughter may ride upon it tomorrow to her wedding at the church."

When the young knight learnt how the maiden he loved was to marry the old lord, he thought that his heart would break, and at first he would have refused with indignation the Duke's request. But then he thought, "Not for the sake of her father, but to do honour to the lady I love, will I lend my palfrey. It is I whom she loves, she will have no joy of this marriage, and perhaps it will comfort her a little if I send her the palfrey which is my friend." So he saddled and bridled the palfrey and gave it to the serving-man, and then he went to his own room and would neither eat nor drink, but flung himself down upon his bed and wept.

In the Duke's castle, on the eve of the wedding, his guests made merry, feasting and drinking deep, and since they were, like himself, all old, when the time came for them to go to rest, they were in truth most weary. But very early in the morning, before dawn indeed, while the moon still shown brightly, the watchman roused them that they might be at the church betimes. Grumbling and half asleep, the guests clothed themselves and gathered in the courtyard where their horses waited. Yawning, they climbed into the saddles and set out upon their way, with the Duke and the old lord at their head. And after all the others came the maiden on the grey palfrey, with her father's old seneschal to watch over her. She was clad in a fair gown, and over it a scarlet mantle trimmed with costly fur, but her face was pale and she wept, and she had not slept all night for sorrow.

In the moonlight they left the castle and took the forest road which led to the church; yet since the way was narrow and branches overhung the track, they might not ride two abreast, but followed each other one by one through the forest, with the old seneschal at the very end, after the weeping bride.

A little way along the road, from habit, the palfrey turned aside, taking the secret path that its master had so often used; and because the old seneschal was nodding and dozing as he rode, he never missed the maiden. Deep into the forest, along the secret way went the palfrey, and in terror the maiden looked about her. But though she was fearful, she did not cry out, for she thought, "I had rather be lost in the forest and devoured by the wild beasts, than live without the knight I love." And she let the palfrey carry her where it would.

After two miles, in the dim light of early dawn, the palfrey stopped before a small manor set among the trees and waited for the gate to be opened. The watchman peeped out through a grille and called, "Who is there?" And, trembling, the maiden answered, "I am alone and lost in the forest. Have pity on me and give me shelter till sunrise."

But the watchman, looking closely, knew his master's palfrey, and made all haste to where he was. "Lord," he said, "at the gate stands your palfrey, and on its back is a lady so lovely that I think she can be no mortal maid. Is it your will that I should let her in?"

The young knight leapt off his bed and ran to the gate and flung it wide and caught the maiden in his arms. When they had done with kissing and weeping for joy, he asked her, "How did you come here?" And she answered, "It was your grey palfrey that brought me, for I should not have known the way."

"Since you are here," said the knight, "here shall you stay, if you will it."

"It is all I ask, to be with you for ever," she said.

So the knight called for his chaplain, and with no delay he and the maiden were married, and in all the manor there was great rejoicing.

When the Duke and the old lord and their friends reached the church they found that the maiden was not with them, and they set themselves to search for her, all about the forest. But by the time the Duke came upon the little manor set among the trees, his daughter was a

wife, and there was nothing he could do about it, save give the marriage his blessing, which he did with an ill grace. But little the young knight and his lady cared for that.

THE MOUSE-PRINCESS

There is something sad about the Mouse-Princess, and the youngest Prince is so humble and so loyal that their story achieves a tenderness unusual in folk tales.

In the days that are passed there lived a king who had three sons. He had ruled well and wisely for more years than he liked to remember, and one day he thought to himself how he was growing old and might well hand the cares of state and governing to a younger man, so that for the time that remained to him he might enjoy a well-earned rest, while one of his sons took his place as king. But the problem that faced him was to which of his three sons he should give his crown and the responsibility that went with it.

The two elder princes were gay, gallant young men, at home in any company and well liked by everyone; but the youngest was a quiet, shy youth, well meaning and kindly enough, but given too much to thinking and reading to meet with his brothers' approval, and, let it be said, over fond of his own company to be altogether pleasing to others. The King saw the merits of each of his sons, but he saw also their disabilities. The two elder were perhaps a little too casual and easy going, a degree too fond of letting things look after themselves; while the youngest was, it is undeniable, rather too serious-minded, and given, besides, to making mountains out of mole-hills.

As the King was pondering his problem, he remembered the young men's mother, his good queen who was dead, and he thought, "Whatever a man is, it is his wife who helps him to be what he will become. Whichever of my sons suc-

"The Mouse-Princess." From *French Legends, Tales and Fairy Stories* by Barbara Leonie Picard. Reprinted by permission of Henry Z. Walck, Inc.

ceeds me, if he has a good queen, he will be half-way to being a good king." He considered then the qualities which go to make a good queen, having always in his mind the picture of his own beloved wife. "She must be patient," he thought, "she must be neat and deft, and she must not despise the simple, necessary things of life. Yet she must have beauty and dignity and noble bearing, and above all, she must be gracious and truly royal."

The King sent for his three sons, and to each of them he handed a hank of flax, saying, "I would know what manner of maiden she is who may one day be queen in your dear mother's place. Go, each of you, and give this flax to the lady of your choice, bid her spin it into thread, and when seven days are passed, bring me the thread she has spun."

The two elder brothers each loved a noble maiden of the court, the one a countess and the other the daughter of a duke, and at once they took the flax and went to their ladies, repeating their father's words and saying that they doubted not that on the results of their spinning would rest the choice of a successor. The Countess and the Duke's daughter were both proud and beautiful; indeed, there was little to choose between them for looks and arrogance. They were skilled in all the accomplishments of noblewomen: they could sing prettily enough and play upon the lute, and they could dance a measure trippingly; but they had never learnt to spin. However, when she saw a crown within her grasp, each of them eagerly set to work upon the flax, bidding her lover have no fear of the result.

But the youngest brother had no lady whom he loved. He was shy and confused in the company of maidens, feeling that they despised him for his lack of gallantry and his inability to talk sweet nonsense which he did not mean. He took his hank of flax, put it in his pocket, and rode out alone from the palace into the forest, depressed and despondent, worrying and teasing himself as to what his father would say to him, in seven days' time, when he gave him back the unspun flax. But he knew that he could not, not even to gain a crown, ask any maiden to spin the flax for him, and risk her scorn and her refusal.

Now, in a neighbouring kingdom, a few years before, the daughter of the King and Queen had had the misfortune to displease a witch, who had immediately turned her into a mouse. "A mouse shall you stay," the witch had said, "until you have made me laugh." As that witch had never been known to laugh, and was, besides, very ill-tempered, there seemed no likelihood of the Princess ever regaining her own shape. The King and the Queen would have been ready to care for their daughter in the form of a mouse for the rest of their lives, and give her every comfort: the best cheese for every meal and a room with ample holes in the wainscotting; but there were too many cats in that palace, and the mouse-princess took fright and ran away, right out of the palace and right out of the kingdom, and into the land ruled over by the old King who had three sons. There in a forest she came upon a ruined tower, all overgrown with ivy and yellow toadflax, and in this tower she made her home.

On the day when the King had given his sons the flax, the mouse was sitting on top of her ruined wall at the time when the youngest Prince rode by. She saw him come, and kept very still. It was a part of the forest where the Prince had never been before, and when he noticed the ruined tower, he felt that it was well fitted to his mood, and he dismounted and sat down upon a fallen block of stone. Seeing him so dejected, the mouse ran down the wall and went to him. Sitting up on her hind legs a yard or so from his feet, she asked him what ailed him. Had he been a less thoughtful person, he might have been surprised to hear a mouse speak, but as it was, he saw no reason why a mouse should not speak as well as a man. Since a courteous question deserves a courteous reply, the Prince told the mouse his troubles, and when he had finished, she said, "If you will permit it, I can help you."

"How can a mouse help me?" asked the Prince.

"Give me the flax and return here in seven days, and you shall see what you shall see."

Since the Prince had no one else to whom he dared give the flax, he saw no harm in giving it to the mouse. He pulled it out of his pocket, laid it down beside her, thanked her politely and rode away.

Seven days later he returned to the ruined tower, and there he found the mouse waiting for him, a little box beside her. "Take this box to the King," she said, "and let him open it."

Being himself kindly and good natured, the Prince did not doubt that the mouse would have done her best for him, and seeing that there was no one else to do as much, he thanked her gratefully and rode back to the palace. When he arrived, he found that his brothers were there before him, bringing the thread spun by their ladies. They laughed at their brother when they saw how he carried no thread but only a little box, and with confidence they gave their spools of thread to the King. He looked at them, turned them this way and that, unwound a length of thread from each, and then he sighed and laid them by. For the Countess's thread was as thick as hempen rope, while the thread spun by the Duke's daughter was so thin and uneven that a child could easily have snapped it. The King smiled encouragingly at his youngest son, who had held back, abashed by his brothers' taunts. "Where is your thread, my son?" The youngest Prince came forward and held out the little box. "It is here, father."

The King took the box and opened it. Inside was a ball of thread as fine as hair and as bright, but so strong that however hard he tugged at it, it would not break.

The two elder brothers looked at one another, eyebrows raised, and the King looked at his youngest son, wondering. But he said nothing, and only laid the ball of thread aside, as he had done with the spools. Then he smiled at his three sons. "The thread is only the beginning," he said, "it is the finished cloth which completes the task." And he gave to each of the young men a reel of linen thread spun by the chief spinning maid of the palace. It was neither so thick as the Countess's thread, nor yet so fine as the thread which the mouse had given the youngest Prince, and unlike the thread of the Duke's daughter, it was strong enough. "Go," he said, "and give this thread to the ladies of your choice, and bid them weave a length of cloth from it. When seven days are passed, bring the cloth to me."

The two elder brothers hurried to their ladies,

who had, naturally, never learnt to weave. But nothing daunted, thinking of the crown that was so close, they set to work as best they might.

The youngest brother put the reel of thread in his pocket and rode from the palace alone. This time he went straight to the ruined tower in the forest. "Little mouse, little mouse," he called, and there she was, her bright eyes gleaming, looking down at him from the top of the wall. "Did you give the box to the king?" she asked.

"I did, little mouse."

"And what did he say?"

"Why, he said nothing."

"That is well," she replied, and ran down the wall to his feet. "But why are you still sad?" He told her. "If you wish it, I will help you," she said.

He smiled, a little cheered. "If you would help me again, I should always be grateful."

"Give me the thread." He took it out of his pocket and laid it before her. "Come back in seven days," she said, "and you shall see what you shall see." And he thanked her and rode away.

Seven days later he returned to the ruined tower, and there was the mouse waiting for him, a little box by her side. "Take this box to the King," she said, "and let him open it."

He spent an hour or two with her, sitting on a block of fallen stone, talking of this and that; and she seemed to him an intelligent and likeable companion indeed. Then he took the little box, thanked her, and rode back to the palace. When he arrived he found his two brothers there before him, bringing the cloth woven by their ladies, and when they saw that he carried nothing but a wooden box which seemed too small to hold a length of cloth, they smiled their relief at each other. With confidence they gave their cloth to the King, who took each length in his hands and sighed and laid it by. The cloth woven by the Countess was so coarse and stiff that it could almost have stood up by itself, while the cloth woven by the Duke's daughter would have made a passable fisherman's net. The King looked at his youngest son. "Where is your cloth?" he asked.

The youngest Prince held out the little box. "It is here, father."

The King opened the box and pulled out, yard by yard, a length of cloth so soft and fine that the small box could easily contain it. Yet it was strong, with the warp and the woof even and smooth.

The two elder brothers looked at one another, frowning and angry, and the King looked at his youngest son, wondering. But he said nothing and only laid the length of cloth aside, next to the others. Then he smiled at his sons. "I have seen," he said, "what your ladies can do, and how skilled they are. But surely the final test of fitness to be a queen is in the bearing of the lady herself, and not in the skill of her hands. At midday tomorrow, let each of you come here with his bride, and I will tell you which of you shall be king in my place."

The two elder brothers hurried off to the Countess and the Duke's daughter, and the two ladies were thrown into a great flutter. The rest of that day they spent trying on their best gowns, choosing out their finest jewels, and strutting and preening themselves before their mirrors.

But the youngest Prince rode out of the palace, and because it was a habit with him by now, he went to the ruined tower. "Little mouse, little mouse, are you there?" And there she was, peeping out through a spray of honeysuckle which hung over a window-sill. "Did you give the box to the King?"

"I did, little mouse."

"And what did he say?"

"Why, nothing."

"That is well," she said. And she ran down the stem of the honeysuckle, out of the window and across to his feet.

"No," said the Prince, "it is not well. I shall never be a king." He sat down upon the grass and the mouse stood beside his hand. "What has your father asked of you now?" she said.

"That at midday tomorrow I shall bring him the lady who is to be my bride, the lady who spun the thread and wove the cloth. But alas, little mouse, there is no lady."

The mouse was silent; and the Prince, too, said nothing for many minutes, then he looked at the mouse and saw a large tear trickling down her nose. He tried hard to smile and to sound as though he did not care. "This time you cannot

help me, little mouse, but you have done enough already, and you must not think that I am ungrateful because I am sad." He took a ring off his finger. "See, here is a gift for you to remember me by." He laid it gently beside her on the grass and stood up. "Good-bye, little mouse, and thank you." He mounted his horse and rode away, and she cried out after him, "I will help you. I will find a way." But he only turned and shook his head and smiled at her.

All that night the mouse-princess thought and thought, but she could think of no way to help the Prince, and in the morning she still had no plan. But as it approached midday, she could not bear not to be with him to comfort him when his brothers came with their brides and he had none. So she picked up his ring in her mouth and she ran and she ran through the forest until she reached the highway. And there she stopped, for she could run no farther. At that moment a man came by with a crate of chickens for the market. The mouse stepped out into his path, dropped the ring, sat up and spoke to him. "Good friend," she said, "give me your black cock, and make me a bridle and saddle, that I may ride on him."

The man was so surprised to hear a mouse speak and so amused by her request, that he thought, "It will be worth the loss of the price of my black cock, just to have such a story to tell." He made a bridle out of plaited grasses and a saddle out of a dock leaf, and saddled and bridled the cock. The mouse thanked him, took up the ring in her mouth and mounted upon the back of the cock, and away they went, towards the palace of the King.

Now, it happened that the way to the palace lay past the castle where the witch lived who had put the spell on the Princess, and her servant was at the window when the mouse rode by on the cock. The servant burst out laughing. "Idle wench," scolded the witch, "what are you laughing at?"

"Why, mistress, I have never seen such a sight in my life!" But the girl could say no more for laughing.

"You foolish creature," said the witch, and she came angrily to the window. But when she looked out and saw the mouse riding on the cock, she, who had never been known even to smile, found herself laughing until the tears ran down her cheeks. And in that moment the mouse became a princess, in silk and velvet and pearls, with a crown upon her head, riding on a black horse with green and golden trappings.

Promptly at midday, the two elder Princes, with their brides beside them, came before the King; and the youngest Prince followed after them, alone.

Nothing could have been more splendid than the sight offered by the Countess and the Duke's daughter. Their gowns were so stiff with jewels that it was a marvel the ladies could move at all, and they flashed so brightly that the King's eyes were almost dazzled. And as for their regal dignity, why, if the Countess had tilted her head much higher, she would surely have tripped and fallen; while as for the disdain of the Duke's daughter, it seemed to include even the King himself.

The two elder brothers presented their brides, and the two ladies curtsied to the King. He spoke to them kindly, and kissed each of them upon the cheek. "You have my blessing, daughters," he said. He turned to the two Princes. "My sons, you have chosen suitably." The Princes bowed to their father and kissed his hand, self-satisfaction glowing in their hearts, for they had not seen the twinkle in his eyes. But the Countess and the Duke's daughter glared haughtily at one another over their bridegroom's heads, all their past friendship forgotten in their present rivalry.

The King beckoned to his youngest son. "Where is your bride?" he asked.

The youngest Prince knelt before his father. "Father, I have none," he said, and hung his head in shame, whilst his brothers grinned at one another.

At that moment the chamberlain hurried in and whispered to the King. The King smiled a little. "Bring her in," he said.

A minute or so later, the Princess was curtseying to the King, and a few seconds after that, she was standing by the youngest Prince; and there was not a lady in all that court who would not have seemed like a serving-wench beside her.

"Look up, my son," said the King, "and see your bride."

The Prince looked up and saw the loveliest maiden he had ever dreamt of, with a crown upon her head; unconscious of the richness of her garments, graceful and gracious and perfectly at ease, she smiled at him, and he felt neither awkward nor shy. He rose and asked in wonder, "Who are you?"

"I am your bride," she said.

He looked at her and loved her in that instant; then he looked at his brothers and saw their anger, he looked at the Countess and at the Duke's daughter and saw their jealousy and of how little worth they were, and he looked at the King and saw the smile on his lips, and he knew that he had but to say a single word and the crown would be his. Yet he could not say that word. He turned away from the Princess and said, "This is not my bride. If any should be my bride, it should be the little mouse who spun the yarn and wove the cloth for me."

"But I was the mouse," said the Princess. "See, here is your ring." And she held it out to him. He took it and put it on her finger and kissed her; and that is the end of the tale.

Italian folk tales

The following two stories are from Old Italian Tales, *retold by Domenico Vittorini. The book is a treasure for the storyteller. Some of the stories are adapted from oral sources, and one is taken from Boccaccio, that master of the storytelling art. The whole collection of twenty tales has unusual variety, an earthy sort of humor, and a vigorous sense of justice. Told with simplicity and respect for sources, these lively tales prove again how little human nature differs from country to country.*

MARCH AND THE SHEPHERD

This duel of wits between two tricksters, with the shepherd always the winner, makes the wry humor of the conclusion quite acceptable.

One morning, in the very beginning of spring, a shepherd led his sheep to graze, and on the way he met March.

"Good morning," said March. "Where are you going to take your sheep to graze today?"

"Well, March, today I am going to the mountains."

"Fine, Shepherd. That's a good idea. Good luck." But to himself March said, "Here's where I have some fun, for today I'm going to fix you."

And that day in the mountains the rain came down in buckets; it was a veritable deluge. The shepherd, however, had watched March's face very carefully and noticed a mischievous look on it. So, instead of going to the mountains, he had remained in the plains. In the evening, upon returning home, he met March again.

"Well, Shepherd, how did it go today?"

"It couldn't have been better. I changed my mind and went to the plains. A very beautiful day. Such a lovely warm sun."

"Really? I'm glad to hear it," said March, but he bit his lip in vexation. "Where are you going tomorrow?"

"Tomorrow I'm going to the plains, too. With this fine weather, I would be crazy if I went to the mountains."

"Oh, really? Fine! Farewell."

And they parted.

But the shepherd didn't go to the plains again; he went to the mountains. And on the plains March brought rain and wind and hail—a punishment indeed from heaven. In the evening he met the shepherd homeward bound.

"Good evening, Shepherd. How did it go today?"

"Very well indeed. Do you know? I changed my mind again and went to the mountains after all. It was heavenly there. What a day! What a sky! What a sun!"

"March and the Shepherd." Reprinted by permission of David McKay Company, Inc., New York, from *Old Italian Tales,* copyright © 1958 by Domenico Vittorini

"I'm really happy to hear it, Shepherd. And where are you going tomorrow?"

"Well, tomorrow I'm going to the plains. I see dark clouds over the mountains. I wouldn't want to find myself too far from home."

To make a long story short, whenever the shepherd met March, he always told him the opposite of what he planned to do the next day, so March was never able to catch him. The end of the month came and on the last day, the thirtieth, March said to the shepherd, "Well, Shepherd, how is everything?"

"Things couldn't be any better. This is the end of the month and I'm out of danger. There's nothing to fear now; I can begin to sleep peacefully."

"That's true," said March. "And where are you going tomorrow?"

The shepherd, certain that he had nothing to fear, told March the truth. "Tomorrow," he said, "I shall go to the plains. The distance is shorter and the work less hard."

"Fine. Farewell."

March hastened to the home of his cousin April and told her the whole story. "I want you to lend me at least one day," he said. "I am determined to catch this shepherd." Gentle April was unwilling, but March coaxed so hard that finally she consented.

The following morning the shepherd set off for the plains. No sooner had his flock scattered when there arose a storm that chilled his very heart. The sharp wind howled and growled; snow fell in thick icy flakes; hail pelted down. It was all the shepherd could do to get his sheep back into the fold.

That evening as the shepherd huddled in a corner of his hearth, silent and melancholy, March paid him a visit.

"Good evening, Shepherd," he said.

"Good evening, March."

"How did it go today?"

"I'd rather not talk about it," said the shepherd. "I can't understand what happened. Not even in the middle of January have I ever seen a storm like the one on the plains today. It seemed as if all the devils had broken loose from hell. Today I had enough rough weather to last me the whole year. And, oh, my poor sheep!"

Then at last was March satisfied.

And from that time on March has had thirty-one days because, as it is said in Tuscany, the rascal never returned to April the day he borrowed from her.

THE MOST PRECIOUS POSSESSION

This tale starts off as if it were to be a variant of "Dick Whittington" without the rags-to-riches theme, but the conclusion is different.

There was a time when Italian traders and explorers, finding the way to the East blocked by the Turks, turned west in their search for new lands to trade with—a search that led to the discovery of the New World.

In those days there lived in Florence a merchant by the name of Ansaldo. He belonged to the Ormanini family, known not only for its wealth but for the daring and cunning of its young men. It happened that on one of his trips in search of adventure and trade, Ansaldo ventured beyond the Strait of Gibraltar and, after battling a furious storm, landed on one of the Canary Islands.

The king of the island welcomed him cordially, for the Florentines were well known to him. He ordered a magnificent banquet prepared and arranged to have it served in the sumptuous hall, resplendent with mirrors and gold, in which he had received Ansaldo.

When it was time to serve the meal, Ansaldo noticed with surprise that a small army of youths, carrying long stout sticks, entered and lined up against the walls of the banquet hall. As each guest sat down, one of the youths took up a place directly behind him, the stick held in readiness to strike.

Ansaldo wondered what all this meant and wracked his brain for some clue to these odd goings-on. He didn't have long to wait. Suddenly, a horde of huge ferocious rats poured into the hall and threw themselves upon the food that was being served. Pandemonium broke loose as

"The Most Precious Possession." Reprinted by permission of David McKay Company, Inc., New York, from *Old Italian Tales,* copyright © 1958 by Domenico Vittorini

the boys darted here and there, wielding the sticks.

For many years the Florentines had enjoyed the reputation of being the cleverest people on earth, able to cope with any situation. Ansaldo saw a chance to uphold the tradition. He asked the king's permission to go back to his ship, and returned shortly with two big Persian cats. These animals were much admired and loved by the Florentines and Venetians who had first seen them in the East and who had brought many of them back to Italy. Ever since, one or two cats always completed the crew of a ship when it set out on a long journey.

Ansaldo let the cats go and before long the entire hall was cleared of the revolting and destructive rats.

The astonished and delighted king thought he was witnessing a miracle. He could not find words enough to thank Ansaldo whom he hailed as the saviour of the island, and when Ansaldo made him a present of the cats, his gratitude knew no bounds.

After a pleasant visit, Ansaldo made ready to sail for home. The king accompanied him to his ship and there he showered him with rich and rare gifts, much gold and silver, and many precious stones of all kinds and colors—rubies, topazes, and diamonds.

Ansaldo was overwhelmed not only by these costly gifts but by the king's gratitude and the praises he heaped upon him and on the cats. As for the latter, they were regarded with awe by all the islanders and as their greatest treasure by the king and the entire royal household.

When Ansaldo returned home he regaled his friends with the account of his strange adventure. There was among them a certain Giocondo de' Fifanti who was as rich in envy as he was poor in intelligence. He thought: "If the island king gave Ansaldo all these magnificent gifts for two mangy cats, what will he not give me if I present him with the most beautiful and precious things that our city of Florence has to offer?" No sooner said than done. He purchased lovely belts, necklaces, bracelets studded with diamonds, exquisite pictures, luxurious garments and many other expensive gifts and took ship for the now famous Canary Islands.

After an uneventful crossing he arrived in

port and hastened to the royal palace. He was received with more pomp than was Ansaldo. The king was greatly touched by the splendor of Giocondo's gifts and wanted to be equally generous. He held a long consultation with his people and then informed Giocondo happily that they had decided to let him share with his visitor their most precious possession. Giocondo could hardly contain his curiosity. However, the day of departure finally arrived and found Giocondo on his ship, impatiently awaiting the visit of the king. Before long, the king, accom-

panied by the entire royal household and half the islanders, approached the ship. The king himself carried the precious gift on a silken cushion. With great pride he put the cushion into Giocondo's outstretched greedy hands. Giocondo was speechless. On the cushion, curled up in sleepy, furry balls, were two of the kittens that had been born to the Persian cats Ansaldo had left on the island.

The old story does not go on to say whether Giocondo, on his return to Florence, ever regaled his friends with the tale of *his* adventure!

Spanish folk tales

So lively and varied are the Spanish folk tales that a good storyteller will wish to look up more of them than this collection has room for. They range from nursery tales to elaborate stories of mature content. See bibliography.

THE HALF-CHICK

Before telling this story, explain to the children about weathervanes, and show them the picture of the weathercock on p. 132.

There was once upon a time a handsome, black Spanish hen, who had a large brood of chickens. They were all fine, plump little birds, except the youngest who was quite unlike his brothers and sisters. This one looked just as if he had been cut in two. He had only one leg, and one wing, and one eye and he had half a head and half a beak. His mother shook her head sadly as she looked at him and said:

"My youngest born is only a half-chick. He can never grow up a tall handsome cock like his brothers. They will go out into the world and rule over poultry yards of their own. But this poor little fellow will always have to stay at home with his mother." And she called him Medio Pollito, which is Spanish for half-chick.

Now though Medio Pollito was such an odd, helpless-looking little thing, his mother soon

found he was not at all willing to remain under her wing and protection. Indeed, in character he was as unlike his brothers and sisters as he was in appearance. They were good, obedient chickens, and when the old hen called them, they chirped and ran back to her side. But Medio Pollito had a roving spirit in spite of his one leg, and when his mother called him to return to the coop, he pretended he could not hear because he had only one ear.

When she took the whole family out for a walk in the fields, Medio Pollito would hop away by himself and hide among the Indian corn. Many an anxious moment his brothers and sisters had looking for him, while his mother ran to and fro cackling in fear and dismay.

As he grew older he became more self-willed and disobedient. His manner to his mother was often rude and his temper to the other chickens disagreeable.

One day he had been out for a longer expedition than usual in the fields. On his return he strutted up to his mother with a peculiar little hop and kick which was his way of walking and, cocking his one eye at her in a very bold way, he said:

"Mother, I am tired of this life in a dull farmyard, with nothing but a dreary maize field to look at. I'm off to Madrid to see the king."

"To Madrid, Medio Pollito!" exclaimed his mother. "Why, you silly chick, it would be a long journey for a grown-up cock; a poor little thing like you would be tired out before you had gone half the distance. No, no, stay at home with your mother and some day, when you are bigger, we will go on a little journey together."

But Medio Pollito had made up his mind. He would not listen to his mother's advice, nor to the prayers and entreaties of his brothers and sisters.

"What is the use of our crowding each other in this poky little place?" he said. "When I have a fine courtyard of my own at the king's palace, I shall perhaps ask some of you to come and pay me a short visit." And scarcely waiting to say good-bye to his family, away he stumped down the high road that led to Madrid.

"Be sure you are kind and civil to everyone you meet," called his mother, running after him. But he was in such a hurry to be off he did not wait to answer her or even to look back.

A little later in the day, as he was taking a short cut through a field, he passed a stream. Now the stream was choked and overgrown with weeds and water plants so its waters could not flow freely.

"Oh, Medio Pollito!" it cried, as the half-chick hopped along its banks. "Do come and help me by clearing away these weeds."

"Help you, indeed!" exclaimed Medio Pollito, tossing his head and shaking the few feathers in his tail. "Do you think I have nothing to do but waste my time on such trifles? Help yourself, and don't trouble busy travelers. I am off to Madrid to see the king." And hoppity-kick, hoppity-kick, away stumped Medio Pollito.

A little later he came to a fire that had been left by some gypsies in a wood. It was burning very low and would soon be out.

"Oh, Medio Pollito," cried the fire, in a weak wavering voice as the half-chick approached, "in a few minutes I shall go quite out unless you put some sticks and dry leaves upon me. Do help me or I shall die!"

"Help you, indeed!" answered Medio Pollito. "I have other things to do. Gather sticks for yourself and don't trouble me. I am off to Ma-

drid to see the king." And hoppity-kick, hoppity-kick, away stumped Medio Pollito.

The next morning, as he was nearing Madrid, he passed a large chestnut tree in whose branches the wind was caught and entangled.

"Oh, Medio Pollito," called the wind, "do hop up here and help me get free of these branches. I cannot come away and it is so uncomfortable."

"It is your own fault for going there," answered Medio Pollito. "I can't waste all my morning stopping here to help you. Just shake yourself off and don't hinder me, for I am off to Madrid to see the king." And hoppity-kick, hoppity-kick, away stumped Medio Pollito in great glee, for the towers and roofs of Madrid were now in sight.

When he entered the town he saw before him

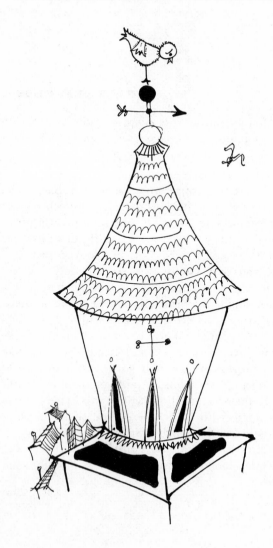

a great splendid house, with soldiers standing before the gates. This he knew must be the royal palace, and he determined to hop up to the front gate and wait there until the king came out. But as he was hopping past one of the back windows, the king's cook saw him.

"Here is the very thing I want," he exclaimed, "for the king has just sent a message that he must have chicken broth for his dinner!" And opening the window he stretched out his arm, caught Medio Pollito, and popped him into the broth pot standing near the fire. Oh, how wet and clammy the water felt as it went over Medio Pollito's head, making his feathers cling to his side.

"Water, water," he cried in his despair, "do have pity upon me and do not wet me like this."

"Ah, Medio Pollito," replied the water, "you would not help me when I was a little stream away in the fields and now you must be punished."

Then the fire began to burn and scald Medio Pollito. He hopped from one side of the pot to the other, trying to get away from the heat, and crying out in pain:

"Fire, fire! Do not scorch me like this. You cannot think how it hurts."

"Ah, Medio Pollito," answered the fire, "you would not help me when I was dying away in the wood. You are being punished."

At last, just when the pain was so great Medio Pollito thought he must die, the cook lifted up the lid of the pot to see if the broth was ready for the king's dinner.

"Look here," he cried in horror, "this chicken is quite useless! It is burned to a cinder. I can't send it up to the royal table." And opening the window he threw Medio Pollito out into the street. But the wind caught him up and whirled him through the air so quickly Medio Pollito could scarcely breathe, and his heart beat against his side till he thought it would break.

"Oh, wind," he gasped out, "if you hurry me along like this you will kill me. Do let me rest a moment, or—" But he was so breathless he could not finish his sentence.

"Ah, Medio Pollito," replied the wind, "when I was caught in the branches of the chestnut tree you would not help me. Now you are punished." And he swirled Medio Pollito over the roofs of the houses till they reached the highest church in the town, and there he left him fastened to the top of the steeple.

And there stands Medio Pollito to this day. If you go to Madrid and walk through the streets till you come to the highest church, you will see Medio Pollito perched on his one leg on the steeple, with his one wing drooping at his side, and gazing sadly out of his one eye over the town.

THE JOKES OF SINGLE-TOE

Padre Porko is a unique character in Spanish folklore. He is the gentlemanly pig, wise, witty, and urbane. He solves his own and his neighbors' problems with nonchalance. Look up the other stories in the book that bears his name. They are all good to tell.

"Chestnuts are ripening and falling on the other side of the canal," said the black-headed sparrow, teetering on the edge of the table.

"Oh, but it's too early for chestnuts," observed the Padre. "It takes two or three frosty nights to open the prickles."

"Well, if you can't believe me," said the sparrow, ruffling his collar, "ask the squirrel. He keeps track of the nuts."

So the Padre asked Single-Toe (so named because he had only one on his left front foot). The squirrel put his paw beside his nose as though he were trying to think up an answer to a riddle. "I'll try to let you know in three days," he mumbled, "but don't do anything about chestnuts until you see me again." And he went off in such a rush that even the good Padre grew suspicious.

An hour later he laid down his pipe and beckoned to Mrs. Wren. "Do you mind having a little fly around the wood to see what the squirrel family is up to this morning?"

She came back twittering all over. "The squirrels, for miles around, are all in the grove across the canal, throwing down the chestnuts for dear life. Single-Toe is making them work all the

"The Jokes of Single-Toe." From *Padre Porko* by Robert Davis, Holiday House. Copyright, 1939, by Robert Davis.

harder, and giggling at something he seems to think very funny."

"Oh, the rascal," chuckled the Padre. "The sly little one-toed sinner! He will give me an answer in three days, will he? Yes, indeed, after he has gathered all the best nuts." He called to his housekeeper. "Mrs. Hedge-Hog, bring me three of the oatmeal sacks from the cupboard and some strong string." And folding the bags inside his belt, he trotted off, pushing his wheelbarrow.

Up among the leaves, busy pulling the polished nuts out of the burrs, Single-Toe and his relatives did not hear the Padre arrive. Patter, plop, plop, plop, patter—the brown nuts were falling on the grass.

"What a lark," beamed the Padre, stuffing four or five into his mouth at once. "And this year they are sweeter and juicier than they have been for a long time." He made little piles of the biggest ones, and began filling his sacks. Finally he had all the wheelbarrow would carry. Bouncing the last bag up and down so he could tie the string around the top, he called out in his silkiest voice, "Many thanks, Single-Toe. You will see that I have taken only the big ones. I do hope that the prickers haven't made your paws sore."

There was a sudden calm in the chestnut grove. The squirrels came leaping down to a low bough, from where they could send sour looks after the Padre, trundling his barrow along toward the bridge. He was singing,

> With chestnuts roasting in a row,
> I love to hear them sizzle.
> I care not how the winds may blow,
> Nor how the rain-drops drizzle.
> I welcome every Jack and Jill
> Who knocks upon my door.
> We toast our toes and eat our fill,
> For there are plenty more.

One day three or four weeks later the Padre was doing a little carpentering under the umbrella pine, when something behind him sniffed. He jumped, and dropped two nails out of his mouth. There, under the table, tears running down their noses, were Mrs. Single-Toe and the four children.

"Bless my blue-eyed buttons," exclaimed the Padre, spitting out the rest of the nails. "What can be as wrong as all that?"

"It's Papa," said the oldest boy. "He's been in a hole by the old oak for four days, and is almost starved."

"But why doesn't he come home?" said the Padre. "The oak isn't far away."

"The fox won't let him," sobbed Madame Single-Toe.

"And why not?"

"He's mad because of Papa's jokes," the youngest child explained.

The Padre's mouth opened in a wide grin. "More of the jokes that other people don't find funny, eh? Well, I'll take a stroll by the twisted oak and have a talk with the fox." As he started off, he called over his shoulder, "Mrs. Hedge-Hog, you might give these youngsters a couple of the pickled chestnuts we keep for company." He winked solemnly at Mrs. Single-Toe, who blushed.

The fox was lying with his muzzle just an inch from the hole. He did not budge, nor lift his eye when the Padre wished him good morning. "I've got him this time," he snarled. "Four days I've been watching this hole. My mother brings my meals and keeps guard while I eat. He'll not get away *this* time!"

"He is a nuisance with his jokes, I admit," said the Padre peaceably, "but he doesn't do any real harm. Don't you think a good scare would be enough for him?"

"No, I don't," snapped the fox. "And don't you mix in this business, Padre, with your talk about kindness. What I've suffered from that little pest you'd never believe. First he dropped a tomato on my nose—a tomato that was too ripe. And then he dribbled pitch all over my head and neck while I was asleep. So don't waste your time." The fox advanced his red tongue hungrily to the very edge of the hole.

The Padre walked away, deep in thought. His generous heart was very unhappy. What should he say to the near-orphans in his kitchen? There must be some way to save him. Suddenly he saw some crows gossiping in a dead pine. "Will one of you black boys do me a favor, in a great hurry?" he called.

"Certainly, Don Porko," they all cawed.

"Fly low through the woods, and tell every

rabbit you see that I want their road commissioner to come to my house for dinner. Say that I'm going to have celery root and cabbage, chopped in parsley."

The Padre's guest was promptness itself. He used a turnip leaf as a napkin, and when he had wiped his whiskers, ate the napkin. "It makes less for Ma'am Hedge-Hog to clear up," he explained.

"Now for serious business," said the Padre, leading the way to the garden, when they had finished their second glass of dandelion wine. "I have invited you here as an expert. We will draw a map." He made a cross in the soft earth with a stick. "Here is the oak that the lightning split. And here in front of it, so, is a rabbit hole that was begun, but never finished. Do you follow me?"

The road commissioner nodded. "I know it perfectly. The workman was caught by an owl when he came up with some dirt."

"Now," continued the Padre, "how far is the bottom of this unfinished hole from one of your regular tunnels, and how long would it take to dig up to it?"

"About half a jump," replied the road commissioner. "The 'Alley to the Ivy Rock' runs very close to that unfinished hole. A good digger can do a medium-sized jump of tunnel in half a day. I should say it would take two hours to dig upwards from 'Ivy Rock Alley' and join the hole."

The Padre beckoned the road commissioner to follow him to the cellar. Scraping away the sand, he laid bare ten carrots, each as smooth and straight as an orange-colored candle. "These are yours, Mr. Commissioner, if you will do this little job of digging for me."

The bargain was soon struck. "One thing more," said the Padre, as the commissioner was lolloping away. "You will find a friend of mine in the unfinished hole. Don't let him make a noise, but bring him here the moment you can get him free. I'll be waiting."

Daylight was fading when the rabbit returned, covered with damp earth to his armpits. He was supporting a hoarse, hungry, and grimy red squirrel. The Padre welcomed them, pointing to the cupboard. "Sh-h-h-sh, go and see what's inside, Single-Toe."

One might have thought a hundred squirrels were behind the cupboard door, such was the hugging and chattering, the rubbing of noses, and the scratching of ears. Single-Toe was invited to stay for a light lunch, even after the road commissioner had left for his burrow, the biggest carrot in his mouth.

Safe, fed, and warmed, the red squirrel became his own gay self again. He began to chuckle, then to shake with merriment. "Ha, ha, ha! That silly old fox is still there, watching an empty hole! Won't it be a priceless joke, if I climb the oak and drop a rotten egg on his nose?"

At the word "joke," Mrs. Single-Toe, the four little squirrels, and the good Padre, all stiffened.

"Don't you ever say that word again," said his wife. "Do you hear, no more jokes, never, never."

Single-Toe wilted. "Yes," he confessed, not daring to meet the Padre's eye, "jokes aren't always so terribly funny, are they? Not even for the joker."

Irish folk tales

How is it possible to characterize the hero tales, the sorrowful romances, the drolls, the strange half-world of faery with its enchantments and spells, which mark the Celtic fairy tales? Great variety of plots and beauty of style have come from the lips of Irish storytellers, and far less humor than most people seem to expect. Indeed, so few and far between are the drolls and so numerous the somber tales of heroism and romance which come to tragic ends that the Irish tales as a whole have never been popular with children. The two examples given here are as different in plot and style as possible. "Connla and the Fairy Maiden" is more typical than the amusing "King O'Toole."

KING O'TOOLE AND HIS GOOSE

Stories of the saints walking the earth and taking part in men's affairs were fairly common in the Middle Ages. Usually, they were serious stories but here is a hilarious exception.

Och, I thought all the world, far and near, had heerd of King O'Toole—well, well, but the darkness of mankind is untollable! Well, sir, you must know, as you didn't hear it afore, that there was a king, called King O'Toole, who was a fine old king in the old ancient times, long ago; and it was he that owned the churches in the early days. The king, you see, was the right sort; he was the real boy, and loved sport as he loved his life, and hunting in particular; and from the rising o' the sun, up he got and away he went over the mountains after the deer; and fine times they were.

Well, it was all mighty good, as long as the king had his health; but, you see, in the course of time the king grew old, by raison he was stiff in his limbs, and when he got stricken in years, his heart failed him, and he was lost entirely for want o' diversion, because he couldn't go a-hunting no longer; and, by dad, the poor king was obliged at last to get a goose to divert him. Oh, you may laugh, if you like, but it's truth I'm telling you; and the way the goose diverted him was this-a-way: You see, the goose used to swim across the lake, and go diving for trout and catch fish on a Friday for the king, and flew every other day round about the lake, diverting the poor king. All went on mighty well until, by dad, the goose got stricken in years like her master, and couldn't divert him no longer; and then it was that the poor king was lost entirely. The king was walkin' one mornin' by the edge of the lake, lamentin' his cruel fate, and thinking of drowning himself, that could get no diversion in life, when all of a sudden, turning round the corner, whom should he meet but a mighty decent young man coming up to him.

"God save you," says the king to the young man.

"God save you kindly, King O'Toole," says the young man.

"King O'Toole and His Goose." From *Celtic Fairy Tales*, edited by Joseph Jacobs. By permission of G. P. Putnam's Sons and Frederick Muller Ltd., London

"True for you," says the king. "I am King O'Toole," says he, "prince and plennypenny-tinchery of these parts," says he; "but how came ye to know that?" says he.

"Oh, never mind," says Saint Kavin.

You see it was Saint Kavin, sure enough—the saint himself in disguise and nobody else. "Oh, never mind," says he, "I know more than that. May I make bold to ask how is your goose, King O'Toole?" says he.

"Blur-an-agers, how came ye to know about my goose?" says the king.

"Oh, no matter; I was given to understand it," says Saint Kavin.

After some more talk the king says, "What are you?"

"I'm an honest man," says Saint Kavin.

"Well, honest man," says the king, "and how is it you make your money so aisy?"

"By makin' old things as good as new," says Saint Kavin.

"Is it a tinker you are?" says the king.

"No," says the saint; "I'm no tinker by trade, King O'Toole; I've a better trade than a tinker," says he—"What would you say," says he, "if I made your old goose as good as new?"

My dear, at the word of making his goose as good as new, you'd think the poor old king's eyes were ready to jump out of his head. With that the king whistled, and down came the poor goose, just like a hound, waddling up to the poor cripple, her master, and as like him as two peas. The minute the saint clapt his eyes on the goose, "I'll do the job for you," says he, "King O'Toole."

"By Jaminee!" says King O'Toole, "if you do, I'll say you're the cleverest fellow in the seven parishes."

"Oh, by dad," says Saint Kavin, "you must say more nor that—my horn's not so soft all out," says he, "as to repair your old goose for nothing; what'll you gi' me if I do the job for you?—that's the chat," says Saint Kavin.

"I'll give you whatever you ask," says the king; "isn't that fair?"

"Divil a fairer," says the saint, "that's the way to do business. Now," says he, "this is the bargain I'll make with you, King O'Toole: will you gi' me all the ground the goose flies over, the first offer, after I make her as good as new?"

Well, my dear, it was a beautiful sight to see the king standing with his mouth open, looking at his poor old goose flying as light as a lark, and better than ever she was; and when she lit at his feet, patted her on the head, and "Ma vourneen," says he, "but you are the darlint o' the world."

"And what do you say to me," says Saint Kavin, "for making her the like?"

"By Jabers," says the king, "I say nothing beats the art o' man, barring the bees."

"And do you say no more nor that?" says Saint Kavin.

"And that I'm beholden to you," says the king.

"But will you gi'e me all the ground the goose flew over?" says Saint Kavin.

"I will," says King O'Toole, "and you're welcome to it," says he, "though it's the last acre I have to give."

"But you'll keep your word true," says the saint.

"As true as the sun," says the king.

"It's well for you, King O'Toole, that you said that word," says he; "for if you didn't say that word, the divil the bit o' your goose would ever fly agin."

When the king was as good as his word, Saint Kavin was pleased with him; and then it was that he made himself known to the king. "And," says he, "King O'Toole, you're a decent man, for I only came here to try you. You don't know me," says he, "because I'm disguised."

"Musha! then," says the king, "who are you?"

"I'm Saint Kavin," said the saint, blessing himself.

"Oh, queen of heaven!" says the king, making the sign of the cross between his eyes, and falling down on his knees before the saint; "is it the great Saint Kavin," says he, "that I've been discoursing all this time without knowing it," says he, "all as one as if he was a lump of a gossoon? —and so you're a saint?" says the king.

"I am," says Saint Kavin.

"By Jabers, I thought I was only talking to a dacent boy," says the king.

"Well, you know the difference now," says the saint. "I'm Saint Kavin," says he, "the greatest of all the saints."

And so the king had his goose as good as new to divert him as long as he lived; and the saint

"I will," says the king.

"You won't go back o' your word?" says Saint Kavin.

"Honour bright!" says King O'Toole, holding out his fist.

"Honour bright!" says Saint Kavin, back again, "it's a bargain. Come here!" says he to the poor old goose—"come here, you unfortunate ould cripple, and it's I that'll make you the sporting bird." With that, my dear, he took up the goose by the two wings—"Criss o' my cross an you," says he, markin' her to grace with the blessed sign at the same minute—and throwing her up in the air, "whew," says he, jist givin' her a blast to help her; and with that, my jewel, she took to her heels, flyin' like one o' the eagles themselves, and cutting as many capers as a swallow before a shower of rain.

supported him after he came into his property, as I told you, until the day of his death—and that was soon after; for the poor goose thought he was catching a trout one Friday; but, my jewel, it was a mistake he made—and instead of a trout, it was a thieving horse-eel; and instead of the goose killing a trout for the king's supper —by dad, the eel killed the king's goose—and small blame to him; but he didn't ate her, because he darn't ate what Saint Kavin had laid his blessed hands on.

CONNLA AND
THE FAIRY MAIDEN

This is an ancient story that goes back to the pre-Christian times of the Druids. Some think it is one of the most ancient of recorded stories. It is a good example of romance between a fairy maiden and a mortal. Notice the description of fairyland, which the poet William Butler Yeats translated as the "Land of Heart's Desire."

Connla of the Fiery Hair was son of Conn of the Hundred Fights. One day as he stood by the side of his father on the height of Usna, he saw a maiden clad in strange attire towards him coming.

"Whence comest thou, maiden?" said Connla.

"I come from the Plains of the Ever Living," she said, "there where is neither death nor sin. There we keep holiday alway, nor need we help from any in our joy. And in all our pleasure we have no strife. And because we have our homes in the round green hills, men call us the Hill Folk."

The king and all with him wondered much to hear a voice when they saw no one. For save Connla alone, none saw the Fairy Maiden.

"To whom art thou talking, my son?" said Conn the king.

Then the maiden answered, "Connla speaks to a young, fair maid, whom neither death nor old age awaits. I love Connla, and now I call him away to the Plain of Pleasure, Moy Mell,

"Connla and the Fairy Maiden." From *Celtic Fairy Tales*, edited by Joseph Jacobs. By permission of G. P. Putnam's Sons and Frederick Muller Ltd., London

where Boadag is king for aye, nor has there been sorrow or complaint in that land since he held the kingship. Oh, come with me, Connla of the Fiery Hair, ruddy as the dawn, with thy tawny skin. A fairy crown awaits thee to grace thy comely face and royal form. Come, and never shall thy comeliness fade, nor thy youth, till the last awful day of judgment."

The king in fear at what the maiden said, which he heard though he could not see her, called aloud to his Druid, Coran by name.

"O Coran of the many spells," he said, "and of the cunning magic, I call upon thy aid. A task is upon me too great for all my skill and wit, greater than any laid upon me since I seized the kingship. A maiden unseen has met us, and by her power would take from me my dear, my comely son. If thou help not, he will be taken from thy king by woman's wiles and witchery."

Then Coran the Druid stood forth and chanted his spells towards the spot where the maiden's voice had been heard. And none heard her voice again, nor could Connla see her longer. Only as she vanished before the Druid's mighty spell, she threw an apple to Connla.

For a whole month from that day Connla would take nothing, either to eat or to drink, save only from that apple. But as he ate, it grew again and always kept whole. And all the while there grew within him a mighty yearning and longing after the maiden he had seen.

But when the last day of the month of waiting came, Connla stood by the side of the king his father on the Plain of Arcomin, and again he saw the maiden come towards him, and again she spoke to him.

"'Tis a glorious place, forsooth, that Connla holds among shortlived mortals awaiting the day of death. But now the folk of life, the ever-living ones, beg and bid thee come to Moy Mell, the Plain of Pleasure, for they have learnt to know thee, seeing thee in thy home among thy dear ones."

When Conn the king heard the maiden's voice, he called to his men aloud and said:

"Summon swift my Druid Coran, for I see she has again this day the power of speech."

Then the maiden said: "O mighty Conn, Fighter of a Hundred Fights, the Druid's power is little loved; it has little honour in the mighty land, peopled with so many of the upright. When the Law comes, it will do away with the Druid's magic spells that issue from the lips of the false black demon."

Then Conn the king observed that since the coming of the maiden Connla his son spoke to none that spake to him. So Conn of the Hundred Fights said to him, "Is it to thy mind what the woman says, my son?"

" 'Tis hard upon me," said Connla; "I love my own folk above all things; but yet a longing seizes me for the maiden."

When the maiden heard this, she answered and said: "The ocean is not so strong as the waves of thy longing. Come with me in my curragh, the gleaming, straight-gliding crystal ca-noe. Soon can we reach Boadag's realm. I see the bright sun sink, yet far as it is, we can reach it before dark. There is, too, another land worthy of thy journey, a land joyous to all that seek it. Only wives and maidens dwell there. If thou wilt, we can seek it and live there alone together in joy."

When the maiden ceased to speak, Connla of the Fiery Hair rushed away from his kinsmen and sprang into the curragh, the gleaming, straight-gliding crystal canoe. And then they all, king and court, saw it glide away over the bright sea towards the setting sun, away and away, till eye could see it no longer. So Connla and the Fairy Maiden went forth on the sea, and were no more seen, nor did any know whither they came.

A Finnish folk tale

The Finns are said to have the largest collection of folk tales in manuscript form of any national group. They are not well known in this country, perhaps because of difficult names and long descriptions but those which have been translated are colorful and worth using.

HIDDEN LAIVA
OR THE GOLDEN SHIP

Men's dreams of flying are so graphically expressed in this story that parts of it sound like a report of an airplane flight. The romance has some amusing ups and downs but the princess seems to improve with age.

In olden days there lived a woodsman whose name was Toivo. Every day, with his bow and arrows slung across his shoulder, he used to wander through the wild forests of Finland. One day in his wanderings he came to a high jagged mountain where no man had ever set foot before. For this was the mountain where the Gnomes lived, and there in a dark hidden cavern lay Hiitola, the Gnomes' home.

"Hidden Laiva or the Golden Ship." From *Tales from a Finnish Tupa* by James Cloyd Bowman and Margery Bianco. Published by Albert Whitman & Company, Chicago

When the Gnomes saw Toivo, they all crowded round him and began shouting: "You come at just the right moment! If you will settle our quarrel and help us to divide our gold fairly between us, we will give you money and a golden ship."

It happened that the parents of these Gnomes had died just a few days before, and the Gnomes had fallen heir to all their wealth. They were very busy trying to divide it up. The whole mountain side was strewn with golden spoons and golden dishes and golden carriages. There was a lot of money, too, great shining gold pieces lying all about. The Gnomes were very greedy; each wanted to have more than his own share and so they couldn't come to any agreement about it all.

Toivo stared about him at all this wealth strewn around. More beautiful than the dishes or carriages was a ship of gold that stood on a high rock shining in the sun. The ship caught Toivo's eye at once.

"How do you make this ship go?" he asked the Gnomes.

The largest of the Gnomes stepped forward. He had a turned-up nose, a shaggy pointed red beard and short bandy legs. He hopped into the golden ship and said:

"Why, you just lift this upper what-you-may-call-it with your hand, and push the lower one with your foot, and the ship will race with the wind like a wild tern."

As soon as Toivo had learned the trick, he made a bargain with the Gnomes.

"If you will give me the golden ship and fill it with golden spoons and dishes, and fill my pockets with money, I'll show you how to settle your quarrel."

"Agreed!" shouted the Gnomes, and they began scrambling about in a great hurry to do as he asked.

Toivo set an arrow to his bow and said:

"I am going to shoot an arrow, and the first one to find it will be your King. He will settle your affairs."

"That's wonderful! Now we'll be happy again," shouted the Gnomes.

Toivo stretched his bow and sent the arrow whistling through the air. All the Gnomes went rushing after it. Then Toivo jumped into the golden ship, he pulled with his hand and he pushed with his foot, there was a loud whir-rr, and the ship leaped down the steep mountain and far out across the sea.

Soon after Toivo brought it to a perfect landing before the King's castle.

It happened that the King's daughter was on the castle steps at that very moment. She was sitting with her chin in her hands, dreaming of the day that some brave prince would come riding up to marry her, when all at once she saw the golden ship.

"This must surely be a prince from some wonderful country," she said to herself, "to come riding over land and sea in a ship like that!"

And she came dancing down the castle steps.

"Take me in your golden ship, dear Prince," she said, "and I will be your bride!"

But Toivo could only stammer, "Sweet Princess, you're making a big mistake, I'm merely Toivo, a common woodsman. I'm not good enough to touch the shoes on your feet. There are plenty of Kings' sons who would be glad and proud to be your husband!"

But the Princess was so excited about the golden ship and the golden spoons and the golden dishes that she didn't care whether Toivo was only a woodsman or what he was.

"It doesn't matter a bit," she said. "Take me in your ship, that's all, and I'll be your bride."

"You're making fun of me," Toivo answered her. "No one but a King's son would be good enough for the likes of you."

The Princess ran into the castle and back again, her arms heaped with costly clothes.

"Dress up in these," she laughed, "and you'll be a Prince too!" And back she ran to fetch food and drink.

Toivo was so humble he dared not even lay a finger on those fine clothes. He felt that he was not even good enough to be the Princess's servant. And he gazed at her in fear and trembling as she paced back and forth before the golden ship, begging him to marry her.

But at the end of seven days he saw that she was really unhappy because he refused her, so he said:

"Gentle Princess, if you really want to make a bargain with a humble woodsman, step into the ship."

As soon as she was seated, he fell on his knees and asked:

"Where would you like to sail, gentle Princess, in this golden ship?"

"To the very middle of the sea. I've heard tell there is an island there ten miles long where the berry bushes are loaded to the ground with red and purple fruit, and where the birds sing day and night."

Toivo pushed with his hand and pulled with his foot, and off flew the golden ship over land and sea. Soon it dived from the sky, right down to the center of an island, and stopped there. Toivo jumped out and ran to look for the purple and red berries.

The first berries that he found were yellow. Toivo tasted them, and before he knew what was happening he fell to the ground in a deep sleep. The Princess waited impatiently for him to come back. At first she thought he was lost. But after three days she decided that he had deserted her, and she grew very angry.

"Die here, you low-bred knave!" she cried. "I shall turn the golden ship round and sail right home again."

So she pulled with her hand and pushed with her foot, and flew back to the castle, while poor Toivo still lay sprawled out on the ground fast asleep.

At the end of another day, Toivo woke up. He searched everywhere, but he could not find the golden ship nor the Princess. His beautiful golden spoons and dishes were gone, too. All he had left was a pocketful of money.

As he hunted high and low, he grew faint with hunger. Before him was a bush laden with purple berries. Toivo filled his left pocket with the fruit, thrust a berry into his mouth and began crunching it between his teeth. All at once he felt horns growing out from his head, monstrous pronged horns like the antlers of a wild moose. They were heavy and they hurt terribly.

"It would be better if I'd stayed hungry," he thought. "These horns are driving me crazy! If a ship should come, the sailors will take me for a wild beast and shoot me."

As he looked for some safe place in which to hide, he saw a bush with red berries on it. He filled his right pocket this time, and crunched one of the red berries between his teeth. No sooner had he done so than the heavy horns fell by magic from his head and he became the most handsome man in the world.

Next day a ship appeared over the edge of

the sea. Toivo ran up and down the beach shouting to the sailors. "Take me with you, good friends, take me away before I die on this island. Bring me to the King's castle and I will pay you well."

The sailors gladly took Toivo and set him down before the King's castle. There he walked through the garden and came to a clear sparkling pool. He sat down on the edge of the pool and dipped his tired feet in the water.

It so happened that the King's Butler was coming to draw water. He said to Toivo:

"My good man, tired you may be, but if the King hears that you've been dipping your dusty feet into his drinking water, he'll have your head cut off!"

"My good sir," said Toivo, "the water will soon be clear again, but I'm sorry for my mistake. Let me show you a secret."

And he took a shining red berry from his right pocket and gave it to the Butler. The Butler crunched the berry between his teeth, and at once became the handsomest man in the kingdom, next of course to Toivo himself. He was so delighted that he hid Toivo in a corner of the pantry where the King would not find him.

At dinner time the Princess saw how wonderfully changed the Butler was in his looks, and it made her very curious.

"What has made you so handsome all of a sudden?" she asked him.

"I met a man in the garden who gave me a shining red berry," he whispered. "I ate it, and the charm worked. I became as you now see me."

"Find that man," the Princess said. "Tell him if he'll only make me beautiful too, I'll marry him."

"I'm afraid he's gone," the Butler said. "He wanted to hide, because he was afraid someone would cut his head off if they found him here."

"Tell him not to be frightened," the Princess said. "I will protect him. Bring him into the secret chamber and I'll give him food and drink."

The Butler went to fetch Toivo, and when they returned they found the Princess waiting with food and drink all set out. When the Princess saw Toivo, he was so handsome that she did not know him at all. While he was eating she said:

"If you can make me as beautiful as you are handsome, I'll be your bride."

Toivo became hot with anger, for he thought the Princess had grown tired of him on the island and had run away, stealing his golden ship and leaving him there to die. He did not know of the long time she had waited there.

"No, gentle Princess," he said. "I'm only a poor servant. There is many a King's son who would gladly marry you."

"Only believe me," she said. "I will dress you in a uniform of a General in the King's Army. I will fill your pockets with gold. I will give you a magic golden ship! Only please, please make me as beautiful as you are handsome, and let us be married."

"Very well," said Toivo at last. "Have it your way. Eat this berry."

He took a purple berry from his left pocket, and as the Princess crunched the berry between her teeth a pair of monstrous pronged horns grew out from her head, as heavy and huge as the horns of a wild elk!

As for Toivo, he got very frightened at what he had done, and ran off to hide.

The Princess set up a great hullabaloo, and everyone came running. When the King saw the horns he tried to cut them away, but they were hard as iron and firmly fixed to her head. So then he ordered his two strongest soldiers to follow behind the Princess everywhere she went and carry the weight of the horns while she walked.

No wonder the whole court was upset! The King and the Queen and all the ladies and gentlemen in waiting could talk of nothing but the poor Princess and her terrible plight. In despair the King at last sent soldiers into every part of his kingdom with this message:

"Whoever will cure the King's daughter by removing her monstrous horns shall receive the hand of the King's daughter in marriage and be raised to the highest command in the King's Army."

From every part of the kingdom came doctors and healers and magicians. They tried all their medicines and potions, all their spells and wonders. But it was wasted work, for the horns still remained.

At last, after many days, Toivo came forward from the crowd and knelt before the King, saying:

"O King, please let me try my cure."

"I doubt if you can do anything, my lad," the King said. "You can see for yourself how all these wise men have failed, one after another. They have eaten and drunk to their own luck, but my poor daughter remains the same."

"But, King, I am the only one who knows the right charm," Toivo begged. "If you'll let me try, I'm sure I can take away the horns."

"Try, then, and if the horns do fall from my daughter's head, I'll make you the highest general in my army."

"Send all these doctors and healers away," said Toivo, "and command your soldiers to make merry, for I will surely make your daughter the most beautiful woman in the kingdom!"

So the King commanded all the doctors and healers and magicians to go home, and the soldiers to make merry, while Toivo was left alone to work his cure.

Toivo said to the maidservant:

"Go, girl, and put dry sticks in the *sauna* (bath house) hearth. Make a hot fire to heat the stones in the Princess's bath house."

And to the page boy he said:

"Run quick to the deep wild forest, boy, and fetch me three long straight willow twigs. With these I will make the horns disappear."

The *sauna* was made ready with warm water and heated stones. The long straight willow twigs were brought and laid in the bath house, too. Then Toivo called for the Princess. He sent the maidservant outside and shut the door. He set the Princess on a bench. He tore the clothing from her shoulders and began to beat her soundly with the willow twigs.

"I'll teach you to run away with my golden ship and leave me to die in the middle of the sea!" he shouted between the strokes. "I'll teach you, you cruel woman, to steal my golden spoons and my golden dishes! I am Toivo, the man you promised to marry if I would take you to a far-off island! I'll teach you!"

The Princess's shoulders were soon red and welted from the blows of the willow twigs. She cried:

"Stop beating me, stop beating me, poor man, and I'll explain everything. Only stop, and I promise never to harm you again!"

"Very well then, explain," said Toivo gruffly.

"It was like this," the Princess began. "For three long days and nights I waited for you. I can't tell you how lonely it seemed, there on that island in the middle of the sea. Every moment I expected some horrible monster to come and swallow me alive. I felt sure you had deserted me, and you can't blame me for being so frightened that I flew back home in your golden ship. How can you doubt that I loved you from the very beginning, and still do!"

When Toivo heard this he threw away the willow twigs and fell on his knees before her. "Forgive me, forgive me for being angry with you, gentle Princess! I will never lift my hand against you again."

As he spoke, Toivo drew a shining red berry from his right pocket. The Princess crunched it between her teeth; at once the ugly horns fell from her head and her face became as fair as a new-blown rose.

Toivo called the maidservant. She dressed the Princess in fine linen; upon her head she set the tall bridal crown, covered with jewels, and upon her feet soft shoes woven of the finest white birch bark in all the King's land.

When the people saw the Princess in her white robe, her thick golden braids falling to her knees, her blue eyes shining and her skin like the fairest rose-petal, they knew she had become the most beautiful woman in the kingdom.

The King was so happy he declared a holiday throughout the whole land. Everywhere people ate, drank and danced all night long.

Toivo became the King's highest general. He married his Princess and they all lived happily ever after.

Czechoslovakian folk tales

The Czech stories have been fortunate in their translator. The clear, vigorous English preserves the peculiar folk flavor of the tales and their humor.

BUDULINEK

It is interesting to note the numbers of stories which warn children not to let anyone in the house when they are alone. This is an exceptionally exciting story for the seven- and eight-year-olds and readily lends itself to amusing illustration.

There was once a little boy named Budulinek. He lived with his old Granny in a cottage near a forest.

Granny went out to work every day. In the morning when she went away she always said:

"There, Budulinek, there's your dinner on the table and mind, you mustn't open the door no matter who knocks!"

One morning Granny said:

"Now, Budulinek, today I'm leaving you some soup for your dinner. Eat it when dinner time comes. And remember what I always say: don't open the door no matter who knocks."

She went away and pretty soon Lishka, the sly

old mother fox, came and knocked on the door.

"Budulinek!" she called. "You know me! Open the door! Please!"

Budulinek called back:

"No, I mustn't open the door."

But Lishka, the sly old mother fox, kept on knocking.

"Listen, Budulinek," she said: "if you open the door, do you know what I'll do? I'll give you a ride on my tail!"

Now Budulinek thought to himself:

"Oh, that would be fun to ride on the tail of Lishka, the fox!"

So Budulinek forgot all about what Granny said to him every day and opened the door.

Lishka, the sly old thing, came into the room and what do you think she did? Do you think she gave Budulinek a ride on her tail? Well, she didn't. She just went over to the table and gobbled up the bowl of soup that Granny had put there for Budulinek's dinner and then she ran away.

When dinner time came Budulinek hadn't anything to eat.

In the evening when Granny came home, she said:

"Budulinek, did you open the door and let anyone in?"

Budulinek was crying because he was so hungry, and he said:

"Yes, I let in Lishka, the old mother fox, and she ate up all my dinner, too!"

Granny said:

"Now, Budulinek, you see what happens when you open the door and let some one in. Another time remember what Granny says and don't open the door."

The next morning Granny cooked some porridge for Budulinek's dinner and said:

"Now, Budulinek, here's some porridge for your dinner. Remember, while I'm gone you must not open the door no matter who knocks."

Granny was no sooner out of sight than Lishka came again and knocked on the door.

"Oh, Budulinek!" she called. "Open the door and let me in!"

But Budulinek said:

"No, I won't open the door!"

"Oh, now, Budulinek, please open the door!" Lishka begged. "You know me! Do you know what I'll do if you open the door? I'll give you a ride on my tail! Truly I will!"

Budulinek thought to himself:

"This time maybe she will give me a ride on her tail."

So he opened the door.

Lishka came into the room, gobbled up Budulinek's porridge, and ran away without giving him any ride at all.

When dinner time came Budulinek hadn't anything to eat.

In the evening when Granny came home she said:

"Budulinek, did you open the door and let anyone in?"

Budulinek was crying again because he was so hungry, and he said:

"Yes, I let in Lishka, the old mother fox, and she ate up all my porridge, too!"

"Budulinek, you're a bad boy!" Granny said. "If you open the door again, I'll have to spank you! Do you hear?"

The next morning before she went to work, Granny cooked some peas for Budulinek's dinner.

As soon as Granny was gone he began eating the peas, they were so good.

Presently Lishka, the fox, came and knocked on the door.

"Budulinek!" she called. "Open the door! I want to come in!"

But Budulinek wouldn't open the door. He took his bowl of peas and went to the window and ate them there where Lishka could see him.

"Oh, Budulinek!" Lishka begged. "You know me! Please open the door! This time I promise you I'll give you a ride on my tail! Truly I will!"

She just begged and begged until at last Budulinek opened the door. Then Lishka jumped into the room and do you know what she did? She put her nose right into the bowl of peas and gobbled them all up!

Then she said to Budulinek:

"Now get on my tail and I'll give you a ride!"

So Budulinek climbed on Lishka's tail and Lishka went running around the room faster and faster until Budulinek was dizzy and just had to hold on with all his might.

Then, before Budulinek knew what was happening, Lishka slipped out of the house and ran off swiftly into the forest, home to her hole, with Budulinek still on her tail! She hid Budulinek down in her hole with her own three children and she wouldn't let him out. He had to stay there with the three little foxes and they all teased him and bit him. And then wasn't he sorry he had disobeyed his Granny! And, oh, how he cried!

When Granny came home she found the door open and no little Budulinek anywhere. She looked high and low, but no, there was no little Budulinek. She asked everyone she met had they seen her little Budulinek, but nobody had. So poor Granny just cried and cried, she was so lonely and sad.

One day an organ-grinder with a wooden leg began playing in front of Granny's cottage. The music made her think of Budulinek.

"Organ-grinder," Granny said, "here's a penny for you. But, please, don't play any more. Your music makes me cry."

"Why does it make you cry?" the organ-grinder asked.

"Because it reminds me of Budulinek," Granny said, and she told the organ-grinder all about Budulinek and how somebody had stolen him away.

The organ-grinder said:

"Poor Granny! I tell you what I'll do: as I

go around and play my organ I'll keep my eyes open for Budulinek. If I find him I'll bring him back to you."

"Will you?" Granny cried. "If you bring me back my little Budulinek I'll give you a measure of rye and a measure of millet and a measure of poppy seed and a measure of everything in the house!"

So the organ-grinder went off and everywhere he played his organ he looked for Budulinek. But he couldn't find him.

At last one day while he was walking through the forest he thought he heard a little boy crying. He looked around everywhere until he found a fox's hole.

"Oho!" he said to himself. "I believe that wicked old Lishka must have stolen Budulinek! She's probably keeping him here with her own three children! I'll soon find out."

So he put down his organ and began to play. And as he played he sang softly:

"One old fox
And two, three, four,
And Budulinek
He makes one more!"

Old Lishka heard the music playing and she said to her oldest child:

"Here, son, give the old man a penny and tell him to go away because my head aches."

So the oldest little fox climbed out of the hole and gave the organ-grinder a penny and said:

"My mother says, please will you go away because her head aches."

As the organ-grinder reached over to take the penny, he caught the oldest little fox and stuffed him into a sack. Then he went on playing and singing:

"One old fox
And two and three
And Budulinek
Makes four for me!"

Presently Lishka sent out her second child with a penny and the organ-grinder caught the second little fox in the same way and stuffed it also into the sack. Then he went on grinding his organ and softly singing:

"One old fox
And another for me,
And Budulinek
He makes the three."

"I wonder why that old man still plays his organ," Lishka said and sent out her third child with a penny.

So the organ-grinder caught the third little fox and stuffed it also into the sack. Then he kept on playing and singing softly:

"One old fox—
I'll soon get you!—
And Budulinek
He makes just two."

At last Lishka herself came out. So he caught her, too, and stuffed her in with her children. Then he sang:

"Four naughty foxes
Caught alive!
And Budulinek
He makes the five!"

The organ-grinder went to the hole and called down:

"Budulinek! Budulinek! Come out!"

As there were no foxes left to hold him back, Budulinek was able to crawl out.

When he saw the organ-grinder he cried and said:

"Oh, please, Mr. Organ-Grinder, I want to go home to my Granny!"

"I'll take you home to your Granny," the organ-grinder said, "but first I must punish these naughty foxes."

The organ-grinder cut a strong switch and gave the four foxes in the sack a terrible beating until they begged him to stop and promised that they would never again do anything to Budulinek.

Then the organ-grinder let them go and he took Budulinek home to Granny.

Granny was delighted to see her little Budulinek and she gave the organ-grinder a measure of rye and a measure of millet and a measure of poppy seed and a measure of everything else in the house.

And Budulinek never again opened the door!

CLEVER MANKA

This is a good example of the humor in Czech stories. It especially delights girls after hearing "The Most Obedient Wife."

There was once a rich farmer who was as grasping and unscrupulous as he was rich. He was always driving a hard bargain and always getting the better of his poor neighbors. One of these neighbors was a humble shepherd who in return for service was to receive from the farmer a heifer. When the time of payment came the farmer refused to give the shepherd the heifer and the shepherd was forced to lay the matter before the burgomaster.

The burgomaster, who was a young man and as yet not very experienced, listened to both sides and when he had deliberated he said:

"Instead of deciding this case, I will put a riddle to you both and the man who makes the best answer shall have the heifer. Are you agreed?"

The farmer and the shepherd accepted this proposal and the burgomaster said:

"Well then, here is my riddle: What is the swiftest thing in the world? What is the sweetest thing? What is the richest? Think out your answers and bring them to me at this same hour tomorrow."

The farmer went home in a temper.

"What kind of a burgomaster is this young fellow!" he growled. "If he had let me keep the heifer I'd have sent him a bushel of pears. But now I'm in a fair way of losing the heifer for I can't think of any answer to his foolish riddle."

"What is the matter, husband?" his wife asked.

"It's that new burgomaster. The old one would have given me the heifer without any argument, but this young man thinks to decide the case by asking us riddles."

When he told his wife what the riddle was, she cheered him greatly by telling him that she knew the answers at once.

"Why, husband," said she, "our gray mare must be the swiftest thing in the world. You know yourself nothing ever passes us on the road. As for the sweetest, did you ever taste

honey any sweeter than ours? And I'm sure there's nothing richer than our chest of golden ducats that we've been laying by these forty years."

The farmer was delighted.

"You're right, wife, you're right! That heifer remains ours!"

The shepherd when he got home was downcast and sad. He had a daughter, a clever girl named Manka, who met him at the door of his cottage and asked:

"What is it, father? What did the burgomaster say?"

The shepherd sighed.

"I'm afraid I've lost the heifer. The burgomaster set us a riddle and I know I shall never guess it."

"Perhaps I can help you," Manka said. "What is it?"

So the shepherd gave her the riddle and the next day as he was setting out for the burgomaster's, Manka told him what answers to make.

When he reached the burgomaster's house, the farmer was already there rubbing his hands and beaming with self-importance.

The burgomaster again propounded the riddle and then asked the farmer his answers.

The farmer cleared his throat and with a pompous air began:

"The swiftest thing in the world? Why, my dear sir, that's my gray mare, of course, for no other horse ever passes us on the road. The sweetest? Honey from my beehives, to be sure. The richest? What can be richer than my chest of golden ducats!"

And the farmer squared his shoulders and smiled triumphantly.

"H'm," said the young burgomaster, dryly. Then he asked:

"What answers does the shepherd make?"

The shepherd bowed politely and said:

"The swiftest thing in the world is thought for thought can run any distance in the twinkling of an eye. The sweetest thing of all is sleep for when a man is tired and sad what can be sweeter? The richest thing is the earth for out of the earth come all the riches of the world."

"Good!" the burgomaster cried. "Good! The heifer goes to the shepherd!"

Later the burgomaster said to the shepherd:

"Tell me, now, who gave you those answers? I'm sure they never came out of your own head."

At first the shepherd tried not to tell, but when the burgomaster pressed him he confessed that they came from his daughter, Manka. The burgomaster, who thought that he would like to make another test of Manka's cleverness, sent for ten eggs. He gave them to the shepherd and said:

"Take these eggs to Manka and tell her to have them hatched out by tomorrow and to bring me the chicks."

When the shepherd reached home and gave Manka the burgomaster's message, Manka laughed and said: "Take a handful of millet and go right back to the burgomaster. Say to him: 'My daughter sends you this millet. She says that if you plant, grow it, and have it harvested by tomorrow, she'll bring you the ten chicks and you can feed them the ripe grain.'"

When the burgomaster heard this, he laughed heartily.

"That's a clever girl of yours," he told the shepherd. "If she's as comely as she is clever, I think I'd like to marry her. Tell her to come to see me, but she must come neither by day nor by night, neither riding nor walking, neither dressed nor undressed."

When Manka received this message she waited until the next dawn when night was gone and day not yet arrived. Then she wrapped herself in a fishnet and, throwing one leg over a goat's back and keeping one foot on the ground, she went to the burgomaster's house.

Now I ask you: did she go dressed? No, she wasn't dressed. A fishnet isn't clothing. Did she go undressed? Of course not, for wasn't she covered with a fishnet? Did she walk to the burgomaster's? No, she didn't walk for she went with one leg thrown over a goat. Then did she ride? Of course she didn't ride for wasn't she walking on one foot?

When she reached the burgomaster's house she called out:

"Here I am, Mr. Burgomaster, and I've come neither by day nor by night, neither riding nor walking, neither dressed nor undressed."

The young burgomaster was so delighted with Manka's cleverness and so pleased with her comely looks that he proposed to her at once and in a short time married her.

"But understand, my dear Manka," he said, "you are not to use that cleverness of yours at my expense. I won't have you interfering in any of my cases. In fact if ever you give advice to any one who comes to me for judgment, I'll turn you out of my house at once and send you home to your father."

All went well for a time. Manka busied herself in her house-keeping and was careful not to interfere in any of the burgomaster's cases.

Then one day two farmers came to the burgomaster to have a dispute settled. One of the farmers owned a mare which had foaled in the marketplace. The colt had run under the wagon of the other farmer and thereupon the owner of the wagon claimed the colt as his property.

The burgomaster, who was thinking of something else while the case was being presented, said carelessly:

"The man who found the colt under his wagon is, of course, the owner of the colt."

As the owner of the mare was leaving the burgomaster's house, he met Manka and stopped to tell her about the case. Manka was ashamed of her husband for making so foolish a decision and she said to the farmer:

"Come back this afternoon with a fishing net and stretch it across the dusty road. When the burgomaster sees you he will come out and ask you what you are doing. Say to him that you're catching fish. When he asks you how you can expect to catch fish in a dusty road, tell him it's just as easy for you to catch fish in a dusty road as it is for a wagon to foal. Then he'll see the injustice of his decision and have the colt returned to you. But remember one thing: you mustn't let him find out that it was I who told you to do this."

That afternoon when the burgomaster chanced to look out the window he saw a man stretching a fishnet across the dusty road. He went out to him and asked: "What are you doing?"

"Fishing."

"Fishing in a dusty road? Are you daft?"

"Well," the man said, "it's just as easy for me to catch fish in a dusty road as it is for a wagon to foal."

Then the burgomaster recognized the man as the owner of the mare and he had to confess that what he said was true.

"Of course the colt belongs to your mare and must be returned to you. But tell me," he said, "who put you up to this? You didn't think of it yourself."

The farmer tried not to tell but the burgomaster questioned him until he found out that Manka was at the bottom of it. This made him very angry. He went into the house and called his wife.

"Manka," he said, "do you forget what I told you would happen if you went interfering in any of my cases? Home you go this very day. I don't care to hear any excuses. The matter is settled. You may take with you the one thing you like best in my house for I won't have people saying that I treated you shabbily."

Manka made no outcry.

"Very well, my dear husband, I shall do as you say: I shall go to my father's cottage and take with me the one thing I like best in your house. But don't make me go until after supper. We have been very happy together and I should like to eat one last meal with you. Let us have no more words but be kind to each other as we've always been and then part as friends."

The burgomaster agreed to this and Manka prepared a fine supper of all the dishes of which her husband was particularly fond. The burgo-master opened his choicest wine and pledged Manka's health. Then he set to, and the supper was so good that he ate and ate and ate. And the more he ate, the more he drank until at last he grew drowsy and fell sound asleep in his chair. Then without awakening him Manka had him carried out to the wagon that was waiting to take her home to her father.

The next morning when the burgomaster opened his eyes, he found himself lying in the shepherd's cottage.

"What does this mean?" he roared out.

"Nothing, dear husband, nothing!" Manka said. "You know you told me I might take with me the one thing I liked best in your house, so of course I took you! That's all."

For a moment the burgomaster rubbed his eyes in amazement. Then he laughed loud and heartily to think how Manka had outwitted him.

"Manka," he said, "you're too clever for me. Come on, my dear, let's go home."

So they climbed back into the wagon and drove home.

The burgomaster never again scolded his wife but thereafter whenever a very difficult case came up he always said:

"I think we had better consult my wife. You know she's a very clever woman."

Russian folk tales

Russian folk tales are, on the whole, bloody and horrible but full of excitement and color. Arthur Ransome in his Old Peter's Russian Tales *has toned them down a bit, and most of the stories in that collection are good for storytelling. Folklore has inspired some well-known Russian music and, since these stories belong to the children eleven to fourteen, it is well to use the stories as introductions to the music. The stories lend themselves to dramatization and illustration.*

SADKO

This story, which has the strangeness of a dream, inspired an opera and may be dramatized by older children, either with puppet or human actors. At the conclusion of the story, the intro-duction of Maroosia and old Peter seems to shatter the spell of the tale. Why not omit them and end with the speculative, "And what happened after that? Well, some say Sadko took his dulcimer and swam out again. . . ."

"Sadko." From *Old Peter's Russian Tales,* edited by Arthur Ransome, Thomas Nelson and Sons Ltd.

In Novgorod in the old days there was a young man—just a boy he was—the son of a rich merchant who had lost all his money and died. So

Sadko was very poor. He had not a kopeck in the world, except what the people gave him when he played his dulcimer for their dancing. He had blue eyes and curling hair, and he was strong, and would have been merry; but it is dull work playing for other folk to dance, and Sadko dared not dance with any young girl, for he had no money to marry on, and he did not want to be chased away as a beggar. And the young women of Novgorod, they never looked at the handsome Sadko. No; they smiled with their bright eyes at the young men who danced with them, and if they ever spoke to Sadko, it was just to tell him sharply to keep the music going or to play faster.

So Sadko lived alone with his dulcimer, and made do with half a loaf when he could not get a whole, and with crust when he had no crumb. He did not mind so very much what came to him, so long as he could play his dulcimer and walk along the banks of the little river Volkhov[1] that flows by Novgorod, or on the shores of the lake, making music for himself, and seeing the pale mists rise over the water, and dawn or sunset across the shining river.

"There is no girl in all Novgorod as pretty as my little river," he used to say, and night after night he would sit by the banks of the river or on the shores of the lake, playing the dulcimer and singing to himself.

Sometimes he helped the fishermen on the lake, and they would give him a little fish for his supper in payment for his strong young arms.

And it happened that one evening the fishermen asked him to watch their nets for them on the shore, while they went off to take their fish to sell them in the square at Novgorod.

Sadko sat on the shore, on a rock, and played his dulcimer and sang. Very sweetly he sang of the fair lake and the lovely river—the little river that he thought prettier than all the girls of Novgorod. And while he was singing he saw a whirlpool in the lake, little waves flying from it across the water, and in the middle a hollow down into the water. And in the hollow he saw the head of a great man with blue hair and a gold crown. He knew that the huge man was the Tzar of the

Sea. And the man came nearer, walking up out of the depths of the lake—a huge, great man, a very giant, with blue hair falling to his waist over his broad shoulders. The little waves ran from him in all directions as he came striding up out of the water.

Sadko did not know whether to run or stay; but the Tzar of the Sea called out to him in a great voice like wind and water in a storm,—

"Sadko of Novgorod, you have played and sung many days by the side of this lake and on the banks of the little river Volkhov. My daughters love your music, and it has pleased me too. Throw out a net into the water, and draw it in, and the waters will pay you for your singing. And if you are satisfied with the payment, you must come and play to us down in the green palace of the sea."

With that the Tzar of the Sea went down again into the waters of the lake. The waves closed over him with a roar, and presently the lake was as smooth and calm as it had ever been.

Sadko thought, and said to himself: "Well, there is no harm done in casting out a net." So he threw a net out into the lake.

He sat down again and played on his dulcimer and sang, and when he had finished his singing the dusk had fallen and the moon shone over the lake. He put down his dulcimer and took hold of the ropes of the net, and began to draw it up out of the silver water. Easily the ropes came, and the net, dripping and glittering in the moonlight.

"I was dreaming," said Sadko; "I was asleep when I saw the Tzar of the Sea, and there is nothing in the net at all."

And then, just as the last of the net was coming ashore, he saw something in it, square and dark. He dragged it out, and found it was a coffer. He opened the coffer, and it was full of precious stones—green, red, gold—gleaming in the light of the moon. Diamonds shone there like little bundles of sharp knives.

"There can be no harm in taking these stones," says Sadko, "whether I dreamed or not."

He took the coffer on his shoulder, and bent under the weight of it, strong though he was. He put it in a safe place. All night he sat and watched by the nets, and played and sang, and planned what he would do.

[1] The Volkhov would be a big river if it were in England, and Sadko and old Peter called it little only because they loved it.

In the morning the fishermen came, laughing and merry after their night in Novgorod, and they gave him a little fish for watching their nets; and he made a fire on the shore, and cooked it and ate it as he used to do.

"And that is my last meal as a poor man," says Sadko. "Ah me! who knows if I shall be happier?"

Then he set the coffer on his shoulder and tramped away for Novgorod.

"Who is that?" they asked at the gates.

"Only Sadko, the dulcimer player," he replied.

"Turned porter?" said they.

"One trade is as good as another," said Sadko, and he walked into the city. He sold a few of the stones, two at a time, and with what he got for them he set up a booth in the market. Small things led to great, and he was soon one of the richest traders in Novgorod.

And now there was not a girl in the town who could look too sweetly at Sadko. "He has golden hair," says one. "Blue eyes like the sea," says another. "He could lift the world on his shoulders," says a third. A little money, you see, opens everybody's eyes.

But Sadko was not changed by his good fortune. Still he walked and played by the little river Volkhov. When work was done and the traders gone, Sadko would take his dulcimer and play and sing on the banks of the river. And still he said, "There is no girl in all Novgorod as pretty as my little river." Every time he came back from his long voyages—for he was trading far and near, like the greatest of merchants—he went at once to the banks of the river to see how his sweetheart fared. And always he brought some little present for her and threw it into the waves.

For twelve years he lived unmarried in Novgorod, and every year made voyages, buying and selling, and always growing richer and richer. Many were the mothers of Novgorod who would have liked to see him married to their daughters. Many were the pillows that were wet with the tears of the young girls, as they thought of the blue eyes of Sadko and his golden hair.

And then, in the twelfth year since he walked into Novgorod with the coffer on his shoulder, he was sailing a ship on the Caspian Sea, far, far away. For many days the ship sailed on, and

Sadko sat on deck and played his dulcimer and sang of Novgorod and of the little river Volkhov that flows under the walls of the town. Blue was the Caspian Sea, and the waves were like furrows in a field, long lines of white under the steady wind, while the sails swelled and the ship shot over the water.

And suddenly the ship stopped.

In the middle of the sea, far from land, the ship stopped and trembled in the waves, as if she were held by a big hand.

"We are aground!" cry the sailors; and the captain, the great one, tells them to take soundings. Seventy fathoms by the bow it was, and seventy fathoms by the stern.

"We are not aground," says the captain, "unless there is a rock sticking up like a needle in the middle of the Caspian Sea!"

"There is magic in this," say the sailors.

"Hoist more sail," says the captain; and up go the white sails, swelling out in the wind, while the masts bend and creak. But still the ship lay shivering, and did not move, out there in the middle of the sea.

"Hoist more sail yet," says the captain; and up go the white sails, swelling and tugging, while the masts creak and groan. But still the ship lay there shivering and did not move.

"There is an unlucky one aboard," says an old sailor. "We must draw lots and find him, and throw him overboard into the sea."

The other sailors agreed to this. And still Sadko sat, and played his dulcimer and sang.

The sailors cut pieces of string, all of a length, as many as there were souls in the ship, and one of those strings they cut in half. Then they made them into a bundle, and each man plucked one string. And Sadko stopped his playing for a moment to pluck a string, and his was the string that had been cut in half.

"Magician, sorcerer, unclean one!" shouted the sailors.

"Not so," said Sadko. "I remember now an old promise I made, and I keep it willingly."

He took his dulcimer in his hand, and leapt from the ship into the blue Caspian Sea. The waves had scarcely closed over his head before the ship shot forward again, and flew over the waves like a swan's feather, and came in the end safely to her harbour.

"And what happened to Sadko?" asked Maroosia.

"You shall hear, little pigeon," said old Peter, and he took a pinch of snuff. Then he went on.

Sadko dropped into the waves, and the waves closed over him. Down he sank, like a pebble thrown into a pool, down and down. First the water was blue, then green, and strange fish with goggle eyes and golden fins swam round him as he sank. He came at last to the bottom of the sea.

And there, on the bottom of the sea, was a palace built of green wood. Yes, all the timbers of all the ships that have been wrecked in all the seas of the world are in that palace, and they are all green, and cunningly fitted together, so that the palace is worth a ten days' journey only to see it. And in front of the palace Sadko saw two big kobbly sturgeons, each a hundred and fifty feet long, lashing their tails and guarding the gates. Now, sturgeons are the oldest of all fish, and these were the oldest of all sturgeons.

Sadko walked between the sturgeons and through the gates of the palace. Inside there was a great hall, and the Tzar of the Sea lay resting in the hall, with his gold crown on his head and his blue hair floating round him in the water, and his great body covered with scales lying along the hall. The Tzar of the Sea filled the hall—and there is room in that hall for a village. And there were fish swimming this way and that in and out of the windows.

"Ah, Sadko," says the Tzar of the Sea, "you took what the sea gave you, but you have been a long time in coming to sing in the palaces of the sea. Twelve years I have lain here waiting for you."

"Great Tzar, forgive," says Sadko.

"Sing now," says the Tzar of the Sea, and his voice was like the beating of waves.

And Sadko played on his dulcimer and sang.

He sang of Novgorod and of the little river Volkhov which he loved. It was in his song that none of the girls of Novgorod were as pretty as the little river. And there was the sound of wind over the lake in his song, the sound of ripples under the prow of a boat, the sound of ripples on the shore, the sound of the river flowing past the tall reeds, the whispering sound of the river at night. And all the time he played cunningly on the dulcimer. The girls of Novgorod had

never danced to so sweet a tune when in the old days Sadko played his dulcimer to earn kopecks and crusts of bread.

Never had the Tzar of the Sea heard such music.

"I would dance," said the Tzar of the Sea, and he stood up like a tall tree in the hall.

"Play on," said the Tzar of the Sea, and he strode through the gates. The sturgeons guarding the gates stirred the water with their tails.

And if the Tzar of the Sea was huge in the hall, he was huger still when he stood outside on the bottom of the sea. He grew taller and taller, towering like a mountain. His feet were like small hills. His blue hair hung down to his waist, and he was covered with green scales. And he began to dance on the bottom of the sea.

Great was that dancing. The sea boiled, and ships went down. The waves rolled as big as houses. The sea overflowed its shores, and whole towns were under water as the Tzar danced mightily on the bottom of the sea. Hither and thither rushed the waves, and the very earth shook at the dancing of that tremendous Tzar.

He danced till he was tired, and then he came back to the palace of green wood, and passed the sturgeons, and shrank into himself and came through the gates into the hall, where Sadko still played on his dulcimer and sang.

"You have played well and given me pleasure," says the Tzar of the Sea. "I have thirty daughters, and you shall choose one and marry her, and be a Prince of the Sea."

"Better than all maidens I love my little river," says Sadko; and the Tzar of the Sea laughed and threw his head back, with his blue hair floating all over the hall.

And then there came in the thirty daughters of the Tzar of the Sea. Beautiful they were, lovely, and graceful; but twenty-nine of them passed by, and Sadko fingered his dulcimer and thought of his little river.

There came in the thirtieth, and Sadko cried out aloud. "Here is the only maiden in the world as pretty as my little river!" says he. And she looked at him with eyes that shone like stars reflected in the river. Her hair was dark, like the river at night. She laughed, and her voice was like the flowing of the river.

"And what is the name of your little river?" says the Tzar.

"It is the little river Volkhov that flows by Novgorod," says Sadko; "but your daughter is as fair as the little river, and I would gladly marry her if she will have me."

"It is a strange thing," says the Tzar, "but Volkhov is the name of my youngest daughter."

He put Sadko's hand in the hand of his youngest daughter, and they kissed each other. And as they kissed, Sadko saw a necklace round her neck, and knew it for one he had thrown into the river as a present for his sweetheart.

She smiled, and "Come!" says she, and took him away to a palace of her own, and showed him a coffer; and in that coffer were bracelets and rings and earrings—all the gifts that he had thrown into the river.

And Sadko laughed for joy, and kissed the youngest daughter of the Tzar of the Sea, and she kissed him back.

"O my little river!" says he; "there is no girl in all the world but thou as pretty as my little river."

Well, they were married, and the Tzar of the Sea laughed at the wedding feast till the palace shook and the fish swam off in all directions.

And after the feast Sadko and his bride went off together to her palace. And before they slept she kissed him very tenderly, and she said,—

"O Sadko, you will not forget me? You will play to me sometimes, and sing?"

"I shall never lose sight of you, my pretty one," says he; "and as for music, I will sing and play all the day long."

"That's as may be," says she, and they fell asleep.

And in the middle of the night Sadko happened to turn in bed, and he touched the Princess with his left foot, and she was cold, cold, cold as ice in January. And with that touch of cold he woke, and he was lying under the walls of Novgorod, with his dulcimer in his hand, and one of his feet was in the little river Volkhov, and the moon was shining.

"O grandfather! And what happened to him after that?" asked Maroosia.

"There are many tales," said old Peter. "Some say he went into the town, and lived on alone until he died. But I think with those who say

that he took his dulcimer and swam out into the middle of the river, and sank under water again, looking for his little Princess. They say he found her, and lives still in the green palaces of the bottom of the sea; and when there is a big storm, you may know that Sadko is playing on his dulcimer and singing, and that the Tzar of the Sea is dancing his tremendous dance, down there, on the bottom, under the waves."

"Yes, I expect that's what happened," said Ivan. "He'd have found it very dull in Novgorod, even though it is a big town."

THE FIRE-BIRD, THE HORSE OF POWER, AND THE PRINCESS VASILISSA

This story has the color and the extravagant magic of an Oriental tale. It may well be used as an introduction to the Stravinsky "Firebird" music. The story also lends itself to dramatization, but because of the bird and the horse, puppets are a better medium than child actors.

Once upon a time a strong and powerful Tzar ruled in a country far away. And among the servants was a young archer, and this archer had a horse—a horse of power—such a horse as belonged to the wonderful men of long ago—a great horse with a broad chest, eyes like fire, and hoofs of iron. There are no such horses nowadays. They sleep with the strong men who rode them, the bogatirs, until the time comes when Russia has need of them. Then the great horses will thunder up from under the ground, and the valiant men leap from the graves in the armour they have worn so long. The strong men will sit those horses of power, and there will be swinging of clubs and thunder of hoofs, and the earth will be swept clean from the enemies of God and the Tzar. So my grandfather used to say, and he was as much older than I as I am older than you, little ones, and so he should know.

Well, one day long ago, in the green time of

"The Fire-bird, the Horse of Power, and the Princess Vasilissa." From *Old Peter's Russian Tales*, edited by Arthur Ransome, Thomas Nelson and Sons Ltd.

the year, the young archer rode through the forest on his horse of power. The trees were green; there were little blue flowers on the ground under the trees; the squirrels ran in the branches, and the hares in the undergrowth; but no birds sang. The young archer rode along the forest path and listened for the singing of the birds, but there was no singing. The forest was silent, and the only noises in it were the scratching of four-footed beasts, the dropping of fir cones, and the heavy stamping of the horse of power in the soft path.

"What has come to the birds?" said the young archer.

He had scarcely said this before he saw a big curving feather lying in the path before him. The feather was larger than a swan's, larger than an eagle's. It lay in the path, glittering like a flame; for the sun was on it, and it was a feather of pure gold. Then he knew why there was no singing in the forest. For he knew that the fire-bird had flown that way, and that the feather in the path before him was a feather from its burning breast.

The horse of power spoke and said,

"Leave the golden feather where it lies. If you take it you will be sorry for it, and know the meaning of fear."

But the brave young archer sat on the horse of power and looked at the golden feather, and wondered whether to take it or not. He had no wish to learn what it was to be afraid, but he thought, "If I take it and bring it to the Tzar my master, he will be pleased; and he will not send me away with empty hands, for no tzar in the world has a feather from the burning breast of the fire-bird." And the more he thought, the more he wanted to carry the feather to the Tzar. And in the end he did not listen to the words of the horse of power. He leapt from the saddle, picked up the golden feather of the fire-bird, mounted his horse again, and galloped back through the green forest till he came to the palace of the Tzar.

He went into the palace, and bowed before the Tzar and said,—

"O Tzar, I have brought you a feather of the fire-bird."

The Tzar looked gladly at the feather, and then at the young archer.

"Thank you," says he; "but if you have brought me a feather of the fire-bird, you will be able to bring me the bird itself. I should like to see it. A feather is not a fit gift to bring to the Tzar. Bring the bird itself, or, I swear by my sword, your head shall no longer sit between your shoulders!"

The young archer bowed his head and went out. Bitterly he wept, for he knew now what it was to be afraid. He went out into the courtyard, where the horse of power was waiting for him, tossing its head and stamping on the ground.

"Master," says the horse of power, "why do you weep?"

"The Tzar has told me to bring him the fire-bird, and no man on earth can do that," says the young archer, and he bowed his head on his breast.

"I told you," says the horse of power, "that if you took the feather you would learn the meaning of fear. Well, do not be frightened yet, and do not weep. The trouble is not now; the trouble lies before you. Go back to the Tzar and ask him to have a hundred sacks of maize scattered over the open field, and let this be done at midnight."

The young archer went back into the palace and begged the Tzar for this, and the Tzar ordered that at midnight a hundred sacks of maize should be scattered in the open field.

Next morning, at the first redness in the sky, the young archer rode out on the horse of power, and came to the open field. The ground was scattered all over with maize. In the middle of the field stood a great oak with spreading boughs. The young archer leapt to the ground, took off the saddle, and let the horse of power loose to wander as he pleased about the field. Then he climbed up into the oak and hid himself among the green boughs.

The sky grew red and gold, and the sun rose. Suddenly there was a noise in the forest round the field. The trees shook and swayed, and almost fell. There was a mighty wind. The sea piled itself into waves with crests of foam, and the fire-bird came flying from the other side of the world. Huge and golden and flaming in the sun, it flew, dropped down with open wings into the field, and began to eat the maize.

The horse of power wandered in the field. This way he went, and that, but always he came

a little nearer to the fire-bird. Nearer and nearer came the horse. He came close up to the fire-bird, and then suddenly stepped on one of its spreading fiery wings and pressed it heavily to the ground. The bird struggled, flapping mightily with its fiery wings, but it could not get away. The young archer slipped down from the tree, bound the fire-bird with three strong ropes, swung it on its back, saddled the horse, and rode to the palace of the Tzar.

The young archer stood before the Tzar, and his back was bent under the great weight of the fire-bird, and the broad wings of the bird hung on either side of him like fiery shields, and there was a trail of golden feathers on the floor. The young archer swung the magic bird to the foot of the throne before the Tzar; and the Tzar was glad, because since the beginning of the world no tzar had seen the fire-bird flung before him like a wild duck caught in a snare.

The Tzar looked at the fire-bird and laughed with pride. Then he lifted his eyes and looked at the young archer, and says he,

"As you have known how to take the fire-bird, you will know how to bring me my bride, for whom I have long been waiting. In the land

of Never, on the very edge of the world, where the red sun rises in flame from behind the sea, lives the Princess Vasilissa. I will marry none but her. Bring her to me, and I will reward you with silver and gold. But if you do not bring her, then, by my sword, your head will no longer sit between your shoulders!"

The young archer wept bitter tears, and went out into the courtyard where the horse of power was stamping the ground with its hoofs of iron and tossing its thick mane.

"Master, why do you weep?" asked the horse of power.

"The Tzar has ordered me to go to the land of Never, and to bring back the Princess Vasilissa."

"Do not weep—do not grieve. The trouble is not yet; the trouble is to come. Go to the Tzar and ask him for a silver tent with a golden roof, and for all kinds of food and drink to take with us on the journey."

The young archer went in and asked the Tzar for this, and the Tzar gave him a silver tent with silver hangings and a gold-embroidered roof, and every kind of rich wine and the tastiest of foods.

Then the young archer mounted the horse of power and rode off to the land of Never. On and on he rode, many days and nights, and came at last to the edge of the world, where the red sun rises in flame from behind the deep blue sea.

On the shore of the sea the young archer reined in the horse of power, and the heavy hoofs of the horse sank in the sand. He shaded his eyes and looked out over the blue water, and there was the Princess Vasilissa in a little silver boat, rowing with golden oars.

The young archer rode back a little way to where the sand ended and the green world began. There he loosed the horse to wander where he pleased, and to feed on the green grass. Then on the edge of the shore, where the green grass ended and grew thin and the sand began, he set up the shining tent, with its silver hangings and its gold-embroidered roof. In the tent he set out the tasty dishes and the rich flagons of wine which the Tzar had given him, and he sat himself down in the tent and began to regale himself, while he waited for the Princess Vasilissa.

The Princess Vasilissa dipped her golden oars in the blue water, and the little silver boat moved lightly through the dancing waves. She sat in the little boat and looked over the blue sea to the edge of the world, and there, between the golden sand and the green earth, she saw the tent standing, silver and gold in the sun. She dipped her oars, and came nearer to see it the better. The nearer she came the fairer seemed the tent, and at last she rowed to the shore and grounded her little boat on the golden sand, and stepped out daintily and came up to the tent. She was a little frightened, and now and again she stopped and looked back to where the silver boat lay on the sand with the blue sea beyond it. The young archer said not a word, but went on regaling himself on the pleasant dishes he had set out there in the tent.

At last the Princess Vasilissa came up to the tent and looked in.

The young archer rose and bowed before her. Says he—

"Good-day to you, Princess! Be so kind as to come in and take bread and salt with me, and taste my foreign wines."

And the Princess Vasilissa came into the tent and sat down with the young archer, and ate sweetmeats with him, and drank his health in a golden goblet of the wine the Tzar had given him. Now this wine was heavy, and the last drop from the goblet had no sooner trickled down her little slender throat than her eyes closed against her will, once, twice, and again.

"Ah me!" says the Princess, "it is as if the night itself had perched on my eyelids, and yet it is but noon."

And the golden goblet dropped to the ground from her little fingers, and she leant back on a cushion and fell instantly asleep. If she had been beautiful before, she was lovelier still when she lay in that deep sleep in the shadow of the tent.

Quickly the young archer called to the horse of power. Lightly he lifted the Princess in his strong young arms. Swiftly he leapt with her into the saddle. Like a feather she lay in the hollow of his left arm, and slept while the iron hoofs of the great horse thundered over the ground.

They came to the Tzar's palace, and the young archer leapt from the horse of power and carried the Princess into the. palace. Great was the joy of the Tzar; but it did not last for long.

"Go, sound the trumpets for our wedding," he said to his servants; "let all the bells be rung."

The bells rang out and the trumpets sounded, and at the noise of the horns and the ringing of the bells the Princess Vasilissa woke up and looked about her.

"What is this ringing of bells," says she, "and this noise of trumpets? And where, oh, where is the blue sea, and my little silver boat with its golden oars?" And the princess put her hand to her eyes.

"The blue sea is far away," says the Tzar, "and for your little silver boat I give you a golden throne. The trumpets sound for our wedding, and the bells are ringing for our joy."

But the Princess turned her face away from the Tzar; and there was no wonder in that, for he was old, and his eyes were not kind.

And she looked with love at the young archer; and there was no wonder in that either, for he was a young man fit to ride the horse of power.

The Tzar was angry with the Princess Vasilissa, but his anger was as useless as his joy.

"Why, Princess," says he, "will you not marry me, and forget your blue sea and your silver boat?"

"In the middle of the deep blue sea lies a great stone," says the Princess, "and under that stone is hidden my wedding dress. If I cannot wear that dress I will marry nobody at all."

Instantly the Tzar turned to the young archer, who was waiting before the throne.

"Ride swiftly back," says he, "to the land of Never, where the red sun rises in flame. There— do you hear what the Princess says?—a great stone lies in the middle of the sea. Under that stone is hidden her wedding dress. Ride swiftly. Bring back that dress, or, by my sword, your head shall no longer sit between your shoulders!"

The young archer wept bitter tears, and went out into the courtyard, where the horse of power was waiting for him, champing its golden bit.

"There is no way of escaping death this time," he said.

"Master, why do you weep?" asked the horse of power.

"The Tzar has ordered me to ride to the land of Never, to fetch the wedding dress of the Princess Vasilissa from the bottom of the deep blue sea. Besides, the dress is wanted for the Tzar's wedding, and I love the Princess myself."

"What did I tell you?" says the horse of power.

"I told you that there would be trouble if you picked up the golden feather from the fire-bird's burning breast. Well, do not be afraid. The trouble is not yet; the trouble is to come. Up! into the saddle with you, and away for the wedding dress of the Princess Vasilissa!"

The young archer leapt into the saddle, and the horse of power, with his thundering hoofs, carried him swiftly through the green forests and over the bare plains, till they came to the edge of the world, to the land of Never, where the red sun rises in flame from behind the deep blue sea. There they rested, at the very edge of the sea.

The young archer looked sadly over the wide waters, but the horse of power tossed its mane and did not look at the sea, but on the shore. This way and that it looked, and saw at last a huge lobster moving slowly, sideways, along the golden sand.

Nearer and nearer came the lobster, and it was a giant among lobsters, the tzar of all the lobsters; and it moved slowly along the shore, while the horse of power moved carefully and as if by accident, until it stood between the lobster and the sea. Then, when the lobster came close by, the horse of power lifted an iron hoof and set it firmly on the lobster's tail.

"You will be the death of me!" screamed the lobster—as well he might, with the heavy foot of the horse of power pressing his tail into the sand. "Let me live, and I will do whatever you ask of me."

"Very well," says the horse of power; "we will let you live," and he slowly lifted his foot. "But this is what you shall do for us. In the middle of the blue sea lies a great stone, and under that stone is hidden the wedding dress of the Princess Vasilissa. Bring it here."

The lobster groaned with the pain in his tail. Then he cried out in a voice that could be heard all over the deep blue sea. And the sea was disturbed, and from all sides lobsters in thousands made their way towards the bank. And the huge lobster that was the oldest of them all and the tzar of all the lobsters that live between the rising and the setting of the sun, gave them the order and sent them back into the sea. And the young archer sat on the horse of power and waited.

After a little time the sea was disturbed again, and the lobsters in their thousands came to the shore, and with them they brought a golden casket in which was the wedding dress of the Princess Vasilissa. They had taken it from under the great stone that lay in the middle of the sea.

The tzar of all the lobsters raised himself painfully on his bruised tail and gave the casket into the hands of the young archer, and instantly the horse of power turned himself about and galloped back to the palace of the Tzar, far, far away, at the other side of the green forests and beyond the treeless plains.

The young archer went into the palace and gave the casket into the hands of the Princess, and looked at her with sadness in his eyes, and she looked at him with love. Then she went away into an inner chamber, and came back in her wedding dress, fairer than the spring itself. Great was the joy of the Tzar. The wedding feast was made ready, and the bells rang, and flags waved about the palace.

The Tzar held out his hand to the Princess, and looked at her with his old eyes. But she would not take his hand.

"No," says she; "I will marry nobody until the man who brought me here has done penance in boiling water."

Instantly the Tzar turned to his servants and ordered them to make a great fire, and to fill a great cauldron with water and set it on the fire, and, when the water should be at its hottest, to take the young archer and throw him into it, to do penance for having taken the Princess Vasilissa away from the land of Never.

There was no gratitude in the mind of that Tzar.

Swiftly the servants brought wood and made a mighty fire, and on it they laid a huge cauldron of water, and built the fire around the walls of the cauldron. The fire burned hot and the water steamed. The fire burned hotter, and the water bubbled and seethed. They made ready to take the young archer, to throw him into the cauldron.

"Oh, misery!" thought the young archer. "Why did I ever take the golden feather that had fallen from the fire-bird's burning breast? Why did I not listen to the wise words of the horse of power?" And he remembered the horse of power, and he begged the Tzar,

"O lord Tzar, I do not complain. I shall presently die in the heat of the water on the fire. Suffer me, before I die, once more to see my horse."

"Let him see his horse," says the Princess.

"Very well," says the Tzar. "Say good-bye to your horse, for you will not ride him again. But let your farewells be short, for we are waiting."

The young archer crossed the courtyard and came to the horse of power, who was scraping the ground with his iron hoofs.

"Farewell, my horse of power," says the young archer. "I should have listened to your words of wisdom, for now the end is come, and we shall never more see the green trees pass above us and the ground disappear beneath us, as we race the wind between the earth and the sky."

"Why so?" says the horse of power.

"The Tzar has ordered that I am to be boiled to death—thrown into that cauldron that is seething on the great fire."

"Fear not," says the horse of power, "for the Princess Vasilissa has made him do this, and the end of these things is better than I thought. Go back, and when they are ready to throw you in the cauldron, do you run boldly and leap yourself into the boiling water."

The young archer went back across the courtyard, and the servants made ready to throw him into the cauldron.

"Are you sure that the water is boiling?" says the Princess Vasilissa.

"It bubbles and seethes," said the servants.

"Let me see for myself," says the Princess, and she went to the fire and waved her hand above the cauldron. And some say there was something in her hand, and some say there was not.

"It is boiling," says she, and the servants laid hands on the young archer; but he threw them from him, and ran and leapt boldly before them all into the very middle of the cauldron.

Twice he sank below the surface, borne around with the bubbles and foam of the boiling water. Then he leapt from the cauldron and stood before the Tzar and the Princess. He had become so beautiful a youth that all who saw cried aloud in wonder.

"This is a miracle," says the Tzar. And the Tzar looked at the beautiful young archer and thought of himself—of his age, of his bent back, and his gray beard, and his toothless gums. "I too will become beautiful," thinks he, and he rose from his throne and clambered into the cauldron, and was boiled to death in a moment.

And the end of the story? They buried the Tzar, and made the young archer Tzar in his place. He married the Princess Vasilissa, and lived many years with her in love and good fellowship. And he built a golden stable for the horse of power, and never forgot what he owed him.

A CLEVER JUDGE

Babette Deutsch, one of the authors of Tales of Faraway Folk *from which this story is taken, identifies "A Clever Judge" as a Kirghiz folk tale. In the introduction she says: "The people who tell this tale live on the vast steppes or prairies of southwestern Asia. They are herders of cattle, sheep, and goats. And they are clever fellows, too, as you shall see."*

There lived a man in the steppes who was famous for his justice and wisdom. At that time if a man was known for his fairness, people came to him from far and wide to ask him to settle their disputes. And so it was that one day two villagers appeared before this wise man and asked him to settle their quarrel.

"Tell me your story," the judge said to the plaintiff.

"I had to leave my village," said the plaintiff, "for I had business elsewhere. And all my wealth was a hundred gold coins. I did not come by them easily. I had to work hard for them, and I did not want them to be stolen while I was away. Nor did I care to carry so much money with me on my journey. So I entrusted these gold coins for safekeeping to this man here. When I got back from my journey, he denied that he had ever received the money from me."

"And who saw you give him these hundred gold coins?" asked the judge.

"A Clever Judge." From *Tales of Faraway Folk* by Babette Deutsch and Avrahm Yarmolinsky. Copyright 1952 by Harper & Brothers

"No one saw it. We went together to the heart of the forest and there I handed him the coins."

"What have you to say to this?" the judge asked, turning to the defendant.

The defendant shrugged his shoulders.

"I don't know what he is talking about," said the man. "I never went to the forest with him. I never saw his gold coins."

"Do you remember the place where you handed over the money?" the judge asked the plaintiff.

"Of course I do. It was under a tall oak. I remember it very well. I can point it out with no trouble at all."

"So you do have a witness, after all," said the judge. "Here, take my signet ring, go to the tall tree under which you stood when you handed over the money, set the seal of my signet ring against the trunk, and bid the tree appear before me to bear out the truth of your story."

The plaintiff took the signet ring and went off to carry out the demand of the judge. The defendant remained behind and waited for his return.

After some time had passed, the judge turned to the defendant and asked, "Do you think he has reached the oak by this time?"

"No, not yet," was the answer.

After further time had passed, the judge again turned to the defendant and asked, "Do you think he has reached the tree by this time?"

"Yes," was the answer, "by now he must have reached it."

Not long after that the plaintiff returned.

"Well?" asked the judge.

"I did just as you said," replied the plaintiff. "I walked as far as the forest and then I went on until I came to the tall oak under which we stood when I handed over my gold coins. I set the seal of your signet ring against the trunk of the tree and I bade it appear before you as a witness. But the tree refused to budge."

"Never mind," said the judge. "The oak has appeared before me and it has borne witness in your favor."

At that the defendant exclaimed, "How can you say such a thing! I have been here all this while and no tree has stalked into the place."

"But," replied the judge, "you said that you had not been in the forest at all. And yet when I asked you whether the plaintiff had reached the oak, first you answered that he could not have reached it, and the second time you said that he must surely have reached it. Therefore, you *were* in the forest and you remembered where the oak was under which you stood when the plaintiff handed his gold coins to you for safekeeping. Now you must not only return him his hundred gold pieces, but you must also pay a fine for having tried to cheat him."

So the tree was a witness without budging, and justice was done.

A Polish folk tale

It has been a long time since the Polish folk tales were available. The tale reprinted here is taken from The Jolly Tailor, *an old and excellent collection of representative stories recently reissued. The ten stories in the collection are all good examples of the storyteller's art, vigorously and sincerely told.*

KING BARTEK

Young girls will like this romantic story of a royal disguise that serves to reveal both the haughty hypocrite and the true-hearted maiden.

"King Bartek." From *The Jolly Tailor and Other Fairy Tales Translated from the Polish* by Lucia Merecka Borski and Kate B. Miller. Copyright 1928, © 1956 by Longmans, Green and Company

On the outskirts of a village, in a hut fallen almost to ruins, there lived a very poor widow with her two daughters, Bialka and Spiewna. Both of them were so beautiful that their fame spread over seven mountains, over seven seas. Even at the king's palace the rumors were heard. Many of the knights wished to go at once and woo the girls.

The King disliked to lose his knights, as he

had planned a great war, and besides he did not have much faith in the rumors. Instead of granting permission to the knights to go, he sent some of his faithful messengers to see the maidens and bring back pictures of Bialka and Spiewna.

The rumors were true. The pictures brought back by the messengers exceeded everybody's expectations. Spiewna was a true sister to the lily; Bialka, to the red rose. The first had azure eyes, the other, eyes dark as the Black Sea; one was proud of her long, golden braids, the other of her raven black braids. The first one had the beauty of a sunny day in her face, the other, the charm of a May night. The knights became enamored of the maidens; no one could keep them from departing. Even the King himself, as he was young and thought of marriage, scratched himself behind the ear and looked at the pictures with great pleasure. The war was put off, the court was desolated, and only the King and his Jester, Pieś, who was old and ugly like the seven mortal sins, were left there.

For a long, long time the knights did not come back. They were enjoying themselves; or it might be the other way around, Bialka and Spiewna, sure of their beauty might be taking their time picking and choosing, like sparrows in poppy seeds. The knights in love unwound entangled thread, killed partridges in the air, and sang serenades. Be it as it may, their long absence annoyed the King and he grew impatient and ill-tempered.

"Pieś," he onced addressed the Jester, "do you know what I am thinking about?"

"I know, Your Lordship!"

"How?"

"Because our thoughts walk the same paths."

"I wonder!" laughed the King.

"Your Lordship wishes to go to the widow's daughters."

"You guessed!" cried the young King, rejoicing.

"Then we shall go together," said Pieś. "But we must change our places; I, a King; Your Lordship, a Jester."

"What an idea!" said the young ruler, shocked a bit.

"There won't be much of a difference," smiled the Jester.

"No, I shall not do it! You may, if you wish, become a King, but I shall put on a peasant's garb and call myself Bartek."

"As you please!" answered Pieś. "Something unpleasant may come of it though."

"Why?" asked the King, now Bartek.

"A King, be he as ugly and humpbacked as I am, will always have preference over Bartek. And then who knows? Your Highness may fall in love with either Spiewna or Bialka."

The youthful lord became alarmed.

"So much the better!" he said after a while, and added in a whisper, "The heart that loves will not fool itself."

They went on their journey.

In the meantime the widow's hut was as noisy as a beehive. One brought musicians, another singers. The hut changed into a music box adorned with garlands and flowers, as if in celebration of a holiday. The knights reveled, the girls danced, song followed song, and jokes, one after another. The mother's white bonnet swung on her white hair from one ear to the other from happiness.

Bialka liked Przegoń (Pshegon) more than all the others. Spiewna chose none as yet. Neither her mother's persuasion nor her sister's scoffs did any good. The girl's heart had not awakened yet, and without love she did not wish to marry even the richest of knights.

The betrothal of Przegoń to Bialka was announced. She had her wedding dress made, goods for which were brought by Przegoń. The jewelry, one could not describe, it could be gathered in measures.

Bialka was overwhelmed with joy, was triumphant with her success. She looked down on her sister with haughtiness and consoled her mother with scornful words.

"Do not worry, Mother! Spiewna awaits a prince. She will become wiser when she has to grow rue, and then I, Przegoń's wife, will try to get her an organist. Also I shall find a suitable nook for you, Mother."

Her mother's heart grieved, but what could she answer?

Then one day a golden carriage drove up before the door. All three of them ran quickly to the window, and Bialka shouted:

"The King has come!"

Sudden confusion possessed the hut. The old

widow trotted to the kitchen to prepare some fowl for His Majesty, the King, while Bialka snatched a hand-mirror and a comb and turning to her sister called in a commanding voice:

"Don't you dare to call the King's attention to yourself!"

Spiewna stopped in astonishment.

"Do you hear me?" shouted Bialka.

"I hear, but I don't understand."

"You don't understand—you don't understand!"

"For—how—" began Spiewna.

"Don't dare to call the King's attention to yourself!"

"What do you care about the King when you have Przegoń?

"Have I or not, that is nothing to you!" grumbled Bialka. "And better take my advice, otherwise—you shall see!"

His Majesty, the King, was far from good looking. He was ugly, old, his right arm was higher than the left, and he was also limping. But all this was covered with the golden crown, was concealed by the purple cloak and was straightened by the long robe richly embroidered with pearls. Upon seeing the sisters, he at once laid his royal gifts at their feet, and loaded them with compliments. Spiewna refused all the gifts, she accepted only a white rose, which she pinned into her hair.

"How beautiful he is!" whispered Bialka.

"How ridiculous he is!" replied Spiewna.

Bialka looked at her with anger.

Among the King's numerous attendants, there was a young and handsome page, called Bartek. Spiewna's eyes met the youth's gaze. Bartek, dazzled with the girl's beauty, did not take his eyes off her, and when the King offered jewels to Bialka, he came near Spiewna and said:

"All my riches is this fife. It plays beautifully and the time will come when I shall present you with its song."

Spiewna, standing on the threshold, blushed like a rose, and Bialka seeing this, maliciously whispered in her ear:

"Just the kind of a husband for you. Keep away from the King!"

"And Przegoń?" questioned Spiewna.

"You may have him," threw out Bialka.

Przegoń did not see the King, but he learned of his arrival and of his gifts to Bialka. He wished to speak to Bialka, but she, busy with her guest, who exaggerated his compliments and promised golden mountains, did not care to see him. He stayed away from his unfaithful sweetheart and waited to see what time would bring forth.

One night, and 'twas a night with the full moon, a scented intoxicating night, under the window of the room where both sisters slept, there came sounds of a guitar accompanied by a song.

"The King!" murmured Bialka and she jumped to the window.

The King sang:

Out of the mist thou shalt have palaces,
For thy comfort and pleasures I will care
And pay with gold for thy every smile.
Attired, bejewelled like a peacock
Thou shalt be Queen in the royal gardens.

"Do you hear, do you hear?" said Bialka to Spiewna. "Thus sings the King!"

Then later under the window fluted the country fife. Bialka looked out of the window and

noticed Bartek. Seeing her sister moved by the sad and sweet tones of the fife, she roared with laughter.

The fife stopped playing and they heard this song:

> Do not come to me with pretense
> But with love in thy pure eyes
> That knows another's love.
> Be not touched with a royal gown
> That is worn by a fool's soul,
> A soul that knows not what is love.

"Thus sings Bartek!" called Spiewna.

"Ha-ha-ha!" rang out Bialka's venomous laughter. She leaned over the window and called aloud into the silent night:

"Drive away the fool, Your Majesty, who has the boldness to interrupt your song and insult your royal soul! Order him away, for he steals from us this beautiful night!"

"I will punish him more severely than you think," was the answer, "because to-morrow he will marry your sister."

"And when we?" asked Bialka.

"Even now. Come to me!"

Bialka jumped out of the window, and there she met face to face with Przegoń.

"What are you doing here?" she asked him haughtily.

"I came to wish you happiness with this— king's Jester," replied Przegoń pointing to Pieś.

"What? What?" cried Bialka, looking with frightened eyes at the splendid dress, like a king's.

And in the room, where Spiewna remained, Bartek's fife rang out followed by a song:

> 'Tis hard to find true love
> Under an alluring purple gown,
> Infirmity shall remain in heart
> With all the roses torn aside.
> Ugly looks and lameness and a hump
> May all be covered with a royal cloak.
> The King wished for a true heart;
> The fool desired fun and laughter;
> And both are satisfied.
> Therefore the fool dressed like a King
> The King put on the peasant's garb.
> Now, maiden, cry for thy alluring loss
> And understand these prophesying words:
> That people are not judged by looks
> But by their hearts and deeds.

The golden carriage came to the door, a thousand torches were lighted, a thousand knights with Przegoń at the head surrounded the royal carriage, into which Spiewna was led with her bridesmaids, and they all went to the King's palace to celebrate the wedding. The mother rejoiced at Spiewna's happiness, but she grieved over the neglected Bialka, who had to grow sixteen beds of rue before she married an old organist.

East Indian folk tales

The East Indian tales are numerically enormous, but only a small percentage of them is suitable for children. The ancestors of many European tales are to be found in the East Indian collections, and also from India comes a multitude of talking beast stories. These are from an ancient collection of Indian fables called the Jatakas, which are birth stories of Gautama Buddha in his progressive reincarnations in the forms of different animals. When references to the Buddha are omitted, a good talking beast tale remains and for this reason the Jatakas are included with the folk tales instead of with the fables. They are generally moralistic in tone but somehow manage to preserve their story values, as these four examples demonstrate. Young children readily accept the animal that speaks, but children over nine or ten are sometimes skeptical.

THE HARE THAT RAN AWAY

This ancient story is one of a series about the wise Buddha in his successive animal incarnations. The story may begin without the reference to Buddha, "Once there was a wise Lion who did much to help his fellow creatures and he found there was much to be done. For instance, there was a little nervous Hare. . . ."

And it came to pass that the Buddha (to be) was born again as a Lion. Just as he had helped his fellow-men, he now began to help his fellow-animals, and there was a great deal to be done. For instance, there was a little nervous Hare who was always afraid that something dreadful was going to happen to her. She was always saying: "Suppose the Earth were to fall in, what would happen to me?" And she said this so often that at last she thought it really was about to happen. One day, when she had been saying over and over again, "Suppose the Earth were to fall in, what would happen to me?" she heard a slight noise: it really was only a heavy fruit which had fallen upon a rustling leaf, but the little Hare was so nervous she was ready to believe anything, and she said in a frightened tone: "The Earth *is* falling in." She ran away as fast as she could go, and presently she met an old brother Hare, who said: "Where are you running to, Mistress Hare?"

And the little Hare said: "I have no time to stop and tell you anything. The Earth is falling in, and I am running away."

"The Earth is falling in, is it?" said the old brother Hare, in a tone of much astonishment; and he repeated this to *his* brother hare, and *he* to *his* brother hare, and *he* to *his* brother hare, until at last there were a hundred thousand brother hares, all shouting: "The Earth is falling in." Now presently the bigger animals began to take the cry up. First the deer, and then the sheep, and then the wild boar, and then the buffalo, and then the camel, and then the tiger, and then the elephant.

Now the wise Lion heard all this noise and wondered at it. "There are no signs," he said, "of the Earth falling in. They must have heard

something." And then he stopped them all short and said: "What is this you are saying?"

And the Elephant said: "I remarked that the Earth was falling in."

"How do you know this?" asked the Lion.

"Why, now I come to think of it, it was the Tiger that remarked it to me."

And the Tiger said: "*I* had it from the Camel," and the Camel said: "*I* had it from the Buffalo." And the buffalo from the wild boar, and the wild boar from the sheep, and the sheep from the deer, and the deer from the hares, and the Hares said: "Oh! *we* heard it from *that* little Hare."

And the Lion said: "Little Hare, *what* made you say that the Earth was falling in?"

And the little Hare said: "I *saw* it."

"You saw it?" said the Lion. "Where?"

"Yonder by the tree."

"Well," said the Lion, "come with me and I will show you how——"

"No, no," said the Hare, "I would not go near that tree for anything, I'm *so* nervous."

"But," said the Lion, "I am going to take you on my back." And he took her on his back, and begged the animals to stay where they were until they returned. Then he showed the little Hare how the fruit had fallen upon the leaf, making the noise that had frightened her, and she said: "Yes, I see—the Earth is *not* falling in." And the Lion said: "Shall we go back and tell the other animals?"

And they went back. The little Hare stood before the animals and said: "The Earth is *not* falling in." And all the animals began to repeat this to one another, and they dispersed gradually, and you heard the words more and more softly:

"The Earth is *not* falling in," etc., etc., etc., until the sound died away altogether.

GRANNY'S BLACKIE

Once upon a time a rich man gave a baby Elephant to a woman.

She took the best of care of this great baby and soon became very fond of him.

"The Hare That Ran Away." From *Eastern Stories and Legends* by Marie Shedlock, published and copyright, 1920, E. P. Dutton & Co., Inc., New York, renewed, 1948. By permission also of George Routledge & Sons Ltd., London

"Granny's Blackie." From *Jataka Tales* by Ellen C. Babbitt. Copyright, 1912, Century Company. Reprinted by permission of the publishers, Appleton-Century-Crofts, Inc.

The children in the village called her Granny, and they called the Elephant "Granny's Blackie."

The Elephant carried the children on his back all over the village. They shared their goodies with him and he played with them.

"Please, Blackie, give us a swing," they said to him almost every day.

"Come on! Who is first?" Blackie answered and picked them up with his trunk, swung them high in the air, and then put them down again, carefully.

But Blackie never did any work.

He ate and slept, played with the children, and visited with Granny.

One day Blackie wanted Granny to go off to the woods with him.

"I can't go, Blackie, dear. I have too much work to do."

Then Blackie looked at her and saw that she was growing old and feeble.

"I am young and strong," he thought. "I'll see if I cannot find some work to do. If I could bring some money home to her, she would not have to work so hard."

So next morning, bright and early, he started down to the river bank.

There he found a man who was in great trouble. There was a long line of wagons so heavily loaded that the oxen could not draw them through the shallow water.

When the man saw Blackie standing on the bank he asked, "Who owns this Elephant? I want to hire him to help my Oxen pull these wagons across the river."

A child standing near by said, "That is Granny's Blackie."

"Very well," said the man, "I'll pay two pieces of silver for each wagon this Elephant draws across the river."

Blackie was glad to hear this promise. He went into the river, and drew one wagon after another across to the other side.

Then he went up to the man for the money.

The man counted out one piece of silver for each wagon.

When Blackie saw that the man had counted out but one piece of silver for each wagon, instead of two, he would not touch the money at all. He stood in the road and would not let the wagons pass him.

The man tried to get Blackie out of the way, but not one step would he move.

Then the man went back and counted out another piece of silver for each of the wagons and put the silver in a bag tied around Blackie's neck.

Then Blackie started for home, proud to think that he had a present for Granny.

The children had missed Blackie and had asked Granny where he was, but she said she did not know where he had gone.

They all looked for him but it was nearly night before they heard him coming.

"Where have you been, Blackie? And what is that around your neck?" the children cried, running to meet their playmate.

But Blackie would not stop to talk with his playmates. He ran straight home to Granny.

"Oh, Blackie!" she said. "Where have you been? What is in that bag?" And she took the bag off his neck.

Blackie told her that he had earned some money for her.

"Oh, Blackie, Blackie," said Granny, "how hard you must have worked to earn these pieces of silver! What a good Blackie you are!"

And after that Blackie did all the hard work and Granny rested, and they were both very happy.

THE TIGER, THE BRAHMAN, AND THE JACKAL

There are a series of jackal stories in which the jackal is generally the trickster who is finally caught and punished, but in this story the tables are turned. Children will be satisfied with the explanation that a brahman is a wise, good man. Further details are unnecessary.

Once upon a time a tiger was caught in a trap. He tried in vain to get out through the bars, and rolled and bit with rage and grief when he failed.

By chance a poor Brahman came by. "Let me out of this cage, O pious one!" cried the tiger.

"The Tiger, the Brahman, and the Jackal." From *Tales of the Punjab* compiled by Flora Annie Steel, Macmillan and Co., Ltd. By permission of The Macmillan Company, New York and Macmillan & Co. Ltd., London

"Nay, my friend," replied the Brahman mildly, "you would probably eat me if I did."

"Not at all!" swore the tiger with many oaths; "on the contrary, I should be for ever grateful, and serve you as a slave!"

Now when the tiger sobbed and sighed and wept and swore, the pious Brahman's heart softened, and at last he consented to open the door of the cage. Out popped the tiger, and, seizing the poor man, cried, "What a fool you are! What is to prevent my eating you now, for after being cooped up so long I am just terribly hungry!"

In vain the Brahman pleaded for his life; the most he could gain was a promise to abide by the decision of the first three things he chose to question as to the justice of the tiger's action.

So the Brahman first asked a *pîpal* tree what it thought of the matter, but the *pîpal* tree replied coldly, "What have you to complain about? Don't I give shade and shelter to every one who passes by, and don't they in return tear down my branches to feed their cattle? Don't whimper—be a man!"

Then the Brahman, sad at heart, went farther afield till he saw a buffalo turning a well-wheel; but he fared no better from it, for it answered, "You are a fool to expect gratitude! Look at me! While I gave milk they fed me on cotton-seed and oil-cake, but now I am dry they yoke me here, and give me refuse as fodder!"

The Brahman, still more sad, asked the road to give him its opinion.

"My dear sir," said the road, "how foolish you are to expect anything else! Here am I, useful to everybody, yet all, rich and poor, great and small, trample on me as they go past, giving me nothing but the ashes of their pipes and the husks of their grain!"

On this the Brahman turned back sorrowfully, and on the way he met a jackal, who called out, "Why, what's the matter, Mr. Brahman? You look as miserable as a fish out of water!"

Then the Brahman told him all that had occurred. "How very confusing!" said the jackal, when the recital was ended; "would you mind telling me over again? for everything seems so mixed up!"

The Brahman told it all over again, but the jackal shook his head in a distracted sort of way, and still could not understand.

"It's very odd," said he sadly, "but it all seems to go in at one ear and out at the other! I will go to the place where it all happened, and then perhaps I shall be able to give a judgment."

So they returned to the cage, by which the tiger was waiting for the Brahman, and sharpening his teeth and claws.

"You've been away a long time!" growled the savage beast, "but now let us begin our dinner."

"*Our* dinner!" thought the wretched Brahman, as his knees knocked together with fright; "what a remarkably delicate way of putting it!"

"Give me five minutes, my lord!" he pleaded, "in order that I may explain matters to the jackal here, who is somewhat slow in his wits."

The tiger consented, and the Brahman began the whole story over again, not missing a single detail, and spinning as long a yarn as possible.

"Oh, my poor brain! oh, my poor brain!" cried the jackal, wringing his paws. "Let me see! how did it all begin? You were in the cage, and the tiger came walking by——"

"Pooh!" interrupted the tiger, "what a fool you are! *I* was in the cage."

"Of course!" cried the jackal, pretending to tremble with fright; "yes! I was in the cage—no, I wasn't—dear! dear! where are my wits? Let me see—the tiger was in the Brahman, and the cage came walking by—no, that's not it either! Well, don't mind me, but begin your dinner, for I shall never understand!"

"Yes, you shall!" returned the tiger, in a rage at the jackal's stupidity; "I'll *make* you understand! Look here—I am the tiger——"

"Yes, my lord!"

"And that is the Brahman——"

"Yes, my lord!"

"And that is the cage——"

"Yes, my lord!"

"And I was in the cage—do you understand?"

"Yes—no—Please, my lord——"

"Well?" cried the tiger, impatiently.

"Please, my lord!—how did you get in?"

"How!—why, in the usual way, of course!"

"Oh dear me!—my head is beginning to whirl again! Please don't be angry, my lord, but what is the usual way?"

At this the tiger lost patience, and, jumping into the cage, cried, "This way! Now do you understand how it was?"

"Perfectly!" grinned the jackal, as he dexterously shut the door; "and if you will permit me to say so, I think matters will remain as they were!"

THE BANYAN DEER

There was once a Deer the color of gold. His eyes were like round jewels, his horns were white as silver, his mouth was red like a flower, his hoofs were bright and hard. He had a large body and a fine tail.

He lived in a forest and was king of a herd of five hundred Banyan Deer. Near by lived another herd of Deer, called the Monkey Deer. They, too, had a king.

The king of that country was fond of hunting the Deer and eating deer meat. He did not like to go alone so he called the people of his town to go with him, day after day.

The townspeople did not like this for while they were gone no one did their work. So they decided to make a park and drive the Deer into it. Then the king could go into the park and hunt and they could go on with their daily work.

They made a park, planted grass in it and provided water for the Deer, built a fence all around it and drove the Deer into it.

Then they shut the gate and went to the king to tell him that in the park near by he could find all the Deer he wanted.

The king went at once to look at the Deer. First he saw there the two Deer kings, and granted them their lives. Then he looked at their great herds.

Some days the king would go to hunt the Deer, sometimes his cook would go. As soon as any of the Deer saw them they would shake with fear and run. But when they had been hit once or twice they would drop down dead.

The King of the Banyan Deer sent for the King of the Monkey Deer and said, "Friend, many of the Deer are being killed. Many are wounded besides those who are killed. After this suppose one from my herd goes up to be killed one day, and the next day let one from your herd go up. Fewer Deer will be lost this way."

The Monkey Deer agreed. Each day the Deer whose turn it was would go and lie down, placing its head on the block. The cook would come and carry off the one he found lying there.

One day the lot fell to a mother Deer who had

a young baby. She went to her king and said, "O King of the Monkey Deer, let the turn pass me by until my baby is old enough to get along without me. Then I will go and put my head on the block."

But the king did not help her. He told her that if the lot had fallen to her she must die.

Then she went to the King of the Banyan Deer and asked him to save her.

"Go back to your herd. I will go in your place," said he.

The next day the cook found the King of the Banyan Deer lying with his head on the block.

The cook went to the king, who came himself to find out about this.

"King of the Banyan Deer! did I not grant you your life? Why are you lying here?"

"O great King!" said the King of the Banyan Deer, "a mother came with her young baby and told me that the lot had fallen to her. I could not ask any one else to take her place, so I came myself."

"King of the Banyan Deer! I never saw such kindness and mercy. Rise up. I grant your life and hers. Nor will I hunt any more the Deer in either park or forest."

A tale from the "Arabian Nights"

The source of the Arabian Nights is lost in antiquity. Some of the tales seem to stem from ancient India, others from North Africa, and others from Persia. In the Moslem world, where they were preserved, they were not considered polite literature but circulated in the market places or the coffee houses. The first translation of the stories into French, in 1704, was made by Antoine Galland from a manuscript that came from Syria but was written in Egypt. However confused their source, the "thousand and one tales" have been spellbinding young readers ever since. Today, perhaps because of rival media of entertainment, they are not so much read. Their interminable length is undoubtedly the chief obstacle to their popularity, for they contain stories within stories, episodes upon episodes, magic and more magic. Modern adapters of these tales have practiced an economy of incident that was lacking in the original, but even greatly cut versions have a color, dramatic plot construction, and a use of magic that are weird and enthralling. Perhaps this sample will send some of the children to a collection of the tales for further reading.

ALADDIN AND
THE WONDERFUL LAMP

There once lived a poor tailor, who had a son called Aladdin, a careless, idle boy who would do nothing but play all day long in the streets with little idle boys like himself. This so grieved the father that he died; yet, in spite of his mother's tears and prayers, Aladdin did

not mend his ways. One day, when he was playing in the streets as usual, a stranger asked him his age, and if he were not the son of Mustapha the tailor. "I am, sir," replied Aladdin; "but he died a long while ago."

On this the stranger, who was a famous African magician, fell on his neck and kissed him, saying: "I am your uncle, and knew you from your likeness to my brother. Go to your mother and tell her I am coming."

Aladdin ran home, and told his mother of his newly found uncle. "Indeed, child," she said, "your father had a brother, but I always thought he was dead." However, she prepared supper, and bade Aladdin seek his uncle, who came laden with wine and fruit. He presently fell down and kissed the place where Mustapha used to sit, bidding Aladdin's mother not to be surprised at not having seen him before, as he had been forty years out of the country. He then turned to Aladdin, and asked him his trade, at which the boy hung his head, while his mother burst into tears. On learning that Aladdin was idle and would learn no trade, he offered to take a shop for him and stock it with merchandise. Next day he bought Aladdin a fine suit of clothes and took him all over the city, showing him the sights, and brought him home at nightfall to his mother, who was overjoyed to see her son so fine.

Next day the magician led Aladdin into some beautiful gardens a long way outside the city gates. They sat down by a fountain and the magician pulled a cake from his girdle, which he divided between them. They then journeyed onwards till they almost reached the mountains. Aladdin was so tired that he begged to go back, but the magician beguiled him with pleasant stories, and led him on in spite of himself. At last they came to two mountains divided by a narrow valley. "We will go no farther," said the false uncle. "I will show you something wonderful; only do you gather up sticks while I kindle a fire."

When it was lit the magician threw on it a powder he had about him, at the same time saying some magical words. The earth trembled a little and opened in front of them, disclosing a square flat stone with a brass ring in the middle to raise it by. Aladdin tried to run away, but the magician caught him and gave him a blow that knocked him down. "What have I done, uncle?" he said piteously; whereupon the magician said more kindly: "Fear nothing, but obey me. Beneath this stone lies a treasure which is to be yours, and no one else may touch it; so you must do exactly as I tell you."

At the word treasure Aladdin forgot his fears, and grasped the ring as he was told, saying the names of his father and grandfather. The stone came up quite easily and some steps appeared. "Go down," said the magician; "at the foot of those steps you will find an open door leading into three large halls. Tuck up your gown and go through them without touching anything, or you

will die instantly. These halls lead into a garden of fine fruit trees. Walk on till you come to a niche in a terrace where stands a lighted lamp. Pour out the oil it contains, and bring it to me." He drew a ring from his finger and gave it to Aladdin, bidding him prosper.

Aladdin found everything as the magician had said, gathered some fruit off the trees, and, having got the lamp, arrived at the mouth of the cave. The magician cried out in a great hurry: "Make haste and give me the lamp." This Aladdin refused to do until he was out of the cave. The magician flew into a terrible passion, and throwing some more powder on the fire, he said something, and the stone rolled back into its place.

The magician left Persia forever, which plainly showed that he was no uncle of Aladdin's, but a cunning magician, who had read in his magic books of a wonderful lamp, which would make him the most powerful man in the world. Though he alone knew where to find it, he could only receive it from the hand of another. He had picked out the foolish Aladdin for this purpose, intending to get the lamp and kill him afterwards.

For two days Aladdin remained in the dark, crying and lamenting. At last he clasped his hands in prayer, and in so doing, rubbed the ring, which the magician had forgotten to take from him. Immediately an enormous and frightful genie rose out of the earth, saying: "What wouldst thou with me? I am the Slave of the Ring, and will obey thee in all things."

Aladdin fearlessly replied: "Deliver me from this place!" whereupon the earth opened, and he found himself outside. As soon as his eyes could bear the light he went home, but fainted on the threshold. When he came to himself, he told his mother what had passed, and showed her the lamp and the fruits he had gathered in the garden, which were in reality precious stones. He then asked for some food.

"Alas! child," she said, "I have nothing in the house, but I have spun a little cotton and will go and sell it."

Aladdin bade her keep her cotton, for he would sell the lamp instead. As it was very dirty, she began to rub it, that it might fetch a higher price. Instantly a hideous genie appeared and asked what she would have. She fainted away, but Aladdin, snatching the lamp, said boldly: "Fetch me something to eat!"

The genie returned with a silver bowl, twelve silver plates containing rich meats, two silver cups, and two bottles of wine. Aladdin's mother, when she came to herself, said: "Whence comes this splendid feast?"

"Ask not, but eat," replied Aladdin. So they sat at breakfast till it was dinner-time and Aladdin told his mother about the lamp. She begged him to sell it, and have nothing to do with devils. "No," said Aladdin, "since chance hath made us aware of its virtues, we will use it and the ring likewise, which I shall always wear on my finger." When they had eaten all the genie had brought, Aladdin sold one of the silver plates, and so on till none were left. He then had recourse to the genie, who gave him another set of plates, and thus they lived for many years.

One day Aladdin heard an order from the Sultan proclaiming that everyone was to stay at home and close his shutters while the Princess, his daughter, went to and from the bath. Aladdin was seized by a desire to see her face, which was very difficult, as she always went veiled. He hid himself behind the door of the bath and peeped through a chink. The Princess lifted her veil as she went in, and looked so beautiful that Aladdin fell in love with her at first sight. He went home so changed that his mother was frightened. He told her he loved the Princess so deeply that he could not live without her, and meant to ask her in marriage of her father. His mother, on hearing this, burst out laughing; but Aladdin at last prevailed upon her to go before the Sultan and carry his request. She fetched a napkin and laid in it the magic fruits from the enchanted garden, which sparkled and shone like the most beautiful jewels. She took these with her to please the Sultan, and set out, trusting in the lamp.

The Grand-Vizier and the lords of council had just gone in as she entered the hall and placed herself in front of the Sultan. He, however, took no notice of her. She went every day for a week, and stood in the same place. When the council broke up on the sixth day the Sultan said to his Vizier: "I see a certain woman in the audience-chamber every day carrying something in a napkin. Call her next time, that I may find out what

she wants." Next day, at a sign from the Vizier, she went up to the foot of the throne and remained kneeling till the Sultan said to her: "Rise, good woman, and tell me what you want." She hesitated, so the Sultan sent away all but the Vizier, and bade her speak freely, promising to forgive her beforehand for anything she might say. She then told him of her son's violent love for the Princess.

"I prayed him to forget her," she said, "but in vain; he threatened to do some desperate deed if I refused to go and ask your Majesty for the hand of the Princess. Now I pray you to forgive not me alone, but my son Aladdin."

The Sultan asked her kindly what she had in the napkin, whereupon she unfolded the jewels and presented them. He was thunderstruck, and turning to the Vizier said: "What sayest thou? Ought I not to bestow the Princess on one who values her at such a price?" The Vizier, who wanted her for his own son, begged the Sultan to withhold her for three months, in the course of which he hoped his son would contrive to make him a richer present. The Sultan granted this, and told Aladdin's mother that, though he consented to the marriage, she must not appear before him again for three months.

Aladdin waited patiently for nearly three months, but after two had elapsed, his mother, going into the city to buy oil, found everyone rejoicing, and asked what was going on. "Do you not know," was the answer, "that the son of the Grand-Vizier is to marry the Sultan's daughter tonight?"

Breathless, she ran and told Aladdin, who was overwhelmed at first, but presently bethought him of the lamp. He rubbed it, and the genie appeared, saying: "What is thy will?"

Aladdin replied: "The Sultan, as thou knowest, has broken his promise to me, and the Vizier's son is to have the Princess. My command is that tonight you bring hither the bride and bridegroom."

"Master, I obey," said the genie. Aladdin then went to his chamber, where, sure enough, at midnight the genie transported the bed containing the Vizier's son and the Princess.

"Take this new-married man," he said, "and put him outside in the cold, and return at daybreak." Whereupon the genie took the Vizier's son out of bed, leaving Aladdin with the Princess. "Fear nothing," Aladdin said to her; "you are my wife, promised to me by your unjust father, and no harm shall come to you." The Princess was too frightened to speak, and passed the most miserable night of her life, while Aladdin lay down beside her and slept soundly. At the appointed hour the genie fetched in the shivering bridegroom, laid him in his place, and transported the bed back to the palace.

Presently the Sultan came to wish his daughter good-morning. The unhappy Vizier's son jumped up and hid himself, while the Princess would not say a word, and was very sorrowful. The Sultan sent her mother to her, who said: "How comes it, child, that you will not speak to your father? What has happened?" The Princess sighed deeply, and at last told her mother how, during the night, the bed had been carried into some strange house, and what had passed there. Her mother did not believe her in the least, but bade her rise and consider it an idle dream.

The following night exactly the same thing happened, and next morning, on the Princess's refusing to speak, the Sultan threatened to cut off her head. She then confessed all, bidding him ask the Vizier's son if it were not so. The Sultan told the Vizier to ask his son, who owned the truth, adding that, dearly as he loved the Princess, he had rather die than go through another such fearful night, and wished to be separated from her. His wish was granted, and there was an end of feasting and rejoicing.

When the three months were over, Aladdin sent his mother to remind the Sultan of his promise. She stood in the same place as before, and the Sultan, who had forgotten Aladdin, at once remembered him, and sent for her. On seeing her poverty the Sultan felt less inclined than ever to keep his word, and asked the Vizier's advice, who counseled him to set so high a value on the Princess that no man living could come up to it. The Sultan then turned to Aladdin's mother, saying: "Good woman, a Sultan must remember his promises, and I will remember mine, but your son must first send me forty basins of gold brimful of jewels, carried by forty black slaves, led by as many white ones, splendidly dressed. Tell him that I await his answer."

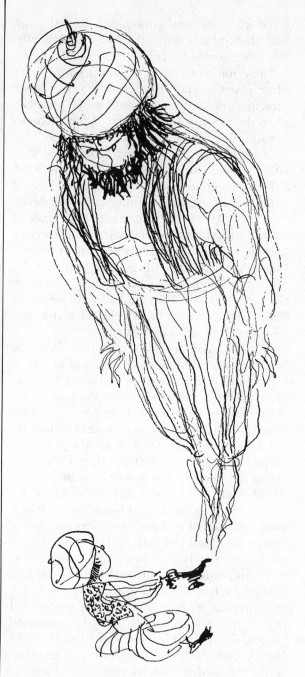

The mother of Aladdin bowed low and went home, thinking all was lost. She gave Aladdin the message, adding: "He may wait long enough for your answer!"

"Not so long, mother, as you think," her son replied. "I would do a great deal more than that for the Princess." He summoned the genie, and in a few moments the eighty slaves arrived, and filled up the small house and garden. Aladdin made them set out to the palace, two and two, followed by his mother. They were so richly dressed, with such splendid jewels in their girdles, that everyone crowded to see them and the basins of gold they carried on their heads.

They entered the palace and, after kneeling before the Sultan, stood in a half-circle round the throne with their arms crossed, while Aladdin's mother presented them to the Sultan. He hesitated no longer, but said: "Good woman, return and tell your son that I wait for him with open arms." She lost no time in telling Aladdin, bidding him make haste. But Aladdin first called the genie.

"I want a scented bath," he said, "a richly embroidered habit, a horse surpassing the Sultan's, and twenty slaves to attend me. Besides this, six slaves, beautifully dressed, to wait on my mother; and lastly, ten thousand pieces of gold in ten purses." No sooner said than done. Aladdin mounted his horse and passed through the streets, the slaves strewing gold as they went. Those who had played with him in his childhood knew him not, he had grown so handsome. When the Sultan saw him he came down from his throne, embraced him, and led him into a hall where a feast was spread, intending to marry him to the Princess that very day. But Aladdin refused, saying, "I must build a palace fit for her," and took his leave.

Once home, he said to the genie: "Build me a palace of the finest marble, set with jasper, agate, and other precious stones. In the middle you shall build me a large hall with a dome, its four walls of massy gold and silver, each side having six windows, whose lattices, all except one, which is to be left unfinished, must be set with diamonds and rubies. There must be stables and horses and grooms and slaves; go and see about it!"

The palace was finished by next day, and the genie carried him there and showed him all his orders faithfully carried out, even to the laying of a velvet carpet from Aladdin's palace to the Sultan's. Aladdin's mother then dressed herself carefully, and walked to the palace with her slaves, while he followed her on horseback. The Sultan sent musicians with trumpets and cymbals to meet them, so that the air resounded with music and cheers. She was taken to the Princess, who saluted her and treated her with great honor. At night the Princess said good-bye to her father, and set out on the carpet for Aladdin's palace, with his mother at her side, and followed by the hundred slaves. She was charmed at the sight of Aladdin, who ran to receive her. "Princess," he said, "blame your beauty for my boldness if I have displeased you." She told him that, having seen him, she willingly obeyed her father in this matter. After the wedding had taken place Aladdin led her into the hall, where a feast was spread, and she supped with him, after which they danced till midnight.

Next day Aladdin invited the Sultan to see the palace. On entering the hall with the four-and-twenty windows, with their rubies, diamonds, and emeralds, he cried: "It is a world's wonder! There is only one thing that surprises me. Was it by accident that one window was left unfinished?"

"No, sir, by design," returned Aladdin. "I wished your Majesty to have the glory of finishing this palace."

The Sultan was pleased, and sent for the best jewelers in the city. He showed them the unfinished window, and bade them fit it up like the others. "Sir," replied their spokesman, "we cannot find jewels enough."

The Sultan had his own fetched, which they soon used, but to no purpose, for in a month's time the work was not half done. Aladdin, knowing that their task was vain, bade them undo their work and carry the jewels back, and the genie finished the window at his command. The Sultan was surprised to receive his jewels again and visited Aladdin, who showed him the window finished. The Sultan embraced him, the envious Vizier meanwhile hinting that it was the work of enchantment. Aladdin had won the hearts of the people by his gentle bearing. He was made captain of the Sultan's armies, and won several battles for him, but remained modest and courteous as before and lived thus in peace and content for several years.

But far away in Africa the magician remembered Aladdin and by his magic arts discovered that Aladdin, instead of perishing miserably in the cave, had escaped and had married a Princess with whom he was living in great honor and wealth. He knew that the poor tailor's son could only have accomplished this by means of the lamp and traveled night and day till he reached the capital of China, bent on Aladdin's ruin. As he passed through the town he heard people talking everywhere about a marvelous palace. "Forgive my ignorance," he said. "What is this palace you speak of?"

"Have you not heard of Prince Aladdin's palace," was the reply, "the greatest wonder of the world? I will direct you if you have a mind to see it."

The magician thanked him who spoke, and having seen the palace knew that it had been raised by the genie of the lamp and became half mad with rage. He determined to get hold of the lamp and again plunge Aladdin into the deepest poverty. Unluckily, Aladdin had gone a-hunting for eight days, which gave the magician plenty of time. He bought a dozen copper lamps, put them into a basket, and went to the palace, crying, "New lamps for old!" followed by a jeering crowd.

The Princess, sitting in the hall of four-and-twenty windows, sent a slave to find out what the noise was about, who came back laughing, so that the Princess scolded her. "Madam," replied the slave, "who can help laughing to see an old fool offering to exchange fine new lamps for old ones?"

Another slave, hearing this, said: "There is an old one on the cornice there which he can have." Now this was the magic lamp, which Aladdin had left there, as he could not take it out hunting with him. The Princess, not knowing its value, laughingly bade the slave take it and make the exchange. She went and said to the magician: "Give me a new lamp for this."

He snatched it and bade the slave take her choice, amid the jeers of the crowd. Little he cared, but left off crying his lamps, and went out of the city gates to a lonely place, where he remained till nightfall, when he pulled out the lamp and rubbed it. The genie appeared and at the magician's command carried him, together with the palace and the Princess in it, to a lonely place in Africa.

Next morning the Sultan looked out of the window toward Aladdin's palace and rubbed his eyes, for it was gone. He sent for the Vizier and asked what had become of the palace. The Vizier

looked out too, and was lost in astonishment. He again put it down to enchantment, and this time the Sultan believed him, and sent thirty men on horseback to fetch Aladdin in chains. They met him riding home, bound him, and forced him to go with them on foot. The people, however, who loved him, followed, armed, to see that he came to no harm. He was carried before the Sultan, who ordered the executioner to cut off his head. The executioner made Aladdin kneel down, bandaged his eyes, and raised his scimitar to strike. At that instant the Vizier, who saw that the crowd had forced their way into the courtyard and were scaling the walls to rescue Aladdin, called to the executioner to stay his hand. The people, indeed, looked so threatening that the Sultan gave way and ordered Aladdin to be unbound, and pardoned him in the sight of the crowd. Aladdin now begged to know what he had done.

"False wretch!" said the Sultan, "come hither," and showed him from the window the place where his palace had stood. Aladdin was so amazed that he could not say a word. "Where is the palace and my daughter?" demanded the Sultan. "For the first I am not so deeply concerned, but my daughter I must have, and you must find her or lose your head."

Aladdin begged for forty days in which to find her, promising if he failed, to return and suffer death at the Sultan's pleasure. His prayer was granted, and he went forth sadly from the Sultan's presence. For three days he wandered about like a madman, asking everyone what had become of his palace, but they only laughed and pitied him. He came to the banks of a river, and knelt down to say his prayers before throwing himself in. In so doing he rubbed the magic ring he still wore. The genie he had seen in the cave appeared, and asked his will. "Save my life, genie," said Aladdin, "and bring my palace back."

"That is not in my power," said the genie; "I am only the Slave of the Ring, you must ask the Slave of the Lamp."

"Even so," said Aladdin, "but thou canst take me to the palace, and set me down under my dear wife's window." He at once found himself in Africa, under the window of the Princess, and fell asleep out of sheer weariness.

He was awakened by the singing of the birds, and his heart was lighter. He saw plainly that all his misfortunes were owing to the loss of the lamp, and vainly wondered who had robbed him of it. That morning the Princess rose earlier than she had done since she had been carried into Africa by the magician, whose company she was forced to endure once a day. She, however, treated him so harshly that he dared not live there altogether. As she was dressing, one of her women looked out and saw Aladdin. The Princess ran and opened the window, and at the noise she made Aladdin looked up. She called to him to come to her, and great was the joy of these lovers at seeing each other again.

After he had kissed her Aladdin said: "I beg of you, Princess, in God's name, before we speak of anything else, for your own sake and mine, tell me what has become of an old lamp I left on the cornice in the hall of windows when I went hunting."

"Alas!" she said, "I am the innocent cause of our sorrows," and told him of the exchange of the lamp.

"Now I know," cried Aladdin, "that we have to thank the African magician for this! Where is the lamp?"

"He carries it about with him," said the Princess. "I know, for he pulled it out of his breast to show me. He wishes me to break my faith with you and marry him, saying that you were beheaded by my father's command. He is forever speaking ill of you, but I only reply by my tears. If I persist, I doubt not that he will use violence."

Aladdin comforted her and left her for a while. He changed clothes with the first person he met in the town, and having bought a certain powder, returned to the Princess, who let him in by a little side door. "Put on your most beautiful dress," he said to her, "and receive the magician with smiles, leading him to believe that you have forgotten me. Invite him to sup with you, and say you wish to taste the wine of his country. He will go for some, and while he is gone, I will tell you what to do."

She listened carefully to Aladdin, and when he left her, arrayed herself gaily for the first time since she left China. She put on a girdle and head-dress of diamonds, and seeing in a glass that she looked more beautiful than ever, received

the magician, saying, to his great amazement: "I have made up my mind that Aladdin is dead, and that all my tears will not bring him back to me, so I am resolved to mourn no more, and have therefore invited you to sup with me; but I am tired of the wines of China, and would fain taste those of Africa."

The magician flew to his cellar, and the Princess put the powder Aladdin had given her in her cup. When he returned she asked him to drink her health in the wine of Africa, handing him her cup in exchange for his as a sign she was reconciled to him. Before drinking, the magician made her a speech in praise of her beauty, but the Princess cut him short, saying: "Let me drink first, and you shall say what you will afterwards." She set her cup to her lips and kept it there, while the magician drained his to the dregs and fell back lifeless. The Princess then opened the door to Aladdin, and flung her arms round his neck, but Aladdin put her away, bidding her leave him, as he had more to do. He then went to the dead magician, took the lamp out of his vest, and bade the genie carry the palace and all in it back to China. This was done, and the Princess in her chamber only felt two little shocks, and little thought she was at home again.

The Sultan, who was sitting in his closet, mourning for his lost daughter, happened to look up, and rubbed his eyes, for there stood the palace as before! He hastened thither, and Aladdin received him in the hall of the four-and-twenty windows, with the Princess at his side. Aladdin told him what had happened, and showed him the dead body of the magician, that he might believe. A ten days' feast was proclaimed, and it seemed as if Aladdin might now live the rest of his life in peace; but it was not to be.

The African magician had a younger brother, who was, if possible, more wicked and more cunning than himself. He traveled to China to avenge his brother's death, and went to visit a pious woman called Fatima, thinking she might be of use to him. He entered her cell and clapped a dagger to her breast, telling her to rise and do his bidding on pain of death. He changed clothes with her, colored his face like hers, put on her veil, and murdered her, that she might tell no tales. Then he went towards the palace of Aladdin, and all the people, thinking he was the holy woman, gathered round him, kissing his hands and begging his blessing. When he got to the palace there was such a noise going on round him that the Princess bade her slave look out of the window and ask what was the matter. The slave said it was the holy woman, curing people by her touch of their ailments, whereupon the Princess, who had long desired to see Fatima, sent for her. On coming to the Princess, the magician offered up a prayer for her health and prosperity. When he had done, the Princess made him sit by her, and begged him to stay with her always. The false Fatima, who wished for nothing better, consented, but kept his veil down for fear of discovery. The Princess showed him the hall, and asked him what he thought of it. "It is truly beautiful," said the false Fatima. "In my mind it wants but one thing."

"And what is that?" said the Princess.

"If only a roc's egg," replied he, "were hung up from the middle of this dome, it would be the wonder of the world."

After this the Princess could think of nothing but a roc's egg, and when Aladdin returned from hunting he found her in a very ill humor. He begged to know what was amiss, and she told him that all her pleasure in the hall was spoilt for the want of a roc's egg hanging from the dome. "If that is all," replied Aladdin, "you shall soon be happy."

He left her and rubbed the lamp, and when the genie appeared commanded him to bring a roc's egg. The genie gave such a loud and terrible shriek that the hall shook. "Wretch!" he cried, "is it not enough that I have done everything for you, but you must command me to bring my master and hang him up in the midst of this dome? You and your wife and your palace deserve to be burnt to ashes; but this request does not come from you, but from the brother of the African magician whom you destroyed. He is now in your palace disguised as the holy woman —whom he murdered. He it was who put that wish into your wife's head. Take care of yourself, for he means to kill you." So saying the genie disappeared.

Aladdin went back to the Princess, saying his head ached, and requesting that the holy Fatima should be fetched to lay her hands on it. But when the magician came near, Aladdin, seizing his dagger, pierced him to the heart.

"What have you done?" cried the Princess. "You have killed the holy woman!"

"Not so," replied Aladdin, "but a wicked magician," and told her of how she had been deceived.

After this Aladdin and his wife lived in peace. He succeeded the Sultan when he died, and reigned for many years, leaving behind him a long line of kings.

Japanese folk tales

Since Japanese folk tales have been out of print for a time, it is good to see them reappearing in fresh editions and excellent translations. Libraries will have some of the earlier collections on their shelves and students of folklore will find them a colorful and rewarding group with strong moral overtones.

MOMOTARO:

BOY-OF-THE-PEACH

After hearing this story, children will be delighted to discover the amusing little poem about Momotaro in Time for Poetry.

Once long, long ago, there lived a kind old man and a kind old woman in a small village in Japan.

"Momotaro: Boy-of-the-Peach." From *The Dancing Kettle and Other Japanese Folk Tales,* copyright, 1949, by Yoshiko Uchida. Reprinted by permission of Harcourt, Brace and Company, Inc.

One fine day, they set out from their little cottage together. The old man went toward the mountains to cut some firewood for their kitchen, and the old woman went toward the river to do her washing.

When the old woman reached the shore of the river, she knelt down beside her wooden tub and began to scrub her clothes on a round, flat stone. Suddenly she looked up and saw something very strange floating down the shallow river. It was a big, big peach; bigger than the round wooden tub that stood beside the old woman.

Rumbley-bump and a-bumpety-bump . . . Rumbley-bump and a-bumpety-bump. The big peach rolled closer and closer over the stones in the stream.

"My gracious me!" the old woman said to herself. "In all my long life I have never seen a peach of such great size and beauty. What a fine present it would make for the old man. I do think I will take it home with me."

Then the old woman stretched out her hand just as far as she could, but no matter how hard she stretched, she couldn't reach the big peach.

"If I could just find a long stick, I would be able to reach it," thought the old woman, looking around, but all she could see were pebbles and sand.

"Oh, dear, what shall I do?" she said to herself. Then suddenly she thought of a way to bring the beautiful big peach to her side. She began to sing out in a sweet, clear voice,

> "The deep waters are salty!
> The shallow waters are sweet!
> Stay away from the salty water,
> And come where the water is sweet."

She sang this over and over, clapping her hands in time to her song. Then, strangely enough, the big peach slowly began to bob along toward the shore where the water was shallow.

Rumbley-bump and a-bumpety-bump . . . Rumbley-bump and a-bumpety-bump. The big peach came closer and closer to the old woman and finally came to a stop at her feet.

The old woman was so happy, she picked the big peach up very carefully and quickly carried it home in her arms. Then she waited for the old man to return so she could show him her

lovely present. Toward evening the old man came home with a big pack of wood on his back.

"Come quickly, come quickly," the old woman called to him from the house.

"What is it? What is the matter?" the old man asked as he hurried to the side of the old woman.

"Just look at the fine present I have for you," said the old woman happily as she showed him the big round peach.

"My goodness! What a great peach! Where in the world did you buy such a peach as this?" the old man asked.

The old woman smiled happily and told him how she had found the peach floating down the river.

"Well, well, this is a fine present indeed," said the old man, "for I have worked hard today and I am very hungry."

Then he got the biggest knife they had, so he could cut the big peach in half. Just as he was ready to thrust the sharp blade into the peach, he heard a tiny voice from inside.

"Wait, old man! Don't cut me!" it cried, and before the surprised old man and woman could say a word, the beautiful big peach broke in two, and a sweet little boy jumped out from inside. The old man and woman were so surprised, they could only raise their hands and cry out, "Oh, oh! My goodness!"

Now the old man and woman had always wanted a child of their own, so they were very, very happy to find such a fine little boy, and decided to call him "Momotaro," which means boy-of-the-peach. They took very good care of the little boy and grew to love him dearly, for he was a fine young lad. They spent many happy years together, and before long Momotaro was fifteen years old.

One day Momotaro came before the old man and said, "You have both been good and kind to me. I am very grateful for all you have done, and now I think I am old enough to do some good for others too. I have come to ask if I may leave you."

"You wish to leave us, my son? But why?" asked the old man in surprise.

"Oh, I shall be back in a very short time," said Momotaro. "I wish only to go to the Island of the Ogres, to rid the land of those harmful creatures. They have killed many good people, and have stolen and robbed throughout the country. I wish to kill the ogres so they can never harm our people again."

"That is a fine idea, my son, and I will not stop you from going," said the old man.

So that very day, Momotaro got ready to start out on his journey. The old woman prepared some millet cakes for him to take along on his trip, and soon Momotaro was ready to leave. The old man and woman were sad to see him go and called, "Be careful, Momotaro! Come back safely to us."

"Yes, yes, I shall be back soon," he answered. "Take care of yourselves while I am away," he added, and waved as he started down the path toward the forest.

He hurried along, for he was anxious to get to the Island of the Ogres. While he was walking through the cool forest where the grass grew long and high, he began to feel hungry. He sat down at the foot of a tall pine tree and carefully unwrapped the *furoshiki*[1] which held his little millet cakes. "My, they smell good," he thought. Suddenly he heard the tall grass rustle and saw something stalking through the grass toward him. Momotaro blinked hard when he saw what it was. It was a dog as big as a calf! But Momotaro was not frightened, for the dog just said, "Momotaro-san, Momotaro-san, what is it you are eating that smells so good?"

"I'm eating a delicious millet cake which my good mother made for me this morning," he answered.

The dog licked his chops and looked at the cake with hungry eyes. "Please, Momotaro-san," he said, "just give me one of your millet cakes, and I will come along with you to the Island of the Ogres. I know why you are going there, and I can be of help to you."

"Very well, my friend," said Momotaro. "I will take you along with me," and he gave the dog one of his millet cakes to eat.

As they walked on, something suddenly leaped from the branches above and jumped in front of Momotaro. He stopped in surprise and found that it was a monkey who had jumped down from the trees.

"Greetings, Momotaro-san!" called the monkey

[1] Pronounced foo-ro-shee-kee, a square cloth used to wrap and carry articles.

happily. "I have heard that you are going to the Island of the Ogres to rid the land of these plundering creatures. Take me with you, for I wish to help you in your fight."

When the dog heard this he growled angrily. "Grruff," he said to the monkey. "*I* am going to help Momotaro-san. We do not need the help of a monkey such as you! Out of our way! Grruff, grruff," he barked angrily.

"How dare you speak to me like that?" shrieked the monkey, and he leaped at the dog, scratching with his sharp claws. The dog and the monkey began to fight each other, biting, clawing, and growling. When Momotaro saw this he pushed them apart and cried, "Here, here, stop it, you two! There is no reason why you both cannot go with me to the Island of the Ogres. I shall have two helpers instead of one!" Then he took another millet cake from his *furoshiki* and gave it to the monkey.

Now there were three of them going down the path to the edge of the woods. The dog in front, Momotaro in the middle, and the monkey walking in the rear. Soon they came to a big field and just as they were about to cross it, a large pheasant hopped out in front of them. The dog jumped at it with a growl, but the pheasant fought back with such spirit that Momotaro ran over to stop the dog. "We could use a brave bird such as you to help us fight the ogres. We are on our way to their island this very day. How would you like to come along with us?"

"Oh, I would like that indeed, for I would like to help you rid the land of these evil and dangerous ogres," said the pheasant happily.

"Then here is a millet cake for you, too," said Momotaro, giving the pheasant a cake, just as he had to the monkey and the dog.

Now there were four of them going to the Island of the Ogres, and as they walked down the path together, they became very good friends.

Before long they came to the water's edge and Momotaro found a boat big enough for all of them. They climbed in and headed for the Island of the Ogres. Soon they saw the island in the distance wrapped in gray, foggy clouds. Dark stone walls rose up above towering cliffs and large iron gates stood ready to keep out any who tried to enter.

Momotaro thought for a moment, then turned

to the pheasant and said, "You alone can wing your way over their high walls and gates. Fly into their stronghold now, and do what you can to frighten them. We will follow as soon as we can."

So the pheasant flew far above the iron gates and stone walls and down onto the roof of the ogres' castle. Then he called to the ogres, "Momotaro-san has come to rid the land of you and your many evil deeds. Give up your stolen treasures now, and perhaps he will spare your lives!"

When the ogres heard this, they laughed and shouted. "HO, HO, HO! We are not afraid of a little bird like you! We are not afraid of little Momotaro!"

The pheasant became very angry at this, and flew down, pecking at the heads of the ogres with his sharp, pointed beak. While the pheasant was fighting so bravely, the dog and monkey helped Momotaro to tear down the gates, and they soon came to the aid of the pheasant.

"Get away! Get away!" shouted the ogres, but the monkey clawed and scratched, the big dog growled and bit the ogres, and the pheasant flew about, pecking at their heads and faces. So fierce were they that soon the ogres began to run away. Half of them tumbled over the cliffs as they ran and the others fell pell-mell into the sea. Soon only the Chief of the Ogres remained. He threw up his hands, and then bowed low to Momotaro. "Please spare me my life, and all our stolen treasures are yours. I promise never to rob or kill anyone again," he said.

Momotaro tied up the evil ogre, while the monkey, the dog and the pheasant carried many boxes filled with jewels and treasures down to their little boat. Soon it was laden with all the treasures it could hold, and they were ready to sail toward home.

When Momotaro returned, he went from one family to another, returning the many treasures which the ogres had stolen from the people of the land.

"You will never again be troubled by the Ogres of Ogre Island!" he said to them happily.

And they all answered, "You are a kind and brave lad, and we thank you for making our land safe once again."

Then Momotaro went back to the home of the old man and woman with his arms full of jewels and treasures from Ogre Island. My, but the old man and woman were glad to see him once again, and the three of them lived happily together for many, many years.

URASHIMA TARO AND THE PRINCESS OF THE SEA

This story is a bit like "Sadko" and Washington Irving's "Rip Van Winkle."

Long, long ago, in a small village of Japan, there lived a fine young man named Urashima Taro. He lived with his mother and father in a thatched-roof house which overlooked the sea. Each morning he was up before the sun, and went out to sea in his little fishing boat. On days when his luck was good, he would bring back large baskets full of fish which he sold in the village market.

One day, as he was carrying home his load of fish, he saw a group of shouting children. They were gathered around something on the beach and were crying, "Hit him! Poke him!" Taro ran over to see what was the matter, and there on the sand he saw a big brown tortoise. The children were poking it with a long stick and throwing stones at its hard shell.

"Here, here," called Taro. "That's no way to treat him! Why don't you leave him alone, and let him go back to the sea?"

"But we found him," said one of the children. "He belongs to us!"

"Yes, yes, he is ours," cried all the children.

Now, because Urashima Taro was a fair and kindly young man, he said to them, "Suppose I give each of you something in return for the tortoise?" Then he took ten shiny coins out of a small bag of money and gave one to each child. "Now, isn't that a fair bargain?" he asked. "A coin for each of you, and the tortoise for me."

"Yes, yes. Thank you!" called the children, and away they ran to the village candy shop.

"Urashima Taro and the Princess of the Sea." From *The Dancing Kettle and Other Japanese Folk Tales*, copyright, 1949, by Yoshiko Uchida. Reprinted by permission of Harcourt, Brace and Company, Inc.

Taro watched the old tortoise crawl away slowly toward the sea and called, "You'd better stay at home in the sea from now on, old fellow!" Then, smiling happily because he had been able to save the tortoise, he turned to go home. There his mother and father were waiting for him with bowls of steaming rice and soup.

Several days passed, and Taro soon forgot all about the tortoise whom he had saved. One day he was sitting in his boat feeling very sad because he could catch no fish. Suddenly he heard a voice from the sea calling, "Urashima-san! Urashima-san!"

"Now who could be calling me here in the earth! But how can I go to the bottom of the sea, and how can I enter her palace?"

"Just leave everything to me," said the old tortoise. "Hop on my back and I will see that you get there safely. I will also take you into the palace, for I am one of the palace guards."

So Urashima Taro jumped onto the smooth round back of the tortoise, and away they went. Swish, swish . . . the waves seemed to part and make a path for them as the tortoise swam on. Soon Taro felt himself going down . . . down . . . down . . . into the sea, but he wasn't getting wet at all. He heard the waves lapping gently about his ears. "That's strange," thought

middle of the sea?" thought Urashima Taro. He looked high and low, but could see no one. Suddenly, from the crest of a big wave, out popped the head of the old tortoise.

"I came to thank you for saving me the other day," said the tortoise.

"Well, I'm glad you got away safely," said Taro.

"This time I would like to do something for you, Urashima-san," said the tortoise. "How would you like to visit the princess who lives in the Palace of the Sea?"

"The princess of the sea!" shouted Taro. "I have heard often of her beauty, and everyone says her palace is more lovely than any place on

Taro. "This is just like a dream—a nice happy dream."

Before long, they were at the bottom of the big blue sea. Taro could see bright-colored fish playing hide and seek among the long strands of swaying seaweed. He could see clams and other shellfish shyly peeking out at him from their shells. Soon Taro saw something big and shiny looming in the hazy blue water.

"Is that the palace?" he asked anxiously. "It looks very beautiful."

"Oh, no," answered the tortoise. "That is just the outer gate."

They came to a stop and Taro could see that the gateway was guarded by a fish in armor of silver. "Welcome home," the guard called to the tortoise, as he opened the gate for them to enter.

"See whom I have brought back with me," the tortoise answered happily. The guard in the armor of silver turned to Urashima Taro and bowed most politely. Taro just had time to return the bow when he looked up and saw another gate. This one was even larger than the first, and was made of silver stones and pillars of coral. A row of fish in armor of gold was guarding the second gate.

"Now, Urashima-san, if you will get off and wait here, I will tell the princess that you have come," said the tortoise, and he disappeared into the palace beyond the gate. Taro had never seen such a beautiful sight in all his life. The silver stones in the gate sparkled and glittered as though they were smiling at him. Taro had to blink hard.

Soon the tortoise was back at his side telling

him that the princess was waiting to see him. He led Taro through the gate of coral and silver, and up a path of golden stones to the palace. There in front of the palace stood the beautiful princess of the sea with her ladies-in-waiting.

"Welcome to the Palace of the Sea, Urashima Taro," she said, and her voice sounded like the tinkling of little silver bells. "Won't you come with me?" she asked.

Taro opened his mouth to answer, but not a sound would come forth. He could only look at the beautiful princess and the sparkling emeralds and diamonds and rubies which glittered on the walls of the palace. The princess understood how Taro felt, so she just smiled kindly and led him down a hallway paved with smooth, white pearls. Soon they came to a large room, and in the center of the room was an enormous table and an enormous chair. Taro thought they might have been made for a great king.

"Sit down, Urashima-san," said the princess, and as he sat in the enormous chair, the ladies-in-waiting appeared from all sides. They placed on the table plate after plate of all the delicious things that Taro could think of. "Eat well, my friend," said the princess, "and while you dine, my maids will sing and dance for you." Soon there was music and singing and dancing. The room was filled with laughing voices. Taro felt like a king now! He thought surely this was all a dream, and that it would end soon. But no, after he had dined, the princess took him all through the beautiful palace. At the very last, she brought him to a room that looked as though it were made of ice and snow. There were creamy pearls and sparkling diamonds everywhere.

"Now, how would you like to see all the seasons of the year?" whispered the princess.

"Oh, I would like that very much," answered Taro, and as he spoke, the east door of the room opened slowly and quietly. Taro could scarcely believe the sight before his eyes. He saw big clouds of pale pink cherry blossoms and tall green willow trees swaying in the beeze. He could hear bluebirds singing, and saw them fly happily into the sky.

"Ah, that is spring," murmured Taro. "What a lovely sunny day!" But before he could say more, the princess led him further on. As she opened the door to the south, Taro could see white lotus blossoms floating on a still green pond. It was a warm summer day, and he could hear crickets chirping lazily, somewhere in the distance. She opened the door to the west and he saw a hillside of maple trees. Their leaves of crimson and yellow were whirling and dancing down among golden chrysanthemums. He had seen such trees each fall in his own little village. When the princess opened the door to the north, Taro felt a blast of cold air. He shivered, and looked up to see snowflakes tumbling down from gray skies. They were putting white caps on all the fence posts and treetops.

"Now you have seen all the seasons of the year," said the princess.

"They were beautiful!" sighed Taro happily. "I have never seen such wonderful sights in all my life! I wish I could stay here always!"

Taro was having such a very good time that he forgot all about his home in the village. He feasted and danced and sang with his friends in the Palace of the Sea, and before he knew it, three long years had gone by. But to Taro they seemed to be just three short days.

At last Taro said to the princess, "Alas, I have been here much too long. I must go home to see my mother and father so they will not worry about me."

"But you will come back?" asked the princess.

"Oh, yes, yes. I will come back," answered Taro.

"Before you go I have something for you," said the princess, and she gave Taro a small jewel box studded with many precious stones.

"Oh, it is beautiful, Princess," said Taro. "How can I thank you for all you have done for me?"

But the princess went on, "There is just one thing about that box," she said. "You must never, never open it if you ever wish to return to the Palace of the Sea. Can you remember that, Urashima Taro?"

"I will never open it, no matter what happens," promised Taro. Then he said good-bye to all his friends in the palace. Once again he climbed on the back of the old tortoise and they sailed toward his village on the seacoast. The princess and her ladies-in-waiting stood at the coral gate and waved to Taro till he could no longer see them. The tortoise swam on and on,

and one by one all the little bright-colored fish that had been following them began to turn back. Before long, Taro could see the seacoast where he used to go fishing, and soon they were back on the very beach where Taro had once saved the tortoise. Taro hopped off onto the smooth white sand. "Good-bye, old friend," he said. "You have been very good to me. Thank you for taking me to the most beautiful place I have ever seen."

"Farewell, Urashima-san," said the old tortoise. "I hope we may meet again some day." Then he turned and crawled slowly back into the sea.

Now that he was in his own village once more, Taro was most anxious to see his parents. He ran along the path which led to their house with his jewel box tucked securely under his arm. He looked up eagerly at each person whom he passed. He wanted to shout a greeting to them, but each face seemed strange and new. "How odd!" thought Taro. "I feel as though I were in some other village than my own. I don't seem to know anyone. Well, I'll soon see Mother and Father," he said, and hurried on. When he reached the spot where the house should have been, there was no house to be seen. There was just an empty lot full of tall green weeds. Taro couldn't believe his eyes. "Why, what has happened to my home? Where are my parents?" he cried. He looked up and down the dusty path and soon saw an old, old woman coming toward him. "I'll ask her what has happened to my home," thought Taro.

"Old woman, please, can you help me?" asked Taro.

The old woman straightened her bent back and cocked her gray head, "Eh, what did you say?" she asked.

"Can you tell me what happened to Urashima Taro's home? It used to be right here," said Taro.

"Never heard of him," said the old woman, shaking her head.

"But you must have," Taro replied. "He lived right here, on this very spot where you are standing."

"Now let me see," she sighed. "Urashima Taro. Yes, it seems I have heard of him. Oh, I remember now. There is a story that he went out to sea in his fishing boat one day and never came back again. I suppose he was drowned at sea. Well, anyway, that was over three hundred years ago. My great-great-grandfather used to tell me about Urashima Taro when I was just a little girl."

"Three hundred years!" exclaimed Taro. His eyes were like saucers now. "But I don't understand."

"Well, I don't understand what you want with a man who lived three hundred years ago," muttered the old woman, and she trudged on down the road.

"So three years in the Palace of the Sea has really been three hundred years here in my village," thought Taro. "No wonder all my friends are gone. No wonder I can't find my mother or father!" Taro had never felt so lonely or so sad as he did then. "What can I do? What can I do?" he murmured to himself.

Suddenly he remembered the little jewel box which the princess had given him. "Perhaps there is something in there that can help me," he thought, and forgetting the promise he had made to the princess, he quickly opened the box. Suddenly, there arose from it a cloud of white smoke which wrapped itself around Taro so that he could see nothing. When it disappeared, Urashima Taro peered into the empty box, but he could scarcely see. He looked at his hands and they were the hands of an old, old man. His face was wrinkled; his hair was as white as snow. In that short moment Urashima Taro had become three hundred years older. He remembered the promise he had made to the princess, but now it was too late and he knew that he could never visit the Palace of the Sea again. But who knows, perhaps one day the old tortoise came back to the beach once more to help his friend.

A Chinese folk tale

We are just beginning to get some translations of the Chinese folk tales in attractive style. The collection from which this story was taken has some delightful tales for telling to older children.

THE FOX'S DAUGHTER

Nothing is luckier than to be the child of a fox, for, without taking the trouble to learn anything, foxes know as much magic as the man who spends his whole life studying it, and when a fox's child takes human form, as sometimes happens, and becomes a boy or a girl, he knows as much magic as his father.

Liu was a young student who should have been working hard for his examinations, but he was rather idle and much preferred wandering about his father's estate, or sailing in a boat on the river which ran through it, to sitting indoors over his books.

One day, when he was occupied—if it can be called occupied—in this way, he saw the form of a young girl among the reeds which grew upon a little island in the river. Quickly he jumped into

his boat and hurried across the water, and, tying the boat up to a willow tree, he began to search the island for her.

For some time he saw nothing, but he heard mocking laughter to the right and to the left, and, running wildly first in one direction and then in the other, he tore his silk robe and broke the strap of one of his sandals. At last he succeeded in running her down, but she looked so beautiful, leaning against a tree and smiling at him, that even after he had got his breath back he could not speak.

"Alas," said the girl in a clear low voice, looking at his torn robe and flapping sandal, "if

"The Fox's Daughter." From *The Treasure of Li-Po* by Alice Ritchie, copyright, 1949, by Harcourt, Brace and Company, Inc. Published in London by The Hogarth Press Ltd.

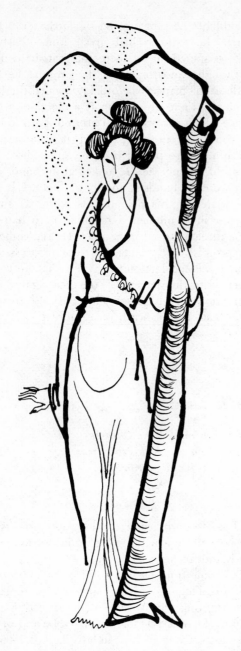

"but as to how I came here, I shall not tell you, and I can go away again as swiftly."

(This was not surprising, because of course she was a fox's daughter, and could appear and disappear at will.) And now she made a movement as if she meant to go, but Liu sprang forward with his hands spread out.

"I beg you to stay," he cried, "or at least tell me where we shall meet again, for you are the most beautiful person I have ever seen."

"Look for me in your books," said the maiden; then, seeing his face become clouded with disappointment, she took a little silver mirror from her girdle and gave it to him. "There," she said, "you shall have something which has belonged to me, but I warn you, you will never see me in it except through your books." And in a moment she had vanished.

Liu went back to his boat feeling very sad, and many times before he reached the house he looked longingly into the silver mirror, but all he saw was the back-view of the beautiful Feng-Lien standing as if she was watching someone going away from her.

As soon as he reached his room, remembering what she had said, he took out the heavy and difficult books which he had never had a mind to study, and laying them on the top of the mirror, he tried to see it through them, but of course he saw nothing, not even its silver handle, buried under those great volumes.

"Feng-Lien meant more than she said," he remarked to himself, and he removed the books from the mirror with a sigh and applied himself earnestly to reading them, refusing to see his friends when they came to the house and not accepting any invitations. After he had spent several days in this way, he looked into the mirror again, and there was Feng-Lien with her face turned towards him, smiling and nodding as if she was pleased.

For a month or more he did nothing but study, looking often into the mirror to be encouraged by the lovely face of Feng-Lien, but presently the fine summer weather came, and he could not force himself to stay in the house. He began once more to wander about the garden and the wild land beside the river, idly enjoying the scent of the newly opened flowers and the sight of the bright birds.

Master Liu pursued his studies with the same zeal as he has pursued me, he would take a high place when the candidates go up to the Examination Hall, and some day he would be a man of great importance—but of course he will do nothing of the sort."

Liu eagerly asked her name and how she happened to know all about him, and also how she came to be upon the island, for he could see no boat except his own.

"My name is Feng-Lien," said the maiden,

"Perhaps I shall see Feng-Lien again," he said. But he did not find her, and in his heart he knew she would not come while he behaved in this way. Then, one evening after he had been on a fishing expedition all day with some friends, when he pulled out the silver mirror he saw Feng-Lien crying bitterly, and the next morning she had her back turned to him.

"It is clear that there is only one thing to be done," he said to himself. "I must make a habit of working all the time."

He took the silver mirror and nailed it on the wall so that whenever he raised his eyes from his difficult reading he would see Feng-Lien's face. She always looked happy now. This went on for two years, and at the end of that time he went up to the Examination Hall and did so well that he took a high place in the final list.

"Now," he said, "at last, I shall surely be allowed to see Feng-Lien herself."

He took up the mirror and looked for a long time at her reflection, at the arched eyebrows and the beautiful eyes and the smiling mouth, until it seemed to him that her lips parted and she spoke, yes, she seemed to be speaking words of welcome and congratulation, and suddenly the mirror dissolved into a drop of dew and instead of her likeness, Feng-Lien herself stood before him.

"Really," she said, bowing very low, "I am quite frightened of this learned young man."

"The success I have had is entirely owing to you," said Liu.

So they were married, and Liu attained to one of the highest positions in China, but Feng-Lien never again had to use the magic she possessed by reason of being a fox's daughter. She found quite simple ways of keeping her husband, who continued to be by nature somewhat lazy, up to the mark.

A Korean folk tale

*The Korean tales are full of ghosts and
magic. They are often beautiful in style and content
and therefore excellent for storytelling.*

WHICH WAS WITCH?

*Here's a story as witty as its title, and a good
tale for Halloween.*

There was once a wise and learned man named Kim Su-ik. He lived just inside the south gate of Seoul but he might as well have lived anywhere for all the thought he gave the matter. His mind was entirely taken up with study and books, and one could say of him, as Im Bang said of another scholar, "He used to awake at first cockcrow, wash, dress, take up his book and never lay it aside. On his right were pictures, on his left were books, and he happy between. He rose to be a Prime Minister."

One night Kim Su-ik was absorbed in studying a Chinese classic when he suddenly felt hungry.

"Which Was Witch?" From *Which Was Witch?* by Eleanore M. Jewett. Copyright 1953 by Eleanore M. Jewett. Reprinted by permission of The Viking Press, Inc.

He clapped his hands to summon a servant, and immediately the door of his room opened.

His wife stepped in.

"What does the master of the house desire?" said she.

"Food," he answered briefly, his attention already returned to the book in his lap.

"I have little in the house but a few roasted chestnuts. If that will suffice I will bring them to you myself. The servants have long since gone to their sleeping quarters."

Kim Su-ik grunted his approval and went on with his studies. In a very short time the door opened again and his wife came in bearing a brass bowl full of hot roasted chestnuts. He helped himself to one and was in the act of putting it into his mouth when once more the door opened and in stepped his wife with a brass bowl full of hot roasted chestnuts.

But his wife was already there, standing beside him with the bowl in her hands!

Kim Su-ik, his mouth still open and a chestnut half in it, looked in astonishment from one to the other of the identical women. They were as like as two pins—faces, features, figures, clothes, the way they stood, the way they used their fingers and moved their shoulders. Never were twins more completely alike. Kim Su-ik passed his hands before his eyes. He must have overdone his studying, he thought to himself, read too late and too steadily. His eyes were playing tricks on him, that was all. He was seeing double.

But when he looked again the two women were still there, and what was stranger still, they seemed not to be aware of each other, but stood quietly, gracefully, their eyes fastened on him as if waiting to know his pleasure.

The scholar leaped to his feet, choking back the cry of terror that rose in his throat. He knew, suddenly, without a doubt, what this meant. It was midnight, the moon was at the full, ghosts, evil spirits, witches and goblins would be abroad, filled with power. One of these two creatures standing before him was his wife, known and loved by him all his wedded life—and perhaps not quite fully appreciated, he hastily decided. The other must be a witch, able to change into any form she chose in the twinkling of an eye. But *which was which?* How could he protect his wife and drive this evil double from beside her?

Being a quick thinker as well as a learned one, Kim Su-ik plunged into action. He seized the arm of one of the women with his right hand and before the other could realize what he was about, he had her arm fast in his left hand. They turned mildly reproachful eyes upon him but made no effort to free themselves.

"My dear," said one, "too much study has fevered your brain."

"My dear," said the other, "too much reading of books has affected your mind."

Kim Su-ik looked from one to the other. Not a particle of difference was there to give him a hint as to which was wife and which was witch. He shook them gently. They smiled indulgently as at a child. He shook harder. No resentment, no struggle to get free. He was tempted to relax his grip on the two arms, but he knew he must not for a moment do that, and hung on more firmly than ever.

Minutes went by, then hours, the dull slow moving hours between midnight and cockcrow. The three stood silent, motionless, in the same spot. Kim Su-ik grew weary beyond words. So, too, must his wife be weary, but neither of the two women he held so tightly by the arm said anything or showed by any movement or expression of the face that she was tired, puzzled or angry. His wife would have been tired and puzzled—angry, too, perhaps, but she would not have blustered or scolded. Any other woman would, were she witch or human. But surely his wife would say *something*. What in the world had got into her? Was she bewitched? Or walking in her sleep? Perhaps she was not either one of these two women. He wanted to rush into the other part of the house to see if she was there, thus proving that both of these were witches. But he did nothing, just hung on, grimly, silently.

At long last a cock crowed. Immediately the woman at his left tried to wrench her arm free. The other remained quiet. Kim Su-ik dropped the unresisting one and threw all his strength into a struggle with the other. Like a wild thing the creature fought, biting, snarling, spitting, leaping back and forth. Still the scholar held on to her and would not let go. The arm in his hand shrank and grew hairy. The whole figure dwindled, the eyes grew round and green and blazed with fury.

Another cock crowed and another, and the first gray light of dawn melted the dark shadows out of doors. But Kim Su-ik had no thought or time to notice the coming of day. With a hideous shriek the creature changed before his very eyes into a powerful wildcat. In horror he loosed his hold, and she leaped through the window and was gone.

"I still think you are studying too much," said a quiet, familiar voice behind him, and there stood his wife, pale, trembling a little, but smiling confidently.

"Why didn't you let me know which was which?" demanded Kim Su-ik.

His wife laughed. "I don't know what you are talking about! You behaved very strangely, but then, one never knows what to expect of a scholar. Which was which what?"

"Witch!" said Kim Su-ik.

A Turkish folk tale

For five centuries the people of Turkey and of all the Near East have been laughing at Nasr-ed-Din Hodja. He is their Paul Bunyan, their Three Sillies all in one, their source of wit and pure foolishness.

HOW MANY DONKEYS?

There was the tinkle of tiny bells, the sharp clip of small hoofs, the throaty drone of a solitary singer. Nasr-ed-Din Hodja was bringing the donkeys back from the mill, their saddlebags filled with freshly ground wheat. The hot Turkish sun beat down on his turbaned head. The brown dust from the donkeys' hoofs puffed about him. The staccato trot of his donkey jiggled him back and forth. But Nasr-ed-Din Hodja was too pleased to be uncomfortable.

"I'll show them," he chuckled. "They gave me plenty of advice about taking care of their donkeys and their wheat. As though I did not know more about donkeys than any man in Ak Shehir."

His eyes rested lazily on the road ahead. At first it followed the brook running away from Mill Valley, the brook that turned the heavy stones to grind the wheat. Then the road disappeared over a hilltop.

"Just over that hill," he mused contentedly, "is Ak Shehir, where they are waiting for their donkeys. There is not a scratch or a bruise on one of the little creatures. No donkeys in all Turkey have had better treatment today than these nine."

Idly he began counting them.

"What?" he gasped. "Eight donkeys?"

He jumped from his donkey and ran hither and yon, looking behind rocks and over hilltops, but no stray donkey could he see. At last he stood beside the donkeys and counted again. This time there were nine. With a sigh of relief he climbed onto his own donkey and went swinging along the road. His long legs in their

"How Many Donkeys?" From *Once the Hodja* by Alice Geer Kelsey, Longmans, Green and Company. Copyright 1943 by Alice Geer Kelsey

baggy pantaloons swung easily back and forth in time to the donkey's trot. Passing through a cluster of trees he thought it time to count the donkeys again.

"One—two—three—" and up to eight he counted, but no ninth donkey was to be seen. Down from his donkey's back he came. Behind all the trees he peered. Not a hair of a donkey could he find.

Again he counted, standing beside his donkeys. There they all were—nine mild little donkeys waiting for orders to move on. Nasr-ed-Din Hodja scratched his poor head in bewilderment. Was he losing his mind or were the donkeys all bewitched? Again he counted. Yes, surely there were nine.

"Ughr-r-r-r," Nasr-ed-Din Hodja gave the low guttural which is Turkish for "Giddap." As he rode on, he looked about him for the evil spirits which must be playing tricks on him. Each donkey wore the blue beads which should drive away the evil spirits. Were there evil spirits abroad stronger even than the blue beads?

He was glad to see a friend coming toward him down the road.

"Oh, Mustapha Effendi," he cried. "Have you seen one of these donkeys? I have lost a donkey and yet I have not lost it."

"What can you mean, Hodja Effendi?" asked Mustapha.

"I left the mill with nine donkeys," explained the Hodja. "Part of the way home there have been nine and part of the way there have been eight. Oh, I am bewitched! Help me! Help me!"

Mustapha was used to the queer ways of the Hodja, but he was surprised. He counted the donkeys silently.

"Let me see you count the donkeys," he ordered the Hodja.

"One—two—three," began the Hodja, pointing at each one as he counted up to eight.

As he said the last number, he stopped and looked at his friend with a face full of helplessness and terror. His terror turned to amazement as Mustapha slapped his knee and laughed until he almost fell from his donkey.

"What is so funny?" asked the Hodja.

"Oh, Hodja Effendi!" Mustapha laughed. "When you are counting your brothers, why, oh why, do you not count the brother on whom you are riding?"

Nasr-ed-Din Hodja was silent for a moment to think through this discovery. Then he kissed the hand of his deliverer, pressed it to his forehead and thanked him a thousand times for his help. He rode, singing, on to Ak Shehir to deliver the donkeys to their owners.

A Costa Rican folk tale

Because of certain references to God and the Saints, the Costa Rican stories should be used with discretion and are better for adult references than for the children's use. The Costa Rican tales include many variants of European, especially Spanish, folk tales.

THE WITCHES' RIDE

Here is as lively a Halloween story as anyone could ask for. It has a familiar theme—the simpleton who comes out on top—but it is extraordinarily eerie. Children may need to know that, according to the story, any sacred name or sign has the power to banish witches or fairies or to put an end to a spell.

Once, in the days of long ago, there lived in Costa Rica a widow who had an only son. Now this son was considered a *bobo,* or simpleton, because he was lazy and, more than that, because in one way or another he muddled everything he set out to do.

One day the bobo's mother was preparing to cook the *chayote* hash and rice which were to be their supper. She went to the shed for wood to burn in the stove, but the shed was empty. So she told the bobo to go to the forest yonder and bring her some sticks for the fire.

Since it was already late afternoon and a chill wind was blowing, the bobo wrapped himself up in a coarse old blanket, wearing it like a cape. Then he set off. He soon entered the forest, but there were no broken branches at hand and since he had no machete, or long, sharp knife, with him to cut branches from the trees, he went on farther and farther, from one thicket to another. Before long he was deep in the forest.

Soon it grew dark and he lost the path. As he groped his way through the dense underbrush and hanging vines, not knowing which way to turn, he suddenly came upon a hut. He was glad to find a shelter and knocked a good round knock. No one answered. So he opened the door and went in. Finding the hut deserted, he proceeded to make himself at home. In a corner behind a pile of straw he found an old mat woven of reeds, and there he snuggled down. Soon, in good comfort, he was fast asleep.

He slept and slept till at the hour of midnight he was awakened with a start by the sound of merry voices. He raised his head a wee bit and looked around with one eye.

Through the open window of the hut the moonlight shone on the clay floor, turning it white. There the bobo saw twelve black shadows —the shadows of twelve old witches. They were jesting and laughing and having altogether a merry time as each witch took a sip from a big

"The Witches' Ride." From *The Witches' Ride and Other Tales from Costa Rica* by Lupe de Osma, copyright 1957 by Lupe de Osma, by permission of William Morrow and Company, Inc.

drinking gourd, then smacked her lips and passed it on.

Meantime, the bobo lay quiet and still behind the pile of straw, scarcely daring to draw his breath lest the witches find him and change him into some bird or beast.

And the riot and revelry went on until the gourd ran dry. Then without any warning at all, a witch cried out in a croaking voice, "Time to be off!" At the same moment she picked up a broom from a pile on the floor, placed herself nimbly upon it, and said these magic words:

"Fly me faster than a fairy,
    Without God—without Saint Mary!"

Away out of the window she flew and soared gracefully up into the air. The others followed quickly—each pouncing upon a broomstick from the pile, then repeating the magic words.

High in the night sky they flew, one behind the other, like a long black waving ribbon. They circled once and again around the big yellow moon and then vanished swiftly from sight beyond the tall mountain peaks.

"A week of Sundays!" cried the bobo in surprise. "Wasn't that neatly done! I wouldn't mind doing it myself! And why not?"

Well, as soon as the last witch had disappeared, up sprang the bobo from the reed mat and straightway went to the corner where the pile of brooms had been. He hoped that the witches might have left one behind. And they had! He snatched it up, and fastening the blanket around his shoulders good and tight, he placed himself upon the stick. Then he shouted with all his might:

"Fly me faster than a fairy,
    Without God—without Saint Mary!"

These words were scarcely out of his mouth when up he shot into the air like a whizzing arrow, and out of the window he flew. Faster and faster he soared, low over the treetops and high toward the moon, like a bird. And he flew and flew and flew, and the higher he went, the more he liked it—so much that every once in a while he would say the magic words again to the broom.

But, alas, he was not called a bobo for nothing. In his great glee he muddled the words, and said to the broomstick:

"Fly me faster than a fairy,
    Fly with God and good Saint Mary!"

No sooner were these words out of his mouth than the broom began to fall. Fast—and faster than fast—it dropped. The poor bobo had no time to think of the right magic words as he tumbled and somersaulted through the air.

Now then, it so happened that some robbers were hiding at the edge of the forest that night. Their booty was spread out on a large cloth, and they were seated around it, counting out each one's share of the treasure by the weak light of their lantern.

"Ho! The Devil himself must have been with us today," cried one of the robbers in delight. "Hope he doesn't take a fancy to drop in for his share!"

And at this very moment the bobo, who was coming down full tilt, saw the group and shouted, "Out of the way! Look out there, all of you! Make way for this poor devil!"

The robbers looked up, each and all of them afraid of the strange sight the bobo made. For his blanket flapped and danced behind him like two big black wings as he plunged down upon them. They sprang up in great fear, thinking they had the Devil on their backs.

"The Devil! The Devil is loose! Here he comes!" they cried in terror. "Run! Let us fly! Away . . . away!" They took to their heels as if they were running a race. And they left their booty behind.

The bobo came down in one enormous swoop upon the pile of riches—plump! There he sat, gazing rapturously at the heap of gold and silver coins. "Bless my soul! Bless my little soul!" he cried.

Straightway he jumped up and piled the coins together again in the center of the large cloth. Then he made a bundle out of it, slung it over his shoulder, and hobbled home very happy, humming a merry tune.

And as for the robbers, they were never seen again.

A Canadian folk tale

*Natalie Savage Carlson has collected a group of Canadian tales under
the title* Sashes Red and Blue *and has told them with her usual charm and humor. The
Nichet stories are traditional tales but are completely realistic.*

LITTLE NICHET'S
BABY SISTER

That little Nichet, Jean LeBlanc's youngest child, was one to keep his parents as busy as all the other thirteen tied together.

One day the little fellow had a new question for his wise father.

"Papa," said Nichet, "where did the Boulangers get their new baby?"

"That is an easy question," answered Jean LeBlanc. "The good Indians brought her, my little nest egg."

"Did the good Indians bring me to you?" asked Nichet.

"Of course," answered his father. "The good Indians bring all the babies."

Little Nichet thought about this for a while.

"Papa," he asked again, "will the good Indians bring us another baby? I would like to have a little sister like Marie Boulanger."

"*Tatata!*" exclaimed Jean LeBlanc. "Already the good Indians have brought us a houseful. Thirteen brothers and sisters are quite enough for such a little fellow as you. And if we had a new baby, you would no longer be our little nest egg."

But Nichet did not think that thirteen brothers and sisters were enough, especially when they were all older and bigger than he.

One afternoon little Nichet wanted to ask his father more about this. But his father and his mother had driven to town in the two-wheeled cart with his eight sisters squeezed together in back.

It was a lonely day for Nichet because his five brothers were out in the field working. And Grandmère kept falling asleep over the rug she was hooking.

So Nichet bravely decided to go to the Indian village himself and ask the Indians if they didn't have an extra baby for the LeBlancs.

Nichet started out on his own two short legs. He walked down the river road. He walked up the Indian trail.

At last he came to the Indian village with its houses scattered over the ground like half-melons.

The Indian village was deserted. The Indians must have gone to town too. Then Nichet saw a few squaws working among the corn sprouts on the hillside. He started toward them.

But he never got as far as the cornfields. For there, propped against a tree trunk, was exactly what Nichet wanted. It was a little papoose laced to its cradle board.

Nichet was so excited that he could scarcely unlace the baby from the board. He lifted it carefully in his arms. The baby did not cry like the Boulanger's new Marie. Nichet looked at its brown skin and its black eyes and its straight black hair. He tried to decide whether it looked more like his papa or his mamma.

The little baby waved its tiny brown arms at him.

"You are my little sister," said Nichet. "I think you look most like me. I will take you home to your papa and mamma."

Nichet LeBlanc carried the papoose down the trail to the river road. It was a long walk and Nichet was so tired he did not think he would ever get the baby to its home. But his sturdy legs carried them both there at last.

Papa and Mamma and the girls had not returned from town yet. The boys were still in the field. Nichet took the baby to show her to Grandmère, but the old lady was asleep with her mouth open and her glasses on the end of her nose.

So little Nichet carried the baby into his parents' bedroom. He carefully laid it in the middle of the bright quilt. Then he ran down the lane to wait for his mamma and papa. He wanted to be the first one to tell them the news that they had a new baby.

At first his papa and mamma thought that little Nichet had a fever. Then they thought that he had fallen asleep like Grandmère and had had a bad dream. But when they saw the brown baby with the black hair and black eyes lying on the bed, they knew that Nichet had told the truth.

"Where did this baby come from?" cried Mamma LeBlanc.

"The Indians brought her," said little Nichet. "That is, I went and got her myself so they wouldn't give her to someone else."

Then there was a great *tohu-bohu* of chattering among the LeBlancs.

"We will have to take it right back," said Jean LeBlanc. "If the Indians think we have stolen their baby, they might burn down our house."

Little Nichet was brokenhearted. He begged and begged his parents to keep his little brown sister with the black hair and black eyes who looked so much like him.

But back to the Indians went the little sister. Little Nichet held her in his arms all the way there in the two-wheeled cart.

There was another *tohu-bohu* of chattering going on at the Indian village.

"A bear has carried off one of the babies," a young brave explained to Jean LeBlanc.

"We have your baby here," said Jean. "It was carried off by a very little bear."

Nichet cried and cried at the loss of his Indian sister. He began feeling sorry for himself. He began thinking that if his papa and mamma had returned the baby to the Indians, they might do the same with him someday.

Little Nichet began feeling sorrier than ever for himself. He decided to return to the Indians of his own free will. How his parents would cry when they found he was gone! They would come galloping to the Indian village. They would take him home again—and his baby sister too.

He packed his nightshirt and his willow whistle and his lynx tail into a sack and set out for the Indian village once more. He walked all the way down the river road. He followed the trail to the houses that were like half-melons.

"I have come back to stay with my little sister," Nichet told one of the Indians.

Then the Indians were as worried as the Le-Blancs had been.

"If we keep you here," said one of them, "your papa will think that we have stolen you. He will burn down our lodges."

Little Nichet refused to leave. "I want to stay here and be an Indian like my little sister," he said.

The Indians gathered together and talked their *micmac* talk, which Nichet could not understand. Then one of them turned to him.

"Can you shoot a bow and arrow?" he asked in Nichet's talk.

"No," said little Nichet.

"Can you skin a moose?"

"No," said little Nichet.

"Can you build a birch canoe?"

"No," said little Nichet.

"Then you cannot stay with us," said the brave. "An Indian must be able to do all those things."

So little Nichet sadly turned and started away. But another Indian came running to him with something furry in his hands.

"A gift for you," said the Indian. "A trade for the baby you returned to us."

He dropped a tiny baby animal into Nichet's arms. It had the head of a beaver, the body of a bear, and the tail of a rabbit.

"What is it?" asked Nichet.

"Your wise father will have a name for it," said the Indian, then he began talking his *mic-mac* talk that Nichet could not understand.

Nichet carried the baby animal home happily. All the way his busy mind wondered if it was a fox or a beaver or a mink or what.

All the LeBlancs were happy to see that Nichet was home again. For truth, they didn't even know he had gone away until they saw the furry little animal in his arms.

"It is a little whistler," said his wise father, Jean LeBlanc. "Some people call them wood-chucks and some people call them groundhogs. But the people back in France call them mar-mots."

"What is it good for?" asked Grandmère. "Will it give milk or pull a cart or lay eggs?"

"It is good for a lonesome little boy who needs a companion smaller than himself," said Jean LeBlanc. He leaned over Nichet and smiled at the new baby. "Across the ocean in France," he said, "chimney sweeps from the mountains keep whistlers for pets. They teach them to do a little dance like a bear's."

"Can I be a chimney sweep when I am big-ger?" asked little Nichet.

"You may be a chimney sweep tomorrow," said Jean LeBlanc generously. "I am going to take down the stovepipe for your mamma and you may help me clean the soot out of it."

So little Nichet thought that he had made a very good trade with the Indians. The boy picked out the name of Pierrette for his tiny pet, and his father helped him to teach that whistler to dance.

Whenever Nichet whistled a special tune, Pierrette would sit up on her hindquarters and wave her forepaws from right to left as she did her dance of the bear. And from time to time she would make polite curtsies. You may be sure that Pierrette was as popular at the stay-awake parties as old Michel Meloche, the storyteller.

Variants of European folk tales
in the United States

Kindergarten teachers who tell their children "Epaminondas" have long known that it is a Negro variant of the English "Lazy Jack" or the German "Clever Hans," and they also know that it is a better story than either of these and much more satisfying to the five-year-olds. Now we know that our American "The Gingerbread Boy" is a variant of the Scotch "The Wee Bannock" or perhaps the Norse "The Pancake" or the English "The Johnny Cake." But it has taken recent research to uncover for us the wealth of European folk tales which have been preserved in typically American vernacular and scene. Not all of these are as good as the European originals, but many of them have a style, a turn of phrase, and characters that are exceedingly fresh and droll. Richard Chase's Jack Tales *are especially amusing, and the bibliography lists other sources of homespun heroes with European relatives.*

THE GINGERBREAD BOY

This American variant of "The Pancake" is a favorite in spite of the urban child's unfamiliar-ity with "threshers" and "mowers." The gay re-frain carries the story.

"The Gingerbread Boy." From *St. Nicholas Magazine*, May 1875

Now you shall hear a story that somebody's great-great-grandmother told a little girl ever so many years ago:

There was once a little old man and a little old woman, who lived in a little old house in the edge of a wood. They would have been a very happy old couple but for one thing—they had no little child, and they wished for one very much. One day, when the little old woman was baking gingerbread, she cut a cake in the shape of a little boy, and put it into the oven.

Presently, she went to the oven to see if it was baked. As soon as the oven door was opened, the little gingerbread boy jumped out, and began to run away as fast as he could go.

The little old woman called her husband, and they both ran after him. But they could not catch him. And soon the gingerbread boy came to a barn full of threshers. He called out to them as he went by, saying:

"I've run away from a little old woman,
  A little old man,
  And I can run away from you, I can!"

Then the barn full of threshers set out to run after him. But, though they ran fast, they could not catch him. And he ran on till he came to a field full of mowers. He called out to them:

"I've run away from a little old woman,
  A little old man,
  A barn full of threshers,
  And I can run away from you, I can!"

Then the mowers began to run after him, but they couldn't catch him. And he ran on till he came to a cow. He called out to her:

"I've run away from a little old woman,
  A little old man,
  A barn full of threshers,
  A field full of mowers,
  And I can run away from you, I can!"

But, though the cow started at once, she couldn't catch him. And soon he came to a pig. He called out to the pig:

"I've run away from a little old woman,
  A little old man,
  A barn full of threshers,
  A field full of mowers,
  A cow,
  And I can run away from you, I can!"

But the pig ran, and couldn't catch him. And he ran till he came across a fox, and to him he called out:

"I've run away from a little old woman,
  A little old man,
  A barn full of threshers,
  A field full of mowers,
  A cow and a pig,
  And I can run away from you, I can!"

Then the fox set out to run. Now foxes can run very fast, and so the fox soon caught the gingerbread boy and began to eat him up.

Presently the gingerbread boy said: "Oh, dear! I'm quarter gone!" And then: "Oh, I'm half gone!" And soon: "I'm three-quarters gone!" And at last: "I'm all gone!" and never spoke again.

THE GIFT OF SAINT NICHOLAS

Here is a novel Christmas story with St. Nick in a new character—a bit of a curmudgeon but an enforcer of justice.

Three hundred years ago in the little city of New Amsterdam lived a young cobbler named Claas. A fortunate young fellow indeed was Claas. He had a lovely brick house with a garden, a big pond full of fat white geese, a thriving trade, and a pretty wife whose name was Anitje. He had worked hard for these blessings from the first bleak day when he landed on the shores of the New World, an orphan boy from Holland. He now was a rich man, rich enough to wear eight pairs of breeches at once.

The only dark cloud in his sky was Roeloffsen, the burgomaster, an old miser who had long been in love with Anitje. As the richest old bachelor in the town, he had expected her to marry him without any question. When she married the poor cobbler boy, the burgomaster's pride was hurt. He swore that he should have his revenge. Whenever Claas and Anitje walked out in their Sunday clothes, with their family of fat Dutch children toddling behind them, he hid behind the heavy curtains of his house and said terrible things.

"The Gift of Saint Nicholas." From *American Myths and Legends* by Charles M. Skinner. As adapted in *Yankee Doodle's Cousins*, edited by Anne Malcolmson. Reprinted by permission of and arrangement with Houghton Mifflin Company and Mrs. Clara A. Skinner

At last his ugly thoughts were put into deeds. He taught the village blacksmith to make hobnails for the townspeople's boots. These nails made a dreadful racket as they clattered over the brick streets. But they kept the boots from wearing out. The boots wore so long that poor Claas had very little business as a cobbler. He had a very hard time of it to make ends meet.

This was not enough for the black-hearted burgomaster, however. Claas and his Anitje still lived in their fine brick house and walked out on Sundays in their handsome clothes. Roeloffsen had to think of something else.

Soon he knew what to do. As an officer of the city he ordered a new street to be built. This street ran right through the middle of Claas's pond. The city builders came and drained the pond. Poor Claas had to sell his beloved geese. This was a great blow to him, because the eggs he sold at the marketplace helped make up for the boots he was unable to sell.

But this was not the worst of it. As Claas sat by his fire sorrowing for the loss of his geese, he had visitors. These were men from the city council. Since the road ran through his land, they said, he should pay for its building. They demanded fifty pieces of gold for this purpose. Fifty pieces of gold! That was all Claas had tucked away in his teapot.

Claas and Anitje had to work harder than ever to keep their family fed and clothed. They sold vegetables from their little garden and managed to make themselves a fair living. Then came the jealous burgomaster. He built another road, through the middle of Claas's garden patch this time. Once again the poor cobbler had to rob his teapot of the vegetable money in order to pay for this road.

And so it went. Every time Claas made a little money, the burgomaster built a new road and made him pay for it. Before long, he had to sell his fine house. No longer could he afford to wear eight pairs of breeches, nor Anitje her twelve petticoats. The little family was poor. They had sold all their belongings except a bare few. They lived in a miserable little cottage with only a dirt floor.

The wicked old burgomaster at last was satisfied. He danced with joy when he saw how low the cobbler had fallen. This would show the

people of New Amsterdam that no orphan boy could outdo the wealthy Heer Roeloffsen!

On Christmas Eve, as the burgomaster was enjoying his fine dinner, Claas and Anitje and their children sat huddled before the fireplace in their little cottage. The very last log burned on the hearth and gave out little heat at best. Their cupboard, like Old Mother Hubbard's, was bare. After their supper of bread and cheese, not a crumb remained. A poor Christmas this would be. No presents, no blazing fire, not even a dinner!

Of all their possessions, only two treasures remained. One was the Bible which Claas's mother had given him long ago. It was bound in beautiful leather and held shut with silver clasps. Claas was tempted to take off these clasps and sell them. They might bring him enough money to provide a Christmas for his children.

No! said Anitje. To sell the clasps from a Bible would be wicked. He should never think of doing such a thing. Better it would be to starve than to feast on the sale of holy things.

The other treasure which remained was a pipe. This was a special, lovely pure meerschaum pipe which to Claas had a magic meaning. As a little boy, leaving his home for the New World, he had found the pipe in his stocking. Where it had come from he could not tell. He was sure it was a present from the good Saint Nicholas himself.

The thought of selling this treasure nearly broke his heart. Even so, it was better than the thought of selling his mother's silver clasps. He reached down into the family chest and took out his beloved meerschaum. Sadly he rubbed it against his trousers and watched it gleam in the firelight.

As he rubbed it the cottage door swung open and a blast of cold air filled the room. There before the fire stood a fat little stranger, about three feet tall. He was dripping with snow, and icicles hung from his shaggy eyebrows and his long white beard.

"Br-r-r!" muttered the stranger crossly. "It's a wonder you wouldn't answer the door when a traveler knocks. Fine manners, I must say, on a night like this!"

All thoughts of the pipe were forgotten as Claas and Anitje stared at their visitor. The children scrambled to hide under the bed. Only their bright blue eyes shone out from behind the curtains.

"Well, come along! Come along!" went on the visitor, growing more angry every minute. "Don't stand there! The least you can do is to put another log on the fire so that I can warm myself. Can't you see I'm half frozen?"

"I-I-I-I'm very sorry, sir," admitted Claas, finding his tongue at last, "but there is no other log to put on the fire. You're very welcome to warm yourself at our poor hearth."

"Well, then," snapped the stranger, "send one of those ragamuffins out to the woodshed. I'm freezing, I tell you!" He glared at the children, who pushed themselves farther back under the bed hangings.

"Oh, sir!" cried Anitje, "if only we had more wood in the shed we would gladly fetch it for you. But, alas, this is our last stick. We have no more to keep ourselves warm."

"Humph!" snorted the little fellow. "That's very careless of you. But what must be, must be." With that he cracked the fine cane he carried over his knee. It broke into several pieces. These he tossed onto the coals. As they struck the fire, something wonderful happened. Each of the pieces of the cane changed into a big birch log. The dark coals blazed up and soon the room was dancing with the light of a huge fire.

"That's better," muttered the stranger. "Upon my life, I thought I should turn to an icicle for all you cared."

The children crept out from their hiding place to gape at the magic blaze. Claas and Anitje rubbed their eyes.

"And now, I suppose, you're going to let me starve to death, too!" sneered the visitor, looking in the direction of the cupboard. "It's a wonder you wouldn't invite me to have some supper. I haven't eaten since this morning."

Tears came to Anitje's eyes. "Oh, sir, whoever you may be, we should indeed be happy to give you our last crumb. But," she sobbed, "we have nothing to eat in the house. We ate our last scrap of cheese for our evening meal."

"That was certainly rude of you," barked the funny little man. "Here I come, after a hard day's tramp over the mountains, through wind and rain and snow! You say you have no fire to warm me! You say you have no bread to feed me! My dear lady, I know better. Your shelves are heaped with cakes and apples. And if that's not roast goose I smell cooking, I'll eat my beard!"

Without thinking, the whole family stopped to sniff. Why, they did smell roast goose! And cabbage and onion and mince pie and pumpkin! These delicious smells were fairly bursting from the oven door. They looked quickly at the cupboard. Its shelves were groaning under bowls of apples and pears and platters of cakes and cookies. The water jug was filled to the brim with sweet cider.

"Don't stand there, don't stand there like a forest of trees!" shouted the stranger. "Can't you see I'm dying of hunger? Get me something to eat and be quick about it. No food, indeed! Why, there's a whole feast in that oven. Put it on the table."

Not knowing whether to be overjoyed or frightened, Claas and Anitje set the table and drew it before the fire. They opened the wide door of the oven. There indeed were the goose and the vegetables and the pies they smelled.

At the sight of the richly spread table, the children forgot their shyness. Hungrily they feasted. But none of them ate so much as did their visitor. Time and again he passed back his plate for another drumstick. An ordinary goose has only two legs, but this one sprouted a new one whenever the little man passed his plate.

When at last the fat little stranger had had enough and the buttons had begun to burst from Claas's coat, the table was cleared away. No longer did the visitor snap angrily at his hosts. He leaned back in his chair and lit his pipe. A twinkle appeared in his eye and he patted the children's blond heads. For an hour he sat talking pleasantly with the happy family, telling strange and marvelous stories of distant lands. But not once did he tell them who he was.

At the stroke of midnight he got up from his chair. "I must be off!" he exclaimed. "Thank you indeed for a pleasant evening and a delicious dinner." He turned to Claas, "Don't ever sell that pipe!" he shouted.

With that, a gust of wind down the chimney filled the whole room with smoke. Before the family could open their smarting eyes again, the stranger was gone without so much as a good-bye.

In the morning Claas was awakened by a great

hammering at his door. There was Burgomaster Roeloffsen and a party of soldiers. "We have come to arrest you!" they screamed. "You are a wizard, a witch, a magician. You are a disgrace to the city of New Amsterdam."

Poor Claas didn't know what to make of it. Why should anyone call him a wizard? He was nothing but a poor cobbler who had had a lovely dream.

"Come!" roared the burgomaster. "Open the door and let us in. We shall have no wizards in our city!"

As he slowly awakened, Claas looked about him. The wretched little cottage had disappeared. He was standing in the hall of a great house. The walls were hung with silks, and from the cupboards shone silver platters and copper bowls. He looked timidly out of the window. Around him spread wide lawns and gardens and in the distance glimmered the ice of a huge pond.

"Open up, I say," bellowed the burgomaster. "Open up in the name of the law. We have come to take you to jail as you deserve." Claas opened the door. In poured the soldiers.

"Aha!" screamed Heer Roeloffsen, his face red with anger. "Seize him! Seize the witch! He has not only changed his cottage to a fine estate. He has filled his chests with gold."

Before the astonished Claas the burgomaster lifted the lid of a chest. The great box was full to the top with pieces of money.

"You thief! You robber! I'll . . ." But before he could finish his sentence, a pair of invisible hands clapped themselves over his mouth. More hands which could not be seen grabbed the soldiers. Then came an awful wacking and thrashing as the unseen arms paddled the burgomaster and his party with unseen switches.

"Ouch! Help! Stop it!" yelled Roeloffsen. But the paddling went on. The soldiers ran down the path to the main road and headed away from town, crying and yelling and trying to defend themselves from the blows of the unseen paddlers.

That was the last ever seen of the jealous burgomaster. Claas and his family lived on in their fine new home, never wanting for food or warmth. How their good fortune had come they did not know. The only clue they had was a piece of paper slipped under the door. It said simply, "Don't ever sell that pipe."

JACK AND THE ROBBERS

The tens and elevens will readily recognize "The Four Musicians" in this homespun variant with the realistic conclusion. They should hear Richard Chase tell it in the laconic drawl of a mountain man.

This here's another tale about Jack when he was still a small-like boy. He was about twelve, I reckon, and his daddy started tryin' to make him help with the work around the place. But Jack he didn't like workin' much. He would piddle around a little and then he'd go on back to the house, till one day his daddy whipped him. He just tanned Jack good. Jack didn't cry none, but he didn't like it a bit. So early the next mornin' he slipped off without tellin' his mother and struck out down the public road. Thought he'd go and try his fortune somewhere off from home.

"Jack and the Robbers." From *The Jack Tales* edited by Richard C. Chase. Copyright 1943 by Richard C. Chase. Reprinted by permission of and arrangement with Houghton Mifflin Company, the authorized publishers

He got down the road a few miles and there was an old ox standin' in a field by a rail fence, a-bellowin' like it was troubled over somethin'—

"Um-m-muh!
Um-m-m—muh-h-h!"

"Hello!" says Jack. "What's the matter?"

"I'll just tell you," says the old ox. "I'm gettin' too old to plow and I heard the men talkin' about how they'd have to kill me tomorrow and get shet of me."

"Come on down here to the gap," says Jack, "and you can slip off with me."

So the old ox followed the fence to where the gap was at and Jack let the bars down and the old ox got out in front of Jack, and they went on down the public road.

Jack and the ox traveled on, and pretty soon they came where there was an old donkey standin' with his head hangin' down over the gate, a-goin'—

"Wahn-n-n-eh!
Wahn-n-n-eh!
Wahn-n-n-eh!"

"Hello," says Jack. "What's troublin' you?"

"Law me!" says the old donkey. "The boys took me out to haul in wood this mornin' and I'm gettin' so old and weak I couldn't do no good. I heard 'em say they were goin' to kill me tomorrow, get shet of me."

"Come on and go with us," says Jack.

So he let the old donkey out and they pulled on down the public road. The old donkey told Jack to get up on his back and ride.

They went on a piece, came to an old hound dog settin' in a man's yard. He would bark awhile and then howl awhile—

"A-woo! woo! woo!
A-oo-oo-oo!"

—sounded awful lonesome.

"Hello," says Jack. "What you a-howlin' so for?"

"Oh, law me!" says the old dog. "The boys took me coon-huntin' last night, cut a tree where the coon had got up in it. I got hold on the coon all right, but my teeth are all gone and hit got loose from me. They said they were goin' to kill me today, get shet of me."

"Come on, go with us," says Jack.

So the old dog scrouged under the gate.

The old donkey says to him, "Get up on my back and ride, if you want to."

Jack holp the old dog up behind him, and they went on down the public road.

Came to an old tomcat climbin' along the fence. Hit was a-squallin' and meowin', stop ever' now and then, sit down on the top rail—

"Meow-ow!
Meow-ow-ow!"

—sounded right pitiful.

"Hello!" says Jack. "What's the matter you squallin' so?"

"Oh, law!" says the old cat. "I caught a rat out in the barn this mornin', but my teeth are gettin' so old and bad I let him go. I heard 'em talkin' about killin' me to get shet of me, 'cause I ain't no good to catch rats no more."

"Come on and go with us," says Jack.

So the old cat jumped down off the fence.

The old donkey says, "Hop up there on my back and you can ride."

The old cat jumped up, got behind the dog, and they went on down the public road.

Came to where they saw an old rooster settin' on a fence post, crowin' like it was midnight, makin' the awfulest lonesome racket—

"Ur rook-a-roo!
Ur-r-r rook-a-roo-oo-oo!"

"Hello!" says Jack. "What's troublin' you?"

"Law me!" says the old rooster. "Company's comin' today and I heard 'em say they were goin' to kill me, put me in a pie!"

"Come on with us," says Jack.

Old rooster flew on down, got behind the cat, says, "All right, boys. Let's go!"

So they went right on down the highway. That was about all could get on the old donkey's back. The old rooster was right on top its tail and a-havin' a sort of hard time stayin' on. They traveled on, traveled on, till hit got plumb dark.

"Well," says Jack, "we got to get off the road and find us a place to stay tonight."

Directly they came to a little path leadin' off in the woods, decided to take that, see could they find a stayin' place in there. Went on a right smart piece further, and 'way along up late in the night they came to a little house, didn't have no clearin' around it. Jack hollered hello at the fence, but there didn't nobody answer.

"Come on," says the old donkey. "Let's go investigate that place."

Well, there wasn't nobody ever came to the door and there wasn't nobody around back of the house, so directly they went on in. Found a right smart lot of good somethin' to eat in there.

Jack says, "Now, who in the world do you reckon could be a-livin' out here in such a wilderness of a place as this?"

"Well," says the old donkey, "hit's my o-pinion that a gang of highway robbers lives out here."

So Jack says, "Then hit looks like to me we might as well take up and stay here. If they've done stole all these vittles, we got as much right to 'em as they have."

"Yes," says the old dog, "that's exactly what I think, too. But if we stay, I believe we better get fixed for a fight. I expect they'll be comin' back in here about midnight."

"That's just what I was goin' to say," says the old cat. "I bet it's pretty close to midnight right now."

"Hit lacks about a hour," says the old rooster.

"Come on, then," says Jack. "Let's all of us get set to fight 'em."

The ox said he'd stay out in the yard. The old donkey said he'd take up his stand on the porch just outside the door. The dog said he'd get in behind the door and fight from there. The old tomcat got down in the fireplace, and the old rooster flew up on the comb of the roof, says, "If you boys need any help now, just call on me, call on me-e-e!"

They all waited awhile. Heard somebody comin' directly; hit was seven highway robbers. They came on till they got pretty close to the house, then they told one of 'em to go on in and start up a fire so's they could have a light to see to get in and so they could divide out the money they'd stole that day.

One man went on in the house, the other six waited outside the gate.

That man went to the fireplace, got down on his knees to blow up the fire. The cat had his head right down on the hearth-rock and that man thought its eyes was coals of fire. Time he blowed in that old cat's eyes, it reached out its claws right quick and scratched him down both cheeks. The robber hollered and headed for the door. The dog ran out and bit him in the leg. He shook it off and ran on the porch and the old donkey raised up and kicked him on out in the yard. The ox caught him up on its horns and ran to the fence and threw him out in the bresh. About that time the old rooster settin' up there on top of the house started in to crowin' right big.

The other robbers, time they heard all that racket, they put out from there just as fast as they could run. The one they'd sent in the house finally got up and started runnin' like a streak, caught up with 'em in no time. They said to him, says, "What in the world was that in there?"

"Oh, I'm killed! I'm killed!" says the man. "I won't live over fifteen minutes!"

The other said, "Well, 'fore ye die, tell us what it was caused all that racket back yonder."

"Law me! That house is plumb full of men, and they've even got one on the roof. I went to blow up the fire and a man in the fireplace raked me all over the face with an awl. Started to run and a man behind the door took me in the leg with a butcher knife. Time I got out the door, a man out there hit me with a knot-maul, knocked me clean off the porch. A man standin' in the yard caught me on a pitchfork and threw me over the fence. And then that man up on the roof hollered out,

'Chunk him on up here!
Chunk him on up here.'

Ain't no use in us goin' back there with all of them men in the house. Let's leave here quick 'fore they come after us."

So them highway robbers ran for their life, and kept on runnin' till they were plumb out the country.

Jack and the ox and the old donkey and the dog and the cat and the rooster, they took possession of that house, and just had 'em a big time.

But the last time I was down that way, Jack had gone on back home to his folks. He was out in the yard a-cuttin' his mother a big pile of stovewood.

FILL, BOWL! FILL!

The old man Jack meets in this tale is strongly reminiscent of the god Odin, gray bearded, with a staff that performs magic deeds.

This here tale's another'n about Jack goin' a-courtin'. And there's some more tales about Jack gettin' married; like that 'un about the doctor's girl, and there was that pretty girl down in Old Fire Dragaman's hole in the ground. 'Course Jack didn't marry all them girls at once. Hit might 'a been one way and hit might 'a been another. There's just different ways of tellin' it.

Well, this time it wasn't no King's girl. There was a farmer lived 'way back in the mountain had two awful pretty girls, and the boys were all crazy about 'em. This farmer, though, he was wealthy, and he didn't want the boys comin' around there, so he fixed up a way to get shet of 'em.

He put out a adver-tize-ment that any boy who wanted one of his girls would have to ketch 'em a wild rabbit and put it in a ring and make it stay there thirty minutes. That was his prop-osition: they would have to bring the rabbit and he'd make a ring ten foot across; then they'd put the rabbit in there and if it stayed thirty minutes, they could have one of the girls. But if the rabbit failed to stay that long, he'd kill the boy that brought the rabbit.

Well, not many went to try, but some did, and the old man cut their heads off. Directly it got so the boys mostly quit goin' down here. That suited the old man fine. But then some boy would get so struck on one of the girls, he'd venture, and get his head cut off. Fin'ly it got so nobody'd go.

Well, Jack he got to studyin' about how he might get one of them girls. His mother told him he better not do that, but Jack said he'd just have to try. So he caught him a rabbit, and put him a little snack of dinner in a poke, and then he got fixed up and started out.

About twelve o'clock in the wilder-ness, Jack met up with an old gray-bearded man. This old man looked like he was about a hundred years old, and he was walkin' with a walkin' stick.

Jack came along, the old man stopped, says, "Howdy do, Jack."

"Howdy do, daddy."

Jack looked at him, says, "I don't believe I know ye."

"No," says the old man. "I know you, though, and I know right where you've started. You're a-fixin' to get killed, now, ain't ye?"

"I might, now," says Jack.

"Are you familiar with what you got to do to get one of them girls?"

"Tol'able familiar," says Jack.

"Don't you think you'd just as well start on back home?"

"Oh, no," says Jack. "I'd never turn back. I'm a-goin' on down there now."

"Well, I might help ye," says the old man, "if ye got any faith. How's your faith, Jack?"

Jack said his faith was pretty good, says, "I'd sure be much obliged was you to help me, daddy."

"Well, if you come down the road a piece with me, I'll test you out a little and we'll see whether you got faith or no."

Got down the road a ways, the old man says, "Now, Jack, you take this stick here and go up there in the woods a ways till you come to a very flush spring. Then you take my stick and stir in that spring till the water turns to wine. And against ye get that done, I'll come up there with somethin' to help ye."

So Jack took that walkin' stick and went on to where there was a very bold spring comin' out the ground. Stuck that stick down in it and com-menced stirrin'.

Jack's faith was sort of weak when he started, but he 'lowed he'd have to keep on tryin'. He stirred right on, stirred right on, and pretty soon it looked like the water *was* turnin' just a little bit pink. So Jack's faith got stronger and stronger and the water got redder and redder.

Well, when that spring turned real red, there was that old man standin' there, says, "Well, Jack, you sure got faith. Now you get out your lunch and we'll eat a little and try some of that and see whether it tastes like wine or not."

So they did, and that water was just as good as any wine.

Then the old man says to Jack, says, "I've done

"Fill, Bowl! Fill!" From *The Jack Tales* edited by Richard C. Chase. Copyright 1943 by Richard C. Chase. Reprinted by permission of and arrangement with Houghton Mifflin Company, the authorized publishers

made ye a drill here, Jack. You can take that and stick it down in the middle of the ring that man'll make and your rabbit'll stay in there till it dies; it don't differ how wild he is."

He gave Jack a drill shaved out of a stick. It was eight-square like a steel drill and about a foot long.

Jack thanked him and started on again.

Got down to that place where the girls were, Jack hollered the old man out and said he'd come to try for one of his girls.

The man told Jack to come around in the yard, and then he marked out a ring, says, "Now, you put your rabbit down in this ring and if it stays in there thirty minutes, you can take whichever girl you want. And if it don't stay in the ring thirty minutes, I'll kill you. You understand now, do ye?"

Jack said he did, made like he was goin' to turn his rabbit loose.

The man says to him, says, "I'll make ye another proposition; if you can make that rabbit stay in there thirty minutes, I'll just let you kill me and take all the money I got."

Jack went and stuck that drill down in the middle of the ring, and dumped the rabbit out the poke he had in it. The rabbit got up on its feet, saw that drill and took out around it hard as it could go, around and around and around.

The old man watched Jack's rabbit a-goin' around in there, and his eyes just stuck out. Walked around the other side the ring, watched it some more. That rabbit ran right on, 'round and 'round the drill. The old man kept takin' out his watch; fin'ly he turned around and went on back in the house.

Told his old woman and the girls, says, "It's my opinion that rabbit is stayin' in there on account of that drill Jack stuck in the ring. One of you go on out there and see can't ye buy that thing off of Jack."

So the oldest girl she went out, says to Jack, "What'll ye take for that drill, Jack?"

Jack says, "I don't know as I'd want to sell it right now."

"I'll give ye a thousand dollars for it."

"No," says Jack, "I'll not sell it."

So she went on back, told her daddy she couldn't make no trade.

Then he sent his youngest girl out.

She came up 'side of Jack, says, "Jack, I'd like awful well to buy that drill."

"Well," says Jack, "you can have it after thirty minutes is up."

"Aw, Jack," she says, "I want it now. I'll pay ye two thousand dollars for it."

"No," says Jack, "you wait till thirty minutes is out, and then we'll trade."

So she saw she couldn't do no good, went on back in the house.

Then the man said to his old lady, says, "You go."

She went out.

"Jack, I'd sure like to trade ye out of that drill. You can have one of the girls, right now; and I'll give ye three thousand dollars and ever'thing on the place."

"No," says Jack, "not till thirty minutes is out."

The old lady went on back, says, "I can't do a thing with him. He won't even talk about sellin'."

The old man looked at his watch, says, "Well, that thirty minutes is about up. I reckon I'll have to go on out and let Jack kill me."

Started out, picked up a big bowl off the table, and took that to Jack, says, "Jack, it looks like your rabbit's goin' to stay in there. You might as well kill me." Says, "'Fore you do, though, I wish you'd sing this bowl full of lies for me."

"All right," says Jack, "I'll try."

"Oh, the oldest daughter she came out
    All for to buy my drill.
I fooled a-round her, kissed her well.
    Fill, bowl! Fill!"

Says, "Is it full?"

"No," says the old man, "only one drop."

"Oh, the youngest daughter she came out
    All for to buy my drill.
I fooled around her, kissed her well.
    Fill, bowl! Fill!"

"Is it full yet?"

"Just two drops, Jack."

"Oh, the old lady she came out
    All for to buy my drill.
I fooled around her, ki . . ."

"Stop, Jack! Hit's full and runnin' over. Just cut my head off."

North American Indian folk tales

*On the whole, the stories of our American Indians are not particularly
appealing unless they are edited to a considerable degree. They are often overly
long and formless. One folklorist said that they "give one an impression
that their narrators were incapable of even preserving an old tale, to say nothing
of inventing a new one." Perhaps they have suffered by translation, but beyond
the mythlike why stories, not many of them are good storytelling material.
Among the various collections, however, there are stories such as the two included
here which are delightful to read or tell.*

LITTLE BURNT-FACE

(Micmac)

*Little Burnt-Face is the scorched face of the
desert in the burning summer. The Great Chief,
whose symbol is the rainbow, is the rain. Invisible for a long time, he comes at last and restores
beauty to the face of the waiting earth child.
This is an interesting variant of the "Cinderella"
theme.*

Once upon a time, in a large Indian village
on the border of a lake, there lived an old man
who was a widower. He had three daughters.
The eldest was jealous, cruel, and ugly; the second was vain; but the youngest of all was very
gentle and lovely.

Now, when the father was out hunting in the
forest, the eldest daughter used to beat the
youngest girl, and burn her face with hot coals;
yes, and even scar her pretty body. So the people
called her "Little Burnt-Face."

When the father came home from hunting he
would ask why she was so scarred, and the eldest
would answer quickly: "She is a good-for-nothing! She was forbidden to go near the fire, and
she disobeyed and fell in." Then the father
would scold Little Burnt-Face and she would
creep away crying to bed.

By the lake, at the end of the village, there
was a beautiful wigwam. And in that wigwam
lived a Great Chief and his sister. The Great

"Little Burnt-Face." From *Red Indian Fairy Book* by
Frances J. Olcott. Copyright 1917, 1945 by Frances J.
Olcott and Houghton Mifflin Company. Reprinted by permission of and arrangement with Houghton Mifflin Company, the authorized publishers

Chief was invisible; no one had ever seen him
but his sister. He brought her many deer and
supplied her with good things to eat from the
forest and lake, and with the finest blankets and
garments. And when visitors came all they ever
saw of the Chief were his moccasins; for when
he took them off they became visible, and his
sister hung them up.

Now, one Spring, his sister made known that
her brother, the Great Chief, would marry any
girl who could see him.

Then all the girls from the village—except
Little Burnt-Face and her sisters—and all the
girls for miles around hastened to the wigwam,
and walked along the shore of the lake with his
sister.

And his sister asked the girls, "Do you see my
brother?"

And some of them said, "No"; but most of
them answered, "Yes."

Then his sister asked, "Of what is his shoulder-strap made?"

And the girls said, "Of a strip of rawhide."

"And with what does he draw his sled?" asked
his sister.

And they replied, "With a green withe."

Then she knew that they had not seen him at
all, and said quietly, "Let us go to the wigwam."

So to the wigwam they went, and when they
entered, his sister told them not to take the seat
next the door, for that was where her brother sat.

Then they helped his sister to cook the supper,
for they were very curious to see the Great Chief
eat. When all was ready, the food disappeared,
and the brother took off his moccasins, and his
sister hung them up. But they never saw the
Chief, though many of them stayed all night.

One day Little Burnt-Face's two sisters put on their finest blankets and brightest strings of beads, and plaited their hair beautifully, and slipped embroidered moccasins on their feet. Then they started out to see the Great Chief.

As soon as they were gone, Little Burnt-Face made herself a dress of white birch-bark, and a cap and leggings of the same. She threw off her ragged garments, and dressed herself in her birch-bark clothes. She put her father's moccasins on her bare feet; and the moccasins were so big that they came up to her knees. Then she, too, started out to visit the beautiful wigwam at the end of the village.

Poor Little Burnt-Face! She was a sorry sight! For her hair was singed off, and her little face was as full of burns and scars as a sieve is full of holes; and she shuffled along in her birch-bark clothes and big moccasins. And as she passed through the village the boys and girls hissed, yelled, and hooted.

And when she reached the lake, her sisters saw her coming, and they tried to shame her, and told her to go home. But the Great Chief's sister received her kindly, and bade her stay, for she saw how sweet and gentle Little Burnt-Face really was.

Then as evening was coming on, the Great Chief's sister took all three girls walking beside the lake, and the sky grew dark, and they knew the Great Chief had come.

And his sister asked the two elder girls, "Do you see my brother?"

And they said, "Yes."

"Of what is his shoulder-strap made?" asked his sister.

"Of a strip of rawhide," they replied.

"And with what does he draw his sled?" asked she.

And they said, "With a green withe."

Then his sister turned to Little Burnt-Face and asked, "Do you see him?"

"I do! I do!" said Little Burnt-Face with awe. "And he is wonderful!"

"And of what is his sled-string made?" asked his sister gently.

"It is a beautiful Rainbow!" cried Little Burnt-Face.

"But, my sister," said the other, "of what is his bow-string made?"

"His bow-string," replied Little Burnt-Face, "is the Milky Way!"

Then the Great Chief's sister smiled with delight, and taking Little Burnt-Face by the hand, she said, "You have surely seen him."

She led the little girl to the wigwam, and bathed her with dew until the burns and scars all disappeared from her body and face. Her skin became soft and lovely again. Her hair grew long and dark like the Blackbird's wing. Her eyes were like stars. Then his sister brought

from her treasures a wedding-garment, and she dressed Little Burnt-Face in it. And she was most beautiful to behold.

After all this was done, his sister led the little girl to the seat next the door, saying, "This is the Bride's seat," and made her sit down.

And then the Great Chief, no longer invisible, entered, terrible and beautiful. And when he saw Little Burnt-Face, he smiled and said gently, "So we have found each other!"

And she answered, "Yes."

Then Little Burnt-Face was married to the Great Chief, and the wedding-feast lasted for days, and to it came all the people of the village. As for the two bad sisters, they went back to their wigwam in disgrace, weeping with shame.

THE TWO-FACES

Here is an authentic Indian story, rich in tribal myths and the everyday activities of a people. It is so long it should probably be read or told to children serially. It will add much to an Indian unit or to a child's understanding of Indian life.

"Now I will tell you a story," said Walks-with-the-wolf when Woodtick had finished.

There was once a tribe of people who had two faces. One was in front where a face ought to be; the other was behind where no face belongs. Nobody knew where their village was; nobody ever saw the Two-faces when they were at home. Old men say they lived somewhere north of here, but nobody knows.

The Two-faces owned a slave who was afraid of them. He was their scout, and they kept him traveling. The Winds were his helpers. He rode them everywhere. No matter which way they were blowing he went along to learn what was going on. After he got there and looked around he waited till a right Wind came along. Then he rode it back to the village of the Two-faces and told their Chief what he had seen and heard. He had to do this, of course, because he was a slave. But he was a very smart Person. He was a Magpie's Feather.

The Two-faces were rich people. They owned many fine lodges, had beautiful clothes and more painted robes than they could use. But they did not work to make any of these things; and they did not steal them. They won everything they possessed by gambling with others. And they kept the Magpie's Feather busy looking for strangers who would play gambling games. He

"The Two-Faces." From *Old Man Coyote* by Frank B. Linderman. The John Day Company, Inc., Publishers. Copyright, 1931, by Frank B. Linderman

would blow into a village, tumble around here and there, into lodges and out again without being noticed, because he was only a Magpie's Feather. But he saw everything everywhere. When he had finished looking and listening he would sleep until the right Wind came blowing along; then he would ride it back to the village of the Two-faces.

The Chief would listen, and if he believed it worth while he would talk things over with the headmen, and if all were agreed, the Chief would give the scout some meat, but never enough! The Magpie's Feather was always hungry!

The next day, if they thought it worth while, the Magpie's Feather would be sent back to the strange village to tell the people there that the Two-faces would visit them and play gambling games, if they were willing. They pretended to be quite polite, always, you see.

Of course all tribes liked to play gambling games. They always listened when the Magpie's Feather came to ask if the Two-faces might come and play games with them, because playing games is friendly. But the tribes did not know that the Two-faces always won, nor that after winning all the property a tribe possessed the Two-faces wagered their lives against the lives of the people they were playing with, so that when the last game was played there was never anybody to tell what had happened. If the tribes had known these things they would not have played with the Two-faces. But you see, no tribe that played with them ever lived to tell the others, because the Two-faces won every game they played. One who gambles must pay if he loses, so that all those who played with the Two-faces paid with their lives in the end.

One day when the North-wind was blowing, the Magpie's Feather rode into the village of the Absanakees. The young men were on the plains hunting, the old men were making weapons and talking of wars, the women were making kettles of Buffalo-paunches, or sewing, or cooking, while the children played. Nobody noticed the black and white Magpie's Feather blowing around.

Four days after this a Person came into the village from the north. Our scouts saw him coming a long time, but he was alone and unarmed, and they let him pass. He was tall and wore a white robe. He spoke softly and was a fine sign-talker. His face was painted, and there was a Magpie's Feather in his hair. He walked straight to the Chief's lodge, and no dogs barked when he passed. After a time men and women saw him leave the Chief's lodge and go out of the village, alone. But nobody, not even the scouts, could tell which way he had gone!

That evening, after the hunters had returned, a crier went about the village saying that four days from then Strangers would visit the Absanakees, and that there would be gambling for four days.

The Absanakees were glad. But when at last the visitors arrived they were not so pleased. The Strangers had *two faces!* No matter which way they turned they were looking at a Person. Nobody could get behind a Two-face, and nobody could be certain that he was in front of him. This would be bad in gambling! Two eyes can never catch all that four eyes can see. Besides this, there were twice as many mouths to feed as there were visitors. But the Absanakees had plenty of meat. And they had invited the Two-faces to their village, or they had told them they might come, which was the same. There was nothing to do about it now.

The Chiefs talked together, and then a crier told the two villages that there would be four games played—one each day for four days. The first was to be the hoop-and-arrow game played twice; once on the first day, and again on the second day. The third day they were to run foot-races, and on the fourth and last day they were to play shinny.

The cunning Two-faces managed things as they had always done. The foolish Absanakees wagered all their property in their lodges against all the property in the lodges of the Two-faces. And the Absanakees lost!

Next day the Absanakees lost all their weapons. The third day the Two-faces won all the lodges of the Absanakees, and on the fourth day —not to be dared by their visitors—the Absanakees bet their lives against the lives of the Two-faces on a game of shinny. The Two-faces won! The Two-faces took the Absanakees' lives, leaving no living thing in the Absanakee village. Yet they did not need all the lodges, and left many standing on the plains when they went back to their own country, wherever it is. They believed that all the Absanakees were dead now.

They did not know that two were still living! One was a middle-aged woman who was away from the village when the Two-faces came. She was far away picking berries. The other was a little boy who had been playing with some puppies in a hole and had gone to sleep there with the baby dogs.

When the Woman came back to the village and found her people dead she did not know what had happened. She was afraid, and she cried among the dead Absanakees, looking to see if any were yet alive. She found the Boy asleep with the puppies in the hole, and together they searched the remaining lodges for property that had been left by the Two-faces. What they found they took, and with the best lodge they saw, they moved up the river to a grove of trees and camped.

The Woman was a good worker and smart. When the Boy grew old enough she made him a bow and arrows and taught him how to use the weapons. He soon became a good hunter. They always had plenty of meat now and skins to make their clothing. The Woman dressed every robe and skin the Boy brought in, so that soon they had more than they needed. They were rich.

One day when the Boy was butchering a Buffalo in a deep coulee a Person came and stood beside him. The Person was tall and wore a white robe. He spoke softly and was a good sign-talker. His face was painted, and there was a Magpie's Feather in his hair.

"Sit down and eat," said the Boy, glad to see anyone. "Eat all you wish."

But the Person did not speak, even after he had eaten all he wished. He did not even say that he was grateful. He only walked away; and when he was gone, the Boy could not tell which way he went.

"Do you ever see anybody when you are hunting?" asked the Woman when the Boy was back in the lodge that night.

"Today when I was butchering a Buffalo a Person came to me," said the Boy.

"How did he look?" she asked, acting afraid.

"He was tall, and wore a white robe. He spoke softly, and was a good sign-talker. His face was painted, and there was a Magpie's Feather in his hair."

"Ha! I know who he is," said the Woman. "He is the scout of the Two-faces—the people who killed all the Absanakees but you and me. If he finds our lodge, and tells the Two-faces, we shall die. Never bring that Person here. Never tell him where we are camped if you do not wish to die."

One windy day the Boy was butchering a Buffalo-cow on the plains when a voice, close behind him, spoke softly. He turned quickly, and there again was the White-robed-person with the Magpie's Feather in his hair.

"Listen, Lives-with-his-grandmother," said the Person, "you were kind to me. You gave me meat —all I could eat—even though I was your enemy. I am the scout of the Two-faces who killed your people, the Absanakees, all but you and one woman. I am their slave and must do as they say. But my heart is bad for the Two-faces, and it is good for you, who gave me meat, all the meat I could eat. The Two-faces give me little to eat. I am always hungry and very tired. I have never had a good sleep in my life."

"Why do you not run away? When you get far off why do you go back?" asked the Boy.

"Because there are Persons who follow: Persons that are never seen, but who would tell the Two-faces where to find me," said the Magpie's Feather. "But I may get away if you will help me," he went on, speaking fast. "First I will help you and the Woman. Then, if I help you, I shall expect you to help me. Will you do this, Lives-with-his-grandmother?"

"Yes, of course I will help you," said the Boy. "What is it you would have me do?"

"This, Lives-with-his-grandmother. The Two-faces know where your lodge is. I told them. I was obliged to tell them. Tomorrow they will come to gamble with you, and you must pretend to be glad. They will play the hoop-and-arrow game twice; one game the first day and another game on the second day. After that they will run a foot-race and play a game of shinny. They have four Medicine-arrows. One is Black, one is Red, one is Yellow, and one is Blue. They will let you choose an arrow for the hoop-and-arrow game. Remember to choose the Black one! Insist that in betting all their property against all your

property they include me, their slave. If you win, you will save me. I will come to your lodge and be your slave. I have spoken."

When the Magpie's Feather had gone the Boy went to his lodge wondering how he could beat the people who had killed all the Absanakees except him and the Woman. Even if he won the first game with the Black arrow what good would this do with the other games to follow? How could the Magpie's Feather help him with the other games? How could any Person help him against the Two-faces?

"Lives-with-his-grandmother! Lives-with-his-grandmother!" Somebody was calling him!

When he raised the lodge-door in stepped Esahcawata, Old-man-coyote. He wore a Wolf's tail tied to each of his moccasins, and he was laughing. "Ha-ha-ha," he cackled like a woman that is very old. "I have come to help my brother, Lives-with-his-grandmother! I have heard that the Two-faces are coming to play gambling games with you. I have come to help. Give me some meat. You have plenty; you are rich!"

"Who told you that the Two-faces are coming here, Esahcawata," asked the Woman, giving him some meat.

"Oh, the Raven, of course; the Raven, and others. I have many friends," said Old-man-coyote, beginning to eat as though he could never get enough to fill his belly. "I'm here in plenty of time, too!" he laughed. "And I've brought my coup-stick. I expect to count some coups here." He showed them a willow-stick to which four small Eagle's feathers were tied. "Oh, it will have more feathers after this, several more," he told them when he saw that the Boy did not think his coup-stick very fine. "You will have to play games with the Two-faces, Lives-with-his-grandmother," said Old-man-coyote, seriously. "You cannot fight them, so you must play with them and be polite."

The Two-faces were there when the Boy wakened in the morning. Old-man-coyote listened through the lodge-skin while the Boy talked to their Chief, who offered to wager all his people's property, except clothes and lodges, against all the property the Boy owned, except his clothes and his lodge.

"I will do as you say if you will include your slave with your other property," said the Boy, remembering what the Magpie's Feather had told him.

"Good!" agreed the Chief of the Two-faces. "Here are four arrows. Choose one for the first game—any one of them."

The Boy pretended he did not know which arrow to choose, the Red arrow, or the Blue arrow, or the Yellow arrow, or the Black arrow. But he took the Black one.

The village crier ran about among the Two-faces saying, "Everybody stand aside! This Boy has bet all his property, except his lodge and clothing, against all our property, except our lodges and clothing, that he can beat us at the hoop-and-arrow game!"

"Hi-Hi-Hi-Hi!" cried all the Two-faces, as though they were surprised.

"And this is the hoop we shall use!" called the camp crier, holding up a painted hoop that all might see that it was fair; that it had four large sections, and a small circle in its center; that it was like this ⊕ and fair.

Then he rolled the hoop. Their player ran after it on one side, and the Boy ran on the other side, each with his bow and arrow. The Two-face shot first. His arrow, the Blue one, went through the rolling hoop, but not through the small circle in its center.

"Ki-yaah—Ki-yaaaaah!" The Two-faces were glad. They cheered their player. "Ki-yaah—Ki-yaaaaah!"

"Zippp!" went the Boy's arrow, straight through the small circle in the hoop's center! He had won! The hoop was pinned to the ground!

"Hi-Hi! Ha-ha-ha!" Old-man-coyote began to sing and dance, the Wolf-tails dangling at his moccasin-heels. "You Two-faced-persons are playing games against a Boy who has powerful friends," he called, tauntingly, jumping over the hoop. Then he struck it down with his coup-stick, as though the hoop were an enemy in war. "Now I will count coup; tie another Eagle's feather on my coup-stick. Watch me, all you Two-faces!" He reached into a pouch, drew out a ruffled Eagle's feather, and tied it with the others to his willow-stick.

"I told you I would help you, Lives-with-his-grandmother!" said Old-man-coyote to the Boy when they went to their lodge with the Magpie's

Feather, after the game. "And I will help you more after this."

"Tomorrow," said the Magpie's Feather, "when they permit you to choose an arrow for the second hoop-and-arrow game, take the Blue one, the arrow the Two-faces used today. Remember this, Lives-with-his-grandmother."

"Yes, that is the best one," said Old-man-coyote, though he knew nothing about the arrows. "That is the best arrow, and I will be thinking of something else to do."

In the morning when the Chief of the Two-faces offered the arrows and said, "Choose," the Boy was a long time deciding. But, of course, he chose the Blue arrow. Then they rolled the hoop again, and again the Boy won. Now he owned all the property of the Two-faces, all their lodges and clothing, and their slave, besides. But he was very unhappy. Tomorrow the game would be a foot-race, and he would be obliged to wager all his winnings against the weapons of the Two-faces. He, himself, was not a swift runner. Old-man-coyote could not run at all, and the Magpie's Feather was a slave. The Two-faces would not play against a slave-person! The Boy was certain of this—and now he was very much afraid.

But Old-man-coyote kept singing and dancing as though there was nothing to fear—as though all things were even between the Two-faces and the Boy. "We are Smart-persons," he kept saying over and over again.

"I am sorry," said the Magpie's Feather that night in the lodge. "I cannot help you further. Tomorrow there will be a foot-race, and the runner for the Two-faces will be The-shadow-of-a-cloud. He is the swiftest Person on this world."

"Oh, no, he isn't—no, he isn't," laughed Old-man-coyote. "No, he isn't. He is fast. But I know some Persons who can beat The-shadow-of-a-cloud, if I can find them."

He stood up. "I will go now, and look for a friend of mine. I may not find him, of course. But remember I will be here in time for the race tomorrow," he said, and went out of the lodge.

The Boy and the Magpie's Feather were asleep when the Woman called them. "Someone is outside," she said, straightening the robes in the lodge.

"Well, I'm back, you see," laughed Old-man-coyote, coming in with a Person. "And I found the Swift-runner, too. Sit down!" he told the Person, as though the lodge were his own.

The Person sat by the fire. He was tall and very thin, and he was white-looking, and there were two heavy stones tied to his feet.

"This Person is fast. One's eyes cannot see him when he runs," said Old-man-coyote. "He must have heavy stones tied to his feet to keep him from running all the time. He cannot walk unless stones are tied to his feet. Tomorrow when we cut them off he will run forever unless we catch him and tie them on again. I guess I am smart enough for those Two-faced-persons."

The race was to be around the edge of the World and back again. The Two-faces had The-shadow-of-a-cloud ready when the Boy brought his runner to the starting place. The Two-faced crier went among the people telling them of the race, and while this was going on the Boy got ready to cut the thongs that held the stones to his runner's feet.

"Ho!" called the Two-faced crier. And the racers were gone! The-shadow-of-a-cloud was behind!

"Hi-Hi-Hi—Ha-ha-ha-ha!" Old-man-coyote began to sing and dance, flipping the Wolf-tails around his heels, and acting silly. The Two-faces were looking at him, and they were scowling, too. But he did not care about their looks, because he could not tell which way they were looking. "Hi-Hi-Hi—Ha-ha-ha-ha! Now get your rope, Lives-with-his-grandmother! Get your rope, and catch your runner when he comes back, or he will run himself to death. He will run forever!" he called.

The Boy got his rope, and when his runner came running back he caught him.

"Hold him! Hold him!" cried Old-man-coyote, tying the heavy stones to the Person's feet. "Now let him up. Ha-ha! We have beaten the Two-faces again."

Night came before The-shadow-of-a-cloud came into the village. He had lost the race around the edge of the World and back again. The Boy had won!

"I'm a pretty smart Person, you'll find," said Old-man-coyote that night in the Boy's lodge. "And you'd better pay attention when I say things to you. Listen now. Tomorrow we play shinny against those Two-faces. It is the last game, and our lives will be wagered on it. Of course they cannot kill me, but they will kill you and the Magpie's Feather and this Woman, if we lose. Go now, and say to the Two-face Chief these words: 'I have played all the games with you, and I have done as you wished in all. Tomorrow when we play shinny I wish to use my own ball.' Say these words, and bring his answer back here. I wish to know it."

The Boy went to the Chief of the Two-faces and said the words Old-man-coyote had spoken. "It is good," answered the Chief. "We will play shinny with your ball. But remember that your lives will be wagered on the game—your lives against ours."

"Hi-Hi! Ha-ha-ha!" laughed Old-man-coyote, when the Boy told him what the Chief had said. "Ha-ha-ha-ha! This game of shinny will be funny! We are to start playing from the center of the World, and put the ball into salt-water east or west. Is this agreed upon, Lives-with-his-grandmother?"

"Yes, Esahcawata, we are to start at the center of the World and knock the ball into salt-water either east or west."

"Good! Good!" chuckled Old-man-coyote. "Who are the swiftest runners that play shinny for the Two-faces?" he asked, counting the feathers on his willow coup-stick.

"Wolf and Coyote," answered Magpie's Feather, uneasily. "But what are we going to use for a shinny-ball?"

"Oh, a good one. One that will do, anyway," laughed Old-man-coyote, rising to go out into the night. "Do not be surprised if the weather turns cold before I come back," he laughed. "I'll be here in time to see the game, remember."

"Why, the snow is falling!" said the Woman, looking up through the smoke-hole of the lodge. "Our lodge is cold!" She put wood on the fire, and drew her robe about her shoulders.

Before morning the snow reached above a man's knees. Then it stopped suddenly, and rain came; then the rain stopped, and the weather turned suddenly cold again and there was a crust on the snow that would bear the weight of a light Person, but not one that was heavy. And now the sky was clear.

"Here I am again; and I've brought a Hot Thing for a shinny-ball." Old-man-coyote came into the lodge with the Morning-star! "This

Person has nothing to do at this time of year," he told them. "The Morning-star does not shine, has no work, until after the Buffalo-calves are born on the plains and stand up. But he will help us. He is the Son of the Sun, and a friend of mine. Now give me some dressed Elk-skin. I shall have to cover this Person so that he will look like a shinny-ball before we use him," he said, beginning to sew Elk-skin around the Morning-star.

The Two-faces were certain they would win the shinny-game and take back their property, even before they killed the Absanakees. But the deep snow worried them a little while they were walking to the center of the World to start the shinny-game. The crust kept breaking. It was only strong enough to hold up the small Persons, like the Fox and the Lynx.

The crier of the Two-faces was ahead. "Here we are! Here we are!" he called, sticking his lance into the snow to mark the place. "This is the center of the World."

The Two-faces gathered around him and his lance that was standing up in the snow just as our people stop to make camp when our Medicine-men stick a lance where our village is to be. "Everybody who desires to play may do so," called out the crier, "but remember the game is for our lives! Our swiftest who will play for us are the Wolf and the Coyote," he finished, stepping back, and waving the people away from the lance in the snow, which was the center of the World.

"And our runners are two Foxes, the Red one and the Silver-cross, first cousins," said Old-man-coyote, who had come up to the lance with the shinny-ball and the Foxes.

There was much talking, and some disputing, over who should first have the Ball. But while this was going on the Ball, in Old-man-coyote's arms, whispered to the Foxes: "Run westward where there are no people at all! I will be there quickly. I will roll under the snow so that they may not see me go. I will melt my way, for I am hot. I will come up out of the snow where you are standing. When you see me, grab me quickly and run west to salt-water. I will not burn you."

The Boy won the Ball, after much talking. "Ho!" called the Two-faced crier. "Play at once!"

Old-man-coyote raised the Ball four times as though he would toss it westward; then, instead, he tossed it eastward where the people were thickest!

There was a mad striking of shinny-clubs! Clubs were so thick there that nobody could see the Ball for flying snow. The Two-faces struck and struck, but not one struck the Ball! It was under the snow and traveling westward.

"Hi-Hi! Ha-ha-ha!" Old-man-coyote ran among the Two-faces, striking frantically, as though he believed the Ball was there. "Do your best, you Two-faces!" he called to them, striking right and left, and making the snow fly. "Remember that we don't love you very much."

They were excited, and all kept striking the snow where Old-man-coyote pretended the Ball was until a Two-face saw the Foxes running away with it, westward. This Person shouted, "There they go! They've got the Ball, and are going westward with it!"

Away went the Wolf and Coyote, their tongues hanging out of their mouths. But they kept breaking through the crust of the snow! They are powerful and swift, but the snow made their work difficult. The rest could not keep up at all.

At length the Wolf and Coyote caught up to the Foxes who were running side by side. The Red-fox was carrying the Ball. The Silver-fox fell back just a little to fool the Wolf and Coyote—to make them believe he was tiring. Then, after a little, he caught up again and the Red-fox passed him the Ball to carry a while. They changed off, you see, and kept running toward the salt-water all the time. Nobody else was near when, out of breath, and very tired, the Red-fox tossed the Ball into the salt-water! The Wolf was reaching for it, too, and nearly took it, but the Red-fox, dodging just when the snow-crust broke with the Wolf, tossed the Ball into the salt-water!

Everybody heard it splash! "Hi-Hi-Hi—Ha-ha-ha!" Old-man-coyote began to laugh. But the Two-faces were crying now.

"Call the Blue-heron," laughed Old-man-coyote. "Call the Blue-heron-person! Let him do this job with his bill. Hi-Hi—Ha-ha-ha! I will call him myself. I planned this thing." He turned his back and sang his Medicine-song.

When the Blue-heron came Old-man-coyote

said, "Brother, kill all these Two-faced ones, and cut off their heads with your bill to make sure your job is well done."

"Boy," he said, "you and this Woman go away from here. Take the Magpie's Feather with you. Do not come back, or even look this way for four days. After four days come back here to your lodge."

The first night the Woman heard men singing back where she and the Boy had left Old-man-coyote. The next night she heard children laughing, and told the Boy. The third night both smelled smoke from many lodges, and the fourth night they could hear war-drums, and people dancing.

The fifth morning they went back. A large village stood where they had left their lodge!

"Welcome—welcome, Lives-with-his-grandmother. Welcome, Woman," many voices were saying. And the words were Absanakee! The Absanakees had come back!

But, of course, Esahcawata, Old-man-coyote, was gone.

"I have finished this story."

Tall tales

England has its giant stories, but the United States of America, with its national symbols a spread eagle and a super-tall figure of a man called "Uncle Sam," has expressed its exuberant sense of bigness in a series of tall tales. Pecos Bill, a western cowboy; Paul Bunyan of the lumber camps; Stormalong, a New England sailor; John Henry, a railroad hand; and some "super-duper" animals like Babe, the Blue Ox, and the Fast Sooner Hound are only a few of our tall tale heroes. Where these stories came from, nobody knows, but they are as indigenous to the United States as its great cornfields, its vast prairies, and its giant trees. These stories voice the philosophy of a new world, a young nation. They say, with tongue in cheek and rare drollery, that our native sons can do anything—"the sky's the limit!" The general formula for these bouncing stories is that the details shall be meticulously realistic and convincing, and the whopping exaggerations shall be told with a straight face and complete gravity. Boys love the stories, and girls like them, too. Told on a picnic, on the beach or around a camp fire, no stories are more fun. But they go almost as well in the home or the classroom, and once the children get the flavor of a series of these hero tales, they want more. Incidentally, when children have caught their style and pattern, they can make up their own tall tales.

THE CAMP
ON THE BIG ONION

With this introduction to Paul Bunyan, the mighty logger, children may want Glen Rounds' delightful book, Ole Paul the Mighty Logger.

That first fall I was workin' for Paul was when he got the big hotcake griddle. Always in the woods in them days the boys was mighty fond of hotcakes—just like men are pretty generally any-

"The Camp on the Big Onion." From *Paul Bunyan*, copyright 1924, 1952 by Esther Shephard. Reprinted by permission of Harcourt, Brace and Company, Inc.

wheres, I guess—and if there was anything could be said for Paul it was that he tried to treat his men right. And so, naturally, he wanted 'em to have hotcakes if there was any way he could fix it, and then besides, the way he ate 'em afterwards, he was more'n a little fond of 'em himself.

Well, in camp before that they hadn't never had hotcakes, because they didn't have no griddle big enough to cook 'em on, and no stove they could of put the griddle on if they'd of had it anyway, and so what they had for breakfast before that and what they was havin' when I went to work for Paul was just sourdough biscuits. And even so the cook used to have to get up twenty-six hours before daylight to get the biscuits cooked in time because all he had to cook 'em on was one of them there drumhead stoves they used to have and he couldn't only cook but sixty-four drippin' pans full at a time.

But that year Paul made up his mind he was goin' to have hotcakes for the men and he was goin' to have a griddle big enough to cook 'em on. And so he went down to the plow-works at Moline, Illinois, and contracted for 'em to make him one to suit him.

The steel that went into this griddle of Paul's was what would have gone into two hundred and sixty breakin' plows, and when it was done finally, it measured two hundred and thirty-five foot across.

And then the men at the plow-works, of course, didn't have no way to ship it up to Paul and they was out there in the yard at the works figgurin' on how they could build some side-tracks and put several flatcars alongside each other and try to ship it up on them, when Paul happened to come along to see if his griddle wasn't finished yet.

"Never mind that," he says to the men when he seen 'em out there. "Never mind tryin' to build any extra tracks. We couldn't never get enough cars anyway, I don't believe. I'll just raise 'er up on edge and hitch my Blue Ox to 'er, and she'll roll right along."

And so after they'd got out of the way he raised 'er up, and hitched on, and started right out for home.

And when he come to within four or five miles of the camp, like he'd calculated it out beforehand, I guess, he just unhitched the Blue Ox and let the griddle spin on by itself. And here she come, rollin' right along. And when she got to just the right place, where he'd figgured to place her, she begun to spin round and round like spin-the-plate at a play-party and dug a nice big hole for the fire to go in under it, and settled right down and was all ready to go.

Paul had the bull-cooks pile in an acre or two of brush for a good fire, and him and Ole the Blacksmith rigged up a tank for the cook to make his batter in and a flume with a stop-cock in it, so's he could run it out onto the griddle and then shut it off whenever he had enough. Paul got flunkies with slabs of bacon strapped to their feet to skate around on the griddle to keep it greased, and a chicken wire fence all around for 'em to climb up on when the batter come in too thick. We rigged up a kind of block and tackle arrangement to haul the hotcake off with when it was done—that's on that first griddle. Afterwards, like in the camp in North Dakota, Paul, of course, always had donkey engines.

There was four hundred bull-cooks bringin' in the spruce-boughs for the bunks in the big bunkhouse at that first camp I was in; it had eighty tiers of bunks, most of 'em muzzle loaders but the two bottom layers, they was sidewinders. And the men used to go to bed in balloons at night and come down in parachutes in the mornin'.

A pretty sight it used to be to watch 'em comin' down.

"R-o-oo-ool out! Daylight in the swamp!" one of the cookees would yell, and then in a minute or two they'd all be rollin' out of their blankets, and the parachutes would open and they'd all come sailin' down. It sure was a pretty sight—about as fine a show as I ever laid eyes on.

Sometimes in the mornin' I used to stop at the door of the bunkhouse, on my way from the barn, to watch 'em. For Bill and I generally used to be on our way in to breakfast about that time, and Bill'd sometimes take the time to stop for a minute or so.

"I like to see 'em," he'd say to me. "Angus, that's a mighty fine show. They come faster now than they used to when it was just for sourdough biscuits. But we'll have to hustle along and get our hotcakes. We got to get back to the Ox."

That spring on the Big Onion we had an awful lot of trouble with the garlic that growed there where Garlic Crick joins the Big Onion River—a kind of V-shaped tract in there along the loggin' road, that was just full of it. The cook tried to use it all up seasonin' the soup but the Frenchies wouldn't stand for it in their pea-soup after the first week, and even with that he only got the top layer off and then there was four more layers growin' under that one. It beats all how thick that wild garlic can grow when it gets a good start. Everybody that even went by that place was seasoned so strong there wasn't nobody else could live with him and, worst of it, he couldn't stand to live with himself even. And we pretty near just had to break up camp, but then Paul heard that the Italian garlic crop was goin' to fail that year and so we grubbed up the whole piece, every last layer of it, and shipped it all to Italy and that way we got rid of it at last; just in time when a good many of us was goin' on the drive anyway, though.

PECOS BILL

AND HIS BOUNCING BRIDE

Here is one of the children's favorites of all the tall tale heroes. As in moving-picture Westerns, women are an unimportant detail, and certainly Pecos Bill's bride must have been glad to see the last of "the Widow-maker." The children will like Le Grand's tall tale, "Why Cowboys Sing in Texas."

There were two loves in the life of Pecos Bill. The first was his horse Widow-Maker, a beautiful creamy white mustang. The second, was a girl, a pretty, gay creature named Slue-Foot Sue.

Widow-Maker was the wildest pony in the West. He was the son of the White Mustang. Like his father he had a proud spirit which refused to be broken. For many years cowboys and *vaqueros* had tried to capture him. At last Pecos Bill succeeded. He had a terrible time of it. For a whole week he lay beside a water hole before he could lasso the white pony. For another week he had to ride across the prairies, in and out of canyons and briar patches, before he could bring the pony to a walk. It was a wild ride indeed. But after Bill's ride on the cyclone it was nothing.

At last the white stallion gave up the struggle. Pecos patted his neck gently and spoke to him in horse language. "I hope you will not be offended," he began as politely as possible, "but beauty such as yours is rare, even in this glorious state of Texas. I have no wish to break your proud spirit. I feel that together you and I would make a perfect team. Will you not be my partner at the I.X.L. Ranch?"

The horse neighed sadly. "It must be," he

"Pecos Bill and His Bouncing Bride." From *Pecos Bill* by James C. Bowman. As adapted in *Yankee Doodle's Cousins* by Anne Malcolmson. Copyright 1941 by Anne Burnett Malcolmson. Reprinted by permission of Albert Whitman & Company and Houghton Mifflin Company.

sighed. "I must give up my freedom. But since I must, I am glad that you are the man who has conquered me. Only Pecos Bill is worthy to fix a saddle upon the son of the great White Stallion, the Ghost King of the Prairie."

"I am deeply honored," said Pecos Bill, touched in his heart by the compliment.

"It is rather myself who am honored," replied the mustang, taking a brighter view of the situation.

The two of them went on for several hours saying nice things to each other. Before they were through, the pony was begging Pecos to be his master. Pecos was weeping and saying he was not fit to ride so magnificent a beast. In the end, however, Pecos Bill made two solemn promises. He would never place a bit in the pony's mouth. No other human would ever sit in his saddle.

When Bill rode back to I.X.L. with his new mount, the second promise was broken. Old Satan, the former bad man, had not completely recovered from his badness. He was jealous of Bill. When he saw the beautiful white stallion he turned green and almost burst with jealousy. One night he stole out to the corral. Quietly he slipped up beside the horse and jumped into the saddle.

Pegasus, as the horse was called, knew right away that his rider was not Pecos Bill. He lifted his four feet off the ground and bent his back into a perfect semicircle. Old Satan flew off like an arrow from a bow. He flew up into the air, above the moon, and came down with a thud on top of Pike's Peak. There he sat howling with pain and fright until the boys at I.X.L. spotted him.

Bill was angry. He knew, however, that Old Satan had had enough punishment. In his kind heart he could not allow the villain to suffer any more than he had to. So he twirled his lasso around his head, let it fly, and roped Old Satan back to the Texas ranch. The former desperado never tried to be bad again.

The cowhands were so impressed by the pony's bucking they decided to change his name. From that time on they dropped the name of Pegasus and called him Widow-Maker. It suited him better.

The story of Bill's other love, Slue-Foot Sue,

is a long one. It began with the tale of the Perpetual Motion Ranch. Bill had bought a mountain from Paul Bunyan. It looked to him like a perfect mountain for a ranch. It was shaped like a cone, with smooth sides covered with grassy meadows. At the top it was always winter. At the bottom it was always summer. In between it was always spring and fall. The sun always shone on one side; the other was always in shade. The cattle could have any climate they wished.

Bill had to breed a special kind of steer for his ranch. These had two short legs on one side and two long legs on the other. By traveling in one direction around the mountain, they were able to stand up straight on the steep sides.

The novelty wore off, however, and at last Bill sold the Perpetual Motion Ranch to an English duke. The day that the I.X.L. boys moved out, the lord moved in. He brought with him trainload after trainload of fancy English things. He had featherbeds and fine china and oil paintings and real silver and linen tablecloths and silk rugs. The cowboys laughed themselves almost sick when they saw these dude things being brought to a cattle ranch.

Pecos Bill didn't laugh. He didn't even notice the fancy things. All he could see was the English duke's beautiful daughter. She was as pretty as the sun and moon combined. Her hair was silky and red. Her eyes were blue. She wore a sweeping taffeta dress and a little poke bonnet with feathers on it. She was the loveliest creature Pecos Bill had ever seen.

She was as lively and gay as she was pretty. Bill soon discovered that Slue-Foot Sue was a girl of talent. Before anyone could say "Jack Robinson," she changed into a cowboy suit and danced a jig to the tune of "Get Along, Little Dogies."

Bill soon lost all his interest in cowpunching. He spent his afternoons at the Perpetual Motion Ranch, teaching Sue to ride a broncho. Sue could ride as well as anyone, but she pretended to let him teach her. After several months of Bill's lessons, she put on a show. She jumped onto the back of a huge catfish in the Rio Grande River and rode all the way to the Gulf of Mexico, bareback. Bill was proud of her. He thought she had learned her tricks all from him.

Sue's mother was terribly upset by her daugh-

ter's behavior. She didn't care much for Bill. She was very proper. It was her fondest hope that Sue would stop being a tomboy and marry an earl or a member of Parliament.

As soon as she realized that her daughter was falling in love with a cowboy, she was nearly heart-broken. There was nothing she could do about it, however. Slue-Foot Sue was a headstrong girl who always had her own way.

At last the duchess relented. She invited Bill to tea and began to lecture him on English manners. She taught him how to balance a teacup,

how to bow from the waist, and how to eat scones and marmalade instead of beans and bacon. He learned quickly, and soon the duchess was pleased with him. She called him "Colonel."

When the boys from the I.X.L. Ranch saw what was going on they were disgusted. Here was their boss, their brave, big, cyclone-riding Pecos Bill, mooning around in love like a sick puppy. They laughed at his dude manners. They made fun of his dainty appetite. When he dressed up in his finery to call on his girl, they stood in the bunkhouse door. They simpered and raised their eyebrows and said to one another, "La-dee-da, dearie, ain't we fine today!"

But for all their kidding they were brokenhearted. None of them had anything against Sue. They admired the way she rode a horse and played a guitar and danced a jig. But the thought of losing Bill to a woman was too much. Even worse was the thought that Bill might get married and bring a woman home to live with them. That was awful.

In spite of their teasing and the duchess's lessons, Bill asked Slue-Foot Sue to marry him. She accepted before he could back out. Her father, the lord, had always liked Bill and was terribly pleased at the match.

On his wedding day Pecos Bill shone like the sun in his new clothes. His boys were dressed in their finest chaps and boots for the occasion. Half of them were going to be groomsmen. The other half were going to be bridesmen. At first Bill asked them to be bridesmaids, but they refused. They said that was going too far.

They rode to the Perpetual Motion Ranch in a fine procession, Bill at the head on Widow-Maker. The white horse pranced and danced with excitement.

At the ranch house waited the rest of the wedding party. The lord had sent back to England for a bishop to perform the ceremony. There stood His Eminence in his lace robes. On his one hand stood the duke in a cutaway coat. On his other hand stood the duchess in a stiff purple gown right from Paris.

Down the stairs came the bride. She was a vision of beauty. She wore a white satin dress cut in the latest fashion. It had a long lace train, but its chief glory was a bustle. A bustle was a wire contraption that fitted under the back of the dress. It made the skirt stand out and was considered very handsome in those days.

As Slue-Foot Sue danced down the steps even the cowhands forgot their sorrow. They jumped down from their horses and swept their sombreros from their heads. Pecos Bill lost his head. He leapt down from Widow-Maker and ran to meet her. "You are lovely," he murmured. "I promise to grant you every wish you make."

That was a mistake. A devilish gleam twinkled in Sue's eye. For months she had been begging Bill to let her ride Widow-Maker. Bill, of course, had always refused.

Now Sue saw her chance. Before she allowed the wedding to proceed, she demanded that Bill give her one ride on his white mustang.

"No, no!" cried Pecos Bill. Before he could stop her Sue dashed down the drive and placed her dainty foot into the stirrup. The duchess screamed. The bishop turned pale.

Widow-Maker gave an angry snort. This was the second time the promise to him had been broken. He lifted his four feet off the ground and arched his back. Up, up, up shot Slue-Foot Sue. She disappeared into the clouds.

"Catch her, catch her!" roared Bill at the boys. They spread themselves out into a wide circle. Then from the sky came a scream like a siren. Down, down, down fell Sue. She hit the earth with terrible force. She landed on her bustle. The wire acted as a spring. It bounced. Up again she flew.

Up and down, up and down between the earth and sky Sue bounced like a rubber ball. Every time she fell her bustle hit first. Back she bounced. This went on for a week. When at last she came back to earth to stay, she was completely changed. She no longer loved Pecos Bill.

The wedding was called off and the boys returned to the I.X.L. with their unhappy boss. For months he refused to eat. He lost interest in cowpunching. He was the unhappiest man Texas had ever seen.

At last he called his hands together and made a long speech. He told them that the days of real cowpunching were over. The prairie was being fenced off by farmers. These "nesters," as he called them, were ruining the land for the ranchers. He was going to sell his herd.

The I.X.L. had its last roundup. Bill gathered all the prime steers together and put them on the train for Kansas City. Then he divided the cows and calves among his boys. He himself mounted Widow-Maker and rode away.

The boys hated to see him go, but they knew how he felt. "Nesters" or no "nesters," the real reason for his going was his broken heart.

None of them ever saw him again. Some of them thought he had gone back to the coyotes. Others had an idea that Slue-Foot Sue had changed her mind and that she and Bill were setting up housekeeping in some private canyon. But they never knew.

Some years later an old cowhand claimed that Bill had died. The great cowpuncher had met a dude rancher at a rodeo. The dude was dressed up in an outfit he had bought from a movie cowboy. The dude's chaps were made of doeskin. His boots were painted with landscapes and had heels three inches high. The brim of his hat was broad enough to cover a small circus. Bill took a good look at him and died laughing.

THE BOOMER FIREMAN'S
FAST SOONER HOUND

Children will enjoy Virginia Burton's pictures in Jack Conroy's and Arna Bontemps' book The Fast Sooner Hound. *They will also be entertained by that super horse, recorded in verse by Dick Jones and called* Platonia the Pride of the Plain.

In the days of the old railroad trains before diesel engines were ever thought of the fireman was an important man. A Boomer fireman could get him a job most anytime on most any railroad and was never long for any one road. Last year he might have worked for the Frisco, and this year he's heaving black diamonds for the Katy or the Wabash. He travelled light and travelled far and didn't let any grass grow under his feet when they got to itching for the greener pastures on the next road or the next division or maybe on the other side of the mountains. He didn't need furniture and he didn't need many clothes, and goodness knows he didn't need a family or a dog.

One day when one of these Boomer firemen pulled into the roadmaster's office looking for a job, there was that Sooner hound of his loping after him. That hound would sooner run than eat and he'd sooner eat than fight or do something useful like catching a rabbit. Not that a rabbit would have any chance if the Sooner really wanted to nail him, but that crazy hound

"The Boomer Fireman's Fast Sooner Hound," by Jack Conroy. From *A Treasury of American Folklore*, edited by B. A. Botkin. Crown Publishers, New York, 1944. Used with the kind permission of Jack Conroy

dog didn't like to do anything but run and he was the fastest thing on four legs.

"I might use you," said the roadmaster. "Can you get a boarding place for the dog?"

"Oh, he goes along with me," said the Boomer. "I raised him from a pup just like a mother or father and he ain't never spent a night or a day or even an hour far away from me. He'd cry like his poor heart would break and raise such a ruckus nobody couldn't sleep, eat or hear themselves think for miles about."

"Well, I don't see how that would work out," said the roadmaster. "It's against the rules of the road to allow a passenger in the cab, man or beast, or in the caboose and I aim to put you on a freight run so you can't ship him by express. Besides, he'd get the idea you wasn't nowhere about and pester folks out of their wits with his yipping and yowling. You look like a man that could keep a boiler popping off on an uphill grade, but I just don't see how we could work it if the hound won't listen to reason while you're on your runs."

"Why he ain't no trouble," said the Boomer. "He just runs alongside, and when I'm on a freight run he chases around a little in the fields to pass the time away. It's a little bit tiresome on him having to travel at such a slow gait, but that Sooner would do anything to stay close by me, he loves me that much."

"Oh, is that so? Well, don't try to tell that yarn around here," said the roadmaster.

"I'll lay my first paycheck against a fin[1] that he'll be fresh as a daisy and his tongue behind his teeth when we pull into the junction. He'll run around the station a hundred times or so to limber up."

"It's a bet," said the roadmaster.

On the first run the Sooner moved in what was a slow walk for him. He kept looking up into the cab where the Boomer was shoveling in the coal.

"He looks worried," said the Boomer. "He thinks the hog law[2] is going to catch us, we're making such bad time."

The roadmaster was so sore at losing the bet that he transferred the Boomer to a local passenger run and doubled the stakes. The Sooner

[1] Five dollar bill.—J. C.
[2] Rule forbidding excessive over time.—J. C.

speeded up to a slow trot, but he had to kill a lot of time, at that, not to get too far ahead of the engine.

Then the roadmaster got mad enough to bite off a drawbar. People got to watching the Sooner trotting alongside the train and began thinking it must be a mighty slow road. Passengers might just as well walk; they'd get there just as fast. And if you shipped a yearling calf to market, it'd be a bologna bull before it reached the stockyards. Of course, the trains were keeping up their schedules the same as usual, but that's the way it looked to people who saw a no-good mangy Sooner hound beating all the trains without his tongue hanging out an inch or letting out the least little pant.

It was giving the road a black eye, all right. The roadmaster would have fired the Boomer and told him to hit the grit with his Sooner and never come back again, but he was stubborn from the word go and hated worse than anything to own up he was licked.

"I'll fix that Sooner," said the roadmaster. "I'll slap the Boomer into the cab of the Cannon Ball, and if anything on four legs can keep up with the fastest thing on wheels I'd admire to see it. That Sooner'll be left so far behind it'll take nine dollars to send him a post card."

The word got around that the Sooner was going to try to keep up with the Cannon Ball. Farmers left off plowing, hitched up, and drove to the right of way to see the sight. It was like a circus day or the county fair. The schools all dismissed the pupils, and not a factory could keep enough men to make a wheel turn.

The roadmaster got right in the cab so that the Boomer couldn't soldier on the job to let the sooner keep up. A clear track for a hundred miles was ordered for the Cannon Ball, and all the switches were spiked down till after that streak of lightning had passed. It took three men to see the Cannon Ball on that run: one to say, "There she comes," one to say, "There she is," and another to say, "There she goes." You couldn't see a thing for steam, cinders and smoke, and the rails sang like a violin for a half hour after she'd passed into the next county.

Every valve was popping off and the wheels three feet in the air above the roadbed. The Boomer was so sure the Sooner would keep up

that he didn't stint the elbow grease; he wore the hinges off the fire door and fifteen pounds of him melted and ran right down into his shoes. He had his shovel whetted to a nub.

The roadmaster stuck his head out of the cab window, and—whosh!—off went his hat and almost his head. The suction like to have jerked his arms from their sockets as he nailed a-hold of the window seat.

It was all he could do to see, and gravel pinged against his goggles like hailstones, but he let out a whoop of joy.

"THE SOONER! THE SOONER!" he yelled. "He's gone! He's gone for true! Ain't *nowhere* in sight!"

"I can't understand that," hollered the Boomer. "He ain't *never* laid down on me yet. It just ain't like him to lay down on me. Leave me take a peek."

He dropped his shovel and poked out his head. Sure enough, the Sooner was nowhere to be seen. The Boomer's wild and troubled gaze swept far and wide.

"Don't see him, do you?" the roadmaster demanded. "He's at least seventy-six miles behind."

The Boomer didn't answer. He just threw his head back into the cab and began to shovel coal. He shoveled without much spirit, shaking his head sadly. There was no need for hard work, anyhow, for the Cannon Ball was puffing into the station at the end of the run.

Before the wheels had stopped rolling, the roadmaster jumped nimbly to the ground. A mighty cheer was heard from a group of people nearby. The roadmaster beamed as he drew near them.

"Here I am!" he shouted. "Where are the cameras? Do you want to take my picture in the cab?"

"Go way back and sit down!" a man shouted as he turned briefly toward the railroad official. "You might as well scrap that Cannon Ball. The Sooner has been here a good half hour and time has been hanging heavy on his hands. Look at him!"

The Sooner was loping easily around a tree, barking at a cat which had taken refuge in the branches and was spitting angrily. The Sooner didn't look even a mite tired, and his tongue was behind his teeth.

"I'm through! Enough is enough, boys!" the roadmaster sputtered. "The rule about passengers in the cab is a dead duck from now on. Let the Sooner ride in the cab as often and as far as he wants to."

The Cannon Ball chugged out of the station with the Boomer waving his shovel in salute and the Sooner yelping proudly beside him. The people cheered until the train disappeared around a bend.

Stories from "Uncle Remus"

The talking beast tales of Uncle Remus are a priceless treasure of Negro folk tales. Many of them had their origin in India, but undoubtedly most of them traveled to this country from Africa. Joel Chandler Harris, a native of Georgia, recorded them from the lips of Negro storytellers. He had an ear for language and a deep love for the philosophy, the canny understanding of human nature, and the humor of the Negroes. In these tales he has preserved the Negro's unsurpassed gifts for storytelling. The hero of the stories is Brer Rabbit, the weakest of all the animals. He is a trickster, but a lovable one, with no meanness in him, just a delight in playing pranks on his bigger neighbors. Occasionally, they turn the tables on him, but his wit and resourcefulness always save him. Those fortunate people who can read and understand the rich dialect in which these stories are recorded should always read or tell them in that form. But for those who find the dialect an impossible barrier to using the stories, two of the stories have been translated into everyday English with every possible effort to retain, in the process, some of the characteristic turns of speech which give the stories their unique charm. Perhaps the examples of translating the stories will encourage grownups who cannot manage the dialect to try the same process with more of the stories. The collection is too rich for children to miss, and every effort should be made to keep these stories in circulation.

THE WONDERFUL
TAR-BABY STORY

This is the best known of all the stories and a perennial favorite with children.

"Didn't the fox *never* catch the rabbit, Uncle Remus?" asked the little boy the next evening.

"He come mighty nigh it, honey, sho's you born—Brer Fox did. One day atter Brer Rabbit fool 'im wid dat calamus root, Brer Fox went ter wuk en got 'im some tar, en mix it wid some turkentime, en fix up a contrapshun wat he call a Tar-Baby, en he tuck dish yer Tar-Baby en he sot 'er in de big road, en den he lay off in de bushes fer to see what de news wuz gwineter be.

"The Wonderful Tar-Baby Story." From *Uncle Remus, His Songs and His Sayings* by Joel Chandler Harris

En he didn't hatter wait long, nudder, kaze bimeby here come Brer Rabbit pacin' down de road — lippity-clippity, clippity-lippity — dez ez sassy ez a jay-bird. Brer Fox, he lay low. Brer Rabbit come prancin' 'long twel he spy de Tar-Baby, en den he fotch up on his behime legs like he wus 'stonished. De Tar-Baby, she sot dar, she did, en Brer Fox, he lay low.

" 'Mawnin'!' sez Brer Rabbit, sezee—'nice wedder dis mawnin',' sezee.

"Tar-Baby ain't sayin' nothin', en Brer Fox, he lay low.

" 'How duz yo' sym'tums seem ter segashuate?' sez Brer Rabbit, sezee.

"Brer Fox, he wink his eye slow, en lay low, en de Tar-Baby, she ain't sayin' nothin'.

" 'How you come on, den? Is you deaf?' sez Brer Rabbit, sezee. 'Kaze if you is, I kin holler louder,' sezee.

"Tar-Baby stay still, en Brer Fox, he lay low.

" 'Youer stuck up, dat's w'at you is,' says Brer Rabbit, sezee, 'en I'm gwineter kyore you, dat's w'at I'm a gwineter do,' sezee.

"Brer Fox, he sorter chuckle in his stummick, he did, but Tar-Baby ain't sayin' nothin'.

" 'I'm gwineter larn you howter talk ter 'spect-tubble fokes ef hit's de las' ack,' sez Brer Rabbit, sezee. 'Ef you don't take off dat hat en tell me howdy, I'm gwineter bus' you wide open,' sezee.

"Tar-Baby stay still, en Brer Fox, he lay low.

"Brer Rabbit keep on axin' 'im, en de Tar-Baby, she keep on sayin' nothin', twel present'y Brer Rabbit draw back wid his fis', he did, en blip he tuck 'er side er de head. Right dar's what he broke his merlasses jug. His fis' stuck, en he can't pull loose. De tar hilt 'im. But Tar-Baby, she stay still, en Brer Fox, he lay low.

" 'Ef you don't lemme loose, I'll knock you agin,' sez Brer Rabbit, sezee, en wid dat he fotch 'er a wipe wid de udder han', en dat stuck. Tar-Baby, she ain't sayin' nothin', en Brer Fox, he lay low.

" 'Tu'n me loose, fo' I kick de natal stuffin' outen you,' sez Brer Rabbit, sezee, but de Tar-Baby, she ain't sayin' nothin'. She des hilt on, en den Brer Rabbit lose de use er his feet in de same way. Brer Fox, he lay low. Den Brer Rabbit squall out dat ef de Tar-Baby don't tu'n 'im loose he butt 'er cranksided. En den he butted, en his head got stuck. Den Brer Fox, he sa'ntered fort', lookin' des ez innercent ez one er yo' mammy's mockin'-birds.

" 'Howdy, Brer Rabbit,' sez Brer Fox, sezee. 'You look sorter stuck up dis mawnin',' sezee, en den he rolled on de groun', en laughed en laughed twel he couldn't laugh no mo'. 'I speck you'll take dinner wid me dis time, Brer Rabbit. I done laid in some calamus root, en I ain't gwineter take no skuse,' sez Brer Fox, sezee."

Here Uncle Remus paused, and drew a two-pound yam out of the ashes.

"Did the fox eat the rabbit?" asked the little boy to whom the story had been told.

"Dat's all de fur de tale goes," replied the old man. "He mout, en den again he moutent. Some say Jedge B'ar come long en loosed 'im—some say he didn't. I hear Miss Sally callin'. You better run 'long."

HOW MR. RABBIT WAS TOO SHARP FOR MR. FOX

"Uncle Remus," said the little boy one evening, when he had found the old man with little or nothing to do, "did the fox kill and eat the rabbit when he caught him with the Tar-Baby?"

"Law, honey, ain't I tell you 'bout dat?" replied the old darkey, chuckling slyly. "I 'clar ter grashus I ought er tole you dat, but old man Nod wuz ridin' on my eyeleds 'twel a leetle mo'n I'd a dis'member'd my own name, en den on to dat here come yo' mammy hollerin' atter you.

"W'at I tell you w'en I fus' begin? I tole you Brer Rabbit wuz a monstus soon creetur; leas'ways dat's w'at I laid out fer ter tell you. Well, den, honey, don't you go en make no udder calkalashuns, kaze in dem days Brer Rabbit en his fambly wuz at de head er de gang w'en enny racket wuz on han', en dar dey stayed. 'Fo' you begins fer ter wipe yo' eyes 'bout Brer Rabbit, you wait en see whar'bouts Brer Rabbit gwineter fetch up at. But dat's needer yer ner dar.

"W'en Brer Fox fine Brer Rabbit mixt up wid de Tar-Baby, he feel mighty good, en he roll on de groun' en laff. Bimeby he up'n say, sezee:

" 'Well, I speck I got you dis time, Brer Rabbit, sezee; 'maybe I ain't, but I speck I is. You been runnin' roun' here sassin' atter me a mighty long time, but I speck you done come ter de en' er de row. You bin cuttin' up yo' capers en bouncin' 'roun' in dis neighberhood ontwel you come ter b'leeve yo'se'f de boss er de whole gang. En den youer allers some'rs whar you got no bizness,' sez Brer Fox, sezee. 'Who ax you fer ter come en strike up a 'quaintance wid dish yer Tar-Baby? En who stuck you up dar whar you iz? Nobody in de roun' worril. You des tuck en jam yo'se'f on dat Tar-Baby widout waitin' fer enny invite,' sez Brer Fox, sezee, 'en dar you is, en dar you'll stay twel I fixes up a bresh-pile and fires her up, kaze I'm gwineter bobby-cue you dis day, sho,' sez Brer Fox, sezee.

"Den Brer Rabbit talk mighty 'umble.

" 'I don't keer w'at you do wid me, Brer Fox,' sezee, 'so you don't fling me in dat brier-patch.

"How Mr. Rabbit Was Too Sharp for Mr. Fox." From *Uncle Remus, His Songs and His Sayings* by Joel Chandler Harris

Roas' me, Brer Fox,' sezee, 'but don't fling me in dat brier-patch,' sezee.

" 'Hit's so much trouble fer ter kindle a fier,' sez Brer Fox, sezee, 'dat I speck I'll hatter hang you,' sezee.

" 'Hang me des ez high as you please, Brer Fox,' sez Brer Rabbit, sezee, 'but do fer de Lord's sake don't fling me in dat brier-patch,' sezee.

" 'I ain't got no string,' sez Brer Fox, sezee, 'en now I speck I'll hatter drown you,' sezee.

" 'Drown me des ez deep ez you please, Brer Fox,' sez Brer Rabbit, sezee, 'but do don't fling me in dat brier-patch,' sezee.

" 'Dey ain't no water nigh,' sez Brer Fox, sezee, 'en now I speck I'll hatter skin you,' sezee.

" 'Skin me, Brer Fox,' sez Brer Rabbit, sezee, 'snatch out my eyeballs, t'ar out my years by de roots, en cut off my legs,' sezee, 'but do please, Brer Fox, don't fling me in dat brier-patch,' sezee.

"Co'se Brer Fox wanter hurt Brer Rabbit bad ez he kin, so he cotch 'im by de behime legs en slung 'im right in de middle er de brier-patch. Dar wuz a considerbul flutter whar Brer Rabbit struck de bushes, en Brer Fox sorter hang 'roun' fer ter see w'at wuz gwineter happen. Bimeby he hear somebody call 'im, en way up de hill he see Brer Rabbit settin' cross-legged on a chinkapin log koamin' de pitch outen his har wid a chip. Den Brer Fox know dat he bin swop off mighty bad. Brer Rabbit wuz bleedzed fer ter fling back some er his sass, en he holler out:

" 'Bred en bawn in a brier-patch, Brer Fox—bred en bawn in a brier-patch!' en wid dat he skip out des ez lively ez a cricket in de embers."

THE WONDERFUL

TAR-BABY STORY[1]

Brer Fox was always fixing some way to catch Brer Rabbit so, one day Brer Fox went to work and got him some tar, and mixed it with turpentine, and fixed up a contraption that he called a Tar-Baby. He took this here Tar-Baby and sat him in the big road, and then he laid off in the bushes for to see what the news was going to be. He didn't have to wait long, neither, for by and

[1] Adapted by May Hill Arbuthnot from the two preceding stories.

by here came Brer Rabbit pacing down the road —*lippity-clippity, clippity-lippity*—just as sassy as a jay-bird. Brer Fox he lay low. Brer Rabbit came prancing along till he spied the Tar-Baby, and then he fetched up on his hind legs like he was astonished. The Tar-Baby, she sat there, she did, and Brer Fox he lay low.

"Morning!" says Brer Rabbit, says he—"nice weather this morning," says he.

Tar-Baby says nothing, and Brer Fox, he lay low.

"How does your symptoms seem to segashuate?" says Brer Rabbit, says he.

Brer Fox, he winked his eye slow, and lay low, and the Tar-Baby, she says nothing.

"How you come on, then? Are you deaf?" says Brer Rabbit, says he. " 'Cause if you are, I can holler louder," says he.

Tar-Baby stay still, and Brer Fox he lay low.

"You're stuck up, that's what you are," says Brer Rabbit, says he, "and I'm going to cure you, that's what I'm going to do," says he.

Brer Fox, he sort of chuckled in his stomach, he did, but Tar-Baby, she says nothing.

"I'm going to learn you how to talk to respectable folks if it's my last act," says Brer Rabbit, says he. "If you don't take off that hat and tell me howdy, I'm going to bust you wide open," says he.

Tar-Baby stay still, and Brer Fox, he lay low.

Brer Rabbit keeps on asking, and the Tar-Baby, she keep on saying nothing, till presently Brer Rabbit draw back with his fist, he did, and *blip* he took her on the side of the head. Right there's where he broke his molasses jug. His fist stuck, and he can't pull loose. The tar held him. But Tar-Baby, she stay still, and Brer Fox, he lay low.

"If you don't let me loose, I'll knock you again," says Brer Rabbit, says he, and with that he fetched a swipe with the other hand, and that stuck fast. Tar-Baby, she say nothing, and Brer Fox, he lay low.

"Turn me loose, before I kick the natural stuffing out of you," says Brer Rabbit, says he, but Tar-Baby, she say nothing. She just held on, and then Brer Rabbit lose the use of his two feet the same way. Brer Fox, he lay low. Then Brer Rabbit squall out that if the Tar-Baby don't turn him loose, he'll butt her cranksided.

And then he butted, and his head got stuck. And there he was. And Brer Fox he sauntered forth looking just as innocent as a mocking-bird.

"Howdy, Brer Rabbit," says Brer Fox, says he. "You look sort of stuck up this morning," says he, and then he rolled on the ground and he laughed and laughed till he couldn't laugh any more. "Well, I 'spect I got you this time, Brer Rabbit," says he; "maybe I ain't but maybe I is. You've been running round here sassing me for a mighty long time but I 'spect you've come to the end of the row. You've been cutting up capers and bouncing round this neighborhood till you've come to believe you're the boss of the whole gang. And then you're always somewhere where you got no business to be," says Brer Fox, says he. "Who asked you to come and strike up an acquaintance with the Tar-Baby? And who stuck you up there where you are? Nobody in the round world. You just took and jammed yourself on that Tar-Baby without waiting for an invitation," says Brer Fox, says he, "And there's where you are, and there you'll stay, till I fix up a brush pile and fires her up, 'cause I'm going to barbecue you this day, sure," says Brer Fox, says he.

Then Brer Rabbit talked mighty humble.

"I don't care what you do with me, Brer Fox," says he, "just so you don't fling me in that brier-patch. Roast me, Brer Fox," says he, "but don't fling me in that brier-patch," says he.

"It's so much trouble for to kindle a fire," says Brer Fox, says he, "that I 'spect I'll have to hang you," says he.

"Hang me just as high as you please, Brer Fox," says Brer Rabbit, says he, "but for the land sakes, don't fling me in that brier-patch."

"I ain't got any string," says Brer Fox, says he, "and now I 'spect I'll have to drown you," says he.

"Drown me just as deep as you please, Brer Fox," says Brer Rabbit, says he, "but don't fling me in that brier-patch," says he.

"There ain't any water nearby," says Brer Fox, says he, "and now I 'spect I'll have to skin you," says he.

"Skin me, Brer Fox," says Brer Rabbit, says he, "snatch out my eyeballs, tear out my hair by the roots, cut off my legs," says he, "but please, Brer Fox, please don't fling me in that brier-patch," says he.

Of course Brer Fox wanted to hurt Brer Rabbit as bad as he could so he caught him by the hind legs and slung him right in the middle of the brier-patch. There was a considerable flutter where Brer Rabbit struck the bushes, and Brer Fox sort of hung around to see what was going to happen. By and by he heard someone call him, way up the hill, and he saw Brer Rabbit sitting cross-legged on a chinkapin log combing the pitch out of his hair with a chip. Then Brer Fox knew he'd been fooled mighty bad. And

Brer Rabbit was obliged to fling back some of his sass, so he hollered out:

"Bred and born in the brier-patch, Brer Fox —bred and born in the brier-patch!" and with that he skipped out as lively as a cricket in the embers.

"HEYO, HOUSE!"

"I don't think Brother Lion had much sense," remarked the little boy after awhile.

"Yit he had some," responded Uncle Remus. "He bleedz ter had some, but he ain't got much ez Brer Rabbit. Dem what got strenk ain't got so mighty much sense. You take niggers—dey er lots stronger dan what white folks is. I ain't so strong myse'f," remarked the old man, with a sly touch of vanity that was lost on the little boy, "but de common run er niggers is lots stronger dan white folks. Yit I done tuck notice in my time dat what white folks calls sense don't turn out ter be sense eve'y day en Sunday too. I ain't never see de patter-roller what kin keep up wid me. He may go hoss-back, he may go foot-back, it don't make no diffunce ter me. Dey never is kotch me yit, en when dey does, I'll let you know.

"Dat de way wid Brer Rabbit," Uncle Remus went on, after a pause. "De few times what he been outdone he mighty willin' fer ter let um talk 'bout it, ef it'll do um any good. Dem what outdo 'im got de right ter brag, en he ain't make no deniance un it.

"Atter he done make way wid ole Brer Lion, all de yuther creeturs say he sholy is a mighty man, en dey treat 'im good. Dis make 'im feel so proud dat he bleedz ter show it, en so he strut 'roun' like a boy when he git his fust pa'r er boots.

"'Bout dat time, Brer Wolf tuck a notion dat ef Brer Rabbit kin outdo ole Brer Lion, he can't outdo him. So he pick his chance one day whiles ole Miss Rabbit en de little Rabs is out pickin' sallid fer dinner. He went in de house, he did, en wait fer Brer Rabbit ter come home. Brer Rabbit had his hours, en dis wuz one un um, en 'twan't long 'fo' here he come. He got a mighty quick eye, mon, en he tuck notice dat ev'ything

"Heyo, House!" From *Uncle Remus and His Friends* by Joel Chandler Harris

mighty still. When he got little nigher, he tuck notice dat de front door wuz on de crack, en dis make 'im feel funny, kaze he know dat when his ole 'oman en de chillun out, dey allers pulls de door shet en ketch de latch. So he went up a little nigher, en he step thin ez a batter-cake. He peep here, en he peep dar, yit he ain't see nothin'. He lissen in de chimbley cornder, en he lissen und' de winder, yit he ain't hear nothin'.

"Den he sorter wipe his mustach en study. He 'low ter hisse'f, 'De pot rack know what gwine on up de chimbley, de rafters know who's in de loft, de bed-cord know who und' de bed. I ain't no pot-rack, I ain't no rafter, en I ain't no bed-cord, but, please gracious! I'm gwine ter fin' who's in dat house, en I ain't gwine in dar nudder. Dey mo' ways ter fin' out who fell in de mill-pond widout fallin' in yo'se'f.'

"Some folks," Uncle Remus went on, "would 'a' rushed in dar, en ef dey had, dey wouldn't 'a' rushed out no mo', kaze dey wouldn't 'a' been nothin' 'tall lef' un um but a little scrap er hide en a han'ful er ha'r.

"Brer Rabbit got better sense dan dat. All he ax anybody is ter des gi' 'im han'-roomance, en dem what kin ketch 'im is mo' dan welly-come ter take 'im. Dat 'zackly de kinder man what Brer Rabbit is. He went off a little ways fum de house en clum a 'simmon stump en got up dar en 'gun ter holler.

"He 'low, 'Heyo, house!'

"De house ain't make no answer, en Brer Wolf, in dar behime de door, open his eyes wide. He ain't know what ter make er dat kinder doin's.

"Brer Rabbit holler, 'Heyo, house! Whyn't you heyo?'

"House ain't make no answer, en Brer Wolf in dar behime de door sorter move roun' like he gittin' restless in de min'.

"Brer Rabbit out dar on de 'simmon stump holler mo' louder dan befo', 'Heyo, house! Heyo!'

"House stan' still, en Brer Wolf in dar behime de door 'gun ter feel col' chills streakin' up and down his back. In all his born days he ain't never hear no gwines on like dat. He peep thoo de crack er de door, but he can't see nothin'.

"Brer Rabbit holler louder, 'Heyo, house! Ain't you gwine ter heyo? Is you done los' what little manners you had?'

"Brer Wolf move 'bout wuss'n befo'. He feel des like some un done hit 'im on de funny-bone.

"Brer Rabbit holler hard ez he kin, but still he ain't git no answer, en den he 'low, 'Sholy sump'n nudder is de matter wid dat house, kaze all de times befo' dis, it been holler'n back at me, Heyo, yo'se'f!'

"Den Brer Rabbit wait little bit, en bimeby he holler one mo' time, 'Heyo, house!'

"Ole Brer Wolf try ter talk like he speck a house 'ud talk, en he holler back, 'Heyo, yo'se'f!'

"Brer Rabbit wunk at hisse'f. He 'low, 'Heyo, house! Whyn't you talk hoarse like you got a bad col'?'

"Den Brer Wolf holler back, hoarse ez he kin, 'Heyo, yo'se'f!'

"Dis make Brer Rabbit laugh twel a little mo' en he'd a drapt off'n dat ar 'simmon stump en hurt hisse'f.

"He 'low, 'Eh-eh, Brer Wolf! dat ain't nigh gwine ter do. You'll hatter stan' out in de rain a mighty long time 'fo' you kin talk hoarse ez dat house!'

"I let you know," continued Uncle Remus, laying his hand gently on the little boy's shoulder, "I let you know, Brer Wolf come a-slinkin' out, en made a break fer home. Atter dat, Brer Rabbit live a long time wid'out any er de yuther creeturs a-pesterin' un 'im!"

BROTHER RABBIT'S
ASTONISHING PRANK

"I 'speck dat 'uz de reas'n w'at make ole Brer Rabbit git 'long so well, kaze he aint copy atter none er de yuther creeturs," Uncle Remus continued, after a while. "W'en he make his disappearance 'fo' um, hit 'uz allers in some bran new place. Dey aint know wharbouts fer ter watch out fer 'im. He wuz de funniest creetur er de whole gang. Some folks moughter call him lucky, en yit, w'en he git in bad luck, hit look lak he mos' allers come out on top. Hit look mighty kuze now, but 'twa'n't kuse in dem days, kaze hit 'uz done gun up dat, strike 'im w'en you might en whar you would, Brer Rabbit wuz de soopless creetur gwine.

"Brother Rabbit's Astonishing Prank." From *Nights with Uncle Remus* by Joel Chandler Harris

"One time, he sorter tuck a notion, ole Brer Rabbit did, dat he'd pay Brer B'ar a call, en no sooner do de notion strike 'im dan he pick hisse'f up en put out fer Brer B'ar house."

"Why, I thought they were mad with each other," the little boy exclaimed.

"Brer Rabbit make he call w'en Brer B'ar en his fambly wuz off fum home," Uncle Remus explained, with a chuckle which was in the nature of a hearty tribute to the crafty judgment of Brother Rabbit.

"He sot down by de road, en he see um go by, —ole Brer B'ar en ole Miss B'ar, en der two twin-chilluns, w'ich one un um wuz name Kubs en de t'er one wuz name Klibs."

The little boy laughed, but the severe seriousness of Uncle Remus would have served for a study, as he continued:

"Ole Brer B'ar en Miss B'ar, dey went 'long ahead, en Kubs en Klibs, dey come shufflin' en scramblin' 'long behime. W'en Brer Rabbit see dis, he say ter hisse'f dat he 'speck he better go see how Brer B'ar gittin' on; en off he put. En 'twa'n't long n'er 'fo' he 'uz ransackin' de premuses same like he 'uz sho' 'nuff patter-roller. W'iles he wuz gwine 'roun' peepin' in yer en pokin' in dar, he got ter foolin' 'mong de shelfs, en a bucket er honey w'at Brer B'ar got hid in de cubbud fall down en spill on top er Brer Rabbit, en little mo'n he'd er bin drown. Fum head ter heels dat creetur wuz kiver'd wid honey; he wa'n't des only bedobble wid it, he wuz des kiver'd. He hatter set dar en let de natal sweetness drip outen he eyeballs 'fo' he kin see he han' befo' 'im, en den, atter he look 'roun' little, he say to hisse'f, sezee:

"'Heyo, yer! W'at I gwine do now? Ef I go out in de sunshine, de bumly-bees en de flies dey'll swom up'n take me, en if I stay yer, Brer B'ar'll come back en ketch me, en I dunner w'at in de name er gracious I gwine do.'

"Ennyhow, bimeby a notion strike Brer Rabbit, en he tip 'long twel he git in de woods, en w'en he git out dar, w'at do he do but roll in de leafs en trash en try fer ter rub de honey off'n 'im dat a-way. He roll, he did, en de leafs dey stick; Brer Rabbit roll, en de leafs dey stick, en he keep on rollin' en de leafs keep on stickin', twel atter w'ile Brer Rabbit wuz de mos' owdashus-lookin' creetur w'at you ever sot eyes on.

En ef Miss Meadows en de gals could er seed 'im den en dar, dey wouldn't er bin no mo' Brer Rabbit call at der house; 'deed, en dat dey wouldn't.

"Brer Rabbit, he jump 'roun', he did, en try ter shake de leafs off'n 'im, but de leafs, dey aint gwine ter be shuck off. Brer Rabbit, he shake en he shiver, but de leafs dey stick; en de capers dat creetur cut up out dar in de woods by he own-alone se'f wuz scan'lous—dey wuz dat; dey wuz scan'lous.

"Brer Rabbit see dis wa'n't gwine ter do, en he 'low ter hisse'f dat he better be gittin' on todes home, en off he put. I 'speck you done year talk ez deze yer booggers w'at gits atter bad chilluns," continued Uncle Remus, in a tone so seriously confidential as to be altogether depressing; "well, den, des 'zactly dat a-way Brer Rabbit look, en ef you'd er seed 'im you'd er made sho' he de gran'-daddy er all de booggers. Brer Rabbit pace 'long, he did, en ev'y motion he make, de leafs dey'd go *swishy-swushy, splushy-splishy,* en, fum de fuss he make en de way he look, you'd er tuck 'im ter be de mos' suvvigus varment w'at disappear fum de face er de yeth sence ole man Noah let down de draw-bars er de ark en tu'n de creeturs loose; en I boun' ef you'd er struck up long wid 'im, you'd er been mighty good en glad ef you'd er got off wid dat.

"De fus' man w'at Brer Rabbit come up wid wuz ole Sis Cow, en no sooner is she lay eyes on 'im dan she h'ist up 'er tail in de elements, en put out like a pack er dogs wuz atter 'er. Dis make Brer Rabbit laff, kaze he know dat w'en a ole settle' 'oman like Sis Cow run 'stracted in de broad open day-time, dat dey mus' be sump'n' mighty kuse 'bout dem leafs en dat honey, en he keep on a-rackin' down de road. De nex' man w'at he meet wuz a black gal tollin' a whole passel er plantation shotes, en w'en de gal see Brer Rabbit come prancin' 'long, she fling down 'er basket er corn en des fa'rly fly, en de shotes, dey tuck thoo de woods, en sech n'er racket ez dey kick up wid der runnin', en der snortin', en der squealin' aint never bin year in dat settlement needer befo' ner since. Hit keep on dis a-way long ez Brer Rabbit meet anybody—dey des broke en run like de Ole Boy wuz atter um.

"C'ose, dis make Brer Rabbit feel monst'us biggity, en he 'low ter hisse'f dat he 'speck he better drap 'roun' en skummish in de neighborhoods er Brer Fox house. En w'iles he wuz stannin' dar runnin' dis 'roun' in he min', yer come old Brer B'ar en all er he fambly. Brer Rabbit, he git crossways de road, he did, en he sorter sidle todes um. Ole Brer B'ar, he stop en look, but Brer Rabbit, he keep on sidlin' todes um. Ole Miss B'ar, she stan' it long ez she kin, en den she fling down 'er parrysol en tuck a tree. Brer B'ar look lak he gwine ter stan' his groun', but Brer Rabbit he jump straight up in de a'r en gin hisse'f a shake, en, bless yo' soul, honey! ole Brer B'ar make a break, en dey tells me he to' down a whole panel er fence gittin' 'way fum dar. En ez ter Kubs en Klibs, dey tuck der hats in der han's, en dey went skaddlin' thoo de bushes des same ez a drove er hosses."

"And then what?" the little boy asked.

"Brer Rabbit p'raded on down de road," continued Uncle Remus, "en bimeby yer come Brer Fox en Brer Wolf, fixin' up a plan fer ter nab Brer Rabbit, en dey wuz so intents on der confab dat dey got right on Brer Rabbit 'fo' dey seed 'im; but, gentermens! w'en dey is ketch a glimpse un 'im, dey gun 'im all de room he want. Brer Wolf, he try ter show off, he did, kase he wanter play big 'fo' Brer Fox, en he stop en ax Brer Rabbit who is he. Brer Rabbit, he jump up en down in de middle er de road, en holler out:

" 'I'm de Wull-er-de-Wust. I'm de Wull-er-de-Wust, en youer de man I'm atter!'

"Den Brer Rabbit jump up en down en make lak he gwine atter Brer Fox en Brer Wolf, en de way dem creeturs lit out fum dar wuz a caution.

"Long time atter dat," continued Uncle Remus, folding his hands placidly in his lap, with the air of one who has performed a pleasant duty,—"long time atter dat, Brer Rabbit come up wid Brer Fox en Brer Wolf, en he git behime a stump, Brer Rabbit did, en holler out:

" 'I'm de Wull-er-de-Wust, en youer de mens I'm atter!'

"Brer Fox en Brer Wolf, dey broke, but 'fo' dey got outer sight en outer year'n', Brer Rabbit show hisse'f, he did, en laugh fit ter kill hisse'f. Atterwuds, Miss Meadows she year 'bout it, en de nex' time Brer Fox call, de gals dey up en giggle, en ax 'im ef he aint feard de Wull-er-de-Wust mought drap in."

MR. RABBIT

MEETS HIS MATCH AGAIN

"Dere wuz nudder man dat sorter play it sharp on Brer Rabbit," said Uncle Remus, as, by some mysterious process, he twisted a hog's bristle into the end of a piece of thread—an operation which the little boy watched with great interest. "In dem days," continued the old man, "de creeturs kyar'd on marters same ez fokes. Dey went inter fahmin', en I speck ef de troof wuz ter come out, dey kep' sto', en had der camp-meetin' times en der bobbycues' w'en de wedder wuz 'greeble."

Uncle Remus evidently thought that the little boy wouldn't like to hear of any further discomfiture of Brer Rabbit, who had come to be a sort of hero, and he was not mistaken.

"I thought the Terrapin was the only one that fooled the Rabbit," said the little boy, dismally.

"Hit's des like I tell you, honey. Dey ain't no smart man, 'cep' w'at dey's a smarter. Ef ole Brer Rabbit hadn't er got kotch up wid, de nabers 'ud er took 'im for a h'ant, en in dem times dey bu'nt witches 'fo' you could squinch yo' eyeballs. Dey did dat."

"Who fooled the Rabbit this time?" the little boy asked.

When Uncle Remus had the bristle "sot" in the thread, he proceeded with the story.

"One time Brer Rabbit en ole Brer Buzzard 'cluded dey'd sorter go snacks, en crap tergedder. Hit wuz a mighty good year, en de truck tu'n out monstus well, but bimeby, w'en de time come fer dividjun, hit come ter light dat ole Brer Buzzard ain't got nuthin'. De crap wuz all gone, en dey want nuthin' dar fer ter show fer it. Brer Rabbit, he make like he in a wuss fix'n Brer Buzzard, en he mope 'roun', he did, like he fear'd dey gwineter sell 'im out.

"Brer Buzzard, he ain't sayin' nuthin', but he

"Mr. Rabbit Meets His Match Again." From *Uncle Remus, His Songs and His Sayings* by Joel Chandler Harris

keep up a monstus thinkin', en one day he come 'long en holler en tell Brer Rabbit dat he done fine rich gole-mine des' cross de river.

"'You come en go 'longer me, Brer Rabbit,' sez Brer Tukky Buzzard, sezee. 'I'll scratch en you kin grabble, en 'tween de two un us we'll make short wuk er dat gole-mine,' sezee.

"Brer Rabbit, he wuz high up fer de job, but he study en study, he did, how he gwineter git 'cross de water, kaze ev'y time he git his foot wet all de fambly kotch cole. Den he up'n ax Brer Buzzard how he gwine do, en Brer Buzzard he up'n say dat he kyar Brer Rabbit 'cross, en wid dat ole Brer Buzzard, he squot down, he did, en spread his wings, en Brer Rabbit, he mounted, en up dey riz." There was a pause.

"What did the Buzzard do then?" asked the little boy.

"Dey riz," continued Uncle Remus, "en w'en dey lit, dey lit in de top er de highest sorter pine, en de pine w'at dey lit in wuz growin' on er ilun, en de ilun wuz in de middle er de river, wid de deep water runnin' all 'roun'. Dey ain't mo'n lit 'fo' Brer Rabbit, he know w'ich way de win' 'uz blowin', en by de time ole Brer Buzzard got his-se'f ballunce on a lim', Brer Rabbit, he up'n say, sezee:

"'W'iles we er res'n here, Brer Buzzard, en bein's you bin so good, I got sump'n fer ter tell you,' sezee. 'I got a gole-mine er my own, one w'at I make myse'f, en I speck we better go back ter mine 'fo' we bodder 'longer yone,' sezee.

"Den ole Brer Buzzard, he laff, he did, twel he shake, en Brer Rabbit, he sing out:

"'Hole on, Brer Buzzard! Don't flop yo' wings w'en you laff, kaze den if you duz, sump'n 'ill drap fum up yer, en my gole-mine won't do you no good, en needer will yone do me no good.'

"But 'fo' dey got down fum dar, Brer Rabbit done tole all 'bout de crap, en he hatter promus fer ter 'vide fa'r en squar. So Brer Buzzard, he kyar 'im back, en Brer Rabbit he walk weak in de knees a mont' atterwuds."

Of all forms of fiction, the fable is the most pedantic and the least appealing to children. It is a lesson in behavior, a kind of sugar-coated moral pill, large doses of which are hard to take. Yet presented occasionally, among other and livelier kinds of stories, fables are not unpalatable. They offer a shrewd appraisal of motives and behavior. Their canny and satiric comments on folly are amusing, and wise behavior is picturesquely presented. Such fables as "The Dog in the Manger," "The Wolf in Sheep's Clothing," "The Fox and the Crow," and "The Hare and the Tortoise" are never forgotten. These and many others have come to occupy a permanent place in our thinking and our speech. Children

OLD MORALITIES: THE FABLES

should know the fables because they contain the distilled wisdom of the ages in striking and memorable form.

Fables might be defined as brief narratives which attempt to make abstract ideas of good or bad, wise or foolish behavior, concrete and sufficiently striking to be understood and remembered. But because they are concerned with abstract ideas of good and evil they are not readily understood by most children until the episodes and their significance have been talked over. Sometimes the characters are men, sometimes, the elements, but chiefly, they are animals. Whatever they are, the characters of a fable are as impersonal and abstract as an algebraic equation. It is never Peter Rabbit with his little brothers and sisters, Flopsy, Mopsy, and Cottontail. It is merely RABBIT and you never care whether RABBIT has a family or is an orphan. He is simply RABBIT. This abstract, impersonal quality of the fable does not appeal to small children, and the obvious intention of teaching a moral lesson grows tiresome if the fables are used too often or with too heavy a hand.

Sources and values

The great fable sources are Aesop, *The Panchatantra,* the *Jatakas,* and La Fontaine,[1] but to most English-speaking people, fables and Aesop are synonymous. A fourteenth-century monk by the name of Planudes added to a collection of fables, supposedly by Aesop, a story of the man's life. Its authenticity is now considered doubtful, and perhaps there never was such a man as the Greek slave Aesop. Picturesque legends about him continued to grow, however, and we like to ascribe those wise and witty stories to some specific source. So, authentic or not, his name goes right on appearing on each new edition and people keep right on hoping that it was an obscure slave, ugly and perhaps deformed as the legends describe him, who collected these priceless tales which mirror man's foibles so relentlessly.

From the time they were collected, translated into Latin in the first or third centuries, and used as a textbook in the medieval schools, the popularity of Aesop's fables has never waned. Undoubtedly adults sensed their teaching values and offered them to children and youth, generation after generation, as guides to wise conduct. Today, there are innumerable beautiful editions of Aesop's fables illustrated by distinguished artists. Appealing as these books are, children should not be expected to sit down and read

[1] See May Hill Arbuthnot, *Children and Books,* pp. 282–288.

them as a whole. They are tiresome when tackled in such a fashion. Fables are for occasional use and they should be presented and discussed with a light touch and the minimum of pedantry. But as carriers of the moral code they are still unforgettable.

Using fables with children

Fables, because they are abstractions, brief sermons on morality, are the least appealing of all story types to children. They are attempting to make abstract ideas striking enough to be understood and remembered.

For young children, five- to nine- or ten-years-old, use anywhere from two to five or six fables a year. Choose those that have the maximum story interest, like "The Lion and the Mouse," and talk the story over without moralizing, just to make sure that the children appreciate the fact that sometimes very small creatures may be useful and helpful and are not to be scorned because they are small and seemingly unimportant.

With older children, the purpose of the fable may be discussed frankly. Then it is fun to have one child read a fable to the whole group and see if the class can make up a pithy moral. Let these upper grade or high school students discover also that fables are still being written. Read them the "Copy-Kitten," p. 281 or "Nothing at All," p. 281 or even Hans Christian Andersen's "The Ugly Duckling," p. 311, to illustrate this point. They will also find it interesting to compare different versions of the same fable, for example, Aesop's "The Fox and the Crow," p. 225 and La Fontaine's version of this tale, p. 232.

When they are still older, children will begin to see how the fable may have grown out of the proverb, which is the most highly condensed commentary on human folly or wisdom, or may develop into an allegory. They will see its similarity to the parable, which also tells a brief story from which a moral truth may be inferred. But in this field of abstract virtues and moral lessons, children are easily bewildered and never too comfortable. The baffled child who defines an allegory as ". . . a story where everything is what it ain't," should be a lesson to grownups. A few fables, a few abstractions go a long way with children.

Aesop's fables

*"The Lion and the Mouse" and "The Town Mouse and the Country
Mouse" are well liked by the five- and six-year-olds because they are simple little
stories and the morals are not too obtrusive. The other fables might
well appear in almost any order you like, three or four a year. Perhaps the moral
of "The Fox and the Grapes," "The Wolf in Sheep's Clothing," "The
Milkmaid and Her Pail," and "The Dog in the Manger" are a little too subtle for
young children and are better reserved for the oldest children. Be
sure to bring from the library some of the illustrated editions of the fables. John
Averill, who illustrated the fables in this section, has stylized the characters with great humor, and after all, the fables are highly stylized stories. It might
be an interesting art project for the oldest children to compare the
fable pictures in three or four major editions and then try some of their own.*

THE HARE WITH MANY FRIENDS

A Hare was very popular with the other beasts who all claimed to be her friends. But one day she heard the hounds approaching and hoped to escape them by the aid of her many friends. So she went to the horse, and asked him to carry her away from the hounds on his back. But he declined, stating that he had important work to do for his master. He felt sure, he said, that all her other friends would come to her assistance. She then applied to the bull, and hoped that he would repel the hounds with his horns. The bull replied: "I am very sorry, but I have an appointment with a lady; but I feel sure that our friend the goat will do what you want." The goat, however, feared that his back might do her some harm if he took her upon it. The ram, he felt sure, was the proper friend to apply to. So she went to the ram and told him the case. The ram replied: "Another time, my dear friend. I do not like to interfere on the present occasion, as hounds have been known to eat sheep as well as hares." The Hare then applied, as a last hope, to the calf, who regretted that he was unable to help her, as he did not like to take the responsibility upon himself, as so many older persons than himself had declined the task. By this time the

"The Hare with Many Friends" and "The Ant and the Grasshopper." From *The Fables of Aesop,* edited by Joseph Jacobs, Macmillan, 1950. By permission of The Macmillan Company, New York and Macmillan & Co. Ltd., London

hounds were quite near, and the Hare took to her heels and luckily escaped.

"He that has many friends has no friends."

THE ANT
AND THE GRASSHOPPER

In a field one summer's day a Grasshopper was hopping about, chirping and singing to its heart's content. An Ant passed by, bearing along with great toil a grain of corn he was taking to the nest.

"Why not come and chat with me," said the Grasshopper, "instead of toiling and moiling in that way?"

"I am helping to lay up food for the winter," said the Ant, "and recommend you to do the same."

"Why bother about winter?" said the Grasshopper. "We have got plenty of food at present." But the Ant went on its way and continued its toil.

When the winter came the Grasshopper had no food, and found itself dying of hunger, while it saw the ants distributing every day corn and grain from the stores they had collected in the summer.

"It is best to prepare for the days of necessity."

THE FOX AND THE CROW

A Fox once saw a Crow fly off with a piece of cheese in its beak and settle on a branch of a tree. "That's for me, as I am a Fox," said Master Reynard, and he walked up to the foot of the tree. "Good-day, Mistress Crow," he cried. "How well you are looking today: how glossy your feathers; how bright your eye. I feel sure your voice must surpass that of other birds, just as your figure does; let me hear but one song from you that I may greet you as the Queen of Birds." The Crow lifted up her head and began to caw her best, but the moment she opened her mouth the piece of cheese fell to the ground, only to be snapped up by Master Fox. "That will do," said he. "That was all I wanted. In exchange for your cheese I will give you a piece of advice for the future——

"Do not trust flatterers."

THE LION AND THE MOUSE

Once when a Lion was asleep a little Mouse began running up and down upon him; this soon wakened the Lion, who placed his huge paw upon him, and opened his big jaws to swallow him. "Pardon, O King," cried the little

"The Fox and the Crow" and "The Lion and the Mouse." From *The Fables of Aesop,* edited by Joseph Jacobs, Macmillan, 1950. By permission of The Macmillan Company, New York, and Macmillan & Co. Ltd., London

Mouse; "forgive me this time, I shall never forget it: who knows but what I may be able to do you a turn some of these days?" The Lion was so tickled at the idea of the Mouse being able to help him, that he lifted up his paw and let him go. Some time after the Lion was caught in a trap, and the hunters, who desired to carry him alive to the King, tied him to a tree while they went in search of a wagon to carry him on. Just then the little Mouse happened to pass by, and seeing the sad plight in which the Lion was, went up to him and soon gnawed away the ropes that bound the King of the Beasts. "Was I not right?" said the little Mouse.

"Little friends may prove great friends."

THE DOG IN THE MANGER

A Dog looking out for its afternoon nap jumped into the Manger of an Ox and lay there cosily upon the straw. But soon the Ox, returning from its afternoon work, came up to the Manger and wanted to eat some of the straw. The Dog in a rage, being awakened from its slumber, stood up and barked at the Ox, and whenever it came near attempted to bite it. At

HERCULES AND THE WAGGONER

A waggoner was once driving a heavy load along a very muddy way. At last he came to a part of the road where the wheels sank halfway into the mire, and the more the horses pulled, the deeper sank the wheels. So the Waggoner threw down his whip, and knelt down and prayed to Hercules the Strong. "O Hercules, help me in this my hour of distress," quoth he. But Hercules appeared to him, and said:

"Tut, man, don't sprawl there. Get up and put your shoulder to the wheel."

"The gods help them that help themselves."

last the Ox had to give up the hope of getting at the straw, and went away muttering:

"Ah, people often grudge others what they cannot enjoy themselves."

"Hercules and the Waggoner" and "The Dog in the Manger." From *The Fables of Aesop*, edited by Joseph Jacobs, Macmillan, 1950. By permission of The Macmillan Company, New York and Macmillan & Co. Ltd., London

THE SHEPHERD'S BOY

There was once a young Shepherd Boy who tended his sheep at the foot of a mountain near a dark forest. It was rather lonely for him all day, so he thought upon a plan by which he could get a little company and some excitement. He rushed down towards the village calling out "Wolf, Wolf," and the villagers came out to meet him, and some of them stopped with him for a considerable time. This pleased the boy so much that a few days afterwards he tried the same trick, and again the villagers came to his help. But shortly after this a Wolf actually did come out from the forest, and began to worry the sheep, and the boy of course cried out "Wolf, Wolf," still louder than before. But this time the villagers, who had been fooled twice before, thought the boy was again deceiving them, and nobody stirred to come to his help. So the Wolf made a good meal off the boy's flock, and when the boy complained, the wise man of the village said:

"A liar will not be believed, even when he speaks the truth."

THE TOWN MOUSE
AND THE COUNTRY MOUSE

Now you must know that a Town Mouse once upon a time went on a visit to his cousin in the country. He was rough and ready, this cousin, but he loved his town friend and made him heartily welcome. Beans and bacon, cheese and bread, were all he had to offer, but he offered them freely. The Town Mouse rather turned up his long nose at this country fare, and said: "I cannot understand, Cousin, how you can put up with such poor food as this, but of course you cannot expect anything better in the country; come you with me and I will show you how to live. When you have been in town a week you will wonder how you could ever have stood a country life." No sooner said than done: the two mice set off for the town and arrived at the Town Mouse's residence late at night. "You will want some refreshment after our long journey," said the polite Town Mouse, and took his friend into the grand dining-room. There they found the remains of a fine feast, and soon the two mice were eating up jellies and cakes and all that was nice. Suddenly they heard growling and barking. "What is that?" said the Country Mouse. "It is only the dogs of the house," answered the other. "Only!" said the Country Mouse. "I do not like that music at my dinner." Just at that moment the door flew open, in came two huge mastiffs, and the two mice had to scamper down and run off. "Good-bye, Cousin," said the Country Mouse. "What! going so soon?" said the other. "Yes, he replied;

"Better beans and bacon in peace than cakes and ale in fear."

THE FROG AND THE OX

"Oh father," said a little Frog to the big one sitting by the side of a pool, "I have seen such a terrible monster! It was as big as a mountain, with horns on its head, and a long tail, and it had hoofs divided in two."

"Tush, child, tush," said the old Frog, "that was only Farmer White's Ox. It isn't so big either; he may be a little taller than I, but I could easily make myself quite as broad; just you see." So he blew himself out, and blew himself out, and blew himself out. "Was he as big as that?" asked he.

"Oh, much bigger than that," said the young Frog.

Again the old one blew himself out, and asked the young one if the Ox was as big as that.

"Bigger, father, bigger," was the reply.

So the Frog took a deep breath, and blew and blew and blew, and swelled and swelled and swelled. And then he said: "I'm sure the Ox is not as big as ——" But at this moment he burst.

"Self-conceit may lead to self-destruction."

"The Shepherd's Boy," "The Town Mouse and the Country Mouse," and "The Frog and the Ox." From *The Fables of Aesop*, edited by Joseph Jacobs, Macmillan, 1950. By permission of The Macmillan Company, New York and Macmillan & Co. Ltd., London

BELLING THE CAT

Long ago, the mice held a general council to consider what measures they could take to out-wit their common enemy, the Cat. Some said this, and some said that; but at last a young mouse got up and said he had a proposal to make, which he thought would meet the case. "You will all agree," said he, "that our chief danger consists in the sly and treacherous manner in which the enemy approaches us. Now, if we could receive some signal of her approach, we could easily escape from her. I venture, therefore, to propose that a small bell be procured, and attached by a ribbon round the neck of the Cat. By this means we should always know when she was about, and could easily retire while she was in the neighbourhood."

This proposal met with general applause, until an old mouse got up and said: "That is all very well, but who is to bell the Cat?" The mice looked at one another and nobody spoke. Then the old mouse said:

"It is easy to propose impossible remedies."

"Belling the Cat," "The Dog and the Shadow," and "The Wind and the Sun." From *The Fables of Aesop,* edited by Joseph Jacobs, Macmillan, 1950. By permission of The Macmillan Company, New York and Macmillan & Co., Ltd., London

THE DOG AND THE SHADOW

It happened that a Dog had got a piece of meat and was carrying it home in his mouth to eat it in peace. Now on his way home he had to cross a plank lying across a running brook. As he crossed, he looked down and saw his own shadow reflected in the water beneath. Thinking it was another dog with another piece of meat, he made up his mind to have that also. So he made a snap at the shadow in the water, but as he opened his mouth the piece of meat fell out, dropped into the water and was never seen more.

"Beware lest you lose the substance by grasping at the shadow."

THE WIND AND THE SUN

The Wind and the Sun were disputing which was the stronger. Suddenly they saw a traveler coming down the road, and the Sun said: "I see a way to decide our dispute. Whichever of us can cause that traveler to take off his cloak shall be regarded as the stronger. You begin." So the Sun retired behind a cloud, and the Wind began to blow as hard as he could upon the traveler. But the harder he blew the more closely did the traveler wrap his cloak round him, till at last the Wind had to give up in despair. Then the Sun came out and shone in all his glory upon the traveler, who soon found it too hot to walk with his cloak on.

"Kindness effects more than Severity."

THE FOX AND THE GRAPES

One hot summer's day a Fox was strolling through an orchard till he came to a bunch of Grapes just ripening on a vine which had been trained over a lofty branch. "Just the thing to quench my thirst," quoth he. Drawing back a few paces, he took a run and a jump, and just missed the bunch. Turning round again with a One, Two, Three, he jumped up, but with no greater success. Again and again he tried after the tempting morsel, but at last had to give it up, and walked away with his nose in the air, saying: "I am sure they are sour."

"It is easy to despise what you cannot get."

THE CROW AND THE PITCHER

A thirsty Crow found a Pitcher with some water in it, but so little was there that, try as she might, she could not reach it with her beak, and it seemed as though she would die of thirst within sight of the remedy. At last she hit upon a clever plan. She began dropping pebbles into the Pitcher, and with each pebble the water rose a little higher until at last it reached the brim, and the knowing bird was enabled to quench her thirst.

"Necessity is the mother of invention."

"The Fox and the Grapes," "The Crow and the Pitcher," and "The Milkmaid and Her Pail." From *The Fables of Aesop*, edited by Joseph Jacobs, Macmillan, 1950. By permission of The Macmillan Company, New York and Macmillan & Co. Ltd., London

THE MILKMAID AND HER PAIL

A farmer's daughter had been out to milk the cows, and was returning to the dairy carrying her pail of milk upon her head. As she walked along, she fell a-musing after this fashion: "The milk in this pail will provide me with cream, which I will make into butter and take to market to sell. With the money I will buy a number of eggs, and these, when hatched, will produce chickens, and by and by I shall have quite a large poultry-yard. Then I shall sell some of my fowls, and with the money which they will bring in I will buy myself a new gown, which I shall wear when I go to the fair; and all the young fellows will admire it, and come and make love to me, but I shall toss my head and have nothing to say to them." Forgetting all about the pail, and suiting the action to the word, she tossed her head. Down went the pail, all the milk was spilled and all her fine castles in the air vanished in a moment!

"Do not count your chickens before they are hatched."

THE WOLF
IN SHEEP'S CLOTHING

A Wolf found great difficulty in getting at the sheep owing to the vigilance of the shepherd and his dogs. But one day it found the skin of a sheep that had been flayed and thrown aside, so it put it on over its own pelt and strolled down among the sheep. The Lamb that belonged to the sheep, whose skin the Wolf was wearing, began to follow the Wolf in the Sheep's clothing; so, leading the Lamb a little apart, he soon made a meal off her, and for some time he succeeded in deceiving the sheep, and enjoying hearty meals.

"Appearances are deceptive."

THE HARE AND THE TORTOISE

The Hare was once boasting of his speed before the other animals. "I have never yet been beaten," said he, "when I put forth my full speed. I challenge any one here to race with me."

The Tortoise said quietly: "I accept your challenge."

"That is a good joke," said the Hare; "I could dance round you all the way."

"Keep your boasting till you've beaten," answered the Tortoise. "Shall we race?"

So a course was fixed and a start was made. The Hare darted almost out of sight at once, but soon stopped and, to show his contempt for the Tortoise, lay down to have a nap. The Tortoise plodded on and plodded on, and when the Hare awoke from his nap, he saw the Tortoise just near the winning post and could not run up in time to save the race.

"Plodding wins the race."

"The Wolf in Sheep's Clothing" and "The Hare and the Tortoise." From *The Fables of Aesop*, edited by Joseph Jacobs, Macmillan, 1950. By permission of The Macmillan Company, New York and Macmillan & Co. Ltd., London

Fables of Bidpai

The fables in the East Indian collections are much longer and more like stories with morals than they are like the spare little abstractions we know as Aesop's fables. The Panchatantra was really a textbook on "the wise conduct of life" and contained stories within stories. Maude Barrows Dutton retold thirty-four of the best-known tales from The Panchatantra and, with the inimitable illustrations of E. Boyd Smith, made an attractive little book called The Tortoise and the Geese and Other Fables of Bidpai. The other source of Indian fables is the group called the Jatakas, which are stories of Gautama Buddha in his progressive reincarnations in the forms of different animals. When references to the Buddha are omitted, these stories become good talking beast tales, and therefore the selections from the Jatakas are included with the folk tales.

THE PARTRIDGE AND THE CROW

A Crow flying across a road saw a Partridge strutting along the ground.

"What a beautiful gait that Partridge has!" said the Crow. "I must try to see if I can walk like him."

She alighted behind the Partridge and tried for a long time to learn to strut. At last the Partridge turned around and asked the Crow what she was about.

"Do not be angry with me," replied the Crow. "I have never before seen a bird who walks as beautifully as you can, and I am trying to learn to walk like you."

"Foolish bird!" responded the Partridge. "You are a Crow, and should walk like a Crow. You would look silly indeed if you were to strut like a partridge."

But the Crow went on trying to learn to strut, until finally she had forgotten her own gait, and she never learned that of the Partridge.

THE TYRANT WHO BECAME A JUST RULER

In olden times there lived a King, who was so cruel and unjust towards his subjects that he was always called The Tyrant. So heartless was he that his people used to pray night and day that they might have a new king. One day, much to their surprise, he called his people together and said to them,——

"My dear subjects, the days of my tyranny are over. Henceforth you shall live in peace and happiness, for I have decided to try to rule henceforth justly and well."

The King kept his word so well that soon he was known throughout the land as The Just King. By and by one of his favorites came to him and said,——

"Your Majesty, I beg of you to tell me how it was that you had this change of heart towards your people?"

And the King replied,——

"As I was galloping through my forests one afternoon, I caught sight of a hound chasing a fox. The fox escaped into his hole, but not until he had been bitten by the dog so badly that he would be lame for life. The hound, returning home, met a man who threw a stone at him, which broke his leg. The man had not gone far when a horse kicked him and broke his leg. And the horse, starting to run, fell into a hole and broke his leg. Here I came to my senses, and resolved to change my rule. 'For surely,' I said to myself, 'he who doeth evil will sooner or later be overtaken by evil.'"

"The Partridge and the Crow" and "The Tyrant Who Became a Just Ruler." From *The Tortoise and the Geese and Other Fables of Bidpai* by Maude Barrows Dutton. Copyright 1908 by Maude Barrows Dutton and Houghton Mifflin Company. Copyright 1936 by Maude Dutton Lynch and Houghton Mifflin Company. Reprinted by permission of and arrangement with Houghton Mifflin Company, the authorized publishers

Fables of La Fontaine

*In France the fables were turned into verse by a skilled poet, Jean de La
Fontaine, a contemporary of Charles Perrault. The sources used by La Fontaine
were Latin versions of Aesop and* The Fables of Bidpai, *and the versions
of Marie de France, who introduced the fable into France in the twelfth century.
La Fontaine's rhymed moralities were so popular in the France of his day
that people called him "le fablier," the "fable-teller." To translate his witty
French verses into English verse is to lose some of their gaiety and charm, so they
are usually translated into prose. "The Grasshopper and the Ant" is an example
of a metrical translation and "The Fox and the Crow" and "The Cricket and the
Ant" are in the vigorous prose of Margaret Wise Brown. In "The Fox
and the Crow" she has used a sing-and-say style that suggests the
original verse form but tells the story clearly.*

THE FOX AND THE CROW

Mister Crow sat on the limb of a tree with a
big piece of cheese in his mouth.

Old Mister Fox smelled the cheese from a
long way off. And he came to the foot of the
tree and spoke to the crow.

"Good morning, Mr. Coal Black Crow,
How beautiful and shining your feathers grow,
Black as the night and bright as the sun,
If you sing as well, your fortune is won."

At these words Mr. Crow joyously opened his
beak to sing his creaky old crow song.

And the cheese fell down to the ground. The
fox snapped it up in his mouth.

As he ran away he called back over his bushy
tail, "My dear Mr. Crow, learn from this how
every flatterer lives at the expense of anybody
who will listen to him. This lesson is well worth
the loss of a cheese to you."

THE CRICKET AND THE ANT

All through the summer the cricket sang. He
sang in the grass when they planted the seed.
And he sang in the grass when the flowers
bloomed. Why should a cricket work on a sunny
day, when he could sing and dance and play? In
the early fall when the seeds were blowing in the
air the cricket chirped his song. But when winter
came and the cold winds blew, the merry little
cricket had nothing to eat and nowhere to go.

So he hopped to the house of his neighbor, the
ant, who had worked all summer storing up her
food for the winter. He knocked at the door and
cried, "Oh, dear! Oh, dear! I am starving, hungry, starving! Kind ant, will you lend me some
seeds to live on until spring? And I will give you
five seeds in the spring for every seed that you
give me today."

But the ant was practical—as ants are.

"What did you do in the summer when the
days were warm and the flowers were going to

seed?" asked the ant. "What did you do in the
early fall when the seeds were blowing through
the air?"

"Night and day I sang," said the cricket.

"You sang!" said the ant. "Then now you can
dance to your own music. I will eat the seed I
gathered and the house I have built will keep
me warm. Maybe your dancing will keep you
warm in the snow."

THE GRASSHOPPER AND
THE ANT

A grasshopper gay
Sang the Summer away,
And found herself poor
By the winter's first roar.
Of meat and of bread,
Not a morsel she had!
So a-begging she went,
To her neighbour the ant,
  For the loan of some wheat,
  Which would serve her to eat,
Till the season came round.
  "I will pay, you," she saith
  "On an animal's faith,

Double weight in the pound
Ere the harvest be bound."
The ant is a friend
  (And here she might mend)
  Little given to lend.
"How spent you the summer?"
  Quoth she, looking shame
  At the borrowing dame.
"Night and day to each comer
I sang if you please."
  "You sang! I'm at ease;
For 'tis plain at a glance,
Now, Ma'am, you must dance."

Myth and epic are a part of that anonymous stream of folklore which includes the folk tales and the fables. All these helped to weld people together with a body of common beliefs, customs, morals, and finally a hero cult. They were indeed the "cement of society," holding it together with a moral code.

Origin of the myth

Mythological stories strike the modern reader as a kind of grown-up fairy tale, strangely beautiful and unearthly, a world of sky dwellers who

GODS AND MEN: MYTH AND EPIC

leave their bright Olympus, now and then, to visit dazzled earth creatures. Actually, such stories are only a part of the varied tales included in the whole body of myth. Taken as a whole, myth attempts to explain in complex symbols:

(1) cosmic phenomena (e.g., how the earth and sky came to be separated); (2) peculiarities of natural history (e.g., why rain follows the cries or activities of certain birds); (3) the origins of human civilization (e.g., through the beneficent action of a culture-hero like

Prometheus); or (4) the origin of social or religious custom or the nature and history of objects of worship.[1]

The stories range from little *why* stories to the most involved and sometimes unpleasant stories of the gods' ways with man or with each other told in symbols which are incomprehensible to children. In spite of the fact that many of the myths because of their complexity and eroticism are unfit for youngsters, there still remain many excellent stories which are enjoyed by children.

The developmental stages of myth-making are interesting because they not only help to explain the variety of the stories, but also help to guide our selection of those that children are most likely to understand and enjoy. No one knows how myth began, except that man seems always to have had the capacity for wondering about himself and his environment. In an age when nature and society were not areas of objective study in our modern scientific sense, but were, instead, areas of unquestioning acceptance, primitive man simply used his imagination to explain their peculiarities. So, the first stage of myth-making was probably submission to and worship of some inexplicable, impersonal force which caused the crops to grow, the rivers to flow, and man to live and die in his appointed time.

The second stage may have followed hard upon the first—the stage of giving body to this impersonal force, personifying it as an animal or a man. One of our American Indian tribes has "Old Man Coyote" among its nature deities, and, for the ancient Greeks, the god Apollo became the embodiment of all the warmth, power, and beauty of the sun. In this personification stage of myth-making, it was natural for men to attribute to their gods a nature like their own on a magnified scale. So it is the anger of a god which accounts for thunderbolts or causes raging storms at sea, and the god must be propitiated. There were so many phenomena to be explained that the Greeks developed more and more gods, of major and minor importance, until G. K. Chesterton sums up their polytheistic mythology by commenting that "the Greeks could not see trees for dryads."

[1] William Reginald Halliday, "Folklore," *Encyclopaedia Britannica*

This multiplication of deities led to the third stage of myth-making, the development of relationships among the gods and the limitations of the powers of each one. In Greek myth, for example, Zeus (Jove or Jupiter)[2] was all powerful; Hera (Juno) was his wife and a jealous guardian of the marriage state; Poseidon (Neptune) ruled the sea, and so the development of relationships and assignment of special powers continued down to those beguiling little creatures of the supernatural world, the local gods of rivers, springs, and groves, and the little dryads, satyrs, and fawns, who followed in the wake of Pan. Unfortunately, the limitation of godly prerogatives led to the same kind of chicanery, squabbles, and warfare that man himself was busily waging on earth. These mythical creatures displayed weaknesses on a grandiose scale sadly like man's own foibles.

The fourth stage of myth-making began when the powers of each god were extended to include certain abstract virtues, so that the god became less human and more of a symbolic figure. Apollo, for instance, began as a sun god, a beautiful young man who daily drove his fiery chariot across the sky. But in this fourth stage, he became a god of health and healing, the patron of physicians. Then, the idea of healing and health was expanded to rites of purification, and the god became a symbol for the abstract idea of purity.

The conversion of these earthy, man-made gods into symbols of moral virtues gave rise to the last and most advanced stage of myth-making, the development of a priesthood, temples, and a ritual of worship. The Apollo myth and other Greek myths reached this last stage of development, but among less civilized peoples myth-making stops at any one of the earlier stages and their myths remain correspondingly primitive.

Kinds of myth

The varying stories of the gods grew, then, out of the various levels of myth-making. The simplest stories, the *why* or *pourquoi* tales, emerge from that first explanatory stage. "Clytie" is the story of why the sunflower turns to the sun

[2] For a fuller list of the Greek and Roman names of the gods and the special powers of each, see May Hill Arbuthnot, *Children and Books*, p. 297.

and "Arachne" explains why spiders spin. Our American Indians have innumerable stories, such as "Why the Woodpecker Has a Red Head."

In both the Greek and Norse mythologies the *why* stories became more complex as the myth itself developed into its second and third stages and grew steadily more symbolic and abstract. The beautiful Greek story "Demeter and Persephone" (Ceres and Proserpine) tells, in symbols, the story of the changing seasons. Demeter, goddess of agriculture, loses her daughter Persephone, or grain, to Hades, the god who rules the dark underground world. The conclusion of the story explains why there is winter on the earth for half of the year. Children accept this story as a kind of super fairy tale and would certainly never catch its seasonal significance if it were not pointed out to them. This is true of the two similar stories in this volume—the Norse "The Death of Balder" and the desert Indian story "Little Burnt-Face."

As man advanced into later myth-making stages, the *why* stories not only became more symbolic and complex but they turned, presently, into full-fledged allegories. King Midas is the personification of greed for gold, and the allegory shows the punishment that follows this offense. Philemon and Baucis, who stand for simple kindness and goodness, are tenderly rewarded by their visitors from Olympus. At precisely what point the explanatory and symbolic character of the *why* story became pure allegory is not important. The changes merely call attention to the progression in complexity, significance, and difficulty to be found in myth.

Another group of stories concerns *the ways of the gods with men* and includes both tales which are best suited and those least appropriate to children. Such tales as "Midas" and "Baucis and Philemon" are delightful, and their meaning is evident. But stories dealing with the gods' amatory adventures among mortals and the revenge their jealous spouses wreak on their rivals are obviously unsuitable for children's reading fare.

This is also true of many of the stories concerned with *the ways of the gods with other gods.* Repellent tales of the creation, matings of brothers and sisters, matings with monsters, and the birth of more monsters, infidelity, jealousy, revenge, are all to be found in this group of stories.

There are noble stories among them, too, but they are often expressed in erotic symbols or ones too difficult for youngsters. For instance, Prometheus, who dared the wrath of the gods to bring fire to man, is so noble a figure of sacrifice that poets have used the story repeatedly. But its symbolism is at once too meaningful and too difficult for children to grasp.

The value of the myths

There is, then, in myth as in the folk tales a great body of material which is adult in form and concept. The myths selected for this collection are the simpler tales—*why* stories, allegories, and a few tales of gods and men. The Greek and Roman stories predominate not only because they are, on the whole, more interesting but also because they are the source of innumerable allusions which the child will encounter now and later on. The modern child sees Mercury or his winged sandals adorning railroad terminals and automobile advertisements. Minerva and her owl stare down at him in libraries. Venus rising from her seashell appears on advertisements for bath salts, and the child eats his morning cereal, a word which goes back to Ceres. Not to know something of Greek mythology is to be deprived of a rich source of linguistic, literary, artistic, and even commercial reference.

It is hoped that this small selection of myth will send teachers and children to whole books of mythology, to be used in connection with their study of a people or just for delight in the stories themselves. For to know the beauty of Olympus or Valhalla and to encounter the gods at their best is to dream with them some of man's ancient dreams of how splendid life may be for those who dare greatly. And some of these old dreams have come true. Icarus today has mastered the air, and modern Phaetons drive their chariots coolly across the sky and do not perish. These are splendid dreams for children to share, couched in symbols whose meaning will grow with the children's maturity.

Epics and Hero Tales

The great epics of literature are book-size collections of tales, far too long to include in such a volume as this. Instead, "The Curse of Polyphemus" one of the stories from the *Odyssey*, and a hero tale "Little John and the Tanner of Blyth" have been included. These samples will, it is hoped, lead children to the collections from which these stories were taken. For to read an epic is to live, day after day, with greatness, and such an experience is good for young spirits.

The epic grew out of or along with myth and consists of a cycle of stories about some human hero, buffeted by gods and men, who suffers greatly and endures staunchly to the end. Myth is still with us in the early epics, for the gods apparently leave their own affairs in Olympus for the express purpose of interfering with man's adventures on earth. But in epics the center of interest shifts from the gods to the human hero, from Olympus to earth. After both the gods and Olympus had faded from man's dreams, culture heroes still excited man's imagination and gained his belief. Tales of greatness would cluster about a single name until a Roland or a Robin Hood assumed the impressive stature of the epic hero even without the background of warring gods.

The epic is strongly national in its presentation of human character. Odysseus may never have lived, but he is the embodiment of the Greek ideals of manly courage, sagacity, beauty, and endurance. Sigurd is the personification of the Norse code of heroism. King Arthur represents chivalry, and Robin Hood, the English love of freedom and justice as well as the ideal of lusty, jovial manhood. Study the epic hero of a nation and you will learn a great deal about the moral code of that nation and era.

Not all epics are suitable for children, but some of them provide a literary and emotional experience as unforgettable as it is precious. *Robin Hood* is certainly the prime favorite with elementary school children, with the *Odyssey* next in appeal. It is probable that *King Arthur, Roland*, the *Iliad*, and perhaps the *Sigurd Saga* are better postponed for the days of adolescence, although if told to children, the Sigurd stories are well liked and so are many of the Arthur cycle. The personification of a great ideal in one hero, the sweep and excitement of epic action, the continuity of the adventures, and the nobility of the stories—these are epic qualities for which there are no substitutes.

Greek and Roman myth and epic

Myth introduces children to a new world of dreams and magic,
where gods and goddesses replace fairies, and golden Olympus becomes
a "land of heart's desire" on a grand scale. Greek myth has the bright beauty
of a southern country and Norse myth the somber, heroic qualities of the north.
Both are for children of eleven and older, with only a few stories
simple enough for the nines or tens. These stories may be used to intro-
duce children to the field of mythology, or to furnish religious background
of a people, or just for their charm and entertainment values.

CLYTIE

The maiden in the process of transformation is an interest-subject for illustration.

Clytie was a water-nymph and in love with Apollo, who made her no return. So she pined away, sitting all day long upon the cold ground,

"Clytie." From *A Book of Myths*, selections from Bulfinch's *Age of Fable*. Copyright, 1942, by The Macmillan Company and used with their permission

with her unbound tresses streaming over her shoulders. Nine days she sat and tasted neither food nor drink. She gazed on the sun when he rose, and as he passed through his daily course to his setting; she saw no other object, her face turned constantly on him. At last, they say, her limbs rooted in the ground, her face became a flower, which turns on its stem so as always to face the sun throughout its daily course; for it retains to that extent the feeling of the nymph from whom it sprang.

ARACHNE

The gods seem to be especially hard on conceit and boastfulness.

Not among mortals alone were there contests of skill, nor yet among the gods, like Pan and Apollo. Many sorrows befell men because they grew arrogant in their own devices and coveted divine honors. There was once a great hunter, Orion, who outvied the gods themselves, till they took him away from his hunting-grounds and set him in the heavens, with his sword and belt, and his hound at his heels. But at length jealousy invaded even the peaceful arts, and disaster came of spinning!

There was a certain maiden of Lydia, Arachne by name, renowned throughout the country for her skill as a weaver. She was as nimble with her fingers as Calypso, that nymph who kept Odysseus for seven years in her enchanted island. She was as untiring as Penelope, the hero's wife, who wove day after day while she watched for his return. Day in and day out, Arachne wove too. The very nymphs would gather about her loom, naiads from the water and dryads from the trees.

"Maiden," they would say, shaking the leaves or the foam from their hair, in wonder, "Pallas Athena must have taught you!"

But this did not please Arachne. She would not acknowledge herself a debtor, even to that goddess who protected all household arts, and by whose grace alone one had any skill in them.

"I learned not of Athena," said she. "If she can weave better, let her come and try."

The nymphs shivered at this, and an aged woman, who was looking on, turned to Arachne.

"Be more heedful of your words, my daughter," said she. "The goddess may pardon you if you ask forgiveness, but do not strive for honors with the immortals."

Arachne broke her thread, and the shuttle stopped humming.

"Keep your counsel," she said. "I fear not Athena; no, nor anyone else."

As she frowned at the old woman, she was amazed to see her change suddenly into one tall,

"Arachne." From *Old Greek Folk Stories Told Anew* by Josephine Preston Peabody. Houghton, Mifflin Co., 1897

majestic, beautiful—a maiden of gray eyes and golden hair, crowned with a golden helmet. It was Athena herself.

The bystanders shrank in fear and reverence; only Arachne was unawed and held to her foolish boast.

In silence the two began to weave, and the nymphs stole nearer, coaxed by the sound of the shuttles, that seemed to be humming with delight over the two webs,—back and forth like bees.

They gazed upon the loom where the goddess stood plying her task, and they saw shapes and images come to bloom out of the wondrous colors, as sunset clouds grow to be living creatures when we watch them. And they saw that the goddess, still merciful, was spinning, as a warning for Arachne, the pictures of her own triumph over reckless gods and mortals.

In one corner of the web she made a story of her conquest over the sea-god Poseidon. For the first king of Athens had promised to dedicate the city to that god who should bestow upon it the most useful gift. Poseidon gave the horse. But Athena gave the olive,—means of livelihood,—symbol of peace and prosperity, and the city was called after her name. Again she pictured a vain woman of Troy, who had been turned into a crane for disputing the palm of beauty with a goddess. Other corners of the web held similar images, and the whole shone like a rainbow.

Meanwhile Arachne, whose head was quite turned with vanity, embroidered her web with stories against the gods, making light of Zeus himself and of Apollo, and portraying them as birds and beasts. But she wove with marvelous skill; the creatures seemed to breathe and speak, yet it was all as fine as the gossamer that you find on the grass before rain.

Athena herself was amazed. Not even her wrath at the girl's insolence could wholly overcome her wonder. For an instant she stood entranced; then she tore the web across, and three times she touched Arachne's forehead with her spindle.

"Live on, Arachne," she said. "And since it is your glory to weave, you and yours must weave forever." So saying, she sprinkled upon the maiden a certain magical potion.

Away went Arachne's beauty; then her very

human form shrank to that of a spider, and so remained. As a spider she spent all her days weaving and weaving; and you may see something like her handiwork any day among the rafters.

ORPHEUS AND EURYDICE

This story makes an invaluable background for the "Orpheus and Eurydice" music by Gluck.

When gods and shepherds piped and the stars sang, that was the day of musicians! But the triumph of Phoebus Apollo himself was not so wonderful as the triumph of a mortal man who lived on earth, though some say that he came of divine lineage. This was Orpheus, that best of harpers, who went with the Grecian heroes of the great ship *Argo* in search of the Golden Fleece.

After his return from the quest, he won Eurydice for his wife, and they were as happy as people can be who love each other and every one else. The very wild beasts loved them, and the trees clustered about their home as if they were watered with music. But even the gods themselves were not always free from sorrow, and one day misfortune came upon that harper Orpheus whom all men loved to honor.

Eurydice, his lovely wife, as she was wandering with the nymphs, unwittingly trod upon a serpent in the grass. Surely, if Orpheus had been with her, playing upon his lyre, no creature could have harmed her. But Orpheus came too late. She died of the sting, and was lost to him in the Underworld.

For days he wandered from his home, singing the story of his loss and his despair to the helpless passers-by. His grief moved the very stones in the wilderness, and roused a dumb distress in the hearts of savage beasts. Even the gods on Mount Olympus gave ear, but they held no power over the darkness of Hades.

Wherever Orpheus wandered with his lyre, no one had the will to forbid him entrance; and at length he found unguarded that very cave that leads to the Underworld where Pluto rules the

"Orpheus and Eurydice." From *Old Greek Folk Stories Told Anew* by Josephine Preston Peabody

spirits of the dead. He went down without fear. The fire in his living heart found him a way through the gloom of that place. He crossed the Styx, the black river that the gods name as their most sacred oath. Charon, the harsh old ferryman who takes the Shades across, forgot to ask of him the coin that every soul must pay. For Orpheus sang. There in the Underworld the song of Apollo would not have moved the poor ghosts so much. It would have amazed them, like a star far off that no one understands. But here was a human singer, and he sang of things that grow in every human heart, youth and love and death, the sweetness of the Earth, and the bitterness of losing aught that is dear to us.

Now the dead, when they go to the Underworld, drink of the pool of Lethe; and forgetfulness of all that has passed comes upon them like a sleep, and they lose their longing for the world, they lose their memory of pain, and live content with that cool twilight. But not the pool of Lethe itself could withstand the song of Orpheus; and in the hearts of the Shades all the old dreams awoke wondering. They remembered once more the life of men on Earth, the glory of the sun and moon, the sweetness of new grass, the warmth of their homes, all the old joy and grief that they had known. And they wept.

Even the Furies were moved to pity. Those, too, who were suffering punishment for evil deeds ceased to be tormented for themselves, and grieved only for the innocent Orpheus who had lost Eurydice. Sisyphus, that fraudulent king (who is doomed to roll a monstrous boulder up-hill forever), stopped to listen. The daughters of Danaus left off their task of drawing water in a sieve. Tantalus forgot hunger and thirst, though before his eyes hung magical fruits that were wont to vanish out of his grasp, and just beyond reach bubbled the water that was a torment to his ears; he did not hear it while Orpheus sang.

So, among a crowd of eager ghosts, Orpheus came, singing with all his heart, before the king and queen of Hades. And the queen Proserpina wept as she listened and grew homesick, remembering the fields of Enna and the growing of the wheat, and her own beautiful mother, Demeter. Then Pluto gave way.

They called Eurydice and she came, like a young guest unused to the darkness of the Underworld. She was to return with Orpheus, but on one condition. If he turned to look at her once before they reached the upper air, he must lose her again and go back to the world alone.

Rapt with joy, the happy Orpheus hastened on the way, thinking only of Eurydice, who was following him. Past Lethe, across the Styx they went, he and his lovely wife, still silent as a Shade. But the place was full of gloom, the silence weighed upon him, he had not seen her for so long; her footsteps made no sound; and he could hardly believe the miracle, for Pluto seldom relents. When the first gleam of upper daylight broke through the cleft to the dismal world, he forgot all, save that he must know if she still followed. He turned to see her face, and the promise was broken!

She smiled at him forgivingly, but it was too late. He stretched out his arms to take her, but she faded from them, as the bright snow, that none may keep, melts in our very hands. A murmur of farewell came to his ears—no more. She was gone.

He would have followed, but Charon, now on guard, drove him back. Seven days he lingered there between the worlds of life and death, but after the broken promise, Hades would not listen to his song. Back to the Earth he wandered, though it was sweet to him no longer. He died young, singing to the last, and round about the place where his body rested, nightingales nested in the trees. His lyre was set among the stars; and he himself went down to join Eurydice, unforbidden.

Those two had no need of Lethe, for their life on earth had been wholly fair, and now that they are together they no longer own a sorrow.

PROSERPINE

This myth, sometimes called "Demeter and Persephone," the Greek names for the mother and child, is the story of winter and summer, of the grains maturing below ground in darkness.

In the vale of Enna there is a lake embowered in woods, which screen it from the fervid rays of the sun, while the moist ground is covered with flowers, and Spring reigns perpetual. Here Proserpine was playing with her companions, gathering lilies and violets, and filling her basket and her apron with them, when Pluto saw her, loved her, and carried her off. She screamed for help to her mother and companions; and when in her fright she dropped the corners of her apron and let the flowers fall, childlike she felt the loss of them as an addition to her grief.

Pluto urged on his steeds, calling them each by name, and throwing loose over their heads and necks his iron-coloured reins. When he reached the River Cyane, and it opposed his passage, he struck the river-bank with his trident, and the earth opened and gave him a passage to Tartarus.

"Proserpine." From *A Book of Myths*, selections from Bulfinch's *Age of Fable*, Macmillan, 1942

Ceres, Proserpine's mother, sought her daughter all the world over. Bright-haired Aurora, when she came forth in the morning, and Hesperus, when he led out the stars in the evening, found her still busy in the search. But it was all unavailing. At length, weary and sad, she sat down upon a stone, and continued sitting nine days and nights, in the open air, under the sunlight and moonlight and falling showers. It was where now stands the city of Eleusis, then the home of an old man named Celeus.

He was out on the field, gathering acorns and blackberries, and sticks for his fire. His little girl was driving home their two goats, and as she passed the goddess, who appeared in the guise of an old woman, she said to her, "Mother,"—and the name was sweet to the ears of Ceres,—"why do you sit here alone upon the rocks?" The old man also stopped, though his load was heavy, and begged her to come into his cottage, such as it was. She declined, and he urged her. "Go in peace," she replied, "and be happy in your daughter; I have lost mine." As she spoke, tears fell down her cheeks upon her bosom. The compassionate old man and his child wept with her. Then said he, "Come with us, and despise not our humble roof; so may your daughter be restored to you in safety."

"Lead on," she said, "I cannot resist that appeal!" So she rose from the stone and went with them. As they walked he told her that his only son, a little boy, lay very sick, feverish, and sleepless. She stooped and gathered some poppies. As they entered the cottage, they found all in great distress, for the boy seemed past hope of recovery. Metanira, his mother, received her kindly, and the goddess stooped and kissed the lips of the sick child. Instantly the paleness left his face, and healthy vigour returned to his body. The whole family were delighted—that is, the father, mother, and little girl, for they were all; they had no servants.

They spread the table, and put upon it curds and cream, apples, and honey in the comb. While they ate, Ceres mingled poppy juice in the milk of the boy. When night came and all was still, she arose, and taking the sleeping boy, moulded his limbs with her hands, and uttered over him three times a solemn charm, then went and laid him in the ashes. His mother, who had been watching what her guest was doing, sprang forward with a cry and snatched the child from the fire.

Then Ceres assumed her own form, and a divine splendour shone all around. While they were overcome with astonishment, she said, "Mother, you have been cruel in your fondness to your son. I would have made him immortal, but you have frustrated my attempt. Nevertheless, he shall be great and useful. He shall teach men the use of the plough, and the rewards which labour can win from the cultivated soil." So saying, she wrapped a cloud about her, and mounting her chariot rode away.

Ceres continued her search for her daughter, passing from land to land, and across the seas and rivers, till at length she returned to Sicily, whence she at first set out, and stood by the banks of the River Cyane, where Pluto made himself a passage with his prize to his own dominions. The river nymph would have told the goddess all she had witnessed, but dared not, for fear of Pluto; so she only ventured to take up the girdle which Proserpine had dropped in her flight, and waft it to the feet of the mother.

Ceres, seeing this, was no longer in doubt of her loss, but she did not yet know the cause, and laid the blame on the innocent land. "Ungrateful soil," said she, "which I have endowed with fertility and clothed with herbage and nourishing grain, no more shall you enjoy my favours." Then the cattle died, the plough broke in the furrow, the seed failed to come up; there was too much sun, there was too much rain; the birds stole the seeds—thistles and brambles were the only growth.

Seeing this, the fountain Arethusa interceded for the land. "Goddess," said she, "blame not the land; it opened unwillingly to yield a passage to your daughter. I can tell you of her fate, for I have seen her. When I passed through the lower parts of the earth, I saw your Proserpine. She was sad, but no longer showing alarm in her countenance. Her look was such as became a queen—the queen of Erebus; the powerful bride of the monarch of the realms of the dead."

When Ceres heard this, she stood for a while like one stupified; then turned her chariot towards heaven, and hastened to present herself before the throne of Jove. She told the story of her bereavement, and implored Jupiter to interfere to procure the restitution of her daughter. Jupiter consented on one condition, namely, that Proserpine should not during her stay in the lower world have taken any food; otherwise, the Fates forbade her release.

Accordingly, Mercury was sent, accompanied by Spring, to demand Proserpine of Pluto. The wily monarch consented; but, alas! the maiden had taken a pomegranate which Pluto offered her, and had sucked the sweet pulp from a few of the seeds. This was enough to prevent her complete release; but a compromise was made, by which she was to pass half the time with her mother, and the rest with her husband Pluto.

Ceres allowed herself to be pacified with this arrangement, and restored the earth to her favour.

ICARUS AND DAEDALUS

Among all those mortals who grew so wise that they learned the secrets of the gods, none was more cunning than Daedalus.

He once built, for King Minos of Crete, a wonderful Labyrinth of winding ways so cunningly tangled up and twisted around that, once inside, you could never find your way out again without a magic clue. But the king's favor veered with the wind, and one day he had his master architect imprisoned in a tower. Daedalus managed to escape from his cell; but it seemed impossible to leave the island, since every ship that came or went was well guarded by order of the king.

At length, watching the sea-gulls in the air— the only creatures that were sure of liberty—he thought of a plan for himself and his young son Icarus, who was captive with him.

Little by little, he gathered a store of feathers great and small. He fastened these together with thread, moulded them in with wax, and so fashioned two great wings like those of a bird. When they were done, Daedalus fitted them to his own shoulders, and after one or two efforts, he found that by waving his arms he could winnow the air and cleave it, as a swimmer does the sea. He

"Icarus and Daedalus." From *Old Greek Folk Stories Told Anew* by Josephine Preston Peabody

held himself aloft, wavered this way and that with the wind, and at last, like a great fledgling, he learned to fly.

Without delay, he fell to work on a pair of wings for the boy Icarus, and taught him carefully how to use them, bidding him beware of rash adventures among the stars. "Remember," said the father, "never to fly very low or very high, for the fogs about the earth would weigh you down, but the blaze of the sun will surely melt your feathers apart if you go too near."

For Icarus, these cautions went in at one ear and out by the other. Who could remember to be careful when he was to fly for the first time? Are birds careful? Not they! And not an idea remained in the boy's head but the one joy of escape.

The day came, and the fair wind that was to set them free. The father bird put on his wings, and, while the light urged them to be gone, he waited to see that all was well with Icarus, for the two could not fly hand in hand. Up they rose, the boy after his father. The hateful ground of Crete sank beneath them; and the country folk, who caught a glimpse of them when they were high above the tree-tops, took it for a vision of the gods—Apollo, perhaps, with Cupid after him.

At first there was a terror in the joy. The wide vacancy of the air dazed them—a glance downward made their brains reel. But when a great wind filled their wings, and Icarus felt himself sustained, like a halcyon-bird in the hollow of a wave, like a child uplifted by his mother, he forgot everything in the world but joy. He forgot Crete and the other islands that he had passed over: he saw but vaguely that wingèd thing in the distance before him that was his father Daedalus. He longed for one draught of flight to quench the thirst of his captivity: he stretched out his arms to the sky and made towards the highest heavens.

Alas for him! Warmer and warmer grew the air. Those arms, that had seemed to uphold him, relaxed. His wings wavered, drooped. He fluttered his young hands vainly—he was falling— and in that terror he remembered. The heat of the sun had melted the wax from his wings; the feathers were falling, one by one, like snowflakes; and there was none to help.

He fell like a leaf tossed down the wind, down, down, with one cry that overtook Daedalus far away. When he returned, and sought high and low for the poor boy, he saw nothing but the bird-like feathers afloat on the water, and he knew that Icarus was drowned.

The nearest island he named Icaria, in memory of the child; but he, in heavy grief, went to the temple of Apollo in Sicily, and there hung up his wings as an offering. Never again did he attempt to fly.

CUPID AND PSYCHE

The theme of this beautiful story is similar to that of "East o' the Sun" and other stories of maidens who doubt and lose their loves but search for them faithfully and successfully.

Once upon a time, through that Destiny that overrules the gods, Love himself gave up his immortal heart to a mortal maiden. And thus it came to pass.

There was a certain king who had three beautiful daughters. The two elder married princes of great renown; but Psyche, the youngest, was so radiantly fair that no suitor seemed worthy of her. People thronged to see her pass through the city, and sang hymns in her praise, while strangers took her for the very goddess of beauty herself.

This angered Venus, and she resolved to cast down her earthly rival. One day, therefore, she called hither her son Love (Cupid, some name him), and bade him sharpen his weapons. He is an archer more to be dreaded than Apollo, for Apollo's arrows take life, but Love's bring joy or sorrow for a whole life long.

"Come, Love," said Venus. "There is a mortal maid who robs me of my honors in yonder city. Avenge your mother. Wound this precious Psyche, and let her fall in love with some churlish creature mean in the eyes of all men."

Cupid made ready his weapons, and flew down to earth invisibly. At that moment Psyche was asleep in her chamber; but he touched her heart with his golden arrow of love, and she opened her eyes so suddenly that he started (forgetting

"Cupid and Psyche." From *Old Greek Folk Stories Told Anew* by Josephine Preston Peabody

that he was invisible), and wounded himself with his own shaft. Heedless of the hurt, moved only by the loveliness of the maiden, he hastened to pour over her locks the healing joy that he ever kept by him, undoing all his work. Back to her dream the princess went, unshadowed by any thought of love. But Cupid, not so light of heart, returned to the heavens, saying not a word of what had passed.

Venus waited long; then, seeing that Psyche's heart had somehow escaped love, she sent a spell upon the maiden. From that time, lovely as she was, not a suitor came to woo; and her parents, who desired to see her a queen at least, made a journey to the Oracle, and asked counsel.

Said the voice: "The princess Psyche shall never wed a mortal. She shall be given to one who waits for her on yonder mountain; he overcomes gods and men."

At this terrible sentence the poor parents were half distraught, and the people gave themselves up to grief at the fate in store for their beloved princess. Psyche alone bowed to her destiny. "We have angered Venus unwittingly," she said, "and all for sake of me, heedless maiden that I am! Give me up, therefore, dear father and mother. If I atone, it may be that the city will prosper once more."

So she besought them, until, after many unavailing denials, the parents consented; and with a great company of people they led Psyche up the mountain,—as an offering to the monster of whom the Oracle had spoken,—and left her there alone.

Full of courage, yet in a secret agony of grief, she watched her kindred and her people wind down the mountain-path, too sad to look back, until they were lost to sight. Then, indeed, she wept, but a sudden breeze drew near, dried her tears, and caressed her hair, seeming to murmur comfort. In truth, it was Zephyr, the kindly West Wind, come to befriend her; and as she took heart, feeling some benignant presence, he lifted her in his arms, and carried her on wings as even as a sea-gull's, over the crest of the fateful mountain and into a valley below. There he left her, resting on a bank of hospitable grass, and there the princess fell asleep.

When she awoke, it was near sunset. She looked about her for some sign of the monster's approach; she wondered, then, if her grievous trial had been but a dream. Near by she saw a sheltering forest, whose young trees seemed to beckon as one maid beckons to another; and eager for the protection of the dryads, she went thither.

The call of running waters drew her farther and farther, till she came out upon an open place, where there was a wide pool. A fountain fluttered gladly in the midst of it, and beyond there stretched a white palace wonderful to see. Coaxed by the bright promise of the place, she drew near, and, seeing no one, entered softly. It was all kinglier than her father's home, and as she stood in wonder and awe, soft airs stirred about her. Little by little the silence grew murmurous like the woods, and one voice, sweeter than the rest, took words. "All that you see is yours, gentle high princess," it said. "Fear nothing; only command us, for we are here to serve you."

Full of amazement and delight, Psyche followed the voice from hall to hall, and through the lordly rooms, beautiful with everything that could delight a young princess. No pleasant thing was lacking. There was even a pool, brightly tiled and fed with running waters, where she bathed her weary limbs; and after she had put on the new and beautiful raiment that lay ready for her, she sat down to break her fast, waited upon and sung to by the unseen spirits.

Surely he whom the Oracle had called her husband was no monster, but some beneficent power, invisible like all the rest. When daylight waned, he came, and his voice, the beautiful voice of a god, inspired her to trust her strange destiny and to look and long for his return. Often she begged him to stay with her through the day, that she might see his face; but this he would not grant.

"Never doubt me, dearest Psyche," said he. "Perhaps you would fear if you saw me, and love is all I ask. There is a necessity that keeps me hidden now. Only believe."

So for many days Psyche was content; but when she grew used to happiness, she thought once more of her parents mourning her as lost, and of her sisters who shared the lot of mortals while she lived as a goddess. One night she told her husband of these regrets, and begged that

her sisters at least might come to see her. He sighed, but did not refuse.

"Zephyr shall bring them hither," said he. And on the following morning, swift as a bird, the West Wind came over the crest of the high mountain and down into the enchanted valley, bearing her two sisters.

They greeted Psyche with joy and amazement, hardly knowing how they had come hither. But when this fairest of the sisters led them through her palace and showed them all the treasures that were hers, envy grew in their hearts and choked their old love. Even while they sat at feast with her, they grew more and more bitter; and hoping to find some little flaw in her good fortune, they asked a thousand questions.

"Where is your husband?" said they. "And why is he not here with you?"

"Ah," stammered Psyche. "All the day long— he is gone, hunting upon the mountains."

"But what does he look like?" they asked; and Psyche could find no answer.

When they learned that she had never seen him, they laughed her faith to scorn.

"Poor Psyche," they said. "You are walking in a dream. Wake, before it is too late. Have you forgotten what the Oracle decreed,—that you were destined for a dreadful creature, the fear of gods and men? And are you deceived by this show of kindliness? We have come to warn you. The people told us, as we came over the mountain, that your husband is a dragon, who feeds you well for the present, that he may feast the better, some day soon. What is it that you trust? Good words! But only take a dagger some night, and when the monster is asleep go, light a lamp, and look at him. You can put him to death easily, and all his riches will be yours—and ours."

Psyche heard this wicked plan with horror. Nevertheless, after her sisters were gone, she brooded over what they had said, not seeing their evil intent; and she came to find some wisdom in their words. Little by little, suspicion ate, like a moth, into her lovely mind; and at nightfall, in shame and fear, she hid a lamp and a dagger in her chamber. Toward midnight, when her husband was fast asleep, up she rose, hardly daring to breathe; and coming softly to his side, she uncovered the lamp to see some horror.

But there the youngest of the gods lay sleeping,—most beautiful, most irresistible of all immortals. His hair shone golden as the sun, his face was radiant as dear Springtime, and from his shoulders sprang two rainbow wings.

Poor Psyche was overcome with self-reproach. As she leaned toward him, filled with worship, her trembling hands held the lamp ill, and some burning oil fell upon Love's shoulder and awakened him.

He opened his eyes, to see at once his bride and the dark suspicion in her heart.

"O doubting Psyche!" he exclaimed with sudden grief,—and then he flew away, out of the window.

Wild with sorrow, Psyche tried to follow, but she fell to the ground instead. When she recovered her senses, she stared about her. She was alone, and the place was beautiful no longer. Garden and palace had vanished with Love. Over mountains and valleys Psyche journeyed alone until she came to the city where her two envious sisters lived with the princes whom they had married. She stayed with them only long enough to tell the story of her unbelief and its penalty. Then she set out again to search for Love.

As she wandered one day, travel-worn but not hopeless, she saw a lofty palace on a hill near by, and she turned her steps thither. The place seemed deserted. Within the hall she saw no human being,—only heaps of grain, loose ears of corn half torn from the husk, wheat and barley, alike scattered in confusion on the floor. Without delay, she set to work binding the sheaves together and gathering the scattered ears of corn in seemly wise, as a princess would wish to see them. While she was in the midst of her task, a voice startled her, and she looked up to behold Demeter herself, the goddess of the harvest, smiling upon her with good will.

"Dear Psyche," said Demeter, "you are worthy of happiness, and you may find it yet. But since you have displeased Venus, go to her and ask her favor. Perhaps your patience will win her pardon."

These motherly words gave Psyche heart, and she reverently took leave of the goddess and set out for the temple of Venus. Most humbly she offered up her prayer, but Venus could not look at her earthly beauty without anger.

"Vain girl," said she, "perhaps you have come to make amends for the wound you dealt your husband; you shall do so. Such clever people can always find work!"

Then she led Psyche into a great chamber

heaped high with mingled grain, beans, and lintels (the food of her doves), and bade her separate them all and have them ready in seemly fashion by night. Heracles would have been helpless before such a vexatious task; and poor Psyche, left alone in this desert of grain, had not courage to begin. But even as she sat there, a moving thread of black crawled across the floor from a crevice in the wall; and bending nearer, she saw that a great army of ants in columns had come to her aid. The zealous little creatures worked in swarms, with such industry over the work they like best, that, when Venus came at night, she found the task completed.

"Deceitful girl!" she cried, shaking the roses out of her hair with impatience, "this is my son's work, not yours. But he will soon forget you. Eat this black bread if you are hungry, and refresh your dull mind with sleep. To-morrow you will need more wit."

Psyche wondered what new misfortune could be in store for her. But when morning came, Venus led her to the brink of a river, and, pointing to the wood across the water, said, "Go now to yonder grove where the sheep with the golden fleece are wont to browse. Bring me a golden lock from every one of them, or you must go your ways and never come back again."

This seemed not difficult, and Psyche obediently bade the goddess farewell, and stepped into the water, ready to wade across. But as Venus disappeared, the reeds sang louder and the nymphs of the river, looking up sweetly, blew bubbles to the surface and murmured: "Nay, nay, have a care, Psyche. This flock has not the gentle ways of sheep. While the sun burns aloft, they are themselves as fierce as flame; but when the shadows are long, they go to rest and sleep, under the trees; and you may cross the river without fear and pick the golden fleece off the briers in the pasture."

Thanking the water-creatures, Psyche sat down to rest near them, and when the time came, she crossed in safety and followed their counsel. By twilight she returned to Venus with her arms full of shining fleece.

"No mortal wit did this," said Venus angrily. "But if you care to prove your readiness, go now, with this little box, down to Proserpina and ask her to enclose in it some of her beauty,

for I have grown pale in caring for my wounded son."

It needed not the last taunt to sadden Psyche. She knew that it was not for mortals to go into Hades and return alive; and feeling that Love had forsaken her, she was minded to accept her doom as soon as might be.

But even as she hastened toward the descent, another friendly voice detained her. "Stay, Psyche, I know your grief. Only give ear and you shall learn a safe way through all these trials." And the voice went on to tell her how one might avoid all the dangers of Hades and come out unscathed. (But such a secret could not pass from mouth to mouth, with the rest of the story.)

"And be sure," added the voice, "when Proserpina has returned the box, not to open it, however much you may long to do so."

Psyche gave heed, and by this device, whatever it was, she found her way into Hades safely, and made her errand known to Proserpina, and was soon in the upper world again, wearied but hopeful.

"Surely Love has not forgotten me," she said. "But humbled as I am and worn with toil, how shall I ever please him? Venus can never need all the beauty in this casket; and since I use it for Love's sake, it must be right to take some." So saying, she opened the box, heedless as Pandora! The spells and potions of Hades are not for mortal maids, and no sooner had she inhaled the strange aroma than she fell down like one dead, quite overcome.

But it happened that Love himself was recovered from his wound, and he had secretly fled from his chamber to seek out and rescue Psyche. He found her lying by the wayside; he gathered into the casket what remained of the philter, and awoke his beloved.

"Take comfort," he said, smiling. "Return to our mother and do her bidding till I come again."

Away he flew; and while Psyche went cheerily homeward, he hastened up to Olympus, where all the gods sat feasting, and begged them to intercede for him with his angry mother.

They heard his story and their hearts were touched. Zeus himself coaxed Venus with kind words till at last she relented, and remembered that anger hurt her beauty, and smiled once more. All the younger gods were for welcoming Psyche at once, and Hermes was sent to bring her hither. The maiden came, a shy newcomer among those bright creatures. She took the cup that Hebe held out to her, drank the divine ambrosia, and became immortal.

Light came to her face like moonrise, two radiant wings sprang from her shoulders; and even as a butterfly bursts from its dull cocoon, so the human Psyche blossomed into immortality.

Love took her by the hand, and they were never parted any more.

ATALANTA'S RACE

Even if Prince Meleager had lived, it is doubtful if he could ever have won Atalanta to be his wife. The maiden was resolved to live unwed, and at last she devised a plan to be rid of all her suitors. She was known far and wide as the swiftest runner of her time; and so she said that she would only marry that man who could outstrip her in the race, but that all who dared to try and failed must be put to death.

This threat did not dishearten all of the suitors, however, and to her grief, for she was not cruel, they held her to her promise. On a certain day the few bold men who were to try their fortune made ready, and chose young Hippomenes as judge. He sat watching them before the word was given, and sadly wondered that any brave man should risk his life merely to win a bride. But when Atalanta stood ready for the contest, he was amazed by her beauty. She looked like Hebe, goddess of young health, who is a glad serving-maiden to the gods when they sit at feast.

The signal was given, and, as she and the suitors darted away, flight made her more enchanting than ever. Just as a wind brings sparkles to the water and laughter to the trees, haste fanned her loveliness to a glow.

Alas for the suitors! She ran as if Hermes had lent her his wingèd sandals. The young men, skilled as they were, grew heavy with weariness and despair. For all their efforts, they seemed to

"Atalanta's Race." From *Old Greek Folk Stories Told Anew* by Josephine Preston Peabody

lag like ships in a calm, while Atalanta flew before them in some favoring breeze—and reached the goal!

To the sorrow of all on-lookers, the suitors were led away; but the judge himself, Hippomenes, rose and begged leave to try his fortune. As Atalanta listened, and looked at him, her heart was filled with pity, and she would willingly have let him win the race to save him from defeat and death; for he was comely and younger than the others. But her friends urged her to rest and make ready, and she consented, with an unwilling heart.

Meanwhile Hippomenes prayed within himself to Venus: "Goddess of Love, give ear, and send me good speed. Let me be swift to win as I have been swift to love her."

Now Venus, who was not far off,—for she had already moved the heart of Hippomenes to love, —came to his side invisibly, slipped into his hand three wondrous golden apples, and whispered a word of counsel in his ear.

The signal was given; youth and maiden started over the course. They went so like the wind that they left not a footprint. The people cheered on Hippomenes, eager that such valor should win. But the course was long, and soon fatigue seemed to clutch at his throat, the light shook before his eyes, and, even as he pressed on, the maiden passed him by.

At that instant Hippomenes tossed ahead one of the golden apples. The rolling bright thing caught Atalanta's eye, and full of wonder she stooped to pick it up. Hippomenes ran on. As he heard the flutter of her tunic close behind him, he flung aside another golden apple, and another moment was lost to the girl. Who could pass by such a marvel? The goal was near and Hippomenes was ahead, but once again Atalanta caught up with him, and they sped side by side like two dragon-flies. For an instant his heart failed him; then, with a last prayer to Venus, he flung down the last apple. The maiden glanced at it, wavered, and would have left it where it had fallen, had not Venus turned her head for a second and given her a sudden wish to possess it. Against her will she turned to pick up the golden apple, and Hippomenes touched the goal.

So he won that perilous maiden; and as for

Atalanta, she was glad to marry such a valorous man. By this time she understood so well what it was like to be pursued, that she had lost a little of her pleasure in hunting.

BAUCIS AND PHILEMON

On a certain hill in Phrygia stand a linden tree and an oak, enclosed by a low wall. Not far from the spot is a marsh, formerly good habitable land, but now indented with pools, the resort of fen-birds and cormorants.

Once upon a time Jupiter, in human shape, visited this country, and with him his son Mercury without his wings. They presented themselves, as weary travellers, at many a door, seeking rest and shelter, but found all closed, for it was late and the inhospitable inhabitants would not rouse themselves to open for them. At last a humble cottage received them, where Baucis, a pious old dame, and her husband, Philemon, had grown old together. Not ashamed of their poverty, they made it endurable by their modest desires and kind dispositions.

When the two heavenly guests crossed the humble threshold and bowed their heads to pass under the low door, the old man placed a seat, on which Baucis, bustling and attentive, spread a cloth, and begged them to sit down. Then she raked out the coals from the ashes and kindled up a fire, fed it with leaves and dry bark, and with her scanty breath blew it into a flame. She brought out of a corner split sticks and dry branches, broke them up, and placed them under the small kettle.

Her husband collected some pot-herbs in the garden, and she shred them from the stalks and prepared them for the pot. He reached down with a forked stick a flitch of bacon hanging in the chimney, cut a small piece, and put it in the pot to boil with the herbs, setting away the rest for another time. A bowl was filled with warm water, so the guests might wash. While all was doing, they beguiled the time with conversation.

On the bench designed for the guests was laid a cushion stuffed with sea-weed; and a cloth, only produced on great occasions, but ancient

"Baucis and Philemon." From *A Book of Myths*, selections from Bulfinch's *Age of Fable*, Macmillan, 1942

and coarse enough, was spread over that. The old lady, with her apron on, with trembling hand set the table. One leg was shorter than the rest, but a piece of slate put under brought it level. When fixed, she rubbed the table down with some sweet-smelling herbs. Upon it she set some olives, some cornel berries preserved in vinegar, and added radishes and cheese, with eggs lightly cooked in the ashes. All were served in earthen dishes, and an earthenware pitcher, with wooden cups, stood beside them. When all was ready, the stew, smoking hot, was set on the table. Some wine, not of the oldest, was added; and for dessert, apples and wild honey. Over and above all, there were friendly faces and a simple, but hearty welcome.

Now, while the meal was being eaten, the old folks were astonished to see that the wine, as fast as it was poured out, renewed itself in the pitcher, of its own accord. Struck with terror, Baucis and Philemon recognized their heavenly guests, fell on their knees, and with clasped hands implored forgiveness for their poor entertainment. There was an old goose, which they kept as the guardian of their humble cottage, and they bethought them to make this a sacrifice in honour of their guests.

But the goose, too nimble with the aid of feet and wings, eluded them and at last took shelter between the gods themselves. They forbade it to be slain and spoke these words: "We are gods. This inhospitable village shall pay the penalty of its impiety; you alone shall go free from punishment. Leave your house and come with us to the top of yonder hill."

They hastened to obey, and, staff in hand, toiled up the steep ascent. They had reached to within an arrow's flight of the top when, turning their eyes below, they beheld all the country sunk in a lake, only their own house left standing. While they gazed with wonder at the sight and lamented the fate of their neighbours, that old house of theirs was changed into a temple. Columns took the place of the corner posts, the thatch grew into a gilded roof, the floors became marble, the doors were enriched with carving and ornaments of gold.

Then spoke Jupiter: "Excellent old man, and woman worthy of such a husband, speak, tell us your wishes; what favour have you to ask of us?"

Philemon took counsel with Baucis a few moments; then they declared to the gods their wish. "We ask to be priests and guardians of your temple; and since we have passed our lives here in love and agreement, we wish that one and the same hour may take us both from life, that I may not live to see her grave nor be laid in my own by her."

Their prayer was granted. They were the keepers of the temple as long as they lived. When grown very old, as they stood one day before the steps of the building and were telling the story of the place, Baucis saw Philemon begin to put forth leaves, and old Philemon saw Baucis changing in the same manner. And now a leafy crown had grown over their heads. They exchanged parting words as long as they could speak. "Farewell, dear spouse," they said together, and at the same moment the bark closed over their mouths. The Tyanean shepherd still shows the two trees, standing side by side, made out of the two good old people.

PEGASUS AND THE CHIMAERA

When Perseus cut off Medusa's head, the blood sinking into the earth produced the winged horse Pegasus. Minerva caught and tamed him and presented him to the Muses. The fountain Hippocrene, on the Muses' mountain Helicon, was opened by a kick from his hoof.

The Chimaera was a fearful monster, breathing fire. The fore part of its body was a compound of the lion and the goat, and the hind part a dragon's. It made great havoc in Lycia, so that the king, Iobates, sought for some hero to destroy it. At that time there arrived at his court a gallant young warrior, whose name was Bellerophon. He brought letters from Proetus, the son-in-law of Iobates, recommending Bellerophon in the warmest terms as an unconquerable hero, but added at the close a request to his father-in-law to put him to death. The reason was that Proetus was jealous of him, suspecting that his wife Antea looked with too much admiration on the young warrior.

Iobates, on perusing the letters, was puzzled

"Pegasus and the Chimaera." From *A Book of Myths*, selections from Bulfinch's *Age of Fable*, Macmillan, 1942

what to do, not willing to violate the claims of hospitality, yet wishing to oblige his son-in-law. A lucky thought occurred to him, to send Bellerophon to combat with the Chimaera. Bellerophon accepted the proposal, but before proceeding to the combat consulted a soothsayer, who advised him to procure if possible the horse Pegasus for the conflict.

For this purpose he directed him to pass the night in the temple of Minerva. He did so, and as he slept Minerva came to him and gave him a golden bridle. When he awoke the bridle remained in his hand. Minerva also showed him Pegasus drinking at the well of Pirene, and at the sight of the bridle the winged steed came willingly and suffered himself to be taken. Bellerophon mounted him, rose with him into the air, soon found the Chimaera, and gained an easy victory over the monster.

After the conquest of the monster Bellerophon was exposed to further trials and labours by his unfriendly host, but by the aid of Pegasus he triumphed in them all, till at length Iobates, seeing that the hero was a special favourite of the gods, gave him his daughter in marriage and made him his successor on the throne. At last Bellerophon by his pride and presumption drew upon himself the anger of the gods; it is said he even attempted to fly up into heaven on his winged steed, but Jupiter sent a gadfly which stung Pegasus and made him throw his rider, who became lame and blind in consequence. After this Bellerophon wandered lonely through the Aleian field, avoiding the paths of men, and died miserably.

MIDAS

This is the meager source (in translation) from which Hawthorne spun the better-known version which follows.

Bacchus, in return for a kindness done him, offered King Midas his choice of a reward, whatever he might wish. Midas asked to have everything he should touch changed into gold. Bacchus consented, though sorry he had not made a better choice. Midas went his way, rejoicing in his new-acquired power, which he hastened to put to the test. He could scarcely believe his eyes when he found a twig of an oak, which he plucked from the branch, become gold in his hand. He took up a stone; it turned to gold. He touched a sod; it did the same. He took an apple from the tree; you would have thought he had robbed the garden of the Hesperides.

His joy knew no bounds, and as soon as he reached home, he ordered the servants to set a splendid feast on the table. Then he found to his dismay that whenever he touched bread, it hardened in his hand, or put a morsel to his lips,

"Midas." From *A Book of Myths*, selections from Bulfinch's *Age of Fable*, Macmillan, 1942

it defied his teeth. He took a glass of wine, but it flowed down his throat like melted gold.

Worried by this affliction, he tried to get rid of the power; he hated the gift he had lately coveted. But all in vain. Starvation seemed to await him. He raised his arms, all shining with gold, in prayer to Bacchus, begging to be delivered from his glittering destruction. Bacchus, merciful deity, heard and consented. "Go," he said, "to the River Factolus, trace the stream to its source, and there plunge your head and body in and wash away your fault and its punishment."

He did so, and scarcely had he touched the waters before the gold-creating power passed into them, and the river sands were changed into gold, as they remain to this day.

Henceforth Midas, hating wealth and splendour, lived in the country and became a worshipper of Pan, the god of the fields. On a certain occasion Pan dared to compare his music with that of Apollo, and to challenge the god of the lyre to a trial of skill. Tmolus, the mountain god, was chosen umpire. He took his seat and cleared away the trees from his ears to listen. At a given signal, Pan blew on his pipes and with his melody gave great satisfaction to himself and his faithful follower, Midas. Then Tmolus turned his head toward the sun-god, and all his trees turned with him.

Apollo rose, his brow wreathed with Parnassian laurel, while his robe of Tyrian purple swept the ground. In his left hand he held the lyre, and with his right hand struck the strings. Ravished with the harmony, Tmolus at once awarded the victory to Apollo, and all but Midas acquiesced in the judgement. He dissented and questioned the justice of the award. Apollo would not suffer such a depraved pair of ears any longer to wear human form, but caused them to increase in length, grow hairy within and without, and become movable at their roots; in short, the perfect pattern of those of an ass.

Mortified enough was King Midas at this mishap; but he consoled himself with the thought that it was possible to hide his misfortune, which he attempted to do by means of an ample turban or head-dress. But his hair-dresser of course knew the secret. He was charged not to mention it, and threatened with dire punishment if he presumed to disobey. But he found it too much to keep such a secret. He went out into the meadow, dug a hole in the ground, and stooping down, whispered the story and covered it up. Before long, a thick bed of reeds sprang up in the meadow, and as soon as it had gained its growth, began whispering the story and has continued to do so from that day to this, every time a breeze passes over the place.

THE GOLDEN TOUCH

Once upon a time, there lived a very rich king whose name was Midas; and he had a little daughter, whom nobody but myself ever heard of, and whose name was Marygold.

This King Midas was fonder of gold than of anything else in the world. He valued his royal crown chiefly because it was composed of that precious metal. If he loved anything better, or half so well, it was the one little maiden who played so merrily around her father's footstool. But the more Midas loved his daughter, the more did he desire and seek for wealth. He thought, foolish man! that the best thing he could possibly do for this dear child would be to bequeath her the immensest pile of yellow, glistening coin, that had ever been heaped together since the world was made. Thus, he gave all his thoughts and all his time to this one purpose. If ever he happened to gaze for an instant at the gold-tinted clouds of sunset, he wished that they were real gold, and that they could be squeezed safely into his strong box. When little Marygold ran to meet him, with a bunch of buttercups and dandelions, he used to say, "Poh, poh, child! If these flowers were as golden as they look, they would be worth the plucking!"

And yet, in his earlier days, before he was so entirely possessed of this insane desire for riches, King Midas had shown a great taste for flowers. He had planted a garden, in which grew the biggest and beautifullest and sweetest roses that any mortal ever saw or smelt. These roses were still growing in the garden, as large, as lovely, and as fragrant, as when Midas used to pass whole hours in gazing at them, and inhaling

"The Golden Touch." From *A Wonder Book for Girls and Boys* by Nathaniel Hawthorne

their perfume. But now, if he looked at them at all, it was only to calculate how much the garden would be worth if each of the innumerable rose-petals were a thin plate of gold. And though he once was fond of music the only music for poor Midas, now, was the chink of one coin against another.

At length Midas had got to be so exceedingly unreasonable, that he could scarcely bear to see or touch any object that was not gold. He made it his custom, therefore, to pass a large portion of every day in a dark and dreary apartment, under ground, at the basement of his palace. It was here that he kept his wealth. To this dismal hole —for it was little better than a dungeon—Midas betook himself, whenever he wanted to be particularly happy. Here, after carefully locking the door, he would take a bag of gold coin, or a gold cup as big as a washbowl, or a heavy golden bar, or a peck-measure of gold-dust, and bring them from the obscure corners of the room into the one bright and narrow sunbeam that fell from the dungeon-like window. He valued the sunbeam for no other reason but that his treasure would not shine without its help. And then would he reckon over the coins in the bag, toss up the bar, and catch it as it came down; sift the gold-dust through his fingers; look at the funny image of his own face, as reflected in the burnished circumference of the cup; and whisper to himself, "O Midas, rich King Midas, what a happy man art thou!"

Midas was enjoying himself in his treasure-room, one day, as usual, when he perceived a shadow fall over the heaps of gold; and, looking suddenly up, what should he behold but the figure of a stranger, standing in the bright and narrow sunbeam! It was a young man, with a cheerful and ruddy face. Whether it was that the imagination of King Midas threw a yellow tinge over everything, or whatever the cause might be, he could not help fancying that the smile with which the stranger regarded him had a kind of golden radiance in it. Certainly, although his figure intercepted the sunshine, there was now a brighter gleam upon all the piled-up treasure than before. Even the remotest corners had their share of it, and were lighted up, when the stranger smiled, as with tips of flame and sparkles of fire.

As Midas knew that he had carefully turned the key in the lock, and that no mortal strength could possibly break into his treasure-room, he, of course, concluded that his visitor must be something more than mortal. Midas had met such beings before now, and was not sorry to meet one of them again.

The stranger gazed about the room; and when his lustrous smile had glistened upon all the golden objects that were there, he turned again to Midas.

"You are a wealthy man, friend Midas!" he observed. "I doubt whether any other four walls, on earth, contain so much gold as you have contrived to pile up in this room."

"I have done pretty well,—pretty well," answered Midas, in a discontented tone. "But, after all, it is but a trifle, when you consider that it has taken me my whole life to get it together. If one could live a thousand years, he might have time to grow rich!"

"What!" exclaimed the stranger. "Then you are not satisfied?"

Midas shook his head.

"And pray what would satisfy you?" asked the stranger. "Merely for the curiosity of the thing, I should be glad to know."

Midas paused and meditated. He felt a presentiment that this stranger, with such a golden lustre in his good-humored smile, had come hither with both the power and the purpose of gratifying his utmost wishes. Now, therefore, was the fortunate moment, when he had but to speak, and obtain whatever possible, or seemingly impossible thing, it might come into his head to ask. So he thought, and thought, and thought, and heaped up one golden mountain upon another, in his imagination, without being able to imagine them big enough. At last, a bright idea occurred to King Midas. It seemed really as bright as the glistening metal which he loved so much.

Raising his head, he looked the lustrous stranger in the face.

"Well, Midas," observed his visitor, "I see that you have at length hit upon something that will satisfy you. Tell me your wish."

"It is only this," replied Midas. "I am weary of collecting my treasures with so much trouble, and beholding the heap so diminutive, after I have done my best. I wish everything that I touch be changed to gold!"

The stranger's smile grew so very broad, that it seemed to fill the room like an outburst of the sun, gleaming into a shadowy dell, where the yellow autumnal leaves—for so looked the lumps and particles of gold—lie strewn in the glow of light.

"The Golden Touch!" exclaimed he. "You certainly deserve credit, friend Midas, for striking out so brilliant a conception. But are you quite sure that this will satisfy you?"

"How could it fail?" said Midas.

"And will you never regret the possession of it?"

"What could induce me?" asked Midas. "I ask nothing else, to render me perfectly happy."

"Be it as you wish, then," replied the stranger, waving his hand in token of farewell. "To-morrow, at sunrise, you will find yourself gifted with the Golden Touch."

The figure of the stranger then became exceedingly bright, and Midas involuntarily closed his eyes. On opening them again, he beheld only one yellow sunbeam in the room, and all around him, the glistening of the precious metal which he had spent his life in hoarding up.

Whether Midas slept as usual that night, the story does not say. At any rate, day had hardly peeped over the hills, when King Midas was broad awake, and stretching his arms out of bed, began to touch the objects that were within reach. He was anxious to prove whether the Golden Touch had really come, according to the stranger's promise. So he laid his finger on a chair by the bedside, and on various other things, but was grievously disappointed to perceive that they remained of exactly the same substance as before. Indeed, he felt very much afraid that he had only dreamed about the lustrous stranger, or else that the latter had been making game of him. And what a miserable affair would it be, if after all his hopes, Midas must content himself with what little gold he could scrape together by ordinary means, instead of creating it by a touch!

All this while, it was only the gray of the morning, with but a streak of brightness along the edge of the sky, where Midas could not see it. He lay in a very disconsolate mood, regretting the downfall of his hopes, and kept growing sadder and sadder, until the earliest sunbeam shone through the window, and gilded the ceiling over his head. It seemed to Midas that this bright yellow sunbeam was reflected in rather a singular way on the white covering of the bed. Looking more closely, what was his astonishment and delight, when he found that this linen fabric had been transmuted to what seemed a woven texture of the purest and brightest gold! The Golden Touch had come to him with the first sunbeam!

Midas started up, in a kind of joyful frenzy, and ran about the room, grasping at everything that happened to be in his way. He seized one of the bed-posts, and it became immediately a fluted golden pillar. He pulled aside a window-curtain, in order to admit a clear spectacle of the wonders which he was performing; and the tassel grew heavy in his hand,—a mass of gold. He took up a book from the table. At his first touch, it assumed the appearance of such a splendidly bound and gilt-edged volume as one often meets with, now-adays; but, on running his fingers through the leaves, behold! It was a bundle of thin golden plates, in which all the wisdom of the book had grown illegible. He hurriedly put on his clothes, and was enraptured to see himself in a magnificent suit of gold cloth, which retained its flexibility and softness, although it burdened him a little with its weight. He drew out his handkerchief, which little Marygold had hemmed for him. That was likewise gold, with the dear child's neat and pretty stitches running all along the border, in gold thread!

Somehow or other, this last transformation did not quite please King Midas. He would rather that his little daughter's handiwork should have remained just the same as when she climbed his knee and put it into his hand.

But it was not worth while to vex himself about a trifle. Midas now took his spectacles from his pocket, and put them on his nose, in order that he might see more distinctly what he was about. In those days, spectacles for common people had not been invented, but were already worn by kings; else, how could Midas have had any? To his great perplexity, however, excellent as the glasses were, he discovered that he could not possibly see through them. But this was the most natural thing in the world; for, on taking them off, the transparent crystals turned out to be plates of yellow metal, and, of course, were worthless as spectacles, though valuable as gold. It struck Midas as rather inconvenient that, with all his wealth, he could never again be rich enough to own a pair of serviceable spectacles.

"It is no great matter, nevertheless," said he to himself, very philosophically. "We cannot expect any great good, without its being accompanied with some small inconvenience. The Golden Touch is worth the sacrifice of a pair of spectacles, at least, if not of one's very eyesight. My own eyes will serve for ordinary purposes, and little Marygold will soon be old enough to read to me."

King Midas went down stairs, and smiled, on observing that the balustrade of the staircase became a bar of burnished gold, as his hand passed over it, in his descent. He lifted the door-latch (it was brass only a moment ago, but golden when his fingers quitted it), and emerged into the garden. Here, as it happened, he found a great number of beautiful roses in full bloom, and others in all the stages of lovely bud and blossom. Very delicious was their fragrance in the morning breeze. Their delicate blush was one of the fairest sights in the world; so gentle, so modest, and so full of sweet tranquillity, did these roses seem to be.

But Midas knew a way to make them far more precious, according to his way of thinking, than roses had ever been before. So he took great pains in going from bush to bush, and exercised his magic touch most indefatigably; until every individual flower and bud, and even the worms at the heart of some of them, were changed to gold. By the time this good work was completed, King Midas was summoned to breakfast; and as the morning air had given him an excellent appetite, he made haste back to the palace.

On this particular morning, the breakfast consisted of hot cakes, some nice little brook-trout, roasted potatoes, fresh boiled eggs, and coffee, for King Midas himself, and a bowl of bread and milk for his daughter Marygold.

Little Marygold had not yet made her appearance. Her father ordered her to be called, and, seating himself at table, awaited the child's coming, in order to begin his own breakfast. To do Midas justice, he really loved his daughter, and loved her so much the more this morning, on account of the good fortune which had be-fallen him. It was not a great while before he heard her coming along the passageway crying bitterly. This circumstance surprised him, be-cause Marygold was one of the cheerfullest little people whom you would see in a summer's day, and hardly shed a thimbleful of tears in a twelve-month. When Midas heard her sobs, he deter-mined to put little Marygold in better spirits, by an agreeable surprise; so, leaning across the table, he touched his daughter's bowl (which was a China one, with pretty figures all around it), and transmuted it to gleaming gold.

Meanwhile, Marygold slowly and disconsol-ately opened the door, and showed herself with her apron at her eyes, still sobbing as if her heart would break.

"How now, my little lady!" cried Midas. "Pray what is the matter with you, this bright morn-ing?"

Marygold, without taking the apron from her eyes, held out her hand, in which was one of the roses which Midas had so recently transmuted.

"Beautiful!" exclaimed her father. "And what is there in this magnificent golden rose to make you cry?"

"Ah, dear father!" answered the child, as well as her sobs would let her; "it is not beautiful, but the ugliest flower that ever grew! As soon as I was dressed I ran into the garden to gather some roses for you; because I know you like them. But, oh dear, dear me! What do you think has happened? Such a misfortune! All the beau-tiful roses, that smelled so sweetly and had so many lovely blushes, are blighted and spoilt! They are grown quite yellow, as you see this one, and have no longer any fragrance! What can have been the matter with them?"

"Poh, my dear little girl,—pray don't cry about it!" said Midas, who was ashamed to confess that he himself had wrought the change which so greatly afflicted her. "Sit down and eat your bread and milk! You will find it easy enough to exchange a golden rose like that (which will last hundreds of years) for an ordinary one which would wither in a day."

"I don't care for such roses as this!" cried Marygold, tossing it contemptuously away. "It has no smell, and the hard petals prick my nose!"

The child now sat down to table, but was so occupied with her grief for the blighted roses that she did not even notice the wonderful trans-mutation of her China bowl. Perhaps this was all the better; for Marygold was accustomed to take pleasure in looking at the queer figures, and strange trees and houses, that were painted on the circumference of the bowl; and these orna-ments were now entirely lost in the yellow hue of the metal.

Midas, meanwhile, had poured out a cup of coffee, and, as a matter of course, the coffee-pot, whatever metal it may have been when he took it up, was gold when he set it down. He thought to himself, that it was rather an extravagant style of splendor, in a king of his simple habits, to breakfast off a service of gold, and began to be puzzled with the difficulty of keeping his treasures safe. The cupboard and the kitchen would no longer be a secure place of deposit for articles so valuable as golden bowls and coffee-pots.

Amid these thoughts, he lifted a spoonful of coffee to his lips, and, sipping it, was astonished to perceive that, the instant his lips touched the liquid, it became molten gold, and, the next moment, hardened into a lump!

"Ha!" exclaimed Midas, rather aghast.

"What is the matter, father?" asked little Marygold, gazing at him, with the tears still standing in her eyes.

"Nothing, child, nothing!" said Midas. "Eat your milk, before it gets quite cold."

He took one of the nice little trouts on his plate, and, by way of experiment, touched its tail with his finger. To his horror, it was imme-diately transmuted from an admirably fried brook-trout into a gold-fish. A very pretty piece of work, as you may suppose; only King Midas, just at that moment, would much rather have had a real trout in his dish than this elaborate and valuable imitation of one.

"I don't quite see," thought he to himself, "how I am to get any breakfast!"

He took one of the smoking-hot cakes, and had scarcely broken it, when, to his cruel mortifica-tion, though, a moment before, it had been of the whitest wheat, it assumed the yellow hue of Indian meal. Almost in despair, he helped him-self to a boiled egg, which immediately under-went a change similar to those of the trout and the cake. The egg, indeed, might have been mistaken for one of those which the famous goose, in the story-book, was in the habit of laying; but King Midas was the only goose that had had anything to do with the matter.

"Well, this is a quandary!" thought he, leaning back in his chair, and looking quite enviously at little Marygold, who was now eating her bread and milk with great satisfaction. "Such a costly breakfast before me, and nothing that can be eaten."

Hoping that, by dint of great dispatch, he might avoid what he now felt to be a considerable inconvenience, King Midas next snatched a hot potato, and attempted to cram it into his mouth, and swallow it in a hurry. But the Golden Touch was too nimble for him. He found his mouth full, not of mealy potato, but of solid metal, which so burnt his tongue that he roared aloud, and, jumping up from the table, began to dance and stamp about the room, both with pain and affright.

"Father, dear father!" cried little Marygold, who was a very affectionate child, "pray what is the matter? Have you burnt your mouth?"

"Ah, dear child," groaned Midas, dolefully, "I don't know what is to become of your poor father!"

Already, at breakfast, Midas was excessively hungry. Would he be less so by dinner-time? And how ravenous would be his appetite for supper, which must undoubtedly consist of the same sort of indigestible dishes as those now before him.

These reflections so troubled wise King Midas, that he began to doubt whether, after all, riches are the one desirable thing in the world. But this was only a passing thought. So fascinated was Midas with the glitter of the yellow metal, that he would still have refused to give up the Golden Touch for so paltry a consideration as a breakfast.

Nevertheless, so great was his hunger, and the perplexity of his situation, that he again groaned aloud, and very grievously too. Our pretty Marygold could endure it no longer. She sat, a moment, gazing at her father, and trying, with all the might of her little wits, to find out what was the matter with him. Then, with a sweet and sorrowful impulse to comfort him, she started from her chair, and, running to Midas, threw

her arms affectionately about his knees. He bent down and kissed her. He felt that his little daughter's love was worth a thousand times more than he had gained by the Golden Touch.

"My precious, precious Marygold!" cried he.

But Marygold made no answer.

Alas, what had he done? The moment the lips of Midas touched Marygold's forehead, a change had taken place. Her sweet, rosy face, so full of affection as it had been, assumed a glittering yellow color, with yellow tear-drops, congealing on her cheeks. Her beautiful brown ringlets took the same tint. Her soft and tender little form grew hard and inflexible within her father's encircling arms. Oh, terrible misfortune! The victim of his insatiable desire for wealth, little Marygold was a human child no longer, but a golden statue!

Yes, there she was, with the questioning look of love, grief, and pity, hardened into her face. It was the prettiest and most woeful sight that ever mortal saw. All the features and tokens of Marygold were there; even the beloved little dimple remained in her golden chin. But, the more perfect was the resemblance, the greater was the father's agony at beholding this golden image, which was all that was left·him of a daughter. It had been a favorite phrase of Midas, whenever he felt particularly fond of the child, to say that she was worth her weight in gold. And now the phrase had become literally true. And now, at last, when it was too late, he felt how infinitely a warm and tender heart, that loved him, exceeded in value all the wealth that could be piled up betwixt the earth and sky!

Midas, in the fulness of all his gratified desires, began to wring his hands and bemoan himself; and how he could neither bear to look at Marygold, nor yet to look away from her. Except when his eyes were fixed on the image, he could not possibly believe that she was changed to gold. But, stealing another glance, there was the precious little figure, with a yellow tear-drop on its yellow cheek, and a look so piteous and tender, that it seemed as if that very expression must needs soften the gold, and make it flesh again. This, however, could not be.

While Midas was in this tumult of despair, he suddenly beheld a stranger standing near the door. Midas bent down his head, without speaking; for he recognized the same figure which had appeared to him, the day before, in the treasure-room, and had bestowed on him this disastrous faculty of the Golden Touch. The stranger's countenance still wore a smile, which seemed to shed a yellow lustre all about the room, and gleamed on little Marygold's image, and on the other objects that had been transmuted by the touch of Midas.

"Well, friend Midas," said the stranger, "pray how do you succeed with the Golden Touch?"

Midas shook his head.

"I am very miserable," said he.

"Very miserable, indeed!" exclaimed the stranger. "And how happens that? Have I not faithfully kept my promise with you? Have you not everything that your heart desired?"

"Gold is not everything," answered Midas. "And I have lost all that my heart really cared for."

"Ah! So you have made a discovery, since yesterday?" observed the stranger. "Let us see, then. Which of these two things do you think is really worth the most,—the gift of the Golden Touch, or one cup of clear cold water?"

"O blessed water!" exclaimed Midas. "It will never moisten my parched throat again!"

"The Golden Touch," continued the stranger, "or a crust of bread?"

"A piece of bread," answered Midas, "is worth all the gold on earth!"

"The Golden Touch," asked the stranger, "or your own little Marygold, warm, soft, and loving as she was an hour ago?"

"Oh, my child, my dear child!" cried poor Midas, wringing his hands. "I would not have given that one small dimple in her chin for the power of changing this whole big earth into a solid lump of gold!"

"You are wiser than you were, King Midas!" said the stranger, looking seriously at him. "Your own heart, I perceive, has not been entirely changed from flesh to gold. Were it so, your case would indeed be desperate. But you appear to be still capable of understanding that the commonest things, such as lie within everybody's grasp, are more valuable than the riches which so many mortals sigh and struggle after. Tell me, now, do you sincerely desire to rid yourself of this Golden Touch?"

"It is hateful to me!" replied Midas.

A fly settled on his nose, but immediately fell to the floor; for it, too, had become gold. Midas shuddered.

"Go, then," said the stranger, "and plunge into the river that glides past the bottom of your garden. Take likewise a vase of the same water, and sprinkle it over any object that you may desire to change back again from gold into its former substance. If you do this in earnestness and sincerity, it may possibly repair the mischief which your avarice has occasioned."

King Midas bowed low; and when he lifted his head, the lustrous stranger had vanished.

You will easily believe that Midas lost no time in snatching up a great earthen pitcher (but, alas me! it was no longer earthen after he touched it), and hastening to the river-side. As he scampered along, and forced his way through the shrubbery, it was positively marvellous to see how the foliage turned yellow behind him, as if the autumn had been there, and nowhere else. On reaching the river's brink, he plunged head-long in, without waiting so much as to pull off his shoes.

"Poof! poof! poof!" snorted King Midas, as his head emerged out of the water. "Well, this is really a refreshing bath, and I think it must have quite washed away the Golden Touch. And now for filling my pitcher!"

As he dipped the pitcher into the water, it gladdened his very heart to see it change from gold into the same good, honest earthen vessel which it had been before he touched it. He was conscious, also, of a change within himself. A cold, hard, and heavy weight seemed to have gone out of his bosom. Perceiving a violet, that grew on the bank of the river, Midas touched it with his finger, and was overjoyed to find that the delicate flower retained its purple hue, instead of undergoing a yellow blight. The curse of the Golden Touch had, therefore, really been removed from him.

King Midas hastened back to the palace; and, I suppose, the servants knew not what to make of it when they saw their royal master so carefully bringing home an earthen pitcher of water. But that water, which was to undo all the mischief that his folly had wrought, was more precious to Midas than an ocean of molten gold could have been. The first thing he did, as you need hardly be told, was to sprinkle it by handfuls over the golden figure of little Marygold.

No sooner did it fall on her than you would have laughed to see how the rosy color came back to the dear child's cheek! And how she began to sneeze and sputter!—and how astonished she was to find herself dripping wet, and her father still throwing more water over her!

"Pray do not, dear father!" cried she. "See how you have wet my nice frock, which I put on only this morning!"

For Marygold did not know that she had been a little golden statue; nor could she remember anything that had happened since the moment when she ran with outstretched arms to comfort poor King Midas.

Her father did not think it necessary to tell his beloved child how very foolish he had been, but contented himself with showing how much wiser he had now grown. For this purpose, he led little Marygold into the garden, where he sprinkled all the remainder of the water over the rose-bushes, and with such good effect that above five thousand roses recovered their beautiful bloom. There were two circumstances, however, which as long as he lived, used to put King Midas in mind of the Golden Touch. One was, that the sands of the river sparkled like gold; the other, that little Marygold's hair had now a golden tinge, which he had never observed in it before she had been transmuted by the effect of his kiss.

When King Midas had grown quite an old man, and used to trot Marygold's children on his knee, he was fond of telling them this marvellous story, pretty much as I have now told it to you. And then would he stroke their glossy ringlets, and tell them that their hair, likewise, had a rich shade of gold, which they had inherited from their mother.

"And to tell you the truth, my precious little folks," quoth King Midas, diligently trotting the children all the while, "ever since that morning, I have hated the very sight of all other gold, save this!"

THE CURSE OF POLYPHEMUS

This excerpt from the great Greek epic, the Odyssey, *is one of the most interesting episodes in the life of the hero Odysseus, whose wanderings lasted for ten years.*

Of all the heroes that wandered far and wide before they came to their homes again after the fall of Troy, none suffered so many hardships as Odysseus. Ten years did he fight against Troy, but it was ten years more before he came to his

"The Curse of Polyphemus." From *Old Greek Folk Stories Told Anew* by Josephine Preston Peabody

home and his wife Penelope and his son Telemachus.

Odysseus set out from Troy with twelve good ships. He touched first at Ismarus, where his first misfortune took place, and in a skirmish with the natives he lost a number of men from each ship's crew.

A storm then drove them to the land of the Lotus-Eaters, a wondrous people, kindly and content, who spend their lives in a day-dream and care for nothing else under the sun. No sooner had the sailors eaten of this magical lotus than they lost all their wish to go home, or to see their wives and children again. By main force, Odysseus drove them back to the ships and saved them from the spell.

Thence they came one day to a beautiful strange island, a verdant place to see, deep with soft grass and well watered with springs. Here they ran the ships ashore, and took their rest and feasted for a day. But Odysseus looked across to the mainland, where he saw flocks and herds, and smoke going up softly from the homes of men; and he resolved to go across and find out what manner of people lived there. Accordingly, next morning, he took his own ship's company and they rowed across to the mainland.

Now, fair as the place was, there dwelt in it a race of giants, the Cyclopes, great rude creatures, having each but one eye, and that in the middle of his forehead. One of them was Polyphemus, the son of Poseidon. He lived by himself as a shepherd, and it was to his cave that Odysseus came, by some evil chance. It was an enormous grotto, big enough to house the giant and all his flocks, and it had a great courtyard without. But Odysseus, knowing nought of all this, chose out twelve men, and with a wallet of corn and a goatskin full of wine they left the ship and made a way to the cave, which they had seen from the water.

Much they wondered who might be the master of this strange house. Polyphemus was away with his sheep, but many lambs and kids were penned there, and the cavern was well stored with goodly cheeses and cream and whey.

Without delay, the wearied men kindled a fire and sat down to eat such things as they found, till a great shadow came dark against the doorway, and they saw the Cyclops near at hand, returning with his flocks. In an instant they fled into the darkest corner of the cavern.

Polyphemus drove his flocks into the place and cast off from his shoulders a load of young trees for firewood. Then he lifted and set in the entrance of the cave a gigantic boulder of a doorstone. Not until he had milked the goats and ewes and stirred up the fire did his terrible one eye light upon the strangers.

"What are ye?" he roared then, "robbers or rovers?" And Odysseus alone had heart to answer.

"We are Achaens of the army of Agamemnon," said he. "And by the will of Zeus we have lost our course, and are come to you as strangers. Forget not that Zeus has a care for such as we, strangers and suppliants."

Loud laughed the Cyclops at this. "You are a witless churl to bid me heed the gods!" said he. "I spare or kill to please myself and none other. But where is your cockle-shell that brought you hither?"

Then Odysseus answered craftily: "Alas, my ship is gone! Only I and my men escaped alive from the sea."

But Polyphemus, who had been looking them over with his one eye, seized two of the mariners and dashed them against the wall and made his evening meal of them, while their comrades stood by helpless. This done, he stretched himself through the cavern and slept all night long, taking no more heed of them than if they had been flies. No sleep came to the wretched seamen, for, even had they been able to slay him, they were powerless to move away the boulder from the door. So all night long Odysseus took thought how they might possibly escape.

At dawn the Cyclops woke, and his awakening was like a thunderstorm. Again he kindled the fire, again he milked the goats and ewes, and again he seized two of the king's comrades and served them up for his terrible repast. Then the savage shepherd drove his flocks out of the cave, only turning back to set the boulder in the doorway and pen up Odysseus and his men in their dismal lodging.

But the wise king had pondered well. In the sheepfold he had seen a mighty club of olivewood, in size like the mast of a ship. As soon as the Cyclops was gone, Odysseus bade his men cut off a length of this club and sharpen it down to a point. This done, they hid it away under the earth that heaped the floor; and they waited in fear and torment for their chance of escape.

At sundown, home came the Cyclops. Just as he had done before, he drove in his flocks, barred the entrance, milked the goats and ewes, and made his meal of two more hapless men, while their fellows looked on with burning eyes. Then Odysseus stood forth, holding a bowl of the wine that he had brought with him; and, curbing his horror of Polyphemus, he spoke in friendly fashion: "Drink, Cyclops, and prove our wine, such as it was, for all was lost with our ship save this. And no other man will ever bring you more, since you are such an ungentle host."

The Cyclops tasted the wine and laughed with delight so that the cave shook. "Ho, this is a rare drink!" said he. "I never tasted milk so good, nor whey, nor grape-juice either. Give me the rest, and tell me your name, that I may thank you for it."

Twice and thrice Odysseus poured the wine and the Cyclops drank it off; then he answered: "Since you ask it, Cyclops, my name is Noman."

"And I will give you this for your wine, Noman," said the Cyclops; "you shall be eaten last of all!"

As he spoke his head drooped, for his wits were clouded with drink, and he sank heavily out of his seat and lay prone, stretched along the floor of the cavern. His great eye shut and he fell asleep.

Odysseus thrust the stake under the ashes till it was glowing hot; and his fellows stood by him, ready to venture all. Then together they lifted the club and drove it straight into the eye of Polyphemus and turned it around and about.

The Cyclops gave a horrible cry, and, thrusting away the brand, he called on all his fellow-giants near and far. Odysseus and his men hid in the uttermost corners of the cave, but they heard the resounding steps of the Cyclopes who were roused, and their shouts as they called, "What ails thee, Polyphemus? Art thou slain? Who has done thee any hurt?"

"Noman!" roared the blinded Cyclops; "Noman is here to slay me by treachery."

"Then if no man hath hurt thee," they called again, "let us sleep." And away they went to their homes once more.

But Polyphemus lifted away the boulder from the door and sat there in the entrance, groaning with pain and stretching forth his hands to feel if any one were near. Then, while he sat in double darkness, with the light of his eye gone out, Odysseus bound together the rams of the flock, three by three, in such wise that every three should save one of his comrades. For underneath the mid ram of each group a man clung, grasping his shaggy fleece; and the rams on each side guarded him from discovery. Odysseus himself chose out the greatest ram and laid hold of his fleece and clung beneath his shaggy body, face upward.

Now, when dawn came, the rams hastened out to pasture, and Polyphemus felt of their backs as they huddled along together; but he knew not that every three held a man bound securely. Last of all came the kingly ram that was dearest to his rude heart, and he bore the king of Ithaca. Once free of the cave, Odysseus and his fellows loosed their hold and took flight, driving the rams in haste to the ship, where, without delay, they greeted their comrades and went aboard.

But as they pushed from shore, Odysseus could not refrain from hailing the Cyclops with taunts, and at the sound of that voice Polyphemus came forth from his cave and hurled a great rock after the ship. It missed and upheaved the water like an earthquake. Again Odysseus called, saying: "Cyclops, if any shall ask who blinded thine eye, say that it was Odysseus son of Laertes of Ithaca."

Then Polyphemus groaned and cried: "An Oracle foretold it, but I waited for some man of might who should overcome me by his valor—not a weakling! And now"—he lifted his hands and prayed—"Father, Poseidon, my father, look upon Odysseus, the son of Laertes of Ithaca, and grant me this revenge—let him never see Ithaca again! Yet, if he must, may he come late, without a friend, after long wandering, to find evil abiding by his hearth!"

So he spoke and hurled another rock after them, but the ship outstripped it, and sped by to the island where the other good ships waited for Odysseus. Together they put out from land and hastened on their homeward voyage.

But Poseidon, who is lord of the sea, had heard the prayer of his son, and that homeward voyage was to wear through ten years more, with storm and irksome calms and misadventure.

HOW THOR FOUND HIS HAMMER

The Norse myths are on a grand scale with little humor. This story is an exception, but even in this ludicrous situation the grandeur of the great god Thor is never forgotten.

The frost-giants were always trying to get into Asgard. For more than half the year they held the world in their grasp, locking up the streams in their rocky beds, hushing their music and the music of the birds as well, and leaving nothing but a wild waste of desolation under the cold sky. They hated the warm sunshine which stirred the wild flowers out of their sleep, and clothed the steep mountains with verdure, and set all the birds a-singing in the swaying tree-tops. They hated the beautiful god Balder, with whose presence summer came back to the ice-bound earth, and, above all, they hated Thor, whose flashing hammer drove them back into Jotunheim, and guarded the summer sky with its sudden gleamings of power. So long as Thor had his hammer Asgard was safe against the giants.

One morning Thor started up out of a long, deep sleep, and put out his hand for the hammer; but no hammer was there. Not a sign of it could be found anywhere, although Thor anxiously searched for it. Then a thought of the giants came suddenly in his mind; and his anger rose till his eyes flashed like great fires, and his red beard trembled with wrath.

"Look, now, Loke," he shouted, "they have stolen Mjolner by enchantment, and no one on earth or in heaven knows where they have hidden it."

"We will get Freyja's falcon-guise and search for it," answered Loke, who was always quick to get into trouble or to get out of it again. So they went quickly to Folkvang and found Freyja surrounded by her maidens and weeping tears of pure gold, as she had always done since her husband went on his long journey.

"The hammer has been stolen by enchant-

"How Thor Found His Hammer." Reprinted from *Norse Stories* by Hamilton Wright Mabie by permission of Dodd, Mead & Company

ment," said Thor. "Will you lend me the falcon-guise that I may search for it?"

"If it were silver, or even gold, you should have it and welcome," answered Freyja, glad to help Thor find the wonderful hammer that kept them all safe from the hands of the frost-giants.

So the falcon-guise was brought, and Loke put it on and flew swiftly out of Asgard to the home of the giants. His great wings made broad shadows over the ripe fields as he swept along, and the reapers, looking up from their work, wondered what mighty bird was flying seaward. At last he reached Jotunheim, and no sooner had he touched ground and taken off the falcon-guise than he came upon the giant Thrym, sitting on a hill twisting golden collars for his dogs and stroking the long manes of his horses.

"Welcome, Loke," said the giant. "How fares it with the gods and the elves, and what has brought you to Jotunheim?"

"It fares ill with both gods and elves since you stole Thor's hammer," replied Loke, guessing quickly that Thrym was the thief; "and I have come to find where you have hidden it."

Thrym laughed as only a giant can when he knows he has made trouble for somebody.

"You won't find it," he said at last. "I have buried it eight miles under ground, and no one shall take it away unless he gets Freyja for me as my wife."

The giant looked as if he meant what he said, and Loke, seeing no other way of finding the hammer, put on his falcon-guise and flew back to Asgard. Thor was waiting to hear what news he brought, and both were soon at the great doors of Folkvang.

"Put on your bridal dress, Freyja," said Thor bluntly, after his fashion, "and we will ride swiftly to Jotunheim."

But Freyja had no idea of marrying a giant just to please Thor; and, in fact, that Thor should ask her to do such a thing threw her into such a rage that the floor shook under her angry tread, and her necklace snapped in pieces.

"Do you think I am a weak lovesick girl, to follow you to Jotunheim and marry Thrym?" she cried indignantly.

Finding they could do nothing with Freyja, Thor and Loke called all the gods together to talk over the matter and decide what should be done to get back the hammer. The gods were very much alarmed, because they knew the frost-giants would come upon Asgard as soon as they knew the hammer was gone. They said little, for they did not waste time with idle words, but they thought long and earnestly, and still they could find no way of getting hold of Mjolner once more. At last Heimdal, who had once been a Van, and could therefore look into the future, said: "We must have the hammer at once or Asgard will be in danger. If Freyja will not go, let Thor be dressed up and go in her place. Let keys jingle from his waist and a woman's dress fall about his feet. Put precious stones upon his breast, braid his hair like a woman's, hang the necklace around his neck, and bind the bridal veil around his head."

Thor frowned angrily. "If I dress like a woman," he said, "you will jeer at me."

"Don't talk of jeers," retorted Loke; "unless that hammer is brought back quickly, the giants will rule in our places."

Thor said no more, but allowed himself to be dressed like a bride, and soon drove off to Jotun-heim with Loke beside him disguised as a serv-ant-maid. There was never such a wedding journey before. They rode in Thor's chariot and the goats drew them, plunging swiftly along the way, thunder pealing through the mountains and the frightened earth blazing and smoking as they passed. When Thrym saw the bridal party coming he was filled with delight.

"Stand up, you giants," he shouted to his companions; "spread cushions upon the benches and bring in Freyja, my bride. My yards are full of golden-horned cows, black oxen please my gaze whichever way I look, great wealth and many treasures are mine, and Freyja is all I lack."

It was evening when the bride came driving into the giant's court in her blazing chariot. The feast was already spread against her coming, and with her veil modestly covering her face she was seated at the great table, Thrym fairly beside himself with delight. It wasn't every giant who could marry a goddess!

If the bridal journey had been so strange that any one but a foolish giant would have hesitated to marry a wife who came in such a turmoil of fire and storm, her conduct at the table ought certainly to have put Thrym on his guard; for never had a bride such an appetite before. The great tables groaned under the load of good things, but they were quickly relieved of their burden by the voracious bride. She ate a whole ox before the astonished giant had fairly begun to enjoy his meal. Then she devoured eight large salmon, one after the other, without stopping to take breath; and having eaten up the part of the feast specially prepared for the hungry men, she turned upon the delicacies which had been made for the women, and especially for her own fastidious appetite.

Thrym looked on with wondering eyes, and at last, when she had added to these solid foods three whole barrels of mead, his amazement was so great that, his astonishment getting the better of his politeness, he called out, "Did any one ever see such an appetite in a bride before, or know a maid who could drink so much mead?"

Then Loke, who was playing the part of a serving-maid, thinking that the giant might have some suspicions, whispered to him, "Freyja was so happy in the thought of coming here that she has eaten nothing for eight whole days."

Thrym was so pleased at this evidence of affection that he leaned forward and raised the veil as gently as a giant could, but he instantly dropped it and sprang back the whole length of the hall before the bride's terrible eyes.

"Why are Freyja's eyes so sharp?" he called to Loke. "They burn me like fire."

"Oh," said the cunning serving-maid, "she has not slept for a week, so anxious has she been to come here, and that is why her eyes are so fiery."

Everybody looked at the bride and nobody envied Thrym. They thought it was too much like marrying a thunder-storm.

The giant's sister came into the hall just then, and seeing the veiled form of the bride sitting there went up to her and asked for a bridal gift. "If you would have my love and friendship give me those rings of gold upon your fingers."

But the bride sat perfectly silent. No one had yet seen her face or heard her voice.

Thrym became very impatient. "Bring in the hammer," he shouted, "that the bride may be consecrated, and wed us in the name of Var."

If the giant could have seen the bride's eyes when she heard these words he would have sent her home as quickly as possible, and looked somewhere else for a wife.

The hammer was brought and placed in the bride's lap, and everybody looked to see the marriage ceremony; but the wedding was more strange and terrible than the bridal journey had been. No sooner did the bride's fingers close round the handle of Mjolner than the veil which covered her face was torn off and there stood Thor, the giant-queller, his terrible eyes blazing with wrath.

The giants shuddered and shrank away from those flaming eyes, the sight of which they dreaded more than anything else in all the worlds; but there was no chance of escape. Thor swung the hammer round his head and the great house rocked on its foundations. There was a vivid flash of lightning, an awful crash of thunder, and the burning roof and walls buried the whole company in one common ruin.

Thrym was punished for stealing the hammer, his wedding guests got crushing blows instead of bridal gifts, and Thor and Loke went back to Asgard, where the presence of Mjolner made the gods safe once more.

THE DEATH OF BALDER

Here is the Norse equivalent of the Greek myth of Demeter and Persephone. Balder, the sun, drifts away in the fiery flames of autumn, leaving the world to darkness.

There was one shadow which always fell over Asgard. Sometimes in the long years the gods almost forgot it, it lay so far off, like a dim cloud in a clear sky; but Odin saw it deepen and widen as he looked out into the universe, and he knew that the last great battle would surely come, when the gods themselves would be destroyed and a long twilight would rest on all the worlds; and now the day was close at hand. Misfortunes never come singly to men, and they did not to the gods. Idun, the beautiful goddess of youth, whose apples were the joy of all Asgard, made a resting place for herself among the massive branches of Ygdrasil, and there every evening came Brage, and sang so sweetly that the birds stopped to listen, and even the Norns, those implacable sisters at the foot of the tree, were softened by the melody. But poetry cannot change the purposes of fate, and one evening no song was heard of Brage or birds, the leaves of the world-tree hung withered and lifeless on the branches, and the fountain from which they had daily been sprinkled was dry at last. Idun had fallen into the dark valley of death, and when Brage, Heimdal, and Loke went to question her about the future she could answer them only with tears. Brage would not leave his beautiful wife alone amid the dim shades that crowded the dreary valley, and so youth and genius vanished out of Asgard forever.

Balder was the most god-like of all the gods, because he was the purest and the best. Wherever he went his coming was like the coming of sunshine, and all the beauty of summer was but the shining of his face. When men's hearts were white like the light, and their lives clear as the day, it was because Balder was looking down upon them with those soft, clear eyes that were open windows to the soul of God. He had always

"The Death of Balder." Reprinted from *Norse Stories* by Hamilton Wright Mabie by permission of Dodd, Mead & Company

lived in such a glow of brightness that no darkness had ever touched him; but one morning, after Idun and Brage had gone, Balder's face was sad and troubled. He walked slowly from room to room in his palace Breidablik, stainless as the sky when April showers have swept across it because no impure thing had ever crossed the threshold, and his eyes were heavy with sorrow. In the night terrible dreams had broken his sleep, and made it a long torture. The air seemed to be full of awful changes for him, and for all the gods. He knew in his soul that the shadow of the last great day was sweeping on; as he looked out and saw the worlds lying in light and beauty, the fields yellow with waving grain, the deep fiords flashing back the sunbeams from their clear depths, the verdure clothing the loftiest mountains, and knew that over all this darkness and desolation would come, with silence of reapers and birds, with fading of leaf and flower, a great sorrow fell on his heart.

Balder could bear the burden no longer. He went out, called all the gods together, and told them the terrible dreams of the night. Every face was heavy with care. The death of Balder would be like the going out of the sun, and after a long, sad council the gods resolved to protect him from harm by pledging all things to stand between him and any hurt. So Frigg, his mother, went forth and made everything promise, on a solemn oath, not to injure her son. Fire, iron, all kinds of metal, every sort of stone, trees, earth, diseases, birds, beasts, snakes, as the anxious mother went to them, solemnly pledged themselves that no harm should come near Balder. Everything had promised, and Frigg thought she had driven away the cloud; but fate was stronger than her love, and one little shrub had not sworn.

Odin was not satisfied even with these precautions, for whichever way he looked the shadow of a great sorrow spread over the worlds. He began to feel as if he were no longer the greatest of the gods, and he could almost hear the rough shouts of the frost-giants crowding the rainbow bridge on their way into Asgard. When trouble comes to men it is hard to bear, but to a god who had so many worlds to guide and rule it was a new and terrible thing. Odin thought and thought until he was weary, but no gleam of

light could he find anywhere; it was thick darkness everywhere.

At last he could bear the suspense no longer, and saddling his horse he rode sadly out of Asgard to Niflheim, the home of Hel, whose face was as the face of death itself. As he drew near the gates, a monstrous dog came out and barked furiously, but Odin rode a little eastward of the shadowy gates to the grave of a wonderful prophetess. It was a cold, gloomy place, and the soul of the great god was pierced with a feeling of hopeless sorrow as he dismounted from Sleipner, and bending over the grave began to chant weird songs, and weave magical charms over it. When he had spoken those wonderful words which could waken the dead from their sleep, there was an awful silence for a moment, and then a faint ghost-like voice came from the grave.

"Who are thou?" it said. "Who breaketh the silence of death, and calleth the sleeper out of her long slumbers? Ages ago I was laid at rest here, snow and rain have fallen upon me through myriad years; why dost thou disturb me?"

"I am Vegtam," answered Odin, "and I come to ask why the couches of Hel are hung with gold and the benches strewn with shining rings?"

"It is done for Balder," answered the awful voice; "ask me no more."

Odin's heart sank when he heard these words; but he was determined to know the worst.

"I will ask thee until I know all. Who shall strike the fatal blow?"

"If I must, I must," moaned the prophetess. "Hoder shall smite his brother Balder and send him down to the dark home of Hel. The mead is already brewed for Balder, and the despair draweth near."

Then Odin, looking into the future across the open grave, saw all the days to come.

"Who is this," he said, seeing that which no mortal could have seen,— "who is this that will not weep for Balder?"

Then the prophetess knew that it was none other than the greatest of the gods who had called her up.

"Thou art not Vegtam," she exclaimed, "thou art Odin himself, the king of men."

"And thou," answered Odin angrily, "art no prophetess, but the mother of three giants."

"Ride home, then, and exult in what thou has discovered," said the dead woman. "Never shall my slumbers be broken again until Loke shall burst his chains and the great battle come."

And Odin rode sadly homeward knowing that already Niflheim was making itself beautiful against the coming of Balder.

The other gods meanwhile had become merry again; for had not everything promised to protect their beloved Balder? They even made sport of that which troubled them, for when they found that nothing could hurt Balder, and that all things glanced aside from his shining form, they persuaded him to stand as a target for their weapons; hurling darts, spears, swords, and battle-axes at him, all of which went singing through the air and fell harmless at his feet. But Loke, when he saw these sports, was jealous of Balder, and went about thinking how he could destroy him.

It happened that as Frigg sat spinning in her house Fensal, the soft wind blowing in at the windows and bringing the merry shouts of the gods at play, an old woman entered and approached her.

"Do you know," asked the newcomer, "what they are doing in Asgard? They are throwing all manner of dangerous weapons at Balder. He stands there like the sun for brightness, and against his glory, spears and battle-axes fall powerless to the ground. Nothing can harm him."

"No," answered Frigg joyfully; "nothing can bring him any hurt, for I have made everything in heaven and earth swear to protect him."

"What!" said the old woman, "has everything sworn to guard Balder?"

"Yes," said Frigg, "everything has sworn except one little shrub which is called Mistletoe, and grows on the eastern side of Valhal. I did not take an oath from that because I thought it was too young and weak."

When the old woman heard this a strange light came into her eyes; she walked off much faster than she had come in, and no sooner had she passed beyond Frigg's sight than this same old feeble woman grew suddenly erect, shook off her woman's garments, and there stood Loke himself. In a moment he had reached the slope east of Valhal, and plucked a twig of the unsworn Mistletoe, and was back in the circle of the gods, who were still at their favourite pastime with Balder. Hoder was standing silent and alone outside the noisy throng, for he was blind. Loke touched him.

"Why do you not throw something at Balder?"

"Because I cannot see where Balder stands, and have nothing to throw if I could," replied Hoder.

"If that is all," said Loke, "come with me. I will give you something to throw, and direct your aim."

Hoder, thinking no evil, went with Loke and did as he was told.

The little sprig of Mistletoe shot through the air, pierced the heart of Balder, and in a moment the beautiful god lay dead upon the field. A shadow rose out of the deep beyond the worlds and spread itself over heaven and earth, for the light of the universe had gone out.

The gods could not speak for horror. They stood like statues for a moment, and then a hopeless wail burst from their lips. Tears fell like rain from eyes that had never wept before, for Balder, the joy of Asgard, had gone to Niflheim and left them desolate. But Odin was saddest of all, because he knew the future, and he knew that peace and light had fled from Asgard forever, and that the last day and the long night were hurrying on.

Frigg could not give up her beautiful son, and when her grief had spent itself a little, she asked who would go to Hel and offer her a rich ransom if she would permit Balder to return to Asgard.

"I will go," said Hermod; swift at the word of Odin Sleipner was led forth, and in an instant Hermod was galloping furiously away.

Then the gods began with sorrowful hearts to make ready for Balder's funeral. When the once beautiful form had been arrayed in grave-clothes they carried it reverently down to the deep sea, which lay, calm as a summer afternoon, waiting for its precious burden. Close to the water's edge lay Balder's Ringhorn, the greatest of all the ships that sailed the seas, but when the gods tried to launch it they could not move it an inch. The great vessel creaked and groaned, but no one could push it down to the water. Odin walked about it with a sad face, and the gentle ripple of the little waves chasing each other over the rocks seemed a mocking laugh to him.

"Send to Jotunheim for Hyrroken," he said at last; and a messenger was soon flying for that mighty giantess.

In a little time, Hyrroken came riding swiftly on a wolf so large and fierce that he made the gods think of Fenrer. When the giantess had alighted, Odin ordered four Berserkers of mighty strength to hold the wolf, but he struggled so angrily that they had to throw him on the ground before they could control him. Then Hyrroken went to the prow of the ship and with one mighty effort sent it far into the sea, the rollers underneath bursting into flame, and the whole earth trembling with the shock. Thor was so angry at the uproar that he would have killed the giantess on the spot if he had not been held back by the other gods. The great ship floated on the sea as she had often done before, when Balder, full of life and beauty, set all her sails and was borne joyfully across the tossing seas. Slowly and solemnly the dead god was carried on board, and as Nanna, his faithful wife, saw her husband borne for the last time from the earth which he had made dear to her and beautiful to all men, her heart broke with sorrow, and they laid her beside Balder on the funeral pyre.

Since the world began no one had seen such a funeral. No bells tolled, no long procession of mourners moved across the hills, but all the worlds lay under a deep shadow, and from every quarter came those who had loved or feared Balder. There at the very water's edge stood Odin himself, the ravens flying about his head, and on his majestic face a gloom that no sun would ever lighten again; and there was Frigg, the desolate mother, whose son had already gone so far that he would never come back to her; there was Frey standing sad and stern in his chariot; there was Freyja, the goddess of love, from whose eyes fell a shining rain of tears; there, too, was Heimdal on his horse Goldtop; and around all these glorious ones from Asgard crowded the children of Jotunheim, grim mountain-giants seamed with scars from Thor's hammer, and frost-giants who saw in the death of Balder the coming of that long winter in which they should reign through all the worlds.

A deep hush fell on all created things, and every eye was fixed on the great ship riding near the shore, and on the funeral pyre rising from the deck crowned with the forms of Balder and Nanna. Suddenly a gleam of light flashed over the water; the pile had been kindled, and the flames, creeping slowly at first, climbed faster and faster until they met over the dead and rose skyward. A lurid light filled the heavens and shone on the sea, and in the brightness of it the gods looked pale and sad, and the circle of giants grew darker and more portentous. Thor struck the fast burning pyre with his consecrating hammer, and Odin cast into it the wonder ring Draupner. Higher and higher leaped the flames, more and more desolate grew the scene; at last they began to sink, the funeral pyre was consumed. Balder had vanished forever, the summer was ended, and winter waited at the doors.

Meanwhile Hermod was riding hard and fast on his gloomy errand. Nine days and nights he rode through valleys so deep and dark that he could not see his horse. Stillness and blackness and solitude were his only companions until he came to the golden bridge which crosses the river Gjol. The good horse Sleipner, who had carried Odin on so many strange journeys, had never travelled such a road before, and his hoofs rang drearily as he stopped short at the bridge, for in front of him stood its porter, the gigantic Modgud.

"Who are you?" she asked, fixing her piercing eyes on Hermod. "What is your name and parentage? Yesterday five bands of dead men rode across the bridge, and beneath them all it did not shake as under your single tread. There is no colour of death in your face. Why ride you hither, the living among the dead?"

"I come," said Hermod, "to seek for Balder. Have you seen him pass this way?"

"He has already crossed the bridge and taken his journey northward to Hel."

Then Hermod rode slowly across the bridge that spans the abyss between life and death, and found his way at last to the barred gates of Hel's dreadful home. There he sprang to the ground, tightened the girths, remounted, drove the spurs deep into the horse, and Sleipner, with a mighty leap, cleared the wall. Hermod rode straight to the gloomy palace, dismounted, entered, and in a moment was face to face with the terrible queen of the kingdom of the dead. Beside her, on a beautiful throne, sat Balder, pale and wan, crowned with a withered wreath of flowers, and close at hand was Nanna, pallid as her husband, for whom she had died. And all night long, while ghostly forms wandered restless and sleepless through Helheim, Hermod talked with Balder and Nanna. There is no record of what they said, but the talk was sad enough, doubtless, and ran like a still stream among the happy days in Asgard when Balder's smile was morning over the earth and the sight of his face the summer of the world.

When the morning came, faint and dim, through the dusky palace, Hermod sought Hel, who received him as cold and stern as fate.

"Your kingdom is full, O Hel!" he said, "and without Balder, Asgard is empty. Send him back to us once more, for there is sadness in every heart and tears are in every eye. Through heaven and earth all things weep for him."

"If that is true," was the slow, icy answer, "if every created thing weeps for Balder, he shall return to Asgard; but if one eye is dry he remains henceforth in Helheim."

Then Hermod rode swiftly away, and the decree of Hel was soon told in Asgard. Through all the worlds the gods sent messengers to say that all who loved Balder should weep for his return, and everywhere tears fell like rain. There was weeping in Asgard, and in all the earth there was nothing that did not weep. Men and women and little children, missing the light that had once fallen into their hearts and homes, sobbed with bitter grief; the birds of the air, who had sung carols of joy at the gates of the morning since time began, were full of sorrow; the beasts of the fields crouched and moaned in their desolation; the great trees, that had put on their robes of green at Balder's command, sighed as the wind wailed through them; and the sweet flowers, that waited for Balder's footstep and sprang up in all the fields to greet him, hung their frail blossoms and wept bitterly for the love and the warmth and the light that had gone out. Throughout the whole earth there was nothing but weeping, and the sound of it was like the wailing of those storms in autumn that weep for the dead summer as its withered leaves drop one by one from the trees.

The messengers of the gods went gladly back to Asgard, for everything had wept for Balder; but as they journeyed they came upon a giantess, called Thok, and her eyes were dry.

"Weep for Balder," they said.

"With dry eyes only will I weep for Balder," she answered. "Dead or alive, he never gave me gladness. Let him stay in Helheim."

When she had spoken these words a terrible laugh broke from her lips, and the messengers looked at each other with pallid faces, for they knew it was the voice of Loke.

Balder never came back to Asgard, and the shadows deepened over all things, for the night of death was fast coming on.

An English hero tale

LITTLE JOHN
AND THE TANNER OF BLYTH

Here is a sample of the Robin Hood hero cycle which children should not miss. The Robin Hood stories may lead into the ballads (see Time for Poetry) *or a medieval unit—or may be used for illustration or dramatization or for pure enjoyment.*

"Little John and the Tanner of Blyth." From *The Merry Adventures of Robin Hood* by Howard Pyle

It often comes about in this world that unlucky happenings fall upon one in such measure that it seems, as the saying is, that every cat that one strokes flies into one's face. Thus it was with Robin Hood and Little John one bright day in the merry Maytime; so listen and you shall hear how Dame Luck so buffeted them that their bones were sore for many a day thereafter.

One fine day, not long after Little John had left abiding with the Sheriff and had come back, with his worship's cook, to the merry greenwood, as has just been told, Robin Hood and a few chosen fellows of his band lay upon the soft sward beneath the greenwood tree where they dwelt. The day was warm and sultry, so that whilst most of the band were scattered through the forest upon this mission and upon that, these few stout fellows lay lazily beneath the shade of the tree, in the soft afternoon, passing jests among themselves and telling merry stories, with laughter and mirth.

All the air was laden with the bitter fragrance of the May, and all the bosky shades of the woodlands beyond rang with the sweet song of birds, —the throstle-cock, the cuckoo, and the wood-pigeon,—and with the song of birds mingled the cool sound of the gurgling brook that leaped out of the forest shades, and ran fretting amid its rough, gray stones across the sunlit open glade before the trysting tree. And a fair sight was that halfscore of tall, stout yeomen, all clad in Lincoln green, lying beneath the broad-spreading branches of the great oak tree, amid the quivering leaves of which the sunlight shivered and fell in dancing patches upon the grass.

The good old times have gone by when such men grow as grew then; when sturdy quarterstaff and longbow toughened a man's thews till they were like leather. Around Robin Hood that day there lay the very flower of English yeomanrie. Here the great Little John, with limbs as tough as the gnarled oak, yet grown somewhat soft from good living at the Sheriff's house in Nottingham Town; there Will Stutely, his face as brown as a berry from sun and wind, but, for all that, the comeliest yeoman in the mid-country, only excepting Allan a Dale the minstrel, of whom you shall hear anon. Beside these was Will Scathelock, as lank as a greyhound, yet as fleet of foot as a buck of three years' growth; young David of Doncaster, with great stout limbs only less than those of Little John in size, the tender beard of early youth now just feathering his chin, and others of great renown both far and near.

Suddenly Robin Hood smote his knee.

"By Saint Dunstan," quoth he, "I had nigh forgot that quarter-day cometh on apace, and yet no cloth of Lincoln green in all our store. It must be looked to, and that in quick season. Come, busk thee, Little John! stir those lazy bones of thine, for thou must get thee straight-way to our good gossip, the draper, Hugh Long-shanks of Ancaster. Bid him send us straightway twentyscore yards of fair cloth of Lincoln green; and mayhap the journey may take some of the fat from off thy bones, that thou hast gotten from lazy living at our dear Sheriff's."

"Nay," muttered Little John (for he had heard so much upon this score that he was sore upon the point), "nay, truly, mayhap I have more flesh upon my joints than I once had, yet, flesh or no flesh, I doubt not that I could still hold my place and footing upon a narrow bridge against e'er a yeoman in Sherwood, or Nottinghamshire, for the matter of that, even though he had no more fat about his bones than thou hast, good master."

At this reply a great shout of laughter went up, and all looked at Robin Hood, for each man knew that Little John spake of a certain fight that happened between their master and himself, through which they first became acquainted.

"Nay," quoth Robin Hood, laughing louder than all, "Heaven forbid that I should doubt thee, for I care for no taste of thy staff myself, Little John. I must needs own that there are those of my band can handle a seven-foot staff more deftly than I; yet no man in all Nottinghamshire can draw gray-goose shaft with my fingers. Nevertheless, a journey to Ancaster may not be ill for thee; so go thou, as I bid, and thou hadst best go this very evening, for since thou hast abided at the Sheriff's many know thy face, and if thou goest in broad daylight, thou mayest get thyself into a coil with some of his worship's men-at-arms. Bide thou here till I bring thee money to pay our good Hugh. I warrant he hath no better customers in all Nottinghamshire than we." So saying, Robin left them and entered the forest.

Not far from the trysting tree was a great rock in which a chamber had been hewn, the entrance being barred by a massive oaken door two palms' breadth in thickness, studded about with spikes, and fastened with a great padlock. This was the treasure-house of the band, and thither Robin Hood went, and, unlocking the door, entered the chamber, from which he brought forth a bag of gold, which he gave to Little John, to pay Hugh Longshanks withal, for the cloth of Lincoln green.

Then up got Little John, and, taking the bag of gold, which he thrust into his bosom, he strapped a girdle about his loins, took a stout pikestaff full seven feet long in his hand, and set forth upon his journey.

So he strode whistling along the leafy forest path that led to Fosse Way, turning neither to the right hand nor the left, until at last he came to where the path branched, leading on the one hand onward to Fosse Way, and on the other, as well Little John knew, to the merry Blue Boar Inn. Here Little John suddenly ceased whistling, and stopped in the middle of the path. First he looked up and then he looked down, and then, tilting his cap over one eye, he slowly scratched the back part of his head. For thus it was: at the sight of these two roads, two voices began to alarum within him, the one crying, "There lies the road to the Blue Boar Inn, a can of brown October, and a merry night with sweet companions such as thou mayst find there"; the other, "There lies the way to Ancaster and the duty thou art sent upon." Now the first of these two voices was far the louder, for Little John had grown passing fond of good living through abiding at the Sheriff's house; so, presently, looking up into the blue sky, across which bright clouds were sailing like silver boats, and swallows skimming in circling flight, quoth he, "I fear me it will rain this evening, so I'll e'en stop at the Blue Boar till it passes by, for I know my good master would not have me wet to the skin." So, without more ado, off he strode down the path that lay the way of his likings. Now there was no sign of any foul weather, but when one wishes to do a thing, as Little John did, one finds no lack of reasons for the doing.

Four merry wags were at the Blue Boar Inn; a butcher, a beggar, and two barefoot friars. Little John heard them singing from afar, as he walked through the hush of the mellow twilight that was now falling over hill and dale. Right glad were they to welcome such a merry blade as Little John. Fresh cans of ale were brought, and with jest and song and merry tales the hours slipped away on fleeting wings. None thought of time or tide till the night was so far gone that Little John put by the thought of setting forth upon his journey again that night, and so bided at the Blue Boar Inn until the morrow.

Now it was an ill piece of luck for Little John that he left his duty for his pleasure, and he paid a great score for it, as we are all apt to do in the same case, as you shall see.

Up he rose at the dawn of the next day, and, taking his stout pikestaff in his hand, he set forth upon his journey once more, as though he would make up for lost time.

In the good town of Blyth there lived a stout tanner, celebrated far and near for feats of strength and many tough bouts at wrestling and the quarterstaff. For five years he had held the mid-country champion belt for wrestling, till the great Adam o' Lincoln cast him in the ring and broke one of his ribs; but at quarterstaff he had never yet met his match in all the country about. Beside all this, he dearly loved the longbow, and a sly jaunt in the forest when the moon was full and the dun deer in season; so that the King's rangers kept a shrewd eye upon him and his doings, for Arthur a Bland's house was apt to have a plenty of meat in it that was more like venison than the law allowed.

Now Arthur had been to Nottingham Town the day before Little John set forth on his errand, there to sell a halfscore of tanned cowhides. At the dawn of the same day that Little John left the Inn, he started from Nottingham, homeward for Blyth. His way led, all in the dewy morn, past the verge of Sherwood Forest, where the birds were welcoming the lovely day with a great and merry jubilee. Across the Tanner's shoulders was slung his stout quarterstaff, ever near enough to him to be gripped quickly, and on his head was a cap of double cowhide, so tough that it could hardly be cloven even by a broadsword.

"Now," quoth Arthur a Bland to himself, when he had come to that part of the road that cut through a corner of the forest, "no doubt at this time of year the dun deer are coming from the forest depths nigher to the open meadow lands. Mayhap I may chance to catch a sight of the dainty brown darlings thus early in the morn." For there was nothing he loved better than to look upon a tripping herd of deer, even when he could not tickle their ribs with a clothyard shaft. Accordingly, quitting the path, he went peeping this way and that through the underbrush, spying now here and now there, with all the wiles of a master woodcraft, and of one who had more than once donned a doublet of Lincoln green.

Now as Little John stepped blithely along, thinking of nothing but of such things as the sweetness of the hawthorn buds that bedecked the hedgerows, or the crab trees that stood here and there all covered with fair pink blossoms, or gazing upward at the lark, that, springing from the dewy grass, hung aloft on quivering wings in the yellow sunlight, pouring forth its song that fell like a falling star from the sky, his luck led him away from the highway, not far from the spot where Arthur a Bland was peeping this way and that through the leaves of the thickets. Hearing a rustling of the branches, Little John stopped, and presently caught sight of the brown cowhide cap of the Tanner moving amongst the bushes.

"I do much wonder," quoth Little John to himself, "what yon knave is after, that he should go thus peeping and peering about. I verily believe that yon scurvy varlet is no better than a thief, and cometh here after our own and the good King's dun deer." For by much roving in the forest, Little John had come to look upon all the deer in Sherwood as belonging to Robin Hood and his band as much as to good King Harry. "Nay," quoth he again, after a time, "this matter must e'en be looked into." So, quitting the highroad, he also entered the thickets, and began spying around after stout Arthur a Bland.

So for a long time they both of them went hunting about, Little John after the Tanner, and the Tanner after the deer. At last Little John trod upon a stick, which snapped under his foot, whereupon, hearing the noise, the Tanner turned quickly and caught sight of the yeoman. Seeing that the Tanner had spied him out, Little John put a bold face upon the matter.

"Hilloa," quoth he, "what art thou doing here, thou naughty fellow? Who art thou that comest ranging Sherwood's paths? In very sooth thou hast an evil cast of countenance, and I do think, truly, that thou art no better than a thief, and comest after our good King's deer."

"Nay," quoth the Tanner boldly,—for, though taken by surprise, he was not a man to be frightened by big words,—"thou liest in thy teeth. I am no thief, but an honest craftsman. As for my countenence, it is what it is; and for the matter

of that, thine own is none too pretty, thou saucy fellow."

"Ha!" quoth Little John, in a great loud voice, "wouldst thou give me backtalk? Now I have a great part of mind to crack thy pate for thee. I would have thee know, fellow, that I am, as it were, one of the King's foresters. Leastwise," muttered he to himself, "I and my friends do take good care of our good sovereign's deer."

"I care not who thou art," answered the bold Tanner, "and unless thou hast many more of thy kind by thee, thou canst never make Arthur a Bland cry 'A mercy.'"

"Is that so?" cried Little John in a rage. "Now, by my faith, thou saucy rogue, thy tongue hath led thee into a pit thou wilt have a sorry time getting out of; for I will give thee such a drubbing as ne'er hast thou had in all thy life before. Take thy staff in thy hand, fellow, for I will not smite an unarmed man."

"Marry come up with a murrain!" cried the Tanner, for he, too, had talked himself into a fume. "Big words ne'er killed so much as a mouse. Who art thou that talkest so freely of cracking the head of Arthur a Bland? If I do not tan thy hide this day as ne'er I tanned a calf's

hide in all my life before, split my staff into skewers for lamb's flesh and call me no more brave man! Now look to thyself, fellow!"

"Stay!" said Little John; "let us first measure our cudgels. I do reckon my staff longer than thine, and I would not take vantage of thee by even so much as an inch."

"Nay, I pass not for length," answered the Tanner. "My staff is long enough to knock down a calf; so look to thyself, fellow, I say again."

So, without more ado, each gripped his staff in the middle, and, with fell and angry looks, they came slowly together.

Now news had been brought to Robin Hood how that Little John, instead of doing his bidding, had passed by duty for pleasure, and so had stopped over night with merry company at the Blue Boar Inn, instead of going straight to Ancaster. So, being vexed to his heart by this, he set forth at dawn of day to seek Little John at the Blue Boar, or at least to meet the yeoman on the way, and ease his heart of what he thought of the matter. As thus he strode along in anger, putting together the words he would use to chide Little John, he heard, of a sudden, loud and angry voices, as of men in a rage, passing fell words back and forth from one to the other. At this, Robin Hood stopped and listened. "Surely," quoth he to himself, "that is Little John's voice, and he is talking in anger also. Methinks the other is strange to my ears. Now Heaven forfend that my good trusty Little John should have fallen into the hands of the King's rangers. I must see to this matter, and that quickly."

Thus spoke Robin Hood to himself, all his anger passing away like a breath from the window-pane, at the thought that perhaps his trusty right-hand man was in some danger of his life. So cautiously he made his way through the thickets whence the voices came, and, pushing aside the leaves, peeped into the little open space where the two men, staff in hand, were coming slowly together.

"Ha!" quoth Robin to himself, "here is merry sport afoot. Now I would give three golden angels from my own pocket if yon stout fellow would give Little John a right sound drubbing! It would please me to see him well thumped for having failed in my bidding. I fear me, though, there is but poor chance of my seeing such a pleasant sight." So saying, he stretched himself at length upon the ground, that he might not only see the sport the better, but that he might enjoy the merry sight at his ease.

As you may have seen two dogs that think to fight, walking slowly round and round each other, neither cur wishing to begin the combat, so those two stout yeomen moved slowly around, each watching for a chance to take the other unaware, and so get in the first blow. At last Little John struck like a flash, and, "rap," the Tanner met the blow and turned it aside, and then smote back at Little John, who also turned the blow; and so this mighty battle began. Then up and down and back and forth they trod, the blows falling so thick and fast that, at a distance, one would have thought that half a score of men were fighting. Thus they fought for nigh a half an hour, until the ground was all ploughed up with the digging of their heels, and their breathing grew labored like the ox in the furrow. But Little John suffered the most, for he had become unused to such stiff labor, and his joints were not as supple as they had been before he went to dwell with the Sheriff.

All this time Robin Hood lay beneath the bush, rejoicing at such a comely bout of quarterstaff. "By my faith!" quoth he to himself, "never had I thought to see Little John so evenly matched in all my life. Belike, though, he would have overcome yon stout fellow before this had he been in his former trim."

At last Little John saw his chance, and, throwing all the strength he felt going from him into one blow that might have felled an ox, he struck at the Tanner with might and main. And now did the Tanner's cowhide cap stand him in good stead, and but for it he might never have held staff in hand again. As it was, the blow he caught beside the head was so shrewd that it sent him staggering across the little glade, so that, if Little John had had the strength to follow up his vantage, it would have been ill for stout Arthur. But he regained himself quickly, and at arm's length, struck back a blow at Little John, and this time the stroke reached its mark, and down went Little John at full length, his cudgel flying from his hand as he fell. Then, raising his staff, stout Arthur dealt him another blow upon the ribs.

"Hold!" roared Little John. "Wouldst thou strike a man when he is down?"

"Ay, marry would I," quoth the Tanner, giving him another thwack with his staff.

"Stop!" roared Little John. "Help! hold, I say! I yield me! I yield me, I say, good fellow!"

"Hast thou had enough?" asked the Tanner, grimly, holding his staff aloft.

"Ay, marry, and more than enough."

"And thou dost own that I am the better man of the two?"

"Yea, truly, and a murrain seize thee!" said Little John, the first aloud and the last to his beard.

"Then thou mayst go thy ways; and thank thy patron saint that I am a merciful man," said the Tanner.

"A plague o' such mercy as thine!" said Little John, sitting up and feeling his ribs where the Tanner had cudgelled him. "I make my vow, my ribs feel as though every one of them were broken in twain. I tell thee, good fellow, I did think there was never a man in all Nottinghamshire could do to me what thou hast done this day."

"And so thought I, also," cried Robin Hood, bursting out of the thicket and shouting with laughter till the tears ran down his cheeks. "O man, man!" said he, as well as he could for his mirth, " 'a didst go over like a bottle knocked from a wall. I did see the whole merry bout, and never did I think to see thee yield thyself so, hand and foot, to any man in all merry England. I was seeking thee, to chide thee for leaving my bidding undone; but thou hast been paid all I owed thee, full measure, pressed down and overflowing, by this good fellow. Marry, 'a did reach out his arm full length whilst thou stood gaping at him, and, with a pretty rap, tumbled thee over as never have I seen one tumbled before." So spoke bold Robin, and all the time Little John sat upon the ground, looking as though he had sour curds in his mouth. "What may be thy name, good fellow?" said Robin, next, turning to the Tanner.

"Men do call me Arthur a Bland," spoke up the Tanner, boldly; "and now what may be thy name?"

"Ha, Arthur a Bland!" quoth Robin, "I have heard thy name before, good fellow. Thou didst break the crown of a friend of mine at the fair at Ely last October. The folk there call him Jock o'Nottingham; we call him Will Scathelock. This poor fellow whom thou hast so belabored is counted the best hand at the quarterstaff in all merry England. His name is Little John, and mine Robin Hood."

"How!" cried the Tanner, "art thou indeed the great Robin Hood, and is this the famous Little John? Marry, had I known who thou art, I would never have been so bold as to lift my hand against thee. Let me help thee to thy feet, good Master Little John, and let me brush the dust from off thy coat."

"Nay," quoth Little John, testily, at the same time rising carefully, as though his bones had been made of glass, "I can help myself, good fellow, without thy aid; and, let me tell thee, had it not been for that vile cowskin cap of thine, it would have been ill for thee this day."

At this Robin laughed again, and, turning to the Tanner, he said, "Wilt thou join my band, good Arthur? for I make my vow thou art one of the stoutest men that ever mine eyes beheld."

"Will I join thy band?" cried the Tanner, joyfully; "ay, marry, will I! Hey for a merry life!" cried he, leaping aloft and snapping his fingers, "and hey for the life I love! Away with tanbark and filthy vats and foul cowhides! I will follow thee to the ends of the earth, good master, and not a herd of dun deer in all the forest but shall know the sound of the twang of my bowstring."

"As for thee, Little John," said Robin, turning to him and laughing, "thou wilt start once more for Ancaster, and we will go part way with thee, for I will not have thee turn again to either the right hand or the left till thou hast fairly gotten away from Sherwood. There are other inns that thou knowest yet, hereabouts." Thereupon, leaving the thickets, they took once more to the highway, and departed upon their business.

Modern fairy tales are said to begin with Hans Christian Andersen, but actually, they began around 1700 when Mme. d'Aulnoy wrote "The White Cat," "Graciosa and Percinet," "The Yellow Dwarf," and other fairy tales which delighted the French court. Some fifty years later, Mme. de Beaumont composed her famous "Beauty and the Beast," a story similar in theme to the Norse folk tale "East o' the Sun and West o' the Moon" and the German "Bearskin," and so successfully done in folk tale style that, like Robert Southey's "Three Bears," it is generally grouped with the folk tales. If grownups are not

NEW MAGIC: MODERN FANCIFUL TALES

always consistent in their classifications of old and new stories, children are even less so. They don't care whether a fairy tale is traditional and anonymous or recently composed by a well-known author. Magic is magic to them, and they demand their favorites from ancient tales like "Snow-White and the Seven Dwarfs" and "The Fisherman and His Wife" to modern science fiction like William Pène du Bois' *Twenty-One Balloons*. Old or new, they love these figments of the imagination which they call "fairy tales."

Hans Christian Andersen

Hans Christian Andersen (1805–1875) did, however, give fresh impetus to the writing of modern fanciful tales. He began by retelling old folk tales and then went on to write new stories in folk tale style. Soon his creative genius was inventing new forms, so fresh and beautiful that they became enormously popular in his own day and pointed the way for writers of a later age. It is interesting to note the types of stories he wrote and to trace some of their modern descendants. Many examples of each could be given, but a few will suffice to indicate relationships:

1. *Retelling of old tales:* Andersen, "The Wild Swans."—Wanda Gág, *Gone Is Gone.*
2. *Original stories in folk tale style:* Andersen, "Thumbelisa."—John Ruskin, *King of the Golden River.* Richard Bennett, *Shawneen and the Gander.*
3. *Inanimate objects personified:* Andersen, "The Steadfast Tin Soldier."—Lorenzini, *Pinocchio.* Virginia Burton, *Mike Mulligan and His Steam Shovel.*
4. *Humorous tales, drolls:* Andersen, "The Emperor's New Clothes."—Theodore Seuss Geisel, *The 500 Hats of Bartholomew Cubbins.*
5. *Talking beasts:* Andersen, "The Ugly Duckling."—Rudyard Kipling, "The Elephant's Child." Marjorie Flack, *Ask Mr. Bear.*
6. *Allegory:* Andersen, "The Real Princess."—Phyllis McGinley, *The Plain Princess.*
7. *Fantasy:* Andersen, "The Snow Queen."—Lewis Carroll, *Alice's Adventures in Wonderland.* Ruth Stiles Gannett, *Elmer and the Dragon.*

To be sure, many of Andersen's stories, and other people's too, will fall under two or more of these groupings. Andersen's "The Emperor's New Clothes" is both a droll and an allegory, "The Ugly Duckling" both a talking beast story and an allegory. Here lies one of the chief difficulties of Andersen's tales for children. Most of them have double meanings which the children sense vaguely but do not understand because the stories are so often satires directed against the foibles of the adult world. The emperor stands for pompous pretentiousness in high places. "The Swineherd" lampoons false values —a preference for the artificial rather than the real and simple things in life. "The Real Princess" makes fun of adult snobbery, the myth of blue-blooded superiority. Fortunately, children usually miss the adult significance of these social satires. If, in discussing one of Andersen's tales, children eleven- or twelve-years-old show any signs of catching the social implications of the stories, by all means amplify the meanings and discuss their application to our world today. Otherwise, let the children enjoy the stories happily, just as stories—funny or fantastic, sad or gay, but invariably beautiful and moving.

The six tales selected for this volume show Andersen's versatility and power. Since many of the tales are quite long, you may wish to cut some of the lengthy descriptions, as you read them aloud, and that is easily done. But this sampling of his stories should send some children to the library for the whole collection of the Andersen *Fairy Tales.* Their simple goodness is armor against the continual impact of banality and brutality to which the modern child is exposed. When Andersen shows the children cruelty, sorrow, and even death, he does it so gently and with such beauty that they are neither shocked nor hurt. He dares to show them fools and rogues, too, and makes children laugh at the absurdities of these pompous knaves. Then, he writes tenderly about the loving, humble folk in the world and paints unforgettable pictures of their kindness, sincerity, and faith in God. It is, indeed, the spiritual overtones in Andersen's stories that make them valuable. Paul Hazard said of them:

> It is this inner life that gives the Tales their deep quality. From it also comes that exaltation which spreads through the soul of the readers. . . . Their mission is to bring to the world a renewal of faith and hope.[1]

Andersen's successors

After Andersen's *Fairy Tales* had captured the imagination of children and adults all over the world, other writers were inspired to try their

[1] *Books, Children and Men,* pp. 104–105.

hands at tales of magic. In England, in 1851, John Ruskin, philosopher and art critic, put aside his adult writing long enough to create for children *The King of the Golden River*. This is an original story in the old fairy tale form, strongly reminiscent of Andersen. It has the same somber, frightening air and the same strange beauty. The fiery little King of the Golden River, who emerges from the melting golden mug and helps to save Gluck from his evil brothers, is a never-to-be-forgotten figure.

But neither this story nor anything in the Andersen tales can account for the daft gaiety and originality of England's great fantasy— Lewis Carroll's *Alice's Adventures in Wonderland*. The story of what happened to Alice after she followed the White Rabbit down the rabbit hole is interspersed with nonsense verses as mad and merry as the prose narrative. Sometimes the words don't even make sense, but they sing in your head when worthier words are forgotten.

Alice broke upon the astonished world in 1851 and has continued to charm each generation ever since. At least, it charms those who like it, but it is not universally popular. There is a great controversy over the proper age to introduce *Alice* to children. Some adults say they loved it before they were ten years old. But upon investigation, that usually means *Alice* was read to them by some grownup who thoroughly enjoyed it himself. Others say they disliked it heartily as children but somewhere around high school age found it exceedingly funny. Extreme points of view are the usual thing where tales of magic are concerned. One child's delight is another child's boredom, and each is entitled to his point of view. In the case of Alice and her fantastic wonderland, perhaps the best advice to grownups is to try it out with your children if you yourself like it. Read the first chapter of it aloud or the famous excerpt included here, "A Mad Tea-Party." If the children like it, go on with the readings. If they reject it firmly, don't be too discouraged; they will probably discover it later with delight.

During the 1870's *The Peterkin Papers* were appearing in the United States. They are direct descendants of the folk tale sillies and are the ancestors of Hope Newell's *Little Old Woman Who Used Her Head*. The stories about the

Peterkin family are a bit dated perhaps, but still funny. When Mrs. Peterkin puts salt in her morning coffee instead of sugar, and the chemist and the herb woman make it worse and worse, the omniscient "lady from Philadelphia" merely suggests that they throw it out and make a fresh cup, and all is well. Eleven- and twelve-year-old children will readily see the relationship of these drolls to the more recent moron stories.

Howard Pyle, also in the United States, published his retelling of the hero cycle, *The Merry Adventures of Robin Hood*, in 1883. This still remains the finest modern source of these stories, and Howard Pyle's own illustrations add greatly to the charm of the book. In 1886 he published his collection of amusing stories in folk tale style, *Pepper and Salt*. These are excellent and are still in continuous use as storytelling sources.

In England around the turn of the century, the publication of two tiny books opened up a new era in writing for children under six years old. These books are *Little Black Sambo* by Helen Bannerman, 1900, and *The Tale of Peter Rabbit* by Beatrix Potter, 1900. These stories, along with their delightful pictures inseparable from the tales themselves, still delight children. They launched the modern picture-story type of book for young children which has continued to multiply from that day to this. The picture-story means, as its name implies, a story in which the pictures are an integral part of the book and in which pictures and text are synchronized and inseparable. Both *Little Black Sambo* and *The Tale of Peter Rabbit* are in folk tale style or pattern but they are told in terms of a four- or five-year-old's imaginary adventures. *Little Black Sambo* is a first-rate hero tale. Sambo encounters danger in the jungle, he uses his wits, gets back all his fine clothes from the tigers, and returns safely to his loving parents, with whom he shares a prodigious number of pancakes. Here's just the kind of conquering hero every child dreams of being.

Peter Rabbit might be any disobedient child, but it is less embarrassing to talk about naughty Peter's adventures, his narrow escape, and his punishment, than to dwell on one's own five-year-old's mistakes. Both stories end on a note of warm security within the family, a reassurance which all small children need. Both stories have a simple, vigorous style that is a model of what good writing for young children should be—no whimsey and no double meanings. Beatrix Potter's little water-color illustrations are exquisite. And in storytelling style, appealing plots, overtones of emotional security, these two small books have not been surpassed and they continue to charm each new generation. Andersen never reached down to the nursery. It took two women to produce the perfect picture-stories for the delight of the small child.

After these epoch-making books at the beginning of the twentieth century, good writing for children increased with astonishing rapidity and diversity. Kipling's *Jungle Book,* preceding them by a few years, appeared in 1894, a strangely convincing story of Mowgli, the boy raised by a wolf pack in the jungle. This was followed in 1902 by Kipling's *Just So Stories,* which pretends, with tongue-in-cheek, to explain such matters as "How the Tiger Got His Spots," "How the Elephant Got His Trunk." The funny sounding words and sonorous sentences in these tales make them most effective when they are read aloud.

The most beautiful of all talking beast stories is probably Kenneth Grahame's *The Wind in the Willows,* published in England in 1908. It is the story of Ratty, Badger, Mole, and the irrepressible playboy, Toad of Toad Hall. These small denizens of the river bank are, of course, prototypes of human beings and, like the Three Little Pigs or Peter Rabbit or Mickey Mouse, they are funnier or more poignant for being animals. Children and adults have apparently always chuckled over the antics of animals used as caricatures of human foibles, and the popularity of the animated cartoons testifies to the permanence of this taste. But Kenneth Grahame's animals are kindly little creatures, loyal friends, patient and forgiving. They succor each other in need, look after the young things, and reclaim sinners from their own misdeeds. The book is full of an earthy delight in sensory pleasures— hot sunshine, moonlight on the river, a warm fire and sizzling bacon after a bitter storm. But it has also spiritual and aesthetic values which children should not miss. Not every child will like it. Long descriptions and British whimsey make it hard reading for average children, but they may enjoy it if it is read aloud by a grownup who

knows and loves it and takes the time to savor it slowly, enjoying both its humor and its beauty.

In 1892 English-speaking children acquired a translation of the Italian story *Pinocchio* by Carlo Lorenzini. This droll account of a puppet which came to life and progressed from one misdeed to another captivated youngsters, probably because Pinocchio does some of the outrageous things they too have yearned to do. The punishments of the puppet are as fantastic and amusing as his adventures, and when he finally reforms and turns into a decent sort of real boy, he is still cocky and on top of the world. This is a face-saving triumph that is seldom possible for the repentant child but always to be hoped for.

Looking over the contribution of these early writers who followed Hans Christian Andersen, we realize that however much the modern fairy tale may owe to Andersen's beautiful innovations, his successors soon broke away from his style, mood, and content. Double meanings, overtones of fable and allegory, so prevalent in Andersen's tales, are also to be found in some of these later writings. In fact, these characteristics seldom seem completely absent from children's fairy stories. But where Andersen's tales are predominantly somber or downright melancholy, Carroll, Hale, Pyle, Bannerman, Potter, Kipling, and Lorenzini introduced gaiety, humor, and nonsense. The content of their stories is also easier for children to understand and much of their writing is simpler. The long descriptions are gone from most of their stories, and Helen Bannerman and Beatrix Potter made enormous strides toward a vigorous, direct style of writing for young children. These are the chief contributions of the early moderns to the development of the fanciful story: a new note of gaiety and the picture-story for children under six written in simple, forthright style.

Modern writers of fanciful tales

Recent writers have added many innovations to the fanciful tales, but most of their stories can be classified under the types listed for Andersen, page 273. In the folk tale section of this book, there are admirable examples of modern *retellings of old tales.* Arthur Ransome, for example, retold the Russian folk tales as he heard them from Russian soldiers in World War I. Andrew Lang has retold "Aladdin" and innumerable other traditional stories. Marie Shedlock's delightful version of "The Hare That Ran Away" and Parker Fillmore's Czech stories illustrate the fascination these old tales have for modern writers. However, in this section our chief concern is with original inventions in the field of the imaginative.

Writing *original stories in folk tale style* has appealed to writers from Andersen, Ruskin, and Pyle to the moderns. Wanda Gág, for instance, heard the folk stories told by family storytellers throughout her childhood. With this background it is not surprising that when she began to write and illustrate her own stories for children, she fell into the folk tale style. Her stories have good plots, a beautiful cadenced rhythm, both in text and pictures, and something of the homely quality of the old tales. Yet nothing could be fresher or more original than the plots of her *Millions of Cats, Snippy and Snappy, The Funny Thing,* and *Nothing at All,* which is included in this book. Each of these is a picture-story with action, suspense, and a satisfying conclusion. They have the fable quality which is characteristic of many of the folk tales, and their quiet humor sets the children to chuckling.

Irish writers and those of Irish descent seem always to have a background of the old tales heard from Irish storytellers whose art is remarkable. Richard Bennett, Arthur Mason, Ella Young, and Eileen O'Faolain show their folk tale heritage in the richness of their own fairy tale invention. Yet they do not write alike nor do their stories have many qualities in common.

Richard Bennett's *Shawneen and the Gander* begins quite realistically. An everyday kind of a child yearns for a trumpet and whoosh! Everything begins to happen. It is soon evident that you can't tamper with leprechauns without getting into hot water. It is the impinging of this strange world of fairy upon everyday mortals that makes these stories convincing to children who have never before heard of leprechauns. This is true also of Arthur Mason's *Wee Men of Ballywooden.* The big wind that blew the Wee Men out to sea also played hob with various humans whose lives were more or less tied up with the Little People. Besides the amusing incidents and characters in these modern Irish fairy tales, it is the continual entanglement of mortals and Wee Men that gives the stories their casual air of veracity. Perhaps no other writers can do this as well as the Irish, brought up on fairylore. Their pookas and leprechauns, their trooping fairies and fairy horses open up a new and strange world to American children, not as readily accepted as other types of make-believe, perhaps, but with a humor, a wonderment, and a poetic quality that seem to explain some of the strangeness of events in everyday life.

Personification of inanimate objects was Andersen's special invention and delight. The Fir Tree, the Darning Needle, the Steadfast Tin Soldier, and other objects which he endowed with a life of their own, are vividly alive to the reader, but all too often they meet with a melancholy end. Not so their modern descendants. From that rascally puppet, Pinocchio, to the most recent tales of inanimate objects which come gaily to life, such personifications make lively and joyous stories, usually of the picture-story type for children four- to eight-years-old.

One of the most successful creators of this type of tale is Virginia Burton, author-artist of *Choo Choo,* a runaway train; *Mike Mulligan and His Steam Shovel,* a story about an intrepid shovel, Mary Anne; and *The Little House* (a Caldecott Award), which tells with pictures and text the fate of a little house which finds itself caught in the evolution of a city. These three picture-stories are not only popular with children five- to eight-years-old, but they have unusual social significance. Virginia Burton, who is Mrs. Demetrios, tells us that her books grew out of the intense interest of her small sons in all sorts of machinery. After hearing *Mike Mulligan* read and poring over the pictures, a second-grade child came dashing into her classroom one morning with the news that "Mary Anne" was working over on the next street. And sure enough, there was a steam shovel labeled "41" but to that child it was indubitably "Mary Anne!"

A. A. Milne's *Winnie-the-Pooh* grew out of his son's personification of his toys. The adventures of Christopher Robin with Pooh, his teddy bear "of little brain"; Eeyore, the old donkey; Kanga and Little Roo, the kangaroos; and Tigger, the tiger, are full of British whimsey but are inexhaustibly funny, once the children catch the pattern of their absurdity. Because the grownup quality of British whimsey is often hard for American children to appreciate fully, the Pooh stories should unquestionably be read aloud to children, with any explanations that seem necessary for enjoyment. The way Christopher walks into his world of fantasy, in which he and the toys get into and out of various difficulties, on the same plane of aliveness, is unique. At the end of the story, Pooh is once more a toy that Christopher Robin carries off to bed. The Pooh books are both fantasy and personifications of inanimate objects and altogether delightful. Their distinctive style is made to order for reading aloud.

Adults may talk about *drolls,* but children call them *"funny stories,"* and their demand for "funny books" never wanes. Looking at a group of modern drolls, we see at once that in this category again there is a greater variety than the folk tales presaged or Andersen developed. The sillies are still with us from "Clever Elsie" to Andersen's "Emperor's New Clothes," Hale's *Peterkin Papers,* and Hope Newell's *Old Woman Who Used Her Head* stories. Hope Newell's tales do not have the literary quality of the Hale stories, but the situations are more modern and therefore more understandable to children today.

Some people might also classify Carl Sandburg's *Rootabaga Stories* as drolls. But if you read the tales aloud and study them, it becomes clear that these are a new type of nonsense. Their repetitious phrases, their airy flights of fancy, and their haunting undertones of almost-making-sense have nothing in common with the drolls of the folk tales or the logical illogic of the *Peterkin Papers.* They are poetic nonsense as light as a puff of cloud and as gay as a spring song. Whether or not children are going to enjoy many of them will depend upon the gaiety with which they are presented. But they are Americana and unique. Certainly, children should have samples of them.

So it is with other modern humorous tales for children. They are fresh inventions, they refuse to be typed, and they fall into almost every category of story writing, but especially fantasy. Indeed all of the stories in this collection which qualify as fantasies are also drolls. Mr. Popper,

in *Mr. Popper's Penguins,* the *Elmer and the Dragon* books, *The Magic Bed-Knob,* and all the others are fantastic nonsense, as funny as they are fantastic and as impossible as *Alice's Adventures in Wonderland.* This type of drollery requires a grave, straight-faced sort of writing that suddenly brings the listener up gasping. In the midst of a realistic setting, it asks its audience to accept one impossible, ridiculous premise, and after that, the story develops easily and convincingly. But the nonsense depends upon this continual admixture of the actual and the wildly absurd.

The books of Theodore Seuss Geisel are fantasies of astonishing originality and variety, but to children they are preëminently "funny books." Grownups find in some of them a rare gift for storytelling and a rhythmic style that is repeated in his illustrations. The books are of two varieties. First there is the accumulative, nonsense narrative, in story style but with no plot, which spins along getting bigger and wilder until it returns to its beginning. *McElligot's Pool,* with its beautiful pictures, is one of the most appealing of this type; *And to Think That I Saw It on Mulberry Street* is the funniest. Such picture narratives are a kind of imaginative play both with words and illustrations, which the children like to carry on, drawing their own candidates for McElligot's pool full of weird fish. The second type of Dr. Seuss book is the plot picture-story of which *The 500 Hats of Bartholomew Cubbins* is probably the best known and the most beloved. Bartholomew has a wistful charm that makes much more of an emotional appeal than the heroes of most nonsense tales, perhaps because we tend to identify ourselves with this harried hero who is always earnestly trying to do the right thing and is forever in the wrong. This droll has grace both in the text and the pictures. It is nonsense-fantasy with beauty. Once children have been introduced to the Dr. Seuss books, they will want to see them all.

These examples suffice to show how far the droll has traveled from the patterns of Andersen and the folk tales. It is today an expertly written tale of great variety and fresh inventiveness.

The allegory with its double meanings and its frankly moral lessons has never been so popular with young children as other types of stories. But when it is lightly written, with humor and charm, it may have considerable appeal. Small children, four- to six-years-old, delight in the *Copy-Kitten,* one of a series of little books by Helen and Alf Evers in fable style. *Nothing at All,* which reads like a folk tale but has a strong allegorical flavor, tells its readers that if you are nothing at all, you have to get dizzy getting busy and the first thing you know you'll be something after all. A plainer lesson could hardly be presented, and yet the story is so amusing and so appealing that children enjoy it without any reservations.

Phyllis McGinley handles the allegory with rare artistry. Her *Plain Princess* will appeal to all little girls who begin to suspect that they are not among the world's beauties. The story is well told, and children seem to take the moral in their stride. Actually, children probably don't mind the moralistic as much as adults have thought. Such stories can be genuinely helpful, and when they are also good entertainment, children accept them readily.

From the time the ass spoke to his obtuse master Balaam and delivered a brief but effective rebuke, *talking beast. stories* have been popular and show no signs of becoming less so. They hold up the mirror to human foibles either in derision or for the purpose of teaching morals. From Aesop to Donald Duck and Bugs Bunny they interest, they preach, and they teach.

Robert Lawson's *Rabbit Hill* (Newbery Award), seems to be a direct descendant of *The Wind in the Willows,* but for younger children. To be sure, the small denizens of Rabbit Hill are concerned with the human beings who impinge on their lives, but otherwise they are much like Kenneth Grahame's river creatures, rugged individualists and prototypes of human beings. Mr. Lawson's wonderful drawings add much to the charm of this story which remains a continuous favorite.

Ben and Me, also by Robert Lawson, is the absurd biography of Benjamin Franklin, supposedly written by Amos, the mouse. Amos considers himself well qualified as a biographer, for he admits that it is to him Franklin owes his many successes. A ludicrous series of misadventures qualifies the book as a droll although it is also a hilarious example of the talking beast type of story.

Ask Mr. Bear by Marjorie Flack could also be grouped in either of two categories. It is in the style of the accumulative folk tale and is also an example of a talking beast story. Its modern plot —a little boy looking for a birthday present for his mother, its repetitional style and the surprise ending, also modern, have endeared it to thousands of pre-school children.

Hugh Lofting's stories about the redoubtable *Dr. Dolittle,* who understood the language of birds and beasts and embarked with them on an endless series. of adventures, have been exceedingly popular with children. In this collection *The Story of Mrs. Tubbs* will introduce the younger children—seven-, eight-, or nine-years-old—to Hugh Lofting's amusing and enterpris-. ing animals.

In all of these tales and dozens more, the talking beast story is pursuing its habitual pattern, with the animals as prototypes of human beings, behaving well or foolishly, teaching morals or playing a moral part, sometimes seriously, sometimes with gay absurdity.

Alice's Adventures in Wonderland set the stage for *fantasy,* by which is meant the whimsical illusory tale. *Pinocchio, Winnie-the-Pooh,* and all of the Dr. Seuss books might well be included in this category. Once the reader accepts its magical premise, he is off to a dream world where anything may happen and strange and curious experiences are guaranteed. This dream world of fantasy ranges from the extremes of make-believe in *Alice's Adventures in Wonderland* to the convincing realism of some of the pseudo-science stories today.

Children five to nine are charmed with the three books about Elmer Elevator and his dragon. Elmer's adventures are as fantastic as Alice's but more easily understood because they are completely modern, for example, Elmer's casual raiding of the refrigerator on his return home after his adventures with the dragon. This same quality of modern situations and action helps children to accept the hilarious escapades of Mr. Popper and his penguins. This story sounds so realistic that the reader must pinch himself to realize that, after all, no one could be quite as penguin-mad as Mr. Popper. The realistic quality of the adventures makes its humor. It is partly the absence of a familiar, modern world setting that makes some of the fantasies of Andersen and Carroll harder for children to follow.

The development of pseudo-scientific fiction is one of the most interesting in the field of fantasy. Older children who begin to read science fiction are completely captivated, and it is hard to get them to read anything else while the interest holds. These stories in modern setting are backed up with all the imposing ramifications of science. In William Pène du Bois' *Twenty-One Balloons* the adventures of a weary ex-professor of mathematics on a mysterious island of diamonds, which finally blows up, are fantastic and absorbing. The action develops with all the serious details of a travel diary. Mr. du Bois' books are all beautifully written and illustrated and *Twenty-One Balloons,* the Newbery Award winner for 1948, is one of the best.

Robert Heinlein's scientific fantasies are more genuinely scientific. It is said that he checks all of the situations in his books for scientific plausibility or even possibility and as a result his books read like factual adventures—*in space,* to be sure, but factual. *Space Cadet* or *Boy on Mars* may sound like a possible story, but it is as much a fantasy as Jules Verne's *Twenty Thousand Leagues under the Sea,* from which it is descended. But no matter how the adventures in space are reinforced with scientific data, the stories are still figments of the imagination and to the average reader they are as fantastic as Professor Sherman's explosive island.

In conclusion, it is well to remind ourselves again that in the field of the folk and fanciful tales, children's tastes differ widely and violently. Some children never enjoy this field of fiction. They remain uneasily conscious of the make-believe or they may reject the magic scornfully. But these young literalists may need exposure to it, nevertheless. The drolleries, the poetry, the high adventures, the moral overtones, the romance and absurdities of modern fairy tales are wholesome antidotes for a too tight literalness which may fossilize young spirits too early.

On the other hand, some children take to the fanciful like ducks to water, and they may begin to reject other types of reading. When this happens, it may mean that the dream world is providing these children with compensation for the drabness or the fearfulness of real life. Up to a point, this is good, but when a child wants nothing but fairy tales he needs help. Look gently into his personal problems first, and then try to balance his reading.

With literary fare as with foods, a varied diet is best. So, don't use the stories in this book in a long series. Intersperse them with poetry, biography, realistic fiction, and science books. But when you use these fanciful stories don't be heavy handed with them and don't label them untrue. It is simply a world of make-believe. If some young realist pins you down with an incredulous—"But that never happened, did it?" you may reply gaily, "Well, maybe it didn't, but wouldn't it be fun if it could happen?"

The modern fanciful tales

ASK MR. BEAR

Marjorie Flack

Although this little story is written like an accumulative tale of talking beasts, the child and the surprise ending are delightfully modern. It is one of the favorites of preschool children.

Once there was a boy named Danny. One day Danny's mother had a birthday.

Danny said to himself,

"What shall I give my mother for her birthday?"

So Danny started out to see what he could find. He walked along, and he met a Hen.

"Good morning, Mrs. Hen," said Danny.

"Can you give me something for my mother's birthday?"

"Cluck, cluck," said the Hen. "I can give you a nice fresh egg for your mother's birthday."

"Thank you," said Danny, "but she has an egg."

"Let's see what we can find then," said the Hen.

So Danny and the Hen skipped along until they met a Goose.

"Good morning, Mrs. Goose," said Danny. "Can you give me something for my mother's birthday?"

"Honk, honk," said the Goose. "I can give you some nice feathers to make a fine pillow for your mother's birthday."

"Thank you," said Danny, "but she has a pillow."

"Let's see what we can find then," said the Goose.

So Danny and the Hen and the Goose all hopped along until they met a Goat.

"Good morning, Mrs. Goat," said Danny. "Can you give me something for my mother's birthday?"

"Maa, maa," said the Goat. "I can give you milk for making cheese."

"Thank you," said Danny, "but she has some cheese."

"Let's see what we can find then," said the Goat.

So Danny and the Hen and the Goose and the Goat all galloped along until they met a Sheep.

"Good morning, Mrs. Sheep," said Danny. "Can you give me something for my mother's birthday?"

"Baa, baa," said the Sheep. "I can give you some wool to make a warm blanket for your mother's birthday."

"Thank you," said Danny, "but she has a blanket."

"Let's see what we can find then," said the Sheep.

So Danny and the Hen and the Goose and the Goat and the Sheep all trotted along until they met a Cow.

"Good morning, Mrs. Cow," said Danny. "Can you give me something for my mother's birthday?"

"Moo, moo," said the Cow. "I can give you some milk and cream."

"Thank you," said Danny, "but she has some milk and cream."

"Then ask Mr. Bear," said the Cow. "He lives in the woods over the hill."

"All right," said Danny, "let's go and ask Mr. Bear."

"No," said the Hen.

"No," said the Goose.

"No," said the Goat.

"No," said the Sheep.

"No—no," said the Cow.

So Danny went alone to find Mr. Bear. He ran and he ran until he came to the hill, and he walked and he walked until he came to the woods and there he met—Mr. Bear.

"Good morning, Mr. Bear," said Danny. "Can you give me something for my mother's birthday?"

"Hum, hum," said the Bear. "I have nothing to give you for your mother's birthday, but I can tell you something you can give her."

So Mr. Bear whispered a secret in Danny's ear.

"Oh," said Danny. "Thank you, Mr. Bear!"

Then he ran through the woods and he

skipped down the hill and he came to his house.

"Guess what I have for your birthday!" Danny said to his mother.

So his mother tried to guess.

"Is it an egg?"

"No, it isn't an egg," said Danny.

"Is it a pillow?"

"No, it isn't a pillow," said Danny.

"Is it a cheese?"

"No, it isn't a cheese," said Danny.

"Is it a blanket?"

"No, it isn't a blanket," said Danny.

"Is it milk or cream?"

"No, it isn't milk or cream," said Danny.

His mother could not guess at all. So—Danny gave his mother a Big Birthday Bear Hug.

COPY-KITTEN

Helen and Alf Evers

A few modern fables, like this one, are popular with small children, but too many of them become monotonous.

No one knew what the Copy-Kitten really looked like—
Because he always tried to look like some other animal.
Sometimes he copied the pigs—
Sometimes he copied the chickens—
But he never copied his mother—
As the other kittens did—
And his mother was worried about him.
One day—
The circus came to town.
The kitten stole away to watch. He crawled under the big tent.
First he looked at the elephant—
The elephant was easy to copy.
Next he saw the monkey—
The Copy-Kitten swung from a bar like the monkey.
Copying the lion was easy, because the kitten looked a little like a lion anyway.
But when the Copy-Kitten came to the giraffe—

And tried to stretch his neck to look like HIM—
He couldn't do it, although he tried and tried.
He stretched his neck, he twisted his head—
He pushed his head with his paws—
But he just couldn't look a bit like the giraffe.
The poor kitten stopped trying—
He had never felt so sad in his life.
He was so sad and disappointed that he made up his mind never to copy anyone again.
When he was home again everyone was very glad to see him—
And everyone was even more glad, because the Copy-Kitten wasn't copying anyone.
But his mother was still worried about him—
Because he wouldn't copy her, as the other kittens did.
All the other young animals copied their mothers—
But the Copy-Kitten was too happy, just being himself at last, to copy anyone at all!

NOTHING AT ALL

Wanda Gág

Wanda Gág not only heard stories well told when she was a child, but she grew up in a family where the father was an artist and every child could and did draw on every scrap of paper he could collect. The Gágs were poor, but Wanda managed to earn enough money to study art even after both parents were gone and she was the head of the family. Her famous Millions of Cats *she made up on the spur of the moment in answer to a child's demand for a cat story. She told it over and over until its rhythm suited her. Then, she made the pictures to go with it. All of her picture-stories have this rhythm of pictures and text, and all of them reflect the style of the old storytellers.* Nothing at All *is a little allegory, but to children it is just an unusual story.*

Once upon a time there were three little orphan dogs. They were brothers. They lived in a far forgotten corner of an old forgotten farm in three forgotten kennels which stood there in a row.

One of the kennels had a pointed roof and in it lived Pointy, the dog with pointed ears.

Another kennel had a curly roof and in it lived Curly, the dog with curly ears.

The middle kennel had a roundish roof and in it lived the third dog, but whether he had round ears nobody knew, for he was a dog whom no one could see. He was invisible.

> He was not very tall
> Nor yet very small;
> He looked like nothing,
> Like nothing at all.

And that was his name—Nothing-at-all.

Nothing-at-all was happy enough, for although no one could see him, he had just as much fun as any other dog.

He could jump and run and eat. He could hear and see and smell. He could bark and romp and play with his two little puppy brothers.

And Pointy said to Nothing-at-all, "We love you even if we can't see you."

And Curly said, "We know you are a really truly dog even if we can't see you. We can't see the wind either but the wind is real. And we can't see smells but smells are *very* real."

And Nothing-at-all said, "Oh, I suppose it takes all kinds of dogs to make a world, both see-able and unsee-able ones, so why should I worry?"

And he was as happy as any dog could be until there came a day when something happened.

It was a warm and drowsy day. Pointy was lying in his pointed kennel, Curly was lying in his curly kennel, and Nothing-at-all was lying in his roundish kennel. They were dozing, all three, when the sound of voices roused them from their dreams.

"Oh look!" cried a boy-voice. "Here are some dog kennels in this far forgotten corner of the old forgotten farm."

"With dogs in them?" asked a girl-voice.

The boy looked into one kennel and said, "Yes! There's a curly-eared dog in here."

Next he looked into another kennel and said, "And a pointy-eared dog in here!"

Then he looked into the middle kennel, but since only invisible Nothing-at-all was in there, he saw nothing. "The roundish kennel is empty," he said. "Nothing in it at all."

Gently and carefully the girl reached for Pointy; gently and carefully the boy reached for Curly, but the two little dogs were frightened and began to whimper.

"Don't cry, little pointy-eared dog," said the girl. "We won't hurt you. We'll adopt you both and give you milk to drink and bones to nibble."

And the boy said, "Don't cry, little curly-eared dog. We'll be kind to you. We won't ever hit you or kick you, or pick you up by your neck or your tail, or with your legs dangling down."

When Pointy and Curly heard this, they knew they would be safe and happy, so they snuggled into the children's arms and went back to sleep.

And then they were carried away to a new and happy home, while poor little Nothing-at-all was left behind. But do you think he sat down and cried? Oh no—he had a plan!

"I'll just be very quiet and go with them," he thought. "After a while they'll get used to me and find out I'm a really truly dog even though they can't see me. Then they'll adopt me too. And they'll never hurt me but will give me milk to drink. And bones to nibble. I think I will like it very much!"

Those were his thoughts as he trotted after the boy and the girl and his two puppy brothers.

But it was a long long road, and soon his little invisible legs felt so weary and his big invisible eyes felt so blinky that he had to sit down and rest. His eyes blinked once and twice and thrice, and then he was fast asleep. When he awoke he was all alone.

"Oh, where is everybody?" he cried. "I must run and find them!"

He ran to the puddle pond. No one was there.

He ran round the blossom bushes. No one was there.

He ran past the poppy patch. No one was there.

Back and forth he went, in and out, over and under, in twists and curves and zigzags, but no one was anywhere.

At last he found a hollow tree which looked something like a kennel. He crept into it—and because he felt so lonely and so very much like nothing, he murmured sadly to himself:

> "Oh, I'm not very tall
> And not very small;
> I look like nothing,
> Like nothing at all!"

As he finished, a voice said, "I can't see you, but aren't you that empty space in the tree trunk?" It was a bird who spoke.

"Yes," said the little dog. "My name is Nothing-at-all, and that's what I look like too. I never minded it before, but now I long to look like other dogs so the boy and the girl can see me, and so they'll give me milk to drink and bones to nibble, and never pick me up by my neck or my tail, but adopt me for their pet as they did my two puppy brothers."

The bird laughed.

"That's a long speech for an empty space to make!" he said. "But I can understand how you feel, and I might be able to help you."

"But you're only a bird," said Nothing-at-all. "How can you help me?"

"I am a JACKDAW," said the bird proudly, "and as such it is my task to carry home everything I see. Once I even found a Book of Magic—wait! I'll be right back," and the bird was gone.

When he returned, the jackdaw said, "It's just as I thought. In the Book of Magic there is a chapter called NOTHINGNESS AND SOMETHINGNESS. And it says that he who is Nothingy, yet wishes to be Somethingy, must get up at sunrise and whirl around and around and around. While whirling thus, he must say this magic chant:

> I'm busy
> Getting dizzy.

This, says the book, he must do nine days in a row at sunrise, and he shall see what he shall see. Goodbye, I'm off!" and the bird was gone.

The next morning before sunrise Nothing-at-all was wide awake and ready to try his magic. As soon as the sun peeped over the hilltop, he began whirling and twirling and swirling, and he said:

> "I'm busy
> Getting dizzy
> I'm busy
> Getting dizzy."

After he had stopped whirling, what do you suppose had happened?

Do you think he was a dog whom anyone could see? No he wasn't. He still looked Nothingy but now his Nothingness had a shape! When he held up his paw, he couldn't see the paw but he could see a paw-shaped space, and he was very happy about that.

"Well done!" cried a voice which was the jackdaw's. "You are a pleasant-looking shape, I must say. Keep it up!" and the bird was gone.

The next day Nothing-at-all worked at his magic as before. As soon as the sun peeped over the hilltop, he whirled and twirled and swirled, and said:

"I'm busy
Getting dizzy
I'm busy
Getting dizzy."

When he stopped, the jackdaw came and said, "Yes, the magic is working well. That's a fine black spot you have on your back now. Keep it up!" and the bird was gone.

The third morning at sunrise Nothing-at-all whirled and twirled and swirled, and said:

"I'm busy
Getting dizzy
I'm busy
Getting dizzy
I'm busy
Getting dizzy."

When he sat down to rest, the jackdaw came and said, "You're doing better than I expected. You've added quite a few spots today. Goodbye!" and the bird was gone.

The fourth day, after Nothing-at-all had whirled and twirled and swirled and repeated his busy-dizzy chant, the jackdaw came and said, "You are certainly working hard at your magic task. That black tail-tip is a beauty, I must say!"

The little dog was so pleased that he wagged his tail wildly, and although the *tail* was still invisible, its black tip showed the wagging plainly enough. The jackdaw laughed at this and then disappeared.

By the fifth day, Nothing-at-all's eyes were visible.

By the sixth day, his nose and mouth could be seen.

On the seventh day his tongue was visible.

On the eighth day his ears and paws could be seen.

And then came the ninth day.

Nothing-at-all whirled and twirled and swirled as he had never done before, and he said:

"I'm busy
Getting dizzy
I'm busy
Getting dizzy
I'm busy
Getting dizzy
I'm busy
Getting dizzy,"

until he was so dizzy that the whole world seemed to swirl around with him.

When he stopped to rest, the jackdaw came.

"Good work!" he cried. "Now you are SOME-THING after all—a really truly see-able dog! And a most lovable round-eared puppy you are, to be sure. Good luck! Goodbye!" and the jackdaw flew away.

Now the little dog was so happy that he jumped to his feet and barked and picked up sticks and tore about wildly.

Round and round in a circle he ran.

With leaps and bounds and somersaults he ran.

In twists and curves and zigzags he ran.

Back and forth, in and out, over and under, around blossom bushes and puddle ponds and poppy patches he ran.

And then he stopped . . . for——

There in front of him were the boy and the girl. They were coming from the far forgotten corner of the old forgotten farm, and were pulling a long red cart on which were:
the pointed kennel
the curly kennel
and the roundish kennel, all in a row!

With a run and a jump, the round-eared puppy hopped into his roundish kennel, and now he too was taken to a new and happy home. All along the way he wagged his black-tipped tail, and with joyful barks he said:

"I've always been small
And not very tall;
I used to look like nothing at all.
I'm still rather small
And not a bit tall,
But now I'm a see-able dog after all!"

But the boy and the girl didn't know what the little dog was saying. Nor did they know what Pointy and Curly were saying when they met their long-lost brother again.
But maybe,
perhaps,
almost surely, they said:
"How happy we'll be, all three of us here; with our dear old kennels to live in, and the two kind children to play with. And oh, little Something-after-all, it *is* so nice to SEE you!"

SONNY-BOY SIM

Elizabeth W. Baker

This delightful tall tale sounds as traditional as "Little Freddy with His Fiddle" and as droll as The Jack Tales. *Sonny-Boy reads aloud as gaily as a jig and the laughing refrain rises like contagious giggles.*

Once a long time ago there was a little log house 'way off in the piney woods. Right through the middle of the house was the dog-trot. The dog-trot was a wide breezeway, like a hall open at each end, with steps at each end to go in and out.

On one side of the breezeway was a long room with a big fireplace in it, and on the other side were three little bedrooms, each with a bed and a chair.

And three people lived in the little log house in the piney woods.

The first person that lived in the little log house in the piney woods was Grandma. She cooked three meals a day at the big fireplace in the long room. She could make the best corn pone you ever ate. She could roast potatoes in the ashes, and barbecue a turkey on a spit in the fireplace until it would melt in your mouth.

And she kept the wide planks in the floor scrubbed with water and wood ashes till they were white, almost, as the lacy bedspreads that she knit.

But in the evenings she liked to pull her rocking chair out into the dog-trot and sit there and rock and rest, and knit on a new bedspread. There she would rock and knit, rock and knit, till the moon came up behind the piney woods.

The second person that lived in the little log house in the piney woods was Grandpappy. All day long Grandpappy plowed the corn or hoed the cotton in the fields. In the fall he cut firewood for the big fireplace, and made sweet cider at the cider mill out back of the house.

But in the evenings he liked to pull his high-backed chair out into the dog-trot, and tilt it back against the wall, and rest while he played the fiddle. He was the champion fiddler of all

that part of the country. He would cross his knees and play that fiddle, and play that fiddle, till the moon went down behind the piney woods.

The third and last person that lived in the little log house in the piney woods was Sonny-Boy Sim. Sonny-Boy Sim roamed the woods all day with his hound-dog, Homer, chasing a bear or a deer, or sometimes maybe just a black-faced coon.

But in the evenings he liked to go out into the dog-trot and dance to the tune of Grandpappy's fiddle. He could bend and turn and leap and clap his hands and lift his feet quicker and lighter than anybody else in all that part of the country. And he would dance to the tune of Grandpappy's fiddle till the moon was sailing through the thin white clouds far above the trees in the dark piney woods.

One day when Sonny-Boy Sim and Homer the hound-dog were out roaming through the piney woods, they came across the biggest black-faced coon they had ever seen.

And Homer the hound-dog opened his mouth and let out a note like a deep-toned bell. And Sonny-Boy Sim and Homer the hound-dog lit out after that coon and chased him clear down to the bayou. And that coon plunged into the water with Homer the hound-dog right after him, close behind.

But just when Homer the hound-dog thought he had that coon, here came a pine stump just showing above the water, and that coon climbed out of the water onto the pine stump.

And when Homer the hound-dog got right up close to the stump all ready to catch that coon, that black-faced coon put out his little black hand and pushed that hound-dog's head right down under the water.

When Homer the hound-dog came up again, he turned around and swam back to where he had started from. And when he had climbed onto the bank and shaken off the water and looked back, that black-faced coon was sitting on the stump, laughing fit to kill.

Then Sonny-Boy Sim remembered that it was just about dinnertime anyway, so he and Homer the hound-dog ran home to get some of Grandma's good corn pone.

One day Sonny-Boy Sim put on a new straw hat that Grandpappy had bought for him at the store, and he and Homer the hound-dog went off into the piney woods. And the first thing you know they ran across a little black bear cub. But as soon as it saw them coming, it climbed right up into a pine tree and sat in the crotch of a limb and looked down at them.

Now, Sonny-Boy Sim wanted that bear cub for a pet. So he said to himself, "I'll climb that tree and catch that bear cub by the tail, and drop it down to Homer the hound-dog, and we'll take it home and make a pet of it."

So he started climbing up that pine tree.

And when Sonny-Boy Sim got nearly up to where that bear cub was sitting in the crotch of a limb, he reached out his hand to take it by the tail.

But all of a sudden that bear cub opened its mouth and showed all its sharp teeth, and stretched out its long claws and snatched that new straw hat right off Sonny-Boy Sim's head. And Sonny-Boy Sim shinned down that tree a good deal faster than he had climbed up. And when he looked back, that bear cub had Sonny-Boy Sim's new straw hat on its head, and it was laughing fit to kill.

About that time Sonny-Boy Sim thought of that good sweet apple cider that Grandpappy made, and he and Homer the hound-dog ran home to get some.

Another time when Sonny-Boy Sim and Homer the hound-dog were roaming through the piney woods, they came across a beautiful deer with wide-branching horns. And Homer the hound-dog opened his mouth and let out a note like a deep-toned bell. And he and Sonny-Boy Sim lit out after that deer and chased him till they had him cornered against a high bank of rocks along a creek.

Sonny-Boy Sim thought, "I'll catch the deer and take its horns and make Grandpappy a hat-rack out of 'em."

So while Homer the hound-dog barked at the deer's heels, Sonny-Boy Sim reached out to catch that deer by the horns.

But all of a sudden, that deer lowered its head, and with its beautiful wide-branching horns caught Sonny-Boy Sim by his suspenders and threw him right up onto a limb of a big pine tree.

And then it caught Homer the hound-dog and threw him on top of the bank of rock where a thick grapevine made a soft bed of green. Then the deer stood there for a minute looking at them, laughing fit to kill.

And as it disappeared into the piney woods, Sonny-Boy Sim got to thinking of that good barbecue that Grandma was cooking, and he and Homer the hound-dog climbed down and ran home to get some.

Not long after that, the coon and the deer and the bear cub met 'way out in the piney woods. And they stopped to talk together.

The deer said, "I'm tired of being chased by Sonny-Boy Sim and his hound-dog Homer."

"So'm I!" said the black-faced coon.

"Me too!" said the bear cub.

"Then," said the deer, "I'll tell you what let's do. Let's get all our sisters and brothers and aunts and uncles and cousins, and go up to that little log house tonight, and show 'em how it feels to be chased about. Let's be there just as the moon is coming up through the piney woods."

That night Grandma pulled her rocking chair out into the dog-trot and got out her knitting. And Grandpappy brought out his high-backed chair and tilted it back against the wall, and began to fiddle. And Sonny-Boy Sim came out and began dancing.

And just as the moon came up behind the piney woods, Homer the hound-dog lifted his head and let out a note like a deep-toned bell.

Sonny-Boy Sim ran to the end of the dog-trot to see who was coming.

Then they heard him call, "Grandma! Grandpappy! Come quick!"

So Grandma and Grandpappy ran to the end of the dog-trot where Sonny-Boy Sim was standing. And there they saw a black-faced coon, and a deer with beautiful wide-branching horns, and a black bear cub, all standing out in the yard. And all around them were more coons and deer and bears—brothers and sisters and aunts and uncles and cousins.

And you can just better believe that Grandma and Grandpappy and Sonny-Boy Sim were scared!

And when they ran to the other end of the dog-trot and saw more deer and coons and bears lined up, they were scared worse than ever.

And Grandpappy said, "Well, they've got us all hemmed in. If they've come here to eat us up, we might as well have one more good time while we can."

So Grandpappy picked up his fiddle and struck up a lively tune, and Grandma ran back and rolled out a barrel of that good sweet cider.

And Sonny-Boy Sim began to dance, and Homer the hound-dog got up and danced all around Sonny-Boy Sim.

And all those deer and bears and black-faced coons came crowding closer and closer, listening to the music and watching Sonny-Boy Sim and Homer the hound-dog dance.

The music got faster and faster, and Sonny-Boy Sim and Homer the hound-dog flung their feet higher and higher.

And presently, all those deer and bears and black-faced coons began to sway from side to side in the moonlight, and the first thing you know, they were all dancing together to the tune of Grandpappy's fiddle.

Then Grandma filled a big tub with that good sweet cider, and set it out where they could all drink as much as they liked. And they all danced to the tune of Grandpappy's fiddle till the moon went down behind the piney woods.

And a soft white mist came up from the bayou, and it wrapped itself about all those deer and bears and black-faced coons, until, the first thing you know, they all went back into the dark piney woods, laughing fit to kill.

MIKE MULLIGAN
AND HIS STEAM SHOVEL

Virginia Burton

This book fits city units and will satisfy every child's interest in modern machines, and will lead children into Virginia Burton's other books, which should be seen as well as heard. The children will like to know that her books were written for her own sons, who criticized them if any detail was omitted or seemed to be wrong. Mike Mulligan reaches down to the youngest children.

Mike Mulligan had a steam shovel, a beautiful red steam shovel. Her name was Mary Anne. Mike Mulligan was very proud of Mary Anne. He always said that she could dig as much in a day as a hundred men could dig in a week, but he had never been quite sure that this was true.

Mike Mulligan and Mary Anne had been digging together for years and years. Mike Mulligan took such good care of Mary Anne she never grew old.

It was Mike Mulligan and Mary Anne and some others who dug the great canals for the big boats to sail through.

It was Mike Mulligan and Mary Anne and some others who cut through the high mountains so that trains could go through.

It was Mike Mulligan and Mary Anne and some others who lowered the hills and straightened the curves to make the long highways for the automobiles.

It was Mike Mulligan and Mary Anne and some others who smoothed out the ground and filled in the holes to make the landing fields for the airplanes.

And it was Mike Mulligan and Mary Anne and some others who dug the deep holes for the cellars of the tall skyscrapers in the big cities. When people used to stop and watch them, Mike Mulligan and Mary Anne used to dig a little faster and a little better. The more people stopped, the faster and better they dug. Some days they would keep as many as thirty-seven trucks busy taking away the dirt they had dug.

"Mike Mulligan and His Steam Shovel." Reprinted by permission of and arrangement with Houghton, Mifflin Company, the authorized publishers

Then along came the new gasoline shovels and the new electric shovels and the new Diesel motor shovels and took all the jobs away from the steam shovels. Mike Mulligan and Mary Anne were VERY SAD.

All the other steam shovels were being sold for junk, or left out in old gravel pits to rust and fall apart. Mike loved Mary Anne. He couldn't do that to her. He had taken such good care of her that she could still dig as much in a day as a hundred men could dig in a week; at least he thought she could but he wasn't quite sure. Everywhere they went the new gas shovels and the new electric shovels and the new Diesel motor shovels had all the jobs. No one wanted Mike Mulligan and Mary Anne any more.

Then one day Mike read in a newspaper that the town of Popperville was going to build a new town hall.

"We are going to dig the cellar of that town hall," said Mike to Mary Anne, and off they started.

They left the canals and the railroads and the highways and the airports and the big cities where no one wanted them any more and went away out in the country. They crawled along slowly up the hills and down the hills till they came to the little town of Popperville.

When they got there they found the selectmen were just deciding who should dig the cellar for the new town hall. Mike Mulligan spoke to Henry B. Swap, one of the selectmen.

"I heard," he said, "that you are going to build a new town hall. Mary Anne and I will dig the cellar for you in just one day."

"What!" said Henry B. Swap. "Dig a cellar in a day! It would take a hundred men at least a week to dig the cellar for our new town hall."

"Sure," said Mike, "but Mary Anne can dig as much in a day as a hundred men can dig in a week." Though he had never been quite sure that this was true. Then he added, "If we can't do it, you won't have to pay."

Henry B. Swap thought that this would be an easy way to get part of the cellar dug for nothing, so he smiled in rather a mean way and gave the job of digging the cellar of the new town hall to Mike Mulligan and Mary Anne.

They started in early the next morning just as the sun was coming up. Soon a little boy came along. "Do you think you will finish by sundown?" he said to Mike Mulligan.

"Sure," said Mike, "if you stay and watch us. We always work faster and better when someone is watching us."

So the little boy stayed to watch.

Then Mrs. McGillicuddy, Henry B. Swap, and the Town Constable came over to see what was happening, and they stayed to watch.

Mike Mulligan and Mary Anne dug a little faster and a little better.

This gave the little boy a good idea. He ran off and told the postman with the morning mail, the telegraph boy on his bicycle, the milkman with his cart and horse, the doctor on his way home, and the farmer and his family coming into town for the day, and they all stopped and stayed to watch.

That made Mike Mulligan and Mary Anne dig a little faster and a little better.

They finished the first corner neat and square . . . but the sun was getting higher.

Clang! Clang! Clang! The Fire Department arrived. They had seen the smoke and thought there was a fire.

Then the little boy said, "Why don't you stay and watch?"

So the Fire Department of Popperville stayed to watch Mike Mulligan and Mary Anne.

When they heard the fire engine, the children in the school across the street couldn't keep their eyes on their lessons. The teacher called a long recess and the whole school came out to watch. That made Mike Mulligan and Mary Anne dig still faster and still better.

They finished the second corner neat and square, but the sun was right up in the top of the sky.

Now the girl who answers the telephone called up the next towns of Bangerville and Bopperville and Kipperville and Kopperville and told them what was happening in Popperville. All the people came over to see if Mike Mulligan and his steam shovel could dig the cellar in just one day. The more people came, the faster Mike Mulligan and Mary Anne dug. But they would have to hurry. They were still only halfway through and the sun was beginning to go down.

They finished the third corner . . . neat and square.

Never had Mike Mulligan and Mary Anne had so many people to watch them; never had they dug so fast and so well; and never had the sun seemed to go down so fast.

"Hurry, Mike Mulligan! Hurry! Hurry!" shouted the little boy. "There's not much more time!"

Dirt was flying everywhere, and the smoke and steam were so thick that the people could hardly see anything.

But listen!

Bing! Bang! Crash! Slam!
LOUDER AND LOUDER, FASTER AND FASTER.

Then suddenly it was quiet. Slowly the dirt settled down. The smoke and steam cleared away, and there was the cellar all finished.

Four corners . . . neat and square; four walls . . . straight down, and Mike Mulligan and Mary Anne at the bottom, and the sun was just going down behind the hill.

"Hurray!" shouted the people. "Hurray for Mike Mulligan and his steam shovel! They have dug the cellar in just one day."

Suddenly the little boy said, "How are they going to get out?"

"That's right," said Mrs. McGillicuddy to Henry B. Swap. "How is he going to get his steam shovel out?"

Henry B. Swap didn't answer but he smiled in rather a mean way.

Then everybody said, "How are they going to get out? Hi! Mike Mulligan! How are you going to get your steam shovel out?"

Mike Mulligan looked around at the four square walls and four square corners, and he said, "We've dug so fast and we've dug so well that we've quite forgotten to leave a way out!"

Nothing like this had ever happened to Mike Mulligan and Mary Anne before, and they didn't know what to do.

Nothing like this had ever happened before in Popperville. Everybody started talking at once, and everybody had a different idea, and everybody thought that his idea was the best. They talked and they talked and they argued and they fought till they were worn out, and still no one knew how to get Mike Mulligan and Mary Anne out of the cellar they had dug.

Then Henry B. Swap said, "The job isn't fin-

ished because Mary Anne isn't out of the cellar, so Mike Mulligan won't get paid." And he smiled again in a rather mean way.

Now the little boy, who had been keeping very quiet, had another good idea. He said, "Why couldn't we leave Mary Anne in the cellar and build the new town hall above her? Let her be the furnace for the new town hall and let Mike Mulligan be the janitor. Then you wouldn't have to buy a new furnace, and we could pay Mike Mulligan for digging the cellar in just one day."

"Why not?" said Henry B. Swap, and smiled in a way that was not quite so mean.

"Why not?" said Mrs. McGillicuddy.

"Why not?" said the Town Constable.

"Why not?" said all the people.

So they found a ladder and climbed down into the cellar to ask Mike Mulligan and Mary Anne.

"Why not?" said Mike Mulligan. So it was decided, and everybody was happy.

They built the new town hall right over Mike Mulligan and Mary Anne. It was finished before winter. Every day the little boy goes over to see Mike Mulligan and Mary Anne, and Mrs. McGillicuddy takes him nice hot apple pies. As for Henry B. Swap he spends most of his time in the cellar of the new town hall listening to the stories that Mike Mulligan has to tell and smiling in a way that isn't mean at all.

Now when you go to Popperville, be sure to go down in the cellar of the new town hall. There they'll be, Mike Mulligan and Mary Anne . . . Mike in his rocking chair smoking his pipe, and Mary Anne beside him, warming up the meetings in the new town hall.

THE STORY OF MRS. TUBBS ✓

Hugh Lofting

This amusing little story should prepare small children to enjoy Hugh Lofting's famous Dr. Dolittle books when they are a little older. They may also like Marie Ets' Mister Penny, another story of enterprising animals who help their human friend.

"The Story of Mrs. Tubbs" by Hugh Lofting. J. B. Lippincott Company, Philadelphia, 1923. Used with the kind permission of Mrs. Hugh Lofting

Once upon a time, many many years ago, there lived a very old woman and her name was Mrs. Tubbs. She lived on a little farm, way off in the country. Her little house stood on the edge of the woods, not very far from a village with a little church, and a little river with a little bridge over it, flowed close by the house. There was a barn too for cows and horses, only the woman hadn't any cows or horses; she lived all alone with a dog and a duck and a pig. The dog's name was Peter Punk, the duck's name was Polly Ponk, and the pig's name was Patrick Pink. The old woman called them Punk, Ponk and Pink for short.

Punk and Ponk had known one another for many years and were very good friends. The pig they treated as a baby because they said he was very young and hadn't much sense.

The old woman did not own the farm although she had lived on it so long. The farm belonged to a man up in London who never came there at all. This man, one fine day at the end of summer when the leaves were beginning to fall in the woods, sent his nephew, a very silly young man with a red face, down from London to live in the farm-house instead of Mrs. Tubbs.

Punk, Ponk and Pink and the old woman were all dreadfully sad at having to leave the home where they had been so happy together for so many years.

As the sun was going down behind the little church one evening at the end of Summer when the leaves were beginning to fall in the woods, they all left the farm together. Punk in front, then Pink, then Ponk and Mrs. Tubbs behind.

They walked a long, long way along the edge of the woods and at last when they saw a seat under a tree they all sat down to rest.

"Oh dear, oh dear," Mrs. Tubbs kept saying, "now I have no home, no place to sleep. And me an old woman. To be turned off the farm after all these years! What shall I do, where shall I go? Oh dear, oh dear!"

Then she stopped talking. Peter Punk and Polly Ponk both understood what she said because they had lived with her so long. Pink couldn't understand because he was only a baby and he kept saying in animal language:—"Let's go on. I don't like this place. There's nothing to eat here."

"I do think it's a shame," Polly Ponk said to Punk, "that the old woman should be turned out. Did you see the way that stupid man slammed the door after we had gone? I'd like to see him turn *me* out of *my* house that way. I'd give him such a peck on his red nose he wouldn't try it again! But of course she is old, very old. I often wonder how old she really is."

"She is over a hundred, I know," said Punk. "Yes, it is a shame she should have to go for that stupid booby. 'Beefsteak-and-Onions' I call him. But it isn't altogether his fault. He's only sent here from London by his uncle who owns the farm."

"Well, what are we going to do with the old lady?" asked Ponk. "She can't stay here."

"We will wait till she falls asleep," said Punk. "Then we'll go into the woods and find a cave for her to spend the night in and cook something to eat."

"Isn't she asleep now?" asked Ponk. "Her eyes are shut."

"No," said the dog, "she's crying. Can't you feel the seat shaking? She always shuts her eyes and shakes when she cries."

Presently the old lady and the pig began to snore together. So they waked poor Pink up and all three went into the woods. They set Pink digging truffles and Polly Ponk went off to the river and caught a fine trout while Punk got sticks together and made a fire.

"Now who's going to do the cooking?" asked Punk.

"Oh, I'll do that," said Ponk.

"Can you cook?" asked the dog.

"Indeed I can," said Polly Ponk. "My Aunt Deborah used to cook at a hotel and she showed me how. You get the fire burning and I'll soon have the fish fried."

So very soon they had a nice meal ready of fried trout and truffles for the old lady.

"Now," said Punk, "we must go into the cave and get a bed ready for Mrs. Tubbs."

So they went into the cave and made a fine, soft bed of leaves.

"What shall we do for a pillow," said Punk. "Shall we use the pig, he would be nice and soft?"

"No," said Ponk, "I'm going to use him as a hot-water bottle. It's very important to keep the old lady's feet warm. But I have some feathers back home which will make a fine pillow. They are some of my own which I kept last moulting season."

"What did you do that for?" asked Punk.

"Well," said the duck, standing first on one foot then on the other, "the fact is I'm not getting any younger myself and I thought that if, when I am very old, I should get bald, I could have them stuck on with glue or something. I'll fly over to the farm and fetch them. I know just where I put them: they're in the left-hand drawer of my bureau under my lavendar bonnet."

With a flap of her wings she flew over the tree-tops to the farm and in a minute was back again with the feathers in a bag.

When they had everything ready they went and fetched Mrs. Tubbs and showed her the supper they had prepared. But the old woman would not eat anything but kept saying,

"Oh dear, oh dear! What shall I do? I am turned out of house and home, and me an old woman!"

So they put her to bed in the cave, covered her over with leaves and placed Pink at her feet as a hot-water bottle. And presently she cried herself to sleep.

Punk and Ponk now began to worry over what they should do with the old woman next.

"She can't stay here," said Ponk. "That's certain. You see, Punk, she isn't eating anything. She is so upset and she is so old. What we've got to do is to find some way to turn that booby out of the farm so she can go back and live there."

"Well, what shall we do?" said the dog.

"I don't just know yet," Polly Ponk answered. "But in the morning before she wakes up, we must go back to the farm and see what can be done."

So next morning, while the old woman was still asleep, off they all went as the sun was getting up behind the woods. Just before they got to the farm as they were crossing the bridge over the stream, they saw Tommy Squeak, the King of the Water-rats coming down for his morning bath in the river.

"Catch him!" said Ponk. "Perhaps he'll be able to help." And they all started running as hard as they could after the water-rat. Poor Tommy Squeak was dreadfully frightened at see-

ing a dog and a pig and a duck coming after him, and he made off for the river as fast as his legs would carry him. When he came to the river he jumped in with a splash and disappeared. Punk and Pink sat down on the grass and said, "We've lost him!"

But Polly Ponk, running up behind, never stopped but dived into the river, swam under the water and just caught poor Mr. Squeak as he was popping into a hole way down at the bottom of the river. She pulled him up by his tail, carried him to the shore and put him on the grass. Then they all gathered round him so he couldn't run away.

"Now," said the duck, "don't be frightened. Stay where you are and do as you are told and we won't hurt you. Listen. Do you remember, last summer, when you were stealing cheese from the pantry up at the farm, and you fell into a bucket of water and Mrs. Tubbs came and caught you? Do you remember?"

"Yes," said Tommy Squeak, shaking the water off his whiskers, still very frightened.

"And she didn't hurt you or give you to the cat. Do you remember?"

"Yes," said Tommy Squeak.

"She let you go and told you never to come back again. Did she not?"

"Yes," said Tommy Squeak.

"You know that she is the kindest woman to animals in all the world, don't you?"

"Yes," said Tommy Squeak.

"Allright," said Polly. "Now listen. A red-faced booby from London Town has been sent down here to turn Mrs. Tubbs out of her house. She is terribly old, as you know; we have taken her up into the woods. But she won't eat her food, she is so sad, and we can't do a thing with her. The Winter is coming on and we must get her back into the farm somehow. Now you are the king of the water-rats and this is what you must do: Call all the rats of the river together—every one of them—thousands of them and take them to the farm. Then worry the booby every way you can think of. Rattle the pans in the kitchen at night so he can't sleep. Pull the stuffing out of the chairs. Eat holes in his best hat. Do everything you can to drive him out. Then, if he goes back to London Town, we can put Mrs. Tubbs back on the farm."

"Allright," said Tommy Squeak. "I'll do my best for the old woman. She certainly ought to be put back on the farm."

Then he stood up on his hind legs by the river-bank and facing up the stream, he gave a long, loud, wonderful squeak. Then he turned and facing down the stream he gave another.

And presently there was a rustling sound in the grasses all around and a whispering sound in the bushes and a splashing sound from the water. And everywhere rats appeared, hopping and jumping towards him—big ones and little ones, black ones, grey ones, brown ones, piebald ones —families of them, hundreds of them—thousands—millions. And they gathered round Tommy Squeak the King-Rat in a great, great big circle. Their beady, black eyes looked very frightened when they saw a dog there but they didn't run away because the king had called them.

Then Tommy Squeak stood up to speak to them and they all stopped cleaning their whiskers to listen.

"Rats," he said, "we have a job of work to do. Follow me." And waving his paw to Punk, Ponk and Pink, he led the way to the farm.

For a whole day and a night the rats worked very hard, trying to turn the man out. They rattled the pans in the kitchens at night. They pulled the stuffing out of his chair. They ate holes in his new, green hat. They stopped the clock. They pulled the curtains down upon the floor. But the man sent to London Town and got three wagon-loads of cats and the rats were all driven back to the river. Tommy Squeak came to Punk, Pink and Ponk on the second day and said,

"I am sorry. We did our best, but we couldn't move him."

So Ponk said to Punk, "Well, we must try something else." And they left the old woman in the woods and started off again.

As they were crossing the river this time before they got to the farm, they saw Tilly Twitter, the Queen of the Swallows, sitting on the corner of the bridge.

"Good-morning!" said Tilly. "You all look very sad."

"Oh, Tilly," said Punk, with tears in his eyes, "Mrs. Tubbs has been turned out of house and home."

"Good gracious!" cried Tilly. "You don't say! Who turned her out?"

"A man from London," said Punk. "I call him 'Beefsteak-and-Onions.' Do you think you can do anything to help us get her back to the farm?"

"Certainly I'll do my best," said Tilly, pushing her crown further back on her head. "I have built my nest over the old woman's door for three Springs now. I would hate to have her leave the farm for good. I'll see what I can do."

Then she flew up into the air going round and round in circles. Higher and higher she flew and all the time she sang a beautiful song at the top of her voice.

And this is the song she sang:

"The leaves are falling in the woods.
  Go get your travelling rugs and hoods.
  The Summer's gone; the snow'll soon be here.
  It's time to fly; but we'll come back next year."

Now every year when all the swallows heard Tilly Twitter sing this song they knew it was time for them to get together to fly to Africa because they don't like the winter's cold in England. So now when they heard it they got their children together and snatching up their bags and bundles, they all flew towards Mrs. Tubb's farm. So many of them came that the sky grew dark and people thought the night was come. And the farm-boys in the country around stopped their plough-horses and said, "There go the swallows, getting ready to fly to Africa. The frost will soon be here."

For five hours they kept coming, more and more and more of them. They gathered around Tilly, sitting on the house, on the barn and the railings, on the gates, on the bridge and on the stones. But never on the trees. Swallows never sit on trees. So many of them came that the whole land seemed covered with the blue of their wings and the white of their breasts.

And when they had all arrived Tilly got up and spoke.

"Swallows," she said, "many years ago, when I first built my mud nest under the eaves of this farm, I had five children in my nest. They were my first family and I was very proud of them. That was before I became the Queen of the Swallows. And being a very inexperienced mother I built the nest too small. When my children grew up there was not proper room for them. Philip—a very strong child—was always twisting and turning in the nest and one day he fell out. He bumped his nose badly on the ground but it was not far to fall and he was not much hurt. I was just going to fly down and try to pick him up when I saw a large weasel coming across the farm-yard to get him. My feathers stood up on the top of my head with fright. I flew to the farm-house window and beat upon the glass with my wings. An old woman came out. When she saw Philip on the ground and the weasel coming to get him she threw her porridge-spoon at the weasel, picked Philip up and put him back in my nest. That old woman's name was Mrs. Tubbs. She has now been turned out of her house and a very stupid red-faced man is living on the farm in her place. We have got to do our best to turn him out and put Mrs. Tubbs back in her house, the same as she put my child back in his nest. So I have called you all together a week earlier than usual this year for our long journey to Africa, and before we leave England we have got to see what we can do. The first thing we'll do is to stop up his chimney so his fire won't burn. Then put mud all over the windows so the light will not come in. Bring all the straw from the barn and fill his bed-room with it. Take his best neck-tie and drop it in the river. And do everything you can to drive him out."

So the swallows set to work and Punk, Ponk and Pink went back to the old woman in the woods.

But after two days Tilly came to them and said, "I am very sorry, but I have not succeeded. The cats have driven my swallows away. He has a thousand cats in the place. What can one do?"

So Punk said to Ponk, "We must go out and try something else."

But Polly Ponk answered,

"No, you go alone this time. The old woman is getting a cold and I must stay and look after her."

So Peter Punk went off with his tail dragging on the ground. He hung about the farm and was very sad and wondered what he could do to drive Beefsteak-and-Onions out of the house.

Presently, feeling hungry, he remembered he had hidden a ham-bone in the trunk of a tree behind the house some weeks ago and he went off to see if it was still there. When he got to the tree he stood up on his hind-legs and looked into the hole. A wasp flew out and stung him on the nose. He sat down on the grass and watched the tree for a minute and saw many wasps coming in and going out through the hole. Then he understood what had happened. Thousands of wasps had made a nest in the hollow tree.

So he thought of a plan. He went and got a big stick and threw it into the hole in the tree. Then all the wasps came flying out and tried to sting him. He went running towards the house with the wasps after him and ran in through the back door of the house. The wasps kept following him—though a few stopped to sting some of the cats that were hanging about the back door. Then he ran up the stairs by the front staircase, into the bedrooms and down by the backstairs. In the hall he found Beefsteak-and-Onions, who had just come in from digging potatoes, with a spade in his hand. Punk ran between his legs and out through the front door.

When the wasps could not find Punk any more they thought the man had hidden him somewhere so they set upon him and stung him. And the rest of them stung all the cats they could find in the house and drove them away across the fields.

Poor Beefsteak-and-Onions ran out into the yard and shut himself up in the barn to get away from the wasps. Then he laid down his spade and put on his coat and said,

"I'll leave this house today. My uncle can come and live here himself if he wants to. But I'm going back to London Town. I didn't want to turn the old lady out anyway. I do not believe my uncle knew anyone was living here at all. I am going today."

Punk was listening outside the door and heard him, so he ran off at once back to the woods. When he got to Ponk and Pink he started dancing on his hind-legs.

"What's the matter?" asked Ponk. "Have you gone crazy?"

But all he answered was:

"Hooray, Hooray!
He's going away,
Old Beefsteak-and-Onions
Is going today."

Then he told them how he had at last succeeded and they both thought he was a very clever dog.

It was now getting late in the evening so they went and got Mrs. Tubbs and they all walked back to the farm by moonlight.

And the old woman was so happy to get back to her little house that she made them all a very fine supper. And Pink said,

"I am glad to get back. There is something to eat here."

And so when the leaves were all fallen in the woods, and the trees stood bare waiting for the snow, they used to sit round the warm fire in the evenings toasting chestnuts and telling stories while the kettle steamed upon the hob and the wind howled in the chimney above. And they never had to leave the farm again and they all lived happily ever after.

HOW SHE KEPT HER GEESE WARM
Hope Newell

There are two books of these "Little Old Woman" stories, and children seem to like them both. With the eights and nines it might be fun to read them "Clever Elsie" and one of the Peterkin stories to see if they will notice the similarity.

One cold winter night, the Little Old Woman was out in the barn putting her geese to bed. She gave them some corn and took off their little red coats. Then she brushed each little coat with a whisk-broom and carefully shook out the wrinkles.

As she was folding the coats in a neat pile, she thought:

"My poor geese must be very cold at night. I have my cozy fire and my feather bed. But they have not even a blanket to keep them warm."

After the geese had eaten their corn, they began to go to roost.

"Honk, honk!" said the big gander, and he hopped up on the roost.

"Honk, honk!" said the grey goose, and she hopped up on the roost.

"Honk, honk!" said all the other geese, and they hopped up on the roost.

Then the Little Old Woman closed the barn door and went into the house. When she went to bed, she lay awake worrying about the geese. After a while she said to herself:

"I cannot sleep a wink for thinking how cold the geese must be. I had better bring them in the house where it is warm."

So the Little Old Woman dressed herself and went out to the barn to fetch the geese. She shooed them off the roost and put on their little red coats. She picked up two geese, and tucking one under each arm, she carried them into the house.

Then she went out to the barn and picked up two more geese. She tucked one goose under each arm and carried them into the house.

When the Little Old Woman had brought all the geese into the house, she said to herself:

"Now I must get them ready for bed again."

She took off their little red coats and gave the geese some corn. Then she brushed each little coat with a whisk-broom and carefully shook out all the wrinkles.

As she was folding the coats in a neat pile, she thought:

"It was very clever of me to bring the geese into the house. Now they will be warm, and I shall be able to sleep."

Then the Little Old Woman undressed herself again and went to bed.

After the geese had eaten their corn, they began to roost.

"Honk, honk!" said the gander, and he hopped up on the foot of the Little Old Woman's bed.

"Honk, honk!" said the grey goose, and she hopped up on the foot of the Little Old Woman's bed.

"Honk, honk!" said all the other geese, and they tried to hop up on the foot of the Little Old Woman's bed.

But it was not a very big bed, and there was not enough room for all the geese to roost. They began to fight. They pushed and shoved each other. They hissed and squawked and flapped their wings.

"How She Kept Her Geese Warm." From *The Little Old Woman Who Used Her Head* by Hope Newell. Thomas Nelson & Sons. Used by permission

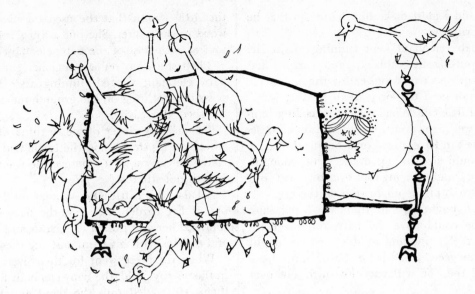

All night long the geese pushed and shoved each other. All night long they hissed and squawked and flapped their wings.

They made so much noise that the Little Old Woman did not sleep a wink.

"This will never do," she said. "When they were in the barn, I did not sleep for thinking how cold they must be. When they are in the house, I cannot sleep because they make so much noise. Perhaps if I use my head, I shall know what to do."

The Little Old Woman tied a wet towel around her forehead. Then she sat down with her forefinger against her nose and shut her eyes.

She used her head and used her head, and after a while she knew what to do.

"I will move the roost into the house," she said. "The geese will have the cozy fire to keep them warm. Then I will move my bed out into the barn. My feather bed will keep me warm, and I will not be worrying about the geese. They will not keep me awake with their noise. I shall sleep very comfortably in the barn."

The Little Old Woman moved the roost into the house, and she moved her bed out into the barn.

When night came again, she brought the geese into the house. After she had fed them some corn, she took off their little red coats. Then they all hopped up on the roost, and the Little Old Woman went out to the barn to sleep.

Her feather bed kept her as warm as toast. She was not worried about the geese, because she knew that they were warm too. So she slept as sound as a top all night long.

HOW SHE MADE
THE BABY ELEPHANT HAPPY

Hope Newell

When the Little Old Woman came in sight of her house, she saw something gray and round and fat running around her garden.

As she came near enough to get a good look at it, she saw that it was a baby elephant.

"Mercy on me!" she said. "This is a great day indeed. First, I see the circus come to town and now I find a baby elephant in my garden."

As she watched the baby elephant running about the garden, and pulling up carrots and cabbages and turnips with his trunk, she thought: "It is not often that I find an elephant eating my vegetables. Indeed, so far as I can recall, I have never seen one in my garden before.

"I wonder where he came from. I could use my head and find out, of course. But this is no time to use my head. The main thing is that he

"How She Made the Baby Elephant Happy." From *More About the Little Old Woman Who Used Her Head* by Hope Newell. Thomas Nelson & Sons. Used by permission

is here, and I must make him happy so that he will not run away."

The baby elephant kept running about the garden pulling up cabbages and carrots and turnips with his trunk and eating them.

"I do not need to worry about feeding him," said the Little Old Woman. "He is feeding himself very well. However, I must find him a house, so that he can have a roof over his head."

"He could live in my house," she thought. "Then he could have my roof over his head. But his feet are so big he might step on the rats.

"Or, he might live in the barn," she said. "Then he could have the barn roof over his head. But, if I put him in the barn, he might step on the geese. I had better build him a little shed and then he will have his own roof over his head."

As soon as she had fed the geese and the rats, the Little Old Woman set to work building a shed for the baby elephant. When the shed was finished she coaxed him into it by feeding him peanuts. She nailed a board across the front of it so that he would stay inside. Then she began to weed her garden.

The baby elephant started running after her and dragging the shed with him.

"What a funny elephant," said the Little Old Woman. "He likes to move his shed around with him."

But the shed was not easy to move. The posts dragged on the ground and made the baby elephant stumble. He did not like this so he lifted up his trunk and squealed. He squealed and squealed.

"Dear me!" said the Little Old Woman. "It is very sad to hear a baby elephant squeal. I must use my head and try to figure out how he can move his shed around without stumbling."

The Little Old Woman went into the house, and tied a wet towel around her head. Then she sat down with her forefinger against her nose and shut her eyes.

She used her head and used her head. Before long she had figured out how the baby elephant could move his shed around without stumbling.

"I will put a wheel on the bottom of each post," she said. "Then he can move his shed around very easily."

The Little Old Woman took the wheels off the little wagon that she used for hauling firewood in the winter. She put a wheel on the bottom of each post of the baby elephant's shed.

Then she went on weeding her garden. The baby elephant started running after her. The posts did not drag on the ground and he moved the shed very easily.

"It was very clever of me to think of putting wheels on his shed," said the Little Old Woman. "Now he can move it wherever he wants to and he will not stumble."

All day the Little Old Woman pulled weeds out of her garden. All day, the baby elephant followed her and pulled up carrots and cabbages and turnips with his trunk and ate them.

When the geese went for their evening swim in the nearby pond, the baby elephant went with them. He waded into the pond and filled his trunk with water. He blew water over the top of his shed, and he blew water on the geese.

He was very happy.

After supper the Little Old Woman took her mending and sat down in her rocking-chair on the porch.

The baby elephant had come back from the pond. He was running about the garden, pulling up carrots and cabbages and turnips with his trunk and eating them.

"I like this baby elephant very much," said the Little Old Woman. "However, I hope no more baby elephants come to live with me. I have no more wood to make sheds and they would have no roofs over their heads.

"Moreover, I would not have enough vegetables to feed them. As it is, this baby elephant will have eaten everything in the garden by morning. Then I shall have to use my head to find out how to feed him."

Just then the Little Old Woman heard a great noise in the distance. Wagon wheels were rumbling, men were shouting, and horses' hoofs were going "plack-plack" over the cobblestones.

"Dear me," said the Little Old Woman. "That must be the circus leaving town."

The baby elephant heard the noise, too. When the Little Old Woman went around to the back of her house where she could watch the circus going over the distant hill, the baby elephant went with her.

They watched the big animal wagons go over

the hill. They watched the camels and they watched the big white circus horses, and the little Shetland ponies.

When the baby elephant saw the big elephants walking slowly over the hill, he dropped the carrot he was eating and his big ears started waving back and forth. Then he lifted up his trunk and squealed. He squealed and squealed and squealed.

One of the big elephants dropped the tail of the elephant in front of her. She lifted up her trunk, and rumbled as loud as thunder.

Before the Little Old Woman could wink her eye, the baby elephant started running in his little shed. When he reached the fence he did not stop. He broke right through the fence and kept on running. He reached the hill just as the big cook-wagon went over its top.

The baby elephant ran up the hill and in a few seconds he too disappeared over the top.

"Dear me," said the Little Old Woman, "I do believe the baby elephant belonged to the circus. The big elephant who rumbled so loudly must have been his mother. Now he has gone back to her and I have no baby elephant."

She went back to the porch and sat down in her rocking chair.

"I shall miss the baby elephant very much," she thought.

"However, perhaps it is just as well that he has gone back to his mother. If he ate as much every day as he did today, I would have to use my head very hard to find out how to feed him.

"I am glad that I made him a little shed so that he will always have a roof over his head. It is a very useful thing to know how to make a shed for an elephant. If ever I find another elephant in my garden, I will know just how to go about it. I am a very wise old woman indeed."

WILLIE'S BAD NIGHT

Robert Lawson

Rabbit Hill was the name of Robert Lawson's own house in the country, and the multitude of small animals that inhabited the place gave him his idea for the story. Undoubtedly the four-footed denizens of the Hill approved of Mr. Lawson's generous theory that "there is enough for all," but Mr. Lawson confessed that in spite of "enough," the moles were a problem.

It was Bluegrass that almost proved the undoing of Willie Fieldmouse. He was on the window sill, as usual, watching and listening to the Folks. This evening, having finished their gardening plans, they were talking of grass seed. Willie was not especially interested and was only half listening when he was suddenly electrified by a familiar word.

"This book," the Man was saying, "recommends a mixture of Red Top, White Clover and Kentucky Bluegrass."

Bluegrass! Kentucky Bluegrass! Wouldn't Father Rabbit be pleased! He must be told at once!

Haste and excitement made Willie inexcusably careless. He should have remembered that the lid of the rainwater barrel was old and rotted, that there were several dangerous holes in it. He did not, and his leap from the window sill landed him squarely in one of the holes. He grabbed frantically as he went through, but the rotten wood crumbled under his claws and with a sickening shock he plunged into the icy water.

He came up gasping. The cold seemed to have driven all the air from his lungs but he managed one wild squeak for help before the water closed over him again. He was very feeble when he came up this time. He struggled weakly toward the side of the barrel but the walls were slippery with moss and his paws too numbed to get a hold. Faintly he squeaked once more—why didn't someone help him—Father or Little Georgie or Phewie? As the water closed over him for the last time he was dimly conscious of a noise and a brilliant glare of light. Then the light went out, everything went out.

A long time later, he never knew how long, Willie's eyes fluttered open. He dimly realized that he was still wet, that uncontrollable fits of shivering shook him. He seemed to be lying in a nest of some soft white stuff, that was very comfortable, he could see the glow of dancing flames and feel a gentle warmth. Then he closed his eyes again.

Later they opened and he saw the faces of the Folks bending over his bed. It was terrifying to see Folks this close. They looked enormous, like something in a nightmare. He tried to burrow into the soft cotton when his nose suddenly caught the smell of warm milk. Someone was holding a medicine dropper before his face—on the end of it a white drop hung. Weakly, Willie licked at it—it was delicious. There was something else in the milk, something that coursed hotly through all his body. He felt stronger already and sucked at the dropper until it was completely empty. Ah, that was better! His stomach was swollen with the comforting warm food, his eyelids drooped and again he slept.

There was consternation among the Animals when Willie failed to report to the group waiting at the burrow. Father and Uncle Analdas immediately organized a searching party but were unable to find any trace of him.

Phewie, who had been enjoying the freedom of the garbage pail, reported that he had heard a mouse-cry, had seen the Folks emerge from the house with flashlights and do something at the rain barrel. Just what, he did not know.

Willie's oldest cousin climbed to the window sill but found the window closed. The Gray Squirrel was wakened and sent to the roof to investigate. He listened at all the upstairs windows without discovering anything unusual.

"It's that dingblasted old Cat," shouted Uncle Analdas. "The sneakin', deceitful, hypocritical scoundrel, makin' out he's old and harmless. Wish I'd kicked him in the face like I planned to."

Porkey was inclined to blame Tim McGrath. "It's him and his traps," he argued. "Always talkin' traps he is, and poisons. Likely he led them Folks into settin' a trap fer Willie."

Father said little, but all the night through he, Uncle Analdas and Little Georgie coursed the Hill like setter dogs, searching every inch of field and wall, looking under every shrub and bush. Not till dawn approached did they admit defeat and return wearily to the burrow where Mother, very red-eyed and sniffly, had a hot breakfast waiting for them.

But of all the Animals the Mole's rage and grief were the most moving. His pal, his Eyes, were lost and he was helpless to join in the search!

"I'll fix 'em," he said grimly. "I'll fix 'em. There won't never a blade of grass take root on this place—never! Never a bulb or a shrub stay set neither. I'll tear 'em up and I'll root 'em out, I'll dig and I'll heave and I'll burrow, I'll fetch in every friend and relation from here to Danbury way and tear this place apart till they wish they'd never—"

His threats were muffled as he plunged frantically into the neatly rolled front lawn. All night the other Animals could hear his grunting, could see the surface of the ground ripple and heave like troubled waters.

It was gray dawn when Willie woke again. The room was chilly but on the hearth a few embers still smouldered and the bricks gave out a comforting warmth. He eased himself out of the cardboard box where he had slept and drew closer to the glowing coals. All his muscles felt stiff and sore, he was still a little wobbly but otherwise he felt very well. He bathed a bit and stretched himself, feeling better all the time. That warm milk and whatever was in it had certainly tasted good. He wished he had some more. He ought to be getting along home but there was no way out—the doors and windows were all closed.

The sun had risen before he heard footsteps approaching through the house. He caught a whiff of the Man's pipe smell, heard the soft pad of Mr. Muldoon's paws. Wildly he looked for a hiding place but no good one offered. On either side of the fireplace bookshelves extended from floor to ceiling and in desperation he leaped to the top of the first row of books and crouched back into the darkest corner just as the door opened.

The Folks came in and at once inspected the box. "Well, well, he's gone," said the Man. "Must be feeling better. Wonder where he is?"

The Lady did not answer. She was watching Mr. Muldoon who had wandered idly over to the bookshelves.

Willie backed as far into the corner as he could squeeze, his heart pounding wildly as the great cat drew closer and closer. The head seemed huge now, the mouth was opening, two rows of white fangs showed, his eyes were gleaming yellow coals. Willie, petrified with fear, could only watch helplessly as the red jaws opened wider and wider. He could feel the hot breath, strong with the odor of canned salmon.

Then Mr. Muldoon sneezed.

"There he is," the Lady said quietly, "on the books, in the corner. Come, Mullie, don't worry the poor little thing. He's had enough trouble already." She seated herself and the cat strolled stiffly over, leaped to her lap and settled down for a nap. The Man opened the outside door and also sat down.

It was some time before Willie's breath came back and his heart returned to normal. When it did he ventured forth, an inch at a time. Nothing happened, so he began the long circuit of the room, staying close to the wall and pausing under each piece of furniture. He was almost to the doorway now and gave one quick survey before the final dash.

The Lady still continued to sit quietly, her fingers slowly stroking Mr. Muldoon's jowls. He snored faintly, with a sound not unlike the steady, gurgling wheeze of the Man's pipe.

One wild scurry and Willie burst out into the sunlight. Across the terrace he went, but even in the excitement of his newly won freedom he was forced to pause at the appearance of the front lawn. The smoothly rolled surface was striped and circled and crisscrossed with a perfect crazy-quilt pattern of mole runs, scarcely a foot of it undisturbed. He skipped to the nearest run, made two digs and plunged beneath the surface.

"Mole! Mole!" he cried as he galloped through the echoing tunnel. "Here I am, Mole, it's me—Little Willie."

Tim McGrath, hands on hips, stood on the front lawn surveying the wreckage of his careful labor. His jaws were a deep, purplish red, his neck seemed swollen with suppressed rage.

"Look at it!" he sputtered, "*Just look at it!* What did I tell you about them moles? But no. No traps, of course not. No poison, oh dear me, no! *Now look!*"

The Man sucked on his pipe rather apologetically. "It is quite a mess, isn't it?" he admitted. "I guess we'll just have to roll it down again."

Tim McGrath gazed at the sky and whispered softly. "*We'll have to roll it again! We'll have to roll it again!* Oh Lord, give me strength." Wearily he trudged away to fetch the rake and roller.

PIPPI PLAYS TAG WITH SOME POLICEMEN

Astrid Lindgren

This is one chapter in a book about the remarkable child Pippi Longstocking. Pippi, who is prodigiously strong, lives all alone except for her monkey and her horse. She is the superchild every child would like to be.

It soon became known throughout the little town that a nine-year-old girl was living all by herself in Villa Villekulla, and all the ladies and gentlemen in the town thought this would never do. All children must have someone to advise them, and all children must go to school to learn the multiplication tables. So the ladies and gentlemen decided that the little girl in Villa Ville-kulla must immediately be placed in a children's home.

One lovely afternoon Pippi had invited Tommy and Annika over for afternoon coffee and *pepparkakor*. She had spread the party out on the front steps. It was so sunny and beautiful there, and the air was filled with the fragrance of the flowers in Pippi's garden. Mr. Nilsson climbed around on the porch railing, and every now and then the horse stuck out his head so that he'd be invited to have a cooky.

"Oh, isn't it glorious to be alive?" said Pippi, stretching out her legs as far as she could reach.

Just at that moment two police officers in full uniform came in through the gate.

"Hurray," said Pippi, "this must be my lucky day too! Policemen are the very best things I know. Next to rhubarb pudding." And with her face beaming she went to meet them.

"Is this the girl who has moved into Villa Villekulla?" asked one of the policemen.

"Quite the contrary," said Pippi. "This is a tiny little auntie who lives on the third floor at the other end of the town."

She said that only because she wanted to have a little fun with the policemen, but they didn't think it was funny at all.

They said she shouldn't be such a smarty. And then they went on to tell her that some nice people in the town were arranging for her to get into a children's home.

"I already have a place in a children's home," said Pippi.

"What?" asked one of the policemen. "Has it been arranged already then? What children's home?"

"This one," said Pippi haughtily. "I am a child and this is my home; therefore it is a children's home, and I have room enough here, plenty of room."

"Dear child," said the policeman, smiling, "you don't understand. You must get into a real children's home and have someone look after you."

"Is one allowed to bring horses to your chil-·dren's home?" asked Pippi.

"No, of course not," said the policeman.

"That's what I thought," said Pippi sadly. "Well, what about monkeys?"

"Of course not. You ought to realize that."

"Well then," said Pippi, "you'll have to get kids for your children's home somewhere else. I certainly don't intend to move there."

"But don't you understand that you must go to school?"

"Why?"

"To learn things, of course."

"What sort of things?" asked Pippi.

"All sorts," said the policeman. "Lots of useful things—the multiplication tables, for instance."

"I have got along fine without any pluttifikation tables for nine years," said Pippi, "and I guess I'll get along without it from now on, too."

"Yes, but just think how embarrassing it will be for you to be so ignorant. Imagine when you grow up and somebody asks you what the capital of Portugal is, and you can't answer!"

"Oh, I can answer all right," said Pippi. "I'll answer like this: 'If you are so bound and determined to find out what the capital of Portugal is, then, for goodness' sakes, write directly to Portugal and ask.'"

"Yes, but don't you think that you would be sorry not to know it yourself?"

"Oh, probably," said Pippi. "No doubt I should lie awake nights and wonder and wonder, 'What in the world is the capital of Portugal?' But one can't be having fun all the time," she continued, bending over and standing on her hands for a change. "For that matter, I've been in Lisbon with my papa," she added, still standing upside down, for she could talk that way too.

But then one of the policemen said that Pippi certainly didn't need to think she could do just as she pleased. She must come to the children's home, and immediately. He went up to her and took hold of her arm, but Pippi freed herself quickly, touched him lightly, and said, "Tag!" Before he could wink an eye she had climbed up on the porch railing and from there onto the balcony above the porch. The policemen couldn't quite see themselves getting up the same way, and so they rushed into the house and up the stairs, but by the time they had reached the balcony Pippi was halfway up the roof. She climbed up the shingles almost as if she were a little monkey herself. In a moment she was up on the ridgepole and from there jumped easily to the chimney. Down on the balcony stood the two policemen, scratching their heads, and on the lawn stood Tommy and Annika, staring at Pippi.

"Isn't it fun to play tag?" cried Pippi. "And weren't you nice to come over. It certainly *is* my lucky day today too."

When the policemen had stood there a while wondering what to do, they went and got a ladder, leaned it against one of the gables of the house and then climbed up, first one policeman and then the other, to get Pippi down. They looked a little scared when they climbed out on the ridgepole and, carefully balancing themselves, went step by step, toward Pippi.

"Don't be scared," cried Pippi. "There's nothing to be afraid of. It's just fun."

When the policemen were a few steps away from Pippi, down she jumped from the chimney and, screeching and laughing, ran along the ridgepole to the opposite gable. A few feet from the house stood a tree.

"Now I'm going to dive," she cried and jumped right down into the green crown of the tree, caught fast hold of a branch, swung back and forth a while, and then let herself fall to the ground. Quick as a wink she dashed around to the other side of the house and took away the ladder.

The policemen had looked a little foolish when Pippi jumped, but they looked even more so when they had balanced themselves backward along the ridgepole and were about to climb down the ladder. At first they were very angry at Pippi, who stood on the ground looking up at them, and they told her in no uncertain terms to get the ladder and be quick about it, or she would soon get something she wasn't looking for.

"Why are you so cross at me?" asked Pippi reproachfully. "We're just playing tag, aren't we?"

The policemen thought a while, and at last one of them said, "Oh, come on, won't you be a good girl and put the ladder back so that we can get down?"

"Of course I will," said Pippi and put the ladder back instantly. "And when you get down we can all drink coffee and have a happy time."

But the policemen were certainly tricky, be-cause the minute they were down on the ground again they pounced on Pippi and cried, "Now you'll get it, you little brat!"

"Oh, no, I'm sorry. I haven't time to play any longer," said Pippi. "But it was fun."

Then she took hold of the policemen by their belts and carried them down the garden path, out through the gate, and onto the street. There she set them down, and it was quite some time before they were ready to get up again.

"Wait a minute," she cried and ran into the kitchen and came back with two cooky hearts. "Would you like a taste?" she asked. "It doesn't matter that they are a little burned, does it?"

Then she went back to Tommy and Annika, who stood there wide-eyed and just couldn't get over what they had seen. And the policemen hurried back to the town and told all the ladies and gentlemen that Pippi wasn't quite fit for an orphanage. (They didn't tell that they had been up on the roof.) And the ladies and gentlemen decided that it would be best after all to let Pippi remain in Villa Villekulla, and if she wanted to go to school she could make the arrangements herself.

But Pippi and Tommy and Annika had a very pleasant afternoon. They went back to their interrupted coffee party. Pippi stuffed herself with fourteen cookies and then she said, "They weren't what I mean by real policemen. No sirree! Altogether too much talk about children's home and pluttifikation and Lisbon."

Afterward she lifted the horse down on the ground and they rode on him, all three. At first Annika was afraid and didn't want to, but when she saw what fun Tommy and Pippi were having, she let Pippi lift her up on the horse's back. The horse trotted round and round in the garden, and Tommy sang, "Here come the Swedes with a clang and a bang."

When Tommy and Annika had gone to bed that night Tommy said, "Annika, don't you think it's good that Pippi moved here?"

"Oh, *yes*," said Annika.

"I don't even remember what we used to play before she came, do you?"

"Oh, sure, we played croquet and things like that," said Annika. "But it's lots more fun with Pippi around, I think. And with horses and things."

THE REAL PRINCESS

Hans Christian Andersen

This is an allegory, a satire on the absurdity of believing in the special delicacy of blue-bloodedness. But children take it literally as a funny story. They enjoy illustrating the princess atop her twenty mattresses.

There was once a prince, and he wanted a princess, but then she must be a *real* princess. He travelled right round the world to find one, but there was always something wrong. There were plenty of princesses, but whether they were real princesses he had great difficulty in discovering; there was always something which was not quite right about them. So at last he had to come home again, and he was very sad because he wanted a real princess so badly.

One evening there was a terrible storm; it thundered and lightened and the rain poured down in torrents; indeed it was a fearful night.

In the middle of the storm somebody knocked at the town gate, and the old King himself went to open it.

It was a princess who stood outside, but she was in a terrible state from the rain and the storm. The water streamed out of her hair and her clothes, it ran in at the top of her shoes and out at the heel, but she said that she was a real princess.

"Well, we shall soon see if that is true," thought the old Queen, but she said nothing. She went into the bedroom, took all the bedclothes off and laid a pea on the bedstead; then she took twenty mattresses and piled them on the top of the pea, and then twenty feather beds on the top of the mattresses. This was where the princess was to sleep that night. In the morning they asked her how she had slept.

"Oh, terribly badly!" said the princess. "I have hardly closed my eyes the whole night! Heaven knows what was in the bed. I seemed to be lying upon some hard thing, and my whole body is black and blue this morning. It is terrible!"

They saw at once that she must be a real prin-

"The Real Princess." From *Fairy Tales* by Hans Christian Andersen, translated by Mrs. Edgar Lucas, Everyman's Library, E. P. Dutton & Co., Inc., New York. By permission also of J. M. Dent & Sons, Ltd., London

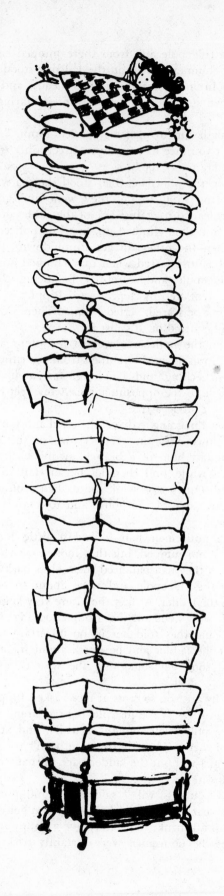

cess when she had felt the pea through twenty mattresses and twenty feather beds. Nobody but a real princess could have such a delicate skin.

So the prince took her to be his wife, for now he was sure that he had found a real princess, and the pea was put into the Museum, where it may still be seen if no one has stolen it.

Now this is a true story.

THE PLAIN PRINCESS

Phyllis McGinley

Phyllis McGinley invariably creates something fresh and original when she writes for children. Look up her alphabet rhymes in Time For Poetry *and then, if they are available, show the children her books with Helen Stone's beautiful pictures. The sixes will like her alphabet book,* All Around the Town, *and the eights and nines will thoroughly enjoy* The Most Wonderful Doll in the World.

Once upon a time, in a distant kingdom, there lived a Princess who was an only child. Her name was Esmeralda and in every way save one she was the most fortunate of young persons.

Her father, the King, was rich and powerful, and the pockets of his waistcoat were always filled with treats. The Queen was an amiable and affectionate mother who dearly loved planning birthday parties and surprises for Esmeralda; and frequently let her dress up in the crown jewels on rainy afternoons.

The Princess's nursery was painted a charming color of her own choosing. In her closet hung dozens of dresses, each more splendid than the other. The court poets composed verses for Esmeralda which were set to enchanting music by the court musicians and sung to her at bedtime.

Did she arrive at the age for roller skates? A skilful workman hurried immediately to his workshop and contrived for her the finest pair to be found in the kingdom. When she outgrew her tricycle and mentioned a two-wheeler, a del-

egation of bicycle experts was dispatched to fetch her the handsomest bicycle possible, with a silver basket attached to the handlebars.

The castle boasted velvety lawns where she might play croquet; there was a pond with ducks to which she could throw bread at feeding time; and from numberless great trees hung swings for her pleasure. (The King employed a tall gardener whose sole duty it was to give her run-unders so that she might swing into the topmost branches.)

Two cooks toiled ceaselessly in the kitchen preparing delicious food—puddings and ice cream and enticing salads to tempt her appetite.

She even owned a pony of her own, with a white and crimson saddle made to her measure.

Nevertheless, Esmeralda was *not* the most fortunate Princess in the world and it was on account of her one lack that the whole kingdom mourned.

For Esmeralda was plain.

There weren't two ways about it—the girl had no beauty, and in a royal Princess that is a serious flaw.

"What," the courtiers used to whisper to each other in the corridors, "will happen when Her Highness comes of age? How can she hope to win the affections of Prince Charles Michael who is destined to share her throne?"

And the prettier maids-in-waiting would smooth their hair before the long mirrors, thinking smugly, "We may not be of royal blood but we're luckier than *some* people we could mention, at that."

Aunts and uncles and other relatives spoke frankly.

"Poor child," they'd cluck, shaking their heads, "Heaven knows where she gets her plainness. Not from *our* side of the family, certainly."

Even the King and the Queen, much as they loved their daughter, had to admit that as good looks went, Esmeralda's were nothing to boast about. And as "Esmeralda the Plain" she began to be known throughout the kingdom.

It wasn't her hair. Esmeralda's hair grew golden as the corn and her handmaiden brushed it a hundred times in the morning (so that it shone like silk) and a hundred times at night again, while singing the Princess's favorite lullaby, which went like this:

NIGHT SONG

Now dark comes creeping,
   Now owls awake,
But the swan is sleeping
   Upon the lake,
The thrushes drowse,
   The wood-folk rest
Under the boughs,
   In hole and nest.
The flower buds furl
   Their petals fast
And the busiest girl
   Must nod at last.
Sleep, Little princess, sleep.

Over your bed
   Night's handmaids hover.
The sky has spread
   You a royal cover—
Laid, unwrinkled
   Between the bars
A counterpane sprinkled
   With sapphire stars.
And the moon (with a curve
   To its silver handle)
Waits to serve
   As your bedside candle.
Sleep, Esmeralda, sleep.

It wasn't Esmeralda's complexion, either. The court physicians saw to that. She was fed on the most Scientific Diet, containing just the proper number of calories and exactly the right amount of vitamins, and nobody ever forgot her cod-liver oil or her wholesome fruit. So there were always roses in her cheeks.

Governesses attended to her posture, insisting that she walk eleven times daily about the nursery with a book balanced on her head. Dancing masters taught her grace, and the royal dentist fashioned golden braces for her teeth so they would grow straight and even.

No—it wasn't any of these things which marred the loveliness of Esmeralda. It was something odd about her face. Her nose went up where it should have gone down, and her mouth went down where it should have gone up, and her eyes—her otherwise nice blue eyes—had no Glow. And since in that particular kingdom upward-tilting mouths and downward-tilting

noses and eyes with a glow and a twinkle to them were generally admired, Esmeralda grew plainer and plainer and the hearts of the King and the Queen grew heavier and heavier.

For a long while the Princess was kept in ignorance of her misfortune. Because she had always been waited on and petted, she had become by the time she was seven years old quite vain and haughty and fancied herself superior to all other young ladies. But on her eighth birthday something rather terrible happened.

The Queen issued invitations to a birthday fête and among those asked was the neighboring Prince, Charles Michael. It was a very elegant party with a cake of seven layers and jeweled gifts for every person present.

Esmeralda sat at the head of the table with her mouth turned down and her nose turned up at an unusually plain angle, and next to her they put the Prince. At least his name was written in gilt letters on the card. But alas! his chair was vacant. He had vanished immediately after pinning the tail on the donkey in the state drawing-room, and when the footmen announced supper he did not come running with the rest. Esmeralda was very cross. She wished Charles Michael to admire the paper crown she had pulled from her snapper; but though the servants scoured the castle, no Prince could they find.

It was only after the feast had been finished that they discovered him down by the duck pond, and with him the daughter of the duck-keeper, who had not been invited to the party at all.

"Your Highness," reproved his tutor after Charles Michael had been fetched in and had made his goodbyes to the King and Queen. "Why ever did you run away from the Princess's fête?"

Charles Michael was a polite boy but he was also honest.

"Because," he answered (and the court could not help but overhear), "I liked the duck-keeper's daughter better. She has a mouth prettily turned up and a nose charmingly tilted down and her eyes have the merriest twinkle in the world."

Well, you can imagine Esmeralda's chagrin! She burst into tears and had to be carried away like a baby by her governess. The King and Queen, casting down their eyes, retired unhappily to their rooms. As for the court, they looked at one another knowingly and murmured, "Just goes to show, doesn't it? It'll be hard, later on, to be ruled over by such a very plain Princess."

All night Esmeralda wept and no one could comfort her. Her father and mother were in despair. They called a consultation of the royal physicians but those sages had little to offer.

"In such cases as this, Your Majesty," said the oldest and wisest of them, "we seldom operate. Tonsils we can take out, but there would be no improvement in cutting off Her Highness's nose. Pills would have no effect upon the shape of her mouth. As for the glow of the royal eye— all the drugs in the kingdom would not bring it there."

"Have you nothing at all to suggest?" asked the King. He looked at the doctors severely, so that they shifted from one foot to the other and fingered their stethoscopes. Finally one of the youngest cleared his throat.

"Your Majesty," he said nervously, "why not try magic?"

"Useless!" snapped the King. "We've been all over that with the Wizard of State."

"Offer a reward," bravely continued the young physician. "In this great country there must be someone who knows the right enchantment."

"We-l-l," meditated the King, "we will take it under our royal consideration." And he dismissed the doctors.

The next day in the newspapers appeared a large advertisement stamped with the King's seal. It went like this:

REWARD

Anyone capable of Transforming a Plain Young Lady into a Beautiful Young Lady will be Given a Purse of Gold. Results must be Guaranteed. Those Failing will Lose Their Heads.

That wasn't a very tactful advertisement, it must be confessed, for the King had thought it up himself without consulting his Royal Board of Public Relations. And for a week no one came forward to seek the reward, since, naturally, few persons wanted to risk having their heads cut off.

Then on the last day of the week there came knocking at the castle gate a strange visitor. It was neither a wizard in a tall hat nor a great doctor in a black robe. It was a woman and an unfashionable one at that, but she clutched a copy of the newspaper in her hand and smiled quite cheerfully at the King when she was admitted to his presence.

Dropping an agreeable curtsey, she said, "Your Majesty, I have come in answer to your advertisement."

The King looked at her in astonishment.

"Nonsense!" he cried, somewhat rudely. "My good woman, I was expecting a powerful magician."

She did not seem one whit abashed.

"The oddest people make magic nowadays," she answered. "Besides, Your Majesty, I am a widow and on practically no income at all I have fed, clothed and educated five daughters. I claim that in these days, taxes being what they are, that takes a magician of sorts."

And she looked so serenely at the King that he was impressed in spite of himself.

"Certainly, you're the only one brave enough to answer my advertisement," he mused. "Perhaps you have some power I have not heard of."

Remembering to be businesslike, he added, "What references can you show from your former empl—I mean, have you any proof of your magic?"

The woman fumbled in her purse and drew out a photograph.

"These are my five daughters," she said. "Not a plain one among them."

Truly the King had to admit, as he scanned the picture, that five handsomer girls he had never seen. Every nose tilted daintily down, every mouth turned up, and the photographer had caught the twinkle in every pair of eyes.

"Nice, very nice," murmured the King. "But could you do the same for a young lady who *wasn't* your daughter?"

"Give me thrice three months," said the woman quietly. "I think I could do it in that time. *If* I have a free hand and no interference."

"You realize you'll lose your head if the magic fails?"

"I'm willing to chance it for your sake, Your Majesty, and for the sake of the poor plain little

Princ—" She stopped suddenly and clapped her hand over her mouth but the King only said sadly, "Never mind. Everybody knows about Esmeralda. Come, now, Mrs.—er—"

"Goodwit. Dame Goodwit."

"Come, then, Dame Goodwit. I am inclined to trust you. I like your courage and I like your manners. Let us but see the Queen, speak to the Princess, and then you can at once take up your residence in the castle."

"Oh," cried the Dame, "that is one thing I cannot do, Your Majesty. Unless Her Highness go with me and live as one of my daughters, the magic is of no avail."

"What!" roared the King. "Esmeralda leave her home and her comforts to live with you in —no offense meant, madam—what is bound to be a style to which she is unaccustomed?"

The Dame was calm but firm.

"Those are my conditions, Your Majesty," she replied. "Your advisers may examine my home. You may keep watch from afar during the Princess's stay. But come with me she must; and what is more she must take little with her. Not one silken gown or jeweled plaything may she bring if my magic is to be effective."

Well, the King argued and he argued but he got nowhere; and finally he gave in. So did the Queen. For once in their lives, also, they were firm with Esmeralda (who did not take kindly to the idea of going away from home with so common a woman) and insisted she try the power of Dame Goodwit.

The very next day, after the royal emissaries had turned in a report that the Dame lived in respectable though very humble circumstances, off they packed her in a hired coach. (For Dame Goodwit had insisted that the journey begin with no royal fanfare.)

Not one thing, either, was Esmeralda permitted to bring along which might remind her of her exalted state—not her bicycle with the silver basket, nor her roller skates, nor her dolls with their numberless costumes, nor her pony, nor any of her beautiful frocks. The Dame went through her closet and selected two or three of the very plainest dresses and a couple of pinafores and a warm coat and hat. Only in one matter did she relent. She permitted Esmeralda to wear about her neck a little trinket, a pearl locket which had been given her by her Godmother and which, though of slight value, the Princess had worn since babyhood. Esmeralda was still clutching tightly to the locket as she rode weeping away in an ordinary coach to the house of Dame Goodwit and her five daughters.

For three hours they rode—out of the city, through a dim forest, into a meadow, and at last the coachman drew up before a small and shabby cottage. The roof was peaked, the shutters a faded blue, the windows insignificant. Flowers of early spring nodded beside the walk, and near the picket fence flamed beds of crocuses. But Esmeralda saw only the shabbiness and the smallness.

"Oh," she sobbed, "to be shut away here in this horrid spot! How can there be magic in such a place?" And she would have run back to the coach if it had not already galloped away.

Dame Goodwit took no notice of her tears and merely said, "Trot along in, my dear, and take a look around." Then, raising her voice, she called, "Come out, daughters, to greet our guest."

Immediately the little front door popped open and out hurried five handsome girls, all beaming at Esmeralda.

"Esmeralda, these are my daughters," said the Dame. "Their names are Annabelle, Christabelle, Dulcibelle, Floribelle, and Echo. Four belles and an echo, you see. Children, Esmeralda will be living with us for a while. You, Annabelle, take her bag. Christabelle, show her where she will sleep. Fetch her, Dulcibelle, something warm to drink, while you, Flory, put on an egg for her supper. And Echo, my pet, give her the kiss of welcome."

Like five stair steps they were, from a very little girl to a very tall girl, and they all smiled shyly at the Princess and ran to assist her. However, it was as if they were greeting a friend instead of a Princess, for not one of them curtsied or kissed her hand. But Esmeralda found no breath to chide them, so briskly did they bundle her in, every damsel talking at once. Her tears, however, began afresh when she saw the tiny cubicle that held her bed, the rough cup out of which she was supposed to drink, the simple kitchen where supper was prepared. Everything was clean as a scrubbed turnip, but to Esmeralda's eyes, dazzled so long by riches, her surroundings seemed too dreary to bear.

Instead of eating the fresh egg which Floribelle obligingly broke for her, she flung herself on the floor, kicking her heels, and indulged, regrettably, in a temper tantrum. At the castle, ten handmaids would have bustled about with spirits of ammonia and soothing words. But Dame Goodwit said only, "Let her be, girls. Esmeralda is possibly homesick. She'll feel better in the morning." And the six of them sat down to eat their wholesome supper. Then they cleared away, stepping neatly around Esmeralda, who was still stretched out on the linoleum.

After a while, since no one paid any attention to her, she left off weeping and kicking, arose, and stated, "I'm hungry."

"Christabelle, see if there's any soup left," instructed the Dame.

Christabelle filled a bowl and set it before Esmeralda, who drank it greedily.

"I am also sleepy," the Princess announced. "Ask one of your daughters, Dame, to attend me to bed."

"People," said that lady cheerfully, "attend themselves here. That is part of the magic." So for the first time in her life, Esmeralda took off her own clothes, turned down her own covers and smoothed her own pillow. She did it with bad grace and clumsily, but she managed, and weary as she was, fell asleep quickly even on the hard mattress.

That was the beginning of a strange life for the Princess. Whatever spells Dame Goodwit knew, they were not, at once, evident. She never said "Abracadabra" or "Hocus Pocus," and there wasn't a single wand anywhere about the cottage. And though Esmeralda looked earnestly in the cracked mirror each day, she could see no improvement in her plainness. In fact, she was, if anything, plainer, for her eyes were continually red from weeping over her lot. No one seemed to recall that she was a royal child, entitled to the privileges of her birth. Only the pearl locket, hung around her neck, reminded her; and that she treasured and fingered constantly, to reassure herself that the castle was not a dream.

The Dame treated her kindly but with no more ceremony than she gave to her own daughters. Esmeralda found, to her horror, that she was even expected to assist with the housework.

"We won't ask you to do much at first," said the Dame. "You'd be only a hindrance. But you aren't really stupid; you'll learn."

"Stupid, indeed!" Esmeralda was outraged.

But as time went on, the Princess secretly discovered that the Dame had been no more than right. Compared to Christabelle and Annabelle and the rest, she *was* quite dull. All the things they could do! They could out-run her at races. They could play innumerable games she had never heard of. Even little Echo could climb into the gnarled apple trees more spryly than she. And at housewifely tasks they were incredibly deft. They sewed and patched and darned and embroidered and whipped up delicate puddings out of practically nothing, while she could scarcely pour water without spilling it.

Not that she tried, at first. She demanded to be waited on. But no one ran to do her bidding. If she neglected to make her bed in the morning, she must sleep that night in rumpled sheets. If she refused to help with the table-setting, no place was laid for her. When she forgot to hang up her clothes, they grew creased and wrinkled and nobody pressed them for her.

What amazed her most was how little the Dame's five daughters minded their humble surroundings. When she wasn't sulking she would spin them long tales of how elegantly she had lived at home, or what tempting meals had been served in her royal nursery, or how remarkably well she rode her pony. But Annabelle and Christabelle and Dulcibelle and Floribelle would mumble politely, "How nice for you," or "Wasn't that pleasant?" and go on digging in the garden or ironing a napkin.

Once, after Esmeralda had regaled them with an especially tedious story of her grand life, good-tempered Dulcy said abruptly (for her), "You may have been a Princess but you never learned to jump rope like us or spell so well or sew a decent seam. You hadn't even any sisters or playmates. What good is it, anyhow, being rich and royal?"

Only little Echo listened attentively to her recountings and followed her about like a shadow. And Esmeralda, who had loved nothing except herself, grew excessively fond of the pretty child, taking comfort in her affection.

After the first bitter weeks, she even stopped being scornful of some of the menial tasks she was called upon to perform. She began to envy the clever hands of Floribelle as she beat up a sponge cake. She noticed what satisfaction Christabelle took in embroidering a pocket on her smock. How awkwardly her own fingers held a needle or wielded a spoon on her rare attempts to compete! Into her mind crept the suspicion that perhaps simply being born a Princess did not make her a really superior person. And one day when the first three months were nearly up, she said grudgingly (watching Floribelle taking delicious gingerbread from the oven), "I wish, Flory, that I could be as clever as you."

At that moment a bird sang loudly, a rainbow appeared in the sky though there had been no rain, and Esmeralda felt a strange sensation. Something odd was happening to her. She ran to the mirror and peered into it. And what do you think?

No longer did Esmeralda's nose turn plainly up. It tilted so charmingly down that she cried out with delight. And with what excitement the generous family gathered 'round to compliment her, for it was indeed an improvement.

"The magic is working!" shouted Esmeralda. "Dame Goodwit, you are an enchantress after all!"

But the Dame only smiled. "That is as may be," she said mildly. "Certainly your nose is more attractive, child. But perhaps that is because you have stopped turning it up at the world in general. Perhaps you have found out there are people just as clever and just as fortunate in their own way, as you."

But Esmeralda was sure it was magic and she began to relent in her feeling toward the Dame and the life of the cottage. Its meanness still irked her and at night she still fondled the pearl locket. But her manners improved and she joined the rest of the girls more frequently in their games and at their chores.

She hung up her clothes, nightly, quite by habit. "Let me gather the eggs," she would sometimes ask at evening when it was time to search the hen-house. Almost humbly she followed at the heels of Christabelle or Floribelle while, singing, they swept or dusted or scoured the hearth. Dame Goodwit gave her a tiny plot of ground for her to plant and she grew reasonably adept at coaxing the seeds to climb up into the sunlight. She burned her thumbs trying to make cookies, she scratched her knees blackberrying, she made up stories for Echo which had nothing to do with how important she had been at the castle.

Then, when save for a day and a night another three months had sped, the second magic came to pass.

It happened on an afternoon when a soft rain was falling. The house was quiet, for the Dame and her daughters were resting after a busy morning. Only Esmeralda was awake, standing by the window watching the drops roll down the pane and thinking with a pang of homesickness about her own nursery at tea-time. She remembered how the lamps would have been lighted and it would have been time for muffins to come up on a tray. She was not sad—merely wistful—but she was seized with a sudden desire to taste again those muffins, so hot, so crisp, so buttery. "Why not make some?" she thought daringly. "Goodness knows I've watched the Dame turn out enough hot breads, and I know exactly where she keeps the cook book."

Without more ado, she crept quietly into the little kitchen, found an apron, and set about her task. The Dame and her daughters must have napped well that day, for Esmeralda made more noise than she had counted on, what with beating the eggs and measuring the sugar and dropping things and opening up drawers and testing the oven to see if it was hot enough. But the batter got itself mixed at last and popped into the stove and, just at the moment the family aroused itself and came looking for Esmeralda, that proud young lady was taking out a batch of crusty, golden-brown muffins.

You can imagine what a stir it created in the house. They may not have been the *best* muffins ever baked—perhaps they were just a bit doughy at the center and a trifle lopsided at the edges if you looked closely—but Esmeralda could not have been more pleased had they been perfection. The Dame praised her, the daughters praised her, and Echo kissed her on both cheeks. And Esmeralda just beamed and beamed. Then suddenly a rose beside the door unfolded its petals, a cricket chirped, and Floribelle cried out, "Esmeralda, your mouth! It turns up!"

Sure enough, when the excited Princess flew to the mirror, she saw a wonderful transformation. Beneath her dainty new nose, her mouth—her drooping, sullen little mouth—turned up as sweetly as that of Echo.

"I'm prettier! I'm growing prettier!" cried Esmeralda.

"She's growing prettier!" sang the sisters and they threw their arms about her and hugged her joyously.

"It was the muffins," said Echo.

"It was the magic," bubbled Esmeralda.

But Dame Goodwit merely smiled and said, "That is as may be. Perhaps your mouth turned down because life was dull. Never before, I think, have you known what it was to be proud of the work of your own hands."

After that famous occurrence, Esmeralda forgot to count the days till her exile ended. She grew happier in the cottage than she had been in the castle—except, of course, for missing her father and mother. She forgot about her pony in caring for the brown hens. She forgot about the tall swings, with clambering up the old apple trees for fruit. She left off yearning for

her usual luxuries in the pleasure of playing Hop Scotch with Floribelle or of beating Christabelle at races or of doing well at household tasks. She tidied her room; she polished the tin pots until they shone bright as copper; she learned to make gingerbread men with raisins for eyes. The pearl locket lay in a drawer of her rickety dresser and although she looked at it each day, its touch was not now her only consolation. The good Dame was well pleased with Esmeralda and remarked it so frequently that the Princess's turned-up smile got quite dimply with happiness.

Autumn waned. The last three months spent themselves in a haze of soft skies and flaming leaves. Light snow fell. In early December the cottage rocked with whisperings and giggles, for little Echo was to have a birthday.

All the sisters were planning surprises for the child—stitching away, after she had gone to bed, on cloth dolls, embroidering aprons and jolly bonnets. Only Esmeralda looked castdown, for she had been able to contrive no gift for her favorite. She couldn't sew as well as Annabelle or knit like Christabelle, or do fine cross-stitch like Dulcy, or twist yarn into cunning toys like Floribelle. There was no use her baking cookies —Dame Goodwit was already frosting an impressive cake. So for the first time in a long while she felt sad and left out.

"Never mind, Esmeralda," Dulcy soothed her. "Echo knows you love her and would give her something if you could."

Yet on the night before the birthday, Esmeralda let fall a salt tear into her pillow. She thought of her thousand riches at home and of how little they helped her now. Her hands, alone, tomorrow would be empty.

Yet need they be? There was her locket. True, it was what she treasured most of all. Without it she might forget altogether that she was the daughter of the King. But Echo had been her admirer, her comforter, her dear friend.

In the darkness, Esmeralda felt for the locket, fitted her hand about it as if in farewell, then fell peacefully to sleep.

At dawn she awoke, found a piece of paper and tied the pearled bauble gaily with a bit of red string from the grocery bundles. When Echo came to the breakfast table, greeted by the

"Happy Birthdays" of the household, there was Esmeralda's present on top of the pile. Echo opened it curiously. Then she cried out, "The locket!" threw herself headlong into Esmeralda's arms, and they both burst into happy tears.

"It was all I had to give you," gulped the Princess. "Wear it for me."

At that moment a gleam of light from the winter morning glittered brightly upon her head, somewhere far off a bell pealed, and Floribelle looked up with amazement.

"Esmeralda," she sang out. "Your eyes! They are glowing like stars."

Once more Esmeralda sped to the cracked mirror and with overwhelming happiness beheld her countenance. What a pair of eyes twinkled back at her, glowing, indeed, like stars!

"The magic," she said softly. "It is complete. I am no longer plain."

Then she turned to Dame Goodwit.

"My father the King will reward you well. You are a powerful enchantress."

"That is as may be," said the Dame placidly. "Perhaps your eyes glow because for the first time in your life you have done an unselfish thing. I am well pleased with you, Esmeralda."

In the midst of the rejoicing there came a rattle of wheels, the sound of horses' hoofs along the frosty road, and someone smote heavily on the door.

It was the King himself, come to fetch his daughter. For thrice three months were gone.

"Come in, Your Majesty, and welcome," spoke the Dame graciously. She dropped a dignified curtsey.

Esmeralda would have run to him but shyness held her and it was only when he called out, "Esmeralda, my child! My lovely child! Is it really you?" that she fled to his embrace.

"Let me look at you," he commanded, holding her at arm's length. "I can scarcely believe it. A mouth like mine, a nose like your mother's, and your eyes, my dear! Such splendid, glowing eyes."

Turning to the Dame, he said, "Well do you deserve the purse of gold which my messengers will shortly bring. I was fearful, very fearful, the magic might not avail. It would have been a sad thing to behead so worthy a widow as yourself."

"The women of my family, Your Majesty," answered the Dame serenely, "seldom lose their heads. As for the purse of gold, I do not want it. Esmeralda herself worked the enchantment."

And try as he would, no reward could he persuade the remarkable woman to accept.

Esmeralda, after bidding a tender goodbye to the Dame and to Annabelle and Christabelle and Dulcibelle and Floribelle and especially to little Echo, stepped into the carriage and was driven away. Strangely enough, as she pressed her face to the coach window, waving her hand as long as the cottage was in sight, her heart seemed almost as heavy as it had been on the journey which had carried her there.

Excitement, however, awaited her at the castle, for the King's messengers had run ahead with the glad news, and now the whole kingdom rejoiced. Flags flew from battlements, cannons fired salutes, and for the occasion the court poets hurried to compose a magnificent ode of fifty verses entitled, simply, *To Esmeralda.*

As the Princess walked gracefully between the silken ropes which had been stretched on either side of the castle steps, an audible gasp arose from all the servants and courtiers and guards of honor who were lined up there in their best livery.

"Is it really Esmeralda?" they whispered. "What poise, what charm, what sparkling eyes!"

The aunts and uncles and cousins nodded their heads complacently, observing, "Gets her looks from our side of the family."

The maids-in-waiting glanced furtively into their hand-mirrors and sighed with envy.

And the court physicians murmured, "Miraculous. We must get the case history."

Only Esmeralda herself kept her composure and was so modest and quiet that the Queen thought she must be ill and insisted she take a spoonful of cod-liver oil at once.

But modest she remained, although pleased with her welcome. And the first thing she did, when the flurry died down, was to persuade the King and Queen to remodel one of the gardener's houses into a comfortable dwelling (with telephone and all modern conveniences) and to send for the Dame and her family. They were naturally reluctant to leave their own home, but when the Queen pointed out what advantages the daughters would enjoy in the matter of schools and of acquiring suitable husbands, she consented finally to move into the cozy residence.

Esmeralda spent much of her time there, keeping up her skill at cookie-making, at climbing apple trees, and at excelling in games of Prisoner's Base.

And she lent her bicycle to Christabelle and her pony to Echo and her roller skates to Dulcy whenever they expressed a wish to try them.

Prince Charles Michael at the next castle party did not run down to the duck pond but paid marked attention to the Princess, helping her adjust her paper crown at the table.

As she grew older she became known far and wide not as "Esmeralda the Plain," but as "Esmeralda the Beautiful." And everyone lived happily ever after—or at least as happily as is possible in this mortal world.

THE UGLY DUCKLING

Hans Christian Andersen

Here is the old "Cinderella" theme of the misunderstood, scorned, and humble creature who finally comes into his own after much suffering. Children eight- or nine-years-old who hear the story read sometimes find it almost unbearably sad. The tens and elevens take it better and will be interested to know that it is much like Andersen's own life. Here is an allegory they can see illustrated in Constance Burnett's life of Andersen, The Shoemaker's Son. *They will also enjoy Will Nickless' illustrated edition of* The Ugly Duckling.

The country was lovely just then; it was summer! The wheat was golden and the oats still green; the hay was stacked in the rich low-lying meadows, where the stork was marching about on his long red legs, chattering Egyptian, the language his mother had taught him.

Round about field and meadow lay great

"The Ugly Duckling." From *Fairy Tales* by Hans Christian Andersen, translated by Mrs. Edgar Lucas, Everyman's Library, E. P. Dutton & Co., Inc., New York. By permission also of J. M. Dent & Sons, Ltd., London

woods, in the midst of which were deep lakes. Yes, the country certainly was delicious. In the sunniest spot stood an old mansion surrounded by a deep moat, and great dock leaves grew from the walls of the house right down to the water's edge; some of them were so tall that a small child could stand upright under them. In amongst the leaves it was as secluded as in the depths of a forest; and there a duck was sitting on her nest. Her little ducklings were just about to be hatched, but she was nearly tired of sitting, for it had lasted such a long time. Moreover, she had very few visitors, as the other ducks liked swimming about in the moat better than waddling up to sit under the dock leaves and gossip with her.

At last one egg after another began to crack. "Cheep, cheep!" they said. All the chicks had come to life, and were poking their heads out.

"Quack! quack!" said the duck; and then they all quacked their hardest, and looked about them on all sides among the green leaves; their mother allowed them to look as much as they liked, for green is good for the eyes.

"How big the world is to be sure!" said all the young ones; for they certainly had ever so much more room to move about, than when they were inside in the eggshell.

"Do you imagine this is the whole world?" said the mother. "It stretches a long way on the other side of the garden, right into the parson's field; but I have never been as far as that! I suppose you are all here now?" and she got up. "No! I declare I have not got you all yet! The biggest egg is still there; how long is it going to last?" and then she settled herself on the nest again.

"Well, how are you getting on?" said an old duck who had come to pay her a visit.

"This one egg is taking such a long time," answered the sitting duck, "the shell will not crack; but now you must look at the others; they are the finest ducklings I have ever seen! they are all exactly like their father, the rascal! he never comes to see me."

"Let me look at the egg which won't crack," said the old duck. "You may be sure that it is a turkey's egg! I have been cheated like that once, and I had no end of trouble and worry with the creatures, for I may tell you that they are afraid of the water. I could not get them into it, I quacked and snapped at them, but it was no good. Let me see the egg! Yes, it is a turkey's egg! You just leave it alone and teach the other children to swim."

"I will sit on it a little longer, I have sat so long already, that I may as well go on till the Midsummer Fair comes round."

"Please yourself," said the old duck, and she went away.

At last the big egg cracked. "Cheep, cheep!" said the young one and tumbled out; how big and ugly he was! The duck looked at him.

"That is a monstrous big duckling," she said; "none of the others looked like that; can he be a turkey chick? well we shall soon find that out; into the water he shall go, if I have to kick him in myself."

Next day was gloriously fine, and the sun shone on all the green dock leaves. The mother duck with her whole family went down to the moat.

Splash, into the water she sprang. "Quack, quack!" she said, and one duckling plumped in after the other. The water dashed over their heads, but they came up again and floated beautifully; their legs went of themselves, and they were all there, even the big ugly gray one swam about with them.

"No, that is no turkey," she said; "see how beautifully he uses his legs and how erect he holds himself: he is my own chick! after all, he is not so bad when you come to look at him properly. Quack, quack! Now come with me and I will take you into the world, and introduce you to the duckyard; but keep close to me all the time, so that no one may tread upon you, and beware of the cat!"

Then they went into the duckyard. There was a fearful uproar going on, for two broods were fighting for the head of an eel, and in the end the cat captured it.

"That's how things go in this world," said the mother duck, and she licked her bill for she wanted the eel's head herself.

"Use your legs," said she; "mind you quack properly, and bend your necks to the old duck over there! She is the grandest of them all; she has Spanish blood in her veins and that accounts for her size, and, do you see? she has a red rag round her leg; that is a wonderfully fine thing, and the most extraordinary mark of distinction any duck can have. It shows clearly that she is not to be parted with, and that she is worthy of recognition both by beasts and men! Quack now! don't turn your toes in, a well brought up duckling keeps his legs wide apart just like father and mother; that's it, now bend your necks, and say quack!"

They did as they were bid, but the other ducks round about looked at them and said, quite loud; "Just look there! now we are to have that tribe! just as if there were not enough of us already, and, oh dear! how ugly that duckling is, we won't stand him!" and a duck flew at him at once and bit him in the neck.

"Let him be," said the mother; "he is doing no harm."

"Very likely not, but he is so ungainly and queer," said the biter; "he must be whacked."

"They are handsome children that mother has," said the old duck with the rag round her leg; "all good looking except this one, and he is not a good specimen; it's a pity you can't make him over again."

"That can't be done, your grace," said the mother duck; "he is not handsome, but he is a thorough good creature, and he swims as beautifully as any of the others; nay, I think I might venture even to add that I think he will improve as he goes on, or perhaps in time he may grow smaller! he was too long in the egg, and so he has not come out with a very good figure." And then she patted his neck and stroked him down. "Besides, he is a drake," said she; "so it does not matter so much. I believe he will be very strong, and I don't doubt but he will make his way in the world."

"The other ducklings are very pretty," said the old duck. "Now make yourselves quite at home, and if you find the head of an eel you may bring it to me!"

After that they felt quite at home. But the poor duckling which had been the last to come out of the shell, and who was so ugly, was bitten, pushed about, and made fun of both by the ducks and the hens. "He is too big," they all said; and the turkey-cock, who was born with his spurs on, and therefore thought himself quite an emperor, puffed himself up like a vessel in full sail, made for him, and gobbled and gobbled till he became quite red in the face. The poor duckling was at his wit's end, and did not know which way to turn; he was in despair because he was so ugly, and the butt of the whole duckyard.

So the first day passed, and afterwards matters grew worse and worse. The poor duckling was chased and hustled by all of them, even his brothers and sisters ill-used him; and they were always saying, "If only the cat would get hold of you, you hideous object!" Even his mother said, "I wish to goodness you were miles away." The ducks bit him, the hens pecked him, and the girl who fed them kicked him aside.

Then he ran off and flew right over the hedge, where the little birds flew up into the air in a fright.

"That is because I am so ugly," thought the poor duckling, shutting his eyes, but he ran on all the same. Then he came to a great marsh where the wild ducks lived; he was so tired and miserable that he stayed there the whole night.

In the morning the wild ducks flew up to inspect their new comrade.

"What sort of a creature are you?" they inquired, as the duckling turned from side to side and greeted them as well as he could. "You are frightfully ugly," said the wild ducks; "but that does not matter to us, so long as you do not marry into our family!" Poor fellow! he had no thought of marriage, all he wanted was permission to lie among the rushes, and to drink a little of the marsh water.

He stayed there two whole days, then two wild geese came, or rather two wild ganders, they were not long out of the shell, and therefore rather pert.

"I say, comrade," they said, "you are so ugly that we have taken quite a fancy to you; will you join us and be a bird of passage? There is another marsh close by, and there are some charming wild geese there; all sweet young ladies, who can say quack! You are ugly enough to make your fortune among them." Just at that moment, bang! bang! was heard up above, and both the wild geese fell dead among the reeds, and the water turned blood red. Bang! bang! went the guns, and whole flocks of wild geese flew up from the rushes and the shot peppered among them again.

There was a grand shooting party, and the sportsmen lay hidden round the marsh, some even sat on the branches of the trees which overhung the water; the blue smoke rose like clouds among the dark trees and swept over the pool.

The water-dogs wandered about in the swamp, splash! splash! The rushes and reeds bent beneath their tread on all sides. It was terribly alarming to the poor duckling. He twisted his head round to get it under his wing and just at that moment a frightful, big dog appeared close beside him; his tongue hung right out of his mouth and his eyes glared wickedly. He opened his great chasm of a mouth close to the duckling, showed his sharp teeth—and—splash—went on without touching him.

"Oh, thank Heaven!" sighed the duckling, "I am so ugly that even the dog won't bite me!"

Then he lay quite still while the shot whistled among the bushes, and bang after bang rent the air. It only became quiet late in the day, but even then the poor duckling did not dare to get up; he waited several hours more before he looked about and then he hurried away from the marsh as fast as he could. He ran across fields and meadows, and there was such a wind that he had hard work to make his way.

Toward night he reached a poor little cottage; it was such a miserable hovel that it could not make up its mind which way to fall even, and so it remained standing. The wind whistled so fiercely round the duckling that he had to sit on his tail to resist it, and it blew harder and harder; then he saw that the door had fallen off one hinge and hung so crookedly that he could creep into the house through the crack and by this means he made his way into the room. An old woman lived there with her cat and her hen. The cat, which she called "Sonnie," could arch his back, purr, and give off electric sparks, that is to say if you stroked his fur the wrong way. The hen had quite tiny short legs and so she was called "Chuckie low-legs." She laid good eggs, and the old woman was as fond of her as if she had been her own child.

In the morning the strange duckling was discovered immediately, and the cat began to purr and the hen to cluck.

"What on earth is that!" said the old woman

looking round, but her sight was not good and she thought the duckling was a fat duck which had escaped. "This is a capital find," said she; "now I shall have duck's eggs if only it is not a drake! we must find out about that!"

So she took the duckling on trial for three weeks, but no eggs made their appearance. The cat was the master of the house and the hen the mistress, and they always spoke of "we and the world," for they thought that they represented the half of the world, and that quite the better half.

The duckling thought there might be two opinions on the subject, but the hen would not hear of it.

"Can you lay eggs?" she asked.

"No!"

"Will you have the goodness to hold your tongue then!"

And the cat said, "Can you arch your back, purr, or give off sparks?"

"No."

"Then you had better keep your opinions to yourself when people of sense are speaking!"

The duckling sat in the corner nursing his ill-humour; then he began to think of the fresh air and the sunshine, an uncontrollable longing seized him to float on the water, and at last he could not help telling the hen about it.

"What on earth possesses you?" she asked; "you have nothing to do, that is why you get these freaks into your head. Lay some eggs or take to purring, and you will get over it."

"But it is so delicious to float on the water," said the duckling; "so delicious to feel it rushing over your head when you dive to the bottom."

"That would be a fine amusement," said the hen. "I think you have gone mad. Ask the cat about it, he is the wisest creature I know; ask him if he is fond of floating on the water or diving under it. I say nothing about myself. Ask our mistress yourself, the old woman, there is no one in the world cleverer than she is. Do you suppose she has any desire to float on the water, or to duck underneath it?"

"You do not understand me," said the duckling.

"Well, if we don't understand you, who should? I suppose you don't consider yourself cleverer than the cat or the old woman, not to mention me. Don't make a fool of yourself, child, and thank your stars for all the good we have done you! Have you not lived in this warm room, and in such society that you might have learnt something? But you are an idiot, and there is no pleasure in associating with you. You may believe me I mean you well, I tell you home truths, and there is no surer way than that of knowing who are one's friends. You just see about laying some eggs, or learn to purr, or to emit sparks."

"I think I will go out into the wide world," said the duckling.

"Oh, do so by all means," said the hen.

So away went the duckling, he floated on the water and ducked underneath it, but he was looked askance at by every living creature for his ugliness. Now the autumn came on, the leaves in the woods turned yellow and brown; the wind took hold of them, and they danced about. The sky looked very cold, and the clouds hung heavy with snow and hail. A raven stood on the fence and croaked Caw! Caw! from sheer cold; it made one shiver only to think of it, the poor duckling certainly was in a bad case.

One evening, the sun was just setting in wintry splendour, when a flock of beautiful large birds appeared out of the bushes; the duckling had never seen anything so beautiful. They were dazzlingly white with long waving necks; they were swans, and uttering a peculiar cry they spread out their magnificent broad wings and flew away from the cold regions to warmer lands and open seas. They mounted so high, so very high, and the ugly little duckling became strangely uneasy, he circled round and round in the water like a wheel, craning his neck up into the air after them. Then he uttered a shriek so piercing and so strange, that he was quite frightened by it himself. Oh, he could not forget those beautiful birds, those happy birds, and as soon as they were out of sight he ducked right down to the bottom, and when he came up again he was quite beside himself. He did not know what the birds were, or whither they flew, but all the same he was more drawn towards them than he had ever been by any creatures before. He did not envy them in the least, how could it occur to him even to wish to be such a marvel of beauty; he would have been thankful if only the ducks would have tolerated him among them—the poor ugly creature!

The winter was so bitterly cold that the duckling was obliged to swim about in the water to keep it from freezing, but every night the hole in which he swam got smaller and smaller. Then it froze so hard that the surface ice cracked, and the duckling had to use his legs all the time, so that the ice should not close in round him; at last he was so weary that he could move no more, and he was frozen fast into the ice.

Early in the morning a peasant came along and saw him; he went out on to the ice and hammered a hole in it with his heavy wooden shoe, and carried the duckling home to his wife. There it soon revived. The children wanted to play with it, but the duckling thought they were going to ill-use him, and rushed in his fright into the milk pan, and the milk spurted out all over the room. The woman shrieked and threw up her hands, then it flew into the butter cask, and down into the meal tub and out again. Just imagine what it looked like by this time! The woman screamed and tried to hit it with the tongs, and the children tumbled over one another in trying to catch it, and they screamed with laughter—by good luck the door stood open, and the duckling flew out among the bushes and the new fallen snow—and it lay there thoroughly exhausted.

But it would be too sad to mention all the privation and misery it had to go through during that hard winter. When the sun began to shine warmly again, the duckling was in the marsh, lying among the rushes; the larks were singing and the beautiful spring had come.

Then all at once it raised its wings and they flapped with much greater strength than before, and bore him off vigorously. Before he knew where he was, he found himself in a large garden where the apple trees were in full blossom, and the air was scented with lilacs, the long branches of which overhung the indented shores of the lake. Oh! the spring freshness was so delicious!

Just in front of him he saw three beautiful white swans advancing towards him from a thicket; with rustling feathers they swam lightly over the water. The duckling recognized the majestic birds, and he was overcome by a strange melancholy.

"I will fly to them, the royal birds, and they will hack me to pieces, because I, who am so ugly, venture to approach them! But it won't matter; better be killed by them than be snapped at by the ducks, pecked by the hens, or spurned by the henwife, or suffer so much misery in the winter."

So he flew into the water and swam towards the stately swans; they saw him and darted toward him with ruffled feathers.

"Kill me, oh, kill me!" said the poor creature, and bowing his head towards the water he awaited his death. But what did he see reflected in the transparent water?

He saw below him his own image, but he was no longer a clumsy dark gray bird, ugly and ungainly, he was himself a swan! It does not matter in the least having been born in a duckyard, if only you come out of a swan's egg!

He felt quite glad of all the misery and tribulation he had gone through; he was the better able to appreciate his good fortune now, and all the beauty which greeted him. The big swans swam round and round him, and stroked him with their bills.

Some little children came into the garden with corn and pieces of bread, which they threw into the water; and the smallest one cried out: "There is a new one!"

The other children shouted with joy, "Yes, a new one has come!" And they clapped their hands and danced about, running after their father and mother. They threw the bread into the water, and one and all said that "the new one was the prettiest; he was so young and handsome." And the old swans bent their heads and did homage before him.

He felt quite shy, and hid his head under his wing; he did not know what to think; he was so very happy, but not at all proud; a good heart never becomes proud. He thought of how he had been pursued and scorned, and now he heard them all say that he was the most beautiful of all beautiful birds. The lilacs bent their boughs right down into the water before him, and the bright sun was warm and cheering, and he rustled his feathers and raised his slender neck aloft, saying with exultation in his heart: "I never dreamt of so much happiness when I was the Ugly Duckling!"

THE 500 HATS
OF BARTHOLOMEW CUBBINS

Dr. Seuss

"Dr. Seuss," who is really Theodore Seuss Geisel, lives on a mountain, in a tall house called "The Tower." When he draws, he looks out of a window to the sea, where the whales go by every spring. When he writes, he can go up to the top of his tower and see mountains in Mexico or mountains in his own state. Sometimes when the fog rolls in from the sea, mountains and land and sea are all hidden and "The Tower" seems to be perched on clouds. Perhaps all this accounts for the wonderful fantasies he has written for children and perhaps the twinkle in his eye explains why children always say his picture-stories are "funny books," the funniest books of all.

In the beginning, Bartholomew Cubbins didn't have five hundred hats. He had only one hat. It was an old one that had belonged to his father and his father's father before him. It was probably the oldest and the plainest hat in the whole Kingdom of Didd, where Bartholomew Cubbins lived. But Bartholomew liked it—especially because of the feather that always pointed straight up in the air.

The Kingdom of Didd was ruled by King Derwin. His palace stood high on the top of the mountain. From his balcony he looked down over the houses of all his subjects—first over the spires of the noblemen's castles, across the broad roofs of the rich men's mansions, then over the little houses of the townsfolk, to the huts of the farmers far off in the fields.

It was a mighty view and it made King Derwin feel mighty important.

Far off in the fields, on the edge of a cranberry bog, stood the hut of the Cubbins family. From the small door Bartholomew looked across the huts of the farmers to the houses of the townsfolk, then to the rich men's mansions and the noblemen's castles, up to the great towering palace of the King. It was exactly the same view that King Derwin saw from his balcony, but Bartholomew saw it backward.

It was a mighty view, but it made Bartholomew Cubbins feel mighty small.

Just after sunrise one Saturday morning Bartholomew started for town. He felt very happy. A pleasant breeze whistled through the feather in his hat. In his right hand he carried a basket of cranberries to sell at the market. He was anxious to sell them quickly and bring the money back home to his parents.

He walked faster and faster till he got to the gates of the town.

The sound of silver trumpets rang through the air. Hoof beats clattered on the cobbled streets.

"Clear the way! Clear the way! Make way for the King!"

All the people rushed for the sidewalks. They drove their carts right up over the curbstones. Bartholomew clutched his basket tighter.

Around the corner dashed fifty trumpeters on yellow-robed horses. Behind them on crimson-robed horses came the King's Own Guards.

"Hats off to the King!" shouted the Captain of the King's Own Guards.

On came the King's carriage—white and gold and purple. It rumbled like thunder through the narrow street.

It swept past Bartholomew. Then suddenly its mighty brakes shrieked. It lurched—and then it stopped. The whole procession stood still.

Bartholomew could hardly believe what he saw. Through the side window of the carriage, the King himself was staring back—straight back at him! Bartholomew began to tremble.

"Back up!" the King commanded the Royal Coachman.

The Royal Coachman shouted to the royal horses. The King's Own Guards shouted to their crimson-robed horses. The trumpeters shouted to their yellow-robed horses. Very slowly the whole procession backed down the street, until the King's carriage stopped right in front of Bartholomew.

The King leaned from his carriage window and fixed his eyes directly on Bartholomew Cubbins. "Well . . . ? Well . . . ?" he demanded.

Bartholomew shook with fright. "I ought to say something," he thought to himself. But he could think of nothing to say.

"Well?" demanded the King again. "Do you

or do you *not* take off your hat before your King?"

"Yes, indeed, Sire," answered Bartholomew, feeling greatly relieved. "I *do* take off my hat before my King."

"Then take it off this very instant," commanded the King more loudly than before.

"But, Sire, my hat *is* off," answered Bartholomew.

"Such impudence!" shouted the King, shaking an angry finger. "How dare you stand there and tell me your hat is off!"

"I don't like to say you are wrong, Sire," said Bartholomew very politely, "but you see my hat *is* off." And he showed the King the hat in his hand.

"If that's your hat in your hand," demanded the King, "what's that on your head?"

"On my head?" gasped Bartholomew. There *did* seem to be something on his head. He reached up his hand and touched a hat!

The face of Bartholomew Cubbins turned very red. "It's a hat, Sire," he stammered, "but it *can't* be mine. Someone behind me must have put in on my head."

"I don't care *how* it got there," said the King. "You take it off." And the King sat back in his carriage.

Bartholomew quickly snatched off the hat. He stared at it in astonishment. It was exactly the same as his own hat—the same size, the same color. And it had exactly the same feather.

"By the Crown of my Fathers!" roared the King, again leaning out of the carriage window. "Did I or did I *not* command you to take off your hat?"

"You did, Sire . . . I took it off . . . I took it off twice."

"Nonsense! There is still a hat upon your head."

"Another hat?" Again Bartholomew reached up his hand and touched a hat.

"Come, come, what is the meaning of all this?" demanded the King, his face purple with rage.

"I don't know, Sire," answered Bartholomew. "It never happened to me before."

The King was now shaking with such fury that the carriage rocked on its wheels and the Royal Coachman could hardly sit in his seat.

"Arrest this impudent trickster," shouted the King to the Captain of the King's Own Guards. "We'll teach him to take off his hat."

The Royal Coachman cracked his long whip. The King's carriage swung forward up the street toward the palace.

But the Captain of the King's Own Guards leaned down from his big brass saddle and grabbed Bartholomew Cubbins by his shirt. Away flew Bartholomew's basket! The cranberries bounced over the cobblestones and rolled down into the gutter.

With a jangling of spurs and a clatter of horseshoes, the Captain and Bartholomew sped up the winding street toward the palace. Out of the narrow streets, on up the hill! Bartholomew clung to the Captain's broad back. On and on they galloped, past the bright gardens of the wealthy merchants. Higher and higher up the mountain, on past the walls of the noblemen's castles. . . .

Flupp! . . . the sharp wind whisked off Bartholomew's hat. *Flupp Flupp* . . . two more flew off. *Flupp Flupp Flupp* flew another . . . and another. ". . . 4 . . . 5 . . . 6 . . . 7 . . ." Bartholomew kept counting as the hats came faster and faster. Lords and ladies stared from the windows of their turrets, wondering what the strange stream of hats could mean.

Over the palace drawbridge they sped— through the great gates, and into the courtyard. The Captain pulled in his reins.

"His Majesty waits in the Throne Room," said a guard, saluting the Captain.

"The Throne Room!" The Captain dropped Bartholomew to the ground. "I'd certainly hate to be in your shoes," he said, shaking his head sadly.

For a moment Bartholomew was terribly frightened. "Still," he thought to himself, "the King can do nothing dreadful to punish me, because I really haven't done anything wrong. It would be cowardly to feel afraid."

Bartholomew threw back his shoulders and marched straight ahead into the palace. "Follow the black carpet," said the guard at the door. All through the long hallway Bartholomew could hear the muttering of voices behind heavy doors. "He won't take off his hat?" "No, he won't take off his hat."

Bartholomew walked on till he stood in the very middle of the Throne Room. The King, in a long scarlet robe, was sitting on his throne. Beside him stood Sir Alaric, Keeper of the King's Records. He wore in his belt, instead of a sword, a long silver ruler. Lords and noblemen of the court stood solemn and silent.

The King looked down at Bartholomew severely. "Young man, I'll give you one more chance. Will you take off your hat for your King?"

"Your Majesty," said Bartholomew as politely as he possibly could, "I will—but I'm afraid it won't do any good." And he took off his hat—and it didn't do any good. Another hat sat on Bartholomew's head. He took off hat after hat after hat after hat until he was standing in the middle of a great pile of hats.

The lords and noblemen were so astonished they couldn't even speak. Such a thing had never happened in the Throne Room before.

"Heavens!" said Sir Alaric, Keeper of the Records, blinking behind his triangular spectacles. "He's taken off 45!"

"And there were 3 more down in the town," said the King.

"And you must add on 87 more that blew off my head as we galloped up the hill," said Bartholomew, trying to be helpful.

"One hundred and thirty-five hats! Most unusual," said Sir Alaric, writing it down on a long scroll.

"Come, come," said the King impatiently. "Sir Alaric, what do you make of all this nonsense?"

"Very *serious* nonsense, Your Majesty," answered Sir Alaric. "I advise you to call in an expert on hats."

"Excellent," agreed the King. "Ho, Guard! Fetch in Sir Snipps, maker of hats for all the fine lords."

Into the Throne Room marched the smallest man, wearing the tallest hat that Bartholomew had ever seen. It was Sir Snipps. Instead of a sword, he wore at his side a large pair of scissors.

"Take a look at this boy's hat," commanded the King. Sir Snipps looked at Bartholomew Cubbins' hat and sniffed in disgust. Then he turned to the King and bowed stiffly. "Your Majesty, I, Sir Snipps, am the maker of hats for all the fine lords. I make hats of cloth of gold,

fine silks and gems and ostrich plumes. You ask *me* what I think of *this* hat? Pooh! It is the most ordinary hat I ever set eyes on."

"In that case," said the King, "it should be very simple for you to take it off."

"Simple, indeed," mumbled Sir Snipps haughtily, and, standing on his tiptoes, he pushed his pudgy thumb at Bartholomew's hat and knocked it to the floor. Immediately another appeared on Bartholomew's head.

"Screebees!" screamed Sir Snipps, leaping in the air higher than he was tall. Then he turned and ran shrieking out of the Throne Room.

"Dear me!" said the King, looking very puzzled. "If Snipps can't do it, this *must* be more than an ordinary hat."

"One hundred and thirty-six," wrote Sir Alaric, wrinkling his brow. "Your Majesty, I advise that you call in your Wise Men."

"A fine idea!" said the King. "Ho, Guard! bring me Nadd. Nadd knows about everything in all my kingdom."

In came an old, old man. He looked at the hat on Bartholomew's head, and he looked at the pile of hats on the floor.

"Nadd, my Wise Man, can you take off his hat?" asked the King. Nadd shook his head solemnly—solemnly no.

"Then fetch me the Father of Nadd," commanded the King. "He knows about everything in all my kingdom and in all the world beyond."

In came an even older man. But when he looked at Bartholomew's hats, the Father of Nadd merely locked his fingers across his beard and said nothing.

"Then bring me the Father of the Father of Nadd!" ordered the King. "He knows about everything in all my kingdom, in all the world beyond, and in all other worlds that may happen to be."

Then came the oldest man of them all. But he just looked at Bartholomew and nibbled nervously at the end of his beard.

"Does this mean there is *no one* in my whole kingdom who can take off this boy's hat?" bellowed the King in a terrifying voice.

A small voice came up through the balcony window. "What's the matter, Uncle Derwin?" To Bartholomew, it sounded like the voice of a boy.

The King stepped out on the balcony and leaned over the marble railing. "There's a boy in here . . . just about your age," the King said. "He won't take off his hat."

Bartholomew tiptoed up behind the King and looked down. There stood a boy with a big lace collar—a very proud little boy with his nose in the air. It was the Grand Duke Wilfred, nephew of the King.

"You send him down here," said the Grand Duke Wilfred. "*I'll* fix him."

The King thought for a minute. He pushed back his crown and scratched his head. "Well . . . maybe you can. There's no harm trying."

"Take him to the Grand Duke Wilfred!" commanded the King. And two of the King's Own Guards led Bartholomew out of the Throne Room.

"Pooh!" said the Grand Duke Wilfred, looking at Bartholomew's hat and laughing meanly. "*That* hat won't come off? You stand over there." He pointed to a corner where the wall curved out. "I need a little target practise with my bow and arrow."

When Bartholomew saw that the Grand Duke Wilfred had only a child's bow he didn't feel frightened. He spoke up proudly, "I can shoot with my father's big bow."

"My bow's plenty big enough for shooting hats—especially hats like yours," answered Wilfred. And he let fly an arrow. zZZ! . . . it grazed Bartholomew's forehead and nipped off his hat. Away it blew, and over the parapet. But another hat appeared on his head. zZZ! . . . zZZ! . . . zZZ! . . . the arrows flew . . . till the Grand

Duke's whole bagful of arrows was gone. And still a hat sat upon Bartholomew's head.

"It's not fair," cried the Grand Duke. "It's not fair!" He threw down his bow and stamped upon it.

"One hundred and fifty-four hats!" gulped Sir Alaric.

"These hats are driving me mad!" The King's voice rang out through all the palace. "Why waste time with a *child's* bow and arrow. Fetch me the mightiest bow and arrow in all my realm—fetch the Yeoman of the Bowmen!"

"Yeoman of the Bowmen," echoed all the lords and noblemen of the court.

A gigantic man strode out across the terrace. His bow was as big as the branch of a tree. The arrow was twice as long as Bartholomew, and thicker than his wrist.

"Yeoman of the Bowmen," said the King, "shoot off this boy's hat . . . and make it *stay* off!"

Bartholomew was trembling so hard that he could scarcely stand straight. The Yeoman bent back his mighty bow.

G—r—r—zibb! . . . Like a mad giant hornet the arrow tore through the air toward Bartholomew Cubbins.

G—r—r—zapp! . . . The sharp arrow head bit through his hat and carried it off—on and on for a full half mile.

G—r—r—zopp! . . . It plunked to a stop in the heart of an oak tree. Yet there on Bartholomew's head sat another hat.

The face of the Yeoman of the Bowmen went white as the palace walls. "It's black magic!" he shrieked.

"Black magic, that's *just* what it is," sighed the King with relief. "I should have thought of that before. That makes things simple. Back to the Throne Room! Call my magicians!"

In the whole Throne Room there wasn't a sound as loud as a breath. But from the spiral stairs that led down from the southwest tower came the shuffling of slow, padded feet. The magicians were coming! Low and slow, they were chanting words that were strange. . . .

"*Dig a hole five furlongs deep,*
Down to where the night snakes creep,
Mix and mold the mystic mud,
Malber, Balber, Tidder, Tudd."

In came seven black-gowned magicians, and beside each one stalked a lean black cat. They circled around Bartholomew Cubbins muttering deep and mysterious sounds.

"Stop this useless muttering," ordered the King. "I want a chant that will charm away this boy's hat."

The magicians huddled over Bartholomew and chanted.

"Winkibus
Tinkibus
Fotichee
Klay,
Hat on this demon's head,
Fly far away!
Howl, men, howl away,
Howl away, howl away,
Yowl, cats, yowl away,
Yowl away, yowl away!
Hat on this demon's head,
Seep away, creep away, leap away, gleap away,
  Never come back!"

"A mighty good chant," said the King, looking very pleased. "Are you sure it will work?"

All the magicians nodded together.

"But," said the King, looking puzzled, "there still *seems* to be a hat upon his head. How long will it take for the charm to work?"

"Be calm, oh, Sire, and have no fears," chanted the magicians.

"Our charm will work in ten short years."

"Ten years!" gasped the King. "Away, fools!" he shouted. "Out of my sight! I can't wait *ten years* to get rid of his hat. Oh, dear, what *can* I do . . . what CAN I do?"

"If I were King," whispered the Grand Duke Wilfred, "I'd chop off his head."

"A dreadful thought," said the King, biting his lip. "But I'm afraid I'll have to."

"Young man," he said to Bartholomew Cubbins, and he pointed to a small door at the end of the room, "march down those steps to the dungeon and tell the executioner to chop off your head."

Bartholomew's heart sank into his boots, but he did as the King commanded. "I *must* take off my hat," he said to himself as he started down the long black stairway. "This is my last chance." One hat after another he tore from his head ". . . 156 . . . 157 . . . 158 . . ." It grew colder and damper. ". . . 217 . . . 218 . . . 219 . . ." Down . . . down . . . down. ". . . 231 . . . 232 . . . 233 . . ." It seemed to Bartholomew he must be in the very heart of the mountain.

"Who's there?" said a voice from the blackness.

Bartholomew turned a corner and stepped into the dungeon.

The executioner was whistling and swinging his axe idly, because at the moment he had nothing to do. In spite of his business, he really seemed to be a very pleasant man.

"The King says you must chop off my head," said Bartholomew.

"Oh, I'd hate to," said the executioner, looking at him with a friendly smile. "You seem like such a nice boy."

"Well . . . the King says you have to," said Bartholomew, "so please get it over with."

"All right," sighed the executioner, "but first you've got to take off your hat."

"Why?" asked Bartholomew.

"I don't know," said the executioner, "but it's one of the rules. I can't execute anyone with his hat on."

"All right," said Bartholomew, "you take it off for me."

The executioner leaned across the chopping block and flipped off Bartholomew's hat.

"What's this?" he gasped, blinking through the holes in his mask, as another hat sat on Bartholomew's head. He flipped this one off . . . then another and another.

"Fiddlesticks!" grunted the executioner, throwing his axe on the floor. "I can't execute you at all." And he shook hands with Bartholomew and sent him back upstairs to the King.

The King had been taking a nap on the throne. "What are you doing back here?" he said to Bartholomew, angry at being awakened.

"I'm sorry, Your Majesty," explained Bartholomew. "My head can't come off with my hat on. . . . It's against the rules."

"So it can't," said the King, leaning back wearily. "Now how many hats does that make altogether?"

"The executioner knocked off 13 . . . and I left 178 more on the dungeon steps," answered Bartholomew.

"Three hundred and forty-six hats," mumbled Sir Alaric from behind his scroll.

"Uncle Derwin," yawned the Grand Duke Wilfred, "I suppose I'll have to do away with him. Send him up to the highest turret and I, in person will push him off."

"Wilfred! I'm surprised at you," said the King. "But I guess it's a good idea."

So the King and the Grand Duke led Bartholomew Cubbins toward the highest turret.

Up and up and up the turret stairs he climbed behind them.

"This is my *last*—my *very last* chance," thought Bartholomew. He snatched off his hat. "Three hundred and forty-seven!" He snatched off another. He pulled and he tore and he flung them behind him. ". . . 398 . . . 399 . . ." His arms ached from pulling off hats. But still the hats came. Bartholomew climbed on.

". . . 448 . . . 449 . . . 450 . . ." counted Sir Alaric, puffing up the stairs behind him.

Suddenly Sir Alaric stopped. He looked. He took off his triangular spectacles and wiped them on his sleeve. And then he looked again. *The hats began to change!* Hat 451 had, not one, but *two* feathers! Hat 452 had three . . . and 453

also had three *and a little red jewel!* Each new hat was fancier than the hat just before.

"Your Majesty! Your Majesty!" cried out Sir Alaric.

But the King and the Grand Duke were 'way up where they couldn't hear. They had already reached the top of the highest turret. Bartholomew was following just behind.

"Step right out here and get out on that wall," snapped the Grand Duke Wilfred. "I can't wait to push you off."

But when Bartholomew stepped up on the wall they gasped in amazement. He was wearing the most beautiful hat that had ever been seen in the Kingdom of Didd. It had a ruby larger than any the King himself had ever owned. It had ostrich plumes, and cockatoo plumes, and mockingbird plumes, and paradise plumes. Beside *such* a hat even the King's Crown seemed like nothing.

The Grand Duke Wilfred took a quick step forward. Bartholomew thought his end had come at last.

"Wait!" shouted the King. He could not take his eyes off the magnificent hat.

"I *won't* wait," the Grand Duke talked back to the King. "I'm going to push him off now! That new big hat makes me madder than ever." And he flung out his arms to push Bartholomew off.

But the King was quicker than Wilfred. He grabbed him by the back of his fine lace collar. "This is to teach you," His Majesty said sternly, "that Grand Dukes *never* talk back to their King." And he turned the Grand Duke Wilfred over his knee and spanked him soundly, right on the seat of his royal silk pants.

"And now," smiled the King, lifting Bartholomew down from the wall, "it would be nice if you'd sell me that wonderful hat!"

". . . 498 . . . 499 . . ." broke in the tired voice of Sir Alaric, who had just arrived at the top of the steps, " and *that* . . ." he pointed to the hat on Bartholomew's head, "makes exactly 500!"

"Five Hundred!" exclaimed the King. "Will you sell it for 500 pieces of gold?"

"Anything you say, Sire," answered Bartholomew. "You see . . . I've never sold one before."

The King's hands trembled with joy as he reached for the hat.

Slowly, slowly, Bartholomew felt the weight of the great hat lifting from his head. He held his breath. . . . Then suddenly he felt the cool evening breezes blow through his hair. His face broke into a happy smile. The head of Bartholomew Cubbins was bare!

"Look, Your Majesty! *Look!*" he shouted to the King.

"No! *You* look at *me*," answered the King. And he put the great hat on right over his crown.

Arm in arm, the King and Bartholomew went down to the counting room to count out the gold. Then the King sent Bartholomew home to his parents . . . no basket on his arm, no hat on his head, but with five hundred pieces of gold in a bag.

And the King commanded that the hat he had bought, and all the other hats, too, be kept forever in a great crystal case by the side of his throne.

But neither Bartholomew Cubbins, nor King Derwin himself, nor anyone else in the Kingdom of Didd could ever explain how the strange thing had happened. They only could say it just "happened to happen" and was not very likely to happen again.

"THAT IS WHY HE WAS ALWAYS CALLED POOH"

A. A. Milne

Younger children like the Pooh books, but sometimes miss part of their humor. In many families parents begin reading Pooh stories to the five- or six-year-olds and are still reading them when the children are ten.

So Winnie-the-Pooh went round to his friend Christopher Robin, who lived behind a green door in another part of the forest.

"Good morning, Christopher Robin," he said.

"Good morning, Winnie-*ther*-Pooh," said you.

"I wonder if you've got such a thing as a balloon about you?"

"*That* Is Why He Was Always Called Pooh." From *Winnie-the-Pooh* by A. A. Milne, published and copyright, 1926, E. P. Dutton & Co., Inc., New York. By permission also of Methuen & Co., Ltd., London

"A balloon?"

"Yes, I just said to myself coming along: 'I wonder if Christopher Robin has such a thing as a balloon about him?' I just said it to myself, thinking of balloons, and wondering."

"What do you want a balloon for?" you said.

Winnie-the-Pooh looked round to see that nobody was listening, put his paw to his mouth, and said in a deep whisper: *"Honey!"*

"But you don't get honey with balloons!"

"I do," said Pooh.

Well, it just happened that you had been to a party the day before at the house of your friend Piglet, and you had balloons at the party. You had had a big green balloon; and one of Rabbit's relations had had a big blue one, and had left it behind, being really too young to go to a party at all; and so you had brought the green one *and* the blue one home with you.

"Which one would you like?" you asked Pooh.

He put his head between his paws and thought very carefully.

"It's like this," he said. "When you go after honey with a balloon, the great thing is not to let the bees know you're coming. Now, if you have a green balloon, they might think you were only part of the tree, and not notice you, and if you have a blue balloon, they might think you were only part of the sky, and not notice you, and the question is: Which is most likely?"

"Wouldn't they notice *you* underneath the balloon?" you asked.

"They might or they might not," said Winnie-the-Pooh. "You never can tell with bees." He thought for a moment and said: "I shall try to look like a small black cloud. That will deceive them."

"Then you had better have the blue balloon," you said; and so it was decided.

Well, you both went out with the blue balloon, and you took your gun with you, just in case, as you always did, and Winnie-the-Pooh went to a very muddy place that he knew of, and rolled and rolled until he was black all over; and then, when the balloon was blown up as big as big, and you and Pooh were both holding on to the string, you let go suddenly, and Pooh Bear floated gracefully up into the sky, and stayed there—level with the top of the tree and about twenty feet away from it.

"Hooray!" you shouted.

"Isn't that fine?" shouted Winnie-the-Pooh down to you. "What do I look like?"

"You look like a Bear holding on to a balloon," you said.

"Not," said Pooh anxiously, "—not like a small black cloud in a blue sky?"

"Not very much."

"Ah, well, perhaps from up here it looks different. And, as I say, you never can tell with bees."

There was no wind to blow him nearer to the tree, so there he stayed. He could see the honey, he could smell the honey, but he couldn't quite reach the honey.

After a little while he called down to you.

"Christopher Robin!" he said in a loud whisper.

"Hallo!"

"I think the bees *suspect* something!"

"What sort of thing?"

"I don't know. But something tells me that they're *suspicious!*"

"Perhaps they think that you're after their honey."

"It may be that. You never can tell with bees."

There was another little silence, and then he called down to you again.

"Christopher Robin!"

"Yes?"

"Have you an umbrella in your house?"

"I think so."

"I wish you would bring it out here, and walk up and down with it, and look up at me every now and then, and say 'Tut-tut, it looks like rain.' I think, if you did that, it would help the deception which we are practising on these bees."

Well, you laughed to yourself, "Silly old Bear!" but you didn't say it aloud because you were so fond of him, and you went home for your umbrella.

"Oh, there you are!" called down Winnie-the-Pooh, as soon as you got back to the tree. "I was beginning to get anxious. I have discovered that the bees are now definitely Suspicious."

"Shall I put my umbrella up?" you said.

"Yes, but wait a moment. We must be practical. The important bee to deceive is the Queen Bee. Can you see which is the Queen Bee from down there?"

"No."

"A pity. Well, now, if you walk up and down with your umbrella, saying, 'Tut-tut, it looks like rain,' I shall do what I can by singing a little Cloud Song, such as a cloud might sing. . . . Go!"

So, while you walked up and down and wondered if it would rain, Winnie-the-Pooh sang this song:

How sweet to be a Cloud
    Floating in the Blue!
Every little cloud
Always sing aloud.

"How sweet to be a Cloud
    Floating in the Blue!"
It makes him very proud
To be a little cloud.

The bees were still buzzing as suspiciously as ever. Some of them, indeed, left their nest and flew all round the cloud as it began the second verse of this song, and one bee sat down on the nose of the cloud for a moment, and then got up again.

"Christopher—*ow!*—Robin," called out the cloud.

"Yes?"

"I have just been thinking, and I have come to a very important decision. *These are the wrong sort of bees.*"

"Are they?"

"Quite the wrong sort. So I should think they would make the wrong sort of honey, shouldn't you?"

"Would they?"

"Yes. So I think I shall come down."

"How?" asked you.

Winnie-the-Pooh hadn't thought about this. If he let go of the string, he would fall—*bump*—and he didn't like the idea of that. So he thought for a long time, and then he said:

"Christopher Robin, you must shoot the balloon with your gun. Have you got your gun?"

"Of course I have," you said. "But if I do that, it will spoil the balloon," you said.

"But if you *don't*," said Pooh, "I shall have to let go, and that would spoil *me.*"

When he put it like this, you saw how it was, and you aimed very carefully at the balloon, and fired.

"*Ow!*" said Pooh.

"Did I miss?" you asked.

"You didn't exactly *miss*," said Pooh, "but you missed the *balloon.*"

"I'm so sorry," you said, and you fired again, and this time you hit the balloon, and the air came slowly out, and Winnie-the-Pooh floated down to the ground.

But his arms were so stiff from holding on to the string of the balloon all that time that they stayed up straight in the air for more than a week, and whenever a fly came and settled on his nose he had to blow it off. And I think—but I am not sure—that *that* is why he was always called Pooh.

POOH GOES VISITING AND GETS INTO A TIGHT PLACE

A. A. Milne

Edward Bear, known to his friends as Winnie-the-Pooh, or Pooh for short, was walking through the forest one day, humming proudly to himself. He had made up a little hum that very morning, as he was doing his Stoutness Exercises in front of the glass: *Tra-la-la, tra-la-la,* as he stretched up as high as he could go, and then *Tra-la-la, tra-la —oh, help!—la,* as he tried to reach his toes. After breakfast he had said it over and over to himself until he had learnt it off by heart, and now he was humming it right through, properly. It went like this:

> *Tra-la-la, tra-la-la,*
> *Tra-la-la, tra-la-la,*
> *Rum-tum-tiddle-um-tum.*
> *Tiddle-iddle, tiddle-iddle,*
> *Tiddle-iddle, tiddle-iddle,*
> *Rum-tum-tum-tiddle-um.*

Well, he was humming this hum to himself, and walking along gaily, wondering what everybody else was doing, and what it felt like, being somebody else, when suddenly he came to a sandy bank, and in the bank was a large hole.

"Aha!" said Pooh. (*Rum-tum-tiddle-um-tum.*)

"If I know anything about anything, that hole means Rabbit," he said, "and Rabbit means Company," he said, "and Company means Food and Listening-to-Me-Humming and such like. *Rum-tum-tum-tiddle-um.*"

So he bent down, put his head into the hole, and called out:

"Is anybody at home?"

There was a sudden scuffling noise from inside the hole, and then silence.

"What I said was, 'Is anybody at home?'" called out Pooh very loudly.

"No!" said a voice; and then added, "You needn't shout so loud. I heard you quite well the first time."

"Bother!" said Pooh. "Isn't there anybody here at all?"

"Nobody."

Winnie-the-Pooh took his head out of the hole, and thought for a little, and he thought to himself, "There must be somebody there, because somebody must have *said* 'Nobody.'" So he put his head back in the hole, and said:

"Hallo, Rabbit, isn't that you?"

"No," said Rabbit, in a different sort of voice this time.

"But isn't that Rabbit's voice?"

"I don't *think* so," said Rabbit. "It isn't *meant* to be."

"Oh!" said Pooh.

He took his head out of the hole, and had another think, and then he put it back, and said:

"Well, could you very kindly tell me where Rabbit is?"

"He has gone to see his friend Pooh Bear, who is a great friend of his."

"But this *is* Me!" said Bear, very much surprised.

"What sort of Me?"

"Pooh Bear."

"Are you sure?" said Rabbit, still more surprised.

"Quite, quite sure," said Pooh.

"Oh, well, then, come in."

So Pooh pushed and pushed and pushed his way through the hole, and at last he got in.

"You were quite right," said Rabbit, looking at him all over. "It *is* you. Glad to see you."

"Who did you think it was?"

"Well, I wasn't sure. You know how it is in

the Forest. One can't have *anybody* coming into one's house. One has to be *careful*. What about a mouthful of something?"

Pooh always liked a little something at eleven o'clock in the morning, and he was very glad to see Rabbit getting out the plates and mugs; and when Rabbit said, "Honey or condensed milk with your bread?" he was so excited that he said, "Both," and then, so as not to seem greedy, he added, "But don't bother about the bread, please." And for a long time after that he said nothing . . . until at last, humming to himself in a rather sticky voice, he got up, shook Rabbit lovingly by the paw, and said that he must be going on.

"Must you?" said Rabbit politely.

"Well," said Pooh, "I could stay a little longer if it—if you—" and he tried very hard to look in the direction of the larder.

"As a matter of fact," said Rabbit, "I was going out myself directly."

"Oh, well, then, I'll be going on. Good-bye."

"Well, good-bye, if you're sure you won't have any more."

"*Is* there any more?" asked Pooh quickly.

Rabbit took the covers off the dishes, and said, "No, there wasn't."

"I thought not," said Pooh, nodding to himself. "Well, good-bye. I must be going on."

So he started to climb out of the hole. He pulled with his front paws, and pushed with his back paws, and in a little while his nose was out in the open again . . . and then his ears . . . and then his front paws . . . and then his shoulders . . . and then——

"Oh, help!" said Pooh. "I'd better go back."

"Oh, bother!" said Pooh. "I shall have to go on."

"I can't do either!" said Pooh. "Oh, help *and* bother!"

Now by this time Rabbit wanted to go for a walk too, and finding the front door full, he went out by the back door, and came round to Pooh, and looked at him.

"Hallo, are you stuck?" he asked.

"N-no," said Pooh carelessly. "Just resting and thinking and humming to myself."

"Here, give us a paw."

Pooh Bear stretched out a paw, and Rabbit pulled and pulled and pulled. . . .

"*Ow!*" cried Pooh. "You're hurting!"

"The fact is," said Rabbit, "you're stuck."

"It all comes," said Pooh crossly, "of not having front doors big enough."

"It all comes," said Rabbit sternly, "of eating too much. I thought at the time," said Rabbit, "only I don't like to say anything," said Rabbit, "that one of us was eating too much," said Rabbit, "and I knew it wasn't *me*," he said. "Well, well, I shall go and fetch Christopher Robin."

Christopher Robin lived at the other end of the Forest, and when he came back with Rabbit, and saw the front half of Pooh, he said, "Silly old Bear," in such a loving voice that everybody felt quite hopeful again.

"I was just beginning to think," said Bear, sniffing slightly, "that Rabbit might never be able to use his front door again. And I should *hate* that," he said.

"So should I," said Rabbit.

"Use his front door again?" said Christopher Robin. "Of course he'll use his front door again."

"Good," said Rabbit.

"If we can't pull you out, Pooh, we might push you back."

Rabbit scratched his whiskers thoughtfully, and pointed out that, when once Pooh was pushed back, he was back, and of course nobody was more glad to see Pooh than *he* was, still there it was, some lived in trees and some lived underground, and——

"You mean I'd *never* get out?" said Pooh.

"I mean," said Rabbit, "that having got *so* far, it seems a pity to waste it."

Christopher Robin nodded.

"Then there's only one thing to be done," he said.

"We shall have to wait for you to get thin again."

"How long does getting thin take?" asked Pooh anxiously.

"About a week, I should think."

"But I can't stay here for a *week!*"

"You can *stay* here all right, silly old Bear. It's getting you out which is so difficult."

"We'll read to you," said Rabbit cheerfully. "And I hope it won't snow," he added. "And I say, old fellow, you're taking up a good deal of room in my house—*do* you mind if I use your back legs as a towel-horse? Because, I mean, there they are—doing nothing—and it would be very convenient just to hang the towels on them."

"A week!" said Pooh gloomily. *"What about meals?"*

"I'm afraid no meals," said Christopher Robin, "because of getting thin quicker. But we *will* read to you."

Bear began to sigh, and then found he couldn't because he was so tightly stuck; and a tear rolled down his eye, as he said:

"Then would you read a Sustaining Book, such as would help and comfort a Wedged Bear in Great Tightness?"

So for a week Christopher Robin read that sort of book at the North end of Pooh, and Rabbit hung his washing on the South end . . . and in between Bear felt himself getting slenderer and slenderer. And at the end of the week Christopher Robin said, *"Now!"*

So he took hold of Pooh's front paws and Rabbit took hold of Christopher Robin, and all Rabbit's friends and relations took hold of Rabbit, and they all pulled together. . . .

And for a long time Pooh only said *"Ow!"* . . . And *"Oh!"* . . .

And then, all of a sudden, he said *"Pop!"* just as if a cork were coming out of a bottle.

And Christopher Robin and Rabbit and all Rabbit's friends and relations went head-over-heels backwards . . . and on the top of them came Winnie-the-Pooh—free!

So, with a nod of thanks to his friends, he went on with his walk through the forest, humming proudly to himself. But, Christopher Robin looked after him lovingly, and said to himself, "Silly old Bear!"

THE MAGIC BED-KNOB

Mary Norton

Only Paul knows that Miss Price is studying to become a witch, but when Carey and Charles hear about it, they persuade Miss Price to give them a little magic too.

Afterwards, on the way home, Carey and Charles tackled Paul.

"Paul, why didn't you tell us you'd seen Miss Price on a broomstick?"

"I dunno."

"But, Paul, you ought to have told us. We'd have liked to see it, too. It was very mean of you, Paul."

Paul did not reply.

"When did you see her?"

"In the night."

Paul looked stubborn. He felt as if he might be going to cry. Miss Price always passed so quickly. She would have been gone before he could call anyone (and they would have said at once, "Don't be silly, Paul"). Besides, it had been his secret, his nightly joy. His bed was beside the window and, when the moon was full, it shone on his pillow and wakened him. It had been exciting to lie there, with his eyes fixed on the pale sky beyond the ragged blackness of the cedar boughs. Some nights, he did not wake up. Other nights, he woke up and she did not come. But he saw her often enough and, each time he saw her, she had learned to fly a little better. At first she had wobbled so, balanced sideways on the stick, that he wondered why she did not ride astride. She would grip the broomstick with one hand and try to hold her hat on with the other, and her feet, in their long shoes, looked so odd against the moonlit sky. Once she fell—and the broomstick came down quite slowly, like an umbrella blown inside out, with Miss Price clinging to the handle. Paul had watched her anxiously until she reached the ground. That time, she did not hurt herself.

Partly, he did not tell because he wanted to be proud of Miss Price. He did not want the others to see her until she was really good at it; until, perhaps, she could do tricks on a broomstick and look confident instead of scared. Once, when she had lifted both hands in the air at the same time, Paul nearly clapped. He knew that was hard to do even on a bicycle. He had another worry, too; that the Home Guard might get her. They were out all night patrolling the hills, on the watch for German parachutists. . . .

"You see, Paul," Carey was saying, "it was really very selfish; now Miss Price has hurt her ankle, she won't be flying again for ages. Charles

"The Magic Bed-Knob," Chapter II. From *The Magic Bed-Knob* by Mary Norton. Copyright 1943 by The Hyperion Press, New York, and used with their permission

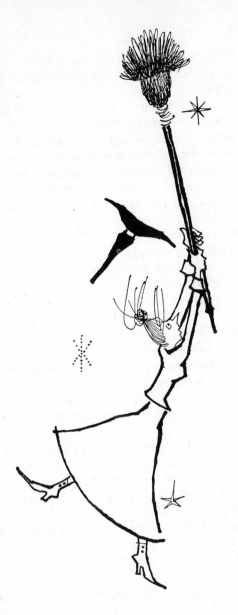

Paul seemed about to burst into speech but was silenced by a kick from Charles; aggrievedly, he swallowed his last mouthful of rice pudding.

"Yes, Aunt Beatrice, we do know where she lives."

It was about four o'clock in the afternoon when the children knocked at Miss Price's neat front door. The path on which they stood was gaily bordered with flowers and, through the half-open windows of the sitting-room, Miss Price's dimity curtains fluttered in the breeze. The door was opened by Agnes, a village girl who served Miss Price for a few hours daily.

As the children entered the little sitting-room for a moment they felt very shy. There lay Miss Price on the sofa, her bandaged foot raised up on pillows. She still looked pale but now her hair was tidy and her white blouse spotlessly neat.

"What lovely peaches! Thank you, my dears, and thank your aunt. Very kind of her, I'm sure. Sit down, sit down."

The children sat down gingerly on the little spindly chairs.

"Agnes is making us some tea. You must stay and keep me company. Carey, can you open that card table?"

The children bustled round and helped to set the room for tea. A little table near Miss Price for the tea-tray and a white cloth on the card table for the scones, the bread and margarine, the quince jelly, and the utility cake.

They enjoyed their tea and, when it was over, they helped Agnes to clear away. Then Miss Price showed Charles and Carey how to play backgammon and loaned Paul a large book full of pictures called "Paradise Lost." Paul liked the book very much. He liked the musty smell of it and the gilt-edged pages.

When they had finished the game of backgammon and it seemed that it must be nearly time to go home, Carey picked up her courage in both hands.

"Miss Price," she said hesitatingly, "If it isn't rude to ask—are you a witch?"

There was silence for a moment and Carey could feel her heart beating. Paul looked up from his book.

Very carefully, Miss Price closed the backgammon board and laid it on the little table

and I may never have the chance of seeing her!"

Later, as they were solemnly eating lunch in the high, dark dining-room, Aunt Beatrice startled them by saying suddenly: "Poor Miss Price!" They all looked up, as if she had read their secret thoughts and were relieved when she went on calmly, "It seems she has fallen off her bicycle and sprained her ankle. So painful, poor soul. I must send her down some peaches."

Paul sat with his spoon halfway to his mouth and his eyes moved round from Charles to Carey.

Carey cleared her throat, "Aunt Beatrice," she said, "could we take the peaches to Miss Price?"

"That's very thoughtful of you, Carey. I don't see why not, if you know where she lives."

beside the sofa. She took up her knitting and unfolded it.

"Well," she said slowly, "I am and I'm not."

Paul sat back on his heels. "You mean, you are sort of," he suggested.

Miss Price threw him a glance. "I mean, Paul," she said quietly, "that I am studying to be a witch." She knitted a few stitches, pursing up her mouth.

"Oh, Miss Price," cried Carey warmly. "How terribly clever of you!"

It was the best thing she could have said. Miss Price flushed but she looked pleased.

"How did you first think of it, Miss Price?"

"Well, ever since I was a girl, I've had a bit of a gift for witchcraft, but somehow—what with piano lessons and looking after my mother—I never seemed to have the time to take it up seriously."

Paul was staring at Miss Price, as if to drink in every detail of her appearance. "I don't think you're a wicked witch," he said at last.

Miss Price dropped her eyes unhappily. "I know, Paul," she admitted in a low voice. "You're quite right. I started too late in life. That's the whole trouble."

"Is being wicked the hardest part?" asked Carey.

"It is for me," Miss Price told her rather sadly. "But there are people who have a natural gift for it."

"Paul has," said Charles.

Paul came nearer and sat down on a chair. He was still staring at Miss Price, as if he longed to ask her something. After a minute, he found courage. "Could you just do a little bit of magic for us now?"

"Oh, Paul!" exclaimed Carey. "Don't worry Miss Price. She can't do magic with a sprained ankle."

"Yes, she could," protested Paul hotly. "She could do it lying down, couldn't you, Miss Price?"

"Well," said Miss Price, "I am a little tired, Paul. But I'll just do a little quick one and then you must all go home. There you are!"

Carey and Charles looked around quickly, following the direction of Miss Price's eyes. Paul's chair was empty. Paul had gone—but where he had been sitting perched a little yellow frog.

Before Carey and Charles had time to exclaim, Paul was back again, still staring expectantly at Miss Price.

"Oh," cried Carey, with a gasp, "That was wonderful, wonderful! How *did* you do it?"

She felt breathless and almost afraid. Magic—a spell—she had seen it with her own eyes.

"I didn't see anything," complained Paul.

Carey looked at him impatiently. "Oh, don't be silly, Paul. You turned into a frog. You must have felt it."

Paul's lips trembled, "I didn't feel anything," he said, in a squeaky little voice. But nobody heard him. Carey was staring at Miss Price with shining eyes."

"Miss Price," she pointed out almost reproachfully, "you could have done that at the Church concert, instead of singing."

Miss Price laid down her knitting. A strange look crept into her face, and she looked hard at Carey as if she were seeing her for the first time. Nervously, Carey drew back in her chair.

"Although you sing so nicely," she added hastily.

But Miss Price did not seem to hear. There was a wild light in her eyes and her lips moved quietly, as if she were reciting. "There must be some way," she was saying slowly. "There-must-be-some-way . . ."

"Some way of what?" asked Charles, after a moment's uncomfortable silence.

Miss Price smiled, showing her long yellow teeth.

"Of keeping your mouths shut," she rapped out.

Carey was shocked. This was far from lady-like. "Oh, Miss Price!" she exclaimed unhappily.

"Of keeping your mouths shut," repeated Miss Price slowly, smiling more unpleasantly than ever.

Paul made a little wriggling movement in his chair. "Now she's getting wicked," he whispered to Carey in a pleased voice.

Carey drew away from him as if she had not heard. She looked worried. "What do you mean, Miss Price? You mean we musn't tell anyone that—" she hesitated.

"That you're a witch?" put in Paul.

But Miss Price was still staring, as if she neither heard nor saw. "In just a minute I'll think of something," she said, as if to herself. "In just a minute—."

Then Carey did something which Charles thought very brave. She got up from her chair and sat down beside Miss Price, on the sofa.

"Listen, Miss Price," she said. "We did try to help you when you hurt your ankle. There isn't any need to use any kind of nasty magic on us. If you want to stop us telling, you could do it in a nice kind of way."

Miss Price looked at her. "How could I do it in a nice kind of way?" she asked, but she sounded more reasonable.

"Well," said Carey, "you could give us something—something magic—and if we told anyone about you, we'd have to forfeit it. You know, like a game. Directly we told, the thing would stop being magic."

"What sort of a thing?" asked Miss Price, but as if the idea held possibilities.

Charles leaned forward. "Yes," he put in, "a ring or something, that we could twist and a slave comes. And, if we told about you, the slave wouldn't come any more. Couldn't you do that?"

Miss Price looked thoughtful. "I couldn't manage a slave," she said after a moment.

"Well, something like that."

Miss Price sat very quiet. She was thinking hard. "I know," she said, after a while. Suddenly, she seemed quite nice and cheerful again. "There's something I've been wanting to try out. Mind you, I'm not sure that it will work. Has anybody got a ring on them?"

Alas, none of them had. Paul felt in his pockets, just in case, but found nothing but the brass knob he had unscrewed from his bed that morning.

"Well, anything. A bracelet would do. It should be something you can twist."

But unfortunately Carey could not produce a bracelet either. "I have one at home," she said, "but I only wear it on Sundays."

"You can twist this," cried Paul suddenly, holding out the bed-knob. "That's just what it does. It twists and it twists and it twists. I twisted it off," he added rather unnecessarily.

Miss Price took the bed-knob and held it thoughtfully between her clean, bony fingers.

"Let me see . . ." she said slowly. Then suddenly she looked up, as if surprised. "Paul I believe this is the best thing you could have given me." (Paul squirmed, pleased but bashful.) "Now, I could do a wonderful spell with this— but I must think it out very carefully. Now, be quiet, children, and let me think—so that I can get this right." Her fingers closed gently round the shining brass. "This should be very good indeed. Now, quiet please!"

The children sat like statues. Even Paul forgot to fidget. A bumblebee came in through the window and buzzed heavily about the room. Except for this, the silence was complete.

After what seemed a long while, Miss Price opened her eyes. And then she sat up, blinking and smiling. "There you are, Paul," she said brightly and handed him back the bed-knob.

He took it reverently. "Is it done?" he asked, in an awe-stricken voice. It looked just the same to him.

"Yes, it's quite done," Miss Price told him. "And it's a very good spell indeed. This is something you'll enjoy. Only don't get yourselves into trouble."

Carey and Charles were looking enviously at Paul.

"What must we do with it?" asked Charles.

"Just take it home and screw it back on the bed. But don't screw it right up. Screw it about half way."

"And then?"

"And then?" Miss Price smiled. "Twist it a little and wish—and the bed will take you to wherever you want to go!"

The children gazed unbelievingly at the gleaming ball in Paul's rather grubby fingers.

"Really?" asked Carey, with a little gasp.

Miss Price was still smiling. She seemed very pleased with herself.

"Well, try it."

"Oh, Miss Price," breathed Carey, still gazing at the knob. "THANK YOU."

"Don't thank me," said Miss Price, taking up her knitting again, "Remember the conditions. One word about me and the spell is broken."

"Oh, Miss Price!" said Carey again. She was quite overcome.

"Well, now off you go. It's getting late. As I say, don't get yourselves into trouble and don't go gallivanting around all night. There's moderation in all things—even in Magic."

SHAWNEEN AND THE GANDER

Richard Bennett

Before you read this story to children, tell them that the leprechaun is an Irish fairy, a fairy shoemaker, in fact. If you can catch one and never take your eye off him, you can make him give you his pot of gold, which he is always guarding. Shawneen knew this, of course, but wait till you hear what happened when he caught a leprechaun.

On the top of a high green hill in Ireland there once lived a little boy and his name was Shawneen.

One bright warm day while his mother was washing out the clothes she said, "The fire is out and there isn't a match in the house. Run down to Mrs. Murphy's shop like a good lad and buy a box. Here is a penny."

Indeed there was no need for a second word about that. Shawneen was always ready to go on errands to Mrs. Murphy's.

"I will to be sure," said he, putting his cap on his head and the penny in his pocket.

Now at the foot of the hill there was a little village with a row of houses and shops up one side of the street and down the other.

Mrs. Murphy's was the prize of the lot. She sold everything.

If you wanted to buy a dress or if you wanted to buy a ham Mrs. Murphy would be sure to have it.

When Shawneen arrived at her shop he was out of breath. He had been running down the hill and it was a good way round when you came by the road.

Before opening the door he stopped for a minute to look in the window.

The first shelf had the usual array of cups and saucers and the second shelf had nothing on it to talk about, but on the third shelf right near the glass Shawneen saw the most beautiful bugle he had ever seen in all his life.

It glistened so brightly in the sun that Shawneen could scarcely look at it.

It was all the color of gold and so shiny he could see himself seven times in it.

When Paddy the postman walked by the window to deliver the letters seven Paddys walked by in the bugle. It was that bright. Oh, I can tell you it was lovely.

Around the middle was tied a blue-and-yellow cord with a silky tassel on each end as big as your hand.

Shawneen went into the shop.

"A box of matches if you please, ma'am," said he to Mrs. Murphy; "and if it wouldn't be asking too much may I have a toot on the bugle?"

"A toot is it?" said Mrs. Murphy. "Indeed you may, my lad, two if you like. There is no harm in a good toot."

So Mrs. Murphy took the bugle out of the window and gave it to Shawneen. The end was cold and smooth and shaped so nicely that it fit snugly over his mouth.

"Now don't be afraid of it, my lad," said Mrs. Murphy. "Give us a good blow."

Shawneen blew very gently at first, then a little louder, and then so loud you could hear it down the street and over the hill and down by the sea.

Shawneen had never heard anything so fine in all his life.

"Ah, it's grand entirely," said he, stroking the tassels. "How much is it?"

"Ah, that's a very fine bugle," said Mrs. Murphy, "I couldn't let you have it for less than ten shillings and sixpence."

Shawneen blew on the bugle again but not so loud this time, then put it back on the counter.

Ten shillings and sixpence was a lot of money. Indeed a pair of shoes would cost as much as that.

Shawneen gave Mrs. Murphy the penny and put the box of matches in his coat pocket.

He walked slowly out the door and down the street.

He was thinking very hard to himself. How could he get ten shillings and sixpence to buy the bugle in Mrs. Murphy's shop window?

There was no money at home to be spent for bugles. Indeed he was well sure of that. Didn't his mother need a new shawl and the donkey a new harness and the window a new pane of glass? Wasn't his mother's teapot badly cracked and she often saying she wished she had the price of a new one? Weren't the soles of his own shoes so thin he decided to take a short cut across the fields as the gravel on the road hurt his feet?

"No, indeed," said Shawneen to himself, "It will be no use asking for ten shillings and sixpence to buy a bugle."

He jumped over the ditch and began to climb the hedge.

The heather and moss at the top felt nice and soft so he sat down for a bit to think the matter over.

He was no sooner nicely settled when all of a sudden he saw a strange little man dressed all in green asleep under a furze bush only a few feet away. He was no more than a foot long and his suit was so much the color of the grass about him that indeed Shawneen had to look sharp to make him out at all.

"It's a Leprechaun surely," whispered Shawneen to himself, "and the very lad who can tell me how I can get ten shillings and sixpence to buy the bugle."

Before you could say two two's Shawneen had the little fellow about the waist.

Now you may be sure it isn't every day you see a Leprechaun and when you do you have to keep your eyes on him or it's off he is in no time at all.

Shawneen lifted the little maneen out from under the bush. The Leprechaun awoke with a great start and let such a yell out of him you wouldn't think he was equal to it. It was that loud.

"Ah, let me down now like a good lad," said the little fellow, kicking this way and that. "This is no way to be treating a gentleman."

"I will, faith," said Shawneen, "but first you must tell me how I can get ten shillings and sixpence to buy the bugle in Mrs. Murphy's shop window."

"Ah, that's easy enough," said the Leprechaun, "but you are hurting me now. Take your thumb off my stomach like a good lad."

Shawneen lifted his thumb a bit and then the Leprechaun began to stretch his arms and stretch his legs and rub his eyes at a great rate.

"This warm weather makes one very sleepy," said he.

"Never mind that now," said Shawneen; "how can I get ten shillings and sixpence to buy the bugle?"

"Ah, you are a very determined lad," said the Leprechaun. "Why, earn it, of course. You can't expect to get something for nothing."

"I know that well enough," said Shawneen, "but how can I earn all that money?"

The Leprechaun put one of his long bony fingers to the side of his nose and leaning forward whispered very mysteriously, "Not a word to a soul now," said he, "hatch the egg and sell the gander."

"What egg?" said Shawneen, squeezing the little fellow tighter than ever.

The Leprechaun didn't say another word but pointed to the earth.

Before Shawneen stopped to think he glanced down and there by the side of the ditch was the biggest goose egg he had ever seen in all his life.

I needn't tell you the Leprechaun was gone in a flash.

"Well, the egg is real enough, faith," said Shawneen, picking it up and putting it in his cap to keep it from breaking.

"An egg the size of this should make a big gander and a big gander should bring a good price at the Fair. I should have enough money in all to buy my mother a new shawl and a new dress and a silver teapot and have still enough left over to buy a bugle."

He was so excited he could hardly wait to get home.

The sooner the hatching began the better.

Over the fields he went, leaping the ditches and climbing the hedges. That the egg wasn't broken was nothing less than a miracle.

When he reached home his mother was hanging out the clothes.

"What have you there, my lad?" said she.

"A goose egg," said Shawneen.

"A goose egg, is it?" said his mother. "I have seen big eggs in my day but nothing the likes of that. Where did you find it?"

Now Shawneen remembered what the Leprechaun had said about keeping quiet.

"I was coming across the field," said he, "and there it was all by itself in the shelter of the ditch."

"And what will you do with an egg like that?" said his mother.

"Hatch it," said Shawneen. "Is there a hen setting?"

"There is, to be sure," said his mother. "Bring it into the shed."

She opened the hen-house door and pointed to a big brown hen nesting in one corner.

"I am afraid she will find it a bit uncomfortable," said Shawneen, pushing the hen aside a bit.

"Oh, in a few days she will be so used to it she will never know it was there at all," said his mother.

Now goodness knows the egg did make the poor hen sit a bit crooked to be sure. But she was a quiet, obliging bird and went on sitting as if nothing had happened.

There she sat with one side up and one side down for days and days, a very mountain of patience.

Every morning Shawneen took a little peek under her wing to make sure all was going well and every now and then he went to have a look at the bugle in Mrs. Murphy's shop window. The bugle seemed to grow more beautiful every day and when Mrs. Murphy let him have a little toot on it now and then it sounded richer and sweeter as the days went by.

Well, the time passed as time will and soon the eggs were hatched—twelve yellow chicks and one yellow gosling. The chicks were fluffy and pretty as you may expect, but the gosling was a sight.

I don't think you could have found an uglier bird in the length and breadth of all Ireland.

His pin feathers stuck out of him like the bristles of an old pig and his feet were so big and red and awkward he was forever stepping on his own toes.

His head was as big as a gosling twice his size and his poor little neck so thin and scrawny that it looked for all the world like a cabbage on the end of a broomstick.

"Ah, he is beautiful," said Shawneen to his mother; "may I raise him myself?"

"Indeed you may," said she. "I am sure I will have nothing to do with him. I have raised ducks and geese in my day but I have never seen anything come out of an egg the likes of that. Goodness knows what kind of a gander he will make. He has altogether too knowing a look in his eye to my notion. Faith, he looks at you as if he knew what you are thinking. Take my word the sooner

you fatten him up and send him off to the Fair the better."

Shawneen thought this was a good idea. The sooner he had the money in his pocket the sooner he could buy his bugle.

So every day he fed his gander the best of this and the best of that. Shawneen thought nothing was too good for him. In no time at all the gander was as big as the hens and as big as the turkeys and soon as big as the geese themselves.

Indeed he grew so fast he became the talk of all the neighbors for lands around.

"That's no common gander," everyone began to say. "He comes from no common stock, I can tell you. Look at the way he carries himself! You would think he owned the world and all!"

Now all this talk and all this attention made the gander very proud. Oh, you have no idea. In fact, he was so carried away with himself that he would have nothing to do with the other birds of the barnyard. With the air of a king he walked before them.

The ducks thought he was very funny and laughed at him.

The hens had never seen his like before and were a bit afraid of him.

But the geese were so put about with his fine airs they couldn't stand the sight of him.

Now with the animals it was a different story.

"Oh, he is only a gander," said they, and went on about their business. They wouldn't even look in his direction.

This didn't please the gander, you may be sure of that. Since they gave him no attention he took great delight in teasing them every chance he could get.

Pulling the pigs' tails while they were eating their supper was one of his favorite tricks.

"Faith, I will wring his neck if he goes on with any more of that," said Shawneen's father.

"Maybe he doesn't like curly tails," said Shawneen; "he was just trying to straighten them out a bit."

"Straighten them out, indeed," said his father. "I'll straighten him out in short order if he goes on with any more of that nonsense."

One day the gander made faces at the donkey and the poor little fellow was so frightened he backed the cart wheel over a boulder and upset two churns of milk and two fine baskets of eggs.

Another day he chased the goats over the young cabbages and the one little patch of potatoes. You can imagine the state of the garden.

One day Shawneen's mother decided to clean out the house. She washed the windows and swept the floor and polished the pots and pans. When everything was nice and neat she went out to get a pail of water.

Meanwhile it started to rain. Over the half door flew the gander as easy as you please and made himself at home in front of the fireplace. He shook the rain off his feathers and flapped his wings, blowing the ashes and cinders all over the house.

"Oh, glory," said Shawneen's mother when she opened the door, "that bird will drive us out of house and home. I think the safest place for him is in the pot."

"Oh, no," said Shawneen, "he was just trying to be helpful and blow up the fire a bit. He is a very thoughtful gander."

"Thoughtful, indeed," said his mother. "It's a nice job he has given me with his thoughtfulness. Another trick like that and into the pot he goes."

I needn't tell you Shawneen was beginning to get worried when he heard this. The gander was acting very strange, to be sure. He would never get to the Fair at the rate he was going. But never a fear had the gander.

He made friends with all the hungry crows of the neighborhood and one evening invited them all in for supper. They ate up the grain in no time at all and the poor hens had to go to bed hungry. Oh, he was a holy terror.

There was no holding him.

Another day Shawneen's mother made some bread. She mixed the dough in a large pan and put it on the table near the fire while she hung out the clothes.

It was a warm afternoon and the gander was feeling a bit drowsy. He jumped over the half door again as familiar as you please and settled himself for a nice comfortable nap in the very middle of the pan.

"Oh, glory," said Shawneen's mother when she opened the door. "This is too much. Tomorrow is Fair day. That gander goes with your father. Whatever price he will bring he will have to go. We can't put up with him a minute longer. There is something very strange about that bird.

Heaven knows what he may do to us all if he takes the notion."

"Sh, sh, sh, sh," said the gander, jumping out of the pan and leaping over the half door. He stood outside for a minute with his ear to the crack and heard the whole story. He knew very well that when ganders or geese went to the Fair they never came back. Oh, he was no fool.

That night he never slept a wink. He stood on one foot and then on the other. When the cock began to crow his mind was made up. He would hide outside the garden wall until Shawneen's father was well out of sight.

Now as luck would have it, who should be sleeping outside the garden wall that very minute but Ned the Napper—the foxiest rogue in all Ireland. He was forever sneaking up and down the countryside stealing everything he could lay his hands on.

Over the wall came the gander and landed squarely on top of his head. Feathers went flying, I can tell you. Such kicking and biting you never saw. For a while in the dim light you couldn't tell which was Ned and which was the gander. But I am sorry to say foxy Ned soon had the upper hand. He tucked the gander safely in his bag, tossed it over his shoulder and made off east the road.

That morning when Shawneen's father had hitched the donkey to the cart and was ready to be off no gander could be found. They all looked high and they all looked low but no gander could they see. They looked behind this and they looked behind that, but not a feather of him was in sight.

"Well, gander or no gander," said Shawneen's father, "I can't wait any longer." So he slapped the lines over the donkey's back and set off to the Fair.

Shawneen watched the donkey cart rattling down the lane and through the gate. Soon it turned a bend of the road and was out of sight. He stood in the middle of the road wondering what to do next. He had waited so long for the egg to hatch and for the gander to grow a bit. Indeed it was a trial keeping him out of the pot with all his strange actions. Now when he was ready for the Fair he was nowhere to be found. Shawneen couldn't help but think of the bugle in Mrs. Murphy's shop window. It was likely to stay just where it was. Shining away for itself on the top shelf.

Shawneen ate his breakfast very slowly, thinking very hard to himself.

"Perhaps he has gone for a walk," said he to his mother.

"Very likely, indeed," said she. "Faith, he was liable to do most anything."

Shawneen decided to take a walk east the road. The gander might have gone in that direction.

Now Shawneen hadn't gone very far when he met two women gathering their washing off the hedges where it had been put out to dry.

"Did you see a big gander pass by here by any chance?" said Shawneen.

"A gander, is it?" said one of the women very crossly. "No, indeed, but I would like to get a glimpse of the rogue that made off with my husband's new Sunday shirt and my two fine linen aprons."

Shawneen went on a little further until he came to a little cottage. Outside the door was an old woman spinning.

"Did you see a big gander pass by here by any chance?" said Shawneen.

"A gander, is it?" said the old woman. "No, my child, but I would like to get a glimpse of my little teapot I put out to dry on the window-sill. A fine, shiny little teapot it was. The fairies must have had their eyes on it."

Shawneen went on his way. Around another bend of the road he met two men cutting turf.

"Did you see a big gander pass by here by any chance?" said Shawneen.

"A gander, is it?" said one of the men very crossly. "Indeed I didn't, but I would like to lay my hands on the rogue that made off with our coats and dinner pail when our backs were turned."

A little way further Shawneen came to a tinkers' van that was standing by the side of the road. Three of the tinkers were talking together in a very wild manner.

"Did you see a big gander pass by here by any chance?" asked Shawneen.

"A gander, is it?" said one of the tinkers very crossly. "No, I didn't, but I would like to lay my hands on the rogue that made off with our finest pots and pans."

Now a little way further Shawneen came to a crossroads where some young people were dancing on a large flat stone by the side of the ditch.

"Did you see a big gander pass by here by any chance?" cried Shawneen.

The young people were so busy laughing and dancing and the fiddler so busy playing and calling out the sets that no one paid any attention.

Shawneen said no more but walked slowly along the little road that ran up the side of a hill.

"A flock of ganders could pass by that crowd and I am sure they would be none the wiser," said Shawneen to himself. "It's too busy dancing they are."

Now he hadn't gone many steps when he met two guards.

"Did you see a big gander pass by here by any chance?" said Shawneen.

"A gander, is it?" said one of the guards. "No, my lad, but we would like to lay our hands on Ned the Napper. We heard he was around these parts."

Shawneen sat on a stone near by and wondered what to do next. His hopes of finding the gander seemed less than ever.

Now during all this time great clouds had been rolling across the sky and soon big raindrops began to fall.

"I'll be drenched surely," said Shawneen, looking about for a bit of shelter. An old ruined castle at the top of a near-by hill was the only thing in sight. He climbed over the hedge and ran up the hill. He walked quickly across the yard and through the castle door.

It was dark and gloomy among the old walls and the ivy rustled and whispered in the wind. In the far corner of the first room Shawneen found a spot that was fairly dry in spite of the wind and rain.

Now he was no sooner nicely settled when all of a sudden he heard a strange noise in the next room.

"Sh, sh, sh, sh," it went very softly.

"Sh, sh, sh, sh," it went again a little louder than before.

"Rain or no rain, I'll stay here no longer," said Shawneen, starting for the door.

"Sh, sh, sh, sh," came the noise again, a little louder this time.

Shawneen stopped a bit. He had heard that sound before.

He tiptoed gently to the door of the next room and peeked in. You can well imagine his surprise. There on the floor was a fierce-looking man fast asleep. By his side was a big bag—and what in the world should be sticking out of the side of it but the gander's head.

The man stirred in his sleep. He began to rub his nose. He was going to wake up, there was no doubt about that. Shawneen held his breath.

Just then the gander leaned over and said "Sh, sh," so softly in his ear the man went on sleeping as sound as ever.

Then the gander began to tear the sack very slowly with his strong bill.

As the hole became bigger and bigger Shawneen suddenly remembered what the guards had said about Ned the Napper. Beyond a doubt this was the very lad the guards were after.

Without a word Shawneen tiptoed across the room. He ran out the door and down the hill.

His feet splashed in all the pools and the rain blinded him so badly he could hardly see. As luck would have it the guards hadn't gone very far. Shawneen came running up puffing and blowing. He was so excited he could hardly speak.

"Up there, up there!" shouted Shawneen, pointing to the castle.

"What's up there, my lad?" said one of the guards.

"Ned the Napper, I think, sir," said Shawneen.

Without another word they all ran up the hill. Before you could say two two's the guards had the fierce-looking man safely between them.

With a few good bites the gander stepped out of the bag and gave himself a good shake. He was as cross as two sticks. And indeed it's well he may be. To be tossed into a bag like an old cabbage head would be hard on anyone's dignity.

"This is a lucky day for you, my lad," said one of the guards to Shawneen. "It will be well worth your while to come down to the barracks with us. This is Ned the Napper all right, all right. It's a long chase he has given us. We will leave his bag here and take care of that later. It will be quite safe in this deserted place."

So down the hill they went—foxy Ned with a guard on each arm and Shawneen and the gander out before.

A few minutes later Shawneen and one of the guards walked out of the barracks door. Shawneen was carrying a little leather sack in one hand. In it was enough money to buy teapots and shoes and dresses and shawls. And bugles!

"Well indeed, my lad," said the guard; "you well deserve this reward for telling us about Ned the Napper. Now that the rain is over let us go back to the castle and see what we can find in the bag."

So up the hill they went. When they reached the castle the guard turned the bag upside down.

Coats and shirts and pots and pans came tumbling out on the floor.

"Why, this must be the old lady's teapot," said Shawneen, "all wrapped up in the turfcutter's coat, and here are the women's aprons and the tinkers' pots and pans."

"Do you know who all these things belong to?" said the guard, scratching his head.

"Indeed I do," said Shawneen, rattling the money in the little sack. "It's scattered west the road they are—tinkers and turfcutters, old ones and young ones. Have a little patience now, your honor. I'll bring them all flying in short order."

Without another word he was down the hill and into Mrs. Murphy's shop. Before you could

say two two's he was out again and up the hill blowing the fine shiny bugle for all he was worth. Ah, indeed, it's fine and clear it sounded ringing out through all the countryside. Through all the lands around its like was never heard before. All who heard it came running up the hill. The tinkers, the women, the turfcutters, the dancers —even the old woman left her spinning wheel and came as far as she could to see what was making such a sweet sound. Soon they all arrived. Shawneen lined them up before the castle door. When each received his bit Shawneen blew a fine lively toot on the bugle. Then there was merry talk, you may be sure. A few minutes later they all went down the hill and west the road. The fiddler played and the young people sang and the gander strutted out before as if he owned the world and all.

"Oh, he is no common gander," everyone said. "It's easy to see that. There isn't a finer bird in the length and breadth of all Ireland."

THE ELEPHANT'S CHILD

Rudyard Kipling

The hilarious Just So Stories *are drolls but may also have been the beginning of science fiction. Probably only adults will fully appreciate Kipling's amusing parodies on processes of evolution, but children enjoy them as fantastic and funny stories. The example chosen for this book is the favorite with children, doubtless because many a child has yearned for the day when he could safely spank his relatives.*

In the high and Far-Off times the Elephant, O Best Beloved, had no trunk. He had only a blackish, bulgy nose, as big as a boot, that he could wriggle about from side to side; but he couldn't pick up things with it. But there was one Elephant—a new Elephant—an Elephant's Child— who was full of 'satiable curiosity, and that means he asked ever so many questions. *And* he lived in Africa, and he filled all Africa with his

'satiable curtiosities. He asked his tall aunt, the Ostrich, why her tail-feathers grew just so, and his tall aunt the Ostrich spanked him with her hard, hard claw. He asked his tall uncle, the Giraffe, what made his skin spotty, and his tall uncle, the Giraffe, spanked him with his hard, hard hoof. And still he was full of 'satiable curtiosity! He asked his broad aunt, the Hippopotamus, why her eyes were red, and his broad aunt, the Hippopotamus, spanked him with her broad, broad hoof; and he asked his hairy uncle, the Baboon, why melons tasted just so, and his hairy uncle, the Baboon, spanked him with his hairy, hairy paw. And *still* he was full of 'satiable curtiosity! He asked questions about everything that he saw, or heard, or felt, or smelt, or touched, and all his uncles and his aunts spanked him. And still he was full of 'satiable curtiosity!

One fine morning in the middle of the Precession of the Equinoxes this 'satiable Elephant's Child asked a new fine question that he had never asked before. He asked, "What does the Crocodile have for dinner?" Then everybody said, "Hush!" in a loud and dretful tone, and they spanked him immediately and directly, without stopping for a long time.

By and by, when that was finished, he came upon Kolokolo Bird sitting in the middle of a wait-a-bit thorn-bush, and he said, "My father has spanked me, and my mother has spanked me; all my aunts and uncles have spanked me for my 'satiable curtiosity; and *still* I want to know what the Crocodile has for dinner!"

Then Kolokolo Bird said, with a mournful cry, "Go to the banks of the great grey-green, greasy Limpopo River, all set about with fever-trees, and find out."

That very next morning, when there was nothing left of the Equinoxes, because the Precession had preceded according to precedent this 'satiable Elephant's Child took a hundred pounds of bananas (the little short red kind), and a hundred pounds of sugarcane (the long purple kind), and seventeen melons (the greeny-crackly kind), and said to all his dear families, "Good-bye. I am going to the great grey-green, greasy Limpopo River, all set about with fever-trees, to find out what the Crocodile has for dinner." And they all spanked him once more for luck, though he asked them most politely to stop.

Then he went away, a little warm, but not at all astonished, eating melons, and throwing the rind about, because he could not pick it up.

He went from Graham's Town to Kimberley, and from Kimberley to Khama's Country, and from Khama's Country he went east and north, eating melons all the time, till he at last came to the banks of the great grey-green, greasy Limpopo River, all set about with fever-trees, precisely as Kolokolo Bird had said.

Now you must know and understand, O Best Beloved, that till that very week, and day, and hour, and minute, this 'satiable Elephant's Child had never seen a Crocodile, and did not know what one was like. It was all his 'satiable curtiosity.

The first thing that he found was a Bi-Coloured-Python-Rock-Snake curled round a rock.

" 'Scuse me," said the Elephant's Child most politely, "but have you seen such a thing as a Crocodile in these promiscuous parts?"

"*Have* I seen a Crocodile?" said the Bi-Coloured-Python-Rock-Snake, in a voice of dretful scorn. "What will you ask me next?"

" 'Scuse me," said the Elephant's Child, "but could you kindly tell me what he has for dinner?"

Then the Bi-Coloured-Python-Rock-Snake uncoiled himself very quickly from the rock, and spanked the Elephant's Child with his scalesome, flailsome tail.

"That is odd," said the Elephant's Child, "because my father and my mother, and my uncle and my aunt, not to mention my other aunt, the Hippopotamus, and my other uncle, the Baboon, have all spanked me for my 'satiable curtiosity —and I suppose this is the same thing."

So he said good-bye very politely to the Bi-Coloured-Python-Rock-Snake, and helped to coil him up on the rock again, and went on, a little warm, but not at all astonished, eating melons, and throwing the rind about because he could not pick it up, till he trod on what he thought was a log of wood at the very edge of the great grey-green, greasy Limpopo River, all set about with fever-trees.

But it was really the Crocodile, O Best Beloved, and the Crocodile winked one eye—like this!

" 'Scuse me," said the Elephant's Child most politely, "but do you happen to have seen a Crocodile in these promiscuous parts?"

Then the Crocodile winked the other eye, and lifted half his tail out of the mud; and the Elephant's Child stepped back most politely, because he did not wish to be spanked again.

"Come hither, Little One," said the Crocodile. "Why do you ask such things?"

" 'Scuse me," said the Elephant's Child most politely, "but my father has spanked me, my mother has spanked me, not to mention my tall aunt, the Ostrich, and my tall uncle, the Giraffe, who can kick ever so hard, as well as my broad aunt, the Hippopotamus, and my hairy uncle, the Baboon, *and* including the Bi-Coloured-Python-Rock-Snake, with the scalesome, flailsome tail, just up the bank, who spanks harder than any of them; and *so,* if it's quite all the same to you, I don't want to be spanked any more."

"Come hither, Little One," said the Crocodile, "for I am the Crocodile," and he wept crocodile-tears to show it was quite true.

Then the Elephant's Child grew all breathless, and panted, and kneeled down on the bank and said, "You are the very person I have been looking for all these long days. Will you please tell me what you have for dinner?"

"Come hither, Little One," said the Crocodile, "and I'll whisper."

Then the Elephant's Child put his head down close to the Crocodile's musky, tusky mouth, and the Crocodile caught him by his little nose, which up to that very week, day, hour, and minute, had been no bigger than a boot, though much more useful.

"I think," said the Crocodile—and he said it between his teeth, like this—"I think today I will begin with Elephant's Child!"

At this, O Best Beloved, the Elephant's Child was much annoyed, and he said, speaking through his nose, like this, "Led go! You are hurtig be!"

Then the Bi-Coloured-Python-Rock-Snake scuffled down from the bank and said, "My young friend, if you do not now, immediately and instantly, pull as hard as ever you can, it is my opinion that your acquaintance in the large-pattern leather ulster" (and by this he meant the Crocodile) "will jerk you into yonder limpid stream before you can say Jack Robinson."

This is the way Bi-Coloured-Python-Rock-Snakes always talk.

Then the Elephant's Child sat back on his little haunches, and pulled, and pulled, and pulled, and his nose began to stretch. And the Crocodile floundered into the water, making it all creamy with great sweeps of his tail, and *he* pulled, and pulled, and pulled.

And the Elephant's Child's nose kept on stretching; and the Elephant's Child spread all his little four legs and pulled, and pulled, and

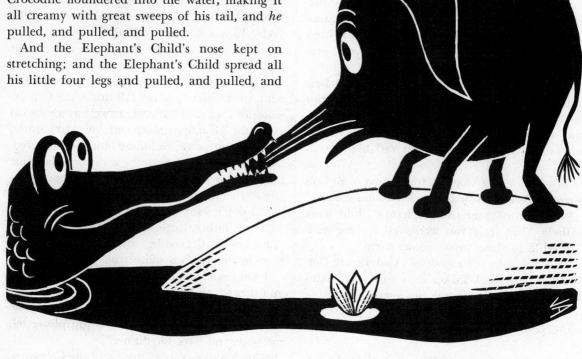

pulled, and his nose kept on stretching; and the Crocodile threshed his tail like an oar, and *he* pulled, and pulled, and pulled, and at each pull the Elephant's Child's nose grew longer and longer—and it hurt him hijjus!

Then the Elephant's Child felt his legs slipping, and he said through his nose, which was now nearly five feet long, "This is too butch for be!"

Then the Bi-Coloured-Python-Rock-Snake came down from the bank, and knotted himself in a double-clove-hitch round the Elephant's Child's hind legs, and said, "Rash and inexperienced traveller, we will now seriously devote ourselves to a little high tension, because if we do not, it is my impression that yonder self-propelling man-of-war with the armour-plated upper deck" (and by this, O Best Beloved, he meant the Crocodile), "will permanently vitiate your future career."

That is the way all Bi-Coloured-Python-Rock-Snakes always talk.

So he pulled, and the Elephant's Child pulled, and the Crocodile pulled; but the Elephant's Child and the Bi-Coloured-Python-Rock-Snake pulled hardest; and at last the Crocodile let go of the Elephant's Child's nose with a plop that you could hear all up and down the Limpopo.

Then the Elephant's Child sat down most hard and sudden; but first he was careful to say "Thank you" to the Bi-Coloured-Python-Rock-Snake; and next he was kind to his poor pulled nose, and wrapped it all up in cool banana leaves, and hung it in the great grey-green, greasy Limpopo to cool.

"What are you doing that for?" said the Bi-Coloured-Python-Rock-Snake.

" 'Scuse me," said the Elephant's Child, "but my nose is badly out of shape, and I am waiting for it to shrink."

"Then you will have to wait a long time," said the Bi-Coloured-Python-Rock-Snake. "Some people do not know what is good for them."

The Elephant's Child sat there for three days

waiting for his nose to shrink. But it never grew any shorter, and besides, it made him squint. For, O Best Beloved, you will see and understand that the Crocodile had pulled it out into a really truly trunk same as all Elephants have to-day.

At the end of the third day a fly came and stung him on the shoulder, and before he knew what he was doing he lifted up his trunk and hit that fly dead with the end of it.

" 'Vantage number one!" said the Bi-Coloured-Python-Rock-Snake. "You couldn't have done that with a mere-smear nose. Try and eat a little now."

Before he thought what he was doing the Elephant's Child put out his trunk and plucked a large bundle of grass, dusted it clean against his forelegs, and stuffed it into his own mouth.

" 'Vantage number two!" said the Bi-Coloured-Python-Rock-Snake. "You couldn't have done that with a mere-smear nose. Don't you think the sun is very hot here?"

"It is," said the Elephant's Child, and before he thought what he was doing he schlooped up a schloop of mud from the banks of the great grey-green, greasy Limpopo, and slapped it on his head, where it made a cool schloopy-sloshy mud-cap all trickly behind his ears.

" 'Vantage number three!" said the Bi-Coloured-Python-Rock-Snake. "You couldn't have done that with a mere-smear nose. Now how do you feel about being spanked again?"

" 'Scuse me," said the Elephant's Child, "but I should not like it at all."

"How would you like to spank somebody?" said the Bi-Coloured-Python-Rock-Snake.

"I should like it very much indeed," said the Elephant's Child.

"Well," said the Bi-Coloured-Python-Rock-Snake, "you will find that new nose of yours very useful to spank people with."

"Thank you," said the Elephant's Child, "I'll remember that; and now I think I'll go home to all my dear families and try."

So the Elephant's Child went home across Africa frisking and whisking his trunk. When he wanted fruit to eat he pulled fruit down from a tree, instead of waiting for it to fall as he used to do. When he wanted grass he plucked grass up from the ground, instead of going on his knees as he used to do. When the flies bit him he broke off the branch of a tree and used it as a fly-whisk; and he made himself a new, cool, slushy-squshy mud-cap whenever the sun was hot. When he felt lonely walking through Africa he sang to himself down his trunk, and the noise was louder than several brass bands. He went especially out of his way to find a broad Hippopotamus (she was no relation of his), and he spanked her very hard, to make sure that the Bi-Coloured-Python-Rock-Snake had spoken the truth about his new trunk. The rest of the time he picked up the melon rinds that he had dropped on his way to the Limpopo—for he was a Tidy Pachyderm.

One dark evening he came back to all his dear families, and he coiled up his trunk and said, "How do you do?" They were very glad to see him, and immediately said, "Come here and be spanked for your 'satiable curtiosity."

"Pooh," said the Elephant's Child. "I don't think you peoples know anything about spanking; but I do, and I'll show you."

Then he uncurled his trunk and knocked two of his dear brothers head over heels.

"O Bananas!" said they, "where did you learn that trick, and what have you done to your nose?"

"I got a new one from the Crocodile on the banks of the great grey-green, greasy Limpopo River," said the Elephant's Child. "I asked him what he had for dinner, and he gave me this to keep."

"It looks very ugly," said his hairy uncle, the Baboon.

"It does," said the Elephant's Child. "But it's very useful," and he picked up his hairy uncle, the Baboon, by one hairy leg, and hove him into a hornet's nest.

Then that bad Elephant's Child spanked all his dear families for a long time, till they were very warm and greatly astonished. He pulled out his tall Ostrich aunt's tail-feathers; and he caught his tall uncle, the Giraffe, by the hindleg, and dragged him through a thorn-bush, and he shouted at his broad aunt, the Hippopotamus, and blew bubbles into her ear when she was sleeping in the water after meals; but he never let any one touch Kolokolo Bird.

At last things grew so exciting that his dear families went off one by one in a hurry to the banks of the great grey-green, greasy Limpopo River, all set about with fever-trees, to borrow new noses from the Crocodile. When they came back nobody spanked anybody any more; and ever since that day, O Best Beloved, all the Elephants you will ever see, besides all those that you won't, have trunks precisely like the trunk of the 'satiable Elephant's Child.

CAPTAIN COOK

Richard and Florence Atwater

When Mr. Popper received the gift of a penguin, the family little knew what that Antarctic bird would do to their lives. Making his home in the refrigerator is only the beginning.

"Call who Captain Cook?" asked Mrs. Popper, who had come in so quietly that none of them had heard her.

"Why, the penguin," said Mr. Popper. "I was just saying," he went on, as Mrs. Popper sat down suddenly on the floor to recover from her surprise, "that we'd name him after Captain Cook. He was a famous English explorer who lived about the time of the American Revolution. He sailed all over where no one had ever been before. He didn't actually get to the South Pole, of course, but he made a lot of important scientific discoveries about the Antarctic regions. He was a brave man and a kind leader. So I think Captain Cook would be a very suitable name for our penguin here."

"Well, I never!" said Mrs. Popper.

"Gork!" said Captain Cook, suddenly getting lively again. With a flap of his flippers he jumped from the tub to the washstand, and stood there for a minute surveying the floor. Then he jumped down, walked over to Mrs. Popper, and began to peck her ankle.

"Stop him, Papa!" screamed Mrs. Popper, retreating into the hallway with Captain Cook after her, and Mr. Popper and the children fol-

lowing. In the living room she paused. So did Captain Cook, for he was delighted with the room.

Now a penguin may look very strange in a living room, but a living room looks very strange to a penguin. Even Mrs. Popper had to smile as they watched Captain Cook, with the light of curiosity in his excited circular eyes, and his black tailcoat dragging pompously behind his little pinkish feet, strut from one upholstered chair to another, pecking at each to see what it was made of. Then he turned suddenly and marched out to the kitchen.

"Maybe he's hungry," said Janie.

Captain Cook immediately marched up to the refrigerator.

"Gork?" he inquired, turning to slant his head wisely at Mrs. Popper, and looking at her pleadingly with his right eye.

"He certainly is cute," she said. "I guess I'll have to forgive him for biting my ankle. He probably only did it out of curiosity. Anyway, he's a nice clean-looking bird."

"Ork?" repeated the penguin, nibbling at the metal handle of the refrigerator door with his upstretched beak.

Mr. Popper opened the door for him, and Captain Cook stood very high and leaned his sleek black head back so that he could see inside. Now that Mr. Popper's work was over for the winter, the icebox was not quite so full as usual, but the penguin did not know that.

"What do you suppose he likes to eat?" asked Mrs. Popper.

"Let's see," said Mr. Popper, as he removed all the food and set it on the kitchen table. "Now then, Captain Cook, take a look."

The penguin jumped up onto a chair and from there onto the edge of the table, flapping his flippers again to recover his balance. Then he walked solemnly around the table, and between the dishes of food, inspecting everything with the greatest interest, though he touched nothing. Finally he stood still, very erect, raised his beak to point at the ceiling, and make a loud, almost purring sound. "O-r-r-r-h, o-r-r-r-h," he trilled.

"That's a penguin's way of saying how pleased it is," said Mr. Popper, who had read about it in his Antarctic books.

Apparently, however, what Captain Cook wanted to show was that he was pleased with their kindness, rather than with their food. For now, to their surprise, he jumped down and walked into the dining room.

"I know," said Mr. Popper. "We ought to have some seafood for him, canned shrimps or something. Or maybe he isn't hungry yet. I've read that penguins can go for a month without food."

"Mamma! Papa!" called Bill. "Come see what Captain Cook has done."

Captain Cook had done it all right. He had discovered the bowl of goldfish on the dining-room window sill. By the time Mrs. Popper reached over to lift him away, he had already swallowed the last of the goldfish.

"Bad, bad penguin!" reproved Mrs. Popper, glaring down at Captain Cook.

Captain Cook squatted guiltily on the carpet and tried to make himself look small.

"He knows he's done wrong," said Mr. Popper. "Isn't he smart?"

"Maybe we can train him," said Mrs. Popper. "Bad, naughty Captain," she said to the penguin in a loud voice. "Bad, to eat the goldfish." And she spanked him on his round black head.

Before she could do that again, Captain Cook hastily waddled out to the kitchen.

There the Poppers found him trying to hide in the still opened refrigerator. He was squatting under the ice-cube coils, under which he could barely squeeze, sitting down. His round, white-circled eyes looked out at them mysteriously from the dimness of the inside of the box.

"I think that's about the right temperature for him, at that," said Mr. Popper. "We could let him sleep there, at night."

"But where will I put the food?" asked Mrs. Popper.

"Oh, I guess we can get another icebox for the food," said Mr. Popper.

"Look," said Janie. "He's gone to sleep."

Mr. Popper turned the cold control switch to its coldest so that Captain Cook could sleep more comfortably. Then he left the door ajar so that the penguin would have plenty of fresh air to breathe.

"Tomorrow I will have the icebox service department send a man out to bore some holes in

the door, for air," he said, "and then he can put a handle on the inside of the door so that Captain Cook can go in and out of his refrigerator, as he pleases."

"Well, dear me, I never thought we would have a penguin for a pet," said Mrs. Popper. "Still, he behaves pretty well, on the whole, and he is so nice and clean that perhaps he will be a good example to you and the children. And now, I declare, we must get busy. We haven't done anything but watch that bird. Papa, will you just help me to set the beans on the table, please?"

"Just a minute," answered Mr. Popper. "I just happened to think that Captain Cook will not feel right on the floor of that icebox. Penguins make their nests of pebbles and stones. So I will just take some ice cubes out of the tray and put them under him. That way he will be more comfortable."

TROUBLES WITH A PENGUIN

Richard and Florence Atwater

The next day was quite eventful at 432 Proudfoot Avenue. First there was the service man and then the policeman and then the trouble about the license.

Captain Cook was in the children's room, watching Janie and Bill put together a jigsaw puzzle on the floor. He was very good about not disturbing the pieces after Bill had spanked him for eating one. He did not hear the refrigerator service man come to the back door.

Mrs. Popper had gone marketing for canned shrimps for the penguin, so that Mr. Popper was alone in the kitchen to explain to the service man what he wanted done to the refrigerator.

The service man put his tool bag down on the kitchen floor, looked at the refrigerator, and then at Mr. Popper, who, to tell the truth, had not shaved yet and was not very tidy.

"Mister," he said, "you don't need no ventilating holes in that there door."

"It's my icebox, and I want some holes bored in the door," said Mr. Popper.

They argued about it for quite a while. Mr. Popper knew that to get the service man to do what he wanted, all he had to do was to explain that he was going to keep a live penguin in the icebox, and that he wanted his pet to have plenty of fresh air, even though the door was closed all night. He felt a little stubborn about explaining, however. He didn't want to discuss Captain Cook with this unsympathetic service man, who was already staring at Mr. Popper as if he thought Mr. Popper was not quite right in his head.

"Come on, do what I said," said Mr. Popper. "I'm paying you for it."

"With what?" asked the service man.

Mr. Popper gave him a five-dollar bill. It made him a little sad to think how many beans it would have bought for Mrs. Popper and the children.

The service man examined the bill carefully as if he didn't trust Mr. Popper too much. But at last he put it in his pocket, took a drill from his tool bag, and made five small holes in a neat pattern on the refrigerator door.

"Now," said Mr. Popper, "don't get up. Wait a minute. There is one more thing."

"Now what?" said the service man. "I suppose now you want me to take the door off its hinges to let in a little more air. Or do you want me to make a radio set out of your icebox?"

"Don't get funny," said Mr. Popper indignantly. "That is no way to talk. Believe it or not, I know what I'm doing. I mean, having you do. I want you to fix an extra handle on the inside of that box so it can be opened from the inside of the box."

"That," said the service man, "is a fine idea. You want an extra handle on the inside. Sure, sure." He picked up his tool bag.

"Aren't you going to do it for me?" asked Mr. Popper.

"Oh, sure, sure," said the service man, edging toward the back door.

Mr. Popper saw that for all his words of agreement, the service man had no intention of putting on an inside handle.

"I thought you were a service man," he said.

"I am. That's the first sensible thing you've said yet."

"You're a fine kind of service man if you don't even know how to put an extra handle on the inside of an icebox door."

"Oh, I don't, don't I? Don't think I don't know how. As far as that goes, I've even got a spare handle in my tool bag, and plenty of screws. You needn't think I don't know how to do it, if I wanted to."

Mr. Popper silently reached into his pocket and gave the service man his last five-dollar bill. He was pretty sure that Mrs. Popper would be annoyed at him for spending all that money, but it could not be helped.

"Mister," said the service man, "you win. I'll fix your extra handle. And while I am doing it, you sit down on that chair over there facing me, where I can keep an eye on you."

"Fair enough," said Mr. Popper, sitting down.

The service man was still on the floor, putting in the final screws that held the new handle in place, when the penguin came out to the kitchen on his silent pink feet.

Surprised at seeing a strange man sitting on the floor, Captain Cook quietly walked over and began to peck him curiously. But the service man was even more surprised than Captain Cook.

"*Ork,*" said the penguin. Or perhaps it was the service man. Mr. Popper was not sure just what had happened when he picked up himself and his chair a moment later. There had been a shower of flying tools, a violent slamming of the door, and the service man was gone.

These sudden noises, of course, brought the children running. Mr. Popper showed them how the refrigerator was now all remodeled for the penguin. He showed Captain Cook, too, by shutting him inside it. The penguin at once noticed the shiny new inside handle and bit it with his usual curiosity. The door opened, and Captain Cook jumped out.

Mr. Popper promptly put Captain Cook back inside and shut the door again, to be sure that the penguin learned his lesson. Before long, Captain Cook became quite skillful at getting out and was ready to be taught how to get inside when the door was shut.

By the time the policeman came to the back door, Captain Cook was going in and out the refrigerator as easily as if he had lived in one all his life.

THE THIRTEENTH FLOOR

Joan Howard

A black cat that answers to no name but Merlin is bound to start things. This four-footed Merlin, by putting out his paw and pressing an unseen spring that leads to a nonexistent 13th floor, proves that magic can be as modern as it is powerful. Use this excerpt to lead the children to the book.

It was still raining, and there did not seem much to do now that they had named their cat, and the cat had made it quite clear he had had enough of sitting on laps for a while and was bored with patting at a spool on a string.

Finding the name for the little black cat had been a peculiar business altogether, and Ronnie and Jill had discovered there was a lot more to it than they would ever have guessed.

They had tried all the names they could think of, like Tommie and Tibbie and Toby; like Jerry and Jumper and James; like Blackie and Bobbie and Bill; and ever so many more. Not by the twitch of a whisker would the black cat show an interest in any of them.

"Butch," suggested Ronnie.

"Oh, no! Not for *this* cat," Jill said, and the little cat walked off in offended dignity, switching his tail.

"Well, I'm sorry then," Ronnie apologized.

"Nightshade might be nice, he's so black," Jill ventured. The cat seemed to prick up an ear to listen.

"It won't do, though," Ronnie decided. "There is really something called nightshade—I'm not sure what it is, but the word deadly goes with it. Deadly Nightshade would be a horrid name for a nice cat. Besides, think of trying to call him. . . . 'Here, Nightshade! Here, Nightshade!' "

Jill gave in to such a convincing argument. She could not think of a single other name, so she began trying to talk like a cat.

"*Meee*-ow!" she said. "*Meee-ow!*"

"That's terrible!"

It was quite clear that the cat thought so too.

"Wait a minute," Jill said. "I think I've just about got it."

She began to practice under her breath. Murrauw! No, not quite right yet.

"Mer . . ." she began. She meant to say, "Merrower," but what came out was "MERLIN!"

She said it again. "Why, that is our cat's name. I'm as sure as sure . . . Merlin!"

Merlin came to his name as if he had been waiting for it and thought they were never going to get it right.

"I read about somebody called Merlin in the *Story of King Arthur and His Knights*," Ronnie said. "He was a magician back in those olden times."

"Our Merlin is magical, too." Jill was certain of that.

Merlin purred softly, but his yellow eyes looked slantwise and mysterious.

After Merlin had got tired of sitting around on laps and bored with patting the spool on a string, he settled himself on the window sill between Jill and Ronnie and watched the rain.

Ronnie and Jill began to play an old game of theirs, racing raindrops down the pane, but that soon grew rather monotonous. Especially since today neither of them ever won with their drops. It was always Merlin who put a sure paw on the right one, a far-behind one that would develop an unaccountable burst of speed at that touch through the glass.

Ronnie finally dug some chalk out of his tool chest and began to draw idly on the black linoleum floor.

"What is it?" asked Jill.

"Just a box, I guess."

"It looks more like a door to me."

"All right. That's what it is then—a trapdoor." Ronnie added a couple of hinges at one side and a sort of latch on the other.

Merlin had been regarding the drawing with critical attention. He put out a soft paw, and the latch unfastened at his touch.

Jill stared at it with wide eyes, and Ronnie began to tug.

The trapdoor lifted quite easily, and Ronnie and Jill followed the sedate Merlin down the steps to the thirteenth floor.

At first glance, the thirteenth floor did not

Ronnie noticed that Merlin was staring at him, with his yellow eyes particularly slanted and mysterious.

"I wonder . . ." he began.

There was a tiny flurry of grey skittering across the floor, and Merlin was off after it. The mouse reached the wall and vanished with a flicker through a hole in one corner. With his whiskers bristling, Merlin sat down to wait, looking no more than a darker shadow in the dim corner.

"I'm glad he didn't catch the poor little mouse," Jill said with a shiver.

Merlin ignored her words as any sensible cat would. His attention was entirely upon the mousehole, so Ronnie and Jill began to explore on their own.

In any other part of the building they would never have gone into a strange apartment, even if the door did stand open. Having their share of curiosity, they might have peeked, of course, but that would have been all. But somehow none of the ordinary rules seemed to apply to the thirteenth floor.

They watched an old man sitting at a desk. His long thin fingers kept picking up bright round discs that gleamed like gold and stacking them in several different piles. Presently Jill and Ronnie edged through the door and into the room, inch by inch, their footsteps silent on the thick rug.

Quiet as they were, the old man heard them and looked up, not at all startled.

"I am a numismatist!" he stated, without bothering about greetings.

Ronnie took a few quick steps backward toward the door. And Jill, who had a very sympathetic nature, said, "That's too bad. I'm terribly sorry."

Behind them in the hall they heard a hoarse chuckle.

"There's no call for you to feel sorry for *him,* my dear. He means that he's a coin collector."

The man who had spoken did not wait for an answer. He rolled on down the hall as if he were balancing himself on a pitching deck in the teeth of a gale; and he wore so many sweaters under his pea jacket that he looked as fat as Humpty Dumpty.

"He must be a sailor," Ronnie said.

"So he is," the coin collector agreed, with the

seem so very different from the fourteenth or the seventh or the second, or any other the Saunders children had inspected. Of course, the doors of the various apartments stood open as they never did either upstairs or down; and the hallway was papered in a rather unusual and complicated all-over pattern of bats and owls and triangles and pentacles and broomsticks and large black cauldrons. Round the borders ran the words of old charms and enchantments. Jill and Ronnie thought it the most attractive wallpaper they had ever seen, and they spent quite a time studying it.

"You know," Ronnie declared, "this would be a fine place for magicians to live, especially absent-minded magicians. If they forgot their spells, all they would have to do is read them off the wall."

"I don't think magicians come absent-minded, do they?" Jill objected. "I've never heard of one."

"Except right when they are doing the magic, maybe they are the same as anybody else. We can't be sure, because we have never known any magicians."

air of a man who resigns himself to a visitation from uninvited children and prepares to make the best of it. "I'm pretty busy today, what with it being the thirteenth and all, but I'll show you a few pieces of my fairy gold here and then you can run along."

Ronnie and Jill examined gleaming coins that were handed them one by one. Each had a different design on its face: owl and bat and toad; a black cock and a black cat; a hemlock branch and a hazel rod and a sprig of a plant the collector said was enchanter's nightshade; a wishbone and a rabbit's foot and a pretty design of crossed broomsticks. There were people, too: a tiny man with long whiskers and pointed ears and an elderly lady with a tall hat of a design commonly seen only on Hallowe'en. They were all quite different from Abraham Lincoln and President Jefferson and Miss Liberty.

The money did not feel exactly like the dimes and nickels and pennies they were used to handling, either. It was softer and it shimmered in their fingers.

"Just what is this fairy gold, anyway?" Ronnie hoped that the amiable coin collector would not think him rude for asking.

"It would take me much too long to explain it to you. In these days gold is not as easily come by as it used to be, even for us numismatists, and you have to take what you can get."

"I think it is much more interesting than ordinary money," Jill said politely.

"So do I," the old man agreed. "I would like to give you some lucky pieces, but perhaps I had better not. You'd find them hard to account for and there'd be no guarantee that they would stay by you."

"That's perfectly all right; thank you just the same." The children tried hard to keep the disappointment out of their voices.

"Come to think of it, though, I do have a few trifles here that you might have fun playing with some day." The collector rummaged round on his littered desk and brushed a lot of bright copper Indian head pennies into a paper sack that had dark shiny spots on it. "I'm sorry it's a little greasy," he apologized. "I brought a ham sandwich home in it from the delicatessen for my lunch."

"That doesn't matter—not a bit," Jill said.

"All right, then, you run along. I have to get back to my work."

Merlin was still sitting at his mousehole and he refused to pay the slightest attention to the children.

They hesitated at another doorway to watch a little man rushing round frantically with brooms and brushes and the kind of squee-gee the window-cleaner uses. His clothes were all covered with a shiny dust and he waved a polishing cloth at them.

"Too busy to talk," he panted. "Come some other day. I've got to go right to work. They've gone and discovered a new star and it's *never* been cleaned."

"Yes, we're too busy," said another voice. It came from a chair by the table but neither Ronnie nor Jill could see anybody there. "Let's see now." The invisible voice sounded cross. "Three warps and five woofs—or is it three woofs and five warps? I simply can't concentrate with people watching me."

"Excuse us," said Jill and Ronnie and they tiptoed away from that door.

Their exploration took them next into an apartment that was just like a ship, except that every part of it—bridge and cabin and deck, and even the engine room and hold—was all jumbled together in one big room that managed to stay shipshape in spite of it all.

And where a regular boat like the one that took them out to the Statue of Liberty last Fourth of July had only one wheel, this had seventeen—and no end of compasses and binnacles and such-like.

The wallpaper was a design in green and white of waves that rolled and swirled and broke into whitecaps till Jill felt quite dizzy. She had never seen water look so real, and while Ronnie was examining some bright brass machinery, she tiptoed over to the wall and touched it. Her finger came away wet.

"Well . . ." she said doubtfully. Somehow she could not think of any words that exactly suited the situation.

They did not find the seafaring gentleman who had spoken to them at the coin collector's door and they decided he must have gone out again. Of course it was possible he was hiding somewhere among a lot of furled sails and canvas-covered lifeboats. But if he was, they thought he couldn't be very anxious to have visitors, and maybe they had better leave.

Their last call was something of a social triumph, for here they found a tenant who was obviously delighted to welcome them.

"Come right in, my dears. It is good of you to find time to visit an old fellow."

He was as thin and grey as fog, and his hair curled round his high domed head like wisps of feathery cloud.

"Weatherbee is the name," he went on, and his voice sounded like a soft wind whistling round the corner of the building. "Elemanzer Pyerocket Weatherbee—and you will be the young Saunderses that my friend Merlin has lately adopted."

"Yes, we are, Mr. Weatherbee."

Ronnie shook a hand that was as brittle as a bundle of twigs, and Jill dropped the curtsy that Mrs. Saunders had tried in vain to have her daughter display when guests came to tea. They both wondered how he knew Merlin's name, and why he thought it was Merlin who had adopted *them* when really they had taken the little black cat home themselves. Somehow, though, they did not like to ask; with Mr. Weatherbee, it did not seem polite to begin right off asking questions and they were very anxious that their manners should match his own.

"We are very happy to find you home," they said. "We have wanted to meet you for a long time, Mr. Weatherbee."

That was not strictly accurate, since they had never heard of Mr. Weatherbee before, but it sounded perfectly true to them when they said it. They had wanted to meet somebody like Mr. Weatherbee for a long time, even if they had not known it till they saw him.

Their new friend seemed to understand all this without any more words. His was a home-like apartment, even if it was such a home as they had never encountered, and his voice that rustled and whispered and whistled softly was a happy, restful sound.

The table was spread with every kind of cake that Ronnie and Jill liked best—angel food and devil's food, jelly roll and Lady Baltimore—and there happened to be exactly the right number of forks and napkins laid out. Mr. Weatherbee

drank tea and the children had raspberry soda that tasted of the ripe, freshly gathered fruit, and afterward they sat in front of a fire that glowed with magical colors while the old gentleman told them about his career in the Weather Bureau.

"I am retired now, of course," he said rather wistfully. "They consider me an old fogy, what with all their brand new instruments and their charts for mapping low pressure areas and high pressure areas, and I don't know what all."

"Well, I'll bet the Weather Bureau was better when you ran it than it is now," Ronnie declared loyally. "They are wrong an awful lot of the time."

"Yes, prophecy is not what it used to be," Mr. Weatherbee admitted. "Times have changed."

"How did you used to tell what the weather was going to be like?" Jill asked, all her shyness about asking questions long since forgotten.

"The way any natural man should be able to tell it. There are signs always—the clouds and the wind, and the way the leaves twist on the trees and the birds twitter in the branches. You knew it was going to be a hard winter when the animals grew heavy coats and there was a plentiful supply of berries and nuts for them to eat and store away. When the groundhog came out to look for his shadow on Candlemas Day, you could be sure of six weeks more snow and ice if he found it. If the blackbird did not sing before seven, it would rain by nightfall. There was red sky at night for a fair day, and red sky at morning for a storm; there were rainbows and rings round the moon and the stars shining with an extra twinkling. A natural man could always tell."

"They ought to have had sense enough to let a natural man go on doing it, then," Ronnie said.

"Not they—they began calling themselves meteorologists and got all tangled up in their fancy apparatus. As Ronnie here mentioned a few minutes ago, they are wrong an awful lot of the time."

The room was growing dimmer in the twilight and Mr. Weatherbee more shadowy. Ronnie and Jill said they had better be getting home before their mother began to worry. There was a special reason why they did not want her to be cross with them tonight.

"That will be Merlin, of course," said Mr. Weatherbee. "But it will come out all right—you can trust Merlin."

The long fingers of shadow that moved steadily across the room toward the fire reminded Jill of one more thing she wanted to know.

"Did you take care of the daylight saving, too, when you managed the Weather Bureau?"

"Daylight saving was something 'I *did* understand, if I do say it myself," Mr. Weatherbee declared with new animation. "The Bureau of Standards and the Interstate Commerce Commission have taken it over now and a fine mess they have made of it between them. Daylight saving, they still call it, but what does it *mean?* What do they do with this daylight; does anyone know? Now, I really *saved* it—why, I've still got rooms full of it here, and every minute a nice bright yellow as new as today. If you children will wait just an instant more, I would like to make you a small present of daylight."

Jill and Ronnie stood in the owl light and watched Mr. Weatherbee open a door just a bright crack and slip through into a clear yellow room. When he came out again, he handed Ronnie a little carved box with a gold padlock on it. The tiny gold key on a chain he hung around Jill's neck.

"You take care of this," he said. "Boys are apt to lose keys."

"I will never, never lose it," Jill promised.

"That's right, my dear. And mind, when you need it, just use one pinch of daylight. A little goes a long way."

"We'll remember," Ronnie declared.

"Thank you for a lovely party, Mr. Weatherbee." Jill curtseyed again.

"And thank you for coming," said Mr. Weatherbee with a courtly bow. "It has been a lovely party for me, too—an old fellow gets lonesome now and then. I see our friend Merlin is waiting for you."

Merlin led the way back up the stairs without a single mew or purr, so Ronnie and Jill were sure the mouse was still safe.

In their playroom, Ronnie shut down the trapdoor. Merlin erased the drawing with his tail and then settled to work washing the chalk off.

From the living room came voices, Mr. Saunders' saying "NO!" very firmly. They could not

catch Mrs. Saunders' answer, but Mr. Saunders' next "No!" was not so firm, and after a while they heard him say, "All right, all right. What chance have I got?"

So Ronnie and Jill knew it was safe to take Merlin in and introduce him to their father.

Merlin behaved with the most commendable tact in permitting a little gentle scratching of his ears, and the day was won.

"Where did you get that pretty key and chain?" Mrs. Saunders asked Jill a few minutes later.

"Mr. Weatherbee gave it to me. He gave Ronnie the box that it opens. He told us how the Weather Bureau works and how it used to work better, and all about daylight saving."

"He sounds like an interesting man," said Mr. Saunders. "I've often wondered myself just what goes on down at that Weather Bureau."

"I suppose it is all right for you to keep the presents the gentleman gave you." Mrs. Saunders still sounded a trifle doubtful. "But after this don't accept anything from people unless Daddy and I know them too."

"Yes, Mummie."

"Does Mr. Weatherbee live here in the building?" Mr. Saunders asked Ronnie.

"Yes, sir, down on the thirteenth floor."

"There is no thirteenth floor in this building."

"Oh, but there is—only you can't visit it except on the thirteenth of the month and if a black cat takes you." Jill sounded very sure of the rules she had learned today.

"Now listen to me, you two. I won't have you growing up superstitious. You are not to believe in any such nonsense as a thirteenth floor."

"But Daddy, don't you see? It is the people who *don't* believe in the thirteenth floor who are superstitious," Ronnie explained earnestly.

Mr. Sidney P. Saunders opened his mouth to utter a few carefully chosen arguments. Then he shut it again before they got out. He seemed to be trying to work out something in his head. He gave it up.

"Do you realize what time it is?" he asked, quite crossly. "Go eat your supper quickly and get right to bed."

"We're not hungry, thank you," Ronnie said,

"We had supper down on the thirteenth floor with Mr. Weatherbee," his sister added.

MRS. WALLABY JONES

Joan Howard

Nearly every day, even in weather that was not fit for ducks, Jill and Ronnie played in the park. But this December afternoon, with the sun shimmering on the first light snowfall of the season, was the only time they had met Mrs. Wallaby-Jones there.

They were used to nice old ladies stopping them to talk and to ask questions, so they chattered with that mixture of open friendliness and polite caution that all sensible children maintain till they are sure of a stranger.

"Are you English?" Jill asked politely.

The lady's speech was rather different from their own, and Jill had heard her mother say once that the English went in for hyphenated names. Mrs. Wallaby-Jones had mentioned *her* hyphen when she introduced herself, as if she considered it a mark of distinction.

"No, not English, my dear," Mrs. Wallaby-Jones replied, "though belonging to the British Empire, of course. We Wallaby-Joneses—with the hyphen—are from Australia. New South Wales, to be more precise. We are a cadet branch of the Macropus family. Surely, even in New York, you have heard of the Macropuses? Australia could hardly be said to have a history at all without the Macropuses—or the Wallabies, if it comes to that. Why, we—"

Ronnie and Jill sighed deeply and wondered if they had not better be going now. Even the nicest grown-ups were bores when they got started on the subject of Family. Their own mother—and she *was* the nicest—went on and on sometimes about her family who had come over from England on a boat called the "Mayflower," and then kept on getting into one bit after another of American history.

"I'm pretty good at the standing broad jump," Ronnie said. He was not so much boasting as trying to change the subject tactfully. "I can do five-feet-ten-and-a-half-inches. Jill can't come anywhere near that, but then girls are never much good at that sort of thing."

"Are they not?" asked Mrs. Wallaby-Jones.

She sounded distinctly huffy, and as they watched she seemed to grow about two feet taller. Maybe she was swelling with rage about something—they had heard about that, though they had never seen it happen. They wondered anxiously what could have upset her. She surely could not be angry about jumping, since jumping was something ladies never went in for, so it must be because they had interrupted her story about the Macropuses and the Wallaby-Joneses.

Suddenly, without any warning at all, she flew through the air in the most spectacular broad jump either of the young Saunderses had ever witnessed. She cleared two park benches, three laurels and two bayberry bushes, and the bridle path; and then there she stood waiting, as primly respectable as ever, but a good twenty-five feet away from them.

"That was a beaut!" Ronnie yelled excitedly.

"You are perfectly wonderful!" his sister called, and both of them ran to catch up to her.

A grown-up who did not let dignity stand in the way of a broad jump like that was a real friend to cultivate. But they were soon reminded not to let her get back to the subject of Family.

"If you think that was good," she said smugly, with her pointed little nose high in the air, "you should have seen my Uncle Hubert Macropus in his younger days. For thirteen years straight he won first prize for the broad jump in the Caledonian Games they hold in Australia on Robert Burns's birthday. He was made an honorary Scot to be eligible and his name was printed in the program as Hubert *Mac*Ropus—to go with MacDuff and MacGregor and MacDonald and all the rest of the Macs, you see."

Jill and Ronnie did not see, quite, and fascinating as broad jumps are when you are making them yourself or even watching them, the illustrious history of Mr. Hubert Macropus, or *Mac*Ropus, did not hold their interest very long.

"Shall we go over to the lake and feed the ducks?" Jill suggested. "I have a bun in my pocket we can crumble up for them."

"A splendid idea, my dear," agreed Mrs. Wallaby-Jones with enthusiasm. "Rules or no rules, I like to see children remember their furred and feathered friends. For myself, I always fancy a nice bit of greens, but I have heard that ducks relish crumbs. There is no accounting for tastes, I always say."

The children were puzzled. "There isn't any rule against feeding the ducks," Ronnie said.

"Is there not? Well, I do call that unfair when there are stupid notices posted on the cages of all the quadrupeds."

Mrs. Wallaby-Jones sounded highly indignant and off she went in another great leap.

"I wish I could do that," Ronnie said wistfully when they had almost caught up with her again.

"Maybe having big feet is a help," his sister suggested, and she pointed to Mrs. Wallaby-Jones's footprints in the light snow. They certainly were enormous for a lady. "I never saw any like that before, and her hands are smaller than mine."

Mrs. Wallaby-Jones was waiting for them, with her tiny gloved hands demurely folded, so Ronnie could see that Jill was quite right.

Just then he caught sight of a policeman friend of theirs. "Hi, Mr. Harrigan," he called. "Do you want to see something that really *is* something? This lady here can do a broad jump that—"

"Hush now, children, don't talk such nonsense," said Mrs. Wallaby-Jones.

She was in a great hurry suddenly, and she had leaped almost out of sight before Ronnie could finish his sentence.

Mr. Harrigan blinked twice and swallowed hard. He pushed his cap back on his head. "Holy Moses, what is your friend, a kangaroo?" he demanded.

"Well, I told you she was a wonderful broad jumper," Ronnie reminded him.

"She's all of that," agreed the policeman. He looked as if he were thinking up some more questions to ask, but Jill and Ronnie had to leave him to catch up with Mrs. Wallaby-Jones.

Their trip across the park was really wonderful, with their new and already dear friend walking in a series of wild leaps, clearing drinking fountains and perambulators and startling some elderly gentlemen who were sunning themselves on the benches. It was such fun that the children hoped they might meet the lady every day after this.

"Look!" Ronnie called. "There are still boats out. Will you come for a row on the lake with us? Our treat!"

"Thank you, I should love to. We Wallaby-Joneses are very fond of water sports. Why, my Great-Aunt Emmeline was the talk of New South Wales when she paddled her own canoe. That was when she was quite a young girl and people had old-fashioned notions about what was ladylike and what was not."

"We'll have to hurry," Jill broke in quickly. "There is Mr. Murphy bringing in his rowboats."

During the summer the children were always coaxing some grown-up or other to take them rowing on the lake. They did the rowing themselves, rather badly, but they had to have an older person with them or they were not allowed out in a boat. There was a printed notice about that rule tacked up on the side of the boathouse where Mr. Murphy took the money.

Mr. Murphy was unusually late storing his boats for the winter this year. Indian summer had continued all through November, and then he had decided to paint up some of them ready for next season. The snow had reminded him that it was near the middle of December, though, so he was working hard today getting them out of the water and stowing them away in a shed. He was closing up shop till next spring.

It took considerable coaxing before he agreed to let them take out a boat for one last hour, but since the lady was with them . . . Jill and Ronnie pooled their allowances to pay the thirty-five cents and two pennies tax.

In the rowboat, Jill and Ronnie sat side by side, each with an oar, while Mrs. Wallaby-Jones settled herself in the stern, an entirely dignified passenger.

Mr. Murphy shoved them off and they started out all right, but as soon as they got really out in the lake their rowing was the kind that always made their father laugh at them. Because Ronnie pulled on his oar so much harder than his sister could, they had a way of going round and round in circles—on their good days in quite large circles, but more often as if they were caught in a small whirlpool.

This promised to be one of their worst days and they were pretty embarrassed about it all until they suddenly straightened out and cut across the ripples in as clean a line as you please.

"Hey!" Ronnie shouted. "Look at us!"

But Jill could not stop to look at them. She was far too intent upon looking at something else. She nudged her brother to watch too. Their eyes got bigger and bigger as they stared at the queerest thing they had ever seen in all their lives.

There was Mrs. Wallaby-Jones, sitting as prim as ever in her sleek fur coat and her fur hat and tippet, her gloved hands folded in her lap. But she had pulled up her skirt just a trifle, probably to keep it dry. And underneath, hanging over the back of the little rowboat and acting as a rudder, was something—something—Jill and Ronnie were not sure *what* it was, but it certainly did look like the tip of a kangaroo's tail.

They were so astonished they could not say a single word. Not even when, encouraged by their fixed attention, Mrs. Wallaby-Jones told them practically *all* about her family. Not until she got to second-cousins-once-removed did Jill find her voice.

"We have a cat," she announced. "A black cat."

"I am not surprised to hear it, my dear,"

Mrs. Wallaby-Jones said amiably. "That would be Merlin, would it not?"

Jill's mouth dropped open and Ronnie's oar hung dripping in midair. But there was no time for questions. Mr. Murphy was waving his arms at them from the shore to signal that their hour was up, so they had to row back quickly.

Ronnie helped their guest out of the rowboat like a perfect gentleman. He could not see anything peculiar about her then, though his sister noticed that Mrs. Wallaby-Jones wore her skirts just a shade longer than was the fashion this year.

"I must get back now, dears," Mrs. Wallaby-Jones said politely. "It has been a most enjoyable outing."

"When can we see you again?" both children wanted to know. "Can we meet you tomorrow? Or next day? Please . . ."

They had never met a grown-up they were more anxious to see again, as much and as often as possible. They were even willing now to let her talk Family in order that they might enjoy her other charms.

"Well, I cannot be sure just when I shall be free again," Mrs. Wallaby-Jones answered. "I would not want to make a promise and not be able to keep it. It is not always easy to get away, and you never know ahead of time when there is going to be a large audience—it depends upon the weather and so forth. I must not disappoint my public, you know, but one of these days we shall meet again."

It was not till they got home and found Merlin waiting for them to give him his catnip mouse from the toy cupboard that either Jill or Ronnie remembered that this was the thirteenth of the month.

At dinner they could talk of nothing but their new friend. They tried to keep their account as matter-of-fact as possible, knowing from past experiences that anything unusual was apt to be regarded with suspicion, if not actually disbelieved. Sometimes grown-up skepticism is really discouraging.

"When she walked, it was sort of in hops," Ronnie said. He remembered just in time not to mention the length of those hops.

"She had a pointed face and bright brown eyes," Jill put in eagerly. "Her clothes were a little bit old-fashioned but they exactly suited her."

"What do you suppose she meant about not disappointing her public?" Ronnie asked.

"Why, it sounds as though she might be an actress," their mother decided.

It was when Mr. Saunders wanted to know if their rowing had improved that Ronnie forgot to be careful.

"I don't know that we're so much better alone," he confessed, "but we're fine when Mrs. Wallaby-Jones is with us. She sort of steers for us. With her tail."

Mr. Saunders choked on a bread crumb and hastily gulped a whole glass of water. Mrs. Saunders was very much upset.

"It is all very well," she said sternly, "to make up stories now and again. I hope I enjoy a bit of fantasy as well as the next person. But it is *not* nice to be rude when the lady was so kind to you. . . ."

The lecture went on all through the chocolate pudding dessert and for quite a long time afterward, with many remarks of a to-think-that-any-child-of-mine nature. Mr. Saunders got tired of listening and left the table to read his evening paper. He finished the front page and the sports page and then turned back to page two. Presently he looked up from it and changed the subject.

"You children didn't happen to meet a kangaroo in the park today, I suppose? It seems one got loose from the menagerie. Just listen to this. . . ." He began to read and the whole family listened.

REMARKABLE OCCURRENCE
IN CENTRAL PARK ZOO

The strange disappearance of a large female wallaby (macropus giganteus) more commonly known as a kangaroo, for two hours today caused considerable excitement at the local menagerie. The animal, who is known to be very friendly and who answers to the name of Jones when called by her keeper, was missing from her cage for that period. At time of going to press, it had not been determined how she got away, nor when and how she was returned. Until her reappearance, her grieving keeper was certain that she had been abducted by a kidnapper disguised as a Miss Smithers, assistant to the curator of the zoo. Their theory was strengthened by the fact that Miss Smithers, an elderly woman, had reported the theft of her outdoor garments—a fur coat, fur hat and tippet—from the closet adjacent to her office. The clothing later reappeared as mysteriously as the missing wallaby, but it was some time before the excitement died down in the zoo.

There was silence for a moment when Mr. Saunders finished reading this extraordinary news item. Then Jill forgot all discretion and burst out in an excited burble of words.

"Why, our Mrs. Wallaby-Jones wore a fur coat and a fur hat an—"

She was stopped short by Ronnie's sharp elbow in her ribs. She yelped, and then the children looked at each other. They both remembered other times when silence had been considerably better than speech.

"Well, I've got some arithmetic homework to do," Ronnie said carelessly. "I expect I'd better get at it. You coming, Jill?"

Jill and Ronnie went off to their own room, followed by a sedate Merlin and the incredulous stares of their parents. Perhaps it was only because it had never before occurred to Ronnie to do his arithmetic homework without being reminded at least three times. Or perhaps . . .

"*What* did they say that woman's name was?" Mrs. Sidney P. Saunders demanded abruptly. "I thought—"

"So did I," admitted her husband. "But it could *not* be that."

ELECTRICITY

Robert Lawson

Children who chuckle over this ridiculous biography of Benjamin Franklin, purportedly written by a mouse, should be urged to read a genuine biography of our "first civilized American." If they are nine or ten, give them Ingri and Edgar d'Aulaire's Ben Franklin. *If they are twelve, give them Enid Meadowcroft's* Benjamin Franklin.

Ben never thereafter mentioned my little adventure in printing, so I tried to be somewhat more lenient about his maxims.

"Electricity." From *Ben and Me* by Robert Lawson, by permission of Little, Brown & Co. Copyright 1939 by Robert Lawson

Trying though they were, however, they were nothing compared to an enthusiasm which beset him about this time. This was the study of what he called "Electricity."

It all started with some glass tubes and a book of instructions sent him by a London friend. These tubes he would rub with a piece of silk or fur, thereby producing many strange and, to me, unpleasant effects. When a tube was sufficiently rubbed, small bits of paper would spring from the table and cling to it, or crackling sparks leap from it to the finger of anyone foolish enough to approach.

Ben derived great amusement from rubbing a tube and touching it to the tip of my tail. Thereupon a terrible shock would run through my body, every hair and whisker would stand on end and a convulsive contraction of all my muscles would throw me several inches in the air.

This was bad enough, but my final rebellion did not come until he, in his enthusiasm, used the fur cap to rub the tube. And *I* was in the cap.

"Ben," said I, "this has gone far enough. From now on, kindly omit me from these experiments. To me they seem a perfectly senseless waste of time, but if they amuse you, all right, go ahead with them. Just leave me out."

"I fear that you are not a person of vision, Amos," said he. "You fail to grasp the worldwide, the epoch-making importance of these experiments. You do not realize the force—"

"Oh don't I?" I replied. "My tail is still tingling."

"I shall tear the lightning from the skies," he went on, "and harness it to do the bidding of man."

"Personally," said I, "I think the sky's an excellent place for it."

Nothing I could say, though, served to dampen Ben's enthusiasm.

Soon he received an elaborate machine that could produce much greater currents than the glass tubes. It was worked by a crank which he ground at happily for hours. Our room became cumbered with rods, wires, tubes, copper plates and glass jars filled with evil-smelling liquids. It was difficult to move about without touching something likely to produce one of those hair-stiffening shocks.

Ben even went so far as to organize a group of similarly obsessed people, calling it "the Philosophical Society." They gathered once a week, armed with their glass tubes, bits of silk and wires. They spent whole evenings fiddling with these things or listening to long speeches about the wonders of "electricity," mostly by Ben. I napped.

After he had played with the new apparatus for a few weeks and had it working well, Ben decided to give an exhibition of his achievements in this field.

A large hall having been secured for the occasion by the Philosophical Society, Ben spent several busy days arranging and testing his apparatus, planning various experiments, writing a speech and inviting prominent people.

Frankly, I was bored by the whole affair, but since Ben seemed rather hurt by my attitude I tried to take a little interest. I read his speech and the descriptions of all the various experiments. By noon I understood everything quite thoroughly.

While we ate a light lunch of bread and cheese I told Ben of my studies. He was delighted and quite touched by my interest.

In the afternoon he went to have his hair curled, leaving me in the hall, where I went on with my research. Determined that no errors should mar this performance, since it meant so much to Ben, I carefully went over each wire and piece of apparatus, comparing them with his diagrams and descriptions.

I discovered that he had apparently made several grave mistakes, for not a few of the wires were connected in a manner that seemed to me obviously incorrect. There were so many of these errors to rectify that I was kept quite busy all afternoon. My corrected arrangements seemed to leave several loose wires and copper plates with no place to go, so I just left them in one of the chairs on the stage. I was barely able to finish before Ben arrived from the hairdresser's.

As we hurried home for supper, he was so filled with pride and excitement that I had no opportunity to tell him how narrowly he had escaped ruining the exhibition by his carelessness.

When we arrived back at the hall in the evening the brilliantly lit auditorium was crowded.

Seated in chairs on the stage were the Governor and his Lady; the Mayor; several of the clergy; and the Chief of the Volunteer Fire Brigade holding his silver trumpet.

Ben made his speech, and performed several simple experiments with the glass tubes. They were watched with great interest by the audience and generously applauded.

He then stepped to the new apparatus and signaled to a young apprentice from the print shop who was stationed at the crank. The lad turned with a will, and a loud humming sound came from the whirling wheel while blue sparks cracked about it.

"And now, my friends," said Ben proudly, "when I turn this knob you shall see, if my calculations are correct, a manifestation of electrical force never before witnessed on this continent."

They did.

As Ben turned the knob the Governor rose straight in the air in much the same manner that I used to when Ben applied the spark to my tail. His hair stood out just as my fur did. His second leap was higher and his hair even straighter. There was a noticeable odor of burning cloth.

On his third rising the copper plate flew from the chair, landing, unfortunately, in his Lady's lap. Her shriek, while slightly muffled by her wig, was, nevertheless, noteworthy.

The Fire Chief, gallantly advancing to their aid, inadvertently touched one of the wires with his silver trumpet. This at once became enveloped in a most unusual blue flame and gave off a strange clanging sound.

Ben leaped toward them, but I clamped on his ear. I had felt those shocks before.

"The boy—" I hissed. "Stop the machine!"

He sprang at the apprentice, who was still grinding merrily. The lad, not an admirer of the Governor, ceased his efforts with some reluctance.

The Governor was stiff and white in his chair, his Lady moaned faintly under her wig, the Fire Chief stared dazedly at his tarnished trumpet, and the audience was in an uproar.

"Never mind, Ben," I consoled as we walked home, "I feel certain that we'll succeed next time."

"Succeed!" shouted Ben. "SUCCEED! Why, Amos, don't you realize that I have just made the most successful, the most momentous experiment of the century? I have discovered the effects produced by applying strong electric shocks to human beings."

"Granted the Governor is one," I said, "we surely did."

THE STEADFAST TIN SOLDIER

Hans Christian Andersen

Andersen seems to have especially enjoyed writing tales endowing inanimate objects with life. These personifications probably grew out of his lonely childhood and his life-long delight in puppets. See The Shoemaker's Son.

There were once five and twenty tin soldiers, all brothers, for they were the offspring of the same old tin spoon. Each man shouldered his gun, kept his eyes well to the front, and wore the smartest red and blue uniform imaginable. The first thing they heard in their new world, when the lid was taken off the box, was a little boy clapping his hands and crying, "Soldiers, soldiers!" It was his birthday and they had just been given to him; so he lost no time in setting them up on the table. All the soldiers were exactly alike with one exception, and he differed from the rest in having only one leg. For he was made last, and there was not quite enough tin left to finish him. However, he stood just as well on his one leg, as the others on two, in fact he is the very one who is to become famous. On the table where they were being set up, were many other toys; but the chief thing which caught the eye was a delightful paper castle. You could see through the tiny windows, right into the rooms. Outside there were some little trees surrounding a small mirror, representing a lake, whose surface reflected the waxen swans which were swimming about on it. It was altogether charming, but the prettiest thing of all was a little maiden standing at the open door of the castle. She, too,

"The Steadfast Tin Soldier." From *Fairy Tales* by Hans Christian Andersen, translated by Mrs. Edgar Lucas, Everyman's Library, E. P. Dutton & Co., Inc., New York. By permission also of J. M. Dent & Sons, Ltd., London

was cut out of paper, but she wore a dress of the lightest gauze, with a dainty little blue ribbon over her shoulders, by way of a scarf, set off by a brilliant spangle, as big as her whole face. The little maid was stretching out both arms, for she was a dancer, and in the dance, one of her legs was raised so high into the air that the tin soldier could see absolutely nothing of it, and supposed that she, like himself, had but one leg.

"That would be the very wife for me!" he thought; "but she is much too grand; she lives in a palace, while I only have a box, and then there are five and twenty of us to share it. No, that would be no place for her! but I must try to make her acquaintance!" Then he lay down full length behind a snuff box, which stood on the table. From that point he could have a good look at the little lady, who continued to stand on one leg without losing her balance.

Late in the evening the other soldiers were put into their box, and the people of the house went to bed. Now was the time for the toys to play; they amused themselves with paying visits, fighting battles, and giving balls. The tin soldiers rustled about in their box, for they wanted to join the games, but they could not get the lid off. The nutcrackers turned somersaults, and the pencil scribbled nonsense on the slate. There was such a noise that the canary woke up and joined in, but his remarks were in verse. The only two who did not move were the tin soldier and the little dancer. She stood as stiff as ever on tip-toe, with her arms spread out; he was equally firm on his one leg, and he did not take his eyes off her for a moment.

Then the clock struck twelve, when pop! up flew the lid of the snuff box, but there was no snuff in it, no! There was a little black goblin, a sort of Jack-in-the-box.

"Tin soldier!" said the goblin, "have the goodness to keep your eyes to yourself."

But the tin soldier feigned not to hear.

"Ah! you just wait till to-morrow," said the goblin.

In the morning when the children got up they put the tin soldier on the window frame, and, whether it was caused by the goblin or by a puff of wind, I do not know, but all at once the window burst open, and the soldier fell headforemost from the third story.

It was a terrific descent, and he landed at last, with his leg in the air, and rested on his cap, with his bayonet fixed between two paving stones. The maid-servant and the little boy ran down at once to look for him; but although they almost trod on him, they could not see him. Had the soldier only called out, "Here I am," they would easily have found him, but he did not think it proper to shout when he was in uniform.

Presently it began to rain, and the drops fell faster and faster, till there was a regular torrent. When it was over two street boys came along.

"Look out!" said one; "there is a tin soldier! He shall go for a sail."

So they made a boat out of a newspaper and put the soldier into the middle of it, and he sailed away down the gutter; both boys ran alongside clapping their hands. Good heavens! what waves there were in the gutter, and what a current, but then it certainly had rained cats and dogs. The paper boat danced up and down, and now and then whirled round and round. A shudder ran through the tin soldier, but he remained undaunted, and did not move a muscle, only looked straight before him with his gun shouldered. All at once the boat drifted under a long wooden tunnel, and it became as dark as it was in his box.

"Where on earth am I going to now!" thought he. "Well, well, it is all the fault of that goblin! Oh, if only the little maiden were with me in the boat it might be twice as dark for all I should care!"

At this moment a big water rat, who lived in the tunnel, came up.

"Have you a pass?" asked the rat. "Hand up your pass!"

The tin soldier did not speak, but clung still tighter to his gun. The boat rushed on, the rat close behind. Phew, how he gnashed his teeth and shouted to the bits of stick and straw.

"Stop him, stop him, he hasn't paid the toll! he hasn't shown his pass!"

But the current grew stronger and stronger, the tin soldier could already see daylight before him at the end of the tunnel; but he also heard a roaring sound, fit to strike terror to the bravest heart. Just imagine! Where the tunnel ended the stream rushed straight into the big canal. That would be just as dangerous for him as it would be for us to shoot a great rapid.

He was so near the end now that it was impossible to stop. The boat dashed out; the poor tin soldier held himself as stiff as he could; no one should say of him that he even winced.

The boat swirled round three or four times, and filled with water to the edge; it must sink. The tin soldier stood up to his neck in water, and the boat sank deeper and deeper. The paper became limper and limper, and at last the water went over his head—then he thought of the pretty little dancer, whom he was never to see again, and this refrain rang in his ears:

"Onward! Onward! Soldier!
For death thou canst not shun."

At last the paper gave way entirely and the soldier fell through—but at the same moment he was swallowed by a big fish.

Oh! how dark it was inside the fish, it was worse than being in the tunnel even; and then it was so narrow! But the tin soldier was as dauntless as ever, and lay full length, shouldering his gun.

The fish rushed about and made the most frantic movements. At last it became quite quiet, and after a time, a flash like lightning pierced it. The soldier was once more in the broad daylight, and some one called out loudly, "A tin soldier!" The fish had been caught, taken to market, sold, and brought into the kitchen, where the cook cut it open with a large knife. She took the soldier up by the waist, with two fingers, and carried him into the parlour, where everyone wanted to see the wonderful man, who

had travelled about in the stomach of a fish; but the tin soldier was not at all proud. They set him up on the table, and, wonder of wonders! he found himself in the very same room that he had been in before. He saw the very same children, and the toys were still standing on the table, as well as the beautiful castle with the pretty little dancer.

She still stood on one leg, and held the other up in the air. You see she also was unbending. The soldier was so much moved that he was ready to shed tears of tin, but that would not have been fitting. He looked at her, and she looked at him, but they said never a word. At this moment one of the little boys took up the tin soldier, and without rhyme or reason, threw him into the fire. No doubt the little goblin in the snuff box was to blame for that. The tin soldier stood there, lighted up by the flame, and in the most horrible heat; but whether it was the heat of the real fire, or the warmth of his feelings, he did not know. He had lost all his gay color; it might have been from his perilous journey, or it might have been from grief, who can tell?

He looked at the little maiden, and she looked at him; and he felt that he was melting away, but he still managed to keep himself erect, shouldering his gun bravely.

A door was suddenly opened, the draught caught the little dancer and she fluttered like a sylph, straight into the fire, to the soldier, blazed up and was gone!

By this time the soldier was reduced to a mere lump, and when the maid took away the ashes next morning she found him, in the shape of a small tin heart. All that was left of the dancer was her spangle, and that was burnt as black as coal.

THE WILD SWANS

Hans Christian Andersen

Andersen has retold this folk tale with beautiful little touches of his own, such as the swans with golden crowns.

"The Wild Swans." From *Fairy Tales* by Hans Christian Andersen, translated by Mrs. Edgar Lucas, Everyman's Library, E. P. Dutton & Co., Inc., New York. By permission also of J. M. Dent & Sons, Ltd., London

Far away, where the swallows take refuge in winter, lived a king who had eleven sons and one daughter, Elise. The eleven brothers—they were all princes—used to go to school with stars on their breasts and swords at their sides. They wrote upon golden slates with diamond pencils, and could read just as well without a book as with one, so there was no mistake about their being real princes. Their sister Elise sat upon a little footstool of looking-glass, and she had a picture-book which had cost the half of a kingdom. Oh, these children were very happy; but it was not to last thus for ever.

Their father, who was king over all the land, married a wicked queen who was not at all kind to the poor children; they found that out on the first day. All was festive at the castle, but when the children wanted to play at having company, instead of having as many cakes and baked apples as ever they wanted, she would only let them have some sand in a teacup, and said they must make-believe.

In the following week she sent little Elise into the country to board with some peasants, and it did not take her long to make the king believe so many bad things about the boys, that he cared no more about them.

"Fly out into the world and look after yourselves," said the wicked queen; "you shall fly about like birds without voices."

But she could not make things as bad for them as she would have liked; they turned into eleven beautiful wild swans. They flew out of the palace window with a weird scream, right across the park and the woods.

It was very early in the morning when they came to the place where their sister Elise was sleeping in the peasant's house. They hovered over the roof of the house, turning and twisting their long necks, and flapping their wings; but no one either heard or saw them. They had to fly away again, and they soared up toward the clouds, far out into the wide world, and they settled in a big, dark wood, which stretched down to the shore.

Poor little Elise stood in the peasant's room, playing with a green leaf, for she had no other toys. She made a little hole in it, which she looked through at the sun, and it seemed to her as if she saw her brothers' bright eyes. Every time the warm sunbeams shone upon her cheek, it reminded her of their kisses. One day passed just like another. When the wind whistled through the rose-hedges outside the house, it whispered to the roses, "Who can be prettier than you are?" But the roses shook their heads and answered, "Elise!" And when the old woman sat in the doorway reading her Psalms, the wind turned over the leaves and said to the book, "Who can be more pious than you?" "Elise!" answered the book. Both the roses and the book of Psalms only spoke the truth.

She was to go home when she was fifteen, but when the queen saw how pretty she was, she got very angry, and her heart was filled with hatred. She would willingly have turned her into a wild swan too, like her brothers, but she did not dare to do it at once, for the king wanted to see his daughter. The queen always went to the bath in the early morning. It was built of marble and adorned with soft cushions and beautiful carpets.

She took three toads, kissed them, and said to the first, "Sit upon Elise's head when she comes to the bath, so that she may become sluggish like yourself. Sit upon her forehead," she said to the second, "that she may become ugly like you, and then her father won't know her! Rest upon her heart," she whispered to the third. "Let an evil spirit come over her, which may be a burden to her." Then she put the toads into the clean water, and a green tinge immediately came over it. She called Elise, undressed her, and made her go into the bath; when she ducked under the water, one of the toads got among her hair, the other got on to her forehead, and the third on to her bosom. But when she stood up three scarlet poppies floated on the water; had not the creatures been poisonous, and kissed by the sorceress, they would have been changed into crimson roses, but yet they became flowers from merely having rested a moment on her head and her heart. She was far too good and innocent for the sorcery to have any power over her. When the wicked Queen saw this, she rubbed her over with walnut juice, and smeared her face with some evil-smelling salve. She also matted up her beautiful hair; it would have been impossible to recognize pretty Elise. When her father saw her, he was quite horrified and said that she could not be his daughter. Nobody would have anything to say to her, except the yard dog, and the swallows, and they were only poor dumb animals whose opinion went for nothing.

Poor Elise wept, and thought of her eleven brothers who were all lost. She crept sadly out of the palace and wandered about all day, over meadows and marshes, and into a big forest. She did not know in the least where she wanted to go, but she felt very sad, and longed for her brothers, who, no doubt, like herself had been driven out of the palace. She made up her mind to go and look for them, but she had only been in the wood for a short time when night fell. She had quite lost her way, so she lay down upon the soft moss, said her evening prayer, and rested her head on a little hillock. It was very still and the air was mild, hundreds of glowworms shone around her on the grass and in the marsh like green fire. When she gently moved one of the branches over her head, the little shining insects fell over her like a shower of stars. She dreamt about her brothers all night long. Again they were children playing together: they wrote upon the golden slates with their diamond pencils, and she looked at the picture-book which had cost half a kingdom. But they no longer wrote strokes and noughts upon their slates as they used to do; no, they wrote down all their boldest exploits, and everything that they had seen and experienced. Everything in the picture book was alive, the birds sang, and the people walked out of the book, and spoke to Elise and her brothers. When she turned over a page, they skipped back into their places again, so that there should be no confusion among the pictures.

When she woke the sun was already high; it is true she could not see it very well through the thick branches of the lofty forest trees, but the sunbeams cast a golden shimmer round beyond the forest. There was a fresh delicious scent of grass and herbs in the air, and the birds were almost ready to perch upon her shoulders. She could hear the splashing of water, for there were many springs around, which all flowed into a pond with a lovely sandy bottom. It was surrounded with thick bushes, but there was one place which the stags had trampled down and Elise passed through the opening to the water side. It was so transparent, that had not the branches been moved by the breeze, she must

have thought that they were painted on the bottom, so plainly was every leaf reflected, both those on which the sun played, and those which were in shade.

When she saw her own face she was quite frightened, it was so brown and ugly, but when she wet her little hand and rubbed her eyes and forehead, her white skin shone through again. Then she took off all her clothes and went into the fresh water. A more beautiful royal child than she, could not be found in all the world.

When she had put on her clothes again, and plaited her long hair, she went to a sparkling spring and drank some of the water out of the hollow of her hand. Then she wandered farther into the wood, though where she was going she had not the least idea. She thought of her brothers, and she thought of a merciful God who would not forsake her. He let the wild crab-apples grow to feed the hungry. He showed her a tree, the branches of which were bending beneath their weight of fruit. Here she made her midday meal, and, having put props under the branches, she walked on into the thickest part of the forest. It was so quiet that she heard her own footsteps, she heard every little withered leaf which bent under her feet. Not a bird was to be seen, not a ray of sunlight pierced the leafy branches, and the tall trunks were so close together that when she looked before her it seemed as if a thick fence of heavy beams hemmed her in on every side. The solitude was such as she had never known before.

It was a very dark night, not a single glowworm sparkled in the marsh; sadly she lay down to sleep, and it seemed to her as if the branches above her parted asunder, and the Saviour looked down upon her with His loving eyes, and little angels' heads peeped out above His head and under His arms.

When she woke in the morning she was not sure if she had dreamt this, or whether it was really true.

She walked a little farther, when she met an old woman with a basket full of berries, of which she gave her some. Elise asked if she had seen eleven princes ride through the wood. "No," said the old woman, "but yesterday I saw eleven swans, with golden crowns upon their heads, swimming in the stream close by here."

She led Elise a little farther to a slope, at the foot of which the stream meandered. The trees on either bank stretched out their rich leafy branches toward each other, and where, from their natural growth, they could not reach each other, they had torn their roots out of the ground, and leant over the water so as to interlace their branches.

Elise said good-by to the old woman, and walked along by the river till it flowed out into the great open sea.

The beautiful open sea lay before the maiden, but not a sail was to be seen on it, not a single boat. How was she ever to get any further? She looked at the numberless little pebbles on the beach; they were all worn quite round by the water. Glass, iron, stone, whatever was washed up, had taken their shapes from the water, which yet was much softer than her little hand. "With all its rolling, it is untiring, and everything hard is smoothed down. I will be just as untiring! Thank you for your lesson, you clear rolling waves! Some time, so my heart tells me, you will bear me to my beloved brothers!"

Eleven white swans' feathers were lying on the sea-weed; she picked them up and made a bunch of them. There were still drops of water on them. Whether these were dew or tears no one could tell. It was very lonely there by the shore, but she did not feel it, for the sea was ever-changing. There were more changes on it in the course of a few hours than could be seen on an inland fresh-water lake in a year. If a big black cloud arose, it was just as if the sea wanted to say, "I can look black too," and then the wind blew up and the waves showed their white crests. But if the clouds were red and the wind dropped, the sea looked like a rose leaf, now white, now green. But, however still it was, there was always a little gentle motion just by the shore, the water rose and fell softly like the bosom of a sleeping child.

When the sun was just about to go down, Elise saw eleven wild swans with golden crowns upon their heads flying toward the shore. They flew in a swaying line, one behind the other, like a white ribbon streamer. Elise climbed up on to the bank and hid behind a bush; the swans settled close by her and flapped their great white wings.

As soon as the sun had sunk beneath the water, the swans shed their feathers and became eleven handsome princes; they were Elise's brothers. Although they had altered a good deal, she knew them at once; she felt that they must be her brothers and she sprang into their arms, calling them by name. They were delighted when they recognized their little sister who had grown so big and beautiful. They laughed and cried, and told each other how wickedly their stepmother had treated them all.

"We brothers," said the eldest, "have to fly about in the guise of swans, as long as the sun is above the horizon. When it goes down we regain our human shapes. So we always have to look out for a resting place near sunset, for should we happen to be flying up among the clouds when the sun goes down, we should be hurled to the depths below. We do not live here; there is another land, just as beautiful as this, beyond the sea; but the way to it is very long and we have to cross the mighty ocean to get to it. There is not a single island on the way where we can spend the night, only one solitary little rock juts up above the water midway. It is only just big enough for us to stand upon close together, and if there is a heavy sea the water splashes over us, yet we thank our God for it. We stay there over night in our human forms, and without it we could never revisit our beloved Fatherland, for our flight takes two of the longest days in the year. We are only permitted to visit the home of our fathers once a year, and we dare only stay for eleven days. We hover over this big forest from whence we catch a glimpse of the palace where we were born, and where our father lives; beyond it we can see the high church towers where our mother is buried. We fancy that the trees and bushes here are related to us; and the wild horses gallop over the moors, as we used to see them in our childhood. The charcoal burners still sing the old songs we used to dance to when we were children. This is our Fatherland, we are drawn toward it, and here we have found you again, dear little sister! We may stay here two days longer, and then we must fly away again across the ocean, to a lovely country indeed, but it is not our own dear Fatherland! How shall we ever take you with us, we have neither ship nor boat!"

"How can I deliver you?" said their sister, and they went on talking to each other, nearly all night, they only dozed for a few hours.

Elise was awakened in the morning by the rustling of the swan's wings above her; her brothers were again transformed and were wheeling round in great circles, till she lost sight of them in the distance. One of them, the youngest, stayed behind. He laid his head against her bosom, and she caressed it with her fingers. They remained together all day; toward evening the others came back, and as soon as the sun went down they took their natural forms.

"Tomorrow we must fly away, and we dare not come back for a whole year, but we can't leave you like this! Have you courage to go with us? My arm is strong enough to carry you over the forest, so surely our united strength ought to be sufficient to bear you across the ocean."

"Oh yes! take me with you," said Elise.

They spent the whole night in weaving a kind of net of the elastic bark of the willow bound together with tough rushes; they made it both large and strong. Elise lay down upon it, and when the sun rose and the brothers became swans again, they took up the net in their bills and flew high up among the clouds with their precious sister, who was fast asleep. The sunbeams fell straight on to her face, so one of the swans flew over her head so that its broad wings should shade her.

They were far from land when Elise woke; she thought she must still be dreaming, it seemed so strange to be carried through the air so high up above the sea. By her side lay a branch of beautiful ripe berries, and a bundle of savory roots, which her youngest brother had collected for her, and for which she gave him a grateful smile. She knew it was he who flew above her head shading her from the sun. They were so high up that the first ship they saw looked like a gull floating on the water. A great cloud came up behind them like a mountain, and Elise saw the shadow of herself on it, and those of the eleven swans looking like giants. It was a more beautiful picture than any she had ever seen before, but as the sun rose higher, the cloud fell behind, and the shadow picture disappeared.

They flew on and on all day like an arrow whizzing through the air, but they went slower than usual, for now they had their sister to carry. A storm came up, and night was drawing on; Elise saw the sun sinking with terror in her heart, for the solitary rock was nowhere to be seen. The swans seemed to be taking stronger strokes than ever; alas! she was the cause of their not being able to get on faster; as soon as the sun went down they would become men, and they would all be hurled into the sea and drowned. She prayed to God from the bottom of her heart, but still no rock was to be seen! Black clouds gathered, and strong gusts of wind announced a storm; the clouds looked like a great threatening leaden wave, and the flashes of lightning followed each other rapidly.

The sun was now at the edge of the sea. Elise's heart quaked, when suddenly the swans shot downwards so suddenly, that she thought they were falling, then they hovered again. Half of the sun was below the horizon, and there for the first time she saw the little rock below, which did not look bigger than the head of a seal above the water. The sun sank very quickly, it was no bigger than a star, but her foot touched solid earth. The sun went out like the last sparks of a bit of burning paper; she saw her brothers stand arm in arm around her, but there was only just room enough for them. The waves beat upon the rock and washed over them like drenching rain. The heavens shone with continuous fire, and the thunder rolled, peal upon peal. But the sister and brothers held each other's hands and sang a psalm which gave them comfort and courage.

The air was pure and still at dawn. As soon as the sun rose the swans flew off with Elise, away from the islet. The sea still ran high, it looked from where they were as if the white foam on the dark green water were millions of swans floating on the waves.

When the sun rose higher, Elise saw before her half floating in the air great masses of ice, with shining glaciers on the heights. A palace was perched midway a mile in length, with one bold colonnade built above another. Beneath them swayed palm trees and gorgeous blossoms as big as mill wheels. She asked if this was the land to which she was going, but the swans shook their heads, because what she saw was a mirage; the beautiful and ever-changing palace of Fata Morgana. No mortal dared enter it. Elise gazed at it, but as she gazed the palace, gardens and mountains melted away, and in their place stood twenty proud churches with their high towers and pointed windows. She seemed to hear the notes of the organ, but it was the sea she heard. When she got close to the seeming churches, they changed to a great navy sailing beneath her; but it was only a sea mist floating over the waters. Yes, she saw constant changes passing before her eyes, and now she saw the real land she was bound to. Beautiful blue mountains rose before her with their cedar woods and palaces. Long before the sun went down, she sat among the hills in front of a big cave covered with delicate green creepers. It looked like a piece of embroidery.

"Now we shall see what you will dream here tonight," said the youngest brother, as he showed her where she was to sleep.

"If only I might dream how I could deliver you," she said, and this thought filled her mind entirely. She prayed earnestly to God for His help, and even in her sleep she continued her prayer. It seemed to her that she was flying up to Fata Morgana in her castle in the air. The fairy came toward her, she was charming and brilliant, and yet she was very like the old woman who gave her the berries in the wood, and told her about the swans with the golden crowns.

"Your brothers can be delivered," she said, "but have you courage and endurance enough for it? The sea is indeed softer than your hands, and it molds the hardest stones, but it does not feel the pain your fingers will feel. It has no heart, and does not suffer the pain and anguish you must feel. Do you see this stinging nettle I hold in my hand? Many of this kind grow round the cave where you sleep; only these and the ones which grow in the churchyards may be used. Mark that! Those you may pluck although they will burn and blister your hands. Crush the nettles with your feet and you will have flax, and of this you must weave eleven coats of mail with long sleeves. Throw these over the eleven wild swans and the charm is broken! But remember that from the moment you begin this work, till it is finished, even if it takes years, you must not utter a word! The first word you say will fall like a murderer's dagger into the hearts of your brothers. Their lives hang on your tongue. Mark this well!"

She touched her hand at the same moment, it was like burning fire, and woke Elise. It was bright daylight, and close to where she slept lay a nettle like those in her dream. She fell upon her knees with thanks to God and left the cave to begin her work.

She seized the horrid nettles with her delicate hands, and they burnt like fire; great blisters rose on her hands and arms, but she suffered it willingly if only it would deliver her beloved brothers. She crushed every nettle with her bare feet, and twisted it into green flax.

When the sun went down and the brothers came back, they were alarmed at finding her mute; they thought it was some new witchcraft exercised by their wicked stepmother. But when they saw her hands, they understood that it was for their sakes; the youngest brother wept, and wherever his tears fell, she felt no more pain, and the blisters disappeared.

She spent the whole night at her work, for she could not rest till she had delivered her dear brothers. All the following day while her brothers were away she sat solitary, but never had the time flown so fast. One coat of mail was finished and she began the next. Then a hunting-horn sounded among the mountains; she was much frightened, the sound came nearer, and she heard dogs barking. In terror she rushed into the cave and tied the nettles she had collected and woven into a bundle upon which she sat.

At this moment a big dog bounded forward from the thicket, and another and another, they barked loudly and ran backwards and forwards. In a few minutes all the huntsmen were standing outside the cave, and the handsomest of them was the king of the country. He stepped up to Elise: never had he seen so lovely a girl.

"How came you here, beautiful child?" he said.

Elise shook her head; she dared not speak; the salvation and the lives of her brothers depended upon her silence. She hid her hands under her apron, so that the king should not see what she suffered.

"Come with me!" he said; "you cannot stay here. If you are as good as you are beautiful, I will dress you in silks and velvets, put a golden crown upon your head, and you shall live with me and have your home in my richest palace!" Then he lifted her upon his horse, she wept and wrung her hands, but the king said, "I only think of your happiness; you will thank me one day for what I am doing!" Then he darted off across the mountains, holding her before him on his horse, and the huntsmen followed.

When the sun went down, the royal city with churches and cupolas lay before them, and the king led her into the palace, where great fountains played in the marble halls, and where walls and ceilings were adorned with paintings, but she had no eyes for them, she only wept and sorrowed; passively she allowed the women to dress her in royal robes, to twist pearls into her hair, and to draw gloves on to her blistered hands.

She was dazzlingly lovely as she stood there in all her magnificence; the courtiers bent low before her, and the king wooed her as his bride, although the archbishop shook his head, and whispered that he feared the beautiful wood maiden was a witch, who had dazzled their eyes and infatuated the king.

The king refused to listen to him, he ordered the music to play, the richest food to be brought, and the loveliest girls to dance before her. She was led through scented gardens into gorgeous apartments, but nothing brought a smile to her lips, or into her eyes, sorrow sat there like a heritage and a possession for all time. Last of all, the king opened the door of a little chamber close by the room where she was to sleep. It was adorned with costly green carpets, and made to exactly resemble the cave where he found her. On the floor lay the bundle of flax she had spun from the nettles, and from the ceiling hung the shirt of mail which was already finished. One of the huntsmen had brought all these things away as curiosities.

"Here you may dream that you are back in your former home!" said the king. "Here is the work upon which you were engaged; in the midst of your splendor, it may amuse you to think of those times."

When Elise saw all these things so dear to her heart, a smile for the first time played about her lips, and the blood rushed back to her cheeks.

She thought of the deliverance of her brothers, and she kissed the king's hand; he pressed her to his heart, and ordered all the church bells to ring marriage peals. The lovely dumb girl from the woods was to be queen of the country.

The archbishop whispered evil words into the ear of the king, but they did not reach his heart. The wedding was to take place, and the archbishop himself had to put the crown upon her head. In his anger he pressed the golden circlet so tightly upon her head as to give her pain. But a heavier circlet pressed upon her heart, her grief for her brothers, so she thought nothing of the bodily pain. Her lips were sealed, a single word from her mouth would cost her brothers their lives, but her eyes were full of love for the good and handsome king, who did everything he could to please her. Every day she grew more and more attached to him, and longed to confide in him, tell him her sufferings; but dumb she must remain, and in silence must bring her labor to completion. Therefore at night she stole away from his side into her secret chamber, which was decorated like a cave, and here she knitted one shirt after another. When she came to the seventh, all her flax was worked up; she knew that these nettles which she was to use grew in the churchyard, but she had to pluck them herself. How was she to get there? "Oh, what is the pain of my fingers compared with the anguish of my heart," she thought. "I must venture out, the good God will not desert me!" With as much terror in her heart as if she were doing some evil deed, she stole down one night into the moonlit garden, and through the long alleys out into the silent streets to the churchyard. There she saw, sitting on a gravestone, a group of hideous ghouls, who took off their tattered garments, as if they were about to bathe, and then they dug down into the freshly-made graves with their skinny fingers, and tore the flesh from the bodies and devoured it. Elise had to pass close by them, and they fixed their evil eyes upon her, but she said a prayer as she passed, picked the stinging nettles and hurried back to the palace with them.

Only one person saw her, but that was the archbishop, who watched while others slept. Surely now all his bad opinions of the queen were justified; all was not as it should be with her, she must be a witch, and therefore she had bewitched the king and all the people.

He told the king in the confessional what he had seen and what he feared. When those bad words passed his lips, the pictures of the saints shook their heads as if to say: it is not so, Elise is innocent. The archbishop, however, took it differently, and thought that they were bearing witness against her, and shaking their heads at her sin. Two big tears rolled down the king's cheeks, and he went home with doubt in his heart. He pretended to sleep at night, but no quiet sleep came to his eyes. He perceived how Elise got up and went to her private closet. Day by day his face grew darker, Elise saw it but could not imagine what was the cause of it. It alarmed her, and what was she not already suffering in her heart because of her brothers? Her salt tears ran down upon the royal purple velvet, they lay upon it like sparkling diamonds, and all who saw their splendor wished to be queen.

She had, however, almost reached the end of her labors, only one shirt of mail was wanting, but again she had no more flax and not a single nettle was left. Once more, for the last time, she must go to the churchyard to pluck a few handfuls. She thought with dread of the solitary walk and the horrible ghouls; but her will was as strong as her trust in God.

Elise went, but the king and the archbishop followed her, they saw her disappear within the gateway of the churchyard. When they followed they saw the ghouls sitting on the gravestone as Elise had seen them before; and the king turned away his head because he thought she was among them, she, whose head this very evening had rested on his breast.

"The people must judge her," he groaned, and the people judged. "Let her be consumed in the glowing flames!"

She was led away from her beautiful royal apartments to a dark damp dungeon, where the wind whistled through the grated window. Instead of velvet and silk they gave her the bundle of nettles she had gathered to lay her head upon. The hard burning shirts of mail were to be her covering, but they could have given her nothing more precious.

She set to work again with many prayers to God. Outside her prison the street boys sang derisive songs about her, and not a soul comforted her with a kind word.

Toward evening she heard the rustle of swans' wings close to her window; it was her youngest brother, at last he had found her. He sobbed aloud with joy although he knew that the coming night might be her last, but then her work was almost done and her brothers were there.

The archbishop came to spend her last hours with her as he had promised the king. She shook her head at him, and by looks and gestures begged him to leave her. She had only this night in which to finish her work, or else all would be wasted, all—her pain, tears and sleepless nights. The archbishop went away with bitter words against her, but poor Elise knew that she was innocent, and she went on with her work.

The little mice ran about the floor bringing nettles to her feet, so as to give what help they could, and a thrush sat on the grating of the window where he sang all night, as merrily as he could to keep up her courage.

It was still only dawn, and the sun would not rise for an hour when the eleven brothers stood at the gate of the palace, begging to be taken to the king. This could not be done, was the answer, for it was still night; the king was asleep and no one dared wake him. All their entreaties and threats were useless, the watch turned out and even the king himself came to see what was the matter; but just then the sun rose, and no more brothers were to be seen, only eleven wild swans hovering over the palace.

The whole populace streamed out of the town gates, they were all anxious to see the witch burnt. A miserable horse drew the cart in which Elise was seated. They had put upon her a smock of green sacking, and all her beautiful long hair hung loose from the lovely head. Her cheeks were deathly pale, and her lips moved softly, while her fingers unceasingly twisted the green yarn. Even on the way to her death she could not abandon her unfinished work. Ten shirts lay completed at her feet—she labored away at the eleventh, amid the scoffing insults of the populace.

"Look at the witch how she mutters. She has never a book of psalms in her hands, no, there she sits with her loathsome sorcery. Tear it away from her, into a thousand bits!"

The crowd pressed around her to destroy her work, but just then eleven white swans flew down and perched upon the cart flapping their wings. The crowd gave way before them in terror.

"It is a sign from Heaven! She is innocent!" they whispered, but they dared not say it aloud.

The executioner seized her by the hand, but she hastily threw the eleven shirts over the swans, who were immediately transformed to eleven handsome princes; but the youngest had a swan's wing in place of an arm, for one sleeve was wanting to his shirt of mail, she had not been able to finish it.

"Now I may speak! I am innocent."

The populace who saw what had happened bowed down before her as if she had been a saint, but she sank lifeless in her brother's arms; so great had been the strain, the terror and the suffering she had endured.

"Yes, innocent she is indeed," said the eldest brother, and he told them all that had happened.

Whilst he spoke a wonderful fragrance spread around, as of millions of roses. Every faggot in the pile had taken root and shot out branches, and a great high hedge of red roses had arisen. At the very top was one pure white blossom, it shone like a star, and the king broke it off and laid it on Elise's bosom, and she woke with joy and peace in her heart.

All the church bells began to ring of their own accord, and the singing birds flocked around them. Surely such a bridal procession went back to the palace as no king had ever seen before!

THE SWINEHERD

Hans Christian Andersen

In folk tale style, a droll but also a satire, this amusing story is for older children. They will catch the silliness of a princess who prefers the artificial to the real, and they will understand that such folly is not limited to princesses.

There was once a poor Prince; he had only quite a tiny kingdom, but it was big enough to allow him to marry, and he was bent upon marrying.

Now, it certainly was rather bold of him to say to the Emperor's daughter, "Will you have me?" He did, however, venture to say so, for his name was known far and wide; and there were hundreds of Princesses who would have said "Yes," and "Thank you, kindly," but see if *she* would!

Just let us hear about it.

A rose tree grew on the grave of the prince's father, it was such a beautiful rose tree; it only bloomed every fifth year, and then only bore one blossom; but what a rose that was! By merely smelling it one forgot all one's cares and sorrows.

Then he had a nightingale which sang as if every lovely melody in the world dwelt in her little throat. This rose and this nightingale were to be given to the Princess, so they were put into great silver caskets and sent to her.

The Emperor had them carried before him into the great Hall where the Princess was playing at "visiting" with her ladies-in-waiting; they had nothing else to do. When she saw the caskets with the gifts she clapped her hands with delight!

"If only it were a little pussy cat!" said she,—but there was the lovely rose.

"Oh, how exquisitely it is made!" said all the ladies-in-waiting.

"It is more than beautiful," said the Emperor; "it is neat."

But the Princess touched it, and then she was ready to cry.

"Fie, Papa!" she said; "it is not made, it is a real one!"

"Fie," said all the ladies-in-waiting; "it is a real one!"

"Well, let us see what there is in the other casket, before we get angry," said the Emperor, and out came the nightingale. It sang so beautifully that at first no one could find anything to say against it.

"*Superbe! charmant!*" said the ladies-in-waiting, for they all had a smattering of French, one spoke it worse than the other.

"The Swineherd." From *Fairy Tales* by Hans Christian Andersen, translated by Mrs. Edgar Lucas, Everyman's Library, E. P. Dutton & Co., Inc., New York. By permission also of J. M. Dent & Sons, Ltd., London

"How that bird reminds me of our lamented Empress's musical box," said an old courtier. "Ah, yes, they are the same tunes, and the same beautiful execution."

"So they are," said the Emperor, and he cried like a little child.

"I should hardly think it could be a real one," said the Princess.

"Yes, it is a real one," said those who had brought it.

"Oh, let that bird fly away then," said the Princess, and she would not hear of allowing the Prince to come. But he was not to be crushed; he stained his face brown and black, and, pressing his cap over his eyes, he knocked at the door.

"Good morning, Emperor," said he; "can I be taken into service in the palace?"

"Well, there are so many wishing to do that," said the Emperor; "but let me see!—yes, I need somebody to look after the pigs, for we have so many of them."

So the Prince was made imperial swineherd. A horrid little room was given him near the pig-sties, and here he had to live. He sat busily at work all day, and by the evening he had made a beautiful little cooking pot; it had bells all round it and when the pot boiled they tinkled delightfully and played the old tune:

"Ach du lieber Augustin,
Alles ist weg, weg, weg!"

Alas! dear Augustin,
All is lost, lost, lost!

But the greatest charm of all about it was, that by holding one's finger in the steam one could immediately smell all the dinners that were being cooked at every stove in the town. Now this was a very different matter from a rose.

The Princess came walking along with all her ladies-in-waiting, and when she heard the tune she stopped and looked pleased, for she could play "Ach du lieber Augustin" herself; it was her only tune, and she could only play it with one finger.

"Why, that is my tune," she said; "this must be a cultivated swineherd. Go and ask him what the instrument costs."

So one of the ladies-in-waiting had to go into his room, but she put pattens on first.

"How much do you want for the pot?" she asked.

"I must have ten kisses from the Princess," said the swineherd.

"Heaven preserve us!" said the lady.

"I won't take less," said the swineherd.

"Well, what does he say?" asked the Princess.

"I really cannot tell you," said the lady-in-waiting, "it is so shocking."

"Then you must whisper it." And she whispered it.

"He is a wretch!" said the Princess, and went away at once. But she had only gone a little way when she heard the bells tinkling beautifully:

"Ach du lieber Augustin."

"Go and ask him if he will take ten kisses from the ladies-in-waiting."

"No, thank you," said the swineherd; "ten kisses from the Princess, or I keep my pot."

"How tiresome it is," said the Princess. "Then you will have to stand round me, so that no one may see."

So the ladies-in-waiting stood round her and spread out their skirts while the swineherd took his ten kisses, and then the pot was hers.

What a delight it was to them! The pot was kept on the boil day and night. They knew what was cooking on every stove in the town, from the chamberlain's to the shoemaker's. The ladies-in-waiting danced about and clapped their hands.

"We know who has sweet soup and pancakes for dinner, and who has cutlets; how amusing it is."

"Highly interesting," said the mistress of the robes.

"Yes, but hold your tongues, for I am the Emperor's daughter."

"Heaven preserve us!" they all said.

The swineherd—that is to say, the Prince, only nobody knew that he was not a real swineherd—did not let the day pass in idleness, and he now constructed a rattle. When it was swung round it played all the waltzes, galops and jig tunes which have ever been heard since the creation of the world.

"But this is *superbe!*" said the Princess, as she walked by. "I have never heard finer compositions. Go and ask him what the instrument costs, but let us have no more kissing."

"He wants a hundred kisses from the Princess!" said the lady-in-waiting.

"I think he is mad!" said the Princess, and she went away, but she had not gone far when she stopped.

"One must encourage art," she said; "I am the Emperor's daughter. Tell him he can have ten kisses, the same as yesterday, and he can take the others from the ladies-in-waiting."

"But we don't like that at all," said the ladies.

"Oh, nonsense! If I can kiss him you can do

see!" So he pulled up the heels of his slippers for they were shoes which he had trodden down.

Bless us, what a hurry he was in! When he got into the yard, he walked very softly and the ladies were so busy counting the kisses, so that there should be fair play, and neither too few nor too many kisses, that they never heard the Emperor. He stood on tiptoe.

"What is all this?" he said when he saw what was going on, and he hit them on the head with his slipper just as the swineherd was taking the eighty-sixth kiss.

"Out you go!" said the Emperor, for he was

the same. Remember that I pay your wages as well as give you board and lodging." So the lady-in-waiting had to go again.

"A hundred kisses from the Princess, or let each keep his own."

"Stand in front of me," said she, and all the ladies stood round, while he kissed her.

"Whatever is the meaning of that crowd round the pig-sties?" said the Emperor as he stepped out on to the verandah; he rubbed his eyes and put on his spectacles. "Why, it is the ladies-in-waiting, what game are they up to? I must go and

furious, and both the Princess and the Prince were put out of his realm.

There she stood crying, and the swineherd scolded, and the rain poured down in torrents.

"Oh, miserable creature that I am! if only I had accepted the handsome Prince. Oh, how unhappy I am!"

The swineherd went behind a tree, wiped the black and brown stain from his face, and threw away his ugly clothes. Then he stepped out dressed as a Prince, he was so handsome that the Princess could not help curtseying to him.

"I am come to despise thee," he said. "Thou wouldst not have an honourable Prince, thou couldst not prize the rose or the nightingale, but thou wouldst kiss the swineherd for a trumpery musical box! As thou hast made thy bed, so must thou lie upon it!"

Then he went back into his own little kingdom and shut and locked the door. So she had to stand outside and sing in earnest—

"Ach du lieber Augustin
Alles ist weg, weg, weg!"

PINOCCHIO

Carlo Lorenzini

Carlo Collodi was the pen name of a witty Italian by the name of Carlo Lorenzini. Italians and Sicilians have always loved puppets so it is not surprising that Lorenzini should write a story about a puppet that comes to life. Anyone who has ever made puppets or played with them has experienced the uncanny feeling that the creatures really do have a life of their own and may take to their heels any minute. This episode finds Pinocchio in a terrible fix. He has run away from school, failed to keep his promises, and is now so conspicuously punished for his sins that he is repenting for dear life.

Every one, at one time or another, has found some surprise awaiting him. Of the kind which Pinocchio had on that eventful morning of his life, there are but few.

What was it? I will tell you, my dear little readers. On awakening, Pinocchio put his hand up to his head and here he found—

Guess!

He found that, during the night, his ears had grown at least ten full inches!

You must know that the Marionette, even from his birth, had very small ears, so small indeed that to the naked eye they could hardly

be seen. Fancy how he felt when he noticed that overnight those two dainty organs had become as long as shoe brushes!

He went in search of a mirror, but not finding any, he just filled a basin with water and looked at himself. There he saw what he never could have wished to see. His manly figure was adorned and enriched by a beautiful pair of donkey's ears.

I leave you to think of the terrible grief, the shame, the despair of the poor Marionette.

He began to cry, to scream, to knock his head against the wall, but the more he shrieked, the longer and the more hairy grew his ears.

At those piercing shrieks, a Dormouse came into the room, a fat little Dormouse, who lived upstairs. Seeing Pinocchio so grief-stricken, she asked him anxiously:

"What is the matter, dear little neighbor?"

"I am sick, my little Dormouse, very, very sick—and from an illness which frightens me! Do you understand how to feel the pulse?"

"A little."

"Feel mine then and tell me if I have a fever."

The Dormouse took Pinocchio's wrist between her paws and, after a few minutes, looked up at him sorrowfully and said:

"My friend, I am sorry, but I must give you some very sad news."

"What is it?"

"You have a very bad fever."

"But what fever is it?"

"The donkey fever."

"I don't know anything about that fever," answered the Marionette, beginning to understand even too well what was happening to him.

"Then I will tell you all about it," said the Dormouse. "Know then that, within two or three hours, you will no longer be a Marionette, nor a boy."

"What shall I be?"

"Within two or three hours you will become a real donkey, just like the ones that pull the fruit carts to market."

"Oh, what have I done? What have I done?" cried Pinocchio, grasping his two long ears in his hands and pulling and tugging at them angrily, just as if they belonged to another.

"My dear boy," answered the Dormouse to cheer him up a bit, "why worry now? What is done cannot be undone, you know. Fate has decreed that all lazy boys who come to hate books and schools and teachers and spend all their days with toys and games must sooner or later turn into donkeys."

"But is it really so?" asked the Marionette, sobbing bitterly.

"I am sorry to say it is. And tears now are useless. You should have thought of all this before."

"But the fault is not mine. Believe me, little Dormouse, the fault is all Lamp-Wick's."

"And who is this Lamp-Wick?"

"A classmate of mine. I wanted to return home. I wanted to be obedient. I wanted to study and to succeed in school, but Lamp-Wick said to me, 'Why do you want to waste your time studying? Why do you want to go to school? Come with me to the Land of Toys. There we'll never study again. There we can enjoy ourselves and be happy from morn till night.'"

"And why did you follow the advice of that false friend?"

"Why? Because, my dear little Dormouse, I am a heedless Marionette—heedless and heartless. Oh! If I had only had a bit of heart, I should never have abandoned that good Fairy, who loved me so well and who has been so kind to me! And by this time, I should no longer be a Marionette. I should have become a real boy, like all these friends of mine! Oh, if I meet Lamp-Wick I am going to tell him what I think of him—and more too!"

After this long speech, Pinocchio walked to the door of the room. But when he reached it, remembering his donkey ears, he felt ashamed to show them to the public and turned back. He took a large cotton bag from a shelf, put it on his head, and pulled it far down to his very nose.

Thus adorned, he went out. He looked for Lamp-Wick everywhere, along the streets, in the squares, inside the theaters, everywhere; but he was not to be found. He asked every one whom he met about him, but no one had seen him.

In desperation, he returned home and knocked at the door.

"Who is it?" asked Lamp-Wick from within.

"It is I!" answered the Marionette.

"Wait a minute."

After a full half hour the door opened. Another surprise awaited Pinocchio! There in the room stood his friend, with a large cotton bag on his head, pulled far down to his very nose.

At the sight of that bag, Pinocchio felt slightly happier and thought to himself:

"My friend must be suffering from the same sickness that I am! I wonder if he, too, has donkey fever?"

But pretending he had seen nothing, he asked with a smile:

"How are you, my dear Lamp-Wick?"

"Very well. Like a mouse in a Parmesan cheese."

"Is that really true?"

"Why should I lie to you?"

"I beg your pardon, my friend, but why then are you wearing that cotton bag over your ears?"

"The doctor has ordered it because one of my knees hurts. And you, dear Marionette, why are you wearing that cotton bag down to your nose?"

"The doctor has ordered it, because I have bruised my foot."

"Oh, my poor Pinocchio!"

"Oh, my poor Lamp-Wick!"

An embarrassingly long silence followed these words, during which time the two friends looked at each other in a mocking way.

Finally the Marionette, in a voice sweet as honey and soft as a flute, said to his companion:

"Tell me, Lamp-Wick, dear friend, have you ever suffered from an earache?"

"Never! And you?"

"Never! Still, since this morning my ear has been torturing me."

"So has mine."

"Yours, too? And which ear is it?"

"Both of them. And yours?"

"Both of them, too. I wonder if it could be the same sickness."

"I'm afraid it is."

"Will you do me a favor, Lamp-Wick?"

"Gladly! With my whole heart."

"Will you let me see your ears?"

"Why not? But before I show you mine, I want to see yours, dear Pinocchio."

"No. You must show yours first."

"No, my dear! Yours first, then mine."

"Well, then," said the Marionette, "let us make a contract."

"Let's hear the contract!"

"Let us take off our caps together. All right?"

"All right."

"Ready then!"

Pinocchio began to count, "One! Two! Three!"

At the word "Three!" the two boys pulled off their caps and threw them high in air.

And then a scene took place which is hard to believe, but it is all too true. The Marionette and his friend, Lamp-Wick, when they saw each other both stricken by the same misfortune, instead of feeling sorrowful and ashamed, began to poke fun at each other, and after much nonsense, they ended by bursting out into hearty laughter.

They laughed and laughed, and laughed again —laughed till they ached—laughed till they cried.

But all of a sudden Lamp-Wick stopped laughing. He tottered and almost fell. Pale as a ghost, he turned to Pinocchio and said:

"Help, help, Pinocchio!"

"What is the matter?"

"Oh, help me! I can no longer stand up."

"I can't either," cried Pinocchio; and his laughter turned to tears as he stumbled about helplessly.

They had hardly finished speaking, when both of them fell on all fours and began running and jumping around the room. As they ran, their arms turned into legs, their faces lengthened into snouts, and their backs became covered with long gray hairs.

This was humiliation enough, but the most horrible moment was the one in which the two poor creatures felt their tails appear. Overcome with shame and grief, they tried to cry and bemoan their fate.

But what is done can't be undone! Instead of moans and cries, they burst forth into loud donkey brays, which sounded very much like, "Haw! Haw! Haw!"

At that moment, a loud knocking was heard at the door and a voice called to them:

"Open! I am the Little Man, the driver of the wagon which brought you here. Open, I say, or beware!"

THE EMPEROR'S NEW CLOTHES

Hans Christian Andersen

This amusing tale is an allegory and a droll. It sounds much like a folk tale, but no folk tale ever had its wit and its tongue-in-the-cheek attitude towards the pompous incompetents of the world. Andersen in this story takes his revenge on the stupid people who made him suffer.

Many years ago there was an Emperor who was so excessively fond of new clothes that he spent all his money on them. He cared nothing about his soldiers, nor for the theatre, nor for driving in the woods except for the sake of show-

ing off his new clothes. He had a costume for every hour in the day, and instead of saying as one does about any other King or Emperor, "He is in his council chamber," here one always said, "The Emperor is in his dressing-room."

"The Emperor's New Clothes." From *Fairy Tales* by Hans Christian Andersen, translated by Mrs. Edgar Lucas, Everyman's Library, E. P. Dutton & Co., Inc., New York. By permission also of J. M. Dent & Sons, Ltd., London

Life was very gay in the great town where he lived; hosts of strangers came to visit it every day, and among them one day two swindlers. They gave themselves out as weavers, and said that they knew how to weave the most beautiful stuffs imaginable. Not only were the colours and patterns unusually fine, but the clothes that were made of these stuffs had the peculiar quality of becoming invisible to every person who was not fit for the office he held, or if he was impossibly dull.

"Those must be splendid clothes," thought the Emperor. "By wearing them I should be able to discover which men in my kingdom are unfitted for their posts. I shall distinguish the wise men from the fools. Yes, I certainly must order some of that stuff to be woven for me."

He paid the two swindlers a lot of money in advance so that they might begin their work at once.

They did put up two looms and pretended to weave, but they had nothing whatever upon their shuttles. At the outset they asked for a quantity of the finest silk and the purest gold thread, all of which they put into their own bags while they worked away at the empty looms far into the night.

"I should like to know how those weavers are getting on with the stuff," thought the Emperor; but he felt a little queer when he reflected that anyone who was stupid or unfit for his post would not be able to see it. He certainly thought that he need have no fears for himself, but still he thought he would send somebody else first to see how it was getting on. Everybody in the town knew what wonderful power the stuff possessed, and everyone was anxious to see how stupid his neighbor was.

"I will send my faithful old minister to the weavers," thought the Emperor. "He will be best able to see how the stuff looks, for he is a clever man and no one fulfils his duties better than he does!"

So the good old minister went into the room where the two swindlers sat working at the empty loom.

"Heaven preserve us!" thought the old minister, opening his eyes very wide. "Why, I can't see a thing!" But he took care not to say so.

Both the swindlers begged him to be good enough to step a little nearer, and asked if he did not think it a good pattern and beautiful colouring. They pointed to the empty loom, and the poor old minister stared as hard as he could but he could not see anything, for of course there was nothing to see.

"Good heavens!" thought he, "is it possible that I am a fool? I have never thought so and nobody must know it. Am I not fit for my post? It will never do to say that I cannot see the stuffs."

"Well, sir, you don't say anything about the stuff," said the one who was pretending to weave.

"Oh, it is beautiful! quite charming!" said the old minister looking through his spectacles; "this pattern and these colors! I will certainly tell the Emperor that the stuff pleases me very much."

"We are delighted to hear you say so," said the swindlers, and then they named all the colours and described the peculiar pattern. The old minister paid great attention to what they said, so as to be able to repeat it when he got home to the Emperor.

Then the swindlers went on to demand more money, more silk, and more gold, to be able to proceed with the weaving; but they put it all into their own pockets—not a single strand was ever put into the loom, but they went on as before weaving at the empty loom.

The Emperor soon sent another faithful official to see how the stuff was getting on, and if it would soon be ready. The same thing happened to him as to the minister; he looked and looked, but as there was only the empty loom, he could see nothing at all.

"Is not this a beautiful piece of stuff?" said both the swindlers, showing and explaining the beautiful pattern and colours which were not there to be seen.

"I know I am not a fool!" thought the man, "so it must be that I am unfit for my good post! It is very strange though! however, one must not let it appear!" So he praised the stuff he did not see, and assured them of his delight in the beautiful colours and the originality of the design. "It is absolutely charming!" he said to the Emperor. Everybody in the town was talking about this splendid stuff.

Now the Emperor thought he would like to see

it while it was still on the loom. So, accompanied by a number of selected courtiers, among whom were the two faithful officials who had already seen the imaginary stuff, he went to visit the crafty impostors, who were working away as hard as ever they could at the empty loom.

"It is magnificent!" said both the honest officials. "Only see, Your Majesty, what a design! What colours!" And they pointed to the empty loom, for they thought no doubt the others could see the stuff.

"What!" thought the Emperor; "I see nothing at all! This is terrible! Am I a fool? Am I not fit to be Emperor? Why, nothing worse could happen to me!"

"Oh, it is beautiful!" said the Emperor. "It has my highest approval!" and he nodded his satisfaction as he gazed at the empty loom. Nothing would induce him to say that he could not see anything.

The whole suite gazed and gazed, but saw nothing more than all the others. However, they all exclaimed with His Majesty, "It is very beautiful!" and they advised him to wear a suit made of this wonderful cloth on the occasion of a great procession which was just about to take place. "It is magnificent! gorgeous! excellent!" went from mouth to mouth; they were all equally delighted with it. The Emperor gave each of the rogues an order of knighthood to be worn in their buttonholes and the title of "Gentlemen Weavers."

The swindlers sat up the whole night, before the day on which the procession was to take place, burning sixteen candles, so that people might see how anxious they were to get the Emperor's new clothes ready. They pretended to take the stuff off the loom. They cut it out in the air with a huge pair of scissors, and they stitched away with needles without any thread in them. At last they said, "Now the Emperor's new clothes are ready!"

The Emperor, with his grandest courtiers, went to them himself, and both the swindlers raised one arm in the air, as if they were holding something, and said, "See, these are the trousers, this is the coat, here is the mantle!" and so on. "It is as light as a spider's web. One might think one had nothing on, but that is the very beauty of it!"

"Yes!" said all the courtiers, but they could not see anything, for there was nothing to see.

"Will Your Imperial Majesty be graciously pleased to take off your clothes," said the imposters, "so that we may put on the new ones, along here before the great mirror."

The Emperor took off all his clothes, and the impostors pretended to give him one article of dress after the other, of the new ones which they had pretended to make. They pretended to fasten something round his waist and to tie on something; this was the train, and the Emperor turned round and round in front of the mirror.

"How well His Majesty looks in the new clothes! How becoming they are!" cried all the people round. "What a design, and what colours! They are most gorgeous robes!"

"The canopy is waiting outside which is to be carried over Your Majesty in the procession," said the master of the ceremonies.

"Well, I am quite ready," said the Emperor. "Don't the clothes fit well?" and then he turned round again in front of the mirror, so that he should seem to be looking at his grand things.

The chamberlains who were to carry the train stooped and pretended to lift it from the ground with both hands, and they walked along with their hands in the air. They dared not let it appear that they could not see anything.

Then the Emperor walked along in the procession under the gorgeous canopy, and everybody in the streets and at the windows exclaimed, "How beautiful the Emperor's new clothes are! What a splendid train! And they fit to perfection!" Nobody would let it appear that he could see nothing, for then he would not be fit for his post, or else he was a fool.

None of the Emperor's clothes had been so successful before.

"But he has got nothing on," said a little child.

"Oh, listen to the innocent," said its father; and one person whispered to the other what the child had said. "He has nothing on; a child says he has nothing on!"

"But he has nothing on!" at last cried all the people.

The Emperor writhed, for he knew it was true, but he thought "the procession must go on now," so he held himself stiffer than ever, and the chamberlains held up the invisible train.

THE OPEN ROAD

Kenneth Grahame

Kenneth Grahame started telling the stories about Ratty, Mole, and all the other denizens of the river bank to his small son at bedtime. When the child did not want to go to the seashore without his father, Grahame promised to send him stories. A careful nurse who read the installments of The Wind in the Willows *to the boy, recognized their worth and saved the letters. From them, the book grew and was finally put together for publication. It remains one of the great juvenile classics in the English language. This does not mean that every child is going to like it, but children should be exposed to its beauty and humor in the hope that the contagion will "take."*

"Ratty," said the Mole suddenly, one bright summer morning, "if you please, I want to ask you a favour."

The Rat was sitting on the river bank, singing a little song. He had just composed it himself, so he was very taken up with it, and would not pay proper attention to Mole or anything else. Since early morning he had been swimming in the river in company with his friends the ducks. And when the ducks stood on their heads suddenly, as ducks will, he would dive down and tickle their necks just under where their chins would be if ducks had chins, till they were forced to come to the surface again in a hurry, spluttering and angry and shaking their feathers at him, for it is impossible to say quite *all* you feel when your head is under water. At last they implored him to go away and attend to his own affairs and leave them to mind theirs. So the Rat went away, and sat on the river bank in the sun, and made up a song about them, which he called

DUCKS' DITTY

All along the backwater,
Through the rushes tall,
Ducks are a-dabbling,
Up tails all!

"The Open Road." Reprinted from *The Wind in the Willows* by Kenneth Grahame; copyright 1908, 1935 by Charles Scribner's Sons; used by permission of the publishers

Ducks' tails, drakes' tails,
Yellow feet a-quiver,
Yellow bills all out of sight
Busy in the river!

Slushy green undergrowth
Where the roach swim—
Here we keep our larder,
Cool and full and dim.

Every one for what he likes!
We like to be
Heads down, tails up,
Dabbling free!

High in the blue above
Swifts whirl and call—
We are down a-dabbling
Up tails all!

"I don't know that I think so *very* much of that little song, Rat," observed the Mole cautiously. He was no poet himself and didn't care who knew it; and he had a candid nature.

"Nor don't the ducks neither," replied the Rat cheerfully. "They say, '*Why* can't fellows be allowed to do what they like *when* they like and *as* they like, instead of other fellows sitting on banks and watching them all the time and making remarks, and poetry and things about them? What *nonsense* it all is!' That's what the ducks say."

"So it is, so it is," said the Mole, with great heartiness.

"No, it isn't!" cried the Rat indignantly.

"Well then, it isn't, it isn't," replied the Mole soothingly. "But what I wanted to ask you was, won't you take me to call on Mr. Toad? I've heard so much about him, and I do so want to make his acquaintance."

"Why, certainly," said the good-natured Rat, jumping to his feet and dismissing poetry from his mind for the day. "Get the boat out, and we'll paddle up there at once. It's never the wrong time to call on Toad. Early or late he's always the same fellow. Always good-tempered, always glad to see you, always sorry when you go!"

"He must be a very nice animal," observed the Mole, as he got into the boat and took the sculls, while the Rat settled himself comfortably in the stern.

"He is indeed the best of animals," replied Rat. "So simple, so good-natured, and so affectionate. Perhaps he's not very clever—we can't all be geniuses; and it may be that he is both boastful and conceited. But he has got some great qualities, has Toady." Rounding a bend in the river, they came in sight of a handsome, dignified old house of mellowed red brick, with well-kept lawns reaching down to the water's edge.

"There's Toad Hall," said the Rat; "and that creek on the left, where the notice-board says, 'Private. No landing allowed,' leads to his boat-house, where we'll leave the boat. The stables are over there to the right. That's the banquet-ing-hall you're looking at now—very old, that is. Toad is rather rich, you know, and this is really one of the nicest houses in these parts, though we never admit as much to Toad."

They glided up the creek, and the Mole shipped his sculls as they passed into the shadow of a large boat-house. Here they saw many handsome boats, slung from the cross-beams or hauled up on a slip, but none in the water; and the place had an unused and deserted air.

The Rat looked around him. "I understand," said he. "Boating is played out. He's tired of it, and done with it. I wonder what new fad he has taken up now? Come along and let's look him up. We shall hear all about it quite soon enough."

They disembarked, and strolled across the gay flower-decked lawns in search of Toad, whom they presently happened upon resting in a wicker garden-chair, with a preoccupied expression of face, and a large map spread out on his knees.

"Hooray!" he cried, jumping up on seeing them, "this is splendid!" He shook the paws of both of them warmly, never waiting for an introduction to the Mole. "How *kind* of you!" he went on, dancing round them. "I was just going to send a boat down the river for you, Ratty, with strict orders that you were to be fetched up here at once, whatever you were doing. I want you badly—both of you. Now what will you take? Come inside and have something! You don't know how lucky it is, your turning up just now!"

"Let's sit quiet a bit, Toady!" said the Rat,

throwing himself into an easy chair, while the Mole took another by the side of him and made some civil remark about Toad's "delightful residence."

"Finest house on the whole river," cried Toad boisterously. "Or anywhere else, for that matter," he could not help adding.

Here the Rat nudged the Mole. Unfortunately the Toad saw him do it, and turned very red. There was a moment's painful silence. Then Toad burst out laughing. "All right, Ratty," he said. "It's only my way, you know. And it's not such a very bad house, is it? You know you rather like it yourself. Now, look here. Let's be sensible. You are the very animals I wanted. You've got to help me. It's most important!"

"It's about your rowing, I suppose," said the Rat, with an innocent air. "You're getting on fairly well, though you splash a good bit still. With a great deal of patience, and any quantity of coaching, you may—"

"O, pooh! boating!" interrupted the Toad, in great disgust. "Silly boyish amusement. I've given that up *long* ago. Sheer waste of time, that's what it is. It makes me downright sorry to see you fellows, who ought to know better, spending all your energies in that aimless manner. No, I've discovered the real thing, the only genuine occupation for a lifetime. I propose to devote the remainder of mine to it, and can only regret the wasted years that lie behind me, squandered in trivialities. Come with me, dear Ratty, and your amiable friend also, if he will be so very good, just as far as the stable-yard, and you shall see what you shall see!"

He led the way to the stable-yard accordingly, the Rat following with a most mistrustful expression; and there, drawn out of the coach-house into the open, they saw a gipsy caravan, shining with newness, painted a canary-yellow picked out with green, and red wheels.

"There you are!" cried the Toad, straddling and expanding himself. "There's real life for you, embodied in that little cart. The open road, the dusty highway, the heath, the common, the hedgerows, the rolling downs! Camps, villages, towns, cities! Here to-day, up and off to somewhere else to-morrow! Travel, change, interest, excitement! The whole world before you, and a horizon that's always changing! And mind, this is the very finest cart of its sort that was ever built, without any exception. Come inside and look at the arrangements. Planned 'em all myself, I did!"

The Mole was tremendously interested and excited, and followed him eagerly up the steps and into the interior of the caravan. The Rat only snorted and thrust his hands deep into his pockets, remaining where he was.

It was indeed very compact and comfortable. Little sleeping-bunks—a little table that folded up against the wall—a cooking-stove, lockers, bookshelves, a bird-cage with a bird in it; and pots, pans, jugs and kettles of every size and variety.

"All complete!" said the Toad triumphantly, pulling open a locker. "You see—biscuits, potted lobster, sardines—everything you can possibly want. Soda-water here—baccy there—letter-paper, bacon, jam, cards and dominoes—you'll find," he continued, as they descended the steps again, "you'll find that nothing whatever has been forgotten, when we make our start this afternoon."

"I beg your pardon," said the Rat slowly, as he chewed a straw, "but did I overhear you say something about 'we' and 'start' and 'this afternoon'?"

"Now, you dear good old Ratty," said Toad imploringly, "don't begin talking in that stiff and sniffy sort of way, because you know you've got to come. I can't possibly manage without you, so please consider it settled, and don't argue—it's the one thing I can't stand. You surely don't mean to stick to your dull fusty old river all your life, and just live in a hole in a bank, and boat? I want to show you the world! I'm going to make an animal of you, my boy!"

"I don't care," said the Rat doggedly. "I'm not coming, and that's flat. And I am going to stick to my old river, and live in a hole, and boat, as I've always done. And what's more, Mole's going to stick to me and do as I do, aren't you, Mole?"

"Of course I am," said the Mole loyally. "I'll always stick to you, Rat, and what you say is to be—has got to be. All the same, it sounds as if it might have been—well, rather fun, you know!" he added wistfully. Poor Mole! The Life Adventurous was so new a thing to him, and so thrilling; and this fresh aspect of it was so tempting; and he had fallen in love at first sight with the canary-coloured cart and all its little fitments.

The Rat saw what was passing in his mind, and wavered. He hated disappointing people, and he was fond of the Mole, and would do almost anything to oblige him. Toad was watching both of them closely.

"Come along in and have some lunch," he said diplomatically, "and we'll talk it over. We needn't decide anything in a hurry. Of course, I don't really care. I only want to give pleasure to you fellows. 'Live for others!' That's my motto in life."

During luncheon—which was excellent, of course, as everything at Toad Hall always was—the Toad simply let himself go. Disregarding the Rat, he proceeded to play upon the inexperienced Mole as on a harp. Naturally a voluble animal, and always mastered by his imagination, he painted the prospects of the trip and the joys of the open life and the roadside in such glowing colours that the Mole could hardly sit in his chair for excitement. Somehow it soon seemed taken for granted by all three that the trip was a settled thing; and the Rat, though still unconvinced in his mind, allowed his good-nature to override his personal objections. He could not bear to disappoint his two friends, who were already deep in schemes and anticipations, planning out each day's separate occupation for several weeks ahead.

When they were quite ready, the now triumphant Toad led his companions to the paddock and set them to capture the old grey horse, who, without having been consulted, and to his own extreme annoyance, had been told off by Toad for the dustiest job in this dusty expedition. He frankly preferred the paddock, and took a deal of catching. Meantime Toad packed the lockers still tighter with necessaries, and hung nose-bags, nets of onions, bundles of hay, and baskets from the bottom of the cart. At last the horse was caught and harnessed, and they set off, all talking at once, each animal either trudging by the side of the cart or sitting on the shaft, as the humour took him. It was a golden afternoon. The smell of the dust they kicked up was rich and satisfying; out of thick orchards on either side the road, birds called and whistled to them cheerily; good-natured wayfarers, passing them, gave them "Good day," or stopped to say nice things about their beautiful cart; and rabbits, sitting at their front doors in the hedgerows, held up their fore paws, and said, "O my! O my! O my!"

Late in the evening, tired and happy and miles from home, they drew up on a remote common far from habitations, turned the horse loose to graze, and ate their simple supper sitting on the grass by the side of the cart. Toad talked big about all he was going to do in the days to come, while stars grew fuller and larger all around them, and a yellow moon, appearing suddenly and silently from nowhere in particular, came to keep them company and listen to their talk. At last they turned into their little bunks in the cart; and Toad, kicking out his legs, sleepily said, "Well, good night, you fellows! This is the real life for a gentleman! Talk about your old river!"

"I *don't* talk about my river," replied the patient Rat. "You *know* I don't, Toad. But I *think* about it," he added pathetically, in a lower tone: "I think about it—all the time!"

The Mole reached out from under his blanket, felt for the Rat's paw in the darkness, and gave it a squeeze. "I'll do whatever you like, Ratty," he whispered. "Shall we run away to-morrow morning, quite early—*very* early—and go back to our dear old hole on the river?"

"No, no, we'll see it out," whispered back the Rat. "Thanks awfully, but I ought to stick by Toad till this trip is ended. It wouldn't be safe for him to be left to himself. It won't take very long. His fads never do. Good night!"

The end was indeed nearer than even the Rat suspected.

After so much open air and excitement the Toad slept very soundly, and no amount of shaking could rouse him out of bed next morning. So the Mole and Rat turned to, quietly and manfully, and while the Rat saw to the horse, and lit a fire, and cleaned last night's cups and platters and got things ready for breakfast, the Mole trudged off to the nearest village, a long way off, for milk and eggs and various necessaries the Toad had, of course, forgotten to provide. The hard work had all been done, and the two animals were resting, thoroughly exhausted, by the time Toad appeared on the scene, fresh and gay, remarking what a pleasant easy life it was they were all leading now, after the cares and worries and fatigues of housekeeping at home.

They had a pleasant ramble that day over grassy downs and along narrow by-lanes, and camped, as before, on a common, only this time the two guests took care that Toad should do his fair share of work. In consequence, when the time came for starting next morning, Toad was by no means so rapturous about the simplicity of the primitive life, and indeed attempted to resume his place in his bunk, whence he was hauled by force. Their way lay, as before, across country by narrow lanes, and it was not till the afternoon that they came out on the high road, their first high road; and there disaster, fleet and unforeseen, sprang out on them—disaster momentous indeed to their expedition, but simply overwhelming in its effect on the after-career of Toad.

They were strolling along the high road easily, the Mole by the horse's head, talking to him, since the horse had complained that he was being frightfully left out of it, and nobody considered him in the least; the Toad and the Water Rat walking behind the cart talking together—at least Toad was talking, and Rat was saying at intervals, "Yes, precisely; and what did *you* say to *him?*"—and thinking all the time of something very different, when far behind them they heard a faint warning hum, like the drone of a distant bee. Glancing back, they saw a small cloud of dust, with a dark centre of energy, advancing on them at incredible speed, while from out the dust a faint "Poop-poop!" wailed like an uneasy animal in pain. Hardly regarding it, they turned to resume their conversation, when in an instant (as it seemed) the peaceful scene was changed, and with a blast of wind and a whirl of sound that made them jump for the nearest ditch, it was on them! The "Poop-poop" rang with a brazen shout in their ears, they had a moment's glimpse of an interior of glittering plate-glass and rich morocco, and the magnificent motor-car, immense, breath-snatching, passionate, with its pilot tense and hugging his wheel, possessed all earth and air for the fraction of a second, flung an enveloping cloud of dust that blinded and enwrapped them utterly, and then dwindled to a speck in the far distance, changed back into a droning bee once more.

The old grey horse, dreaming, as he plodded along, of his quiet paddock, in a new raw situation such as this simply abandoned himself to his natural emotions. Rearing, plunging, backing steadily, in spite of all the Mole's efforts at his head, and all the Mole's lively language directed at his better feelings, he drove the cart backwards towards the deep ditch at the side of the road. It wavered an instant—then there was a heart-rending crash—and the canary-coloured cart, their pride and their joy, lay on its side in the ditch, an irredeemable wreck.

The Rat danced up and down in the road, simply transported with passion. "You villains!" he shouted, shaking both fists. "You scoundrels, you highwaymen, you—you—road-hogs! —I'll have the law of you! I'll report you! I'll take you through all the Courts!" His home-sickness had quite slipped away from him, and for the moment he was the skipper of the canary-coloured vessel driven on a shoal by the reckless jockeying of rival mariners, and he was trying to recollect all the fine and biting things he used to say to masters of steam-launches when their wash, as they drove too near the bank, used to flood his parlour carpet at home.

Toad sat straight down in the middle of the dusty road, his legs stretched out before him, and stared fixedly in the direction of the disappearing motor-car. He breathed short, his face wore a placid, satisfied expression, and at intervals he faintly murmured "Poop-poop!"

The Mole was busy trying to quiet the horse, which he succeeded in doing after a time. Then he went to look at the cart, on its side in the ditch. It was indeed a sorry sight. Panels and windows smashed, axles hopelessly bent, one wheel off, sardine-tins scattered over the wide world, and the bird in the bird-cage sobbing pitifully and calling to be let out.

The Rat came to help him, but their united efforts were not sufficient to right the cart. "Hi! Toad!" they cried. "Come and bear a hand, can't you!"

The Toad never answered a word, or budged from his seat in the road; so they went to see what was the matter with him. They found him in a sort of trance, a happy smile on his face, his eyes still fixed on the dusty wake of their destroyer. At intervals he was still heard to murmur "Poop-poop!"

The Rat shook him by the shoulder. "Are you coming to help us, Toad?" he demanded sternly.

"Glorious, stirring sight!" murmured Toad, never offering to move. "The poetry of motion! The *real* way to travel! The *only* way to travel! Here to-day—in next week to-morrow! Villages skipped, towns and cities jumped—always somebody else's horizon! O bliss! O poop-poop! O my! O my!"

"O *stop* being an ass, Toad!" cried the Mole despairingly.

"And to think I never *knew!*" went on the Toad in a dreamy monotone. "All those wasted years that lie behind me, I never knew, never even *dreamt!* But *now*—but now that I know, now that I fully realize! O what a flowery track lies spread before me, henceforth! What dust-clouds shall spring up behind me as I speed on my reckless way! What carts I shall fling carelessly into the ditch in the wake of my magnificent onset! Horrid little carts—common carts—canary-coloured carts!"

"What are we to do with him?" asked the Mole of the Water Rat.

"Nothing at all," replied the Rat firmly. "Because there is really nothing to be done. You see, I know him from of old. He is now possessed. He has got a new craze, and it always takes him that way, in its first stage. He'll continue like that for days now, like an animal walking in a happy dream, quite useless for all practical purposes. Never mind him. Let's go and see what there is to be done about the cart."

A careful inspection showed them that, even if they succeeded in righting it by themselves, the cart would travel no longer. The axles were in a hopeless state, and the missing wheel was shattered into pieces.

The Rat knotted the horse's reins over his back and took him by the head, carrying the bird-cage and its hysterical occupant in the other hand. "Come on!" he said grimly to the Mole. "It's five or six miles to the nearest town, and we shall just have to walk it. The sooner we make a start the better."

"But what about Toad?" asked the Mole anxiously, as they set off together. "We can't leave him here, sitting in the middle of the road by himself, in the distracted state he's in! It's not safe. Supposing another Thing were to come along?"

"O, *bother* Toad," said the Rat savagely; "I've done with him!"

They had not proceeded very far on their way, however, when there was a pattering of feet behind them, and Toad caught them up and thrust a paw inside the elbow of each of them; still breathing short and staring into vacancy.

"Now, look here, Toad!" said the Rat sharply; "as soon as we get to the town, you'll have to go straight to the police-station, and see if they know anything about that motor-car and who it belongs to, and lodge a complaint against it. And then you'll have to go to a blacksmith's or wheelwright's and arrange for the cart to be fetched and mended and put to rights. It'll take time, but it's not quite a hopeless smash. Meanwhile, the Mole and I will go to an Inn and find comfortable rooms where we can stay till the cart's ready, and till your nerves have recovered from their shock."

"Police-station! Complaint!" murmured Toad dreamily. "Me *complain* of that beautiful, that heavenly vision that has been vouchsafed me! *Mend* the *cart!* I've done with carts forever. I never want to see the cart, or to hear of it, again. O, Ratty! You can't think how obliged I am to you for consenting to come on this trip! I wouldn't have gone without you, and then I might never have seen that—that swan, that sunbeam, that thunderbolt! I might never have heard that entrancing sound, or smelt that bewitching smell! I owe it all to you, my best of friends!"

The Rat turned from him in despair. "You see what it is?" he said to the Mole, addressing him across Toad's head: "He's quite hopeless. I give it up—when we get to the town we'll go to the railway-station, and with luck we may pick up a train there that'll get us back to River Bank to-night. And if ever you catch me going a-pleasuring with this provoking animal again!" —He snorted, and during the rest of that weary trudge addressed his remarks exclusively to Mole.

On reaching the town they went straight to the station and deposited Toad in the second-class waiting-room, giving a porter twopence to keep a strict eye on him. They then left the horse at an inn stable, and gave what directions they could about the cart and its contents. Eventually, a slow train having landed them at a station not very far from Toad Hall, they escorted the spell-bound, sleep-walking Toad to his door, put him inside it, and instructed his housekeeper to feed him, undress him, and put him to bed. Then they got out their boat from the boat-house, sculled down the river home, and at a very late hour sat down to supper in their own cosy riverside parlour, to the Rat's great joy and contentment.

The following evening the Mole, who had risen late and taken things very easy all day, was sitting on the bank fishing, when the Rat, who had been looking up his friends and gossiping, came strolling along to find him. "Heard the news?" he said. "There's nothing else being talked about, all along the river bank. Toad went up to Town by an early train this morning. And he has ordered a large and very expensive motor-car."

THE LADY
WHO PUT SALT IN HER COFFEE

Lucretia Hale

One account of the beginnings of these tales is that "Aunt Lucretia," on the spur of the moment, told the story about salt in the coffee for a sick child. Another account insists that the episode of the lady who wished to go for a drive really happened and gave the author the idea for these tales. However they began, Lucretia, the gifted sister of Edward Everett Hale, learned to pick up every silly mistake which she or any of her friends blundered into, and turn it into a problem for the "lady from Philadelphia."

"The Lady Who Put Salt in Her Coffee." From *The Peterkin Papers* by Lucretia P. Hale, Houghton Mifflin Company

This was Mrs. Peterkin. It was a mistake. She had poured out a delicious cup of coffee, and, just as she was helping herself to cream, she found she had put in salt instead of sugar! It tasted bad. What should she do? Of course she couldn't drink the coffee; so she called in the family, for she was sitting at a late breakfast all alone. The family came in; they all tasted, and looked, and wondered what should be done, and all sat down to think.

At last Agamemnon, who had been to college, said, "Why don't we go over and ask the advice of the chemist?" (For the chemist lived over the way, and was a very wise man.)

Mrs. Peterkin said, "Yes," and Mr. Peterkin said, "Very well," and all the children said they would go too. So the little boys put on their india-rubber boots, and over they went.

Now the chemist was just trying to find out something which should turn everything it touched into gold; and he had a large glass bottle into which he put all kinds of gold and silver, and many other valuable things, and melted them all up over the fire, till he had almost found what he wanted. He could turn things into almost gold. But just now he had used up all the gold that he had round the house, and gold was high. He had used up his wife's gold thimble and his great-grandfather's gold-bowed spectacles; and he had melted up the gold head of his great-great-grandfather's cane; and, just as the Peterkin family came in, he was down on his knees before his wife, asking her to let him have her wedding-ring to melt up with all the rest, because this time he knew he should succeed, and should be able to turn everything into gold; and then she could have a new wedding-ring of diamonds, all set in emeralds and rubies and topazes, and all the furniture could be turned into the finest of gold.

Now his wife was just consenting when the Peterkin family burst in. You can imagine how mad the chemist was! He came near throwing his crucible—that was the name of his melting-pot—at their heads. But he didn't. He listened as calmly as he could to the story of how Mrs. Peterkin had put salt in her coffee.

At first he said he couldn't do anything about it; but when Agamemnon said they would pay in gold if he would only go, he packed up his bottles in a leather case, and went back with them all. First he looked at the coffee, and then stirred it. Then he put in a little chlorate of potassium, and the family tried it all round; but it tasted no better. Then he stirred in a little bichlorate of magnesia. But Mrs. Peterkin didn't like that. Then he added some tartaric acid and some hypersulphate of lime. But no; it was no better. "I have it!" exclaimed the chemist—"a little ammonia is just the thing!" No, it wasn't the thing at all.

Then he tried, each in turn, some oxalic, cyanic, acetic, phosphoric, chloric, hyperchloric, sulphuric, boracic, silicic, nitric, formic, nitrous nitric, and carbonic acids. Mrs. Peterkin tasted each and said the flavor was pleasant, but not precisely that of coffee. So then he tried a little calcium, aluminum, barium, and strontium, a little clear bitumen, and a half of a third of a sixteenth of a grain of arsenic. This gave rather a pretty color; but still Mrs. Peterkin ungratefully said it tasted of anything but coffee. The chemist was not discouraged. He put in a little belladonna and atropine, some granulated hydrogen, some potash, and a very little antimony, finishing off with a little pure carbon. But still Mrs. Peterkin was not satisfied.

The chemist said that all he had done ought to have taken out the salt. The theory remained the same, although the experiment had failed. Perhaps a little starch would have some effect. If not, that was all the time he could give. He should like to be paid, and go. They were all much obliged to him, and willing to give him $1.37½ in gold. Gold was now 2.69¾, so Mr. Peterkin found in the newspaper. This gave Agamemnon a pretty little sum. He sat himself down to do it. But there was the coffee! All sat and thought awhile, till Elizabeth Eliza said, "Why don't we go to the herb-woman?" Elizabeth Eliza was the only daughter. She was named after her two aunts,—Elizabeth, from the sister of her father; Eliza, from her mother's sister. Now, the herb-woman was an old woman who came round to sell herbs, and knew a great deal. They all shouted with joy at the idea of asking her, and Solomon John and the younger children agreed to go and find her too. The herb-woman lived down at the very end of the street; so the boys put on their india-rubber boots again, and they set off. It was a long walk through the village, but they came at last to the herb-woman's house, at the foot of a high hill. They went through her little garden. Here she had marigolds and hollyhocks, and old maids and tall sunflowers, and all kinds of sweet-smelling herbs, so that the air was full of tansy-tea and elder-blow. Over the porch grew a hop-vine, and a brandy-cherry tree shaded the door, and a luxuriant cranberry-vine flung its delicious fruit across the window. They went into a small parlor, which smelt very spicy. All around hung little bags full of catnip, and peppermint, and all kinds of herbs; and dried stalks hung from the ceiling; and on the shelves were jars of rhubarb, senna, manna, and the like.

But there was no little old woman. She had gone up into the woods to get some more wild herbs, so they all thought they would follow her —Elizabeth Eliza, Solomon John, and the little boys. They had to climb up over high rocks, and in among huckleberry-bushes and blackberry-vines. But the little boys had their india-rubber boots. At last they discovered the little old woman. They knew her by her hat. It was steeple-crowned, without any vane. They saw her digging with her trowel round a sassafras bush. They told her their story—how their mother had put salt in her coffee, and how the chemist had made it worse instead of better, and how their mother couldn't drink it, and wouldn't she come and see what she could do? And she said she would, and took up her little old apron, with pockets all round, all filled with everlasting and pennyroyal, and went back to her house.

There she stopped, and stuffed her huge pockets with some of all the kinds of herbs. She took some tansy and peppermint, and caraway-seed and dill, spearmint and cloves, pennyroyal and sweet marjoram, basil and rosemary, wild thyme and some of the other time—such as you have in clocks,—sappermint and oppermint, catnip, valerian, and hop; indeed, there isn't a kind of herb you can think of that the little old woman didn't have done up in her little paper bags, that had all been dried in her little Dutch-oven. She packed these all up, and then went back with the children, taking her stick.

Meanwhile Mrs. Peterkin was getting quite impatient for her coffee.

As soon as the little old woman came she had it set over the fire, and began to stir in the different herbs. First she put in a little hop for the bitter. Mrs. Peterkin said it tasted like hop-tea, and not at all like coffee. Then she tried a little flagroot and snakeroot, then some spruce gum, and some caraway and some dill, some rue and rosemary, some sweet marjoram and sour, some oppermint and sappermint, a little spearmint and peppermint, some wild thyme, and some of the other tame time, some tansy and basil, and catnip and valerian, and sassafras, ginger, and pennyroyal. The children tasted after each mixture, but made up dreadful faces. Mrs. Peterkin tasted, and did the same. The more the old woman stirred, and the more she put in, the worse it all seemed to taste.

So the old woman shook her head, and muttered a few words, and said she must go. She believed the coffee was bewitched. She bundled up her packets of herbs, and took her trowel, and her basket, and her stick, and went back to her root of sassafras, that she had left half in the air and half out. And all she would take for pay was five cents in currency.

Then the family were in despair, and all sat and thought a great while. It was growing late in the day, and Mrs. Peterkin hadn't had her cup of coffee. At last Elizabeth Eliza said, "They say that the lady from Philadelphia, who is staying in town, is very wise. Suppose I go and ask her what is best to be done." To this they all agreed, it was a great thought, and off Elizabeth Eliza went.

She told the lady from Philadelphia the whole story,—how her mother had put salt in the coffee; how the chemist had been called in; how he tried everything but could make it no better; and how they went for the little old herb-woman, and how she had tried in vain, for her mother couldn't drink the coffee. The lady from Philadelphia listened very attentively, and then said, "Why doesn't your mother make a fresh cup of coffee?" Elizabeth Eliza started with surprise. Solomon John shouted with joy; so did Agamemnon, who had just finished his sum; so did the little boys who had followed on. "Why didn't we think of that?" said Elizabeth Eliza; and they all went back to their mother, and she had her cup of coffee.

MRS. PETERKIN

WISHES TO GO TO DRIVE

Lucretia Hale

One morning Mrs. Peterkin was feeling very tired, as she had been having a great many things to think of, and she said to Mr. Peterkin, "I believe I shall take a ride this morning!"

And the little boys cried out, "Oh, may we go too?"

Mrs. Peterkin said that Elizabeth Eliza and the little boys might go.

So Mr. Peterkin had the horse put into the carryall, and he and Agamemnon went off to their business, and Solomon John to school; and Mrs. Peterkin began to get ready for her ride.

She had some currants she wanted to carry to old Mrs. Twomly, and some gooseberries for somebody else, and Elizabeth Eliza wanted to pick some flowers to take to the minister's wife; so it took them a long time to prepare.

The little boys went out to pick the currants and the gooseberries, and Elizabeth Eliza went out for her flowers, and Mrs. Peterkin put on her cape-bonnet, and in time they were all ready. The little boys were in their india-rubber boots, and they got into the carriage.

Elizabeth Eliza was to drive; so she sat on the front seat, and took up the reins, and the horse started off merrily, and then suddenly stopped, and would not go any farther.

Elizabeth Eliza shook the reins, and pulled them, and then she clucked to the horse; and Mrs. Peterkin clucked; and the little boys whistled and shouted; but still the horse would not go.

"We shall have to whip him," said Elizabeth Eliza.

Now Mrs. Peterkin never liked to use the whip; but, as the horse would not go, she said she would get out and turn his head the other way, while Elizabeth Eliza whipped the horse, and when he began to go she would hurry and get in.

So they tried this, but the horse would not stir.

"Mrs. Peterkin Wishes to Go to Drive." From *The Peterkin Papers* by Lucretia P. Hale

"Perhaps we have too heavy a load," said Mrs. Peterkin, as she got in.

So they took out the currants and the gooseberries and the flowers, but still the horse would not go.

One of the neighbors, from the opposite house, looking out just then, called out to them to try the whip. There was a high wind, and they could not hear exactly what she said.

"I have tried the whip," said Elizabeth Eliza.

"She says 'whips,' such as you eat," said one of the little boys.

"We might make those," said Mrs. Peterkin, thoughtfully.

"We have got plenty of cream," said Elizabeth Eliza.

"Yes, let us have some whips," cried the little boys, getting out.

And the opposite neighbor cried out something about whips; and the wind was very high.

So they went into the kitchen, and whipped up the cream, and made some very delicious whips; and the little boys tasted all round, and they all thought they were very nice.

They carried some out to the horse, who swallowed it down very quickly.

"That is just what he wanted," said Mrs. Peterkin; "now he will certainly go!"

So they all got into the carriage again, and put in the currants, and the gooseberries, and the flowers; and Elizabeth Eliza shook the reins, and they all clucked; but still the horse would not go!

"We must either give up our ride," said Mrs. Peterkin, mournfully, "or else send over to the lady from Philadelphia, and see what she will say."

The little boys jumped out as quickly as they could; they were eager to go and ask the lady from Philadelphia. Elizabeth Eliza went with them, while her mother took the reins.

They found that the lady from Philadelphia was very ill that day, and was in her bed. But when she was told what the trouble was she very kindly said they might draw up the curtain from the window at the foot of the bed, and open the blinds, and she would see. Then she asked for her opera-glass, and looked through it, across the way, up the street, to Mrs. Peterkin's door.

After she had looked through the glass she laid it down, leaned her head back against the pillow, for she was very tired, and then said, "Why don't you unchain the horse from the horse-post?"

Elizabeth Eliza and the little boys looked at one another, and then hurried back to the house and told their mother. The horse was untied, and they all went to ride.

ABOUT ELIZABETH ELIZA'S PIANO

Lucretia Hale

Elizabeth Eliza had a present of a piano, and she was to take lessons of the postmaster's daughter.

They decided to have the piano set across the window in the parlor, and the carters brought it in, and went away.

After they had gone the family all came in to look at the piano; but they found the carters had placed it with its back turned towards the middle of the room, standing close against the window.

How could Elizabeth Eliza open it? How could she reach the keys to play upon it?

Solomon John proposed that they should open the window, which Agamemnon could do with his long arms. Then Elizabeth Eliza should go round upon the piazza, and open the piano. Then she could have her music-stool on the piazza, and play upon the piano there.

So they tried this; and they all thought it was a very pretty sight to see Elizabeth Eliza playing on the piano, while she sat on the piazza, with the honeysuckle vines behind her.

It was very pleasant, too, moonlight evenings. Mr. Peterkin liked to take a doze on his sofa in the room; but the rest of the family liked to sit on the piazza. So did Elizabeth Eliza, only she had to have her back to the moon.

All this did very well through the summer; but, when the fall came, Mr. Peterkin thought the air was too cold from the open window, and the family did not want to sit out on the piazza. Elizabeth Eliza practised in the mornings with

"About Elizabeth Eliza's Piano." From *The Peterkin Papers* by Lucretia P. Hale

her cloak on; but she was obliged to give up her music in the evenings the family shivered so.

One day, when she was talking with the lady from Philadelphia, she spoke of this trouble.

The lady from Philadelphia looked surprised, and then said, "But why don't you turn the piano round?"

One of the little boys pertly said, "It is a square piano."

But Elizabeth Eliza went home directly, and, with the help of Agamemnon and Solomon John, turned the piano round.

"Why did we not think of that before?" said Mrs. Peterkin. "What shall we do when the lady from Philadelphia goes home again?"

THE NIGHT OF THE BIG WIND

Arthur Mason

Some of the Irish folk have a seeing eye for the fairies that other people lack. Danny O'Fay was such a one. He thought kindly of the Wee Men even when he himself was in trouble. And surely the Big Wind was trouble enough for men, beasts, and fairies.

"The Night of the Big Wind," Chapters I and II. From *The Wee Men of Ballywooden* by Arthur Mason. Used with the kind permission of Arthur Mason

Old Danny O'Fay and his donkey lived in a hut by the sea, and Danny sold fish through the country. People wondered how he got his fish. He was never known to buy from fishermen, nor did he ever fish himself. But before he went to bed, he put the wee saddle on his donkey. Another thing he did, and he never missed a night. He would fill his clay pipe, and light it and puff on it for a bit. Then he'd open the door and lay the smoking pipe on the doorstep, saying as he yawned, "A fine night it is, with the sea talking and the corncrake singing. Well, have your smoke and take your donkey ride. You'll not be forgetting my fish for the morning. Good-night to yez all." Then he'd close and bar the door and lie down on his bed of straw and sleep until Jerry, his donkey, hee-hawed him awake. Then up he'd get and open the door and out to his two-wheel cart he'd go, to look at his fish. There they'd be, fresh from the sea, every one of them. Old Danny would smile the gouged wrinkles from his face. "Ah, and it's the fine catch they had last night," he'd say.

This had been going on for quite a while, and old Danny and his donkey thrived fairly well. He had his bowl of red tea, and potatoes and cabbage, and once in a while the leg of a duck. Old Danny was happy as he drove through the country shouting his song, "Fresh fish! Fresh fish! Fresh fish!"

Then came a day when old Danny's customers questioned his honesty.

"Say, Danny O'Fay," they asked, "where do you get your fish? You never buy from fishermen, nor do you ever fish yourself."

"Is it stealing fish you're thinking I am?"

"Oh, the Lord forbid," said Mrs. Blaney, "and us eating every morsel of them! It isn't that at all, at all, Danny O'Fay, but worse. Our eyes we've been keeping on you lately, and it's said by word of mouth, that in the dark of the moon, wee lights are seen dancing around your hut. Now, Danny O'Fay, if it's harboring Willie the Wisp you are, and all of his clan, not a fish will we buy from you."

"Tut, tut," said Danny, "You're all astray in your mind. It's eating too much oatmeal you are, and not enough fish out of the sea."

"Away with you, Danny O'Fay," they scolded.

"Look at the saddle marks on your donkey! How do you explain that?"

"I do a bit of riding in my sleep," answered Danny. "And as for the wee lights you do be seeing in the dark of the moon, sure it may be the flicker of your own candle lights that you haven't blinked out of your eyes."

"Oh, no, Danny O'Fay, it's pious men have seen the lights, and they have warned us to buy no more of your fish. Away with you, now!"

"Get up!" said Danny to his donkey. "It's terrible times we do be having, with people not believing, not buying my fish. Well, well, what will become of us anyway?"

All day long he drove through the country but not a fish could he sell. Nor would the farmers speak to him when he passed. They looked the other way. So heartsore and weary, he turned his donkey homeward, and by the time he reached the four roads, a mile or more from his hut, a wall of clouds banked the setting sun.

Old Danny looked up at the cloud-growing sky. Said he to himself, "I hear the crows scolding on the wing to their nests, but not a sight of one do I see. Put longer strides into your steps!" he shouted to his donkey. "Is it blind you are, that you can't see the clouds falling? Don't be listening to the frogs croaking or the crickets a-singing. Can't you hear the wind starting a fight in the whins? On with you, I say, before the pitch of the night swallows us up!" And Danny trudged on behind his donkey cart, thinking the while of the wind, and the power of it, and of the morrow with the fish in his cart left to rot.

The road now ribboned itself along the strand, and Danny looked out at the sea. "The Wee Men will be doing no fishing to-night," said he to himself, "not with the waves coughing the hearts out of themselves the way they are. Ah, and sure I'll have to be telling them to put their wee nets away. I can't sell a fish. There's a blight upon me. But they'll have their smoke and their donkey ride just the same."

Night came in like a crow lighting on a nest of eggs. Danny was home, unhitching his donkey.

"Ah, what a night! What a night!" he was saying. But he couldn't hear himself talk, for the wind stole the words out of his mouth as fast as his tongue could twist them. "Ah, there'll be a world of trouble to-night. I, with my five and seventy winters, have never listened to the lung-moanings of the wind like this before." He fumbled for the buckle on the donkey's collar. "Keep your ears away from my hands, bad cess to you, and me trying to get you out of the wind."

He opened the door of his hut. There was a wee turf fire burning in the grate. "Good-evening to yez all," he said. "My eyes don't see one of you, but sure that's nothing at all, with a night of nights outside. Come in, Jerry," he said to the donkey, "and be thankful you have a roof over your head." At that moment, the wind lifted a blanket of thatch off the roof. "I may have spoken a bit too quick; anyway, there's a fire in the grate, and your stall is over yonder."

Danny closed and barred the door. The wind tumbled through the hole in the roof and filled the hut. He tried to light a candle but the wind wouldn't let him. He pulled off his cap, scratched a wisp of hair over his ear, and looked up at the roof.

"Where's the moon to-night? Bad luck to her, the hag that she is. You never can see her when you want her. Oh, it's not angry I am at all. It's feeding the donkey I'll be doing." He felt his way to the stall. There stood the donkey eating oats. "What!" exclaimed old Danny. "Did they feed you before they left? Well, well, God bless every one of them! May the roots of the trees take a good grip of the ground while the Wee Men hold onto them, for it's something firm they'll be needing to-night. Ah, why don't they have houses like human beings? But it's not for me to tamper with things that are and things that are not. Anyway, they'll have their smoke, even if the wind lifts the world on its wings."

Danny sat down by the fire and filled his pipe and lit it. He smoked for a bit, then he got up and opened the door to lay his pipe down on the doorstep. The storm, like a byre full of bullocks chased by bumblebees, knocked the pipe out of his hand, and the mouth of the wind gulped its sparks.

"You gluttonous villain!" shouted old Danny. "May the sparks burn a hole in your thrapple!" He placed his back against the door and with his sharp shoulder blades he closed it. "Sure," said he, "it feels as if the tops of the mountains were playing hop, skip, and jump. Oh, what a night

for my wee friends to be out in. No shelter, no smoke, and the world rolling under them."

As old Danny hobbled over to the fire the only window in the hut blew in and crashed around his feet. A roar ran up the chimney and the wee fire chased after it. And to make matters worse, the thatched roof was stripped entirely. Danny was blown against the door, and he stood there, rubbing his hands.

"Is it afraid I am?" he cried. "Tut, tut, Danny O'Fay, put that thought out of your head. It's not the wind you're listening to, at all. It's the music from the big tumbling waves you're hearing." He got down on his hands and knees, and crawled to the donkey stall. "Get over there, Jerry. It's Danny that's talking. Don't you hear me? Get over, I say. Shake the roar out of your ears. There isn't an eye-cup of sleep in the world to-night, but it's alongside of you I'll be doing. If the wild mane of the blow leaves the walls standing, we'll both be here in the morning. Whist! Is that whispering I'm hearing, or is it the wind counting the spokes in the wheels of my cart?"

Old Danny lay down under the Manger, talking to himself, and closed his eyes.

CHAPTER II

The big wind wrought havoc through the country that night. Nothing escaped. Cattle sheds were up-ended. Chimneys tumbled down. Sheets of bog water went flying through the air. The four roads were choked with haystack tops and jaunting cars. Thorns and whin bushes were plucked out by the roots. Hedgehogs, wheelbarrows—all sorts of things were loose and on the run.

Blaney's rooster, that weighed a stone and could crow louder than any rooster in the parish, got stuck in the garden gate. The wind nibbled him naked. The old windmill on Murry's Brae, that hadn't run for years, was spinning to-night, and the squeaks from it sounded louder than a drove of hungry pigs.

The oak tree in the lonely lane had been the talk of generations. It was whispered in the ears of young and old that the Wee Men spent some of their nights in the lonely lane and played around the oak tree. And there wasn't a man in the parish who would pass it after dark. Anyway, the wind hurled against it and it came crashing to the ground. There was no shelter anywhere.

The cow paths looked twisted, and the stepping stiles were open gaps. Even the rushes in the meadow lay like combed hair.

Down by the sea, where a mossy rock lipped over a cove, swarms of Wee Men were hanging, clinging to the moss. The chief of the clan—the Paver-of-Caves—was renowned among the Wee Men for his ability to bend moonflakes with white heather for the flooring of the caves. To-night he was so fearfully frightened that he could hardly make himself heard, even though he spoke in his loudest voice.

"I hope the moss on this rock holds," he cried. "Were there any of you scratched when the oak tree fell?"

"No, no," came wee whines, "but we're all warped and twisted. Our eyes are webbed with eyebrows, and our beards are whistling tunes such as we never heard before!"

"That's to be expected," answered the Paver. "Keep your heads! Don't let the belching waves or the sky wheezings upset you. If the moss holds, well and good. If it doesn't, keep together, what-ever happens!"

A wee wail of a voice reached the Paver's ears. "The moss on this rock is as straggly as the down on a young linnet's breast!"

"Who is that I hear?" asked the Paver.

"The Midsummer Mower," came back the an-swer.

"I thought as much," cried the Paver. "You're always complaining of a poor harvest. Now then, weigh down your minds," commanded the Paver. "Weigh them down well, with the work you've left undone—and trust to that to hold you to the rock!"

The Wee Men had no difficulty weighing down their minds, but even that weight was no match for the night. All of a sudden, without the yelp of a warning, the arms of the wind be-gan wrestling with the rock.

"Let go," roared the Paver, "before we're tossed into the cove! There's slugging behind us, but nowheres ahead of us. Unballast your minds! Take hold of each other!"

A buzzing of wee voices hummed through the blackness.

"Oh, where are we going?"

"That," shouted the Paver, "is a question I can't answer."

The words were no sooner out of his mouth than the tail of the wind wound itself around the Wee Men and lifted them high in the air.

"We're all right, so far!" the Paver cried out. "Stick together! Don't let go of each other! If I had an eyeful of moonlight, I could tell you which way we're going."

"The sea is under us!" screamed the Crane Chaser.

The Midsummer Mower, who had hold of the Paver's hand, cried out in a tremble, "Have you no power at all?"

"Power?" shrieked back the Paver. "With my feet off the ground? Why, man, what are you thinking about? Power? I'd have you all know that, with the stars mired, and the moon choked, I can do nothing but blow away with the rest of you."

The gale was sweeping them out over the sea. The wee Cradle Rocker began to cry. "I'm get-ting dizzy from whirling and circling," he whined.

"Stop your crying!" commanded the Paver. "There's noise enough in the world to-night."

"If only I had a light," called out the Cradle Rocker, "I could find myself."

"Hold on," shouted the Paver, "there may be a remedy after all. Is Willie the Wisp among you?"

"That I am," piped up Willie, "but I haven't a spare breath to blow my light lit."

"Where do you think we are now?" spoke the Stooker-of-Wheat-Sheaves.

Grunty, the fisherman, answered, "Over Dun-drum Bay."

"If the clouds should let go of us," shouted the Wee Weaver, "I won't have to do any more weaving!"

"Stop your complaining," ordered the Paver. "I'll need a suit the minute we alight."

"How about me?" It was the Quarryman's voice. "My schisty shirt is slit up the back. My cap is gone and my pulse heaters, too. How are we going to get back? Can you answer me that, Paver-of-Caves?"

"We're speeding so fast," answered the Paver, "that my mind can't keep up with me."

There was silence among the Wee Men for a long time, for they had little breath to waste in words. They held tight to each other's hands, while the Big Wind made serpentine curves out of them, as on it swept over the sea, driving them ahead of it. But after a while the Counter-of-Lark-Eggs spoke. Said he, "I smell the morn, and it's fighting its way to be seen."

"Good," said the Paver, "I thought we were nearing something, for I just bumped my chilblain on the top of a mountain."

Far, far away, the tired eye of the morn squeezed through the clouds. Ribbons of sunken sunlight fluttered up and into the sky. And then something happened that brought cheer to the Wee Men, for all of a sudden they found themselves astride the arch of a rainbow.

"Let go of hands," commanded the Paver, "and every man of you slide down the rainbow legs to the ground! But mind and keep your heads, for we don't know what's waiting below."

The Wee Men began to argue about what colors they would choose to slide down.

"Look here," said the Paver, "there are colors enough for all of you. I'm going down on the peacock band."

"I'll follow you on the purple," said the Weaver. "I might even do a bit of weaving on my way down."

"Good!" cried the Paver. "I'm in need of a cloak. Have an eye out for color; it's a green cloak I want."

The Paver looked over his men. "Are you all ready?" he asked.

"We are!"

"Then let us slide down to the ground!"

The Wee Men lay flat on their little bellies, and each one twisted his short legs around the color band he liked best. Then down the rainbow legs they banistered.

The Weaver was the last to land, for he had a large bundle of woven rainbow web under his arm.

THE SKILLFUL HUNTSMAN

Howard Pyle

After Howard Pyle had illustrated his own retelling of the Robin Hood stories, he decided to continue writing the text for his pictures. Pepper and Salt *began as a series of humorous verses,* *but Pyle soon found it easier to write stories than verse. Children and storytellers have been equally delighted with the two collections that resulted.*

Once upon a time there was a lad named Jacob Boehm, who was a practical huntsman.

One day Jacob said to his mother, "Mother, I would like to marry Gretchen—the nice, pretty little daughter of the Herr Mayor."

Jacob's mother thought that he was crazy. "Marry the daughter of the Herr Mayor, indeed! You want to marry the daughter of the Herr Mayor? Listen; many a man wants and wants, and nothing comes of it!"

That was what Jacob Boehm's mother said to him.

But Jacob was deaf in that ear; nothing would do but his mother must go to the Herr Mayor, and ask for leave for him to marry Gretchen. And Jacob begged and begged so prettily that at last his mother promised to go and do as he wished. So off she went, though doubt was heavy in her shoes, for she did not know how the Herr Mayor would take it.

"So Jacob wants to marry Gretchen, does he?" said the Herr Mayor.

Yes; that was what Jacob wanted.

"And is he a practical huntsman?" said the Herr Mayor.

Oh yes, he was that.

"So good," said the Herr Mayor. "Then tell Jacob that when he is such a clever huntsman as to be able to shoot the whiskers off from a running hare without touching the skin, then he can have Gretchen."

Then Jacob's mother went back home again. "Now," said she, "Jacob will, at least, be satisfied."

"Yes," said Jacob, when she had told him all that the Herr Mayor had said to her, "that is a hard thing to do; but what one man has done, another man can." So he shouldered his gun, and started away into the world to learn to be as clever a huntsman as the Herr Mayor had said.

He plodded on and on until at last he fell in with a tall stranger dressed all in red.

"The Skillful Huntsman." From *Pepper and Salt* by Howard Pyle, Harper & Brothers

"Where are you going, Jacob?" said the tall stranger, calling him by his name, just as if he had eaten pottage out of the same dish with him.

"I am going," said Jacob, "to learn to be so clever a huntsman that I can shoot the whiskers off from a running hare without touching the skin."

"That is a hard thing to learn," said the tall stranger.

Yes; Jacob knew that it was a hard thing; but what one man had done another man could do.

"What will you give me if I teach you to be as clever a huntsman as that?" said the tall stranger.

"What will you take to teach me?" said Jacob; for he saw that the stranger had a horse's hoof instead of a foot, and he did not like his looks, I can tell you.

"Oh, it is nothing much that I want," said the tall man; "only just sign your name to this paper—that is all."

But what was in the paper? Yes; Jacob had to know what was in the paper before he would set so much as a finger to it.

Oh, there was nothing in the paper, only this: that when the red one should come for Jacob at the end of ten years' time, Jacob should promise to go along with him whithersoever he should take him.

At this Jacob hemmed and hawed and scratched his head, for he did not know about that. "All the same," said he, "I will sign the paper, but on one condition."

At this the red one screwed up his face as though he had sour beer in his mouth, for he did not like the sound of the word "condition." "Well," said he, "what is the condition?"

"It is only this," said Jacob: "that you shall be *my* servant for the ten years, and if, in all that time, I should chance to ask you a question that you cannot answer, then I am to be my own man again."

Oh, if that was all, the red man was quite willing for that.

Then he took Jacob's gun, and blew down into the barrel of it. "Now," said he, "you are as skillful a huntsman as you asked to be."

"That I must try," said Jacob. So Jacob and the red one went around hunting here and hunting there until they scared up a hare. "Shoot!" said the red one; and Jacob shot. Clip! off flew the whiskers of the hare as neatly as one could cut them off with the barber's shears.

"Yes, good!" said Jacob, "now I am a skillful huntsman."

Then the stranger in red gave Jacob a little bone whistle, and told him to blow in it whenever he should want him. After that Jacob signed the paper, and the stranger went one way and he went home again.

Well, Jacob brushed the straws off from his coat, and put a fine shine on his boots, and then he set off to the Herr Mayor's house.

"How do you find yourself, Jacob?" said the Herr Mayor.

"So good," said Jacob.

"And are you a skillful huntsman now?" said the Herr Mayor.

Oh yes, Jacob was a skillful huntsman now.

Yes, good! But the Herr Mayor must have proof of that. Now, could Jacob shoot a feather out of the tail of the magpie flying over the trees yonder?

Oh yes! nothing easier than that. So Jacob raised the gun to his cheek. Bang! went the gun, and down fell a feather from the tail of the magpie. At this the Herr Mayor stared and stared, for he had never seen such shooting.

"And now may I marry Gretchen?" said Jacob.

At this the Herr Mayor scratched his head, and hemmed and hawed. No; Jacob could not marry Gretchen yet, for he had always said and sworn that the man who should marry Gretchen should bring with him a plough that could go of itself, and plough three furrows at once. If Jacob would show him such a plough as that, then he might marry Gretchen and welcome. That was what the Herr Mayor said.

Jacob did not know how about that; perhaps he could get such a plough, perhaps he could not. If such a plough was to be had, though, he would have it. So off he went home again, and the Herr Mayor thought that he was rid of him now for sure and certain.

But when Jacob had come home, he went back of the woodpile and blew a turn or two on the little bone whistle that the red stranger had given him. No sooner had he done this than the other stood before him as suddenly as though he had just stepped out of the door of nowheres.

"What do you want, Jacob?" said he.

"I would like," said Jacob, "to have a plough that can go by itself and plough three furrows at once."

"That you shall have," said the red one. Then he thrust his hand into his breeches pocket, and drew forth the prettiest little plough that you ever saw. He stood it on the ground before Jacob, and it grew very large.

"Plough away," said he, and then he went back again whither he had come.

So Jacob laid his hands to the plough and—whisk!—away it went like John Stormwetter's colt, with Jacob behind it. Out of the farm-yard they went, and down the road, and so to the Herr Mayor's house, and behind them lay three fine brown furrows, smoking in the sun.

When the Herr Mayor saw them coming he opened his eyes, you may be sure, for he had never seen such a plough as that in all his life before.

"And now," said Jacob, "I should like to marry Gretchen, if you please."

At this the Herr Mayor hemmed and hawed and scratched his head again. No; Jacob could not marry Gretchen yet, for the Herr Mayor had always said and sworn that the man who married Gretchen should bring with him a purse that always had two pennies in it and could never be emptied, no matter how much was taken out of it.

Jacob did not know how about that; perhaps he could get it and perhaps he could not. If such a thing was to be had, though, he would have it, as sure as the Mecklenburg folks brew sour beer. So off he went home again, and the Herr Mayor thought that now he was rid of him for certain.

But Jacob went back of the woodpile and blew on his bone whistle again, and once more the red one came at his bidding.

"What will you have now?" said he to Jacob.

"I should like," said Jacob, "to have a purse which shall always have two pennies in it, no matter how much I take out of it."

"That you shall have," said the red one; whereupon he thrust his hand into his pocket, and fetched out a beautiful silken purse with two pennies in it. He gave the purse to Jacob, and then he went away again as quickly as he had come.

After he had gone, Jacob began taking pennies

out of his purse and pennies out of his purse, until he had more than a hatful—hui! I would like to have such a purse as that.

Then he marched off to the Herr Mayor's house with his chin up, for he might hold his head as high as any, now that he had such a purse as that in his pocket. As for the Herr Mayor, he thought that it was a nice, pretty little purse; but could it do this and that as he had said?

Jacob would show him that; so he began taking pennies and pennies out of it, until he had filled all the pots and pans in the house with them. And now might he marry Gretchen?

Yes; that he might! So said the Herr Mayor; for who would not like to have a lad for a son-in-law who always had two pennies more in his purse than he could spend.

So Jacob married his Gretchen, and, between his plough and his purse, he was busy enough, I can tell you.

So the days went on and on and on until the ten years had gone by and the time had come for the red one to fetch Jacob away with him. As for Jacob, he was in a sorry state of dumps, as you may well believe.

At last Gretchen spoke to him. "See, Jacob," said she, "what makes you so down in the mouth?"

"Oh! nothing at all," said Jacob.

But this did not satisfy Gretchen, for she could see that there was more to be told than Jacob had spoken. So she teased and teased, until at last Jacob told her all, and that the red one was to come the next day and take him off as his servant, unless he could ask him a question which he could not answer.

"Prut!" said Gretchen, "and is that all? Then there is no stuffing to that sausage, for I can help you out of your trouble easily enough." Then she told Jacob that when the next day should come he should do thus and so, and she would do this and that, and between them they might cheat the red one after all.

So, when the next day came, Gretchen went into the pantry and smeared herself all over with honey. Then she ripped open a bed and rolled herself in the feathers.

By-and-by came the red one. Rap! tap! tap! he knocked at the door.

"Are you ready to go with me now, Jacob?" said he.

Yes; Jacob was quite ready to go, only he would like to have one favor granted him first.

"What is it that you want?" said the red one.

"Only this," said Jacob: "I would like to shoot one more shot out of my old gun before I go with you."

Oh, if that was all, he might do that and welcome. So Jacob took down his gun, and he and the red one went out together, walking side by side, for all the world as though they were born brothers.

By-and-by they saw a wren. "Shoot at that," said the red one.

"Oh no," said Jacob, "that is too small."

So they went on a little farther.

By-and-by they saw a raven. "Shoot at that, then," said the red one.

"Oh no," said Jacob, "that is too black."

So they went on a little farther.

By-and-by they came to a ploughed field, and there was something skipping over the furrows that looked for all the world like a great bird. That was Gretchen; for the feathers stuck to the honey and all over her, so that she looked just like a great bird.

"Shoot at that! shoot at that!" said the red one, clapping his hands together.

"Oh yes," said Jacob, "I will shoot at that." So he raised his gun and took aim. Then he lowered his gun again. "But what is it?" said he.

At this the red one screwed up his eyes, and looked and looked, but for the life of him he could not tell what it was.

"No matter what it is," said he, "only shoot and be done with it, for I must be going."

"Yes, good! But what *is* it?" said Jacob.

Then the red one looked and looked again, but he could tell no better this time than he could before. "It may be this and it may be that," said he. "Only shoot and be done with it, for they are waiting for me at home."

"Yes, my friend," said Jacob, "that is all very good; only tell me what it is and I will shoot."

"Thunder and lightning!" bawled the red one, *"I do not know what it is!"*

"Then be off with you!" said Jacob, "for, since you cannot answer my question, all is over between us two."

At this the red one had to leave Jacob, so he fled away over hill and dale, bellowing like a bull.

As for Jacob and Gretchen, they went back home together, very well pleased with each other and themselves.

And the meaning of all this is, that many another man beside Jacob Boehm would find himself in a pretty scrape only for his wife.

THE KING
OF THE GOLDEN RIVER,
OR THE BLACK BROTHERS

John Ruskin

This long, rather somber tale in folk style by an art critic and author of many adult books is so dramatic that children do not forget it.

Chapter I: How the Agricultural System of the Black Brothers was interfered with by South-West Wind, Esquire.

In a secluded and mountainous part of Stiria, there was, in old time, a valley of the most surprising and luxuriant fertility. It was surrounded, on all sides, by steep and rocky mountains, rising into peaks, which were always covered with snow, and from which a number of torrents descended in constant cataracts. One of these fell westward, over the face of a crag so high, that, when the sun had set to everything else, and all below was darkness, his beams still shone full upon this waterfall, so that it looked like a shower of gold. It was, therefore, called by the people of the neighborhood the Golden River. It was strange that none of these streams fell into the valley itself. They all descended on the other side of the mountains, and wound away through broad plains and by populous cities. But the clouds were drawn so constantly to the snowy hills, and rested so softly in the circular hollow, that, in time of drought and heat, when all the country round was burnt up, there was still rain in the little valley; and its crops were so heavy, and its hay so high, and its apples so red, and its grapes so blue, and its wine so rich, and its honey so sweet, that it was a marvel to every one who beheld it, and was commonly called the Treasure Valley.

The whole of this little valley belonged to three brothers, called Schwartz, Hans, and Gluck. Schwartz and Hans, the two elder brothers, were very ugly men, with overhanging eyebrows and small, dull eyes, which were always half shut, so that you couldn't see into *them,* and always fancied they saw very far into *you.* They lived by farming the Treasure Valley, and very good farmers they were. They killed everything that did not pay for its eating. They shot the blackbirds, because they pecked the fruit; and killed the hedgehogs, lest they should suck the cows; they poisoned the crickets for eating the crumbs in the kitchen; and smothered the cicadas, which used to sing all summer in the lime trees. They worked their servants without any wages, till they would not work any more, and then quarrelled with them, and turned them out of doors without paying them. It would have been very odd, if, with such a farm, and such a system of farming, they hadn't got very rich; and very rich they *did* get. They generally contrived to keep their corn by them till it was very dear, and then sell it for twice its value; they had heaps of gold lying about on their floors, yet it was never known that they had given so much as a penny or a crust in charity; they never went to mass; grumbled perpetually at paying tithes; and were, in a word, of so cruel and grinding a temper, as to receive from all those with whom they had any dealings, the nickname of the "Black Brothers."

The youngest brother, Gluck, was as completely opposed, in both appearance and character, to his seniors as could possibly be imagined or desired. He was not above twelve years old, fair, blue-eyed, and kind in temper to every living thing. He did not, of course, agree particularly well with his brothers, or rather, they did not agree with *him.* He was usually appointed to the honorable office of turnspit, when there was anything to roast, which was not often; for, to do the brothers justice, they were hardly less sparing upon themselves than upon other people. At other times he used to clean the shoes, floors, and sometimes the plates, occasionally getting what was left on them, by way of encourage-

ment, and a wholesome quantity of dry blows, by way of education.

Things went on in this manner for a long time. At last came a very wet summer, and everything went wrong in the country round. The hay had hardly been got in, when the haystacks were floated bodily down to the sea by an inundation; the vines were cut to pieces with the hail; the corn was all killed by a black blight; only in the Treasure Valley, as usual, all was safe. As it had rain when there was rain nowhere else, so it had sun when there was sun nowhere else. Everybody came to buy corn at the farm, and went away pouring maledictions on the Black Brothers. They asked what they liked, and got it, except from the poor people, who could only beg, and several of whom were starved at their very door, without the slightest regard or notice.

It was drawing towards winter, and very cold weather, when one day the two elder brothers had gone out, with their usual warning to little Gluck, who was left to mind the roast, that he was to let nobody in, and give nothing out. Gluck sat down quite close to the fire, for it was raining very hard, and the kitchen walls were by no means dry or comfortable looking. He turned and turned, and the roast got nice and brown. "What a pity," thought Gluck, "my brothers never ask anybody to dinner. I'm sure, when they've got such a nice piece of mutton as this, and nobody else has got so much as a piece of dry bread, it would do their hearts good to have somebody to eat it with them."

Just as he spoke, there came a double knock at the house door, yet heavy and dull, as though the knocker had been tied up,—more like a puff than a knock.

"It must be the wind," said Gluck; "nobody else would venture to knock double knocks at our door."

No; it wasn't the wind; there it came again very hard, and what was particularly astounding, the knocker seemed to be in a hurry, and not to be in the least afraid of the consequences. Gluck went to the window, opened it, and put his head out to see who it was.

It was the most extraordinary looking little gentleman he had ever seen in his life. He had a very large nose, slightly brass-colored; his cheeks were very round, and very red, and might have warranted a supposition that he had been blowing a refractory fire for the last eight-and-forty hours; his eyes twinkled merrily through long silky eyelashes, his moustaches curled twice round like a corkscrew on each side of his mouth, and his hair, of a curious mixed pepper-and-salt color, descended far over his shoulders. He was about four feet six in height, and wore a conical pointed cap of nearly the same altitude, decorated with a black feather some three feet long. His doublet was prolonged behind into something resembling a violent exaggeration of what is now termed a "swallow-tail," but was much obscured by the swelling folds of an enormous black, glossy-looking cloak, which must have been very much too long in calm weather, as the wind, whistling round the old house, carried it clear out from the wearer's shoulders to about four times his own length.

Gluck was so perfectly paralyzed by the singular appearance of his visitor, that he remained fixed without uttering a word, until the old gentleman, having performed another, and a more energetic concerto on the knocker, turned round to look after his fly-away cloak. In so doing he caught sight of Gluck's little yellow head jammed in the window, with its mouth and eyes very wide open indeed.

"Hollo!" said the little gentleman, "that's not the way to answer the door; I'm wet, let me in."

To do the little gentleman justice, he *was* wet. His feather hung down between his legs like a beaten puppy's tail, dripping like an umbrella; and from the ends of his moustaches the water was running into his waistcoat pockets, and out again like a mill stream.

"I beg pardon, sir," said Gluck, "I'm very sorry, but I really can't."

"Can't what?" said the old gentleman.

"I can't let you in, sir,—I can't indeed; my brothers would beat me to death, sir, if I thought of such a thing. What do you want, sir?"

"Want?" said the old gentleman petulantly, "I want fire and shelter; and there's your great fire there blazing, crackling, and dancing on the walls, with nobody to feel it. Let me in, I say; I only want to warm myself."

Gluck had had his head, by this time, so long out of the window, that he began to feel it was really unpleasantly cold, and when he turned, and saw the beautiful fire rustling and roaring, and throwing long bright tongues up the chimney, as if it were licking its chops at the savory smell of the leg of mutton, his heart melted within him that it should be burning away for nothing. "He does look *very* wet," said little Gluck; "I'll just let him in for a quarter of an hour." Round he went to the door, and opened it; and as the little gentleman walked in, there came a gust of wind through the house, that made the old chimneys totter.

"That's a good boy," said the little gentleman. "Never mind your brothers. I'll talk to them."

"Pray, sir, don't do any such thing," said Gluck. "I can't let you stay till they come; they'd be the death of me."

"Dear me," said the old gentleman, "I'm very sorry to hear that. How long may I stay?"

"Only till the mutton's done, sir," replied Gluck, "and it's very brown."

Then the old gentleman walked into the kitchen, and sat himself down on the hob, with the top of his cap accommodated up the chimney, for it was a great deal too high for the roof.

"You'll soon dry there, sir," said Gluck, and sat down again to turn the mutton. But the old gentleman did *not* dry there, but went on drip, drip, dripping among the cinders, and the fire fizzed, and sputtered, and began to look very black, and uncomfortable; never was such a cloak; every fold in it ran like a gutter.

"I beg pardon, sir," said Gluck at length, after watching the water spreading in long, quicksilver-like streams over the floor for a quarter of an hour; "mayn't I take your cloak?"

"No, thank you," said the old gentleman.

"Your cap, sir?"

"I am all right, thank you," said the old gentleman rather gruffly.

"But,—sir,—I'm very sorry," said Gluck, hesitatingly; "but—really, sir,—you're—putting the fire out."

"It'll take longer to do the mutton then," replied his visitor drily.

Gluck was very much puzzled by the behavior of his guest; it was such a strange mixture of coolness and humility. He turned away at the string meditatively for another five minutes.

"That mutton looks very nice," said the old

gentleman at length. "Can't you give me a little bit?"

"Impossible, sir," said Gluck.

"I'm very hungry," continued the old gentleman; "I've had nothing to eat yesterday, nor today. They surely couldn't miss a bit from the knuckle!"

He spoke in so very melancholy a tone, that it quite melted Gluck's heart. "They promised me one slice to-day, sir," said he; "I can give you that, but not a bit more."

"That's a good boy," said the old gentleman again.

Then Gluck warmed a plate, and sharpened a knife. "I don't care if I do get beaten for it," thought he. Just as he had cut a large slice out of

dle of the kitchen, bowing with the utmost possible velocity.

"Who's that?" said Schwartz, catching up a rolling-pin, and turning to Gluck with a fierce frown.

"I don't know, indeed, brother," said Gluck in great terror.

"How did he get in?" roared Schwartz.

"My dear brother," said Gluck, deprecatingly, "he was so *very* wet!"

The rolling-pin was descending on Gluck's head; but, at the instant, the old gentleman interposed his conical cap, on which it crashed with a shock that shook the water out of it all over the room. What was very odd, the rolling-pin no sooner touched the cap, than it flew out

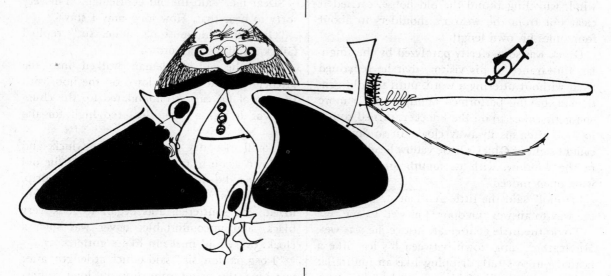

the mutton, there came a tremendous rap at the door. The old gentleman jumped off the hob, as if it had suddenly become inconveniently warm. Gluck fitted the slice into the mutton again, with desperate efforts at exactitude, and ran to open the door.

"What did you keep us waiting in the rain for?" said Schwartz, as he walked in, throwing his umbrella in Gluck's face. "Ay! what for indeed, you little vagabond?" said Hans, administering an educational box on the ear, as he followed his brother into the kitchen.

"Bless my soul!" said Schwartz when he opened the door.

"Amen," said the little gentleman, who had taken his cap off, and was standing in the mid-

of Schwartz's hand, spinning like a straw in a high wind, and fell into the corner at the further end of the room.

"Who are you, sir?" demanded Schwartz, turning upon him.

"What's your business?" snarled Hans.

"I'm a poor old man, sir," the little gentleman began very modestly, "and I saw your fire through the window, and begged shelter for a quarter of an hour."

"Have the goodness to walk out again, then," said Schwartz. "We've quite enough water in our kitchen, without making it a drying house."

"It is a cold day to turn an old man out in, sir; look at my gray hairs." They hung down to his shoulders, as I told you before.

"Ay!" said Hans, "there are enough of them to keep you warm. Walk!"

"I'm very, very hungry, sir; couldn't you spare me a bit of bread before I go?"

"Bread, indeed!" said Schwartz; "do you suppose we've nothing to do with our bread, but to give it to such red-nosed fellows as you?"

"Why don't you sell your feather?" said Hans, sneeringly. "Out with you."

"A little bit," said the old gentleman.

"Be off!" said Schwartz.

"Pray, gentlemen."

"Off, and be hanged!" cried Hans, seizing him by the collar. But he had no sooner touched the old gentleman's collar, than away he went after the rolling-pin, spinning round and round, till he fell into the corner on the top of it. Then Schwartz was very angry, and ran at the old gentleman to turn him out; but he also had hardly touched him, when away he went after Hans and the rolling-pin, and hit his head against the wall as he tumbled into the corner. And so there they lay, all three.

Then the old gentleman spun himself round with velocity in the opposite direction; continued to spin until his long cloak was all wound neatly about him; clapped his cap on his head, very much on one side (for it could not stand upright without going through the ceiling), gave an additional twist to his corkscrew moustaches, and replied with perfect coolness: "Gentlemen, I wish you a very good morning. At twelve o'clock to-night, I'll call again; after such a refusal of hospitality as I have just experienced, you will not be surprised if that visit is the last I ever pay you."

"If ever I catch you here again," muttered Schwartz, coming, half frightened, out of the corner—but, before he could finish his sentence, the old gentleman had shut the house door behind him with a great bang; and there drove past the window, at the same instant, a wreath of ragged cloud, that whirled and rolled away down the valley in all manner of shapes; turning over and over in the air; and melting away at last in a gush of rain.

"A very pretty business, indeed, Mr. Gluck!" said Schwartz. "Dish the mutton, sir. If ever I catch you at such a trick again—bless me, why the mutton's been cut!"

"You promised me one slice, brother, you know," said Gluck.

"Oh! and you were cutting it hot, I suppose, and going to catch all the gravy. It'll be long before I promise you such a thing again. Leave the room, sir; and have the kindness to wait in the coal-cellar till I call you."

Gluck left the room melancholy enough. The brothers ate as much mutton as they could, locked the rest in the cupboard, and proceeded to get very drunk after dinner.

Such a night as it was! Howling wind, and rushing rain, without intermission. The brothers had just sense enough left to put up all the shutters, and double bar the door, before they went to bed. They usually slept in the same room. As the clock struck twelve, they were both awakened by a tremendous crash. Their door burst open with a violence that shook the house from top to bottom.

"What's that?" cried Schwartz, starting up in his bed.

"Only I," said the little gentleman.

The two brothers sat up on their bolster, and stared into the darkness. The room was full of water, and by a misty moonbeam, which found its way through a hole in the shutter, they could see, in the midst of it, an enormous foam globe, spinning round, and bobbing up and down like a cork, on which, as on a most luxurious cushion, reclined the little old gentleman, cap and all. There was plenty of room for it now, for the roof was off.

"Sorry to incommode you," said their visitor, ironically. "I'm afraid your beds are dampish; perhaps you had better go to your brother's room; I've left the ceiling on there."

They required no second admonition, but rushed into Gluck's room, wet through, and in an agony of terror.

"You'll find my card on the kitchen table," the old gentleman called after them. "Remember the *last* visit."

"Pray Heaven it may!" said Schwartz, shuddering. And the foam globe disappeared.

Dawn came at last, and the two brothers looked out of Gluck's little window in the morning. The Treasure Valley was one mass of ruin, and desolation. The inundation had swept away trees, crops, and cattle, and left, in their stead, a waste of red sand, and gray mud. The two brothers crept, shivering and horror-struck into the kitchen. The water had gutted the whole first floor; corn, money, almost every movable thing had been swept away, and there was left only a small white card on the kitchen table. On it, in large, breezy, long-legged letters, were engraved the words:—*South-West Wind, Esquire*.

Chapter II: Of the Proceedings of the Three Brothers after the Visit of South-West Wind, Esquire; and how little Gluck had an Interview with the King of the Golden River.

South-West Wind, Esquire, was as good as his word. After the momentous visit above related, he entered the Treasure Valley no more; and what was worse, he had so much influence with his relations, the West Winds in general, and used it so effectually, that they all adopted a similar line of conduct. So no rain fell in the valley from one year's end to another. Though everything remained green and flourishing in the plains below, the inheritance of the Three Brothers was a desert. What had once been the richest soil in the kingdom, became a shifting heap of red sand; and the brothers, unable longer to contend with the adverse skies, abandoned their valueless patrimony in despair, to seek some means of gaining a livelihood among the cities and people of the plains. All their money was gone, and they had nothing left but some curious old-fashioned pieces of gold plate, the last remnants of their ill-gotten wealth.

"Suppose we turn goldsmiths?" said Schwartz to Hans, as they entered the large city. "It is a good knave's trade; we can put a great deal of copper into the gold, without any one's finding it out."

The thought was agreed to be a very good one; they hired a furnace, and turned goldsmiths. But two slight circumstances affected their trade: the first, that people did not approve of the coppered gold; the second, that the two elder brothers, whenever they had sold anything, used to leave little Gluck to mind the furnace, and go and drink out the money in the ale-house next door. So they melted all their gold, without making money enough to buy more, and were at last

reduced to one large drinking-mug, which an uncle of his had given to little Gluck, and which he was very fond of, and would not have parted with for the world; though he never drank anything out of it but milk and water. The mug was a very odd mug to look at. The handle was formed of two wreaths of flowing golden hair, so finely spun that it looked more like silk than metal, and these wreaths descended into, and mixed with, a beard and whiskers, of the same exquisite workmanship, which surrounded and decorated a very fierce little face, of the reddest gold imaginable, right in the front of the mug, with a pair of eyes in it which seemed to command its whole circumference. It was impossible to drink out of the mug without being subjected to an intense gaze out of the side of these eyes; and Schwartz positively averred, that once, after emptying it full of Rhenish seventeen times, he had seen them wink! When it came to the mug's turn to be made into spoons, it half broke poor little Gluck's heart; but the brothers only laughed at him, tossed the mug into the melting-pot, and staggered out to the ale-house; leaving him, as usual, to pour the gold into bars, when it was all ready.

When they were gone, Gluck took a farewell look at his old friend in the melting-pot. The flowing hair was all gone; nothing remained but the red nose, and the sparkling eyes, which looked more malicious than ever. "And no wonder," thought Gluck, "after being treated in that way." He sauntered disconsolately to the window, and sat himself down to catch the fresh evening air, and escape the hot breath of the furnace. Now this window commanded a direct view of the range of mountains, which, as I told you before, overhung the Treasure Valley, and more especially of the peak from which fell the Golden River. It was just at the close of the day, and, when Gluck sat down at the window, he saw the rocks of the mountain tops, all crimson, and purple with the sunset; and there were bright tongues of fiery cloud burning and quivering about them; and the river, brighter than all, fell in a waving column of pure gold, from precipice to precipice, with the double arch of a broad purple rainbow stretched across it, flushing and fading alternately in the wreaths of spray.

"Ah!" said Gluck aloud, after he had looked at it for a little while, "if that river were really all gold, what a nice thing it would be."

"No it wouldn't, Gluck," said a clear metallic voice, close at his ear.

"Bless me, what's that?" exclaimed Gluck, jumping up. There was nobody there. He looked round the room, and under the table, and a great many times behind him, but there was certainly nobody there, and he sat down again at the window. This time he didn't speak, but he couldn't help thinking again that it would be very convenient if the river were really all gold.

"Not at all, my boy," said the same voice, louder than before.

"Bless me!" said Gluck again, "what *is* that?" He looked again into all the corners and cupboards, and then began turning round, and round, as fast as he could, in the middle of the room, thinking there was somebody behind him, when the same voice struck again on his ear. It was singing now very merrily "Lala-lira-la;" no words, only a soft running effervescent melody, something like that of a kettle on the boil. Gluck looked out of the window. No, it was certainly in the house. Up stairs, and down stairs. No, it was certainly in that very room, coming in quicker time, and clearer notes, every moment. "Lala-lira-la." All at once it struck Gluck, that it sounded louder near the furnace. He ran to the opening, and looked in; yes, he saw right, it seemed to be coming, not only out of the furnace, but out of the pot. He uncovered it, and ran back in a great fright, for the pot was certainly singing. He stood in the farthest corner of the room, with his hands up, and his mouth open, for a minute or two, when the singing stopped, and the voice became clear, and pronunciative.

"Hollo!" said the voice.

Gluck made no answer.

"Hollo! Gluck, my boy," said the pot again.

Gluck summoned all his energies, walked straight up to the crucible, drew it out of the furnace, and looked in. The gold was all melted, and its surface as smooth and polished as a river; but instead of reflecting little Gluck's head, as he looked in, he saw meeting his glance, from beneath the gold, the red nose and sharp eyes of his old friend of the mug, a thousand times redder and sharper than ever he had seen them in his life.

"Come, Gluck, my boy," said the voice out of the pot again, "I'm all right; pour me out."

But Gluck was too much astonished to do anything of the kind.

"Pour me out, I say," said the voice rather gruffly.

Still Gluck couldn't move.

"*Will* you pour me out?" said the voice, passionately, "I'm too hot."

By a violent effort, Gluck recovered the use of his limbs, took hold of the crucible, and sloped it, so as to pour out the gold. But instead of a liquid stream, there came out, first, a pair of pretty little yellow legs, then some coat tails, then a pair of arms stuck akimbo, and, finally, the well-known head of his friend the mug; all which articles, uniting as they rolled out, stood up energetically on the floor, in the shape of a little golden dwarf, about a foot and a half high.

"That's right!" said the dwarf, stretching out first his legs, and then his arms, and then shaking his head up and down, and as far round as it would go, for five minutes, without stopping; apparently with the view of ascertaining if he were quite correctly put together, while Gluck stood contemplating him in speechless amazement. He was dressed in a slashed doublet of spun gold, so fine in its texture, that the prismatic colors gleamed over it, as if on a surface of mother-of-pearl; and, over this brilliant doublet, his hair and beard fell full halfway to the ground, in waving curls, so exquisitely delicate, that Gluck could hardly tell where they ended; they seemed to melt into air. The features of the face, however, were by no means finished with the same delicacy; they were rather coarse, slightly inclining to coppery in complexion, and indicative, in expression, of a very pertinacious and intractable disposition in their small proprietor. When the dwarf had finished his self-examination, he turned his small sharp eyes full on Gluck, and stared at him deliberately for a minute or two. "No, it wouldn't, Gluck, my boy," said the little man.

This was certainly rather an abrupt, and unconnected mode of commencing conversation. It might indeed be supposed to refer to the course of Gluck's thoughts, which had first produced the dwarf's observations out of the pot; but whatever it referred to, Gluck had no inclination to dispute the dictum.

"Wouldn't it, sir?" said Gluck, very mildly, and submissively indeed.

"No," said the dwarf, conclusively. "No, it wouldn't." And with that, the dwarf pulled his cap hard over his brows, and took two turns of three feet long, up and down the room, lifting his legs up very high, and setting them down very hard. This pause gave time for Gluck to collect his thoughts a little, and, seeing no great reason to view his diminutive visitor with dread, and feeling his curiosity overcome his amazement, he ventured on a question of peculiar delicacy.

"Pray, sir," said Gluck, rather hesitatingly, "were you my mug?"

On which the little man turned sharp round, walked straight up to Gluck, and drew himself up to his full height. "I," said the little man, "am the King of the Golden River." Whereupon he turned about again, and took two more turns, some six feet long, in order to allow time for the consternation which this announcement produced in his auditor to evaporate. After which, he again walked up to Gluck and stood still, as if expecting some comment on his communication.

Gluck determined to say something at all events. "I hope your Majesty is very well," said Gluck.

"Listen!" said the little man, deigning no reply to this polite inquiry. "I am the King of what you mortals call the Golden River. The shape you saw me in, was owing to the malice of a stronger king, from whose enchantments you have this instant freed me. What I have seen of you, and your conduct to your wicked brothers, renders me willing to serve you; therefore attend to what I tell you. Whoever shall climb to the top of that mountain from which you see the Golden River issue, and shall cast into the stream at its source three drops of holy water, for him, and for him only, the river shall turn to gold. But no one failing in his first, can succeed in a second attempt; and if any one shall cast unholy water into the river, it will overwhelm him, and he will become a black stone." So saying, the King of the Golden River turned

away, and deliberately walked into the centre of the hottest flame of the furnace. His figure became red, white, transparent, dazzling,—a blaze of intense light,—rose, trembled, and disappeared. The King of the Golden River had evaporated.

"Oh!" cried poor Gluck, running to look up the chimney after him; "Oh, dear, dear, dear me! My mug! my mug! my mug!"

Chapter III: How Mr. Hans set off on an Expedition to the Golden River, and how he prospered therein.

The King of the Golden River had hardly made the extraordinary exit related in the last chapter, before Hans and Schwartz came roaring into the house, very savagely drunk. The discovery of the total loss of their last piece of plate had the effect of sobering them just enough to enable them to stand over Gluck, beating him very steadily for a quarter of an hour; at the expiration of which period they dropped into a couple of chairs, and requested to know what he had got to say for himself. Gluck told them his story, of which of course they did not believe a word. They beat him again, till their arms were tired, and staggered to bed. In the morning, however, the steadiness with which he adhered to his story obtained him some degree of credence; the immediate consequence of which was that the two brothers, after wrangling a long time on the knotty question, which of them should try his fortune first, drew their swords, and began fighting. The noise of the fray alarmed the neighbors, who, finding they could not pacify the combatants, sent for the constable.

Hans, on hearing this, contrived to escape, and hid himself; but Schwartz was taken before the magistrate, fined for breaking the peace, and, having drunk out his last penny the evening before, was thrown into prison till he should pay.

When Hans heard this, he was much delighted, and determined to set out immediately for the Golden River. How to get the holy water, was the question. He went to the priest, but the priest could not give any holy water to so abandoned a character. So Hans went to vespers in the evening for the first time in his life, and, under pretence of crossing himself, stole a cup-ful, and returned home in triumph.

Next morning he got up before the sun rose, put the holy water into a strong flask, and two bottles of wine and some meat in a basket, slung them over his back, took his alpine staff in his hand, and set off for the mountains.

On his way out of the town he had to pass the prison, and as he looked in at the windows, whom should he see but Schwartz himself peep-ing out of the bars, and looking very disconso-late.

"Good morning, brother," said Hans; "have you any message for the King of the Golden River?"

Schwartz gnashed his teeth with rage, and shook the bars with all his strength; but Hans only laughed at him, and advising him to make himself comfortable till he came back again, shouldered his basket, shook the bottle of holy water in Schwartz's face till it frothed again, and marched off in the highest spirits in the world.

It was, indeed, a morning that might have made any one happy, even with no Golden River to seek for. Level lines of dewy mist lay stretched along the valley, out of which rose the massy mountains,—their lower cliffs in pale gray shadow, hardly distinguishable from the floating vapor, but gradually ascending till they caught the sunlight, which ran in sharp touches of ruddy color along the angular crags, and pierced, in long level rays, through their fringes of spear-like pine. Far above, shot up red splintered masses of castellated rock, jagged and shivered into myriads of fantastic forms, with here and there a streak of sunlit snow, traced down their chasms like a line of forked lightning; and, far beyond, and far above all these, fainter than the morning cloud, but purer and changeless, slept, in the blue sky, the utmost peaks of the eternal snow.

The Golden River, which sprang from one of the lower and snowless elevations, was now nearly in shadow; all but the uppermost jets of spray, which rose like slow smoke above the un-dulating line of the cataract, and floated away in feeble wreaths upon the morning wind.

On this object, and on this alone, Hans's eyes and thoughts were fixed; forgetting the distance

he had to traverse, he set off at an imprudent rate of walking, which greatly exhausted him before he had scaled the first range of the green and low hills. He was, moreover, surprised, on surmounting them, to find that a large glacier, of whose existence, notwithstanding his previous knowledge of the mountains, he had been ab-solutely ignorant, lay between him and the source of the Golden River. He entered on it with the boldness of a practised mountaineer; yet he thought he had never traversed so strange, or so dangerous a glacier in his life. The ice was excessively slippery, and out of all its chasms came wild sounds of gushing water; not monot-onous or low, but changeful and loud, rising occasionally into drifting passages of wild mel-ody, then breaking off into short melancholy tones, or sudden shrieks, resembling those of human voices in distress or pain. The ice was broken into thousands of confused shapes, but none, Hans thought, like the ordinary forms of splintered ice. There seemed a curious *expres-sion* about all their outlines,—a perpetual re-semblance to living features, distorted and scorn-ful. Myriads of deceitful shadows, and lurid lights, played and floated about and through the pale blue pinnacles, dazzling and confusing the sight of the traveller; while his ears grew dull and his head giddy with the constant gush and roar of the concealed waters. These painful cir-cumstances increased upon him as he advanced; the ice crashed and yawned into fresh chasms at his feet, tottering spires nodded around him, and fell thundering across his path; and though he had repeatedly faced these dangers on the most terrific glaciers, and in the wildest weather, it was with a new and oppressive feeling of panic terror that he leaped the last chasm, and flung himself, exhausted and shuddering, on the firm turf of the mountain.

He had been compelled to abandon his basket of food, which became a perilous incumbrance on the glacier, and had now no means of refresh-ing himself but by breaking off and eating some of the pieces of ice. This, however, relieved his thirst; an hour's repose recruited his hardy frame, and with the indomitable spirit of ava-rice, he resumed his laborious journey.

His way now lay straight up a ridge of bare red rocks, without a blade of grass to ease the foot, or a projecting angle to afford an inch of shade from the south sun. It was past noon, and the rays beat intensely upon the steep path, while the whole atmosphere was motionless, and penetrated with heat. Intense thirst was soon added to the bodily fatigue with which Hans was now afflicted; glance after glance he cast on the flask of water which hung at his belt. "Three drops are enough," at last thought he; "I may, at least, cool my lips with it."

He opened the flask, and was raising it to his lips, when his eye fell on an object lying on the rock beside him; he thought it moved. It was a small dog, apparently in the last agony of death from thirst. Its tongue was out, its jaws dry, its limbs extended lifelessly, and a swarm of black ants were crawling about its lips and throat. Its eye moved to the bottle which Hans held in his hand. He raised it, drank, spurned the animal with his foot, and passed on. And he did not know how it was, but he thought that a strange shadow had suddenly come across the blue sky.

The path became steeper and more rugged every moment; and the high hill air, instead of refreshing him, seemed to throw his blood into a fever. The noise of the hill cataracts sounded like mockery in his ears; they were all distant, and his thirst increased every moment. Another hour passed, and he again looked down to the flask at his side; it was half empty, but there was much more than three drops in it. He stopped to open it, and again, as he did so, something moved in the path above him. It was a fair child, stretched nearly lifeless on the rock, its breast heaving with thirst, its eyes closed, and its lips parched and burning. Hans eyed it deliberately, drank, and passed on. And a dark gray cloud came over the sun, and long, snake-like shadows crept up along the mountain sides. Hans struggled on. The sun was sinking, but its descent seemed to bring no coolness; the leaden weight of the dead air pressed upon his brow and heart, but the goal was near. He saw the cataract of the Golden River springing from the hill-side, scarcely five hundred feet above him. He paused for a moment to breathe, and sprang on to complete his task.

At this instant a faint cry fell on his ear. He turned, and saw a gray-haired old man extended on the rocks. His eyes were sunk, his features deadly pale, and gathered into an expression of despair. "Water!" he stretched his arms to Hans, and cried feebly, "Water! I am dying."

"I have none," replied Hans; "thou hast had thy share of life." He strode over the prostrate body, and darted on. And a flash of blue lightning rose out of the East, shaped like a sword; it shook thrice over the whole heaven, and left it dark with one heavy, impenetrable shade. The sun was setting; it plunged towards the horizon like a red-hot ball.

The roar of the Golden River rose on Hans's ear. He stood at the brink of the chasm through which it ran. Its waves were filled with the red glory of the sunset: they shook their crests like tongues of fire, and flashes of bloody light gleamed along their foam. Their sound came mightier and mightier on his senses; his brain grew giddy with the prolonged thunder. Shuddering, he drew the flask from his girdle, and hurled it into the centre of the torrent. As he did so, an icy chill shot through his limbs; he staggered, shrieked, and fell. The waters closed over his cry. And the moaning of the river rose wildly into the night, as it gushed over THE BLACK STONE.

Chapter IV: How Mr. Schwartz set off on an Expedition to the Golden River, and how he prospered therein.

Poor little Gluck waited very anxiously alone in the house for Hans's return. Finding he did not come back, he was terribly frightened, and went and told Schwartz in the prison all that had happened. Then Schwartz was very much pleased, and said that Hans must certainly have been turned into a black stone, and he should have all the gold to himself. But Gluck was very sorry, and cried all night. When he got up in the morning, there was no bread in the house, nor any money; so Gluck went and hired himself to another goldsmith, and he worked so hard, and so neatly, and so long every day, that he soon got money enough together to pay his brother's fine, and he went, and gave it all to Schwartz, and Schwartz got out of prison. Then Schwartz was quite pleased, and said he should have some of the gold of the river. But Gluck only begged he would go and see what had become of Hans.

Now when Schwartz had heard that Hans had stolen the holy water, he thought to himself that such a proceeding might not be considered altogether correct by the King of the Golden River, and determined to manage matters better. So he took some more of Gluck's money, and went to a bad priest, who gave him some holy water very readily for it. Then Schwartz was sure it was all quite right. So Schwartz got up early in the morning before the sun rose, and took some bread and wine, in a basket, and put his holy water in a flask, and set off for the mountains. Like his brother he was much surprised at the sight of the glacier, and had great difficulty in crossing it, even after leaving his basket behind him. The day was cloudless, but not bright: there was a heavy purple haze hanging over the sky, and the hills looked lowering and gloomy. And as Schwartz climbed the steep rock path, the thirst came upon him, as it had upon his brother, until he lifted his flask to his lips to drink. Then he saw the fair child lying near him on the rocks, and it cried to him, and moaned for water.

"Water indeed," said Schwartz; "I haven't half enough for myself," and passed on. And as he went he thought the sunbeams grew more dim, and he saw a low bank of black cloud rising out of the West; and, when he had climbed for another hour, the thirst overcame him again, and he would have drunk. Then he saw the old man lying before him on the path, and heard him cry out for water. "Water, indeed," said Schwartz, "I haven't half enough for myself," and on he went.

Then again the light seemed to fade from before his eyes, and he looked up, and, behold, a mist, of the color of blood, had come over the sun; and the bank of black cloud had risen very high, and its edges were tossing and tumbling like the waves of the angry sea. And they cast long shadows, which flickered over Schwartz's path.

Then Schwartz climbed for another hour, and again his thirst returned; and as he lifted his flask to his lips, he thought he saw his brother Hans lying exhausted on the path before him, and, as he gazed, the figure stretched its arms to him, and cried for water. "Ha, ha," laughed Schwartz, "are you there? remember the prison bars, my boy. Water, indeed! do you suppose I carried it all the way up here for *you?*" And he strode over the figure; yet, as he passed, he thought he saw a strange expression of mockery about its lips. And when he had gone a few yards farther, he looked back; but the figure was not there.

And a sudden horror came over Schwartz, he knew not why; but the thirst for gold prevailed over his fear, and he rushed on. And the bank of black cloud rose to the zenith, and out of it came bursts of spiry lightning, and waves of darkness seemed to heave and float between their flashes, over the whole heavens. And the sky where the sun was setting was all level, and like a lake of blood; and a strong wind came out of that sky, tearing its crimson clouds into fragments, and scattering them far into the darkness. And when Schwartz stood by the brink of the Golden River, its waves were black, like thunder clouds, but their foam was like fire; and the roar of the waters below, and the thunder above met, as he cast the flask into the stream. And, as he did so, the lightning glared in his eyes, and the earth gave way beneath him, and the waters closed over his cry. And the moaning of the river rose wildly into the night, as it gushed over the TWO BLACK STONES.

Chapter V: How little Gluck set off on an Expedition to the Golden River, and how he prospered therein; with other Matters of Interest.

When Gluck found that Schwartz did not come back, he was very sorry, and did not know what to do. He had no money, and was obliged to go and hire himself again to the goldsmith, who worked him very hard, and gave him very little money. So, after a month, or two, Gluck grew tired, and made up his mind to go and try his fortune with the Golden River. "The little king looked very kind," thought he. "I don't think he will turn me into a black stone." So he went to the priest, and the priest gave him some holy water as soon as he asked for it. Then Gluck took some bread in his basket, and the bottle of water, and set off very early for the mountains.

If the glacier had occasioned a great deal of fatigue to his brothers, it was twenty times worse for him, who was neither so strong nor so practised on the mountains. He had several very bad falls, lost his basket and bread, and was very much frightened at the strange noises under the ice. He lay a long time to rest on the grass, after he had got over, and began to climb the hill just in the hottest part of the day. When he had climbed for an hour, he got dreadfully thirsty, and was going to drink like his brothers, when he saw an old man coming down the path above him, looking very feeble, and leaning on a staff. "My son," said the old man, "I am faint with thirst, give me some of that water." Then Gluck looked at him, and when he saw that he was pale and weary, he gave him the water; "Only pray don't drink it all," said Gluck. But the old man drank a great deal, and gave him back the bottle two-thirds empty. Then he bade him good speed, and Gluck went on again merrily. And the path became easier to his feet, and two or three blades of grass appeared upon it, and some grasshoppers began singing on the bank beside it; and Gluck thought he had never heard such merry singing.

Then he went on for another hour, and the thirst increased on him so that he thought he should be forced to drink. But, as he raised the flask, he saw a little child lying panting by the road-side, and it cried out piteously for water. Then Gluck struggled with himself, and determined to bear the thirst a little longer; and he put the bottle to the child's lips, and it drank it all but a few drops. Then it smiled on him, and got up, and ran down the hill; and Gluck looked after it, till it became as small as a little star, and then turned, and began climbing again. And then there were all kinds of sweet flowers growing on the rocks, bright green moss, with pale pink starry flowers, and soft belled gentians, more blue than the sky at its deepest, and pure white transparent lilies. And crimson and purple butterflies darted hither and thither, and the sky sent down such pure light, that Gluck had never felt so happy in his life.

Yet, when he had climbed for another hour, his thirst became intolerable again; and, when he looked at his bottle, he saw that there were only five or six drops left in it, and he could not venture to drink. And as he was hanging the flask to his belt again, he saw a little dog lying on the rocks, gasping for breath,—just as Hans had seen it on the day of his ascent. And Gluck stopped and looked at it, and then at the Golden River, not five hundred yards above him; and he thought of the dwarf's words, "that no one could succeed, except in his first attempt;" and he tried to pass the dog, but it whined piteously, and Gluck stopped again. "Poor beastie," said Gluck, "it'll be dead when I come down again, if I don't help it." Then he looked closer and closer at it, and its eye turned on him so mournfully that he could not stand it. "Confound the King and his gold too," said Gluck; and he opened the flask, and poured all the water into the dog's mouth.

The dog sprang up and stood on its hind legs. Its tail disappeared, its ears became long, longer, silky, golden; its nose became very red, its eyes became very twinkling; in three seconds the dog was gone, and before Gluck stood his old acquaintance, the King of the Golden River.

"Thank you," said the monarch; "but don't be frightened, it's all right;" for Gluck showed manifest symptoms of consternation at this unlooked for reply to his last observation. "Why didn't you come before," continued the dwarf, "instead of sending me those rascally brothers of yours, for me to have the trouble of turning into stones? Very hard stones they make too."

"Oh dear me!" said Gluck, "have you really been so cruel?"

"Cruel!" said the dwarf, "they poured unholy water into my stream; do you suppose I'm going to allow that?"

"Why," said Gluck, "I am sure, sir,—your majesty, I mean,—they got the water out of the church font."

"Very probably," replied the dwarf; "but," and his countenance grew stern as he spoke, "the water which has been refused to the cry of the weary and dying, is unholy, though it had been blessed by every saint in heaven; and the water which is found in the vessel of mercy is holy, though it had been defiled with corpses."

So saying, the dwarf stooped and plucked a lily that grew at his feet. On its white leaves there hung three drops of clear dew. And the dwarf shook them into the flask which Gluck held in his hand. "Cast these into the river," he said, "and descend on the other side of the mountains into the Treasure Valley. And so good speed."

As he spoke, the figure of the dwarf became indistinct. The playing colors of his robe formed themselves into a prismatic mist of dewy light; he stood for an instant veiled with them as with the belt of a broad rainbow. The colors grew faint, the mist rose into the air; the monarch had evaporated.

And Gluck climbed to the brink of the Golden River, and its waves were as clear as crystal, and as brilliant as the sun. And when he cast the three drops of dew into the stream, there opened where they fell, a small circular whirlpool, into which the waters descended with a musical noise.

Gluck stood watching it for some time, very much disappointed, because not only the river was not turned into gold, but its waters seemed much diminished in quantity. Yet he obeyed his friend the dwarf, and descended the other side of the mountains, towards the Treasure Valley; and, as he went, he thought he heard the noise of water working its way under the ground. And, when he came in sight of the Treasure Valley, behold, a river, like the Golden River, was springing from a new cleft of the rocks above it, and was flowing in innumerable streams among the dry heaps of red sand.

And as Gluck gazed, fresh grass sprang beside the new streams, and creeping plants grew, and climbed among the moistening soil. Young flowers opened suddenly along the river sides, as stars leap out when twilight is deepening, and thickets of myrtle, and tendrils of vine, cast lengthening shadows over the valley as they grew. And thus the Treasure Valley became a garden again, and the inheritance, which had been lost by cruelty, was regained by love.

And Gluck went, and dwelt in the valley, and the poor were never driven from his door; so that his barns became full of corn, and his house of treasure. And, for him, the river had, according to the dwarf's promise, become a River of Gold.

And, to this day, the inhabitants of the valley point out the place, where the three drops of holy dew were cast into the stream, and trace the course of the Golden River under the ground, until it emerges in the Treasure Valley. And, at the top of the cataract of the Golden River, are still to be seen two BLACK STONES, round which the waters howl mournfully every day at sunset; and these stones are still called by the people of the valley, THE BLACK BROTHERS.

HOW THEY BRING BACK THE VILLAGE OF CREAM PUFFS WHEN THE WIND BLOWS IT AWAY

Carl Sandburg

When a poet turns to nonsense, something unusual is bound to result. Carl Sandburg, poet, newspaperman, and biographer, declared that he was tired of reading his little girls stories about castles and kings. Why not something American, something in a lingo they would understand? With this declaration of independence, he created his Rootabaga Stories. *The fantastic nonsense about a boy who lived in the Village of Liver and Onions or about a Village of Cream Puffs that blew away sent his own three little girls into gales of laughter. Of course, they were luckier than the rest of us because they heard the author of the stories read them in his wonderful voice and manner. But the airy lightness of these tales carries over for any reader. You have to know them well to read them well because they run on like a patter-song with hardly a chance to catch your breath.*

A girl named Wing Tip the Spick came to the Village of Liver-and-Onions to visit her uncle and her uncle's uncle on her mother's side and her uncle and her uncle's uncle on her father's side.

It was the first time the four uncles had a chance to see their little relation, their niece. Each one of the four uncles was proud of the blue eyes of Wing Tip the Spick.

The two uncles on her mother's side took a long deep look into her blue eyes and said, "Her eyes are so blue, such a clear light blue, they are the same as cornflowers with blue raindrops shining and dancing on silver leaves after a sun shower in any of the summer months."

And the two uncles on her father's side, after taking a long deep look into the eyes of Wing Tip the Spick, said, "Her eyes are so blue, such a clear light shining blue, they are the same as cornflowers with blue raindrops shining and dancing on the silver leaves after a sun shower in any of the summer months."

And though Wing Tip the Spick didn't listen and didn't hear what the uncles said about her blue eyes, she did say to herself when they were not listening, "I know these are sweet uncles and I am going to have a sweet time visiting my relations."

The four uncles said to her, "Will you let us ask you two questions, first the first question and second the second question?"

"I will let you ask me fifty questions this morning, fifty questions tomorrow morning, and fifty questions any morning. I like to listen to questions. They slip in one ear and slip out of the other."

Then the uncles asked her the first question first, "Where do you come from?" and the second question second, "Why do you have two freckles on your chin?"

"Answering your first question first," said Wing Tip the Spick, "I come from the Village of Cream Puffs, a little light village on the upland corn prairie. From a long ways off it looks like a little hat you could wear on the end of your thumb to keep the rain off your thumb."

"Tell us more," said one uncle. "Tell us much," said another uncle. "Tell it without stopping," added another uncle. "Interruptions nix nix," murmured the last of the uncles.

"It is a light little village on the upland corn prairie many miles past the sunset in the west," went on Wing Tip the Spick. "It is light the same as a cream puff is light. It sits all by itself on the big long prairie where the prairie goes up in a slope. There on the slope the winds play around the village. They sing it wind songs, summer wind songs in summer, winter wind songs in winter."

"And sometimes like an accident, the wind gets rough. And when the wind gets rough it

picks up the little Village of Cream Puffs and blows it away off in the sky—all by itself."

"O-o-h-h," said one uncle. "Um-m-m-m," said the other three uncles.

"Now the people in the village all understand the winds with their wind songs in summer and winter. And they understand the rough wind who comes sometimes and picks up the village and blows it away off high in the sky all by itself.

"If you go to the public square in the middle of the village you will see a big roundhouse. If you take the top off the roundhouse you will see a big spool with a long string winding up around the spool.

"Now whenever the rough wind comes and picks up the village and blows it away off high in the sky all by itself then the string winds loose off the spool, because the village is fastened to the string. So the rough wind blows and blows and the string on the spool winds looser and looser the farther the village goes blowing away off into the sky all by itself.

"Then at last when the rough wind, so forgetful, so careless, has had all the fun it wants, then the people of the village all come together and begin to wind up the spool and bring back the village where it was before."

"O-o-h-h," said one uncle. "Um-m-m-m," said the other three uncles.

"And sometimes when you come to the village to see your little relation, your niece who has four such sweet uncles, maybe she will lead you through the middle of the city to the public square and show you the roundhouse. They call it the Roundhouse of the Big Spool. And they are proud because it was thought up and is there to show when visitors come."

"And now will you answer the second question second—why do you have two freckles on your chin?" interrupted the uncle who had said before, "Interruptions nix nix."

"The freckles are put on," answered Wing Tip the Spick. "When a girl goes away from the Village of Cream Puffs her mother puts on two freckles, on the chin. Each freckle must be the same as a little burnt cream puff kept in the oven too long. After the two freckles looking like two little burnt cream puffs are put on her chin, they remind the girl every morning when she combs her hair and looks in the looking glass. They remind her where she came from and she mustn't stay away too long."

"Oh-h-h-h," said one uncle. "Um-m-m-m," said the other three uncles. And they talked among each other afterward, the four uncles by themselves, saying:

"She has a gift. It is her eyes. They are so blue, such a clear light blue, the same as cornflowers with blue raindrops shining and dancing on silver leaves after a sun shower in any of the summer months."

At the same time Wing Tip the Spick was saying to herself, "I know for sure now these are sweet uncles and I am going to have a sweet time visiting my relations."

A MAD TEA-PARTY

Lewis Carroll

When an astonished England began investigating the author of Alice's Adventures in Wonderland, *it was soon discovered that there was no such person as Lewis Carroll. The name concealed a staid lecturer in mathematics at Oxford, Charles Lutwidge Dodgson. This young man liked children, and on one famous summer afternoon, he rowed three little girls up the River Cherwell. On the river bank, while they were having tea, the children asked for a story, and the young man told them his masterly concoction of sense and nonsense, nightmares and pleasant dreams, the world up-side-down and hind-side-before—fantasia unlimited! If the children enjoy this excerpt, try the whole book.*

There was a table set out under a tree in front of the house, and the March Hare and the Hatter were having tea at it: a Dormouse was sitting between them, fast asleep, and the other two were using it as a cushion, resting their elbows on it, and talking over its head. "Very uncomfortable for the Dormouse," thought Alice; "only, as it's asleep, I suppose it doesn't mind."

The table was a large one, but the three were all crowded together at one corner of it: "No

"A Mad Tea-Party." From *Alice's Adventures in Wonderland* by Lewis Carroll

room! No room!" they cried out when they saw Alice coming. "There's *plenty* of room!" said Alice indignantly, and she sat down in a large arm-chair at one end of the table.

"Have some wine," the March Hare said in an encouraging tone.

Alice looked all round the table, but there was nothing on it but tea. "I don't see any wine," she remarked.

"There isn't any," said the March Hare.

"Then it wasn't very civil of you to offer it," said Alice angrily.

"It wasn't very civil of you to sit down without being invited," said the March Hare.

"I didn't know it was *your* table," said Alice; "it's laid for a great many more than three."

"Your hair wants cutting," said the Hatter. He had been looking at Alice for some time with great curiosity, and this was his first speech.

"You should learn not to make personal remarks," Alice said with some severity: "It's very rude."

The Hatter opened his eyes very wide on hearing this; but all he *said* was, "Why is a raven like a writing-desk?"

"Come, we shall have some fun now!" thought Alice. "I'm glad they've begun asking riddles—I believe I can guess that," she added aloud.

"Do you mean that you think you can find out the answer to it?" said the March Hare.

"Exactly so," said Alice.

"Then you should say what you mean," the March Hare went on.

"I do," Alice hastily replied; "at least—at least I mean what I say—that's the same thing, you know."

"Not the same thing a bit!" said the Hatter. "Why, you might just as well say that 'I see what I eat' is the same thing as 'I eat what I see'!"

"You might just as well say," added the March Hare, "that 'I like what I get' is the same thing as 'I get what I like'!"

"You might just as well say," added the Dormouse, who seemed to be talking in his sleep, "that 'I breathe when I sleep' is the same thing as 'I sleep when I breathe'!"

"It *is* the same thing with you," said the Hatter, and here the conversation dropped, and the party sat silent for a minute, while Alice thought over all she could remember about ravens and writing-desks, which wasn't much.

The Hatter was the first to break the silence. "What day of the month is it?" he said, turning to Alice: he had taken his watch out of his pocket, and was looking at it uneasily, shaking it every now and then, and holding it to his ear.

Alice considered a little, and said, "The fourth."

"Two days wrong!" sighed the Hatter. "I told you butter wouldn't suit the works!" he added, looking angrily at the March Hare.

"It was the *best* butter," the March Hare meekly replied.

"Yes, but some crumbs must have got in as well," the Hatter grumbled: "you shouldn't have put it in with the bread-knife."

The March Hare took the watch and looked at it gloomily: then he dipped it into his cup of tea, and looked at it again: but he could think of nothing better to say than his first remark, "It was the *best* butter, you know."

Alice had been looking over his shoulder with some curiosity. "What a funny watch!" she remarked. "It tells the day of the month, and doesn't tell what o'clock it is!"

"Why should it?" muttered the Hatter. "Does *your* watch tell you what year it is?"

"Of course not," Alice replied very readily: "but that's because it stays the same year for such a long time together."

"Which is just the case with *mine*," said the Hatter.

Alice felt dreadfully puzzled. The Hatter's remark seemed to her to have no sort of meaning in it, and yet it was certainly English. "I don't quite understand you," she said, as politely as she could.

"The Dormouse is asleep again," said the Hatter, and he poured a little hot tea on to its nose.

The Dormouse shook its head impatiently, and said, without opening its eyes, "Of course, of course: just what I was going to remark myself."

"Have you guessed the riddle yet?" the Hatter said, turning to Alice again.

"No, I give it up," Alice replied: "what's the answer?"

"I haven't the slightest idea," said the Hatter.

"Nor I," said the March Hare.

Alice sighed wearily. "I think you might do something better with the time," she said, "than wasting it in asking riddles that have no answers."

"If you knew Time as well as I do," said the Hatter, "you wouldn't talk about wasting *it!* It's *him.*"

"I don't know what you mean," said Alice.

"Of course you don't!" the Hatter said, tossing his head contemptuously. "I dare say you never even spoke to Time!"

"Perhaps not," Alice cautiously replied: "but I know I have to beat time when I learn music."

"Ah! That accounts for it," said the Hatter. "He won't stand beating. Now, if you only kept on good terms with him, he'd do almost anything you liked with the clock.

"For instance, suppose it were nine o'clock in the morning, just time to begin lessons: you'd only have to whisper a hint to Time, and round goes the clock in a twinkling! Half-past one, time for dinner!"

("I only wish it was," the March Hare said to itself in a whisper.)

"That would be grand, certainly," said Alice thoughtfully; "but then—I shouldn't be hungry for it, you know."

"Not at first, perhaps," said the Hatter; "but you could keep it to half-past one as long as you liked."

"Is that the way *you* manage?" Alice asked.

The Hatter shook his head mournfully. "Not I!" he replied. "We quarreled last March—just before *he* went mad, you know—" (pointing with his teaspoon at the March Hare,) "—it was at the great concert given by the Queen of Hearts, and I had to sing

'Twinkle, twinkle, little bat!
How I wonder what you're at!'

You know the song, perhaps?"

"I've heard something like it," said Alice.

"It goes on, you know," the Hatter continued, "in this way:—

'Up above the world you fly,
Like a teatray in the sky.
Twinkle, twinkle—' "

Here the Dormouse shook itself, and began singing in its sleep *"Twinkle, twinkle, twinkle, twinkle—"* and went on so long that they had to pinch it to make it stop.

"Well, I'd hardly finished the first verse," said the Hatter, "when the Queen bawled out 'He's murdering the time! Off with his head!'"

"How dreadfully savage!" exclaimed Alice.

"And ever since that," the Hatter went on in a mournful tone, "he won't do a thing I ask! It's always six o'clock now."

A bright idea came into Alice's head. "Is that the reason so many tea-things are put out here?" she asked.

"Yes, that's it," said the Hatter with a sigh: "it's always tea-time, and we've no time to wash the things between whiles."

"Then you keep moving round, I suppose?" said Alice.

"Exactly so," said the Hatter: "as the things get used up."

"But when you come to the beginning again?" Alice ventured to ask.

"Suppose we change the subject," the March Hare interrupted, yawning. "I'm getting tired of this. I vote the young lady tells us a story."

"I'm afraid I don't know one," said Alice, rather alarmed at the proposal.

"Then the Dormouse shall!" they both cried. "Wake up, Dormouse!" And they pinched it on both sides at once.

The Dormouse slowly opened his eyes. "I wasn't asleep," he said in a hoarse, feeble voice: "I heard every word you fellows were saying."

"Tell us a story!" said the March Hare.

"Yes, please do!" pleaded Alice.

"And be quick about it," added the Hatter, "or you'll be asleep again before it's done."

"Once upon a time there were three little sisters," the Dormouse began in a great hurry; "and their names were Elsie, Lacie, and Tillie; and they lived at the bottom of a well—"

"What did they live on?" said Alice, who always took a great interest in questions of eating and drinking.

"They lived on treacle," said the Dormouse, after thinking a minute or two.

"They couldn't have done that, you know," Alice gently remarked. "They'd have been ill."

"So they were," said the Dormouse; *"very* ill."

Alice tried a little to fancy to herself what such an extraordinary way of living would be like, but it puzzled her too much, so she went on: "But why did they live at the bottom of a well?"

"Take some more tea," the March Hare said to Alice, very earnestly.

"I've had nothing yet," Alice replied in an offended tone, "so I can't take more."

"You mean you can't take *less,*" said the Hatter: "it's very easy to take *more* than nothing."

"Nobody asked *your* opinion," said Alice.

"Who's making personal remarks now?" the Hatter asked triumphantly.

Alice did not quite know what to say to this: so she helped herself to some tea and bread-and-butter, and then turned to the Dormouse, and repeated her question. "Why did they live at the bottom of a well?"

The Dormouse again took a minute or two to think about it, and then said, "It was a treacle-well."

"There's no such thing!" Alice was beginning very angrily, but the Hatter and the March Hare went "Sh! Sh!" and the Dormouse sulkily remarked, "If you can't be civil, you'd better finish the story for yourself."

"No, please go on!" Alice said very humbly. "I won't interrupt you again. I dare say there may be *one.*"

"One, indeed!" said the Dormouse indignantly. However, he consented to go on. "And so these three little sisters—they were learning to draw, you know—"

"What did they draw?" said Alice, quite forgetting her promise.

"Treacle," said the Dormouse, without considering at all this time.

"I want a clean cup," interrupted the Hatter: "let's all move one place on."

He moved on as he spoke, and the Dormouse followed him: the March Hare moved into the Dormouse's place, and Alice rather unwillingly took the place of the March Hare. The Hatter was the only one who got any advantage from the change: and Alice was a good deal worse off than before, as the March Hare had just upset the milk-jug into his plate.

Alice did not wish to offend the Dormouse again, so she began very cautiously: "But I don't understand. Where did they draw the treacle from?"

"You can draw water out of a water-well," said the Hatter; "so I should think you could draw treacle out of a treacle-well—eh, stupid?"

"But they were *in* the well," Alice said to the Dormouse, not choosing to notice this last remark.

"Of course they were," said the Dormouse,—"well in."

This answer so confused poor Alice, that she let the Dormouse go on for some time without interrupting it.

"They were learning to draw," the Dormouse went on, yawning and rubbing his eyes, for it was getting very sleepy; "and they drew all manner of things—everything that begins with an M—"

"Why with an M?" said Alice.

"Why not?" said the March Hare.

Alice was silent.

The Dormouse had closed its eyes by this time, and was going off into a doze, but, on being pinched by the Hatter, it woke up again with a little shriek, and went on: "—that begins with an M, such as mousetraps, and the moon, and memory, and muchness—you know you say things are 'much of a muchness'—did you ever see such a thing as a drawing of a muchness?"

"Really, now you ask me," said Alice, very much confused, "I don't think—"

"Then you shouldn't talk," said the Hatter.

This piece of rudeness was more than Alice could bear: she got up in great disgust, and walked off: the Dormouse fell asleep instantly, and neither of the others took the least notice of her going, though she looked back once or twice, half hoping that they would call after her: the last time she saw them, they were trying to put the Dormouse into the teapot.

"At any rate I'll never go *there* again!" said Alice as she picked her way through the wood. "It's the stupidest tea-party I ever was at in all my life!"

Just as she said this, she noticed that one of the trees had a door leading right into it. "That's very curious!" she thought. "But everything's curious today. I think I may as well go in at once." And in she went.

Once more she found herself in the long hall, and close to the little glass table. "Now, I'll manage better this time," she said to herself, and began by taking the little golden key, and unlocking the door that led into the garden. Then she set to work nibbling at the mushroom (she had kept a piece of it in her pocket) till she was about a foot high: then she walked down the little passage: and *then*—she found herself at last in the beautiful garden, among the bright flowerbeds and the cool fountains.

AIRY-GO-ROUND

William Pène du Bois

The "intermission" with which this story begins is in Professor Sherman's lecture on his escape from an island that exploded. In this part of his talk he describes one of his surprising adventures on the Island of Krakatoa.

During the intermission, the mayor and the Chief Surgeon of the San Francisco General Hospital rushed to Professor Sherman's bedside to see if he was all right. "Are you tired?" they asked in one voice. "Would you rather resume tomorrow?" asked the Mayor. "How do you feel?" asked the Chief Surgeon. "Is there anything we can do for you?"

"I feel fine," said Professor Sherman.

"Would you like one of the nurses to change the drinking water in your carafe?" asked the Chief Surgeon.

"I don't care, it tastes all right to me."

"Could I fetch you a little refreshment?" asked the Mayor. "Something to renew your strength?"

"If you insist," said the Professor. The Mayor ran off at a fast puffing trot while the Chief Surgeon busied himself tucking in the comforter on the Professor's bed. It should have been obvious to anyone, even two such important personages as the Mayor and Chief Surgeon, that all Professor Sherman wanted during this intermission he had called was a few minutes of rest.

The Mayor came back with a nip and the Professor swallowed it in one gulp. Then, looking at the Mayor and Surgeon, he said with a smile on his face, "You know, Gentlemen, this to me is very funny. A little over a month ago, I was an insignificant arithmetic teacher who would have found it almost impossible to get to see either one of you. Now you are waiting on me like a pair of well-trained valets. I thank you for your kind attention. It goes to show how wonderful ballooning can be. You never can tell where the winds will blow you, what fantastic good fortune they can lead you to. *Long live balloons!*" he shouted. The Mayor and the Chief Surgeon joined in with a few sheepish giggles, then backed away.

By this time the fifteen minutes were up and Professor Sherman was gratified to see that the people of the audience had quietly returned to their seats and were sitting attentively. The packed auditorium wasn't making a sound. It was waiting anxiously to hear the end of his extraordinary story.

The Chief Surgeon saw, as before, that the Professor was comfortably propped up with pillows, and the Mayor walked over to the Professor's bedside. With one hand resting on the head of the bed, he turned to the audience and said:

"Again it gives me great pleasure to present Professor William Waterman Sherman."

The Professor thanked the Mayor, cleared his throat, and resumed his talk:

Mr. F. led me to the first invention he had promised to show me, the Balloon Merry-Go-Round. On our way I told Mr. F. that the name of the invention suggested something at an amusement park. "Just what is this invention for?"

"It is part of an amusement park," said Mr. F., "which the children of Krakatoa are planning for themselves. You see, our children now are between the ages of ten and fifteen. When we return from our trips to other countries, they help us unload our freighter with great interest. It suddenly dawned on them a year or so ago that it would be an excellent idea if a few boatloads were brought back full of supplies exclusively for them; for after all they do own a share in the mines, too. We agreed to give them two boatloads a year, so all of the children held a meeting to decide how best to fill their freighters.

This amusement park they have started to build is the result of their planning. The Balloon Merry-Go-Round is their own invention, designed with but little help from us."

"Is there any school here?" I asked.

"The children have no formal schooling. We have taught them how to read and write, and we have tried to teach them a little arithmetic. They have all taken part in the building of our international houses—which is most educating in itself. But all in all, a school is sorely needed here. You aren't by any chance a teacher, are you? Just what does the title Professor stand for in your case?"

"Professor of, uh, Aeronautics," I stuttered. "I teach Balloon Theory at, uh, the San Francisco Lighter than Air School." I felt a flush of heat in my cheeks as I waded through this fabulous lie. I had no intention of getting involved again in teaching, the very thing from which this trip of mine was intended to take me.

"How interesting," said Mr. F. "That goes to show how quickly one gets out of touch with one's native city. I can't say that I even recall hearing of such an institution."

"It's one of the latest," I muttered, "practically brand new." Then quickly changing the subject, I asked what other forms of amusement could be found at the park.

"So far, they have just had time to design and build the Merry-Go-Round, but they have a lot more planned. Most of the usual rides found at amusement parks are impractical for Krakatoa because they are higher than the jungle life on the Island and would be visible from the sea. As a matter of fact, we only take rides on the Balloon Merry-Go-Round after thoroughly scanning the horizon for passing ships. We never use it if anything is in sight. Do you see that tall pole in the distance?"

"Yes, I do," I said. The pole was straight and the same width at the bottom as at the top. It was threaded like a gigantic screw and it was about seventy-five feet tall.

"That's part of the Balloon Merry-Go-Round, the axle around which it revolves to give it its spin when it is gaining altitude."

"Can't that be seen from the ocean?"

"Yes, it can. But one lone pole isn't enough to attract much attention from passing ships."

We came to a little forest of palm trees, the same sort of neatly kept little forest I had seen the day before, with freshly cut lawn instead of the usual jungle underbrush. We walked through this forest for a hundred yards or so and then came upon a clearing. In the middle of this clearing was what was apparently the Balloon Merry-Go-Round. There were eight little boats around the base of the pole, all joined together bow to stern. In the place of oarlocks, there were two brass rings on these boats, and through these rings passed poles which all met at the main vertical pole of the Merry-Go-Round where they were screwed into the hub of another large brass ring around the pole, forming spokes of a giant wheel. Each boat was covered with a protective tarpaulin. Mr. F. removed one of the tarpaulins and showed me one. They were nice little centerboard sailboats, sturdy and quite seaworthy. The sails were neatly stowed in trim lockers. I didn't notice any masts, but there was definitely a place for them. Alongside of each of these boats was a large deflated balloon painted a pale sky-blue. Off to one side in the clearing there was a little shack made of bamboo which reminded me very much of my basket house. On its walls outside, eight silk hoses were hanging, neatly coiled up and in line. There was a bell on top of this little shack, which could be reached by climbing a ladder.

Mr. F. walked over to the shack, went inside, and came out again with a spyglass. He climbed up the ladder to the roof of the shack and carefully looked over the horizon around him, apparently for ships. "Would you care to risk a trip in it?" he asked me. "The weather today is ideal."

"As an ardent balloonist, I accept with enthusiasm; but as a sixty-six-year-old man I must confess that I accept with some trepidation. Is it safe?"

"Absolutely," answered Mr. F. "You don't believe that we would allow our children to make ascensions in dangerous contraptions, do you?"

"I guess not," I said, reassured. "I am sure that any invention using balloons and wind as motive power cannot but be enjoyable."

"Very well, then," said Mr. F. He then loudly rang the bell on top of the shack. This sound produced the same reaction, only considerably

happier and more excited, as a school bell back home. We were shortly surrounded by children. These children didn't seem to need to be explained anything either; as soon as they arrived in the clearing they made themselves extremely busy readying the Balloon Merry-Go-Round. They took the tarpaulins off all the boats and rolled them up neatly. Four of the children ran into the shack where they prepared the hydrogen machine and pumps. Another eight each grabbed a silk hose, attached it to the hydrogen machine in the shack on one end, and to one of the balloons on the other. The balloons were all carefully unfolded and laid out flat on the ground, and the nets and ropes which attached them to the boats were carefully placed around and beside them so that they wouldn't get tangled up when the balloons were filled with gas. Slowly the balloons started to fill with hydrogen, the ones nearest the pumps filling faster than the others. They lazily lifted themselves off the ground with the children watching them carefully, constantly straightening the ropes so they wouldn't get tangled. Soon they were all full of hydrogen and straining at the boats which were roped to the ground. All forty children were present, working efficiently on the Merry-Go-Round, although it was apparent that there was only room for fourteen of them on this trip. There was room for two in each boat, making a total of sixteen seats, but Mr. F. and I were going to occupy two of the seats. There was no arguing among the children as to whose turn it was; they must have had some sort of passenger schedule they followed closely. I did notice that neither B-1 nor B-2 were among the children who climbed into the boats when they were ready. I suppose that this was because it was "B" Day of the Month of Lamb and they had plenty of work to do at their British chop house. I sat in a boat with Mr. F's son, F-1, and Mr. F. sat with a child in a boat which was on the opposite side of the big pole from ours. "This will make the Merry-Go-Round balance better," said F-1.

There were two children on the ground near each boat. When we were all aboard, they detached the silk hydrogen hoses and rolled them back up to the shack where they carefully hung them up. They then returned to us and one held a rope at the bow of each boat and the other held a rope at the boat's stern. One of the children passengers had a blank pistol, the sort used for starting races at track meets. He stood up and yelled in a high clear voice, *"Is everybody ready?"*

A shrill and deafening *"yes"* was heard, mixed with the deeper voices of Mr. F. and myself. At this signal, the children standing near the boats all gave their ropes a sharp pull, which seemed to unhook the boats from the ground, and they all ran around the pole in the direction we were heading, giving us a good fast start.

The boats were joined together to form the rim of a wheel. The poles going through the brass oarlocks of the boats formed the spokes of this wheel. The spokes were attached to a big brass ring, or hub of the wheel, and this whole gigantic Merry-Go-Round revolved around the seventy-five-foot pole which was pointing straight up to the sky and was threaded like a screw. The balloons lifted the boats around and around the huge screw up into the air. The Balloon Merry-Go-Round gained speed as it gained altitude. The pole was well greased so that by the time we neared the top we were going very fast. I asked F-1 what happened when we reached the top of the pole. "Do we quickly deflate the balloons and revolve back down to the ground around the pole in the opposite direction?"

"Of course not," said F-1. "We fly right off the pole into the air."

"You'll see," he said.

We soon reached the top and the Merry-Go-Round lunged upward as it lost its grip on the pole. The wind immediately started to carry us off over the Island. We were gaining altitude fast and, of course, still spinning around at great speed. I must admit this was truly a delightful and exciting ride, unlike any other balloon experience I have ever had. I saw now how the boats were kept level. A child in each boat held the ripcord of his boat's balloon. Whenever a boat went a little higher than the others, the ripcord would be pulled releasing a little hydrogen until the boat was again on the same level.

"You must only be able to take short trips," I told F-1, "if you constantly have to release gas to keep the Merry-Go-Round level."

"That's right," he answered. "The length of our trips depends on many things such as the calmness of the weather, how well we distribute the weight in the boats, and how skillfully we control the ripcords. But you understand," he added, "the Balloon Merry-Go-Round wasn't built for travel but rather for short pleasure trips."

"Oh, of course," I said.

The Balloon Merry-Go-Round was heading directly for the mountain. I saw that we were going to fly over it. I asked F-1 if this were not dangerous.

"It isn't dangerous, but it's rather unfortunate because it always means a short trip."

"Why?" I asked.

"Because the huge crater of the volcanic mountain is full of hot air which forms sort of a vacuum. When we fly over the crater, the Merry-Go-Round is sucked downward rather violently and we always use up a lot of gas controlling it and keeping it level."

"Isn't this hazardous?" I asked.

"No," said F-1, "by the time we reach the mountain, we will be high enough to clear it by a great distance. The only danger in taking a ride in this is landing on the ground or on the mountain, or worst of all, in the mountain when the wind is calm. Krakatoa is a small island, and if there is any wind at all, it will carry the Merry-Go-Round out to sea. Once when we first got it, we took a trip on a very calm day. We went straight up, spun around a while, and gradually lost altitude, landing in a forest of palm trees. No one was hurt, but some of the boats were damaged and one of the balloons was torn. Since then, we have only risked trips when there is wind."

We were nearing the mountain and I leaned over the side of my boat to look down at the crater. There was a thick gray smoke crawling around inside. It was like looking into a horrible pit full of elephants. When we were directly over the mountain there was a sickening atmosphere of hot air permeated with sulphurous gases. The Merry-Go-Round started tossing around violently over the pit, and the children with the ripcords kept a careful watch directly across our giant wheel at opposite boats to keep the Merry-Go-Round as steady and level as possible. Hanging on tightly, I leaned over the side of the boat in order to have a direct look into the volcanic

crater itself. In places where the smoke had cleared a bit I could see a lake of thick molten lava boiling and bubbling in slow motion. It was a sickening, frightening sight. As I was leaning over, the Merry-Go-Round suddenly plunged downward, then swayed from side to side as the children steadied it. I must have taken a deep gasp of breath, out of fear, I suppose, and my lungs were suddenly filled with hot sulphurous fumes. The Merry-Go-Round was still spinning fast, as well as pitching and rocking in the air. I hastily drew my head back into the boat, shut my eyes, and lay down on the bottom of the boat. I could hear the rumbling of the mountain beneath me mixed with the hissing noise of hydrogen being released from the balloons. I think I was as close to being sick then as it is possible for anyone to be. We were soon over the mountain, and in fresh, calm air again and I sat up feeling considerably better.

"To tell you the truth, Sir," said F-1, who apparently could well see that I had nearly lost my British breakfast, "I was nearly sick myself that time. The mountain seems unusually violent this morning. I hope this isn't a bad sign."

I took this to be the remark of a younger balloonist comforting an older one who had nearly made a fool of himself. I told him that my behavior was quite inexcusable.

Flying over water in this spinning airship was completely enjoyable. The magnificent seascape of the Pacific Ocean passed before your eyes half of the time, and Krakatoa in its entirety was beneath you for your careful observation with each turn of the Merry-Go-Round. The Island looked beautiful from the air. Its vegetation was so rich, warm, and soft-looking. The mountain looked so fearful and exciting. The magnificent houses of all nations looked like extraordinary doll's houses on felt lawns, and the Krakatoan crystal house shone like a jewel. The contrast between the trimmed interior and untrimmed ring of jungle around the Island was easy to see from our boats. The Island looked like a formal garden surrounded by a bushy untrimmed hedge.

After a flight lasting approximately thirty-five minutes we were near the surface of the water. The children, controlling their ripcords like experts, lowered the Merry-Go-Round gently and smoothly into the Ocean. We made one complete turn in the water and came slowly to a stop. "Well," I exclaimed, "that was undoubtedly the most thrilling and unusual trip I have ever had the pleasure of taking."

The children in the boats, Mr. F., and I then all leaned back and relaxed a while in the sun, looking up at the balloons which were now half empty and bobbing back and forth with the wind. Suddenly one of the boys, the same one who had fired the starting gun, stood up and said, "All right, everybody, let's go."

At this command, the rest of the children stood up and carefully deflated their balloons and folded them up in their boats without letting any part of them touch water. They folded them lengthwise first, then rolled them from the top toward the bottom where the gas escape was, thus forcing all of the gas out of them and making small neat bundles. They opened the little lockers in the boats, where the sails were, took the sails out, and replaced them with the folded balloons. Each boat had one mainsail.

"How do you sail these boats when they are all attached together like a wheel?" I asked. "And what do you use for masts?" These were foolish questions, I immediately realized, for while I was asking them I managed to figure out these problems for myself.

First of all, the children detached the boats one from the other at their bows and sterns. When this was done, they were still attached to each other by the poles which formed the spokes of the giant wheel. These poles were obviously the masts when the boats were used for sailing. The children, two on each pole, all pushed together toward the center hub until the poles slid out through the brass oarlock rings on their boats. Then, still working two on each pole, they unscrewed the poles from the brass hub in the center. They all unscrewed their poles except one boy, the boy who gave the commands. He pulled his pole in with the hub still attached to it, unscrewed the hub in his boat, and put it away in a separate locker. Now that they each had their masts, it was a simple problem to put them into the mast holes. Mr. F. and I did our best to work as efficiently as any of the other crew members. Soon the mainsail was rigged up and we were ready to sail back to the Island. Only the need for a boom was absent from this compact invention. We lowered centerboards and lined up. It was evidently the custom to race home. The boy who gave the signals took out his gun, fired it, and we were homeward bound as fast as the wind would take us. I am afraid I was more of a hindrance than a capable assistant to young F-1. We finished the race last by about seven minutes. The boats were moored to a dock near the freighter in the hidden inlet and we assembled on shore. F-1 explained to me that the boy who had given the signals was the "Captain of the Day," some sort of honor each child received in turn.

The Captain of the Day told the rest of us that since this was my first trip in the Balloon Merry-Go-Round, the results of the boat race wouldn't count on the Official Scoring Sheet. F-1 let out a whooping cheer at this which made me feel quite badly. The Captain of the Day then took me aside and told me, in a most polite way, that he thought it would be an excellent idea if I learned a bit about sailing since I now found myself to be a citizen of Krakatoa. I assured him that I would.

The Captain of the Day then closed the meeting by saying that the Merry-Go-Round would be reassembled around the flying pole right after supper. "And I want you all to be here and help," he said, looking sternly in my direction.

After forty years of schoolteaching I found myself being ordered about by a child. I couldn't help but find this heretofore impossible turnabout amusing. I was indeed far away from the usual dull school routines I so disliked.

"I'll be there!" I said in a loud voice, as everybody looked at me and laughed.

The whole trip had taken about five hours and we had therefore missed lunch. I devoured an excellent supper at the B.'s chop house, and then Mr. F. and I reported to the flying pole. The Captain of the Day rang the bell on top of the shack assembling all of the children and we were divided into eight groups of five. (B-1 and B-2 were still busy.) With five on each boat, we had the Merry-Go-Round reassembled and ready to go in less than half an hour. I will confess, though, that after this busy second day on the fabulous Island, I was well ready for bed and slept like a top.

from THE CHILDREN

OF GREEN KNOWE

Lucy Maria Boston

This book is one of the most unusual and beautiful ghost stories ever written. It is about Toseland (Tolly), a lonely boy, staying with his great-grandmother in a big stone castle. It suggests witches, ghosts, and spells. Tolly encounters all three and comes to love the ghost children from the long, long ago of his own family. Here is the first chapter.

A little boy was sitting in the corner of a railway carriage looking out at the rain, which was splashing against the windows and blotching downward in an ugly, dirty way. He was not the only person in the carriage, but the others were strangers to him. He was alone as usual. There were two women opposite him, a fat one and a thin one, and they talked without stopping, smacking their lips in between sentences and seeming to enjoy what they said as much as if it were something to eat. They were knitting all the time, and whenever the train stopped the click-clack of their needles was loud and clear like two clocks. It was a stopping train—more stop than go—and it had been crawling along through flat flooded country for a long time. Everywhere there was water—not sea or rivers or lakes, but just senseless flood water with the rain splashing into it. Sometimes the railway lines were covered by it, and then the train-noise was quite different, softer than a boat.

"I wish it was *the* Flood," thought the boy, "and that I was going to the Ark. That would be fun! Like the circus. Perhaps Noah had a whip and made all the animals go round and round for exercise. What a noise there would be, with the lions roaring, elephants trumpeting, pigs squealing, donkeys braying, horses whinnying, bulls bellowing, and cocks and hens always thinking they were going to be trodden on but unable to fly up on to the roof where all the other birds were singing, screaming, twittering, squawking and cooing. What must it have sounded like, coming along on the tide? And did Mrs. Noah just knit, knit and take no notice?"

The two women opposite him were getting ready for the next station. They packed up their knitting and collected their parcels and then sat staring at the little boy. He had a thin face and very large eyes; he looked patient and rather sad. They seemed to notice him for the first time.

"What's your name, son?" asked the fat woman suddenly. "I've never seen you on this train before." This was always a question he dreaded. Was he to say his unexpected real name or his silly pet names?

"Toseland," he said.

"Toseland! That's a real old-fashioned name in these parts. There's Fen Toseland, and Toseland St. Agnes and Toseland Gunning. What's your Christian name?"

"That is it—Toseland."

"Do your mum and dad live round here, son?"

"No, they live in Burma."

"Fancy that now! That's a long way away. Where are you going, then?"

"I don't know. That is, I'm going to my great-grandmother Oldknow at Green Noah. The station in Penny Soaky."

"That's the next station after this. We get out here. Don't forget—the next station. And make sure there's some dry land before you get out of the train. The floods are bad there. Bye-bye, cheerio."

They got out, shouting and joking with the porters and kissing the people who had come to meet them. They started off into the hissing rain as if they loved it. Toseland heard the fat woman's loud voice saying, "Oh, I don't mind this. I like it, it's our home-rain, not like that dirty London water."

The train jogged on again and now Toseland was quite alone. He wished he had a family like other people—brothers and sisters, even if his father were away. His mother was dead. He had a stepmother but he hardly knew her and was miserably shy of her. He had been at a boarding-school, and for the last holidays he had been left behind to stay with the head mistress, Miss Spudd, and her old father. They meant to be kind to him, but they never spoke to him without saying "dear." It was "Finish up your porridge, dear, we don't want you to get thin," or "Put on your coat, dear, we don't want you to catch cold," or "Get ready for church, dear, we don't want you to grow up a heathen." And every day after breakfast, "Run along to your room, dear, we want to read the papers."

But now his great-grandmother Oldknow had written that he was to come and live with her. He had never seen her, but she was his own great-grandmother, and that was something. Of course she would be very old. He thought of some old people he had seen who were so old that it frightened him. He wondered if she would be frighteningly old. He began to feel afraid already, and to shake it off he thought about Green Noah and Penny Soaky. What queer names! Green Noah was pure mystery, but Penny Soaky was friendly like a joke.

Suddenly the train stopped, and the porters were shouting "Penny Soaky! Penny Soaky!" Toseland had no sooner got the door open than a man wearing a taxi-driver's hat came along calling:

"Anybody here for Green Noah? Are you Master Toseland for Green Noah?"

"Oh yes, please. It's me."

"This your luggage? Two more in the van? You stand here out of the rain while I get it."

There were a few houses to be seen on one side of the line, and on the other nothing but flooded fields with hedges standing in the water.

"Come along," said the taxi-man. "I've put all your luggage in the car. It'll be dark before we get there and we've got to go through a lot of water."

"Is it deep?"

"Not so deep, I hope, that we can't get through."

"If it rains forty days and forty nights will it be a real flood?"

"Sure enough it would."

Toseland sat by the driver and they set off. The windscreen wipers made two clear fans on the windscreen through which he could see the road half covered with water, with ditches brimming on either side. When they came near the bridge that crossed the river, the road disappeared under water altogether and they seemed to drive into the side of the river with a great splash that flew up against the windows; but it was only a few inches deep, and then they reached the humpbacked bridge and went up and over it, and down again into deeper water on the other side. This time they drove very carefully like bathers walking out into cold water. The car crept along making wide ripples.

"We don't want to stick here," said the driver, "this car don't float."

They came safely through that side too, and now the headlights were turned on, for it was growing dark, and Toseland could see nothing but rain and dazzle.

"Is it far?" he asked.

"Not very, but we have to go a long way round to get past the floods. Green Noah stands almost in the middle of it now, because the river runs alongside the garden. Once you get

there you won't be able to get out again till the flood goes down."

"How will I get in, then?"

"Can you swim?"

"Yes, I did twenty strokes last summer. Will that be enough?"

"You'll have to do better than that. Perhaps if you felt yourself sinking you could manage a few more?"

"But it's quite dark. How will I know where to swim to?"

The driver laughed. "Don't you worry. Mrs. Oldknow will never let you drown. She'll see you get there all right. Now here we are. At least, I can't go any further." Toseland pushed the car door open and looked out. It had stopped raining. The car was standing in a lane of shallow water that stretched out into the dark in front and behind. The driver was wearing Wellington boots, and he got out and paddled round the car. Toseland was afraid that he would be left now to go on as best he could by himself. He did not like to show that he was afraid, so he tried another way of finding out.

"If I am going to swim," he said, "what will you do with my luggage?"

"You haven't got no gum boots, have you?" said the driver. "Come on, get on my shoulders and we'll have a look round to see if anyone's coming to meet you." Toseland climbed on to his shoulders and they set off, but almost at once they heard the sound of oars, and a lantern came round the corner of the lane rocking on the bows of a rowing boat. A man called out, "Is that Master Toseland?" The driver shouted back, "Is that Mr. Boggis?" but Toseland was speechless with relief and delight.

"Good evening, Master Toseland," said Mr. Boggis, holding up the lantern to look at him, while Toseland looked too, and saw a nice old cherry-red face with bright blue eyes. "Pleased to meet you. I knew your mother when she was your size. I bet you were wondering how you were going to get home?" It was nice to hear somebody talking about "home" in that way. Toseland felt much happier, and now he knew that the driver had been teasing him, so he grinned and said: "I was going to swim."

The boat was moored to somebody's garden

gate while the two men put the trunk and tuck-box into it.

"You'll be all right now," said the taxi-man. "Goodnight to you both."

"Goodnight, and thank you," said Toseland. Mr. Boggis handed him the lantern and told him to kneel up in the bows with it and shout if they were likely to bump into anything. They rowed round two corners in the road and then in at a big white gate. Toseland waved the lantern about and saw trees and bushes standing in the water, and presently the boat was rocked by quite a strong current and the reflection of the lantern steamed away in elastic jigsaw shapes and made gold rings round the tree trunks. At last they came to a still pool reaching to the steps of the house, and the keel of the boat grated on gravel. The windows were all lit up, but it was too dark to see what kind of a house it was, only that it was high and narrow like a tower.

"Come along in," said Mr. Boggis. "I'll show you in. I'd like to see Mrs. Oldknow's face when she sees you."

The entrance hall was a strange place. As they stepped in, a similar door opened at the far end of the house and another man and boy entered there. Then Toseland saw that it was only themselves in a big mirror. The walls round him were partly rough stone and partly plaster, but hung all over with mirrors and pictures and china. There were three big old mirrors all reflecting each other so that at first Toseland was puzzled to find what was real, and which door one could go through straight, the way one wanted to, not sideways somewhere else. He almost wondered which was really himself.

There were vases everywhere filled with queer flowers—branches of dry winter twigs out of which little tassels and rosettes of flower petals were bursting, some yellow, some white, some purple. They had an exciting smell, almost like something to eat, and they looked as if they had been produced by magic, as if someone had said "Abracadabra! Let these sticks burst into flower." "What if my great-grandmother is a witch!" he thought. Above the vases, wherever there was a beam or an odd corner or a doorpost out of which they could, as it were, grow, there were children carved in dark oak, leaning out over the flowers. Most of them had wings, one had a real bird's nest on its head, and all of them had such round polished cheeks they seemed to be laughing and welcoming him.

While he was looking round him, Boggis had taken his coat and cap from him and hung them up. "Your great-grandmother will be in here," he said, and led him to a little old stone doorway such as you might find in a belfry. He knocked on the door. "Come in," said a clear voice. Boggis gave Toseland a shove, and he found himself inside.

The room seemed to be the ground floor of a castle, much like the ruined castles that he had explored on school picnics, only this was not a ruin. It looked as if it never possibly could be. Its thick stone walls were strong, warm and lively. It was furnished with comfortable polished old-fashioned things as though living in castles was quite ordinary. Toseland stood just outside the door and felt it must be a dream.

His great-grandmother was sitting by a huge open fireplace where logs and peat were burning. The room smelled of woods and woodsmoke. He forgot about her being frighteningly old. She had short silver curls and her face had so many wrinkles it looked as if someone had been trying to draw her for a very long time and every line put in had made the face more like her. She was wearing a soft dress of folded velvet that was as black as a hole in darkness. The room was full of candles in glass candlesticks, and there was candlelight in her ring when she held out her hand to him.

"So you've come back!" she said, smiling, as he came forward, and he found himself leaning against her shoulder as if he knew her quite well.

"Why do you say 'come back'?" he asked, not at all shy.

"I wondered whose face it would be of all the faces I knew," she said. "They always come back. You are like another Toseland, your grandfather. What a good thing you have the right name, because I should always be calling you Tolly anyway. I used to call him Tolly. Have you got a pet name? I'm sure they don't call you Toseland at school."

"No, I get called Towser."

"And at home?"

"My stepmother calls me Toto, but I hate it. It's worse than Towser."

"I think I agree with you. Here we are all used to Toseland, it's the family name and doesn't seem queer to us. So you shan't be Toto here. Do you mind Tolly?"

"I like it. It's what my mother used to call me. What shall I call you?"

"Granny," she said. "What does one generation more or less matter? I'm glad you have come. It will seem lovely to me."

Tolly watched the flames tugging loose from the logs and leaping up the black chimney. They reminded him of bonfire flames wrestling and tearing and whistling in the sky on the fifth of November. Those had been frightening, but these were wonderful.

"Are these our flames?" he asked. "I mean, are they our own?"

"The blue ones are yours and the orange ones are mine."

"And the candle-flames?"

"All yours."

Tolly hesitated, then asked in a very little voice because he hardly dared, "Is it my house— I mean, partly?"

"Of course it is—partly, as you say. Well, now that you are here what shall we do first? Are you hungry?"

She rose and, standing, looked much older. Her figure was bent and shrunken, her face no higher than Tolly's own. The folds of her dress seemed both to weigh her down and hold her up. She brought a tray that was laid ready for him on the sideboard, and put it on a low table in front of the fire. There were egg sandwiches and chicken sandwiches and iced orange cake and jelly and chocolate finger biscuits. Toseland ate happily and tried not to make crumbs.

"I came in a boat with a lantern," he said. "I played the house was Noah's Ark."

"Oh, the Ark! So you played it was the Ark."

"Yes. Do you think Noah had a whip like a circus man and made the animals run round and round for exercise?"

"Yes. And Ham juggled with clubs and plates to pass the time away, and Shem and Japhet were clowns and tried to make Mrs. Noah laugh. But she never did, because if she had done, all her buttons would have burst off. She was done up very tight."

At that moment the fire went *pop!* and shot a piece of wood out into the room. *Pop!* again.

"Buttons! Who said buttons? Poor Mrs. Noah." Tolly chased the sparks and trod on them to put them out.

"Why do you live in a castle?" he said, looking round.

"Why not? Castles were meant to live in."

"I thought that was only in fairy tales. Is it a real castle?"

"Of course."

"I mean, do things happen in it, like the castles in books?"

"Oh yes, things happen in it."

"What sort of things?"

"Wait and see! I'm waiting too, to see what happens now that you are here. Something will, I'm sure. Tomorrow you can explore the inside of the house up and down, and learn your way about and to feel at home in it, because you won't be able to go outside until the floods go down. And now you must come and see your own room, and you must go to bed early tonight."

She led him up winding stairs and through a high, arched room like a knight's hall, that she called the Music Room, and on up more stairs to the very top of the house. Here there was a room under the roof, with a ceiling the shape of the roof and all the beams showing. It was a long room with a triangle of wall at each end and no walls at the sides, because the sloping ceiling came down to the floor, like a tent. There were windows on three sides, and a little low wooden bed in the middle covered with a patchwork quilt, as unlike a school bed as anything could be. There was a low table, a chest of drawers and lots of smooth, polished, empty floor. At one side there was a beautiful old rocking-horse—not a "safety" rocking horse hanging on iron swings from a centre shaft, but a horse whose legs were stretched to full gallop, fixed to long rockers so that it could, if you rode it violently, both rear and kick. On the other side was a doll's house. By the bed was a wooden box painted vermilion with bright patterns all over it, and next to it all Tolly's luggage piled up, making the room look really his.

A wicker bird-cage hung from one of the beams. On the only side that had no window there hung a big mirror reflecting all the rest—the rafters, the wicker cage, the rocking-horse, the doll's house, the painted box, the bed.

"In this house," said Tolly, "everything is twice!" He tried the lid of the painted box, but could not open it.

"The key is lost," said Mrs. Oldknow. "I don't know what's in it. It used to be the children's toy-box."

He put his hand on the rocking-horse's mane, which was real horse-hair. Its tail was real hair too, black and soft and long. He started it rocking. It made a nice creaky sound, like a rocking-chair. He opened the front of the doll's house. "Why, it's this house!" he said. "Look, here's the knight's hall, and here's the stairs, and here's my room! Here's the rocking-horse and here's the red box, and here's a tiny bird-cage! But it's got four beds in it. Are there sometimes other children here?"

Mrs. Oldknow looked at him as if she would like to know everything about him before she answered.

"Yes," she said, "sometimes."

"Who are they?"

"You'll see when they come, if they come."

from THE BORROWERS

Mary Norton

If you know exactly where you put your favorite pencil, but it is not there when you return for it, then probably your house has THEM *—the* BORROWERS. *They are tiny ingenious folk who live under the floor and who borrow what they need from "human beans"—such as a thimble for a kettle or a stamp for a portrait to hang on their walls. Their greatest danger is being seen by the giant humans. In this chapter, Pod returns from a borrowing expedition, thoroughly frightened—he has been seen!*

Pod came in slowly, his sack on his back; he leaned his hat pin, with its dangling name-tape, against the wall and, on the middle of the kitchen table, he placed a doll's tea cup; it was the size of a mixing bowl.

"Why, Pod—" began Homily.

"Got the saucer too," he said. He swung down the sack and untied the neck. "Here you are," he said, drawing out the saucer. "Matches it."

He had a round, currant-bunny sort of face; tonight it looked flabby.

"Oh, Pod," said Homily, "you do look queer. Are you all right?"

Pod sat down. "I'm fair enough," he said.

"You went up the curtain," said Homily. "Oh, Pod, you shouldn't have. It's shaken you—"

Pod made a strange face, his eyes swiveled round toward Arrietty. Homily stared at him, her mouth open, and then she turned. "Come along, Arrietty," she said briskly, "you pop off to bed, now, like a good girl, and I'll bring you some supper."

"Oh," said Arrietty, "can't I see the rest of the borrowings?"

"Your father's got nothing now. Only food. Off you pop to bed. You've seen the cup and saucer."

Arrietty went into the sitting room to put away her diary, and took some time fixing her candle on the upturned drawing pin which served as a holder.

"Whatever are you doing?" grumbled Homily. "Give it here. There, that's the way. Now off to bed and fold your clothes, mind."

"Good night, Papa," said Arrietty, kissing his flat white cheek.

"Careful of the light," he said mechanically, and watched her with his round eyes until she had closed the door.

"Now, Pod," said Homily, when they were alone, "tell me. What's the matter?"

Pod looked at her blankly. "I been 'seen,' " he said.

Homily put out a groping hand for the edge of the table; she grasped it and lowered herself slowly on to the stool. "Oh, Pod," she said.

There was silence between them. Pod stared at Homily and Homily stared at the table. After a while she raised her white face. "Badly?" she asked.

Pod moved restlessly. "I don't know about badly. I been 'seen.' Ain't that bad enough?"

"No one," said Homily slowly, "hasn't never been 'seen' since Uncle Hendreary and he was the first they say for forty-five years." A thought struck her and she gripped the table. "It's no good, Pod, I won't emigrate!"

"No one's asked you to," said Pod.

"To go and live like Hendreary and Lupy in a badger's set! The other side of the world, that's where they say it is—all among the earthworms."

"It's two fields away, above the spinney," said Pod.

"Nuts, that's what they eat. And berries. I wouldn't wonder if they don't eat mice—"

"You've eaten mice yourself," Pod reminded her.

"All draughts and fresh air and the children growing up wild. Think of Arrietty!" said Homily. "Think of the way she's been brought up. An only child. She'd catch her death. It's different for Hendreary."

"Why?" asked Pod. "He's got four."

"That's why," explained Homily. "When you've got four, they're brought up rough. But never mind that now. . . . Who saw you?"

"A boy," said Pod.

"A what?" exclaimed Homily, staring.

"A boy." Pod sketched out a rough shape in the air with his hands. "You know, a boy."

"But there isn't—I mean, what sort of a boy?"

"I don't know what you mean 'what sort of a boy.' A boy in a night-shirt. A boy. You know what a boy is, don't you?"

"Yes," said Homily, "I know what a boy is. But there hasn't been a boy, not in this house, these twenty years."

"Well," said Pod, "there's one here now."

Homily stared at him in silence, and Pod met her eyes. "Where did he see you?" asked Homily at last.

"In the schoolroom."

"Oh," said Homily, "when you was getting the cup?"

"Yes," said Pod.

"Haven't you got eyes?" asked Homily. "Couldn't you have looked first?"

"There's never nobody in the schoolroom. And what's more," he went on, "there wasn't to-day."

"Then where was he?"

"In bed. In the night-nursery or whatever it's called. That's where he was. Sitting up in bed. With the doors open."

"Well, you could have looked in the nursery."

"How could I—halfway up the curtain!"

"Is that where you was?"

"Yes."

"With the cup?"

"Yes. I couldn't get up or down."

"Oh, Pod," wailed Homily, "I should never have let you go. Not at your age!"

"Now, look here," said Pod, "don't mistake me. I got up all right. Got up like a bird, as you might say, bobbles or no bobbles. But"—he leaned toward her—"afterwards—with the cup in me hand, if you see what I mean. . . ." He picked it up off the table. "You see, it's heavy like. You can hold it by the handle, like this . . . but it drops or droops, as you might say. You should take a cup like this in your two hands. A bit of cheese off a shelf, or an apple—well, I drop that . . . give it a push and it falls and I climbs down in me own time and picks it up. But with a cup—you see what I mean? And coming down, you got to watch your feet. And, as I say, some of the bobbles was missing. You didn't know what you could hold on to, not safely. . . ."

"Oh, Pod," said Homily, her eyes full of tears, "what did you do?"

"Well," said Pod, sitting back again, "he took the cup."

"What do you mean?" exclaimed Homily, aghast.

Pod avoided her eyes. "Well, he'd been sitting up in bed there watching me. I'd been on that curtain a good ten minutes, because the hall clock had just struck the quarter—"

"But how do you mean—'he took the cup'?"

"Well, he'd got out of bed and there he was standing, looking up. 'I'll take the cup,' he said."

"Oh!" gasped Homily, her eyes staring, "and you give it him?"

"He took it," said Pod, "ever so gentle. And then, when I was down, he give it me." Homily put her face in her hands. "Now don't take on," said Pod uneasily.

"He might have caught you," shuddered Homily in a stifled voice.

"Yes," said Pod, "but he just give me the cup. 'Here you are,' he said."

Homily raised her face. "What are we going to do?" she asked.

Pod sighed. "Well, there isn't nothing we can do. Except—"

"Oh, no," exclaimed Homily, "not that. Not emigrate. Not that, Pod, now I've got the house so nice and a clock and all."

"We could take the clock," said Pod.

"And Arrietty? What about her? She's not like those cousins. She can *read,* Pod, and sew a treat—"

"He don't know where we live," said Pod.

"But they look," exclaimed Homily. "Remember Hendreary! They got the cat and—"

"Now, now," said Pod, "don't bring up the past."

"But you've got to think of it! They got the cat and—"

"Yes," said Pod, "but Eggletina was different."

"How different? She was Arrietty's age."

"Well, they hadn't told her, you see. That's where they went wrong. They tried to make her believe that there wasn't nothing but was under the floor. They never told her about Mrs. Driver or Crampfurl. Least of all about cats."

"There wasn't any cat," Homily pointed out, "not till Hendreary was 'seen.' "

"Well, there was, then," said Pod. "You got to tell them, that's what I say, or they try to find out for themselves."

"Pod," said Homily solemnly, "we haven't told Arrietty."

"Oh, she knows," said Pod; he moved uncomfortably. "She's got her grating."

"She doesn't know about Eggletina. She doesn't know about being 'seen.' "

"Well," said Pod, "we'll tell her. We always said we would. There's no hurry."

Homily stood up. "Pod," she said, "we're going to tell her now."

SPACE SHIP *BIFROST*

Robert A. Heinlein

Robert Heinlein's books are usually listed for teen-age reading. They are not easy, but this one sample is included because of the tremendous interest of older boys in the whole idea of space and the mastery of space travel. These books of Mr. Heinlein will interest adults as well as children, and interplanetary travel will begin to seem as possible as an airplane ride from here to England. This episode has to do with the beginning of a journey to Ganymede, where the boy and his family are going to settle.

I woke up hungry but I suddenly remembered that this was it!—my last day on Earth. Then I

"Space Ship *Bifrost*." Reprinted from *Farmer in the Sky* by Robert A. Heinlein; copyright 1950 by Robert A. Heinlein; used by permission of the publishers, Charles Scribner's Sons

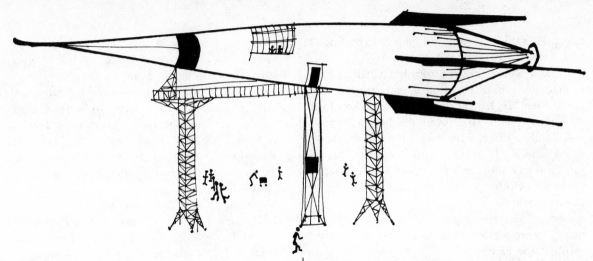

was too excited to be hungry. I got up, put on my Scout uniform and my ship suit over it.

I thought we would go right on board. I was wrong.

First we had to assemble under awnings spread out in front of the hotel near the embarking tubes. It wasn't air conditioned outside, of course, but it was early and the desert wasn't really hot yet. I found the letter "L" and sat down under it, sitting on my baggage. Dad and his new family weren't around yet; I began to wonder if I was going to Ganymede by myself. I didn't much care.

Out past the gates about five miles away, you could see the ships standing on the field, the *Daedalus* and the *Icarus,* pulled off the Earth-Moon run for this one trip, and the old *Bifrost* that had been the shuttle rocket to Supra-New-York space station as far back as I could remember.

The *Daedalus* and the *Icarus* were bigger but I hoped I would get the *Bifrost;* she was the first ship I ever saw blast off.

A family put their baggage down by mine. The mother looked out across the field and said, "Joseph, which one is the *Mayflower?*"

Her husband tried to explain to her, but she still was puzzled. I nearly burst, trying to keep from laughing. Here she was, all set to go to Ganymede and yet she was so dumb she didn't even know that the ship she was going in had been built out in space and couldn't land anywhere.

The place was getting crowded with emigrants and relatives coming to see them off, but I still didn't see anything of Dad. I heard my name called and turned around and there was Duck Miller. "Gee, Bill," he said, "I thought I'd missed you."

"Hi, Duck. No, I'm still here."

"I tried to call you last night but your phone answered 'service discontinued,' so I hooked school and came up."

"Aw, you shouldn't have done that."

"But I wanted to bring you this." He handed me a package, a whole pound of chocolates. I didn't know what to say.

I thanked him and then said, "Duck, I appreciate it, I really do. But I'll have to give them back to you."

"Huh? Why?"

"Weight. Mass, I mean. I can't get by with another ounce."

"You can carry it."

"That won't help. It counts just the same."

He thought about it and said, "Then let's open it."

I said, "Fine," and did so and offered him a piece. I looked at them myself and my stomach was practically sitting up and begging. I don't know when I've been so hungry.

I gave in and ate one. I figured I would sweat it off anyhow; it was getting hot and I had my Scout uniform on under my ship suit—and that's no way to dress for the Mojave Desert in June! Then I was thirstier than ever, of course; one thing leads to another.

I went over to a drinking fountain and took a very small drink. When I came back I closed the candy box and handed it back to Duck and told him to pass it around at next Scout meeting and tell the fellows I wished they were going along. He said he would and added, "You know, Bill, I wish I was going, I really do."

I said I wished he was, too, but when did he change his mind? He looked embarrassed but about then Mr. Kinski showed up and then Dad showed up, with Molly and the brat—Peggy—and Molly's sister, Mrs. van Metre. Everybody shook hands all around and Mrs. van Metre started to cry and the brat wanted to know what made my clothes so bunchy and what was I sweating about?

George was eyeing me, but about then our names were called and we started moving through the gate.

George and Molly and Peggy were weighed through and then it was my turn. My baggage was right on the nose, of course, and then I stepped on the scales. They read one hundred and thirty-one and one tenth pounds—I could have eaten another chocolate.

"Check!" said the weightmaster, then he looked up and said, "What in the world have you got on, son?"

The left sleeve of my uniform had started to unroll and was sticking out below the half sleeve of my ship suit. The merit badges were shining out like signal lights.

I didn't say anything. He started feeling the lumps the uniform sleeves made. "Boy," he said, "you're dressed like an arctic explorer; no wonder you're sweating. Didn't you know you weren't supposed to wear anything but the gear you were listed in?"

Dad came back and asked what the trouble was? I just stood there with my ears burning. The assistant weightmaster got into the huddle and they argued what should be done. The weightmaster phoned somebody and finally he said, "He's inside his weight limit; if he wants to call that monkey suit part of his skin, we'll allow it. Next customer, please!"

I trailed along, feeling foolish. We went down inside and climbed on the slide strip, it was cool down there, thank goodness. A few minutes later we got off at the loading room down under the rocket ship. Sure enough, it was the *Bifrost,* as I found out when the loading elevator poked above ground and stopped at the passenger port. We filed in.

They had it all organized. Our baggage had been taken from us in the loading room; each passenger had a place assigned by his weight. That split us up again; I was on the deck immediately under the control room. I found my place, couch 14-D, then went to a view port where I could see the *Daedalus* and the *Icarus.*

A brisk little stewardess, about knee high to a grasshopper, checked my name off a list and offered me an injection against dropsickness. I said no, thanks.

She said, "You've been out before?"

I admitted I hadn't; she said, "Better take it."

I said I was a licensed air pilot; I wouldn't get sick. I didn't tell her that my license was just for copters. She shrugged and turned away. A loudspeaker said, "The *Daedalus* is cleared for blasting." I moved up to get a good view.

The *Daedalus* was about a quarter of a mile away and stood up higher than we did. She had fine lines and was a mighty pretty sight, gleaming in the morning sunshine. Beyond her and to the right, clear out at the edge of the field, a light shone green at the traffic control blockhouse.

She canted slowly over to the south, just a few degrees.

Fire burst out of her base, orange, and then blinding white. It splashed down into the ground baffles and curled back up through the ground vents. She lifted.

She hung there for a breath and you could see the hills shimmer through her jet. And she was gone.

Just like that—she was gone. She went up out of there like a scared bird, just a pencil of white fire in the sky, and was gone while we could still hear and feel the thunder of her jets inside the compartment.

My ears were ringing. I heard someone behind me say, "But I haven't had breakfast. The Captain will just have to wait. Tell him, Joseph."

It was the woman who hadn't known that the *Mayflower* was a space-to-space ship. Her husband tried to hush her up, but he didn't have any luck. She called over the stewardess. I heard her answer, "But, madam, you can't speak to the Captain now. He's preparing for blast-off."

Apparently that didn't make any difference. The stewardess finally got her quiet by solemnly promising that she could have breakfast after blast-off. I bent my ears at that and I decided to put in a bid for breakfast, too.

The *Icarus* took off twenty minutes later and then the speaker said, "All hands! Acceleration stations—prepare to blast off." I went back to my couch and the stewardess made sure that we were all strapped down. She cautioned us not to unstrap until she said we could. She went down to the deck below.

I felt my ears pop and there was a soft sighing in the ship. I swallowed and kept swallowing. I knew what they were doing: blowing the natural air out and replacing it with the standard helium-oxygen mix at half sea-level pressure. But the woman—the same one—didn't like it. She said, "Joseph, my head aches. Joseph, I can't breathe. Do something!"

Then she clawed at her straps and sat up. Her husband sat up, too, and forced her back down.

The *Bifrost* tilted over a little and the speaker said, "Minus three minutes!"

After a long time it said, "Minus two minutes!"

And then "Minus one minute!" and another voice took up the count:

"Fifty-nine! Fifty-eight! Fifty-seven!"

My heart started to pound so hard I could hardly hear it. But it went on: "—thirty-five! Thirty-four! Thirty-three! Thirty-two! Thirty-one! *Half!* Twenty-nine! Twenty-eight!"

And it got to be: *"Ten!"*

And "Nine!"

"Eight!

"Seven!

"And six!

"And five!

"And four!

"And three!

"And two—"

I never did hear them say "one" or "fire" or whatever they said. About then something fell on me and I thought I was licked. Once, exploring a cave with the fellows, a bank collapsed on me and I had to be dug out. It was like that —but nobody dug me out.

My chest hurt. My ribs seemed about to break. I couldn't lift a finger. I gulped and couldn't get my breath.

I wasn't scared, not really, because I knew we would take off with a high *g*, but I was awfully uncomfortable. I managed to turn my head a little and saw that the sky was already purple. While I watched, it turned black and the stars came out, millions of stars. And yet the Sun was still streaming in through the port.

The roar of the jets was unbelievable but the noise started to die out almost at once and soon you couldn't hear it at all. They say the old ships used to be noisy even after you passed the speed of sound; the *Bifrost* was not. It got as quiet as the inside of a bag of feathers.

There was nothing to do but lie there, stare out at that black sky, try to breathe, and try not to think about the weight sitting on you.

And then, so suddenly that it made your stomach turn flip-flops, you didn't weigh anything at all.

BOOK 3: TIME FOR TRUE TALES

and almost true

BOOKS AND CHILDREN

Time and the child

Only grownups know the swiftness of time's passing. To children and young people it moves as slowly as a snail, with long intervals when nothing seems to happen. In those intervals, between play and routines, the child needs something to feed upon. Food for the body is essential but there must also be food for the mind and spirit of the child. And what do children find to feed upon in this modern age! They may turn to soap operas, television cowboys, the comics, or little gilded books with abbreviated content —pacifiers, not food, designed to kill time, not to fill it richly and fully. If they turn to these pacifiers, it is often because many adults have no respect for the child's time. They say, "Don't bother me just now. Go turn on the television." Or they ask, "Where is that pretty book I bought for you at the grocery store?" They don't even remember the title. It doesn't matter. It is just something to keep the child occupied and out of the way. Yet who should know better than adults the touching swiftness with which childhood passes? And who should be more aware than they of its exuberant eagerness, its hungry curiosities? What happens to a child's dreams and his hungers if he is fed only intellectual chaff? And what may happen if his curiosities are met with strong books which feed his young spirit and give him something to grow on?

Clifton Fadiman, exploring modern books for children, makes this statement,

Consider, though, how little the child actually *does* read. Librarians estimate that about 500 books represent the *maximum* the average child can get through between seven and fourteen. That's about 70 per year. Hence the child simply cannot afford the commonplace.[1]

Perhaps Mr. Fadiman is a bit too exacting. Perhaps if grownups can lull themselves happily with pulp fiction or "whodunits" from time to time, their offspring might be allowed a few commonplaces. But, in the main, Mr. Fadiman's concern is sound. Childhood *is* brief. Its reading is even briefer. The least adults can do is to see that children encounter a variety of fine books and some of the great books which can minister most effectively to their maturing minds, growing responsibilities, and changing needs.

Books and children's needs

But how can grownups learn to know and select the best books for children from the enormous mass of juveniles available? First, they should understand that children should find in reading vicarious satisfaction for their basic needs. In the opening chapter of *Children and Books*[2] there is a full discussion of those needs and the kinds of books which help to meet them. For example, *security*—physical or material, emotional, spiritual, and intellectual—continues to be a basic need even in an age of social unrest, wars, and atom bombs. Children and men alike dream of being safe, comfortable, wealthy, and wise. It is the superman dream that persists no matter how far short of the goal individuals

[1] Clifton Fadiman, "Party of One," *Holiday*, August 1952, p. 6
[2] May Hill Arbuthnot, *Children and Books*, Scott, Foresman, 1957, Chapter 1

and the world may fall. Fairy tale fantasies on the one hand and the biographies of real heroes on the other minister to this dream and keep young spirits soaring.

The *need to achieve,* to do or be something worthy of admiration, is even more pressing than the need for security. This is fortunate or the human race would grow too cautious to survive. Stories built around adventure from *Peter Rabbit* to *Treasure Island* satisfy this need grandly. Stories for the oldest children along with adventurous action begin to emphasize moral achievement. Kate with the help of the Good Master becomes a self-controlled and useful child. Johnny Tremain abandons his plans for revenge in a self-forgetting absorption in the prerevolutionary plots. Achievement has progressed from riding up a glass hill to moral victory over self.

The *need to belong,* to be an accepted and liked member of a group, motivates the child's desire to achieve and is a part of the maturing process. Stories about family life, neighborhood and gang activities are built around this need to be a part of a social group as well as around the child's *need to love and to be loved.* These latter needs give rise presently to the romance literature of adolescence.

But neither life nor the child is always in earnest and there seems to be a healthy rhythm of work and play rising out of a basic *need for change.* Humorous verses and stories meet this desire for fun and change, either realistically as in "The Story of Johnny Head-in-Air"[1] and *The Adventures of Tom Sawyer,* or fantastically as in "Alas, Alack!" and in such tall tales as *Pecos Bill.*

And finally there is the *need for aesthetic satisfaction.* We know that children are lusty little animals, but we know that they are far more than this. They reach out for beauty as well as food. They respond to the beauty of the world around them and to the beauty of decent human beings doing the best they can, and to the varied expressions of this beauty and goodness as we find them in the arts. So children need to discover in books this nebulous experience that we call aesthetic satisfaction—a sense of the signifi-

[1] May Hill Arbuthnot, *Time for Poetry,* "The Story of Johnny Head-in-Air," "Alas, Alack!"

cance of life in terms so arresting and so beautiful that life takes on richer meaning.

This brief review of children's basic needs omits one important consideration—namely, that no two children bring precisely the same needs and interests to a book. One child may be developing happily and normally in his social relationships but with a tight literalness of mind that knows nothing about imaginative play and brooks no nonsense. Such a child needs imaginative beauty in his reading, a little fantasy and sheer hilarity to keep him flexible. Another child is pampered and therefore socially immature. He needs stories that will help him to see himself in relation to other people and to develop increasing social responsibility. The withdrawing child, the overly aggressive one, the indecisive or the insensitive youngsters are all victims of maladjustment to the tasks with which they are confronted. Probably books alone cannot cure their maladjustments, but two things are certain. Trashy, trivial, or second-rate reading may afford these children temporary entertainment and escape from their problems, but it will give them no insight into dealing with those problems. On the other hand, strong books, worth-while books, even while they entertain young readers, will also supply them with clues to a better understanding of themselves and other people.

Qualities that make a child's book worth while

Probably no two people would agree upon all the qualities that must go into a book for children to make it worth while. But there may be a few qualities without which, most people would agree, no book can hope to win both the approval of children and critics of literature.

Of course, poetry is a special kind of writing that must be considered by itself. It is generally difficult to define the qualities that set authentic poetry apart from the commonplace, but many of the criteria have been discussed in the introduction to *Time for Poetry.* Melody and movement or, as Walter de la Mare calls them, "tune and runningness" are the qualities that set poetry apart from prose most conspicuously. In light verse or nonsense jingles the melodies are gay and the movements light, dancing, and strongly marked. The child soon discovers that the Mother Goose verses hop, skip, walk, run, gallop, or swing as tunefully as music. As he progresses to poetry with more content, the melodies are more subtle and the movement less marked and more varied. But in good poetry there is always a compatibility between the tune and runningness and the action, mood, or meaning of the poem. The words poetry employs are used with precision and chosen for their rich sensory and associative values. These in turn stimulate a sensory response in the person who speaks or hears poetry. Melody and movement, sensory imagery, and the associative values of words all work together with magical results to make experiences suddenly stirring and to give them a significance that was lacking when they were merely experiences.

But prose is another matter. If children were literary analysts, they would probably insist that the first requisite of a good story is lively *action* or *plot*. It is true that children accept and even like gentle, charming stories without plot, especially if they are illustrated, but the prime favorites, the stories that survive for generations, the stories children wear out with rereading or wear out the grownups with rereading or retelling are plot stories. Such favorites as "The Three Little Pigs," *The Five Hundred Hats of Bartholomew Cubbins, The Adventures of Tom Sawyer, Caddie Woodlawn,* all have lively plots, with a great deal happening and with the heroes progressing merrily from deed to deed or escapade to escapade. Even the long descriptions in the idyllic *Wind in the Willows* are endured by children because of the unexpected scrapes Toad gets into and the exciting action involved in getting him out.

The stream of consciousness style of writing, the stories which begin in the middle and end up in the air, may pass with adults, but they won't with children. They like stories in which there is a brisk introduction that launches the plot, a development full of action and growing suspense, and conclusions that settle everything including the villain. To be sure, the plots for the nursery age are pretty mild, but even *Angus and the Ducks* has a definite plot, amusing action and suspense, and a satisfying conclusion with Angus safe and sound under the sofa.

An interesting *idea* or *theme* is essential to the development of a good plot. The theme is not always easy to define, but one explanation is that it is the motivating idea for the whole story. *Treasure Island,* for example, has a theme clearly indicated in the title and one sufficiently robust to support a thriller whose popularity has never waned in the more than thirty years of its existence. *The Good Master* is, of course, a gentle, juvenile version of the old *Taming of the Shrew* theme, and *Angus and the Ducks* turns upon the dog's curiosity. But whether or not a theme can be readily defined, it is the backbone of a story. The absence of a dominant idea results in a lot of the "so what?" type of stories that may be beautifully illustrated and momentarily entertaining but which will soon be forgotten.

Another characteristic of a superior book for children is *unique and memorable characters.* Stereotypes are soon forgotten, but unique, salty, vivid characters capture the imagination and affection of young readers. Rumpelstiltskin, Padre Porko, Br'er Rabbit, Ping, Smoky, Pinocchio, Huck Finn, Heidi and her grandfather, Long John Silver, Young Fu, Hetty and Hank, the Defender, Mr. Jerome Kildee—such characters as these are not easily forgotten. They add spice to reading and to life. Young readers are apt to say, "Oh, I wish I could have known"— Kate or Caddie or Tom or Jancsi or whoever the character happens to be. Or when they are grown up, they still chuckle over the wickedness of Long John Silver or the pranks and cockiness of Br'er Rabbit. Book characters like these broaden children's understandings and deepen their responses to people, animals, and life in general.

The fourth requisite of a first-rate story is that nebulous quality called *style.* Unfortunately, the lack of good prose style is not always noticed, particularly in the field of children's books, but good style makes itself felt in many ways. The text moves and flows smoothly. Reading is effortless and agreeable, not because of a denuded vocabulary and short sentences but because words and meaning are compatible and the phrasing is staccato or sonorous, serene or brisk, according to mood and meaning. If the text reads aloud delightfully, it has good prose style. Folk tales are obvious examples of this. Notice their dramatic dialogues, which characterize without descriptions. Sometimes the narrative has a cadenced swing, sometimes it is literally in a minor key. The beginnings often set the mood and tempo of the whole story and the conclusions are likewise gay or grave or romantic in the mood of the adventure. There are similar virtues in the modern fairy tales. The books of Dr. Seuss or A. A. Milne or Wanda Gág cry out for reading aloud, so delightful is their style. In the field of realism the style is different but may be equally well done. The laconic vernacular of *Smoky* suits the story. Not a word of *Tom Sawyer* can be changed to advantage.

There are, of course, other requisites to good fiction[3] such as close unity of interest centered in the theme, a decent economy of incidents, and balanced proportions in the parts of the story. These contribute, too, but for a child's story, the essentials are *plot* growing out of a worth-while *theme, memorable characters,* and *distinguished style.*

Values from books

Taking for granted that grownups know something about the basic needs of children in general and the particular needs of individual children and have also adequate criteria for judging the worth of poetry, stories, and biography for children, what may they hope from a program of exposing children from their early years to good literature? What should fine books do for children?

Insight into living

One virtue of good reading is that it widens the child's limited experience and teaches him more about himself and others. Intensely personal in his interests, the small child identifies himself with story characters. *He* is the wise, clever pig. No wolf can get him. He would never think of being as foolish as Henny Penny or Budulinek. He would outwit them all, like Br'er Rabbit, or astonish them like William or Yonie. By way of stories, the child discovers that prying curiosity or irresponsibility may get him into hot water. But though these gay, first stories show

[3] For detailed discussion of these see May Hill Arbuthnot, *Children and Books,* Chapter 2

him the cause and effect of behavior or teach him manners and morals, they do so with a smile.

As the child and his reading mature together, he begins to see himself with ever-widening social relationships and social responsibilities. Ellen Tebbits pays dearly and absurdly for an inadvertent misrepresentation. The All-of-a-Kind family suffer acutely over the loss of a library book. The Wilder boy learns the meaning of money in terms of human labor, and Steppin has to get over his high-and-mighty opinion of himself before he makes much progress as a dancer. Standards of home life, of loyalty to a friend or a member of the family, family struggles, and family frolics may become a part of a child's social concepts as a result of his reading.

As the young reader acquires a widening knowledge of people, he also explores the world of nature, of pets and of wild animals—especially of animals that exist in a secret world and order of their own. He soon discovers that some people and animals enjoy security while others must face dangerous insecurity, that some people and animals are accepted and others rejected by the group they value. Children never forget the touching rejection of Wanda by her school group in *The Hundred Dresses.* In biography, the child sees his hero suffering humiliation, failures, even defeat, before he achieves success. Gradually, from the vicarious experiences of reading, the child's insight into his own personal problems grows and his understanding of people and creatures outside his immediate experience is enormously increased.

Reverence for life

That remarkable and dedicated man, Albert Schweitzer, used the phrase "reverence for life" as the summation of his philosophy of living. In this day of wars, atom bombs, and a growing callousness toward violence and death, "reverence for life . . . all life capable of development" is an ideal to cherish for ourselves and for our children. It is an extension of our own self-respect and self-love to a respect and love for others. Good books without sermonizing reinforce this attitude toward life. *The Blind Colt, Smoke Above the Lane,* and *Kildee House,* for example, leave children not only with a better understanding of animal life but also with a deep sympathy and tenderness for animals. *The Defender,* with its unforgettable account of the hunted mountain rams, also gives a picture of social injustice which rouses the reader's pity for the misjudged and rejected man. Books which show animals or men suffering from cruelty or misunderstanding, or sacrificing themselves for another's welfare build in young readers an abiding reverence for the valiant spirit that won't be downed. Poetry develops the child's sensitivity to beauty, to the significance of brief moments or great episodes, in short, to the significance of life and loveliness in all their strange variety. Biography reveals dedicated human beings and cannot help but nourish the child's response to goodness and decency and his "reverence for life . . . all life capable of development."

Zest for life

Finally, most children come into the world with exuberant energy and a zest for life that is glorious to behold. Alas, before they have reached maturity these may be sadly diminished. That is a pity. Life can be tragic or dull, but it can also be triumphant and gay. Some-

times it is downright comic. Also, human beings are endowed with a mechanism denied to animals, namely laughter, and it is good for man to use all of his endowments. So children should discover in their experience with books some reasons for laughter. There are drolls in the fairy tales, humor and nonsense in poetry, and delicious absurdities in realistic stories and even biography. Top off a dull day by reading a selection from this rich store. "Life is real and life is earnest" for most of us most of the time. But the therapy of laughter is a healthy medicine to be administered frequently. Some forgotten philosopher from the teaching profession once said, "Count the day lost in which your children have not laughed." Sometimes a smile or even a sudden twinkle in the eye means as much as a laugh. It means that tensions are broken and the young spirit is relaxed and at ease. A renewed zest for life will follow soon.

These, then, are some of the desirable outcomes of good reading. Supply the child with worth-while, entertaining reading and share it with him and he will gain *insight* into his own behavior, his social relationships, and responsibilities. He will grow in *reverence for life* and sensitivity to beauty and goodness. And he will keep his God-given *zest for life* and the gift of laughter.

Stories about animals are so popular with modern children that it is sometimes a problem to get them to read anything else. Perhaps the reason is that over half the world's population is now living in cities and the urban child misses the everyday contact with animals which is the rural child's heritage.

To meet children's demands for exciting chronicles of animal adventure, authors and publishers are turning out such stories in quantities. There are books about every kind of beast from rabbits to elephants, from minks to mustangs. Many of these books are excellent, most of them are fairly good, but some of them are stereotypes or juvenile thrillers, as sensational as fights and gore can make them. To appraise this offering,

ANIMAL STORIES

it is well to know something about the different types of animal stories, their values and limitations.

Animals as prototypes of human beings

The animals of folk tales and fables are not, of course, authentic animals at all, but symbols or even caricatures of human beings. "The Three Little Pigs" behave like foolish or wise people and "The Fox and the Crow" are flatterer and flattered. These ancient stories are ancestors of modern allegories like *Nothing at All* and modern fables like *Copy-Kitten.* When illustrators add clothes to these creatures, as in *Peter Rabbit,* their similarity to people is even more apparent. Oddly enough, this scientific generation, young and old, thoroughly enjoys animal tales in which the beasts are used as prototypes of human beings. Small children still love "Henny-Penny," their older brothers and sisters weep over "The Ugly Duckling," and both children and adults chuckle at the absurdities of "Donald Duck," "Bugs Bunny," and "Pogo." Ourselves in fur or feathers seem irresistibly comic or pathetic, both in stories and pictures.[1]

Animals as animals but talking

The second type of animal tale is partly make-believe and partly natural science, a hybrid form. The animals in such stories are portrayed with fidelity to the nature and behavior of the species, but they are given the human attributes of thoughts and speech. To be sure, the beasts don't discuss politics, but they do talk at length about their own affairs. The classic example is not *Black Beauty,* in which the horse is much too human for horse nature, but Felix Salten's *Bambi.*[2] In *Bambi,* the deer talk, are puzzled or afraid, warn each other, grieve or rejoice in words, but always in terms of deer life and deer problems. For example, the deer parents do not admonish their fawns to be courteous to their uncles and aunts, but they do warn them to be on watch for the pale, hairless creature which walks upright and carries a stick that sends out fire and death to animals far away. This type of story is difficult to write with integrity. If the animals are overly humanized, they cease to be authentic animals, and the story tends to become didactic or mawkishly sentimental. Not that children object to sentimentality or moralizing. Like adults, they will take considerable second-rate reading matter, but they deserve better fare.

[1] See May Hill Arbuthnot, *Time for Fairy Tales,* Scott, Foresman, 1961, for the following stories: "The Three Little Pigs," "The Fox and the Crow," "Nothing at All," "Copy-Kitten," "Henny-Penny," "The Ugly Duckling," "Puss in Boots" (The Master Cat) , "Ask Mr. Bear."
[2] Not the altered Disney versions but the original stories.

Animals objectively reported

The third type of animal story is told from the outside, as if the narrator were able to observe everything the animal does. The best of these stories re-create with scientific accuracy the animal and his environment within the framework of an exciting plot. Whether the animals are household pets, farm animals, or denizens of forest, swamp or jungle, they speak no words, but the noises they make are subject to general interpretations, as the cat's purr of contentment, a dog's bark of welcome, a lion's menacing roar or the loud churr of Mr. Kildee's "Old Grouch," which marked a full stomach and a dry, warm shelter. Beyond such guesses at meaning, which all humans seem to indulge in, the reader knows nothing about the inside workings of the animal's thoughts and emotions.

It is this third type of animal story which is enormously popular with children today. Even when they are still accepting the folk tale animal fantasy like "Puss in Boots," and "Ask Mr. Bear," they will also enjoy *Hodie* or one of the *Blaze* books and other stories that are scrupulously objective, realistic, and possible. It is this latter type of animal story, in contrast with the fanciful animal stories of *Time for Fairy Tales,* which has been chosen for this book.

These stories were selected with certain criteria in mind which may serve as standards for evaluating other animal tales. In addition to the usual criteria for evaluating any story for children—interesting plot, strong theme, memorable characters, and good style—there are also specific standards for judging the merit of this third type of animal tale. The first is, of course, integrity to the species of animal described. Hodie, for instance, has the gaiety and clownishness that are characteristic of the French poodle, but he also learns with true poodle quickness and amiability. The Wahoo Bobcat saves a little boy's life, not from any humanitarian motives, but from sheer blind rage and the instinct to defend a cub. The baby skunk in *Smoke Above the Lane* makes friends with the tramp because of desperate fear and hunger. The authors of the stories in this section never allow their animals to function from human motives, nor do they sentimentalize them, but the creatures run true to species.

Second, if there are people in these animal tales, they should be real people, not stereotypes of cruelty or goodness. Both Marguerite Henry in her horse stories and Jim Kjelgaard in his dog stories give children unique human characters, who are as memorable as the animal heroes of the books. So, the old man in that remarkable story *The Defender* is unlike any other character in children's books. Delightful as the wild mountain rams are, it is the old man, the defender, who gives the story greatness.

Avoidance of unnecessary cruelty and violence is a third criteria for evaluating animal stories. Because animals are vulnerable and suffer both from man and from other animals, some of the stories in this field go to sensational lengths to achieve a high degree of reading interest. They play up suffering and brutality to a disproportionate degree. The animal stories presented in this book often show animal tragedies and frequently man's injustice or brutality to beasts, but they are written with compassion, and the gory details are kept within bounds. Too much brutality can rouse latent sadism in young readers or develop in them a callous tolerance of suffering. This field of animal stories is one in which adults who guide children's reading need to distinguish between necessary violence and sensationalism.

Values of animal stories for children

Well-written animal stories have unique values for young readers. Over and over again, they teach him the curious vulnerability of animals, at the mercy of man with his guns and his greedy desire to exploit animals. The animal's lack of language subjects him to injustice and misunderstanding. The dog can't explain that he did not kill the sheep, nor can he help himself if his master wishes to sell him or give him away. It is this helplessness of animals which calls out the child's pity and love. And it is quite as important for the child to wish to love and cherish another creature as it is for him to be loved. In many city homes the animal story is vicarious satisfaction for the pets the child is not permitted to own.

Animal stories also give the child vicarious experiences with a variety of wild animals he cannot know in any other way. He learns the habits and needs of a great many beasts, and his admiration for them grows as he understands their problems, their nature, and their hazardous lives. A book like *Kildee House* or *My Friend Flicka* supplies him with considerable information on the biology of mating, birth, and death, which comes in casually and naturally in the midst of an exciting story. Indeed, poor Jerome Kildee's survival in his unique house came to depend upon his ability to cope with the birth of more and more baby animals. The way nature marches on in the animal world takes on meaning for children who read this story.

Finally, animal stories are good for children because they find in their animal heroes the virtues they most admire in human beings and would like to achieve themselves. Look over any first rate group of animal adventures and see if these virtues are not paramount—courage in the face of danger, fortitude under suffering or injustice, loyalty to cub, mate, or master, and, above all, a shining zest for life that is like the child's own. Colts, cubs, kittens, children take life gaily with splendid prancings and cavortings. And even mature animals seem to find life good and go proudly and gallantly to meet its challenge. These are some of the reasons why children love good stories about animals and should have them, the soundest and the best to be found.

Animals we know best

ANGUS AND THE DUCKS

Marjorie Flack

Marjorie Flack is an artist with words as well as with brush. Her long series of picture-stories for small children—her Angus *books,* Wag-tail Bess, Tim Tadpole, Walter the Lazy Mouse, Ask Mr. Bear (Time for Fairy Tales) —*have set high standards for the literature of the early years. Each story is unique, each has a well-defined plot, delightful style, and just enough suspense or surprise to keep children interested.*

Once there was a very young little dog whose name was Angus, because his mother and his father came from Scotland.

Although the rest of Angus was quite small, his head was very large and so were his feet.

Angus was curious about many places and many things:

He was curious about what lived under the sofa and in dark corners and who was the little dog in the mirror.

He was curious about things-which-come-apart and those things-which-don't-come-apart; such as slippers and gentlemen's suspenders and things like that.

Angus was also curious about things-outdoors but he could not find out much about them because of a leash.

The leash was fastened at one end to the collar around his neck and at the other end to somebody else.

But Angus was most curious of all about a noise which came from the other side of the large green hedge at the end of the garden.

The noise usually sounded like this: Quack! Quack! Quackety! Quack!!

But sometimes it sounded like this: Quackety! Quackety! Quackety! Quack!!

One day the door between outdoors and indoors was left open by mistake; and out went Angus without the leash or somebody else.

Down the little path he ran until he came to the large green hedge at the end of the garden.

He tried to go around it but it was much too long. He tried to go over it but it was much too high. So Angus went under the large green hedge and came out on the other side.

There, directly in front of him, were two white ducks. They were marching forward, one-foot-up and one-foot-down. Quack! Quack! Quackety! Quack!!!

Angus said, WOO-OO-OOF!!!

Away went the ducks all of a flutter. Quackety! Quackety! Quackety! Quackety! Quackety!!!

Angus followed after.

Soon the ducks stopped by a stone watering trough under a mulberry tree.

Angus stopped, too. Each duck dipped a yellow bill in the clear cool water. Angus watched. Each duck took a long drink of the cool clear water. Still Angus watched. Each duck took another long drink of cool clear water.

Then Angus said: WOO-OO-OOF!!!

Away the ducks scuttled and Angus lapped the cool clear water.

Birds sang in the mulberry tree.

The sun made patterns through the leaves over the grass.

The ducks talked together: Quack! Quack! Quack!

Then: HISS-S-S-S-S-S-S!!! HISS-S-S-S-S-S-S!!!

The first duck nipped Angus's tail! HISS-S-S-S-S-S!!! HISS-S-S-S-S-S-S!!!

The second duck flapped her wings!

Angus scrambled under the large green hedge, scurried up the little path, scampered into the house and crawled under the sofa.

For exactly three minutes by the clock, Angus was not curious about anything at all.

HODIE

Katharine and Bernard Garbutt

Mrs. Garbutt was the author and Mr. Garbutt the illustrator of this book about their dog, Hodie. In California, where they lived, even in some of the polite suburbs of Los Angeles, the coyotes hunt dogs and howl dismally when they miss their prey. Hodie learned not to follow these creatures when they smiled invitingly at him.

Hodie was a city dog.

He lived in an apartment. As he grew bigger and bigger the apartment grew smaller and smaller. He ran into the walls, and the furniture was in the way. Little tables tipped over as he raced by and his ball got lost under the large chairs.

So one spring he went to the country to live on a farm.

The Farmer had a horse and a cow and a goat and a pig and chickens and, of course, a cat. But he had mostly turkeys.

The minute Hodie reached the farm, he ran round and round in circles. He jumped on the Farmer and tipped over the milk pail.

The Farmer did not like it at all. He said, "Why! He can't stay here. I need a sensible dog that can work on the farm. This dog will chase the cat and frighten the chickens and annoy the goat and bother the pig and worry the cow and scare the horse and kill my turkeys. He's just a spoiled city dog. He can't stay here!"

What the Farmer did not know was that Hodie was really just a happy dog. He did not want to scare anything or kill anything. He only wanted to make friends and play. He wanted to please everyone.

The cat found that out at once. Hodie played gently with her and she purred.

Hodie followed the horse and the horse felt comfortable to have him close by.

He lay quietly beside the cow and she liked him too. Hodie jumped up and down in front of the goat. The goat pretended to butt. It was just a game between them. He rubbed noses with the pig in the pigsty.

Once Hodie ran over a hen's nest and broke an egg. The hen pecked him on the nose and after that he watched where he ran. The chickens learned to go about their business as if he were not there.

Hodie could look at the turkeys only through a fence. He sat down to do that and spent hours each day watching them. They grew used to him too.

Hodie was the first one to see the eight baby pigs the morning they were born. That was very exciting.

The cat had her four kittens in the barn. As soon as they were old enough she taught them to play with Hodie too. And the goat let him play with her kid. And the cow let him play with her calf.

When the colt was born Hodie liked him the best. They played tag and hide-and-go-seek and were very gay together.

Hodie was careful not to touch the twelve baby chickens because their mother asked him not to. And all the baby turkeys were out of reach behind the fence.

"Well," said the Farmer. "He's friendly and he does no harm, but what good is he? I can't be feeding him just to play around all day. As soon as the summer is over, he'll have to go back to the city."

Early one morning the Farmer rode the horse over the hill to the river. He let the colt and Hodie go along.

The sun was not yet up and the sky was gray with red streaks in the East. Hodie ran happily on ahead, out of sight. "Ki-yi-yi-yi!" the Farmer heard and he galloped his horse fast around a curve to see what had happened to Hodie.

Nothing had happened to Hodie. He was just looking at a coyote. She was the one who was screaming, "Ki-yi-yi-yi!" at Hodie. Then the coyote saw the Farmer and ran away, but she glanced back over her shoulder and smiled at Hodie.

Hodie started to follow her. And another coyote came out of the bushes behind him.

"Hodie, come here!" yelled the Farmer. He knew the coyotes would kill Hodie if he went with them. So Hodie had to turn and trot back with the Farmer, though he did not want to.

"Hodie is the silliest dog I ever saw," said the Farmer when he reached the farm. "Why, he even likes *coyotes!* He's no use, I need a dog like Jake."

Now Jake was the neighbor's dog and he was different. He was cross but he worked hard. One day he saw Hodie and wanted to fight. He put his hair up along his back. But Hodie did not even notice. He wanted to play.

First Jake was just surprised. Then he decided he liked Hodie after all. He smoothed his hair back again and wagged his tail. The dogs were friends after that.

Jake did not know how to play but he knew how to work. He herded cows at home and so he showed his new friend how to herd. They practiced on the chickens. When the chickens wandered from the barnyard, Jake showed Hodie how to drive them back. Jake walked slowly, now behind them, now this side, now that, never scaring them or hurrying them. He let Hodie help.

Later when the baby pigs got out, Hodie found them. He was able to herd them gently back to their mother all by himself.

When the summer was nearly over, Hodie saw the coyote again. She was near the end of the turkey yard. This time she did not smile at him. He didn't think she should look at the turkeys the way she did. It bothered him, and he waited until she went away.

But the Farmer did not see the coyote. He was too busy to watch Hodie. He did not know Hodie was learning to herd and to guard. He did not think that Hodie was learning anything.

One evening when the sun went down, the Farmer went to feed his turkeys. Hodie was not in sight and the Farmer thought again how useless he was.

"He'll have to go back to the city tomorrow." he said. Just then the Farmer reached the turkey yard.

"HEY!" he shouted. "The gate is open! A lot of my turkeys are gone!" The Farmer was worried. He could hear the coyotes calling over by the river and coyotes eat fat turkeys. But nobody knew where the turkeys had gone.

Nobody knew except Hodie. He had seen them wander away. When the turkeys did not come back he was worried too. He thought they should stay where they belonged. Hodie set off to follow them and found them eating by the river.

It was getting dark and the coyotes were hunting. Their "Ki-yi-yi-yi!" sounded nearer. Hodie knew he must herd the turkeys home. He drove them carefully as Jake had taught him, now behind them, now this side, now that, never scaring or hurrying them.

Soon the Farmer saw his turkeys coming back over the hill and he saw Hodie driving them. Hodie looked happy because it was such fun. He herded them all the way through the gate and behind the fence. The Farmer closed the gate. Not a turkey was missing. The Farmer was astonished.

"I didn't know he had it in him," he said. Suddenly he knew that the turkeys were not afraid of Hodie because he was so friendly and happy. But what surprised the Farmer the most was that even work was play to Hodie. "Why, he *likes* to work!" said the Farmer.

The Farmer patted Hodie on the head and smiled at him. "The farm is all yours," he told him.

Hodie danced with joy because the Farmer praised him and he loved the Farmer and the farm. Now he could stay and herd the chickens and the turkeys. He could play with the horse and the cow and the goat and the pig and the cat and all their babies.

Hodie was a farm dog now.

MICHAEL

WHO MISSED

HIS TRAIN

Dorothy and Marguerite Bryan

This delightful story of an unwanted but ingratiating puppy has remained a favorite ever since it first appeared in 1932.

One morning the expressman delivered a large box to the mother of Mary and David. The children wondered what was in it.

It humped! It heaved! It sniffed!

A shiny eye peered out between the slats that were nailed across the side. Then there was a bark!

"It's a dog!" shouted Mary and David.

"Yes, it's Michael from Boston," said their mother. "But we already have Patsy, and we really cannot keep more than one dog on this small place, so Michael will have to go back to Boston as soon as he has had a little rest."

When Michael was taken out of the box, he proved to be a very friendly Sealyham terrier with big feet, big brown eyes, and a fine, strong tail for wagging.

He did not have the big brown spot over his right eye that Patsy had but he had small spots on his ears.

Mary and David and Patsy decided that they did not want Michael to go back to Boston. So they all met out under the dogwood tree to plan what to do about it.

"Mother loves Patsy and wants *her* to stay," David said. "Do you suppose it is because Patsy does tricks?"

They all turned and looked at Patricia.

She sat up and waved her paws.

"Patsy sits up," said Mary. "Why don't you sit up, Michael?"

Michael tried very hard, but when he had lifted his big front paws off the ground he leaned way toward one side, then way toward the other side, then w-a-y, w-a-y back, and over he rolled!

But Michael tried again and again until he could sit up, too—though he did not look very steady.

What to do? Michael was so willing—so loving—so anxious to make himself wanted.

Michael chased balls and sticks.

But he chased the cat next door, and *that* did not help!

They all ran indoors to Mother. "Sit up," Mary ordered.

Patsy sat up very straight, lightly waving her paws.

Michael tried once and fell over; tried twice and fell over; tried the third time, and sat up! His chest stuck way out; his paws dangled way

down; he wobbled and he tottered—but he did *not* tumble over.

"That is very smart," admired Mother. "But one beggar is bad enough around this house. What would we do with two? Michael must go back to Boston."

Michael stretched himself tenderly on Mother's feet whenever she sat down.

But he stretched himself tenderly on the best silk cushion when he was lonesome for Mother's feet and that did not help!

When Patsy was eating her dinner, Michael just sat and watched politely, and no matter how s-l-o-w-l-y Patsy mincey-moused her dinner he would not steal a crumb.

But he brought home a large soup bone that belonged to somebody else and that did not help!

Michael taught himself to sing softly—woo! woo!! woo!!!

But he taught Patsy to sing, too, and whenever those two were left alone on the front seat of the automobile they w-o-o! w-o-o!! w-o-o-ed!!! together, louder and louder until everybody came running to see what the trouble was.

And that certainly did not help!

Whenever Michael did anything wrong, he put himself in the corner behind the door and tried not to do it again.

But somehow he was apt to forget to be a good dog, and that did not help at all!

So Mother said, "Michael means well, but he *must* go back to Boston."

Mary, David, Patsy, and Michael all met out under the weeping-willow tree. Patsy sat close beside Mary and kissed the tip of Michael's nose. "What shall we try now?" asked David.

"We will have to try a brand new surprise trick," answered Mary. "We must all put on our thinking caps."

So Mary made them each a newspaper hat, and they sat thinking—and thinking—and thinking—and thinking.

Then strange sounds began to come out from under the weeping-willow tree—whistlings and tootlings and thumpings and excited yippings. And a whole barrel of ginger snaps was used up as rewarding tid-bits.

After a long, long time Mary, David, Patsy, and Michael went tramping in to Mother.

David kept whistling the first few bars of "Yankee Doodle," over and over.

They all came to a stop in front of Mother's chair.

Patsy and Michael listened carefully. Everything was very quiet. Then—"Ta-Ra-Ra-Ra-Ra Boom!" said David.

At the word "Boom!" Patsy and Michael fell on their sides and lay just as still as still.

"Di-Yay!" cried Mary.

Patsy and Michael jumped to their feet as though they had been pulled by one string.

"They died for their country," explained David.

"And came alive again for you," added Mary.

"That is very clever," applauded Mother. "But Michael must really go back to Boston!!"

Mournful Michael!

So Michael was put into his box again and the slats were nailed across the side.

Mary and David counted out enough dog biscuits to last during the whole trip to Boston.

Crunch! Scrunch! Munch-munch!! went Michael—and all his meals for his trip to Boston were eaten up before he had even started. Michael was very loving and very sad at leaving—but, somehow, he was *always* hungry.

When the last biscuit crumb was licked up all was still.

The box humped! It heaved! It sniffed!

A sorrowful eye peered out between the slats nailed across the side.

Then there was a moan!

"I will get out the car and take Michael to his train," Mother said hastily.

"Oh, please! Won't you let us carry him down ourselves?" begged Mary. "He isn't heavy."

"And it isn't far," added David.

"Well, all right," said Mother. "Be careful. Good-bye, Michael. I am sorry to see you leave, but we really cannot keep more than one dog on this small place, so you must go back to Boston." She patted Michael's nose through the slats and went quickly into the house.

"Let's give him some soft leaves for a bed on his way to Boston," Mary suggested.

So they put down the box and gathered oak leaves and pushed them between the slats.

Michael scratched round and round and made himself a cosy nest.

Slowly, slowly they moved on.

"He likes to toss pine cones," David said. "Let's find a nice big one for Michael to play with on his way to Boston."

So they put down the box and Patsy found a big pine cone that they squeezed in between the slats.

Michael nosed it and nibbled it but he could not toss it very well. There was not enough room. So he buried it under the oak leaves.

Slowly, slowly they trudged on.

"Do you want to change hands?" Mary asked. "My right arm is getting tired."

"All right," answered David. "So is my left arm."

So they put down the box and changed sides. They both patted Michael between the bars on the way around the box.

Slowly, slowly they tramped on.

Mary and David had just changed hands again when—

Toot! Toot!

"It's the train!" cried Mary.

"And we haven't Michael's ticket or anything," shouted David. They started to run.

The box kept bumping their legs.

Michael rolled from side to side, barking and scratching.

Patsy ran, too.

Just as they rushed around the last curve in the path, Toot! Toot—Toot!! the train gave a warning whistle and Puff—*puff*—*puff*, it pulled out of the station.

They put down the box.

"Michael has missed his train!" cried David.

"So he has," said Mary.

Mary and David pulled Michael out of the box and put him down beside Patsy. Slowly, slowly they trudged back to Mother, who was waiting at home, feeling rather lonely.

"Michael has missed his train," cried Mary and David.

There was a pause. They waited anxiously.

"What! Michael has missed his train," said Mother. "Well, then, of course—

"Michael *cannot* go back to Boston."

from BLACK BRUCE

Margaret S. and Helen Lossing Johnson

Harry Simpson's collie dog, Black Bruce, was injured during their stay in Newfoundland and had to be left behind to recover. The pup was overjoyed when he was reunited with his master, and the two of them set sail for Prince Edward Island, where new and happier adventures began for Bruce. Margaret Johnson and her mother have done many dog stories together. Each book concerns a particular breed of dog, and the story turns upon the peculiar gifts of that breed. In this book, Bruce does not come into his own until he finds farm animals to herd.

[A Collie Finds His Work]

When Bruce jumped out of the wagon in the big barnyard at "Fair Acres Farm," his ears were pricked, his plumy tail was wagging, and there was an interested light in his brown eyes.

A herd of cows, which to him were like large goats, were standing near one of the barn doors, quietly chewing their cuds and regarding the strange dog doubtfully. The collie felt a rush of friendliness for these creatures, and he went forward to make friends. But in the same way that Bess had warned him away from the goats, so the strangest-looking dog he had ever seen now warned him away from the cows. Short-legged, broad-chested, brindle and white in color, with a huge head and undershot jaw, Topsy, the English bulldog, trotted towards him growling low in her throat.

Bruce was only too ready to defend himself, but he meekly retreated before Topsy's fierce rush, for no dog will willingly fight a female dog. Duncan McGregor spoke sternly to Topsy and said: "I hope she will decide to like Bruce; a bulldog's grip is a dangerous thing, and we will have to watch her."

It was evident that the collie liked Topsy, and he walked around with her with wagging tail and a pleased expression. After sniffing him scornfully, Topsy apparently made up her mind that she would not hurt him for the present, but she would keep an eye on him and see that he did just what she told him to do.

Harry and his uncle drew a breath of relief. "Well, I guess she's going to let him stay," said Mr. McGregor. "Topsy is a grand watchdog and sleeps in the stable, where I have some valuable horses; but she's no good at caring for cattle and sheep; that will be Bruce's job." Harry looked at his collie and hoped that Bruce would be as fine a shepherd dog as some of his illustrious ancestors had been.

Mrs. McGregor and the two children, Mary, eight years old, and Bob, six, were very glad to see Harry again and welcomed and admired the beautiful dog whom they had heard so much about.

Bruce had never known any children and drew back when Mary and Bob came near, and Harry told the two that they had better leave the young collie alone for a few days, until he had become accustomed to his new home.

When Harry first took Bruce to the beautiful hillside pasture, bordered by woods of beech and birch and maple, where the fine flock of sheep was kept, he held the collie's collar, for he was not sure what Bruce would do when he saw his first sheep.

"Steady, boy, steady," said Harry, walking quietly towards the sheep. Raising their heads, they stopped cropping the short grass and pointed their ears towards Harry and the collie, ready to run at the slightest quick movement.

Bruce, walking softly, was deeply interested in these timid creatures and waved his tail and whined eagerly, but was puzzled by their strange woolly coats. Suddenly he heard a familiar sound, a gentle "baa," which was quickly repeated several times, and he saw a beautiful lamb run to its mother. With a joyous look in his eyes, he turned to his master, begging Harry to release him, for he believed the young creature might be his beloved baby goat whose life he had saved in Newfoundland.

Bruce had to learn many new things during the next few weeks, while the long, warm days and cool nights went slowly by, filled with the work of the big farm and the happy companionship of his master.

By the end of August, Bruce was able to drive the big herd of cows to the pasture, and if one tried to stray down the road, eating the roadside grasses, she would be quickly driven back by the collie and forced to go through the gate with the others. Then Bruce would stand in the gateway until someone came to close it. In the evening the gate would be opened, and Bruce would dash off across the pasture, and soon the cows would all walk into the barnyard, the panting, watchful collie at their heels.

When the sheep broke out of the pasture one Sunday morning while the family were at church, and immediately made their way into a field of ripe oats, it was Bruce who put every sheep and lamb back where it belonged and stood guard at the break in the fence, barking until one of the men found him and repaired the fence.

Gradually Bruce gained the confidence of every living creature on the farm except Topsy. She still expected him to do something for which she would have to punish him, and she never allowed him to set one paw inside the house. Even on Sunday afternoon when Harry took the children and the two dogs for a walk in the woods, Topsy waddled along close to Mary and Bob and rolled a warning eye at Bruce when he came near. The collie was so wildly happy at being with his master, and the woods were so delightful with the mossy paths and sweet-smelling ferns, that he forgot his sober dignity and was like a playful puppy again.

One path in the woods led steeply down to a

broad stream, and here Bruce loved to swim. Topsy was fond of the water, too, and once in it, it was hard to persuade her to come out. She swam around happily, and here Bruce dared to play with her, for his longer legs made him a faster swimmer, and he teased Topsy by always keeping just out of her reach.

After Bruce had shown his intelligence by putting the sheep back in the pasture all by himself, Duncan McGregor decided that Bruce should have the freedom of the farm at night, as well as in the daytime. So a big, warm kennel was built for him and placed under a shed, and when this kennel was filled with sweet-smelling hay, Bruce decided that it was the most comfortable bed he had ever had.

Bruce began to feel that everything on the farm was under his care, especially helpless creatures like young calves and sheep, and it was not long before he included the two children. As it turned out, it was fortunate for the youngsters that he felt that way about them.

Mary and Bob went to the little, country school about a mile from their home, and each morning they started off, Mary carrying the lunch box filled with sandwiches and cake.

One golden afternoon early in September, Bruce had nothing to do, for Harry had gone off for the day, and the men were all in a distant part of the farm cutting a big field of grain. The collie knew it was nearly time for the children's return and trotted down the road to meet them. Soon he saw the two little figures and ran gaily forward, sure of an enthusiastic welcome.

"Oh, Bruce, I'm so glad you came!" said Mary. "Now I know it will be perfectly safe for us to go to the woods to find raspberries. I know where there are a lovely lot of late ones, and we can fill our lunch box with them."

Bruce was delighted at the prospect of a ramble, and the three adventurers climbed a fence and crossed a big pasture, making for the distant woodland. The light was dim, and the air was cool in the shadow of the big trees, and Bob drew back a little, feeling that his sister was being rather daring in going farther into these green depths.

Even Mary hesitated, but Bruce was running cheerfully down the mossy wood-road, coming back to the children from time to time, then dashing off after squirrels, and she felt encouraged to go on. After what seemed a very long time, the three emerged into the bright sunlight again; they had come to a clearing, where the trees had been cut off, and here the raspberry bushes grew in a wild tangle.

Mary picked berries busily for a while, Bob occasionally dropping one into the box; but there were not so many as they thought there would be, and the best ones seemed always to be in the center of the prickly tangle. Bruce had found a rabbit in a pile of brushwood and was trying to dig in to it, panting and barking, and the children encouraged him for a while. At last they gave up, and Bob said, "Mary, I'm tired and *awful* thirsty; I can't walk any more unless I have a drink."

Then Mary remembered a quiet little brook which ran through a deep ravine in the woods, and she decided to go there before returning home. "Father showed me some lovely, big mushrooms there last Sunday," said the little girl. "We can fill our box with them."

So the three turned off into the woods again, following no road this time but making their way through beds of ferns and over fallen trees. Before long they came to the brook, and the children quenched their thirst, while Bruce wallowed in the cool water. Mary saw and picked a fine mushroom, then there was a group of them farther on, and before they knew it, the children were completely lost and had no idea how to get back to the road.

For some time Bruce had been worried and had stayed behind, trying to make Mary and Bob turn back. He knew it was time to go after the cows, and that Harry would soon be home, and he wanted to go back to his master; but the children were in his care, and he couldn't leave them alone, so the faithful collie was very unhappy.

Bob commenced to cry from weariness and fear, and Mary was very near tears. She was a brave little girl, however, and told Bob not to worry. "Bruce will take us home; he knows the way. Go home, Bruce, find Harry," she said, and was delighted when he barked and wagged his tail and started off confidently. The climb up the steep sides of the ravine seemed twice as long as the trip down to the tired children, and they stumbled over logs, and caught their feet under roots, trying to keep up with Bruce. Mary dragged Bob along, and the collie stopped and waited for them several times, wagging his tail, and licking their faces to comfort them. When the three finally found the wood-road again, it was growing dark in the woods, and chilly, and soon the autumn night would close down. The walking was easier on the road, and the children hurried after Bruce, and soon came to the edge of the woods, and the field. At the gate stood Topsy, anxiously peering and sniffing into the dim woodland. When she saw the children, she rushed forward, wagging her stubby tail, and licking their hands with her big wet tongue.

Led by the happy dogs, Mary and Bob crossed the field, and on the other side met their father, starting out to look for them.

"We got lost in the woods," shouted Bob, very brave now that home was in sight, "but Bruce knew the way back, and made us come with him!" Mr. McGregor praised the collie, and Topsy gave him a friendly glance, and much to Bruce's surprise, when the house was reached, the bulldog allowed him to follow her inside, and she lay contentedly beside him while the children told their story. It was the first time the collie had been in the house, and he felt that he now was really a member of the family.

Harry was proud of his splendid Black Bruce, and in November, when Bruce was two years old, the McGregor family gave a birthday party for him. The pleased collie was escorted into the dining room by Mary and Bob, and there he found the whole family and several young friends of the children. The table was covered with plates of cake and sandwiches, and in the center was a special cake with two candles burning.

As the collie appeared, everyone called out, "Happy birthday, Bruce!" and the sensitive dog was so embarrassed that he ran to Harry and hid his head against his master. A crackling wood fire burned in the big fireplace and sent a warm glow over the room.

As Bruce stood beside the fine old mahogany sideboard, over which hung a painting of a beautiful house in the Highlands of Scotland,

Mr. McGregor said to his wife, pointing to the picture, "Who knows, perhaps Bruce's ancestors were related to the fine shepherd dogs my grandfather had in that old house in the hills!"

The party was a gay one, and Bruce had his full share of the good things from the table. When all was over, the collie lay before the fire beside Harry, on a soft, bright-colored hooked rug, with perfect contentment shining out of his brown eyes.

All was now ready for winter on the big farm. The barns were full of hay and straw and the bins were full of grain, and in the cellar were apples as well as potatoes and other vegetables. There were warm quarters for all the cows and horses, sheep, pigs, and chickens, and Bruce slept in his cozy kennel, making the rounds of the place at least once during the night, to see that all was well.

The winters are long and cold in that north country, for the ice in the great Gulf of St. Lawrence packs solidly around Prince Edward Island, and the snow lies deep on the ground. Bruce loved the cold and the snow, for his glorious thick coat kept him warm and he was always ready to join in any work or play.

Harry stayed on with his uncle, for he liked a farm better than the sea, and Bruce had plenty to do. One of his great delights was to go to market, following the sleigh drawn by one of the big farm horses, and sometimes riding, tucked in between Harry and Mr. McGregor. Often darkness overtook them and they came home guided by the light of the wonderful Aurora Borealis, or northern lights.

Harry had not forgotten that Bruce was a trained sled dog, and he fashioned a harness and taught the collie to haul wood to the house. Mary and Bob were delighted with this accomplishment of their beloved collie and it was not long before they were riding on the sled; and finally Bruce learned to haul them to school on very cold or stormy days, and the children would unharness him when they reached the schoolhouse. Running home by himself, he would return for them in the afternoon to be re-harnessed, and with his head held high and his tail proudly waving, and the two sleigh bells jingling gaily on his collar, he would bring them home.

There were days when the wind howled and the snow drifted and only the men who had to feed and water the animals ventured outside the house. Bruce was always on hand, full of eager interest, and he thought it great fun to watch the men as they shoveled the snow, making paths from the house to the barn.

But at last the spring came and with it the first melting of the snow.

The large flock of sheep at "Fair Acres Farm" was kept in a barn of their own, with a big fenced-in yard on the south side, where they were allowed to stay on sunny days. One old sheep, the leader of the flock, and several yearlings were in a separate yard, and very early one morning this old leader found a place in the fence which he could manage to crawl under. He promptly made his way to freedom, followed by the five young sheep. Down through the pasture went the six runaways, slipping and sliding in the mud and melting snow, until they came to the stream. A tiny peninsula jutted out into the stream at this spot and here the warm sun had melted the snow very early, and bits of fresh green grass were showing. The sheep immediately smelled and saw this and, overjoyed at the thought of green food after the long winter, they splashed out through the muddy ground near shore and started eagerly nibbling at the grass.

A short distance up this stream, in a ravine, was a sawmill and, above it, a deep millpond. This pond was made by building a dam of stones and logs across the stream. The rapidly melting snow had filled the pond almost to overflowing, and now a heavy rainstorm had increased the pressure on the dam, until it began to give way in the weakest spot. Gradually the break grew bigger, until, with a terrific roar, the whole structure went down and the racing water poured downstream. Suddenly, the six sheep, happily cropping the grass at the tip of the peninsula, found themselves surrounded by foaming water. Fortunately for them, the ground on which they stood was several feet higher than that near shore, or they would have been drowned in the first rush. The water was rising, however, and the runaways huddled close together, helpless and terrified.

Bruce had, as usual, wakened early that morning and he came out of his warm kennel yawning and stretching; turning his cold black nose this way and that, he sniffed the chilly air, then trotted off on a tour of inspection. It was not long before he came to the place where the sheep had crawled through the fence, and his keen nose found their trail, which he followed at a gallop. The collie came in sight of the stream, just as the waters roared down from the broken dam, and he stopped, astonished at the change in the well-known stream. Probably he would not have gone any nearer, but he heard the cry of a sheep in distress and, going to the edge of the wild water, he saw the runaways and recognized them as the ones whose trail he had been following. Half frantic, Bruce barked excitedly and started into the stream; but the current ran so strongly that he drew back, for he was not accustomed to rough water. Hoping that his barking had been heard, the collie looked eagerly about, but there was no one in sight. It was then that the sheep called again, and Bruce saw that the water had risen until it touched the hoofs of the frightened creatures. With a howl he launched himself, but was immediately carried downstream, and struggled back to shore again with difficulty. Twice more he tried, but was defeated, and then his intelligence came to his aid. Going upstream, he struck out and, swimming strongly, he was carried down to the island. Barking, nipping at their heels, Bruce tried to drive the sheep into the water, but the terrified creatures would not move.

Finally, made desperate by their stupidity, Bruce seized one by the wool with his teeth and dragged it into the stream. Guided and partly upheld by the brave dog, the sheep swam shoreward and landed, panting with exhaustion, some distance downstream. Again Bruce swam out, and this time with difficulty he pushed and dragged the old sheep ashore. He was tired now but could not stop until all were safe.

The third sheep was a weak swimmer and once disappeared under the water; and it was only by a great effort that the collie pulled him to the surface again. This time he had to lie down and rest before again braving the flood. The island was all under water now, and the three remaining sheep were in water up to their knees. One more was pulled ashore by the tired dog, and then he looked back to see the other two floating away. Into the water, which was beginning to flow less strongly now, Bruce plunged again and brought one sheep ashore, but the other was carried some distance before it finally crawled out weakly and collapsed on the ground.

For a few minutes Bruce lay panting and exhausted; but the courage of the real shepherd dog was strong within him, and he could not rest until his charges were safe at home. The sheep had recovered and felt safe with the collie, and he soon had them bunched together and started them up the hill. About halfway home, Bruce was met by Mr. McGregor and Harry, running down to meet him. A neighbor had been on the opposite side of the stream while the collie made his splendid rescue, and he had hurried over to "Fair Acres Farm" to tell about it.

"Good dog, Bruce, brave dog!" called Harry, when he saw the wet and bedraggled group toiling up the hill. Mr. McGregor added his words of praise, and Bruce was content. Now that there was someone else to look after the sheep, the collie found that he felt very weary, and he willingly followed Harry into the house and lay down before the kitchen stove, while his master dried his wet coat.

"I won't let you catch pneumonia again, Brucie," said Harry, rubbing him vigorously. Bruce felt a little stiff the next day, but he soon forgot his experience in the flood. Harry and the McGregors did not forget, however, and never tired of telling about the courage of their splendid dog.

from IRISH RED

Jim Kjelgaard

The author said he always had a dog and sometimes "as many as seven at a time." This helps to explain his understanding of and sympathy for dogs. But he knew wild animals too, as his story of a polar bear, Kalak of the Ice, bears witness. No one who likes dogs should miss Big Red *and* Irish Red, Son of Big Red. Snow Dog *is equally popular, and all of the Kjelgaard books are well written and intensely exciting. In* Irish Red *Big Red's son, Mike, proved to be a self-willed mutt instead of the great bird dog the Picketts had expected. But Danny still believed in the pup. These two chapters tell of the near tragedy which changed a silly pup into a disciplined hunting dog.*

White Prison

Danny stirred, and fought sluggishly to a bewildered awakening. For a few minutes he lay still, unable to think where he was or what had happened. Bit by bit, like crooked pieces of a jigsaw puzzle, he fitted the picture together.

He was up on Tower Head, he remembered, where he had come to investigate marten sign. Summer had suddenly become winter, and winter had been ushered in by a terrible wind storm which had ripped through the beech trees. Some had broken. Great boughs had been torn like match sticks from their parent trunks, and one had hit him.

Danny lapsed into a numbed slumber and a second time fought to wakefulness. A thousand drums seemed to pound within his aching head and for a moment he felt very sick. The spasm passed, and when it did he could think more clearly. It had, he remembered, been daylight when he decided to return to Budgegummon. Now inky blackness surrounded him. Danny stretched his hand forth and a warm, wet tongue licked it gently. His exploring fingers found Mike's silky coat. At once he felt a tremendous rush of gratitude. Until now he had not remembered bringing Mike.

He sat up, and when he did his head broke through the fresh, fluffy snow that covered him. It had, then, snowed while he lay unconscious and the fact that it had covered him was the reason why he had not frozen to death. That and Mike, for the red puppy had found him, and was crouching as close as he could get to his injured master. Again Danny gratefully stroked the red puppy's fur.

The snow was still falling fast; even in the darkness Danny felt its soft, deadly caress as he stood erect. He stumbled and almost fell, but by a mighty effort stiffened his legs.

He was aware of Mike pressing closely against his feet, but he could see nothing whatever.

Overwhelmed by another spasm of illness, and weighed down by an unbearable burden on his back, Danny crouched in the snow and gave himself over to sheer misery. When he recovered he felt better and could think more clearly.

The burden he bore was only his pack, Danny realized, and forced himself to be calm. What had happened? First, winter had struck with savage fury. There had been no snow at all during the afternoon, but now it was up to Danny's knees and still falling. He was in the forest, and therefore the snow would not have drifted much. However, there was no possible way he could get to Budgegummon without crossing open spaces where there would be deep drifts, and he had no snowshoes. Even with every possible bit of good luck, it would take him days just to get off the mountain.

Then he did his best to forget it and give his thoughts to immediate problems. Falling snow had prevented his freezing to death, but he was numb with cold and ached in every muscle. Before he did anything else he must get a fire going.

Danny plowed forward, a step at a time, groping hands stretched out before him. A few feet from where he had started, he stopped to rest. He was panting, and beads of sweat clung to his forehead. As soon as he stopped, the cold attacked again; he licked frost particles from his upper lip. Starting forward again, he stumbled over a snow-covered limb, and fell on his hands and knees. For a moment he rested where he was, too tired to get up. A delicious, soothing warmth enveloped him. Then Mike's questing nose touched his face.

Danny fought his way to a standing position. Now he must keep going or die. The snow would not save him again for he had started to sweat. Should he relax for more than a few seconds the sweat would freeze, and if it did he was all through. Danny forced his numb body forward.

He jarred his shoulder against a standing tree and stopped, raising cold hands to feel the tree. It was small, scarcely a foot through, and ragged wisps of paper-thin bark hung like shedding fur from it. A great hope leaped in Danny.

Solely by accident he had bumped into a birch. The parchment-like bark covering the trunk was

as thin as paper and burned as readily. Keeping hold of the tree with one hand, Danny trampled a hole in the snow.

Carefully feeling his way, he stripped handfuls of bark from the tree and put it in the hole he had trampled. Then he knelt down, holding both hands firmly against Mike's warm fur. When circulation returned to his hands, Danny felt in his pocket for the metal match box he always carried. He unscrewed the top, extracted one match, and carefully tightened the cover down. Striking the match against the box's rough side, Danny held the tiny flame against his pile of birch bark. The match died, and almost went out. Danny's hand trembled, and a cold shiver rippled up his spine. Then a corner of bark curled, smoldered, and burst into flame. Almost instantly the whole pile was alight.

Danny's happy shout vied with the softly ominous sound of falling snow and the whine of the wind that sighed through the beech forest. Guiding himself by the fire's light, he turned back to the tree and feverishly groped for the outer tips of small dry twigs that broke easily. He filled his hands with them and went back to throw them on his dying fire. Hungry flames crackled their way into this stronger nourishment. Turning back to the tree, Danny wrenched off an inch-thick limb, broke it into sections, and heaped them on the flames. The fire climbed higher.

Danny gratefully appreciated his good luck in having an ample supply of wood practically within reach of his fire. Very few trees on Tower Head were dead, and chance alone had guided him to one of them. Fuel awaited only the taking.

He broke off more and bigger branches and carried them to his fire. He laid them the long way, pushing them farther up as the ends burned, and arranged a layer of dead sticks to sit on. There were blankets in his pack, but Danny was too tired to try making a proper bed. Heat from the fire melted an increasing circle of snow, and Danny changed his seat.

Mike, for once subdued, crouched down beside him. Danny put a hand on the red puppy's ruff and drew him close. Mike had already atoned for all his past sins merely by providing company. Danny spoke softly to him.

"Tomorrow we'll see about getting out of

here, pup. Sure wish I had a pair of snowshoes."

As soon as he had spoken, Danny wished that he had not even thought about what tomorrow would bring. Certainly there was no immediate hope of rescue for he had told Ross that he was going up Stoney Lonesome. Ross would not worry unduly for a couple of days, and if he did start out, it would not be toward Tower Head. If they were going to be helped, Danny and Mike would have to help themselves.

Danny gazed soberly into the fire. It was ordinarily a few hours' walk back to Budgegummon. Now deep snow covered every inch of the way, and progress would be painfully slow. It would take several days to reach Budgegummon, or even to get down into one of the sheltered valleys where, Danny hoped, the snow would not be so deep.

He knew he was in serious trouble, but bewailing the fact, or worrying about what might happen, would not help at all. Tonight, certainly, he could do nothing except sit here by the fire. He pushed a couple of sticks farther up, bent his head forward so that the collar of his jacket came up around his neck, and dozed fitfully. Creeping cold awakened him when the fire burned low, and Danny built it up again.

He was awakened by Mike's warning bark. He jerked erect, one hand stealing to the grip of his .22, but he could see nothing. Mike touched his hand with a cold nose, and Danny lifted his head to find that dawn had come. He stared around in bewilderment.

The once stately forest on Tower Head had become a shambles. Big trees were piled helter-skelter, a Gargantuan jumble of jackstraws. Boughs and branches had blown down among them in a litter of kindling. As Danny plodded over to get more wood for his fire, he thought of the food in his pack.

Expecting to be away for only two days, he had not packed much food. There was a little slab of bacon, flour, syrup, a chunk of meat, salt and pepper, and coffee. There was not nearly enough of anything. Bucking deep snow would require effort and burn up energy fast. The food that Danny had would have to be conserved to the utmost.

Reluctantly he unbuckled the straps that closed his pack and took out the package of flour. He sliced four strips of bacon from his small chunk and put them into the skillet. Melting snow in the coffee pot, he mixed flapjack batter, and pushed the sizzling bacon to one side of the skillet. He poured a flapjack and let it cook. When it was finished he gave it to Mike, along with two strips of bacon.

The red puppy wagged his appreciation, and gulped his food. He looked on with great interest as Danny fixed the same amount for himself. Mike licked his chops eagerly, and begged with limpid eyes. Danny looked at him.

"Nix," he said. "We're on short rations until we find something else. If one of us eats then both of us will, and there'll be no stealing from each other."

Danny washed the coffee pot with more melted snow and brewed coffee. Letting it cool a little, he drank it directly from the pot. Then he brushed snow over the fire, buckled his pack on, and stood for a moment as he tried to pick out a route through the fallen trees.

Danny plunged his foot into deep snow, and almost collapsed as a red-hot iron seemed to flash across his right side. He felt a momentary dizziness, then eased back into his tracks.

Obviously he was hurt more than he knew. He had not felt it last night either because he was partly dazed or because his injury had not had time to stiffen. Possibly he had a couple of broken ribs or internal injuries. Still, there was no one to help him. What was to be done, he must do alone. Days might elapse before anyone thought of looking for him on Tower Head. Danny tried another experimental step, this time with his left foot.

He stepped into deep snow and brought his right foot up. Danny gritted his teeth. The pain was there, but it was not as intense as when he had tried to walk with his right foot forward. He plowed ahead, favoring his right side as much as possible. He had to keep on.

Mike plodded along in the trail Danny broke, the top of his head four inches below the snow line. The red puppy's eyes were anxious, and he whined at intervals. He was worried, but had every faith in the man he was following.

Danny stopped to rest, leaning against a tree to ease the burden on his back. When he cast his eye over the trail he had made he was panicky.

He must have been on the move for half an hour, yet last night's camp was no more than a stone's throw away. He was making very poor time.

It was impossible to go any faster in his condition. He was already panting from exertion. It was turning warmer, too, he noticed. The snow was stopping and the clouds overhead were breaking. A slanting ray of warm sun stole down; the soft snow would soon begin to melt. Danny unbuttoned his jacket, pushed his knitted cap back on his head, and went on.

Two hours later the top of the snow was a soggy mess. Dark wet patches appeared here and there, dips and hollows in what had been a perfectly smooth blanket. Hard to buck before, now the settling snow became doubly difficult to wade through. Danny stopped again to rest.

Hunger that would not be subdued arose within him. Danny licked his lips, and tried not to think of the food in his pack. But he could not help thinking of it, and the very fact that he had food within reach seemed to induce a strange weakness. Danny turned to look at Mike, who was sitting in the snow looking expectantly up at him. Again Danny licked his lips.

The proper course, he had always heard, was to hoard every scrap of food when one had little. But, even though he had come only a short distance, he had burned a terrific amount of energy doing it. It was impossible to continue without eating; he would just have to take a chance of getting some sort of food later on.

Danny stopped and cooked more of his scanty supplies, dividing them equally with Mike. When he had eaten he felt better, but by then it was even more difficult to travel through the wet snow. Every foot he advanced was a foot that had to be fought for, and every step cost pain. He tried counting his steps, then gave it up. The *next* step was the thing. It was all-important, and if he could make that one he could also make the one to follow. Every step he took carried him that much nearer Budgegummon and that much farther away from Tower Head. Distance lost its meaning because of the effort it cost to make that all-important next step.

The sun went down and Danny buttoned his jacket, for with the approach of twilight the cold returned. He stopped to wipe the sweat from his forehead, and considered. He had to rest, for if he tried going on through the darkness he would only exhaust himself and probably fall. Danny glanced at Mike, who sat in the snow, ears erect and tail flat behind him. He whined apprehensively and Danny made up his mind. It was time to camp.

He was very tired, and when he chopped wood for a fire his axe seemed a wooden thing with no edge at all. Danny stopped twice while he was chopping to look at the pile of wood, then wearily turned to cut more. Finally he scooped the snow away, built a fire, laid a mat of twigs, and put one blanket on it. The other he laid on top, and made a pillow with his pack. Mike crowded close to him, and Danny stroked the red puppy's ears.

"Poor pup," he soothed. "You sure got in a fix when you went out with me, didn't you?"

As he comforted Mike, a sudden relief overcame Danny himself. It had been a terrible, endless day. But it had ended, and not until tomorrow must he resume fighting his way through the snow. Tomorrow was a long while away, and they were in camp. At least for the moment their troubles were ended, and within itself that was a relief. The moment was the thing and the future he could work out. Danny prodded the pack with his foot.

"We got this far," he told Mike. "Let's celebrate."

Danny dived recklessly into his store of food and prepared a filling meal for Mike and himself. After eating, he drowsed in front of the fire, then crawled into his blankets. Ordinarily it would have been a hard bed, but not tonight. Danny dropped at once into a deep and untroubled sleep from which he did not awaken until dawn had again come.

He sat up to look at his dead fire. During the night Mike had become cold, and had crawled underneath the blankets to take advantage of the warmth offered by Danny. Now he tumbled unwillingly out of his comfortable sleeping place, stretching and yawning. Danny looked at him and felt comforted just from the puppy's presence.

Yesterday had been a sick day. Still suffering from the effects of the blow when the branch had struck him, Danny had done what he could do. This morning, after a good night's sleep, he could look at their predicament sanely. They were still trapped in a white prison from which there was scant hope of escape, but they must get out if they were to live. It was that simple.

Methodically Danny set about the preparation of a scanty breakfast. He divided the food exactly in half, fed the red puppy and himself. Then he gathered his blankets, shouldered his pack, and started off. After two steps he stopped and looked down at the snow in dismay.

During the night it had turned much colder, and a crust had formed on top of the soggy snow. Mike, climbing up, could run about on it at will. But at every step Danny's foot broke the brittle crust. He shivered, then plodded doggedly ahead.

Mike skipped happily about on the crust, no longer finding it necessary to plod in his master's trail. Danny kept envious eyes on the puppy. If there was some way to make him go there, Mike could reach Budgegummon by nightfall. If Mike came in alone, Ross would set out at once to find Danny. Then he shook his head in despair; it would be hopeless to try to make the obstinate puppy return to the cabin. If only Red were with him!

Mike stopped suddenly, and froze in his tracks. For a moment Danny forgot to breathe; Mike was on partridges! Danny's hand slid to the grip of his .22 revolver.

"Whoa, Mike!" he said tensely. "Whoa!"

Intently he searched the little scattering of evergreens at which Mike was pointing. Partridges were hard to see, but if he could catch one on the ground he had a chance of getting it.

Then Mike went in to flush. There was a thunder of wings and Danny saw five partridges rise. He shot at them, pulling the trigger time after time as he sent the little leaden pellets flying after the grouse. But he knew it was hopeless.

Mike dashed out of sight, and Danny looked after him with sick eyes.

A Rebel's Heart

Trying to keep the partridges in sight, Mike raced happily across the frozen crust. He slipped, went down, and rolled into a small tree.

Mike picked himself up and looked about for the birds he had flushed. They were gone, and he could neither see nor smell them. The puppy sat down to puzzle out their probable whereabouts. Then he started toward a copse of evergreens. Halfway there he turned and looked back at Danny. Never before, when partridges were near, had he let anything interfere with their pursuit. But never before had he found himself in a situation such as this one. What should he do?

When the great wind storm had struck, Mike, unlike Danny, had not tried to make his way through it. Instead, the red puppy had curled at the base of a great boulder and waited there, shivering as the mighty beeches trembled and crashed all around him. When the wind died, Mike had started out at once to reach Danny. He had found him before the snow started, lying motionless where he had fallen. The red puppy, sensing something wrong, had tried to awaken Danny by whining, then by pawing, and when he could get no response had curled up beside him. Even though Mike, the rebel, acknowledged no master, the age-old bond between dog and man had instinctively kept him by Danny's side in time of trouble.

So Mike hesitated now, instead of rushing after the partridges, because he knew that Danny was still in trouble. There was an urgency in the way Danny plodded on, and a tense desperation, both of which were entirely foreign to any normal state.

The red puppy turned halfway around to go back. But the will to hunt, as powerful as it had ever been, held him where he was. Mike trembled uncertainly, pulled in two directions at once and wholly undecided as to what he had better do. Then the lure of the hunt prevailed, and he started toward the evergreens.

Because he was certain his game had gone into them, he did not bother to swing downwind where he could get a better scent. He raced full speed toward his objective, then slowed down as he approached it. Wrinkling his nose to clear it, he detected the partridges and stiffened in a point.

He did not rush in at once because there was another faint scent, one he had never smelled before, underlying the odor of partridges. The

smell had something of fear in it, and evil, something Mike did not like. He did not know what it was and because nothing except the porcupine had ever hurt him he eased cautiously forward.

The partridges were in the very center of the thicket, where green branches intertwined so closely that they were almost impenetrable. Mike located the birds exactly and flung himself forward. He heard a partridge's alarmed cluck, and dashed insanely toward the sound. Then his quarry drummed upward and Mike threw himself to one side after it.

A second later and he would have been too late to avoid the beast that had been in the thicket even before the partridges, the thing Mike had smelled and ignored. It was a snow-bound puma, a tawny, rippling beast almost invisible in the hemlocks.

The puma had stared with hungry eyes at the partridges when they flew into the thicket, but he had not moved a muscle. They alighted a dozen feet away, too far to let him catch one.

But he knew himself unseen; if he did not move one or more of the birds might venture within striking distance.

The hungry puma instantly transferred all his attention to Mike when the red puppy entered the thicket. Here was food in plenty, good food; he had eaten a dog before. He waited until Mike seemed near enough, then launched his lithe spring.

However, the puma did not distinguish between dogs and he had previously caught and eaten only an aging, lost hound. Mike was much younger and infinitely more agile. The puma's outstretched claws missed their target by three inches and Mike dodged out of the thicket.

He ran as fast as he could, with healthy fear lending speed to his legs. Mike had never been hurt by anything except the porcupine, but the law of survival was part of his heritage and he knew that the puma intended to kill him. Furthermore, he knew that it could. Mike raced full speed back toward Danny and found him resting wearily in the snow with his pack braced against a dead stump. Mike slid to a halt beside him and turned around to bristle and bark.

He faced the direction from which he had come, testing the wind with his nose, while the hungry puma lingered behind some brush a few hundred feet away. Having caught man scent, the big cat had no wish to come any nearer. Mike barked again, challenging his enemy, and Danny's hand played around the red puppy's ears.

"What's the matter?" Danny asked. "What's up, Mike? You see your own shadow out there?"

Without understanding the words, Mike sensed the comradeship in the tone of voice.

Danny could not know, nor could Mike himself reason out, that a change had been worked within him. The days when he had been only a senseless puppy, with never a thought except for himself, were definitely in the past. Time, and affection, and now shared trouble, were all combining to work the change. Mike was growing up.

Being a dog, neither the past nor the future mattered to him. The moment was the thing, and now Mike sat on the crusted snow reading the wind that told him of the puma's movements. The big cat had made a circle and gone to one side. Now he lay behind a fallen beech, eyes and ears alert and tail twitching as he studied the situation. The puma had no desire to expose himself to a man, but neither did he have the slightest intention of abandoning the trail until he had caught Mike. Cunning and wise, he would follow the pair until he found an opportunity to catch and kill the dog.

Mike growled low in his throat, and Danny looked questioningly in the direction the red puppy was looking, then turned to go on. Mike stayed behind him, making short little excursions out on the crust to read the wind to better advantage. The puma was coming, slinking along their trail like a tawny shadow. But so woods-wise was he that he never once showed himself. Mike knew he was coming only because his nose told him.

With only a mouthful of cold food at noon, they plodded slowly on. The sun started its downward sweep and with its descent the cold became more intense. Accustomed to being out-

side, and provided by nature with a suitable coat for all seasons, Mike did not feel it. Danny tried to tighten his jacket and shivered as he stopped in a cluster of big beech trees.

A squirrel chattered in one of the beeches. Mike glanced disinterestedly up, not caring about such game. It was fun to chase squirrels, and to watch them leap with panicky haste into the trees. That was all. But now Mike sensed the change in Danny.

Dead-tired and almost apathetic for the past hour, Danny was now tensely alert. The revolver in his hand, he stood in his tracks and looked eagerly into the towering trees. Nothing happened; the squirrel did not even chatter again. Mike knew what Danny did not, that it had gone into a hole in one of the trunks, but long after the squirrel had found safety Danny continued to stare up into the trees.

Then, with a despairing little gesture, he sheathed his gun and set about gathering firewood. Mike crowded anxiously in, staying as close to Danny as he could get and risking a burned nose when Danny lighted a match with which to start his fire. An eddying breeze brought him the puma's scent. It had come in very close, but when smoke started curling from the fire it retreated. The ravenous cat was not so desperately hungry that he would risk getting near a fire. Mike followed the puma's progress with his nose. He also watched Danny's preparation of their meager meal.

The red puppy had never wondered about the source of his food. He knew only that humans had never let him go hungry. When his belly was empty, they gave him something to fill it and he was sure that it would be filled now. Mike gobbled the tiny piece of meat and the bit of bread Danny gave him, and looked questioningly about for more. He whined when Danny ate an equal amount and sat staring dully into the fire. The red puppy scraped his master's arm with an impatient paw. Danny stirred angrily.

"There's no more!" he half shouted. "See?"

Mike sniffed distantly at the pack when Danny opened it for him. He flattened his ears and rolled appeasing eyes, not understanding the fact that food supplies were practically gone and uncomfortable because he was still hungry. Mike knew only that, for some unaccountable reason, Danny was angry with him and he did not like it.

He retreated to the edge of the light circle cast by the fire, then came back within it, for his nose told him that the hungry puma still lingered in the shadows. It was no place for him. In the semi-darkness, he moved confidently closer to Danny. His paws twitched.

He was hungry, but neither exhausted nor terrified. Mike knew that he had been near death when he met the puma, but now that he was again with Danny, that threat was removed. Today, for the first time, he had learned that he was not self-sufficient, but part of a team. He moved softly over to be nearer Danny, and stared steadily into the unfriendly night.

The puma was creeping nearer. A weak moon had risen, casting moving shadows across the snow, and the puma was taking advantage of them to get nearer the camp. He felt bolder now, for the fire sent up only straggling wisps of smoke. Wrapped in his blankets, Danny had surrendered to exhaustion. Mike snuffled again at the creeping puma, then edged in until his rear paws were braced against the sleeping Danny. There fear left him. Alone he could do little, but together he and Danny could face any threat.

The red puppy growled harshly, and the advancing puma stopped. Then he came on, slowly and furtively. Mike growled again, fiercely this time. The numbed Danny stirred fretfully in his blankets.

The puma was very near now; a little more and he would be within leaping distance. Mike snarled again, and again, as he made ready to repel the attacker. Danny stirred, rolled over, and woke up.

He did not make any noise or cry out when he came awake because he had been born to the woods and wild places. He knew the value of silence, and even sick exhaustion could not make him forget it. When Danny rolled out of his blankets he did so carefully and silently. He inched himself to a sitting position and drew the .22 from its holster.

Mike pricked up his ears and stared intently at a motionless shadow. He knew the puma was there for his nose told him, but he could not be certain he saw it. Danny fixed his eyes on the place, like a hundred other shadows but still unlike any of them. Moving ever so slowly, Danny raised the .22 and squeezed the trigger.

When the little revolver snapped, the shadow melted into the night. The puma, taken by surprise, had silently backed away. He was not hurt and he did not run, for to run would be to expose himself. When he knew he could no longer be seen, the puma turned and loped away after easier game. He had gambled and lost.

Knowing the enemy vanquished, Mike relaxed. For a few minutes Danny remained in a sitting position, the little revolver in his hand. What had he shot at? Had he really seen anything? In any event, Mike was now quiet, so Danny put more wood on the fire and returned to his blankets. When he did, Mike lifted a corner with his nose, crawled in beside him, and snuggled up against Danny's back. They did not awaken until dawn had come.

Mike waited hopefully, expectantly, as Danny built up the fire and brewed a pot of coffee. There was nothing else, and Mike tried to stay his rising hunger by licking his chops. He snuffled at the steaming coffee, then turned his nose away.

When Danny resumed his heartbreakingly slow progress toward the distant valleys, Mike climbed out of the trail he broke to run about on the crust. He liked that better, for in the trail the sharp edges of the broken snow were like glass, and hurt his feet. Mike looked back to see if Danny was coming, then gave all his attention to what lay ahead.

They were crossing a small clearing where blackberry brambles barred their path. Tall weeds had found a rooting in the brambles, and their seeded tops still protruded above the snow. Mike caught the scent of partridges that were eating the seeds, and started toward them. Then he heard Danny's tense voice.

"Whoa! Whoa, Mike!"

The red puppy paused, and looked around. Again he swung his head to drink in the entrancing scent of partridges. He froze into a point.

The old urge was there, the driving impulse to rush furiously upon his game and see if he could overwhelm it. But for the first time something in Danny's voice stopped him. The sound of the familiar command had a new meaning, the end of a long chain of occurrences. Mike was no longer the wild, undisciplined puppy who had escaped from the Haggin estate. A thousand wild chases were behind him, and Red's punishment, and the endless patience and affection offered by Danny and Ross. And fresh in his mind was the realization that he and Danny had faced, and overcome, danger and terror—together. He quivered with eagerness, but held his point.

There was motion in the brambles. One of the partridges thrust a curious head straight up, then sat still. Mike drooled, and tensed his muscles. Before he could move, he heard the snap of Danny's .22.

Utterly bewildered, the red puppy paused. Two partridges thundered away. But another one remained in the brambles, an inert heap of brown feathers. Mike felt an overwhelming flood of excitement; at last his dearest wishes were realized. Everything else was forgotten as he bounded toward the partridge. Mike closed his jaws about the bird, then Danny's voice penetrated his delirious haze.

"Mike. Come here, Mike."

The puppy stood still, not knowing in this joyful moment just what he should do. Again he heard Danny's voice.

"Fetch, Mike."

Then, at long last, Mike gave his whole heart to a master. He started back toward Danny.

Two days later, well down in a sheltered valley, Mike pricked up his ears and looked at the snowbound trees ahead of them. He barked, then started happily forward. Danny's incredulous eyes followed him. A moment later Big Red burst out of the trees. A little way behind him was Ross, on snowshoes and pulling a toboggan.

"Danny!" Ross's voice broke. "Boy, I'm right glad to see you!"

"I'm kind of glad to see you," Danny admitted. "What brought you up here?"

"That Red dog," said Ross. "We looked every other place we could think of, and Red wanted to come up here. I figured I might as well follow him. What happened? You hurt bad?"

"Well," Danny said lamely, "I went up Tower Head to look for marten, only there weren't any, and then a big windstorm came, and a limb hit me, and—"

"Save it," Ross commanded. "Climb aboard."

Danny settled gratefully on the toboggan and let Ross wrap him in warm blankets. He fought the drowsiness that overcame him, for he had a very important message. It had nothing to do with marten, or money, or broken ribs. It was something far more important. He fingered the two partridges at his belt.

"We've got a partridge dog, Pappy." Then he fell asleep.

FACTORY KITTY

Helen Hoke

Helen Hoke writes and has helped guide young writers in their efforts. She loves cats, and this story shows her understanding of a courageous kitten.

Everybody remembers the day the kitten came to the Ritz Print and Dye Works.

Tony, the head dyer, is the one who started it all. One noontime when the whistle blew, he decided it was such a nice sunny day he would eat his lunch outside. In no time at all, all the other workers brought their lunch boxes outside, too. And the big yard in front of the factory turned into a picnic ground.

And then, suddenly, there was the kitten. Perhaps it had smelled the delicious salami that Mrs. Tony had put in Tony's lunch box. Perhaps it just liked picnics. Certainly, it had no way of knowing it had entered the private property of a big noisy factory filled with machines that clattered and giant cutters that slashed through heavy cloth with a dangerous swish, and great vats of boiling hot dye, all colors of the rainbow.

It was a very small kitten and a very sad-looking kitten, with a torn ear and its ribs sticking out. But it was a very brave kitten, standing there in a strange place, facing all the strange men like a fierce little orange-and-yellow-and-black tiger.

"Well, I'll be," said Tony, "if that isn't a regu-

lar Calico Cat. My grandmother had one . . . a little tiger of a cat, fierce and proud and full of beans."

"Well *this* one's certainly full of beans." Mike laughed because the kitten had quietly begun to nibble at the nice little pot of beans that Mrs. Mike had put in the lunch box.

"Makes himself at home, doesn't he?" said Jake.

"Sure, makes himself at home out here in the yard—but I'll bet he turns scaredy-cat just like the others when we get him *inside* the factory," Mike said.

But Mike was wrong. After lunch, when they all went back to work, Calico followed right along. He gave one small leap in the air when the machinery began to roar. But that was all. Then he began to explore. Delicately, he picked his way between whizzing wheels and rows of cloth that zoomed up and down on a thing that looked like a roller coaster. He stood with his small head cocked beside the dye bath and saw yards and yards of material go in grey and come out red. He watched the workmen load the cloth on little trucks to be carried down to the storeroom. He peered into the quiet office where the Big Boss sat at an ordinary desk, but he didn't stay very long.

"Too peaceful for him around here," the Big Boss said.

There was only one place Calico didn't go. That was down in the basement where the goods were stored. The basement belonged to Big Tom, the black cat who had been with the factory for years. Big Tom would not bother with the rest of the factory. The basement—where there was a danger of rats eating the cloth—was his Hunting Ground. And the big barred iron door to the basement was kept carefully closed.

"Wait till tomorrow—Calico won't be here," the Big Boss said when he left that evening. "No kitten has ever stayed for more than a day. But I hope he does—and that he's a good mouser. Big Tom has all he can handle, downstairs."

"Well, he seems to be settling down for the night," said Tony.

Sure enough, Calico, all by himself, had found an old heap of rags and made himself a bed.

The next morning all the workmen brought something extra in their lunch pails. If that little Calico was still around, he was going to have his reward. And indeed he *was* still around. And what a story the night watchman had to tell!

"That little critter turned up every hour just as if he knew when I had to punch the time clock. He followed me all over the place. And *mice*—he's a born mouser. Little as he is, he's tough! Had 'em laid out in *rows*. Big Tom didn't even need to inspect, upstairs, last night, when I left the door open for him. Only place Calico *won't* go is down in the storeroom. Reckon Big Tom told him that was Private Property."

Within a week, Calico knew just what he liked to do, every hour. He liked to be in the spot with the most action. At seven o'clock he was in the dye room, where he ate the salami that Tony gave him, drank a saucer of coffee, and then sat quietly studying the colors the men were mixing.

"Blue is his favorite color," Tony said.

"Aw—how do you reckon that?" Jake asked.

"Begins to lick himself and purr whenever we make blue," Tony said.

By noon, Calico was hungry again and after lunch he took a nap. He liked to put his head on an old scrap of blue velvet, as soft as his own kitten's fur.

After his nap, he did his exercises, climbing up and down the ropes and sharpening his claws on them. Sometimes the men gave him a ride in a truck with the goods that were being carried off the floor.

"Look at that, turns his claws in so he won't pull the cloth . . . smart cat," Mike said.

"Smart cat" began to be a phrase that was heard often in the factory. Whoever would suppose, the men said, that a little scrawny kitten could turn into such a daring acrobat!

"Better than a tightrope walker," they said when Calico picked his way daintily along a narrow ledge only half-a-kitten wide.

"Better than a whole circus," they said when Calico did his once-a-day Special Trick. Every day, just before the going-home whistle blew, Calico began his long ride down the newly dyed strip of cloth. It was hot. So he kept dancing from one foot to another until *just* before the cloth turned over into the series of steam rollers that dried the wet cloth. At just that moment, easily—no trouble at all—Calico leaped across the space between the two banks of steam rolls, and slid happily down the dry cloth to the heap on the floor below. It made a first-rate toboggan slide, and the men watched, every night just before the whistle, to see Calico do his Special Trick.

He *was* a smart cat all right. He got fooled only once and that was the day that the Ritz Print and Dye Works had the big order to print some leopard cloth. When Calico woke up from his nap, the whole factory was filled with leopards. Up and down the roller coaster came the long lengths of material, yellow with black spots

. . . furry, moving spots. Calico gave a frightened yelp and began tearing up and down the aisles between the busy machines.

"Silly critter—what's got into him?" Tony asked, shaking his head in bewilderment.

When the Big Boss came walking by just then, he began to laugh. "It's the leopards!" he cried. "Stop the machines."

So for the first time since the electricity failed in a thunderstorm, the machines at the Ritz Print and Dye Works were stopped. All because of Calico.

"Now," said the Big Boss, "pick him up, Tony, and show him it's only cloth.

"Reckon you feel pretty silly," Tony said tenderly, as Calico put out a brave paw and touched the leopard cloth.

And Calico must have felt *very* silly because when the machines began to roar again, he stalked with great dignity back to his bed and pretended to be asleep the rest of the day.

It was the next morning that Calico's love of blue got him into real trouble. When he started on his regular inspection of the dye room, there on the floor was a little pan of blue color, as blue as a lake on a summer's day. It was hot in the dye room. And the blue in the pan looked very cool. Suddenly Calico could stand it no longer. He dipped his nose into the cool blue. But it wasn't cool. It was hot. Burning hot. Calico yelped with surprise and misery.

"Jumping Jupiter," Tony cried, "get Miss Alice."

Miss Alice sat in the office with the Big Boss. She was the one who fixed the cuts and burns.

Poor Calico. He had burned his nose. Miss Alice put some salve on it, but Calico kept licking off the salve. And the salve had a horrid taste. Miss Alice finally put a bandage over Calico's nose to cover the salve.

Calico felt very sick. All day long he lay on his heap of rags with his head on the piece of blue velvet. He was very brave, but occasionally the men heard a faint moan and they knew he was suffering.

When it was time to go home, no one wanted to leave him. Finally the Big Boss himself said: "I think I'd better take him home with me. He's a fine brave little kitten, but this noisy factory is no place for him. Jimmy and Jill, my two young ones, will love him and there is a big green lawn where he can play."

Nobody said a word because the Big Boss was usually right about things. But it was a very sad crowd of men who gathered up their empty lunch boxes and started home.

"Reckon we'll miss Calico a lot," Tony said sadly.

"Yes," said Jake, "and what's more—I reckon Calico'll miss us!"

And Jake was right. At first, things happened so quickly that Calico didn't miss anyone. He was whisked into a big automobile and driven to a big white house on a hill. He saw lots of grass, as green as the beautiful green dye Tony mixed. And blue, blue sky, his favorite shade of blue.

Then, as soon as the Big Boss carried him inside the house, things happened even faster. A pretty little girl took him from the Big Boss's arms and hugged him tight. But the Big Boss said: "You'll have to wait till his nose gets better, Jill. Better put him down now. You can play with him all you want when he's well again."

Calico stood in the middle of a big soft rug and stared up at Jill. She was a nice little girl, but he was not at all sure he wanted her to hug him. Then a little boy came running up. He was even smaller than the little girl, and right away he reached for Calico's tail.

"No, Jimmy, no!" said his father. "Poor Calico doesn't feel well. You can play with him when he gets better."

Calico stared at Jimmy and sighed. Jimmy looked like a nice little boy, but Calico was not at all sure that he wanted anybody to pull his tail.

A lady in a stiff, starched dress brought him a dish of warm milk. It was very nice milk, but it did not have the flavor of onions or salami or beans. Calico sighed again.

Then the lady said, "Shouldn't we give him a bath? He must have picked up all kinds of germs in the factory."

"Not yet," the Big Boss told her. "He doesn't feel well enough to have a bath yet."

Calico didn't know what the lady meant by "bath," but he felt it was probably not anything pleasant.

Calico shivered. Everything was so quiet here,

and so strange. He felt sure he wasn't going to like it anywhere nearly as much as he did the factory.

Sure enough, Calico didn't like it. The pretty little girl named Jill dressed him up in her doll clothes and took him for a ride in a buggy. Calico was miserable. It was nothing like the rides in a real truck he had had. The little boy Jimmy pulled his tail every chance he got. And that nurse in the stiff, starched clothes spent all her time giving people—and kittens—baths.

Calico got fatter and healthier, and his nose was all well. But he kept on being unhappy. Sometimes he woke up with a start, thinking it was time for him to catch up with the night watchman. Sometimes in his dreams he heard the whir of the machinery and the swish of the giant cutters. But when he woke, he heard nothing more exciting than the tinkling of chimes of the big clock in the hall.

Then one day Calico saw a big truck outside the door, and the man in the truck was the very same man who had always given him a piece of herring out of his lunch box at the factory. Sure enough, the man was carrying a big bolt of cloth into the house—leopard cloth—the very same yellow cloth with black spots that had scared poor Calico so much.

Calico jumped all the way down to the ground from the second-story window and, before anyone saw him, hopped up into the truck and hid under a big parcel. When the driver came down the walk and got back into the truck, Calico's heart beat fast with excitement. He was with his friends again.

Whizz-grrr went the engine of the truck. *Squeak* went the brakes. And off they went.

After a long ride, the truck stopped and Calico peered out. His heart stopped beating. No factory. No familiar workmen. This was a big building with a roof, but no sides. And there was noise all around, and whistles tooting all the time. Calico saw two silver rails shining in the sun. The next minute a big black engine came roaring along, and the silver rails were hidden by a long row of cars. And now hundreds of people were suddenly on the platform, most of them carrying suitcases and boxes. Calico began to worry about losing the nice man from the factory who had driven him here in the truck.

Calico scrambled out, looking eagerly for the man who always gave him a piece of herring. But the man had disappeared. Calico knew there was just one thing to do. He must find his friend at once. Like a flash, he streaked across to the platform.

"Get out of here," a strange man said, reaching out with his foot toward Calico. Calico streaked off in another direction. And then, another. His friend wasn't anywhere. And the truck! Where had it gone to? Calico couldn't find it, either.

For days, poor Calico wandered. He found that some people pushed him away; some yelled "S-C-A-T!" at him. Life was a weary round of ducking and dodging and keeping one jump ahead of big dogs and ladies with brooms and bad little boys with sling shots. He slept in strange places. And it wasn't long before he had very little to eat. By this time Calico looked very much the way he had looked that first day at the factory—thin and bedraggled and sad. But he was still a fierce tiger cat at heart. And everywhere he went, he looked for just one thing— his beloved factory where he had so many fine friends.

And then one day he saw a big cat eating a piece of fish. The fish looked delicious. And it smelled very much like the herring from the lunch box at the factory. Calico was hungry. He

was much smaller than the big cat, but he was willing to fight for just one taste of that fish.

At first, the big cat did not even bother to fight. He just brushed Calico away with his paw. But when Calico nipped the big cat from behind, the big cat snarled. And in a minute the fur began to fly!

"Just one bite of that fish," thought Calico. "I don't care if I do lose an ear trying to get it."

"Oh," screamed a lady in a big automobile parked at the curb, near by. "Oh, oh!"

And the next thing Calico knew, the lady had come to his rescue.

She waved her umbrella at the big cat.

"Brute," she cried angrily at the big cat, "what do you mean, trying to steal from this little kitty?"

Lickety-split, the big cat ran, and Calico gulped down the fish. It was even more delicious than he had thought it would be. But he was not so happy when the lady picked him up and carried him into her automobile. He already knew that he didn't like trucks that took him to strange places. So, when the engine started up and went *whizz-grrr,* just like the truck, even though there wasn't any squeak, Calico was very much upset.

Then, in a little while, there he was in another strange place. It was an apartment house, and he had to ride in an elevator to get up to the tenth floor, where the lady lived. Calico didn't like her apartment at all. It had too many things in it. He wanted to get out. But when he ran over to the window in the living room, he saw it was much too high to jump down from.

Even though he had plenty to eat, Calico was unhappy. The lady, who was called Miss Muff, patted him too much. Every day she took him for a ride. And whenever she took him for a walk, she put a leather thing around his neck so he couldn't run away. That was even worse than being dressed in doll clothes! Every day, Calico felt more and more bored.

Then a wonderful thing happened. It happened one day when Miss Muff took him for his daily ride. When Miss Muff did that, she never bothered to put the leather thing around his neck. Calico always sat beside her on the front seat on a fat satin pillow, looking wistfully out of the window. Miss Muff thought he was having a good time. But he wasn't having a good time.

Now on this particular day, Miss Muff was driving along when all of a sudden there was a big bang and the car stopped.

"Oh, dear," said Miss Muff. "A blow-out. A real blow-out. What shall I do?"

"There's a garage about two blocks back, ma'am," a man on the sidewalk said. "Walk down there and they'll send someone back to fix your tire."

"Oh, thank you," said Miss Muff. She was so excited about the tire she forgot all about the open window beside her. She almost forgot Calico—but not quite. "Be a good boy, kitty," she called back as she got out of the car and hurried away.

No sooner had Miss Muff disappeared around the corner, than with one flying leap Calico was out of the window and streaking away in the opposite direction. All day long he ran and ran and ran. He hid in alleys and behind bushes, and he wandered for miles and miles.

When at last it was night and the dark was all around him, Calico went more and more slowly. It was a very hot night, and he began to wish he could find some cool water. He suddenly remembered that it had been a long time—hours and hours—since he had had a drink of water. He remembered all the nice cool water at the factory. Oh, to be back at the factory!

Slowly, Calico kept on walking. And after a while he smelled a faint fishy smell. Following the smell, he came to a little canal. The moonlight made stripes of gold on the water. The little canal looked familiar. Was it? Yes, it was! Suddenly he saw a big building rising out of the shadows. It looked almost like . . . it was . . . the factory itself! Calico started to run, then stopped in his tracks. For along the canal, a black slow-moving shape came stalking. It was Big Tom out for a walk. Calico slid back into the shadows and watched.

Big Tom stepped slowly along the canal. He seemed to be looking for something in the water. And then, quick as a flash, his paw darted into the water and out it came with something shiny.

"A fish! He's caught a fish," thought Calico.

Big Tom ate the fish and then walked on, once more. He was coming nearer and nearer,

and Calico felt his heart beat faster. In the factory, Big Tom had never hurt him. Big Tom had just paid no attention to him at all. Big Tom had merely acted as if Calico didn't belong to the factory. But what would he do now if he saw Calico trying to get into the factory?

Then and there Calico made up his mind. He wasn't going to let Big Tom or anything else scare him away. Now that he had found the factory again, he intended to stay there. So he stepped bravely out into the moonlight where Big Tom could see him.

Big Tom stopped walking. For a long time, he stared at Calico, then came closer and closer. Calico stood still and stared back. After a long time, Big Tom did a most surprising thing. He turned and walked back to the canal. In a second, flash went his paw, and out came another fish. Then Big Tom brought the fish back to where Calico was standing and dropped it in front of him. Would Big Tom fight for the fish? Suddenly, Calico knew he was so hungry he didn't care. Thrusting out his paw, he pulled the fish toward him and started gobbling it down. He ate it all. And Big Tom didn't even growl. He simply stood and watched, then turned around and went back to the canal.

Calico waited a minute. "Well!" thought Calico, "well!" and he knew at once that this was his chance. And quick as a wink, there he was, streaking off toward the factory.

Next morning, what a story the night watchman had to tell Tony and Jake and all the others!

"There he was, smiling, if you please, standing by the time clock when I came to ring in. First he showed me the mice he had caught—lots and lots of mice. Then he went to my lunchbox for something to eat. Then he went right over to that old heap of rags and fussed around until he found his special piece of blue velvet, curled up and went off to sleep. Just too tired to follow me around and help me punch the time clock."

"Told you he could take care of himself," said Tony. "Wonder where he went when he ran away from the Big Boss. He looks pretty well fed."

"Anyway he got back—so who cares where he went," said Jake.

"Do you suppose the Big Boss will want to

take him home again?" Mike asked in a worried voice, as the Big Boss came out of his office.

Calico woke up, stretched himself, and began to purr so loudly that the men were sure he understood what the Big Boss said to Mike then, "Take him home? No, I don't think so. He's a Career Kitty at heart, that's exactly what he is. It's on the job for him from now on!"

Bbbrr-BBBBRRRRRR went the machines as the factory day began and the work got under way. *Purr*RRRRR went Calico happily, head cocked and four feet poised for the flying leap into the big room full of noise and action. He was on the job and so was everyone else—and they were all much too busy to see Old Tom peering around the corner of the basement door with what might almost have been a grin on his battered old face.

BLAZE AND THE FOREST FIRE

C. W. Anderson

The fact that Mr. Anderson calls his country house "The House That Blaze Built" is a testimony to the popularity of his Blaze *books. They are excellent horse stories for children 4 to 8, and the drawings that illustrate them are superb. These simple stories will lead the children, when they are older, to Mr. Anderson's* Salute *and* High Courage *and to his magnificent sketches and brief biographies of race horses,* Black, Bay *and* Chestnut *and* Deep Through the Heart, *which are enjoyed from twelve years old on. Emphasis on character, both in the horses and human beings, makes Mr. Anderson's books of more than ordinary significance. This story is an excellent illustration of the courage of a horse and boy.*

Billy was a boy who loved horses more than anything else in the world. He loved his own pony, Blaze, best of all. After his father and mother gave him Blaze, Billy spent most of his time with the pony. Blaze would come whenever Billy called. He seemed to like the rides through the woods or along the roads as much as Billy did. Billy felt sure that Blaze understood him

when he talked; and the pony really did seem to understand what Billy said.

Billy's dog, Rex, usually went with them on their rides. But one day he was sick; so Billy's mother kept him at home. It was a beautiful day, and Billy decided to ride along a little winding road. It passed through some woods, and not many people used it. Both Billy and Blaze liked to ride through the woods, because there were so many things to see. They always met rabbits and squirrels and saw many birds. Flowers grew along the way, and the big trees were green and cool after the hot dusty roads. The summer had been very warm, and there had been little rain.

They had gone quite a long way when Blaze suddenly stopped. Billy looked ahead and saw smoke coming out of a pile of dry brush at the side of the road. He knew that it was against the law to build fires in the woods during the dry season. It was not a safe thing to do because of the danger of starting a forest fire.

Even as Billy looked, the flames burst out. He knew that these flames were the beginning of a forest fire unless they could be put out. If a breeze came up and carried the fire to the big pine trees near by, the whole countryside might burn. Not only the grass and trees would be burned. Fences and barns and houses would also go up in flames.

Billy had once seen a place where a forest fire had been. He remembered how bare and black it had looked, with burnt stumps where beautiful trees had been. He knew he must try to save the woods he loved so much. He must go quickly and get help.

The nearest place to go for help was a large farm. It was a long way to this farm by the road, and there was no time to lose. Billy knew they could save much time if they cut across country through the fields. But to reach the first field they would have to jump a high stone wall, higher than anything Blaze had ever jumped. But Blaze seemed to understand that they needed to hurry. He jumped the high wall perfectly.

Then they went on as fast as they could across the wide field. Billy did not need to urge Blaze. The pony was going like the wind. If he could only keep up this speed, they would soon reach the farmhouse. Billy could see it far off in the distance.

In the middle of the field was a brook. There was no bridge and no time to look for a shallow place to cross. "Come on, Blaze," called Billy, and Blaze went even faster than before. The nearer they came to the brook, the wider it seemed. It was too late to stop now. They were right at the water's edge. Blaze made a tremendous leap. Billy could feel how hard he was trying. It seemed that they would surely get over the brook safely.

As they landed, the bank gave way under the pony's hind feet. For a moment Billy thought they would fall back into the brook. But Blaze scrambled up the bank, and Billy held on somehow, his arms around the pony's neck.

In a flash Billy had his feet in the stirrups again; and they were off as fast as the faithful pony could go. Blaze was breathing hard now, but the farmhouse was near.

Suddenly Billy pulled Blaze to a stop. There, right in front of them, was a high wall with barbed wire at the top. He looked both ways but there was no gate in sight. Billy almost gave up, but the thought of the fire sweeping across the countryside was too much. They must go on.

"Just once more, Blaze," he whispered to the pony. Poor Blaze was very tired, but he galloped bravely toward the fence. He was straining every muscle for the jump.

They were almost over when Billy felt Blaze's hind legs catch on the wire, and they began to fall. Down went Blaze to his knees, and Billy slipped out of the saddle and up on the pony's neck. It seemed certain that Blaze would go down all the way, taking Billy with him. But, with a great effort, Blaze scrambled to his feet; and Billy, holding on to the pony's neck, stayed on. Then Blaze started at a gallop for the farmhouse, which was just across the field.

They galloped into the farmyard. The farmer and his son hurried over to meet Billy. All out of breath, he told them about the fire. At once they got some things to use in putting it out. Then they climbed into a car and drove off very fast. The farmer's wife quickly telephoned to the neighbors to send all the help they could.

Blaze was covered with sweat and dirt. He was a very tired pony, but he rubbed his nose against Billy and seemed to know that the boy was proud of him.

"You're the best pony in the world, Blaze— the very best!" said Billy, and he felt sure that what he said was true.

The barbed wire had cut Blaze's legs. So the farmer's wife brought warm water and medicine and helped Billy wash the cuts clean and bandage them. They were not deep cuts, and the farmer's wife said she was sure they would soon heal.

Billy and Blaze had a good rest at the farmhouse and something to eat. Then Billy started for home, letting Blaze walk slowly. On the way they met the farmers coming back. They said that they had been able to put out the fire before it did any real harm. They all thanked Billy for what he had done. They made him feel quite grown up. They said nice things about Blaze, too; so Billy was very happy as he rode home.

When Billy got home, his father and mother were waiting for him. The farmer's wife had telephoned to tell them what had happened. Billy's father took some salve and put it on Blaze's cuts so that they would heal more quickly. Blaze got much petting, and had some carrots with his supper. He was very fond of carrots. Billy had some chocolate cake with his supper. He liked that just as much as Blaze liked carrots. Billy's father and mother were very proud of both Billy and Blaze.

One evening, two weeks later, there was a rap at the door. Billy's mother asked him to go and see who was there. It was one of the farmers who had helped put out the fire. He held a big box on which was written "For Billy and Blaze."

Much excited, Billy opened the box. He found a beautiful new bridle, with a silver headband on which was printed one word—BLAZE. The box held also a pair of shining new boots and a fine pair of riding breeches. They were just the right size for Billy. The people of the countryside had bought all these things for him. They wanted to show Billy how grateful they were that he had saved them from a forest fire.

It was hard to sleep that night. It seemed to Billy that daylight would never come. He got up several times to look at the new boots and the beautiful bridle. He wanted to be sure he hadn't dreamed them.

No one else was awake when Billy brought the new bridle down to the stable and put it on

Blaze. Even Rex was still asleep. When Billy got into the saddle wearing his new breeches and boots, he felt fine. He was sure he could ride better because he had them on. Blaze arched his neck proudly. Even in the early dawn the silver headband on the new bridle shone brightly. His cuts were all healed; and he felt fine, too. So the two friends started happily off for their early-morning ride.

from THE BLIND COLT

Glen Rounds

Raised on a ranch, Glen Rounds can spin a tall tale or a western horse story and illustrate them to perfection. "The Camp on the Big Onion," in Time for Fairy Tales, *is an example of his robust style. The episode given here from* The Blind Colt *is quite different—poignant, tender, and true to horse and boy nature. Glen Rounds says perhaps he wrote this story because he was homesick for horses, and he adds that there really was such a colt as the one he tells about, blind and smart.*

The Bad Lands

It was near sundown of an early spring afternoon when the brown mustang mare left the wild horse band where it grazed on the new spring grass and climbed carefully to the top of a nearby hogback.

All afternoon she had been restless and nervous, spending much of her time on high ground watching the country around her. Now she stood and stamped her feet fretfully while she tipped her sharp-pointed ears forward and back as she looked and listened. And her nostrils flared wide as she tested the wind for any smells that might be about.

The rain-gullied buttes and pinnacles of the Badlands threw long black shadows across the soft gray and brown and green of the alkali flats below her. A few jack rabbits had already left their hiding places and were prospecting timidly around in the open, searching out the tender shoots of new grass. They, too, threw long black shadows that were all out of proportion to their size.

A few bull bats boomed overhead, and a meadow lark sang from the top of a sagebrush nearby. Below her the rest of the mustang band grazed quietly except for an occasional squeal and thump of hoofs as some minor dispute was settled. Otherwise everything was quiet.

But still the little mare didn't leave the ridge. She stood watching while the flats grew darker, and while the darkness crept up the sides of the buttes, until at last the sun touched only the very tip tops of the highest pinnacles. Then after a look back to where the rest of the horses were bedding down for the night, she slipped quietly down the far side of the ridge and was soon hidden in the darkness.

Next morning she was in a grassy hollow at the head of a dry coulee where the rolling prairie and the Badlands meet. And lying at her feet, sound asleep, was her colt, that had been born during the night.

The early sun touched the top of the rim rock behind her, then gradually crept down until it was warming the grass where the little mustang lay. As soon as the ground had begun to steam and the touch of frost was out of the air, she nudged him with her muzzle and waked him. For a little while he lay there, sniffing around in the grass as far as he could reach, and flapping his tail to hear it thump against the ground, while the mare stood relaxed on three legs and watched him.

But after a while she seemed to figure it was time for him to be up and about so she urged him to his feet. And he was as awkward looking a scamp as you'd care to see as he stood with his long, knobby legs braced wide apart and caught his breath after the effort of getting up.

His body was close knit and compact and his back was flat and strong. His muzzle was delicately shaped but his forehead bulged as all colts' do. His neck was so short he couldn't get his nose closer to the ground than his knees, and his legs were so long he seemed to be walking on stilts. His ears were trim and sharply pointed but looked as though they should belong to a horse much larger than he.

The mare saw all this but she knew that all colts were put together so, and that those extra long legs of his were specially made that way so that by the time he was a day or two old he would be able to travel as fast and as far as the grown horses in case of danger. And besides, she thought that his blue-gray coat was especially handsome.

For a few minutes the colt was kept busy trying to balance himself on his legs while he sniffed and snorted at everything in reach. As long as he stood still he was all right but when he tried walking he found he was engaged in a mighty ticklish business, what with his being so high in the air with nothing holding him up but those four knobby legs. They had to be lifted and swung just so or they got all tangled up and started him kiting off in some entirely unexpected direction.

But he was hungry, and the only way he could get anything to eat was to go after it himself, so it wasn't long before he was able to scramble around against the mare's side. After a little nuzzling around he found her teats and settled down to sucking noisily, flapping his tail with excitement.

Before long his sides began to stick out, he was so full of milk, and he was quite ready to enjoy the business of having his coat groomed by the mustang mare. She was fair bursting with pride, as this was her first colt. She whickered softly and caressed him with her muzzle every now and again as she scrubbed him with her rough tongue. When she hit a ticklish spot he'd flap his tail and squirm and snort his tiny snorts. When he did that she'd nip him gently with her big yellow teeth to warn him that wild young ones must learn to obey, and he'd better stand still until she was done or he might get worse.

And not an inch of his hide did she overlook. The white snip on his nose, his speckled blue sides and flanks and his legs that shaded down to black shiny hoofs, all got their share of combing and washing. By the time he had been thoroughly polished the sun was warm in the hollow and he began practising his walking again, and his smelling, and his hearing.

He started taking little exploring trips, a few wobbly steps in one direction, then another, with much snuffing and snorting as the brittle last year's grass crackled under foot. As he got the hang of operating his walking apparatus more smoothly he became bolder and extended the range of his explorations until sometimes he

traveled as far as ten or twenty feet from the brown mare's side.

His black-tipped, pointed ears were fixed to turn in all directions, to help him locate the source of sounds he heard. He pointed them forward and back, and the soft wind that springs up on the desert in the morning brushed against them, feeling sweet and clear and smooth. What few sounds he heard at first seemed to float separately through the warm silence as though there was all the time in the world and no need for two noises to be moving at the same time. Meadow larks whistled from nearby sagebrush, and far off he heard the harsh bickering of magpies as they quarreled over a dead rabbit or gopher.

Later on he discovered that down close to the ground there was a thin blanket of bug sounds. Flies buzzed and grasshoppers whirred. And buryer beetles made clicking noises as they busily buried a small dead snake.

Sniffing through his nose, he caught the sharp clean smell of the sagebrush, and the more pungent smell of the greasewood as the sun began to heat it up. Occasionally he got a whiff of wild plum and chokecherry blossoms from the thickets down below the rim of the Badlands.

Of course, these were the big plain smells, easily discovered. Later on he would learn to identify others that had to be searched for with flared nostrils, and carefully and delicately sifted for the story they could tell him of friends, or danger, or the location of water holes in the dry times. But for now the simpler lessons were enough to keep him busy, and the mustang mare was mighty proud of him.

But for all her pride, she was a little troubled, too. For there was something strange about the colt, although she couldn't tell exactly what the matter was. He was as lively as you'd expect any colt only a few hours old to be. He snorted and kicked up his heels when a ground squirrel whistled close by. And he put on a mock battle with a tumble weed when it blew against his legs, rearing up and lashing out with his front feet. When he came back from his trips he'd pinch her with his sharp teeth, and pretend to fight, like any healthy colt should do. But none the less, she felt that something was wrong.

The sun climbed higher, and the colt finally

tired himself out and lay down to doze at the mare's feet. She thought about starting back to join the mustang band, but it seemed so safe and peaceful there in the pocket that she hated to leave. And by tomorrow the colt's legs would be stronger and he would be able to follow her with no difficulty.

But before the morning was half gone she heard the sound of danger; an iron shod hoof striking a stone, and looked up to see two cowboys between her and the mouth of the pocket.

It was Uncle Torwal and Whitey out to see how their range stock was getting along. Torwal was a slow speaking fellow with a droopy red moustache, and a good many of the horses running in the Badlands belonged to him. Whitey, who was probably ten years old or thereabouts, had lived with him on the ranch for several years. Almost since he could remember. He wore a cast-off Stetson hat of Torwal's and high-heeled riding boots from the same source. They lived alone like any two old sourdoughs and were a familiar sight at all the roundups, and in town of a Saturday, Torwal on a crop-eared black and Whitey on a pot-bellied old pinto named Spot. Torwal usually spoke of Whitey as his "sawed off" foreman.

The little mare had whirled to face them, keeping the colt behind her. With her teeth bared and her ears laid back, she looked half wolf for sure.

"Spunky crittur, ain't she?" Whitey remarked as they rode carefully around, trying to get a good look at the colt.

"She's a wolf, all right," Torwal agreed. "An' if you ain't careful she's agoin' t' paste you plumb outta your saddle. Better not crowd her."

They sat on their horses and watched a while and admired the colt. "Purty as a picture, ain't he, Uncle Torwal?" said Whitey. "Reckon we better take him home so the wolves won't get him?"

"Don't reckon we'll take him anywheres," Torwal told him. "Looks like I'm a-goin' to have to shoot him!"

"Shoot him! Why?" squalled Whitey. "Why he's the purtiest colt on the ranch!"

"Better look him over closer, Bub," said Torwal. "See if you notice anything outta the way about him."

"I don't see anything wrong, myself," Whitey told him, after he'd walked Spot in a circle around the mare and colt again. "He looks to me just like the kind of crittur I'd like to have for a 'Sunday' horse."

"Look at his eyes; they're white." Torwal growled. "That colt's blind as a bat!"

"Aw, them's just china eyes, Uncle Torwal," Whitey said. "Lotsa horses has china eyes. Even ol' Spot has one."

"Them ain't no china eyes, not by a long shot," said Torwal. "If you look close you'll see that they're pure white without no center. He's blind, and we gotta shoot him. Otherwise he'll fall in a hole somewheres or get wolf et."

"Well, even if he is blind do we *hafta* shoot him?" Whitey asked. "Couldn't I take him home an' keep him at the ranch?"

"All he'd be is a mess of trouble even if you got him home, and I doubt that he'd go that far without somethin' happening to him anyways," Torwal told him. "An' besides, he wouldn't be good for nothing."

"Well anyway, do we hafta shoot him?" Whitey said. "Couldn't we just let him go loose?"

"Now quit your squallin'," Torwal told him, patiently. "I don't like it any more than you do, but if we leave him he'll either fall in a hole and starve or else he'll get wolf et. Lookit her tracks where she circled during the night. Fighting off an ol' 'gray,' I bet she was."

While Whitey sat with his lip hanging down almost to his collar, Torwal took another chew from his plug and got his rifle out of his saddle scabbard. But whenever he tried to get near the colt the little mare was there, lashing out with her hoofs and showing her teeth to bite either man or horse that got too near. Before long she was covered with lather and her eyes showed white, and the ground was plowed and trampled in a circle. But still the colt was safe.

Then Whitey spoke up again. "Lissen, Uncle Torwal," he said. "Lookit the way she fights. I don't believe any wolf could get to that colt, the way she uses them heels. If you'll let him go I'll watch mighty close to see if he falls in anything. I'll ride out everyday to see that he's all right. An' if he does fall in I—I—I'll shoot him myself!"

Uncle Torwal thought the matter over awhile.

"You want that colt mighty bad, don't yuh?" he said at last.

"Yeah, I sure do! He's the purtiest thing I've ever seen!" said Whitey. "I don't think anything will happen to him, really, Uncle Torwal! He's too smart lookin'!"

"Well, I tell yuh," Torwal said, doubtfully. "Since you feel like that about it we'll let him go awhile. We'll be a-ridin' over here every day for a while, anyways, so we can always shoot him later."

"But don't go gettin' your hopes up," he added. "The chances are he won't last a week. An' if he does he ain't good for nothing except to eat up good grass an' be a gunny sack full of trouble."

"Nothing is going to happen to him," Whitey exclaimed, "You'll see."

"Maybe," said Uncle Torwal, but Whitey could see that he was glad to have an excuse for not shooting the colt. Uncle Torwal put his rifle back in the scabbard, and they sat for a minute watching the colt, and then rode off to attend to their other affairs.

The little mare watched them until they were out of sight, and finally when she could no longer hear them she turned to the colt. She nuzzled him all over to make sure that nothing had happened to him. Then after letting him suck again she started down the trail toward the place she'd left the mustang band, with the blind colt following close against her flank.

Sounds and Smells

Back with the mustang band, the brown mare and the blind colt settled into the routine of range life. Early mornings they moved to their favorite feeding grounds where they grazed until the sun got hot when they dozed and rested. Late afternoons they grazed slowly towards some nearby water hole for their daily drink.

And the blind colt began learning the thousand and one things that a colt must know before he can take care of himself. Because he was blind he not only had to learn the things all colts must learn, but many others besides. For a week or so he stuck pretty close to the mare's side, and she saw to it that they stayed out where the ground was level with nothing for the colt to run into.

So it was only natural that he soon came to the conclusion that all the world was flat, and that he could travel safely anywhere.

What he did not know was that this Badlands country was criss-crossed and honeycombed with gulleys and washouts of every size, shape and description, and that sooner or later he would have to learn about them.

And sure enough, before long he did. It came about one morning when the horses were grazing on a grassy bench between gray shale bluffs on one side and a deep gulley on the other. The blind colt had wandered off a little farther than usual, when the mare looked up and whinneyed sharply for him to come back. He had learned that she usually punished him with her big teeth when he disobeyed, but he was feeling spooky this morning and figured that a little gallop the way he was going before he turned and came back wouldn't really be disobeying. So he flirted his tail over his back, snorted as loud as he could and made a few buck jumps straight ahead. The third jump sent him over the edge of the gulley and he found there was no more solid ground under his feet!

The sensation was one he never did forget. He turned head over heels and rolled to the bottom unhurt but considerably shaken up, and thoroughly frightened. After he had picked himself up he whinneyed shrilly and stood trembling and snorting until the mare came to the edge of the bank. She made comforting noises to him and with her encouragement he soon found a place where he could scramble back up the bank to where she stood.

For several days after that he stayed almost as close as if he had been glued to the brown mare's side, and carefully felt out the ground ahead at every step. He was afraid it would fall away from under him again.

But after a few days his curiosity got the better of his fear, and he started cautiously exploring again. He soon discovered that it wasn't enough to be careful not to fall over these banks, but that sometimes they stuck up and when he ran into them they were apt to jar the daylights out of him.

However, he learned fast and in a surprisingly short time he developed a sense that warned him of these things in his path even though he could not see them.

Whitey and Uncle Torwal, riding across the range, often saw him as he picked his way cautiously over strange ground or traveled with the rest of the horses to water, pressed up close to the brown mare's side.

"Well, he ain't got himself wolf et so far," Uncle Torwal would say.

"Nossir!" Whitey would answer. "An' he ain't a-goin' to, either. He's too smart."

Uncle Torwal would spit and say nothing.

During the late spring and early summer, the band of mustangs didn't travel much. There was plenty of grass on the flats and the water holes were nearly all full. In the cool hours of the mornings the older horses grazed quietly while the colts ran and kicked among themselves. The long middle hours of the day they spent contentedly dozing in the sun.

One or another of the mares usually was to be found a little distance from the rest, where she could keep a watchful eye on the surrounding country. When it was the brown mare who was standing guard the colt stayed close to her side. When she looked he listened, and when she listened, he listened too, and stretched his nostrils wide to smell. This way he learned many things. Things surrounding him were only Sounds and Smells, as far as he could tell. Unable to see them, they of course had no shapes. Bull bats catching bugs overhead in the evening were only Booming Sounds. Coyotes skulking around about their business of catching small rodents and robbing birds' nests were Rank Furry Smells. Jack rabbits were Furry Smells too, but smaller and dustier. The rabbits were also Small Sneezes and Thumping Noises. He learned to recognize the step of every horse in the band, and could spot the step of a strange horse immediately. He learned to tell the difference between the irregular movements of a loose horse and the steady purposeful gait of one ridden by a man.

The blind colt often heard Whitey and Spot go by these days, recognizing them by the lazy clop of Spot's big feet and his habit of blowing imaginary bugs out of his nose every few steps.

By the time summer came on and the band started climbing to the tops of high buttes in the middle of the day to escape the flies, the Colt's nose and his ears were giving him almost as good a picture of the things around him as if he'd had eyes.

Now most of these things were friendly and harmless, but the slightest taint of wolf smell, even before he knew what it was, would send him racing to his mother, stamping and snorting with excitement. For the fear of wolves has been born in the bones of horses for centuries. Before long he was to learn of other unfriendly and dangerous things.

On a drowsy afternoon in the middle of the summer, the blind colt was browsing among the broken banks of a black shale butte some distance from the other horses. In little pockets here and there were scattered bunches of grass high enough for him to reach.

He didn't really need the grass, but finding it was a sort of game. He had to work his way carefully along the rainwashed banks, exploring each projecting shelf with delicate sniffings, and when he discovered a green stalk he'd reach out his long upper lip and wrap it around the grass to get it in reach of his biting teeth.

When he succeeded in pulling up a mouthful, he'd stand and grind it busily with his small milk teeth, and flap his tail and nod his head with enjoyment.

After a time he noticed an odd smell. One that was new to him. It was sharp, but not very strong. He lowered his head and snorted his nostrils clear, to catch the new scent better. It didn't have the warmth and body of an animal smell, and yet there was something about it that frightened him a little, he didn't know why.

He stamped and snorted, but nothing happened, and there was nothing moving that he could hear. So after a little he went on with his search for grass. He had worked around a jutting shoulder of the butte when he noticed the smell was suddenly stronger and then he heard a buzzing—something like a grasshopper. But a grasshopper's buzzing had never given his skin the tingly feeling he had now. He was puzzled. He listened in all directions, pointing his ears this way and that, but the sound had stopped. As soon as he stepped forward, he heard the buzz again, and this time it was sharper and louder. It came from somewhere on the ground nearby, but as soon as he stopped to locate it, the sound stopped. He stood motionless for sev-

eral minutes, waiting for it to come again, and when it didn't he figured that whatever had made it must be gone, and returned to his search for grass.

But when he stepped forward again the buzz returned, and this time it had a nervous, angry sound. The smell was stronger, too. The colt was frightened, but hadn't been able to figure out where the sound came from so he didn't know which way to run. He stamped his foot, and as he did there was a dry rustling and a sudden movement from under an overhanging ledge at his feet as something struck his foreleg a sharp blow. The colt snorted with terror, whirled and ran for his mother, bumping into things as he went.

He'd been bitten by a rattlesnake that had crawled under the ledge for shade.

The mare fussed over him and worried about him, for in a short time he was a very sick colt indeed. His leg began to swell and he grew sick and feverish all over. Before long he was thirsty. And as he waded around in the nearby water hole he found that the mud cooled and soothed him. By evening his leg had swollen so much he could only hobble around with great difficulty. The rest of the band went away after a time, but

for several days the mare and the blind colt stayed by the edge of the water hole. The colt spent the greater part of his time standing deep in the churned-up mud while the mare grazed nearby, coming back to nuzzle him and to groom his hide with her tongue every few minutes.

In a few days the swelling began to go down and before long he was able to travel slowly, by favoring the sore leg, and they set out to find the rest of the horses. A couple weeks more and he was about as well as ever. But after that, the slightest smell of rattlesnake was enough to set him to snorting and plunging with fear.

The Water Hole

As the summer advanced the hot dry winds blew up from the south with the heat from a thousand miles of desert, and the country turned dry and brown. The small springs with their trickles of clear water were the first to dry up. Then the smaller water holes began to show wider and wider bands of dried and trampled mud around their edges, and finally they too were completely dry.

By late August the only water to be found was in the few large sinks and behind the scattered earth dams thrown up by the ranchers to hold snow water in the spring.

Old trails that had lain hard and untracked all summer now were inches deep in dust, ground up by the hoofs of the wild horse bands and the herds of cattle on their trips to water.

With so many bands coming into the few big water holes, the grass near them was soon gone, so the horses had to travel farther and farther from water to feeding grounds. When the weather was cool and overcast, they sometimes went to water only once in three days. But when the hot winds blew they had to drink every day.

Before long the blind colt's band was traveling so far that the trip to water and back left little time for rest or grazing.

The blind colt was still fat and sassy, growing like a weed, but the heat and traveling were beginning to show on the brown mustang mare. Her coat had begun to look rough, and her hip bones and ribs to show.

The trips in to water were full of excitement for the colt. Early in the afternoon the band would start slowly grazing in that direction. The nearer they came to the water the shorter the grass was, having been eaten down by the stock that had passed before. After a time they'd fall into one of the well-worn paths and follow it. Before long they'd see the dust of other bunches moving in the same direction. And the last mile or so there would be flocks of sage hens plodding along in single file, also on the way for their evening drink.

When they finally reached the rim overlooking the water hole, the whole band stopped while the leader looked the country over carefully. If there was another band of horses ahead of them they waited until they'd finished and gone away, for two strange bands will not drink at the same time. And, too, there was always a certain amount of danger connected with these isolated water holes. Wild horse hunters sometimes waited there, and the big gray wolves skulked about looking for a chance to pull down any animal that got trapped in the deep mud.

The blind colt enjoyed these trips, however. His ears picked up the disgruntled cluckings of the waddling sage hens, and he smelled the fresh scent of the sagebrush and any number of other pungent desert weeds drying in the hot wind. And while still a long way from the water hole all the horses would smell the water and hurry a little faster.

When they reached the ridge he stood with the others examining the country for danger, throwing his head high and distending his nostrils as far as he could. When the stallion bugled through his nose, the colt tried to do the same.

When they finally started down the trail he'd kick and squeal with excitement, nipping the flanks and hocks of whatever horse was nearest and generally stirring up confusion.

But the water hole itself always frightened him a little, for it was surrounded by a wide band of mud, dried and cracked on top, and thick and gummy under the crust. It wasn't like the nice squishy stuff he'd waded in earlier in the summer. This mud made strange sucking noises around the horses' feet and seemed to be trying to pull them down.

At first he always stayed on firm ground while the brown mare drank, waiting for her. But as the summer got drier and the colt older the mare's supply of milk grew less and less. By this

time the colt was able to graze a little so he wasn't troubled by lack of food, but he did begin to get thirsty. So one day he ventured out across the mud himself, being careful to pick a place that had been packed firmer than the rest. Except for the sucking noises around his feet, nothing happened, so after that he always drank with the others.

But one day he accidently shoved up against a short-tempered old mare and she whacked him in the ribs with her heels. The colt was startled and plunged away, landing in a boggy spot the others had been avoiding.

His hoofs, being small and sharp, didn't give him the support that flatter ones of an older horse would have, and he felt himself sinking. The harder he tried to pull his feet loose the deeper he sank. He whinneyed in terror and lunged with all his power, but all he could do was work himself deeper and deeper into the sticky mud.

The brown mare had left her drinking as soon as she heard him squall, but there was nothing she could do but nuzzle him and whicker encouragingly. By the time he was exhausted he had thrown himself partly on his side and was trapped beyond any chance of escape without help. He lay there, covered with mud, his sides heaving and his nostrils showing their red inner side.

The horses milled round, excited by his struggles and his frightened whinneying, but after a time they all went away except for the brown mare standing guard.

She stood over him and nuzzled him with her nose and wiped mud off with her tongue, comforting him as much as possible. By spells he struggled, trying to get to his feet. But after a time he wore himself out completely and just lay and shivered.

That night was the longest he'd ever known. He heard the sound of other horses coming to drink, and the squeals and thump of hoofs on ribs as the brown mare drove them off.

Somewhere in the night there was the smell of a big gray wolf prowling near, and the snorting and stamping of the mare as she circled between the blind colt and the danger.

In the morning he heard the small sounds of sage chickens and little animals drinking, but

nothing else. He and the brown mare were alone. She grazed nearby, returning to the trapped colt whenever he moved or made a sound.

It was late in the morning when the mare threw up her head to listen for a sound the colt had heard some time before. The sound of a shod horse, and from his steady gait it was plain there was a cowboy on his back. In a little while Whitey showed up on old Spot. There was much to be done these days, what with riding out to check the water holes and the like, so Torwal quite often sent him out to ride alone. And when Whitey saw the colt bogged down he was mighty glad that Torwal was not along this particular morning, because he felt sure Torwal would have argued that the colt had best be shot.

He rode up and sat a minute in his saddle while the mare watched him. This time she didn't show fight. Perhaps somehow she knew there was no need. Whitey talked soothingly to her and to the colt while he took down his rope. Shaking out a noose as he'd seen Uncle Torwal do in such cases, he rode carefully out across the mud as close as possible to the colt. The mare followed anxiously, but still not interfering. After a few unsuccessful attempts he got the loop around the colt's neck and took a dally around the saddle horn. Then, working carefully, he edged Spot towards solid ground. As the noose tightened on the colt's neck he began to struggle again. But now with the pull of the rope to help him, he was soon dragged out to firm ground.

He was a messy looking sight, with all that mud caked on him, as he lay there getting his breath. But luckily he wasn't chilled as he would have been later in the year. The brown mare trotted around like an old hen with a bunch of ducks, snorting and whinneying to herself and smelling and nudging the colt. Working very carefully and without getting out of his saddle, Whitey shook the muddy noose from the colt's neck and rode off a few yards to watch.

For a while the colt was content to lay on the grass and rest while the mare nosed him over to see if he was all right, and licked the mud off his coat. But after being in the mud all night he was mighty hungry, so it wasn't long before he struggled to his feet. His legs were pretty wobbly under him, but beyond that he didn't seem to be damaged any. And by the time the mare had nursed him and polished him from head to foot he looked and felt about as good as new, so they started slowly up the trail the way the other horses had gone.

All this time Whitey had quietly watched them from a distance, with his chest thrown out and as near strutting as is possible for a fellow sitting on a sleepy old pinto horse to be. He'd been busting for some time to get a chance to pull a bogged crittur out of the mud by himself. And for it to be his blind colt was almost more excitement than he could hold!

After the mare and colt had disappeared over the ridge he managed to get his attention back on his business and climbed down to clean the mud off his rope before he coiled it back on the saddle.

When that was finished he cocked his hand-me-down Stetson as far on one side as it would go and rode away, admiring his shadow more than a little. He kind of hoped he'd get a chance to rope a wolf or some such thing to sort of finish his day out right.

from JUSTIN MORGAN
HAD A HORSE

Marguerite Henry

No one has written more thrilling tales of different breeds of horses than has Mrs. Henry, who, like the illustrator of her books, Wesley Dennis, knows and loves horses. The little wild horse about whom she wrote a book, Misty of Chincoteague, *lives with Mr. and Mrs. Henry, and eats Christmas dinner with them each year.* King of the Wind, *the story of the ancestor of the famous race horse, Man o' War, won the Newbery Award in 1949. The episode given here comes from a book about the ancestor of a special breed of horses, the sturdy and willing Morgan horse. Little Bub, the horse hero, is given to the schoolmaster Justin Morgan in payment of a debt. Young Joel Goss, who has been apprenticed to Miller Chase and who is also a friend of the schoolmaster, loves the colt from the time he first sets eyes on him, and undertakes to gentle him.*

Little Bub Is Rented Out

Never was a colt so willing to be gentled. After but two lessons, he wore a halter as if it were part of him. Like his forelock. Or his tail.

Next Joel tried the harness, and slipped a bit between his nippers and his back teeth. Bub hated the bit. He did not mind rope or leather things, but this iron was cold and frightening.

One night Joel warmed the bit in his hands, and from then on, the colt accepted it without even jerking.

Whenever Bub behaved well, Joel let him bury his nose in a bucket of oats—all the while telling him what a fine, smart horse he was. "You're my reddish-brown stallion," he would say. "Soon you'll be *big* for your size! And then you've got to be so smart and willing that even an ornery man will have no excuse to touch a whip to you. I couldn't abide that!" he added, his fists doubled.

Some nights Joel fastened a horn lantern to an old two-wheeled cart of his father's. Then, filling the cart with stones for weight, he would drive the horse over the rolling hills. Some nights he rode bareback. He practiced pulling the colt up

From *Justin Morgan Had a Horse,* by Marguerite Henry. By permission of Wilcox & Follett Co.

short. He practiced walking him, trotting him, racing him. Often they would travel ten miles in an evening.

Late on one of these evenings Joel burst into the schoolhouse so full of laughter he could scarcely talk.

The children were gone, and the boy's laughter was so hearty that the schoolmaster joined in without knowing why.

Between spasms, Joel managed to gasp, "You should have seed that little hound-dog run!"

"What little hound-dog?"

"Why Abel Hooper's," giggled Joel, bursting into fresh laughter. "He comes a-tearing out the gate and begins yammering at Little Bub and nipping his forelegs. Oh ho, ho, ho!"

"What did Bub do?"

"What did he *do*?" shrieked Joel. "Why he sprung forward like a cat outen a bag. And that idiot hound was too muddled to go home. He turned tail and streaked down the road with Bub after him."

Joel had to wipe away his tears before he could go on. "Finally," he chuckled, "the hound got so beat out I took pity on him and reined in. Why the way Little Bub can climb hills," breathed Joel, "it's like he had wings!"

When Mister Goss discovered Joe training the colt, he was furious at first. Then he boasted and bragged about it at Chase's Inn: "All that boy knows about horses he got from me!"

But the truth of the matter was that in watching his father train a colt, Joel had learned what not to do, as well as what to do. While his father could break a horse in a matter of hours, his horses often seemed broken in spirit, too. The boy was determined that this should not happen to his colt. And it had not. Little Bub's eyes were still dancy. He still tossed his mane and nosed the sky. He still had a frisky look about him. No, he had lost none of his spirit.

The moon waned and became full again. Not once, but many times. For months the schoolmaster said no more about selling the colt. And about the time when Joel began to think that Little Bub might be his forever, a man came to call on the schoolmaster. He was Ezra Fisk, a new settler.

"I've been watching a lad drive a smallish horse in the moonlight," Mister Fisk said, "and by inquiring at the Inn, I understand the horse belongs to you, sir."

The schoolmaster nodded.

"Now I have fifteen acres of wooded land, and Evans, my hired man, will need a horse to clear it. This Evans is a wiry hand, and I figure that he and a horse with a little getup about him could clear the land in a year's time."

"You would like to buy the horse?" asked Master Morgan.

"No indeed, sir. I do not wish to buy such a *little* animal. I merely wish to rent him. I stand ready to pay fifteen dollars a year, *and* his keep of course. I'll send Evans around in the morning to fetch him."

Joel was setting a log in the sawmill when he heard the cloppety-clop of hoofs coming down the river road. This in itself was nothing to make him stop work, but from the uneven beat of the hoofs he could tell that the animals were not traveling in a team. And then without looking up at all he knew. He knew that the lighter hoofbeats were those of Little Bub. Not until he had started the saw, did he face the road.

It *was* Little Bub all right, not ten rods away. He was tied on to the back of a wagon pulled by a fat ox. His reddish coat glinted in the sunlight. And he held his head high, as if he found nothing at all disgraceful in being tied to an oxcart.

The blood hammered in Joel's head. He might have whistled and felt the hot pride of having the little horse nicker in answer. Instead, he kept murmuring the schoolmaster's words: "I've got to pay off my debts before I die. Will you gentle the colt, lad?"

Well, Bub had been gentled all right. *Any-*one could see that. With a heavy heart, he watched the procession as it clattered over the log bridge and climbed up and up the steep hill. Finally it disappeared over the brow, and nothing was left of it. Nothing but a wisp of dust.

The Pulling Bee

By the time spring came on, Joel and Miller Chase were friends. In the late afternoons, while Mistress Chase napped, the miller often gave Joel a whole hour to himself.

One afternoon early in May Joel stood look-ing out the inn door. Suddenly the yard began filling with big-faced dray horses and oxen, and men were gathering about a huge pine log.

"Is it a pulling bee?" asked Joel, turning to Miller Chase quickly.

"If Nathan Nye is about, looking mighty important and bossy, you can be expecting most anything. He was ever good at fixing contests."

"He's there!" exclaimed Joel. "And he's got tug chains."

"H'm," mused the miller, tapping his cheek, "if I was a boy now with no chores to do, it seems like I'd skedaddle right out there."

Joel grinned over his shoulder, and in no time at all he was helping Mister Nye fasten the tug chains to a big dappled mare.

The mare's owner, Abel Hooper, was too busy boasting to the farmers to be of any help. "A mighty lucky thing I'm first," he was saying. "Lucy and me'll pull this here piece a kindling to the sawmill in one pull. Then you can all hyper on home whilst it's still daylight."

But Abel Hooper had to eat his words, for Lucy barely caused the log to tremble.

One after another, the beasts had their turn, and no matter how whips cracked or masters yelled, the log seemed rooted to the earth.

"Folks, I guess it's up to the oxen now," Nathan Nye was saying, when into the yard came Evans riding Little Bub.

"Hey, Nathan," called Evans, "what's all the hullabaloo?"

"'Tis a pulling bee," answered Mister Nye, "but can't none of the beasts pull that there pine log to the sawmill in three pulls or less. Just look at Hooper's big mare! She's roaring from the try. And Biggle's gelding—his muscles are still a-hitching and a-twitching. Even Ezra Wiggins' beast failed. None of them can budge the log."

"None except my one-horse team!" crowed Evans.

Joel held his breath. He felt scared right down to his toes.

The crowd snickered. Then it hooted.

"*That* little flea? Why, he's just a sample of a horse. He ain't no bigger than a mouse's whisker! Besides, his tail is so long, he's liable to get all tangled up and break a leg."

Evans looked over the horseflesh. "Little Bub," he said slowly, "ain't exactly what you'd call a dray horse, but whatever he's hitched to generally has to come the first time trying."

"Take him on home," scoffed Nathan Nye. "When we have a contest for ponies, we'll be letting you know."

Above the man-talk Joel heard the sharp voice of Mistress Chase. "Boy! You come here!"

On his way in Joel stopped only long enough to press his face hard against Little Bub's nose.

At the door Mistress Chase handed him a kettle of hasty pudding and a long stick.

"Hang the kettle over the fire," she said, "and stir and stir until I tell you to quit."

"*Hasty* pudding!" muttered Joel to himself. "It beats me how it got its name!"

Evans strutted into the room just then. "Chase!" he called to the miller. "I'll wager a barrel of cider that my horse can move that pine log to the sawmill in two pulls. But first, pour me a mugful. I'm dying of thirst."

At sound of Evans' voice Joel almost upset the pudding.

"Boy!" shrilled Mistress Chase. "Mind your work. Hasty pudding's not meant to feed the fire!"

For once Joel paid no heed. He tore across the room and grabbed Mister Evans by the sleeve.

"Mister Evans!" he cried. "Little Bub's been dragging logs all day. You hain't going to enter him in the pulling bee?"

Evans gulped his drink. "Go away, Joel," he snapped in annoyance. "When I want advice, I'll not ask it of a whippersnapper."

The little horse meanwhile was feasting upon all the fresh green shoots within his range. They tasted juicy and delicious after the business of logging.

One by one the stars dusted the sky. Nathan Nye brought out a lanthorn so Mister Evans could see to fasten his tugchains to the log.

Joel followed Evans about like a puppy. Evans stood it as long as he could. Finally he shoved the boy aside.

"A nettle hain't half as pesky as you," he growled. "Stand back or I'll clout you."

Now Evans was stepping off the ten rods from the log to the mill.

"Want to give up before you start?" scoffed Nathan Nye.

"No such a thing. Why, I'm actually ashamed to ask my horse to pull such a little log. Now if you'll find me three stout men to sit astride the log, why then I'll ask him."

Joel bit his lips to keep from crying out. He hid his face in the horse's tangled mane. "Oh, Bub, my poor little Bub," he choked, "none of the big creatures could budge the log, and now with three men besides. Oh Bub, Bub . . ."

Laughter rang up and down the valley. "Ho-ho-ho—that pint-sized cob to pull such a big log! Ho-ho . . ."

Nathan Nye had no trouble at all in finding three brawny volunteers. As the men straddled the log, they joked and laughed and poked one another in the ribs.

"Look to your feet, men!" warned Evans. "This horse means business. Something's got to give."

Nye held the lanthorn aloft. It lighted the circle of faces. They were tense with excitement. Some of the men were placing last-minute bets with one another. Some were whittling like mad. Others twirled their whips nervously. Joel was white with anger.

Nye repeated the warning. "Look to your feet, men!"

Someone tittered.

Evans felt to see if the little horse was hitched securely. Then, "Git up!" he roared, as he slashed the whip across Bub's back.

The little horse galvanized into action. First, he backed ever so slightly. Then his powerful neck bent low, as if to give every muscle a chance to get going. Now he was straining forward. You could see his muscles grow firm and swell up like rubber balls. You could see the white foam come out on his body.

Joel, too, was drenched in sweat. The silence was heavy, like a gray blanket.

At last there was the groaning of chains. The log trembled. Slowly it moved. It kept on moving. It was more than halfway to the saw!

The little horse stopped. His sides were heaving. Joel breathed in and out with the horse. He felt as if his lungs were on fire. There was no sound at all from the crowd. Overhead a baby robin, trying to get settled for the night, chirped insistently.

Now Evans commanded again. And again the horse went through the same motions. He backed slightly. He bent his head. He strained every muscle. Again the log was moving, moving, moving. This time it did not stop until it reached the sawmill!

And still nobody had made a sound. The three men were as silent as the log they sat upon. Only the horse's breathing pierced the quiet.

Then everyone began shouting at once. "Hooray for Morgan's colt! Hooray! Hooray! Hooray for the big-little horse."

Joel had his arms around Bub's neck. His whole body ached, as if he had moved the log himself. "It's over! It's over! You did it, Bub! You did it!" he kept repeating. Then he sobbed a little from exhaustion and relief.

The horse lipped Joel's cheek and neck. He almost tried to say, "It's all right, Joel; don't be taking it so hard." He was steaming and tired, but it was good to be near the boy again. It was good. He nickered softly.

A RANGE COLT

Will James

Will James was a cowboy, and he wrote in the cowboy vernacular. But don't be deceived by the bad grammar. The story of Smoky the cowhorse is told with consummate skill and feeling. It sets a high standard for telling stories about animals of any sort because it is told with complete fidelity to the species. Smoky lives, enjoys, and suffers as a horse, never as a human being. This book won the Newbery Award in 1927, and its popularity has never waned.

It seemed like Mother Nature was sure agreeable that day when the little black colt came to the range world, and tried to get a footing with his long wobblety legs on the brown prairie sod. Short stems of new green grass was trying to make their way up thru the last year's faded growth, and reaching for the sun's warm rays. Taking in all that could be seen, felt, and inhaled, there was no day, time, nor place that could beat that spring morning on the sunny side of the low prairie butte where Smoky the colt was foaled.

"Smoky" wouldn't have fitted the colt as a name just then on account he was jet black, but that name wasn't attached onto him till he was a four-year-old, which was when he first started being useful as a saddle horse. He didn't see the first light of day thru no box-stall window, and there was no human around to make a fuss over him and try to steady him on his feet for them first few steps. Smoky was just a little range colt, and all the company he had that first morning of his life was his watchful mammy.

Smoky wasn't quite an hour old when he begin to take interest in things. The warm spring sun was doing its work and kept a-pouring warmth all over that slick little black hide, and right on thru his little body, till pretty soon his head come up kinda shaky and he begin nosing around them long front legs that was stretched out in front of him. His mammy was close by him, and at the first move the colt made she run her nose along his short neck and nickered. Smoky's head went up another two inches at the sound, and his first little answering nicker was heard. Of course a person would of had to listen mighty close to hear it, but then if you'd a-watched his nostrils quivering you could tell that's just what he was trying to do.

That was the starting of Smoky. Pretty soon his ears begin to work back and forth towards the sound his mammy would make as she moved. He was trying to locate just where she was. Then something moved right in front of his nose about a foot; it'd been there quite a good spell but he'd never realized it before; besides his vision was a little dim yet and he wasn't interested much till that something moved again and planted itself still closer.

Being it was right close he took a sniff at it. That sniff recorded itself into his brain and as much as told him that all was well. It was one of his mammy's legs. His ears perked up and he tried nickering again with a heap better result than the first time.

One good thing called for another and natural like he made a sudden scramble to get up, but his legs wouldn't work right, and just about when he'd got his belly clear of the ground, and as he was resting there for another try at the rest of the way up, one of his front legs quivered and buckled at the elbow, and the whole works went down.

He layed there flat on his side and breathing hard. His mammy nickered encouragement, and it wasn't long when his head was up again and his legs spraddled out all around him the same as before. He was going to try again, but next time he was going to be more sure of his *ground*. He was studying, it seemed like, and sniffing of his legs and then the earth, like he was trying to figger out how he was going to get one to stand up on the other. His mammy kept a-circling around and a-talking to him in horse language; she'd give him a shove with her nose, then walk away and watch him.

The spring air, which I think is most for the benefit of all that's young, had a lot to do to keep Smoky from laying still for very long. His vision was getting clearer fast, and his strength was coming in just as fast. Not far away, but still too far for Smoky to see, was little calves, little white-faced fellers a-playing and bucking around and letting out wall-eyed bellers at their mammies, running out a ways and then running back, tails up, at a speed that'd make a greyhound blush for shame.

There was other little colts too all a-cavorting around and tearing up good sod, but with all them calves and colts that was with the bunches of cattle or horses scattered out on the range, the same experience of helplessness that Smoky was going thru had been theirs for a spell, and a few hadn't been as lucky as Smoky in their first squint at daylight. Them few had come to the range world when the ground was still covered with snow, or else cold spring rains was a-pouring down to wet 'em to the bone.

Smoky's mother had sneaked out of the bunch a few days before Smoky came, and hid in a lonely spot where she'd be sure that no cattle nor horses or even riders would be around. In a few days, and when Smoky would be strong enough to lope out, she'd go back again; but in the meantime she wanted to be alone with her colt and put all her attention on him, without having to contend with chasing off big inquisitive geldings or jealous fillies.

She was of range blood, which means mostly mustang with strains of Steeldust or Coach throwed in. If hard winters come and the range was covered with heavy snows, she knowed of high ridges where the strong winds kept a few spots bare and where feed could be got. If droughts came to dry up the grass and water holes, she sniffed the air for moisture and drifted out acrost the plain which was her home range, to the high mountains where things was more normal. There was cougars and wolves in that high country, but her mustang instinct made her the "fittest." She circled around and never went under where the lion was perched a-waiting for her, and the wolf never found her where she could be cornered.

Smoky had inherited that same instinct of his mammy's, but on that quiet spring morning he wasn't at all worried about enemies. His mammy was there, and besides he had a hard job ahead that was taking all of his mind to figger out: that was to stand on them long things which was fastened to his body and which kept a-spraddling out in all directions.

The first thing to do was to gather 'em under him and try again. He did that easy enough, and then he waited and gathered up all the strength that was in him. He sniffed at the ground to make sure it was there and then his head went up, his front feet stretched out in front of him, and with his hind legs all under him, he used all that strength he'd been storing up and pushed himself up on his front feet, his hind legs straightened up to steady him; and as luck would have it there was just enough distance between each leg to keep him up there. All he had to do was to keep them legs stiff and from buckling up under him, which wasn't at all easy, cause getting up to where he was had used up a lot of his strength, and them long legs of his was doing a heap of shaking.

All would of been well maybe, only his mammy nickered "that's a good boy," and that's what queered Smoky. His head went up proud as a peacock and he forgot all about keeping his props stiff and under him. Down he went the whole length of his legs, and there he layed the same as before.

But he didn't lay long this time. He either liked the sport of going up and coming down or else he was getting peeved; he was up again, mighty shaky, but he was up sure enough. His mammy came to him. She sniffed at him and he sniffed back. Then nature played another hand and he nursed, the first nourishment was took in, his tummy warmed up and strength came fast. Smoky was an hour and a half old and up to stay.

The rest of that day was full of events for Smoky. He explored the whole country, went up big mountains two feet high, wide valleys six or eight feet acrost, and at one time was as far as twelve feet away from his mammy all by himself. He shied at a rock once; it was a dangerous-looking rock, and he kicked at it as he went past. All that action being put on at once come pretty near being too much for him and he come close to measuring his whole length on Mother Earth once again. But luck was with him, and taking it all he had a mighty good time. When the sun went to sinking over the blue ridges in the west, Smoky, he missed all the beauty of the first sunset in his life—he was stretched out full length, of his own accord this time, and sound asleep.

The night was a mighty good rival of what the day had been. All the stars was out and showing off, and the braves was a-chasing the buffalo plum around the Big Dipper, the water hole of The Happy Hunting Grounds. But all that was lost to Smoky; he was still asleep and recuperating from his first day's adventures, and most likely he'd kept on sleeping for a good long spell, only his mammy who was standing guard over him happened to get a little too close and stepped on his tail.

Smoky must have been in the middle of some bad dream. His natural instinct might of pictured some enemy to his mind, and something that looked like a wolf or a bear must of had him cornered for sure. Anyway, when he felt his tail pinched that way he figgered that when a feller begins to *feel* it's sure time to act, and he did. He shot up right under his mammy's chin, let out a squeal, and stood there ready to fight. He took in the country for *feet* and *feet* around and looking for the enemy that'd nipped him, and finally in his scouting around that way he run acrost the shadow of his mammy. That meant but one thing, safety; and that accounted for and put away as past left room for a craving he'd never noticed in his excitement. He was hungry, and proceeded right then and there to take on a feed of his mammy's warm, rich milk.

The sky was beginning to get light in the east, the stars was fading away and the buffalo hunters had went to rest. A few hours had passed since Smoky had been woke up out of his bad dream and there he was, asleep again. He'd missed his first sunset and now he was sleeping thru his first sunrise, but he was going to be prepared for that new day's run, and the strength he was accumulating through them sleeps and between feeds would sure make him fit to cover a lot of territory.

There wasn't a move out of him till the sun was well up and beginning to throw a good heat. He stacked up on a lot of that heat, and pretty soon one of his ears moved, then the other. He took a long breath and stretched. Smoky was coming to life. His mammy nickered, and that done the trick; Smoky raised his head, looked around, and proceeded to get up. After a little time that was done and bowing his neck he stretched again. Smoky was ready for another day.

The big day started right after Smoky had his feed; then his mother went to grazing and moving away straight to the direction of some trees a mile or so to the south. A clear spring was by them trees, and water is what Smoky's mammy wanted the most right then. She was craving for a drink of that cold water, but you'd never thought it by the way she traveled. She'd nose around at the grass and wait for spells, so as little Smoky could keep up with her and still find time to investigate everything what throwed a shadow.

A baby cottontail had jumped up once right under his nose, stood there a second too scared to move, and pretty soon made a high dive between the colt's long legs and hit for his hole; Smoky never seen the rabbit or even knowed he was there or he might of been running yet, cause that's what he'd been looking for, an excuse to run. But he finally made up an excuse, and a while later as he brushed past a long dry weed and it tickled his belly, he let out a squeal and went from there.

His long legs tangled and untangled themselves as he run, and he was sure making speed. Around and around he went and finally lined out straight away from where his mammy was headed. She nickered for him and waited, all patience. He turned after a spell and headed for his mammy again the same as tho he'd run acrost another enemy at the other end; and as he got close to his mammy he let out a buck, a squeal, a snort, and stopped—he was sure some little wild horse.

It took a couple of hours for them two to make that mile to the spring. The mother drank a lot of that good water, a few long breaths and drank some more till the thirst was all gone. Smoky came over and nosed at the pool, but he didn't take on any of the fluid, it looked just like so much thin air to him, the same with the tender green grass that was beginning to grow in bunches everywhere; it was just growing for him to run on.

The rest of that day was pretty well used up around that one spot; adventures of all kinds was numerous for Smoky, and when he wasn't stretched out and asleep there was plenty of big stumps in the cottonwood grove that could be depended on to give him the scare he'd be looking for.

But there was other things and more threatening than stumps which Smoky hadn't as yet spotted, like for instance,—a big cayote had squatted and been watching him thru dead willow branches. He wasn't at all interested in the action Smoky was putting into his play, and only wished the colt's mammy would move away a little further when he would then take a chance and try to get him down—colt meat was his favorite dish and he sure wasn't going to let no chance slip by even if it took a whole day's waiting for one to show itself.

A couple of chances had come his way but they was queered by Smoky's mammy being too close, and he knowed better than show himself and get run down by them hoofs of hers. Finally, and when he seen his appetite wouldn't win anything by sticking around that spot any longer, he took a last sniff and came out of his hiding place. Keeping the willows between him and the horses, he loped out till he was at a safe running distance and where he could see all around him, and there he squatted again, in plain sight this time. He hadn't quite made up his mind as yet whether to go or stick around a while longer. Just about then Smoky spots him.

To him, the cayote was just another stump, but more interesting than the others he'd kicked at, on account that this stump moved, and that promised a lot of excitement. With a bowed neck and kinked tail Smoky trotted up towards the cayote. The cayote just set there and waited and when the colt got to within a few feet from him, he started away and just fast enough so as the colt's curiosity would make him follow. If he could only get the colt over the ridge and out of his mammy's sight.

It all was only a lot of fun to Smoky, and besides he was bound to find out what was that gray and yellow object that could move and run and didn't at all look like his mammy. His instinct was warning him steady as he went, but curiosity had the best of him, and it wasn't till he was over the hill before his instinct got above his curiosity and he seen that all wasn't well.

The cayote had turned and quicker than a flash made a jump for Smoky's throat. The generations of mustang blood that'd fought the lobo and cougar, and which was the same blood that flowed in Smoky's veins, is all that saved the colt. That inherited instinct made him do the right thing at the right time, he whirled quicker than lightning and let fly with both hind feet with the result that the cayote's teeth just pinched the skin under his jaws. But even at that, he wasn't going to get rid of his enemy (it was a sure enough enemy this time) that easy, and as he kicked he felt the weight of the cayote, and then a sharp pain on his hamstrings.

Smoky was scared, and he let out a squeal that sure made every living thing in that neighborhood set up and wonder; it was a plain and loud distress signal, and it was answered. His mammy shot up the hill, took in the goings on at a glance, and ears back, teeth a-shining, tore up the earth and lit into the battle like a ton of dynamite.

The battle was over in a second, and with hunks of yellow fur a-flying all directions it wound up in a chase. The cayote was in the lead and he stayed in the lead till a second hill took him out of sight.

Smoky was glad to follow his mammy back to the spring and on to the other side a ways. He didn't shy at the stumps he passed on the way, and the twig that tickled his tummy didn't bring no play. He was hungry and tired, and when the first was tended to and his appetite called for no more he lost no time to picking out a place to rest his weary bones. A thin stream of blood was drying on one of his hind legs, but there was no pain, and when the sun set and the shadow of his mammy spread out over him he was sound asleep, and maybe dreaming of stumps, of stumps that moved.

When the sun came up the next morning, Smoky was up too, and eyes half closed was standing still as the big boulder next to him and sunned himself. A stiff hind leg was a reminder of what happened the day before, but the experience was forgotten far as dampening his spirits was concerned, even the stiffness wouldn't hold him back from whatever the new day would hold. He'd always remember the cayote, and from then on never mistake him for a stump, but that sure wasn't going to take any play out of him.

He was two days old now and strength had piled up fast, he felt there was no trail too long for him and when the sun was a couple of hours high that morning and his mother showed indications that she wanted to drift he sure wasn't dragging along behind. The stiffness gradually went out of his hind leg as he traveled, and by the afternoon of that day he was again shying at everything and sometimes even shying at nothing at all.

They kept a-traveling and traveling, and it seemed like to Smoky that the trail was getting pretty long after all. They skirted the flat along the foot of the mountains, crossed one high ridge, and many creeks, and still his mother was drifting on. She wouldn't hardly even stop for him to nurse, and Smoky was getting cranky, and tired.

The pace kept up till the sun was well on its way down, when it slackened some and finally the mother went to grazing. A short while later Smoky was layed out full length and dead to the world.

Smoky didn't know and didn't care much just then, but his mammy was headed back to her home range, where there was lots of horses and other little colts for him to play with; and when late that night she lined out again traveling steady he wasn't in any too good a humor.

Finally it seemed like they'd got there, for his mammy after watering at a creek went to grazing at the edge of some big cottonwoods; she showed no indications of wanting to go any further. Right there Smoky was willing to take advantage of the chance and recuperate for all he was worth. The sun came up, but Smoky was in the shade of the cottonwoods what was beginning to leaf out. He slept on and a twitching ear once in long spells is all that showed he was still alive.

That day never seen much of him; once in a while he'd get up and nurse but right away after he'd disappear again and stretch out flat on the warm earth.

He kept that up till way in the middle of the next night, and it was well towards morning before he felt like he was all horse again.

He come out of it in fine shape though, and he was stronger than ever. His vision was taking more territory too, and he was getting so he could see near half as far as his mammy could. She was the first to see the bunch of range horses trailing in to water early that morning. Smoky heard her nicker as she recognized the bunch and it drawed a heap of interest as to what she nickering about, for he was right there alongside of her and he couldn't see nothing for her to nicker at, but pretty soon he could hear the horses as they trailed towards him. His ears straightened towards the sound and a while later he could make out the shapes of 'em. Smoky just kind of quivered at the sight of so many that looked like his mammy. He was all interested, but at the same time, and even tho his instinct told him that all was well, he had no hankering to leave his mammy's side till he knowed for sure just what was up.

The mother watched the bunch coming closer with ears pointed straight ahead, but soon as some of the leaders discovered little Smoky there was a commotion and they all begin crowding in to get a look at and greet the newcomer, about which time the mother layed her ears back. It was a warning that none of 'em come too close.

Little Smoky's knees was a-shaking under him at the sight of so many of his kind; he leaned against his mammy half afraid, but his head was up far as he could get it and facing 'em and showed by the shine in his eyes that he liked the whole proceeding mighty well at that. He rubbed nostrils with a strange gelding which was braver than the rest and dared come close, and when that gelding was nipped at by his mammy he had a mighty strong hankering to help her along just for fun, and nip him himself.

The preliminary introduction took a good hour, and the mother stood guard; not for fear that any of 'em would harm Smoky, but she wanted it understood from the start that he was her little colt and she had the say over him. It finally *was* understood, but it took all that day and part of the next for the bunch to get used in having the new little feller around and quit making a fuss over him.

They was all jealous of one another and fought amongst themselves to be the only one near him, and his mother, of course she'd declared herself from the start, and it was took for granted from all around that her place in Smoky's heart couldn't be considered, and all knowed better than try and chase her away from him. Fillies and old mares, young geldings and old ponies and all, had it out as to which was the most fit to tag along and play with Smoky and keep a watchful eye over him along with his mammy. All wanted the job, but a big buckskin saddle horse who all the time had been the boss of the herd took it to hand to show them that *he* would be the all around guardeen for Smoky, and second only to his mammy. He delivered a few swift kicks, pounded on some ribs, left teeth marks on shiny hides, and after taking one last look and making sure that all was persuaded, grazed out towards Smoky who by his mammy had watched the whole proceeding with a heap of interest.

There was three other little colts in the bunch besides Smoky, and each time one of them little fellers came the buckskin horse had to whip the bunch so as he'd have the say over the newest one. Now Smoky was the newest one, and the buckskin horse had first rights as an outsider once again. He was an old horse full of scars showing where he'd had many a scrap; there was saddle marks on his back and at one time he had been a mighty fine cowhorse. Now he was pensioned; he'd more than earned a rest and all he had to do for the rest of his life was to pick out good feed grounds for the winter, shady places and tenderest green grass for the summer,

and his other interest in life was them little colts that came in springtime.

Smoky's mother was young, at least ten years younger than the buckskin horse, but the buckskin was like a colt compared to her when it come to be playful. She had the responsibility of Smoky and while she let him play with her, kick or bite at her, she never played with him and once in a while if he'd get too rough she'd let him know about it. She loved little Smoky with all her heart and would of died for him any time, and her main interest was to see that she kept in condition so that Smoky would never be stunted by lacking of rich milk. She had no time for play.

And that's where the old buckskin came in. Him and Smoky was soon acquainted, in a short while they was playing, Smoky would kick at him while the big buckskin nipped him easy and careful along the flank, then he'd run away from him, and the little colt had a lot of fun chasing that big hunk of horseflesh all over the country. The rest of the bunch would watch the two play and with no effort to hide how jealous they felt.

Smoky's mother kept her eye on the buckskin, but never interfered, she knowed, and it was only when Smoky came back to her, tired and hungry, that she put her ears back and warned him to keep away.

It took a few days before the buckskin would allow any of the other horses to get near Smoky, and then he had no say about it for he found that Smoky had his own ideas about things, and if he wanted to mingle in with the other horses that was his business, and all the buckskin could do then was to try and keep the other horses away. That was quite a job, specially if Smoky wanted to be with them. So the buckskin finally had to give it up and do the best he could which was to see that none of 'em done him any harm. But none of 'em had any intentions of doing the little colt any harm, and as it was it looked like Smoky had 'em all buffaloed. He'd tear in after some big horse like he was going to eat him up and all that big horse would do was to scatter out like the devil was after him.

Smoky was the boss and pet of the herd for a good two weeks and then one day, here comes another little feller, a little bay colt just two

days old and trailing in alongside his mammy. Smoky was left in the background and witnessed the same fuss and commotion that was done over him that morning by the creek. The buckskin horse once again fought his way in that new little feller's heart, and right away he forgot Smoky.

But Smoky never seen anything wrong to that, he went on to playing with every horse that would have him and it wasn't long till he picked up with a young filly and afterwards went to mingling with other young colts.

From then on Smoky had more freedom, he could go out a ways without having some big overgrowed horse tagging along, but he never went far and if he did he always came back a heap faster than when he started out. But them spring days was great for Smoky; he found out a lot of things amongst which was, that grass was good to eat, and water mighty fine to drink when the day was hot. He seen cayotes again and the bigger he got the less he was afraid of 'em till he finally went to chasing every one of 'em he'd see.

Then one day he run acrost another yellow animal. That animal didn't look dangerous, and what's more it was hard for Smoky to make out just what it was, and he was bound to find out. He followed that animal plum to the edge of

some willows, and the queer part of it was that animal didn't seem at all in a hurry to get away, it was mumbling along and just taking its time and Smoky was mighty tempted to plant one front foot right in the middle of it and do some pawing, but as luck would have it he didn't have the chance, it'd got in under some willows and all that was sticking out was part of the animal's tail. Smoky took a sniff at it without learning anything outside that it shook a little. There didn't seem to be no danger, so the next sniff he took was a little closer, and that done the trick. Smoky let out a squeal and a snort as he felt his nostrils punctured in half a dozen places with four-inch porcupine quills.

But Smoky was lucky, for if he'd been a couple of inches closer there'd been quills rammed into his nose plum up to his eyes, which would've caused a swelling in such size that he couldn't of been able to eat and most likely starve to death. As it was there was just a few of them quills in his nostrils, and compared to the real dose he might of got, it was just a mild warning to him. Another lesson.

It was a few days later when he met another strange animal, or strange animals, for there was many of 'em. He didn't get much interest out of them somehow, but while they was handy maybe it was just as well for him to have a close look at one. Besides he had nothing else to do, and mammy wasn't far away.

His instinct had no warning to give as he strutted towards the smallest one of the strangers which he'd picked to investigate. He wasn't afraid of this animal and this animal didn't seem afraid of him so Smoky kept a-getting closer till one was within a couple of feet of the other. Both Smoky and this stranger was young, and mighty inquisitive, and neither as yet knowed that they'd sure be seeing plenty of each other's kind as they get older, that they'll be meeting thru the round-ups at the "cutting grounds," on "day herd" and on "night guard," on the long, hot, dusty trails. A cowboy will be riding Smoky then and keeping a whole herd on the move, a whole herd of the kind that little Smoky was so busy investigating that day. They'll be full grown then, and there'll be other young ones to take the place of them that's trailed in to the shipping point.

But Smoky wasn't as yet worried or even thought on what was to come, neither was the little white-faced calf he was exchanging squints with; and when the critter called her long-eared, split hoofed baby to her side, Smoky just kicked up his heels, put his head down, and bucked and crowhopped all the way to where his mammy and the rest of the bunch was grazing.

Animals of field, forest, and jungle

from SMOKE ABOVE THE LANE

Meindert DeJong

Here is told an amusing and touching story of a strange friendship.

[A Tramp and a Baby Skunk]

In the wood there was a tramp—making pancakes. And in the wood there was a little skunk, sitting in a hollow stump—watching the tramp. Beside the wood there stood a long, old freight train. The freight train stood beside the wood, and stretched away beyond the wood, for it was easily a mile long. And there it stood. And it was early in the morning.

It was so early in the morning in this little wood in the far North country, that the morning sun was not even up. It was cold in the wood, even though this was a morning in the first week of September. It was so cold that the big tramp stopped making pancakes to rub his big cold hands.

The big tramp did not know the little skunk was watching him. He was too busy making pancakes. He fried them on a piece of tin over a little fire. Above the fire he had hung a big tomato can—the tramp was also making coffee. No, the big tramp did not know the skunk was there, and he was cheerfully humming as he made breakfast for himself over a little fire on the bank of a creek in the little wood. "Carry me back to old Virginny," he was humming.

But the tramp knew that the train was there! Busy as he was, from time to time he would stop his cheerful humming, and peer under the trees at the long, old freight train. He kept his eye on the train.

The little skunk kept his eye on the tramp. He sat in the dark, hollow stump, watching the tramp and listening to his cheerful humming. He sat and sniffed the wood smoke, and the lovely odor of pancakes and coffee that drifted on the wood smoke. He gurgled happily to himself—a tiny little gurgle. He was waiting for the tramp to leave. Then he would go to the little fire and pick up all the pancake crumbs. He did it every morning—ever since the tramp had come to the little wood, oh, many weeks ago.

The little skunk knew the tramp. The little skunk liked the tramp. He liked the tramp for his pancake crumbs and for his cheerful humming. And often he would follow the footsteps of the tramp—oh, just for fun. Just because he liked the tramp. But the tramp had never seen the little skunk.

This morning the tramp was in a hurry. He hurriedly took a last bite of pancake, he gulped a last swallow of coffee out of the tomato can, he stuffed some hot, left-over pancakes in a coat pocket, stamped out the fire, and hurried to the creek with the tomato can. He rinsed out the

coffee and filled the tomato can with water. He stuffed the tomato can with water into his other coat pocket. Then the big tramp hurried through the little wood toward the long, old freight train.

As soon as the big tramp was gone, the little skunk came out of the stump and ambled to the stamped-out fire. He found a crumb of pancake, he nibbled the crumb. He searched for more, but there were no more. He ambled to the creek, and took a little drink. He went back to the fire, but there just were no more pancake crumbs. So then the little skunk just went to the creek for still another little drink.

But the tramp had reached the edge of the wood, the tramp had come to the railroad fence that ran along the little wood. The big tramp looked carefully up and down the long train. He saw no one, he heard no one, and that pleased the tramp. With all his strength he hurriedly tore a board from the fence. And, with the heavy board on his shoulder, the big tramp hurried along the train until he came to a boxcar that he liked. He took the board and rammed the door of the boxcar open.

Once more the tramp looked up and down the train. He heard no one, he saw no one. He peeked inside the boxcar and saw that it was empty. That pleased the tramp. He grinned, and placed one end of the board in the open doorway of the boxcar. He hurried up the slanting board into the boxcar.

The tramp went to the farthest, darkest corner of the boxcar. He tugged the tomato can out of his pocket, and he carefully set it on the floor. And then he stretched himself down on the floor beside the old tomato can. He did not bother to close the door of the boxcar. He did not bother to throw the board down—it still slanted up into the open doorway. He went to sleep!

In the little wood the baby skunk had gone for still another drink to the clear, cool-water creek. The clear, cool-water creek wound in and out between the trees. It gurgled under fallen trees. It curled around the stumps of trees long gone. The little skunk dug at the foot of one of the stumps. He found a nice, fat grub. He nibbled the grub. He gurgled happily—a tiny little gurgle. It was such a delicious grub! But then he went back to the stamped-out fire. But now he

was not looking for pancake crumbs, now he was looking for footsteps—the footsteps of the long-legged tramp. And then he found one!

The little skunk hurried from that first invisible footstep to the next invisible footstep. He began following them through the wood. The footsteps of the tramp were far apart. Here a footstep, there an invisible footstep, but the little skunk followed them as surely as if he could see them. He could not see them—he was a near-sighted little skunk but it was as if he saw them with his little crinkling nose, so surely did he follow them.

The little skunk followed the footsteps, and he gurgled his tiny little gurgle. He knew the tramp! He liked the tramp! And he liked to follow the tramp's big footsteps—just for fun. Just because he liked the tramp.

The little skunk came to the railroad fence. He stopped exactly where the tramp had stopped. But he did not watch the train! He was near-sighted, he could not see that far. No, he was following the footsteps. He followed them under the fence, he followed them along the train, and then he came to the slanting board. He stretched up to sharpen his nails on the slanting board. He smelled the footsteps going up the board. He went up the board! It was a big mistake.

The little skunk had hurried and hurried all the time as fast as a little skunk can hurry. But that was slow as slow. And now, when the skunk

went up the board, the Northern sun was shining over the trees into the doorway of the boxcar. The little skunk felt the warm sun. The sun was warm, the sun was good, the sun was warming his fur and his bones. The little skunk felt so good with the sun, he sank down in the sunny, sheltered doorway, curled his bushy tail over his nose and eyes—and went to sleep!

It was a terrible mistake.

It was a terrible mistake because the long, old freight train, standing on the railroad siding beside the little wood, was waiting for the fast express to come roaring by. Once the fast express train had rushed by on the main track, the slow old freight train would start up, and rattle and bang on its own slow way out of the far North country. The little skunk did not know that. The little skunk did not understand trains.

The tramp lay sleeping in the corner. The little skunk lay sleeping in the sunny doorway. And there—with a roar and a swoosh and a shriek—the fast express went thundering by. The shriek and roar so scared the tramp and skunk, they both jumped up, they both leaped high. But just as the tramp jumped to his feet, there with a mighty jolt and jerk the freight train started into motion. The mighty jerk knocked the big tramp right down again.

The mighty jerk had not only knocked the tramp down. The mighty jerk of the freight train knocked the slanting board out of the open doorway. The mighty jerk rammed the door of the boxcar tightly shut. The door flew shut— the empty boxcar became black and dark.

The terrified little skunk lay flat against the floor—lay trembling. But the tramp had gone down hard and lay where he had fallen—he lay still. He had hurt his head. He was stunned. He did not move.

Far up ahead on the mile-long train, the whistle of the old locomotive moaned and hooted. Far up ahead, the bell clanged. The whole train groaned and shook and rattled as the locomotive huffed and strained away from the little wood, back to the main track.

There went the train. It rolled and banged around a bend, and then the little wood was gone. There went the train, there went the baby skunk. Away from the wood that had been his home. Away from the clear, cool-water creek, and the big trees, and the stumps of trees where he had dug for grubs. Away and away. It was a terrible mistake.

But now at last the long-legged tramp in the corner of the dark boxcar was coming to his senses. He sat up, he rubbed his sore head. "Is that a way to start a train?" he grumbled. "Is that an engineer?" He rubbed his head again, but then he thought of something. He hastily felt around in the dark for the tomato can. He poked a long finger down in the can and felt for the water. "Oh, oh, just as I thought," he groaned. "Knocked more than half the water out. And that man calls himself an engineer!"

Now the tramp's eyes were getting used to the dark. Suddenly he leaned forward. He peered hard at the closed door. He peered again, then he sat back with a jerk. "No!" he told himself. "No, don't tell me that's a skunk! Don't tell me I've got myself locked in here with a skunk. Oh, no!"

The tramp became quiet. He sat studying the flattened little skunk. He sat thinking hard. "Now what am I going to do?" he asked in the darkness.

The big tramp did not dare move because of the skunk. The little skunk did not dare move at all. He kept himself squashed flat against the floor. The little skunk was terrified. He did not understand trains. He was used to solid ground. The solid ground had never bounced and banged, and rocked and rattled. The little skunk did not know what to do. He was too terrified to move a muscle.

When the big tramp saw that the little skunk was too terrified to stir, it gave the big tramp courage. "Look, little fellow," he said to the skunk, "you're scared, aren't you? You don't want to be here, do you? Well, I'm the man to help you. Look, I'll get that door open, then I'll wait until we come to a nice, soft pile of leaves, and then with one swoosh of my foot I'll send you flying into the leaves."

The big tramp sat waiting, as if he were waiting for the little skunk to answer him. "One swoosh," he said again. "But to do it, I've got to get at the door. But you're sitting right in front of the door! And I'm afraid that when you see me coming right at you, you'll get so scared you'll throw your scent—swish it all over with your tail. All over me—all over the boxcar! And I'm just a poor old tramp. I haven't any clothes to change. And I can't get off this train to bury my clothes in the ground for a week to rid them of your awful scent. And I can't take a bath in a tomato can half full of water!"

The tramp stopped pleading with the little skunk. He waited still a little longer, but then he came. He edged along the wall of the boxcar, he inched closer and closer to the skunk, but all the while he kept talking in the softest, friendliest voice. And then he reached the little flattened skunk, who clung to the floor with every nail and every muscle!

Now the tramp could see how really terrified and miserable the little skunk was. "Ah, you little tike," he said softly. "Scared to death, aren't you? You're petrified. Well, you just let me get at that door!"

And then the tramp stepped right over the skunk, and turned to the closed door! The little skunk lay flat and miserable between the tramp's big feet. The tramp took hold of the door to shove it open. He struggled and pushed, he pulled and he grunted. The door would not yield. He dug all his fingers into the old door, and tried again. He broke his fingernails, but the door did not stir. At last the tramp looked helplessly down at the little quivering skunk. "I'm afraid you're in for it, little fellow. That door's rammed shut. It's absolutely stuck. You and I are in here till they let us out."

And now at last the terrified little skunk looked up at the big man.

"Ah, little tike," the big tramp said, "I'd better not scare you any more. I'll get back to my corner. But, look, you and I will make out all right. We've some water and some pancakes. We can hold out until they let us out. Who knows, maybe we can even become friends."

The big tramp moved softly away to his dark corner so as not to worry the little skunk. The big tramp was mistaken. He did not see it as he walked away, but the little skunk lifted his head and looked desperately after the tramp. He kept his head turned, trying to see the tramp. He was afraid of the banging train, not of the friendly, soft-spoken tramp.

In the far corner the tramp stretched himself out to go to sleep. He lay there humming him-self to sleep. "Carry me back to old Virginny," he was humming. The little skunk listened to the humming. It was some comfort to the little skunk as the slow old train banged on and on.

That is how they rode—the little skunk at the closed door, the tramp in the far corner. The tramp lay sleeping, but the little skunk sat listening anxiously to every rattling sound as the slow old train banged on. He kept turning his head toward the dark corner. He listened wistfully to every snoring sound from the sleeping tramp—it was a little comfort. But he stayed at the closed door. He did not dare to move.

A mile up ahead the old locomotive whistled and hooted its way around a bend. The whole train slowed as it went around the bend, and when it slowed the boxcar did not bang and rattle quite so much. The little skunk looked longingly toward the far corner with the tramp. The boxcar was a little quieter. The little skunk began moving toward the tramp! He still did not dare to get to his feet. He dragged himself along the floor, inch by slow inch. Oh, it took long! The slow old train went many slow miles, before the little flattened skunk at last reached the big feet of the sleeping tramp. He was so relieved when he got there, so tired from the strain, he cuddled himself tightly against the tramp's big shoe. He pressed himself against it.

Just being pressed against the tramp's big shoe seemed to give the little skunk courage. Now the slow old train went around a long bend again, it slowed again. It was less noisy, less rocky. It hardly swayed. And now the little skunk dared to pull himself up by the big shoe and crawl up on the leg of the man! He crawled along the tramp's long leg while the train went slowly around the bend. And then—then he came to the man's stomach!

There the little skunk discovered something. The man was soft! Softer than leaves! The man was warm! Warmer than a whole pile of leaves in the sun! The man was soft and warm—he did not bounce and rattle! The man swayed with the swaying of the train, the man quivered and jiggled with the motions of the train, but the man was soft and warm. And safe! And for the first time on that terrifying ride the little skunk felt safe enough, and cozy enough, to sink himself down on the tramp. He was so tired from the strain and fright! It was so wonderful to feel safe! He went to sleep.

The big tramp slept. The little skunk slept on the tramp. The slow old banging train rolled on.

The tramp and skunk woke up together. They woke up from the quiet. They woke because the train was standing still. Outside the train a bird sang, and then a cow mooed. The slow old train must be standing on a railroad siding somewhere in the country, it must be waiting for a faster train to pass again.

The big tramp slowly opened his eyes. He carefully peered around the dark boxcar. He searched the darkness for the little skunk. Then his eyes fell on the little skunk curled up on his stomach! "Oh, ho!" the big tramp rumbled. "So there you are! I was looking everywhere, but not on my own stomach. Using me for a mattress, eh? Didn't I tell you we'd be friends? If you aren't as cute as a kitten! If you aren't something!"

The big tramp chuckled and chuckled. The little skunk sat jiggling up and down on the big tramp's chuckling stomach. Suddenly he crinkled his nose, and sniffed. He smelled pancakes! He was hungry! And now that the train was still, the little skunk was bold enough, and hungry enough, to follow his nose right across the tramp, right to the pocket where the pancakes were. The floor was still, the floor was not rocking and banging. The little skunk climbed down from the tramp to get at the pocket with the pancakes. But there stood the tomato can with water! The little skunk was terribly thirsty, too —from all the fright. He put his forepaws on the rim of the tomato can, and peered in.

The big tramp hastily sat up. "Careful, don't tip it," he warned anxiously. "It isn't even half full. We can't waste it. There's no telling how long we may be locked up in this boxcar. Here, let me help you." He took the tomato can and carefully poured a few drops into the palm of his hand. He held out his hand with the water. The little skunk shrank away from the hand. The little skunk was timid, but the tramp was worried too—afraid that if he alarmed the skunk, the little skunk might suddenly throw his awful scent. The worried tramp held his hand steady, but because he was worried, he started humming. When the little skunk heard the hum-

ming sound he knew so well, he came to the cupped hand, dipped his chin down in, and drank! "There," said the tramp, and he was so relieved, he took a small drink from the tomato can himself.

"Well, that's all the water for now," the tramp announced, after he had put the tomato can down. "Now let's see about pancakes." He pulled the pancakes out of his pocket, and held them close to his face to count them in the dark. "Hey, only five!" he said disappointedly. "I thought I'd taken more."

He sorted out the smallest pancake and broke it in two. "One half for me, and a half of one half for you—because I'm bigger," he told the little skunk. "Wait a minute—I had breakfast, but I suspect you didn't. Okay, one half of one half for you, and none for me. There's no telling how long we may have to stay in this boxcar."

The big tramp gave the skunk his piece of pancake, but he carefully put the other pieces back in his pocket with the other pancakes. On the floor the little skunk had just begun to nibble the piece of pancake when, with a terrific jolt, the old train started into motion. The tramp grabbed the tomato can with water, but the little skunk lay flat and trembling on the floor.

"Look," said the tramp, now that the tomato can was safe, "you'd better get back on me. It rides better." But the little skunk was too terrified to move.

"Now what to do?" the tramp said. "I don't dare pick you up, I don't dare handle you yet. You might not understand, and then you'd swish your tail and throw that miserable scent of yours all over me."

The big tramp puzzled a while. Then he took the piece of pancake and held it on his hand before the little skunk. Even that wouldn't lure the little skunk to crawl up on his hand—he was too frightened. "Careful now," the tramp warned. "You know I mean you no harm." Quickly he slid his flat hand under the little skunk, lifted him up, and set him on his lap. He slid his hand from under him. "There," said the tramp, much relieved. "Now you feel safer, don't you? And I feel better myself." He placed the piece of pancake on his lap before the little skunk. The little skunk almost began to nibble and eat, but first he looked up at the man.

"You're welcome," the big tramp said. And he chuckled and chuckled until the little skunk sat jiggling and eating in his chuckling lap.

That is how they rode from that time on—with the little skunk in the big tramp's lap when they were both awake, or with the little skunk curled up on the stretched-out man when they were both asleep. And all the time the slow old train rolled on and on.

The train kept going through that day, it kept on going through that night. But the big tramp and the little skunk in the tightly shut boxcar did not know where they were. They did not know where they were going. They did not even know what time it was, or what day it was. It hardly made any difference. They ate when they got hungry—but one small mouthful of pancake was hardly enough for hunger. They drank when they got thirsty—but half a mouthful of water was hardly enough for thirst. They slept when they got sleepy. Mostly they slept—for when they slept they could not feel their hunger and their thirst. It was best to sleep as much as possible.

During the day the tramp would just stretch out and go to sleep, but when night came it was different. When night came he would take his shoes off. "Now it is night," the tramp would say, and then he'd take his shoes off, and that would make it bedtime. The little skunk would curl himself up on the stretched-out tramp, and then they both would try to sleep. It was best to sleep as much as possible.

They would wake up to another day. "We must be in another state by now," the tramp would say the first thing in the morning. Slow as this train runs, we must have come through three or four states by now—we've been on here so long." The little skunk would perk up his head and listen to the talking voice.

The big tramp talked quite a lot to the little skunk on the slow, dark, rattling journey through the countryside that they could not see at all. He would sit and stare at the solid wall of the boxcar, and then he'd suddenly say: "You can see for yourself that now we're going along a lake. Isn't it pretty? Look at the gulls!" And then he'd laugh and laugh until the wondering little skunk sat jiggling in his chuckling lap.

But whenever the train would stop the big tramp would become quiet. He would listen long and carefully until he heard the sound of birds, or a cow lowing, or other farm sounds. "Huh," he would whisper then, much relieved, "I was afraid maybe we were stopping at a station in some city, but there's a cow, so we must be in the country. Guess we're stopping so the old locomotive can take on water again. Guess the old locomotive leaks at every seam—it's so old." The little wondering skunk would listen to his whispering voice.

Suddenly the train would jerk to a start again, rattle and roll on again—endlessly. But sometimes the train *would* stop at a railroad station in a town. And that was altogether different. There would be noises all along the train—great bangings as boxcars were loaded and unloaded. Trucks roared, voices shouted, doors of boxcars slid open, slid shut. "Now we've got to be mighty quiet," the tramp would warn. "Hush now, because if they catch me stealing a ride on this train, they'll march me straight to jail!"

The noises would come and the noises would go. Doors of boxcars slid open, slid shut. But no one ever came to the empty boxcar with the tramp and skunk. No one ever slid that door open. The last truck would roar away, the last voices would fade away into the railroad station, and the old train would slowly roll out of the town.

At first when the train would roll through a town, the big tramp was still jolly and chuckly. He would amuse himself by pointing out things in the town that he could not see at all. "See that blue suit in that window?" he would say. "Now a blue suit is just what I need. I'm getting to be quite a raggedy old tramp. . . . Wait a minute, though! Seeing that shoe store reminded me, I need shoes much worse than a blue suit. There's holes in my soles big enough for one of my pancakes to go through. I should have made my pancakes bigger! No, we'll stop at a shoe store, then I can buy a little leash for you, too. Because you and I have just got to travel together from now on." He looked down at the little skunk. "You know, little tike, you've been great company for me on this miserable, hungry, dark journey. Yes, sir, and I've become mighty fond of you. You and I just have to stay together from now on."

That was the day when they shared the last pancake together. They were too hungry for a half, and half of one half. They ate the whole pancake. The old tomato can was dry. It wasn't even damp any more. The tramp could not shake out so much as a drop to give to the little skunk.

That day the tramp did not chuckle any more. He hardly talked. He did not hum. Only once all that day did he say anything, and then it was to warn the little skunk to be mouse quiet, because the train was rolling into a station in another town. "Just this time yet," he pleaded. "Just this time we'll be real quiet. You know, I could bang on the door, and they'd come to let us out, but they'd march me straight to jail." He peered at the little skunk. "We can hold out this day, can't we? I'd much rather be hungry and thirsty and free—than full of food and water in a jail. And you would be, too, because even if they wouldn't put you in jail, they might put you in a zoo. And that's no better than a jail!"

This time when the train finally rolled out of the town, the tramp did not point out the stores. He was too miserable from thirst and hunger. The little skunk, even though the floor was rocking and banging, made many trips to the pocket where the pancakes had been. It still smelled of pancakes, but in it there was not a crumb. The little skunk crawled in the tomato can and licked the bottom.

"It's bedtime," the tramp said shortly when he saw that. "It had better be bedtime! We'd better sleep, if we can." He hastily took his shoes off.

The slow old train rolled on all through that night, and the tramp did manage to sleep a little in spite of hunger and thirst. But when he woke up early in the morning there were strange sounds inside the boxcar. Sharp nibbling, gnawing sounds. He could hear them above the noise of the boxcar. "Hey, mice!" the startled tramp said. "Don't tell me—mice have got more sense than to get on a car where there isn't even a crumb."

It was the little skunk. The little skunk was sitting in his shoe, gnawing and nibbling at the leather! "Aw," said the tramp, "it's come to that! Well, at the next stop they ought to open that door, they can't leave it shut forever. And then we'll take our chance, little tike. I'll put you in

my pocket, and we'll jump out and run. Listen! Doesn't it sound as if we're rolling into a town?"

The little skunk did not listen—he went on gnawing at the tough shoe leather. The tramp took the shoe away from him. "I'll need it if we're coming into a town, and if they open the door, and we have to make a run for it." But the little skunk looked up at the shoe so pitifully, the tramp did not have the heart to put it on his foot. "Here, then," he said gruffly, and he tore the tongue out of the shoe. "Here, chew on that, I can get along without it. I know how you feel, it just feels better to be chewing on something. Remind me next time to buy better-tasting shoes."

The tramp was suddenly quiet. The train had stopped. The tramp got to his feet, he stood listening hopefully. Soon there were sounds—great sounds, hopeful sounds, great noises all along the train. It sounded as if all along the train the doors of the boxcars were being slid open. Somebody had started at the front and was going along the train opening up the boxcars. The noise of sliding doors came closer and closer.

"Now," whispered the tramp, "now at last it sounds like we're going to be set free. But now you've got to help me, little tike. I'm going to set you right before the door, then when they slide it open—there you'll sit. And if I know anything, whoever it is that's opening the doors, when he sees a skunk, he'll run. That'll be my chance. I'll scoop you up and stick you in my pocket, and then I'll run. Then we'll soon find food and water!" He stopped to listen. "Hush, now," he cautioned. "And stay right at that door!"

The tramp pressed himself against the wall next to the door. He waited. The door of the boxcar ahead slid open with a squealing, grinding sound. "Now," said the tramp to himself.

Outside the boxcar a man's voice could be heard. The man was right outside the door, mumbling to himself. The tramp held his breath. But the mumbling went away, and then the door of the boxcar right behind slid open with a squeal.

"No!" said the tramp. "No, they didn't pass us up again!" But already the door of a farther boxcar slid open.

The disappointed tramp stood listening. Then he looked down at the little skunk where he should be sitting, but the little skunk wasn't at the door. Tiny gnawing sounds came from the dark corner—the little skunk had gone back to the leather tongue. "Aw," said the tramp, "that does it. This can't go on—eating shoe leather! We've got to get out. Okay, I'll take my chances, and if I can get away, I'll be back to pick you up. But if I take you with me and I get caught, then we're both caught. So we'll see." He went to the door, he started pounding on it with all his might. "Let me out! Let me out!" he yelled as loud as he could.

Feet came running along the wooden loading platform just outside the boxcar. A man's voice yelled for other men to come. More feet pounded on the hollow-sounding platform. And then the stuck door of the boxcar was wrenched open by many hands. The big tramp tried to make a leap out of the boxcar over the open space between the loading platform and the doorway, but he had been in the dark so long, the sudden light blinded him. Before he could jump three men had jumped into the boxcar. They grabbed the tramp. He struggled, he wrestled, he threw himself and the three men all over that boxcar. But he was too weak from hunger to tear himself away from three big men. He broke away once and ran to the corner where the scared little skunk sat, but the men seized him again.

In the running and rolling and wrestling all over the boxcar, nobody noticed the confused little skunk. He was pushed here, and shoved there, and then he was shoved right over the edge of the doorway. He fell! He fell between the doorway and the loading platform. He landed under the boxcar.

Nobody noticed, for now in the boxcar the three men had overpowered the tramp. Now they were leading him away down the long loading platform. They were taking him to jail.

At the far end of the loading platform, there were steps that led down to the street. The men were going to lead the tramp down those steps. But just before they came to the steps, the tramp took a sudden, sideways, flying leap right over the edge of the high platform—down into the street. The sudden jump tore him out of the grasp of two of the men, the other man went down with him. They rolled over and over in the street. But the tramp was up first, and then the tramp was free. On his long legs he went flying across the street, into an alley, around a corner, and then the tramp was gone.

The three men chased him, but on his long legs the tramp easily outran them all. The three gave up. They came back to the loading platform, they stopped and peered into the empty boxcar. All three were breathing heavily. "Well, well, that was quite a way to start the day," one of them said, panting. "I'm all tuckered out already."

"So am I," said another voice. "And this is supposed to be a holiday. It's Labor Day today, isn't it? Labor—is right! That tramp sure put up a fight. And how that man can run!"

Under the boxcar the little skunk sat listening to the voices. They moved away, and then the sound of feet and voices disappeared into the railroad station. Everything was quiet. Under the boxcar the little skunk sat listening and waiting. He was waiting for the tramp. Nothing happened. There were no footsteps, the voice of the tramp did not come. Still the little skunk waited. The tramp did not come.

At last the little confused skunk began poking and circling and sniffing under the boxcar. He was searching for the footsteps of the tramp, the way he had always done in the little wood up North. But here were no leaves and grass, here were only bricks. Here were only town smells. The little skunk did not understand town smells.

He circled and searched. There were no footsteps. But he *had* to find the footsteps. If he found the footsteps, the footsteps would lead him back to the tramp, and the tramp would lead him back to the little wood that was his home. Back to the clear, cool-water creek, for he was terribly thirsty. Back to the stumps where he could dig for grubs, for he was terribly hungry. Back to the nest of leaves in the hollow stump, for he was terribly lost. Back to his home! He was a little skunk, he did not understand that since he had been on the train for nights and days, that he was hundreds and hundreds of miles from home.

And since he did not understand about trains, and hundreds and hundreds of miles, the little skunk stopped circling and searching uselessly under the boxcar. He had decided to go home! He walked from under the boxcar, he walked into the street. In the middle of the street, the little skunk found rails! He gurgled at the rails, for he knew rails. He had often followed the rails back home when he had wandered from his little wood. But these were not the rails of a railroad siding beside a little wood up North. These were streetcar rails! And these rails merely led down the main street of this town—into the heart of town. The little skunk did not know that. The little skunk was sure that now at last he was going home. In spite of hunger and in spite of thirst, he gurgled happily—a tiny, little gurgle—as he followed the streetcar rail that led him into the town.

. . . .

"There's a tramp loose in town," the steam-shovel man shouted.

"A tramp loose in town? Isn't it bad enough to have a skunk loose in town?" the alarmed mayor shouted back. "Throw the fellow in jail!"

The news went traveling up Main Street. "The mayor says to throw the tramp in jail."

There everything stood while the mayor's words went traveling up Main Street until they reached the streetcar. Then after a while the news came traveling back from the streetcar: "Tell the mayor the tramp got away. He was too fast, his legs were too long—nobody could catch him." The steam-shovel man shouted it to the mayor. "The tramp is gone. They couldn't catch him. He's gone—they think he ran clear out of town."

"Couldn't catch him!" the mayor fumed. "Well, all right. If that tramp is out of town, let's get that skunk out of town, and get on with our Labor Day parade. Let's get on with it."

"The mayor says to get on with it," the steam-shovel man bellowed up the street. "Never mind the tramp."

There the words went from car to car, and mouth to mouth: "On with it. On with it. Never mind the tramp."

At last the distant words reached the streetcar, the streetcar started up, then the long row of cars started up. Everything began to move again. This time everything could move quite a way, for all the time that things had been standing still, the little skunk had hurried right ahead for water.

Now, with the long row of cars out of the way, the big steam shovel could at last make its turn into Main Street. After the steam shovel, the jeep, the bulldozer, the farmer and his wagon, and last of all the crawling fire engine, could all turn into Main Street. But now that everything was moving at last, everybody became excited, everybody cheered and shouted.

It was a racket and a din, and it alarmed the little skunk. Never had he heard such a noise and such a racket—not even on the rattlebang train. He did not like it, he was afraid of it, but since he was a slow little skunk—too slow to run away from it—he did the only thing he could do. He stopped and turned to face it! He raised his warning tail straight up, he quirked and quirked his warning tail!

The motorman saw it. He hastily stopped the streetcar. When the streetcar stopped, everything stopped. When everything stood still, there was nothing to shout and cheer about, so then everything became quiet. When everything was quiet, the little skunk turned and hurried down the track to find himself some water.

The moment the little skunk went ahead, the streetcar started up. Everything started up. But the moment everything moved again, everybody became excited again. Everybody started cheering and shouting, blowing horns, roaring motors, clanging bells, shrieking sirens.

The little skunk stopped. The little skunk turned. Up came his warning tail! Everything stopped again.

Now that the fire engine was on Main Street, the mayor on the high seat could see what was the trouble. He could see something had to be done, but he did not know what to do, he did not know about skunks.

The farmer standing on the wagon could see what was the trouble, too. "Mister Mayor, Mister Mayor, sir, I've got a plan," the farmer said politely. "And it's the only way to keep the little skunk moving. If you will back out of my way, I'll turn around and go up an alley and get on Main Street between the streetcar and the skunk. Then, with my horses I'll keep the little skunk moving. I'm a farmer and I know about skunks. Skunks don't mind horses, and horses don't mind skunks. They often see each other when the horses are in pasture—they know each other. So when Faber and Elizabeth come clopping on behind the little skunk, he won't be alarmed about all the noise any more, and they will keep him moving."

"Fine, fine," the mayor shouted. "Would you do that? If you'll do that for me, then I'll let you ride in our Labor Day parade."

When the farmer heard that now at last, after ten long years, he was going to ride in the Labor Day parade, the farmer became all excited. He hardly waited for the fire engine to back up, he squeezed his horses from between the fire engine

and the bulldozer, he turned them down the side street, he turned them into an alley. When they got in the alley the farmer stood up in the wagon, and shouted so excitedly that his two old horses really flew. The sparks flew. But when they turned into Main Street between the streetcar and the little skunk, the whispering farmer slowed his two old horses to a crawl, so as not to alarm the little skunk. They hardly moved, they hardly lifted their heavy feet as they swung ahead of the streetcar and fell in line behind the skunk.

The little skunk heard the two old horses coming. The little skunk smelled the smell of horses, and gurgled happily—a tiny, little gurgle. He liked the smell of horses, he liked horses—horses were his friends.

Faber and Elizabeth walked sedately on behind the skunk. They lowered their big old heads to look at the skunk. They did not mind the little skunk right before their noses. In fact, they liked the little skunk much better than the oily, machinery smell of the big bulldozer. Faber and Elizabeth had often seen skunks at night by moonlight in their pasture. They liked skunks because skunks were slow and poky—not jumpy and scary in the shadowy, moonlit pasture.

The two old horses clopped on behind the skunk. The little skunk hurried ahead as fast as

a little skunk can hurry, for he was very thirsty.

The little skunk hurried along. The horses clopped along. The streetcar crawled on behind the old farm wagon and the quiet farmer. The cars came creeping on behind the crawling streetcar. Everything came on. But now the fire chief did not clang his bell and shriek his siren, horns did not blow, motors did not roar, people did not cheer and shout. The mayor had forbidden it. The farmer had not heard the mayor's order, but he knew enough to be quiet, now that he was right behind the skunk. He knew about skunks!

In the new quiet, the little skunk hurried down the streetcar track. But all of a sudden there wasn't any more streetcar track. And then there wasn't any more street. Instead, there was a country road. And when there was no more track, and no more street—there was no more town. Instead, there was the quiet, lovely country.

When he saw the lovely country the little skunk sat down. He gurgled at the quiet country. He gurgled at the country and at the little country road, and at the lovely country smells. Here were no town smells and town noises. Here was the smell of trees and grass, of cows and sheep in pastures. And the little skunk got up to go into the lovely country.

The road went straight, the little skunk went straight—straight down the road that led into the country.

Behind him in the little town down south in warm Virginia, the streetcar had reached the end of the track, and there the streetcar had to stop. Then everything and everybody had to stop. But nobody turned away, everybody stayed to watch a little skunk, with his happy, bushy tail straight up, march off into the country. Only the quiet farmer and his two old heavy horses still kept on behind the skunk, to help the little skunk get deep into the country.

And then—then there was a bend in the road. The road went around a bend, the little skunk went around the bend in the road. But the farmer quietly turned his horses there and started to go back to the town.

The crowd at the end of Main Street all saw the little skunk marching around the distant bend. Then nobody could keep quiet any

longer. The people shouted and cheered, the streetcar clanged its warning bell, the car horns blew and blasted, the steam shovel and the bulldozer roared and rumbled, and the fire chief clanged his bell and twirled his shrieking siren. But the mayor grabbed the shotgun, and shot the single shell into the air. Now they could hold their Labor Day parade!

The little skunk heard the distant noise and racket, but he paid it no attention, for now the noise was far away, and he was in the country. He heard the horses going away, and now he heard the farmer begin shouting to his horses. "Giddap, Faber! Giddyap, Elizabeth! Now we're going to ride in the parade! Giddap, Faber! Giddyap, Elizabeth! You and I are in the parade." How those two old horses ran. They liked parades. It was much better than plowing.

The little skunk went on alone around the bend in the little road.

At the bend in the little road, there was a narrow country lane. And because the lane went straight out from the bend, and because the little skunk was going straight, the little skunk went down the lane. He left the road and took the lane. But that was good! And that was right! For it was a long lane, and a straight lane, and it did not have a single turning. And since the little skunk was going straight, he would go straight down that straight lane. And at the end of that long lane—there was a wood! There was a little wood, and in that wood there was a creek, and there were trees, and fallen trees, and stumps of trees long gone. The clear, cool-water creek in the wood wound in and out between the trees, it gurgled under fallen trees, it curled around the stumps of trees long gone.

The little skunk did not know that. The little near-sighted skunk could not see that far. He could not even smell that far. But because the lane went straight without a single turning, the little skunk would also go straight—straight to the little wood, and to the clear, cool-water creek.

At last the little skunk was half way down the lane. And suddenly he rose up on his hind legs like a squirrel. He crinkled his nose, he sniffed and sniffed the air. He did not smell the little wood and the clear, cool-water creek—he could not smell that far. No, he smelled something else. And at what he smelled that little skunk gurgled and gurgled. Something came drifting on the air over the fields and down the lane. It was smoke! And in the smoke the little skunk smelled something—he smelled coffee. Then he smelled something else—he smelled pancakes frying. He smelled bacon. Pancakes and bacon!

The little skunk dropped to his feet to hurry down the lane toward the lovely odors. But as he hurried farther down the lane, suddenly the little skunk smelled something else. This wasn't on the air, this wasn't far away! This was right before his nose. This was a footstep, and then another big footstep. These were footsteps coming from the field into the lane, and going down the lane. Big footsteps, far-apart footsteps—the footsteps of a long-legged man. Oh, how that little skunk gurgled! Oh, how that little skunk hurried from one invisible footstep to the next invisible footstep going down that country lane. He crinkled and crinkled his little nose. He gurgled.

In the little wood, on the bank of the clear, cool-water creek, a tramp was sitting by a fire. He was frying pancakes on a piece of tin over the little fire. Above the fire hung a tomato can. The tramp was also making coffee. The tramp was also frying bacon—pancakes and bacon. But now he rose to peer under the trees and spy out the fields to see that nobody had followed him from the town to throw him into jail. He looked across the hills and fields and pastures, but nowhere did anything move. He looked down the lane! At what he saw coming down that lane, the big tramp had to lean against a tree and laugh and laugh and chuckle.

"Well, I'll be kicked! Well, I'll be kicked," he softly told himself. "Don't tell me. Don't tell me that that's the little tike following my footsteps down the lane. Well, I'll be kicked—the little smarty-pants. I told him we had to stay together!"

The big tramp leaned against the tree, and watched and waited for the little skunk. He waited with his pancakes and his bacon for the little skunk to come. He leaned against the tree and chuckled. "Well, I'll be kicked," he said again. "Didn't I tell him that from now on we had to stay and travel together?" He slapped his two coat pockets! "That's it! That's it!" he said

excitedly. "One pocket for my pancakes—one for my little skunk! From this time on, we live and travel together." And then the tramp leaned back against the tree and laughed and chuckled loud and long.

Down the long lane came the little skunk, hurrying as fast as a little skunk can hurry. Oh, it would take him long, because the lane was long. But the long lane had no turning, and he would get there sure. Oh, he would get there sure!

And when at last he got there, the little skunk would have his tramp, and he would have a home. The little skunk would have a home again in a little wood with a clear, cool-water creek, and trees, and stumps of trees long gone, where he could dig for grubs. He would have a little wood home almost exactly like his little wood home up North. But this winter his little wood home would not be far up North in the cold, blizzard country, where winter came down, and the snow and ice heaped ten feet deep. This time his home would be down south in warm Virginia!

Down the long lane hurried the little gurgling skunk, as fast as a little skunk can hurry. Oh, he was slow as slow, but he would surely get there. Oh, he would surely get there! For he was following the footsteps.

from KILDEE HOUSE

Rutherford Montgomery

This opening chapter of Kildee House *should lead straight into the book. It is a tender and amusing story about Jerome Kildee's problems in preventing the animals from taking over his house entirely and in resolving the enmity between two strong-minded young neighbors.*

[Mr. Kildee Makes Friends with Old Grouch]

Jerome Kildee had built himself a house on the mountainside. It was an odd house because Jerome Kildee was an odd man. He built his house under a giant redwood tree on Windy

Point. Since the days of Julius Caesar creatures had been building homes at the foot of the redwood or in its branches. At the time Jerome built his house most folks did not build on knobs high on a mountainside, even the round-topped, wooded mountains of the Pacific Coast Range.

What the neighbors said or what they thought was of no concern to Jerome. The day he walked out on Windy Point, and looked up at the giant redwood towering into the sky, and stood savoring the deep silence, he knew he was going to stay. When he turned from the great tree and looked down over the green ridges, the smoky valley, into the gray-white haze of the Pacific, he smiled. This was a land of silence, the place for a silent man.

The house Jerome built was not as wide as the redwood; to have made it so wide would have been a waste of space, because Jerome did not need that much room. He toted the biggest window he could buy to the cabin, and set it in the wall which faced a panorama of ridges and valleys. The window was as high as the wall; it was

one wall as far across as the door. It had been rolled out as a plate-glass window for a store.

The back wall was the redwood trunk. It made an odd house, one wall curved inward, and finished with shaggy redwood bark. Jerome rented a horse and packed Monterey stone up for a fireplace. The fireplace was a thing of beauty. It filled one end of the room. The cream Monterey stone, traced through with threads of red, was carefully fitted and matched for grain; the hearth was wide, and the mantel was inlaid with chips of abalone shell. It was the last piece of stonework Jerome planned to make, and he made it a masterpiece. In a recess back of the last slab of stone he tucked away the tools of his trade and sealed them into the wall. Jerome Kildee, maker of fine monuments was no more. There remained only Jerome Kildee, philosopher, a silent little man, seeking to become a part of a silent mountain.

Jerome Kildee did not work. He owned the hundred acres of woods and hillside around him, but he did not clear any of it. He bought all of his food, and he had stove and fireplace wood hauled up and stacked outside his door. Jerome hired the Eppys to haul the wood to the bottom of the hill, then up the hill with their tractor because there was only a winding footpath up from his mailbox. The Eppys laughed and made quite a bit of it. Jerome had hundreds of cords of oak and madroña close to his cabin. The farmer and his sons would have cut it and sawed it for a tenth of what Jerome paid for the wood and the hauling.

Jerome had no near neighbors, nor would he ever have any, because he had built in the exact center of his hundred acres. He had gone through life silent, unable to talk to people, expecting them to leave him to his own thoughts. He had never visited the Eppy family after they hauled his wood, although they lived at the foot of his hill on the north side. They put him down as a queer one. The nine Eppys, as they were known locally, were robust folks. The six sons were all over six feet tall. Emma Lou would someday be almost as tall as her brothers. The Cabot place, at the foot of the mountain on the other side of the hill, was certainly not a place where Jerome would care to go. It was a fine estate with landscaped gardens and a swimming pool. The Cabots had one son, Donald Roger, who had never given Jerome more than a brief look.

But Jerome Kildee found he was not without friends. He had a host of friends and he didn't have to talk to them to keep their friendship. In fact, his silence helped to keep them friendly. They were all interested in him, a new experience for Jerome, and he was interested in them. Jerome found that they were not unlike the people back where he had operated his monument shop. They were willing to take advantage of him, they were selfish, and some of them were thieves, like the trade rats who packed off anything they could carry, regardless of whether or not they could use it. He soon learned that none of the raccoons could be trusted inside the cabin. They unscrewed the caps off ketchup bottles as easily as he could do it; they unlatched cupboard doors or opened them if there was a knob on them. One old raccoon, who was the neighborhood grouch, lived in a hole in the trunk of his redwood tree. Old Grouch had refused to move when Jerome built his house. He considered the redwood tree his tree. He made it clear to Jerome that he was trespassing.

The pair of spotted skunks who set up housekeeping under his floor were folks of a different sort from the raccoons. They were not dull-witted stinkers of the sort Jerome had known in his boyhood, dumb fellows who for ages had been depending upon poison gas instead of their wits for protection. They carried guns but seldom used them. The little spotted skunks were as smart as the raccoons, and about as curious. They had a real sense of humor and were always playing pranks on the raccoons. With them around, Jerome always had to get down on his hands and knees and explore the chimney of his fireplace before he built a fire. The skunks liked the fireplace and would gladly have traded it for their nest under the floor. They were not big stinkers like the swamp skunks, so Jerome could always fish them out of the chimney with his broom.

Jerome would probably have been crowded out of his house by the assortment of mice that found his house and the fine bark wall of the redwood to their liking if it had not been for the spotted skunks. The skunks had large appetites,

so they kept the mouse population on an even keel. Two big wood mice lived in a bark nest back of a knot in the tree trunk. They furnished dinners for the spotted skunks with a regularity which should have become monotonous. How they could go on having big families, nursing them to a size to go out into the world, only to have them gobbled up one at a time as they left the nest, was more than Jerome could understand.

There was another pair of mice who lived under his bed in a box of old letters, which they made good use of without snooping into the contents, or trying to figure out why Jerome had tied them in bundles. They chewed up all of the letters except those written in indelible pencil. This removed from Jerome's life any desire to brood over the past. The spotted skunks could not get into the box. The mice went in through a knothole in the end. But their families suffered the same fate as the wood mice. And they went on having big families.

Jerome's wooded acres harbored many black-tailed deer and many gray foxes and possums. The foxes never made friends, and the possums ignored him because he never kept chickens. They had no bump of curiosity to draw them to his house. He saw them often and had a nodding acquaintance with them, so to speak. The black-tails visited his garbage pit regularly. The does often brought their fawns into his yard. But they did not bother much with him because he did not grow a garden or set out young fruit trees. He was about like any other dweller on the wooded mountain: he just lived there.

It was during the second year that Old Grouch turned the head of a dainty little miss. She was just sixteen months old, and like many another lass before her, she fell in love with a good-for-nothing. Old Grouch brought her to his nest in the redwood. It was high up on the tree where a burl formed a deep pocket. Old Grouch had learned that a redwood tree was a safe haven. When coon dogs chased him, followed by yelling humans, all he had to do was shinny up the giant tree. The hunters could not shake him out or climb the tree. Of course after Jerome came, the coon dogs and the hunters stayed away.

Old Grouch brought his bride home in January during the heavy rains. In April she presented him with a family. Like many another good-for-nothing, Old Grouch failed to provide for his family, though he did share the nest with them, taking the dry side and grabbing any of the food she rustled which suited his taste. Jerome couldn't climb the tree to look into the nest, but he heard the babies and listened to the family chitchat over them.

Old Grouch mildly irritated Jerome. He was smug and fat, always ready to march into the cabin and demand part of Jerome's fried egg or lamb chop, but never thanking his host for anything, and always staying outside unless there was food. Any friendly advance was always met with a snarl or a snapping of white fangs. He was a surly fellow, but Jerome admired the way he had with the ladies.

His wife was of a different sort. She was friendly and thankful to Jerome for bits of food he gave her. She visited the cabin while he was in it, and not just when it was mealtime. She would have taken over his larder if he had allowed it. Her willingness to shift Old Grouch's responsibility for the family to him gave Jerome a problem. He was forced to invent new catches for his cupboard doors, and to fashion latches for his pull drawers.

Outwitting the slim little bride was no easy matter. With feminine wile she made up to Jerome, letting him stroke her head and scratch around her ears, smiling coyly up at him as he sat in his padded chair, but raiding his cupboard as sure as he went for a walk. Jerome fixed inside catches for the doors worked by wires which went up through the inside of the cupboard and were pulled by strings dangling from the ceiling, well out of reach of a raccoon. The pull drawers became pop-out drawers worked by wires with dangling strings attached to them. Jerome's house was well decorated with strings hanging from the ceiling. A large button dangled at the end of each string like a black spider.

When Jerome wanted an egg for breakfast he pulled a string, and open popped a drawer exposing the egg carton. Then Jerome always had to take out two eggs because the minute the door popped open in popped Mrs. Grouch, and Jerome had to split fifty-fifty with her. He could have closed and barred the door, but then he would have had to sit by the big window eating his egg with Mrs. Grouch's furry bangs pressed against the plate glass, her bright eyes watching every bite he took, her little tongue dripping hungrily.

The rains lasted a long time that spring, keeping on until June. Mrs. Grouch stood the home her old man had provided for her as long as she could. The babies were growing and taking up more room, the roof leaked, and Old Grouch always took the dry side. When the wind blew from the north there might as well have been no roof at all. One afternoon while Jerome was tramping in the woods, snug in oilskins and rubber boots, she moved her babies into the house. Helping herself to the stuffing in his mattress, she made a nest in the oven. She had long ago learned how to open the oven door. The smell of the oven pleased her. It had a faint food smell which was elegant. She could feed her babies and lick the oven walls, nibbling bits of burned meat as she came to them.

Jerome discovered the family at once because the oven door was open. He did not scold about the mattress when she showed him her brood of silky raccoons. But he was hungry and this was Saturday afternoon. Jerome always fixed a beef roast for Saturday supper. Once a week the mailman left the meat in his mailbox at the foot of the hill. Jerome got a wooden box and put it in a corner, then he moved the family. Mrs. Grouch was miffed, but she accepted the change with a sly smile. Later she would slip her family back into the oven.

Old Grouch stamped up on the porch and seated himself in the open doorway. He scolded his wife in proper style; he glared at Jerome and tossed a few nasty cracks at him. Between growls he kept sniffing the roast cooking in the oven, and shaking his fur to get the raindrops off it. With a final warning to his wife he turned about, climbed the redwood trunk, and got into his nest. The wind was from the north, and his wife was not there to keep the rain off his back. He stayed in the nest for half an hour, then he climbed back down the tree trunk and walked to the door. Jerome grinned at him. He was cutting the roast. He sliced off a piece and laid it on a saucer. He set the saucer on the floor.

Old Grouch looked at the saucer. This was

dangerous business. Going into a cabin was like stepping into a box trap. But he was wet and cold; his wife had walked out on him. He needed food and warmth. Ruffling his scruff, he walked into the house. He paused at the saucer and sniffed the good smell of the roast. He took a bite. When Mrs. Grouch scurried across the floor to share with him, he caught up the piece of meat in his forepaws. He sat up and glowered at her. Then he began munching the roast. His wife sniffed eagerly. She looked up at Jerome. He handed her a slice of meat. She took it and seated herself beside her husband. They sat there eating very much like humans, using their small hands to tear bits of meat from the large pieces, then stuffing the bits into their mouths.

By the time Jerome had finished his supper Old Grouch had made up his mind. He had marched to the door three times, and each time the cold rain had spattered into his face. He knew his wife and babies were going to sleep warm and dry inside the cabin. She had already returned to the box, where she sat with her small black eyes just above the edge. Old Grouch felt he could do with some more roast, too. He was still a bit hungry. He would stay in the cabin.

After the dishes were washed Jerome lighted his pipe. He was faced with a new problem. He had been trying for weeks to get Old Grouch into the cabin. Now that the old fellow and his family had moved in he dared not close the door. If he closed the door it was hard to say what Old Grouch would do. Jerome was sure it would be pretty wild.

But the night air was growing chilly. The wind was blowing into the room, wet and cold. Even if he did chase Old Grouch out into the rain he couldn't put Mrs. Grouch and the babies out. Jerome got to his feet. Old Grouch took one look at Jerome towering above him, then scuttled out into the night.

Jerome set the gasoline mantel lamp on the table so the white light would flood the door. He got his tool chest from under the bed. Mrs. Grouch kept her eyes just above the edge of the box. Jerome cut a small door in the bottom of his big door. He swung the small door by a pair of butterfly hinges and bored three holes in it.

As he gathered up his saw and auger and screw driver Jerome realized that the little door would offer welcome to any and all who roamed. It would mean keeping open house to all, except, of course, those neighbors too big to squeeze through the little door. He had never been able to make friends; it might be that the little door would change everything. He took the lamp and examined the chimney of his fireplace. The little skunks were not sleeping on the damper, so he lighted the fire he had laid earlier in the day. Pulling his padded chair up to the fireplace, he set his tobacco jar on the chair arm. As an afterthought he got a saucer and stacked a few squares of roast on it. He set the saucer on the floor beside the chair.

Jerome puffed slowly on his pipe. He watched the red tongues of flame lick around the oak and madroña logs in the fireplace. The beating warmth made him feel drowsy. He was on his second pipe when Old Grouch solved the mystery of the little door. He had peeped in through the three holes and discovered that Jerome had turned out the gasoline lamp, that his wife was snug and dry in the box with the babies. He sniffed and caught the rich smell of roast beef. He was wet and cold. He eased through the little door just as his wife hopped from the box, carrying one of the babies. She had her teeth set in the scruff. Shaking the water from his fur, he watched her put the youngster into the oven. He scowled at her, but he didn't make a sound. The warmth of the fireplace and the smell of the roast in the saucer drew him. He moved warily toward the fire. His experience with men had made him wary. But he was cold and he had an idea he could eat some more. Seating himself in the deep shadows near the chair, he stretched his snout toward the dish. He kept his eyes on Jerome. When Jerome did not move Old Grouch eased forward and picked up a piece of meat. He sat up and began munching it.

Mrs. Grouch had finished transferring her babies to the oven. She sat on the door for a while, watching the two males at the fireplace. Shaking her head, she turned her back upon them and curled up with her brood.

Jerome had never been able to talk with people. He had always known he was missing a great deal, but he had never been able to say the weather was nice or that the weather was bad when people came into his shop. He set his pipe on the arm of the chair and tossed another log on the fire Old Grouch ducked into a patch of deep shadow, but he came out again and got another piece of meat. The warmth of the fire was beating against his fur. He felt contented and happy. Jerome leaned back and spoke out loud. When he spoke the sound of his voice startled even himself. Old Grouch, now gorged with roast and sleepy from the heat, toppled off the hearth and had to make quite an effort to right himself. Mrs. Grouch thrust her head out of the oven and stared at Jerome wildly. If it had not been for her babies she would have fled into the night.

"When I came up here I was licked," Jerome had said. It was as though a stranger had spoken to him; he heard his own voice so seldom. He felt called upon to answer the stranger.

"And were you licked?"

Old Grouch batted his eyes fearfully. He looked all around the room but saw no human being except Jerome, whom he had ceased to consider a man, because Jerome never shouted or whistled or talked at all.

"I've spent a lifetime carving cherubs and angels on tombstones. I've cut many a nice sentiment on a gravestone, but never was able to recite a single line before company." Jerome pointed his pipestem toward the fire. "It's a sad business, dealing with sad people, and not being able to say a word to comfort them."

Old Grouch braced himself and let his stomach ease down until he was resting comfortably. He had room for a bite or two more, and the fire was very nice. Jerome smiled down at him. Old Grouch looked like a small bandit with the black patches which circled his eyes and extended along his cheeks like black bands, making a perfect mask against the lighter coloring of his fur. He cocked his head. He was in a mellow mood. His stomach was full to bursting; his furry hide was warm. He felt like singing.

He started out with a soft "Shur-r-r-r," then went into a deeper note, a long-drawn, tremulous "Whoo-oo-oo," not unlike the call of a screech owl, only softer and sweeter, much more mellow. Jerome's smile widened. He had never dared venture a note himself. In all of the hundreds of times he had sat alone in his pew in church he had never dared open his mouth and sing.

"I have missed much," he said.

"Whoo-oo-oo," Old Grouch sang, his head swaying sleepily.

From the oven door came an answering trill. Never had Mrs. Grouch heard her husband put so much tenderness, so much romance into his song. It touched her deeply, so deeply she closed her eyes and sang back to him. Jerome laid down his pipe.

Turning to catch the high soprano from the oven, Jerome noticed that the little door was bobbing back and forth. He fixed his attention upon it. A small head with black shoe-button eyes appeared. The head moved into the room, followed by a slim body. A moment later another slim body moved through the door. Two tall white plumes lifted. The little spotted skunks had come visiting. Papa waved his plume and stamped his feet; Mama waved her plume and stamped her feet. Like a good host, Jerome arose from his chair. Instantly the two little skunks vanished through the door. Jerome filled a saucer with canned milk and set it near the door, then he went back to his chair before the fire.

Almost at once the little door opened and the skunks marched in. They sat down and began lapping eagerly. When Mrs. Grouch hopped off the oven door and started toward the saucer, Papa elevated his plume and stamped his forefeet. He rushed at her, did a handstand, flipped his hind feet down again, then stamped some more. Mrs. Grouch knew what that meant, as did every other living thing in the woods. She hastily retreated to the oven door. Papa went back to his milk.

Jerome leaned back in his chair. Old Grouch was in full voice now; his whoo-oo-oo was deep and bell-like. Jerome tried an experimental note himself. He was amazed at its quality. It was a baritone note with feeling and depth in it. But it sent Mrs. Grouch scrambling back into the oven; Papa and Mama left without waiting to stamp their feet. Only Old Grouch was not startled at all. He just sat and swayed back and forth and sang. He seemed to have caught the fine flavor of Jerome's baritone. Jerome tried a few more notes. Mrs. Grouch stayed in the oven;

the spotted skunks stayed under the floor. Old Grouch picked up the last square of roast and ate it slowly. When he swallowed it his stomach bulged bigger. He cocked an eye at Jerome. Jerome tried a few hymns he remembered. Old Grouch joined in. He had only one song, but it blended well with any hymn.

After a bit Jerome began to feel sleepy. He was sleepy and he was happy. He leaned back and closed his eyes. Old Grouch yawned. He ambled toward the oven door. After two tries he managed to hop up on the door. Easing into the oven, he curled up with his family. Jerome sighed deeply. Here among friends he could talk about things he had always wanted to talk about, and he could sing when he felt like it. He got to his feet and took his flannel nightgown from its hook. He smiled as he got ready for bed.

from MASKED PROWLER

John L. and Jean George

John L. George in this talented husband and wife team is a zoologist, and his wife is an artist. Both write, and their books reveal a special sympathy for the creatures man hunts so relentlessly. But the authors are realists too, and the uneven battle of wits between hunter and hunted is not softened. In this chapter, Procyon, a young raccoon, has his first encounter with his lifelong enemies, the hunting dogs. The price of life is eternal vigilance, but Procyon triumphs grandly in the end. Don't miss Vulpes, the Red Fox *and* Meph, the Pet Skunk *by the Georges.*

[First Adventures of a Young Raccoon]

When the hay was baled and stored in the mow, the harvesting of the oat crop began. All day the whisk of the binder sounded across the field. At ten minutes to five Joe looked at his big gold pocket watch.

"What time do you have, Gib?" he called.

"Five to five," the farmer answered. Joe's watch was always clogged with chaff and grit from the fields, and at least once a day it

stopped. He shook it, set the hands and mumbled, "About chore time."

He turned away from the fields and walked toward the barn. The cows were in the barnyard waiting to be fed and milked. Joe opened the east door and they filed into the barn and each walked to her own stall. He took down the electric milking machines and was well along with the chores when Gib came into the barnyard with the team. He unhitched the horses from the binder and gave them a spank on their broad haunches to let them know they were free. They galloped ponderously to the water tank and from there to their stalls. Gib joined Joe in the barn.

"The white cow didn't come up from the woods," Joe said as he poured a bucket of foamy milk through the strainer.

"She's about due to calf," the farmer said. "If she's got a calf we'd better go back and get her now, or she'll hide it in the underbrush, and it will take us a couple of hours to find it."

They finished the milking and started to the woods. As they opened the gate in the lane, Fanny, the Blue Tick hound, trotted around the grainery to join them. She dashed ahead, searching for meadow mice, but waited for them at the end of the lane.

The men separated in the forest. Joe walked to the woodland meadow, scouted the edges and started back to meet Gib at the sugar house.

"Ka Bos, Ka Bos," he would call from time to time to the cow.

Gib was standing motionless at the corner of the shack. He was peering intently across the hill. Several howls from Fanny signaled the presence of some woodland creature.

"Coon family," Gib mumbled. "Four little ones and a big one." Clinging to the dipping limbs of a sugar maple were Procyon, his brother, sisters and mother. They were staring silently at Fanny barking below them.

"Here, Fanny, come on, come here!" Gib called. "Leave them alone, dog."

Fanny did not respond and he went to get her. She was jumping and clawing at the tree in an effort to climb to the limbs where the raccoons clung. Gib clutched her collar between bounds and looked steadily at the picture above him. Frightened by the man, the mother and two of the youngsters galloped higher into the tree. They disappeared in the dense foliage. The other two did not move, but with eyes and ears fixed curiously upon Fanny and then Gib, they stared down quietly.

Suddenly the raccoons had an unexpected ally. The missing cow rushed from a nearby thicket, lowered her head and charged Fanny. Gib released the hound and she dashed for shelter behind the sugar house. Joe heard the noise and came running. As he passed a raspberry and prickly ash thicket, he found the calf. He prodded it to its feet. The cow, still alarmed, bellowed and rushed him but she stopped short beside her calf. Each of the men picked up a stout club and expertly herded the cow toward the lane. She moved reluctantly stopping frequently to call her calf.

"Whey, Boss, Whey Boss. The calf will follow you, he'll follow," Joe told her. And the calf did follow although occasionally he found his untried legs too far apart to move. Joe would straighten him out with a lift from the rear and he would stumble after his mother.

At the edge of the woods Fanny trotted up to the heels of the men. The cow turned and charged the dog. Gib pushed her off with a well-timed shove on her nose.

"Go on home. Git!" He shouted at Fanny. The hound was only too happy to obey. She slipped under the fence and took the field route home.

Once in the lane, the cow started homeward with more willingness. The calf trotted behind her. Joe and Gib discussed the coon family as they herded the cow and the little bull up the lane.

"Weren't they nice little coons?"

"Sure were," Joe laughed. "Wonder where they came from."

"Whey Boss!" shouted Joe as the cow hesitated.

"Fanny brought them out of that old stream bed."

"Maybe there'll be good hunting this fall. Must be a lot more around."

And so they whooped and chatted as they drove the cow and the newest addition to the herd back to the barn. In the barn the cow headed for her stanchion with her calf at her heels. Gib let the calf nurse, then slipped a collar around its neck and tied it to the wall just behind the cow. The cow turned her head and bawled to her calf, who had now dropped on a pile of sweet yellow straw that Gib had thrown down for him.

Gib took the remaining milk from the cow by hand. It was a thick yellow fluid which she would give for several days. It was designed by nature to make the digestive tract of the new born calf begin its work. In a day or so the white milk would come. Gib did not put this fresh milk in with the milk from the other cows, for he could not send it to the dairy. What the calf did not need he fed to the hogs. After the ninth milking he would put the milk in with that of the herd.

Back in the woods the raccoon family relaxed as the men disappeared down the lane. Procyon had been one of the youngsters who had hidden in the leaves with his mother. His sister pushed close beside him, still hugging him and watching the dark tree so recently alive with a barking clawing hound. She shivered. As the forest quieted down, the mother raccoon whistled to her youngsters and descended to the forest floor. Procyon dug his foreclaws into the tree bark and pushed out from the limb. He swung like a pendulum a few times as he hung by his hands, then grabbed the tree with his hind feet, turned around head first and climbed to the earth. The family reassembled and trekked off to the great marsh that spread to the north of the forest.

Procyon left the group at the edge of the cat-tail border. He crossed a garden of wild iris, pushed through a relentless mat of sedges and came to a fallen cottonwood, four feet through, that had tumbled from the shore into the marsh. He scrambled up this and walked along it. Beneath him he could hear open water, and ripples lapping around the old tree.

Farther along the trunk he came to a massive limb that sloped downward into the grasses. In the fork of this limb, Procyon stopped. He had come upon the scat pile of a raccoon. He sniffed it, circled the pile with careful steps and followed the limb down to a basin of water. The smell of silt and mud filled his nose. Here he had the feel of pollywogs and frogs.

Procyon lifted his head. To his right the

grasses parted and a giant raccoon moved before him. Procyon could see his black mask and the bulging muscles of his forearms. The spread of that broad tapered face made Procyon back against the log.

The old raccoon surveyed the young hunter solemnly. He moved a few steps closer, sniffed him and stepped into the water. The marsh basin muddied as his feet moved nimbly among the roots and down into the muck. The little coon watched in fascination. He had known no other raccoon of comparable stature other than his mother. Even she had not such tremendous jaws. Her haunches were not as high, nor her wrists as large and powerful. Should this giant decide that Procyon was intruding, there would

be little scuffle, little battle. The power and force of those great legs gave him the right to anything in the marsh and woods.

Procyon did not retreat, rather he pushed up on his toes and walked gingerly into the water. Surprised by the audacity of the youngster's movements, the old coon stopped his fishing and looked up. He snarled gruffly and his white teeth made Procyon uneasy. The young coon knew it was useless to run. The old giant still paused as if wondering whether to permit this young one to remain. He seemed to be waiting for the scurry of the cub's retreat. Procyon dug his toes into the mud. He shifted his feet automatically, his eyes on the big raccoon.

There was a deep snarl—the great male had made a decision. He turned away and went back to his work. As he fished he waded off, paying no more attention to the young one. Procyon lost his fear, and once more admired the greatness of the hunter's size. Still eyeing him, he moved deeper into the water and searched the stem of a bull rush. From it he picked off a water snail and brought it up to his mouth. The old coon heard the shell crunch and turned around. Ferocity seemed to have left his face. Procyon stopped to listen more keenly for he thought he detected the murmur of a purr deep in that round chest. The old one moved on through the shallows.

Procyon watched him go, then turned to find his mother. He climbed back on the log and raced for the cattails and reeds where he had left her and his sisters and brother. He found them not far from the base of the log. They were whistling and calling as they rounded up for the trip home.

Tonight they did not return to the red oak. The mother led her family into a grove of basswoods and willows. Here she selected a tilted tree and took the four youngsters to a dry hollow about twenty feet above the ground. The cavity was deeper than the familiar one in the red oak. In fact, it seemed to the young coons that they climbed right back to the earth on the inside of the tree.

The bottom of the retreat was roomy and Procyon and his brother explored the cracks and crevices with their hands before settling down to sleep. When he had satisfied his curiosity about the interior of this marshland home, Procyon snuggled up to his mother for milk. There was none to be had. He pushed and shoved her, but he had had the last of his mother's milk that morning. This was as it should be, for the litter which had weighed little more than half a pound at birth, now weighed well over twenty pounds. The young cubs were ready to go without milk. For a month their mother had taught them how to find and eat other foods.

The family spent much of their time during late August at the basswood retreat in the marsh. Here Procyon often found the old male coon. He followed him, but the two were never intimate, for Procyon kept a respectful distance. The old coon taught the youngster many secrets of the marshes. Procyon tracked him to the elderberry bushes and the gooseberry bushes. Through the old one he became aware of a vast assortment of foods to be found in August.

On an afternoon late in August, Procyon and his bigger sister were wrestling in the bottom of the basswood den. The rest of the family were out on the limbs where they had sunned themselves during the day. His sister grew tired of the tumbling and rolling and meant to end the play. She bit Procyon sharply on the ear. He jumped on her, growled and returned her bite with a sound nip on the chest. She galloped up the tree. Procyon chased her out of the hole and down the outside. She stopped at the first limb. Procyon nipped her while hanging above her, then passed on down the tree and walked off to the gooseberry bushes.

He ate until he was contentedly full and stretched out to play on the back of an old log. He found a walnut and took it in his paws. Rolling around on his back he tossed it between his feet. He was twisting and biting it when the old coon came by. Procyon dropped his walnut and rolled off the log. He crouched against it looking at the hunter. Suddenly the marshland birds became silent.

The old coon was looking up, the young cub followed his gaze. Above them came the winged hunter, Circus, the marsh hawk. He hovered for a minute over the raccoons. His feet swung half extended as his sharp eyes surveyed the scene. Then gracefully he veered and flew toward an abandoned meadow. Undisturbed, the old coon looked away from the soaring hunter. He did not look at Procyon again, but turned away and bounded off along the edge of the reeds hoping to surprise a vole he scented in the meadow. As he left, Procyon reached out and rolled the walnut, his eyes still focused on the path the old giant had taken.

When the corn had tasseled and eared, the coon family moved back to the red oak den for it was closer to this source of food than the basswood. It was with some reluctance that Procyon left the long grasses, protected pools and tangled avenues of the marshland.

About four-thirty in the afternoon of a September day, Procyon was curled on the limb of the red oak. The air was cool as it came rushing through the woods, and Procyon shifted in his sleep, tucking his nose deeper into his fur. He was awakened by a beetle climbing up his nose toward his ear. He snapped at it, but it winged off and he dropped his head back to the limb to sleep. His eyes would not close. He found himself watching the limbs dip deeper and deeper as a storm circled the woods and emptied itself some miles to the north.

He finally arose and climbed down the tree to the ground. His hind legs and haunches were well developed. They were longer than his forelegs and tilted his body forward, giving him the shape of a plump pear. They no longer wobbled when he walked but propelled him through the woods with agility and sent him galloping along the limbs of the trees as deftly as a squirrel. Procyon now weighed eight pounds. He was big, but not full grown or mature. Despite his power and versatility on land and in the trees,

he was still a comedian. Masked and fuzzy, this harlequin of the woods was a limber acrobat. He hung by his hind legs from limbs, frisked along the narrow avenues of the trees, rolled and tumbled on the ground, and climbed hand over hand along low branches.

Procyon was off to the stream this September afternoon. He ran and trotted toward the water, turning off the trail frequently to investigate a rattling leaf, a smell, a hollow log. At the edge of the stream he heard a noise behind him. He jumped to the foot of a tree, looked around, heard it again and galloped up a few paces.

"Who-oo?" a voice called.

"Who-oo," Procyon answered. He turned around sideways and looked down at his sister who had followed him. Bracing himself with his chin he started down. He came down as always, head first. He hung by his big hind feet that curved snugly around the tree. With this support a forearm shot out, and back to his side. It took the weight while he brought the hind foot on that side forward. In this manner he climbed down to the base of the tree and ran to his sister. He nipped her on the ear and raced to the water. The sister buckled up, danced a few side steps in the leaves and chased after him.

Side by side they took a long drink. Their chins seemed to float on the very surface of the water as they drank, for their lower jaws were so far behind their noses that if they had tried to lap like a dog their noses would have been submerged. Then they resumed their sparring again. Finally Procyon crossed the shallows to the roots of a sugar maple. The tree was being undermined by the creek and tilted across the stream at a forty-five degree angle. Its massive roots still retained the soil above, but were washed out below.

The meandering creek had dug into the ground behind the roots leaving a cave barred by the grill work of interlacing roots. Procyon wove his way through this screen and splashed in the shallow water. This was one of his favorite hunting grounds for it was protected from the woodland; and into the net of roots came many creatures of the stream. After a brief survey of his cave, Procyon stuck his head out through a small opening in the lattice work. He looked brightly around the stream bed and watched his sister hunt water-food then run toward him. She slipped and soaked her tail and hind legs. Ears back, he wedged out through the grill and galloped along the shore. She pulled herself from the water and galloped after him.

As he raced along, his antics frightened a minnow. It swam up the creek ahead of him, trying to escape, and stranded itself in a shallow rapid. Procyon pounced upon it as it flopped helplessly. He rolled it over and over in his paws, flipped it to the bank, jumped on it, picked it up in his teeth and tossed it into the sand. Again he grabbed it, then carried it ten feet up the bank. Here he lost it momentarily, found it again, bit it several times and carried it back to the creek. At the spot where he had caught it, he rolled it over and over in the water as if he were washing it. He was merely feeling it in water just as he had felt it on land. Finally the fish became a

pulpy mass that fell apart. The head and gills were carried away by the current. He ate the rest.

Meanwhile his sister had felt her way up the stream beyond him and was crunching loudly on what seemed to be a stone, but what proved to be a fresh water mussel. She could not open it and dropped it. It rocked back to the bottom of the stream, scratched white where her little milk teeth had raked across it. But one tooth would never scratch again. Her vigorous bite had knocked it loose from its shallow socket. Where it had been was the gleaming white tip of her permanent canine tooth.

About this time Gib's herd of cattle came crashing through the woods to the creek for water. Procyon ran up a ten inch basswood that leaned over the stream. His sister went up a large silver maple. While the cattle drank below them the coons descended slowly. A cow at the foot of Procyon's basswood caught his scent, looked up and snorted. Procyon, only a few feet above her wide twitching nostrils, turned around and went back up a short distance.

A black heifer seeing the sister, crossed the creek and went to look at her. The raccoon spiraled to the other side of the tree and came around almost face to face with the heifer. Taken by surprise the heifer leaped backward and stumbled down the bank into the stream. Procyon galloped down the sloping basswood and ran for the base of the washed out maple. Before he could gain the protection of the tangled roots, the cow lowered her head and chased him some thirty feet into the woods trying to bunt him with her nose. The young cow stopped and stared at him. Procyon, unafraid, came toward her taking time to investigate every interesting sight along the woodland floor. The cow charged him again, but this time Procyon curved around her to the creek. He found his sister had also come back to the stream. Little disturbed by the herd, they climbed down the lattice work of roots and resumed their fishing. Several cows stood close together on the opposite bank and for a long time watched them curiously.

When the cattle had wandered back toward the fields, the coons left the security of the maple root grill and worked up stream. After they tired of fishing they climbed a flaky barked sugar maple. They walked out onto the far ends of the branches and fingered the terminal shoots and buds. They dipped and swayed with the limbs as the wind rocked the young tree. Procyon and his sister pulled the twigs to their mouths and picked off the buds with their teeth. The leaves spiraled to the ground as they ate. Occasionally they pried loose a sliver of bark and it plopped to the forest floor.

Balancing on the pencil thin limbs they sparred and fought as easily as they did on the ground. Frolicking, swinging and hanging, the fat cubs entertained themselves on the zig-zag playground of the tree. Presently Procyon climbed high in the maple and settled his haunches in the sharp angle of a crotch. Draping his forepaws and head over the branch above, he fell asleep. His sister dozed in a fork below him.

To the east along the horizon a gaudy moon was rising. The scent of goldenrod and milkweed was on the wind, and the air had a taste of nuts, grapes and plump berries. A great horned owl boomed from the forest to the north, and the eerie howl of a red fox was followed by silence.

After an hour's nap Procyon and his sister rejoined the family. The family feasted on the many woodland delicacies that comprised their varied taste. They enjoyed a wide assortment of foods; that of mice, of fish and water animals, nuts, corn, insects and all berries and succulent fruits. This night they dined from the stream to the highlands. They were ready to go home about midnight, but it was dawn before they reached the base of the big red oak and climbed to the den, for they wandered home slowly, checking each scent and sound. They stole quietly down into the hollow.

One bright September night when the stars glittered through the tops of the trees like fireflies, and the air was so clear that each tree looked crisp and fresh, the coon family awoke and prepared themselves for hunting. Stretching and yawning, they gradually came to life. Procyon rolled his sister's tail between his hands and scratched her stomach with his hind foot. He nipped her until she sputtered and then shoved his brother. His mother moved and Procyon reached out and tapped her cheek. She looked at him casually, then turned and climbed out of the den.

Procyon rolled over on his back with his feet in the air and watched the others leave for their night trip through the September woods.

Somewhat later he poked his head out of the den and smelt the night air. Slowly he climbed to the ground and joined the family in the cornfield. Procyon broke off an ear of corn with his nimble hands and peeled back the husk. Biting and chewing he devoured half of this and began on another when the scent of pheasant rode to him on the wind. He turned away quietly and traced the wind to its source. An old cock pheasant sleeping in a dense pocket of goldenrods and asters that grew along the edge of the field, awoke with a start as Procyon raked a corn stalk. The pheasant clattered into the darkness and flew blindly for the woods. Procyon looked after him. The wind carried off his scent and the coon turned to find his family.

He picked up his mother's trail and wove through the corn in search of her. She was sitting over an ear of corn that she held between her forepaws. As she wrinkled up her lips to sink her front teeth in the kernels, she saw her son galloping up the green corridor toward her. She did not stop eating but purred and pressed back her ears as Procyon rose to his back feet, touched her on the forearm then swung gently away. His brother was behaving strangely, and Procyon found his actions more interesting than his mother's. He crossed into the next alley of corn passing through a cobweb that stuck to his black mask. His brother had a young meadow vole under his paw, and was nipping it as it scurried to get loose. When he saw Procyon he stopped playing with it, killed it quickly and ran down the furrow holding it in his teeth. Procyon chased him, overtook him and knocked his feet out from under him. He snatched the mouse and galloped to the next row of corn as his brother scrambled into action and came charging after him.

While the raccoon family was raiding Gib's cornfield, Ruff, the vagrant wild hound slipped under the gate at the end of the lane and stole toward the woods. He was lean and thin for he did not eat regularly. Occasionally he was fed by a family that lived on Ford Road, but for the most part he lived on mice in the fields, muskrats, woodchucks and anything he could hunt or steal. Ruff had no certain ancestry, he was a mixture of terrier, hound and others. During the day he stuck to the woods almost as wild as a fox or coyote. When he came near the farmhouses he did so with his tail between his legs and his head crouched. He hid from the farmers and was chased by their dogs.

Ruff slunk down the lane to the woods, his nose pressed to the earth, trying to pick out the scent of some animal on the dry ground. He circled the sugar house and trotted up the ravine that ran west through the woods past the red oak den. Ruff turned around suddenly and jogged back a few steps. His tail stiffened as he came upon the trail of the coon family leading south to the cornfield.

Ruff understood that the scent he was following was that of a raccoon. The hound knew from experience that the raccoon was a formidable animal and he stole along the trail silently without snapping a stick. Slinking close to the ground he followed the trail to the fence.

Ruff became tense, he could hear the scrapping growls of Procyon and his brother as they fought over the mouse. They were just beyond the fence, four rows into the cornfield. Ruff glided under the fence, still silent.

The brothers heard the fence rattle and as the dog crashed through the first row, they sped up the furrow toward their mother. Ruff strained into action, the exertion forcing a yipe from his throat. He gained rapidly on Procyon and his brother. With a snarl, Ruff sank his teeth into the fleshy hind leg of the brother. The brother rolled into the dusty earth and turned from the

attacking hound. Ruff checked his speed and swung. He lunged again. With a howl the hound went down writhing and yelping in pain. With a vicious snarl the mother coon had caught the dog in complete surprise from the rear. By the time the hound had gathered his wits, the family followed by their mother was through the fence. Ruff bounced to his feet but followed them with less interest.

The wire fence checked him long enough for the coons to put ten yards between them. The brother, slowed by his wounded leg, jumped to the first tree beyond the fence and scurried out of reach of the dog. The sisters who had had more time, had run into the woods about fifty yards before climbing a young maple. They were safely out of reach when their mother and Procyon passed them and took to the security of the next maple. Ruff followed them cautiously. He slid up to the tree and stopped. With tongue hanging from his mouth, he looked into the branches. The raccoons were safe in the trees. Ruff limped off.

from THE WAHOO BOBCAT

Joseph Wharton Lippincott

An animal story by Mr. Lippincott, publisher as well as author, is invariably exciting. In this first episode the bobcat has been discovered by a hound, and begins the adventures that are going to lead to his strange friendship with a boy.

Fight with a Hog

The Tiger, completely taken by surprise, waited to see what the big dog would do, and the dog, a hound, just stood there looking at him in the dim light. The hound was trying hard to understand the weird combination of a wildcat's body and a skunk's smell which made his eyes mistrust his nose. At length, the hair began to rise on his back, and with a bellow of combined glee and fury he sprang at the fence, forcing the cat to leap back to the protection of the bushes. Over the fence then came the hound with a clatter of rails, and after the cat he dashed with bellow after bellow fairly bursting from his chest.

Shrill yaps of delight now sounded behind him as the three other dogs heard the row and could not resist running from the house to join in the chase. Down the hog path went the Tiger in long, easy bounds, toward the Prairie and the swamps that he knew so well, the briar thickets in which he could hide and the deep mud holes over which he could leap. He drew away from the bellows and the thumping feet and sprang out of the path into the thick bushes to confuse his followers and give himself more time to elude them, for instinct told him that a hound like this one would trail him as long as his scented tracks could be followed.

The four dogs were all together now, thrashing about in the bushes to find where he had dodged. Occasionally they yelped with excitement, occasionally too there were distant shouts indicating that a man had joined the hunt. Fiercely the Tiger fought his way through the swamp growth, reached the Prairie and dashed along its edge among the tussocks of heavy grass and the tricky holes that had no bottom, places where snakes lurked and the barbed briars would rip any creature that did not understand their tangles.

Bellows from the black hound began again; he was once more on the trail and coming fast. The cat stopped for a moment to listen and make sure he was not too close, then deliberately turned back and followed his own tracks until he came to a tree whose limbs hung low. With a mighty leap the Tiger reached one of these stout limbs, climbed along it to the tree's trunk and crouched there, twenty feet from the ground, so high that his scent would be caught by the rising currents of night air and kept away from pursuers below. If they discovered him he would jump into the bushes and run again.

He was not afraid now. His pounding heart slowed down and he rested. As presently the dogs came bounding single file along the Prairie's edge on the trail he had left, he stood up to watch them flounder in the mud and fight the tangles. They passed him and reached the place where he had doubled back, but then their glad tonguing ceased and they searched in all directions for more tracks. It did not occur to them to turn back on the trail and look up the tree. Once, a circle made by the black hound in his hunting brought him directly under the cat, but there was no scent on the ground and he did not guess that he was so close to the Tiger.

Gradually the dogs worked their way farther into the swamp and far from the cat, the crashing and splashing sounds they made dying out and the shouts of the man growing dim as he tired of the fruitless hunt in the musk-laden air and returned to his house. The moon was rising and filling the swamp with remarkable shadows; the Prairie shimmered wherever there were grassless pools and the frogs were yelling as if their lives depended on the noise, but no creature appeared to notice the Tiger as he climbed down the tree, backwards like a bear, sniffed at his fur, rolled a few times in a sandy spot and once more hungrily began his search for food.

Everywhere was the smell of musk. It had bothered almost all the little furry creatures and made them hide or travel beyond the reach of the fumes; this meant that some had to go into the pine woods or far down the Prairie's edge, others into holes in the ground or in hollow trees; even the hum produced by the countless insects of the swamp seemed to have changed.

Like a ghost in the deserted swamp the cat wandered, ever on the alert but more and more discouraged. He did not want to go near the home of the dogs, so at length he trotted to the second-best field, arriving at its edge just as dawn grayed the sky and the birds of day began to awake and give their first morning cries. Soon they would sing and play and feed on all sides and the creatures of the night would vanish into hiding. Hunger, however, kept the Tiger on the move. Even more stealthy now, he crept along the fence, looking well ahead for gray squirrels and unwary birds of any kind, ears cocked at every sound and muscles ready for instant leaps.

He belonged to the creatures of the night and therefore was too easily spotted now by his intended prey; the birds scattered before him in alarm and the squirrels barked derisively from safe perches over his head, advertising his presence wherever he went. The Tiger, however, was resourceful; he knew that if he found a good hiding place he could crouch there unseen and spring upon unwary creatures that came near him in their own feeding. Such a place was inside the fenced area, in an unplowed corner where tall briars gave perfect cover. So, after leaping the worm fence to this corner he sneaked, and under the green cover of the thorny tangle he hid himself.

A hundred yards across the field stood the house where humans lived and already were clattering about. Their breakfast was finished and the two children, a boy of nine and a girl somewhat smaller, were out on the back porch playing. But the Tiger was not afraid of children.

The grunt of a hog sounded some distance to the right and presently a lean, brown-black sow grubbed her way under the fence and led six very young black piglets into the forbidden area. She was nearer to him than to the house and at the edge of a strawberry patch where her rooting could do much harm. Under some of the plants went her powerful snout and contentedly she munched the roots and grunted while the piglets clustered around her legs.

The half wild sow was having a very happy time until the little boy happened to see her. He knew that hogs had to be chased out of the field whenever they came under the fence, so he shouted to his parents and, seizing a stick, bravely jumped from the porch and ran at the hogs, waving the stick and still yelling.

The old sow looked up, realized at once that this was an attack on her for trespassing, and, with a grunt of alarm led the piglets towards the hole through which they had come. The little ones toddled after her with might and main but were held back by a stretch of soft, ploughed ground and were continually falling into the furrows and having to climb out. The smallest, a mere runt with tiny legs and a very wrinkled snout, was having the worst time of all and suddenly got into a furrow from which he could not climb.

The runt kept very quiet for a few moments, but when the others left him and the boy came running, he gave a shrill squeal of fear and struggled anew with the crumbling furrow. The boy's first instinct was to help him out, so he stooped and put his hands under the runt, whereupon the tiny pig thought his doom was sealed and let out piercing squeals which went to his mother's heart and brought her back on the run to his rescue.

She charged across the soft ground in wild

mother rage, reached the boy, knocked him head over heels with her snout and began to rip at him with her toothed mouth, furiously grunting amid the squeals of the piglet and the sudden howls of the boy who was pummeling her as best he could with his fists. The noise reached every corner of the field and brought the father out of the house in his bare feet, running so fast that he tripped on a bush and fell full length in the sand. Behind him came the yelling mother, brandishing a saucepan, her face white with fear as she ran toward her son. The squeals, grunts, shrieks and yells continued unabated as the sow furiously rolled the boy over and over, biting and rooting at him and trampling him into the sand.

Strangest of all was the action of the wildcat. A sudden fury took possession of his brain and blotted out all else. He rushed along the fence, then cut across the ploughed ground and coming close to the battling mass of screaming bodies, threw himself on top of the sow and hurled her to the ground. Buffeting her head with his two forepaws, he raked at her snout and clawed her sides, bit with all his strength into her thick neck and in spite of her kicks held on and rolled about with her in the heavy sand, now on top now underneath, his screams and growls joining the high pitched voices of the others as he ripped and tore and tried to batter the black, fighting body locked in his embrace.

Suddenly the big sow, with a great heave of her snout, threw him away from her, rose to her feet and stood facing him with mouth open, little eyes sparkling and wicked. The cat got his paws under him and crouched, when suddenly he seemed to awaken. He looked this way and that in a daze. He saw the man and the woman standing over him holding the boy between them in their arms, saw the bare, sandy field around him all white in the sun that was rising over the trees. Gone was the old sow in a whirl of dust and gone all of a sudden was his fury and his courage.

He got shakily to his feet, looked for an instant at the man and woman standing there so oddly quiet, then started for the fence, slowly at first until his legs unlimbered and he could take the furrows in his great, graceful bounds. He scarcely touched the top of the fence as he went over it and he did not stop until he was far in the cool, shadowed swamp, among the silent places, away from all signs and sounds of the strange, wild fight. Throwing himself flat on the ground under the green tangles he lay with heaving sides pulling himself together and getting back his normal balance. Forever in his memory, however, would be the very strange adventure of this day.

Small birds sang as if nothing at all had happened. The gray moss swayed and the leaves rustled in the growing breeze; ants ran up and down the tree trunks; buzzards circled like kites, with flattened wings and tails spread. Gradually the Tiger relaxed, dozed a little, licked his rumpled fur, tested his bitten legs a few times and arranged himself into a ball that could lie snugly among the dead leaves. Night would come again and with it the hunting time, the magic hour, when the rabbits and mice would appear from their hiding places and again the chance would come for him to still his hunger pains. Yes, night would come and night was really cat time; then he would hunt again and eat frogs if nothing better came his way.

Sammy and the Wildcat

The day dawned like any other day. The swamp, never entirely asleep, teemed with life and pleasant sounds as birds and beasts went about their usual pursuits. Cattle lowed and hogs grunted as if to show that man was nearby, and far away a railroad engine tooted mournfully as though tired of sticking to the same old track.

Stretched on a low limb of a moss-festooned live oak, with his four feet under him, the Tiger dozed and dreamed. Occasionally his claws moved and often his ears wiggled to ward off flies, but otherwise he was as motionless as the limb itself. The hours passed until the August sun overhead marked high noon and soon began to sink toward the western horizon, its heat growing slowly less as the rays slanted more and more.

The cat was becoming restless. He stretched his legs and yawned, and he began to look around and listen attentively to the sounds in the swamp. An unusual noise came faintly from the direction of the clearings and at once caught his attention. It was whistling, for Sammy liked to whistle whenever he was alone, and now he was making his way to the Prairie, taking what he thought was a short cut to the boat that his father kept moored at the water's edge. He should have stayed on the little path that led there from the house, but Sammy had ideas of his own and wanted to explore. In his bare feet he found it easier to walk under the oaks where the briars were not so tangled, and he was heading in almost a straight line for the tree in which the Tiger rested.

It was not difficult for the cat to tell by the sounds that only one person was approaching, and this a youngster with no evil intentions. A hunter would keep as quiet as possible and sneak along the paths, instead of whistling loudly and padding carelessly over the dry leaves.

Presently he sighted Sammy's head above the palmettos, then his thin body; there seemed nothing dangerous about this little human and, besides, the cat felt that if he kept still he would not be seen on his limb. As he watched, his memory brought him back to the time when he had seen this boy before, running across the field, and he felt curiosity about this small edition of dangerous man.

Sammy came whistling past the tree and then stopped. The vague feeling that he was being watched had come to him as it comes to many creatures more sensitive than the average. He stood quite still and looked around him. The swamp seemed deserted to his eyes, but he continued to turn them this way and that until suddenly they met the stare of the big cat crouching on the limb not twenty feet away. Sammy wasn't scared, but he was mightily surprised. He could not remember ever having seen a cat one quarter as large as this one, which must be the daddy of them all, the kind he had heard his parents speaking about. They liked cats and so did he.

"Kitty, Kitty! Here Kitty!" said Sammy; but as the cat did not stir and continued to gaze at him he grew disconcerted and took several steps backward. He decided something must be wrong with it because it did not move, and he was troubled by the fixed stare of its round, yellow eyes. He walked farther, still looking back and calling "Kitty," and when it was out of sight he thought about it and wondered whether it was hungry, out here in the swamp all by itself.

He found the boat, pulled a bait can from under the seat and put a white worm on the hook which dangled from a fishing pole he had hidden in the bushes at his last visit. The worm was one of a number he had found under the bark of a fallen and partly decayed pine. The nose of the boat was stuck in the mud and the stern projected into the Prairie to the edge of a little pool surrounded by grass. In this pool he dropped his hook and waited expectantly until the line began to move and he felt a nibble. He gave the fish time enough to swallow the worm, then jerked and brought out a flopping bream the size of a pancake.

The bream flopped about on the bottom of the boat but was soon unhooked. Another worm, then another bream. In all, he landed four before they stopped biting. To carry them he strung them on a little forked stick, one end of which he passed through their gills. Now he was ready to go home, so he hid his pole and started up the path, whistling as before and holding the stick on his shoulder so that the fish dangled behind him. He was feeling happy and carefree until all at once he remembered the cat and again wondered whether it was hungry.

He decided then to leave the path and have another look at the big animal, if it was still in the same place; and this time, when he came near the tree, he saw the yellow eyes immediately.

"Here Kitty," he called. "Here Kitty." The cat did not move, and Sammy went quite close, until he was almost directly under it. This was too close for the Tiger, who immediately leaped noiselessly to the ground and vanished in the bushes, leaving the boy surprised and disappointed by its lack of friendliness. He thought of the fish and, acting on a generous impulse, pulled one off the stick and laid it on the ground. Again he called, but getting no response, decided he would leave the fish for the cat to find, because he was sure all cats were hungry like his cat at home. Now he began to whistle again and continued his walk through the swamp to the field and then to the house, where he gave the three remaining bream to his mother to clean and cook for supper.

"Did you have a nice time?" asked Eliza.

"Oh, yes, and I caught another bream, but I gave that one to a great big cat."

"What?" gasped his mother. "What kind of a cat?"

"An awful big one. It looked hungry."

His mother dropped her dish cloth and sat down in a chair beside him.

"Tell me all about it," she demanded. And Sammy, excited by her interest, gave a very good description of the cat in the tree and how it had jumped down and run away, although he had left the bream for it to find because he knew it was hungry.

For once Eliza was speechless, but when Bill returned from a trip into the woods to feed his wandering hogs a little corn and keep them gentle and tame, she gave him Sammy's story word for word.

"I wonder if it was the Tiger?" mused Bill.

"Aren't you worried about the boy walking in the swamp and running into catamounts like that?"

"Not one bit," he answered. "I was like him when I was a little feller and the swamp was swarming with varmints. Nothing ever happened to me."

"Well, I don't feel it's safe. Suppose that critter had jumped on him?"

"It wouldn't. He's safer with the cats around than if they were all dead; that fuss with the old sow proved it."

Eliza calmed down after that.

"At least, it's better, I guess, for him not to be made timid," she said. And so Sammy was not prevented from continuing his walks to the Prairie.

The Tiger found the bream and ate it. He had gone only a few yards into the bushes and had waited there until Sammy was out of sight; then he returned to the tree to look around and at once saw the fish as well as scented it. Fearing a trap, he walked around it very carefully before daring to pick it up and swallow it with a few guarded chews before the gulp that took down head, bones and all. The good-tasting tidbit was definitely associated in his mind with the tree and Sammy, which led to his resting on the same limb during the next day and listening for the whistling which heralded the boy's approach.

And since Sammy had been greatly interested in his experience with the cat, the two met again in the same place. This time Sammy lingered longer and talked to him.

"Why you stay up there?" he wanted to know. "You come down here or maybe I won't bring you a bream. You're bad; when I call you, you got to mind!" He did bring a bream, however, and this time had the luck to look back just as the Tiger jumped from the tree and picked up the fish.

At the house he told his mother that the poor cat had only half a tail as if it had been run over by a wagon. He wanted to know who owned it.

"You own it as much as anyone," his mother told him. "That cat's wild. It stays in the swamp and never goes near anyone's house."

"It's my cat?" he asked just to make sure.

"Yes, it's yours just as I said, as much as it's anyone's."

"It's my cat!" he repeated several times. After that he never caught bream without leaving one and sometimes two of them under the tree. If the Tiger was not on his favorite limb, the fish were left anyway with much calling of "Kitty." And never was a fish wasted because sooner or later the Tiger always came to look for it and to follow Sammy's trail as far as the field as if hoping he would drop others. There came the day when he jumped from his limb to take the fish as soon as the boy left it, and later the day when he circled the boy on the ground, waiting for him to drop the fish.

Sammy now accepted his timidity as he accepted everything when he got used to it, and so gradual was the cat's growth of confidence that the boy was not at all surprised when the big, beautiful animal at last followed him to the boat and sat on its haunches watching him fish. Sammy talked to the Tiger as he would to a companion, and if the cat did not understand the words, at least he knew that they indicated good feeling between them. The Tiger, indeed, while in awe of the boy as a superior being, had no longer any real fear; he knew that Sammy was a very friendly benefactor, and he liked Sammy. He was restless and nervous whenever the boy did not come on time or was kept in the house on account of rainy weather.

Bill and Eliza knew what was going on and never ceased to marvel. They would see the boy and the bobcat come out of the swamp together, the cat trotting ahead of the lad or directly behind him until the field was reached, whereupon the cat would stop and the boy would turn around to talk to him and say goodby.

"I can't understand it," Eliza would exclaim again and again. "It isn't human; maybe we ought to stop it."

"What for?" Bill would ask. "The boy is healthy and happy and keeps up his work. He's got a way with animals that seems to make them trust him. It's a sign of character. Let him develop it."

"But we're not raising a son of ours to be a wild animal trainer in a circus!"

"That's true, but he's nearly ten and there are no boy companions his age around here. That's hard on him, and certainly he won't play with doll babies like Mary does."

"Well, keep your eye on them and don't let anything happen to Sammy," was Eliza's final word. "A catamount is always a catamount even if he gets tame."

Those were warm days, when the black hound did not feel like going into the swamp to hunt cats or anything else. They were beautiful days that made the acorns fatten and the berries and seeds develop over all the land as if in preparation for the autumn chills that were sure to come. The young birds and animals grew large and strong and learned to shift for themselves in the big world, and the snakes began to grow lazy with all the food they could hold, and the fish swarmed in the tepid water of Wahoo Prairie.

JUNGLE BROTHERS

Kenneth Gilbert

Cappy, Dirk Fallon's little Capuchin monkey, sat in the strange forest gazing mournfully at his motionless master.

Exhausted by tropical fever, Dirk, a broad shouldered young gold hunter, lay beside an animal trail that twisted here and there under the thick canopy of the Guatemalan rain forest

"Jungle Brothers." Used by permission of the author, Kenneth Gilbert

When the first hot dizziness warned him that he had been stricken with the dread jungle malady, he knew a weakening moment of terror at the thought of dying alone in the wilderness. Then he grew delirious, and finally he fell into the coma of the crisis. Eventually, he would awaken clearheaded and free from fever, or he would slip into eternal slumber, reaching adventure's end there in the jungle—alone.

And yet he was not alone, for Cappy sat on guard. He crouched beside Dirk, bewildered by the strange unresponsiveness of the big, kind man-god and fearful of the unseen menace that seemed to lurk everywhere in the dense bush. This was the land of Cappy's ancestors, but the little gray monkey was seeing it for the first time. Before this, Dirk Fallon had done his exploring in more temperate regions, but stories of the gold to be found along the Guatemalan rivers had lured him to the tropics, and he had brought Cappy for company.

"You can look up all your relatives, Cappy," he had grinned, and Cappy had no way of telling him that Dirk meant more to him than a treeful of relatives.

Now Cappy crouched miserably beside Dirk, well-aware that something terrible had happened to his master. He knew too that darkness was creeping over the rain forest, and that the jungle life was awakening. Instinctively he feared the night prowlers, most of them dangerous to little monkeys who foolishly stayed on the ground instead of taking to the trees. He whimpered and with soft little paws rubbed Dirk's fevered cheeks, trying to say that it was time to leave this dreadful place. But Dirk lay there motionless, and Cappy's features wrinkled as though he were close to tears. Yet he would not leave the man he adored, even though remaining might mean swift death.

His bright eyes observed ghostly butterflies and giant moths drifting among the trees, but he was not in the mood to pursue them. There were vague stirrings and rustlings near-by that would ordinarily have demanded curious investigation, but now they only alarmed him. He heard the raucous cries of parrots, and their harsh calls seemed to awaken old memories buried deeply in his brain. Suddenly he heard monkey voices speaking his own language!

He had seen no other monkeys in this land, and for a moment he forgot his uneasiness, and sat up to peer about. Again he heard the monkey talk, and this time it came from a point much nearer.

His excitement mounted. Here were friends. His lips shaped themselves, and in his squeaky little voice he called a greeting, to let them know he was lonely and wanted companionship.

He listened intently for a reply, but none came. Soon, however, he saw a slender, thick-leafed limb sway unaccountably, and then he glimpsed gray forms running among the branches and leaping dexterously from one to another, drawing closer. Again he called out, this time questioningly.

Now there came an answer. It was a hoarse, barking reply, and all at once the trees seemed filled with monkeys who were counterparts of himself. Their leader, a surly-looking old fellow with an age-whitened face, chattered excitedly.

Much of it was unintelligible to Cappy, for these were wild brothers and their language was somewhat different from that of the tame monkeys he had once lived with in a zoo, although their coloring was identical. Yet he understood the drift of their talk. The old king was asking where he came from, to which tribe he belonged, and why he traveled with a man-ape.

Cappy answered them, but his actions roused their suspicion. He slapped at the mosquitoes buzzing about Dirk's face, and disgustedly brushed off a red-striped beetle crawling on his master's sleeve. His wild brothers could not understand this and came closer, hurling abuse at him and demanding that he come into the trees and fight. But Cappy had resources new to these jungle dwellers.

Just inside Dirk's pack, which lay on the trail, was a little silver bell of which Cappy was inordinately fond. He used this bell to express anger, joy, or excitement. Now he leaped nimbly to the pack, and his slender fingers hauled forth the precious trinket. He jingled it violently, and looked up at the strangers to see if they were properly astonished.

Apparently they were stricken speechless. Some of them were plainly frightened. Baby monkeys ran to their mothers, and big males drew together in an attitude of defense. These wild Capuchin brothers had never heard such a sound, and it puzzled them greatly. They knew what to expect when they heard the coughing roar of a jaguar, the plaintive yowl of an ocelot, the bellow of a bull alligator, or the hiss of a huge water boa. But this musical tinkle was beyond their comprehension.

The old king's curiosity got the better of his natural caution. With a questioning bark, he dropped to a lower limb, and hung there while he eyed Cappy and the mysterious and shiny thing in the tame monkey's fist. Cappy gave the bell another jingle.

This completely captivated the king. He came closer, making soothing, persuasive sounds deep in his throat. Other members of the tribe, fully a hundred of them, also drew near.

But Cappy did not mistake this advance for friendliness. He saw the avaricious look in the king's eyes, and jingled the bell violently, at the same time wrinkling his lips suggestively in an insulting snarl.

Ordinarily, this would have been sufficient cause for combat, but now the king was wholly bent on getting possession of the marvelously gleaming thing that made such a pleasing noise. He ignored Cappy's defiance and drew even closer. Growing alarmed at the king's determined manner, Cappy backed closer to his unconscious master and tugged frantically at his sleeve to awaken him.

Suddenly the king lost patience. With an angry bark he dropped to a lower limb, raced along it, and gathered himself to leap upon the stubborn Cappy.

But at that instant one of the watchful males in the higher branches gave a frantic cry of alarm. Forgetting Cappy, the king sprang to safety. The ruff of bristly hair around his neck and along his spine lifted, while he bared his fangs and chattered ominously. The mother monkeys shrieked as they tried to gather their young. In the face of imminent danger, the fighting males formed a group that swung low and hurled defiance at a sinuous, mottled length weaving noiselessly in and out of the undergrowth along the game trail.

Never before had Cappy seen a boa constrictor, that dreaded foe of jungle folk, and particularly monkeys, but instinct told him it was an enemy. He hesitated, torn between his longing to flee into the trees with the wild monkeys, and his reluctance to desert his master. Then, in a frenzy of excitement, he jingled the bell, caught up a short length of rotted limb, and hurled the stick straight at the huge snake's head.

The boa, surprised and angered, looped its coils and hissed a warning. Then its flat, expressionless eyes fell on the man lying there as though dead. Instantly it was aroused and alarmed.

Under other circumstances, it is probable that the boa would have avoided the man and been content to go in peace, but the attack Cappy had launched could be interpreted in only one way by the great snake. Therefore, it offered battle.

With another terrifying hiss it prepared to strike, its strong jaws parted for a death grip before it wound powerful coils around the unconscious victim. The boa was not venomous, but its loops had strength enough to crush life even from a big wild boar.

Before the snake could strike, however, Cappy had stirred into valiant action. He caught up another stick and bravely smashed at the fearsome, scaled head with the lidless eyes.

It was a blow that ordinarily would have meant nothing to the boa, whose muscular length had a toughness almost capable of withstanding the fangs of a jaguar. But the move diverted the snake's attention, and instead of striking at the man, it struck at Cappy.

The little Capuchin, however, was too nimble to be caught in this fashion, and he leaped aside with a shriek of derision, at the same time jingling the bell he still clutched. And, as though at a signal, the tribe of wild kinsmen rallied to his support.

With deafening cries they began raining missiles on the hated destroyer. Sticks, small branches, even green coconuts, were hurled unerringly at the boa, who once more coiled in an attitude of defense. A flock of green-and-gold macaws added to the tumult, while in the distance a band of howler monkeys boomed in reply. Tragedy again stalked the jungle, so the wild things believed.

The assault and noise became too much for the boa to endure. Battered on head and body, he was unable to retaliate, and could only lie there and hiss horribly at his swarming foes. After a minute or so of it he gave up, and slid into the cool sanctuary of the undergrowth, where his assailants dared not follow.

This was Cappy's moment of triumph! As if he alone had routed the monster, he sent a shrill paean of victory through the green forest aisles, and rang his silver bell madly.

His jungle brothers did not dispute his claims. Possibly they felt that the bell possessed some power of driving off all foes. Never before had they dared attack a boa. This strange Capuchin from another world had led them successfully against one of their most fearsome enemies. Surely there was hidden magic in the silver bell.

The monkey king looked at the marvelous treasure, and curiosity and greed once more overcame his natural caution. Again he approached Cappy and made clucking, reassuring noises; he made a show of vast friendliness. If he could get near enough, he could snatch the tinkling thing from the little stranger's hand, and perhaps with a bite or a blow teach the upstart what it meant to be defiant of one who ruled a hundred monkeys.

Cappy was fearful. Again he shook the arm of his fever-stricken master, to apprise him of danger from the gray brethren who were swarming closer from every side. But Dirk Fallon, still in that coma which precedes death or recovery, did not respond.

Nearer and nearer came the monkey king, his gray old face masking determination to get the bell at any cost. Yet he was uncertain about the man lying there so still. Was this a trap? It might be, but he would not be satisfied until he had the gleaming thing in his own sinewy fingers.

His boldness gave courage to the others. Of a sudden Cappy found himself ringed by many little-old-man faces that were not at all reassuring. Most truculent of all was the king. He sidled toward Cappy with a soothing mutter, but his eyes glistened purposefully. Cappy clung to his master, chattering uneasily and baring his fangs. The king was not impressed, however, and continued to approach, stretching out his paws as though demanding the precious bell that Cappy clutched more tightly than ever.

Suddenly Dirk Fallon stirred and groaned, and the wild monkeys, with exclamations of alarm, fled to the heights, the king with them. Cappy shrieked triumph.

Yet one wild monkey lingered. This was a sleek young female with limpid eyes, and she fascinated Cappy with a show of shy friendliness. Though she withdrew a little when the king voiced alarm, she returned presently and became greatly interested in a white lichen on the bole of a bacaba palm near-by. Deftly she tore it loose, sniffed it, and picked it apart, all the while with feigned indifference watching the strange Capuchin with the silver bell.

Cappy was enchanted—here was a chance for sympathy and understanding. Eagerly he drew nearer. Too late, then, he saw through her guile, for he heard a sound behind him and whirling abruptly, found himself confronting the baleful eyes of the monkey king. Cappy couldn't retreat to the safety of his master's presence for, with a savage snarl, the king leaped.

The next moment Cappy was battling frantically with a skilled and ruthless fighter—a jungle veteran who was king by right of might. Wounded in a dozen places, Cappy was putting up a game but losing battle when the element of chance, which so often determines situations in the wilderness, came to his aid.

For the sounds of fighting were obliterated suddenly by a hoarse, blood-chilling roar. It wiped out the fierce outcries of the tribesmen as they crowded near and shrieked for the monkey king to "kill." Their triumph turned to terror. Cappy, released by the king, caught sight of a huge, thick-muscled cat with a curiously spotted coat, the most fearsome killer in the jungle—a jaguar!

It was a female, savage with hunger, for her cubs were hidden in a near-by den and she had to hunt constantly to keep herself and them alive. Lean and ravenous, she would not have hesitated to attack a man if she discovered him in the vicinity of her den.

Her keen ears had heard the insane chattering of the monkeys when they had driven off the boa, and her cunning told her that here was an opportunity to stalk her excited victims when they would be less on guard. Now she was among them, her evil, painted face snarling as

she struck right and left at the screaming monkeys fleeing for the treetops. Miraculously they escaped, but Cappy and the fighting king were slower. The jaguar charged.

They saw her coming, and separated instantly as though blown apart by a mighty gust of wind, the king leaping for the nearest limb. But Cappy instinctively turned to the one being who had always offered protection in the past, big Dirk Fallon, lying unconscious of peril. As the jaguar missed, she pivoted to follow Cappy—and saw the man but a short leap distant!

At once she crouched, tail twitching, ears flattened to skull, fangs bared in a terrifying snarl that split her mottled face. Her lambent eyes seemed molten with green flame, while muscles rippled under her sleek skin. She feared the man, but there were reasons why she did not run.

She was mad with hunger, and ferocious because this man's presence might be a threat to her cubs. His seeming helplessness there on the ground gave her confidence, and yet she had the feeling of being cornered. She would fight, kill! Her muscles grew taut, rigid, as she gathered herself for a quick spring.

Frozen by terror, Cappy crouched on Dirk Fallon's breast. The little Capuchin did not understand that his own act was bringing death to his beloved master. He was chained to the spot by the hypnotic power of those blazing jade-green eyes. Moreover, this was his man-god, and he would not leave him. Crouching close to

Dirk, Cappy bared his puny teeth in defiance—saw the tip of the jaguar's tail lift suddenly as she tensed for the leap.

That very act broke the spell which gripped him. What he did then was an involuntary thing, governed by no reason, but it had magic results. His thin fingers still clutched the bell that he had not given up in fighting the monkey king, and now with all his strength he hurled the thing straight at the jaguar's head!

It struck her with a tinkling clink, and she recoiled at the sound as though bitten by a snake. In a single movement almost too quick for the eye to follow, she leaped aside with explosive snarl. Never before had she heard such a sound as the tinkle of a bell. She was puzzled, fearful again of the man. Doubt and uncertainty replaced her killing urge, and she hesitated.

But as swiftly there came reassurance. The shining thing had not hurt her. The man was still helpless, an easy victim. Her baleful eyes swung on him once more—but at that instant she stiffened as her ears caught a sound too faint for even Cappy to hear.

Now fear did get the upper hand. Only an instant longer she waited, then melted disappointedly into the brush. She would not fight where the odds were against her. A minute later and there was the soft pat of bare feet on the trail as a dozen rubber-workers hurried up.

They were wispy-haired natives, very swarthy and their black eyes widened at sight of Dirk, who was now stirring, strengthened by his long sleep. They understood what was wrong, and they acted quickly. One went for water, while another disappeared in the brush, to return in a few minutes with pungent leaves that he crushed between his palms. A few drops of the juice were mixed with the water in a gourd dipper, and held to Dirk's lips.

He choked at the bitter draught, but after a time his eyes opened, and he stared at the men with his senses rapidly clearing of the fever fog.

"Gracias," he thanked them in Spanish. "Lucky you came along."

"Si," grinned their leader. "You've been ver' sick, but now you be well. Our camp is near. Mos' fortunate, señor, that we hear the tinkle of a bell, and come to fin' you."

Dirk frowned, puzzled. "Bell?" he asked. Then he understood, so he thought, and grinned and stroked Cappy, who was snuggled contentedly against his shoulder. "Oh—my monkey's. He's probably been having a fine time playing around with it while I've been asleep. Even got himself scratched up. But nothing ever happens to Cappy. Does it, fellow?"

Cappy chattered back in great content, not in the least disturbed because he could not tell his master how he, Cappy, one small monkey with a toy bell, had saved them both from the two most dangerous killers of the jungle. What did it matter? The man-god was himself again—and here were treasures. Cappy glanced down happily. In one tiny fist he gripped a handful of bristly hair wrenched from the royal neck of the vanished monkey king, and in the other he held the precious bell that had wrought magic when magic was needed.

from THE DEFENDER

Nicholas Kalashnikoff

The mountain rams, ruthlessly hunted by greedy men, are a noble and pathetic herd, struggling for survival in the remote fastness of the mountains. The man Turgen has been cruelly misjudged by his fellows, and he too has taken refuge in the mountain tops. How he becomes the defender of the mountain rams and of an un-fortunate family and finds himself, in the process, is a moving story. "Everywhere there is life and everywhere there are warm human hearts" is the theme of the book.

[*The Wild Rams Find a Friend*]

By stepping on to a ledge outside his door, Turgen on a clear day had a wonderful view of the valley below and the mountains above him. When he tired of watching the tiny figures of men and women scurrying about at the foot of his hill, he had only to turn his eyes upward to see a different and fascinating sight. For there, dodging among the crags, were specks which he knew to be wild rams.

"How do they live?" he asked himself one evening. The hills were barren except for sparse tufts of moss, an occasional thin clump of grass, and now and then a tough, hardy shrub that could not contain much nourishment.

His curiosity and pity aroused, Turgen watched the rams intently all that season and the next. He could make out nine individuals of what he assumed to be a family—or, as he called it, a tribe. In summer one lamb—or it might be two—were added to the number, but they disappeared with cold weather.

Then Turgen began to worry. For with the cold weather came snow to cover the moss and grass and dry up the meagre shrubs. Even at a distance he could sense the animals' despair as they searched avidly beneath the snow for any poor morsel to chew upon. Their grey-brown wool hung loosely on them now, and they moved indifferently, without spirit. Unless there was a hint of danger. Then they would lift their heads proudly and take themselves into the distance with incredible lightness and speed.

"Poor things." Turgen spoke his thoughts aloud. "To think that I used to hunt you to kill you! What harm are you to anyone? You who ask only for freedom."

But pity could not help them. He must find a way to give them practical aid. He considered one thing, then another. At last he fixed upon a plan.

First he built a light sleigh which he loaded with hay. Then, putting on skis, he pulled the sleigh to the ridge of the next mountain, dumped the hay, and returned home. Not a ram was in sight, but he could feel their inquisitive and fearful eyes upon him from behind the boulders farther up the hill.

From his own door he watched them approach the hay warily, circle it and trample it, and stoop to nibble at it. They seemed to fear a trap. But when he went back to the spot the hay was gone. After that he took frequent offerings of food to them, and gradually the rams came to accept his gifts without hesitation. Although they never approached him when he visited the feeding ground, he caught glimpses of them in hiding, awaiting his coming. In order to gain their greater confidence, he made it a point never to carry a gun. He even gave up his habit of carrying an iron-tipped stick which helped him in climbing. For he knew that all animals fear the rod which gives forth noise and fire.

It was not easy to conquer the fear of these wild creatures. It needed patience as well as understanding. But Turgen had both. Season after season he gave them care and attention, and was rewarded by knowing that they accepted him and depended upon him even though they did not fully trust him. A time came when they no longer hid from him but stood watching from a safe distance as if to determine what sort of being this was from whom they received nothing but good. And he had another satisfaction. The food he gave them worked a miracle in their appearance. They were no longer the sad, dishevelled animals of former days.

His heart leaped for joy one day when he went to the feeding ground and discovered the entire ram family gathered in a group on a little mound near by.

"Eh!" Turgen declared with pleasure. "You are truly a good-looking band—strong and healthy. And you eat now as if you enjoyed it."

The rams eyed him gravely, with an expression that might have been gratitude on their long homely faces.

"Yes," they seemed to be saying. "Perhaps your pampered cattle down below would not thrive on this fare, but for savages like us it is nourishing. You see, we are not looking to put on fat, merely to survive."

With these friends, who had become like his own children, Turgen knew that he would never again be lonely as before.

[New Life on the Mountains]

"A good man greets each new day as if it were a holiday." Turgen thought of this proverb upon waking every morning now, because it described exactly the way he felt. By becoming the protector of these defenseless animals, he had found a mission which used all the warmth of his lonely heart. He only regretted that the idea of feeding the rams had occurred to him so late. "But why waste time in regret?" he reflected. "Better rejoice that the idea came to me at last."

In order not to give the rams occasion for fright, it was necessary to change certain of his habits. For one thing, he did no hunting at all in the neighborhood of his yurta and the rams' feeding ground, but travelled some distance before permitting himself to fire a shot. He was gratified to discover before long that with the coming of spring birds and small animals, especially squirrels, flocked to his mountain side in great numbers. It was as if a rumor had spread that his place was their assurance of safety. The next spring and the next it was the same. Gay and charming visitors he had never known before came to delight him with their presence, and he felt himself being drawn into another world. How wonderful to be looked upon as a friend rather than as an enemy of these creatures!

In three years the rams, too, showed growing confidence in him. He fed them regularly, even when the snow melted and the crevices of the rocky hills revealed young grass and tender new shoots on the shrubs.

One sunny day he had gone as usual to the Rams' Mountain and was standing on a ledge near the feeding ground waiting for them to appear. Soon he saw three coming cautiously toward him. Quickly he stepped out of sight. By their watchful movements he judged that they had been sent to reconnoitre, and he was more sure of this a moment later when they bleated a piercing "Ma-a! Ma-a!"

He could not doubt that this was a signal to inform hidden companions that all was well, for the entire ram family now appeared, led by a huge powerful fellow who held his head with its sharp spiralling horns proudly. "What strength!

What assurance!" Turgen thought, enchanted. The long beard and tail indicated that the leader ram was not young, but his legs were slender and built to endure. He had a reddish-brown coat flecked here and there with white. By his extraordinary size and confident attitude he impressed his authority on the herd.

When the leader after a brief survey had satisfied himself that there was no danger he spoke calmly to his charges. "Ma-a!" he said. Whereupon all the rams fell to eating.

Turgen counted them: six females and three males—with two lambs not more than three weeks old, which he had not seen before. Unlike the lambs he had noticed briefly in previous seasons, these were gay and frisky and seemed prepared to enjoy a long life. Two lambs to six females was not a large increase. Still they were promise of new generations. Turgen was overjoyed. Surely the smaller one must be a girl, the larger one a boy. He watched them drink greedily of their mothers' milk, then pick at some grass only to reject it disdainfully and return to their mothers. Clearly they preferred milk to the food of grown-ups.

Turgen could not take his eyes from the rams, his wild mountaineers. In his imagination he saw this little family grow into a great herd.

. . . .

[Tragedy]

September came, bringing its customary changeable weather. One damp and windy day when all the furies seemed loose, Turgen went as usual to take food to his charges and stand watch.

"Though why anyone should come out in this weather I don't know," he thought. "Even the rams will surely keep under shelter."

But no. He had time only to drop the hay and retreat to his watching post when there they were in full strength—the whole family. The rain annoyed them and they shook themselves from time to time. Otherwise they showed no discomfiture. While the leader and two other males circled the clearing on the alert for danger, the rest stood quietly in the lee of the cliff waiting for the rain to abate. Looking for the lambs, Turgen saw them lying snugly under their mothers' bellies.

At the first sign of the weather's clearing Turgen's favorite jumped up and ran to urge the second lamb to romp with him. She refused, preferring her comfort.

He then advanced on the older rams, trying by all the wiles he could command to get their attention. Turgen almost laughed aloud watching his antics.

"What a show-off!" Then he worried. "It is cold and wet for one so young. He will get sick. —But that's an absurd idea. He is not made of clay that he will melt."

Soon after this the rain stopped and Turgen started for home. He had gone only a few steps when a shot rang out. There were hunters somewhere in the hills nearby—too far away to menace the herd of rams but the sound of gunfire alone was enough to cause panic. While the echo was still curling around the mountains the rams crowded around the leader as he stood irresolute, his head raised, his nostrils distended to test the air. It was he who must say what they should do.

In a minute the old ram turned and came at a light trot across a narrow stone abutment that formed a natural bridge between the clearing and the adjoining hill where Turgen stood. Without hesitation the other rams followed him in single file, males and females alternating. Turgen's lamb was behind his mother and just in front of the male ram who brought up the rear. The bridge led to a labyrinth of caves where escape was easy. That it led past Turgen seemed a matter of no concern to the rams in the face of great danger.

The bridge was no doubt slippery but the rams were sure-footed and they did not give way to panic. They were moving in a direction away from the gunfire. But Turgen had another plan. He would go toward the place from which the shot came. Should he meet the hunter, the hunter would understand that he was trespassing and leave the neighborhood—for such was the custom. Only one hunter was allowed to a region.

But before Turgen could act on his resolve, there was another shot. The ram at the rear of the line, hearing it, jumped, made an incautious step, and knocked against the lamb, who fell from the bridge.

Turgen's heart turned in him as he watched the small body hurtle down the crevasse. Then, peering over, he saw the lamb lying motionless on the mountain slope. Quickly, he made his way to the spot, fearing that wild animals would get there first.

The lamb's eyes, raised to his, were black with terror. It tried convulsively to rise but could not.

"Thank God, he's alive," was Turgen's first thought. "There's a chance I can save him."

With that he stooped and lifted the lamb gently.

"Ma-a," said the lamb in a weak, childish whimper. And from a distance came a mournful answering bleat. "Ma-a! Ma-a!" that might have been the old leader. Then fog enveloped the mountain.

The lamb was surprisingly heavy, but Turgen hardly noticed the burden in his anxiety and excitement. Carefully he made his way to the yurta through the darkness, and as he went he murmured reassurance to his patient, who made no further effort to escape.

"It is not far to go. Be quiet. Rest. Do not fear —I'll do you no harm." Over and over Turgen said it, like a chant.

At the yurta Turgen laid the lamb on some soft pelts to examine him. Noticing fresh blood stains, he looked for a wound and found a flesh cut under the right front leg. It took but a minute to wash it clean and cover it with a poultice of plantain leaves to stop the bleeding.

The lamb's fright returned now and he struggled to gain his feet. But his hind legs would not obey him.

"There, there, lad," Turgen soothed him with tender strokes and pats. "What are you afraid of? I will soon make you well and take you back to your family. Who am I but an old man? There is no harm in me. Besides, who would dare to lift a hand against such a splendid fellow? Lie still. Trust me."

Pain, weariness, and the strange but unterrifying sound made by a human voice finally had their effect. The lamb rested while Turgen explored more thoroughly for possible injuries. There were scratches and bruises, none of them serious. And one hind leg was plainly swollen.

"God forbid that it should be broken," Turgen thought in dismay. For he was expert with animals and he knew the difficulty of keeping a wild young thing quiet while bone mended.

Fortunately, he found that the injury was no more than a dislocation, but extremely painful to the touch. With practiced skill, while the patient bleated piteously, he swathed the whole body to keep it immobile except for the head. Then, quickly and deftly, he set the bone, bandaged the leg and hoof between splits and satisfied himself that the lamb could do no harm to the injury should he get on his feet. As he worked the lamb regarded him with fixed and startled eyes. It was breathing heavily and clearly would have liked to offer resistance.

The bandaging operation finished, the lamb grew calm, fright gave way to weariness.

"Why," Turgen thought. "There is the same look in his eyes that I saw in Tim's when I set his arm. Children are alike. They suffer more from fright than pain." To the lamb he said: "That other little fellow drank some milk and fell asleep when I had doctored him. And so should you."

Fortunately, Turgen had only the day before brought milk from Marfa's cow. It stood untouched in the cellar. He poured some into a large wooden bowl and offered it to the lamb. At first the lamb turned his head away in distaste, but when by accident a few drops found their way into his mouth he smacked his lips with enjoyment. After that he drank willingly, with relish, looking at Turgen as if to say: "Really, this isn't bad at all."

Turgen was beside himself with joy as his charge finished his meal and promptly went to sleep.

"Food and attention—that's all anyone wants," Turgen reflected. "Just food and attention."

It was late when he himself was ready for bed, and after the agitating events of the day he slept fitfully. Whenever he wakened, as he did frequently, his first thought was for the lamb—and this stranger in his yurta seemed not a wild ram but a person close and dear to him. By going to his rescue, Turgen had found someone to share his yurta.

It is true, he marvelled, what our people say: "Misfortune can sometimes bring happiness."

The world the child lives in is to him an endless source of wonder and curiosity. People and places, birds, beasts, and stars, cities and farms, all the modern means of communication and travel engage his attention. Good factual books in the fields of science and social studies answer many of his questions, but so far as human relationships are concerned, sound, lively stories tell the child more about himself and his ever widening social world than encyclopedias or other factual books possibly can. Realistic stories help the child to understand himself, and they orient him in the wide and varied world of people in which he lives. Such stories can be as

TODAY IN THE UNITED STATES

exciting as fairy tales and as full of humor or adventure or romance. The difference lies in their plausibility. A realistic story is one in which everything that happens is possible and seems probable. The plot may turn simply upon a child's need to stoop down and tie his shoelaces (*Wait for William,* p. 105), or it may involve a tremendous adventure like the Little Paiute's difficulties in leading his grandmother across the mountains and desert to her home. But whatever the action of the realistic story, it must carry the conviction of complete plausibility so that the reader can identify himself with the hero and believe in his mistakes or triumphs as if they were his own and had really happened.

Didacticism past and present

Such is the pattern of the modern realistic story, which, oddly enough, has its roots in the didacticism of the past. In the eighteenth and nineteenth centuries, little juvenile tracts in story form with children as the characters were designed to teach the young to be pious or industrious or honest.[1] Many years went by before *Hans Brinker, Heidi, Tom Sawyer,* and *Little Women* broke this pattern of unrelieved didacticism. These remarkable books were thoroughly entertaining, moral but not moralistic, and so popular that their success would seem to be sufficient to wipe out forever the juvenile tract type of story. But not so. Didacticism in books addressed to children seems to rise in one form or another in every generation. The theological didacticism of the Puritans hung grimly over the heads of their children. And the intellectual didacticism of the eighteenth century and the moralistic didacticism of Maria Edgeworth in the early nineteenth century were almost equally oppressive. Now we are developing a kind of sociological didacticism for children that closely parallels the "How to Win Friends and Influence People" sort of books for adults. Today there are little stories about a child who goes to kindergarten, knocks over the other children's blocks, and grabs their possessions until he is shunned by all. Then, one day he learns to share and lo, he becomes a beloved member of the group, immediately. This sort of thing might seem harmless enough, except that it induces the same kind of priggish self-righteousness that the *Elsie Dinsmore* books used to breed. Upon hearing such a story, normally grabby five-year-olds remark piously, "Wasn't he *bad? I* never do that." And momentarily the little hypocrites believe it. A story about a child's rejection of his small brother as a pest brought horrified condemnation from a family of four children who were normally fond of each other but were always protesting the hampering presence of the baby sister. These stories are numerous today. Their realism

[1] See May Hill Arbuthnot, *Children and Books,* Scott, Foresman, 1957, p. 48

is not real, but is a priggish picture of sinning and reforming to the point of perfection. Besides being dull reading, such stories promote unwholesome feelings of self-righteous superiority.

There have even been some picture-stories for young children on interracial relationships, stories about white sheep with one black brother or white rabbits with one spotted brother. In both cases the black or spotted animal has been shunned by his family although the children can never see why. The solution of these problems is as synthetic as the situations. Good race relationships are not taught this way. They develop from agreeable first-hand contact with people of another race or from vicarious experience through books in which peoples of other races are shown to be more like than different from ourselves. Adults who read *Heidi* when they were children can remember how much they wished to know Swiss children and to see Heidi's mountain home. They were predisposed to like the Swiss people because of Heidi. So white children who enjoy *Steppin and Family* discover, in the midst of a thoroughly entertaining story, that this Negro family is much like other families they know and that Steppin, once he gets over his cockiness, is the kind of boy they would like. *Steppin and Family* is not a tract on race relationships but a picture of normal, likable people, making mistakes and enjoying occasional triumphs—in short, it is a good story.

Didacticism is not dead, and something called bibliotherapy may nurture its continuance. But, on the whole, the fine realistic literature written for the modern child is free of this taint. The adult, who guides children's reading, needs to know the books he selects for children so that he can avoid the dull little tracts and select the fine vigorous stories which give children insight into their own personal problems and social relationships without smugness.

Values of realistic stories

Realism for the youngest begins with himself, his personal problems and needs, and those of other children like himself. The children's mistakes are often shown, but their stories are full of reassurance. Paddy has to learn that church is no place for pets. Andrewshek, in *Poppy Seed Cakes*, is saved from the sad results of his irresponsibility by the all-enveloping love of Auntie Katushka. William, although deserted by his impatient brothers and sisters, who won't wait for him, triumphs grandly. And Dr. Trotter's visit turns out to be a delightful event with a surprise ending, thanks to the doctor's gold watch and ingenuity. Family life in stories for the youngest is full of affectionate reinforcement and understanding. Such stories build the small child's confidence and keep alive his sense of being loved and of finding life full of delightful possibilities.

Gradually, stories for young children spur them on to further achievement and responsibility and, at the same time, orient them into the everyday institutions of their community and their country. Hank and Hetty want "squeaky, creaky shoes," but know they have to earn them by their own efforts. The insatiable curiosity of Yonie Wondernose proves invaluable to his family, and Roger's patient persistence wins him a glimpse of the fox and more. Even in this small selection of stories from the great body of realistic tales for children, the stories for the sixes, sevens, and eights show the characters living in cities and suburbs, on farms, deserts, and mountain tops. The children go to school, dancing school, church, stores, the county fair, the library, the circus, and even live joyously on a riverboat bound for the south.

Children who read these stories or hear them read share vicariously these experiences. Moreover, they discover in the process that their country is made up of different kinds of people living in different parts of the country, with different problems, different religious customs but with the same family affection and loyalties—mountaineers, riverboat people, cotton pickers, Pennsylvania Dutch, Indians, Negroes, Japanese, Jews, Poles, and Quakers, all citizens of the same country. Here, indeed, in the realistic stories for children is a little cross section of "life in these United States." Through such stories, sometimes hilarious, sometimes serious, but invariably representative of the people and the section of the country in which they live, children will begin to take this variety for granted. They may even sense the underlying unity of these people. Certainly young readers of these stories will grow in social sympathy and understanding.

The writers of realistic stories

The stories in this section have been chosen for their content, age appeal, and variety, but the table of contents reveals the fact that this group also includes a cross section of major writers in the field of realistic fiction for children. Not all the outstanding writers are here, but it is a representative selection. Marguerite de Angeli, Newbery Award winner, 1950, has written a series of delightful books about minority groups in this country—the Pennsylvania Dutch, Quakers, Negroes, and a Polish community in a big city. Florence Crannell Means has also made notable contributions, chiefly for adolescents, to the literature of minority groups. Lois Lenski's regional stories are some of the most important contributions of the last decade to children's social understandings and entertainment. They are distinguished by a unique gallery of characters brought vividly to life. They may be migrant workers, berry pickers, or astonished beneficiaries of a gusher oil well. They may be ignorant, inefficient, or downright ornery, but they are lifted out of their sordidness by warm family affection and pride. No child who has identified himself with Shoestring Slater or Joanda could make fun of "Crackers" or "Oakies." These stories build respect for people, all kinds of people.

Marjorie Flack has made a notable contribution to literature for the youngest, and Carolyn Haywood for the next age group, the sixes, sevens, and eights. Lavinia Davis writes for children of various ages, and her books have a warm, earthy quality that is well illustrated by the selection in this group, *Roger and the Fox*. Robert McCloskey, Eleanor Estes, and Beverly Cleary have written some of the gayest stories children have enjoyed since Tom Sawyer was set to whitewashing a fence. So each author could be singled out for a unique addition to the realism of the modern child in his modern world. It is hoped that the samples in this section will send children to the books of each author and to the stories of other excellent writers listed in the bibliography. Meanwhile, here are stories as real as the children next door, stories which will give children a clearer understanding of themselves, greater social insight, a happy sense of life's gaieties and a warm liking for the people who make this country.

PADDY'S THREE PETS

Mary G. Phillips

*This lends itself to storytelling and is a favorite
with the four- and five-year-olds.*

Once upon a time there was a big fat father
who had a fat little boy named Paddy. One evening, when fat Father came home from the office,
he wiped his feet on the mat, opened the door
with his jingly key, and whistled. Down the
stairs ran fat Paddy as fast as his short legs
would carry him—paddity-pat, paddity-pat, paddity-pat. First he hugged Father then he put his
hand into one of the big overcoat pockets. And
what do you think he pulled out? A white
guinea pig with pink eyes.

"Squeak! Squeak! Squeak!" cried the guinea
pig.

"What will you do with him?" asked fat Father.

Fat Paddy stroked the soft fur of the little
guinea pig. "I'll give him some lettuce and play
with him," he replied. And so he did, until the
guinea pig grew fat and fatter.

One evening, when fat Father came home
from the office again, he wiped his feet on the
mat, opened the door with his jingly key, and
whistled. Down the stairs came fat Paddy as fast
as his short legs would carry him—paddity-pat,
paddity-pat, paddity-pat! First he hugged Father
then he put his hand into one of the big over-

"Paddy's Three Pets." Used by permission of the author,
Mary G. Phillips

coat pockets. And what do you think he pulled
out? A little gray kitten with white paws.

"Miaow! Miaow! Miaow!" cried the kitten.

"What will you do with him?" asked fat Father.

Fat Paddy stroked the soft fur of the little
gray kitten. "I'll give him some milk and play
with him," he replied. And so he did, until the
kitten grew fat and fatter. Paddy and the guinea
pig and the kitten all played together.

One more evening, when fat Father came
home from the office, he wiped his feet on the
mat, opened the door with his jingly key, and
whistled. Down the stairs came fat Paddy as fast
as his short legs would carry him—paddity-pat,
paddity-pat, paddity-pat. First he hugged Father then he put his hand into one of the big
overcoat pockets. And what do you think he
pulled out? A little brown puppy with one
black ear.

"Bow-wow! Bow-wow! Bow-wow!" cried the
puppy.

"What will you do with him?" asked fat Father.

Fat Paddy stroked the soft brown puppy. "I'll
give him some milk and play with him," he replied. And so he did, until the brown puppy
with one black ear grew fat and fatter.

One Sunday morning fat Paddy, the fat
guinea pig, the fat kitten, and the fat puppy
were all playing together on the sunny porch.
It was a quiet day. No grocer's wagon rumbled
over the street. No children's feet skipped and

scuffled on the way to school. Far away fat Paddy heard the church bell.

"Ding-dong! Ding-dong! Ding-dong!" it called and that meant "Come to church! Come to church! Come to church!"

Fat Paddy scrambled to his feet and gathered his pets gently in his arms. He said to them, "It is time for me to wash my face and hands and put on my best suit and new shoes, for I am going to church with Father. I will put you, fat guinea pig, and you, fat kitty, and you, fat puppy, in a warm, cozy place for a nap."

Hanging in the hall was fat Father's overcoat. Into one deep, warm pocket he put the kitten; into another the guinea pig; and into the inside pocket, dark, deep, and warm, he squeezed the puppy. Then fat Paddy went upstairs—up one step, up two steps, up three steps, up, up, up, up went his feet to the very top.

When he was quite ready for church, he came down the stairs—paddity-pat, paddity-pat, paddity-pat—and there was fat Father waiting for him in the hall. Fat Father had on his overcoat. The pockets bulged and were quite heavy, but then Father's pockets always did bulge, and they always were heavy, for he kept lots of nice things in those pockets. Fat Paddy was thinking of his own best suit and his own new shoes. He did not remember what was in those deep, warm pockets.

Around the corner fat Father and little fat Paddy walked together and their feet kept time with the bell which was calling again: "Ding-dong! Ding-dong! Ding-dong! Come to church! Come to church! Come to church!"

Fat Father and little fat Paddy walked together into the church and up the wide aisle. They walked very quietly with hushed feet, for the church was still. At one pew they stopped and fat Paddy sat down. Fat Father took off his coat and put it over the back of the seat. Bump! went the fat guinea pig's sides against the pew.

"Squeak! Squeak!" cried the guinea pig, waking from his nap.

Quickly fat Father picked up his coat, but he did not see the guinea pig. The people sitting near by smiled. Fat Father turned the coat around and again put it over the back of the seat. This time the kitten's fat sides went Bump! against the pew. The gray kitten woke up.

"Miaow! Miaow!" cried the kitten.

People near by smiled again and so did Paddy. Father did not smile. He was puzzled. Where did the sound come from? Once more he picked up his coat. This time he squeezed the fat sides of the brown puppy. The puppy awoke from his nap.

"Bow-wow! Bow-wow!" cried the puppy.

More people smiled and Paddy leaned over to Father and whispered, "They are taking their naps in your pockets."

Fat Father smiled at Paddy and whispered back, "Home is the place for naps. I'll take them home and come back." Then fat Father picked up his coat very carefully and walked softly down the aisle.

And after that the guinea pig with pink eyes, the gray kitten with white paws, and the brown puppy with one black ear each had a little box in the garage for naps.

THE PICNIC BASKET

Margery Clark

Stories for small children repeatedly sound a reassuring note. Andrewshek is irresponsible, but Auntie Katushka's all-enveloping love saves him over and over again. The "author" of this favorite book, Poppy Seed Cakes, *is really plural. Two librarians, Margery Quigley and Mary Clark, combined their names and their talents in composing these stories which they say grew up around two children they knew.*

One cool summer morning Andrewshek's Auntie Katushka said, "Andrewshek, I think I will put some sandwiches and some cottage cheese and some poppy seed cakes and two eggs in our picnic basket. Then we will go to the park and eat our lunch there, near the water."

"May I go with you, Auntie Katushka?" said Andrewshek.

"Of course you may go to the park with me," said Auntie Katushka. "But first we have a great many things to do, before we can start to the park. I must go into the garden and catch the white goat. I will tie her up so she will not run away. Please find the kitten, Andrewshek, and put her in the cellar, so she will not worry the chickens while we are gone."

"Yes, indeed, I will find the kitten and put her in the cellar," said Andrewshek, "so she will not worry the chickens while we are gone."

But all Andrewshek really did was to lift up the red and white napkin which Auntie Katushka had laid over the picnic basket and look at the eggs and the poppy seed cakes and touch the sandwiches and taste the cottage cheese.

The goat was not easy to catch. The goat wanted to go to the park, too. She galloped round and round the garden.

At last Auntie Katushka caught her and tied her firmly to a post.

Then Auntie Katushka went into the house to get Andrewshek and the lunch basket. She saw Andrewshek peeping under the red and white napkin and tasting the cottage cheese. He had forgotten all about the kitten.

The kitten was nowhere to be found. "I think she must be paying a visit to the Mouse family," said Auntie Katushka.

Then Auntie Katushka put on her bright shawl and took her umbrella with the long crooked handle under one arm. Then she picked up the lunch basket with the red and white napkin on top and she and Andrewshek started for the park.

They went down the hill and across the tracks and past the market and down a long street until they came to the park by the water.

Andrewshek sat down on the grass beside a little stream. Andrewshek's Auntie Katushka laid her umbrella with the long crooked handle and the basket of lunch on the grass beside Andrewshek.

"Andrewshek," said Auntie Katushka, "I must go to the spring and get some water for us to drink. Please watch the basket with the eggs and the sandwiches and poppy seed cakes and cottage cheese while I am gone."

"Yes, indeed, I will watch the basket of lunch," said Andrewshek.

But what Andrewshek really did was to say to himself, "I would like to take off my shoes and my stockings and wade in the little stream. I believe I will!"

Andrewshek took cff his shoes and his stockings and went wading in the little stream.

A big white swan came floating calmly down the stream. He saw the picnic basket lying on the grass. He stopped and stretched and stretched his long neck, till he could touch the basket. "Honk! honk! honk!" said he. "I wonder what is under the red and white napkin."

The big white swan lifted the napkin with his red bill and looked in the basket. "Oh, oh, oh! Won't Mother Swan be pleased with this nice lunch!" said he. "Sandwich bread makes fine food for baby swans."

He picked up the basket in his strong red bill and floated it ahead of him down the stream.

Andrewshek could not wade after the big white swan. The water was too deep.

"Stop! Stop! White Swan!" cried Andrewshek. "That is my Auntie Katushka's picnic basket and it has our lunch in it. Please put it back on the grass."

"No, indeed! I will not put the basket back," honked the big white swan. "Sandwich bread makes fine food for baby swans and I have ten baby swans to feed."

The big white swan gave the picnic basket a little push with his red bill. The basket floated on down the little stream. The big white swan floated calmly behind it.

Just then Andrewshek's Auntie Katushka came hurrying up with the spring water. She saw the big white swan floating down the stream, with the lunch basket floating ahead of him.

Andrewshek stood in the middle of the stream, crying.

Auntie Katushka picked up her umbrella with the long crooked handle. Auntie Katushka ran along the shore until she overtook the big white swan, with the lunch basket floating ahead of him.

She caught the handle of the picnic basket in the crook of her long handled umbrella. She drew the basket safely to shore.

"Well! well!" said Auntie Katushka, as she spread the red and white napkin on the grass, and laid the sandwiches and the poppy seed cakes and the cottage cheese and the eggs upon it. "It always pays to carry an umbrella to a picnic."

DR. TROTTER AND
HIS BIG GOLD WATCH

Helen Earle Gilbert

The amusing device of a wise old doctor for allaying the fears and worries of his small patients should work vicariously for those who read or hear this story.

One fine afternoon, in the little village of Green Hill, Dr. Trotter was getting ready to go out and make his calls.

Ting-a-ling-a-ling went the telephone.

"Is that you, Doctor?" asked a worried voice. "Will you please come over? Baby Agatha's cheeks are all puffed up."

"Be right over," the doctor answered in his deep, comforting voice. "Sounds like the mumps to me. Who did you say it was?"

"This is Mrs. Cousins. Please hurry. And thank you."

Dr. Trotter picked up his hat and his doctor bag. Then he felt in the left-hand pocket of his Scotch-plaid vest, as he always did when he was going to call on a child, to be sure that he had his big watch with him.

Not that there was much chance of his losing it. For this old-fashioned round gold watch was fastened to one end of a heavy gold chain. On the other end, in his right-hand vest pocket, was the small new silver watch by which he took pulses and told the time.

Dr. Trotter and His Big Gold Watch by Helen Earle Gilbert. Copyright 1948 by Stone and Pierce. Used by permission of Abingdon Press, the publishers

Then he went out to his car. He hurried, for of all the people Dr. Trotter took care of, his favorites were the children. He was a friend to all of them. What is more, every one of them would do whatever he wanted, the moment he asked.

Baby Agatha's cheeks were plump and pink, but she was all right. Mrs. Cousins drew a long breath of relief. She bustled about to make the doctor a cup of tea, piping hot and strong. For although she had not lived on Green Hill very long, she knew, as everyone did for miles around, that the doctor liked his tea.

Dr. Trotter took the cup with a sigh of pleasure and sat down in the big corner chair. Nubbin, the little gray kitten, climbed out of her basket and up into his lap. "Ouch!" the doctor said as her claws went in. But he let her stay.

In the yard outside, Katherine and Tom Cousins, with the Butterworth boys, Hank and George Jr., were climbing in the cherry tree. They began to see how high they could climb and then jump.

Mrs. Cousins glanced out with a worried look. "I'm so afraid one of them will fall," she said.

"Tell me, Doctor, what it is that you do or say

to make the children do whatever you want, the moment you ask?"

"Well, well!" The old doctor set down his cup. "Children can always keep a secret, can't they?" He leaned back and felt in the left-hand pocket of his Scotch-plaid vest. "It's really not my secret but my grandfather's. He was a doctor, too, and this was his watch."

He pulled out the heavy old-fashioned round gold watch.

Mrs. Cousins leaned forward.

Dr. Trotter opened the back of the watch, and there was a little round keyhole.

From his right-hand vest pocket he drew out the other watch (the small new silver one with which he took pulses and told the time) and there —beside it on the heavy gold chain—hung a little shining gold key. Dr. Trotter took it off the chain and thrust it into the keyhole.

Just then the telephone rang. Mrs. Cousins ran to answer it.

"It's for you," she said. "It's Mrs. Oldfield. The minister's cut his thumb. They want you right away."

Dr. Trotter put back his watches and picked up his bag.

Nubbin yawned, curled up in her basket, and dropped off to sleep.

Out in the cherry tree the children climbed higher and higher.

The little old car carried Dr. Trotter to the minister's house where Mrs. Oldfield met him at the door. The doctor dressed the minister's thumb (which wasn't very badly cut after all). Then he went on to the Dwinney's where Jane Dwinney, who was nine, had broken out with a rash.

Just as Jane was putting out her tongue for the doctor, the telephone rang. It was Mrs. Oldfield again.

"Is the doctor there?" she asked. "Will you send him right back to the Cousins'? Tommy's fallen out of that cherry tree and hurt his ankle."

"Be right over," the doctor promised.

"Now Jane, I'll stop in on my way home. You know what for. . . . I think it's measles," he said to her mother. "Keep her warm." And he was gone.

People along the roadside and at their windows saw the doctor's car flying past and won-dered. "What's happened now?" they asked. He turned the corner into the Cousins' driveway in a great cloud of dust.

Dr. Trotter saw that the yard was empty. There was no one in the cherry tree.

With one hand in the left-hand pocket of his Scotch-plaid vest, he hurried up the steps.

He found Tommy lying on the couch, with his swollen ankle on a pillow. He was trying not to cry. The other children stood around him. Mrs. Cousins was hurrying with ice in one hand and a hot-water bottle in the other. (In the excitement she had forgotten which one was right for swell-ings.)

The instant he saw, with his professional eye, that it was only a sprain, Dr. Trotter reached for his watch. Tommy wiped his face and smiled. The children looked at one another.

Out came the big old round gold watch. The doctor reached into his right-hand pocket, and out came the small new silver watch. He looked on the chain for the little gold key.

But the little gold key was gone!

Dr. Trotter felt in all his pockets. He hunted through his bag and poked down into the sides of the corner chair.

Katherine and Hank looked under the sofa.

George Jr. looked under the rug.

Mrs. Cousins lifted the kitten basket carefully, not to wake little sleeping Nubbin, and looked under that.

But no one could find the little gold key.

"Wait!" cried Mrs. Cousins. "I may have a key that will fit!" She ran and got her key ring, her key case, and an old desk drawer full of keys. But not one of them fitted the little round key-hole.

"Maybe the Oldfields have one!" shouted Tommy.

Mrs. Cousins rushed to the telephone. She was so excited that Mrs. Oldfield got excited, too.

"A key for Dr. Trotter, you say?" she asked. "Well, I'll see. And I'll call up the neighbors and ask them."

In no time at all Mrs. Oldfield was at the door.

"Here's my key ring," she puffed. "Here's the key to our front door, to the garage, to Fred's case of stuffed birds, and to the minister's type-writer. . . . The neighbors will be right along with their keys," she added.

Tommy laughed.

In bounced Mrs. Dwinney. She had got a ride with the bread man. "Here's the key to our barn," she said, "and to our front-hall closet. Here are some drawer keys and keys to two chests and to the station wagon."

"My goodness!" exclaimed Mrs. Cousins. "All we want is a little bit of a watch key."

In trotted Miss Fuller, the milliner. She had a bunch of Yale keys on a ring and an old satchel. "This," she said with pride, "has in it all the keys that have been in our family for sixty-seven years."

Behind her came Mr. Pound, the grocer, with the keys to his store.

Then came Mrs. Pound with two very ancient clock keys, and Mrs. Trotter with all the doctor's other keys.

"The sexton's even bringing the key to the church," cried Mrs. Cousins from the doorway, "and it's thirteen inches long!"

The door flew open again. There stood Grandma Stepney, the oldest person for miles around.

"It was *tea* you wanted, wasn't it?" she asked, panting a little. "I couldn't quite hear over the telephone, but you said it was for the doctor."

On a tray she held her pink luster teapot, steaming hot, and a large plate of warm cinnamon buns.

Katherine ran to bring her a chair.

Mrs. Cousins took the tray and said, "Thank you."

The doctor looked a little worried.

But Tommy's eyes were bright with excitement.

Just at that minute Nubbin stood up in her basket. She rounded her back, rolled out her red tongue, and yawned. Down in the basket something glittered.

"What's that?" shrieked Tommy.

Katherine rushed over and picked it up.

"Nubbin, you bad kitty!" cried Tommy. "You went to sleep on the little gold key!"

Dr. Trotter took the key and hurried over to Tommy. He opened the back of his big round watch, thrust in the key and turned it a few times.

Then he lowered the watch into Tommy's outstretched hands.

Tick-a-tick-a-tick-a-tick! Everybody listened. Tommy held the watch tight against his ear.

"Before we begin," said the doctor as he took the iodine and dressings from his bag, "where would you like to have me set my watch Tom? At what time?"

His fingers moved deftly over Tommy's anklebone. "Some people," he went on, "like to have it tell them how old they are. What will you have?"

"I'll have twelve," Tommy answered firmly. "That's the highest one. And anyway, I'll be twelve in two years more."

Dr. Trotter nodded. He set the hands at two minutes before twelve o'clock.

"*Ssh-sh-h-h!*" cried all the children.

The room grew very quiet. Mrs. Cousins stared, her finger on her lip. Grandma Stepney stopped rocking. Mrs. Pound looked at Mrs. Dwinney and smiled.

Tommy's eyes shone. He hardly felt the old doctor's gentle hands on his ankle. He hardly felt the dressing that Dr. Trotter was putting on.

Tick-a-tick-a-tick-a-tick went the big round watch against Tommy's ear.

And then!

RING-RING-RING-RING-RING-RING-RING-RING-RING-RING-RING-RING!

Tommy's face broke into a smile.

"A watch that strikes," said Mrs. Cousins. "Well, I never!"

DOWN DOWN THE MOUNTAIN

Ellis Credle

It is especially good for city children to encounter stories about mountaineer children whose environment is less complex and more challenging than their own. The ingenuity and self-reliance of Hetty and Hank in solving their problems and achieving their heart's desire are admirable.

Once upon a time, in a little log cabin away up in the Blue Ridge Mountains, there lived a little girl named Hetty and her brother Hank.

Although their home was a small one, it was a cozy place to live. There was a big stone fireplace at one end. That was where Mammy cooked beans and cornmeal mush and fried pork in a big, black, frying pan.

There was a big bed in one corner and a little bed in the other corner, and in the middle of the room there was a long table made of planks. That was where Mammy and Pappy and Hetty and Hank ate their dinner every day.

All kinds of things hung from the rafters,

Down Down the Mountain, by Ellis Credle. New York: Thomas Nelson & Sons

strings of shucky beans, bunches of bright red peppers, ears of popcorn all tied together, hams, and sausages, and baskets full of this and that.

Never in all their lives had Hetty or Hank had a pair of shoes. In the summer it was fun to run around barefoot, but when winter came, and the snow lay on the mountains like a chilly white blanket, their little feet were blue with cold and they longed for a pair of shoes.

They each wanted a beautiful shining pair that sang, "Creaky—squeaky—creaky—squeaky," every time they walked.

They begged their mammy to buy them some shoes, but she said, "You can't find shoes like that in these hills! Such shining shoes come from the town, away down down at the foot of the mountain."

So they asked their Pappy, but he said, "There's not a cent of money in this household. We've everything we need right here in these hills."

Hetty and Hank felt very sad, but they did not give up.

"Let's ask our Granny," said Hetty. And they did.

"Some shining shoes?" chirped Granny. "I'll tell you how you can get them yourselves."

"How? How?" cried Hetty and Hank.

"Plant some turnip seeds," said Granny, "and when they have grown into fine big turnips, you can take them all the way down to town and trade them off for some shining, creaky, squeaky shoes."

"Thanky' Ma'am, that's what we'll do," cried Hetty and Hank.

They raced away and planted some turnip seeds in a tilted field right next to Pappy's corn patch.

Home they went singing,

"Our fields are high up in the air,
We wouldn't dare plant pumpkins there,
For pumpkins grow so big and round,
They'd break right off and tumble down.
But turnips grow on hills or vales,
Because they twist their little tails
Around the rocks and hold on tight
And don't let go for day or night!"

When Hetty and Hank got home it was dark. The whippoorwills were calling sadly from the deep woods, "Whip-poor-will! Whip-poor-will!" and a little owl was asking "Who? Who-o-o?"

Mammy was waiting for them. She gave them a nice supper of corn bread and butter and yellow honey. Then she tucked them snugly into bed. They dreamed all night about shining shoes that played a creaky, squeaky tune, just like Pappy's fiddle.

The next day they climbed up the steep, steep mountain-side to see if the turnip seeds had come up. But they had not, and Hetty and Hank had to wait and wait and wait, before they spied the baby turnip leaves peeping out of the ground.

Then there was plenty of work for Hetty and Hank! They had to chop away the weeds each day, and chase away the worms and the bugs and the grasshoppers that come for a taste of nice green turnip leaves.

When there was no rain and the little turnips felt dry and thirsty, Hetty and Hank had to bring big buckets of water to make them fresh and green again.

The little turnips were very grateful. They grew and grew until they were the finest and the biggest turnips to be found any where in the hill country.

Then Hetty and Hank brought Granny and Mammy and Pappy up to see them.

"Sakes alive!" cried Mammy, "I never saw such big turnips!"

"Yes siree!" smiled Granny, "These are mighty juicy turnips."

"And they'll fetch a fine price in the town," said Pappy. "Hetty and Hank shall have the old gray horse to take them down the mountain."

So Hank quickly brought the gray horse. Then they pulled up all the beautiful turnips and packed them into a big bag.

Pappy laid the bag proudly across the gray horse's back, then he gave Hetty and Hank a boost and settled them safely right behind the turnips. Now they were ready to go.

"It's no trouble to find the town," said Granny. "Just you keep to the road and it will lead you down. Sometimes it's steep—just like the stair. Sometimes it's narrow—like a hair. It turns and twists and winds around, but at the end you'll find the town!"

"We'll keep to the road," promised Hetty and

Hank. Hank pulled on the reins. Hetty gave the gray horse a slap on the side, and they were off.

"Goodby!" cried Granny and Mammy and Pappy.

"Goodby!" waved Hetty and Hank. And away they went, clippity, cloppity, down the road to town.

They had not gone very far before they came to an old man cutting sugar cane in a field beside the road.

"Howdy young ones!" he called. "What have you in that big bag?"

"Some turnips we're taking to sell in the town," said Hank proudly.

"Oh, my! Turnips!" cried the old man. "How I'd love some nice juicy turnips for my dinner. Couldn't you spare me just a few?"

"I suppose we wouldn't miss just a few," said Hetty, and she gave him some.

On they jogged between great bushes of pink mountain laurel, and after awhile they came to an old woman who was making soap in a big black kettle.

"Howdy, children!" she called. "What have you in that big bag?"

"Some turnips we're taking down to town," said Hank.

"Turnips!" cried the old woman. "Mercy me! How I'd love just a taste of turnip for my dinner. Couldn't you spare me just two, one for my old man and one for me?"

"I suppose we wouldn't miss just two," said Hetty and she gave her two big ones.

Down, down, down they went between the rows of tall blue mountains, down, down, down until they came to a little stream flowing over the rocks. There the little road ended. They looked here, they looked there they looked everywhere but it was nowhere to be seen.

But just then along came a woman on horseback, splishing and splashing right down the middle of the stream.

"What's the matter young ones?" she called.

"We've lost the little road to town," said Hank.

"Follow the creek," said the woman. "That's all the road there is in these parts."

So Hetty and Hank went splashing along and along and pretty soon they spied the little road leading up from the water.

They said goodby to the kind woman and gave her a bunch of turnips for her dinner.

On they went along the little road beneath the tall pine trees. After awhile they overtook a man who was driving flock of turkeys down to town. "Howdy," greeted the man. "What have you in that big bag?"

"Some turnips we're taking to sell in the town," said Hank.

"Oh my stars!" said the man. "Turnips! and I've had nary a bit to eat since break of dawn. A nice, juicy turnip would taste mighty good now, for I've been running after these turkeys 'til I'm nigh worn out."

"We'll have to give him a handful of turnips," said Hetty. And she did.

"Thanky, thanky," said the man, "you're kind and generous young ones!"

Now they were very near to town. They could look down and see the roof tops in the valley.

The little road became so smooth and straight that the gray horse broke into a gallop.

"Here's the town!" cried Hank.

Along they went, clippity clop, clippity clop, past the schoolhouse, past the church, past the courthouse, and suddenly there was the little red store.

"Whoa!" cried Hank, pulling on the reins. "Here's the place to trade our turnips off for some shining shoes!"

They climbed down and lifted off the sack. Somehow it felt very light and very, very empty. Had they given all their turnips away?

Hetty put her hand into the bag and brought out one large, fat, lonesome turnip. It was the only one left.

And there—shining through the store window were those beautiful, creaky, squeaky, shining shoes!

Hetty and Hank gazed at them longingly. But one turnip would not buy a pair of shoes.

Two big tears began to roll down Hetty's cheeks.

"There! There!" said Hank. "No use crying. We'll just walk around and see the sights. Come on."

So they walked along the little road looking this way and that way. They saw the big covered wagons, all loaded with apples, come rumbling down from the hills. They saw the men trading horses in the courthouse square. Then a train went thundering past and they watched it with round eyes.

Along and along they went and after awhile they came to a field where there were many, many people. A big sign over the gate said "COUNTY FAIR."

Hetty and Hank went hustling and bustling about in the crowd. Pretty soon they came to a long row of tables, each one groaning with a different kind of vegetable. There were tomatoes on this one, and beans on that one, and pumpkins on the other one.

"Oh, here are some turnips!" cried Hetty.

"Are they as big as ours?" asked Hank.

Hetty held up her turnip. It seemed larger and juicier than the rest.

"Howdy, young ones," said the old man who was looking at the turnips. "Do you want to enter that turnip in the contest?"

"What contest?" asked Hank.

"Why there's a prize offered for the finest turnip at the fair," replied the old man.

"Mercy me!" said Hetty. "Let's try it."

"You bet your life!" said Hank.

So the old man wrote their names on a tag and tied it to the fat turnip. Then he laid it carefully among all the other turnips.

"You are just in the nick of time," he said, "for I was just a-getting ready to do the judging."

He began to examine the turnips. He weighed each one to see how heavy it was. He felt each one to see how firm it was. And when he had tried them all he held one large turnip high above his head.

"Folks!" he cried. "Here's the finest turnip at the fair. It belongs to a little girl and a little boy!"

Hetty and Hank listened with all their ears.

"Come forward, young ones and receive the prize!"

Hetty held out her hand and there shining up at her was a bright five-dollar gold piece.

"Oh thank you sir!" cried Hetty and Hank. "Now we can buy our shining shoes!"

They dashed along past the beans and tomatoes. They ran past the squash and skipped past the potatoes. They dodged through the hustle and the bustle on the fair grounds. They raced

along the street until they came to the little, red store.

The storekeeper was standing behind the counter.

"We want to buy some beautiful, creaky, squeaky shoes!" said Hank all out of breath.

The storekeeper got down his brightest shoes, and Hetty and Hank each chose a pair that played a creaky, squeaky tune.

Then they bought some gifts to take home with them. A yellow hat for Pappy, a bright sash for Mammy and a big, red handkerchief and a package of needles for Granny.

And off they started on the long trip home. Up, up, up they wound, round and round the mountain, past the pink laurel flowers, along the little stream and underneath the tall pine trees.

After a long, long climb they reached their own little cabin. There sat Mammy and Pappy and Granny waiting on the porch. How pleased they were to see Hetty and Hank and all the new things they had brought!

The next day was Sunday, so they put on their beautiful things and went to preaching.

Hetty and Hank walked proudly into the meeting-house. Their shoes were playing such a creaky, squeaky tune that all the people craned their necks to see who could be wearing such beautiful shoes.

YONIE WONDERNOSE

Marguerite de Angeli

There could hardly be a more appealing introduction to the Pennsylvania Dutch than Yonie. *Young children will also enjoy Marguerite de Angeli's* Henner's Lydia, Thee, Hannah! *and many others, and when they are a little older, her medieval story* The Door in the Wall, *which won the Newbery Award. Mrs. De Angeli's beautiful illustrations for her books add to their charm.*

Yonie was a little Pennsylvania Dutch boy. He was seven. He lived with Mom and Pop, Malinda, Lydia, and little Nancy on a farm in Lancaster County. His brother Ammon was grown up and had been away for a long time. Granny lived on the farm, too. She lived in her own part of the house. But most of the time she was in the kitchen helping Mom and Malinda.

Yonie's real name was Jonathan, but everyone called him Yonie. Pop called him "Yonie Wondernose" because he was so curious. He wanted to know about everything. If Pop brought a package into the house, he must see what was in it. If the Bishop came to talk to Pop, he must listen. If Mom had a pot boiling on the stove, he must lift the lid to see what was cooking. Sometimes the steam burned his nose, but it didn't keep him from looking the next time. If Malinda was baking a cake, Yonie was sure to open the oven door to see what kind it was.

"A Wondernose you are for sure!" she would scold. "Look now how it falls so fast!"

When Yonie and Lydia were on their way to school, he stopped so many times that they were often late. He hung over the fence to watch the men filling the wagons with stones from the stone crusher. He stood watching while a man changed a tire on a car, or while Nathan Straub seeded the bean field.

"We'll be late!" wailed Lydia. "Come now!" But she stood to watch, too!

Yonie's jacket was fastened with hooks and eyes instead of buttons. Pop didn't have buttons on his suit either. That is because he was an Amishman. And the Amish people never use buttons unless they are necessary. Yonie wore a broad hat just like Pop's hat, too—a straw one in summer and a black felt one in winter. And Mom cut Yonie's hair around a bowl, just like she cut Pop's. But Pop wore a beard such as all Amishmen wear.

This afternoon Pop and Mom were going visiting. They were taking Malinda and Lydia with them in the Germantown wagon, and they would stay overnight. Granny, Yonie, and Nancy stood in the doorway to see them off.

"Good-by," said Pop. "Don't be a Wondernose, now, and forget what you are doing!"

"No, Pop, I won't," Yonie answered.

"Remember, you are the man of the house now," said Mom.

"Ya, I will." Yonie nodded and stood straighter.

"Take good care of the barn creatures," called Pop again. "Feed and water them well. Don't forget, if anything happens, be sure to look after the horses first. They get scared so fast. Next, look after Dunder the red bull. He cost a lot of money, so take good care of him, don't forget! We see, now, if you are a man!"

Then he winked, and Yonie knew what he meant. Pop had promised him something when he was old enough to be trusted like a man but no one, not even Mom, knew about that promise. It was a secret between Pop and Yonie.

"I won't forget!" he called back.

As the wagon drove off, he thought, "Now Pop thinks I'll be a Wondernose, but I'll show him! I'll show him how big and smart I can be! When he comes home tomorrow, he'll see that I can take care of the animals by myself. Then, maybe, he'll let me do what he promised!"

"Ya, vell," said Granny. "Soon it makes time for supper. More rount-wood I need for the fire, and the cistern water iss all! The last I used for sprinkling the plants and for scrubbing."

Cistern water was soft rain water that Granny liked best for washing dishes and such things. Pop teased Granny because she was always scrubbing.

"It's a wonder you don't scrub the hoe handles and the fence posts, you are so clean!" he would say.

But Granny only said, "Better so, as like some I know, with floors all smeary and things all hoodled up!" and went on scrubbing. Yonie

knew he must pump a lot of water to keep Granny supplied. He must get the wood for the kitchen stove. But he must take care of the animals, too.

He went first to the pasture for the cows, Blossom, Bluebell, and Buttercup. As they ambled down the lane, a squirrel scolded at Yonie from the fence rail, then scampered up a tree and into a knothole. Yonie *must* see where he went. Up the tree he scrambled and peered into the hole. He thrust his finger in to see what he could find. But he drew it out again in a hurry, for Mr. Squirrel gave it a sharp bite!

"Ach!" Yonie scolded himself, "here I am, being a Wondernose, just like always."

When he climbed down from the tree, the cows had scattered to nibble the grass at the edges of the lane. It took Yonie some time to get them started again in the right direction and to their places in the cowshed. He hurried to throw down fresh straw for their beds, while Granny milked. He carried water for them and called Nancy to come and put milk in the cats' dish for Malta and the four kittens.

He took the horses to the trough for water. He patted Star's broad back and thought of what Pop had promised. Then he went to look after Dunder. Dunder was kept in a pen and shed of his own on the far side of the barn.

Yonie had helped Pop, but he had never taken care of Dunder by himself as Ammon always had. He knew he must speak quietly to the great beast. He knew how to use the staff that Pop kept handy, too, and how to attach it to the ring in the bull's nose. So he felt safe, even though Dunder was so big and fierce.

The summer was really over. The hay was in the barn and the harvest gathered. But it had turned very warm again. Yonie's shirt was damp from the heat, and his yellow hair clung to his forehead. He wished he could stop work and go wading in the creek. The Little Conestoga ran through the meadow, and Yonie knew how cool it would be in the shade of the willow tree on its bank. He dropped the bucket he was carrying and started toward the creek. Then he remembered his promise to Pop—and Pop's promise to him. He picked up the bucket and went to pump more water for the rest of the animals and the chickens.

"Ach, vell," he told himself, "I can douse good, once, when I get the chores done."

He grunted as he lifted the heavy pail out of the trough. The water spilled a little onto his bare feet. It felt good and made clean patterns where it washed off the dust. He carried the bucket as full as he could. The chicken pans had to be filled, the calves needed a drink, the pigs had to be fed, and there was still the water to carry in for Granny.

When Yonie had filled the pans in the chicken yard, he made sure to lock the chicken house door. He knew the eggs had been gathered, so he didn't bother to look inside again.

He picked up the buckets in a hurry to water the calves and then stopped. Was that an airplane he heard? He couldn't see it but now he remembered that Granny wanted the roundwood for the fire.

"Rount-wood gives a hot fire," she had said, "and supper makes soon."

So Yonie went to the woodpile to get it. He could see Nancy under the big tree happily playing with her doll.

He started to gather the wood, and again came the deep purr of an airplane. This time he was sure. It might even be a new kind. He dropped the wood and ran to the corner of the house where he could see better.

As he craned his neck to follow the flight of the plane, he heard Nancy call, "Wonderno-ose Yonie! Wonderno-ose Yonie!" she teased.

He made a face in Nancy's direction, but turned back to the woodpile. When he carried the wood into the kitchen, Granny wasn't there. Something was bubbling on the stove. It smelled so good! He *must* see what was inside! Could it be apple dumplings? He lifted the lid. Ouch! The steam burned his nose, as usual.

He wondered where Granny could have gone, leaving the supper to cook by itself. But there was more work to do, so he went out to pump water for the calves. The water made him think again of the cool Conestoga. How he wished he were in it! It wouldn't take long for a splash, he thought, and it would feel so good! Suddenly he dropped the pump handle and started for the creek. He had his shirt and trousers off almost before he got there, and then—in he went.

The coolness and the quiet murmur of the creek made Yonie stay longer than he meant to. Then in the stillness he heard the bleating of the calves, and suddenly remembered that they were thirsty. He pulled on his clothes as best he could without drying and hurried back to the pump.

When he opened the barnyard gate, the calves came running to get at the water. The little black-and-white one nipped at Yonie's trousers, butted him with his knobbly head, and licked at his hands to see if he had any sugar.

Yonie thought, "That little runt now, if he was mine, I'd call him Wondernose like Pop calls me, the way he's nosing into my hand for sugar! I wish he *was* mine! It would be more fun to water them if one could be mine. If Pop would give me even a little pig the next time there are any, I'd take care of it till it grew big."

But more than he wanted the calf, more than the little pig, Yonie wanted what Pop had promised. He closed the gate and hurried to get the sour milk for the pigs. He could hear them squealing around beyond the corner of the barn.

When they saw Yonie coming with their supper, they squealed more loudly than ever. There were vegetable parings, bits of bread, and celery tops floating in it. But the pigs thought it was delicious. The great big old sow put both feet in the trough so as to be sure and get her share.

When Yonie went to the kitchen with the water for Granny, she still wasn't there. He thought, once, that he heard her call. But when he listened again he heard nothing.

The food in the kettle had boiled over and didn't smell so good as it had before. He called up the stairs, "Granny! Oh, Granny! Somesing smells like burning!" But there was no answer.

He called again, then listened. But there was still no answer. Then he went upstairs and looked in all of the rooms. But still he saw no one and heard nothing. He went downstairs and over into Granny's part of the house.

"Granny!" he shouted, but only the ticking of the clock answered him.

As he stood wondering where Granny might be, his eyes lighted on the painted chest. There Granny kept the old book. It was full of stories that Yonie loved to hear. Granny never allowed the children to open the chest themselves.

She always said, "The things in it are over two hundred years old. That's when your great-great-

great-grandfather came with his family and many others from the old country. They came so they might worship God in their own way."

Yonie thought, "It wonders me, now, what else is in there besides the book. I could just look once, and Granny would never know."

He went to the chest where it stood under the window and lifted the lid. But before he could even begin to see anything, he seemed to hear Pop's voice, saying, "Yonie! Yonie Wondernose!"

He stood for a second, then was sure that he heard a voice.

It sounded like a real voice coming through the open window.

He listened. He could just barely hear it. But it called, "Yonie! Oh, Yonie!"

He dropped the lid with a bang! Out he flew, through to the kitchen, to the porch, down the yard, through the arbor, and to the chicken house.

Now he could hear the voice plainly, and it was coming from inside the chicken house. "Yonie! Ach, Yonie! Let me out of here!"

He turned the lock and opened the door and out fell Granny! She had been shut up in the heat of the chicken house ever since Yonie filled the water pans! Yonie helped her to a seat in the arbor and ran to get her a drink of water.

When she could speak, she said, "Ach, Yonie! Why didn't you be *this* time a *Wondernose*? Always look *first* inside, *then* lock the door." But Yonie looked so sorry that Granny had to laugh.

"Never mind," she said. "You locked the door like your Pop said. You didn't know Granny was in there. Next time—look inside first." She sniffed the air. "Somesing smells like burning," she said. "Supper, I guess. Ach, vell, ve have spreadin's anyways on our bread, and shoofly pie. Call Nancy."

They went in to supper.

Nancy helped Granny put the "spreadin's" on the table. There was apple butter, currant jelly, stewed apples, and piccalilli. Then there was the pie. It was a shoofly pie made with soft molasses cake baked in a piecrust. Yonie was very fond of it. While they were eating, Granny told how it felt to be shut up in the chicken house.

"Hot as seven in a bed it was in there! I count the chickens over and over. They stare at me, and cluck like I don't belong in there. And I stare back. I try to get out by the place where the chickens go in, but for a long time now I'm too big for that!"

Yonie and Nancy laughed to think of Granny down on her hands and knees trying to get through that little opening. Yonie thought how it would be to sleep seven in a bed!

"Whew!" he said.

Yonie wished he could douse again in the creek, it was so warm in the kitchen. Granny looked warm, too, and fanned herself with her apron. Even Nancy pushed little wisps of hair up onto her braids.

Suddenly, as they finished eating, the spot of sunlight faded from the table, and there was a growl of thunder.

"It makes like a storm, ain't, Granny?" said Yonie.

"*Ya,*" agreed Granny. "The heat iss something wonderful. It makes a storm, maybe. Make everything fast by the barn."

Nancy ran out to get her doll. And Yonie went to make sure he had done all that Pop told him to do. Yes, he had fed and watered the barn creatures. They were all quiet for the night. When he came in, it was time for him to go to bed.

There was another grumble of thunder, but Yonie didn't hear it. He was asleep.

Suddenly a bright flash woke him with a start. With the flash came a sizzling "bang" of thunder! Yonie jumped out of bed. He knew the storm had broken right overheard and that something might have caught fire from the lightning.

"Ach!" he thought. "Somesing does happen maybe, like Pop said. Now I have to see if Star and Blackie are all right and Dunder."

He reached for his breeches just as Granny came hurrying to the foot of the stairs. She called, "Yonie! Oh, Yonie! Come quick!"

But she didn't need to tell him the barn was afire. He could see it as he ran past the window and down the steep, twisty stairs. Then the rain began.

Yonie didn't wait for Granny, who was tying her shoes. He ran headlong through the shower toward the barn. Something black flew past him, then four somethings. It was Malta and the four kittens. A cloud of pigeons fluttered about, then flew off toward the woods. They lived in the cupola of the barn.

Now a blaze came out of the barn like a great red flower that grew and grew, even though the rain was coming down faster and faster. Yonie had to hold his breath as he tried to go through the thick smoke that already filled the barn. If he was going to get the horses out he would have to cover their heads. Otherwise, Pop had told him, they would run right back into the fire again.

Yonie knew where to find the old carriage robe that Pop kept hanging near the horses just in case of need. Stumbling toward it, he got it in his hands at last. Then he hurried to hang it over Star's head. Granny came running in with her shawl to put over Blackie and got him out of the barn door just behind Yonie and Star.

Lightning flashed and thunder banged. Rain poured down, but the fire burned fiercer and roared louder, for now it had reached the hay.

"Run!" cried Granny. "Quick now! Over past the house, and we tie the horses to the fence post."

Blackie tossed his head and tried to get away, but Granny held on. Star snorted and neighed and tried to fling off the cover from his head. But Yonie held it tight till they reached the fence. The rain stopped as suddenly as it had begun, and a breeze sprang up.

Back raced Yonie and Granny toward the barn. Granny was breathing hard.

"Run ahead and let loose the chickens!" she cried. "The wind blows that way and sparks soon set fire to the roof."

"Ya!" Yonie shouted, as he turned off to let out the chickens. They ran out scolding and clucking, and scattered over the road and fields.

"It's good I ain't in there still!" panted Granny. "The fire makes worse on this side, so we loose the cows next. Then Dunder."

They got Blossom and Buttercup out safely and left them to run toward the orchard. But before they could get Bluebell out of the way, a burning brand fell across her back. It rolled off, but left a scorched place. She leaped clear of the door in one jump, then ran off after the other cows.

Granny and Yonie got out just in time, and ran to open the calf pen, which was close by.

"How shall we fix poor Bluebell, so the burn won't hurt?" panted Yonie.

"Apple butter," gasped Granny, spreading her skirts to head off the calves so they would go the right way. "Apple butter makes the pain go away. I fix it while you get Dunder out. Get him quick! He's such a fine bull, your Pop gets mad if he's hurt! Quick!"

Granny started off toward the house, and Yonie hurried around to the front of the barn toward Dunder's shed. He could see the bare frame of the roof through the fire. And just as he looked up, a great timber fell.

"It must be right on the ground near the pigpen!" he thought excitedly. "I must see where it went. Besides, what of the pigs and the old sow?"

He turned back the way he had come and went around to where the pigs were shut in beyond the calf pen. The timber had fallen inside the barn, and not on the pigpen. But Yonie opened the door and called to them, making a sucking noise with his mouth as if he were going to feed them. They came rushing up. And Yonie guided them through the gate and down the slope to the field where Pop had been digging potatoes. There they began rooting in the ground, so Yonie knew they were safe.

Back he started across the muddy field toward Dunder's pen, for now he could hear great roars from that direction.

"That Dunder, now," he thought, "he might do me somesing, he's so mad. He bellers wonderful! If only Pop would come home!"

A sudden burst of flame made him stop to look and wonder. A great rafter fell with a shower of sparks as he watched.

"It's like a picture in a book!" he thought.

Dunder bellowed again, more loudly than ever. Yonie set his tired legs in motion. How he wished Pop were here! But Pop wasn't here, and Dunder must be gotten out!

Then, above the whooshing and the crackling of the fire, Yonie heard a new noise. He stopped again. He looked out toward the highway.

The road leading down from it was crowded with people! There were people in wagons, people in carriages, people in automobiles, and people on foot! Yonie stared. Then a siren shrieked, and he heard a bell clanging. That must be the fire engine! He started to run toward the crowd. He must see that beautiful, bright red engine that now turned into the road. It puffed and clanged. It made the horses step lively. It pushed the people off the road and sent the chickens squawking in every direction.

Yonie was so excited that he forgot everything else. He forgot about the tools and farm gear that needed to be moved from the fire. He forgot that Granny might need his help with Bluebell. He forgot Nancy, who was still asleep in the brick house. He even forgot Dunder. All he could think of was that red engine with the shiny trim. Just as he was about to cross the cornfield Dunder bellowed again loud and long. Yonie stopped short.

"Ach!" he thought, "that Dunder!"

He stood for a second, longing to go where the red engine was already at work. He could see the stream of water it was pouring into the fire from the Little Conestoga. He could see the fire dying down.

Then he seemed to hear Pop say, "Wondernose!"

He turned and ran as fast as he could go to Dunder's pen. Beside the gate into the pen Pop kept the long staff with the hook at the end. Yonie made sure to have it securely in hand before he opened the gate. He could tell that Dunder was not very happy.

Yonie crept up toward the big bull's head. Dunder started to roar, and Yonie quickly snapped the staff into place. Dunder tossed his head, but not far! He was stopped suddenly by the pain in his nose, for the staff thrust his head up into the air and he was helpless.

Yonie was very proud to lead him through the gate toward the field that sloped up the hill. He wrapped Dunder's chain around the trunk of a tree and left the staff where it would be handy. But Dunder still bellowed as if he were in pain.

"Now, what makes it that you holler still?" Yonie said out loud. "Maybe you don't like all this fire, but to make so much noise is no good." He turned to go back toward the fire engine. And then he saw the cause of Dunder's bellows. Across Dunder's back where there should have been glossy brown hair there was no skin at all! A burning timber had fallen on the big bull before Yonie had moved him. Yonie ran tearing down the hill to find Granny and the apple butter.

He had to push his way through the crowd of people. Granny was on the back porch comforting Nancy, who stood there crying in her little nightgown.

He could see her in the light from the kitchen where neighbor women were already setting about making coffee.

"Why," thought Yonie, "it's almost like a picnic!"

He started to cross the wagon track. But just then a shiny black car drove in and stopped. Yonie forgot Dunder again. He *must* see that car! Pop said automobiles were worldly, but Yonie loved to look at them. He stood staring.

The door opened and someone got out— someone who looked like Pop! Someone who said, just like Pop, "A Wondernose still!" It *was* Pop! A neighbor had gone to bring him home!

"And are the barn creatures all safe?" asked Pop.

But before Yonie had time to answer, the Bishop and several neighboring farmers came up to tell Pop they would help him to rebuild the barn and get things in order again.

Yonie wished he could see Pop alone for just one minute, then he could explain that Dunder was hurt because he had taken care of the pigs first! What would Pop do when he knew that Yonie almost forgot Dunder because he stopped to look at the red engine?

He stood waiting till the men were through talking. Then he took a long breath and began: "Apple butter makes good for the burns on Dunder's back, Granny says. And I forgot and took the pigs out first." There! It was out!

What would Pop say? Would he say, "Now you are too little still for me to keep that promise?"

But Pop didn't say anything. He just took Yonie up in his arms and held him tight. Then he put him down again, and said, "Now, come, we see where all the animals are. Star and Blackie I saw when we come in the lane. Where's Dunder?"

When they reached the top of the field where Dunder was tied, some of the neighbor women were there, putting a poultice on Dunder's back. Dunder was quiet.

"He's not bad hurt," said Katie Lapp. "We heard him beller as we come over the field. I bring apple butter like always when there is a fire, to put on the animals when they get hurt."

Pop thanked them. Then he and Yonie went on down to the potato field where the pigs were. They were still hunting out roots in the mud, all but the mother sow. She lay over in the fence corner. When Yonie leaned over to see if she was all right, what do you think he saw? Ten little new baby pigs! Pop saw them, too. He laughed.

"*Ya*, vell," he said, "this time it pays to be a Wondernose! Better Dunder gets a pain in his back as lose the old mother sow!"

Yonie felt happy.

"Now," said Pop, "for being such a big smart boy, one of these little pigs belongs to you. Choose which one."

Yonie didn't speak. He just laid his hand on the little pink one that couldn't find room to get his share of dinner. Now he had a pet that was all his own.

The calves came bleating to the other side of the fence. The little black one put his nose

through the rails and sniffed in Yonie's pocket as he leaned over.

"He's a Wondernose just like you," said Pop. "Would you like to have him, too?"

"*Ya*, Pop," said Yonie. "I'd like fine to have him!"

"It takes a *man* to care for barn creatures and get them safe out of a fire. Soon it makes time for fall planting." He winked again at Yonie. "I need a man for that, too!" he said.

Now Yonie knew that Pop would keep his promise! At last he could do what he had hoped for ever since Ammon left. He was big enough now to guide the two great work horses to harrow the field for winter wheat all by himself. He could see himself astride Star's back, high above the ground, above the fence posts, even above Pop's head! He could hear himself saying, "Gee! Haw!" and whichever way he said, the horses would go! He slipped his hand into Pop's big one.

"Yonie Wondernose!" said Pop.

JIMMY AND JEMIMA

Helen Sewell

This humorous fable could be entitled "Pride goeth before a fall."

When Jemima was born Jimmy thought she was the most beautiful baby sister in the world. And so did his Mother and his Daddy and his Granny.

Sometimes Jimmy took her out in her carriage.

And when she was older he gave her rides in his express wagon.

Or they rode together on his bike.

But when Jimmy was a big boy he joined the Scouts. Then he had no time to play with girls.

Jimmy wanted more than anything else to earn the lifesaving medal. So he took swimming lessons.

One day all the family came to see Jimmy swim five strokes.

Then Jemima jumped in and swam way to

"Jimmy and Jemima." Reprinted by permission of the author, Helen Sewell

the other end of the pond. And no one knew that she could swim at all!

Jimmy wanted to learn to ride a horse. So he took riding lessons.

The whole family came out to see him ride.

But when the horse stopped suddenly, poor Jimmy slid right on his head.

Jemima climbed up on the horse's back and rode him all the way home!

One morning Jimmy and the Scouts started out very early, for they were going to climb a high mountain. Jimmy said that Jemima could not go because it was much too far for girls.

They climbed and climbed and climbed.

And when they reached the top Jemima was already there!

One day in the winter Jimmy and Jemima went skating.

Jimmy could skate very well but once he slipped and fell down on the ice. Then Jemima was *too* proud and she skated *too* far.

And Jemima fell in.

But Jimmy was a good Boy Scout. He had learned all about lifesaving. He found a board and he fished Jemima out.

When Jemima was safe in bed with a hot-water bottle she thought about Jimmy. It was nice to have a brother to pull her out when she fell into the water.

And when the Mayor presented the lifesaving medal to Jimmy he thought about Jemima.

It was nice to have a sister to fall into the water so that he could pull her out.

WAIT FOR WILLIAM

Marjorie Flack

This amusing little circus story turns upon the most natural conflict in the world—a four-year-old's trouble with his shoelace and the older children's impatience with his slowness. Its conclusion demonstrates delightfully that "The humble shall be exalted."

Once there were three children who lived in a white house in Pollywinkle Lane in the village of Pleasantville.

The oldest of these three children was a big boy whose name was Charles and he was eight years old.

The middle one was a girl whose name was Nancy and she was six years old.

The youngest was a little boy and his name was William and he was just four years old.

One summer morning when William was riding his scooter up and down the walk Charles said,

"Hurry up, William, put away your scooter and we will take you down to Main Street to see the Circus Parade."

And Nancy said,

"Hurry up, William, wash your hands and comb your hair and we will take you down to Main Street to see the Circus Parade."

So William put away his scooter and he washed his hands and combed his hair, and they all started down Pollywinkle Lane on their way to Main Street to see the Circus Parade.

"Hurry up, William," said Charles. "Walk faster, William. We must not be too late when we get to Main Street to see the Circus Parade."

"Hurry up, William, walk faster, William," said Nancy, "or we shall be too late when we get to Main Street to see the beginning of the Circus Parade."

William walked faster but Charles walked faster and Nancy walked faster as they all hurried along down Pollywinkle Lane on their way to Main Street to see the Circus Parade.

"Wait!" called William. "Wait for me, my shoe is untied!"

"We can't wait," said Charles.

"We can't wait," said Nancy, "or we shall all be too late when we get to Main Street to see the Circus Parade."

So William walked faster and faster, but *flap, flap* went the shoestring, so William hopped and William galloped as he hurried along down Pollywinkle Lane on the way to Main Street to see the Circus Parade.

Then *flop*, off came William's shoe, and there he stood with one shoe off and one shoe on. "Wait for me!" called William. "Wait for me, my shoe's come off!"

But Charles and Nancy did not answer. They did not answer because they did not hear Wil-

liam. They did not hear William because they were too far away, as they hurried along down Pollywinkle Lane on their way to Main Street to see the Circus Parade.

So William stopped and he put on his shoe and he tied the shoestring in a tight firm knot, and then he slowly and carefully made the ends into a proper, neat bow.

But when it was all done, Nancy and Charles were gone, they were nowhere in sight! So William ran alone. He ran all alone down Pollywinkle Lane on his way to Main Street to see the Circus Parade.

Then William stopped, he stopped at a corner because he heard Music, William heard Circus Music coming nearer and nearer and then William saw the Circus Parade coming to him, coming to William on its way to Main Street.

First came the horses—then came the band—and then came the Camels—and then came a man leading an Elephant.

The man saw William. He saw William standing all alone, all alone because Charles and Nancy and everybody else, everybody else in the whole village of Pleasantville had gone to Main Street to see the Circus Parade.

"Want a ride?" called the man.

"Yes!" said William.

So the man lifted William up, up high on the Elephant and William and the Elephant paraded along to Main Street.

William was so high the branches of the trees were near him and he looked down, way down on all the people of Pleasantville as they stood on Main Street to see the Circus Parade!

William passed by the Drug Store, he passed by the Grocery Store, and he passed by the church and then, when he came to the Post Office William looked down, way down, and there he saw Charles and Nancy and all their friends!

Charles and Nancy and all their friends looked up, way up, and there on top of the Elephant they saw William riding the Elephant in the Circus Parade!

"Look at William!" shouted Charles.

"Look at William!" shouted Nancy.

"Look at William!" shouted all their friends.

Then they all ran along beside William as he rode the Elephant in the Circus Parade.

They went up Summer Street, and then down High Street, and then they came to the corner of Pollywinkle Lane.

Then the man lifted William down. He lifted William down, down to the ground again.

"Thank you for the Elephant Ride," said William. The man said, "You're welcome." Then the man and the Elephant went away.

"Tell us about it," begged Charles.

"Tell us about it," begged Nancy.

"Tell us about riding the Elephant in the Circus Parade," begged all their friends.

But William said, "Wait. Wait. My other shoe is untied."

So Charles waited, and Nancy waited, and all their friends waited, while William tied the shoe-string in a good firm knot and they waited while he slowly and carefully made the ends into a proper, neat bow.

Then slowly they walked, walked slowly with William as he told them about riding the Elephant down Main Street, down Main Street in the Circus Parade.

from KI-KI A CIRCUS TROUPER

Edith Janice Craine

[A New Act for the Circus]

Ki-Ki was lost!

Ki-Ki did not know that he was lost.

The little dog did know that things all about him were strange. There was not one familiar pair of feet, not one familiar sniff, not one familiar voice.

Ki-Ki knew that he was tired. He was so tired that he could hardly keep his chin up. So tired there was hardly a wag left in his wee tail. So tired that he straddled his legs wide apart to keep them from doubling under him. The tiredness came from running and running, here and there, from one place to another, in search of something he knew, something familiar. He braced himself against a railing and blinked bravely to keep his eyes open.

Suddenly, an enormous wagon rumbled past and something inside roared furiously as though very angry. It was a fearful sound.

The little dog was so frightened that he forgot his weariness. He did not take an instant to look where he was going. But he jumped as high and as far as he could, and he landed on the cushioned seat of a basket wagon.

With a faint yap, Ki-Ki rolled himself into a tight ball and snuggled down. He tucked his

nose under his forepaws, and closed his eyes. Right away he went fast asleep, without knowing where he was, or what had given him such a fright.

While he slept, Ki-Ki dreamed of familiar things and his tiny body quivered happily. He slept and slept and slept. He was awakened by the sound of laughter. It was the sort of laughter that just pops right out of people when there is a pleased, very kindly feeling deep inside them. It comes when something makes them feel so good they have to smile out loud.

That laugh took away every speck of Ki-Ki's tiredness. With a gay little spring he was on his feet. He stood straight and firm now, and he held his head up.

Just ahead, the little dog saw that a great pair of gates was standing wide open, and that he was going forward in a basket wagon. The wagon had shafts at the back, and a spotted pony was harnessed between the shafts, with his head facing the wagon. He was pushing the wagon. A small boy, under a very big hat, was astride the back of the pony, and the jolliest clown was driving.

"It's the clown!"

"He said that he would come!"

"The circus! Oh! Oh! Oh!"

"The clown and his little boy!"

"See the pony. Ha-ha-ha! He's pushing the wagon!"

"Oh, look!"

"Elephants, with royal covers!"

"I hear bears!"

"There are bears. Brown ones. And look, a big white one!"

"Here they come!"

"Real tigers, and real lions!"

"Wild ones!"

"Wild as anything!"

There were so many shouts from all sides that the noise became a great roar that rolled right into the air.

Ki-Ki did not know that those shouts came from boys and girls of a hospital. There were boys and girls, big ones and little ones, who had to be in chairs, or on couches, or had to hold themselves up with crutches until doctors and nurses could make their bodies well and strong.

But, Ki-Ki could tell that they were very, very happy, so he lifted himself right up in plain sight, and barked as hard as he could. To be sure it wasn't very loud barking. Only those who were nearby could hear him at all, but he did not mind that. A big, kindly hand kept him from jumping under the feet of the elephant, or into a cage and down the throat of a lion. The lion was yawning at the moment.

"Hello, Trouper! Want to help with the show?" said the clown, as he lifted the little dog up into his arms.

Ki-Ki did not answer, but his red tongue went out, swift as lightning, in a wide lick on the clown's face. The lick nearly took the clown's paint off.

"There, there. All right, it's settled, but you must not spoil my looks," laughed the clown. He tucked Ki-Ki under his arm where everyone could see the dog and the pair led the great circus parade around the courtyard.

Everywhere boys and girls were watching eagerly. Some were on a platform so low they could reach out and touch the animals, or talk to the performers. Others were on balconies, and they leaned over. There were three rows of those balconies.

Besides the children, there were grown-ups. They all wore smiles that went from ear to ear. Why, there were even twitches and twinkles about the lips and eyes of the most serious-looking doctors.

Around and around went the parade, so that everybody could see every single thing. The ele-

phants poked out their long trunks for peanuts. The lions roared their fiercest, as they balanced on huge balls. Cowboys, on plunging, bucking broncos, whooped and threw their big hats into the air. Their long lariats opened into wide loops with a delightful swish, then poised and dropped. One caught the clown just as he was alighting from his wagon.

"What do you mean, sir?" The clown pretended to be very angry.

"Sorry! So sorry, sir. You see, my rope slipped," said the cowboy very politely.

"I do not see! It is disgraceful," answered the clown. He had the worst time getting rid of that lariat. It tangled first in one place, then another.

The clown's little boy tried to help. Ki-Ki tried to help and was tossed over and over. A little lame girl with a crutch tried to help, and nearly got caught. It was all so funny that the hospital children laughed and laughed until their sides ached.

The doctors and nurses laughed until their sides ached.

"Ladies and gentlemen," someone shouted. "Attention!"

"It is time for ice cream," roared someone else.

"Hurrah!"

"Hurrah for the circus!"

"Hurrah for the clown!"

"We thank you," the clown waved his hat and bowed very low.

"We thank you for giving us such a good time," called the children.

"Ladies and gentlemen," said the clown. "I want to return this lovely little dog." He held Ki-Ki up, but no one seemed to understand. "I guess he belongs to one of you boys or girls. When I first saw him, I thought he was a brown, woolly muff on legs. He is so little, he surely could get lost in my pocket." The clown balanced Ki-Ki on the palm of his hand.

"Hurrah for the little dog," shouted a girl with a crutch.

"Who owns him?"

"He does not belong to us—"

"He doesn't belong to us—"

Ki-Ki did not belong to any boy or girl there.

"Then, he must belong to a doctor or a nurse," said the clown.

"Not to us," said the nurses.

"Nor to us," said the doctors.

"Land of Liberty! Where, in the name of curly lollipops did you come from, Trouper?" said the clown. He was puzzled as he could be.

"Oh, Dad, I saw something jump into the wagon when we hitched up this afternoon," said the clown's little boy.

"Was it this fellow?"

"I was going to get some water for the pony, and did not stop to look. But, maybe it was."

"My word, Trouper. Did you run away?"

"Perhaps he is lost," said a nurse.

"He looks like a thoroughbred toy 'Pom' to me," said one of the doctors.

"We must watch the newspapers and find out who lost you," the clown told Ki-Ki.

The tiny dog snuggled close on the clown's arm, his tail wagging as hard as it could wag, as if to say that he did not feel lost a bit, and that he was quite content to be a trouper forever and ever.

"Cupid! Cupid! Cupid!" The clown's little boy called three times. The little boy was named Peter Webber. He was stretched out on his stomach on the floor, but his heels were in the air, his chin resting on one palm, and his other hand held a newspaper. He was reading about dogs in the Lost and Found column.

A few feet away from Peter, Ki-Ki was lapping water out of a shiny new pan, which was all his own. He knew very well that his name was Ki-Ki, but he couldn't tell that to Peter. Of course, he couldn't tell anyone. After all, what did it matter? He would jump and frisk when they called him Trouper.

"What do you find in the newspaper, Peter?" the clown asked.

"Pom-er-an-ian—"

"Pomeranian?"

"Yes, sir. The newspaper says that the dog answers to the name of Cupid," Peter read slowly.

"This pup does not answer to that name. What else does the newspaper say, son?"

"Two years old—"

"This chap isn't more than a year old. Any more lost dogs?"

"Yes, Dad. Listen to these. Lost, a brindle bull pup—"

"That does not fit."

"Lost, a small brown terrier," Peter read aloud.

"We did not find a terrier."

"A black Scottie. That's all." Peter folded the newspaper, and Ki-Ki was sure it was time for a romp.

"We must keep watching," said the clown. "After a while, we shall find out who owns him."

The clown's name was John Webber and he had deep lines in the corners of his eyes. These lines made his face look as if he were always ready for a good laugh.

"I wonder how the little dog got away from his master," said Mrs. Webber.

"Perhaps he jumped out of an automobile when no one was looking," her husband answered.

"Maybe his owner thought he was asleep among the cushions," suggested Peter.

"He is so little," said Mrs. Webber. "That might have happened."

"And we must be careful he does not do it again," Peter declared. "I am going to keep watch over you, little fellow." Peter caught the dog in his arms and held him close.

A whole week had passed since Ki-Ki had been found on the front seat of the circus wagon, and he had helped the clown give the crippled children at the hospital so much fun.

Now, it was the very last night the circus would be in town. So the clown and his family were in their own dressing room packing boxes and bags for a journey.

· · · · · · · · · · · ·

When Peter awakened, the caravan was not moving. He was in his pajamas, snug in his own cot, where his mother had tucked him gently, hours before. The long caravan had come to a halt, and the cot was in the Webbers' own tent. From outside came familiar sounds. They were sounds that the little boy knew very well were made by men putting things into shape for the opening of the circus.

There were smells too, very pleasant ones. One was the sweet fragrance from a meadow where the hay had just been cut. Another fragrance came from the campfire breakfasts. These were enough to make any boy hurry out of bed and into his clothes.

Peter found that his mother and father were waiting breakfast for him. Ki-Ki was waiting too, but he did not mind because he had eaten a biscuit.

"Good morning, Mother and Dad," said Peter.

"Good morning," they answered.

"Hungry, dear?" asked his mother.

"Hollow as a bass drum," he said.

"Well, pitch in," invited his father.

The boy did not need to be urged. He had nearly finished his breakfast when something popped into his head.

"Dad, this is the country, isn't it?"

"It certainly is."

"You and Mother promised that when we were in the country, I might ride the big elephant, Queen Bess, some afternoon."

"So we did. Are your lessons finished?"

"They are, Dad, every single lesson."

"Very well. I see no reason why you should not ride Queen Bess this afternoon, if Mr. Lawrence does not object. If he says that it is safe, you may."

"Thanks, Dad. I'll find out." Peter had finished his breakfast, so he gave them both a good hug. Then he hurried out to find Mr. Lawrence.

Things were coming along pretty well. The enormous tent was in place. Ropes and braces were being made fast on the outside. Small tents were going up for the side shows. Many-colored flags and streamers, that Peter had seen being packed the night before, were now waving gaily in the breeze. In the sky, not a cloud could be seen. The sun was beaming down on the circus, and crowds of people were gathering to enjoy the fun.

"You will have to stay inside, Trouper," Peter explained as they hurried along, but the little dog only frisked. Soon the small boy found Mr. Lawrence, who said that it would be quite all right for him to ride Queen Bess that afternoon. So Peter raced back to the family tent to tell his mother.

"I'll get you ready, dear," Mrs. Webber said as she set to work adding: "you will be very careful, son."

"Of course, Mother. Will you watch?"

"I can watch the start, at least," she told him.

"Where's my elephant boy?" Mr. Lawrence shouted a bit later.

"Right here. All ready," Peter called. He wore red sandals with a high turban to match, and brown tights.

"Run along," urged his mother.

"Be a good fellow, Trouper," the boy said, as he fastened the leash to the leg of the cot. "I'll come for you soon." He raced off to his place in the parade, leaving Ki-Ki looking dreadfully disappointed. The little dog tugged at the leash and barked woefully.

"Speed up there," roared the elephant-man.

The elephant's trunk coiled gently about Peter's waist.

"Going up!" Mr. Lawrence laughed as he caught Peter's hand to steady him.

"Whew!" said Peter as he took his place between the elephant's great ears.

"Forward—march!"

Queen Bess moved forward majestically and Peter was so happy that he could hardly contain himself. He wished that he could stand on his head, but that would surely spoil the wonderful turban.

Inside the huge tent, the band was playing such lively music that it made everyone quite gay.

The parade formed as it did for the children at the hospital, with the clown in his funny wagon, pushed by the spotted pony. Only this time, there was no small boy astride the pony's back.

Then came Queen Bess with Peter Webber seated cross-legged on her broad head. There were more elephants, followed by cages of wild animals, roaring and snarling furiously.

Through the performers' entrance went the clown, straight to the center ring, under the gay banners and swinging festoons. From all sides of the arena arose a rousing cheer of welcome. Boys and girls, big and little; men and women, large and small, clapped and shouted at the top of their voices. Around the center ring went the grand parade.

Suddenly, it seemed to Peter, that he heard a different sort of sound. As soon as he could, he looked around to see what it was. Peter was so startled that he forgot how high he was sitting. But the man behind him caught hold of his arm.

"Steady, big boy," said Mr. Lawrence.

"Yes, sir." Peter's teeth chattered. "O-o—oh, Trouper!"

The small dog, his leash dragging, was dashing headlong into the center ring. Heedless of swinging tight-rope tackle, tramping hoofs, and busy performers, he leaped on and on. Two men raced to his rescue and tried to toss him to safety, but the small dog slipped from their hands.

Ki-Ki landed on his side and rolled and tumbled before he regained his feet. With an impudent little yap, he started again.

"Hurrah for that dog!"

The audience thought it a part of the show, and cheered lustily.

"Good boy!"

"Go to it, Old Timer!"

One end of the leash caught the end of a pole, but held only an instant, then Ki-Ki pulled himself free.

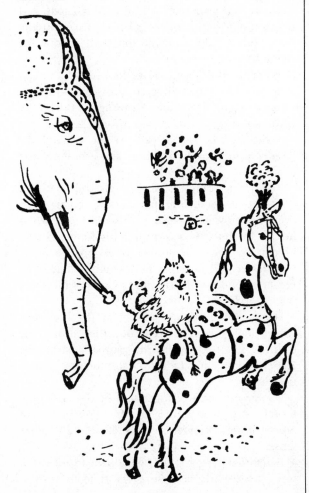

"Woof! Woof!" He headed straight for the parade.

"He'll be trampled. He'll be hurt," Peter choked.

By that time, Peter could not see the dog. Bravely he blinked back tears that welled in his eyes, and gulped down a great lump that rose in his throat. He was sure that Queen Bess would crush the tiny dog. The caravan kept moving steadily, then Peter felt the elephant sway slightly. Her long trunk was swinging from side to side.

Then, just as she had lifted Peter up to his place on her head, so Queen Bess picked up Ki-Ki.

"Oh, Trouper, Trouper!" Peter choked. He could hardly believe his eyes. He leaned forward to catch his pet, but Queen Bess had another idea. She waved the small dog back and forth so that everyone could see him. Then she set him down on the broad back of the spotted pony right in front of her. How everyone laughed!

Of course Ki-Ki had no idea what it was all about, but he understood merry laughs, chuckles, and ha-ha's. He gave his head a funny little shake, then stood on his hind feet, his forefeet waving, as if he were greeting the cheering crowd.

"Good Queen Bess!"

"Cunning pup!"

More cheers and shouts. The shouts were so thunderous that they nearly brought down the tent poles.

"Cheers for the pup! Cheers for the elephant!"

That is how a little lost dog became a really-for-real trouper.

ROGER AND THE FOX

Lavinia R. Davis

This is a sensitively perceptive story about a little boy's interest in a wild creature and his patient, persistent lookout, which is finally rewarded. Such a story has great value in setting a pattern for a boy's approach to wild life, not as a hunter or a molester, but as a thrilled observer of the creature's secret life. Children who like this story will enjoy the second one, The Wild Birthday Cake.

The fall wind swished through the leaves of the trees. The leaves floated to the ground like little umbrellas. And the wind, still chasing and teasing, rolled and tossed them across the road. Roger's feet, in his new school shoes, scuffled through the dried leaves.

Rustle-rustle-crack went the leaves. Roger, who was six, and walking home from school, grinned to himself. He loved the sound of rustling leaves. It was a fine, dry, corn-popping, pie-eating, cider-drinking, *fall* sound.

At the bend in the road the wind died down. Roger heard another noise. It was a little, shy, scurrying noise deep in the leaves. Roger started forward. Then he remembered what Seth had said and he stood still as a fence post and waited. Seth was the hired man on Roger's father's farm and he knew everything.

"If you want to see wild animals," Seth had said, "you can't just rush in on 'em. You have to wait and be patient."

This time Roger didn't have to wait long. There was another stir in the leaves, and then, plain as a pumpkin, out came the chipmunk and darted across the road.

Roger hurried home to tell Seth. He stayed at the house only long enough to help himself to ginger cookies and then he ran up to the barn.

Seth was milking when Roger told him about the chipmunk. "I saw it all by myself," Roger said. "I just stood still and I saw it."

Seth went right on squirting milk into the pail. "Saw a big fox myself this morning," he said finally. "Fine red one down at the river by that ironwood tree that was blown over in the hurricane."

"A fox!" said Roger, and suddenly he felt as flat as a pricked balloon. What was a little old chipmunk compared to a fine red fox?

Roger left the barn and went straight down the long hill toward the Still River. Roger wanted to see that fox himself. Since he and his family had moved to the farm he had seen squirrels, rabbits, field mice, turtles, and of course chipmunks. Once from a safe distance his big brother Dick had shown him a skunk. But

until today Roger hadn't even been sure that there were foxes in Connecticut.

Even after Roger reached the river he had a long walk ahead of him. The cold black water twisted and turned between the trees like a pretzel. It was damp and chilly walking along the riverbank, and Roger began to rustle leaves again because the sound made him feel warmer.

It was nearly dark by the time Roger reached the fallen-down tree where Seth had seen the fox. He looked and looked. He couldn't see a thing except the big ironwood tree arching over the river like a shadowy bridge. Roger was colder than ever now and hungry, and there wasn't so much as ginger dust left from his cookies. Pretty soon he started for home. He'd come back tomorrow and bring Scamper with him. Scamper was a fox terrier and almost as smart as Seth's coon hound, Ranger. Roger felt sure if he had Scamper along he'd see the fox.

There was always a lot to do after school, and it was more than two weeks before Roger finally took Scamper down to the long hill to look for the fox.

When he did go, the river looked colder than ever. Even Scamper shivered with cold and then shot through the woods, running as fast as he could to keep warm. By the time Roger caught up with him he was already at the fallen-down tree, yipping and barking and snuffing the ground.

"Be quiet, Scamper!" Roger said, but it didn't do a bit of good. Scamper barked louder than ever. Roger was just going to scold again when he saw the hole! It was quite a big hole and half hidden by the fallen-down tree. Roger's heart beat faster and faster as he looked at that hole. He knew, he just knew, that that was the fox's front porch.

Scamper snuffed and pawed at the hole and Roger looked and looked, but they didn't see a thing. The fox had heard Scamper's barks and Roger's shouts and he didn't so much as put his nose out.

"Come on home," Roger said finally, and now he felt very cross with Scamper. "You made too much noise. Ranger would have had more sense."

After that Roger didn't get down to the river for a long while because every time he started out Scamper came after him. He tried shutting Scamper up, but somebody always let him out and then he was noisier than ever.

Finally one Saturday Dick started to teach Scamper tricks and then Roger knew he was safe. He hurried down to the river, and this time he went very quietly indeed.

He walked through the woods without even rustling a leaf, but he hadn't counted on the crows. He didn't even see the crows sitting in the birches and the oak trees and the thorn apples. But the crows saw Roger. All of a sudden they began to caw, caw, CAW, and flew off, flapping their great black wings. They were so noisy and so unexpected that Roger jumped! The fox must have jumped too! He must have jumped right down into his deep hole because when Roger reached it there was nothing to be seen.

The very next Saturday Roger started off right after breakfast to try to see the fox.

"Seen the fox yet?" Seth asked as he passed the barn. Roger shook his head, but he didn't say a word. He wasn't going to take a chance by boasting to Seth, but in his heart he felt that this would be his lucky day. Scamper was off on a hunting trip of his own, the weather was warmer, he himself had just finished a specially good breakfast, and he just felt like fooling that fox.

Roger walked on tiptoes until he was near the fallen-down tree. Then he hid behind an oak tree and peered cautiously out at the fox hole. He looked at the hole and then he took a deep excited breath! There was something big and reddish-brown. Was it—surely it must be—the fox?

Roger never had a chance to make sure. Just at that moment a big pointer dog jumped through the brush. Right behind him were three duck hunters with their guns under their arms. Roger started forward with his finger on his lips, but it was no use. He had forgotten the cat briers that grew along the riverbank. The next instant Roger tripped over a cat brier and fell flat in front of the hunters!

"Well, sonny," said one of the hunters when they had picked him up and made sure he wasn't hurt, "what are you doing out so early?"

"Fox!" panted Roger, and nodded toward the hole. The three hunters looked and Roger looked, but there wasn't anything there. Even the pointer just sniffed the hole and then went down toward the river looking for duck. "But —but I saw it!" Roger began. "At least I think—"

"Sure, Sonny." The biggest hunter grinned down at Roger. "When I was your size I used to see lions and tigers and giraffes in these woods."

Roger knew when he was being teased, so he started for home. As he walked up the long hill he knew it wasn't his lucky day after all. He didn't mind tripping over the cat brier. He didn't mind the hunter's teasing. What he did mind was that he couldn't honestly be sure if he had seen the fox or just imagined him. And if he told that to Seth he knew he'd be laughed at and he would mind that most of all.

Soon after that the Christmas vacation began and Roger was very busy making his presents. Then the day after Christmas Roger caught a bad cold and had to stay in bed. He spent the time drawing pictures of the fallen-down tree with his new Christmas paints and tracing the outline of a fox in one of his new books. And all the time he wished that the weather would clear up and his cold go away so that he could get back to the river and make sure about the fox.

Roger's cold was soon gone, but the weather wasn't in any hurry to get better. First it rained, then it froze, and then it rained some more. Finally a day came when it was clear and dry, and Roger was well enough to put on his new snow suit and rubber boots and go outside. He felt nice and warm as he started down for the river, but he also felt a bit stiff because the suit and the boots were so very new.

When Roger reached the river the bank was all covered with gleaming sheets of melted-then-frozen snow. It was fine and flat and glistening and just made to be jumped on. Roger took his first jump, and the thin sheet of ice cracked and splintered. He took another jump and listened to the crackle. He jumped again. It was a wonderful noise. It was a sharp, biting, where-are-my-mittens, *midwinter* noise.

Roger jumped almost all the way to the fallen-down tree. It was great fun, but it wasn't the way to see a fox. The fox must have heard all that cracking and splintering a long way off because by the time Roger reached his home no one was there.

There was nothing for Roger to do but turn around and walk up the long, steep hill toward home. He was very tired when he reached the top, and his beautiful new snow suit had rubbed chapped places under his knees.

Seth came out of the barn just as Roger passed it on his way to the house. "Seen the fox?" he asked.

"No!" Roger said, and now he was so discouraged he was sure he never would see the fox. "He's always just gone. Always!"

Seth grinned, but his voice was friendly enough. "You have to be real quiet to see a fox," he said. "Quiet and mighty quick. It wouldn't be easy for a city boy."

Roger hated being called a city boy and he walked away without saying a word. Someday he was going to see that fox all by himself. He just had to see it!

The next day it was Roger's seventh birthday, and that was so exciting he almost forgot about the fox. Mother and Dad gave him skis. Grandma gave him a box of tin soldiers. Dick gave him a duck whistle. And Seth—well, Seth gave him the very best present of all. It was a cap, a regular Dan'l Boone hunting cap, made out of the skin of a coon that Seth and Ranger had caught.

Roger put on his new snow suit, his new coonskin cap, and his new skis. It was easy to wear the cap. It was easy to wear the snow suit now that the new stiffness had worn off. But it was unexpectedly hard to wear the skis. They were longer than Roger was tall, and when he stood up on them they shot out in different directions.

Roger practiced skiing all that week and all the next week. First he learned to glide in a straight line on the flat snow-covered stretch of lawn behind the house. When there was another snowfall Roger and Dick made a huge snow man called Henriques De Pew, and after a while Roger learned to zigzag on skis around Henriques.

In another ten days Roger even learned how to ski down little hills, though he took a lot of snow baths while he was learning. It was very deep snow indeed, and Roger was glad he had

his skis to play with because no one, not even Seth, could have walked down to the river through the thick white drifts.

So Roger kept on practicing, and then one day Dad said he could try the long, steep hill that led down to the river. Dad skied down the hill first, and when he reached the valley he turned and waved. Roger waved back. Daddy looked a long way off, but Roger gave himself a push with his ski poles and started after him.

He flew down that hill so fast that he lost his breath. He just swooped down, but he didn't fall once. "Good boy!" Dad said when he reached the valley. "That's skiing."

Well, of course, after that Roger didn't want to stop skiing. Even after Dad left to cut wood he kept right on skiing by himself up and down the long, steep hill. It was hard work zigzagging up to the top, but it was worth it to come zooming down again.

It was quite late, and Roger had just reached the valley after a specially good run when he heard the far-off tinkling of a big cowbell. Roger knew that Mother was ringing that cowbell because it was suppertime.

Roger zigzagged up the hill for the last time. Now that the bell had stopped ringing the world seemed quieter than ever. There were no voices, no crows, no dogs to bark. There was only the cold, lonely wail of the wind in the telephone wires and the faint squeak-squeak of his own ski harnesses.

When Roger reached the hilltop he looked back proudly at the fine, clean tracks his skis had made on all his runs downhill. The snow was pale blue and purple now in the fading light, and the tracks stood out clear and bold.

Roger turned away and skied cross-country toward the house. He was just sliding down the last little slope to the front door when Mother came out to ring the bell again. She had just lifted up the bell when Roger snow-plowed to a stop beside her. She was so surprised she jumped and dropped the bell in the snow.

"Why, Rog!" she said. "You did surprise me. I didn't hear you coming at all!"

When she said that Roger had a wonderful idea. If he had surprised Mother he could surprise the fox! At last he'd found a way to go places that was very fast and very quiet and, what was more, the deep drifts wouldn't bother him a bit. Tomorrow he'd put on his snow suit, his hunting cap, *and* his skis and just fool that fox.

It snowed while Roger and Dick made popcorn that evening. It snowed while they were asleep. It snowed and snowed great, soft, white flakes that covered up the bushes, and covered up the dog kennel, and covered up the fences so that only the tops of the tallest fence posts stuck out like little black rabbit ears.

When Roger woke up the next morning the ceiling in his room glistened with reflected light. Roger lay still for a moment under his patchwork quilts and blinked up at the brightness. Then slowly he understood. There was more new snow. Piles and drifts of it, and he could ski soundlessly over it all and surprise Mr. Fox!

When Roger reached the top of the long hill again there wasn't a single sign of a living creature and there wasn't a sound either. The ski tracks he had made yesterday were gone, and no wind whistled through the telephone wires. There was nothing but new snow and the breathless quiet of the hill listening to itself.

Roger pulled down his coonskin cap and hugged himself because he was so glad he was the first person out in that brand-new world. He felt like a real hunter now, a frontiersman, a breaker of trails.

Roger pushed off and sifted soundlessly down the long, steep hill to the river valley. He never stopped until he reached the wood lot nearest the fallen-down tree. Then he stood so still that even Henriques De Pew, the snow man, seemed like a jitterbug in comparison. There, straight ahead of Roger's nose, was the fox standing beside his hole!

The fox's head was up, his bushy tail was out like a flag. Except for the slight twitching of his whiskers, he was just as still as Roger himself!

All of a sudden the fox put back his head and barked. It didn't sound like Scamper or Ranger. It sounded like nothing on earth but a big, red fox, and it was the wildest, eeriest sound Roger had ever heard.

Only Roger's eyeballs moved as he saw the second fox come out of the hole. She was smaller and lighter-colored and more timid-looking than

the first fox. By this time Roger was so excited he was shaking! He took a step forward to balance himself, and the tip of one ski hit into a tree trunk and knocked the snow from its branches. There wasn't much noise. Just the very soft plopping sound of snow from the trees falling onto snow on the ground. It was hardly a noise at all, but it was enough!

The two foxes disappeared!

One moment they were right there in front of Roger and the next they were not. They had melted away faster than the noise of an exploded firecracker. Roger stared, and then a grin spread from one side of his coonskin cap all the way to the other side. Right before him where the foxes had stood were new, clear tracks in the snow. Roger looked at the tracks and looked again. The tracks were fox paw prints and they were right where he had seen the foxes!

After that Roger did not wait another minute. He made a kick turn and started straight up the hill to tell Seth. This time he hadn't been fooled. He had seen the fox and there were paw prints to prove it. More than that, he had seen two foxes, which was just twice as many as Seth himself had seen!

THE GOLDFISH

Julian Street

This is a wonderful Christmas story, but it is much more fun to tell to children than to read to them.

The first thing Mrs. Harman saw when she opened the nursery door was the cat crouched upon the table, tense and motionless, watching Peter, the goldfish, in his glass bowl.

"Shoo! You're a bad cat! Shoo!" she cried, stamping her foot.

The cat shot her a quick, guilty glance, and was gone like a shadow through the doorway.

"Shoo!" cried Mrs. Harman after her, and turned to her son.

"You shouldn't let the cat in here, Don. She'll get Peter."

Seven-year-old Don was seated on the floor struggling with a shoe lace.

"Now—" he began, "now—I didn't see her, Mother. I've been tying my laces. Mother, will you telephone for Craig to come over and play? You know I was disappointed yesterday and day before, and— Will you, Mother?"

"Have you spotted today?" asked Mrs. Harman.

"A little jelly spot at lunch. It was very little, and—now—I didn't spot at breakfast."

"Very well," said Mrs. Harman, "I'll see if Craig can come."

But Craig could not come and for the third successive day Don was disappointed.

"You see it's near Christmas, dear," the mother explained, "and all the boys are busy."

"I'm not busy," Don told her wistfully.

"I'll tell you what you can do." Mrs. Harman spoke brightly. "You can write a letter to Santa Claus. Won't that be fun? It's only three weeks to Christmas, and he'll be wondering what you want."

"I don't know what I want." His tone was listless.

"Snow shoes?" she suggested.

"Oh, I don't know."

"A sled?"

Don brightened. The sled gave him an idea.

"I know what. I want a brother. Not a little one. A regular brother. Big, you know, with lots and lots of teeth."

"They're hard to get in those large sizes," Mrs. Harman said, "and it's so near Christmas they must be pretty well picked over. The best plan is to write to Santa about it. Here's paper with lines, and a nice sharp pencil."

Don sat down at his little desk and in a round laborious hand began to write. The letter, when completed, ran uphill and down and read as follows:

> Dear Santy
> i am well i hope you are well i would like a boy with teeth the biggest one you can spair for a brother
> yours truly
> D Harman

The paper, originally white, was changed to gray in the process of writing, and smudges had somehow been communicated to Don's face and hands.

"Now," said his mother, "we'll send it."

"Do you think he'll get it tonight?"

"He ought to."

They moved to the fireplace; Mrs. Harman touched a match to the letter and they watched it burn to a black, wavering crisp, and disappear.

That night Mrs. Harman told her husband she was worried about Don.

"He needs boys to play with," she said.

"There seem to be plenty of boys in the neighborhood," Mr. Harman replied.

"Yes, but they're not his age. Craig is Don's age but he lives almost a mile away, and Don doesn't see much of him except at school. I was thinking—" She sighed and broke off.

"What were you thinking, dear?"

"I was thinking of little Fred, your sister Helen's boy. He's just three months older than Don, you know."

"Isn't he getting on all right at Aunt Henrietta's?"

"I suppose so. But your Aunt Henrietta is growing old, and—well, it's not as if he had a father and a mother."

"Look here, Sallie," her husband said, "you've

got something in your mind. What is it? Do you feel that we ought to—" He did not finish the question, for his wife was nodding at him, smiling. ——

Meanwhile, up in the nursery, Don was eating his supper and his nurse was watching every mouthful.

"Will you never learn to be a little gentleman?" she demanded. "Look at your napkin. One mass of jelly. I'll have to show it to your mother. A big boy like you, and Christmas so near, too!"

"I don't care," said Don, defiantly.

"One mass of jelly," she repeated. "I'll certainly have to show it to your mother." So saying, she took the offending napkin from the boy's neck and left the room.

"I don't care!" he said again, and moved slowly over to the table where, with chin on hands, he sat and gazed at Peter, the goldfish, in his bowl.

He was not thinking of the bowl; he was not staring into it as the cat had stared, but through it at something far beyond—just what, I do not know. Nor do I know how long he sat there gazing beyond the glass and the water and the weeds and the little castle and even Peter himself. It may have been a long time or a short time, but whether it was long or short his attention was at last attracted by a tiny squeaky sound. He listened and the sound grew plainer. Somehow it suggested words—words which at first seemed to come from so far away you couldn't understand them. Then suddenly he realized that the sound was coming from inside the goldfish bowl.

Don looked at Peter. He was not swimming now, but was lying motionless, nose pressed against the glass, staring out into the nursery. His mouth was moving. It opened and shut, opened and shut, and the squeaky little sound continued.

Don leaned forward and turned one ear to the bowl. The sound grew plainer.

"Is that you, Peter?"

"Yes! Yes! Yes! Yes!" the little squeak responded instantly.

"Don't talk so fast," said Don. "What do you want?"

"Help me out!"

"All right," said the boy, but when he dipped his hand into the water, Peter darted to his castle.

"Not like that! You'll drown me!"

"You can't drown a fish."

"Have you ever been a fish?" asked Peter sharply.

"Of course not."

"Then what do you know about it?"

"I'm a boy, and a boy knows more than a fish."

"He thinks he does!" As Peter spoke, four round bubbles issued from his mouth and followed one another to the surface, where they broke with a chuckling sound: "Ha-ha-ha-ha!"

Don did not like to be laughed at by grownups, let alone fish.

"If that's how you're going to talk," he said, "I won't help you."

"Wait a minute! I want to tell you something. Will you promise not to tell?"

"Yes, what?"

"Put your ear close."

Don hesitated. "No tricks, now! If you jump up and nip my ear, or yell in it, or anything like that, I'll grab you out and have you cooked."

Peter looked shocked. "I wouldn't think of playing tricks on you," he said. "May I float belly-up if I would."

"Well, go ahead, then."

"I'm ashamed to tell it." The little fish looked very red. "It happened through my messy way of eating. They all warned me—my mother, my aunt, my nurse—but I—"

"Your nurse? Fish don't have nurses."

"That was before I *was* a fish. It was when I was a boy."

"Were you a boy?" Don was hardly able to believe his ears.

"Yes."

"What happened to you?"

"Spilling did it—spilling food on my napkin and the tablecloth."

"A fish hasn't napkins and tablecloths."

"Of course not; that's just it," said Peter. "That's how I happened to become a fish. They told me I didn't deserve a napkin on a lap. They told me I ought to be kept in water. But I never dreamed I'd come to this." A little groan came from the bowl.

"Don't you like to be a fish?" asked Don. "You don't have to go to school."

"Swimming was fun at first," said Peter, "but I'm awfully tired of it. The bowl's so round—one side just like another. And when my nose tickles I miss my hands terribly. Really there's nothing as nice as being a boy with hands and a clean white napkin and a lap."

"I wish I could get you out," said Don, "but you'd flip around on the table and die, wouldn't you?"

"Yes, there's only one way to turn me back into a boy."

"How?"

"Another boy must do it for me. He has to keep his napkin clean for a week."

"A whole *week?*" Don gasped.

"Only a week. After that I'll be his brother. I can make box kites, and we could dig caves, and keep rabbits, and get some garter snakes, and some—"

"I'll try!" exclaimed Don. "I'll try like everything!"

"Oh, thanks!" said Peter. "I can't tell you what it's going to mean to me!" He looked through the other side of the bowl at the calendar on the wall. "This is the seventeenth. You begin tomorrow morning. You only have to keep your napkin clean until the twenty-fourth, and then—why, my scales! That will be Christmas Eve! How jolly!"

"If I should spot just once," Don asked, "would that spoil everything?"

Peter quivered.

"Don't speak of such a thing!" he begged. "And remember, you are not to breathe a word of what I've told you. If you tell, the whole thing will be—"

"There you are!" cried the nurse, appearing in the doorway. "You're supposed to be in bed. Now, I'll have to tell your mother."

Don turned and blinked at her. Then he arose, shuffled over to his bed, slipped out of his bathrobe and tumbled in.

The week dragged along. The Christmas preparations, the mysterious packages, the crackling of wrapping paper Don heard through the closed door of his mother's room—none of these things occupied his mind as they had the year before. His thoughts were fixed on the tremen-dous task of freeing Peter. Somehow, somehow he must manage to keep his napkin spotless for a week. He must!

At first he thought the safest plan would be to go without meals altogether; but when he tried it Nurse scolded, and besides he got hungry. His one idea when he sat down to eat was to keep from splattering and spilling. When there was meat with gravy he cut it into little pieces with the utmost care, never allowing his knife or fork to slip. He spread his apple sauce and jelly very thin upon his bread and butter, and saw to it that none was hanging to the edges. He pushed his glass of water or milk far back from the table's edge, and when he drank he took the smallest swallows. As for cereals, eggs and soft, custardy desserts, he ate such little spoonfuls that Nurse could not believe her eyes, and wondered "what ailed the child."

To his surprise he found the task less difficult as meals and days went by. There were little tricks, he learned, to keep from making spots, and the more you practiced them the better you got. But as the work grew easier, responsibility increased. It would be awful to dribble something on his napkin after having kept it clean three days . . . four days . . . five days.

When Nurse was absent from the room he would go to Peter's bowl and whisper reassuring words; but Peter never spoke again, although he looked at Don with sad, appealing eyes, especially during meals.

At breakfast on the seventh day Peter was plainly nervous. At luncheon he was more excited still. And when night came his fins and tail were all a-quiver as he gazed through the glass wall.

This made it hard for Don. He tried not to watch Peter. At lunch he made a slip with some potato but caught it in his hand before it reached his napkin. As this occurred, a great big bubble rose like a sigh from Peter's mouth.

Having safely disposed of the last spoonful of custard, Don gave a joyful cry. He removed his napkin, and raised it like a fair white banner.

"Look!" he cried. "A whole week, and not a single spot!"

"Now, I do declare!" exclaimed the nurse, who thought he was showing it to her. "How good little boys do get when Christmas is coming. It shows what you can do. Look at it, all clean and white! I'll have to show it to your mother." She took the napkin and left the room.

Don placed his elbows on the table, rested his chin in his hands, and gazed intently at the goldfish bowl.

"Peter!" he whispered softly.

But Peter only swam about, as much a goldfish as he ever was.

Don was disappointed. He had hoped the thing would happen after supper, while Nurse was there. He had imagined Peter rising from the water, changing shape, and dropping off his scales—until he stood a full-fledged boy. How Nurse's eyes would bulge! But though this didn't happen, Don never lost his faith; he only sat there wondering how and when the change would come.

"There you are!" cried the nurse, appearing in the doorway. "You're supposed to be in bed. Now, I'll have to go and tell your mother."

Don skipped over to the bed and leaped in.

"You such a big boy," Nurse went on, "and this Christmas Eve, and your stocking hanging in the living room! I'll really have to tell your mother." She was muttering and puttering around the nursery as he fell asleep.

"Shoo! Shoo! You bad cat!" It was Mrs. Harman's voice.

Don turned over in his bed and squinted at the early morning light.

"Merry Christmas, dear!"

"Merry Christmas, Mother!" He sat up suddenly and stared with wide eyes at the goldfish bowl.

"Why, Peter's gone!" he cried, jumping out of bed.

"Never mind that now," said his mother. "You must hurry down and see all the lovely things Santa left in the living room. Get into your bathrobe and slippers. Hurry, son!"

As she spoke Don heard a motor in the driveway. Then the slam of the front door and his father's voice in the hall below.

"Dad! Dad!" he shouted, rushing down the stairs.

On the bottom step he stopped abruptly. There, holding tightly to his father's hand, stood another boy, a boy just Don's size. He grinned,

and as he did so Don saw that he had lots and lots of teeth.

The two stared at each other for a moment. Then Don moved slowly forward.

"We can make box kites," he said, "and dig caves, and keep rabbits and—"

"And garter snakes," put in the other boy.

EDDIE GOES TO DANCING SCHOOL

Carolyn Haywood

Once the children discover Eddie, they will want to read all the Eddie *books and the* Betsy *books too. No one writes about pleasant family life and the mild adventures of children 4 to 7 more happily than Carolyn Haywood.*

One day when Eddie came home from school his mother said, "Eddie, Mrs. Wallace was here this afternoon."

"You mean Toothless's mother?" Eddie asked.

"Eddie, that's a dreadful way to speak of Anna Patricia," said Mrs. Wilson.

"Well, it's true!" said Eddie. "She hasn't had any front teeth for such a long time that I guess she's never going to get any. And anyway, Anna Patricia is a silly name. Why don't they call her Anna or Patricia? Or just Pat? If I had a name like that I'd make everybody call me Pat."

"I guess Anna Patricia likes to be called by her full name," said Eddie's mother.

"Well, in school we all call her Toothless," said Eddie.

"Mrs. Wallace is forming a dancing class," said his mother. "She came to invite you to join."

Eddie looked at his mother with a face filled with horror. "A dancing class!" he cried. "What would I want to do that for?"

"Now, Eddie," said Mrs. Wilson, "it will be very nice for you to learn to dance. Dancing school is fun."

"Fun for the girls maybe, but not for boys. Are Rudy and the twins going?"

"Eddie Goes to Dancing School." From *Eddie and the Fire Engine* by Carolyn Haywood, copyright 1949 by William Morrow and Company, Inc., by permission of William Morrow and Company, Inc.

"It's just for the children in your room in school," said his mother.

"That's tough," said Eddie. Then his face brightened. "I know, Mama! You tell her Papa can't afford to send me to dancing school."

"But it's free, Eddie," said his mother. "Only the girls have to pay."

"That's a mean trick," said Eddie. "And I bet I'll have to dance with Toothless. And she lisps!"

"Of course you'll dance with Anna Patricia," said Mrs. Wilson. "The dancing class is going to be held at her home."

Eddie sat down and held his head. "Ugh!" he said. "When?"

"Friday afternoon, at half past four," replied Mrs. Wilson.

"Friday afternoon!" wailed Eddie. "That's when we practice for the Saturday ball game."

"Eddie," said his mother, "you wouldn't want it to be on Saturday, would you?"

"Of course not," Eddie moaned. "But why does it have to be at all? Why do I have to learn to dance? Rudy and the twins don't have to learn to dance. Why do you pick on me?"

"Eddie, you will have a very nice time," said his mother. "Don't raise such a fuss. Go and see."

"If I don't like it can I stop?" Eddie asked.

"Yes, if you don't like it you can stop," his mother replied.

"O.K.!" said Eddie. "But don't tell Rudy and the twins that I have to go to dancing school."

"O.K.!" said Mrs. Wilson.

On Friday, when Eddie came home from school, his mother said, "Eddie, put on your best suit for dancing class."

"You mean my best Sunday suit?" said Eddie.

"Yes, dear," replied Mrs. Wilson.

"Golly! This dancing school business gets worse all the time," said Eddie.

Eddie washed his face and hands and soaked his hair with water. Then he took off his blue jeans and put on his best suit. "What will I do if I meet Rudy and the twins, all dressed up in my Sunday suit on Friday?" Eddie shrieked from his bedroom.

When he came downstairs his mother handed him a package. "These are your pumps, dear," she said.

"My what, Mama?" said Eddie, screwing up his nose.

"Your pumps," replied Mother, "your dancing pumps."

"What do I do with 'em?" Eddie asked.

"You wear them on your feet," said Mrs. Wilson.

"You mean I can't dance in my shoes?" Eddie cried.

"You would step on the little girls' feet, Eddie, in those clumsy shoes," said his mother.

"Serves 'em right!" said Eddie. "I'll walk all over Toothless's feet. Just let me at 'em."

"Eddie, do stop dawdling and get off," said his mother. "Have you money for bus fare? And don't forget to ask for a transfer."

Eddie pulled some change out of his pocket and looked at it. "O.K.," he said.

Just then he heard the twins coming in the front door. Eddie leaped like a deer and was out of the back door in a flash. He did not stop running until he reached his bus stop.

When the bus arrived Eddie stepped in. He knew the bus driver. He often rode with him. His name was Mike.

"Hi!" said Mike. "You look like a movie actor. All you need is a carnation in your buttonhole. Where you going, all dressed up?"

"Don't ask me," Eddie moaned. He flopped into the seat nearest the door.

"Come on, tell me. You'll feel better if you tell me," said Mike.

"You promise you won't tell anybody?" said Eddie.

"On my honor," said Mike.

Eddie got up and whispered in Mike's ear. "I'm going to dancing school. Isn't that horrible?"

"Oh! Cheer up!" said Mike. "I went to dancing school once. And look at me now."

"You did?" said Eddie, with a brighter face. He leaned over and whispered, "And did you have pumps?"

"Sure! Sure!" said Mike. "I was the best pumper in the crowd. You'll learn to pump. It's easy."

"No, Mike," said Eddie. "They're some kind of shoes. They're in this package."

"Oh, I thought that was your supper," said Mike. "Oh, sure! Pumps. Sure, you gotta have pumps."

"I have to change buses at Brewster Road," said Eddie.

"Righto!" said Mike. "Three more stops before we get there."

When the bus reached Brewster Road, Mike drew up to the curb. As Eddie stepped out he said, "So long, Mike."

"So long, pal!" said Mike. "I'll wait for you to cross the street."

Eddie crossed the street in front of the bus. When he reached the opposite corner, he heard Mike calling, "Hey, Eddie!"

Eddie looked back and saw a package flying toward him. It landed at his feet. "Your pumps," Mike called out, as he started the bus.

Eddie picked up the parcel and put it under his arm. He stood on the corner and waited for the other bus. Across the street there was a used car lot. It belonged to Mr. Ward, a friend of Eddie's father. Eddie looked over the cars while he waited. Suddenly, he caught sight of something bright red. Eddie's heart began to beat faster. He ran across the street and over to the lot. Sure enough! It was just what he thought. There was the fire engine he had ridden on at the Fair. A man was lying under it, working with a hammer.

Eddie stooped down and looked under. There was Mr. Ward. "Hello, Mr. Ward!" said Eddie. "I rode on this fire engine once. It was super!"

"You did, Eddie?" said Mr. Ward, pushing himself out from between the wheels. "Well, how would you like to ride on it again?"

"Now?" said Eddie, his eyes shining.

"I want to see how it runs," said Mr. Ward. "I just put in a new part."

"Swell!" said Eddie, climbing right up into the front seat. "This is great!" he added, as the fire engine started.

Then Mr. Ward looked down on the ground. "Does that bundle belong to you?" he asked.

"Oh, golly! Yes," said Eddie. "Stop."

The fire engine stopped and Eddie got down. He ran back and picked up his package. Then he climbed up again. He put the package on the seat beside him and they started off. "I sure like this fire engine," he said.

"You going anywhere special?" Mr. Ward asked.

"Oh, not very special," Eddie replied.

"Got plenty of time?" said Mr. Ward.

"Oh sure!" said Eddie.

"Very well! She's going good. We'll take a spin around," said Mr. Ward.

Eddie held onto the seat and swung his legs. This was wonderful! "Can I pull the bell?" he asked.

"No, we can't ring the bell," said Mr. Ward. "The fire company would object. Might look like a false alarm."

Mr. Ward drove Eddie way out into the country before he said, "I guess I had better get back. Where can I drop you?"

Eddie thought of dancing school for the first time since he had been on the bus. "Oh! I have to go to Beech Tree Road," he said.

"Beech Tree Road?" said Mr. Ward. "What's going on there? By the way, you look all slicked up."

"Yeah," said Eddie. "I forgot all about it. I'm going to dancing school."

"You don't say!" said Mr. Ward. "What have you got in the package?"

Eddie looked sheepish. "Aw, pumps," he said.

"Pumps!" said Mr. Ward. "What the heck are pumps?"

"I don't know," said Eddie. "Something you wear on your feet."

"Well, suppose I take you right over to the place," said Mr. Ward.

"Oh, that would be great!" said Eddie.

Mrs. Wallace was standing at the front door when Eddie drove up in the fire engine. As he jumped down she said, "Why, Eddie! You're very late. I've been wondering why you didn't get here."

"I guess I am a little late," said Eddie. "Mr. Ward gave me a lift."

Eddie could hear the boys and girls laughing. They were all in the dining room.

"It's too bad you missed the dancing class," said Mrs. Wallace. "The children are having their ice cream now."

Eddie's face shone. "Ice cream?" he said. "Gee, that's great!"

"Hello, Eddie!" the children called out when Eddie walked into the dining room.

"Hello!" said Eddie, sitting down at the table.

Mrs. Wallace handed him a large plate of ice cream and Eddie lost no time in eating it. Just as he swallowed the last spoonful, the doorbell rang. Mrs. Wallace went to the front door and opened it. Eddie heard Mr. Ward's voice say, "Is Eddie Wilson still here?"

"Yes, he is," said Mrs. Wallace.

"Well, here are his pumps," said Mr. Ward.

The children had caught a glimpse of the fire engine through the open door. They rushed to the door to look at it. "Oh, here's the fire engine that was at the Fair!" they cried.

"I had a ride on it this afternoon," said Eddie.

"Oh, can we have a ride?" the children shouted. "Can we have a ride?"

"You have on your best clothes," said Mrs. Wallace. "You can't go riding on a fire engine in your best clothes, in your dancing clothes."

"We won't hurt them," the children cried.

"I didn't hurt mine, did I?" said Eddie.

"I'll take them all home," said Mr. Ward.

The children rushed to the fire engine, the little girls in their ruffled dresses and the boys in their Sunday suits.

"Now, everybody sit still," said Mr. Ward. "You have to keep your clothes clean."

Just as everyone was settled Eddie jumped down. "Wait a minute," he said.

He ran into the house and came back with his package. He looked up at Mr. Ward and grinned. "Forgot my pumps," he said.

Mr. Ward dropped the children off, one by one. Eddie was the last. When he drove up to the house, the twins were looking out of the window. When they saw Eddie, they rushed to the front door.

"What's the idea," cried Joe, "riding on the fire engine?"

"Where have you been?" cried Frank.

"I've been to dancing school," said Eddie.

"Dancing school!" cried the twins in chorus.

"Gee, it's swell!" said Eddie, as he waved good-by to Mr. Ward.

When dinner was almost over, the doorbell rang. Mr. Wilson went to the door and opened it and everyone around the dining-room table heard Mr. Ward's voice say, "Here are Eddie's pumps. He left them on the fire engine."

When Mr. Wilson came back to the dining room, he was carrying a package. He put it on the window sill. "Here are your pumps, Eddie," he said.

"Pumps!" cried Rudy and the twins together. "What are pumps?"

"I don't know," said Eddie. "I haven't had time to look at 'em. But dancing school was swell, Mama. Dancing school was swell!"

from BENJIE'S HAT

Mabel Leigh Hunt

[Hat Trouble]

Every First Day, which was Sunday, Hamish hitched the horse to the carriage. Grandmother put on her best bonnet and one of her good dresses and her softest, finest kerchief. Benjie cleaned his shoes and scrubbed his cheeks and put on his tow suit and the straw hat bound round with gray flannel. He and Grandmother climbed into the carriage. Grandmother took up the reins, clucked to the horse, and off they went to Meeting.

When they arrived at the meeting-house,

Reprinted by permission of the publishers from *Benjie's Hat* by Mabel Leigh Hunt. Copyright, 1938, by J. B. Lippincott Company

Grandmother patted Benjie's shoulder, and said, "Now thee be a good boy, Grandson," which was rather unnecessary, as Benjie behaved himself very well indeed. He may have squirmed a little when his feet went to sleep, or when the day was warm and his tow breeches scratched, but that was all.

Then he and Grandmother parted, for Grandmother must sit on the women's side of the meeting-house with the women and girls, and Benjie must sit with the men on the men's side. He felt very grown-up sitting there without his father and Milo and Matthew, as at home, and for several First Days this was enough to keep Benjie completely satisfied throughout the long silent meeting. For when Benjie was a little boy, the Friends had no music at their religious services, and only rarely did they have preaching. Children must "wait in stillness upon the Lord," as their elders did, and receive comfort and strength through silent meditation and prayer.

On a certain October morning Benjie and Grandmother went to meeting. There never was a more perfect day. The long needles of the pines glittered in the golden sunlight. The red and golden leaves fluttered lazily down from the trees that were all red and golden. Through the open windows of the meeting-house Benjie could hear the horses moving lazily and stamping at their hitching-rack. From afar came the whistle of quail. For the first time Benjie felt fidgety. The coarse stuff of his clothing made him itch, and although no one paid him any attention, he knew that he must not scratch. The world outside seemed to be saying, "Come out, Benjie. Come out and play in the golden morning." Benjie kept hearing this soft and golden voice, and as there seemed to be no probability of the meeting ever coming to an end, and as the prickles on his legs seemed to be getting worse, he arose at last from his place, very softly. He squeezed past several large knees, whose owners looked at him gravely from under their broad hats. But Benjie knew that they scarcely saw him, for their thoughts were far removed from worldly things. He tiptoed down the aisle of the men's side and out into the meeting-house grounds.

The stillness outside was almost as deep as it had been in the meeting-house, a charmed and golden stillness, and Benjie, now that he had come, scarcely knew what to do with himself. It was very queer, but he didn't itch a bit any more. He looked about, and felt lonely. The world seemed an empty golden shell, with no one in it but the horses and a stranger named Benjamin Bartholomew Barnett. Oh, dear, whatever had made him come? How shocked and sorry Grandmother would be if she knew that he had run away from Meeting! A little lump came into Benjie's throat when he thought of Grandmother, whom he loved so much, and who loved him. Forlornly he wandered to the fence and began to stroke the noses of the horses, since there was no joy for him in the lovely day, after all. He gathered handfuls of grass for them. They nosed him eagerly.

And then a most surprising thing happened.

For all of a sudden Benjie heard a loud crunching noise. His head was jerked violently sidewise. A damp breath blew through his hair, and he looked up to see an old white horse at his shoulder. And he had Benjie's hat in his mouth. He was chewing with all his might and main. He was chewing up Benjie's hat!

"Ow!" cried Benjie. "Gimme my hat!" He reached up as far as he could and began tugging at the object that was no longer a hat, but a crushed and mangled fragment. A long strip of gray flannel hung from the horse's mouth. Bits of straw fell to the ground. The hat was gone, all but one little piece in Benjie's hand—the hat that had been a fine store hat, the hat that had once been Milo's pride, that had been worn less proudly by Matthew, and was, until a moment ago, Benjie's only hat.

Oh, the mean old horse! The meanest old horse in the world! What could Benjie do? He couldn't slip back into Meeting and sit with uncovered head. That was unthinkable, for the Friends wore their hats throughout the Meeting. What would Grandmother say when she found that Benjie had not only "played hooky" from Meeting, but had lost his hat as well. "Wilful waste, woeful want," that's what Grandmother would say. Oh, she would think him a very bad boy! Well, he was, although he hadn't really meant to be. Losing his hat was a punishment for stealing away from Meeting. At last Benjie climbed up into Grandmother's carriage, with the one remnant of his hat in his hand, and made himself as small as possible.

Presently the people began coming slowly out of the meeting-house, looking refreshed and calm and cheerful. They shook hands with each other in the autumn sunshine. There was a pleasant hum of talk.

Benjie screwed himself into a tighter knot on the carriage seat, but kept a weather eye open for Grandmother. Yes, there she was! Beloved Grandmother, folded so neatly into her shawl; her face placid and rosy in its neat frame of bonnet. There! She was looking for him! Oh, dear! Benjie turned his head away sadly. He couldn't bear to see Grandmother looking for the *good* boy that should have come out of the meeting-house with all the good people when Meeting broke.

And then he heard the soft rustle of Grandmother's skirts. He felt her near him.

"Why, Benjie-boy!" she cried. "Is thee ill? Did thee have to leave the Meeting?"

"No, Grandmother," answered Benjie. He turned and looked at her, full of misery. "I didn't have to leave. Just see what happened, Grandmother." He held out the piece of straw. "An old horse chewed up my hat!"

"Thy hat! Benjie! Does thee mean to say that a horse reached into the meeting-house and took the very hat off thy head? Never did I hear the like!" And as Grandmother climbed into the carriage she looked about indignantly as if to say, "Where is that rude creature that ate the hat off the grandson of Judith Cox?"

"Oh, no, Grandmother!" Benjie could not help smiling a little at the impossible picture that Grandmother had imagined. Nothing short of a giraffe could have reached into the meeting-house.

"No, Grandmother," he went on. "I did leave Meeting. It's a nice day, and my pants scratched me, and my feet were going to sleep, and before I thought what I was doing, I was walking out of Meeting."

"Benjamin Bartholomew Barnett!" exclaimed Grandmother. "Thee left Meeting just because thee was fidgety?"

"But I didn't have a bit good time, Grandmother!" cried Benjie hastily. "I wished and wished I hadn't come. And then the old horse grabbed my hat. If he'd just waited a minute I'd have given him some nice grass. I was taking turns feeding them all grass. But he couldn't wait—the old greedy!"

"A just punishment for thee, Benjie," declared Grandmother. "Now thee has no hat. And thee sinned besides." Grandmother shook her head sorrowfully.

"Maybe next year the hat would've been too small for me, Grandmother," suggested Benjie.

"That does not alter the situation, Grandson. Some other boy could have worn it."

The remainder of the ride home was very quiet. Dinner was very quiet. The afternoon bade fair to be very quiet and very long. So that the sound of the music from Hamish's banjo twanging across the October fields was welcome to Benjie, even though it was so surprising. He looked at Grandmother quickly. Her mouth was set in a straight line.

"Someone else sinneth," she said. "Go down, Benjamin, and ask Hamish what he means by playing the banjo on my farm on First Day. And come back the moment thy errand is done."

Benjie went along the edge of the corn-field, going to meet the gay little banjo notes that seemed to be running, in spite of First Day, to meet him. And there was Hamish, seated in his doorway, his head bent over his beloved banjo, his fingers strumming happily. And there was Eliphalet, doing a buck-an'-wing in the red-colored dust in front of the cabin.

"Hamish!" cried Benjie sternly. "Grandmother says thee is not to play the banjo on her farm on First Day."

Hamish's mouth fell open. Eliphalet stopped, frozen in his tracks.

"Ah plum fo'got mahse'f," said Hamish, sheepishly. "Reckon hit am de weathah. Reckon hit am a day foh pickin' de banjo. Reckon dis niggah done los' my min' disrememberin' dat Ol' Miss cain' have no music on Fus' Day."

"Grandmother says thee sinneth," announced Benjie. It was rather pleasant to be able to tell Hamish that he, too, was a sinner.

Hamish's face fell. Tenderly he put down his banjo. He looked so sad that Benjie cried, "But I sinned, too, Hamish." And he told his friend all about the morning's sad incident.

At first Hamish looked very sympathetic. But presently his mouth began to spread. The laughter that seemed to have its home in Hamish's toes was coming up, shaking his body, up, up, until it burst from mouth and nose in snorts and chuckles.

"Yoh mean—yoh mean dat ol' white hoss et up dat hat uv yo-alls? Dat ol' white hoss jus' natchally lean hisse'f ovah an' grab dat hat an' chew an' chew twell hit all chewed up?" Hamish flung up his hands in delight. He rocked back and forth, hugging his mirth.

"An' chew an' chew an' chew," echoed Eliphalet. "De hat, de hoss. De hat, de hoss!"

And soon Hamish and Eliphalet and Benjie, too, for he could not help it, were rocking with laughter. And Dilcey came and stood in the doorway. "Dat ol' white hoss don' need no dinnah dis day," she chuckled. "No, 'deedy. He

done had a pow'ful good dinnah eatin' off Benjie's hat."

Benjie wished that he could stay in this jolly place. But Grandmother's word was law, and he trudged dutifully back home. He was relieved to see that Grandmother seemed much more cheerful. She and Benjie carried chairs out to the yard and sat together in the mild autumn sunshine. Presently Jerushy came waddling along, and Grandmother picked her up, and allowed the old hen to rest upon her aproned lap, for Jerushy and Grandmother were great friends, after all these thirteen years together.

And while Benjie leaned against Grandmother's chair, and stroked Jerushy's soft old feathers, Grandmother told him stories. She told him of his great-grandfather, whose home had been on Nantucket Island, but who had spent most of his life at sea, for he had been a whaling master. "A very good man," said Grandmother. "He held silent meeting on his ship every First and Fourth Days, just as if he were in the meeting-house at home." She told Benjie of his great-uncle, who had once lain in prison for many weeks, because he refused to bear arms against his fellow-man. She spoke of Benjie's great-great-grandfather, who had lived in England before sailing to America as a young man, and who had been able to tell his children of the days when George Fox, the great founder of the Society of Friends, used to come to his father's house in that English village where he lived as a boy.

And Grandmother said, "The good people before thee were God-fearing people. *They* had no worldly thoughts at Meeting. None of them would ever have strayed away from Meeting at the slightest excuse, as thee did, Benjamin."

And she looked at Benjie, and Benjie looked at her. It was a long moment, and when it was over, it seemed that Benjie and his Grandmother loved each other even more than ever. And Grandmother reached into her deep pocket, and brought forth a handful of peanuts, and she and Benjie broke them and ate them, which made old Jerushy sit up and jerk her head about, as if to say, "What! Something to eat?" Jerushy made Benjie and Grandmother both smile.

After supper, and six o'clock, when First Day was over, and Benjie was getting ready for bed, he saw Grandmother's eyes begin to twinkle.

Her rosy face grew rosier. She held her apron up to her mouth, and she began to shake all over. Grandmother was laughing! It made Benjie laugh to see Grandmother laughing so hard. And when she had calmed down and wiped her eyes, and tucked Benjie into bed, she looked down at him, and she said, "Don't thee be thinking that I considered it funny of thee to run away from Meeting, Benjamin Bartholomew Barnett. It's just the idea of that old horse chewing up thy hat. All of a sudden it struck my funny bone."

And Benjie said, "Grandmother, next First Day I shall go to Meeting, and I shan't *move*, no matter how much my britches scratch me." He suddenly sat up in bed. "But what shall I do? I can't go to Meeting without a hat!"

"That's true, Grandson," answered Grandmother. "And of course it is almost too late in the season to wear thy tow breeches and thy straw hat, anyway. Why didn't thee bring thy winter hat with thee?"

"It was too little for me," said Benjie. "Mother gave it to Cousin Daniel. Mother said that thee would buy me a winter hat over in Friendship."

"Tut, tut!" exclaimed Grandmother. "Does thy mother think that money grows on my peanut vines, or that I dig it up with my yams? But a hat thee must have. That's plain. We'll see what can be done about it. We'll see."

And as Benjie fell asleep, full of Grandmother's loving forgiveness, he thought to himself, "How nice it will be to have a hat all my own, a hat that is bought just for me!"

But the pine woods through which Benjie ran to school still murmured softly of Indian summer, and he did not really need a hat, except for Meeting. So for two days he almost forgot about the hat which had disappeared down the throat of the old white horse. And while he played *Ant'ny-Over* and *Prison Base* with the boys at recess, the thought of a nice new hat lay half-forgotten, too, but warmly treasured in his mind.

On the evening of Third Day, Grandmother said, "To-morrow thee must march with the other children to regular Fourth Day Meeting. Therefore thee must wear thy new hat to school.

Thee didn't know I had a surprise for thee, now did thee?"

She opened the door of the fireside cupboard and drew out a hat.

"There, Benjie!" she exclaimed. "While thee was at school, I was busy plying my needle. There was no need to spend good silver, nor good trade, either, for a store hat, when thy grandfather's nap beaver lay unused in its box. See? I cut a mite off the crown, though it was a pity to waste even that bit. I took some pleats in crown and brim, to make it more thy size. Then I sewed them back together again. And there is thy hat!" She held it up proudly.

Benjie stared and stared. "It's a very peculiar-some hat," he murmured, and burst into tears. "The b-b-boys will laugh."

"Tut, tut, Benjie," scolded Grandmother. "Is thee a girl, to be so vain of thy looks? 'Tis a good hat, and 'twill serve the purpose. Thee should feel honored to wear the hat thy grandfather wore for fifteen years."

Benjie set off for school the next morning, wearing the tall hat. In spite of Grandmother's careful pleatings, it was still much too large for him, and only his ears held it up. In the woods he reached up and felt it carefully. How smooth

and furry it was! No doubt Grandfather had once paid a good round sum for it. Perhaps, after all, the boys would not laugh.

But when Benjie entered the school yard, up went shouts of derision, and soon the whole world, as it seemed to Benjie, was echoing with the chorus:

"Look at Benjie's ha-yat!
Look at Benjie's ha-yat!"

Oh, how red and unhappy Benjie was!

But he laughed as hard as anyone when his tormentors flung the hat into the air, and it caught on the high limb of a tree. He hoped that it would hang there forever. When the hour came to march to the meeting-house, it was very fortunate for Benjie that one of his schoolmates was absent that day, but had left his hat hanging on a nail in the school entry. So Benjie wore it, and was completely satisfied.

He went home that evening to tell Grandmother cheerfully that his new hat was entirely out of reach on the limb of a very tall tree. But the next day, while school was keeping, Grandmother and Hamish came with a long pole and rescued the hat. What a craning of necks as the children watched them through the windows! And presently, to the delight of every boy in the room, Grandmother opened the door, and said, "Benjamin Barnett, thee will find thy hat hanging in the entry." For a few hours after that it seemed to Benjie that he didn't even *like* his grandmother!

Soon Benjie began to feel that nothing on earth could harm that hat. For instance, it blew off one day in a windy gust of rain. He carried it home hopefully, for it was smeared with the gummy red clay of North Carolina. But Grandmother let it dry, scraped off the dirt and washed and brushed it carefully. It looked just as good as ever.

"Is this my hat, Grandmother, or is it Grandfather's hat?" asked Benjie.

"It is thy hat now," answered Grandmother.

So, after thinking it over carefully, Benjie argued to himself that he had a perfect right to give the hat to Eliphalet, for it seemed that the little colored boy was the only one in all the world, except Grandmother, of course, who did not laugh at Benjie's hat.

"Dis heah am a sho-nuff gif'," declared Eli-

phalet, grinning from ear to ear, and holding the hat reverently in his hands. "Dat ol' Mistuh Beavah, he des' as smove an' slick as evuh he am."

Eliphalet put on the hat, but it would fall down over his eyes, and even over his nose. Benjie could see nothing of his friend's face but a pair of grinning lips, a row of white teeth, and a little black chin. Eliphalet had to perch the hat on the back of his head, to be able to see at all. When Benjie went home, feeling generous, but a little doubtful, he looked back and saw Eliphalet strutting all around the cabin as proudly as a king.

But when Dilcey saw the hat decorating her son's woolly head, she shouted, "Yo-all march straight up to de big house wid dat hat, an' don' be delayin' yo'se'f. Benjie's gran'mammy—she gwine be in a big huff when she fin' dat boy gib ol' dead Massa's hat away. N' ol' Massa's gwine steal back an' ha'nt folkses dat weah his hat when dey ain' got no right."

In a very few moments the hat was lying on Grandmother's doorstep, and Eliphalet running home again with all his might and main, for fear of the *ha'nt*. So the hat was Benjie's once more, and there was nothing to do but wear it.

Whenever he went to Meeting, he could think of nothing but his hat. His ears burned scarlet with shame. He would turn suspiciously, to catch a frosty twinkle in a pair of elderly eyes, or a smothered giggle from some boy.

Therefore one morning, as he and Grandmother rode to Meeting, Benjie said, "I guess *thee* wouldn't wear this hat!"

"Indeed I would, and proud to," answered Grandmother tartly. And to Benjie's horror, she removed her bonnet and put on the hat, sitting as straight as a ramrod, glancing neither to the right nor the left. She looked ridiculous. Oh, dear! Grandmother was certainly very difficult to look after. He couldn't allow *her* to make a laughingstock out of herself. Personal pride was one thing, but family pride was another. He sighed. "Never mind, Grandmother. *I'd* better wear it," he said.

Just then a dog came running out from nowhere, barking furiously. The horse jumped, and thundered down the road, almost shaking Grandmother and Benjie to pieces. Afterward it was discovered that Benjie's hat was missing. He went back to search for it, praying that it had been trampled beyond repair, or that the dog had carried it off. But no! There it was, lying in a fence corner, with only one small dent in the brim.

"A little steaming and pressing will attend to that," said Grandmother.

"Grandfather certainly bought a good hat, didn't he?" remarked Benjie.

"Yes," answered Grandmother. "He had the hat made at Beard's Hatter Shop. A good nap beaver will last a lifetime."

Benjie's heart sank. A lifetime seemed a very long time.

So when next Peter Kersey had an errand to Randolph County, Benjie gave him a letter, secretly, with the request that it be delivered to his mother. It said:

"Dear Mother—
I am middling well, and hope thee is the same. Grandmother is well. Jerushy is still alive and shows no sines of dyeing. But I wish thee would send me a Cap, and oblige
Thy obeedyunt son,
Benjie Barnett."

But when Peter returned, and Benjie unwrapped the eagerly-awaited parcel, there was nothing but a yarn muffler. To tie his head up like a baby! Oh, it was terribly disappointing!

One evening Benjie sat on a stump in the woods. There was a dark scowl on his face. His lower lip stuck away out. At school that afternoon when Susan Bond was supposed to be doing a sum on the blackboard she had drawn a picture. First she had made a very tall hat. Beneath that, two enormous ears. Then she had drawn a teeny-tiny body, and underneath she had printed BENJIE. She had rubbed it out quickly before the teacher had suspected, but most of the scholars had seen it.

So Benjie, very angry, sat alone on the stump. He was angry at everybody in the world.

Presently Peter Kersey came riding through the wood. He jumped off his horse and sat down by the boy. But Benjie did not speak. He only scowled the darker. Peter picked the hat up and turned it thoughtfully in his hands. "Thy grandfather was a fine man, Benjie," he began quietly, "one of the finest North Carolina has ever produced. He and I were boys together. He was my great friend. Did thee ever hear about the time thy grandfather—" And Peter began telling stories about Grandfather Cox—things that Benjie had never heard before. Soon the scowl faded. The sulky lower lip slipped back. Benjie was smiling, and his eyes were shining. He began to think that perhaps he might wear cheerfully a hat that such a fine grandfather had worn.

"And I'll tell thee, Benjie," said Peter, when he had finished, "Thy grandmother is a fine woman, too. There's no one quite like her. But between me and thee, women never understand just how a man feels about his hat. A man's hat is his own. Let it be suitable, and he can face the world with his head up."

Even if Peter Kersey was an Elder, and sat at the head of the Meeting, he understood a fellow!

But the next morning Benjie remembered Susan's drawing, and he said to himself, "I'll not wear this hat to school if I catch the quinsy and die!" So he took to hiding the hat in the woods, and nobody knew.

One afternoon in the early winter Peter Kersey, with his gun over his shoulder, went into the woods after rabbits. He had bagged three and was just turning homeward, when he saw another plump cotton-tail bounding ahead. He took aim, and missed. The rabbit disappeared into one end of a hollow log just as Peter fired his second shot. He walked forward and peered into the log. And there, in the end of it, was Benjie's hat, with the top of the crown almost torn off by the force of the shot, and the dead rabbit trapped inside!

"Now what have I done?" asked Peter of himself. "I'll have to wait for Benjie to come along this way from school."

When Benjie saw the hat—oh, what joy! "Now I'll never have to wear it again!" he cried.

"Don't thee be too sure of that," warned Peter. "Thy grandmother is a very resourceful woman. But now we must go and tell her what has happened."

Very slowly Peter and Benjie walked through the woods toward Grandmother's house. Benjie was wondering just how he would explain the fact that his hat was in the end of the log. And

Peter was wondering just how he could help Benjie. Presently he said, "A thought has suddenly occurred to me. Put on the hat, boy. And can't thee look a trifle pale?"

Indeed Benjie's cheeks were not so rosy as usual, for what would Grandmother say? What would she do?

Arrived at the house, Peter confronted Grandmother bravely. He kept Benjie well behind him. His face was long and serious.

"I have something to tell thee, Judith," he said. "I hope thee will not take it too hard. This afternoon I was hunting in the woods. And I— I shot thy—thy grandson's hat." He reached around quickly and plucked the hat off Benjie's head.

Grandmother stared at the bullet holes. She saw the stains in the crown. She went white as a sheet. "O Benjie-boy!" she cried. "Is thee hurt?"

Benjie could not bear to see his grandmother looking so white and distressed. But neither could he keep his face straight a moment longer. Laughing, he flung his arms around Grandmother's waist. And then Peter began laughing. And as soon as Grandmother heard about the rabbit, her relief was so great that she laughed as heartily as anyone.

"I do declare," she said, "this hat has had so many misfortunes that I'm beginning to believe the Lord never intended that Benjie should wear it."

"Then thee'll throw it away?" cried Benjie.

"Throw this good hat away?" echoed Grandmother. "Just hearken to him, Peter. I'm sure I don't know where he gets such notions. 'Wilful waste, woeful want,' Grandson. Thee knows that other old saying, too—'Keep a thing seven years, and thee will find a use for it.' So of course I won't throw the hat away. It will come in handy for something one of these days. But thee can't wear it any more. As a matter of fact, Peter," she said, gravely, turning to Peter Kersey, "I don't believe Benjie ever liked this hat, fine as it was. I thought it was very suitable for him. But there's no accounting for a boy's taste. So to-morrow, Benjie, we shall drive over to Friendship and buy thee just an ordinary cap."

An ordinary cap! Why, that was just what Benjie wanted! A fellow didn't have to be careful of an ordinary cap. It was all that Benjie could do to keep from turning a handspring or shouting or clapping his hands. But because of Grandmother's feelings about Grandfather's fine hat, it would never do to shout his joy.

But he ran to the stone jar, and he selected the very biggest and brownest cooky for his friend, Peter Kersey. And the next biggest for himself. As Peter accepted the cooky, he and Benjie looked at each other, as man to man, and smiled.

from AUGUSTUS AND THE RIVER

LeGrand

Our hero is a little "grape of wrath" without knowing it. He and his happy-go-lucky family adventure joyously through innumerable books. This episode is the beginning of one of their long and satisfying jaunts.

[Going South]

Augustus stood on the low bank of the Mississippi River and shuffled his bare feet in the thick coarse grass. Absent-mindedly picking up a stick with his toes, he looked out over the river.

Below him bobbed the houseboat where he lived with his sister Glorianna, his brother Jupiter, Pop, Ma, Tom Cat and the chickens.

Down the shore a way, he saw Glorianna and Jupiter hunting for doodlebugs. Augustus thought maybe he would get them to play pirate. Then he decided he wouldn't. Jupiter was just five—only half as old as Augustus, and that wasn't old enough to be a good pirate. Glorianna was eight, and old enough, but she was only a girl.

Feeling restless, Augustus picked up another stick with his toes. He kicked it deftly into the air, caught it and tried to balance it on the end of his nose.

On a log near by, a big old bullfrog blinked sleepily, and swelling his throat, rumbled, "Kerchunk."

That was a mistake.

Augustus saw him, and threw the stick. It was a good shot, and he felt a mild glow of pride as the frog squawked and jumped into the water.

The stick drifted out away from shore, and Augustus watched as the current whirled if off down-river.

"Wonder if it will drift clean down to the ocean?" he mused.

There was a quacking overhead and a flock of ducks flew by, headed down-river too.

"Going south for the winter," thought Augustus. "Wish I was going—"

Suddenly he understood the restlessness that had been bothering him. He wanted to go south too.

The ducks were going, the stick was going; why, even the river was going, moving on always past new strange places, way down there beyond where the earth and the sky met.

"We've been living in this ol' bend more than a year now," muttered Augustus.

There was a scrambling on the bank and Glorianna and Jupiter came sliding down beside him.

"What you doing?" asked Glorianna.

"Just wishing I had a boat of my own, so I could go south."

"Bet you'd be scared all alone on the river."

"Huh, would not. I guess I'd show that ol' river something."

Glorianna looked doubtful.

"What you want to go down-river for?" she asked.

"Huh," thought Augustus, "just like a girl—not to understand about things like that."

"Well," he said aloud, "we've been living on this ol' river all our lives, and never been farther south than this bend right here in Iowa."

Glorianna looked puzzled.

"Well, this is pretty far south from Minnesota where we used to live," she said.

Augustus snorted.

"Aw, you don't understand," he grumbled. "I mean really south."

He had a far-off expression as he went on. "Folks say there's some mighty wonderful things to see down there—alligators big as a house—"

Glorianna shuddered.

"—Sugar cane they grind up and boil, and it comes out sugar—"

"Good ol' sugar," said Jupiter, patting his stomach.

Augustus paid no attention to him and went on: "Ol' man Hawkins says there's pirates down

there too. An' way down at the end is the blue ocean. I'd mighty like to see the ocean. . . ."

Augustus was thinking so hard about the ocean he didn't notice anything, but Glorianna heard the creaking of oarlocks and looked around.

She jumped up, saying, "Here comes Pop." Turning to Augustus, she added, "Maybe we'll all be going off down-river if the fishing stays bad here. Pop's been talking some about going."

Augustus' face brightened as he said, "Yeh, I heard him tell Ma he was studyin' about it . . . said at least a body could keep warm in the winter if he went far enough south."

The creaking of the oarlocks grew louder and Pop came into sight around the bend, rowing his skiff up to the bank.

"Catch anything, Pop?" yelled Augustus as they all ran down to meet him.

"Nothin' much," grumbled Pop. "Only a few ghoul."

"A ghoul's a right good eatin' fish, Pop," said Jupiter.

Pop looked at him and grinned.

"Trouble is," he said, "only river folks like ghoul. Can't trade 'em down at the store for side meat and beans and coffee and sugar and such-like."

Augustus helped Pop pull the skiff up on the bank. There was a lot of water in the bottom and it poured out over the stern as the boat tilted.

"Ol' boat leaks worse every day," said Pop. "I aim to fix it sometime. Trouble is, when I'm out on the river I can't fix it, and when I'm on shore I don't need to fix it."

Pop grinned and winked at Augustus, who grinned and winked back. Augustus had yellow hair like Pop's, and they looked a lot alike when they grinned. Ma always said the river had got into their blood, because their hair was so like the color of the muddy yellow water. Glorianna and Jupiter took after Ma and had black hair.

"Are we going south, Pop?" asked Augustus anxiously.

"Maybe," said Pop, going up the narrow gangplank to the houseboat. "I aim to make up my mind right soon."

It was bright and cheerful-looking in the little cabin as they clattered in the door and down the two steps to the floor. The walls were lined with newspapers to keep the wind out. One was a colored funny paper. It looked very pretty, and so did the big calendar Glorianna had fished out of the river one day. The calendar part was gone but the picture part had lots of red roses and white doves and bluebirds and a lady with wings. The lady was spoiled some by the big black mustache Jupiter had marked on her. Next to the calendar hung a map of the United States. It showed the Mississippi River, and Pop had made a mark that showed where the houseboat was.

"Any luck?" asked Ma as Pop came in the door.

"No luck," said Pop. "Nothing but some ghoul. Seems as if all the good fish I can trade have moved on away from here."

Pop looked thoughtful as Ma bustled around getting dinner.

Augustus broke up some driftwood and stuffed it into the potbellied stove. It popped and crackled loudly as Ma fried the fish. Soon there was corn hoecake getting nice and brown in the pan, and the smell of the fish almost brought tears of joy to Jupiter's eyes.

"You Augustus," said Ma, "fetch some water."

Augustus got a bucket of water from the river for washing and another for drinking water. He put the drinking water aside to give the mud a chance to settle to the bottom.

"Now all of you get yourselves cleaned up. The vittles are most done," said Ma.

Augustus filled the tin washbasin and went out on deck. The houseboat rocked in the swells from a passing steamboat. The water in the basin jiggled back and forth, slopping over the edge until most of it was gone. Augustus looked at what was left, thought a while about getting some more, decided he probably wasn't very dirty anyway and managed to get his face and hands damp. Then he rubbed vigorously with the flour-sack towel. A lot of fertile soil went from Augustus to the towel in that process. Then, happily satisfied that he had done all that could reasonably be asked of him, he gave the basin to Glorianna.

By the time everyone had washed, Ma had the food on the table.

She looked hard at Jupiter as they sat down.

"I declare," said Ma, "you haven't done more than wipe the mud off your nose."

"That's the only place there was mud, Ma," said Jupiter in a puzzled tone.

Ma led him out on deck. Mournful sounds drifted into the cabin, followed by splashings and a tinny clattering from the washbasin. When Jupiter burst through the door, his face was pink and shiny.

Pop didn't laugh and carry on as he usually did at dinner; he just sat there dipping his hoecake in the rich side-meat gravy and looking thoughtful. When Pop took a bite, he parted his mustache with one hand as if he were moving a curtain aside. Then he popped the food in and let the curtain fall.

Augustus knew Pop was trying to decide whether to go south or not. He remembered how ol' man Hawkins said if you want someone to do something, you cross all your fingers and look cross-eyed. Then you think about what you want him to do. Ol' man Hawkins said that always worked.

Augustus crossed his fingers and looked cross-eyed at Pop. Scowling fiercely, he muttered under his breath, "Please make Pop go on down-river, because I'm tired of just staying here."

Pop looked up to get another piece of hoecake and saw Augustus scowling at him cross-eyed. Pop's eyes widened slowly and he jerked up in his chair.

"Skin me for a catfish," he said, "what ails you, boy?"

Augustus uncrossed his eyes as quickly as he could, but not before Ma had seen him.

"He needs a tonic," said Ma.

Augustus shivered.

Ma's tonics were a painful subject to the whole family. Whenever anyone stubbed his toe, or looked a little pale, or not pale enough, or ran too hard, or didn't run at all, Ma made a tonic. One thing all Ma's tonics had in common was a bad smell and an even worse taste. Another thing was that she always made everyone take some. She even took a little herself—just to show it didn't taste bad. Ma reasoned that if it was good for one it must be good for all.

So when Ma said "tonic," everyone looked unhappy. Pop pushed his chair back with a clatter and jumped up.

"I've made up my mind," he said. "We'll move on down-river—"

Pop was going to say some more but he didn't get a chance. Augustus jumped up, his eyes shining. He opened his mouth until it formed a perfect circle. Then a wild yell came out.

"Yay, yay!" he shouted. "When do we start?"

Pop blinked and looked startled.

"Well," he said mildly, "I figure we might as well go right soon—maybe in the morning. The fishin's plumb worn out here."

Augustus began to run around the cabin.

"Goin' south!" he shouted. "Yay! Goin' south!"

He butted Glorianna in the stomach. She screeched, and Ma reached for Augustus. He ducked and tackled Jupiter around the knees. They rolled and tumbled on the floor until Ma caught them each by an ear and hauled them to their feet.

"A body'd think you were touched in the head," said Ma, but her eyes twinkled.

Ma liked to travel too, and she was beginning to feel the excitement that is part of going places.

"Goin' south," shouted Augustus and tried to butt Ma.

She boxed his ears and tried to look stern, but her mouth twitched.

"What a young 'un!" said Ma, and began to laugh with Augustus.

Pop had stopped by the door, surprised by all the carrying-on. Pop liked a good time, and when Ma started to laugh, he ran over, grabbed her and started to jig. The floor squeaked under Pop's weight, and the houseboat rolled and lurched.

"I declare," gasped Ma, "I believe you're all jelly-brained."

"Yep," chuckled Pop, "likely we are, but don't we have fun!"

He went to the door and, looking down-river toward the south, shouted, "Look out down there below! We're a-coming!"

Everyone went to bed real early that night because Pop said they had to get up early to get a good start. Augustus was too excited to sleep. Once he heard the whistling sound of wings and the faint honking of wild geese flying past, high over the houseboat.

"We're goin' south too, ol' geese," he muttered happily.

Through the window he could see the moonlight sparkling on the water like a path leading off down-river. Way off down there a steamboat whistled soft and low in the distance. The sound seemed to come up the path of light. And then the two got all mixed up in Augustus' mind. His eyes closed.

"Get up out of there," shouted Pop.

Augustus opened his eyes and groaned. It was still dark and his bed was mighty comfortable.

"Getting folks out of bed in the middle of the night," he grumbled; he blinked as he looked at the lighted lamp, dazzled by the yellow flame.

"Hurry up," said Pop. "I want to start before sunup."

"Start?" thought Augustus. "Start where?"

Then, with a warm glow rushing all through him as he remembered, Augustus jumped up.

Jupiter was bouncing up and down on his bed shouting, "Wheee! Going south!" as loud as he could.

Everybody scrambled around and got in everybody else's way.

Pop stood in the middle of the floor and shouted, "Hurry up, hurry up," at everyone. That was the way Pop was; when he really wanted to do something, he wanted to do it right now.

Augustus rushed through breakfast so fast he scalded his mouth with hot coffee. It burned all the way down. He grabbed a dipper of water and drank it down fast. Finding he had finished his breakfast before anyone else, he went out on the bank to wait for Pop to get through.

It was nice and fresh out on the bank. Everything was pale gray and misty. There was a bright patch in the sky just over the trees on the other side of the river.

A soft breeze came up and made little gurgling ripples that rolled across the river and splashed at Augustus' feet. He stuck his toes out, letting the fresh coolness of the water roll over them. The little waves chuckled against his ankles and clunked against the hull of the houseboat with a thin, musical splashing.

It sounded like a song, Augustus thought, and tried to think of words to go with the music. He had got as far as "Ol' Glorianna looks like a banana" when Pop came out.

Pop stood for a moment, sniffing the damp, cool air. Then seeing Augustus, he said, "All right, let's go."

"Okay, Pop," said Augustus and ran to untie the rope that held the houseboat to the shore. Jupiter and Glorianna picked up the gangplank and pushed and shoved and grunted as they hoisted it up on the roof.

Pop pushed against the bank with the pike pole.

"Here we go," yelled Augustus as he waded out into the river and pushed and pried.

There was a grating noise, the houseboat swung free of the sand and Augustus jumped on deck as the boat drifted off.

"Whee!" yelled Jupiter.

The shore slid past as the current took the little houseboat out toward the middle of the river. Pop got in the skiff, which he had tied to the boat, and rowed to steer the houseboat away from the banks and snags.

Augustus and Glorianna and Jupiter crawled onto the roof. The sun was up now and there was a warm smell from the tar-paper roofing. The chickens in their coop on the roof were cackling sort of drowsily. It was mighty comfortable just being lazy and watching things go past. Augustus sat with his legs dangling over the edge and rolled happily from side to side with the motion of the waves.

The buoys marking the deep-water steamboat channel made splotches of color against the shining water. The red buoys on the left side of the channel and the black ones on the right swayed and bowed at one another with stiff politeness.

Sometimes the narrow channel led almost straight across the wide shallow river, turning back at the bank to make a long slanting crossing to the other side.

On the banks, marking the ends of the crossings, were white wooden towers called "daymarks." Augustus thought that was a silly name for them; they were just as useful at night, he thought, when the lights at the top of the towers were the only marks to guide boats through the darkness. Pop didn't pay much attention to the buoys and daymarks, because the houseboat needed only a few inches of water and could go anywhere.

A steamboat puffed slowly by, pushing a long line of barges ahead of it. The big paddle wheel whirled around, splashing spray high into the air and making swells that rolled across the river, rocking the houseboat.

Zigzagging up the river, the steamboat came close enough for Augustus to see the pilot. High up in the pilothouse, easing the great wheel a spoke at a time, he balanced the long line of barges against the rush of the current.

Augustus jumped up and waved both arms in salute.

The pilot saw him and grinned. Reaching up, he pulled the whistle cord in a series of short, sharp blasts.

Augustus nearly burst with pride. He had been saluted by a steamboat! He started to walk over to Glorianna to make sure she knew what had happened when the houseboat gave a sudden lurch.

Teetering on the edge of the roof, trying to get his balance, Augustus looked over the side and gasped. He was looking straight down into a swirling hole in the water. The houseboat was heeling over into the edge of a whirlpool, swaying from side to side and bucking up and down all at the same time.

"Hold on," shouted Pop from the skiff.

The rope between the skiff and the houseboat quivered and stretched as Pop struggled to pull away from the drag of the whirlpool. Augustus threw himself flat on the roof and held on with both hands.

Ma was out on the back deck holding on to the doorway and shouting, "Look out! Look out!"

The houseboat heeled over farther. The chickens cackled frantically and, flapping their wings, hit the side of their coop as the roof tilted and jerked.

Suddenly Pop stopped trying to row away. He turned the skiff, set its nose against the side of the houseboat and rowed hard, pushing straight into the middle of the whirlpool.

Leaning over the edge, Augustus stared down at the skiff. What was Pop doing? Had he gone crazy?

Digging his oars deep, Pop grunted as he threw all his weight against the blades.

"You're rowing the wrong way!" shouted Augustus.

The houseboat began to spin around crazily. There was a loud "galumph" and a choking sucking noise as the broad flat bottom suddenly slid sideways and covered the hole in the center of the eddying water. Immediately everything was quiet. The water calmed; the whirling stopped; the houseboat straightened and bobbed peacefully off down-river.

"Whew," gasped Pop, wiping the sweat from his forehead; "that was close."

Then he looked up and grinned at Augustus.

"Now you've learned something," he said. "Don't forget it the way I did. Steer right into the middle of an eddy like that, and if your boat is big enough you're all right. Stay off on the side and likely it'll turn you over."

Augustus felt a little shaky. Glorianna was holding on to him. He turned and started to say, "Guess we showed the ol' river," when suddenly he stopped and blinked. Where was Jupiter? He had been on the roof. He wasn't there now. Augustus scrambled down to the deck. Jupiter wasn't there. He wasn't in the cabin either.

"Pop, Pop," shouted Augustus. "Jupiter—he's gone."

Pop's jaw dropped. He sprang from the skiff to the deck as Augustus climbed up to the roof again. Ma clambered up from the other side. Glorianna started to cry.

"He's gone. He's gone," she wailed.

"I am not gone," said a small muffled voice.

Augustus whirled around as the door of the chicken coop opened and a small tousled head popped out. Then the rest of Jupiter followed his head out of the chicken coop. Brushing the feathers off his face, he grinned at everyone and said, "I just got in the chicken coop so's I wouldn't fall off."

Ma came up intending to put her arms around him, but she was so excited she boxed his ears instead. Everyone laughed without knowing exactly why.

"It's a good thing I nailed that chicken coop to the roof," said Pop.

The little houseboat drifted on through the golden autumn day. Augustus sprawled on the roof and wiggled his toes as he soaked up the warm sunlight.

Along about dusk Pop rowed the houseboat to shore in back of a bar. It was a mudbar but the mud wasn't too soft and it looked like a good place to tie up for the night. There were no trees near enough to tie to, so, while Augustus and Ma held the ropes, Pop went up the bank with the ax and cut some stakes. Using the back of the axhead as a hammer, he drove the stakes deep into the mud and tied the ropes to them.

Ma had supper ready before dark really settled down. Augustus laughed and carried on at supper. He poured water on Jupiter's chair and slipped fishbones down Glorianna's back.

"You're so frisky you can just go up on the bank and get some wood for the stove after supper," said Ma.

"Aw," said Augustus.

But he brightened when Pop said, "I'll go along and help you."

"Don't get to walking and forget the wood," said Ma as they went out.

There was a sandy place up above the mud on the bank. The soft sand scuffed out ahead of their feet in little puffs that fell with a dry rattling sound.

"Ouch," said Augustus suddenly as he stubbed his toe on something that clinked.

He poked under the sand and uncovered a big rusty iron ring attached to a cement block.

"Steamboat ring," said Pop, scratching his chin. "Must have been a landing here long ago —maybe even a town."

Augustus looked around at the tangled underbrush and scrub trees that covered the bank.

"I don't see any signs of a town," he said.

"Oh, it was long ago—if there was one," said Pop. "There are a lot of ghost towns along the river. Some of them were busy places too, in the old days. Not a trace of them left now; nothing, except maybe an old rusty steamboat ring like this one."

Augustus chipped at the ring with a stone and broke off a chunk of rust.

"What happened to the towns, Pop?" he asked.

Pop pointed across the river to the lights of a railroad train that wound snakelike around a curve.

"That's what happened," he said. "The railroads came and the steamboats lost out. There wasn't any use for the ol' steamboat towns then."

Augustus watched the train as it crawled out of sight.

"I like steamboats better, anyway," he muttered.

"Most river folks do," said Pop, grinning. "And they're coming back too. They say there's more freight moving on the river right now than ever before."

"What's in those ol' freight barges, Pop?" asked Augustus.

"Well, mostly coffee and sugar and oil, coming up from the south. Going down-river they carry iron and coal, flour and machinery and such."

Pop stopped and shook his head sadly.

"But there are just freight boats pushing barges on the river now," he said. "The ol' packet boats are gone for good. Oh, they were pretty, all glittery white and handsome, fancy carving all over them. Why, some even had pictures of scenery and such painted on the paddle-wheel boxes."

Pop kicked at the old steamboat ring and it clanked sadly.

"Those old boats were back even before my time on the river," said Pop. "I never saw them, only pictures of them."

The stars glittered in the black sky as Pop and Augustus walked slowly back to the houseboat. Far out on the river a steamboat puffed along with a slow even sound like a giant panting. The lights in the windows sparkled brightly and were reflected in bright paths on the water.

The red light that marked the left side of the steamboat was a gleaming spot of bright color that wove through the white reflections. Suddenly the red light blinked out as the steamboat turned, and the green light that marked the right side sparkled where the red had been.

"I think steamboats are still mighty pretty, even if they are just freight boats now," said Augustus.

"Most any kind of boat is pretty," said Pop.

They walked up the gangplank and into the houseboat. Ma looked up.

"Where's the wood?" she asked.

Pop and Augustus looked at each other sheepishly.

"We just plumb forgot it," said Pop. "I'll get some in the morning."

Ma snorted. "Just like a man," she said.

That night Augustus dreamed of a great white steamboat that sailed over the land, throwing rusty iron rings at frightened trains which scuttled off promising never to come back.

"Jumpin' catfish!" Pop was shouting when Augustus woke up.

Pop was standing on deck blinking in the gray morning light. The mist was just rising from the river and the fresh damp smell of early morning, wet wood and mud came through the open door as Augustus scrambled out of bed.

He slipped into his overalls and went out. Pop was looking over the side of the houseboat as Augustus came on deck.

"Look," said Pop, pointing.

Augustus looked.

There wasn't any water under the houseboat —nothing but mud. The river had fallen during the night and left the houseboat high and dry on a mudbank.

"That's a river for you," said Pop. "Up and runs away just when you need it most."

Ma and Jupiter and Glorianna came out on deck. They all stood and looked at the mud.

"Well," said Pop, "only one thing to do . . ."

He rolled up the legs of his overalls and got but in the mud. It was soft and sticky and Pop sank almost to his knees as he leaned against the houseboat and pushed. Augustus jumped down in the mud to help. They pushed and pushed, but the houseboat didn't move.

"No use," said Pop and climbed back on deck.

Augustus started to follow him. He tried to lift his right foot. It wouldn't come. He pulled at his left foot. It wouldn't come, and his right foot sank deeper. The mud oozed up past his knees.

"Hey, help," shouted Augustus. "I'm sinking."

Pop turned and saw him.

"Hold on," shouted Pop.

He threw the gangplank down on the mud beside Augustus and crawled out on it. Pop grabbed Augustus and pulled. The mud made squishy noises. Augustus felt himself lift a little. A little more. With a loud "galumph" his feet came out of the mud and he scrambled up on deck.

"I bet you were scared!" said Jupiter.

"Naw," said Augustus.

Then he saw Pop looking at him. Pop was sort of grinning.

"Well," said Augustus, "anyway—not much."

Pop looked at the river. "She's still a-falling," he said. "Won't be any water anywhere near us by nighttime."

Ma sat down gloomily.

"Likely we'll be stuck here until spring high water," she grumbled.

Glorianna's eyes widened.

"You mean we'll be stuck here all winter?"

"Huh," grunted Augustus, "just you wait. Pop and I will get us off this ol' mudbank."

"How?"

"Oh, that's easy."

"Well, how then?"

Augustus looked all around. He looked down at his muddy feet and wiggled his toes. The mud had dried some and little chunks cracked off and fell in the water. Augustus let on as though he couldn't be bothered explaining things to just a girl and such a small boy as Jupiter.

He looked off up-river as if he expected to see the answer up there somewhere. There was a smudge of smoke over the treetops. Augustus watched it. The smoke swirled closer and a big white steamboat puffed around the bend. It was going down-river and going fast.

"If we had enough money," said Augustus, "I betcha that ol' steamboat would pull us off here pretty quick."

"Hmm," said Pop, "river folks don't have that much money."

The steamboat came roaring past close to shore. The big paddle wheel in the stern slapped around, sending out swells that rolled out across the river and splashed high on the muddy bank.

As the steamboat came closer, one of the swells rolled under the houseboat. Another—and the houseboat lifted and rocked.

Pop jumped up and pushed hard against the bank with the pike pole. The houseboat moved a little. It was afloat! Slowly it slid off the mud, away from shore and out into deep water.

"There," said Augustus. "I guess Pop and I showed you."

from ALL-OF-A-KIND FAMILY

Sydney Taylor

The book from which this episode is taken is a heart-warming story of an affectionate Jewish family that will be enjoyed by all children.

The Library Lady

"That slowpoke Sarah!" Henny cried. "She's making us late!"

Mama's girls were going to the library, and Henny was impatient.

"If it was Charlotte, I could understand," said Ella, who was the eldest and very serious. "I'd know Charlotte was off dreaming in some corner. But what can be keeping Sarah?"

From *All-of-a-Kind Family* by Sydney Taylor. By permission of Wilcox & Follett Co.

"All the best books will be gone," complained Henny. "Maybe she forgot it's Friday."

"No!" interrupted Charlotte. "Not Sarah!"

No, not Sarah, nor any of the girls could forget that Friday was library day.

Almost no East Side child owned a book when Mama's children were little girls. That was an unheard-of luxury. It was heavenly enough to be able to borrow books from the public library and that was where the children always went on Friday afternoons. Right after school, they rushed off happily to get fresh reading material for the week end. Even Gertie who was not yet old enough to "belong" took the weekly trip to look at the picture magazines.

Where *was* Sarah? Mama was beginning to be concerned too. It wasn't like the child to be late.

At last footsteps could be heard on the creaky back steps. Henny ran to open the kitchen door and poked her head out. "Here she comes," she called.

"Well, it's about time," said Ella. "Come on, let's get our books."

Henny opened the door wider. "What's the matter?" her sisters heard her asking.

A woebegone little figure, face streaked with tears, walked slowly into the kitchen.

"Mama," piped up Gertie, "Sarah's crying."

"Sarah, what's the matter? What's happened?"

Sarah didn't answer. Walking over to the hard brown leather couch, she threw herself face downward, weeping bitterly. Her sisters gathered in a little group around her.

Mama came over and sat down beside Sarah. Gently she stroked her hair and let the child weep. After a while she said softly, "Sarah, tell us what happened."

Between sobs, the muffled words came slowly, "My—library book—is—lost."

Lost! The children looked at each other in dismay. Such a thing had never happened in the family before. "Ooh—how awful!" Ella said, and then was sorry that the words had escaped her for they seemed to bring on a fresh burst of tears.

"Now, now, stop crying, Sarah," Mama said. "You'll only make yourself sick. Come, we'll wash your face and then you'll tell us all about it."

Obediently Sarah followed Mama to the kitchen sink.

"Does it mean we can't go to the library ever again?" Charlotte whispered to Ella.

Ella shook her head. "I don't think so."

"Maybe we could change over to another branch," suggested Henny.

The cold water felt good on Sarah's flushed face. She was quiet now and could talk.

"It wasn't really me that lost the book. It was my friend, Tillie. You know how Tillie never takes a book out herself, but she's always wanting to read mine. When I told her about *Peter and Polly In Winter,* she begged me to lend it to her. She promised she'd give it back to me on Friday.

"When I asked her for it today, she said that she put it in my desk yesterday, but Mama, she didn't! She really didn't!"

"Are you sure?" asked Mama. "Maybe you left it in school."

"I looked a thousand times. That's why I came so late. I kept hunting and hunting all over the schoolroom."

"Maybe you brought it home with you yesterday and left it here in the house."

"Then it should be on the shelf under the whatnot," Ella said.

Hopefully, everybody rushed over to the whatnot where the library books were kept, but alas, there was no *Peter and Polly* book there today.

"I cleaned the house pretty thoroughly this morning," said Mama. "I don't remember seeing the book anywhere. But let's all look again anyway."

How anxiously everyone searched. The children peered into every corner of the two bedrooms and they poked under beds and dressers. No one believed it was in the front room, but still they searched it diligently. They searched and searched until they had to agree that it was useless to continue.

When they were back in the kitchen again, Sarah said tearfully, "How can I go and tell the library that the book is lost?" She was ready to cry again.

"I'm afraid they won't let you take out any more books until we pay for this one," Mama worried. "And a book costs a lot of money."

"But Tillie lost the book," argued Sarah. "She should pay."

"We can't be sure of that," Mama said. "Tillie

claims she returned it. Maybe someone else took it."

"No library could make me pay for any old book." Henny was just trying to cover up how bad she felt too.

"I'm afraid the library will expect you to pay for it. And it's only right," continued Mama. "You borrowed the book and that makes you responsible. The library lets you borrow the book and you're not supposed to lend it to anybody else. I know you wanted to be kind to Tillie, but if Tillie wants to read a library book, then she should take out her own. I wish I could help you pay for this, but you know, Sarah, there's no money for such things."

"But Mama, will you come with me and talk to the library lady?"

Mama shook her head. "No, Sarah, that's something you must do yourself. If you explain just how it happened, I'm sure the library lady will understand that you didn't mean to be careless. Find out what you have to do, and we'll talk about it when you get back. Now you'll all have to hurry. There's not much time left before supper. So, the rest of you, see if you can choose your books quickly today."

Mama had said to hurry but Sarah's feet wouldn't walk. They felt like lead. In her chest was a lump of lead too. Ella put her arm around Sarah's shoulder. Even Gertie forsook her idol Charlotte and came over to Sarah. She slipped her little hand into Sarah's, her brown eyes large in sympathy.

A branch of the New York Public Library was only a few blocks from their home; soon the familiar brown building came into view. Through the high door and up the staircase they went. With each step, Sarah grew more despairing. They'll take my card away, she thought. I just know they will. I'll never be able to take out any more books.

Once inside the room, Sarah hung back, fearing to join the line at the "in" desk. She looked back down the staircase longingly. It would be so easy to run down the stairs and out into the street and just never come back.

"Come on, Sarah," Ella said. "Let's get it over with." Gently she pulled Sarah towards the desk and the five children fell in line.

Henny nudged Sarah. "Look," she said, "isn't that a new library lady? She's pretty!" she added.

Sarah studied the new library lady anxiously. She looked so fresh and clean in a crisp white shirtwaist with long sleeves ending in paper cuffs pinned tightly at the wrists. Her hair is light, just like mine, Sarah said to herself. And she has such little ears. I think she has a kind face. She watched as the librarian's slender fingers pulled the cards in and out of the index file. How does she keep her nails so clean, Sarah wondered, thinking of her own scrubby ones.

It was Ella's turn to have her book stamped. The library lady looked up and Sarah could see the deep blue of her eyes. The library lady smiled.

She has dimples, Sarah thought. Surely a lady with dimples could never be harsh.

The smile on the library lady's face deepened. In front of her desk stood five little girls dressed exactly alike.

"My goodness! Are you all one family?"

"Yes, all one family," Henny spoke up. "I'm Henrietta, Henny for short; I'm ten. Ella's twelve, Sarah is eight, Charlotte is six, and Gertie is four."

"A steps-and-stairs family!" The library lady laughed and the tiny freckles on her pert nose seemed to laugh with her.

"That's a good name for us," Ella said. "Some people call us an all-of-a-kind family."

"All of a very nice kind," smiled the library lady. "And you have such nice names! I'm Miss Allen, your new librarian. I'm very glad to meet you."

Her eyes travelled over the five little girls. Such sad-looking faces. Not a smile among them.

"Better tell the teacher what happened," Charlotte whispered to Sarah.

"She's not a teacher, silly. She's a library lady." Henny's scornful reply was loud enough for Miss Allen to hear. The dimples began to show again.

Sarah stepped forward. "Library lady," she began, twisting and untwisting the fingers of her hands.

Miss Allen looked at Sarah and suddenly noticed the red-rimmed eyes and the nose all swollen from weeping. Something was wrong. No wonder the faces were so unhappy.

"Let me see, now. Which one are you?" she asked.

"Sarah," the little girl replied and the tears began to swim in her eyes.

The library lady put her hand under the little girl's chin and lifted it up. "Now, now, Sarah. Nothing can be that bad."

Sarah said tearfully, "Yes, it can. I—I—" She couldn't go on.

"Here." Ella put a handkerchief to her sister's nose.

Miss Allen went on speaking as if she did not notice anything unusual. "Did you enjoy your book?"

Sarah's voice broke. "I loved it. But nobody else will ever be able to read it again . . ."

"She means she lost it!" Henny blurted out.

"She didn't lose it. It was Tillie." Charlotte rushed to Sarah's defense.

"Oh, I'm so sorry," said the library lady, looking bewilderedly from one to the other. "Who is Tillie?"

Thereupon Ella unfolded the whole story and the library lady listened sympathetically.

"Mama says I must pay for the book and I'm going to—every cent." Sarah was trembling. "But I don't have enough money now."

"How much will she have to pay?" Ella asked.

"I'll have to look it up in the catalogue," Miss Allen answered. She pulled out a big book and began to look through its pages. It really was a shame that this had happened. She knew that the people who lived on the East Side had to count their pennies carefully. Even a small sum would seem like a fortune to these children.

Her heart went out to the little group. How sincere they were and how anxious to do the right thing. She wished that she could pay for the book herself. But she could not risk hurting either the children or their parents by making the offer.

She made her voice as cheerful as she could. "Well, it's not nearly as bad as I thought. Let's see now. Do you have any spending money, Sarah?"

"A penny a day . . . and I can save my pennies. I don't care for candy anyway." She added quickly, "I have seventeen cents saved up in my penny bank."

Seventeen cents! thought the library lady. How can I tell her that the book costs a dollar? "It that all you have?"

Sarah nodded shyly. "Yes."

"She was going to buy a doll." Gertie's voice filled the silence. "A doll with real hair."

The library lady looked at the sad little figure for a moment.

"Sarah," she said, "the book costs a dollar. If you pay the seventeen cents the next time you come, you will owe eighty-three cents. After that, I will make a special arrangement so you can pay one penny each week. I know it will take a very long time to pay the whole amount but you can save for your doll at the same time."

Sarah's eyes opened wide in unbelief. "You mean, I can save for my doll and still pay for the book?"

"That's right," said the library lady, and they both smiled.

Meanwhile the other children were whispering among themselves. Finally Ella spoke up. "Could we help pay? Each of us can bring a penny every week. We've collected three cents right now."

Henny said shamefacedly, "I already spent my penny today but I promise I'll bring it next week like the others."

"That's a wonderful idea! Sarah must be very proud to have such thoughtful sisters."

Sarah was proud. She gave them each a hug. "And when I get my doll, you can all play with her."

"Isn't it nice to have a family to share your troubles?" asked the library lady.

"Have you any sisters?" Sarah asked shyly.

"No, dear. Nor brothers. I'm the only one."

"Isn't that lonesome?" Charlotte asked. The children all felt sorry for the library lady now.

"Yes, dear, it is lonesome. But come now, aren't you going to take out any books today?"

"Can Sarah take out a book too?" questioned Henny.

"Yes, she can, so long as you'll be paying for the lost book."

Sarah clasped her hands together joyfully. "Oh, thank you! I think you're the nicest, kindest library lady in the whole world."

Miss Allen's smile was warm and friendly. "Run along now, dear, and get your book."

As she worked, Miss Allen found herself watching the five little girls. How quaint they were in their stiffly starched white aprons over dark woolen dresses. They looked for all the world like wide-open umbrellas.

Had she been able to peek under those dresses, she would have understood why they billowed out in such a manner. Underneath were *three* petticoats, a woolly, flannel one first, a simple cotton one next, with both of these topped by a fancy muslin garment which was starched to a scratchy crispness. In order to save money, Mama made those petticoats herself. Still further underneath was long woolen underwear, over which were pulled heavy knitted woolen stockings, making thin legs look like well-stuffed frankfurters. How the girls hated those stockings! They itched so! *And they never wore out!* Mama knitted them herself on long needles and she could always reknit the holes the children made.

Miss Allen could see that the stockings were bothering Sarah. She looked very comical as she kept rubbing one leg against the other. Clutching her new book tightly to her, she made her way back to the desk.

"Come on, everybody. It's late," Ella warned.

The children quickly chose their books and gave them to the library lady for stamping.

They raced home on happy feet. They couldn't wait to tell Mama that their beloved Friday afternoons at the library were not going to be spoiled after all.

The Sabbath

The Sabbath begins Friday evening at dusk and for two days Mama was busy with her preparations. On Fridays she cleaned, cooked, and baked. On Thursdays she shopped. Sabbath meals had to be the best of the whole week so it was most important that she shop carefully. Every Thursday afternoon, Mama went to Rivington Street market where prices were lower than in her neighborhood stores.

Usually she left Gertie in Papa's care and set off alone right after lunch. This Thursday Mama was rather late. The children would soon be home from school so Mama decided that it would be nice if for once shopping for the Sabbath could be a family affair.

"Who wants to come to market with me?" she asked the children as soon as they came trooping in.

"I do! I do!" Everybody wanted to go along.

"Gracious, hasn't anybody any other plans for this afternoon?" asked Mama.

"Nothing as exciting as going to market," Ella declared, and her sisters all agreed.

But what about Gertie? It was a long walk for little feet.

Gertie spoke up as if she knew what Mama was thinking. "Oh, Mama," she pleaded, "me too!"

Mama wasn't going to disappoint her. "All right, but I think it would be a good idea to take the baby carriage along."

"Baby carriage!" Gertie was indignant. "I'm too big for a baby carriage!"

"Of course you are," Mama assured her, "but the carriage will come in handy for all the bundles and if you should happen to get too tired to keep on walking, why, we can have the bundles move over and make room for a very nice little girl. Now hurry, everybody. Into your hats and coats."

"Mama," said Sarah, "we'll be passing right by the library. Couldn't we go up for just a minute so you could meet the library lady?"

"Well—I don't know. I have a lot of shopping to do." Mama hesitated. "I would like to see her."

"Please, Mama, for just a minute."

"She's asked us a number of times to bring you over," Ella said.

"All right," replied Mama. "But we can't stay long."

The children were pleased. At last the library lady was going to see Mama. The children were very proud of Mama. Most of the other Jewish women in the neighborhood had such bumpy shapes. Their bodies looked like mattresses tied about in the middle. But not Mama. She was tall and slim and held herself proudly. Her face was proud too.

Once inside the library, the children scrambled eagerly up the stairs while Mama followed at a more sedate pace. They stood in a small group waiting for a moment when the library lady would be free. Then Sarah approached the desk.

Miss Allen looked up and smiled. "Hello, Sarah. It can't be Friday already?"

"No," laughed Sarah. "It's only Thursday, but we brought Mama."

"How nice!" the library lady said, and came from behind her desk to join the family.

"Mama," said Sarah proudly, "this is Miss Allen."

"I'm so glad you came," said the library lady as she extended her hand in greeting. "My, you couldn't possibly be the mother of five—you look young enough to be their eldest sister."

"I don't feel that young," said Mama laughing. "But thank you for the compliment. I've been wanting to meet you for a long time. But you know how it is with a family this size. There's always something to do. The children talk about you so much at home though, I feel that I already know you."

"They've told me all about you, too," replied Miss Allen.

"Sarah has never forgotten your kindness to her," continued Mama. "For that matter, all the children are always telling me such nice things about you. How you're always ready with a suggestion about what they should read, and how interested you are in discussing the books with them. I appreciate that."

"It's a pleasure to help such eager readers," the librarian said, smiling at the upturned faces.

"Well," Mama said, beaming, "I'm afraid we'll have to be running along."

"We're all going to market," Sarah explained.

"Good," said Miss Allen, "and when you come tomorrow, you can tell me all about it."

"Do you like her, Mama?" asked Sarah as they walked downstairs.

"Yes," answered Mama. "She's very sweet—and so pretty too!" Mama was thoughtful for a moment. She turned to Ella and added, "She smiles at you, but somehow the face is wistful, don't you think?"

Back on the street, the children danced along sometimes beside, sometimes just behind Mama. That is, all except Henny. She kept racing ahead and dashing back again, just like a small, impatient puppy.

Already their ears were filled with the shrill cries of street hawkers. Already they could smell the good smells, and in another minute, they were themselves part of the crowd.

"Just look at all the pushcarts!" exclaimed Sarah.

Heaped high with merchandise, they stretched in endless lines up and down the main street and in and out the side streets. They were edged up close to the curb and wedged together so tightly that one could not cross anywhere except at the corners. The pushcart peddlers, usually bearded men in long overcoats or old women in heavy sweaters and shawls, outdid each other in their loud cries to the passers-by. All promised bargains—bargains in everything—in fruits and vegetables, crockery, shoelaces, buttons, and other notions, in aprons and housedresses, in soap and soap powders, and hundreds of other things.

There were stores in which you could buy fish and stores that carried only dairy products. There were bakeries and meat shops, shoe stores and clothing establishments. In delicatessen shops, fat "specials" (frankfurters) hung on hooks driven into the walls and big chunks of "knubble" (garlic) wurst were laid out in neat rows on white trays which bore the sign "A Nickel a Schtickel" (a nickel for a piece). The counters overflowed with heaps of smoked whitefish and carp, and large slabs of smoked red salmon. If one wished, firm plump salt herrings were fished out of barrels for inspection before buying. Men's red flannel drawers and ladies' petticoats flew in the wind from their showhooks on dry-goods store fronts.

But it was not enough that the merchandise sold behind closed shop doors could be displayed in showcase windows and store fronts. Their owners had to come out in the open too. They built stands which they either used themselves or rented out to others. Almost anything could be bought at these stands. There were pickle stands where the delicious odor of sour pickles mingled with the smell of sauerkraut and pickled tomatoes and watermelon rind. There were stands where only cereal products were sold— oats, peas, beans, rice and barley—all from open sacks. At other stands, sugar and salt were scooped out of large barrels and weighed to order. Here coffee was bought in the bean, for every household had its own wooden coffee grinder.

And wherever there was a bit of space too small for a regular stand, one could be sure to find the old pretzel woman. Her wrinkled face was almost hidden inside of the woolen kerchief bound round her head. Her old hands trembled as they wrapped up the thick, chewy pretzels.

The sidewalks were choked with people. It was not easy for Mama to push the carriage through the narrow aisles left between pushcarts and stands. The children followed behind in twos and whenever Mama stopped either to buy or look, they stopped too.

"Say, Gertie," Charlotte cried out, "how would you like a necklace like that?" She pointed to the garlic peddler who was coming towards them. No need for a store, a stand, or a pushcart for this peddler. With a basket full of garlic on one arm and a spicy necklace of the same looped around his neck, he was all set for business.

The dried mushroom peddlers did business in the same way except that, as Charlotte laughingly said, "They were better dressed." They wore long, heavy mushroom bracelets about their arms as well as necklaces.

How sharply the shoppers hunted for bargains! And what bargains, if one could believe the peddlers. How carefully every article was examined to make sure it was perfect! It always was, according to the shopkeepers. How the buyers haggled over the price of everything. And how the peddlers swore on their very lives that the price of anything was the lowest at which they could afford to part with it! But above and through all the noise and confusion, ran a feeling of great good nature and cheery contentment.

Only one tongue was spoken here—Yiddish. It was like a foreign land right in the midst of America. In this foreign land, it was Mama's children who were the foreigners since they alone conversed in an alien tongue—English.

At the next corner, Henny bought a fat, juicy sour pickle with her after-lunch penny. She ate it greedily, with noise and gusto, while her sisters watched, their mouths watering. "Selfish! How about giving us a taste, huh?"

Henny pretended that she didn't hear them, but before the pickle was half gone, she stopped teasing and gave each a bite.

Inside Mama's favorite fish store the smell was not so pleasing. "Gertie," suggested Charlotte, "let's squeeze our noses tight and talk to each other while we're squeezing."

And that's just what they did, talking about anything at all just so they could hear the funny sounds which came through their squeezed noses. "Look at the big fish with goggly eyes," said Gertie.

"I hope Mama is not getting any live fish this week," Charlotte said. "I like to see them swimming around in the bathtub but I don't like it when Papa cleans them afterward."

But Mama was not getting any live fish this time, only pieces of several different kinds of fish, whitefish, yellow pike and winter carp—that meant gefüllte fish (stuffed fish) for the Sabbath, yum, yum!

"I wish Mama would hurry up," said Gertie. "I can smell the fish right through my squeezed nose. And I do want to buy something for my penny, don't you?"

"Yes, and no fish!"

Out on the street again, the air seemed sharper and colder. Some of the peddlers had been standing in their places since early morning. They stamped their feet and slapped their arms across their chests trying to warm their chilled bones. But the sweet potato man did not mind the cold. Why should he when he had his nice hot street oven to push before him? When Ella caught sight of him, she said at once, "Just the thing for a cold day." The sweet potato man stopped before her and pulled open one of the drawers of his oven. There arose on the air such a delicious smell that Ella smacked her lips expectantly. Inside she saw the plump sweet potatoes in their gray jackets. Some were cut open in halves and their rich golden color gave promise of great sweetness. For her penny, Ella got a large half and as she bit into it, she wondered why sweet potatoes baked at home never tasted half so good. When she rejoined the family, four other mouths helped to make short work of that potato.

The chicken market was the next stopping place. It was smelly and noisy with the squawking of fowl. The children gathered about the crates and watched the roosters sticking their long necks through the slats. Mama donned an apron she had brought with her and began to pluck the fowl she selected.

After Mama finished her plucking, the chicken was wrapped up and added to the other bundles in the shopping bag. The family continued on its way.

Gertie turned to Charlotte. "What'll we buy with our pennies?" The answer to that question was just then coming along the street. Candied slices of tangerine and candied grapes mounted on sticks lay in rows on white trays. The peddler stopped when he heard Gertie's delighted cry. "Penny a stick, little darlings," he said. Char-

lotte chose grape and Gertie took tangerine. Thus two more pennies were spent.

"I'm almost through," Mama told them, but still Sarah's penny lay warm and snug in her coat pocket. "Aren't you going to spend your penny?" the children asked her. They couldn't be sure because Sarah was saving all her pennies these days—six for the dolly and one penny for the library lady. But today was something special. She had shared in the goodies her sisters had bought. It would only be fair for her to return their generosity. But what could she get?

Arbis! Shaynicke, guttinke arbislach! Keuf meine heise arbis!" (Chick peas. Fine, nice chick peas. Buy my hot chick peas!)

The hot-chick-pea peddler was singing the words over and over in a funny Yiddish chant as he rolled a small white oven along the streets. Before Mama could stop her, mischievous Henny gave the carriage a big push so that it rolled away from under Mama's hands. She stooped over it as if she were pushing a great weight and began to chant in imitation:

"Arbis! Shaynicke, guttinke arbislach!"

The children roared with laughter. Even Mama could not hide a smile while she ordered Henny to stop. "Leave her alone, lady," the peddler told Mama. "She's helping me in mine business."

Because he was so good-natured, Sarah decided to give up her penny to him. Everyone watched as he fished out the peas. First he took a small square of white paper from a little compartment on one side of the oven. He twirled the paper about his fingers to form the shape of a cone and then skillfully twisted the pointed end so that the container would not fall apart. He lifted the wagon cover on one side revealing a large white enamel pot. The steam from the pot blew its hot breath in the little girls' faces so they stepped back a bit while the peas were ladled out with a big soup spoon. The wagon cover was dropped back into place and the paper cup handed over to Sarah. The peas were spicy with pepper and salt, and how good they were! They warmed up the children's tummies and made them very thirsty.

With the purchase of a pound of pumpernickel bread, the shopping tour came to an end. They left behind the life and activity of the market and started the weary walk home. By now the children were tired. Gertie uttered not a single word of protest when Mama lifted her up and put her into the carriage together with the bundles. The others wished they were young enough to join her.

The next afternoon, when they had chosen their books, they told the library lady all about their marketing trip. Ella was a good actress and could imitate voice and gestures marvelously well. The children and the library lady went into gales of laughter as she mimicked the various peddlers. They made so much noise that the other librarian stared at them reprovingly.

"I guess we'd better be quiet," Miss Allen whispered.

The children started for the staircase walking exaggeratedly on tiptoes and giggling softly.

At home, the kitchen was warm with the smell of fresh-baked white bread. The room sparkled with cleanliness. The table, which wore only an oilcloth covering all through the week, now had on a snowy white tablecloth. On it stood the brass candlesticks, gleaming brightly from the polishing that Ella and Sarah had given them the day before. They were just in time to see Mama saying the prayer over the candles.

The children stood around the table watching her. A lovely feeling of peace and contentment seemed to flow out from Mama to them. First she put a napkin on her head; then placing four white candles in the brass candlesticks, she lit them. She extended her arms to form a circle. Over the lighted candles the encircling gesture was repeated. After that Mama covered her eyes with her hands, softly murmuring a prayer in Hebrew.

Thus was the Sabbath ushered in.

Mama set two braided loaves of white bread on the table at Papa's place. She covered them with a clean white napkin. Then from the whatnot, she took a wine bottle full of the dark sweet red wine which Papa always made himself. She also took a small wine glass and put these on the table next to the loaves.

The children lined up before Papa. He placed his hand on each child's head, asking God's blessing for his little one. When this ceremony was over, Papa left for the synagogue.

It's so lovely and peaceful, thought Ella. Now if only Charlie were here, everything would be just perfect. Had Mama invited him for the Sabbath supper? She hadn't said.

"Is Charlie coming tonight?" she asked.

"No," answered Mama. "Papa tells me Charlie hasn't been in the shop for over a week."

So Charlie was gone again. For how long this time, wondered Ella.

"Where do you suppose he goes?"

"Who knows?" Mama answered with a sigh.

"Doesn't Papa ever ask him?"

Mama shook her head. "You don't ask people about their personal lives."

"It's queer. Charlie isn't at all like the other peddlers, is he, Mama? He seems so educated and so fine. Why does he live like this? What do you suppose happened to him?" Ella's questions caught the attention of the other children.

"I guess he likes it this way," Henny remarked airily.

"Has he a Mama and a Papa?" Sarah asked. She could not imagine life without parents.

"We don't know, Sarah. He never mentions them."

"He comes and goes," began Charlotte.

Henny finished, "And nobody knows."

Papa came in. "Good Sabbath," he said.

"Good Sabbath," each replied.

Papa washed his hands. It was time for supper, but first he must pronounce the prayer in praise of his wife for her fine Sabbath preparations. Then he must say a prayer of thanksgiving for the Sabbath. To do this, Papa filled the glass full of wine, raised it aloft and said a short prayer in Hebrew, then drank some of it. Everyone had a sip from the glass.

Another short prayer was said over the loaves. Papa uncovered them and cut a thick piece for Mama and smaller pieces for the girls. In turn, Mama and the children recited the prayer thanking God for giving them this bread. Now, at last, supper could be eaten.

Such a good supper! *Gefüllte* fish, chicken soup with homemade noodles, chicken, carrots prepared in a sweet way, and applesauce.

Afterward, the children helped with the clearing of the table and the dishwashing. In the lovely hush of the Sabbath eve, they once more gathered around the table, the children with their books, Mama with her magazine, and Papa with his Jewish newspaper. All heads were bent low over their reading while the candles flickered and sputtered. It was quiet except for the whispered sounds of Charlotte's voice as she read aloud from her primer to wide-eyed Gertie.

So they would continue reading until the candles burnt low. Then they would undress and go to bed—for after the candles died out, the room would be in complete darkness. There could be no light struck on the Sabbath. That was the law.

ELLEN RIDES AGAIN

Beverly Cleary

Beverly Cleary is a Californian whose first book, Henry Huggins, *was an instantaneous success. There are now several other books about Henry, all of them equally funny and popular. Ellen in* Ellen Tebbits *is the feminine counterpart of Henry. This book about Ellen's adventures is just as hilarious as the other books and especially popular with girls. As American as supermarkets and completely true to child nature, Mrs. Cleary's stories are hilarious commentaries on modern life.*

The arrival of spring meant different things to different people. To Mrs. Tebbits it meant spring cleaning. To Mrs. Allen it meant planting seeds and setting out new flowers. To Ellen and Austine spring meant something much more important. It meant no more winter underwear.

The two girls were walking home from the library one warm spring afternoon. They felt light and carefree in their summer underwear. It was a wonderful feeling. It made them want to do something exciting.

At the library Austine had been lucky enough to find two horse books. "I wish I could ride a horse sometime," she said.

"Haven't you ever ridden a horse?" asked Ellen.

"No. Have you?" Austine sounded impressed.

"Oh, yes," said Ellen casually. "Several times."

It was true. She had ridden several times. If she had ridden twice she would have said a couple of times. Three was several times, so she had told the truth.

"Where? What was it like? Tell me about it," begged Austine.

"Oh, different places." That was also true. She had ridden at the beach. Her father had rented a horse for an hour and had let Ellen ride behind him with her arms around his waist. The horse's back had been slippery and she had bounced harder than was comfortable, but she had managed to hang on.

And she had ridden at Uncle Fred's farm. Uncle Fred had lifted her up onto the back of his old plow horse, Lady, and led her twice around the barnyard. Lady didn't bounce her at all.

And then there was that other time when her father had paid a dime so she could ride a pony around in a circle inside a fence. It hadn't been very exciting. The pony seemed tired, but Ellen had pretended it was galloping madly. Yes, it all added up to several times.

"Why haven't you told me you could ride?" Austine demanded. "What kind of saddle do you use?" Austine knew all about different kinds of saddles, because she read so many horse books.

"Oh, any kind," said Ellen, who did not know one saddle from another. "Once I rode bareback." That was true, because Lady had no saddle.

"Golly," said Austine. "Bareback!"

Ellen was beginning to feel uncomfortable. She had not meant to mislead Austine. She really did not know how it all started.

"Oh, Ellen, you have all the luck," exclaimed Austine. "Imagine being able to ride horseback. And even bareback, too."

"Oh, it's nothing," said Ellen, wishing Austine would forget the whole thing.

But the next day at school Austine did not forget about Ellen's horseback riding. She told Linda and Amelia about it. They told Barbara and George. Barbara and George told other boys and girls. Each time the story was told, it grew.

Even Otis was impressed and he was a difficult boy to impress. When the girls started home after school, he was waiting on the edge of the school grounds. He had a piece of chalk and was busy changing a sign from "Bicycle riding forbidden at all times" to "Bicycle riding bidden at all times." Otis crossed out "for" every time he had a chance, but the rain always washed away the chalk marks.

"Hello, Ellen," he said, walking along beside her in his cowboy boots. Since Christmas Otis had worn boots instead of Oxfords. He was not wearing spurs today. Miss Joyce had asked him not to wear them to school.

Ellen and Austine ignored him.

Otis kicked at the grass along the edge of the sidewalk. "Say, Ellen, is it true you ride a lot? Even bareback?"

"Of course it's true," said Austine.

"I wish people would stop talking about it," said Ellen crossly. "What's so wonderful about riding a horse, for goodness' sake?"

"Gee whiz," said Otis enviously. "Some people have all the luck."

The girls continued to ignore him. He followed them for a while, kicking at the grass, and then turned down another street.

When the girls came to Austine's house, they found Mrs. Allen on her knees beside a flat box of pansy plants. She was taking them out of the box and setting them into a border along the driveway.

"Hello there," she said. "Since tomorrow is Memorial Day and there isn't any school, how would you like to go on a picnic?"

Ellen did not say anything. She thought Mrs. Allen meant her, too, but she was not sure. She hoped so. That was the trouble with the word *you*. Sometimes it meant one person and sometimes it meant a lot of people. Maybe Mrs. Allen was talking to Austine and not to both of them.

Mrs. Allen said, "Ellen, I have already asked your mother and she says you may go."

"Thank you. I'd love to go." Maybe a picnic would make Austine forget about horses. And if they went on a picnic, Austine couldn't come to Ellen's house to play and perhaps say something about horseback riding in front of Mrs. Tebbits. Ellen was worried about what her mother would say if she found out how Ellen had exaggerated.

"Where are we going?" asked Austine.

"We're going to drive out toward Mount Hood. The rhododendrons are beginning to bloom, and I thought it would be nice to see them blooming in the woods."

The next morning at ten o'clock Ellen ran down Tillamook Street and around the corner to Austine's house. For her share of the picnic she carried eight deviled eggs carefully packed in a cardboard box. Mr. Allen was backing out the car. Mrs. Allen sat in the front seat and Austine in the back.

"Hop in," said Mr. Allen. "Bruce isn't going with us. The boy scouts are marching in a parade."

Ellen was glad she and Austine could each sit by a window. That made it easier to look for white horses and to play the alphabet game. The first one to see a white horse got to make a wish. Ellen was going to wish Austine would forget about her horseback riding.

The girls always played the alphabet game when they rode in a car. Each watched the signs on her own side of the road for the letters of the alphabet. Each letter had to be found in order or it did not count. The *k* in a Sky Chief Gasoline sign could not be used unless a *j* had already been seen. The girl who had a Burma Shave sign on her side of the road at the right time was lucky because it contained in the right order both *u* and *v*, two hard letters to find. The game went quickly at first, because there were lots of signs, but as they neared the mountains the signs became more scarce.

Ellen was looking for a Texaco filling station for an *x* when Austine shouted, "Look, a white horse! I've got dibs on it." She shut her eyes to wish.

Ellen was sorry she had not seen the horse first. She needed a wish. Finally both girls were down to *z*. By then the car was winding along the mountain roads.

"Z!" shouted Ellen. "I win. There was a sign by that bridge that said 'Zigzag River.'"

"That's all right," said Austine generously. "I'm going to get my wish."

It was a few more miles along the highway that Austine saw the horses. "Look, Daddy! Horses for rent, fifty cents an hour! Please stop," she begged.

Mr. Allen drew over to the side of the road near some horses in a makeshift corral. Austine scrambled out of the car and ran to the horses, while the others followed.

"Daddy, please let us go horseback riding. All my life I've wanted to ride a horse. Please, Daddy. You and Mother could go on and look at the rhododendrons and come back for us."

"Would it be safe for the girls to ride alone?" Mrs. Allen asked the man with the horses.

"Please, Mother," begged Austine. "Make my wish come true."

"Sure. Kids do it all the time," answered the man. "They ride up that dirt road as far as the old sawmill and turn around and come back. The horses know the way. Takes about half an hour. Road runs right along the highway."

"They won't be thrown from the horses?" asked Mrs. Allen.

"From these horses?" said the man. "No, lady. These horses worked at a riding academy for years."

"You're sure they're gentle?"

"Yes, ma'am. Gentle as kittens."

"The girls could hang onto the saddle horns," suggested Mr. Allen.

"Oh, Daddy, you aren't supposed to hang onto the saddle horn. Only tenderfoots, I mean tenderfeet, do that. We'll be safe, because Ellen has ridden a lot and I know all about riding from books."

Ellen wished Austine would keep still. She was not at all sure she wanted to ride, especially without a grownup along.

"I suppose it would be safe to let the girls ride for half an hour," said Mrs. Allen. "We could walk along the dirt road and look at the rhododendrons while they rode. That way they would be within shouting distance."

"All right, girls, which horses do you want to ride?" asked Mr. Allen, taking a handful of change out of his pocket.

Ellen thought she had better act brave even if she didn't feel that way. "The spotted horse is nice, but I think I'd rather have the brown one over in the corner of the pen." She thought the brown horse looked gentle.

"I'll take the pinto on this side of the corral," said Austine, glancing at Ellen.

Oh dear, thought Ellen. I've said the wrong thing. I wish I'd read some horse books.

Austine watched eagerly and Ellen watched uneasily while the man saddled and bridled the two horses. "O.K., kids," he said.

Ellen walked over to the brown horse and patted him gingerly. He seemed awfully big when she stood beside him. But he looked down at her with large gentle eyes, and Ellen felt braver.

The man held out his hand, palm up.

Oh, I wonder if he wants me to give him some money, thought Ellen. It must be that, but I'm sure Austine's father paid him. Or maybe he wants to shake hands. A sort of farewell.

"Come on, girlie. Step up," said the man. "Don't be scared. Brownie isn't going to hurt you."

My goodness, thought Ellen. I guess he expects me to step in his hand. I suppose it's all right. His hand is dirty anyway.

She put her foot into his hand and he boosted her onto the horse. The ground seemed a long way below her. And Ellen had forgotten how wide a horse was. The man shortened her stirrups and then helped Austine onto the pinto. Ellen patted Brownie on the neck. She was anxious to have him like her. If only she had a lump of sugar in her pocket.

"Look," cried Austine. "I'm really on a horse."

Ellen knew she was expected to take the lead. "Giddap," she said uncertainly. Brownie did not move.

The man gave each horse a light slap on the rump. They walked out of the corral and ambled down the dirt road as if they were used to going that way. Austine's mother and father followed on foot.

Ellen carefully held one rein in each hand. As she looked at the ground so far below, she hoped Brownie wouldn't decide to run.

"I'm going to call my horse Old Paint like in the song," said Austine, who never missed the Montana Wranglers on the radio and knew all about cowboy songs. "I wish I'd worn my cowboy neckerchief."

"Yes," said Ellen briefly. She didn't feel like making conversation.

When Austine's horse moved in front, Ellen took hold of the saddle horn. It wasn't so much that she was scared, she told herself. She just didn't want to take unnecessary chances.

"I wish we'd worn our pedal pushers," said Austine. "It's sort of hard to feel like a cowgirl in a dress."

"I wish we had, too."

Maybe this wasn't going to be so bad after all. The horses seemed to know the way, and Ellen found the rocking motion and the squeak of the saddle rather pleasant. She was even able to look around at the trees and enjoy the woodsy smell.

Then when they had gone around a bend in the road, Brownie decided it was time to go back to the corral. He turned around and started walking in the direction from which they had come.

"Hey," said Ellen anxiously. She pulled on the right rein, but Brownie kept on going. "Stop!" she ordered, more loudly this time.

"What are you going that way for?" asked Austine, turning in her saddle.

"Because the horse wants to," said Ellen crossly.

"Well, turn him around."

"I can't," said Ellen. "He won't steer."

Austine turned Old Paint and drew up beside Ellen. "Don't you know you're supposed to hold both reins in one hand?" Austine was scornful.

Ellen didn't know. "I just held them this way to try to turn him," she said. She took them in her left hand. They were so long she wound them around her hand.

Austine leaned over and took hold of Brownie's bridle with one hand. "Come on, Old Paint," she said, and turned her horse forward again. Brownie followed.

"Thanks," said Ellen. "My, you're brave."

"Oh, that's nothing," said Austine modestly. "You don't steer a horse," she added gently. "You guide him."

"Oh . . . I forgot." Ellen wondered how she would ever explain her ignorance to Austine. What would her best friend think when she found out how Ellen had misled her?

The horses plodded on down the woodsy road. Through the trees the girls could see the highway and hear cars passing. Austine's mother and father appeared around the bend, and Ellen began to feel brave again.

"Let's gallop," suggested Austine.

Ellen's legs were beginning to ache. "How do you make them gallop?"

"Dig your heels in," said Austine.

"Oh, I wouldn't want to hurt the horse," said Ellen.

"You won't hurt him, silly. Cowboys wear spurs, don't they?"

Ellen timidly prodded Brownie with her heels. Brownie ambled on.

Austine dug in her heels. Old Paint began to trot. At first Austine bounced, but soon she rode smoothly. Then her horse began to gallop.

When Old Paint galloped, Brownie began to trot. Ellen began to bounce. She hung onto the saddle horn as hard as she could. Still she bounced. Slap-slap-slap. Her bare legs began to hurt from rubbing against the leather of the saddle flap. Slap-slap-slap. Goodness, I sound awful, she thought. I hope Austine doesn't hear me slapping this way.

Austine's horse, after galloping a few yards, slowed down to a walk. "Whoa, Old Paint," cried Austine anyway, and pulled on the reins. Old Paint stopped and Austine panted a minute.

"I did it, Ellen!" she called. "It was just a few steps, but I really, truly galloped. I hung on with my knees and galloped just like in the movies."

"Wh-wh-oa-oa!" Ellen's voice was jarred out between bounces. Brownie trotted on. Slap-slap-slap.

Austine began to laugh. "I can see trees between you and the saddle every time you go up. Oh, Ellen, you look so funny!"

Slap-slap-slap. Ellen didn't think she could stand much more bouncing. It was worse than being spanked.

"Ellen Tebbits! I don't think you know a thing about horseback riding."

"Wh-wh-oa-oa!" When Brownie reached Old Paint he stopped. After Ellen got her breath, she gasped, "I do, too. It's just that the other horses I rode were tamer."

The horses walked on until the road curved down to the edge of a stream.

"Oh, look. There's a bridge," exclaimed Ellen, looking up.

"I guess the highway crosses to the other side of the stream," said Austine. "I wonder if the poor horses are thirsty."

There was no doubt about Brownie's wanting a drink. He left the road and picked his way down the rocky bank to the water.

"Poor horsie, you were thirsty," said Ellen, patting his neck.

But Brownie did not stop at the edge of the stream. He waded out into it.

"Whoa," yelled Ellen, above the rush of the water. "Austine, help!"

Brownie waded on.

"Austine! What'll I do? He's going swimming!"

"Here, Brownie! Here, Brownie!" called Austine from the bank. Her voice sounded faint across the surging water.

When Brownie had picked his way around the boulders to the middle of the stream, he stopped and looked around.

"Look, he's in over his knees!" Ellen looked down at the swirling water. "Giddap, Brownie!"

"Kick him in the ribs," yelled Austine from across the stream.

"I don't want to hurt him," called Ellen, but she did kick him gently. Brownie did not appear to notice.

"Slap him on the behind with the ends of the reins," directed Austine from the bank.

Ellen slapped. Brownie turned his head and looked at her reproachfully.

By this time some hikers had stopped on the bridge. Looking down at Ellen, they laughed and pointed. Ellen wished they would go away.

Brownie lowered his head to drink. Because Ellen had the reins wound around her hand, she could not let go. As she was pulled forward, the saddle horn poked her in the stomach.

"Oof," she said. Hanging over the horse's neck, she clung to his mane with one hand while she unwound her other hand.

Brownie looked at her with water dripping from his chin. Ellen thought it was his chin. Maybe on a horse it was called something else.

Austine broke a branch from a huckleberry bush that grew out of an old log at the edge of the stream. She waved it toward Brownie. "Here, horsie. Nice horsie."

Brownie glanced at her with mild interest.

"Oh, go on, Brownie," said Ellen in disgust. She kicked him hard this time. Brownie looked at her sadly and swished his tail.

A couple of cars stopped on the bridge and the occupants looked down at Ellen and laughed. "Yippee!" yelled one of the hikers and everyone laughed. "Ride 'em, cowboy!"

"Do something, Austine," Ellen called across the water. "Our half hour must be nearly up."

"Maybe I could ride back and get the man who owns the horses," Austine yelled back.

"No, Austine. Don't leave me here alone," begged Ellen. "Maybe I could get off and wade. I don't think the water would come up to my shoulders."

"The current's too strong," called Austine. "And anyway, we're supposed to bring the horses back. You can't go off and leave Brownie."

Austine was right. Ellen knew that she couldn't leave Brownie. She might lose him, and the man would probably make her pay for him. At least, she thought he would. She had never heard of anyone losing a horse, so she wasn't sure. "I can't stay here forever," she called.

"Mother and Daddy should catch up with us in a minute," Austine called. "They'll know what to do."

That was just what was worrying Ellen. She didn't want the Allens to see her in such a predicament. What would they think after Austine had told them she had ridden before? Maybe they had wandered off to look at rhododendrons and were lost in the woods by now.

Still Brownie did not move. Ellen wondered what it would be like to try to sleep on a horse. Again she wished she had brought some lumps of sugar. She could have eaten them herself when she became hungry.

One of the hikers climbed down the bank to the edge of the water. "Need some help, little girl?" he called.

"Oh yes, please," answered Ellen gratefully.

Jumping from boulder to boulder, the man drew near her, but he could not get close enough to reach Brownie's bridle. "Throw me the reins, little girl," he directed.

Ellen threw them as hard as she could. They fell into the water, but the man grabbed them as the current carried them toward him.

"Come on, old fellow," he said, pulling at the reins. Meekly Brownie began to pick his way around the boulders toward the bank.

"Oh, thank you," said Ellen, when they reached dry ground. "I guess I would have had to stay out there all day if you hadn't come for me."

"That's all right," said the man. "The trouble is, you let the horse know you were afraid of him. Let the old nag know you're boss and you won't have any trouble."

"Thank you, I'll try," said Ellen, taking a firm grip on the reins. "Good-by."

Just then Austine's mother and father appeared around the bend in the road. "Enjoying your ride, girls?" asked Mr. Allen.

"Oh yes," said Austine. "We just stopped to give the horses a drink."

"It's time to turn back now," said Mrs. Allen.

"All right, Mother," said Austine.

The girls headed their horses toward the corral. Ellen was so embarrassed she didn't know quite what to say to Austine. What would Austine think of her after this? What would she tell the kids at school?

Finally, when Austine's mother and father were a safe distance behind, Ellen said in a low voice, "I guess I didn't know quite as much about horseback riding as I thought I did."

"Your horse was just hard to manage, that's all," said Austine generously.

"Austine?" said Ellen timidly.

"What?"

"You won't tell anybody, will you? You won't tell that Otis Spofford what happened, will you?"

Austine smiled at her. "Of course I won't tell. We're best friends, aren't we? It'll be a secret like the underwear. Giddap, Old Paint."

"Thank you, Austine," said Ellen gratefully. "You're a wonderful friend. And you know what? I'm going to look for some horse books the next time we go to the library."

The horses, knowing they were headed toward hay, showed more spirit. Ellen held the reins firmly. That Brownie was going to know who was boss. She began to enjoy herself. She pretended she was returning to a ranch after a hard day riding the range.

"I didn't know horses had such long hair," she remarked.

"It's their winter coat," explained Austine. "They'll shed it this summer."

Ellen laughed. "Just like winter underwear," she said.

HOME

Lois Lenski

Lois Lenski has given children a wonderful picture of life in the United States and of its diverse people. Among her regional stories are Strawberry Girl *(Florida), 1946 Newbery Award winner,* BoomTown Boy *(Oklahoma),* Bayou Suzette *(Louisiana),* Blue Ridge Billy *(North Carolina),* Judy's Journey *(migrant workers),* Prairie School *(Dakota prairies), and* Cotton in My Sack *(Arkansas), from which this excerpt is taken. Every one of these is a lively, enjoyable story. What the people in the stories lack in money and education, they make up for in pride and family loyalties. Young readers who share the problems, hardships, and occasional fun of the children in these books will have a deeper understanding of people and of what Albert Schweitzer calls "reverence for life." Joanda in* Cotton in My Sack *is one of the most appealing little girls in the series. This excerpt, together with the song, lends itself to dramatization. Other chapters in this book and many of Lois Lenski's stories will prove admirable for dramatization.*

"Sun up in the mornin'
Hot upon my back,
Got to go start pickin'
Cotton in my sack . . ."

Joanda's voice rang out clearly over the cotton field. She had made up the song herself and its simple tune wavered uncertainly. Then it stopped.

"Oh!" she cried. "Don't you put that worm on me."

"I will so!" answered Ricky.

She ducked to get out of her brother's way.

"There it is *on* you," said Ricky.

"Git it off! Git it off!" screamed Joanda, shaking herself. "If there's one thing I can't stand about cotton pickin', it's worms. Where'd it go? What kind was it—a fuzzy one, or one that's speckeldy-like with lots of feet?"

"I don't know," said Ricky. "You lost it. It's gone now."

"You better git busy and pick," said Joanda.

Five-year-old Ricky sat down in the cotton row. "I *can't* pick and I *won't* pick," he said.

"When you take a notion to pick, you *can* pick," said Joanda.

"What we got to pick for?" asked Ricky.

"This is Daddy's cotton," explained Joanda. "We're pickin' for Big Charley, Daddy's boss-man."

"Is Daddy gonna pay me?" asked Ricky.

"Daddy's *s'posed* to pay *me* for pickin', but sometimes he don't," said Joanda.

"When I git my money, I'm gonna git me a new coat," said Ricky.

"You'll be an old man before you git it," said Joanda.

Ricky slung his tow sack over his shoulder and began to pick. "I'm gonna git my sack full."

Joanda started a game she had made up: "Do you chew tobacco?"

"No," said Ricky, shaking his head.

"Do you dip snuff?"

"NO!" answered Ricky.

"Do you smoke a pipe?"

"NO, NO, NO!" shouted Ricky.

"Do you eat popcorn?"

"Home" from *Cotton in My Sack*. Copyright, 1949, by Lois Lenski; used by permission of the author and publisher, J. B. Lippincott Co.

"No—oh yes! YES!"

"Do you chew gum?"

"YES MA'M, when I can git it!" laughed Ricky.

The small boy held out both hands filled with cotton. "Look how much cotton I got!" He had a sweet smile. His face was plump, but it was very dirty. "For Christmas I want a tractor. I'm gonna be a farmer."

"It's a long time 'fore Christmas comes," said his sister. She stopped in her row and lifted the middle of her seven-foot pick sack to shake the cotton down to the end. Her face was pretty, but had a wistful, sad expression. Dark brown eyes looked out from under her floppy checked sun-bonnet. Tangled brown hair hung beside her cheeks. She wore baggy patched blue jeans and a faded red plaid shirt.

"After it's shook down it's not half full," she said. "If I could only git it full once, I'd be happy. Daddy says I won't be even half-a-hand till I git it full."

"Am I a full hand?" asked Ricky.

Joanda laughed. "You? Course not. Mavis is fourteen—she's a full hand, only she can't pick now 'cause she's got a boil on her neck. Steve's twelve, but he's not half-a-hand 'cause he stands and looks around so much. You have to be eleven or twelve to be a full hand."

"Oh!" said Ricky.

"Bless Pat!" cried Joanda suddenly. "That's our baby crying."

"Maybe it's Mr. Burgess's cotton pickers singin'," said Ricky. "I hear our dog barking. *Here, Trouble, here, Trouble!*" He called, but the dog did not come.

The children looked down to the far end of the rows, where three bent figures were picking.

"Listen how the baby's hollerin'," Joanda went on. "Bet she's cryin' to come over here to me. Bet she'd be quiet if she was here with me. Mama won't git her sack full if Lolly keeps on yellin'."

"I'm gonna pull my shoes off," announced Ricky.

"Mama'll whoop you. Daddy'll whoop you," said Joanda.

"No, they won't," answered Ricky.

"Big Charley, the boss-man will whoop you."

"No, he won't!"

"Miz Shands will whoop you."

Cotton in My Sack

The song *Cotton in My Sack*. Copyright by Lois Lenski and Clyde Robert Bulla; used by permission of author and composer

"She jest better not try it," laughed Ricky. "She'd have to ketch me first."

"You'll git sandburrs in your feet," warned Joanda.

Ricky walked around in the dirt. "I ain't got no cuckleburrs," he said.

"Pick some more, sugar," said Joanda. "Pick four more pounds, then you can rest."

"I'm tard of pickin'," said Ricky. "I ain't never gonna pick no more cotton as long as I live."

Joanda laughed. The children had picked to the end of their row and now came out on the turn-row between two cotton fields. Here stood the trailer, three-quarters full of cotton. It was an old rickety cotton wagon, with high board sides. Ricky started to climb up the ladder at the back.

"Daddy don't want you to git on the cotton," warned Joanda. "Git down, Ricky." He kept on climbing.

"Cotton feels good on my bare feet, so soft and squnchy," said the boy. He jumped and came down *plop*. He rolled over and over, the fuzzy cotton sticking to his clothes. "I like to go barefooted. It feels good on my toes!"

"We don't have to go barefooted now," said Joanda. "We got shoes to wear. We used to go barefooted when we didn't have money to buy any."

"My shoes hurt my feet," said Ricky. "One time I had some money and I spent it."

"I got $3.45 now, I had $5.00," said Joanda proudly. "I spent it for groceries. I got baloney and bread and two cans of fish and two candy bars. Steve owes me a quarter. He better pick cotton and pay it back. If he don't, I'll make him. He says he's goin' to, but if he don't, I'll take my switch after him."

The Negro pickers in the next field were singing. Joanda stood still to listen:
"Oh, the cotton needs pickin' so bad!
Cotton needs pickin' so bad,
Cotton needs pickin' so bad,
Gonna pick all over dis field" . . .

"Mama and Daddy's pickin' fast," said Ricky. The children looked at the three figures who were coming closer and closer.

"Why is Steve so far behind the others?" asked Ricky.

"He's lookin' at every bird and wishin' it was an airplane," said Joanda. "He's lookin' at the cars along the road." She pointed to the highway off on the right.

"Where's all the cars a-goin'?" asked Ricky.

"To town," said Joanda.

"I don't want to live in town," said Ricky. "You can't make any money in town."

"I do," said Joanda. "You can spend all your money in town. Let's ask Daddy to go to the gin this evenin', when he takes the cotton in."

"Goody, goody!" cried Ricky, jumping up and down.

All the time she had been talking, the girl's nimble fingers had been putting cotton in her sack, as she started on the next row. Her bent back moved from plant to plant, and her thin arms moved in a steady rhythm.

"Why don't you rest a while?" asked Ricky.

"I don't rest, I have to keep on workin'," said Joanda. "I picked twenty-seven pounds one evenin'. Maybe if I try hard, I'll git my pick sack *full*."

"*Here, Trouble, here, Trouble!*" called Ricky.

A little gray dog came tearing down the cotton middle, barking. Then Daddy came, carrying his bulging sack over his shoulder. He was a thin man with a weathered face, and he wore a slouchy felt hat. Mama came more slowly, dragging her heavy load. Joanda ran to meet her. Mama's load was not all cotton, for there on her pick sack rode the baby, Lolly, as comfortable as a bird in a nest.

"Lolly rolled off back down there," said Mama, "and how she did yell. When I looked around, there was Trouble sittin' in her place as smart as you please, expectin' a ride."

"Betcha he pushed her off," said Joanda. "Can I take her, Mama?"

"Land sakes, yes, git her off," said Mama. "My back's nigh broke. She's as heavy as a ton o' bricks."

"Betcha she was hollerin' for me," said the girl. "Betcha she missed me all right."

Mama had so many clothes on, it was hard to tell whether she was a large or small woman. She wore pants to cover her legs, her cotton dress came to her knees, and over it she wore one of Daddy's old shirts to cover her arms. Brown eyes peered out from under her large slat bonnet. Hot, tired and dirty, she slipped down on her cotton sack to rest.

Joanda took Lolly on her lap, her thin arms squeezed tightly around the heavy two-year-old. The baby was plump and had curly red hair. She was dressed in a khaki coverall suit with red buttons down the front. Joanda looked down at her, adoration in her eyes.

"Lolly pick cotton? Lolly like to pick cotton?" she asked.

Lolly reached over and pulled off a fluffy boll. She began to make a humming sound.

"You singin', Lolly? You singin' *Cotton in my Sack?*" Joanda turned to Mama. "Lolly makes out like she's singin', Mama."

"Only time that young un's quiet is when she's eatin' or sleepin'," said Mama. "She's the noisiest little somebody."

Joanda gave the baby a tight hug.

Daddy began weighing. He tied the two ends of his long pick sack together and hooked them over the scales. "Fifty-two pounds," he said. "Git off that sack, you two."

Mama and Joanda stood up and watched as he weighed the others. Mama had forty-four pounds, Joanda eighteen and Ricky seven. Daddy marked all the weights down in a little green record book. Steve came up, and he had thirty pounds. Daddy shook his head. "We'd a had more if Mavis coulda picked today. Cotton's light. It don't weigh much when it's plumb dry."

Each sack, after being weighed, was thrown up on top of the load. Mama took the baby and Joanda climbed up to help. Ricky and Joanda and Steve and Daddy jumped up and down, emptying the sacks and tramping the cotton. Trouble jumped and bounced and barked.

Mama looked down at Lolly and said, "They're havin' a time, ain't they?" Lolly clapped her hands and laughed.

"Can we go to the gin?" "Oh, Daddy, can we?" "Mama, can we ride to the gin?" begged the children.

Mama looked at Daddy who nodded his head.

"I reckon so," answered Mama. "Come, Trouble. We'll go see if Mavis has got supper cooked." She started across the field, baby in arms and dog at her heels.

Daddy's truck, already full of cotton, had been left parked in the turn-row. He backed it up, hitched the trailer on, and drove out of the cotton field. Joanda threw off her sunbonnet to cool her face in the breeze. The children sat down on the cotton. Their bright faces and figures, seated on the white cotton, made a colorful pattern against the blue of the sky. A radiant sunset threw out flames of red and gold, casting changing shadows across the level Arkansas fields. The truck bumped along the dirt road until it came to the crossroads center, where beside a garage and a country store, stood the White Top cotton gin.

Daddy drove up under the shed until the trailer was on the scales.

A man hurried out. "Hi there, Dave Hutley!"

The children hopped down and the man weighed the cotton. He went in the building to mark down the weight, came out and hooked a tag on the trailer. Then Daddy backed up and he weighed the cotton in the truck.

"O. K., Hutley," the man called out.

Daddy drove the trailer under a large round pipe which came down from the main part of the gin. The man jumped on the load and began to move the pipe about. A loud noise was heard as the motor was turned on and the fan began to operate. The suction pulled the cotton up into the pipe.

"That's the suck!" Joanda explained to Ricky. "See how it sucks up all the cotton?" She turned to Steve. "What do they do with the cotton after they git it in the gin?"

"Don't *you* know?" answered Steve. "They've got big machinery in there. It separates the seeds from the cotton and blows the hulls out in a big pile at the back. The seeds go out in another place. And the cotton goes round and round till it gits clean of leaves and trash, then it's pressed in a bale."

"They put a tow sack around it and tie it with wires," said Joanda. "I know that much."

"Big Charley, our boss-man, took me in and showed me all over one time," said Steve.

"Oh look, what's that up there in our cotton?" cried Joanda. "It's something blue . . . it's . . . whish! There, it's gone. *It was my sunbonnet!*"

"It went so quick!" cried Ricky, laughing. "I saw it go."

"You left it on the cotton," said Steve. "Wasn't it funny to see it go up?"

Joanda didn't know whether to laugh or cry. She started for the door of the gin.

"Where you a-goin'?" called Steve. "Kids are not allowed in there."

"Gonna git my sunbonnet," said Joanda, "before anything happens to it."

Daddy came up and the children explained.

"You're too late, sugar," said Daddy. "It's all chawed up to bits by this time."

"Chawed up?" Joanda blinked. She was used to sudden losses and things she could not help.

After the cotton was unloaded, the man said, "Goin' home now? You live in that shotgun house out on the by-o road, don't you?"

The children climbed into the cab of the truck with Daddy. As they rode along the dusty dirt road, Ricky asked, "Daddy, what's a shotgun house?"

Daddy laughed. "Where'd you hear that, son?"

"The man at the gin said we lived in one," answered Ricky.

"That's right," said Daddy. Now they were close enough to see the house, which was painted red. "It has three rooms in a row. I can take my shotgun and shoot through the front door and the bullet will go out the back door. It will go plumb through all four doors in a straight line."

The children laughed.

"But you won't do it, will you, Daddy?" asked Ricky.

"I got better use for my gun than any sech fool doin's," said Daddy. "Might better go squirrel huntin' over in them woods along the Mississippi River, eh, boys?"

"You bet!" agreed Steve.

The small yard around the house was bare of grass and untidy with trash. Near the back door was a pile of coal and beyond were several rickety sheds. Cotton grew close on all sides. There was just room for Daddy to park the truck and trailer close to the front porch.

The children ran around and went in at the back door. Mama was bent over the stove, putting coal in. Hot bacon fat sizzled angrily and sent up an appetizing odor. A few dishes were set on the oilcloth table.

"I lost my sunbonnet, Mama," said Joanda. "I left it on top of the cotton. It went up in the suck and got chawed to bits."

"Why didn't you keep it on your head where it belongs?" said Mama. "You'll have to find another old one to wear. Mavis didn't even git the fire started. She's still in bed in there. And Lolly's been cryin' so . . . Take her, Nannie."

Joanda picked up the baby and went through to the front part of the house. Mavis lay on one of the two double beds that nearly filled the middle room. Joanda was hot and tired after her all-day picking. A gentle breeze came in at the open front door. Joanda sat on the floor and played with the baby. Then Lolly crawled off to explore. Joanda stretched out full length.

Her tired back felt better when she lay flat on the floor. She rested, not moving, her head placed near the wall. Then she looked up. There on the wall old newspapers were pasted, in place of plaster. They were stained and dirty, but she could still read the words and study the pictures and advertisements. The papers were pasted on upside-down. She could read them better lying on the floor.

Joanda loved to read. There were no books or magazines in the house, only the newspapers on the wall. The words—strange words she did not know the meaning of—had a fascination for her. She used to ask Daddy to explain what they meant. But he couldn't—he only went to the third grade, he said. Joanda could pronounce them, if she took one syllable at a time and tried to say them slowly.

" 'Perm—a—nent, permanent—lasts forever.' They do something to the hair, I reckon. $5.00—that's too much," Joanda said to herself. "But it sure does look purty." She must save up all the hard words she did not know and ask the teacher when she went back to school.

"Supper's ready!" called Mama from the kitchen.

Mama knew how to cook supper, but she did not know the magic of words.

CHI-WEÉ RUNS A RACE

Grace Moon

Mr. and Mrs. Moon spent many years in the Indian country of our Southwest. Mrs. Moon's stories, which her husband illustrated, are not only exciting but also authentic.

Here is a tale of the desert wide,
A tale of the Mesa high,
With sage and sand on every side,
And the blue of a cloudless sky.

Here is a tale of a little maid,
And a boy of a desert band;
Of the things they did and the games they
        played,
In far-off Indianland!

Chi-weé wriggled! Chi-weé squirmed! Out
there in the sunlight the call of the little hoot-
owl had sounded three times. In the broad day
when there were no hoot-owls. That meant that
Loki was waiting for her, outside in the dancing
sunlight where he could hear all the sounds of
the desert and see the thousand play places that
called louder than voices. And here, in the dark
house, she must sit and listen to the words of old
Mah-pee-ti while he talked and talked endlessly
to her mother.

Her mother had told her she must sit quietly,
and the *outside* of her was as quiet as possible,

but no little girl could be quiet *inside* while old
Mah-pee-ti talked, and the hoot-owl called, and
on the very end of her tongue was a secret so
big she had to close her lips *tight* to keep from
shouting it out loud to the whole world.

How could big people sit so quietly, and talk
and talk when there were such wonderful things
to do, and all outdoors called with tongues that
would not be still?

Chi-weé belonged to the outdoors. She was a
little Pueblo Indian girl and lived in a town
built like an eagle's nest high on the top of a
mesa. For all the eight years of her life she had
lived in this little town overlooking the desert—
this queer little town built of stone, that had
houses whose flat roofs were the front-door yards
of other houses built above them and whose
crooked little streets led nowhere in particular
except that sometimes they ran to the edge of the
mesa so that they too might look out over the
desert.

The houses had ladders for stairways and
often no doorways at all in the first story. That
was because long, long ago when many other
tribes were at war with them, each house was
really a fort, and to keep the enemies from surprising them at night they would pull up their
ladders and then go to sleep in peace knowing
that no one could get into the house. But no one
came to fight now, as their enemies were not so
brave as they used to be and would only steal in
secret. There were many children in the little
town, and dogs and wild turkeys playing all together in the streets, and women sitting on the
roof-tops painting jars and bowls of pottery and
stringing long strands of red chili peppers to dry
in the sun. They had always many smiles and
nods for Chi-weé, who, with her shy little ways,
was well loved in the town. Chi-weé was small
for her age, with a great mop of black hair and
a serious manner, but she was not serious *inside,*
and those who knew her well could see in her
black eyes a little fairy of mischief ever dancing,
and in her heart she said there were wings—
wings like those of the little bird for which she
was named.

It did not seem that old Mah-pee-ti *ever*
would stop—but *now*—he was slowly rising—
and at a little nod from her mother Chi-weé was
through the door and out to the head of the

mesa trail like a tumbleweed blown by a strong wind.

There was Loki waiting as she knew he would be waiting, at the top of the trail that led down the mesa side to the spring below—Loki, who kept sheep in the desert and was Navajo, but who was her very best friend. Better than all else she liked to play with him in the desert, to see the strange places he would find and hear the wonderful tales he would tell. Loki was not very much older than Chi-weé, but he liked to have her *think* that he was very old and wise. Oh, yes—better than with the little chubby baby brother who gurgled, and better than with Ba-ba, her little goat, Chi-weé liked to play with Loki. And now, when she saw him, she called aloud before she came very near.

"Three times must you guess the great surprise secret I have to tell!" she cried, and she jumped up and down in her excitement. "Three times, like *this*—" and she held up three fingers, wiggling them in front of Loki—"and *never* will you guess it!"

"But, how can I guess," he said, with a little pretend-frown. "How can I guess when I do not know what you speak about?"

"W-e-e-ll," said Chi-weé slowly, "I will tell this much—it is about the Trader—a *little* of it is about him. Did you know," she asked excitedly then, "that he had brought a lady wife to the Cañon—a lady with a white face—and she wears shiny clothes?"

"Yes, I know," said Loki. "One time I saw her."

"She knows magic," said Chi-weé with much impressiveness. "*Great* magic she knows—I have seen how she knows it."

"What kind of magic?" asked Loki, and he tried not to appear too interested.

"Listen, and I will tell you," said Chi-weé, and she felt very important, to know more than Loki. Usually *he* was the one who knew everything. "One day—it was yesterday, I think—I found a little flower in the desert. It was one I have not seen before—and, as it was the day when we rode to the trading store, I took the little flower with me and gave it to the white lady. She has a smile that is nice, and she said, 'Oh, but that is a pretty flower, it is one I have wanted to see.' 'Did someone tell you about this flower?' I said, and

she said, 'No, I saw it in a book.' Now, that is great magic, to see a flower in a book."

"Pooh!" laughed Loki. "That is nothing—in school places they teach about *everything, all* from books."

"I know about school places," said Chi-weé eagerly. "Once, the mission lady asked me to come in and sit down. It is a very, very bad place."

"Why is it a bad place? I think it is good to know about things," said Loki.

"Oh, but it is bad to sit very still all day in a house, and if you say one *word* the lady says, 'S-S-S-SH!' and waggles her finger at you, and if you move your foot she goes, 'Bang—Bang!' with a little stick on a table, and when the very, very little ones come in with no clothes on she says, 'Shame—shame! Run home to your mamma and get a dress!' No, that school place is a bad place. I do not have to look in a book or ask a teacher lady to know things. If I want to know about a little flower I run out and find it; *then* I know —and how can a book or a teacher lady show to me the sunshine and the little dawn wind and the song of the night hawk? But the magic of the white lady of the trader was different from the books in the school, for she said it had a long, long name, that little flower, and she told me what it was—and she told me——"

"But what is that great surprise?" interrupted Loki. "Listen, I will guess one time—that you go to some place soon?"

"No—no!" cried Chi-weé, all excitement again. "It is a *big* surprise, and maybe a part is for you."

"Then it is seed cakes your mother has made."

"Oh, no!" cried Chi-weé, dancing around him, "and two times you have guessed. Look! Two fingers are gone. Now, one more time——"

Loki grinned. "It is that you can come down in the desert and play with me. Is that the great secret—is it, mesa girl?"

Chi-weé laughed in answer to his grin and made a little face at him. "*That* would be no great secret—many times I come down to the desert to play with you. This is a very different thing. Listen——" and she waited just a little to see if she could make Loki eager to listen, but he made a great show of indifference, and when she waited, he looked across the desert as if he saw something there.

"Well," continued Chi-weé, after a very little, for she was too excited to wait long herself, "listen, Loki—we are to have races and games and prizes"—she was dancing again, up and down—"a whole day—and dances and good things, *many* good things to eat—and——"

Loki too, was excited now, and his eyes sparkled.

"Where will it be—and who will race—and when is this to be?"

Chi-weé laughed joyously.

"I *told* you how it was a great secret. It is that the Trader is very happy to bring the white lady to the Cañon, and in three days from now everyone is to come to the ranch where he lives, and it will be a great day—and *you* will come, Loki— and will play in the games?" she questioned eagerly.

"I will put the sheep in corral that day and I will come," answered Loki joyously, and it was hard to keep his feet from dancing a little jig as the feet of Chi-weé were dancing, but it would

not do for him to jump up and down like a little girl.

Those were long days, those three days in between, but at last came the big one. Bright and clear it dawned, and from every direction came people riding to the dance.

"It is like the 'Chicken-pull'!" shouted Loki, when he saw Chi-weé coming down from the mesa; Chi-weé all dressed in her very best, with a green waist and long, brown skirt, and a woven red belt with bobby tassels hanging down. She wore white boots too, and silver bracelets, and a string of silver beads at her throat, and she was very conscious of all this splendor.

"It is like the time at Ganado," called Loki. "*Now* you will see how that was like. I could not tell you much—it is a *see* thing, not a *tell* thing. But now you will know."

"Yes, I will know," shouted Chi-weé in answer, though she was so near she did not need to shout. "And see how I have wings in my feet," and she jumped high with no effort at all. "To-day I could run faster than the wind—to-day the little hares in the desert could not run so fast as I can run. I will be the one that will win in those races—you shall see!"

"If you will talk so much, Chi-weé," called her mother, laughing, "you will have no breath to win races."

But Chi-weé and Loki gave little heed to words. They climbed into the back of the wagon, for Loki was to ride with them this day, and Loki, too, was dressed as Chi-weé had never seen him; with a plum-colored velvet waist with silver buttons and soft buckskin pants, and a woven red belt around his waist and a red band about his black hair, and in his ears bits of turquoise as blue as the deepest blue of the sky. Chi-weé's father drove the wagon and the mother sat beside him holding the fat baby brother, and in the back, on a pile of blankets sat Loki and Chi-weé, and they all felt that they looked very fine in their best bright clothes.

After this they spoke but little, for the eyes of each were big with thoughts of what was to come this day.

Over the glowing desert they drove, down sandy washes and up again—the steep other side —over rocky stretches and past rocks and buttes of the strangest shape and color. Past clumps of pinyon trees, mesquite and cactus, and always, everywhere, were tumbleweed and sagebrush and the little scurrying animals of the wild places. Other wagons, many of them, were driving in the same direction, and people on horses and burros, and many walking. It was the sort of excitement that Chi-weé and Loki loved, and their hearts sang within them.

Finally, they came to the place. It was at the mouth of a broad cañon, and in this sheltered place were the ranch and the store of the Trader.

Now, it was filled with many people and the noise and wagons and confusion made it seem almost like a town, but a town on a holiday, and there was an air of happy excitement over everything.

After a little while, the Trader came out of his store and he told them all that this was a very happy time for him, and that he wanted everybody else to be happy, and so he started the games and said there would be many fine prizes, and especially he said there would be a prize of a big piece of beautiful cloth stuff for the little girl who won in the race. Chi-weé's eyes sparkled at that—and then he said there would be a great feast and everyone was to eat more than they had ever eaten before. The men laughed then, but Chi-weé did not laugh, for it was a serious matter. If she obeyed the Trader she was not just certain what would happen, for there had been times—at other feasts, when good things had tempted very, very strongly—that she had eaten until she had been very sure that she had heard the sewed places of her little dress stretching, and if she ate *more* than that—she wondered if she had better *see* what would happen—and her eyes grew thoughtful for a moment—and then—!

"Look—look!" cried someone. "There go the pony races!" and she ran to where the crowd was thickest, to see. Young men and boys were mounted on ponies and were to race down a place cleared for them. Buried in the sand near one end of the cleared place was a bag with money in it, and just a piece of the neck of the bag stuck out of the sand so the men could reach down and grab for it as they rode past. It was a very exciting race, and many times they grabbed for the bag before one man got it. There were many games that followed the race, some

played with balls and some with arrows, and there were other races and tests of strength, and so many things that Chi-weé grew dizzy with trying to see them all. Loki won a game with arrows, and he came running to show how they had given him a beautiful belt with silver buttons on it. And then, at last, came the race for little girls!

When they stood in line for the race, Chi-weé was so excited that at first she could hardly think; and then, very suddenly, she grew quiet and looked around her at the other little girls. Two or three she knew and the others she did not know. They were all as eager and excited as herself and she knew they thought longingly of that beautiful piece of cloth stuff that would make such a lovely warm dress for a little girl. One little girl looked as if the dress she had on could not last much longer than this day. It was very thin and worn and Chi-weé saw that the little girl was thin too. Two red spots were burning in her cheeks and she looked at Chi-weé with eyes that were very bright.

"If I win this race," she almost whispered to Chi-weé, "my mother will be very glad, and I will be glad. I can run fast—I—I think that I will win."

Chi-weé did not answer, for she thought how fast she too could run. And then came the word to be ready, and then—BANG!—they were off!

At first, they ran all together. But very soon first one and then another dropped behind, and then Chi-weé saw that the little thin girl had told true, for just they two together led all the rest and quickly got a great way ahead. They were running very fast now, but Chi-weé could breathe easily, and she heard the breath of the other girl coming quickly in little short sounds.

"I can win," thought Chi-weé, with fast-beating heart. "Something has said that I could win and it told true. That is very beautiful cloth stuff they will give for a prize—and, look—there is the line that makes the race to end, and I am a great way ahead."

It was true—the other little girl had run slower and slower as they came near to the winning place—and then—such a strange thing happened! As she came almost to the line, Chi-weé dug her little toe into the earth and dropped down in a little bunch on the ground.

"Oh!" cried the other girl, panting as she came close, and she would have stopped, but then *another* strange thing happened, for Chi-weé, without speaking, reached up and gave her a push that sent her stumbling across the winning line, and then she got up and walked slowly across the line herself.

"I stumbled my foot on a little stone," said Chi-weé then to the other girl. "I am glad that you won the race. You run very fast."

At first the thin little girl did not know what to do, but the others crowded around her and told her that she had won the race.

"Often people fall when they race," they said, "and that makes them to lose. Look how you have won this beautiful cloth stuff."

"And for *you*," said the Trader, then turning to Chi-weé with a twinkle in his eye that spoke of understanding, "for you there is *this*," and he shook out of a little bundle a beautiful shawl, the most beautiful shawl Chi-weé had ever seen, with flowers along the border and a fringe as soft as baby hair. Her eyes flew wide and her little mouth dropped open as she saw it, but longingly her arms reached wide to receive it.

"I—I—do not understand," she said tremblingly. "I did not win a prize."

"You did not *think* you won a prize," said the Trader smilingly, "but for *this* race there are *two* prizes—and this one is for you," and he placed the shawl in her arms.

That night, when they were back in the home place, after a long, long happy day, and Chi-weé was tucked safely in her blankety bed, she held her shawl close to her cheek and remembered the smile of the thin little girl. "How nice to win *two* prizes," she whispered into the soft folds, and settled down to sleep with a great content.

SUGAR HILL

Arna Bontemps

Arna Bontemps is a distinguished Negro writer. His understanding of boys and the problems of the country boy in a big city is evident in Sad-Faced Boy. *Rags, Willie, and Slumber have hitchhiked from Alabama to New York to visit their Uncle Jasper in Harlem. In this chapter the boys encounter a bossy little girl, who starts training them in spite of themselves.*

Slumber stretched out in the warm water of his bath. Rags and Willie had already dried themselves and put on the clean clothes that Uncle Jasper Tappin went out and got for them. Slumber's new things were hanging on a nail, waiting for him. As soon as he could get himself clean, dinner would be ready. Aunt Ludy had already called from the kitchen to remind him of that. And there she was calling again.

"Hurry up, you old slow poke boy. Remember you're in Harlem now. You got to get a move on."

Slumber heard what she said, but he couldn't get a move on. The warm bath felt too good. He had never been in a tub like this one, and he had begun to think that a bath tub was just about the finest thing in the world. He stood up and soaped himself all over again. Then once more he rolled in the water, washing the soap from his body. Yes, a bath tub was a fine thing for sure. Ho-hum, and the warm water was fine, too. It made you feel like closing your eyes and staying there a long, long time. Yes, ho-hum. Slumber closed his eyes. It would just be for a minute. He felt so comfortable in the long tub, the warm water. In one more minute he'd open his eyes and get out of the tub. Ho-hum!

But a minute passed and Slumber had not moved. Two minutes passed, five minutes, fifteen, *twenty-five* minutes! Uncle Jasper Tappin and Rags and Willie took their places at the table. Aunt Ludy started bringing things from the kitchen to the dining room. As she went back and forth, she called to Slumber three times. "Come on, slow poke, we just about ready to eat. Come on, you sad-faced boy, I'm putting the dishes on the table. Hurry up, you Slumber, you."

"Wonder what's keeping that boy," Uncle Jasper Tappin said.

"Maybe he got drowned in that bath tub," Willie said. "Slumber can't swim so good, you know."

The others laughed at little Willie, but they were tired of waiting for Slumber. After a few more minutes Aunt Ludy lost her patience.

"Sugar Hill," from *Sad-Faced Boy* by Arna Bontemps. Reprinted by permission of and arrangement with Houghton Mifflin Company, the authorized publishers

"Jasper Tappin," she said, "go in there and see what's holding that boy back. The dinner's going to be all cold."

So Uncle Jasper Tappin went to the bathroom door and opened it. Slumber was not drowned. Nothing was holding him back, either. He was just fast asleep in the bath tub.

"Well, dog my cats," Uncle Jasper Tappin exclaimed. "This beats Jack Robinson, and *he* beat the *band*. Gone to sleep in the bath tub, and all of us sitting at the table waiting for him. You Slumber! You better get up from there, boy. Don't you know the dinner will get cold? Wake up, I say. Rags and Willie and me is about starving. We can't wait for you to take a nap in the bath tub."

Slumber opened his eyes, rolled them sadly. Ho-hum, the warm water felt *so* good.

"I didn't go to do it, Uncle Jasper Tappin. For a fact, I really didn't. But this old bath tub feels so good, this old water is so warm and nice, this old soap smells so good, I just couldn't help it. But I'm coming directly now. I'll be there before you can bat your eye. You just see if I don't."

It did not take Slumber long to get himself dried and dressed, but by the time he reached the table the others were eating.

"Well, that's a new something you bringing up here," Aunt Ludy said, "going to sleep in the bath tub. But never mind, you'll learn to keep your eyes open if you stay up here long."

The dinner was good. The boys finished eating and Uncle Jasper Tappin pushed his chair back from the table.

"Well, has everybody got a plenty?" he asked.

"Yes, sir," the boys murmured.

"No more greens and back bone? No more salad? No more rice and gravy? No more strawberry short cake?"

"No more nothing," Slumber said slowly. "We can't hardly move now. This the best dinner we had in a month or more."

"Well, I'm glad you got enough," Aunt Ludy said. "We'll just have something light for supper when you come in this evening."

"It's most too late to do any real work today," Uncle Jasper Tappin said. "Yet and still we can look the apartment house over and get you ready to do some real helping later on."

The boys followed him out to the elevator and Uncle Jasper Tappin rang the bell.

"Isn't that an elevator over there, too?" Slumber asked as they waited for the door to open.

"Yes," Uncle Jasper Tappin said. "That's what you call the service elevator. We use that for hauling freight and trash. But we're not working just now, so we'll go up on the regular elevator if that boy ever gets here."

The door opened finally, and the three boys stepped in ahead of Uncle Jasper Tappin.

The elevator boy wore a red uniform with large gold buttons.

"Which floor?" he asked.

"Thirteen," Uncle Jasper Tappin told him.

The thirteenth floor was really the roof. The boys, walking behind their uncle, went outside and looked at the blue sky.

Then they walked to the front wall and looked down on the park. They looked at all the rooftops of Harlem and the streets far below. There was so much to see Slumber scarcely knew what to look at.

"This here is New York?" he whispered.

"Yes," Uncle Jasper Tappin said. "This is New York. See up there . . . That's the downtown part."

"What's that great tall building?" Rags asked.

"The Empire State Building, that is. And up this-a-way is the Bronx. And all down below, all around the park there and up that-a-way towards that other park yonder—well, that's all Harlem."

"There's a plenty to see," Slumber said.

"You mighty right about that. More than you can see in one day, or one week either," the old man said.

Slumber slipped his mouth organ from his pocket and began playing softly. The other two boys leaned their elbows on the wall and continued to look at the sights. After a while Slumber paused to rub his lips and think up a new song to play.

"I always wanted to see New York," he told Uncle Jasper Tappin.

"Well, you boys just look around for a while," the old man said. "I'm going down to see if the halls are all clean. I'll be back soon."

Slumber began a new tune when the three boys were alone.

"What that you playing now?" Willie asked. "I never heard you play that before."

"No, I reckon you never did," Slumber said. "I'm just making it up as I go. It's a song about three country boys in a great big city."

"About you and me and Rags?"

Slumber just nodded his head. He was playing again and he couldn't stop to talk. Soon he began patting his foot. The music trickled out sweetly. Willie sat down and began drumming on a tin can with two sticks. Rags put his fingers in his mouth and whistled like an old train whistling as it leaves Alabama. He shuffled his feet slowly, began dancing.

As he danced lazily to the music of Slumber and Willie, Rags began to think of words to go with the music.

"Aw, blow your whistle, Mister Railroad Train," he said. "Blow your whistle on the Dixie line. Sun in the sky, not a tree in sight. Country boys in a big man's town."

Slumber was playing for all he was worth by now. Willie was trying to beat holes in his tin can. Rags made the sound of that train whistle again and continued to shuffle drowsily. "Aw, blow your whistle on the Dixie line."

Then suddenly Slumber observed that someone else was listening to the music. It was no-

body he knew, nobody he had ever seen before. She wore a little checkered skirt with suspender-like straps over the shoulders, and there was a red tam on her head. She had come out of the door quietly, but now that she was near the music, she began to clap her hands. The girl watched the boys for a while, then clicked her heels and made a few little steps of her own.

"Where you learn that music, you sad-faced boy, you?" she said pleasantly. "Who taught you how to blow that harp?"

Slumber shook his head.

"Don't ask me nothing," he told her, pausing. "Don't ask me a thing. We just got to Harlem and we can't sit down."

"Well, listen to me," the girl said, putting her feet down emphatically. "You do right well yourself, old sad-faced boy, but your two brothers here need to learn something if they want to play music in this town. Let me show you how to beat that drum there, little bubber. Move over." She shoved Willie aside. Then, turning to Rags, she added, "When I get through here, I'll show you how to dance, tall boy."

Willie gave up his sticks reluctantly. Slumber rubbed his lips and knocked the harmonica against his knee. Then he began playing again.

"See there," the girl said, catching the rhythm and tapping the can like a real drummer. "It's easy when you know how."

"Hum!" Willie said unpleasantly. "Hum!"

Anybody could see that the happy-faced little girl could do more good drum beating in a minute than Willie could do in an hour. Even Willie could see that, so there was nothing for him to say but *hum*.

Rags had quit dancing and stood beside his small brother observing carefully every move the newcomer made as she beat the traps to Slumber's harmonica playing. When he was thoroughly convinced that she knew her business and that there was no fault to be found with her playing, he said softly, "What's your name, anyhow?"

"Daisy Bee," she said. A little later she asked, "Where did you boys come from?"

"Way down the line," Rags told her. "Alabama. We come up here to see our Uncle Jasper Tappin. We heard a lot of talk about New York and Harlem."

"Oh, he's your uncle! Well, did you ever hear about Sugar Hill?" she asked.

The boys shook their heads.

"Where'bouts is that?" Willie said.

"Right here," Daisy Bee explained. She stopped and pointed with one of the drum sticks. "All the hill up on this side of the park is Sugar Hill. This is about the best row of apartment houses in Harlem, and this one that we're on is the tallest of all. Look down that way and you can see."

Slumber paused to look with the others.

"Oh, yes."

"But we haven't got time for a lot of looking now," Daisy Bee said, getting up from the floor. "Take your drum back, little bubber. Let me see if you can beat it any better since I showed you how. Strike up another tune, sad-faced boy. Come on, tall boy, let me show you how to get those steps right. Maybe I can make something out of you three yet."

The boys didn't exactly like the way Daisy Bee talked. She was high-handed. She simply told you what she wanted you to do and you had to do it. She didn't give you a chance to answer. This irritated Slumber as well as Rags and Willie, but none of them did more than frown a little before they obeyed.

"Take your hands out your pockets and do what she says," Slumber told his brothers. "You can see well as me what we're up against. It's the best thing to let a girl like Daisy Bee have her own way."

The others seemed to agree. They had to let her teach them.

THE HUNDRED DRESSES

Eleanor Estes

Unlike most of Eleanor Estes' other books—the popular Ginger Pye *(Newbery Award),* The Moffats, The Middle Moffat, *and* Rufus M., *which are exceedingly funny—this book is a serious treatment of a grave problem. Children are not likely to forget Wanda, who was rejected by the group, nor the culprits who taunted her.*

Wanda

Today, Monday, Wanda Petronski was not in her seat. But nobody, not even Peggy and Madeline, the girls who started all the fun, noticed her absence.

Usually Wanda sat in the next to the last seat in the last row in Room 13. She sat in the corner of the room where the rough boys who did not make good marks on their report cards sat; the corner of the room where there was most scuffling of feet, most roars of laughter when anything funny was said, and most mud and dirt on the floor.

Wanda did not sit there because she was rough and noisy. On the contrary she was very quiet and rarely said anything at all. And nobody had ever heard her laugh out loud. Sometimes she twisted her mouth into a crooked sort of smile, but that was all.

Nobody knew exactly why Wanda sat in that seat unless it was because she came all the way from Boggins Heights, and her feet were usually caked with dry mud that she picked up coming down the country roads. Maybe the teacher liked to keep all the children who were apt to come in with dirty shoes in one corner of the room. But no one really thought much about Wanda Petronski once she was in the classroom. The time they thought about her was outside of school hours, at noontime when they were coming back to school, or in the morning early before school began, when groups of two or three or even more would be talking and laughing on their way to the school yard.

Then sometimes they waited for Wanda—to have fun with her.

The next day, Tuesday, Wanda was not in school either. And nobody noticed her absence again, except the teacher and probably big Bill Byron, who sat in the seat behind Wanda's and who could now put his long legs around her empty desk, one on each side, and sit there like a frog, to the great entertainment of all in his corner of the room.

But on Wednesday, Peggy and Maddie, who sat in the front row along with other children who got good marks and didn't track in a whole lot of mud, did notice that Wanda wasn't there. Peggy was the most popular girl in school. She was pretty; she had many pretty clothes and her auburn hair was curly. Maddie was her closest friend.

The reason Peggy and Maddie noticed Wanda's absence was because Wanda had made them late to school. They had waited and waited for Wanda—to have some fun with her—and she just hadn't come. They kept thinking she'd come any minute. They saw Jack Beggles running to school, his necktie askew and his cap at a precarious tilt. They knew it must be late, for he always managed to slide into his chair exactly when the bell rang as though he were making a touchdown. Still they waited one minute more and one minute more, hoping she'd come. But finally they had to race off without seeing her.

The two girls reached their classroom after the doors had been closed. The children were reciting in unison the Gettysburg Address, for that was the way Miss Mason always began the session. Peggy and Maddie slipped into their seats just as the class was saying the last lines . . . "that these dead shall not have died in vain; that the nation shall, under God, have a new birth of freedom, and that government of the people, by the people, for the people, shall not perish from the earth."

The Dresses Game

After Peggy and Maddie stopped feeling like intruders in a class that had already begun, they looked across the room and noticed that Wanda was not in her seat. Furthermore her desk was dusty and looked as though she hadn't been there yesterday either. Come to think of it, they hadn't seen her yesterday. They had waited for her a little while but had forgotten about her when they reached school.

They often waited for Wanda Petronski—to have fun with her.

Wanda lived way up on Boggins Heights, and Boggins Heights was no place to live. It was a good place to go and pick wild flowers in the summer, but you always held your breath till you got safely past old man Svenson's yellow house. People in the town said old man Svenson was no good. He didn't work and, worse still, his house and yard were disgracefully dirty, with rusty tin cans strewn about and even an old straw hat. He lived alone with his dog and his cat. No wonder, said the people of the town.

Who would live with him? And many stories circulated about him and the stories were the kind that made people scurry past his house even in broad daylight and hope not to meet him.

Beyond Svenson's there were a few small scattered frame houses, and in one of these Wanda Petronski lived with her father and her brother Jake.

Wanda Petronski. Most of the children in Room 13 didn't have names like that. They had names easy to say, like Thomas, Smith, or Allen. There was one boy named Bounce, Willie Bounce, and people thought that was funny but not funny in the same way that Petronski was.

Wanda didn't have any friends. She came to school alone and went home alone. She always wore a faded blue dress that didn't hang right. It was clean, but it looked as though it had never been ironed properly. She didn't have any friends, but a lot of girls talked to her. They waited for her under the maple trees on the corner of Oliver Street. Or they surrounded her in the school yard as she stood watching some little girls play hopscotch on the worn hard ground.

"Wanda," Peggy would say in a most courteous manner, as though she were talking to Miss Mason or to the principal perhaps. "Wanda," she'd say, giving one of her friends a nudge, "tell us. How many dresses did you say you had hanging up in your closet?"

"A hundred," said Wanda.

"A hundred!" exclaimed all the girls incredulously, and the little girls would stop playing hopscotch and listen.

"Yeah, a hundred, all lined up," said Wanda. Then her thin lips drew together in silence.

"What are they like? All silk, I bet," said Peggy.

"Yeah, all silk, all colors."

"Velvet too?"

"Yeah, velvet too. A hundred dresses," repeated Wanda stolidly. "All lined up in my closet."

Then they'd let her go. And then before she'd gone very far, they couldn't help bursting into shrieks and peals of laughter.

A hundred dresses! Obviously the only dress Wanda had was the blue one she wore every day. So what did she say she had a hundred for?

What a story! And the girls laughed derisively, while Wanda moved over to the sunny place by the ivy-covered brick wall of the school building where she usually stood and waited for the bell to ring.

But if the girls had met her at the corner of Oliver Street, they'd carry her along with them for a way, stopping every few feet for more incredulous questions. And it wasn't always dresses they talked about. Sometimes it was hats, or coats, or even shoes.

"How many shoes did you say you had?"

"Sixty."

"Sixty! Sixty pairs or sixty shoes?"

"Sixty pairs. All lined up in my closet."

"Yesterday you said fifty."

"Now I got sixty."

Cries of exaggerated politeness greeted this. "All alike?" said the girls.

"Oh, no. Every pair is different. All colors. All lined up." And Wanda would shift her eyes quickly from Peggy to a distant spot, as though she were looking far ahead, looking but not seeing anything.

Then the outer fringe of the crowd of girls would break away gradually, laughing, and little by little, in pairs, the group would disperse. Peggy, who had thought up this game, and Maddie, her inseparable friend, were always the last to leave. And finally Wanda would move up the street, her eyes dull and her mouth closed tight, hitching her left shoulder every now and then in the funny way she had, finishing the walk to school alone.

Peggy was not really cruel. She protected small children from bullies. And she cried for hours if she saw an animal mistreated. If anybody had said to her, "Don't you think that is a cruel way to treat Wanda?" she would have been very surprised. Cruel? What did the girl want to go and say she had a hundred dresses for? Anybody could tell that was a lie. Why did she want to lie? And she wasn't just an ordinary person, else why would she have a name like that? Anyway, they never made her cry.

As for Maddie, this business of asking Wanda every day how many dresses and how many hats and how many this and that she had was bothering her. Maddie was poor herself. She usually wore somebody's hand-me-down clothes. Thank

goodness, she didn't live up on Boggins Heights or have a funny name. And her forehead didn't shine the way Wanda's round one did. What did she use on it? Sapolio? That's what all the girls wanted to know.

Sometimes when Peggy was asking Wanda those questions in that mock polite voice, Maddie felt embarrassed and studied the marbles in the palm of her hand, rolling them around and saying nothing herself. Not that she felt sorry for Wanda exactly. She would never have paid any attention to Wanda if Peggy hadn't invented the dresses game. But suppose Peggy and all the others started in on her next! She wasn't as poor as Wanda perhaps, but she was poor. Of course she would have more sense than to say a hundred dresses. Still she would not like them to begin on her. Not at all! Oh, dear! She did wish Peggy would stop teasing Wanda Petronski.

A Bright Blue Day

Somehow Maddie could not buckle down to work.

She sharpened her pencil, turning it around carefully in the little red sharpener, letting the shavings fall in a neat heap on a piece of scrap paper, and trying not to get any of the dust from the lead on her clean arithmetic paper.

A slight frown puckered her forehead. In the first place she didn't like being late to school. And in the second place she kept thinking about Wanda. Somehow Wanda's desk, though empty, seemed to be the only thing she saw when she looked over to that side of the room.

How had the hundred dresses game begun in the first place, she asked herself impatiently. It was hard to remember the time when they hadn't played that game with Wanda; hard to think all the way back from now, when the hundred dresses was like the daily dozen, to then, when everything seemed much nicer. Oh, yes. She remembered. It had begun that day when Cecile first wore her new red dress. Suddenly the whole scene flashed swiftly and vividly before Maddie's eyes.

It was a bright blue day in September. No, it must have been October, because when she and Peggy were coming to school, arms around each other and singing, Peggy had said, "You know what? This must be the kind of day they mean when they say, 'October's bright blue weather.' "

Maddie remembered that because afterwards it didn't seem like bright blue weather any more, although the weather had not changed in the slightest.

As they turned from shady Oliver Street into Maple, they both blinked. For now the morning sun shone straight in their eyes. Besides that, bright flashes of color came from a group of a half-dozen or more girls across the street. Their sweaters and jackets and dresses, blues and golds and reds, and one crimson one in particular, caught the sun's rays like bright pieces of glass.

A crisp, fresh wind was blowing, swishing their skirts and blowing their hair in their eyes. The girls were all exclaiming and shouting and each one was trying to talk louder than the others. Maddie and Peggy joined the group, and the laughing, and the talking.

"Hi, Peg! Hi, Maddie!" they were greeted warmly. "Look at Cecile!"

What they were all exclaiming about was the dress that Cecile had on—a crimson dress with cap and socks to match. It was a bright new dress and very pretty. Everyone was admiring it and admiring Cecile. For long, slender Cecile was a toe-dancer and wore fancier clothes than most of them. And she had her black satin bag with her precious white satin ballet slippers slung over her shoulders. Today was the day for her dancing lesson.

Maddie sat down on the granite curbstone to tie her shoelaces. She listened happily to what they were saying. They all seemed especially jolly today, probably because it was such a bright day. Everything sparkled. Way down at the end of the street the sun shimmered and turned to silver the blue water of the bay. Maddie picked up a piece of broken mirror and flashed a small circle of light edged with rainbow colors onto the houses, the trees, and the top of the telegraph pole.

And it was then that Wanda had come along with her brother Jake.

They didn't often come to school together. Jake had to get to school very early because he helped old Mr. Heany, the school janitor, with the furnace, or raking up the dry leaves, or other odd jobs before school opened. Today he must be late.

Even Wanda looked pretty in this sunshine, and her pale blue dress looked like a piece of the sky in summer; and that old gray toboggan cap she wore—it must be something Jake had found —looked almost jaunty. Maddie watched them absent-mindedly as she flashed her piece of broken mirror here and there. And only absent-mindedly she noticed Wanda stop short when they reached the crowd of laughing and shouting girls.

"Come on," Maddie heard Jake say. "I gotta hurry. I gotta get the doors open and ring the bell."

"You go the rest of the way," said Wanda. "I want to stay here."

Jake shrugged and went on up Maple Street. Wanda slowly approached the group of girls. With each step forward, before she put her foot down she seemed to hesitate for a long, long time. She approached the group as a timid animal might, ready to run if anything alarmed it.

Even so, Wanda's mouth was twisted into the vaguest suggestion of a smile. She must feel happy too because everybody must feel happy on such a day.

As Wanda joined the outside fringe of girls, Maddie stood up too and went over close to Peggy to get a good look at Cecile's new dress herself. She forgot about Wanda, and more girls kept coming up, enlarging the group and all exclaiming about Cecile's new dress.

"Isn't it lovely!" said one.

"Yeah, I have a new blue dress, but it's not as pretty as that," said another.

"My mother just bought me a plaid, one of the Stuart plaids."

"I got a new dress for dancing school."

"I'm gonna make my mother get me one just like Cecile's."

Everyone was talking to everybody else. Nobody said anything to Wanda, but there she was, a part of the crowd. The girls closed in a tighter circle around Cecile, still talking all at once and admiring her, and Wanda was somehow enveloped in the group. Nobody talked to Wanda, but nobody even thought about her being there.

Maybe, thought Maddie, remembering what had happened next, maybe she figured all she'd have to do was say something and she'd really be one of the girls. And this would be an easy

thing to do because all they were doing was talking about dresses.

Maddie was standing next to Peggy. Wanda was standing next to Peggy on the other side. All of a sudden, Wanda impulsively touched Peggy's arm and said something. Her light blue eyes were shining and she looked excited like the rest of the girls.

"What?" asked Peggy. For Wanda had spoken very softly.

Wanda hesitated a moment and then she repeated her words firmly.

"I got a hundred dresses home."

"That's what I thought you said. A hundred dresses. A hundred!" Peggy's voice raised itself higher and higher.

"Hey, kids!" she yelled. "This girl's got a hundred dresses."

Silence greeted this, and the crowd which had centered around Cecile and her new finery now centered curiously around Wanda and Peggy. The girls eyed Wanda, first incredulously, then suspiciously.

"A hundred dresses?" they said. "Nobody could have a hundred dresses."

"I have though."

"Wanda has a hundred dresses."

"Where are they then?"

"In my closet."

"Oh, you don't wear them to school."

"No. For parties."

"Oh, you mean you don't have any everyday dresses."

"Yes, I have all kinds of dresses."

"Why don't you wear them to school?"

For a moment Wanda was silent to this. Her lips drew together. Then she repeated stolidly as though it were a lesson learned in school, "A hundred of them. All lined up in my closet."

"Oh, I see," said Peggy, talking like a grownup person. "The child has a hundred dresses, but she wouldn't wear them to school. Perhaps she's worried of getting ink or chalk on them."

With this everybody fell to laughing and talking at once. Wanda looked stolidly at them, pursing her lips together, wrinkling her forehead up so that the gray toboggan slipped way down on her brow. Suddenly from down the street the school gong rang its first warning.

"Oh, come on, hurry," said Maddie, relieved. "We'll be late."

"Good-by, Wanda," said Peggy. "Your hundred dresses sound bee-you-tiful."

More shouts of laughter greeted this, and off the girls ran, laughing and talking and forgetting Wanda and her hundred dresses. Forgetting until tomorrow and the next day and the next, when Peggy, seeing her coming to school, would remember and ask her about the hundred dresses. For now Peggy seemed to think a day was lost if she had not had some fun with Wanda, winning the approving laughter of the girls.

Yes, that was the way it had all begun, the game of the hundred dresses. It all happened so suddenly and unexpectedly, with everybody falling right in, that even if you felt uncomfortable as Maddie had there wasn't anything you could do about it. Maddie wagged her head up and down. Yes, she repeated to herself, that was the way it began, that day, that bright blue day.

And she wrapped up her shavings and went to the front of the room to empty them in the teacher's basket.

The Contest

Now today, even though she and Peggy had been late to school, Maddie was glad she had not had to make fun of Wanda. She worked her arithmetic problems absent-mindedly. Eight times eight . . . let's see . . . nothing she could do about making fun of Wanda. She wished she had the nerve to write Peggy a note, because she knew she'd never have the courage to speak right out to Peggy, to say, "Hey, Peg, let's stop asking Wanda how many dresses she has."

When she finished her arithmetic, she did start a note to Peggy. Suddenly she paused and shuddered. She pictured herself in the school yard, a new target for Peggy and the girls. Peggy might ask her where she got the dress she had on, and Maddie would have to say that it was one of Peggy's old ones that Maddie's mother had tried to disguise with new trimmings so that no one in Room 13 would recognize it.

If only Peggy would decide of her own accord to stop having fun with Wanda. Oh, well! Maddie ran her hand through her short blonde hair as though to push the uncomfortable thoughts away. What difference did it make? Slowly Maddie tore the note she had started into bits. She was Peggy's best friend, and Peggy was the best-liked girl in the whole room. Peggy could not possibly do anything that was really wrong, she thought.

As for Wanda, she was just some girl who lived up on Boggins Heights and stood alone in the school yard. Nobody in the room thought about Wanda at all except when it was her turn to stand up for oral reading. Then they all hoped she would hurry up and finish and sit down, because it took her forever to read a paragraph. Sometimes she stood up and just looked at her book and couldn't, or wouldn't, read at all. The teacher tried to help her, but she'd just stand there until the teacher told her to sit down. Was she dumb or what? Maybe she was just timid. The only time she talked was in the school yard about her hundred dresses. Maddie remembered her telling about one of her dresses, a pale blue one with cerise-colored trimmings. And she remembered another that was brilliant jungle green with a red sash. "You'd look like a Christmas tree in that," the girls had said in pretended admiration.

Thinking about Wanda and her hundred dresses all lined up in the closet, Maddie began to wonder who was going to win the drawing and color contest. For girls this contest consisted of designing dresses, and for boys, of designing motor boats. Probably Peggy would win the girls' medal. Peggy drew better than anyone else in the room. At least that's what everybody thought. You should see the way she could copy a picture in a magazine or some film star's head. You could almost tell who it was. Oh, Maddie did hope Peggy would win. Hope so? She was sure Peggy would win. Well, tomorrow the teacher was going to announce the winners. Then they'd know.

Thoughts of Wanda sank further and further from Maddie's mind, and by the time the history lesson began she had forgotten all about her.

The Hundred Dresses

The next day it was drizzling. Maddie and Peggy hurried to school under Peggy's umbrella. Naturally on a day like this they didn't wait for Wanda Petronski on the corner of Oliver Street, the street that far, far away, under the railroad tracks and up the hill, led to Boggins Heights. Anyway they weren't taking chances on being late today, because today was important.

"Do you think Miss Mason will surely announce the winners today?" asked Peggy.

"Oh, I hope so, the minute we get in," said Maddie, and added, "Of course you'll win, Peg."

"Hope so," said Peggy eagerly.

The minute they entered the classroom they stopped short and gasped. There were drawings all over the room, on every ledge and window sill, tacked to the tops of the blackboards, spread over the bird charts, dazzling colors and brilliant lavish designs, all drawn on great sheets of wrapping paper.

There must have been a hundred of them all lined up!

These must be the drawings for the contest. They were! Everybody stopped and whistled or murmured admiringly.

As soon as the class had assembled Miss Mason announced the winners. Jack Beggles had won for the boys, she said, and his design of an outboard motor boat was on exhibition in Room 12, along with the sketches by all the other boys.

"As for the girls," she said, "although just one or two sketches were submitted by most, one girl —and Room 13 should be very proud of her— this one girl actually drew one hundred designs —all different and all beautiful. In the opinion of the judges, any one of her drawings is worthy of winning the prize. I am happy to say that Wanda Petronski is the winner of the girls' medal. Unfortunately Wanda has been absent from school for some days and is not here to receive the applause that is due her. Let us hope she will be back tomorrow. Now, class, you may file around the room quietly and look at her exquisite drawings."

The children burst into applause, and even the boys were glad to have a chance to stamp on the floor, put their fingers in their mouths and whistle, though they were not interested in dresses. Maddie and Peggy were among the first to reach the blackboard to look at the drawings.

"Look, Peg," whispered Maddie, "there's that blue one she told us about. Isn't it beautiful?"

"Yeah," said Peggy, "and here's that green one. Boy, and I thought I could draw!"

While the class was circling the room, the monitor from the principal's office brought Miss Mason a note. Miss Mason read it several times and studied it thoughtfully for a while. Then she clapped her hands and said, "Attention, class. Everyone back to his seat."

When the shuffling of feet had stopped and the room was still and quiet, Miss Mason said, "I have a letter from Wanda's father that I want to read to you."

Miss Mason stood there a moment and the silence in the room grew tense and expectant. The teacher adjusted her glasses slowly and deliberately. Her manner indicated that what was coming—this letter from Wanda's father—was a matter of great importance. Everybody listened closely as Miss Mason read the brief note:

"Dear teacher: My Wanda will not come to your school any more. Jake also. Now we move away to big city. No more holler Polack. No more ask why funny name. Plenty of funny names in the big city. Yours truly,

Jan Petronski."

A deep silence met the reading of this letter. Miss Mason took her glasses off, blew on them and wiped them on her soft white handkerchief. Then she put them on again and looked at the class. When she spoke her voice was very low.

"I am sure none of my boys and girls in Room 13 would purposely and deliberately hurt anyone's feelings because his name happened to be a long unfamiliar one. I prefer to think that what was said was said in thoughtlessness. I know that all of you feel the way I do, that this is a very unfortunate thing to have happen. Unfortunate and sad, both. And I want you all to think about it."

The first period was a study period. Maddie tried to prepare her lessons, but she could not put her mind on her work. She had a very sick feeling in the bottom of her stomach. True, she had not enjoyed listening to Peggy ask Wanda how many dresses she had in her closet, but she had said nothing. She had stood by silently, and that was just as bad as what Peggy had done. Worse. She was a coward. At least Peggy hadn't considered they were being mean, but she, Maddie, had thought they were doing wrong. She had thought, supposing she was the one being made fun of. She could put herself in Wanda's shoes. But she had done just as much as Peggy to make life miserable for Wanda by simply standing by and saying nothing. She had helped to make someone so unhappy that she had had to move away from town.

Goodness! Wasn't there anything she could do? If only she could tell Wanda she hadn't meant to hurt her feelings. She turned around and stole a glance at Peggy, but Peggy did not look up. She seemed to be studying hard.

Well, whether Peggy felt badly or not, she, Maddie, had to do something. She had to find Wanda Petronski. Maybe she had not yet moved away. Maybe Peggy would climb the Heights with her and they would tell Wanda she had won the contest. And that they thought she was smart and the hundred dresses were beautiful.

When school was dismissed in the afternoon, Peggy said with pretended casualness, "Hey, let's go and see if that kid has left town or not."

So Peggy had had the same idea as Maddie had had! Maddie glowed. Peggy was really all right, just as she always thought. Peg was really all right. She was o.k.

Up on Boggins Heights

The two girls hurried out of the building, up the street toward Boggins Heights, the part of town that wore such a forbidding air on this kind of a November afternoon, drizzly, damp, and dismal.

"Well, at least," said Peggy gruffly, "I never did call her a foreigner or make fun of her name. I never thought she had the sense to know we were making fun of her anyway. I thought she was too dumb. And gee, look how she can draw! And I thought I could draw."

Maddie could say nothing. All she hoped was that they would find Wanda. Just so she'd be able to tell her they were sorry they had all picked on her. And just to say how wonderful the whole school thought she was, and please not to move away and everybody would be nice. She and Peggy would fight anybody who was not nice.

Maddie fell to imagining a story in which she and Peggy assailed any bully who might be going to pick on Wanda. "Petronski—Onski!" somebody would yell, and she and Peggy would pounce on the guilty one. For a time Maddie consoled herself with these thoughts, but they soon vanished and again she felt unhappy and wished everything could be nice the way it was before any of them had made fun of Wanda.

Br-r-r! How drab and cold and cheerless it was up here on the Heights! In the summer time the woods, the sumac, and the ferns that grew along the brook on the side of the road were lush and made this a beautiful walk on Sunday afternoons. But now it did not seem beautiful. The brook had shrunk to the merest trickle, and today's drizzle sharpened the outlines of the rusty tin cans, old shoes, and forlorn remnants of a big black umbrella in the bed of the brook.

The two girls hurried on. They hoped to get to the top of the hill before dark. Otherwise they were not certain they could find Wanda's house. At last, puffing and panting, they rounded the top of the hill. The first house, that old rickety one, belonged to old man Svenson. Peggy and Maddie hurried past it almost on tiptoe. Somebody said once that old man Svenson had shot a man. Others said "Nonsense! He's an old good-for-nothing. Wouldn't hurt a flea."

But, false or true, the girls breathed more freely as they rounded the corner. It was too cold and drizzly for old man Svenson to be in his customary chair tilted against the house, chewing and spitting tobacco juice. Even his dog was nowhere in sight and had not barked at the girls from wherever he might be.

"I think that's where the Petronskis live," said Maddie, pointing to a little white house with lots of chicken coops at the side of it. Wisps of old grass stuck up here and there along the pathway like thin wet kittens. The house and its sparse little yard looked shabby but clean. It reminded Maddie of Wanda's one dress, her faded blue cotton dress, shabby but clean.

There was not a sign of life about the house except for a yellow cat, half grown, crouching on the one small step close to the front door. It leapt timidly with a small cry half way up a tree when the girls came into the yard. Peggy knocked firmly on the door, but there was no answer. She and Maddie went around to the back yard and knocked there. Still there was no answer.

"Wanda!" called Peggy. They listened sharply, but only a deep silence pressed against their eardrums. There was no doubt about it. The Petronskis were gone.

"Maybe they just went away for a little while and haven't really left with their furniture yet," suggested Maddie hopefully. Maddie was beginning to wonder how she could bear the hard fact that Wanda had actually gone and that she might never be able to make amends.

"Well," said Peggy, "let's see if the door is open."

They cautiously turned the knob of the front door. It opened easily, for it was a light thing and looked as though it furnished but frail protection against the cold winds that blew up here in the winter time. The little square room that the door opened into was empty. There was absolutely nothing left in it, and in the corner a closet with its door wide open was empty too. Maddie wondered what it had held before the Petronskis moved out. And she thought of Wanda saying, "Sure, a hundred dresses . . . all lined up in the closet."

Well, anyway, real and imaginary dresses alike were gone. The Petronskis were gone. And now how could she and Peggy tell Wanda anything? Maybe the teacher knew where she had moved to. Maybe old man Svenson knew. They might knock on his door and ask on the way down. Or the post office might know. If they wrote a letter, Wanda might get it because the post office might forward it. Feeling very downcast and discouraged, the girls closed the door and started for home. Coming down the road, way, way off in the distance, through the drizzle they could see the water of the bay, gray and cold.

"Do you suppose that was their cat and they forgot her?" asked Peggy. But the cat wasn't anywhere around now, and as the girls turned the bend they saw her crouching under the dilapidated wooden chair in front of old man Svenson's house. So perhaps the cat belonged to him. They lost their courage about knocking on his door and asking when the Petronskis had left and anyway, goodness! here was old man Svenson himself coming up the road. Everything about Svenson was yellow; his house, his cat, his trousers, his drooping mustache and tangled hair, his hound loping behind him, and the long streams of tobacco juice he expertly shot from between his scattered yellow teeth. The two girls drew over to the side of the path as they hurried by. When they were a good way past, they stopped.

"Hey, Mr. Svenson!" yelled Peggy. "When did the Petronskis move?"

Old man Svenson turned around, but said nothing. Finally he did answer, but his words were unintelligible, and the two girls turned and ran down the hill as fast as they could. Old man Svenson looked after them for a moment and

then went on up the hill, muttering to himself and scratching his head.

When they were back down on Oliver Street again, the girls stopped running. They still felt disconsolate, and Maddie wondered if she were going to be unhappy about Wanda and the hundred dresses forever. Nothing would ever seem good to her again, because just when she was about to enjoy something—like going for a hike with Peggy to look for bayberries or sliding down Barley Hill—she'd bump right smack into the thought that she had made Wanda Petronski move away.

"Well, anyway," said Peggy, "she's gone now, so what can we do? Besides, when I was asking her about all of her dresses she probably was getting good ideas for her drawings. She might not even have won the contest otherwise."

Maddie carefully turned this idea over in her head, for if there were anything in it she would not have to feel so bad. But that night she could not get to sleep. She thought about Wanda and her faded blue dress and the little house she had lived in; and old man Svenson living a few steps away. And she thought of the glowing picture those hundred dresses made—all lined up in the classroom.

At last Maddie sat up in bed and pressed her forehead tight in her hands and really thought. This was the hardest thinking she had ever done. After a long, long time she reached an important conclusion.

She was never going to stand by and say nothing again.

If she ever heard anybody picking on someone because they were funny looking or because they had strange names, she'd speak up. Even if it meant losing Peggy's friendship. She had no way of making things right with Wanda, but from now on she would never make anybody else so unhappy again. Finally, all tired out, Maddie fell asleep.

The Letter to Room 13

On Saturday Maddie spent the afternoon with Peggy. They were writing a letter to Wanda Petronski.

It was just a friendly letter telling about the contest and telling Wanda she had won. They told her how pretty her drawings were, and that now they were studying about Winfield Scott in school. And they asked her if she liked where she was living now and if she liked her new teacher. They had meant to say they were sorry, but it ended up with their just writing a friendly letter, the kind they would have written to any good friend, and they signed it with lots of X's for love.

They mailed the letter to Boggins Heights, writing "Please Forward" on the envelope. The teacher had not known where Wanda had moved to, so their only hope was that the post office knew. The minute they dropped the letter in the mail box they both felt happier and more carefree.

Days passed and there was no answer, but the letter did not come back so maybe Wanda had received it. Perhaps she was so hurt and angry she was not going to answer. You could not blame her. And Maddie remembered the way she hitched her left shoulder up as she walked off to school alone, and how the girls always said, "Why does her dress always hang funny like that, and why does she wear those queer, high, laced shoes?"

They knew she didn't have any mother, but they hadn't thought about it. They hadn't thought she had to do her own washing and ironing. She only had one dress and she must have had to wash and iron it overnight. Maybe sometimes it wasn't dry when it was time to put it on in the morning. But it was always clean.

Several weeks went by and still Wanda did not answer. Peggy had begun to forget the whole business, and Maddie put herself to sleep at night making speeches about Wanda, defending her from great crowds of girls who were trying to tease her with, "How many dresses have you got?" Before Wanda could press her lips together in a tight line the way she did before answering, Maddie would cry out, "Stop! This girl is just a girl just like you are. . . . " And then everybody would feel ashamed the way she used to feel. Sometimes she rescued Wanda from a sinking ship or the hoofs of a runaway horse. "Oh, that's all right," she'd say when Wanda thanked her with dull pained eyes.

Now it was Christmas time and there was snow on the ground. Christmas bells and a small tree decorated the classroom. And on one narrow blackboard Jack Beggles had drawn a jolly fat Santa Claus in red and white chalk. On the last day of school before the holidays, the children in Peggy's and Maddie's class had a Christmas party. The teacher's desk was rolled back and a piano rolled in. First the children had acted the story of Tiny Tim. Then they had sung songs and Cecile had done some dances in different costumes. The dance called the "Passing of Autumn" in which she whirled and spun like a red and golden autumn leaf was the favorite.

After the party the teacher said she had a surprise, and she showed the class a letter she had received that morning.

"Guess who this is from," she said. "You remember Wanda Petronski? The bright little artist who won the drawing contest? Well, she has written me and I am glad to know where she lives because now I can send her medal. And I hope it gets there for Christmas. I want to read her letter to you."

The class sat up with a sudden interest, and listened intently to Miss Mason as she read the letter.

"Dear Miss Mason: How are you and Room 13? Please tell the girls they can keep those hundred dresses because in my new house I have a hundred new ones all lined up in my closet. I'd like that girl Peggy to have the drawing of the green dress with the red trimming and her friend Maddie to have the blue one. For Christmas. I miss that school and my new teacher does not equalize with you. Merry Christmas to you and everybody. Yours truly, Wanda Petronski."

The teacher passed the letter around the room for everybody to see. It was pretty, decorated with a picture of a Christmas tree lighted up in the night in a park surrounded by high buildings.

On the way home from school Maddie and Peggy held their drawings very carefully. They had stayed late to help straighten up after the play and it was getting dark. The houses looked warm and inviting with wreaths and holly and lighted trees in their windows. Outside the grocery store hundreds of Christmas trees were stacked, and in the window candy peppermint canes and cornucopias of shiny bright transparent paper were strung. The air smelled like

Christmas and bright lights everywhere reflected different colors on the snow.

"The colors are like the colors in Wanda's hundred dresses," said Maddie.

"Yes," said Peggy, holding her drawing out to look at it under the street lamp. "And boy! This shows she really liked us. It shows she got our letter and this is her way of saying that everything's all right. And that's that," she said with finality.

Peggy felt happy and relieved. It was Christmas and everything was fine.

"I hope so," said Maddie sadly. She felt sad because she knew she would never see the little tight-lipped Polish girl again and couldn't ever really make things right between them.

She went home and she pinned her drawing over a torn place in the pink-flowered wall-paper in the bedroom. The shabby room came alive from the brilliancy of the colors. Maddie sat down on the edge of her bed and looked at the drawing. She had stood by and said nothing, but Wanda had been nice to her anyway.

Tears blurred her eyes and she gazed for a long time at the picture. Then hastily she rubbed her eyes and studied it intently. The colors in the dress were so vivid she had scarcely noticed the face and head of the drawing. But it looked like her, Maddie! It really did. The same short blonde hair, blue eyes, and wide straight mouth. Why, it really looked like her own self! Wanda had really drawn this for her. Wanda had drawn her! In excitement she ran over to Peggy's.

"Peg!" she said. "Let me see your picture."

"What's the matter?" asked Peggy as they clattered up the stairs to her room, where Wanda's drawing was lying face down on the bed. Maddie carefully lifted it up.

"Look! She drew you. That's you!" she exclaimed. And the head and face of this picture did look like the auburn-haired Peggy.

"What did I say!" said Peggy. "She must have really liked us anyway."

"Yes, she must have," agreed Maddie, and she blinked away the tears that came every time she thought of Wanda standing alone in that sunny spot in the school yard close to the wall, looking stolidly over at the group of laughing girls after she had walked off, after she had said, "Sure, a hundred of them—all lined up . . ."

HATSUNO'S GREAT-GRANDMOTHER

Florence Crannell Means

Hatsuno Noda walked alone in the crowd of girls and boys pouring out of school. She held her head so straight that her chubby black braids spatted her trim shoulders, and her step was so brisk that you would have thought she enjoyed walking by herself. Hatsuno could not bear to let anyone guess how lonesome she felt in the gay throng.

Brother Harry and six-year-old brother Teddy were deep in clumps of their schoolmates, but the girls from Hattie's class streamed by her without pausing. Behind her Patty White, whom she liked best of all, skipped along between Sue and Phyllis, giggling and talking. Hattie wondered what they were talking about. Often they were chattering about Hattie's secret dream; but today it sounded as if they were discussing the Mother's Day tea next month. This morning the teacher had appointed Patty chairman of the decorating committee.

Hattie could have helped decorate. Her slim fingers knew how to fold amazing Japanese paper birds, flowers, dolls. And at the old school the teacher would have had her do colored drawings on the blackboard, along with Tommy Lin, who was Chinese, and Consuelo, who was Mexican. The three drew better than any of the "plain Americans." But in this new school, where almost all were "plain Americans," no one knew what Hattie's fingers could do.

No, the girls were not talking about the tea.

"If you join now," Patty was saying, "you can go up to camp this summer—"

Oh, if only Patty were saying it to Hatsuno! But she wasn't. She broke off as she danced past with the others.

"Hi, Hattie!" she called, wrinkling her up-tilted nose in a smile and tossing back her thistle-down curls.

Hattie smiled a small, stiff smile, though she ached to shout "Hi!" and fall in step with Patty. Then maybe Patty would think to ask her.

"Hatsuno's Great-Grandmother" by Florence Crannell Means from *Told under the Stars and Stripes*, compiled by the Literature Committee of the Association for Childhood Education, The Macmillan Company, 1945

"Join"—"camp": those words were the keys to one of Hattie's dearest dreams.

Hatsuno had never been in the mountains. All her life she had lived where she could see them, stretching like a purple wall across the end of the dingy downtown street. They were beautiful, with snow-capped peaks shining pink and lavender and gold in the sunrise, and Hatsuno had always longed to explore them; but though they looked so near, they were miles and miles away.

The new school had given her hope. In the new school there was a Camp Fire group; and every summer it spent a few days at a camp far up in the mountains. Hattie had seen pictures of its bark-covered lodges climbing steeply among the tall evergreens beside a sparkling stream. She had heard Patty tell of the camp-fires and the horse-back rides. For Patty was a Camp Fire girl, and Patty's mother was the guardian of the group. Yet, friendly though Patty was, she never spoke of Hattie's joining. And Hattie was far too shy to bring up the subject.

In her old home she had not been so shy; but the old house had grown too small, and they had had to move to a larger one. Hattie, the first Noda baby, had been followed by five boys, and, as Harry said, each child shrunk the house a little bit more. This spring brought not only a new baby but a new grandmother, and the house was as small as Hattie's year-before-last coat. Even Mother couldn't let out its hems enough to make it do.

Mother could manage almost anything. During the depression, when Father was out of work, Mother had kept the children neat as wax and even stylish. She was always up, working, when Hattie woke in the morning, always up, mending and making over, when Hattie went to sleep at night. Mother was proud that even in the bad years Denver had few Japanese Americans "on relief": almost as few as in jail.

Even Mother could not stretch the house enough for the new baby and Great-Grandmother. So the Nodas had moved, uprooting the children from neighborhood and school. The new school was pleasant; Hattie's teacher, Miss Bender, was lovely; Patty White was the gayest, prettiest girl Hattie had ever met. But Hattie didn't fit in.

So here she was, walking home alone, with Camp Fire and the mountains as far away as ever. Teddy overtook her, making noises like a machine gun—like a railway train—like an airplane. Teddy's face was as round as a button, his eyes as black as coal, his teeth as white as rice.

"Last one home's a lame duck!" he chirped at her.

She did not hurry as once she would have done. Home was a changed place now; changed by Grandmother as well as by the new house.

Though Great-Grandmother had come from Japan ten years ago, Hattie had never seen her till this month. Great-Grandmother had lived with Aunt Kiku in San Francisco, until Aunt Kiku's death had left Grandmother alone.

She was not at all what Hattie had expected; not at all like grandmothers in books, comfortable, plump people who loved to spoil their grandchildren. No, Grandmother was not that kind.

Hattie slowly opened the door, which still quivered from Teddy's banging it. Little gray Grandmother sat stiffly erect, only her head bent toward the sock she was darning, her small feet dangling.

"How do you do, Grandmother?" said Hattie.

"How do you do, Elder Daughter?" Grandmother responded. There is no easy way to say "granddaughter" in Japanese.

Under their folded lids Grandmother's eyes traveled down Hattie. Hattie, feeling prickly, smoothed her hair, straightened her collar, twitched her checked skirt, and finally shifted her weight to one knee as Grandmother reached her feet.

"A cold day for bare legs," Grandmother observed. Hattie thought her look added, *And a great girl twelve years old should wear long stockings.*

Self-consciously Hattie's eyes pulled free from Grandmother's. "Oh," she cried, "Dicky's climbed on the piano again." She ran over and replaced the box of satiny white wood in which her latest—and last—doll always stood on view, fairly safe from the six boys. It was an enchanting doll, with glossy black hair and a silk kimono. "The other boys at least keep off the piano," Hattie scolded, "but not Dicky."

Grandmother's cool eyes seemed to say, *Boys*

have to be excused, since they're so much more important than girls. And why should a great girl of twelve care about dolls?

Hattie hurried on into the good-smelling kitchen. "Mother," she complained, "Grandmother doesn't understand that we're Americans, not Japanese. I bet she'd like me to flop down on my knees and bump my head on the floor the way you used to have to, and say, 'Honorable Grandmother, I have returned.'"

"Wash your hands," said Mother, "and help me get dinner on the table."

Hattie slapped her shoes down hard, as she went to the sink to wash. She wished her heels weren't rubber; they didn't make enough noise to express her feelings.

"Of course you will give proper courtesy to the old," Mother said quietly.

"Why? She doesn't even like me." The question was useless. Hattie had grown up knowing that politeness to the old was as much a law as honesty, industry, self-control—and minding parents.

Mother only said, "Stop and buy grapefruit on your way from school. Be sure to pick out heavy ones."

"Of course," Hattie grumbled. Hadn't she known how to choose good fruit and vegetables since she was nine?

Dinner was Japanese American. Seven Nodas —and Grandmother—crowded around an ordinary American table; but the utensils were chopsticks instead of knives and forks. The fish soup and the pickled radish were Japanese; the *pakkai* were American spareribs and the fluffy white rice was international. Bread and butter were pure American, and the dessert was Japanese gelatin, too firm to quiver. "It's not so nervous as American jelly," Harry said, and made Teddy laugh till his eyes went shut.

Only Grandmother seemed all Japanese; in the way she sipped her soup and tea, with a noise that was polite in Japan but not in America; in the way she refused bread and butter; in the way she greeted an old neighbor of the Nodas', who came in as they were finishing the meal.

Grandmother shuffled across the room, toeing in, because for sixty-five of her seventy-five years she had worn clogs; and she bowed the deep bow

of old Japan, her withered hands sliding down to her knees. Why couldn't Grandmother be more American?

The neighbor had come to remind them that tonight was the festival called Buddha's Birthday. Grandmother's eyes brightened at the news. But Mother apologized: she could not go with Grandmother, for Saburo the new baby was feverish, and she could never bear to leave her babies when they were sick. Father? He had to work tonight. Thoughtfully Grandmother looked at Hattie. Hattie excused herself and hurried back to school.

Right up to the time school opened, she kept seeing Grandmother's eyes brighten and grow dull. If Hattie had been with Patty and the others on the schoolground, as she longed to be, she might have forgotten Grandmother. But sitting lonesomely at her desk, pretending to read, she could not forget.

Maybe it was good, after all, to have a rule about being kind to old people whether they like you or not. Hattie thought of Mother, taking care of her and her brothers when they were young and helpless. How dreadful if, when Mother grew old and helpless, they did not take turn about and care for her! Hattie frowned at her book, thinking.

"Mad, Hattie? My, but you're scowling!" teased Patty, pausing as she came in from the schoolground.

Hattie shook her head and smiled. If only Patty would sit down beside her and say the thrilling words, "Oh, Hattie, wouldn't you like to join Camp Fire?" If she would even say, "Can't you come over after school?"

But after school Hattie walked home alone, as usual, stopping for the grapefruit on her way. When she had put them in the home cooler, she hunted up Grandmother, and ducked her head in a shy bow. "Grandmother," she said, "if you want to go to Buddha's Birthday tonight, I'm sure Mother will let Harry and me go with you."

The Nodas were Methodists, so the Buddhist church was strange to Hattie and Harry. Tonight it was crowded, and all through the program small children trotted in and out and climbed over people's feet, with nobody minding. There were songs and dances and pantomimes, graceful kimonos, stately poses, dignified steps; and voices in the high falsetto which was the proper tone for Japanese actors, but which gave Hattie a funny, embarrassed feeling. "Such squeaky doors!" Harry whispered comically.

Coming home by street-car and bus, the three arrived so late that the house was all sleeping. Harry bade Grandmother good-night and stumbled drowsily to his room, but Grandmother lingered, eyes bright and cheeks flushed.

Hattie hunted for something to say. "The dancing was lovely," she said. "And the kimonos."

"I have one old kimono," Grandmother said, turning toward her door. With Hattie at her heels, she opened a dresser drawer and took out a silken bundle which she unfolded and held out, smiling faintly at Hattie's gasp of admiration.

"Chrysanthemums, for your aunt's name, Kiku, Chrysanthemum," said Grandmother. Gorgeous blossoms in many rich colors grew across the heavy blue crepe. "It was the only one saved from the great San Francisco fire. She wrapped it round one of her doll boxes." Grandmother motioned toward the drawer and a white wood box that lay there.

"Could I see?" Hattie stuttered.

"You may," Grandmother answered.

When Hattie slid open the box the breath of the Orient puffed out into her nostrils. She lifted the bag that protected the doll's hair and face, and gazed at the miniature lady, exquisitely moulded, and robed in brocades, padded, corded, embroidered. Clasping the box to her breast with one hand, Hattie pulled out a chair for Grandmother. "I don't know much about the doll festival," she coaxed shyly. "Here in Denver we don't."

She curled up on the floor at Grandmother's feet. "O Kiku San brought her doll set with her," Grandmother said, "when she married and came to America. This one is more than a hundred years old. We were taught to take care of things. The girls' festival—O Hina Matsuri—was a great day. It was play, but it taught us history and manners."

Looking from the doll to Grandmother, Hattie listened with all her might. She missed some words, for the Japanese the Nodas used at home was simple, and, to Hattie's relief, there had

been no Japanese Language School for some years now. Still, she could follow the story, and it made pictures for her in the quiet night: little-girl-Grandmother wearing enchanting kimonos, in charming rooms carpeted with cushiony mats; spending long hours learning to serve tea just so, to arrange flowers just so, to paint the difficult Japanese letters just so; learning to hold her face and voice calm no matter how she felt. Girl-Grandmother, writing poems with her friends and going to view the full moon, valuing beauty above riches. Grandmother, hearing about America, and longing to go where life was free for women. Grandmother, never able to come until she was too old to fit herself into this new land.

When the parlor clock struck one, Grandmother stopped short. "A girl of twelve should be asleep!" she said severely.

Next morning Hattie wondered if she had dreamed that companionable midnight visit, for Grandmother looked coldly at Hattie's bare knees and said, "Since you must run and jump like a boy, I suppose those ugly short clothes are necessary." But even while Hattie was biting her lip uncomfortably, Grandmother added, "Hatsuno, the chrysanthemum kimono and the doll are to be yours. After all, you are our only girl."

Home was beginning to seem homelike again.

That was fortunate for Hattie, since neighborhood and school were still strange. It was a relief to go back to their old district on Sundays, to the Japanese Methodist Church. And once Mother took the older children to an evening carnival at their old school. On the way they stopped at the store where they used to buy Japanese food, dishes, cloth. Clean and bright itself, it was jammed in among grimy second-hand stores and pawn shops. It was queer, Hattie thought, but no matter how clean people were, or what good citizens, if they happened to be born Chinese or Japanese or Mexican, they were expected to live down on these dirty, crowded streets, with the trucks roaring past. Yes, the new neighborhood and school were far pleasanter than the old—if only Hatsuno could fit in.

As Mother's Day approached, Hattie felt lonelier than ever. When she came into school two days before the tea, Patty, Sue and Phyllis were huddled round the teacher's desk. Miss Bender smiled approvingly at Hattie, who was already top student in Seventh Grade. Patty smiled, too, and looked at her expectantly. Hattie's heart thumped with the wish to push herself in amongst them. But how could she? She smoothed her starched skirt under her, sat down, and pretended to clean out her desk.

"It's such a late spring," Miss Bender was saying, "the lilacs aren't out. But I'll bring sprays of cherry-blossoms. And we must find out how many mothers to expect. I hope your mother is coming, Hattie."

"No, ma'am," Hattie said soberly. "The baby has chickenpox, and Mother just won't leave a sick baby."

"Haven't you an aunt or grandmother who could come in her place?"

Oh, dear! Grandmother would be so different from the rest. What would Patty think of her? Then Hattie's head came up. "I'll ask Great-Grandmother," she said.

She thought Grandmother would refuse. She hoped Grandmother would refuse. Instead, Grandmother asked, "Every girl should have mother or grandmother at this tea?"

"Yes, Grandmother."

"And your mother will not leave the baby. Elder daughter, you went with me to Buddha's Birthday. I go with you to school."

Hattie swallowed a lump in her throat. Grandmother was doing this because she thought Hattie wished it. Tea—Grandmother would sip it in Japanese fashion. Would she notice if the girls giggled? She would hide the fact if she did. Hattie thought of Grandmother's long training in the concealment of pain or disappointment. Well, that was a good heritage for anybody. Hattie would use it now. "Thank you, Grandmother," she said. "I will come and get you Friday, after school."

When the two came into the schoolroom that afternoon, the mothers were all there and having their tea, and it seemed to Hattie that everyone stopped talking and turned to gaze. Well, she and Grandmother must look pretty funny, Hattie thought.

Hattie was dressed like the other girls, in white sweater and short white skirt, her white anklets folded neatly above her oxfords, and her black hair out of its braids and done in another favorite style of the season. Grandmother, as short and slim as Hattie, wore a dress nicely made over from a kimono, but looking a little strange; and her gray hair was combed straight back from the withered little face with its slanting eyes.

Politely Hattie introduced Miss Bender to Grandmother, and pulled up one of the visitor's chairs, since Grandmother had never been to a tea where people stood up and balanced the dishes on their hands. Patty brought her a plate, Phyllis the sandwiches, Sue a cup of tea. Then Patty returned, pulling her mother after her. "Mom," she said, "here's Hattie. And here's her great-grandma." Patty dropped her mother's hand and stood beaming.

Hattie looked anxiously at Grandmother. She could not speak a word of English, nor the others a word of Japanese. But, instead of words, Seventh Grade and its mothers were bringing sandwiches and cakes till Grandmother's plate was heaped. And Grandmother sat there, as stately and self-possessed and smiling as if she went to seven teas a week.

Hattie studied her more closely. Others might think Grandmother's little face a mask, but Hattie saw that the eyes were bright again, and that the wrinkled cheeks were pink. Grandmother liked it! Grandmother felt happy and at home!

Maybe even a great-grandmother could be lonesome, especially when she was too old to learn the ways of a new land. Thinking so happily of Grandmother that she forgot all about her own shyness, Hattie squeezed Patty's arm, just as she might have squeezed Teddy's on some rare occasion when he was sweet instead of maddening.

Patty squeezed back—quickly, as if she had been waiting for the chance. "Mother!" she stuttered, in a voice that matched her gay fluff of curls. "Mother, I think maybe I was mistaken. I think Hattie might like to—" She looked eagerly up into her mother's questioning eyes— "You ask her, Mother!" she begged.

"About Camp Fire? Hattie, would you like to join our Camp Fire group?"

Hattie was silent from pure joy and astonishment.

"If I got your name in this week," Mrs. White continued, "you could go to camp with us. A camp in the mountains; do you know about it?"

"Oh, yes, ma'am, *I know*," Hattie said with shining eyes. "Oh, yes, ma'am!"

STEPPIN'S FIRST

PUBLIC APPEARANCE

Hope Newell

This first chapter from Steppin and Family *is a good introduction to an appealing hero and a lively story. Steppin, a Harlem Negro lad, hopes to dance like Bojangles Robinson, and who wouldn't want to, once having seen that remarkable tap dancer? Unfortunately, Steppin starts out with much too good an opinion of himself. His ups and downs are mostly downs for awhile, but he does begin to climb eventually.*

To see Steppin Stebbins racing down the street one warm afternoon in June, no one would have believed that he was on his way to school. Every other school day in the whole year it had needed his mother's warning, "You'll be late," and his little sister Mary Ellis' constant scolding to get Steppin through his lunch and

From *Steppin and Family,* by Hope Newell. Copyright 1942, by Oxford University Press, Inc.

back to his desk before the tardy bell rang. But this day was different.

It was the last day of school. No more lessons, no more homework, no more scrambling out of bed in a hurry, nothing but fun for two blessed months! But it was not so much the thought of freedom to come as the great event of that very afternoon that made Steppin hurry. For he was to do a solo tap dance at the closing exercises of his class. "My first public appearance," he thought proudly as he ran down the street.

A changing traffic light on Eighth Avenue brought him to an abrupt halt. Hopping up and down on the curb, Steppin stared impatiently at the stream of automobiles, trucks and street cars roaring by. The thunder of the elevated trains overhead, the clank and clatter of street cars and honks of taxis went unnoticed. His ears were tuned to city din.

"School is out
Hear me shout,"

he crooned under his breath, while his feet beat out a tap in the same rhythm. Brush, brush, hop with his right foot, and brush brush, hop with the left foot, over and over. While he danced Steppin kept an eye on the green signal light. Was it going to stay that way all day? Wouldn't it ever turn red?

At last it changed and Steppin darted across the street like a flash and scurried down the street. Out of habit he looked up at the street clock which generally told him he was in danger of being late. But today he saw that it had taken him only five minutes to come this far. As school was only two blocks away, Steppin slowed down to a walk and stopped before his favorite window, the pawn shop.

Treasures of all kinds were heaped together in the dusty shop window; guns, tennis rackets, telescopes, banjos, roller skates and jack knives. Steppin always played a game before that window. He picked out the thing he would most like to buy if he had all the money he wanted. He usually spent a long time over that choice, weighing values carefully. But this day he paid no attention to the wonderful display. He had caught sight of his reflection in the gilt mirror that stood at the back of the show case.

He eyed himself proudly. "Boy, I sure do look

like a professional," he murmured, strutting a little and grinning broadly. His coffee-brown face, shining with the scrubbing he had given it, grinned back at him, showing all of his ivory white teeth. His hair under the tight skull cap he wore was slicked so close to his skull that it looked as if it was painted on. His big black eyes took in the navy blue coat of his Sunday suit, the stiffly starched white shirt with a little black bow tie, and the white duck trousers which his friend Charley Kee, the Chinese laundry man, had pressed for him in exchange for errands. Steppin sighed with satisfied approval.

Steppin had pored over the pictures of Negro celebrities who performed in night clubs and theatres, and this costume was the best imitation of his idols that he could manage. Except for one thing Steppin was greatly pleased with the elegant entertainer he saw reflected in the mirror. His shoes were all wrong. He had no soft flexible slippers with metal taps on their tips like a real dancer. He wore a pair of old sneakers and had stuck a cluster of thumb tacks in the tip of each sole to use for taps. They did pretty well, but Steppin was not satisfied with them.

"Oh, well, you can't have everything at once, I suppose," he consoled himself. "Anyway when I get to be a professional I'm going to have six dozen pairs of dancing shoes at a time, with solid silver taps on every single one of them. Even platinum, maybe, if I want to."

Steppin's dreams of the future carried him happily on to school. A few boys were playing ball in the playground. They called to Steppin to join them. "Not a chance," thought Steppin, not when he was about to make his first public appearance as a dancer. He must keep his clothes in order for an occasion like this. So he entered the large brick building and ran up the stairs to his class room.

Steppin hardly recognized the familiar room, it looked so festive with garlands of evergreens on the walls and bowls of flowers on the window sills. Some of the girls, who were helping the teacher, Miss Blair, decorate the room, looked festive too, in their frilly dresses of pink and blue and white, their hair gay with bows of bright ribbons. Miss Blair herself, in a blue silk dress, with her blond hair fluffed out around her face, looked young as a girl, Steppin thought.

Miss Blair's desk had been taken away, and two big jars of lilacs stood one on each side of the platform. A bright poster painted by some of the children served as a back drop. Steppin surveyed it with approval. It looked almost like a stage.

But suddenly he thought of the moment when he would have to step up there before all the boys and girls. Cold shivers went up his spine. A strange sinking feeling gripped him in the stomach. He was scared! Steppin had never thought of that.

"Oh my gosh, I've got to make good, and here I am as jumpy as a cat," he thought as he slid into his seat. His own name, Stephen A. Stebbins, seemed to jump at him from the neatly printed program on his desk. He stared at it and clenched his clammy hands under the desk.

While the other boys and girls, demure and solemn in their best clothes, took their seats, Steppin anxiously went over in his mind the dance routine he had so carefully worked out. He counted out the steps to the tune of *Marching Through Georgia* which his sister, Mary Ellis, was to play for his accompaniment. Brush, brush, hop and brush, brush, hop; and heel and toe and break. "Gee, I wish I could have a tune with some snap to it," he thought. But the few selections which Mary Ellis could play by ear on the wheezy old organ at home did not include pieces with snap.

In a daze Steppin heard Miss Blair make her little opening speech and then announce: "And now we will have the first number on our program, a recitation of Kipling's poem *If* by Martin Burns, Junior." Martin had been speaking that piece on every school program since he was in the fourth grade and never yet had he been able to get through all the "ifs" without help. Steppin had never before felt the slightest interest in his struggles, but now he found himself waiting in an agony of suspense every time Martin hesitated. When for the fourth time he began "Eff you can" and stopped, open mouthed, with imploring eyes fixed on Miss Blair, Steppin knew how he felt. Suppose I forget my dance steps! But Miss Blair, with whispered prompting, urged Martin on to the final line which he knew by heart and which he spoke in ringing triumphant tones. "AND WHAT IS MORE, YOU'LL BE A MAN, MY SON."

Steppin's place was fifth on the program. It had seemed a long way down the list, but now the time was coming, quickly, surely, when he would have to get up on the platform and dance. He saw Mary Ellis come in quietly and take a seat. She had been excused early from her class so that she might play for him. Oh, if only something had happened to keep her from coming! But there she was, smiling at him as calmly as though he were not crazy with stage fright and about to be disgraced before the whole school.

The sweet, clear notes of a cornet recalled Steppin from his miserable thoughts. That was David Harmon and he was playing the Shubert *Serenade*. David played in the school orchestra and was an old hand at public appearances. Watching him standing there so easy and calm, Steppin felt sick with envy and fright. "I would have to be billed next to him," he thought unhappily. "Oh my gosh, why didn't I practice more on cartwheels, so I could do a cartwheel, then go into a split to finish the act? I could try, maybe, but like as not I'd land on my head and a fine finale that would be."

The last soft note of the *Serenade* died away. David bowed gracefully and returned to his seat. "That was lovely, David." Miss Blair rose and beamed on him, then, still smiling, she glanced kindly at Steppin. "The next number will be a tap dance by Stephen A. Stebbins, and"——she smiled at Mary Ellis——"his little sister will play his accompaniment."

Like one in a dream Steppin found himself getting to his feet, while before him the big yellow bow on Mary Ellis' hair bobbed up as she rose and went to the piano. His knees trembled and his legs felt like cooked noodles, thought Steppin miserably, but somehow he mounted the platform and bowed gravely. This wasn't a bit the way he had dreamed it—this horrible nightmare. But there was nothing to do about it, nothing to do but dance. Mary Ellis struck the first chord. To his surprise his feet responded, although they felt like solid blocks of wood. Mechanically he went through the simple steps of his dance. In a few moments he forgot the staring boys and girls in front of him and began to dance as though his life depended on it. He thought of nothing but the rhythm and the beat of his dancing feet. He varied his few steps with

pantomime, making himself very tall, then letting his arms hang perfectly limp from his shoulders so that they flapped queerly with every step. Someone giggled. Then a chuckle swept over the room. That did it. It was all fun now. Joyously he hopped and whirled. No longer afraid, he varied his pantomime, now grinning at his audience, now looking very solemn.

He had just completed a quick whirl on one foot and was finishing with a split when he felt a stinging in the soles of his feet. Steppin knew very well what that meant. The thumbtacks were working through the soles of his shoes! Every time he hopped the pain grew worse. Brush, brush, tap; brush, brush, tap, ouch! Steppin nearly yelled out with pain. "I can't give up, the show has got to go on," he reminded himself, like an old trouper. And all the while his feet tapped and his face wore a stiff frozen smile.

Then one of the boys began clapping in time to the music. Soon others joined in, marking the beat. "Boy, they're with me. I got to go on if it kills me." Steppin flashed his white teeth in a bright agonized grin and spread out his hands in an inviting gesture to his friends. The whole room broke into clapping. Almost over now, thought Steppin. Mary Ellis was pounding out the last chorus—"Hurrah, hurrah, the flag that makes us free."

Suddenly Steppin tripped! The thumbtacks in his shoes had caught on a rough spot of the floor.

Quick as a flash, even as he stumbled, Steppin knew there was only one thing to do. He threw out his arms, and, hurling himself forward with all his might, tried to turn his fall into a cartwheel. He felt himself flying through space and in the next instant he was teetering on his feet, gasping for breath as he slid to the floor in a fast split.

In a daze he heard the loud applause and suddenly he realized that in his cartwheel he had flung himself right off the platform. A pleased grin spread from ear to ear. "Well, tie my shoes! I didn't know I had it in me."

Just then Mary Ellis, who had gone placidly on with her piece, struck the last chord with a resounding thump. Steppin scrambled to his feet, bowed politely as Miss Blair had taught him, and limped to his seat. The continued clapping was music in his ears. He looked over at Miss Blair who smiled and nodded encouragingly. Steppin rose and bowed again with a flourish, glowing with pride and happiness.

The program continued, but Steppin hardly heard or saw what was going on, though he clapped heartily for each performer. He was lost in a haze of glory and triumph. "Boy, applause sure is jam on my bread," he chuckled while he slyly removed the torturing thumbtacks from his shoes. "From now on, nothing is going to stop me. I'm going to be a first class dancer or bust."

THE DOUGHNUTS

Robert McCloskey

Homer Price *is one of the most amusing boy stories of recent years, and the doughnut episode is the favorite. Robert McCloskey won the Caldecott Award in 1942 for* Make Way for Ducklings, *and any one of his other picture-stories might well have won it—*Lentil, *choice Americana,* Blueberries for Sal *or* One Morning in Maine. *His illustrations for* Trigger John's Son *by Tom Robinson are equally delightful.*

One Friday night in November Homer overheard his mother talking on the telephone to Aunt Agnes over in Centerburg. "I'll stop by with the car in about half an hour and we can go to the meeting together," she said, because tonight was the night the Ladies' Club was meeting to discuss plans for a box social and to knit and sew for the Red Cross.

"I think I'll come along and keep Uncle Ulysses company while you and Aunt Agnes are at the meeting," said Homer.

So after Homer had combed his hair and his mother had looked to see if she had her knitting instructions and the right size needles, they started for town.

Homer's Uncle Ulysses and Aunt Agnes have a very up and coming lunch room over in Centerburg, just across from the court house on the town square. Uncle Ulysses is a man with advanced ideas and a weakness for labor saving devices. He equipped the lunch room with automatic toasters, automatic coffee maker, automatic dish washer, and an automatic doughnut maker. All just the latest thing in labor saving devices. Aunt Agnes would throw up her hands and sigh every time Uncle Ulysses bought a new labor saving device. Sometimes she became unkindly disposed toward him for days and days. She was of the opinion that Uncle Ulysses just frittered away his spare time over at the barber shop with the sheriff and the boys, so, what was the good of a labor saving device that gave you more time to fritter?

When Homer and his mother got to Centerburg they stopped at the lunch room, and after Aunt Agnes had come out and said, "My, how that boy does grow!" which was what she always said, she went off with Homer's mother in the car. Homer went into the lunch room and said, "Howdy, Uncle Ulysses!"

"Oh, hello, Homer. You're just in time," said Uncle Ulysses. "I've been going over this automatic doughnut machine, oiling the machinery and cleaning the works . . . wonderful things, these labor saving devices."

"Yep," agreed Homer, and he picked up a cloth and started polishing the metal trimmings while Uncle Ulysses tinkered with the inside workings.

"Opfwo-oof!!" sighed Uncle Ulysses and, "Look here, Homer, you've got a mechanical mind. See if you can find where these two pieces fit in. I'm going across to the barber shop for a spell, 'cause there's somethin' I've got to talk to the sheriff about. There won't be much business here until the double feature is over and I'll be back before then."

Then as Uncle Ulysses went out the door he said, "Uh, Homer, after you get the pieces in place, would you mind mixing up a batch of doughnut batter and put it in the machine? You could turn the switch and make a few doughnuts to have on hand for the crowd after the movie . . . if you don't mind."

"O.K." said Homer, "I'll take care of everything."

A few minutes later a customer came in and said, "Good evening, Bud."

Homer looked up from putting the last piece in the doughnut machine and said, "Good evening, Sir, what can I do for you?"

"Well, young feller, I'd like a cup o' coffee and some doughnuts," said the customer.

"I'm sorry, Mister, but we won't have any doughnuts for about half an hour, until I can mix some dough and start this machine. I could give you some very fine sugar rolls instead."

"Well, Bud, I'm in no real hurry so I'll just have a cup o' coffee and wait around a bit for the doughnuts. Fresh doughnuts are always worth waiting for is what I always say."

"O.K.," said Homer, and he drew a cup of coffee from Uncle Ulysses' super automatic coffee maker.

"Nice place you've got here," said the customer.

"Oh, yes," replied Homer, "this is a very up and coming lunch room with all the latest improvements."

"Yes," said the stranger, "must be a good business. I'm in business too. A traveling man in outdoor advertising. I'm a sandwich man, Mr. Gabby's my name."

"My name is Homer. I'm glad to meet you, Mr Gabby. It must be a fine profession, traveling and advertising sandwiches."

"Oh no," said Mr. Gabby, "I don't advertise sandwiches, I just wear any kind of an ad, one sign on front and one sign on behind, this way. . . . Like a sandwich. Ya know what I mean?"

"Oh, I see. That must be fun, and you travel too?" asked Homer as he got out the flour and the baking powder.

"Yeah, I ride the rods between jobs, on freight trains, ya know what I mean?"

"Yes, but isn't that dangerous?" asked Homer.

"Of course there's a certain amount a risk, but you take any method a travel these days, it's all dangerous. Ya know what I mean? Now take airplanes for instance . . ."

Just then a large shiny black car stopped in front of the lunch room and a chauffeur helped a lady out of the rear door. They both came inside and the lady smiled at Homer and said, "We've stopped for a light snack. Some doughnuts and coffee would be simply marvelous."

Then Homer said, "I'm sorry, Ma'm, but the doughnuts won't be ready until I make this batter and start Uncle Ulysses' doughnut machine."

"Well now aren't you a clever young man to know how to make *doughnuts!*"

"Well," blushed Homer, "I've really never done it before but I've got a receipt to follow."

"Now, young man, you simply must allow me to help. You know, I haven't made doughnuts for years, but I know the best receipt for doughnuts. It's marvelous, and we really must use it."

"But, Ma'm . . ." said Homer.

"Now just *wait* till you taste these doughnuts," said the lady. "Do you have an apron?" she asked, as she took off her fur coat and her rings and her jewelry and rolled up her sleeves. "Charles," she said to the chauffeur, "hand me that baking powder, that's right, and, young man, we'll need some nutmeg."

So Homer and the chauffeur stood by and handed things and cracked the eggs while the lady mixed and stirred. Mr. Gabby sat on his stool, sipped his coffee, and looked on with great interest.

"There!" said the lady when all of the ingredients were mixed. "Just *wait* till you taste these doughnuts!"

"It looks like an awful lot of batter," said Homer as he stood on a chair and poured it into the doughnut machine with the help of the chauffeur. "It's about *ten* times as much as Uncle Ulysses ever makes."

"But wait till you taste them!" said the lady with an eager look and a smile.

Homer got down from the chair and pushed a button on the machine marked, "Start." Rings of batter started dropping into the hot fat. After a ring of batter was cooked on one side an automatic gadget turned it over and the other side would cook. Then another automatic gadget gave the doughnut a little push and it rolled neatly down a little chute, all ready to eat.

"That's a simply *fascinating* machine," said the lady as she waited for the first doughnut to roll out.

"Here, young man, *you* must have the first one. Now isn't that just *too* delicious!? Isn't it simply marvelous?"

"Yes, Ma'm, it's very good," replied Homer as the lady handed doughnuts to Charles and to Mr. Gabby and asked if they didn't think they were simply divine doughnuts.

"It's an old family receipt!" said the lady with pride.

Homer poured some coffee for the lady and her chauffeur and for Mr. Gabby, and a glass of milk for himself. Then they all sat down at the lunch counter to enjoy another few doughnuts apiece.

"I'm so glad you enjoy my doughnuts," said the lady. "But now, Charles, we really must be going. If you will just take this apron, Homer, and put two dozen doughnuts in a bag to take along, we'll be on our way. And, Charles, don't forget to pay the young man." She rolled down her sleeves and put on her jewelry, then Charles managed to get her into her big fur coat.

"Good night, young man, I haven't had so much fun in years. I *really* haven't!" said the lady, as she went out the door and into the big shiny car.

"Those are sure good doughnuts," said Mr. Gabby as the car moved off.

"You bet!" said Homer. Then he and Mr. Gabby stood and watched the automatic doughnut machine make doughnuts.

After a few dozen more doughnuts had rolled down the little chute, Homer said, "I guess that's about enough doughnuts to sell to the after theater customers. I'd better turn the machine off for a while."

Homer pushed the button marked *"Stop"* and there was a little click, but nothing happened. The rings of batter kept right on dropping into the hot fat, and an automatic gadget kept right on turning them over, and another automatic gadget kept right on giving them a little push

and the doughnuts kept right on rolling down the little chute all ready to eat.

"That's funny," said Homer, "I'm sure that's the right button!" He pushed it again but the automatic doughnut maker kept right on making doughnuts.

"Well I guess I must have put one of those pieces in backwards," said Homer.

"Then it might stop if you pushed the button marked *"Start,"* said Mr. Gabby.

Homer did, and the doughnuts still kept rolling down the little chute, just as regular as a clock can tick.

"I guess we could sell a few more doughnuts," said Homer, "but I'd better telephone Uncle Ulysses over at the barber shop." Homer gave the number and while he waited for someone to answer he counted thirty-seven doughnuts roll down the little chute.

Finally someone answered, "Hello! This is the sarber bhop, I mean the barber shop."

"Oh, hello, sheriff. This is Homer. Could I speak to Uncle Ulysses?"

"Well, he's playing pinochle right now," said the sheriff. "Anythin' I can tell 'im?"

"Yes," said Homer. "I pushed the button marked *Stop* on the doughnut machine but the rings of batter keep right on dropping into the hot fat, and an automatic gadget keeps right on turning them over, and another automatic gadget keeps giving them a little push, and the doughnuts keep right on rolling down the little chute! It won't stop!"

"O.K. Wold the hire, I mean, hold the wire and I'll tell 'im." Then Homer looked over his shoulder and counted another twenty-one doughnuts roll down the little chute, all ready to eat. Then the sheriff said, "He'll be right over. . . . Just gotta finish this hand."

"That's good," said Homer. "G'by, sheriff."

The window was full of doughnuts by now so Homer and Mr. Gabby had to hustle around and start stacking them on plates and trays and lining them up on the counter.

"Sure are a lot of doughnuts!" said Homer.

"You bet!" said Mr. Gabby. "I lost count at twelve hundred and two and that was quite a while back."

People had begun to gather outside the lunch room window, and someone was saying, "There are almost as many doughnuts as there are people in Centerburg, and I wonder how in tarnation Ulysses thinks he can sell all of 'em!"

Every once in a while somebody would come inside and buy some, but while somebody bought two to eat and a dozen to take home, the machine made three dozen more.

By the time Uncle Ulysses and the sheriff arrived and pushed through the crowd, the lunch room was a calamity of doughnuts! Doughnuts in the window, doughnuts piled high on the shelves, doughnuts stacked on plates, doughnuts lined up twelve deep all along the counter, and doughnuts still rolling down the little chute, just as regular as a clock can tick.

"Hello, sheriff, hello, Uncle Ulysses, we're having a little trouble here," said Homer.

"Well, I'll be dunked!!" said Uncle Ulysses.

"Dernd ef you won't be when Aggy gits home," said the sheriff.

"Mighty fine doughnuts though. What'll you do with 'em all, Ulysses?"

Uncle Ulysses groaned and said, "What will Aggy say? We'll never sell 'em all."

Then Mr. Gabby, who hadn't said anything for a long time, stopped piling doughnuts and said, "What you need is an advertising man. Ya know what I mean? You got the doughnuts, ya gotta create a market . . . Understand? . . . It's balancing the demand with the supply . . . That sort of thing."

"Yep!" said Homer. "Mr. Gabby's right. We have to enlarge our market. He's an advertising sandwich man, so if we hire him, he can walk up and down in front of the theater and get the customers."

"You're hired, Mr. Gabby!" said Uncle Ulysses.

Then everybody pitched in to paint the signs and to get Mr. Gabby sandwiched between. They painted "SALE ON DOUGHNUTS" in big letters on the window too.

Meanwhile the rings of batter kept right on dropping into the hot fat, and an automatic gadget kept right on turning them over, and another automatic gadget kept right on giving them a little push, and the doughnuts kept right on rolling down the little chute, just as regular as a clock can tick.

"I certainly hope this advertising works," said

Uncle Ulysses, wagging his head. "Aggy'll certainly throw a fit if it don't."

The sheriff went outside to keep order, because there was quite a crowd by now—all looking at the doughnuts and guessing how many thousand there were, and watching new ones roll down the little chute, just as regular as a clock can tick. Homer and Uncle Ulysses kept stacking doughnuts. Once in a while somebody bought a few, but not very often.

Then Mr. Gabby came back and said, "Say, you know there's not much use o' me advertisin' at the theater. The show's all over, and besides almost everybody in town is out front watching that machine make doughnuts!"

"Zeus!" said Uncle Ulysses. "We must get rid of these doughnuts before Aggy gets here!"

"Looks like you will have ta hire a truck ta waul 'em ahay, I mean haul 'em away!!" said the sheriff who had just come in. Just then there was a noise and a shoving out front and the lady from the shiny black car and her chauffeur came pushing through the crowd and into the lunch room.

"Oh, gracious!" she gasped, ignoring the doughnuts, "I've lost my diamond bracelet, and I know I left it here on the counter," she said, pointing to a place where the doughnuts were piled in stacks of two dozen.

"Yes, Ma'm, I guess you forgot it when you helped make the batter," said Homer.

Then they moved all the doughnuts around and looked for the diamond bracelet, but they couldn't find it anywhere. Meanwhile the doughnuts kept rolling down the little chute, just as regular as a clock can tick.

After they had looked all around the sheriff cast a suspicious eye on Mr. Gabby, but Homer said, "He's all right, sheriff, he didn't take it. He's a friend of mine."

Then the lady said, "I'll offer a reward of one hundred dollars for that bracelet! It really *must* be found! . . . it *really* must!"

"Now don't you worry, lady," said the sheriff. "I'll get your bracelet back!"

"Zeus! This is terrible!" said Uncle Ulysses. "First all of these doughnuts and then on top of all that, a lost diamond bracelet . . ."

Mr. Gabby tried to comfort him, and he said, "There's always a bright side. That machine'll probably run outta batter in an hour or two."

If Mr. Gabby hadn't been quick on his feet Uncle Ulysses would have knocked him down, sure as fate.

Then while the lady wrung her hands and said, "We must find it, we *must!*" and Uncle Ulysses was moaning about what Aunt Agnes would say, and the sheriff was eyeing Mr. Gabby, Homer sat down and thought hard.

Before twenty more doughnuts could roll down the little chute he shouted, "SAY! I know where the bracelet is! It was lying here on the counter and got mixed up in the batter by mistake! The bracelet is cooked inside one of these doughnuts!"

"Why . . . I really believe you're right," said the lady through her tears. "Isn't that *amazing?* Simply *amazing!*"

"I'll be durn'd!" said the sheriff.

"OhH-h!" moaned Uncle Ulysses. "Now we have to break up all of these doughnuts to find it. Think of the *pieces!* Think of the *crumbs!* Think of what *Aggy* will say!"

"Nope," said Homer. "We won't have to break them up. I've got a plan."

So Homer and the advertising man took some cardboard and some paint and printed another sign. They put this sign

FRESH DOUGHNUTS
2 for 5¢
WHILE THEY LAST
$100.00 PRIZE
FOR FINDING
A BRACELET
INSIDE A DOUGHNUT
P.S. You have to give the
bracelet back

in the window, and the sandwich man wore two more signs that said the same thing and walked around in the crowd out front.

Then . . . The doughnuts began to sell! *Everybody* wanted to buy doughnuts, *dozens* of doughnuts!

And that's not all. Everybody bought coffee to dunk the doughnuts in too. Those that didn't buy coffee bought milk or soda. It kept Homer and the lady and the chauffeur and Uncle Ulysses and the sheriff busy waiting on the people who wanted to buy doughnuts.

When all but the last couple of hundred doughnuts had been sold, Rupert Black shouted, "I GAWT IT!!" and sure enough . . . there was the diamond bracelet inside of his doughnut!

Then Rupert went home with a hundred dollars, the citizens of Centerburg went home full of doughnuts, the lady and her chauffeur drove off with the diamond bracelet, and Homer went home with his mother when she stopped by with Aunt Aggy.

As Homer went out of the door he heard Mr. Gabby say, "Neatest trick of merchandising I ever seen," and Aunt Aggy was looking sceptical while Uncle Ulysses was saying, "The rings of batter kept right on dropping into the hot fat, and the automatic gadget kept right on turning them over, and the other automatic gadget kept right on giving them a little push, and the doughnuts kept right on rolling down the little chute just as regular as a clock can tick—they just kept right on a comin', an' a comin', an' a comin', an' a comin'."

THE GLORIOUS WHITEWASHER

Mark Twain

This is one of the most famous scenes in American literature, and should lead children to the book.

Saturday morning was come, and all the summer world was bright and fresh, and brimming with life. There was a song in every heart; and if the heart was young the music issued at the lips. There was cheer in every face and a spring in every step. The locust trees were in bloom and the fragrance of the blossoms filled the air. Cardiff Hill, beyond the village and above it, was green with vegetation, and it lay just far enough away to seem a Delectable Land, dreamy, reposeful, and inviting.

Tom appeared on the sidewalk with a bucket of whitewash and a long-handled brush. He surveyed the fence, and all gladness left him and a deep melancholy settled down upon his spirit. Thirty yards of board fence nine feet high. Life

"The Glorious Whitewasher." From *The Adventures of Tom Sawyer* by Mark Twain (pseud. for Samuel L Clemens), 1876

to him seemed hollow, and existence but a burden. Sighing he dipped his brush and passed it along the topmost plank; repeated the operation, did it again; compared the insignificant whitewashed streak with the far-reaching continent of unwhitewashed fence, and sat down on a tree-box discouraged. Jim came skipping out at the gate with a tin pail, and singing "Buffalo Gals." Bringing water from the town pump had always been hateful work in Tom's eyes, before, but now it did not strike him so. He remembered that there was company at the pump. White, mulatto, and negro boys and girls were always there waiting their turns, resting, trading playthings, quarreling, fighting, skylarking. And he remembered that although the pump was only a hundred and fifty yards off, Jim never got back with a bucket of water under an hour—and even then somebody generally had to go after him. Tom said:

"Say, Jim, I'll fetch the water if you'll whitewash some."

Jim shook his head and said:

"Can't, Mars Tom. Ole missis, she tole me I got to go an' git dis water an' not stop foolin' roun' wid anybody. She say she spec' Mars Tom gwine to ax me to whitewash, an' so she tole me go 'long an' 'tend to my own business—she 'lowed she'd 'tend to de whitewashin'."

"Oh, never you mind what she said, Jim. That's the way she always talks. Gimme the bucket—I won't be gone only a minute. *She* won't ever know."

"Oh, I dasn't, Mars Tom. Ole missis she'd take an' tar de head off'n me. 'Deed she would."

"*She!* She never licks anybody—whacks 'em over the head with her thimble—and who cares for that, I'd like to know. She talks awful, but talk don't hurt—anyways it don't if she don't cry. Jim, I'll give you a marvel. I'll give you a white alley!"

Jim began to waver.

"White alley, Jim! And it's a bully taw."

"My! Dat's a mighty gay marvel, *I* tell you! But Mars Tom, I's powerful 'fraid ole missis ——"

"And besides, if you will I'll show you my sore toe."

Jim was only human—this attraction was too much for him. He put down his pail, took the white alley, and bent over the toe with absorbing interest while the bandage was being unwound. In another moment he was flying down the street with his pail and a tingling rear, Tom was whitewashing with vigor, and Aunt Polly was retiring from the field with a slipper in her hand and triumph in her eye.

But Tom's energy did not last. He began to think of the fun he had planned for this day, and his sorrows multiplied. Soon the free boys would come tripping along on all sorts of delicious expeditions, and they would make a world of fun of him for having to work—the very thought of it burnt him like fire. He got out his worldly wealth and examined it—bits of toys, marbles, and trash; enough to buy an exchange of *work,* maybe, but not half enough to buy so much as half an hour of pure freedom. So he returned his straitened means to his pocket, and gave up the idea of trying to buy the boys. At this dark and hopeless moment an inspiration burst upon him! Nothing less than a great, magnificent inspiration.

He took up his brush and went tranquilly to work. Ben Rogers hove in sight presently—the very boy, of all boys, whose ridicule he had been dreading. Ben's gait was the hop-skip-and-jump —proof enough that his heart was light and his anticipations high. He was eating an apple, and giving a long, melodious whoop, at intervals, followed by a deep-toned ding-dong-dong, ding-dong-dong, for he was personating a steamboat. As he drew near, he slackened speed, took the middle of the street, leaned far over to starboard and rounded to ponderously and with laborious pomp and circumstance—for he was personating the *Big Missouri,* and considered himself to be drawing nine feet of water. He was boat and captain and engine-bells combined, so he had to imagine himself standing on his own hurricane-deck giving the orders and executing them:

"Stop her, sir! Ting-a-ling-ling!" The headway ran almost out and he drew up slowly toward the sidewalk.

"Ship up to back! Ting-a-ling-ling!" His arms straightened and stiffened down his sides.

"Set her back on the stabboard! Ting-a-ling-ling! Chow! ch-chow-wow! Chow!" His right hand, meantime, describing stately circles—for it was representing a forty-foot wheel.

"Let her go back on the labboard! Ting-a-ling-ling! Chow-ch-chow-chow!" The left hand began to describe circles.

"Stop the stabboard! Ting-a-ling-ling! Stop the labboard! Come ahead on the stabboard! Stop her! Let your outside turn over slow! Ting-a-ling-ling! Chow-ow-ow! Get out that head-line! *Lively* now! Come—out with your spring-line—what're you about there! Take a turn round that stump with the bight of it! Stand by that stage, now—let her go! Done with the engines, sir! Ting-a-ling-ling! *Sh't! s'h't! sh't!*" (trying the gaugecocks).

Tom went on whitewashing—paid no attention to the steamboat. Ben stared a moment and then said:

"Hi-*yi! You're* up a stump, ain't you!"

No answer. Tom surveyed his last touch with the eye of an artist, then he gave his brush another gentle sweep and surveyed the result, as before. Ben ranged up alongside of him. Tom's mouth watered for the apple, but he stuck to his work. Ben said:

"Hello, old chap, you got to work, hey?"

Tom wheeled suddenly and said:

"Why, it's you, Ben! I warn't noticing."

"Say—*I'm* going in a-swimming, *I* am. Don't you wish you could? But of course you'd druther *work*—wouldn't you? Course you would!"

Tom contemplated the boy a bit, and said:

"What do you call work?"

"Why, ain't *that* work?"

Tom resumed his whitewashing, and answered carelessly:

"Well, maybe it is, and maybe it ain't. All I know is, it suits Tom Sawyer."

"Oh come, now, you don't mean to let on that you *like* it?"

The brush continued to move.

"Like it? Well, I don't see why I oughtn't to like it. Does a boy get a chance to whitewash a fence every day?"

That put the thing in a new light. Ben stopped nibbling his apple. Tom swept his brush daintily back and forth—stepped back to note the effect—added a touch here and there—criticized the effect again—Ben watching every move and getting more and more interested, more and more absorbed. Presently he said:

"Say, Tom, let *me* whitewash a little."

Tom considered, was about to consent; but he altered his mind:

"No—no—I reckon it wouldn't hardly do, Ben. You see, Aunt Polly's awful particular about this fence—right here on the street, you know—but if it was the back fence I wouldn't mind and *she* wouldn't. Yes, she's awful particular about this fence; it's got to be done very careful; I reckon there ain't one boy in a thousand, maybe two thousand, that can do it the way it's got to be done."

"No—is that so? Oh come, now—lemme just try. Only just a little—I'd let *you,* if you was me, Tom."

"Ben, I'd like to, honest injun; but Aunt Polly—well, Jim wanted to do it, but she wouldn't let him; Sid wanted to do it, and she wouldn't let Sid. Now don't you see how I'm fixed? If you was to tackle this fence and anything was to happen to it——"

"Oh, shucks, I'll be just as careful. Now lemme try. Say—I'll give you the core of my apple."

"Well, here—No, Ben, now don't. I'm afeard——"

"I'll give you *all* of it!"

Tom gave up the brush with reluctance in his face, but alacrity in his heart. And while the late steamer *Big Missouri* worked and sweated in the sun, the retired artist sat on a barrel in the shade close by, dangled his legs, munched his apple, and planned the slaughter of more innocents. There was no lack of material; boys happened along every little while; they came to jeer, but remained to whitewash. By the time Ben was fagged out, Tom had traded the next chance to Billy Fisher for a kite, in good repair; and when *he* played out, Johnny Miller bought in for a dead rat and a string to swing it with—and so on, and so on, hour after hour. And when the middle of the afternoon came, from being a poor poverty-stricken boy in the morning, Tom was literally rolling in wealth. He had beside the things before mentioned, twelve marbles, part of a jews'-harp, a piece of blue bottle-glass to look through, a spool cannon, a key that wouldn't unlock anything, a fragment of chalk, a glass stopper of a decanter, a tin soldier, a couple of tadpoles, six firecrackers, a kitten with only one eye, a brass door-knob, a dog-collar—but no dog—the handle of a knife, four pieces of orange-peel, and a dilapidated old window-sash.

He had had a nice, good, idle time all the while—plenty of company—and the fence had three coats of whitewash on it! If he hadn't run out of whitewash, he would have bankrupted every boy in the village.

Tom said to himself that it was not such a hollow world, after all. He had discovered a great law of human action, without knowing it—namely, that in order to make a man or a boy covet a thing, it is only necessary to make the thing difficult to attain. If he had been a great and wise philosopher, like the writer of this book, he would now have comprehended that Work consists of whatever a body is *obliged* to do, and that Play consists of whatever a body is not obliged to do. And this would help him to understand why constructing artificial flowers or performing on a treadmill is work, while rolling tenpins or climbing Mont Blanc is only amusement. There are wealthy gentlemen in England who drive four-horse passenger-coaches twenty or thirty miles on a daily line, in the summer, because the privilege costs them considerable money; but if they were offered wages for the service, that would turn it into work and then they would resign.

The boy mused awhile over the substantial change which had taken place in his wordly circumstances, and then wended toward headquarters to report.

from TRAIL OF THE LITTLE PAIUTE

Mabel O'Moran

After white settlers invaded the arid hunting grounds of the Paiute Indians, there was often insufficient food, and it was necessary to enforce the tribal law that in time of famine the old and helpless must leave the camp and walk away into the wilderness and certain death. When Inyo discovers that his grandmother is the first one to be sent away, the boy rebels at the law and determines to lead her across the desert to California. Trail of the Little Paiute is an authentic account of the Paiute's last stand against the white men.

The Talk Is Good

The winter of 1859 was going to be an early winter in the Waucobi. The Waucobi is a high mountain valley wedged in between the Sierra Nevada on the west and the Panamints on the east, and for thousands of years it has been the home of not only the Paiute Indians but also the home of the grizzly bear, the Bighorn sheep, and the fleet-footed deer.

Now an early winter in the Waucobi is a long and hungry winter. And all the signs were out. The wild geese were wedging south, the rabbits and the squirrels were thickening their fur, and the ants were getting frantic with haste.

Man and beast, bird and reptile, those who walk upright on two legs and those who skim along the ground on their bellies, each could read in his own way the warning to get under cover, to gather in food and lay it up for that time when there would be none to gather, or else go into the long sleep which lasts until spring, like the grizzly bear and the wise old rattlesnake.

But the Indian must shiver out the winter in his own wickiup. Well for him that he get busy while the piñon nuts are ripe, and the deer fat and juicy. There are the agave worms to dry, the taboose to dig. Food must be stored and quickly. Winter is coming on.

Inyo, the little Paiute boy, broke away from the slow steadiness of the tribe beginning the long climb to the dark upsweep of the piñon forests. He noticed that the pack baskets of the women were deeper and wider this year, that the men carried a double load of arrows. It was because they had all read the signs. And this year, having nine winters behind him, Inyo too carried arrows. His grandmother had made them for him.

She saw he was now big enough for the hunting, and today he had arrows and was wearing a breechclout. His grandmother had made them for him. His grandmother, who had once been a Chumash woman, was smart, smarter than the other squaws. Doomdah, the woman from Far Away.

When he had left the tribe well behind him, when he could no longer hear them or see them,

Inyo sprang to a ledge jutting out over a cliff, and looked back on Lake Waucobi. He could see the flash of the morning sunshine on it, and he took a long, long look.

He felt the points of his arrows; one after another he touched them. Doomdah had made the points of obsidian, just like the arrows the braves had. These were big game arrows, and as such he would use them. Let the women and the girl children gather the piñon nuts, but he would be trailing the horizons. He would be up with the winds, he would be edging along the clouds. He would track down the Bighorn sheep that jumps over glaciers and balances on ice peaks.

Inyo's blood raced at the thought of it, and standing there on the outjutting rock he put his thought into song:

> "You are quick, Bighorn sheep,
> You touch crag after crag
> Like Paiute brave dancing.
> I will aim for big throat
> With obsidian point arrow.
> I will watch you fall
> With arrow in throat.
>
> When the wind whips ice
> On Paiute tepee
> Your coat will feel warm
> To little papooses,
> To the squaw and the brave
> Your coat will feel warm.
>
> When the snow is white feathers
> To world turned black,
> Then your full-flavored meat
> Will taste good to the tribes
> In the hungry tepees.
>
> I come, Bighorn sheep,
> I come with my arrows."

He left the ledge and went back to the softer ground. Here he looked for the tracks of the big brown bear in the pine needles. The big brown bear, heavy with weight, slow with the load of fat that must carry him through the winter, dim of eye and dull of thought, the big brown bear lumbering toward the caves for his long winter sleep.

Inyo, not being fat with the summer feeding; Inyo, with light feet and many arrows, would jump into his path and shoot him in the mouth; would send the arrow straight through to his brain. That was why his grandmother had made him the arrows—to shoot the Bighorn sheep, to bring her the paws of the grizzly for her pot basket, to fill up her tepee with hides and horns and hoofs, and maybe the feathers from a golden eagle. If he saw an eagle.

He came to a patch of warm sunshine, and stretching out on his back he stared up into the deeps of the blue September sky for sight of an eagle. But although he waited and waited he saw none. He saw the black crows who go by pairs the whole year round, he watched the rising and falling of robins, of orioles, of larks, he heard the loud and hearty laugh of the woodpecker rapping at the trees. But nowhere at all did he see an eagle.

When the sun had left the warm patch of pine needles he got up and drank from a near-by spring. Then he crept along on hands and knees to read sign on which and how many of his animal brothers had passed that way and when. And all he could find was the wriggly line where a snake had crossed the trail.

A big snake—a rattlesnake. Should he track it? No, let the snake go. Because smart as it is in knowing how to grow together again if cut in two, and how to make a new skin when it wants one, and also many other things that the Indian has not yet learned, it isn't smart enough to get away from a squaw with a stick in her hand. If she is quick—and of course she had better be quick—she can lean over and break its neck with a short, heavy stick. So he'd not waste time on a rattler. Let the squaws do that.

Seeing no other sign on the trail, the little Paiute took another drink and went back to the ledge. Here he could again look down on the valley below. He could see it as the eagle sees it—a land checkered with meadows and clear, cold streams. Lake Waucobi was blue now, blue and far away. Blue as turquoise, and far away as the sky.

The Paiute land. A land of mountains and meadows, of streams and lakes, of towering black trees looking down on tawny desert, of hot springs and cold springs, and far off in the desert, poison springs. The land that had nourished and clothed and sheltered his race since the beginning of time.

It was like looking at part of himself, and it filled him with a happiness that was primitive and simple and satisfying. For the moment the meaning of his own name took on a deep significance—Inyo, the dwelling place of a great spirit.

Moving from dream to dream as clouds form and reform in a summer sky Inyo suddenly realized that the shadows had got long and the mountains were turning cold. He was still far below the trails of the Bighorn sheep. He listened for the soft pad on the pine needles of hoof or paw. But the antelope and the deer had not yet come out of hiding, and the bear must have seen him first.

Then he saw the spirals of smoke drifting up from the woodlands below him, and his hand fell slowly away from his arrows. The smoke was sign that the campfires had been lighted. The boys down there would be running and jumping, the girls on rope swings hung from the branches—ropes made from the strong fibers of the Joshua tree that grows down where the valley borders the desert.

There would be much laughing and singing. The hunters would be showing the game they had brought in, and the squaws would be proud over their full baskets. The porcupines and the rabbits that the hunters had shot would be sizzling over the fires, and the grass nuts roasting in hot ashes. Doomdah's tepee would be already set up and bedded down in soft fir plumes and dried grasses—warm, sweet-smelling grasses. Her basket would be overflowing with big piñon nuts, her fire burning, and the hot stones ready for the pot basket.

The little Paiute shivered. The wind was beginning to whoosh through the treetops. It was time to go, and with a glance back at the heights he had never reached he named the place "Not Shoot Arrows," and broke into a short steady trot down the trail.

Inyo edged into the camp as if he had never been away. His head was downcast, his heart shamed. He had hunted and come back empty handed. But nobody seemed to notice it. Only Doomdah would notice it, Doomdah who had made him the bow and arrows. What would she say to him, what would she ask him: "Where is the game? I have gathered the piñon nuts alone, I have set up the tepee. I have broke off the fir plumes for our beds, and pulled the wild grasses with my own hands. Where is the game?"

Then he would tell her about tomorrow, how tomorrow he would be shooting what he hadn't shot today. Tomorrow the bear would be slower, tomorrow the deer would be less wary, tomorrow the eagle would be flying low. Doomdah would understand. He must find Doomdah and tell her about tomorrow.

But he couldn't see her anywhere. He went from fire to fire looking for his grandmother. If he could have asked: "Where is Doomdah?" someone might have told him. But while one has eyes it is for his eyes to seek out the answers. And his eyes saw everything but his grandmother. They saw the braves making big talk about their hunting, the squaws bending over the fires and cooking, the girls on swings under the trees, and the boys running foot races. And all he wanted to see was Doomdah.

Then he noticed that as he came to each fire the talking there stopped, and those who turned to smile at him—the kindly squaws and the braves who had brought in the meat—smiled without words. Smiles of compassion and comfort. But no words. Some of the squaws made a place for him by the fire. He just looked, and passed on. Where was Doomdah?

When he had gone by all the fires, and when he saw she was at none of them, he looked in all the tepees. And wherever he looked and wherever he stopped there came a hush as if it were something he had brought with him. Finally he went back to one of the first fires and sat down on the outermost edge of those who were sitting there. A squaw brought him food to eat, and he ate it.

When the eating was over the fires were allowed to die down—all except one. More wood was thrown on this one, but not too much, for if a fire is too large the heat and the smoke will drive you back into the cold again.

The Indians had gathered around this special fire. Now was the time for the Chief to speak, and brave after brave settled back on his haunches, and squaw after squaw hushed child and papoose, while all prepared to listen to what would be said—tales of that time when the Paiute heroes walked the earth, stories of those happy days when the desert was all meadows and forests, full of fruits and game.

Inyo had heard all this before, as had the other Indians. Year following year they had heard it, but still they listened. The glow from the pine logs etched each passive copper face against the black night, the occasional cry of a child was quickly stifled, the inattention of the young was corrected with a slight shove.

There was no argument. The talk came from the man who knew. He was never interrupted nor was he asked to prove his statements, but was listened to with a nod here and a smile there, and because what he said set the pattern of life for the Paiute, and because it was full of the wonder and the grandeur and the greatness of the race, the Indian could sit there and listen to it forever.

All except Inyo. He did not want ancestral heroes tonight. He wanted Doomdah. His thoughts went farther and farther away from the speaker, and closer and closer to his grandmother. Where was she? If there was no tepee where would she sleep tonight?

Inyo could not remember ever having had the care of either father or mother. Both had died back in those days when the white man's sickness, cholera, had touched the tribe. Since then it had been Doomdah's love that stood between him and the little griefs of his life. Now it was only Doomdah's stories that held interest for him. For Doomdah was a Chumash, and had come from Far Away, where the Chiefs were called Padres, where there were strange fruits and flowers, where there were sheep who ate from your hand, and cattle—

The little Paiute felt a heavy hand on his shoulder that unbalanced him and sent him sprawling over into the ashes. He looked up into the face of Hard Hoof, the Medicine Man, with the firelight shining back from his deep-set eyes.

"The talk is good," said Hard Hoof.

Inyo wiped the ashes out of his eyes with the back of his hand, and wondered how Hard Hoof had known he wasn't listening. He tried to forget about Doomdah and think only of Hy-nan-u, the ancestor that the speaker was now talking about. Hy-nan-u who was everybody's ancestor, who had taught the Paiute to be happy by going about doing good.

But how could Inyo be happy without Doomdah? From the time he had learned the difference between words and signs he had listened more to Doomdah than to anybody else. And there was more than Paiute words to her talk. She spoke words she had learned from the Padres, and she taught those words to him—Mission words. But this kind of talk was always a secret between them, and only when they were alone did they speak them, these strange, soft words of the Far Away.

Again Hard Hoof's heavy hand brought Inyo's thoughts back to the campfire.

"The talk is good," warned Hard Hoof.

Seeing that it was going to be more comfortable if he listened to what the speaker was saying, Inyo leaned well forward and stared at Chief Jobouri. He was the finest looking of a race of free-living men, straight and of good height, and neither young nor old. The firelight flickered over his headband of yellow quills, and when he waved his arms his skin shone like polished bronze, and his eyes flashed black fire.

"The Paiute never grows old," said Chief Jobouri.

There were nods of assent, and almost without his seeing them there were many quick glances shot at Inyo. The Chief was not looking at him, but most of the other Indians were, and those who weren't seemed to want to be looking.

The Waucobi land stretched from mountain to mountain, from desert to desert, pointed out the Chief. It was a beautiful land, but it was not a big land.

"This home of ours is a good home." The deep, rich voice was like music to those who listened. "The Waucobi gives generously to the Paiute. She gives us food and shelter, the red joy of the hunt and the pale peace of the tepee. But the Waucobi has a law, and only as we keep that law does she give these things to us." He waited for the hushing of a baby's cry before he went on.

"Everything changes—day is ever becoming night, summer keeps birthing into winter, sleep nourishes our activity. But the law itself never changes. As fire is dry and water is wet the law is absolute." He looked into the faces around him.

The braves nodded and the squaws nodded. They knew what he was going to say, but they could hear it again and again because it was the truth. Jobouri extended his arms to the great piñon trees and the stars shining through them.

"It was the law a thousand years ago, it is the law today—there shall not be a hundred deer in a meadow meant for fifty."

There was a moment's silence. A little sigh went through the camp like the light sweep of air in the branches above. The fire crackled, the baby again cried, and far off in the distance came the mournful hoot of an owl. Everybody was now looking at Inyo, Chief Jobouri as well as the others, and nobody tried to pretend that he wasn't looking.

"The earth will nourish just so many," said the Chief. "When there is too much asked of it, the earth dies. Where there are too many people some must go.

"The Paiute knows this. He lives out his full measure of years, and then he goes. He goes like the great Chief Puma did, Puma who walked away to die that he should not live too long. And squaws, when they age, walk away too."

Inyo jumped to his feet, his bow still slung on his shoulder, his ten arrows still in the quiver. And this time Hard Hoof did not molest him. Now only the little Paiute and the Chief were standing. Each took a long look at the other, and there was no talk. No talk from the hunters, no talk from the squaws, no talk from Hard Hoof, the Medicine Man.

Then Inyo turned swiftly. For he knew what the others had forgotten—Doomdah was Chumash, not Paiute. He stepped back into the darkness, and left the tribe looking after him. He must find Doomdah before she walked too far. Doomdah was Chumash, and the Chumash do not walk away to die.

Lake Waucobi

It was a dark night. Although the stars were shining above the trees they were all so far away that they were able to withhold their light from the earth. There was no way for Inyo to tell where he was going except by looking back at the campfire and judging from that. A few steps, a look back, a few more steps. And each time he

looked it got smaller and smaller. Then the trees began to get between him and the fire, and finally there was nothing at all there—no fire and no trees.

The voices too faded out, and new sounds began to beat through the black night, and while he knew what each was, he had to remind himself that the wind in the trees was nothing more than just wind, that the coyote has always howled at the stars and always will. When his hand touched a rotten twig and it broke off he thought it was something alive, and he struck out at it. His hand bruised against the tree, and he felt the warm blood gush out.

As he got farther and farther down the trail the stealth of movement around him increased, noises became more distinct and more frequent. There was the bloodcurdling shriek of a lynx, the yowl of a wolf. For the moment he forgot they were just animals like himself, eating from the earth and drinking its waters, because he knew they could be U-nu-pits too. The snarls of the panther were right behind him now, the hoots of an owl, remote and melancholy, were answered by the growls of a grizzly. And when the clouds came over the sky and the friendly stars were gone, then he indeed was alone.

However, there was no turning back. The things that were here were all around him. They were as much in back of him as in front of him.

Inyo was still on the mountainside when daylight grayed over the world. He was scratched, muddy, and bleeding, he had bumps on his head and bruises on his body, and for all that he had come as fast as he could, it had taken him a whole night to cover the distance that the tribe had climbed up in a few hours.

He jumped into the nearest pool to wash off his stains, to clear his eyes, and to start his blood racing again. Then, with his bow slung jauntily from his shoulder, and his ten arrows all safe and intact, he climbed out onto a ledge to see how much farther he had to go, or for that matter, where to go.

Where to find Doomdah. Doomdah wouldn't want to die, he was sure of that. Doomdah, who had once been a Chumash woman, would have to be Chumash again. And to be Chumash, and not Paiute, she must go back to Far Away, to that land she had often told him about where there were sheep and horses and bells and prayers and Padres.

With the rising sun touching their uppermost branches the trees were all bright and friendly again, the birds were singing, the ants beginning to swing into action. Below him, and some miles away, was the wide sweep of Lake Waucobi. It lay softly misted in the chill of the early morning, and on its near shore he caught a pinprick of light. He stared at it intently. That would be somebody's campfire, someone who had not slept, someone who was waiting—for what?

Then his heart beat faster. That would be Doomdah's fire, and she would be waiting for him.

He had not gone far before a new thought troubled him—could that fire belong to pale-faces, those strange men with colorless eyes and black beards who had been seen crossing the Paiute land when the moon was young?

What was he going to see, what was he going to hear?

The seeing came first, and it was all that he wanted to see—a solitary Indian woman standing by a small fire. This could be no one but

Doomdah herself. His fears fell from him as a bird plummets down, and he ran forward.

She did not see him, and because she was singing he stopped before he reached her. One does not interrupt song. He saw that she was dressed in her feast clothes—soft doeskin trousers covered with a tunic made of birdskins and trimmed with the small white shells that at times are brought in from the distant shores of the Big Water.

Beside the fire was a pack basket and a water basket. Inyo, full of hunger, nodded with joy. The pack basket would hold a pot basket full of food, the water basket would have sweet water in it.

He was now close enough to see her face. If she had come to the lake to make a swift end of her life, if walking away from the tribe meant walking into the water—but no, she did not look like things that are about to die. He thought of the glazed, imploring eyes of the deer with the hunter's knife at its throat, of the frenzied eyes of the rabbit snarled up in the rabbit net, of the sad little eyes of the woodrat with the arrow in its vitals.

But Doomdah's eyes were wide and bright, and were fixed on the lake as if she were looking at something very wonderful to see. The pack basket had not been touched. She had forgotten to eat, forgotten to drink, and her whole soul was in her song:

"Tomorrow I am the high mountain,
Tomorrow I am the white cloud.
Wolf in the dark night,
Do not touch me.
What can you do to me?
Tomorrow I am the white cloud.

Tomorrow I am the great rocks,
Tomorrow I am the clear starshine.
Panther in the piñon tree,
Do not touch me.
What can you do to me?
Tomorrow I am the clear starshine.

Tomorrow I am the south wind—"

Inyo could endure no more. He made a rush at her, and his arms went around her neck and half strangled her. "No, no," he cried. "Tomorrow you are Doomdah."

Except for the strength in her firm, straight legs the impact would have knocked her over. She unlocked his hands from her neck and set him on his feet. All the light was gone from her face, the unfinished song sank back in her throat.

"This is not place for you," she said sternly. "Return to tribe."

"Where you are that is place for me," answered the boy. "What you do now is for only Paiute to do. Not for you. You are not Paiute, you are Chumash."

Doomdah breathed like one coming in from a hard race. "That is true," she said slowly. "I am Chumash."

"What is right for Paiute is not right for Chumash."

"That is truth too," she admitted. The wisdom of his few years brought a warm light into her eyes.

"Tell me where is trail to Far Away, and I take you back to Chumash."

"You? You, my little bear's cub?" For a minute or two she looked out at the immensity of Lake Waucobi. The mist was gone and the blue water sparkled under the rising sun. Then she turned her back to the lake, and a great peace flooded over her face. "Let be. A Paiute brave who was big brought me from Far Away, a Paiute brave who is little takes me back again. Today I am Chumash, tomorrow I am still Chumash. Life is good, life is good. Come, we eat now."

There were piñon nuts in the basket, and little cakes made of seed and sweetened honey. There was a big roasted rabbit, and some agave worms crisped in porcupine fat. There was also a small jar of cactus wine. A full pack basket was the tribe's gesture of the last farewell.

Inyo kept his eyes watchfully on his grandmother that he might not lose her again, and found her pleasant to look on. Doomdah, unlike the Paiute squaws, had held to her youth. The Paiute girl is bright and happy until she marries. Then the many labors of camp and trail cut deep wrinkles into her face, and the overloaded pack basket curves her back down toward the earth.

But Doomdah's eyes were large and clear, her brown face smooth, her teeth strong and white, and lithe grace was still in her body. It was her Chumash heritage. Unlike the Paiute, the Chumash had been a well-fed, joyous race living on the rich lands around Santa Barbara, and as is true of every race, the well-fed are strong and joyous.

"Life is good," said Doomdah again when the basket was empty. She spoke in Spanish, the Mission tongue that she had taught Inyo was for these two alone.

"You are strong," said the boy.

"Yes, I am strong."

"You bring in twice what you eat."

"Three times," she corrected. "I bring in for three. For you, for me, and for such other as may need it."

"It is not time to die," said Inyo. "The strong must not die. I take you back to Padre, and I leave you there." He broke open some piñon nuts and gave them to his grandmother. "Where is Far Away?" he asked.

"It is across burning sands, it is across high mountains. It is many, many moons away from here."

Inyo put another chunk of wood on the fire. He shook out the pack basket but there was nothing more in it now except a few nut shells and half an agave worm. He threw the nut shells on the fire and ate the piece of worm.

"Let us sleep," said Inyo. "Let us rest for this trail to Far Away."

from ALL-AMERICAN

John R. Tunis

No one writes better sports stories than John R. Tunis. But in addition to sports, his books center on the problems of adolescents resulting from religious and racial prejudices.

[The Academy Versus the High School]

When you win, when passes click, when the interference forms smoothly in front and you cut in for five, ten, twenty yards, when the sun shines and your girl's sitting up there in the High School stands and the score mounts, yes, then football's fun. That's grand, that's something like.

But this sort of thing wasn't fun; it was agony. For almost the first time since he began playing football he longed to hear the sound of the whistle.

Of all days to have it rain, the day of the Academy game, the one day we want a good dry field and firm footing! The rain pelted down his neck, oozed into his shoes, made each pad a sodden lump of lead. He looked around. The 16-yard line! One more touchdown and we'll be licked; surely, positively licked. Ruefully he remembered standing on the same spot and saying that same thing to himself before the second touchdown. And the third.

Then the whistle blew.

The team picked itself out of the mud and straggled across the mire into the gymnasium. Into the lockers and clean clothes; relief from that incessant pounding, a chance to rest, to stretch out quietly, to pull themselves together.

The familiar room was warm and dry; in one corner steam was hissing cheerfully from the pipes, and the sight of those little piles of fresh, clean clothes before every locker was comforting. They trooped in, sodden and dripping, saying nothing because there wasn't much you could say, chucking their headgears across the benches in disgust, despondent and disappointed. 19–0. What could anybody say about that kind of a score? To think this was the team that had been talked of as possibly playing an Intersectional game!

"Ok, boys." The coach brought up the rear, slamming the door on an especially severe gust of wind and rain. If he was distressed by the upset he showed no evidence of it. "Ok now, boys, get those clothes right off. Mike! Give us a hand here. Goldman, I'll fix that cut up over your eye. Doc, take a look at Jake's leg."

They hauled off their clothes, wet, soggy, disagreeable to touch, and dropped them to the floor. A small pool of water immediately collected about each pile. Mike and the Doc and the assistant coaches went around rubbing them down, repairing them for the second half. Ah, that's good. Good to be stretched out and relaxed on the hard board while Mike assailed you with the coarse, dry towel. But that score, 19–0.

Gee, that's terrible, you can't laugh that off. And we were the team mentioned in the papers as going south to play Miami High. Sure, in all the newspapers!

Slowly they dressed once more. Dry socks, underwear, supporters, pads, pants, jerseys, and shoes. There. That's better. That's something like. The coach came past and slipped to the bench where Ronny was leaning over to tie his shoelaces.

"Ronald!" His voice was low. "What seems to be the trouble out there this afternoon?"

Ronny knew perfectly well what the trouble was but he didn't like to say. So he just kept leaning over his shoes. When he didn't answer, the coach continued in a low voice. "I know it's wet out there; this kind of weather hurts the T-formation the worst way. But from the bench it kinda looks as if the boys aren't together."

Nope, we surely aren't together. Of course we aren't together; how can we be together when some of the crowd are set on something besides winning a football game? That's what he wanted to say, tried almost to say as loud as he could; but it refused to come out. He mumbled something about the bad weather, the storm, the wet ball, the footing.

The coach rose. He clapped his hands. The squad gathered about, everyone's hair still wet and damp. Behind in the rear Mike passed with an armful of soaking uniforms and equipment.

"Boys, this weather is certainly tough. No use talking. I recognize what you are up against out there. The T-formation needs good firm ground to be effective. But I still feel somehow you're better'n what you've shown, and I've still got confidence in you to win, yes, even with this score. I have confidence, that is, if you'll only get going. Nineteen points a lot? Sure. But the test of a player is what he can do when he's tired. This half go out and play the kind of ball you can."

Then they were outside, out in that deluge once more. Across the way the Academy stands rose in a roar as Keith led his team at the same moment onto the field. Over the end zone was the scoreboard with those dreadful figures staring at them: H.S. 0   Visitors 19.

The ball was low, and from his position Ronald could watch the backs of his teammates converge on the runner, on Keith, no, on Heywood. That big halfback, heavy, powerful, fast, had been slashing holes in their line all afternoon. In the mud and slime he seemed impossible to stop, and Ronny himself had tackled him half a dozen times.

The teams lined up. Heywood took the ball once more for a sizeable gain. But Ronald was noticing something else; he was watching Mike and two others break through and pile up on Keith. It was what they'd been doing ever since the kick-off. To his astonishment some of his teammates hadn't forgotten Goldman's injury of the previous season. They were still trying to pay Keith for his share in it.

There's a guy we don't like, so we'll bang him off at the start. This was their attitude. Ronny knew what they didn't seem to know, that Keith could take it. All the time they were attempting to bang him off, Steve Ketchum and Heywood had plowed through for those touchdowns.

Once again Heywood sliced into the line and out into the secondary. He was nearly clear before he slipped and fell. That's a break, that is. On the next play they made a first down, and then Keith got loose off tackle, his most dangerous run. It was Ronny who, seeing the danger on that sloppy field, managed to knock him outside after a thirty-yard gain. He picked himself up, now as wet and soggy as he had been at the end of the first half.

"C'mon, gang, get in there, get in there and play ball like you can, will ya? Block that end, Mike, watch him every minute; get in low, Jake."

But slowly, surely, steadily, the Academy came toward their goal, toward a fourth touchdown, toward the worst licking the High School had ever taken. Keith charged in low and hard between Vic and Don Westcott who alone seemed to be holding up the center of the line, playing a magnificent defensive game. Don slapped at him and threw him off his stride as Ronny came running up. The whole play was clear before him. Keith with one arm out, stumbling in the mud; Mike and Dave rushing in hard to fall on him so that if he wasn't knocked out he'd at least know he'd been hit. It made Ronald furious. He closed in, determined not to permit them to get away with it, to block off Dave anyway. He did block him off, and as he did so Mike

accidentally slipped and hit him on the chin with the full force of his fist.

He saw stars. When he came to they were standing around in the mud. Doc Roberts was leaning over, wiping his face and holding smelling salts under his nose.

"I'm ok, Doc." He rose unsteadily, feeling dizzy, tried to step out a little, managed to trot a few steps. "I'm ok." But he was not ok, and he was mad clean through. This had to end. One thing or the other. They'd have to quit and play ball—or he would.

"C'm here, gang. This way. Look. This has gotta stop. It's gotta stop or I quit. If you guys don't lay off that bird, I'll leave the field, here, right now, and I'll tell Coach why. C'mon, gang, what say, gang, let's go. Let's forget that stuff. Let's get together, let's play against that crowd there, not against each other."

"You're dead right, Ronald!" Jim Stacey, adjusting his headgear, stepped in toward the center. "Listen, you guys, lay off that fella from now on and play ball. I've been watching you, and Ronny's quite right. We've been playing against each other, not together. Let's all shoot together for the team."

"Ok, Jim."

"All right, Jim-boy."

"Sure, let's go, gang."

"Yeah, let's go."

"All right now, get in there, you guys."

The whistle blew. The teams lined up. Ronald looked around. He was standing on the 8-yard line!

It was raining harder than ever. The Academy leaned over the ball. It was snapped to Heywood, who for the first time started a fraction of a second too soon. The ball was over his shoulder, he stabbed at it, deflected it in the air. A wet figure dashed past and snatched at it in the mist. He had it. Never missing a stride he was five yards down the field before anyone turned.

"Go on, Ned, go on Ned-Boy, for Pete's sake, go on. Don't slip, Ned, go on, Ned!"

The two teams picked themselves up out of the mud and streamed along behind him, but the fleet colored boy gained with every stride.

"Yeah, team! Team, team, team. Yeah, team!" The cymbals clashed and clanged from the High

School side of the field. The first chance they had had to cheer since the kick-off.

Now then, we're moving. We're really moving. For the rest of the third quarter the teams slithered up and down the center of the gridiron, both Keith and Ronald punting and handling that juicy sphere as if it were dry and easy to hold. Somehow they managed to cling to the thing.

Then toward the end of the quarter the High School team got moving. A quarterback sneak was good for a long gain. On the Academy 30-yard line, however, they were held for two plays. Third and six. They went into their huddle.

"Ok, gang. 39 on 5 count." He was winded, he puffed hard. This was Meyer's play. They went into formation.

"Hike. 27 . . . 38 . . . 40 . . . hike . . ." He leaned over, his hand on Don's wet rump. The ball came and for once the play was perfectly executed. He faked with his empty left hand to Jake, the halfback, and then in the same motion tucked the ball in Meyer's stomach, continuing back himself as if he were about to throw a pass. Meyer roared off Roger Treadway's end into the secondary, he bounced off Steve, straightarmed Rex Heywood, and carried Keith along on his back almost five yards. The High School stands were jumping, shrieking, yelling.

Then someone shouted. Over to the left in clear territory a figure lay in the wet. Jim had gone down on the play to fake catching a possible forward and draw in one of the defensive backs in their 5–4–2 alignment. Doing so he had turned, slipped, and fallen in the open. When Ronny reached him a group of players was huddled round and he was writhing in agony on the ground.

The Doc rushed up, shoving them aside. He knelt down in a puddle, began feeling of the thigh, the leg, the calf, the ankle.

"Ouch!" Jim perked up. "Ow . . . that hurts . . . ow . . ."

The Doc beckoned to the sidelines. "You lay still, young man. Lay still now, don't move."

Silence came over the field, and Ronny could hear them from the stands. . . . "It's Jake . . . naw . . . it's Perry . . . no, he's up there . . . it's Jim Stacey."

Two managers ran out with a stretcher. They rolled him over, protesting. Ronny saw he was in acute pain. On the bench Jack Train, his substitute, leaned over toward the coach. Then they were carrying Jim from the field.

The team stood disconsolately in the rain. Aw, shoot! Shucks, don't we get the breaks against us! How's that for rotten luck! First this stinking lousy weather. Then we lose our captain, the key of our passing attack, the man who was our best pass catcher.

Jack Train came running on, adjusting his dry headgear. His uniform was unsoiled, his hands were fresh and clean. Ronny looked at him almost with disgust. Heck! What good is he? Couldn't catch a dry ball at ten feet. What use is he on a day like this?

They tried a play. Then another. Something had gone, the mainspring of their nervous energy had snapped, there was no punch left. Baldy was a bear on scouting other teams, and Ronald well knew they'd been told that with Stacey out the High School's passing attack wasn't to be feared. He saw the defensive halfback in one zone slide up. Ideal for a pass if only he had a receiver.

Looking over the situation he called for a fake split buck-end run with Jake carrying the ball. But they were waiting, and although Meyer blocked out the defensive end, the halfbacks smeared the play for a small gain. Third and nine! Shoot! Just as we were rolling, too. That's lousy luck all right. Then he heard a voice at his elbow as they went into the huddle. It was Ned, who never raised his voice, who never spoke unless you spoke to him first—Ned, who was the best defensive end in the State but never carried the ball.

"Ronny. Lemme have a look at that thing. Shoot me that flat pass up the center. I b'lieve I kin hang on to that thing."

Why not? They were stopped now. Why not have a try at it? "Ok, gang. Number 46 on 4. Got it, everyone?" He looked round at their muddy faces, heard their panting, saw their affirmative nods. "C'mon now. Formation T. 46 on 4. Hike. 27–38–40–39 . . . hike . . ." He leaned over, patting Don on his wet back. Here it comes!

Taking the ball, he turned and scuttled to the

rear. Careful. Keep your balance. Watch your feet now. Both defensive halfbacks anticipating a thrust at the line had sneaked up, and Ronald, as he'd been coached, shot the flat pass over their heads into empty territory. Like lightning Ned was there, cutting in with a swerve and taking that greasy thing in midair on the dead run. He had it! Doggone, he had it! He was off. Ronald could see nothing more, for he himself was buried under a swarm of resentful tacklers.

He didn't need to see. When he shook himself free and got the mud out of his eyes, Ned was standing beneath the goal posts and the umpire had his hands high in the air.

Another touchdown. 19–13.

You can't keep a good gang down! The band blared, squeaky noises came from the brasses, but the cheering drowned everything. Yeah, team! Team, team! Watch it, Meyer. Watch it, boy; watch that kick, it's terribly important. He remembered the coach's words as the ball was snapped back to Bob who always held it for Meyer. Give Meyer a chance, and he'll come through. He's only missed two out of the last fourteen tries.

Swell! Atta boy, Meyer, great work, Meyer. 19–14. Great work for you too, Ned. Boy, you're hot! "C'mon now, gang, c'm here, c'm over here. Look. We got eight minutes to score. Let's get this one for Jim, gang. You bet, we'll get this one for Jim."

It was the longest eight minutes of his life. In that eight minutes he lived a hundred lives, died and was reborn a hundred times. In that space of time he suffered ages of agonies. For he was weary, beaten, his whole frame ached as it had never ached before, he seemed to be carrying around twenty pounds of heavy mud. Each step was a horrible effort. Every fall, every tackle, jarred him badly.

They kicked off, downed them close to their goal line, held them after several rushes, and got the ball near midfield.

"Ok, gang, here's our chance. Here's where we go. 48 on 3. Hip-hip. Hike." Get outa the way, Mike, get outa the way or I'll tattoo your backbone. No gain? Shoot! Third and eight to go.

He punted, poorly. But then their own line

held and once more the Academy was forced to kick back. Now he gave everything he had, a delayed straight buck, a short forward to Ned which was knocked down, a forward to Bob which was incomplete. Again he had to kick.

For the third time they held despite the fierceness of the Academy attack. Dusk was descending fast in the wet and mist. You could hardly see the opposite goal posts. He called for 80. It was one of the coach's favorites, a play in which he handed the ball to Meyer who tossed it to Bob, the man in motion. His play which had been stopped three times in the first half for no gain went for twenty yards. They were creeping along, well in enemy territory now; but time was running out fast.

A fumble! A fumble! The ball slithered through the mud. He could see it, in the open. Then a figure shot toward it almost parallel to the ground. How he ever managed to hold that greasy object Ronny never knew. There he was, however, with the ball in his stomach when six men piled on top.

Ned LeRoy! Good boy, Ned! You saved us that time. Gee, that's great work, Ned, that's really super. They went into the huddle. Why not? Sure it was growing dark. Sure the ball was wet and hard to handle. But why not try it?

The defensive backs were sneaking up again, so he called for a pass down the sidelines in which the left end ran down and cut over to take the ball. Number 86 on 3. He leaned over, panting. Whew! Gosh, I'm all in. The words of the coach came suddenly to mind.

The test of a player is what he can do when he's tired.

He looked at them. Meyer on his knees in a pool of water. Ned with his mouth open and his white teeth showing. Don hardly able to stand up, Mike with the gash in his forehead open and bleeding, everyone done in, beaten, exhausted. But the test of a player is what he can do when he's tired.

"Look, gang, let's give 'em one good one for Stacey. What say, hey, gang . . . let's give 'em this one for Jim. One good play. Everyone in it. 86 on 3. Dave, watch that defensive halfback. Jake, fade out a little more. End around direct pass. Everyone got it? Remember, they're scared now. They're plenty worried. And they're just as tired as we are. Ok, gang, let's make this a good one for Jim."

They went into formation. He leaned over, took the ball, and faded slowly back. Meyer and Bob and Jake ran out ahead to form interference; Ned slipped around and then, going ahead, cut toward the sidelines. Ronald saw a form rushing toward him, dodged, and then let loose. This time he had the whole panorama of the play before his eyes.

The pass was true and straight out to the side. This time Ned was there waiting. Gee, if he only holds it. Cool as ice, the end gathered the ball in, turned and cut across the field behind Jake and Meyer. Someone went down. Gosh, is that Ned? Nope, they're still after him. The pursuit continued. Running forward, Ronny could see scattered bodies writhing on the ground in the mud and mist up ahead. Ned was crossing over now, heading for the opposite sideline. He was in the clear.

A wild spontaneous cheer came from his side. From Abraham Lincoln High.

KILLER WHALES

Archie Bins

Clint Barlow, an only child living with his parents in a remote region of Puget Sound, knows that he wants to be an oceanographer, and uses his wonderful outdoor life for observations which he carefully records. But in this chapter the loss of Buster, his pet seal and constant companion, has made Clint indifferent to everything else, even danger.

The school bus stopped at the mailbox with James Barlow printed on the side, and Clint got out into the pouring rain.

"Don't get your feet wet!" Len Decker called after him.

George Lawson raised his hand in his usual friendly salute.

"Killer Whales." From *Sea Pup* by Archie Binns, by permission of Duell, Sloan & Pearce, Inc. Copyright 1954 by Archie Binns

Then the door closed and the bus went on as Clint started down the hill toward the house.

From the road, all you could see of the Barlow place were the wet shake roofs of farm buildings and the bare orchard with a few dozen forgotten yellow apples on a Bellflower tree. Orchard and land and roofs looked wetter than the gray plain of water beyond them. But smoke from the kitchen chimney was wrestling with the rain. Inside it would be warm and dry, with good cooking smells.

Going back to school hadn't turned out as bad as Clint had feared. The worst part had been worrying about what might happen to Buster while he was away. He had told the neighbors for miles in every direction that Buster was his pet seal; they wouldn't hurt him. But there was always the danger of his being shot by a stray hunter or fisherman.

Nothing bad had happened. And Buster had learned to tell time, though no one knew how he did it. Mom said he might be out in the water half a mile away from the house at ten minutes to four—and at four o'clock, when Clint was due home, he would be rocking up the front steps.

Buster had never disappointed Clint, but in these days of autumn rains the boy had to disappoint the seal. At each home-coming Buster would coax and coax Clint to go swimming, and when he refused because the weather was too cold and wet, the seal would pretend to fall over dead with disappointment. While he lay there Clint pounced on him, and they wrestled until the dogs came barking and joined in the tussle.

Usually Mom came out and told them to stop the racket. Once, when she didn't, Clint and Buster fell off the edge of the front porch and Clint rolled all the way down the steps.

Buster wasn't around the back of the house this afternoon. Probably he had been in swimming and was rocking his way up the front steps as Clint hung his dripping slicker on one of the hooks on the back porch. He opened the door and stepped into the warm kitchen, full of good smells.

Mom, who knew the time as well as Buster, was taking a big pan out of the oven.

"Just in time, Clint! I made coffee cake. You

can have some if it won't spoil your appetite for supper."

"It won't, Mom. How's everything?"

"Just a quiet rainy day. Your dad went to town this morning; he'll be back for supper. There's a letter from Aunt Harriet you must see—"

"How's Buster?"

"He was out swimming. He's probably waiting for you; he always is."

As Clint opened the front door Wolf and Jerry scrambled to their feet in the shelter of the porch, wagging and barking their welcome.

Buster was nowhere in sight.

"Here, Buster! Here, Buster!"

There was no answer.

Clint looked up and down the Canal, but there was no smooth seal head pointed toward home.

Mom came out on the porch.

"Isn't he here, Clint? His clock must have been slow for once. Come in where it's warm, and have your cake. Buster's sure to be back by the time you're done."

His appetite was spoiled before he started. He ate one piece of coffee cake, then went back to the porch. As far as he could see, the gray rainy water was unbroken. He scowled at it, thinking of the time he had waited on Toandos for Buster's mother to come home. . . .

After a while Mom came out again.

"Worrying won't bring him any faster, Clint— and there's something in Aunt Harriet's letter about you. It could be important."

He might have known he would have bad luck when there was a letter from Aunt Harriet. She had tried to talk him out of having a seal for a pet—and now Buster was missing!

In the kitchen Mom unfolded a letter.

"Harriet sent this in her letter. It's from Professor Wills at the University. He's in the department that studies the ocean."

Dear Miss Hall:

Thank you for letting me see Clint Barlow's excellent paper on the geoduck. Several of his observations are original and, quite possibly, scientifically sound. Of at least equal interest to me is the imagination shown in the paper. As you know, Oceanography is a new science, pioneering in the last great unexplored region of the world—the ocean. And one of the first requirements for this field is the kind of scientific imagination Clint shows. Tell him from me to keep up his good work; also that I hope someday to have him as one of my students. Meanwhile, if Clint is ever in Seattle, I should like to show him through our laboratory. I feel sure he would see things there that would open new horizons for him.

Sincerely,
Herbert Wills

"Gee!" Clint said. Then he remembered about Buster, and nothing seemed good any more.

"Isn't that wonderful?" Mom said. "And you only in junior high!"

"I guess so. Yes." He stared at the letter without seeing it. "Where did Aunt Harriet get my paper?"

Mom hesitated. "She saw it when she was here last time, and borrowed it. She was going to ask you—"

"It's all right," Clint said. "I wish I knew where Buster is."

There still wasn't any sign of him; Dad wasn't home, and there were the chores to do. Clint took one more look at the darkening water, and went for his slicker and boots.

When he was milking he thought of the letter again. Dr. Wills had written about "pioneering in the last great unexplored region of the world —the ocean." That was what Clint had wanted to do, only he hadn't been able to put it in words. And Dr. Wills was going to show him the laboratory where they studied the ocean. Imagine Aunt Harriet making something like that happen! She was always meddling; trying to take him away from what he wanted to do. No, she had brought him nearer. She couldn't do both. Somewhere in his mind he thought the letter was the biggest thing that had ever happened to him. But it had come at the wrong time, when he was too worried for anything but Buster to seem important.

It was dark when Clint heard the truck, and saw the shine of headlights in the pouring rain. For the minute it seemed to him that his father could find Buster at once and make everything all right. Actually he couldn't do any more about it than Clint. But he could make things seem better.

"There's no use fretting, boy," he said in the shelter of the porch. "If he isn't back soon it's because he's found other seals, as he was intended to. You did a good job of raising him, and he's on his own now."

It sounded all right then, but at supper Clint couldn't eat much. He knew the seal better than anyone else; and Buster would have been there to meet him if he hadn't been shot, or trapped somewhere. If he knew that Buster was dead he would have to take it, and go on from there. But he felt hollow and sick when he thought of his friend suffering somewhere with no one to help him. Buster had so much good will toward everyone; he wouldn't understand Clint's not coming to help him when he was in trouble.

While Mom and Dad were eating Clint thought how wonderful it would be if there were a sound outside and Buster's funny seal face looked in the window while he tapped on the glass with a flipper. But supper ended without any sound outside except the wind and rain.

As soon as Clint could get away he put on his slicker and boots, and got his flashlight. As he was going out his father spoke to him.

"You won't be out long, will you, boy?"

"I was just going to look around the beach, Dad."

Mom said, "You shouldn't be out at all on such a night."

At the landing he shone the flashlight up and down the beach; it didn't light up anything but rain beating on wet sand; and when he swept the water with it the choppy waves broke up the light.

"Here, Buster! Here, Buster! Buster!"

When he didn't get any answer, Clint launched the little skiff, and clawed off the beach with the oars. He wasn't coming back until he found Buster. The water was rougher than he expected, and the skiff pounded and jumped as he rowed upwind.

"Here, Buster! Here, Buster!"

Every few minutes he steadied the boat with both oars in one hand while he swept the water with his flashlight. If Buster was within range his eyes would reflect the light. But there was no answering shine of eyes.

"Here, Buster! Here, Buster!"

In the distance, down-wind, Clint heard his father shout. He didn't answer because he didn't want to come home without his friend. The skiff was pounding heavily and throwing spray, but he was all right while he kept headed up into the wind.

After a while he heard the far-off sound of a boat being launched.

"I'm all right, Dad!" he yelled. "Don't come after me!" Probably his father couldn't hear him. Clint held the boat steady while he flashed his light over the short steep waves.

"Here, Buster! Here, Buster!"

He was rowing again when he heard the rumble of the outboard motor. Why couldn't Dad leave him alone?

A light flashed astern, and his father's voice shouted above the sound of the motor.

"Clint, show your light!"

He flashed the light on, shouting,

"I'm all right, Dad! Don't come after me!"

His father brought the big boat abreast of him, a dozen feet away, and throttled down the motor.

"Come back, boy! It's too rough for that little skiff, and we're in four hundred feet of water. You wouldn't stand a chance if you capsized!"

Clint was almost crying.

"I'm all right, Dad! I've got to find Buster—"

"Listen!"

The boy had already heard the giant breathing sound. It came again, louder and deeper; great calm breath after breath that filled the night as it bore down on them. Over his shoulder he saw a long blaze of phosphorescent fire leap toward his father's boat.

"Dad, look out!"

His yell was lost in a giant breathing sound and a rush of water. Out of the cold fire there heaved a great gleaming back with a fin that rose like a sickle against the sky above Dad's head. The back swerved a little at the last second, rolling forward as it swept past the boat and submerging until there was only a six-foot fin tearing through the water, shining with sparks of phosphorus.

"Killer whale!"

Clint heard his own shout, like a whisper; then his father's voice that seemed to come from a long way off.

"Look out, boy!"

He looked over his shoulder and saw the black water boil into fire as the next killer rolled to the surface, directly ahead of his boat. It was too close and coming too fast for him to move; he could only wait for the crash. The back swerved and rushed by his tossing skiff, with a great sickle fin high above his head, dripping fire. The night was still full of vast breathing sounds and the roar of water. Over his shoulder Clint saw more of the killers, like a string of cars lit with phosphorus and carrying snoring giants. One after another, close together, they roared out of the

darkness, swerved a little at the last moment, and went rolling by, some on one side of the boats and some on the other. The big solid backs and fins, glittering with sparks of phosphorus, seemed blacker than anything Clint had ever seen.

Nine of the killer whales had passed and the boats were still afloat. Clint saw his father's light flash on and heard his faint yell,

"Look out, boy! This is it!"

The flashlight shone on a great back and fin rolling up too close for any turning aside. It rushed down on them until it seemed to Clint that he could have touched it with an oar—then it submerged swiftly, with only a great fin ripping through the water between the two boats. The skiff tipped crazily in the fierce surge of power rolling under it, and shipped water. It righted itself; and Clint heard the rain rattling on his slicker, the rush of waves, the slow, oily pulse of the outboard motor; then his father's voice:

"Was that close enough for you, boy? Come alongside and get in before you swamp!"

On the way home, above the sound of the motor, they could hear the vast breathing of the killer whales in the distance.

"I could have hung my hat on any one of their fins," Dad said. "I never want to be that close to blackfish again—but I wouldn't have missed it! Did you see the phosphorus on them? They were lit up like Christmas trees!"

Clint knew that in daylight killer whales liked to see how close they could come to boats without hitting them. He had never heard of one making a mistake. But he didn't think these had sensed the boats in the dark until they were almost on top of them. Clint had been there because he wanted to be; but Dad had only come out to help him—and he could have lost his life. That took the fight out of the boy.

When they had hauled the boats to safety, Clint's father said, "Let's not say anything to your mother about that close shave. She'll be worried enough as it is."

"That's right, Dad."

In his room, trying to do his homework, Clint still saw the killer whales charging by in the dark, blacker than night and shining with sparks of phosphorus. It had been the biggest adventure of his life; but he couldn't enjoy it when he thought of Buster away somewhere in the dark, dead or trapped . . . and Clint working on Social Studies!

He remembered with sudden dread that killer whales came into Puget Sound *after seals*. They might have got Buster hours ago! If they hadn't yet, he could only hope that they would miss him; the Canal was so wide, and Buster so small. . . .

MEET AMIGO

Page Cooper

Here is the first chapter of a thrilling story of circus life. It is told from the standpoint of the circus performers and concerns the struggles of three teen-agers who are trying to qualify for the big center ring. Franz is an equestrian who has lost his heart to a beautiful but excitable horse, Amigo. The horse, a palomino, belongs to Señor

Gonzales, who does a juggling act. Dolores, an orphan called Dizzy by the boys, is also working to become an equestrienne. And Mulk, an East Indian, is all for the elephants although his father trains the big cats. The story not only gives a vivid picture of circus life—its disciplines, fun, dangers, and glories—but also deals with the lives of the circus animals and their temperamental ups and downs.

Franz stared at Amigo, caressing with his eyes the horse's trim, sturdy body, the color of light coffee, and the splendid cream mane and tail. He wasn't listening to his father and the slim-hipped Mexican talking at the entrance to the horse tent. If he had dared, he would have run his hand over the horse's flank. Amigo had cocked his ears inquiringly and thrust out his nose toward the boy. Franz took a slight step forward, as much as to say "Hello," but he kept his hands in his pockets. It wasn't courteous to touch a circus performer's horse. His father would have been furious if someone had tried to touch Uncle or Allodria.

The Mexican, Señor Gonzales, smiled at Franz. "Glad to be back with the show?"

Captain Szabo put his arm proudly around his son's shoulder.

"Now the boy's really going to work. He's spinning candy for Eddy this season. Come on, Franz. I want to sponge out Uncle's eyes. There was a lot of dust this afternoon."

With a backward look at the palomino, Franz caught up with his father. They circled the menagerie end of the big tent and came to a red wagon with a canvas lean-to and two white horses staked out behind it, nibbling at the coarse, beaten grass. They were magnificent horses, snow-white Lippizans from the stud that had belonged to Franz Joseph, the Emperor of Austria in the old days when there was an emperor. Their haunches were thick and their bodies shorter than those of an English thoroughbred, but their small feet and arched necks showed their Arabian blood.

Alexander Szabo took a pan of water from a bucketful that had been warming in the sun, and bathed Uncle's eyes; then he climbed into the wagon and sat in the door with his feet on the detachable steps. Franz swung up beside him. The languor of the early summer evening lay like a hush over the field. Most of the performers were loafing in camp chairs before their dressing rooms under the big tent. Those who were coming back from the "grease wagon," with a coke or an ice cream cone in hand, moved in slow motion. Even the noises of children, whose harassed mothers had brought them early to the evening performance, were muted as they circled outside the rope fence that shut in the circus back yard.

In front of the red wagon, the wall of the big top was pulled up about halfway, showing the rumps of the elephants staked inside. Sadie towered higher than the others, and baby Toto's stubby tail twitched as he shuffled on his chain. Franz sniffed the scent of elephant dung and hay, hot dogs and polished leather. These two months that he had stayed behind to finish the school term had seemed endless. Now, at last, it was June and he was home again.

"What does Señor Gonzales do?" Franz asked, his mind returning to Amigo.

"A juggling act on horseback. It's unusual. He's a splendid rider."

"I liked his horse."

"The palomino? That's his spare. He's too nervous and excitable, but he's a handsome animal. Uncle and Allodria have missed you."

The mellow notes of a bugle drifted across the field. Captain Szabo jumped to the ground and stretched. Time to dress. Franz's heart swelled with pride as he looked at his father, straight as a flagpole, his black mustache making a dashing smudge on his lean, sunburned face. Distinction, that's what his father had—an air of importance. You would know he was somebody special if you saw his back going down the street.

"Coming in?"

"No, I'll wait. You riding Uncle? I'll hold him for you."

Captain Szabo climbed into the wagon, switched on the light, and shut the door. Franz stuck his head into the lean-to and spoke to Jake, the groom who had just come back from the cook tent. He had brought Uncle in and was giving him a final polishing.

Jake was an old cowpoke who had been around horses all his life. He took three gold tassels from their tissue-paper wrappings and tied them into Uncle's mane. Uncle gravely arched his neck with the air of a prince of the church about to pronounce a benediction.

"Ain't he first cousin to God Almighty?" Jake circled about like a privileged courtier, half mockingly, wholly devoted. He always called Uncle "he" or "him."

The Lippizan had a long high-sounding name that told his pedigree, but as soon as Franz could talk he had named the horse "Uncle" and Uncle he had remained.

· Uncle was twenty-five years old and one of the most highly trained high school horses alive. In the circus they called this high art of horsemanship "high school," but in Vienna where Franz was born they called it the French term, *waute école*. There were not more than two or three others who could perform a courbette five times in a row—five successive leaps into the air from the back feet, remaining upright without touching the ground with the forefeet. Uncle had such perfect balance that there was nothing he couldn't do.

To tell the truth, Franz was both a little overawed and at the same time bored with Uncle. The horse had taught him how to ride. Uncle had tolerated the boy's clumsiness and uncertain commands, and had gone right ahead performing faultlessly, never losing his dignity for a moment. Now that he was an expert rider, Franz couldn't help feeling satisfaction in the perfect co-ordination between him and Uncle, but Uncle was the dominant one. He was in command. You always knew exactly what he would do. There was no excitement in riding him.

Allodria was more fun. He was younger and couldn't do to perfection all the steps that Uncle did, but he had a mischievous habit of trying to play jokes on you and kept you on your toes. Not in the ring. When he was performing, nothing would tempt him to playfully toss the rider over his tail, then stand by and laugh at him. But of a morning when Franz put him through his paces, they had a lot of fun together.

It was understood that next year when Franz was sixteen, old enough to get a contract with the show, he would have Allodria and his father would bring over another Lippizan to train. That was all very well, but Allodria was a one-man horse. He liked to play with Franz as he would with a young colt, but he belonged single-heartedly to Alexander Szabo, and nobody else would ever be his master.

Above everything in the world Franz wanted a horse of his own. One that he had trained, one who would owe allegiance to nobody but him. If only he had a horse like Amigo, for instance! The palomino liked him. There was a certain kinship between them, a current of understanding. He had felt it as he stood in the tent door wanting to stretch out his hand and touch Amigo's velvet side.

Alexander Szabo snapped out the light and opened the door. He looked very grand in his tight, black, braided jacket and flat-brimmed, high-crowned Spanish hat, like a captain in some fabulous Balkan army. And indeed he had been a Hungarian captain in the days before the war.

The second bugle had sounded. The performance was on. At the back door, Franz could see the elephants lined up for the spectacle with girls, wearing pink tights and crinoline, perched on their heads. Captain Szabo's act was next. Franz tightened Uncle's girth and brought him around to the wagon steps. His father always mounted at the steps to keep from soiling his boots. Franz proudly took a last flick at them with his handkerchief.

Uncle, glad to be under the saddle, moved across the field at a dignified high trot, lifting his feet with the precision of a ballet dancer, his neck arched, his head held on a perfect vertical line. He was just too perfect.

Franz shut the wagon door and looked around to see if he could find Mulk, the son of the Hindu lion tamer. Mulk was working for his father this season, beginning at the bottom, helping to clean out the cages and feed the animals. His father, whose name was Chandu, expected him to uphold the family tradition and train the big cats, but Mulk liked the elephants. He would rather teach Toto to walk on bottles than to drive Mogul, the king of black panthers, through a flaming hoop.

Franz made for the grease wagon. If Mulk had a dime he would be hanging around it trying to decide what kind of ice cream cone to buy. He was like that; he always had so many arguments on both sides of a question that he never could make up his mind.

In front of the hospital wagon, Franz came upon Mulk and Dolores, the Argentine girl, conferring with the nurse. Last season the three of them had been inseparable. "The Three Musketeers," Charley the clown had called them, and the name had stuck.

"Hi, Dizzy! Hi, Mulk!" Franz always called Dolores by her nickname. "What you doing?"

Dizzy turned mournful eyes toward him. On her finger perched Coco, her pet parakeet, drowsily blinking, his topknot sunk almost to his breast. He didn't even squawk at Franz his usual greeting, "You bum! You greasy bum!"

"We gotta have aspirin. Coco sick," Dolores was explaining to the nurse. She could speak six languages fluently, but her English was not very good. Her enormous eyes gleamed as though they were filling up with tears, and her small dark face looked so forlorn that the nurse checked a smile.

"He won't take aspirin. It's too bitter. Probably he's eaten a bug that disagreed with him. One of you boys hold him while Dolores opens his beak, and I'll give him a drop of oil."

Mulk grinned at Franz.

"You do it. You're the new boy around here." Franz kicked Mulk's shin.

"Give him here, Dizzy."

Ordinarily Coco would have flapped and screamed at anyone who took him off of Dizzy's finger, but as Franz held down his wings, he didn't even open his beady eyes. Franz tipped him on his back, Dizzy opened his beak and the nurse carefully dropped into his mouth a few globules of oil from a medicine dropper.

"There now, scat," she said, squeezing the remains of the oil back into the bottle. "He'll be all right tomorrow."

Dizzy thanked her, then took Coco back and smoothed his ruffled feathers.

"Come on," Franz suggested. "Let's go down by the horse tents and I'll show you a palomino that's a beauty."

The three walked across the field, skirting the wet wash that hung from tent ropes, their feet making little crunching sounds in the grass. Dizzy held Coco protectively against her chest.

"There he is. That one in front. Isn't he terrific!"

Franz indicated the palomino at the near end of the double line of horses tied to ropes that stretched along the sides of the tent.

Amigo heard Franz's voice and pulled at his halter, thrusting out his nose.

"You kids keep out of here." A groom got up out of the straw at the far end of the tent where he had been polishing a bridle. "You know you mustn't hang around the horses."

"We weren't doing anything. We were just looking," Franz explained. "Honest, we were just admiring the palomino."

"Well, go admire somewhere else. That horse is nervous as a witch. Goes into a tizzy if you so much as speak to him."

"Ow!" Dizzy screamed, covering her head with her free hand. "Fledermaus!"

"A bat." The groom snatched a pitchfork and jabbed at the black flapping creature that swooped and rose to beat upon the canvas roof. The horses stirred restlessly and pulled at their halters. Amigo was quivering, his ears laid back.

The bat swooped toward the door. Dizzy screamed. It turned and flapped against the side wall in front of Amigo's face. He reared, heaved, tore loose his halter and dashed out of the tent as though he were pursued by a thousand demons. Skimming over the rope fence he ran blindly toward a dark clump of buildings at the other end of the fair grounds.

Franz caught his breath first. He dashed after Amigo, with Mulk at his heels, and Dizzy chasing after them, hampered by her attempt to protect Coco. The groom was slower to get started. He waited to collect a half-dozen hands who were lazily guarding the fence.

It was almost dark now. Amigo looked like a phantom horse with his long cream tail streaming. Franz lost him behind one of the buildings, then caught sight of him again. There he was, cornered in the angle of a wall. He reared, wheeled, and came pounding toward Franz, swishing past him, then, as he saw the running figures coming at him across the field, he charged back toward the buildings. It was like a game of hide-and-seek. At one moment you saw him like a white shadow; at the next, he was lost. Franz was gaining on him, following him around each corner.

Amigo was blocked again, stopped by a four-foot cattle gate. Would he jump it and run loose in the town? The horse paused a moment, eying the gate, sucking in his breath, his ribs heaving.

"Amigo," Franz called softly. Motioning Mulk and Dizzy back, he took a step toward the horse, then stood perfectly still. "Amigo, old boy, wait for me."

The horse turned his head. Franz saw him thrust up his ears. He swirled around, facing the sound.

"Amigo." Franz took another step forward. "It's only me." The horse lowered his head and waited, watching, quivering, ready to break away.

"Hold still, old boy." This time Franz took two steps. He was almost within reach of the halter rope. Slowly he picked up the end of the rope. The horse stretched forward and thrust his nose against the boy's shoulder, then tautened. Running feet were thudding around the building at their rear and voices shouting, "There he is!"

Amigo reared and jerked at the rope, flailing the air with his hoofs. Dizzy screamed, and Mulk's tongue froze in his mouth. An inch lower and the hoofs would crack Franz's skull.

"Back, back," the groom shouted. "The brute'll kill you." But Franz hung on.

"I've got him. Clear them out, Mulk," he shouted.

Mulk understood. He had seen Amigo respond to Franz, and he knew that this shouting mob would drive the horse mad. He grabbed the groom by the arm and turned him around.

"Stay back behind that house and don't breathe," he ordered in a shrill whisper, pushing the groom back toward the half-dozen men who had followed him. Mulk was an authority. He was supposed to be an animal trainer. The groom motioned his helpers back and then peered curiously around the corner of the building.

Franz talked quietly to the frenzied horse and held onto the rope. He kept his eyes lowered, away from the hoofs flailing so near his head. The blood was throbbing in his temples but from excitement, not fear. Somehow he knew that Amigo wouldn't hurt him. "Quiet, boy, quiet." He held himself motionless while Amigo's paroxysm wore itself out. Finally the horse came down on all fours and stood dripping with sweat, his wet coat gleaming and his snorts splattering Franz's face with foam. One ear was cocked forward, the other lay back. He was ready to escape or fight.

Slowly Franz held out his hand. Amigo hesitated, sniffed, then nuzzled it.

"See, we're friends." He shortened the rope a bit. Amigo reared back but it was a half-hearted rear, no more than a gesture. Franz pulled gently on the rope. Amigo yanked on the halter but followed. Franz took another step, then two or three, talking to Amigo all the time. The horse came with him. Slowly they walked back across the fair ground. At first the halter rope was taut, but by the time they had reached the horse tent, Amigo was almost beside Franz, occasionally nudging the boy's shoulder.

Captain Szabo and Señor Gonzales were waiting in front of the tent.

"That horse is crazy as a loon. I'll have to kill him someday, but he's the smartest horse I ever had." The Mexican's voice was edged with annoyance. "Thank you, Franz. You are a real horseman, eh? You know how to manage Amigo." He took the rope from the boy, tied Amigo in his stall, found a cloth, and began to dry the horse's wet flanks. Then he threw a

blanket over the palomino, came to the door, and shook Franz warmly by the hand.

Captain Szabo caught his son by the shoulder and turned him firmly around toward the big top.

"You youngsters have had enough excitement for one evening. Time to turn in. You'd better go back to the train." Franz could tell by the sound of his father's voice that he was pleased.

"Yes, sir," Mulk and Franz answered in one voice. Dizzy paid no attention. She was stroking the drooping parakeet.

"Come on, Dizzy," Mulk said, taking her arm. "All Coco needs is a little sleep." Franz took her other arm. He was sorry for her too, but his heart was pounding with elation. Amigo liked him. Amigo knew that somehow they were going to belong to each other.

After he had said good night to Mulk and Dizzy and found his own car on the siding, Franz climbed into the upper berth of his father's stateroom and quickly fell asleep. In his dreams he was riding Amigo into the center ring. He swept off his hat. Amigo took a bow to the tiers of blurred, admiring faces. The whole tent rocked with cheers. Franz pushed the sheet back from his hot face and turned over with an ecstatic sigh.

It is well for American children to discover early that their country is made up of many kinds of people, of many races, religions, and customs. Then, the transition to thinking about peoples of other countries is an easy and a natural one, founded on familiarity with and liking for many kinds of people in their own land. It is only a step from Hatsuno's charming little grandmother in America to Chinese Little Pear's understanding family. Swiss Kobi's acceptance of responsibility in the terrifying storm is close kin to the Little Paiute's brave decision. Pennsylvania Dutch Yonie Wondernose and French Ca-

OTHER LANDS

nadian Pierre Pidgeon are equally full of curiosity and resourcefulness. And Chinese Young Fu and Negro Steppin are both ambitious and well-intentioned boys but subject to mistakes nevertheless. In short, human nature is human nature whether it is the American smart aleck, Jemima, paying dearly for showing off or Hungarian Kate eating too many sausages in an equally absurd bit of exhibitionism.

Like the varied peoples in our United States, the heroes and heroines of these stories of other lands are a lovable group that American children will discover are more like themselves than different. For example, a third-grade class was talking about Kintu's fear of the jungle, and the teacher asked the children what they thought had cured Kintu of his fear. They decided that it wasn't the "charm" because that was "nothing but an old fruit pit." After considerable discussion, they thought perhaps Kintu got over being afraid when he had to stay in the jungle and found out that he could use the skills he had already learned to keep himself safe. Then the teacher asked the children if they had ever been afraid of something that they were not afraid of now. Practically every child had. Fear of the dark, of dogs, of deep water, and of a new school were mentioned most often. In each case, the children decided they had recovered from their fear when they did something about it and found out that they could take care of themselves in the dark or in deep water or in a new classroom or with strange dogs. After this discussion, Kintu seemed more than ever like themselves and fears a common difficulty to be dealt with and banished.

One thing children should find in books about other countries is authenticity in all the details and a true picture of the *everyday* life of the people. For a while, children's books about foreign lands read like travel folders. They presented the bizarre, the unusual, and the exotic. Life was a series of fiestas, gaily costumed and picturesque. The toil and struggle were missing. The stories chosen for this section, unlike such unrealistic tales, present everyday people faced with everyday problems, sometimes worried or frightened, sometimes gay or triumphant, but normally doing the best they can at work and play.

This is what stories about people of other lands should do for children—make them kindred under the skin. From such stories young readers develop a warm interest in people and in ways of living different from their own. What child, after reading *Heidi,* has not wanted a bed of straw in a loft and goat's milk and cheese to eat? The silversmiths of Mexico in "Four Silver Pitchers," the Hungarian ranch of *The Good Master,* Young Fu's work with the coppersmiths, the Iceland farm in *Smoky Bay,* little Pedro's jungle hut so lovingly prepared for his grandmother— these people and their ways of life seem as admi-

rable as the child's own family and community. As a result of knowing vicariously peoples of other countries, children are predisposed to warm and friendly relationships with foreign groups when they encounter them in real life. To this end the stories in this group have been chosen.

TIM ALL ALONE

Edward Ardizzone

In this story as in all the Tim stories, the young seafaring lad is a real hero, the very personification of achievement.

One day Tim arrived back at his home by the sea. He had been away for a long holiday and was therefore longing to see his mother and father again.

Imagine, however, his surprise when he found the windows shuttered and the door locked.

He looked through the keyhole and found nobody. He shouted but no one answered.

Then he noticed a bit of paper pinned beside the door. It said 'Gone away. House to Let.'

Poor Tim. He sat down on the step and wondered and wondered what strange thing could have happened.

However, when he had cried a little—and he could not help that—he remembered to say his prayers and felt a little comforted. Then he got up, turned his back on the house and set out on his way once more.

He was determined to search, if necessary, the whole wide world until he had found his parents.

But Tim had no money, so he stopped at a farm-house and asked the farmer to give him a bed for the night.

'You can sleep in my hay loft,' said the farmer, 'and I will give you breakfast and dinner too, but first you must dig my potato patch.' He gave Tim a fork and set him to work.

When night came and Tim lay down in the hay, he felt too tired to be sad, but went straight to sleep.

Tim All Alone, by Edward Ardizzone. Reprinted by permission of Henry Z. Walck, Inc.

At breakfast the next morning Tim told his story.

The good farmer's wife felt sorry for him, so when he came to leave she gave him a large packet of sandwiches and two very rosy apples, slipped some money in his pocket and kissed him goodbye.

Tim's plan was to join one of the small ships which stopped at all the little ports up and down the coast where he could inquire for his parents. He knew they loved the sea and would not live far away from it.

So Tim marched to the seaport town and here his luck was good, for lying in the dock was the very ship he wanted. A little old ship with a tall red funnel, called the *Amelia Jane*.

Luckier still, when Tim went on board, he found they were short of crew and he was signed on at once as a cabin boy.

Once at sea Tim was kept so busy painting, scrubbing, running errands and helping the steward serve the officers' meals that he had little time to fret.

The *Amelia Jane* was a happy ship and all the officers and crew were kindly men and particularly kind to Tim.

The days and weeks went by and at every little port at which they stopped, and there were many of them, Tim would hurry ashore and inquire for his father and mother.

How unhappy he felt when he heard no news of them and how sadly he went back to join his ship.

It was then that the officers and crew were specially nice to him and tried their best to cheer him up.

But perhaps Tim's best friend on board was the ship's cat.

Many a time when work was done Tim would sit in some sheltered corner of the deck and talk to the cat and tell him his life's story.

The cat would answer 'Prrmp, prrmp, miaou, miaou,' as if he understood every word of it.

Now don't forget this cat because, later on, he is going to play a very important part in this tale.

One day the *Amelia Jane* was docked in a small port and Tim, as usual, had been on shore looking for his parents.

He was hurrying back to the ship, having searched in vain, when he saw a lady standing on the pavement. He stopped and, as a last chance, asked her if she knew of them.

'What! lost your parents, have you?' said the lady catching hold of Tim by the hand. 'Then you must come with me to the home for lost children!'

'No, no,' said Tim, 'I don't want to go to a home for lost children; I'm a sailor and must get to my ship now, or I will miss it. Please do let go.'

But the lady held on to his hand as tightly as ever and dragged him 'along the streets till they came to a great dark house with a great dark door.

'Here we are,' she said, taking out a big key and trying to fit it into the keyhole.

At that moment Tim gave a sharp tug which made her drop the key. Then, when she bent down to pick it up, he tugged again and she fell over and let go his hand.

Away went Tim, running as fast as he could, back towards the docks.

But you can imagine his dismay, for when he arrived at the quayside he saw the *Amelia Jane* steaming out to sea. He had missed his ship.

There was only one thing for Tim to do, he must hide. So he slipped on board another steamer and hid under one of the boats.

It was not long before he heard the engines being started and the sound of ropes being let go and he was out at sea once more.

But this new ship was not a happy one like the old *Amelia Jane*. The captain was a horrid man and the crew were a rough and unfriendly lot. They were all particularly horrid to Tim because he was a stowaway.

The weather was bad, yet every day Tim was made to work on deck. He was frozen by the cold North wind and often soaked with rain or salt sea spray.

After a time Tim felt sick, too sick to work.

The captain was furious. 'I can't have sick boys on board,' he shouted. 'Send him ashore.'

The ship was hove-to near a small grey seaside town and a signal was sent for a boat to come to the ship.

When it was alongside, Tim was lowered into the boat and away it went.

Arriving at the town Tim was landed on the stone jetty of the little harbour.

Among the people watching him being lifted out of the boat was a middle-aged lady who took pity on him.

'Ah! the poor wee lad,' she said. 'Carry him to my house and I will nurse him and look after him.' So the boatman carried him up to a small grey house on the hill behind the town, where he was put to bed.

Here he lay sick for many days and Miss Hetty McBain, for that was the lady's name, was very kind to him and nursed him very well.

She gave him porridge and cream, good rich milk and new laid eggs.

Gradually Tim became better, and one day when he was nearly well Miss Hetty said, 'Tim, my boy, I have a plan. I am getting old now and lonely. Stay with me and be my son.'

Tim asked if he could first go away and look for his parents, but Miss Hetty would not hear of it. This made Tim sad because he loved Miss Hetty and did not want to hurt her feelings.

Every day, when Tim was allowed out, he would walk down to the little harbour and stare out to sea and long so much to be away, and every day he became sadder and sadder.

One morning at breakfast Miss Hetty said, 'Tim, my boy, how sad you look. I see now that I must let you go.' Then she gave him a suitcase full of new clothes and some money and kissed him goodbye.

Tim set off feeling both happy and sorry too. But when he reached the harbour he saw something that made him feel really happy, for lying by the jetty was the old *Amelia Jane*.

What a welcome he had on board! How pleased they all were to see him! And the ship's cat was the most pleased of all.

Of course the captain insisted that he should be their cabin boy again.

But Tim's troubles were not over yet. They had not been at sea many days when they ran into bad weather, and, worse still, the ship caught fire.

Tim smelt the smoke first and rushed to tell the captain.

Alas, the strong wind fanned the flames and though the crew worked like heroes they could not put the fire out. At last all the forward part of the ship was ablaze

Sadly the captain gave the order to abandon ship and they clambered into the remaining boats.

At that moment Tim remembered the cat which had been shut up in the mate's cabin.

'Oh, poor cat! I must save it,' he cried, and dashed back on deck, though the crew tried to stop him.

He reached the cabin and caught the cat, but when he turned to go back he found that the flames had leapt up behind him and he could not return.

All that Tim could do was to plunge into the sea with the cat in his arms.

Luckily Tim saw a hatch cover floating nearby which the crew had thrown overboard earlier. He and the cat climbed on to it.

Now the waves were too high and the spray too thick for the crews of the boats to find them, so all that day Tim and the cat drifted across the stormy sea.

At dusk they were cast up on a sandy beach.

They climbed the steep beach and found themselves in the streets of a seaside town.

They stopped at a café and peered through the lighted windows. They were both cold, wet, tired and very very hungry. But Tim had no money for food.

Then Tim noticed through the glass a lady sitting all by herself at a table. She was holding a handkerchief to her eyes as if she was crying.

COULD IT BE HIS MOTHER?

Yes it was.

In a moment Tim was in the café and in his mother's arms.

How happy they were and what a lot they had to tell each other!

Tim's mother explained that when he was on holiday, they read in a newspaper that a pleasure steamer had been lost at sea with all on board. By some terrible mistake Tim's name was given as one of the passengers. They were so sad that they could not bear to live any longer in the old house and so had decided to go away.

Tim told her all about his adventures.

The next day Tim and his parents and the ship's cat all went back to the old home by the sea.

They found it was still un-Let and just the same as before.

Tim's friends Charlotte and Ginger came back to stay with them and they all lived happily there ever afterwards

BUT

You may be sure Tim did not forget Miss Hetty.

Nor did he forget his good friends on the *Amelia Jane,* who had all landed safely.

SNIPP, SNAPP, SNURR
AND THE RED SHOES

Maj Lindman

This story of the Swedish triplets by the au-thor-artist Maj Lindman is one of a series. This little tale has a gaiety about it that matches the colorful illustrations of the original book. It is as popular as that other birthday story Ask Mr. Bear *by Marjorie Flack* (Time for Fairy Tales.)

Snipp, Snapp, and Snurr were three little boys who lived in Sweden.

One day Snipp said, "Mother, dear, tomorrow will be your birthday. Snapp and Snurr and I have talked about it, but we can't decide what to get you for a birthday present."

Snipp said, "I thought you might like a train."

Snapp said, "I thought you might like a pony."

Snurr said, "I know! You would like to have a red wagon!"

Mother thought for a moment. Then she said, "I would like a pair of red slippers, red slippers lined with gold."

Snipp, Snapp, and Snurr decided that mother must have her shoes.

They ran upstairs to their playroom to get their bank which was a white china pig with brown spots. The bank was on the high book-case.

Snipp brought a chair.

Snapp climbed upon the chair, stood on tip-toe, reached for the bank, and handed it to Snurr. Then he climbed down.

The three little boys ran over to the table. They rattled their bank. They shook it, and

Snipp, Snapp, Snurr and the Red Shoes by Maj Lind-man. Albert Whitman & Co., 1932. Used by permission of the publisher

rolled it from side to side to try to get out all their money.

But as long and as hard as they shook it, they could not get out enough money to buy the red shoes.

Snipp, Snapp, and Snurr decided that they must find a way to earn money.

The three little boys asked their mother if they might go out. They ran down the steps and walked toward the corner. All three of them were looking for ways to earn money.

Down the street, near the corner light they saw a neighbor painting a high board fence. It was a very high fence, so high that the man had to stand on a wooden box to reach the top.

Snipp said politely, "Do you need help, sir? I am quite sure that I could finish painting the fence."

The neighbor had many other things to do, so he was glad to have Snipp finish painting.

Snapp and Snurr walked on down the street. They were thinking of ways to earn money to buy the red shoes.

High on the red roof of a house they saw the village chimney sweep. He was cleaning out the chimney with brushes.

Suddenly he called loudly to one of the boys, "Snapp, come and help me!"

Both boys climbed up the tall ladder to the roof, and across the roof, to the very tallest chim-ney.

The man was nearly as black as the chimney he was sweeping. But he smiled kindly as he said, "Snapp, you are so little you can get into the chimney and sweep it cleaner than I can. I will pay you if you will help me.

So Snurr left Snapp on the roof and climbed down all alone.

Snipp was painting a bright red fence.

Snapp was cleaning out the very blackest chimney he had ever seen.

Snurr walked on, wondering to himself what he could find to do. He must earn money to help buy the red shoes.

At last Snurr saw a big mill where wheat was ground into flour. Before the mill stood his friend, the miller. He wore a bright red cap and was smoking his longest pipe.

Snurr stepped up to him and said, "Please, sir, will you give me a job?"

The miller laughed, "Well, well, Snurr, what

do you say? You want to be a miller? Good! You can begin work now."

All three boys were very happy. Each one had found some way to earn money to help buy the red shoes for his mother.

Snipp drew his brush up and down the fence busily. He felt most important.

The fence grew brighter and brighter until it glistened in the sun.

Snipp worked so fast and used so much red paint that he spilled some of it all over his clothes. He even splashed red paint on his cheeks and his bare legs. So as the fence grew redder and redder, Snipp grew redder and redder, too.

His suit which was once such a pretty blue was all spattered with red.

Snapp's suit was not much better! Snapp pushed the brush up and down the dirty chimney. The black soot flew all over his nose, and his hair and his clothes. Soon his pretty blue suit was gray. Then it grew darker. And the longer he worked the blacker he got.

The cat which sat on the roof watching him was sure that a little black boy was hard at work!

But Snapp was very happy. Soon bright coins would jingle in his pocket which would help to buy the red slippers for mother.

And Snapp worked harder than ever, whistling a little tune as he worked.

Snurr was finishing his work. He had worked hard at the mill. Once he had surprised the miller by carrying a large sack of flour.

Snipp worked painting a fence, and he grew red.

Snapp worked cleaning a chimney, and he grew black.

Snurr worked at the flour mill, and he grew white from head to foot. He looked just like a snowman.

Money jingled cheerily in Snurr's pockets as he left the mill. The miller had been much pleased with his work.

Snurr now had his share of the money to help buy the red shoes for his mother.

Snipp, Snapp, and Snurr all finished their work at the same time.

As they were running happily home they met in the market place.

The little boy in red was Snipp.

The little boy in black was Snapp.

The little boy in white was Snurr.

Each took his money out of his pocket.

When they counted all their money they found that now they had enough to buy the red shoes.

Snipp, Snapp, and Snurr were very happy!

They decided to hurry to the shoemaker right away to see if he had the red shoes.

Down the street they went. It was nearly sunset and they were afraid the shop might close.

They ran into the shoemaker's shop, each carrying his part of the money.

Because Snipp was in the lead, he began, "Mr. Shoemaker, have you—"

Because Snapp was next, he said, "red shoes lined with gold?"

Because Snurr was last he finished, "Shoes that will fit our mother's feet?"

The shoemaker laughed, "Have I red shoes lined with gold that will fit your mother's feet? That I have. They are right here on the shelf, the finest you can buy, near or far."

Snipp, Snapp, and Snurr each gave the shoemaker his part of the money.

The shoemaker wrapped the shoes up in a box, and the three little boys hurried home, each taking his turn to carry the package.

At last they were home. Because Snipp was the first to find work, Snapp and Snurr agreed that he should be the one to give the package to Mother.

"Here is a present for you, Mother!" they cried as they burst into the door.

Mother was surprised to see a red boy, a black boy, and a white boy, instead of her three little boys in blue.

"Snipp, Snapp, Snurr! Where have you been?" she cried.

"We have been earning money to buy you a birthday present, Mother dear, and here it is!" they answered.

Mother untied the string, unwrapped the box, and took out the red shoes lined with gold.

"Why, here are the red shoes that I wanted more than anything else," she cried. "They are the most beautiful slippers in the world!"

She was so happy that she waved her lovely red slippers in the air.

Snipp, Snapp, and Snurr, the three little boys, joined hands and danced around their mother.

As they danced, they sang, "Happy birthday!"

PIERRE PIDGEON

Lee Kingman

It is hoped that the children who enjoy this unusual story will, when they are older, discover Lee Kingman's The Best Christmas. *Pierre is French Canadian and the Christmas story is about a Finnish-American family. Both stories have a convincing realism and warmth that are characteristic of this writer's work.*

Pierre Pidgeon was seven years old, waiting to be eight. He lived in a part of Canada called the Gaspé, which is a large piece of land surrounded on three sides by water.

His father was a fisherman who sailed out in his boat every day. Very often, he left early in the morning when Pierre was still asleep.

But every afternoon Pierre went down to the dock to watch his father's boat come in and to help unload the fish.

Since fishing didn't bring in much money to take care of the Pidgeon family, Pierre's mother baked bread in an outdoor oven and sometimes sold it to tourists who came along the road, and Pierre liked to help her.

Pierre liked to do lots of things. He liked to drive a dogcart—and sail on his father's boat.

But most of all he liked to build ship models. It took a great deal of patience to do this, but when he grew tired of it, Pierre would always run down to the beach to play.

He liked, too, visiting the store near the dock where the boats came in. The shelves were full of canned foods and fishing tackle and cloth and clothes for the people who lived in the town, and there were wood carvings for tourists who liked to buy souvenirs. But most of all Pierre liked the shelf halfway up on the right just inside the door. For one day when he walked into the store to buy a spool of thread for his mother, he looked at that shelf and right in the middle of it, he saw a beautiful ship model.

It was the nicest he had ever seen, and he thought it was even better than the ones he made because it was all inside a bottle!

Mr. LeClerc, who ran the store, saw Pierre

looking at the boat-in-the-bottle. "How do you like that ship model, Pierre?" he asked.

"I like it very much!" said Pierre, "but how did the man ever make it inside the bottle?"

"Ah," said Mr. LeClerc, and smiled at Pierre. "There is only one way for ships to get inside bottles. They grow inside!"

Pierre looked at Mr. LeClerc. "But boats aren't alive! How can they grow inside a bottle, if they aren't alive?"

Mr. LeClerc shook his head. "I don't know, Pierre. But ships can move just like dogs and horses and oxen, and how else could a boat get inside a bottle if it weren't very small indeed, as small as a seed bean?"

Every time he went to the store, he stopped to look at the boat-in-the-bottle and wish it belonged to him. Once he asked Mr. LeClerc how much it cost, and Mr. LeClerc put his head on one side and said, "That's a very good bottle. I should say a dollar."

Pierre felt very sad inside, because he knew he would never have a whole dollar all his own to spend.

His mother knew Pierre was seven, waiting to be eight, and one day when they were all sitting out by the windmill, she asked him what he would like for his birthday. Pierre thought of the shelf halfway up on the right just inside the door of the store by the dock and his eyes grew very bright. "I should like the boat in Mr. Le-Clerc's store!" he cried. "The boat-in-the-bottle!"

Pierre's mother smiled at him. "But you can make boats," she said.

Pierre sighed. "But I can't bottle them!" he said.

One day Pierre walked along the road driving Henri, the ox, to the pasture. Henri was not an ox to be hurried, so Pierre strolled behind, only switching him once in a while when he stopped to munch clover by the roadway.

When they came to the pasture, there was a

fine long view of the sea and Pierre sat down to look at it. As it was a very warm day, he soon put his cap over his face and went to sleep.

But it did not take him long to wake up, when he heard someone calling, "Oh, help!"

He jumped up!

He saw a lady caught in a corner of the pasture fence by a very large ox. His horns were lowered, but Pierre knew from the spots on his back that it was Henri. Pierre ran up and held onto his tail. "He will not hurt you," he told the lady. "Henri is a very gentle ox."

"That may be," said the lady, "but I'd just as soon he stopped staring me in the face."

Pierre tugged at Henri's tail and the ox turned away and went back to the clover. The lady brushed her skirts and picked up the little camp stool and small easel she had dropped.

"I want to paint a picture," she said. "Do you think you can keep that ox from pushing me off the edge of the cliff while I do it?"

Pierre said he thought he could, so the lady set up her camp stool and sat on it and balanced her easel so that it stood up straight. She took out her sketch pad and arranged her paints on the ground. Pierre sat down where he could watch Henri, who was not fierce at all when you knew him. And he also kept an eye on the lady, who squinted out at the ocean as she painted.

"What is that odd-looking rock out there?" she asked Pierre.

"That is the ship of stone," Pierre explained, "because it is shaped like a boat."

The lady worked a long time and Pierre felt that she kept looking at him, too. When she put her paints away and finished washing off her paint brushes, Pierre jumped up. He wanted to see what she had painted.

The lady let him look and right spank in the middle of the picture was Pierre Pidgeon, keeping an eye on Henri.

"That's me!" cried Pierre.

"So it is," said the lady. "And here is something for rescuing me from the ox." She gave Pierre a dollar!

When he had stopped looking hard at the dollar and said thank you, he gave Henri a warm slap and ran off down the road to the village.

There was Mr. LeClerc's store and Pierre stopped short just outside the door. Suppose someone else had bought the boat-in-the-bottle! His heart beat three times as fast as it usually did, when he walked in the door. And then his heart beat even faster than that—the boat-in-the-bottle was still there!

"Good afternoon, Mister Pidgeon," said Mr. LeClerc smiling at him. "Have you come for another look at your boat?" Pierre nodded and looked at it speechlessly. The bottle shone in the afternoon sunlight and the little boat inside looked as if it were sailing along on a good stiff breeze.

Pierre felt the dollar in his hand and then he walked all around the store. There were the big round balls of colored candy that his little sister liked, and there were the silky skeins of embroidery thread his mother liked. But Pierre came back to the shelf halfway up on the right, just inside the door.

"Mr. LeClerc," said Pierre, swallowing hard. "I want the boat-in-the-bottle." He held out the dollar, which was now well crumpled by his fist.

Mr. LeClerc blinked. "Well, well!" he said, and reached up for the bottle. He put it down on the counter in front of Pierre, who picked it up very carefully in both hands.

"Do you want a box for it?" Mr. LeClerc asked.

"No, thank you," said Pierre. "I shall carry it very carefully and take it straight home so it won't break." He looked at it again. "The bottle has much too small a neck for anyone to push the boat through it. How do you suppose the boat *does* get in the bottle, Mr. LeClerc?"

"I don't know, Pierre. But if you ever find out, you'll be a very smart boy indeed."

Pierre walked out very carefully and watched his feet as he went down the three front steps of the store. He went along the rocky road by the beach and up the hill to the house.

There was his mother smiling from the doorway. Running around the corner of the house came his little sister—and the Newfoundland dog, Geneviève, who often pulled their dogcart, came bounding around the corner, too. She was a very big dog and was very fond of Pierre. She was so glad to see him now that she sprang toward him happily. Pierre held the bottle high over his head. "Be careful, Geneviève!" warned Pierre, but he felt the bottle slip. Out it flew from his hands!

"Oh!" he wailed, and shut his eyes tight. Crash! When he opened his eyes, there was the bottle in a hundred pieces on a stone at his feet.

"Bad Geneviève!" said Pierre, and the big dog hung her head and looked at Pierre sadly.

Pierre bent over to see how much of a shipwreck it was, and found that the little boat was still whole, but the masts and sails had fallen lengthwise along the top of the deck. It looked as if it had fought through a very bad storm.

He held it up to his mother. "This was the boat-in-the-bottle," he said.

Mother knew Pierre's heart was as broken as the bottle. "Come inside for supper," she said. "It looks like a very nice boat, even without the bottle."

"But it's broken," said Pierre and put it down tenderly on the shelf in the kitchen. He succeeded very well in keeping the tears from rolling down his cheeks while he ate his boiled potatoes and fish for supper.

His father and little sister were very sorry, too. "I remember seeing that a good many times in the store," Father said. "And just last month I picked up a bottle like it that was washed up on the beach. It's down in the boathouse."

"Maybe I could put the boat in it," cried Pierre, and then felt very sad, because he didn't know how the boat could possibly get inside of the bottle. It just seemed as if Mr. LeClerc were right—and they did grow up inside.

But after a while, he told them how he earned the dollar to buy the boat and they were all delighted. Everyone agreed that Henri was a very smart ox.

After supper his father sat on the front doorstep with his pipe, while his mother put his little sister to bed.

Pierre took the shipwrecked boat off the shelf and ran around to the back of the house where the boathouse stood.

He took Geneviève along, too, because if he kept her with him, she couldn't come bounding out to meet him. In a corner he found the bottle his father had told him about, and it was just the same as the bottle he had broken.

He rubbed the dust off on his shirt, but the narrow neck still looked much too small to put a boat with all its masts and tiny sails through.

Inside the bottle was a rusty fish hook. Pierre poked his finger in and as he pulled the hook out, he had an idea. He picked up the little boat and pushed the masts down flat along the deck the way they had fallen when the bottle broke. Then the boat just slid through the neck of the bottle! Pierre stared and stared! He had a boat-in-the-bottle!

He tied a piece of string to the fish hook and dangled it inside the bottle until the prong caught lightly in one of the little sails. Then he pulled until the masts stood up, as firm and straight as ever. He tugged gently until the fish hook came out, and then the little boat looked just as if it were sailing along on a good stiff breeze inside the bottle.

Pierre called out, "Oh!" and ran into the house as fast as he dared. Father jumped up to keep Geneviève away, and his mother came running downstairs with his baby sister in her arms.

"Look!" cried Pierre. "It's really my own boat-in-the-bottle now!"

They put it over the mantelpiece in the house, where Geneviève couldn't reach it, and Pierre looked at it proudly. He ran to the front door, but his mother called, "Pierre, where are you going? It's time for bed."

"Oh, please!" cried Pierre. "I want to tell Mr. LeClerc how to grow a boat-in-a-bottle!"

Pierre's mother smiled. "All right," she said, and Pierre ran off down the road as fast as he could.

MADELINE

Ludwig Bemelmans

This amusing jingle sounds as if it should be in Time for Poetry, *and perhaps it should. But, we suspect it is more story than poetry and more Bemelmans than anything else. Of course, you must see the book with its marvelous Bemelmans' illustrations. Poor Madeline! She inhabits a French boarding school, hence the "twelve little girls in two straight lines" doing everything in two straight lines except the appendix. Only Madeline managed that. This story is fun to illustrate. Be sure to look up Ludwig Bemelmans'* Hansi, *too.*

In an old house in Paris
that was covered with vines
lived twelve little girls in two straight lines.
In two straight lines they broke their bread
and brushed their teeth
and went to bed.
They smiled at the good
and frowned at the bad
and sometimes they were very sad.
They left the house
at half past nine
in two straight lines
in rain
or shine—
the smallest one was Madeline.
She was not afraid of mice—
she loved winter, snow, and ice.
To the tiger in the zoo
Madeline just said, "Pooh-pooh,"
and nobody knew so well
how to frighten Miss Clavel.
In the middle of one night
Miss Clavel turned on the light
and said, "Something is not right!"
Little Madeline sat in bed,
cried and cried; her eyes were red.
And soon after Dr. Cohn
came, he rushed out to the phone
and he dialed: DANton-ten-six—
"Nurse," he said, "it's an appendix!"
Everybody had to cry—

not a single eye was dry.
Madeline was in his arm
in a blanket safe and warm.
In a car with a red light
they drove out into the night.
Madeline woke up two hours
later, in a room with flowers.
Madeline soon ate and drank.
On her bed there was a crank,
and a crack on the ceiling had the habit
of sometimes looking like a rabbit.
Outside were birds, trees, and sky—
And so ten days passed quickly by.
One nice morning Miss Clavel said—
"Isn't this a fine—
day to visit
Madeline."
VISITORS FROM TWO TO FOUR
read a sign outside her door.
Tiptoeing with solemn face,
with some flowers and a vase,
in they walked and then said, "Ahhh,"
when they saw the toys and candy
and the dollhouse from Papa.
But the biggest surprise by far—
on her stomach
was a scar!
"Good-by," they said, "we'll come again,"
and the little girls left in the rain.
They went home and broke their bread
brushed their teeth
and went to bed.
In the middle of the night
Miss Clavel turned on her light
and said, "Something is not right!"
And afraid of a disaster
Miss Clavel ran fast
and faster,
and she said, "Please children do—
tell me what is troubling you?"
And all the little girls cried, "Boohoo,
we want to have our appendix out, too!"
"Good night, little girls!
Thank the lord you are well!
And now go to sleep!"
said Miss Clavel.
And she turned out the light—
and closed the door—
and that's all there is—
there isn't any more.

Text from *Madeline* by permission of Simon and Schuster, Publishers. Copyright, 1939, by Ludwig Bemelmans

KINTU

Elizabeth Enright

Kintu lives in the African Congo, but his problem is universal—how to get over a particular fear. After the children have enjoyed the story, an interesting discussion can grow out of this problem. What cured Kintu of his fear? Was it the charm, which was only a fruit pit? Let the children argue it out. They will probably conclude that Kintu got over his fear when he discovered that the things he knew how to do kept him safe in the jungle. Ask the children if they have ever been cured of a fear they had when they were younger—fear of the dark, perhaps, or of dogs or of deep water or what not? The conclusion is, of course, that we get over being afraid when we do something about the thing we fear and discover that we can take care of ourselves.

The Jungle Village

Kintu was a little black boy who lived in Africa. He lived with his father and mother and his five brothers and sisters in a big mud hut with a straw roof, shaped like a beehive. The beehive in which Kintu lived was the largest of a great group of beehives in the middle of the jungle, for Kintu's father, Kitomba, was the chief of his tribe, and therefore a very important person. Kintu was his eldest son, which meant that he, too, would one day be a chief.

He had two brothers and three sisters to play with. There was Timbo, who could throw a spear farther than Kintu could, although he was a year younger. And there were Kakopa and Kaku, who were twins and who looked so much alike that Kakopa had to wear a ring in her nose so that people could tell which was which. Then there was Wapi, who was fat, and rather bow-legged, and always eating something. And last of all there was Nomba, who was the baby and who spent most of her time in a little hammock which hung from her mother's shoulders.

They were very busy children; their days were filled with lessons—most exciting ones. Kintu had more of these than anyone else, because he

was the eldest son and to be a chief you must know many things.

You must know, for instance, how to throw a spear faultlessly, how to shoot an arrow perfectly; and every day Kintu practiced for hours, hurling his spear and shooting his arrows at a red circle painted on the trunk of a baobab tree.

He learned how to play the drums, and with the palms of his hands make them talk the drum language which in Africa is the way that messages are sent from village to village.

"Look out, look out," say the drums, beating deeply, "an enemy tribe is coming down the river"; or "Look out, look out, an angry storm approaches from the east!" Usually they send warning messages but sometimes they only converse together.

Kintu would sit with his drum (n'goma) before him, his hands thumping on the tightly stretched skin, and for miles around the jungle murmured with the sounds he made.

A chief's son must be able to dance to the drums as well as to play them. Kintu learned devil dances, and fever dances, dances of triumph, dances to bring good hunting, or fine weather, or the rain, and all of them were different. Kintu liked the devil dances best because when he did them, he wore a magnificent headdress made of crimson feathers and telephone wire. (His father considered the telephone wire a great bargain; he had got it from a white trader who had passed that way several years before, and he had only given four leopard skins and a pair of elephant's tusks in exchange for a big coil of it. They used it for all sorts of things: Kintu's mother wove it into their headdresses, and made baskets out of it; it even held their roof together in places.)

The devil dances took longer than any of the others, and were more interesting because there was a great deal of leaping and shouting to them. The drumbeats grew louder and louder till your ears rang with the sound of them, and you kept on dancing till you fell exhausted in the dust, and had to be taken home.

Kintu learned many other things, too. He was taught how to cure the hides of wild animals, and how to make arrowheads and spearheads of metal and stone. He learned how to kindle a fire with two sticks, how to set a trap, how to climb trees almost as fast as a monkey. He learned which berries were poisonous, and which ones were the best cure for snakebite.

Timbo and Wapi had lessons much the same as his own, but Kakopa and Kaku learned other things; they made pottery and cooked and wove mats of grass and palm leaves. They had their dances, too. All of the children were dressed alike in little colored skirts except for Nomba who was attired simply in a bracelet and a head necklace. All of them had brass ornaments on their ankles and around their necks, and would have felt strange without the quiet jingling which accompanied their walking.

Every day the children awoke at the very first light of dawn, and rising from the hard earth which was the only bed they had, shook themselves like little dogs and walked straight out of the hut to work or play as they pleased. Kintu took up his spear and practiced throwing it. Kakopa and Kaku wove their mats; and Timbo and Wapi played leapfrog or pretended to be hunters stalking a panther in the jungle. Nomba was too fat and too young to do anything but lie in the sun, chewing a piece of sugar cane.

In the middle of the morning, their mother made a fire by rubbing two sticks together till a spark caught the leaves and kindling on the flat stone which was her fireplace. Then in a great earthenware pot she cooked their breakfast— corn and manioc root and eggs (and sometimes chicken).

When it was done she called them, and they all sat down around the big pot and dipped into it with their fingers. Wapi usually managed to get the most, and often burned himself because he never could bear to wait for things to cool.

Their only other meal was in the evening and was usually exactly the same as the first; but sometimes as a special treat, their mother made them a delicious pudding of corn flour and palm oil and dried white caterpillars.

After supper the people of the village would gather around a fire and talk or sing. The men spoke of hunting, and the oldest ones had stories to tell of the times when lions were fiercer and elephants bigger than any found nowadays. Kintu, sitting beside his father, would shiver and try not to listen, because though nobody knew it, he was afraid of the jungle!

Magic

Now living in a jungle is very much like living next door to the zoo, except that the animals are not in cages, which makes quite a difference. Sometimes at night Kintu would lie awake and listen to the strange sounds made by wild creatures in the jungle, and be very afraid.

There was an insect which ticked all night long like a little watch, and an insect which made a loud noise like an alarm clock. There were the excited voices of suddenly awakened monkeys, and the croaking of big frogs which sounded like old men talking together in deep hoarse voices. There were panthers and leopards whose snarls were like the sound of thick canvas being torn. And there were the grunts of hippopotami who left the river and walked on land at night. There were noises made by nightjars and cicadas, and all the other hundreds of creatures who preferred to do their talking after dark.

Kintu would lie on his hard earthen bed and shake with fright, because he knew that when he was older his father would expect him to hunt in the jungle and to know it as well as he knew his own village. It would never do for a chief's son to be afraid!

It worried Kintu badly, and finally he decided to go and see the witch doctor and ask him for a spell to make him braver.

So one morning, after breakfast, he stole away from his brothers and sisters and playmates, and all by himself walked to the witch doctor's hut.

It was set apart from the rest of the village, and on either side of the door were little idols carved of black wood. One had a very ugly, cross face, and one grinned from ear to ear showing a double row of square, ivory teeth. Kintu bowed and raised his spear to each of them, then he entered the hut and came face to face with the witch doctor.

The witch doctor was very old and very wise, and he wore a derby hat, which he had got from the same trader who brought the telephone wire. From his great height he looked down at Kintu, without smiling, and Kintu would have shaken in his shoes if he had any to shake in.

"Chief's son," said the witch doctor, "why have you come to see me?"

"Witch doctor," began Kintu bravely, "I am in great trouble. I am afraid of the jungle!" He

After several minutes (long ones, they seemed) the witch doctor stood up, pushing back his hat. Still without smiling he looked down at Kintu.

"Chief's son," he said, "I believe I have a cure for you." He leaned down, took something out of a red earthenware bowl, and put it into Kintu's little black hand.

"Take this," he said, "and tomorrow, when the sun is at its highest, walk three hundred paces into the jungle towards the east. After you have walked for three hundred paces, plant this charm at the foot of the first baobab tree you find; then, when you have buried it, say these words—" (But what the words were I cannot tell you for they were black magic, and a secret.)

"In the jungle? All by myself?" asked Kintu in a timid voice.

"All by yourself, chief's son," said the witch doctor firmly.

Kintu walked slowly home. Once he stopped and opened his hand to see what the charm was like; it was nothing but the dry stone of a fruit and didn't look as though it had much magic in it; but the witch doctor had said it had, and Kintu believed him.

That evening he couldn't eat his supper and his mother was worried about him.

"You have been eating between meals again," she said. "When *will* you learn to leave that monkey-bread tree alone?"

But Kintu only sighed, and said nothing. Very late that night he lay awake and listened to the jungle sounds which seemed louder and more terrifying than ever. He thought the cicadas were chanting a jeering song: "Afraid, afraid, afraid," they cried, over and over again.

"Perhaps after tomorrow you'll be singing another song," whispered Kintu into the darkness; and feeling a little more cheerful, he went to sleep.

In the Jungle

The next day dawned bright and very hot; and Kintu went through his duties in a daze.

When, soon after their morning meal, the sun had ridden to its highest point, and everybody else had gone to sleep in the shade, Kintu picked up his spear (ekonga), and holding the charm in his other hand, tiptoed through the drowsy village and into the jungle.

paused, and glanced up to see if the witch doctor looked disapproving, but there was no change in the old man's expression, so he continued. "Yes, I'm afraid of it. All of it. Its beasts, its noises and its huge trees. I don't even like the way it smells. How can I ever be a great chief like my father when I am such a coward?"

He hung his head for he was very much ashamed.

"This is bad!" said the witch doctor. "I must think." And he sat down on the floor, pulled his derby hat over his nose and thought. Kintu leaned against the wall and watched him almost without breathing, he was so terribly excited.

It was hot and steamy under the great trees; it smelled like the inside of a greenhouse, warm and damp. Everywhere the silk cotton trees raised their great trunks; and high, high overhead a whole, separate airy world existed: parrots called in cross voices, a thousand birds sang different songs, and monkeys leapt nimbly along the boughs, chattering and scolding.

Counting all the time, and forgetting to be afraid, Kintu looked up and stubbed his toe badly on a root. By this time he had walked his first hundred paces and was beginning his second hundred. The farther he walked the wilder the jungle grew, and he had to beat back the undergrowth and tear apart the vines which hung, covered with flowers, from every tree.

Once he surprised a group of little brown monkeys who were sitting sociably on the ground in a circle, eating berries. They simply leapt up the trunk of a palm tree when they saw him, and sat high in the leaves telling him what they thought of him till long after he had passed.

Great moths flew blindly into his face; and once he came upon a hibiscus bush so beautiful, with its flaming red flowers, that he stopped and stared at it.

All this time he had forgotten about being afraid, but now as he came to the middle of his last hundred paces the shadows seemed suddenly darker, and the trees taller than before, and he found himself counting more and more rapidly.

"Two hundred and eighty," said Kintu, leaping over a log, "two hundred and eighty-one—eighty-two—eighty-three . . ." On his right something gave a squeal and plunged into the bushes.

"Eighty-four, eighty-five," shouted Kintu in a loud, bold voice (he was running now), "eighty-six, eighty-seven, eighty-eight, eighty-nine . . ."

At last the three hundred paces were behind him, and he began to look about for a baobab tree.

There were silk cotton trees, and gum trees, and pandanus trees, and borassus trees, and ebony trees, and rubber trees, and mahogany trees, and kakula trees; but there was not a single baobab tree in sight!

Kintu sighed; his heart was beating like a tomtom and the palms of his hands felt cold and damp; but he had come this far and he simply couldn't turn back till he had buried the magic fruit pit.

So he hunted and he hunted, and went farther and farther into the jungle, and at last he came upon an enormous baobab tree standing all by itself in a clearing.

He felt safer somehow now that he had found it, and with relief he knelt among its great roots and scooped out a hole in the ground with the head of his spear; he buried the charm and covered it with earth. After that, he said the words of black magic which the witch doctor had taught him.

Then he picked up his spear and started back.

It had taken him a long time to find the baobab tree and by now it was the middle of the afternoon; the shadows were growing longer.

A crowd of little gnats circled around his head as he walked, buzzing in high thin voices till his ears rang and he felt dizzy. He kept waving his spear at them to drive them away, but they didn't mind it in the least and came back again as soon as he stopped.

On and on stumbled Kintu, among flowers, and tendrils, and great leaves. He realized that he had lost his way, and that so far the magic had not worked, because he felt more frightened than ever.

He thought about his family all safe together in the village, and wondered when they would miss him and begin to look for him. He thought about the stories told by the old hunters of fierce lions who sometimes come into the jungle at night, of hyenas whose cry is like the laughter of a devil-god, of great elephants with tusks of ivory who can uproot small trees with their trunks. He thought about the buried fruit pit and the magic words, and they seemed small protection against the jungle and its many dangers. He wished that he had never gone to see the witch doctor at all, and that he had allowed himself to be a coward in peace.

Kintu began to cry quietly, because he was sure that he would never see his family again, and he was terribly afraid. He stopped walking and stood very still among great ferns like giant feather dusters: it seemed foolish to go on when whatever direction he took was bound to be the wrong one.

It was growing darker now, and already the

tree toads had begun their evening conversation. "Wack-a-wack-a-wack," they cried in harsh voices from every tree. The gnats, fortunately, had got tired of Kintu's waving spear and had all gone off together to find some other creature to torment; so except for the remarks of the tree toads, and the occasional cry of a bird, it seemed very still.

Then, all at once, quite near, he heard a sound like that of thick canvas being torn in two. The snarl of a leopard!

It no longer seemed useless to go on; in fact, it seemed most necessary to go somewhere very quickly; and Kintu, spear in hand, began to run faster than he had ever run before.

Ahead of him, six little monkeys, who had also heard the dangerous sound, went leaping and skipping along the ground at great speed. Kintu, feeling somehow that they were his friends, followed them; and when they came to a huge tree hung with creepers which the monkeys swarmed neatly up, like little sailors climbing up a rigging, he went right after them as fast as he could go.

Up and up he struggled, with his spear between his strong teeth, and his little black fingers and toes curling around the thick vine almost as cleverly as the monkeys' did. The creeper looped itself over one of the lower branches and returned to earth on the other side, so Kintu began climbing up the boughs; stretch, pull, swing! Stretch, pull, swing!—till he had nearly reached the top of the tree, and then he sat down on a huge limb with his shoulder against the broad trunk, and his spear across his knees. His heart was thumping like anything and he was out of breath, but he felt slightly safer.

The six little monkeys, who didn't seem to mind him at all, sat on a branch just above him, and said things very fast in monkey language about leopards. Kintu wished that he could understand them and join in their conversation; he wanted to ask them if leopards were any good at climbing trees. Still, even if he couldn't speak to them, it was a comfort just to have them there, and he hoped they wouldn't go away.

All about him stretched the strange leaves and branches of jungle trees, and below him he saw the great ferns and flowers through which he had beaten his way. Overhead the sky was a darker blue, with a little purple in it, and already there was a star, pale and cold, shining just over the place where the sun had set.

The air was filled with queer smells. A clump of yellow orchids bloomed in a deserted bird's nest several feet below him and gave off a perfume so strong and heavy that he grew tired of it very soon. There were big red berries on a tree nearby that had an odor rather like cough medicine; and you've been in the monkey house at the zoo, haven't you? So you know how the monkeys smelled.

It was really twilight, now; and Kintu saw the bright busy lights of fireflies everywhere. Huge mosquitoes came whining out of the shadows; cicadas sang at the tops of their voices, and the tree toads almost screamed at each other. An evening wind stirred for a moment in the feathery treetops and moved the branch above Kintu where the monkeys were dozing in a row. It woke them up, and they chattered anxiously at each other for a minute. But they soon went back to sleep; and Kintu, feeling like the loneliest person on earth, continued to stare at the sparkling patterns made by fireflies against the darkness.

Presently the moon rose, huge and lopsided, above the world; each leaf glittered in its light, and the brass bracelets on Kintu's ankle looked as if they were made of purest gold.

The night was full of sounds: rustling sounds and scratchings and scamperings; squeaks and grunts in the darkness below; the singing of the night birds in the leaves above.

Then Kintu heard another sound—a new one. He heard the heavy, soft footsteps of an enormous creature stepping quietly; the snapping of shrubs and the squelching sound of wet earth under huge feet. He leaned forward and peered still more intently into the blackness below him. A tremendous shape, darker than the shadows from which it came, moved gently and ponderously towards the tree where he was hidden. Bigger than a house, it looked; almost as big as a mountain, Kintu thought. Slowly, slowly the Thing approached; then paused directly below him. Suddenly there was a faint sound of scraping, and the tree began to quiver as though in an earthquake; the monkeys jabbered nervously, and Kintu knew that an elephant, the largest of all wild creatures, was scratching his back on a branch.

Then slowly, as before, the great beast went on its way; the noise of snapping twigs and heavy tread grew fainter, and it was seen no more.

Hours passed; the moon was high in the sky; and Kintu, too tired to think of fear any longer, settled himself against the tree trunk and slept with the monkeys.

The Leopard

He must have slept a long time, because when the shrill, excited voices of the monkeys woke him, he saw that the moon had set, and the world was as black as the inside of a pocket.

He looked down wondering what was the matter. At first he saw nothing but the roaming lights of the fireflies. And then a chill of fear ran up the calves of his legs and along his spine to the nape of his neck; for below him he saw two small lights, side by side, which did not move; two small lights which he knew were the eyes of an animal watching him.

Squealing and scolding, the monkeys bounded along the branches, dived into the boughs of another tree and were gone.

Kintu faced real danger, alone.

Once more he heard the low snarl which had so frightened him earlier in the evening. The leopard had found him, after all.

The two lights moved a little; Kintu knew that the animal was crouching, making sure of the distance before he sprang.

Then the eyes leapt forward; there was the swish of a heavy body flying through the air, the impact of it against the tree, and the sound of sharp claws tearing wood.

Determinedly, the leopard climbed the tree towards Kintu.

It was useless to be frightened now. Something would have to be done, and quickly too.

Swiftly and quietly Kintu stood up on the branch. He held on to the trunk with his left hand, and in his right he raised the spear high above his shoulder.

He could hardly see the dark shape of the animal climbing towards him, but he would have to take a chance.

"Now or never," said Kintu in a small voice, and hurled the spear.

Then there was a grunt and the thud of a soft, heavy weight falling upon the earth. After that there were no more sounds at all: and Kintu knew that the leopard would not bother him again. Not this one, anyway.

Trembling all over, but almost shouting with triumph, he climbed, feeling his way, a little higher in the tree. How glad he was, now, that his father had made him practice throwing the spear hour after hour, day after day.

"I certainly won't sleep again," said Kintu; and slept.

Drumbeats

The next time he woke up it was morning. Long pale fingers of early sunlight slanted through the leaves. Every bird was singing as though it were necessary to sing louder than any other bird. The world was golden and fresh and drenched with dew.

Kintu stretched his stiff arms and legs, and yawned with a great noise. He looked for his spear and wondered for a moment if he had dropped it. Then he remembered about the leopard.

Quickly he climbed down the branches and slid along the creepers to the ground.

There, stretched at the foot of the tree, lay the leopard, so beautiful with its tawny dark-spotted fur that Kintu was sorry he had killed it. But when he looked closer and saw the cruel curving white teeth, and the glittering claws half hidden in the soft paws, he was sorry no longer.

"It is better to kill than to be killed," said Kintu wisely; and pulling his spear from the leopard's hide, he started off once more to find his village.

It was a beautiful morning! Wet leaves glittered in the sun like leaves of gold. Great drops of dew fell on his head; and there was a little pool in the cup of every flower.

Feeling thirsty, he tipped a big leaf down to his open mouth, and water poured into it as if from a pitcher.

He was hungry, too, and stopped for a minute to pull some purple berries from a vine. Nothing had ever tasted so delicious.

He felt like a king as he strode through the

jungle, brandishing his spear and singing: "I am not afraid!"

The wild creatures, watching him, knew that this was true.

"He is not afraid," screamed the gray parrots in the treetops. "He is not afraid," sang all the birds together. "He is not afraid, he is not afraid," chattered the noisy monkeys; and great serpents, sunning themselves on branches, watched him through the leaves, and said in slow voices, "He is not afraid."

The leopards saw him, too, and the black panther with golden eyes, hidden behind a screen of flowers. "No, he is not afraid," they said, and turned away into the shadows feeling fear themselves.

Never had Kintu been so happy; he was filled with hope, and was sure that he would find his village, and that everything would be all right after all. He listened with joy to all the shrieking, babbling, singing, chattering noises of the early morning jungle. He liked its noises. He loved the way is smelled.

Then something made him stop, quite still, in his tracks. He held his breath, and listened with ears which had been trained to sharpness by the jungle, to another sound. Far, far to the right of him, there was a faint throbbing in the air. Yes! There could be no doubt about it; it was the beating of drums that he heard and this is what they were saying:

"Chief Kitomba's eldest son has disappeared. Has he been seen? Has he been seen?"

And then, still farther away, to his left, the drums of another village replied, "Chief Kitomba's son has not been seen. Chief Kitomba's son has not been seen."

Kintu's heart skipped a beat. The drums which had spoken first were the drums of his village, he knew. If he turned to the right and followed their sound he would surely find his way home.

He couldn't go fast enough! He ran; and skipped over creepers and leapt high in the air, twirling his spear, and yelling for joy. But he did not forget to stop now and then and make a scratch on the bark of a tree with his spearhead. When he got back to the village he would ask some of the men to get the leopard for him. And he wanted them to be sure and find it.

The jungle was loud with the sound of drumbeats now. All the villages for miles around were answering the message from his village, and relaying it to others still farther away.

It grew very hot; yellow mist rose from the damp ground. The gnats came after him in swarms; but he didn't care: the world was beautiful and exciting and full of adventures, and he was no longer afraid.

Then he saw the hibiscus bush with its scarlet flowers, the very same one that he had noticed the day before; and he knew that he was near his home! He broke one of the bright blossoms from its stem and stuck it behind his ear as a badge of triumph.

There was a shout behind him suddenly, and turning he saw his father running towards him between the trees.

"Father!" cried Kintu, throwing his spear to the ground and leaping into Chief Kitomba's arms.

"I was lost! I spent the night in a tree, I saw an elephant, I killed a wicked n'gwe, and I'm not afraid," said Kintu all in one breath.

"You are safe, my son; you are not hurt?" asked Chief Kitomba anxiously.

"No, but I am very, very hungry," answered Kintu.

The Celebration

His mother was so glad to see him that she cooked him the special pudding which is made of corn flour and palm oil and dried white caterpillars. Then she stood over him and watched to see that he ate it all.

His brothers and sisters sat round him in a circle, each of their mouths hanging open an inch, and listened to the story of his night in the jungle. He had to tell it three times.

"Let us play a game about it," said Wapi to Timbo; "you can be the leopard and I will be Kintu in the tree."

"No, indeed," said Timbo; "you forget that I'm the eldest. I will be Kintu, and you can be the leopard!"

All the people of the village were so glad that Kintu had returned and was unharmed, that Chief Kitomba said, "Light the bonfires; bring out the big n'gomas; we will have a jubilee, as soon as the leopard's brought back to the village."

"A jubilee!" screamed everybody in delight, and clapped their hands and ran to fetch wood for the bonfires. Half a dozen men followed Kintu's markings to the place where the slain leopard lay beneath a tall tree. Cutting a slim strong sapling with their knives they lashed the heavy animal to it and, raising the burden to their strong right shoulders, walked singing and laughing back to the village. When they had reached it they went at once to the hut of Kintu's father, and set the leopard down beside the door. Everybody came to look at it, and said what a big one it was, and what a fine coat it had, and how wicked and dangerous it must have been when it was alive.

Kintu could feel happiness and pride swelling inside of his chest like a big balloon. His ribs felt almost too narrow to hold it. He looked downwards and drew a circle in the dust with his big toe.

"Now we will celebrate," said Chief Kitomba.

Kintu went into the hut and put on his favorite headdress of crimson feathers and telephone wire, for he felt that this was a very special occasion. Then he walked to the central clearing in the village where all the tribe was gathered.

The fires had been lighted, and were burning like five great towers of flame and smoke, soaring and snapping. Half a dozen of the bravest warriors in the village stood behind the big drums, waiting to play them.

"Come here, my son," said Chief Kitomba, and Kintu went to him. Around his neck his father fastened a necklace made of leopards' teeth; and around his waist he tied a leopard's skin so that the tail hung down behind just as it should.

"Now dance," said Chief Kitomba, and Kintu for the first time in his life was allowed to do the Dance of the Victorious Hunter; for had he not killed the leopard, that creature feared and hated by all jungle dwellers, men and beasts alike?

"Boom. Boom. Boom-a-diddy-boom!" sang the drums, and Kintu's feet moved swiftly through the dust, hopping and leaping. Around him all the people of the village clapped their hands and stamped in time to the music.

Kintu finished his dance with a whoop and a yell. And then everybody danced!

Drums boomed, brass anklets jingled, spears clashed together, dry gourds were shaken like rattles, people sang and monkeys screamed in the thickets. Never had there been such a loud and joyful jubilee in the history of the village!

It went on till very late at night. They brought out delicious things to eat: hot things in big earthenware pots, fruits of all kinds on round platters. There were delicious things to drink, too, in tall black jars.

Long after it was dark the fires still burned high, and the village was filled with flickering lights and dark moving shadows.

Everyone was happy, and Kintu was the happiest of all, for his father had said to him, "I am well pleased with you, my son; you will be a good chief to our people when I am gone. Only fear can make a strong man weak, and you have conquered that."

At last, when they had all grown tired of dancing and had eaten too much, they sat down around one of the dying bonfires and asked Kintu to tell them his story.

He told them about climbing the tree after the monkeys and about the elephant who had come unsuspectingly so near to him; he told them all about the leopard. But he did not tell them why he had gone into the jungle in the first place or about the magic charm; that was a secret between the witch doctor and himself and the baobab tree.

Finally, when he was sure that he couldn't stay awake more than two minutes longer, Kintu stood up and said goodnight to all his proud, well-fed relatives and friends. But before he went to his father's hut, he tiptoed through the shadowy village to the hut which was surrounded by little black idols. The witch doctor was leaning in his doorway.

"Well, chief's son," he said, and from his great height he looked down at Kintu without smiling. But this time Kintu was not timid in the least.

"Well, witch doctor," he said, "I am very grateful to you. I did everything you told me to, and then I got lost. I spent the night in the jungle among wild creatures; I even killed a leopard. And this morning when I woke up, I knew I wasn't frightened any more!"

The witch doctor didn't look very much impressed.

Kintu waited for him to speak. At last he

nodded his head slowly up and down and said "Good." That was all, but Kintu felt that it was enough.

Turning, he left the witch doctor's hut and walked slowly through the darkness. It was quieter, now. There were occasional bursts of laughter from groups of people, but the voices were subdued, and the fires had died into heaps of glowing coals.

Kintu entered his hut and removed the headdress of crimson feathers and telephone wire. Then he lay down on the earth against the wall. Above the voices and the laughter he heard the night sounds of the jungle. He heard the tree toads, and the monkeys, and the insects which tick like little watches. Far, far away he heard a sound like that of thick canvas being torn in two. Kintu knew that another leopard roamed the jungle, terrifying all creatures. He reached out and patted the handle of his spear companionably.

But above all these noises he was aware of the song of the cicadas. No longer could he make the words "Afraid, afraid, afraid" fit their chanting. There were no words for it. The thousands of voices pulsed together like the sound of a heart beating and the longer Kintu listened to them the drowsier he became. And at last with his cheek pressed against the earth and with one hand on his spear he went to sleep.

LITTLE PEAR FALLS
INTO THE RIVER
AND DECIDES TO BE GOOD

Eleanor Frances Lattimore

A little girl exclaimed after reading Little Pear, *"You know he is just like my little brother, always getting into scrapes." The author, Mrs. Lattimore, spent many years in China and must have known and loved many children there, she writes about them so delightfully.*

It was a hot day in the middle of the summer. The sun blazed down on the village and on Little Pear, who was strolling along the street, eating a cucumber. His bare feet shuffled through the thick yellow dust. "Ay-ah," he sighed, "how hot it is!—and where are all my friends?"

The street was deserted, and the reason was that nearly every one was asleep. It was too hot for most people to want to walk about. It was even too hot for the children to want to play. Little Pear, though, always wanted to be doing something. "I know what I shall do," he thought. "I shall go and watch the boats on the river." Just then he saw a child trotting around the corner. He felt quite excited for a minute, because he had walked nearly through half the village and had seen only a pig and a few chickens. But when the child came nearer he saw that it was only Big Head's baby brother.

The baby was dressed in a little red apron shaped like a diamond. It was all that he had on, because Chinese babies don't wear very much in the summer. His head was shaved except for a fringe of hair across his forehead. He was trotting along in a great hurry until he met Little Pear, who stopped him. "You must not run away," said Little Pear, and he took the baby's hand and led him back to the home of Big Head, who was leaning against the doorway, fast asleep. Little Pear lifted the little brother over the doorstep and gave him the rest of his cucumber. "Stay where you are," he said. "You might get lost if you run away." Then he had a good idea. He took the good-luck chain off his own neck and put it around the baby's. "Now you will be safe," he said, and he patted the baby kindly on the head and strolled on, feeling very good. Again he thought, "I shall go to the river and watch the ships," and he started off in the direction of the river.

It was a long way to the river. Little Pear followed the path that cut across the fields, and soon left the village far behind him. The sun blazed down on Little Pear as he pattered along in his bare feet. The fields were as deserted as the village. There was no sound except for the singing of cicadas in the willow trees as he drew near the river.

Presently he stood on the high bank, looking down at the river. First he looked up the river, and then he looked down the river; and all the time he remembered to hold tight to a willow tree with both hands.

The river was swift and muddy. The sun shining on it made the ripples first brown and then blue. The bank opposite Little Pear, like the bank that he was standing on, was bordered by rough-barked willow trees leaning out over the water. Between the banks the boats went busily up and down. Here everybody seemed to be very wide awake. Little Pear thought of the sleepy village he had left and was glad that he had come to the river.

There were all kinds of boats. Big boats with masts and sails and smaller boats with none, and boats with great fishing-nets spread out like huge spider-webs. There were flat boats, too, laden with things to sell. Some had cabbages, and some had rolls of matting, and some had bags that might be filled with all sorts of interesting things, Little Pear thought.

The big boats had eyes painted on them in front, so that they could see where they were going. The owners of these boats were careful not to let anything hang over the edge in front of the eyes, for then the boats could not have seen their way as they sailed in and out among the smaller boats.

Little Pear wished that he had a boat of his own, but he couldn't decide whether he would rather have a small one that he could row, or a larger one that he could push with a pole, or a *big* one with a sail.

Finally Little Pear decided that what he would like most of all to have when he grew up would be a fishing-boat. For then he could catch fish for his meals and take fish to the city to sell, and what fun that would be!

Little Pear held tight to the willow tree and gazed at the ships going up and down. He was wishing that he would grow up soon, when suddenly he saw, drawing nearer and nearer, the loveliest kind of boat on the river. It was a houseboat!

"That is the kind of boat I should like to have," thought Little Pear, as he watched it drawing nearer and nearer. It was a long flat boat with a real little house on it, with a hole in the ceiling for the smoke to go through, and paper windows. A man was walking up and

down the side of the deck, shoving with a long pole.

Little Pear looked admiringly at the clothes hanging out to dry and watched the children playing about the deck, and the boat sailed gayly along until it was quite close to Little Pear.

Suddenly one of the children saw him. He called to his brothers and sisters, and they all flocked to the edge of the boat and waved to Little Pear as he stood alone on the bank. It made him feel very happy, and without thinking he let go of his tree to wave back. *Slip,* went his feet on the steep bank—slip, slide—and *plop,* into the river fell Little Pear! . . .

The brown water whirled round and round him in circles as he rose to the surface, choking and sputtering. "Ay-ah!" cried the children on the boat. "He is drowning, he is drowning!" For Little Pear could not swim, and the swift current was carrying him away from the bank. He splashed around wildly with his arms and was about to sink again when the man on the boat rushed forward and reached out his pole. "Catch hold!" he cried.

Little Pear couldn't hear what the man said,

for there was water in his ears. He could scarcely see the man, for there was water in his eyes! He couldn't say anything himself, for he had swallowed so much water—but he splashed around with his arms—and—he caught hold of the pole! Then he held on tight while the man pulled him to the side of the boat and lifted him safely to the deck.

For some time he lay there, wondering to himself whether he was drowned or not, and thinking that perhaps he would never see his family again. Then he opened his eyes and saw above him a circle of faces. Here he was on the houseboat, and here were the children who had waved to him and the man who had saved him. There was the kindly face of the mother, too, who had hurried out of the little house to see what had happened.

Little Pear smiled at them, and they all exclaimed over him, saying what a wonder it was that he wasn't drowned; and they admired his flowered jacket and the green string around his pigtail.

"Will you stay with us?" asked the children.

But their mother said, "No, this little boy comes from the shore, and his family will wonder where he is. He must go home when we come to the next landing-place."

The boat sailed on down the river. Little Pear sat drying in the sun, while the children sat around him in a circle, telling him about their life on the river, and asking him eager questions about the land. "We have never lived on the land," they told him, "because this boat has always been our home." Then Little Pear told them about his village, and about his family and friends and his canary. As he talked he began to think how glad he would be to see them all again. But the boat sailed on down the busy river, taking Little Pear farther and farther away from home.

When they finally reached the next landing-place, the houseboat stopped and Little Pear was set ashore. He felt very sorry to say good-by to his new friends. He climbed the path up the bank and watched until the boat had sailed on, far down the river. The children were still waving to him, but Little Pear held tight to a tree with both hands, because he didn't want to fall into the water again. The boat disappeared around a bend in the river, and Little Pear started for home.

Away across the fields the sun was setting. Little Pear walked on, and on, and on. The way home was long, as the boat had sailed a mile or two down the river. "Ay-ah," thought Little Pear, "soon it will be dark!" And he hurried his tired feet along more quickly. He wished that he might meet another kind man like his friend who had taken him to the city. But the path along the river bank was deserted, the fields were deserted, and it seemed as though in all the world there was nobody except Little Pear.

Little Pear walked on, and on, and on. The sun had been down for a long time, and the night was very dark, when at last Little Pear saw ahead of him the dim outline of the village. Dogs barked at him as he approached. "Don't bark!" he cried. "Don't you know me? This is Little Pear!" When he reached his own gateway the stone lions on either side of it looked very fierce. "They are roaring now, not laughing," he thought, and he said aloud, "Don't bite me. This is Little Pear!" He ran across the courtyard to the house. "Open the door!" he cried. "It is Little Pear!"

Then the door was flung open, and "It is Little Pear!" cried his mother and Dagu and Ergu all at once, throwing their arms around him.

How glad Little Pear was to be at home again! And how glad his family were to see him! "Where have you been?" they cried. "We have hunted for you all afternoon, and the men are still out with lanterns, looking for you."

Little Pear told them all that had happened, how he had left the village and had gone to the river, and how he had fallen into the river and been rescued. Then his mother prepared some hot food for him while Dagu put the kettle on to boil and Ergu sped away to tell all the village that Little Pear had returned.

Soon there was the sound of many feet in the courtyard, and then the tiny room was filled with people. There were Little Pear's father and the other men who had been searching with him for Little Pear. There was Ergu, out of breath and with shining eyes. There were all the nearest neighbors and best friends. There was Big Head, looking very excited, and Big Head's baby brother, eating a tang-hulur. He still had the good-luck chain around his neck.

"You may keep the chain," Little Pear told him, "for you are very little and something might happen to you. But I am a big boy, and I am never going to run away again."

Then everybody was very happy. They patted Little Pear on the head, and the baby brother gave him the rest of his tang-hulur.

"We all loved you very much when you were naughty," they said, "but we shall love you even more if you are good."

"I will always be a good boy, now," Little Pear promised, nodding his head very hard. Ergu looked at her small brother and suddenly felt rather sad.

"Little Pear is growing up," she said.

A LONELY NIGHT

Mary and Conrad Buff

Conrad Buff, who made the beautiful pictures for Kobi, is a Swiss and in this story he has re-called his childhood experiences in that beautiful country. His wife Mary Buff wrote them down, and together they made this book. So also they made The Apple and the Arrow, *a thrilling story of the Swiss people's fight for freedom.* Dash and Dart *is about twin fawns and reflects the Buffs' California life, part of which is spent high in the mountains where deer, squirrel, and other small animals share the forest with them.*

When Kobi had finished milking the cows, he carried the milk into the hut and poured it out into flat wooden bowls, which he put away in the cool milk room. Then he ate his usual supper of goats' milk and great hunks of heavy bread. Supper over, the boy sat on an old bench just outside the cabin, watching the evening shadows.

It was a warm summer evening, and so clear that Kobi could see the cows grazing on Schwarz Alp across the valley. He could even hear Sepp's dog bark.

"A Lonely Night." From *Kobi, a Boy of Switzerland* by Mary and Conrad Buff. Copyright 1939 by Mary and Conrad Buff. Reprinted by permission of The Viking Press, Inc., New York

Shadows slowly drowned each bright green Alp in gray, as night crept up and up along both sides of the valley. In a short time, only the tops of the mountains shone with the last rays of the sun. Soon the gray shadows covered them too, and the world faded into darkness.

Slowly stars came out. By the faint glow in the eastern sky, Kobi knew the moon would rise. As it grew still darker, a bird called sadly in the forest beyond the hut. It sang as if it had lost something it would never find again.

Kobi saw a light flicker in Sepp's hut. On Hoch Alp the cows grazed restlessly. Every few minutes they stopped in their feeding and looked around as if they heard someone coming. Blass the dog lay panting at Kobi's feet, his red tongue hanging from his mouth, for it was warm. Usually when the sun went down the night was cold, but this night Kobi thought the air very sultry.

The world outside was so unfriendly that Kobi went into the cabin and lit the lamp. Blass always slept in the barn, but on this strange night Kobi called him into the hut for company.

But even with the light shining in the old lamp on the rough table and Blass panting beside him, Kobi still felt the world was unfriendly. Earlier than usual he put out the light, and crawled into bed. But it too was lonely, without Uncle Jacob.

Kobi lay thinking about the day that had just gone: the edelweiss he had picked high on the top of the mountain; the chamois that crept along the cliffs; Grittli, Mother, Aunt Marie.

It was so hot, Kobi threw off the goose-feather pad. The wind rose. A shutter banged. Kobi heard a stick of wood slip from the woodpile outside. An ax leaning against the hut fell to the ground with a soft thud.

Kobi would never have heard these little noises if Uncle Jacob had been there. But tonight they made him afraid.

He thought of Franzli in the story Grandfather had told so often, the old story of "The Boy Who Wanted to Yodel." That boy had slept all alone in an Alpine hut too. What if a giant should come to this cabin tonight and give to him, Kobi, the gift of yodeling like Uli the cheesemaker? Everything seemed possible tonight.

The wind whined louder as it rose. Kobi heard the goats bleating outside. Even Blass was restless. He could not find a comfortable place to sleep. He walked around the cabin from spot to spot, never quiet.

Suddenly the door blew open. Blass growled. Kobi was so startled he jumped out of bed to bolt the door. But before he did this, he peered out of doors. The sky was overcast with clouds. The stars were gone. Was a storm coming?

Hurriedly he climbed back into bed. But he did not stay long, for drops of rain began to fall gently upon the roof. Through the window Kobi saw a bright fork of lightning flare and disappear.

Grandfather had told him many a story from his own boyhood of storms that came and disappeared in an hour, leaving behind them ruined bridges, dead cattle, broken barns.

He knew how suddenly the weather changed in the mountains. Animals felt it before people did. Kobi thought of the panting dog, the restless cows, the sad bird in the forest. He must drive the cows into the barn at once.

He jumped out of bed and lit the lamp. He pulled on his heavy woolen trousers, his hobnailed shoes, and a warm coat. By the time his black leather cap was on his head, the rain was pouring down.

He unbolted the door and ran into the storm; it was so dark he could see only when the lightning flashed. When he reached the barn he pulled open the door, and the cows and goats piled in pell-mell, happy for a roof. Kobi lit a lantern. Each cow stood in her own stall. But thirteen stalls were still empty. Thirteen cows were missing. He must find them.

When Kobi, followed by Blass, raced once again into the night, the rain was coming down so hard he was soon wet to the skin. His feet sloshed about in his soggy shoes as he ran here and there over Hoch Alp, looking everywhere for the lost cows. The thunder was deafening. Each peal bounded back from the sides of the mountains, echoing time and time again. Before one died away another peal of thunder had taken its place. The noise was earsplitting. Lightning flashed every second. Kobi could see everything clearly, but he did not see any cows.

Then he remembered Uncle Jacob had told him never to let cows stand under trees during a storm. He said lightning often hit the trees.

There was but one tree on Hoch Alp. That was the crooked old pine tree on the north side, near the steep cliffs. It's a long way to the old tree, thought Kobi as he slipped through the wet grass. Once he fell headlong on his face. But he struggled up and on. He was so worried about the lost cows that he had no time to fear the wind, the thunder, the lightning.

When at last he reached the tree, Kobi saw a dark mass of animals huddled together under it. Cows! He yelled and called; Blass barked; each tried to make himself heard above the storm. Boy and dog ran this way and that, chasing the frightened animals toward the distant barn. It took a long time, but when at last each cow stood in her stall, Kobi saw by the light of the flickering lantern that one stall was still empty. It was Roslie's stall—Roslie, the fine prize heifer he had promised Mrs. Bach to guard so carefully and bring back to Wolfram's Castle in September. Where could Roslie be?

Once more the boy and his dog went into the storm. It was even worse than before. Peals of thunder boomed against the rocks like giant cannon. Kobi and Blass raced from one end of the Alp to the other, looking everywhere.

Perhaps I have missed her near the tree, thought Kobi, and he ran on and on until he could hardly breathe and his heart beat wildly.

He was near the old tree when suddenly a sheet of living white fire dropped out of the sky and struck the ground before him. Kobi fell on his knees. He covered his eyes with his hands. He smelled burning wood.

He was helpless, afraid, trembling all over. His ears hurt and he could not see—he could not get to his feet.

Strangely enough this last fierce blinding stroke of lightning was the last to flash that night on Hoch Alp. Kobi heard the thunder die slowly away, growing fainter and fainter, as the sound of the great bells died in the church tower on feast days. The wind drove the sullen clouds before it like an army beaten in battle. The rain stopped. The moon looked through a clear bit of sky.

Kobi could hardly believe the world had not ended. As he looked around, his trembling stopped. He saw where the lightning had struck. It had split the tree in two. One great gnarled limb lay across the fence, breaking it down. The old pine had lost its last battle with the storm.

In the strange calm that followed, Kobi heard a faint sound. It seemed to come up from between the canyon walls. He ran to the tree and leaned over the broken fence, peering down into the dark canyon. He heard a soft sad "moo." As he looked into the darkness, he thought he saw something move. He called:

"Roslie, Roslie!" and another "moo" came out of the canyon.

Kobi knew the cliff wall as well in the darkness as he knew it in the daylight. Many an afternoon he had sat there and studied its rocky forms from the edge, the cliff sloped gently down and ended in a narrow shelf of rock in the side of the canyon wall. Then it plunged straight down for over a hundred feet to meet the noisy stream far below.

Roslie must have been knocked over by the broken limb. Or she might have jumped over in fright. "Be still, Roslie." He slid down the incline and landed beside the heifer. She licked his hands.

"Don't move, Roslie," Kobi whispered to her. "Don't move." And with these words the boy clambered up the cliff and raced with all his strength toward the distant barn, to get a rope. Fear lent him wings.

When Kobi returned to the edge of the canyon, and once more slid down to the rocky shelf, Roslie was still there. He tied the rope around her neck and fastened it to a stout root that stuck out of the rocks. Then he said to her: "Roslie, I'm going away. But I'll be back soon and pull you up. Stay here, Roslie, I'll be back."

As Kobi had raced to the barn for the rope, he had thought of a plan. He would go down into the valley, cross the river, climb up to Schwarz Alp, and get Sepp. Sepp was strong. He and Sepp together could pull the heifer out of the canyon.

The moon shone so brightly as Kobi hurried down the muddy trail into the valley that he could hardly believe death had walked on the Alp only a few minutes before. The creek in the bottom of the valley roared, swollen into a river. The foot bridge seemed to hang by a thread.

Kobi crossed it carefully. As he climbed up toward Schwarz Alp Sepp saw him coming.

"Come and help me!" cried Kobi to his friend, and then he hurriedly told him the story of Roslie. "Hurry up," he cried, plucking at Sepp's sleeve. "Of course I'll come," Sepp said. He ran to the barn, and came back with a thick heavy rope curled over his shoulder.

When the boys arrived on Hoch Alp a half-hour later, Roslie was still there. They could hear her chewing her cud on her little haven of rock.

"Imagine that," laughed Sepp, out of breath with the steep climb, "chewing her cud! She's not hurt at all."

Kobi grabbed one end of the rope, and slid down the embankment. He put the rope around the heifer's neck, and threw the other end to his friend on the bank, who wound it around the old tree-trunk, which was still standing. Then Sepp called: "Steady, Kobi. Push!"

Kobi pushed, Sepp pulled on the rope. Roslie did her best. She knew the boys were trying to help her, but the rocks were slippery and she always slid back. The boys tried time and time again until they were both out of breath.

"We may have to wait until Uncle Jacob comes," cried Kobi.

"Let's try once more," argued Sepp. "If she doesn't come up then, I'll go and get Father."

So once more they pushed and pulled Roslie. The bank was full of holes, washed out by the storms that had fallen on the Alp in many years. By accident Roslie put a hind foot in a hole just as Kobi pushed her from behind. Suddenly, almost without knowing how it happened, Roslie walked up the cliff and stood safely on the Alp.

The faint gray of dawn was pouring over the mountains as the tired, sleepy boys drove the heifer into the barn. "Come and have something to eat," said Kobi to Sepp, putting his arm over his shoulder in affection.

"No, sorry, Kobi. I've got to get home and help Father milk. But tonight I'll come over." Sepp hurried down the trail.

Kobi could hardly drag himself into the cabin, he was so tired and hungry.

He took off his muddy shoes and his wet coat; he poured himself a bowl of milk and cut a thick piece of bread. Then he sat down on a bench, his back to the door.

Kobi did not hear the quick footstep, until he felt a pair of strong arms around him, holding him tight. And Uncle Jacob's voice was saying: "Kobi, Kobi, my brave herder."

Uncle Jacob had met Sepp as he crossed the broken bridge in the valley, and Sepp had told him about the long fight to save Roslie. But Kobi was so tired he could not say a single word. He burst into tears as Uncle Jacob patted him on the shoulder and said: "Never mind, Kobi. You are a brave boy! I woke up when I heard the thunder and saw lightning flash on the mountain. I came as fast as I could, my boy, but the roads were rivers of mud. Many of the bridges were washed away. In all of my life in the mountains I've never seen a storm like this. Many a cow was lost, I know. I prayed for you, Kobi, all alone with those cows in such a storm. Your mother will be proud of you. You are a real cowherd now, Kobi, as good as any man!" But the real cowherd was fast asleep, worn out with the work and the excitement.

Early in September, a snow storm fell over the Alps. In the morning when Kobi woke, everything was white. When the sun came out, the snow melted. But it was a warning to the herders that autumn had come.

Uncle Jacob told Kobi: "If we have another snow storm like this, we must go home. The grass is short now. When snow covers it for a few hours, the cows don't get enough to eat."

The grass was very short. Only a few fall flowers still bloomed in the pastures. On a clear day Kobi could see the beech trees, in the valley below, turned red.

Then another snow storm came, covering the roofs of the barn and hut. The snow did not melt quickly.

"Kobi," said Uncle Jacob as they were milking that morning, "I think we must go home, and go today. Bring down the big bells. We will start as soon as the hut and barn are in order."

So without any more talk, Kobi and Uncle Jacob drove the cows down the trail toward home. When they reached the lowlands, everything seemed new to Kobi. The villages were so crowded. There were so many people everywhere. He had lived for three months in a world of only Uncle Jacob, Sepp, Uli, the cows, Blass, the goats; he had forgotten how crowded the villages were, how close to each other the farmhouses were, and how tiny the fenced pastures of the lowlands were.

As he and Uncle Jacob went through the villages they saw many other processions of cattle. The snow storm had driven the wise herders from the mountains that September day.

When they reached Uncle Jacob's house, Kobi did not stay long enough to eat. He wanted to get home. He wanted to see Mother, Grandfather, Father. He wanted to play with Grittli, and he wanted to eat fried potatoes covered with caraway seeds, and hot sausage.

It was late afternoon when he saw his old brown house far in the distance. The red geraniums were not in the windows. The fields were shaved close by the mowers. The leaves were falling from the pear trees. There were late apples still clinging to the apple trees.

Kobi ran the last half mile, he was so anxious to get home. He pulled open the heavy kitchen door, and rushed through the house, calling: "Grittli, Mother, where are you? I'm home! It's me—Kobi!"

Then he saw his mother. She was very beautiful, for she wore her fine dress that she wore only on Sundays and feast days. But this is not Sunday, thought Kobi.

As the boy hugged her, he cried: "Mother, you have on your Sunday dress; this is not Sunday. And how beautiful you are, Mother!"

Mother smiled down at him, tears in her eyes, as she said: "Brave Kobi, I heard all about that night in the storm. Do you remember that Aunt Marie told you we had a surprise at home for you? It is upstairs in my room. Come, Grittli, we'll show him."

Up the rickety stairs Kobi followed his Mother. Grittli danced on ahead of them both. The three entered Mother's bedroom. Beside her bed was the old wooden cradle. Kobi's grandfather had slept in it when he was a baby; so had Kobi's father, and Kobi himself. There were roses painted on the headboard, and between the roses it read: "1842."

Kobi's mother lifted a white cloth. Kobi peered inside as she said:

"This is the surprise for you, Kobi. This is why I have on my best dress. We have just come from the christening. This is your baby brother —Conrad Tobler."

from PEDRO'S COCONUT SKATES

Esther Wood

Esther Wood has the knack of re-creating the work and play, longings and achievements, the sadness and fun of children of other lands. Pedro's Coconut Skates is the tender story of a little Filipino boy's desire to have a house for his grandmother. Great Sweeping Day, *house cleaning in Japan, and* Silk and Satin Lane, *a charming story of an unwanted Chinese girl who makes some grave blunders in her efforts to be indispensable, are two other fine books by Esther Wood.*

From *Pedro's Coconut Skates,* copyright 1938 by Esther Wood Brady, and Longmans, Green and Co., Inc.

Singing Souls

Hundreds of little candles twinkled in the darkness of All Saints' Eve. They looked as if the stars might have fallen, and, just for one night, snuggled down against the earth.

Aunt Valentina dressed herself in her best clothes. She put on a long skirt, tucking the train up neatly to show her embroidered petticoat and her green velvet chinelas. Her blouse was thin and crisp with big, bell-like sleeves. When she had tied on her best black apron, she called to Uncle Manuel that she was ready.

He finished the song he was singing and tucked his guitar under his arm. "Time for bed," he called to the children, who were playing tubigan in the moonlight.

Pedro stamped out the water marks they had made in the road for their game and followed the three little girls into the house. Great Aunt Trinidad had spread their mats on the floor, and hung up the mosquito nets around each bed. In no time at all the four of them were in bed; even Magellan was tucked in, much against his will.

"Well," said Great Aunt Trinidad, "you never know about children. It's always trouble, trouble, trouble, putting them to bed; and now on All Saints' Eve they're asleep almost before I get the mats on the floor." She held the lamp high that Aunt Valentina might see her way down the ladder and out the gate.

"They're too good to be true," she said, holding the lamp to look at the children, who already seemed to be sound asleep. With that she blew out the light, and leaned back against the wall where her eyes were shaded from the moonlight coming through the door. In a few minutes she was asleep and snoring softly.

Pedro raised his head. "Are you ready?" he whispered.

Three black heads popped out from under three mosquito nets, and nodded. Three little girls slipped on their dresses and quietly stole down the ladder to the gate where Pedro waited for them.

"Where is Magellan?" asked Pedro. "I thought you had him."

Magellan scampered out from under the house. He was carrying Pedro's coconut skates.

"Oh, Magellan," cried Pedro, "I don't want them now." He put the skates back of the fence and picked up the monkey. "But—" he said, "you're a smart monkey. You gave me a good idea."

Juana stopped. "I forgot the coconut shell," she said. "Singing souls always carry a coconut shell."

"And the candle," said Marciana.

"And the bell," said Nene.

Juana climbed back into the house and presently came out with a bell, a candle, and half a coconut shell. She gave the bell to Nene and the candle to Marciana, keeping the coconut shell for herself.

Pedro led the way down the dark street, staying well in the shadows that no one might see them. Instead of crossing the moonlit plaza, they slipped around its edge where the houses cast deep, black shadows. Past the old stone church they crept and across the market place, until they came to the big house of the landlord.

"Do you think they'll hear us?" whispered Nene.

"Perhaps they aren't at home," said Juana.

The shell windows had been closed and the house looked quite dark.

"Well, sing as loudly as you can," said Marciana. She started the song, for she was the only one who knew all the verses of the long ballad that told of the travels of the Singing Souls from heaven to earth. Nene rang her bell, and they all sang very loudly when Marciana came to the parts they knew.

The door was opened a crack, and someone looked out at them. Then it was opened wider. A servant in a long, white apron shuffled out and put five centavos in Juana's coconut shell.

Juana excitedly poked Marciana. "Look!" she whispered. "Five centavos!"

The man shuffled back into the house, but just as he was about to close the door, he popped his head out again. "Is that Magellan?" he asked, peering at the monkey in Pedro's arms.

"Yes," said Pedro. "I found him, and I am bringing him back to the Señor."

Magellan jumped to the ground, bounded through the man's outstretched arms, and ran into the hall.

"Oh, Magellan!" cried a woman's voice from inside. "Where have you been?"

"The Señora was very sad to lose that little monkey," said the servant to the children. Then he whispered behind his hand, "As for myself—" He shrugged.

"Bring the children inside," said the Señora, coming to the door, with Magellan sitting on her shoulder. "And, Vicente, bring my purse to me."

The servant ran down the hall, the wooden soles of his shoes clattering on the floor.

"Come in." The Señora smiled at them.

The four children followed her down the hall and out into the patio. The moonlight made everything look white in the little garden, surrounded by the four walls of the house. They climbed the stairs and crossed the balcony to a sitting room where the Señor sat reading.

"Look! Here is Magellan home again!" cried the Señora.

Magellan bounded across the room and jumped on the Señor's shoulder, where he snuggled his head against the man's collar.

"Where did you find him?" the Señor asked, as he stroked the monkey's back. His stern face softened, and he smiled.

The three girls said nothing. They were afraid of the landlord.

"In—the haunted house," stammered Pedro.

"That old house by the river?" asked the Señor.

"Yes," said Pedro.

"What were you doing there?" asked the man sharply.

"I—I just wanted to see what it was like," explained Pedro. "I didn't touch anything."

The Señora interrupted, "Oh, I know you didn't," she said. "It's such a tumble-down house, anyway." She took the purse the servant had brought her.

"Weren't you afraid to go there?" asked the landlord.

"No. It's just like any other house," said Pedro, "only old."

"What's your name?" asked the Señor.

"Pedro."

"Well, Pedro, I like you," said the Señor. "You're one boy who doesn't believe the old women's stories."

The Señora slipped five centavos apiece into the coconut shell. "For the Singing Souls," she said. "And now," she said to her husband, "what about a reward for bringing back Magellan?"

"Good," said the man, turning to Pedro. "What do you want?"

"Well—" said Pedro, "I don't want a reward. But, you know, that little, old house by the river is just the kind of house my grandmother has always wanted."

"Yes?" said the Señor.

"It's very old," said Pedro, "but she wouldn't mind. We could mend it."

"Yes?" said the Señor.

"Well—it's like this," said Pedro. "I haven't any money, but I could work for you. I'm a good houseboy; I could bring my coconut skates and polish your floors every day."

The old servant poked the Señora and vigorously nodded his head. She smiled and nodded to her husband.

"I could come every day on my way to school," said Pedro.

"It seems to me," said the Señor, "that would be enough rent for the little old house."

"Do you mean it?" cried Pedro. "Could we really have it?"

"Yes, of course," said the landlord, "but don't let it fall down on you."

"Oh, thank you, Señor," said Pedro.

The man laughed and patted his head. "I like you, Pedro," he said. "Do whatever you want with the little old house."

The children went down the stairs and across the moonlit patio to the hall, where the servant held the door open for them. Pedro saw nothing. He was too excited. Christmas was coming, and maybe—! Perhaps it was too much for a little boy to do, but it wasn't too much for a little boy to think about.

Mending the Nipa House

Early the next morning the Cruz family went down to the bamboo grove to see Pedro's house. Even Great Aunt Trinidad left her sunny doorway and stomped along with her cane. She took a special interest in the house, for wasn't it she who had told Pedro to find out about things? And if it had not been for Pedro's curiosity, he would not have had the little house.

Pedro was proud to show them his house, old and wornout though it was. To be sure, it was very small, but Grandmother Paz had always wanted a wee nipa house. There were four win-

dows, one on each side, and a door. In the open space beneath the house, Grandmother Paz could keep her chickens.

"It's a bit dilapidated, to be sure," said Uncle Manuel, shaking the old ladder by the front door.

"And there are holes in the roof," said Aunt Valentina, peering up at the ceiling.

"And the floor sags a little," said Great Aunt Trinidad, poking through the cracks in the bamboo floor with her cane.

"Oh, but we can fix it!" cried Pedro. "We can mend the holes and make a new ladder."

"Well, you children go to work," said Uncle Manuel. "There's plenty of bamboo and nipa palm around."

"There's a nice mango tree out there," said Aunt Valentina.

Pedro looked out the door. "Grandmother Paz likes mangoes," he said.

"And Pedro can have his bananas," said Great Aunt Trinidad, poking her cane into the banana tree by the window.

Uncle Manuel took down the shutters, the worn and sagging shutters that all but fell apart when they were touched. The house looked bare, but much neater without them. They made a great bonfire and burned up all the rubbish they could find.

With great enthusiasm Pedro and the three girls started mending the house for Grandmother Paz. Before they knew it, the bamboo grove had become the most popular place in the village. It was like a new game; after school everyone raced down to the river to see who would be allowed to help the Cruz children that day.

Even the older boys and girls came to help, for building a house by themselves was fun. The boys borrowed their fathers' bolo-knives and cut down the bamboo shoots in the yard. The girls brought mangrove leaves and mended the holes in the walls. With the help of Uncle Manuel they made four new shutters, weaving strips of bamboo into mats and tying them tightly with rattan. Each one they hung by rings on a bamboo pole, so that it could be slipped back along the wall, or propped out to make a window shade.

Finally, the parents had heard so much about Pedro's house, that they, too, came to the bamboo grove by the river. They came to watch, but they stayed to help. Some said it should be done this way, and others that, and before they knew it, they were putting in new beams of nibong to make the house stronger and weaving new laths of bamboo to make the floor firmer.

There was little need for furniture inside the house. Few people had tables and chairs. Grandmother Paz would have her own mats and mosquito nets and a woven tampipi basket for her clothes.

The only thing that bothered Pedro was the roof. To be sure it could be mended with nipa palm that would do very well in good weather. But perhaps, when the rainy season came, it would leak like a fish net. Pedro decided not to think about the roof for a while. The dry season was ahead.

One day Ignacio, the rope maker, and his wife came to see what was happening in the bamboo grove. "Oy," cried Ignacio, "I see you have a fine house here."

"But what about a kitchen?" said Maria. "Now to my mind, every house needs a kitchen. You can't live on mangoes and bananas day in and day out."

"I forgot about a kitchen," said Pedro. "Maybe we could build a bonfire at mealtime."

"No, you must have a stove," said Maria.

"And a stove you shall have" said Ignacio, "if you don't mind a stove that's a bit used."

"Oh, no!" cried Pedro.

Then the two of them brought out their gift for Grandmother Paz's nipa house. Ignacio carried an earthen pot which he put down on the ground by the door. "That's for the fire," he said.

Maria brought a round earthen pot that fitted on top and put it in place. "And that's for the rice and the fish and the stew," she said. "Now you have a kitchen."

For plates Grandmother Paz could use banana leaves, and for cups and bowls she could use coconut shells. It was very simple, for they grew right in the yard.

Then Great Aunt Trinidad came hobbling over with a treat for all the children. She had a basketful of coconut cakes and suman, which was sweetened rice sticks. She made a fire in the lower part of the stove, and in the pot on top

she put cacao beans, ground up and mixed with sugar and water. In no time at all there was a pot full of hot chocolate. Each child found a coconut shell for his cup.

With most of the children of the village there, the little nipa house had its first housewarming.

Christmas

Pedro and the three girls could hardly wait for Christmas. The little nipa house, with its new roof, was to be a Christmas surprise for Grandmother Paz.

Pedro built a chicken coop, and Aunt Valentina said she would give him two of her chickens to put in it. Uncle Manuel hollowed out the trunk of a bamboo tree for a water bucket. Marciana and Juana scrubbed the little stove until it looked almost new.

When everything was ready, they wrote a letter to Grandmother Paz and asked her to come to visit them for Christmas. They didn't say a word about the little house. They only asked her to bring her sleeping mat and her mosquito net. Pedro asked her to bring something for him, but he wouldn't tell anyone what it was. He wanted it very much, he said.

At last the day came when Uncle Manuel was to bring her from Manila in the carabao cart. He would get back in time for Christmas Eve, he said, as he left.

Pedro put a banana tree by the gate and tied it to the fence post. Then he helped the three girls trim it with lanterns and chains of colored paper. It was a gay little Christmas tree. In the window they hung a star lantern with a long swishing tail and a candle to light at night.

All through the village banana trees and arches were trimmed with lanterns and colored papers. A warm breeze, blowing through the palms, stopped to touch the Christmas trees and make them dance.

"And now it's time for a siesta," said Aunt Valentina, spreading their mats on the floor. "If you're going to stay up until midnight, you'll have to have your siesta."

The children slowly climbed up the ladder and lay down on the floor. That night they would go to church, at the nativity hour, and after that there would be a midnight feast. Small wonder they couldn't sleep, thinking about it all.

Pedro lay on his back, watching the lizards scamper up the walls in search of mosquitoes. Outside Aunt Valentina was swishing rice back and forth in her flat bamboo basket to let the wind blow the chaff away. She sang happily to herself:

> My nipa house is very small
> But in gathering seeds, it houses
>   them all;
> Sincamas and talong,
> Seguidillas and mani,
> Sitao, batao, patani.

Great Aunt Trinidad sat in the doorway, grinding cacao beans with a stone. The smell of chocolate made Pedro hungry. He could smell, too, the chicken adobo in the pot on the stove.

Just as he was about to ask for something to eat, he heard the squeaking of cart wheels down the street. He rolled over, and looked out the door. There was Domingo, and behind him sat Uncle Manuel and Grandmother Paz with the tampipi basket between them.

"Oy!" shouted Pedro, jumping out of the door with one bound. Behind him came Marciana and Juana and Nene. The four of them raced down the street to meet their grandmother.

"Well," said Grandmother Paz, gathering them all in her arms, "if my children can't come 'to kiss the hand of Grandmother' at Christmas, then Grandmother will come to them."

Joyfully they led her back to the house where Aunt Valentina and Great Aunt Trinidad came to the gate to meet her.

"Did you bring my Christmas present?" whispered Pedro when Uncle Manuel had carried the tampipi basket indoors.

"Do you want it now?" asked Grandmother Paz.

"Yes," said Pedro. "I am going to give it to Uncle Manuel."

Grandmother Paz opened the tampipi basket and took out a package tied up in red tissue paper.

"Uncle Manuel," called Pedro, "here is a Christmas present for you."

Everyone crowded around to watch Uncle Manuel open the package from Manila. Out of the red tissue paper came a round black record. "For your victrola," said Pedro.

"For my victrola!" exclaimed Uncle Manuel, beaming. "Where is my victrola?"

The three little girls dragged it from the corner and lifted the lid. They all listened in delight while the music came from somewhere in the box:

> Jingle bells, jingle bells,
>   jingle all the way
> Oh, what fun it is to ride
>   in a one-horse open sleigh!

They loved it. None of them had ever seen snow or even heard of a sleigh, but it was such a jolly tune that they all began to sing with the victrola. The three little girls and Pedro danced round and round the room, until their mother said they'd fall through the floor if they didn't watch out.

"When are we going to give Grandmother Paz her surprise?" asked Nene, in a whisper so loud that it could be heard all through the house. Everyone laughed, while Grandmother Paz pretended she hadn't heard.

Pedro, who was almost bursting with the secret, jumped up. "Right now," he cried, taking Grandmother Paz's hand and leading her down the ladder.

The whole family went with them. Even Great Aunt Trinidad left her sunny doorway and stomped along with her cane. Grandmother Paz was quite breathless by the time she reached the river bank. "Wherever are we going, Pedro?" she asked, as she followed them through the bamboo grove.

"Here it is!" cried Pedro, who had run on ahead.

Then she saw the wee nipa house sitting in the middle of a tidy yard. In every window hung a star lantern with a long swishing tail.

"It's for you," said Pedro.

"Oh-h-h," breathed Grandmother Paz. "What a dear little house." Then she turned to her grandson. "What did you say, Pedro?"

"It's for you," said Pedro.

Everyone began talking at once, telling Grandmother Paz how Pedro had found the little house and the whole village had helped mend it for her.

Grandmother Paz couldn't say a word. But her

shining eyes told everyone she was too happy to speak.

"There is a mango tree near the door," said Nene, remembering that her grandmother liked mangoes.

"So there is," said Grandmother Paz.

"And look!" cried Pedro. "Here is the chicken coop; there are two chickens in it."

"It is just as I have dreamed a little house should be," said Grandmother Paz.

They went inside and lighted the candles in the star lanterns that hung in the windows. Then the neighbors began to come to welcome Grandmother Paz home. Each one brought a gift—a few eggs or a basket of rice or even a live chicken to put in her chicken coop.

Uncle Manuel played his guitar. What with the laughing, and the talking, and the singing, and the noise of firecrackers, it was a very gay housewarming.

Darkness came quickly, and outside the Christmas stars twinkled through the palm trees. The candles in the windows lighted the laughing faces of friends and neighbors. Pedro stood in the doorway watching them. He said, "Grandmother, do you think this little old house was ever so happy before?"

"Oh, Pedro," Grandmother Paz laughed, "are you still asking funny questions?"

"You're all right, Pedro," said Great Aunt Trinidad, playfully tapping him on the head with her knuckles, "if you don't ask questions, you'll never know anything."

from THE GOOD MASTER

Kate Seredy

The Good Master *is an exceedingly popular book with children all over this country. These opening chapters should send the children straight to the library for the book. One group of children argued about what made Kate behave so badly when she first came to her uncle's ranch. See what your children think. This group thought she was angry with her father because he had sent her away from him and was "taking it out" on these strangers. Most of us do foolish things when we think we are unjustly treated.*

Cousin Kate from Budapest

Jancsi was up bright and early that morning and at work milking the cows. He was so excited he couldn't stay in bed. For today Cousin Kate was coming. She was the only cousin he had, and she was a city girl. A real city girl from Budapest. Ever since the letter came from his uncle, Jancsi had been the proudest boy on the big Hungarian plain. He was the only boy in the neighborhood who had a cousin in the city. And she was coming today, to stay for a long time. Father had told Jancsi what was in the letter. It said that Kate had had the measles last winter. Jancsi had never had the measles—he thought it must be something wonderful to have. And she was delicate, the letter said, too, so she was coming to the country. A *delicate* city cousin, who had had the *measles*—that was something.

If it were only Sunday, they would go to church and he could tell everybody about her. Sunday was the only time when Jancsi saw anyone outside his own family. Father had a ranch, with thousands of sheep, horses, cows, and pigs. He had chickens and ducks and geese; he even had donkeys, but he didn't have enough children to suit Jancsi. It got so lonesome for poor Jancsi, he would have given ten horses for a brother. He had it all figured out—he would give a donkey for even a sister. Not horses, just a donkey.

The ranch was miles and miles from the village. It was too far to walk, and they were too busy to drive on weekdays. So, although Jancsi was ten years old and quite a man if you asked his opinion, he had never been to school, and he did not know how to read or write. The ranch was the only reality to him—the world outside was just a fairy story. Mother knew lots of fairy stories about dragons and golden-haired princesses who lived in glittering castles. Jancsi thought that houses in Budapest were made of gold and had diamond windows. All the city people rode around on pure white horses and wore silk gowns. Cousin Kate would have golden curls, rosy cheeks, big blue eyes; she would wear a white silk flowing gown, and her voice would be like honey. Now—Jancsi is off in dreamland

—some day a dragon will capture her, and it will be up to Jancsi to go to the rescue. He is clad in green velvet, red boots, riding a coal-black steed. Here comes the dragon! Jancsi pulls out his golden sword, and one-two-three heads are at his feet! All good dragons have twelve perfectly hideous heads. Four—slash, five—swish goes his sword——

"Mo-o-o-o!" bellowed something close to him. And crash-bang went Jancsi together with the milking-stool. He sat and blinked. Máli, the mottled cow, looked at him with reproachful eyes. Reality closed around the hero—oh yes, here he was in the barn, milking the cow.

"Jancsi! Ja-a-ncsi-i! Hurry up with the milk or you'll be late for the train!" It was his mother's voice calling from the house. He scrambled to his feet, scowled at Máli, and picking up the full pails made his way back to the kitchen. Mother took the milk from him. "I'll strain it today, Jancsi. You eat your breakfast and get dressed. And get a good scrub—why, you're all full of mud!"

Jancsi kept his back out of Mother's sight—the seat of his white pants would need explaining. He gulped down his bread and milk. Then, backing out of the kitchen, he ran to the well. He filled a wooden bucket with the icy water and, stripping off his clothes, stepped into it. With great splutters and groans he scrubbed himself, using sand on the most disgraceful spots. Then he took a bit of salt from a mug and scrubbed his teeth with his fingers. Squirting out the salty water, he set a new long-distance record; he even paused long enough to gaze at it admiringly and mark the spot with a stone "Can spit almost as far as Father," he muttered with pride.

He ran back to the house. His very best Sunday clothes were all laid out on the bench, near the big white stove—his embroidered shirt, the wide pleated pants, his shiny black boots, his round hat with the bunch of flowers. He put them on. Mother wasn't in the kitchen. He went to the bedroom. No Mother in the bedroom. But on the windowsill, glittering in the sunshine, was a green bottle. He gazed at it for a while, torn between desire and discipline. It was too much for him. Tiptoeing to the window, he took the bottle and the little red comb next to

it. It was perfumed hair oil—and only *men* used perfumed hair oil! He put a little on his hair. Then a little more, and still more, until his hair looked as if it were made of black enamel. Then with a sigh of satisfaction he put on his hat and strutted out. He heard the wagon—time to go!

When he saw the wagon drive up to the door, he gave a whoop of joy. Father had harnessed his four black horses with the very best brass-studded harness. Each horse had a big bunch of geraniums fastened to the headband, and long streamers of gayly colored ribbons floated in the breeze. He jumped up next to Father, and off they went down the long poplar-lined lane leading to the main road.

It was early April, and fields and pastures were a fresh pale green. The poplars stood like solemn sentinels, whispering to the wind. Father was a man of few words; men never spoke, he believed, unless they had something important to say. Gossip was only for the womenfolks. Jancsi was quiet, too, busy with his own thoughts. He was going to the town for the first time in his life—he would see a train. Trains were a mystery to him. One of the shepherds had told him trains were fire-eating dragons; they roared, and snorted black smoke. "They pull little houses; people go from one place to another in the little houses. And trains kill everybody who gets in their way." Jancsi wondered if he could hitch their own house to one of these dragons. Then he could go and see the world. But he would take his dog Peti, he'd take his favorite horse, he'd take Máli, the cow . . . No, he scowled and rubbed his side, remembering this morning. No, he wouldn't take Máli. Deeply absorbed in deciding whom he would take with him, he hardly noticed how fast they were traveling. Soon they left the open country and entered the long village street. The village was always interesting to him, so he began to look around. Father turned to him. "I'll stop at the store to buy some tobacco. You hold the reins, Jancsi." Jancsi slid over to Father's seat and grabbed the reins. He sat there, head up, shoulders erect, looking straight ahead. Just then a village boy walked by. He stopped and looked at Jancsi with open admiration.

"Hey! You driving *alone?*"

Jancsi gulped and replied evasively: "Going to fetch my cousin from the train. She comes from Budapest." Then, unable to keep from gossiping like womenfolks, he blurted out his news: "She had the measles and is delicate and her name is Kate! She'll live with us!"

Father came down the store steps, stuffing his pipe. Jancsi prayed for a miracle. If the boy would only go away or if Father would only let him drive . . . !

The miracle came. Father walked around the wagon and, getting up next to Jancsi, said: "Let's see how you handle wagon and four!"

So they left the boy staring after them open-mouthed. Jancsi drove through the village like a king in a golden coach. The clouds of white dust around the horses' hoofs were like stardust to him. The glittering hoofs were made of diamonds. Everything looked new and beautiful to him today. The endless rows of snow-white houses with their gayly painted doors and shutters were like pearls in a row. The geraniums in the windows were a brighter red than ever. The church seemed taller, the grass greener. He flipped his whip impatiently at the barking dogs and almost rode over a flock of honking geese slowly plodding across the street. Then they were in the open country again. It was almost noon; the spring sun beat down on the shimmering fields. They passed a long fence. Horses were grazing placidly in the pasture.

"Good horseflesh," remarked Father. "See how meek they look now, but it's a man's job to stay on one of those beasts."

"I can get on one and stay on it, Father. Those aren't worse than your own horses."

"Think you can, Son?"

"I *know* I can!" asserted Jancsi hastily, forgetting that this would call for explanations. He was not yet allowed to ride unbroken horses.

"You *know* you can?" said Father, reaching for his pocket knife. Jancsi watched him in shocked silence. He knew he was in for it, but somehow he didn't mind. After the pocket knife came a little round stick of wood with many cross-marks cut into it. It was the score pad. One notch was cut in for each sin Jancsi committed, and after a while it was crossed out. But the "after a while" usually included moments Jancsi didn't like to remember. Holding knife and stick in his hands, Father looked at Jancsi. Jancsi looked far, far ahead. Suddenly Father

laughed and, putting away the "score," slapped Jancsi on the back.

"You're no worse than I was at your age, Son. You'll make a good rancher."

Jancsi heaved a sigh of relief. This was a man's world, and he was accepted!

Father pointed ahead. "See those houses and chimneys? That's the town and the station." Jancsi was all eyes and ears now. Soon the wagon was rattling on the cobbled street. They passed lots of buildings, and there were a great many people walking around. Father told him where to stop and, after the horses were hitched to a post, said: "Well done, boy!" This made Jancsi feel still better. Praises from Father were few and far between, but they were all the more satisfying.

Walking through the station building, they came to the platform. "Those long shiny snakes are rails, Son; the train travels on them. It'll be here soon now."

Jancsi heard a great rumbling, snorting, and pounding in the distance. He felt the platform shake under his feet. Casting a frightened look at his father, he saw that Father wasn't afraid, so it must be all right. Then he saw a black monster rushing around the curve. It must be the dragon. It had an immense eye glittering in the sunshine. Vicious-looking black teeth, close to the ground. And black smoke poured out of its head. Then it gave a shrill scream, blew white smoke out of its ears, and came to a groaning halt. Men jumped down, opened the doors of the funny little black houses. Jancsi waited with eyes round and shiny like big black cherries. He expected to see people in silks and velvets, glorious people. But not one of them had good clothes on; they were just everyday people dressed in drab grays and browns. Then he heard someone shouting: "Márton Nagy! Is Márton Nagy here?"

Father yelled back: "Here! Márton Nagy!" A man hurried toward them, dragging a little girl with him. Just any kind of little girl, with plain black hair, a smudgy face, and skinny legs.

"Well, thank goodness you're here," said the man, wiping his forehead. "Here, take this—this imp, this unspeakable little devil—take her and welcome." He pushed the girl to Father. "Never again in my life will I take care of girls. I'm a self-respecting railroad guard. I handle anything from baggage to canaries, but I'd rather travel with a bag of screaming monkeys than her, any time." He gave her a final push. "Here's your uncle, he'll take care of you now. G'bye and—good luck to you, Mister Nagy!"

All this tirade left Jancsi and Father speechless. Here was Kate, looking as meek as Moses, but evidently something was wrong with her. Father bent down and said: "Well, Kate, I am your Uncle Márton and this is Jancsi, your cousin. We'll take you home now."

Cousin Kate looked up. Her dirty little face broke into a grin. "Oh, but you look funny!" she cried. "And I thought my cousin was a boy, and she's nothing but a girl!"

"But, Kate," said Father, "can't you see he's a boy?"

"I only see that she has skirts on and an embroidered blouse. Nobody's wearing embroidered blouses this season, they're out of style!"

Jancsi just began to realize that this dirty, skinny little girl in the plain blue dress was his cousin. He felt cheated—that was bad enough—but she called Father "funny" and said he was a *girl*—that was really too much! With fists clenched, chin stuck out, he advanced toward Kate. "I am a girl, am I? . . . I'm funny, am I? . . . I'll show you!"

Kate was ready. She dropped her bag, took a threatening step toward Jancsi. They were face to face now, tense, poised like two little bantam roosters, ready to settle the argument on the spot. Suddenly Father's hearty laugh broke the tension. "You two little monkeys," he cried, "now I'll tell you that you are both funny! Stop this nonsense, both of you. Jancsi! Gentlemen don't fight girls. Come on, we'll go home."

He grabbed their hands and, still laughing, walked to the baggage-room. Jancsi and Kate had no choice, they had to go, but at least they could make faces at each other behind his back. The fight was not over, it was just put off for the moment.

When they reached the wagon, there was more trouble. Kate declared that since the wagon had no top, she'd get a sunstroke. It didn't have cushions on the seat, so she'd break to pieces. She told Father to "phone" for a "taxicab."

"I'll wash your mouth out with soap, if you swear at *my* father!" cried Jancsi. "Phone" and "taxicab" sounded like swearing to him.

"She wasn't swearing, Jancsi," said Father; "she is just talking city language. 'Phone' is a little black box, you can talk into it, and people many miles away hear you. 'Taxicab' is a horseless wagon city people travel in." He turned to Kate. "We haven't any taxicabs here, Kate, so come on, hop on the seat."

Kate shook her head. "I will not. Ride in this old wagon indeed! Why, everybody will laugh at me."

Father's patience was wearing out. He just grabbed Kate under the arms and lifted her into the seat before she knew what had happened. "Come on, Son, we can't waste the whole day. You sit on the outside so she won't fall off." They both got on the wagon. Kate almost disappeared between them. Father was a very big man, and Jancsi a big husky boy for his age. But what Kate lacked in size, she made up in temper. When she realized what had happened, she turned into a miniature whirlwind. She kicked and screamed, she pinched Jancsi, she squirmed like a "bag of screaming monkeys."

"Father, the man was right, she's a bag of screaming monkeys!" said Jancsi, half angry, half amused, holding on to Kate.

Father was busy holding the horses in check. They were respectable farm horses, not used to the unpleasant sounds Kate managed to make. Soon they left the town and were traveling at a fast clip on the country road. Little by little Kate subsided. The long trip in the train and all the excitement were beginning to wear her out. She looked around. She saw the great Hungarian plain unfold before her eyes. Something in her was touched by the solemn beauty of it. Its immense grassy expanses unbroken by mountains or trees, shimmering under the spring sun. The dark blue sky, cloudless, like an inverted blue bowl. Herds of grazing sheep, like patches of snow. No sound, save the soft thud of the horses' hoofs on the white dusty road, and now and then the distant tinkle of sheep's bells, or the eerie sound of a shepherd's flute, the tilinkó. At times these plains, called the "puszta," are the very essence of timeless calm. At times the puszta wakes up and resembles an ocean in a storm. Clouds, so low it seems you can reach up and touch them, gather above. Hot winds roar over the waving grass. Frightened herds stampede,

bellowing and crying. But calm or stormy, it is magnificent. Its people are truly children of the soil, they are like the puszta itself. Good-natured, calm, smiling, they, like the plain, can be aroused to violent emotions.

Kate did not know all this, but she was touched by the greatness and calm of it. She was very quiet now. Jancsi looked at her and touched Father's shoulder. They smiled at each other— she seemed asleep. Jancsi felt almost sorry for her now, she was so little and thin, so funny with her dirty little face. "Like a kitten," he thought, "the poor little kitten I found after the storm." He moved, to give her more room. She leaned heavily against him, her head nodding. He didn't see her face now, didn't see the slow impish grin, the awakening mischief in her eyes. He moved a little more, balancing on the edge of the seat. "Poor little kitten," he thought again—and "poor little kitten" suddenly gave him a hearty push which sent him off the wagon like a bag of flour. He landed in the dusty road, resembling a bag of flour indeed. He hurt something awful where he landed; it was the same spot Máli the cow had kicked that morning. Through the dust he saw the wagon come to a stop.

Father jumped down and, reaching Jancsi, be-

gan to feel his arms and legs for broken bones. "You great big baby," he scolded, "you want to ride wild horses? Can't even stay on a wagon!"

"Hey! Hey! Father! Stop Kate! Look, Father!" Jancsi yelled, struggling away from Father.

There was Kate, standing bolt upright on the seat, reins and whip in hand. She was grinning from ear to ear.

"Pushed you off, didn't I, little girl? Catch me if you can!" She whipped the horses, screaming at them: "Gee, git up, git up!" This was too much for one day even for the horses. They lunged forward, and broke into a wild gallop.

Father, shocked speechless for a moment, grabbed Jancsi by the arm.

"Come on, Son, we've got to catch this screaming monkey before the horses break their legs, or she breaks her neck!"

They ran, panting and choking in the hot dust. The wagon was almost out of sight now.

"Got-to-get-horses!" panted Father.

"We-could-catch-two from the herd here!" choked Jancsi, pointing to the herd they had passed that morning.

They jumped the fence and were among the surprised horses before the animals became alarmed.

"Run with the horse, Son," cried Father. "Run with it, grab its mane, and *swing!*"

Exciting moments followed. They were used to horses, but this was hard business, without rope or halter. Jancsi singled out a young chestnut horse. The animal reared, shied, baring his teeth, and started to run. But Jancsi's hands were already clutching his mane. The horse broke into a wild run, Jancsi clinging to him for dear life. He was carried like a piece of cloth, almost flying beside the horse. With a supreme effort he pulled himself up. Clutching his legs around the animal's neck, he reached forward to pull its nose down. Horse and rider were a mass of plunging, snorting animation. Jancsi was dizzy, but he gritted his teeth and hung on. Then he heard Father's voice through the tumult. "Let him run and guide with your knees. Come on, 'csikós,' you're a real son of mine!"

Slowly the horse quieted down. Jancsi pulled him around and headed for the fence. Father was riding a big mare, waving to him to follow. Soon they were traveling side by side—hot, dirty, exhausted, and, judging by Father's face, madder than hornets.

They rode through the village without stopping to ask questions. The poplars on the ranch road whizzed past them. There was the house now! There was Mother, at the gate, waving madly with one hand. With her other hand she was clutching the blue skirts of a dancing, struggling little imp—a dirty, disheveled, but grinning little girl—Cousin Kate from Budapest!

Motherless Lamb

While Kate told her story, Jancsi cast half-amused, half-admiring glances at her. She might be just a plain little girl, but she certainly wasn't a sissy.

She was sitting in Mother's ample and protective lap, looking once more like a sleepy kitten. Father was very angry at first, but he was so relieved to see her alive, he just couldn't stay angry.

"We were going almost as fast as Ben Hur in the movies," Kate said. "Only I lost those long strings tied to the horses and then I had to sit down, I had nothing to hang on to. And the chariot was swaying so I got dizzy!" She kept on calling the wagon a "chariot." Jancsi didn't like

it, it sounded almost as bad as "taxicab." "Then we came to a long street with houses. Men in petticoats, like yours, Jancsi, came running out of the houses. They were all yelling, but couldn't stop the horses. But after a while the horses got tired running, an' I was sick to my stomach anyway, so I crawled back and lay down on the straw, and went to sleep."

"The poor mite was still sleeping when I found her," said Mother. "I saw the wagon turn in at the gate without a living soul on it. The horses were heading for the stable. I ran out. There was a girl curled up in the straw! When I woke her up, she started to jabber a lot of nonsense about 'chariots' and 'Ben Hurs' and Uncle Márton and Jancsi. 'Glory be,' I said, 'are you Cousin Kate from Budapest?' I picked her up and brought her in! The very idea, leaving a delicate child alone in the wagon with four wild horses!"

"Leaving—what's this?" cried Father, but Kate broke in hurriedly: "And then we saw you and Jancsi riding like the devil was after you!"

"Only it was the other way round—*we* were riding after the devil!" said Father. "Luckily the horses had sense enough to bring you home. But listen, my girl, you are rather a wolf in sheep's clothing!"

"M-m-m," said Kate with satisfaction. "I know. That's what Father always said. Oh! He sent you a letter!" She reached down into her blouse and produced an envelope.

Father read the letter aloud:

"My dear Brother:

"I feel guilty for misleading you, so forgive me. My dear daughter Kate had the measles, and she is delicate and in need of fresh country air—all this is true. But she is more than delicate. She is the most impossible, incredible, disobedient, headstrong little imp. And she needs more than fresh air—she needs a strong hand! Pray don't let her innocent face take you in; when she looks like an angel, she's contemplating something disastrous. She is beyond me. I confess I have spoiled her since her blessed mother died. You always had a good hand with wild young things, your people always called you the Good Master, so I send Kate to you. I'll miss her terribly, but this is the best thing I can do for her.

"So forgive me, Márton, and try to put a halter on my wild colt.

"Your loving brother,
"Sándor."

There was a long silence. Everybody looked at Kate. She, with her eyes cast down demurely, was the very picture of innocence.

"My poor little motherless lamb," cried Mother, gathering Kate in her arms. "I don't believe a word of it. Why, look at her, Father, isn't she like an angel?"

Jancsi felt gooseflesh creeping up his spine. He had seen this angelic expression before—his uncle was right, it was a danger signal. He looked at Father and caught his eye. Father was actually winking at him. Then he stood up, and said:

"Jancsi and I are going to look after those 'wild horses,' Mother; you watch our new angel. See that she doesn't fly away."

The horses were a sorry sight indeed, caked with dust. Father and Jancsi worked hard for a long time. Under the currycomb and brush the black coats of the animals were glossy once more. After the cleaning Father gave them their rations. The stable was spick and span, the wagon put in the shed. "Time for our supper, Jancsi. Let's see what Mother is doing with the 'angel.'"

"There's Mother calling now," cried Jancsi, "but she's calling Kate."

Mother was running toward them, flushed, with all her numerous petticoats swaying around her.

"Kate! Where is Kate? Have you seen Kate? She was in the kitchen one minute, making the most awful faces at the bowl of milk I gave her for supper. Then she disappeared in thin air while I went out for water!"

They looked high and low. No Kate. No sign, no sound, of Kate. In the sheep house, the chicken coop, pigsty, cowbarn—no Kate. They looked up the roof and down the well. Back to the house, maybe she was just hiding. She wasn't in the house.

Utterly exhausted, Father sank into a kitchen chair. "If she's still alive, she's going back to the city tomorrow, so help me! I wasn't made for this sort of thing, it gives me a pain in my side," he said.

"Send the poor little motherless lamb away,

Father? You couldn't," cried Mother. "Her very own father calling her names. I just know her poor little heart is broken. And you two looking at her as if she were a bug. It's enough to kill the child!"

"Tee-hee!" a sound came from the rafters. "Tee-hee!"

"Mice or rats after the sausages again. Light a candle, Jancsi," said Father. He was very fond of sausages. Mother made quantities of them in the winter. Thin long ones with lots of paprika, short fat ones with liver; she made head cheese, smoked hams. When they were ready, Father hung them on the rafters in the kitchen. He hung long rows of peppers and strings of corn on the cob. He kept bacon on one rafter, his carving tools on another. Even Jancsi wasn't allowed to touch anything stored up there.

When the candle flared up, Father was ready with a broom. Rats were his personal enemies.

"Tee-hee!" came the sound again. There sat Kate, straddling the smoky beam, skinny legs dangling, munching one end of a long sausage. Gulping down a huge mouthful, she volunteered an explanation to her thunderstruck relatives. "She gave me milk for supper. Hate milk! I like sausages!"

As long as Jancsi lived, he never forgot the uproar that followed the discovery of Kate. He wanted to laugh, but didn't dare, Father was too mad! Grasping the broom, Father roared: "Come down!" Kate shook her head. "COME DOWN!" Kate moved like lightning, out of the path of the swinging broom. Mother was wringing her hands, trying to calm Father, and imploring Kate to come down, all at once. There was a cascade of assorted sausages, pepper, and corn. Father got red and redder in the face. Kate was scurrying like a monkey from one beam to the other, screaming like a tin whistle. It went on and on. It was Father who gave in first. He sank into his chair, wiping his forehead. "Angel . . . motherless lamb," he panted. "Look at her now. Her little heart is broken." And with utter contempt: "Delicate! Devouring yards of sausages!"

"Come down, my lamb, he won't hurt you." Mother held out her arms to Kate.

"Can't," was the laconic answer.

"How did you get up there anyway? If you

went up, you can come down," growled Father.

"I climbed on that big white beehive in the corner, but it's hot now, she made a fire in it," said Kate. She meant the stove. It did look like a beehive, squatting in the corner. There was a bench around it. Jancsi loved to cuddle on the bench, propping his back against the warm side of the "kemence."

"Well, now you'll stay there until the 'beehive' cools down. Jancsi! Mother! I forbid you to take her down. She can stay there all night!" said Father. And no amount of Mother's begging and crying softened him. There she was, and there she stayed.

Mother began to serve supper. They ate in silence. Jancsi was grinning secretly. Once he looked up. Kate was peering down, her face black, her dress smoky, her stockings torn, but she grinned back.

Suddenly Father began to laugh. "Screaming monkey! Poor kitten! Colt! Motherless lamb! Why, she's a whole menagerie! You always wanted to go to a circus, Jancsi; now the circus has come to you!"

"I'm thirsty," announced Kate unexpectedly.

"Anybody would be after eating two yards of sausages. If you want a drink, come down and get it!" was Father's answer.

She tried "I'm sleepy," "I'm tired," without any satisfactory results. In fact, they were going to bed, actually leaving her perched on the rafters, and the "beehive" still too hot. She began to whimper. Jancsi felt sorry for her, but orders were orders.

Mother prepared the beds. The guest bed for Kate. This was seldom in use, all the fancy embroidered pillows were piled up to the ceiling on it. Mother carried them to a chest, put down two huge featherbeds for mattresses, and a lighter featherbed for a cover. She was shaking her head, looking at Kate, looking at Father, but he wouldn't soften. Finally they put out the candles and silence settled upon the house.

Jancsi fell asleep. The sound of soft footsteps woke him up. Then he heard whispers and a giggle. He tiptoed to the kitchen door. There was Father, holding Kate in his arms, stroking her hair.

Something made Jancsi feel all shaky inside —he felt like crying, but he was happy.

He crawled back to his bed. A little later he heard Father's voice whisper: "Good night, little screaming monkey."

Dozing off to a contented sleep, Jancsi's last thought was: "I'm glad she isn't a golden-haired princess—she's almost as good as a real boy!"

AT THE GRANDFATHER'S

Johanna Spyri

College girls have frequently said that Heidi *was one book they brought with them when they first came to college. It is easy to see why.* Heidi *is the homeless, forlorn child trying to make a place for herself. Like* The Wind in the Willows, *this is a reassuring book, and the gallant spirit of that little girl is unforgettable.*

After Dete had disappeared, the uncle sat down again on the bench and blew great clouds of smoke from his pipe, while he kept his eyes fixed on the ground without saying a word. Meanwhile Heidi was content to look about her. She discovered the goats' shed built near the hut and peeped into it. It was empty.

The child continued hunting about and came to the fir trees behind the hut. The wind was blowing hard, and it whistled and roared through the branches, high up in the tops. Heidi stood still and listened. When it stopped somewhat she went round to the other side of the hut and came back to her grandfather. When she found him in the same place where she had left him, she placed herself in front of him, put her hands behind her, and gazed at him. Her grandfather looked up.

"What do you want to do?" he asked, as the child continued standing in front of him without moving.

"I want to see what you have in the hut," said Heidi.

"Come along, then!" and the grandfather rose and started to go into the hut.

"Bring your bundle of clothes," he said as he entered.

"I shan't want them any more," replied Heidi.

The old man turned round and looked sharply

From *Heidi* by Johanna Spyri, translated by Helen B. Dole. Used by permission of the publishers, Ginn and Company.

at the child, whose black eyes shone in expectation of what might be inside the hut.

"She's not lacking in brains," he said half to himself. "Why won't you need them any more?" he asked aloud.

"I'd rather go like the goats, with their swift little legs."

"So you shall, but bring the things along," commanded the grandfather; "they can be put into the cupboard."

Heidi obeyed. The old man opened the door, and Heidi followed him into a good-sized room, which occupied the whole hut. In it were a table and a chair; in one corner was the grandfather's bed, in another the fireplace where hung the large kettle; on the other side, in the wall, was a large door, which the grandfather opened; it was the cupboard. There hung his clothes, and on one shelf lay his shirts, stockings, and linen; on another were plates, cups, and glasses, and on the topmost a loaf of bread, smoked meat, and cheese. Everything the Alm-Uncle owned and needed for his living was kept in this closet. As soon as he had opened the door, Heidi came running with her bundle and pushed it in, as far back of her grandfather's clothes as possible, that it might not be easy to find it again. Then she looked carefully round the room and said:

"Where shall I sleep, grandfather?"

"Wherever you like," he replied.

This was quite to Heidi's mind. She looked into every nook and corner to see where would be the best place for her to sleep. In the corner by her grandfather's bed stood a little ladder, which led to the hayloft. Heidi climbed this. There lay a fresh, fragrant heap of hay, and through a round window one could look far down into the valley below.

"This is where I will sleep," Heidi called down; "it is lovely! Just come and see how lovely it is up here, grandfather!"

"I know all about it," sounded from below.

"I am going to make a bed," called out the child again as she ran busily to and fro in the loft; "but you must come up here and bring a sheet, for the bed must have a sheet for me to sleep on."

"Well, well," said the grandfather below; and after a few moments he went to the cupboard and rummaged about; then he drew out from under his shirts a long, coarse piece of cloth, which might serve for a sheet. He came up the ladder and found that a very neat little bed had been made in the hayloft; the hay was piled up higher at one end to form the pillow, and the bed was placed in such a way that one could look from it straight out through the round open window.

"That is made very nicely," said the grandfather; "next comes the sheet; but wait a moment,"—and he took up a good armful of hay and made the bed as thick again, in order that the hard floor might not be felt through it; "there, now put it on."

Heidi quickly took hold of the sheet, but was unable to lift it, it was so heavy; however, this made it all the better because the sharp wisps of hay could not push through the firm cloth. Then the two together spread the sheet over the hay, and where it was too broad or too long Heidi quickly tucked it under. Now it appeared quite trim and neat, and Heidi stood looking at it thoughtfully.

"We have forgotten one thing, grandfather," she said.

"What is that?" he asked.

"The coverlet; when we go to bed we creep in between the sheet and the coverlet."

"Is that so? But supposing I haven't any?" asked the old man.

"Oh, then it's no matter," said Heidi soothingly; "we can take more hay for a coverlet"; and she was about to run to the haymow again, but her grandfather prevented her.

"Wait a moment," he said, and went down the ladder to his own bed. Then he came back and laid a large, heavy linen bag on the floor.

"Isn't that better than hay?" he asked. Heidi pulled at the bag with all her might and main, trying to unfold it, but her little hands could not manage the heavy thing. Her grandfather helped, and when it was finally spread out on the bed, it all looked very neat and comfortable, and Heidi, looking at her new resting-place admiringly, said:

"That is a splendid coverlet, and the whole bed is lovely! How I wish it were night so that I could lie down in it!"

"I think we might have something to eat first," said the grandfather. "What do you say?"

In her eagerness over the bed, Heidi had forgotten everything else; but now that eating was suggested to her, a great feeling of hunger rose within her, for she had taken nothing all day, except a piece of bread and a cup of weak coffee early in the morning, and afterward she had made the long journey. So Heidi heartily agreed, saying:

"Yes, I think so too."

"Well, let us go down, since we are agreed," said the old man and followed close upon the child's steps. He went to the fireplace, pushed the large kettle aside and drew forward the little one that hung on the chain, sat down on the three-legged wooden stool with the round seat and kindled a bright fire. Almost immediately the kettle began to boil, and the old man held over the fire a large piece of cheese on the end of a long iron fork. He moved it this way and that, until it was golden yellow on all sides. Heidi looked on with eager attention. Suddenly a new idea came to her mind; she jumped up and ran to the cupboard, and kept going back and forth. When the grandfather brought the toasted cheese to the table, it was already nicely laid with the round loaf of bread, two plates, and two knives, for Heidi had noticed everything in the cupboard, and knew that all would be needed for the meal.

"That is right, to think of doing something yourself," said the grandfather, laying the cheese on the bread and putting the teapot on the table; "but there is something still lacking."

Heidi saw how invitingly the steam came out of the pot, and ran quickly back to the cupboard. But there was only one little bowl there. Heidi was not long puzzled; behind it stood two glasses; the child immediately came back with the bowl and glasses and placed them on the table.

"Very good. You know how to help yourself; but where are you going to sit?"

The grandfather himself was sitting in the only chair. Heidi shot like an arrow to the fireplace, brought back the little three-legged stool and sat down on it.

"Well, you have a seat, sure enough, only it is rather low," said the grandfather; "but in my chair also you would be too short to reach the table; still you must have something anyway, so come!"

Saying which he rose, filled the little bowl with milk, placed it on the chair, and pushed it close to the three-legged stool, so that Heidi had a table in front of her. The grandfather laid a large slice of bread and a piece of the golden cheese on the chair and said:

"Now eat!"

He seated himself on the corner of the table and began his dinner. Heidi grasped her bowl and drank and drank without stopping, for all the thirst of her long journey came back to her. Then she drew a long breath and set down the bowl.

"Do you like the milk?" asked her grandfather.

"I never tasted such good milk before," answered Heidi.

"Then you must have some more"; and the grandfather filled the bowl again to the brim and placed it before the child, who looked quite content as she began to eat her bread, after it had been spread with the toasted cheese soft as butter. The combination tasted very good, with frequent drinks of milk.

When the meal was over, the grandfather went out to the goat-shed to put it in order, and Heidi watched him closely as he first swept it clean with a broom and then laid down fresh straw for the animals to sleep on. Then he went to his little shop, cut some round sticks, shaped a board, made some holes in it, put the round sticks into them, and suddenly it was a stool like his own, only much higher. Heidi was speechless with amazement as she saw his work.

"What is this, Heidi?" asked the grandfather.

"It is a stool for me, because it is so high; you made it all at once," said the child, still deeply astonished.

"She knows what she sees; her eyes are in the right place," remarked the grandfather to himself as he went round the hut driving a nail here and there; then he repaired something about the door, and went from place to place with hammer, nails, and pieces of wood, mending and clearing away wherever it was needed. Heidi followed him step by step and watched him with the closest attention, and everything he did interested her very much.

Evening was coming on. It was beginning to blow harder in the old fir trees, for a mighty wind had sprung up and was whistling and moaning through their thick tops. It sounded so beautiful in Heidi's ears and heart that she was quite delighted, and skipped and jumped under the firs as if she were feeling the greatest pleasure of her life. The grandfather stood in the doorway and watched the child.

A shrill whistle sounded. Heidi stopped her jumping, and the grandfather stepped outside. Down from above came goat after goat, leaping like a hunting train, and Peter in the midst of them. With a shout of joy Heidi rushed in among the flock and greeted her old friends of the morning one after the other.

When they reached the hut, they all stood still, and two lovely slender goats—one white, the other brown—came out from the others to the grandfather and licked his hands, in which he held some salt to welcome them. This he did each evening. Peter disappeared with his flock. Heidi gently stroked first one goat and then the other and ran round them to stroke them on the other side; she was perfectly delighted with the little creatures.

"Are they ours, grandfather? Are they both ours? Will they go into the shed? Will they stay with us always?" asked Heidi, one question following the other in her delight. When the goats had finished licking their salt, the old man said:

"Go and bring out your little bowl and the bread."

Heidi obeyed, and came back at once. The grandfather milked the goat and filled the bowl and cut off a piece of bread, saying:

"Now eat your supper and then go up to bed! Your Aunt Dete left a bundle for you; your nightgowns and other things are in it. You will find it downstairs in the closet if you need it. I must attend to the goats now; so sleep well!"

"Good night, grandfather! Good night—what are their names, grandfather? what are their names?" cried the child, running after the old man and the goats as they disappeared into the shed.

"The white one is named Schwänli[1] and the brown one Bärli,"[2] answered the grandfather.

"Good night, Schwänli! good night, Bärli!" called Heidi at the top of her voice. Then Heidi sat down on the bench and ate her bread and

[1] Schwänli = little swan.
[2] Bärli = little bear.

drank her milk; but the strong wind almost blew her off her seat; so she finished hastily, then went in and climbed up to her bed, in which she immediately fell asleep and slept as soundly and well as if she had been in the loveliest bed of some royal princess.

Not long after, even before it was entirely dark, the grandfather also went to bed; for he was always up with the sun, and it came climbing over the mountain very early in the summer time. In the night the wind blew with such force that its blasts made the whole hut tremble, and every rafter creaked. It howled and groaned down the chimney like voices in distress, and outside in the fir trees it raged with such fury that now and then a bough was broken off.

In the middle of the night the grandfather rose and said half aloud to himself:

"She may be afraid."

He climbed the ladder and went to Heidi's bedside. The moon outside shone brightly in the sky for a moment and then disappeared behind the driving clouds, and everything grew dark. Then the moonlight came again brightly through the round opening and fell directly on Heidi's couch. Her cheeks were fiery red as she slept under the heavy coverlet, and she lay perfectly calm and peaceful on her little round arm. She must have been dreaming happy dreams, for a look of happiness was on her face. The grandfather gazed long at the sweetly sleeping child until the moon went behind a cloud again and it was dark. Then he went back to his own bed.

FOUR SILVER PITCHERS

Ann Weil

The Silver Fawn, *from which this selection is taken, presents an excellent picture of the skillful craftsmen of Mexico and the beautiful things they make. It is also a moving story of one boy's achievement.*

Señor Bill was right. With the coming of the weavers, more and more Mexicans found their way to the little shop in Taxco. First they came only to buy the *serapes,* but it was not long before they were buying the silver, too. The months passed quickly, and with their passing the shop grew both in size and popularity.

And as the months passed Chico, too, grew rapidly. Now, when he was almost sixteen, he had the clear bright eyes and steady hands of a real silversmith. The other workmen in the shop saw his work grow better and better. They began to admire his well-formed pieces and his clear-cut designs. All of the beautiful things that Chico had dreamed of making—these, one by one, were becoming real. Now Chico worked beside Alfonso, Alfonso who was the most famous silversmith in all of Taxco. True, Chico was only Alfonso's helper, but the very fact that he worked beside him every day made Chico happy. Chico watched this fine artist while he modeled and soldered and formed the silver. "Someday," Chico whispered to the fawn, "someday I, too, will be an artist." When such ideas popped into his head these days, Chico did not shake them impatiently away. It was nice to dream again as he had when he was a little boy. It was nice to know that much of the hard work was well behind him. It was nice to know that his fingers had learned how to obey his commands —that they no longer behaved like ten useless sticks.

So the shop and Chico grew and grew, and it was not long before the dry season came again bringing with it the tourists. By the time the shop was two years old, it was one of the show places of Taxco. Tourists asked to see it as they asked to see other places of interest. They wanted to see the parrots who walked round the shop and talked to the customers. They wanted to see the kid and the fawn who were always there to be petted. They watched the weavers carding, spinning, weaving. They watched the silversmiths molding and hammering. They looked at the beautiful things on display. Certainly it was a workshop, a museum and a zoo all rolled into one.

And then one day a very important woman came into the shop. She was a Mexican from Mexico City. Señor Bill recognized her at once as Donna Gamanio who was known all over Mexico for her interest in art. She had helped and encouraged many young artists. She had helped revive the interest in Indian art. At her home all artists were always welcome. Certainly her presence in the shop was a thing to be proud of.

"I wish to order four pitchers," she said to Señor Bill. "A small one for cream and a larger one for milk. A fat, round one for chocolate and a tall one for water. They are to be given as a wedding present," she said as she left. "I must have them in two weeks."

Four silver pitchers! Everyone in the shop was excited about the order. Certainly it was exciting for two reasons. First, the order was big. Never before had one person ordered so much. Second, if Donna Gamanio was pleased, she would probably tell her friends, and her friends were the most important people in Mexico City.

Señor Bill could not hide his delight with the order. Donna Gamanio did not spend her money carelessly. If she had not heard good things about the shop, she would never have come all the way from Mexico City to give an order. Her coming was an honor he had not expected.

The whole shop seemed to work on the pitchers. True, only one workman, Alfonso, did the actual work, but everyone was interested; everyone wanted to help. Chico watched each step, fascinated. He saw the silver bars melted. He saw the pitchers taking form beneath the hands of Alfonso. Finally three were finished. They stood in a row in a place of honor.

Everyone who came into the shop saw and admired them. "They are for Donna Gamanio," the workmen whispered to the customers. "*The* Donna Gamanio?" the people answered. "No wonder, then, they are so beautiful." Yes, everyone in Mexico knew that Donna Gamanio accepted only the best.

And then, with three pitchers finished, an accident happened! Alfonso was all ready to start on the fourth and last pitcher. The soldering pot stood before him, boiling and bubbling. Everything was ready. That was *one* second! The *next* second Alfonso's foot slipped, and he fell against the table. But that was not all! In falling he upset the soldering pot, and the hot lead ran all over his fingers. Certainly the pain from the burns was great, but as Alfonso looked down at his blistering fingers, he thought only of the one unfinished pitcher. He had only three days in which to finish it. He shook his head sadly. He

knew it would take more than three days for his burns to heal.

Señor Bill tried to comfort him as best he could. "Such accidents cannot be helped," he said. "Certainly you would be the last one to want it to happen. Donna Gamanio will just have to give three pitchers instead of four. We can only hope that she will not be too disappointed."

Nevertheless the whole shop worried about the fourth pitcher. It was known that Donna Gamanio was not used to being disappointed. Everyone always tried hard to please her. With all of her kindness she could, at times be very unreasonable. If she had made up her mind to give four pitchers, she would never be content to give only three. To all of them the whole future of the little shop seemed to depend upon that one pitcher. If a word from Donna Gamanio could make them famous, it was just as true that a word from her could ruin them forever. Let her tell her friends that the shop in Taxco promised one thing and did another. Let her tell them that it was not to be trusted. That would be all her friends needed. There were many shops in Mexico City more than eager to win their favor. Everyone was sure that once Donna Gamanio had been disappointed, she would never come back again.

Chico, particularly, could scarcely stand it. He looked as though he carried the worries of the world on his shoulders. "We have to do something," he said to Señor Bill that afternoon. "We have to do something. We can't just stand here."

"Well," said Señor Bill, half-annoyed, half-joking, "if you think there is something that can be done, why don't you do it? I, for one," he added, "can think of nothing. The other men in the shop are good workmen, but they are not artists. I know that their work would never please Donna Gamanio. Unless the pitcher is as good as the other three, it would be better not to have it at all."

Chico nodded his head and turned away. He could tell that Señor Bill did not wish to be bothered. When a person was worried, he wanted to be alone with his thoughts. Chico knew how he felt. He, himself, did not feel like talking to anyone. He went over to the table and sat down.

Ever since they had started to work on the pitchers, Chico had been helping Alfonso. Now, with Alfonso gone, he had the big table all to himself. He looked round at all the work to be done, but now none of it seemed very important. His fingers felt lifeless; the tools seemed like so many worthless objects whose use he had forgotten; the silver looked dull and heavy. If he made six more buttons, or four more bracelets or two more spoons, what did it matter? He had been delighted when he thought the shop had raised itself from a little tourist shop to a place where the cultured people of Mexico came to buy. Now that hope was gone. With a heavy heart he picked up a bar of silver and laid it on the table.

Just then the little fawn came up and licked his hand—and suddenly Chico felt unhappy no longer. An overturned pot—a missing pitcher—surely the success or failure of the little shop could not hang on such small things. He bent down and patted the little fawn. Then he went to work.

All afternoon Chico worked, all afternoon and the next day and the day after that. With Alfonso gone, everyone had to work hard. Chico, like everyone else, kept himself busy.

On the day that Donna Gamanio was to come after her order, everyone in the shop wore a long face. The morning seemed endless. The minutes stretched themselves into hours, and the hours were days that had to be lived through. "What would she do?" everyone asked. "What would she say?" Some said that she would fly into a rage and stamp out of the shop. Some said that she would leave without a word. Some said— The stories grew and grew. If Donna Gamanio were a dragon about to descend upon them they would not have feared her more. Still, behind all of the stories, there was a real reason for their concern. It was true that Donna Gamanio was as temperamental as any of the artists she had helped. She could be kind and helpful and considerate; she could also be very unreasonable. The whole shop waited breathlessly for her coming.

They worried and talked. They gathered in small groups and shook their heads. Everyone deserted his work to add a bit to the growing stories; everyone, that is, except Chico. He sat all alone at the big table in the back of the showroom, his head bent over his work. "He is unhappy," the other workmen said; "we will leave him alone."

Later that afternoon, however, Chico did leave his table. Señor Bill saw him standing in front of the three silver pitchers, looking at them as though he had never seen them before. "It is too bad," said Señor Bill. "The three that are made are certainly lovely." He turned at the sound of an automobile, and looked out of the window. There down the street came Donna Gamanio, only a block from the shop. Señor Bill shrugged his shoulders and turned around. "Well," he began, then stopped short. Where the three pitchers had stood there were now four. He put his hand to his forehead and blinked his eyes, What had happened? A silver pitcher did

not appear out of thin air. He looked expectantly at Chico.

Chico, however, merely looked frightened. "I," he began, "I—I—" he stopped and looked hurriedly at the door. Donna Gamanio was already on the steps. "I came back to the shop every night and worked on it," Chico said in a low whisper. "Do you think it will do?"

"Do?" Señor Bill picked it up and held it in his hand. The workmen around the shop stopped where they were as though they had been suddenly turned into stone. They stared as though they had suddenly seen a vision. "Do?" Señor Bill smiled as he turned the pitcher round and round in his hand. He looked at its satinlike finish, at its well-formed shape. He smiled again when he saw, on one side, an etching of a little fawn. It was the simplest design imaginable—just a few little strokes; still those few little lines, some long, some short, set off the pointed ears, the stubby tail, the delicate throat and the slender legs. Just a few little lines; still the fawn was there. One had only to look at the etching to see it.

Señor Bill put it down next to the other three pitchers just as Donna Gamanio walked into the room. She smiled pleasantly and then she stopped. "Are those mine?" she asked. "Are those my pitchers?"

Señor Bill nodded. "Yes," he said, "do you like them?"

"They're lovely," she answered. "I couldn't ask for lovelier ones."

Chico walked over to a corner of the room where the little fawn stood. It seemed that he was breathing easily for the first time in three days. Then, suddenly, he stopped breathing altogether. Donna Gamanio walked over to the table and picked up his pitcher. "This one," she said, "does not look like the others. Yes," she said, "I am sure of it. It is different—quite different."

Señor Bill nodded his head. There was no use trying to fool Donna Gamanio.

"Yes," she repeated, "quite different. I do not know who made the other three, but I do know that this one was made by an artist." She smiled at the outline of the little fawn. "It is amazing," she said. "When you first look at the design, it is merely a few little lines mixed up together—

then all of a sudden you see the fawn. You feel that any moment it might twitch its ears or flick its tail or run away on its slender legs."

She put the pitcher down on the table. "You can tell it was made by an artist," she said. "See, it holds itself proudly."

Señor Bill looked at it fondly and nodded his head. Hard work, time and patience—certainly one could tell that Chico had used them, as well as the silver, in making the pitcher.

"Wait," he said to Donna Gamanio as she started to leave. "Wait, I will introduce you to the artist and to the little fawn who posed for the etching." But when he looked over in the corner, both Chico and the fawn had disappeared.

"IN THE BEGINNING ALL THINGS ARE DIFFICULT"

Elizabeth Foreman Lewis

Young Fu of the Upper Yangtze *won the Newbery Award in 1933. This book gives us a graphic picture of the inner strife and conflict in the life of a young Chinese boy. The details are Chinese, but Fu is any boy of any country trying to make his way in the world and blundering now and then in spite of good intentions. The country boy poked fun at by city boys, the conflict between Fu's point of view and his mother's, and the picture of the coppersmith's shop make this selection an excellent lead into the book.*

The room was quite dark when Fu Be Be's repeated callings aroused him. "What is it?" he asked sleepily.

"Already the Hour of the Tiger draws to a close. That we have moved to this city is no reason for your sleeping like a gentleman."

Young Fu sat up. "But it is still black as midnight." He pulled the pu-gai about his shoulders. "Ai! it is cold."

"Laziness never filled a rice bowl. And Chung-

"In the Beginning All Things Are Difficult." From *Young Fu of the Upper Yangtze*, by Elizabeth Foreman Lewis, and used by permission of the publishers, The John C. Winston Company, Philadelphia

king is famous throughout the land for its bad weather, so I have heard." She shivered. "Cold it is." Loosening the latch, she glanced outside. "And the rain falls."

Yawning, her son struggled into his outer jacket. Fu Be Be was working over the dilapidated clay stove built into the chimney place. She rubbed stinging eyes as she blew the charcoal into flame. There was a breakfast of hard puffed rice. This, with hot water to drink, completed the meal. Then, dressed in their best garments, the boy and his mother set out for the coppersmith's.

Mist and fine rain sifted in the streets. Sedan chairs still bore lighted lanterns. A man carried a small oil lamp burning brightly. Its glass shade was wet. Young Fu looked after him. An uncovered light continuing to flame steadily in spite of falling water! This Chungking rain was different from that of the open country.

At Tang's, business was already in progress. They stood in admiration before the establishment. Trays and kettles, jars and vases, braziers and water pipes—everything that might be desired in white and yellow brass, or red-gold copper—were displayed on the shelves of the shop. An apprentice dusted stock and a clerk stood behind the counter and deftly counted with the wooden beads strung on the wires of an abacus. Before acknowledging the presence of these new arrivals, he laid down the frame, took up a small camel's-hair brush, dampened it leisurely on a black slab of ink, and wrote several characters in an account book.

At last he turned to Fu Be Be. "What do you wish?"

"To give this to your proprietor." She held out a long, narrow envelope.

He accepted it and addressed his assistant, "Take this, Den, to the master."

The boy laid aside the feather duster and moved to an inner room. As he did so, he eyed the two callers with a glance of derision. Young Fu reddened. He felt suddenly at a loss what to do with his hands and feet. With his chin he pointed to a table and two empty stools. "Let us sit," he suggested in a whisper.

Fu Be Be shook her head. "It is not custom; we have come to obtain work, not to buy."

After what seemed an hour, an older man appeared. He walked directly to them and spoke courteously. Behind him the apprentice, Den, stared in an unblinking gaze at the new applicant. Fu Be Be explained their errand.

"This is the youth of whom Wen, the farmer wrote?"

Fu Be Be bowed.

"And his age?"

"Thirteen years and seven moons."

"That is older than I wish, but he has strength which apprentices sometimes lack." Without turning, he raised his voice, "This early in the day they are forced to rest a little."

The idler flushed guiltily and reached for the duster. Young Fu hid a smile. One thing was certain—this man missed nothing. His mother asked the coppersmith timidly about rules.

"The guild to which all of our artisans belong had in the past required five years of training for an apprentice, but at present, war changes conditions. The two I now have serve three years; your son may do the same. He will eat and sleep here at my expense; you will clothe him. What he earns after he becomes a journeyman, will depend on himself."

Fu Be Be nodded. All of this was as it should be. There was, however, one small matter. "I am one person living alone. Would your guild permit my son to spend his nights in his home?"

The coppersmith thought for a moment. "It can be arranged. He must present himself daily at the Hour of the Hare and remain until his duties are finished at night."

Fu Be Be thanked him for this consideration and promised that her son's punctuality would be on her body.

"A contract!" Tang called to the accountant. When it was brought, he read the terms aloud. "Now a pen!" He turned from the clerk to Fu Be Be. "This man will sign your name for you if you will tell him what it is. Is it the Fu character for happiness or the one for a worker?"

Fu Be Be looked up timidly. "It is the character for teacher, Honorable Proprietor, and uses twelve strokes in the writing."

Tang and the clerk stared at her in amazement. "You recognize written words?" asked the coppersmith.

Young Fu watched his mother shake her head in denial. "No, I am but a stupid countrywoman, but my husband knew several tens of characters, and he taught me our name."

Her son noticed the accountant's expression change, and his body grew hot with disappointment. That his mother had been able to tell them the correct word for their name was good; if only she might have written it as well! In these people, respect for such ability was plain to see. At home there had been little talk of learning. With the earth demanding a man's entire attention, there was no time for books. Their village was too small to support a school, and if there had been one, no child could have been spared from the fields. Yes, girls perhaps might, but who would waste good money trying to educate girls?

When letters needed to be sent, the Head of the Village would draft a few crude sentences explaining the matter in hand. Sayings from the Classics, handed down from one generation to another, were a part of daily speech. And occasionally a· wandering story-teller would appear at the small inn and regale those who could stay to listen with tales drawn from centuries of history. Once or twice his father had taken him to hear these romancers, but that had been before the soldiers had made life an impossible hardship. Such slight contacts had been his only ones with the knowledge to be found in books. His mind formed a swift decision: he would not remain ignorant; in some way he would learn to read and write.

When the ceremonies of contract were completed, Fu Be Be whispered to her son, "Give heed to all that you are told and say little! It is the good listener who learns well. This new master of yours is, I believe, a wise one." She finished swiftly as Tang's attention centered once more on them. "Remember the turns by which we arrived here this morning, two to the left—"

Young Fu interrupted with a nod, "I know the way," and then waited silently while his mother bowed herself out of the shop.

In the street the mist had lifted and Fu Be Be gazed on either side with interest. Her bound feet made slow progress. The flagstone pavings were loose and slippery with mire, and everywhere thoroughfares were separated by flights of steps, for Chungking climbed high on its rocky promontory above the swirling currents of the Lin and the still more treacherous Yangtze.

Today she had leisure, but work must be found for the future. In this city living costs were exorbitant. To retain the shelter of the room in Dai's tenement, she would have to pay, each moon, one half of a Szechuen silver dollar. Besides the rent, there was the problem of food for herself. She was thankful that her son would be fed by Tang. She herself could live on little. Rice and sometimes chin-t'sai, the cheapest of green vegetables, would satisfy her needs. Meat, except on feast days, she had learned to do without, and in brewing tea she would use fewer of the precious leaves. As for clothing, their present garments would last for some time; when they became too threadbare, she would purchase material on Thief Street, where stolen goods were offered for cheap sale, and make others.

The shops about her were busy, but most of them employed men only. The sound of light chatter attracted her attention. Women sat in a room close by and gathered pig bristles of varying lengths into uniform bunches. Fu Be Be wondered if more workers were needed. To inquire would harm no one. She came out with the promise of work to begin the next morning. After three days of learning to sort properly, she would receive ten coppers a day for twelve hours of labor, until the Great Heat arrived. Bristles to be marketable had to be thick and wiry, and summer robbed them of these qualities. But she would not worry about that now; when the time came, some other means of livelihood would present itself.

At the coppersmith's, her son was led to the farthest room and taught his first lesson in tending the fire. This he soon discovered, though no one wished to be responsible for it, was a task of the utmost importance. The heat had to be held to an even temperature, and to do this required constant attention. Fuel was fed the small furnace regularly, and if the flame failed to respond promptly, a pair of bellows flared it into life. The workmen plied from anvils to fire, and between the moments of concentration the new apprentice studied his associates.

Five journeymen there were, and he soon connected them with their names. Tsu, an old man and second in importance to Tang, was short and his face was a network of wrinkles. His

speech, though Young Fu could not hear it, kept his companions in high humor. At the anvil next him worked a sharp-featured man named Lu; Young Fu thought he had never seen anyone so long of body. When Old Tsu happened to stand beside the other, the contrast was comic. But there was no underestimating the importance of this pair; that Tang counted on them was very evident, and the whole shop deferred to them in most matters. The accountant and his assistant apprentice conducted the store. On one of his errands to the furnace room, this boy, whom the workmen called by every epithet possible except his real name, Small Den, watched the new stoker critically.

"That you have been used to tilling the soil and nothing else, I can see," he remarked with a smirk.

Young Fu, sweating in the effort to place a glowing coal in a strategic position, made no reply. He would never care much for this fellow, he felt sure. As for the others, time would tell.

At midday rice he experienced the first taste of that torment with which a new apprentice is always greeted. Without acknowledging his presence, the men began to discuss the differences between city and country people, and the first seemed to have everything in their favor.

"Countrymen are always stupid!"

"Yes, but that can be forgiven; it is their appearance I find hardest to bear. Their heads are usually the shape of a turnip, and their hands and feet are twice the size of a normal being's."

"I, myself, could like them, if I had no nose. As it is, the odor of manure about their garments makes me hurry in the opposite direction."

"And such garments!"

"And their talk!"

One remark followed the other, and the men, with sly glances at the newcomer, agreed gravely to all that was said. Old Tsu's quips, though few in number, were more to the point than the rest, and Den, aping his elders, wagged his tongue incessantly.

Young Fu burned with shame and anger. He was aware of the sting of truth in much that they said. His trousers and short coat were made differently from theirs, and the earth language he spoke did contain words these people did not use. He himself had to listen sharply to catch all that they said. As for his appearance, he thought miserably that perhaps his head was the shape of a turnip. He would look into the next puddle he came to and find out. Hungry as he was, the hot rice stuck in his throat. He wanted nothing so much as to get back to that village which only last night he had scorned. He forced the food down his throat as Den's voice ran on; he would not let these city people see how much he suffered at their hands.

Unexpected relief came with Tang's entrance. The master sat down and told Den to bring him food. Old Tsu squinted in mock horror, "Let me bring it, please, instead of this honorable apprentice. His talk this noon has been weighted with wisdom. I had not guessed he knew so much about this business. Is it possible that you have offered him a partnership?"

Tang joined with the others in laughter, and Young Fu forgot his own wretchedness long enough to appreciate this fun at Den's expense. The talk turned abruptly to politics, and the men were soon in a hot discussion as to what would happen to Chungking if the present Tuchun should be defeated.

After a while Lu told the new apprentice to clear away the bowls. The youth collected them and carrying them to the rear room set them down on a table while he blew the fire once more to intense heat. Then pouring hot water over a dirty, gray rag he swabbed the inside of the bowls and wiped off the chopsticks. As he placed them neatly on a shelf, a boy's voice called out, "Give me a bowl! Is there rice still in the pot?"

Young Fu whirled about. This was someone he had not seen before. "There is rice in plenty," he replied.

The newcomer used his sleeve to wipe perspiration from his face. "That is good, for I am starved to death. So you are the new apprentice! What is your name?"

"Fu."

"Mine is Li." He lifted the food to his lips.

Young Fu made no effort to continue the conversation. While the newcomer assumed no superior airs, he might if opportunity arose find delight in exercising his talents along this line. The tall Lu entered and held a sheet of metal in the heat. He poised the tongs carefully and

spoke: "When Small Li has eaten, you will go with him to deliver a mei-shiang-tz of kettles. It is too heavy for him to carry alone; also, in this fashion you will become familiar with the city."

They set out, the mei-shiang-tz suspended from a carrying pole, the flat ends of which rested on a shoulder of each boy. Young Fu soon learned the swinging stride which load-bearers used, and Li cleared a path for them through the crowded thoroughfares by yelling, "Open the way for a load of brasses!"

Li was shorter in stature than himself, but older. He seemed genial and inclined to ask questions.

"Where is your home?"

Young Fu hesitated. If he told, this fellow would mock him too. Then let him! He was not ashamed of his native place. "The village of Three Pools, near Tu-To," he replied sharply.

"My grandfather was a farmer," proffered his companion, "and while my father's house has lived nowhere but Chungking, we do not, of course, consider it our home. But one is safer behind strong city walls than in open fields. There, nothing checks soldiers and bandits."

"A true saying!"

"But," the other continued, "my father misses the soil. And I can understand. Once last spring we went through the land gate to the village of Dsen Gia Ngai. There were fields of rice and mustard, and, on the paths, grass. It was good to look at and very clean. Some day I hope to cross the Great River to the hills. From their highest points, it is said, one can see long distances, even to the provinces of Kweichow and Yunnan, but that naturally is on a day when the sky holds no cloud."

Young Fu warmed to this companion. They moved aside to flatten against a compound wall that two sedan chairs might pass in the narrow street. The two passengers were gentlemen of wealth and, as they recognized each other, fans were raised hurriedly before their faces in greeting. The ceremonies attendant on stopping would have required some time, and by this gesture each indicated courteously that he was in a great hurry.

The sedan chairs having passed, the boys once more swung into step. "Where do you now dwell?" asked Li.

"On Chair-Makers' Way."

"My family lives on Chicken Street, but I, of course, share the coppersmith's roof. You will sleep next me, I suppose."

"No, my mother is alone and this morning she asked the master if I might return to keep her company each night."

"That is not the custom." Small Li's eyes were wide with surprise. "But then Tang's payments to the Brassworkers' Guild are so large that it is easier for him than for most to arrange things to his own liking." He sighed. "I am sorry. Den is a poor companion. He wishes to forget he is still an apprentice and his ears are only for the men."

Young Fu thanked him for this friendly advance. He was moved to frankness, "Den, I think, will not regret my absence."

Small Li threw him a questioning glance. "So this early he vented his bitterness, did he? A member of his house, a cousin, wished to become Tang's apprentice. The coppersmith would not consider him. It was bad fortune enough to have one in his shop like Den; he did not wish a second. I myself heard him say it. Den will not soon forgive you for filling the place."

When they reëntered the store late that afternoon, Young Fu felt braced to meet anything. One in this place was his friend, the others did not matter. As they appeared, Tang called out, "Did you enjoy yourselves playing about this afternoon? Or can it be that the customer has moved?"

Small Li bowed with a grin. Noticing his companion's confusion, he waited until they had reached the rear, then told him, "Tang is always like that. His tongue is sharp and his wit worse than Old Tsu's, but he does not beat his apprentices, and that is a great blessing. My cousin who works for a tanner bears scars from the bamboo's strokes—and for no reason but that he placed a skin with a tear on a pile of perfect ones."

That Tang had another side to his character, Young Fu discovered later. At dusk the coppersmith beckoned to him. "You need not remain to finish tonight. The ways of this city are new to you, and your mother will carry a heavy heart until you return. Do you know the direction to Chair-Makers' Way?" The youth nodded. "Then follow it without delay." His eyes held a kindly expression, and through the devious turns that led him home, Young Fu remembered it.

The light was still dim when he arrived at the shop next morning. Lanterns suspended from the ceiling softened the brasses to a satiny sheen, and Young Fu was held for a moment by the beauty on display. His pride increased; these objects were the work of men who had at one time started as apprentices. In time he, too, would be permitted to do something more than tend fires and run errands. Small Den's challenge broke the spell, "Did you never see a piece of brass before, countryman?"

Young Fu's countenance hardened. This morning was not yesterday! Coolly he faced his antagonist, "If I have not, is it your affair?"

"Ai!" exclaimed Den turning to the accountant for appreciation, "his temper is easily fired!"

Tang, suddenly appearing, took the conversation into his own control. "As is mine, when I see the dust still thick where you have left it."

Small Den began to whisk furiously at the offending tables, and the other boy lost no time in applying himself to the fire. Twice his enemy had lost face in his presence. This would be something to remember for future consolation. Also, his first opinion that the coppersmith missed nothing was being momentarily proved. Wherever Tang was needed at the moment, there he was to be found. No smallest detail of the work escaped him, and he gave the impression of being in all three rooms at once. There was nothing he did not know about his craft. A hint from him saved a sheet of metal from an unnecessary degree of heat; a stroke of his thumb nail hastily corrected a weak line in a design. Under his suave influence, customers whom the clerk was unable to interest would invariably buy.

When Tang was in the store, Old Tsu would chuckle: "There is no better bargainer in this city than the master. Never does he follow a patron into the street; always they tug at their moneybags before they leave this place. I have seen his competitor, Wu, a half li from his shop trying to persuade a reluctant buyer to return and purchase." And the men would acknowledge the truth of these statements.

Tang, though he demanded the utmost in effort and artistic achievement from his workmen, held their respect. He wasted none of his suave manner on them, he was blunt and his tongue could flay like a whip, but Young Fu soon recognized the fact that the coppersmith was just in all of his dealings, and no artisan in Chungking gave better quality of work for value received.

From sunrise to nightfall, the new apprentice had no free minutes except those stolen from errands. The workrooms were a bedlam of noise— hammers beating against anvils, chisels screeching their way into designs, voices calling out, tongs clattering beside the fire. And the oven, stretching out long tongues of green and gold flame, added its contribution of soot to the blackened figures of the journeymen and recalled to Young Fu's mind pictures he had seen of the realms in which evil spirits dwell.

His thoughts of evil spirits became vividly real one afternocn as he squatted in the middle room and polished a brazier which a workman, named Dsen, had just finished. Through the doorway he watched coolies lower an open sedan chair from which a tall, strangely dressed person stepped out. The apparition sauntered into the store and Young Fu stopped his work and gazed open-mouthed. It was a foreigner. In the weeks of living in Chungking, he had not yet been close to one. Occasionally he saw them at a distance, but they were usually so well hidden by the inquisitive crowds that always accompanied their appearance, that he still had no idea what they were like. Tang took immediate charge of the stranger, and the clerk and Den rushed about displaying goods.

Young Fu turned to the journeyman beside him. "Is that a man?"

Dsen laughed. "Truly you are from the country. Have you never seen a foreigner before?"

"Not so close. And if it is a man, even you will agree that he wears the jacket and loose trousers of a woman."

"All of their men dress in this fashion, and their women clothe their bodies in men's skirts. Everything they do is the opposite of accepted custom. The women all have feet as large as coolies', and they go about, even the young ones, in open chairs that expose their faces to the gaze of the world. The shoes they wear have thin pegs under the heels, to make them taller, I suppose, though High Heaven knows they are ungainly

enough by nature. And their hair flies loosely about their faces and they laugh and talk as freely as a man. But they are as all other barbarians: they have no polite rules of conduct, and we of the Middle Kingdom can feel pity."

The boy listened attentively, but his eyes never left the figure in the store. The foreigner moved restlessly about the room, pointing out objects with a long stick and refusing to sit down and drink tea, which was what any Chinese gentleman would have done in the same circumstances.

"I like not his face," Young Fu told the journeyman. "The skin is white with bristles and resembles a poorly plucked fowl, and his nose is twice the size it should be."

Dsen went on with his work. "I felt the same about the first one I saw. When he opened his mouth to smile, he was so ugly I thought it would kill me. But I am used to them now, and while I see no good in them, I do not believe

with the women that they cause bad fortune. Indeed, they are too stupid for any sensible man to fear. With money they are fools, paying coolies for every service twice what they ought to receive. But they are rich, and silver means nothing to them. They have meat every meal, it is said, and the choicest vegetables and fruit. Even the poorest among them lives like a Mandarin."

The foreigner, who showed no particular interest in the objects before him, was attempting to explain his dissatisfaction to Tang. Young Fu strained to hear, but nothing reached him above the usual uproar of the room.

"What language does he speak?" he asked Dsen.

"English, and some few words of Chinese, I suppose."

"Does Tang understand English?"

"No, but what the fellow cannot say in Chinese, the coppersmith will guess."

Tang came swiftly toward them. "With such industry in an apprentice, my fortune is made already," he remarked wryly in passing.

Old Tsu called out, "Does nothing suit your rich customer?"

"Nothing in the store. He wishes a finer piece to send as a gift to his friend in America. He shall see the best that we have." The master moved to a large chest, pulled a key from his belt, inserted it in the triangular hanging lock, and lifted the lid.

Young Fu's hands moved rhythmically over the surface of the brazier, but stolen glances told him everything. He had noticed that chest many times but he had paid it little attention. That shopkeepers did not show their finest stock in the open store, was news to him.

Tang beckoned. "Wipe your greasy hands and carry these to Den."

At the partition to the outer room, the youth halted. Fu Be Be's warnings about foreigners returned to him in full force. Suppose evil should fall on him as a result of being close to this creature. His skin prickled; then he moved forward. Evil was certain to follow if he made Tang angry by not obeying orders, and the unknown seemed the lesser of the two. He gave the articles carefully to Small Den. On his third return to the inner room, a voice called after him, "Tell your master I wish to hurry."

Startled, Young Fu glanced over his shoulder. That had been the foreigner speaking. He could not believe his own ears. He himself knew no English, so the man must have used Chinese words. In a daze he repeated the message to Tang.

"Always these foreigners must hurry," remarked the coppersmith. "They waste good time studying their watches. They hasten to earn money and hasten to spend it. Why then trouble to gain it? Careful spending increases riches."

Old Tsu was now helping Tang to choose from the hidden treasures. "His hurry will be to your advantage," he said. "He will not linger over the bargaining."

Carrying a tray and a jar, Tang and the apprentice strode toward the customer. In a moment the latter had selected the tray and asked its price. Young Fu was amazed at the stupidity of such a course. Even a child knew better than to let a merchant guess which purchase pleased him most. One pretended interest in everything else and asked the price only after the storekeeper had, himself, centered attention on the article desired. Tang mentioned a sum at which Young Fu caught his breath. The foreigner looked up quizzically, then offered half the amount. Tang raised it to three fourths of the original and the other man met this compromise with one of two thirds. He accompanied the last figure with action. His hand drew from a slit in the side of his trousers—a queer place, indeed, to keep money!—several silver dollars. They were accepted. Small Den wrapped the gleaming tray in tissue paper and carried it to the chair. With a nod, the foreigner was gone.

That night on Chair-Makers' Way, Young Fu told his mother, "Today a foreign man bought a tray in our store."

"He did not see you, I hope!"

"He did. Tang told me to carry brasses into his presence. Also, he spoke to me." At his mother's exclamation of fright, he reassured her, "Do not fear! He was ugly, but harmless."

"When did you acquire so much wisdom? Already you copy these city people. You are like a man who sits at the bottom of a well and boasts about his knowledge of the world. No one now is wise save those within the walls of the brass shop! But in the country we still know a few things, and one is that foreign barbarians should be avoided."

"But do you wish me to disobey Tang's orders?"

No reply came, and rolling in his pu-gai, her son fell asleep.

THE SNOWSTORM

Steingrimur Arason

An Iceland farm and the continual struggle of the farmers against the short season and violent weather are the setting for this story. This chapter gives a picture of the people and their quiet fortitude. To make the excerpt easier to follow, it helps to know who the characters are. Erik and Helga are master and mistress of the farm; Nonni is their son, Skuggi his dog and companion; Sigga and Gudda are maids, and Snorri and Thor are farmhands.

Everyone seemed uneasy all day. Nonni noticed first when he dropped his spoon on the floor during breakfast and Sigga looked at him too quickly, with startled eyes. His mother went about her work absent-mindedly, in an unusually silent mood, and when he called to Skuggi the dog refused to leave his warm corner by the fire and only thumped his tail.

By afternoon Helga stated her worry. "I don't like that whistling sound up in the mountain pass," she said, with a frown.

Erik got up and went to the window. "I wonder if the farmhands have gone for the sheep?"

Gudda chimed in, shaking her head dolefully. "I had a bad dream last night. I spilled a whole pail of milk on the dairy floor."

Nonni laughed, but Sigga looked up with interest. "That was bad, to spill the milk, Gudda. What do you think it means?"

"It means a terrible storm is sure to come. I have never known it to fail."

Nonni looked at her quickly. She was making it all up, of course.

And yet, when he went over to the window-pane, he was not so sure. "The frost roses are all turned down!"

Sigga swung around at his shout, her face bright with excitement. "Go, Nonni, and find out how the bladder is!"

Storms were frequent enough, but one that had announced itself beforehand in Gudda's dream was certainly out of the ordinary. When Nonni reported that the sheep's bladder, hung up to serve as barometer, was very hard, she stared at Gudda with fascinated eyes.

Erik had paid no attention to the chatter in the room, but now he turned from the window and began getting into his sheepskin coat.

"I must go and help the farmhands before it gets quite dark," he said.

Gudda smiled and nodded her head, but Helga took alarm at his tone.

"Please be careful, Erik. It is bad enough knowing the sheep and the farmhands are out in a storm without being afraid for you too."

"Oh, I'll be in no danger."

He put on his storm cap while Nonni watched enviously. It came way down and completely covered his head, all but his eyes and nose. Then he took his walking stick, six feet high and tipped with sharp steel, and left.

Nonni watched at the window. It was really growing steadily darker; and every now and then Gudda would shuffle up behind him and peer out with a satisfied air, as though she were cooking up the storm by a special recipe. Half an hour after Erik had gone, the snow began. In a few minutes the air was full of fine, driving flakes, and a little later the house began to shake as though it were pummeled by giants' fists.

"God help all those who are outside now," Helga said softly.

She had her embroidery in her lap, and in the light from the kerosene lamp she appeared peaceful in contrast with the nervous Sigga. But Nonni saw the knotted frown between her eyes and noticed that her hands lay frequently idle on the embroidery frame.

Sigga could not sit still. She walked up and down, and shivered with each onslaught of wind.

"I am afraid the house will be blown away."

Nonni laughed. "No danger of that," he assured her. "It is frozen too solidly into the ground!"

He was enjoying the storm, and wished he

might have gone with his father into the arctic darkness. With a cap like Erik's, to keep his neck and ears warm, and a staff in his hand, he would have felt equal to anything. He was sorry his mother could not see it that way.

Gudda looked up from her spinning and listened to the wind.

"In all my eighty years I have never seen weather like this," she said with evident pride. "Well, once it was like this. That was when the brothers from Bakki died. They were coming from town just before Christmas, and they lost their way on the lowland. They had heavy burdens on their backs, and they kept walking through the night. In the morning they were found far up the valley, dead, stiff, and frozen."

Helga got up abruptly, letting her sewing fall to the floor.

"Let's put lights in all the windows," she said. Her voice was quick and frightened. "Sigga, you go put one in the guest-room window, and fasten a mirror behind it. There may be someone out on the lowland now, coming from the town. Nonni, you put one in the south window, facing the highland."

Three long hours passed, during which they were all unwillingly conscious of the storm and the angry knocking of the wind. It sounded so sharp and insistent that Nonni wondered how they dared refuse it. Each knock sounded angrier than the one before. He could not think of the storm as just wind and weather swirling impersonally about the farmhouse. He saw it now as a huge giant towering over them in a purple cloak; tossing his head in a fury and kicking his boots against the little house; roaring that he would come and get them anyway, so they had better open the door.

Suddenly the outer door was opened. A sharp cold wind with snow in it rushed through the long hall and came right into the *badstofa*. Nonni jumped up, his heart leaping with unreasonable fear. Helga caught up a lamp and rushed out, followed by Sigga and Nonni. The hall was already white with fine snow. Two men, looking unnaturally large in their storm coats and so covered with snow that they were almost unrecognizable, stood there, beating themselves free. Snow fell in showers all about them. They were Snorri and Thor.

"Where is Father?" Nonni called.

"Where is Erik?"

They stopped beating away the snow and stared as though they had not heard correctly.

Then, "Isn't he here?" Snorri asked.

Thor said, "I saw him over two hours ago. Some of the sheep were missing, and he said he would go up to the mountains to look for them. It wasn't bad then," he ended lamely as he saw the look on Helga's face.

There was a short stillness. Then Snorri turned back to the door.

"Come on. We'll go look for him."

Helga caught his arm. "No, you don't." Her voice was small and determined. "If you go, you will not find him; and you will be of no help to any of us, lost yourselves. Erik can take care of himself and come home as soon as it's possible to do so."

There was so much truth in this that they could not deny it, and they were soon warming themselves at the fire and drinking hot coffee while their outer clothes were hung up to dry. Their coffee finished, they brought some harness out of the storeroom and went to work mending it. Everyone was busy at something and everyone worked silently, listening for the door to open once more and trying not to show the anxiety they felt.

The storm kept hammering on the house. Helga went into her bedroom once and closed the door. Nonni knew that she went to read the Bible. After a time she came out again, seemingly calmer.

"Your father has been out in bad storms before this," she told Nonni. "He will be able to stand this one just as he stood those."

Surprisingly, Gudda lifted her wrinkled face.

"Yes, I know," she said. "He has the warmth of a bear in him. Anyone who has that has a gift from God."

They all felt vaguely comforted after that. It was so seldom that Gudda had anything good to say. Nevertheless, the night passed very slowly. They lay on beds in the *badstofa* and seldom spoke. Nonni slept a little and roused at times from a light slumber to hear Gudda chanting some dreary rhyme and the storm still beating its drum.

He awoke the next morning aware of a great

stillness. The storm had worn itself out and the sky was clear, with all the stars shining. The windows were coated with frost, and Nonni blew his warm breath on the glass until a round, clear spot appeared. Through this he looked into the dim, snow-covered farmyard and immediately gave a glad shout.

"Father is coming!"

Everyone ran eagerly to open the door for him. Helga's wan face was shining with relief and joy. Erik came in walking heavily, too tired to scrape the snow from his heavy boots. He tracked it straight into the *badstofa* and sank onto a bed, clothes and all. Helga helped him out of his coat.

"Where have you been all the night?" Nonni demanded.

"I have been walking all night, my boy."

"Oh, your poor toes!" Helga cried, struggling with his boots. "Aren't they frozen?"

Erik roused enough to smile at her. "I should say not. I was warm enough." Then he looked grave as he added, "The worst of it all is I did not find the sheep. It was not easy to look for them. I never could see a yard from me. Every hollow is filled up. They must be under the snow, or I would have found them. Ah, well, I will have to go out again, later, to see what I can do."

Helga had pulled off the boots and now began brushing the snow from his clothes.

"Go to the kitchen, Sigga, and heat a quart of milk," she said. "You, Erik, no more talking about going out again. You must get in bed and go to sleep, right away."

Erik started to protest, but at that moment there was a loud knocking at the outer door. Helga hurried to open it, and was astonished to see Karl, the postman, standing on the threshold.

He smiled at her. "I am in poor condition to enter your house," he said, glancing down at his wet, half-frozen clothes. "I have been sleeping under the snow. Could you give me dry clothing?"

"Of course, Karl. Come in," Erik cried. He had left his bed at the sound of Karl's voice and now stood in the hallway in his stocking feet. "You and I are a fine pair. I have been out all night, too, but not sleeping."

"Oh, Erik, get in bed! And you, too, Karl—

you must get into dry clothes and rest a while."

But Helga's solicitude was wasted. Tired as the men were, they wanted to talk about the storm more than they wanted to sleep. When Karl had changed into some clothes of Erik's, much too large for him, the two sat at the table and ate a hearty meal.

"How did it happen that you were out last night?" Erik asked.

"I was caught on the mountain, coming from Reykjavik, when the storm broke out. When I became aware of it I did as I always do, stopped and stood still for a long time."

"Why did you do that?" Nonni asked curiously.

Karl was long-winded and could make a story out of almost anything. It was not often he had such good material as this to work with.

He leaned back in his chair and prepared his explanation slowly. "When the blizzard is just beginning, the wind is blowing from all directions at once. Then people are apt to get confused and lose their way. It is necessary to think hard at that moment. When the wind has grown very strong and the blizzard is well under way, it seldom changes direction until it clears up. After that it is all right to plot your course. Just so, last night. When the wind was blowing steadily, and I had made sure of the direction, I noticed that it was blowing straight against the outer end of my left eyebrow."

Nonni giggled, but Karl's face was grave.

"After that," he continued, "I kept on walking, keeping the wind always on that spot—except where there were windings on the road and, after traveling that same road ever since I was a lad of eighteen, I guess I know those pretty well. I wasn't really lost once. When I had walked about three hours, I said to myself, 'Karl, you have walked far enough. If you can't find Fairdale here, you will not look for it any farther.'"

"And you did not find it!" Nonni said.

Karl nodded. "And I did not find it. It was about the darkest dark I have ever met with. You couldn't have seen your hand five inches from your eyes. And the storm was sweeping over me so fast that I could not stand on my feet at times."

"What did you do?"

"Well, there was only one thing I could do. I

lay down in a little hollow at the south of a hill. I put the mailbag under my head and turned down the flap, to be sure the letters wouldn't get wet. In no time at all the snow had covered me as snug as your mother would, with an eider down quilt, if I would let her."

He cackled as Helga smiled in spite of herself and gave an impatient shake of her head.

"I don't care what becomes of the two of you," she said. "Out all night in a storm and then sit there talking your heads off all day!"

"Never had a better sleep in my life," Karl assured her gravely, though his blue eyes twinkled.

"You must have been very hungry," Nonni said, thinking what it would be like to go to bed in the snow and deciding it would be a lot of fun.

"Oh, no," Karl cried quickly. "I forgot to tell you I had some sandwiches in my pocket. Never travel without them. When the snow had covered me all up, I moved around so as to hollow out a little elbow room for myself; and I made space enough to get out those sandwiches."

"So you had a comfortable night out there in the blizzard after all." Erik smiled.

"Yes, yes, a very fine night," Karl said. "The trouble did not start until I climbed out of bed this morning. Then it occurred to me that I was all dripping wet. The frost was so hard that I thought I would freeze all through in a moment. You may believe that I walked fast to this house. And, surprisingly enough, I was only a few yards from your house all the time!"

Everyone laughed, but Sigga gave a little shudder and said, "I would go crazy right now if I were buried like that!"

"I wouldn't!" Nonni cried.

It was very exciting to think that Karl, the postman, had been sleeping only a few yards from them under the snow all night!

Nonni's thoughts turned to the sheep, still out in the snow. Karl had dug himself out, little the worse, but the sheep were too foolish to do that. They would freeze to death if they were not found soon. He remembered how the ewes had behaved during sudden windstorms in the summer. They had huddled together in little groups, in the lee of a big rock. He remembered the ravine where Halli had found Flenna. The sheep would be sure to go to some such place as that when the storm broke. Perhaps they had not been able to reach it and were snowed under on the way. Suddenly he wanted to be out over the unbroken pastureland.

"Mother, let me go skiing!"

"Yes, do that," she agreed. "The snow must be good. But put on your hood. I don't want you coming back with your ears frozen."

He went into the storeroom for his skis. As an afterthought he took a shovel with him. He called to Skuggi, put on his skis, and climbed up to the pastureland. The skis left a clean herringbone track behind him. When he had gone a long way and was approaching the place where the sheep usually grazed, he brushed the snow from a rock and sat down to rest. Skuggi came to him and sat in front of him. He found it hard work, floundering through the snow, and was glad for once to stop when Nonni did. Nonni took the dog's head in his hands and looked into his eyes.

"You have a good sense of smell, Skuggi. I want you to find the sheep that are buried somewhere near here. You must try your very best!"

Then they went higher up into the hills. Skuggi really was sniffing and running about as though vigorously searching for something. Sometimes the snow got into his nose and made him sneeze. The two of them searched the snow all around for a long time. They had covered nearly all the pastureland, and Nonni, tired and hungry, was ready to turn back in disappointment when Skuggi commenced to scratch at the snow and bark furiously.

Nonni's spirits rose at once, and he rushed to Skuggi's aid with the shovel. It was no easy task. The snow was heavy, and wherever he shoveled it away more tumbled in from the sides. At last he discovered that it was better to make big blocks of the snow and push these away down the hillside. Even though this involved more work, it was the only way he could make any progress. He worked hard for a long time; then, panting and damp with perspiration, he sat down to rest. Even now, it seemed, after all his work, he would have to make the hole much wider or there would not be room enough, as he got down deeper, to wield the shovel. If only Skuggi had not been barking and scratching merely in play! He looked sharply at him, but the dog was nosing eagerly at the snow and scratching it away with his claws.

Nonni picked up the shovel and went to work again, standing in part of the hole while trying to enlarge it. Suddenly, without even a crack to warn him, the snow under his feet gave way, and he fell into a dark cave. At the same time he heard the bleating of sheep! He was so happy he shouted; and above him he saw Skuggi, waving his tail and barking. Several sheep lay close together in the darkness, in a little room. The heat from their bodies had melted the snow from the ground around them, leaving a roof of snow over their heads. They appeared warm and comfortable.

How to get them out was a problem. Nonni looked at the gaping hole through which he had tumbled. It was too steep for sheep to scramble through. He looked at his shovel, which his fall had brought down with him. He had had enough of that for a while. But it was the only way. He took it up and once more bent his aching back to the task of digging. He had to make a great many steps, close together yet on a gradual slope away from the sheep, before he was through. At last the animals could climb out of the cave, and Nonni was surprised to count ten of them.

Even now the work was not over. The sheep were heavy and sank too far into the snow with every step. He would have to walk slowly, dragging his skis behind him by a piece of string luckily found in his pocket, and try to beat some sort of solid path in front of the sheep so they could follow him.

It was quite a procession that came into the farmyard an hour later. Nonni tramped slowly along. Behind him came the sheep in single file; and bringing up the rear was Skuggi, carrying his plumed tail proudly. Erik, who had just opened the door to start out after the lost sheep, could hardly believe his eyes. He stared for a moment at the little figure stamping toward him through the snow, and then he gave such a shout of joy, pride, and sheer amazement that all inside the house rushed out.

Nonni came carefully forward, and the sheep crowded as close as the skis would allow. He could not keep the delighted grin from his face, although he would have liked to hide it.

"Now you can go back to bed, Father," he called.

"What a wonderful thing!" said the farmhands, marveling. "Who would have thought he could find them!"

Helga only smiled from the doorway, her face rosy with pleasure, but Erik went over to Nonni and led him into the house almost as though he were an important guest.

"Let's have food for this shepherd, Helga," he said. "What do you have extra fine in the storeroom?"

Nonni noticed, as he entered the door, that Sigga put out her foot to bar the way to the dog.

"No, no! Let Skuggi come in," he said, and Skuggi jumped over the outstretched ankle. "I did not discover the sheep." he said stoutly. "It was Skuggi who did that, and I want him to have the best supper he has ever had."

from DOBRY

Monica Shannon

Dobry *won the Newbery Award in 1935, and it still remains one of the finest in the list of Newbery winners. Beautifully written, rich in unique characters, this slow-moving story does not make an immediate appeal to children. Reading it aloud and discussing it will help. Should Dobry do as his mother wishes, stay on the farm, or go away to study art as he yearns to do?*

[Everything Is Different]

Dobry ran to a window, slid back its windowpanel carved with buffalo heads. "Snow! Why, it's snowing, Grandfather! The courtyard is white already." Snow was never rare in a mountain village of Bulgaria, but nobody, not even Dobry's grandfather, had seen snow coming down to hide red apples on the tree, late corn on the stalk, ripe peppers in the field, grapes on the vine. The golden-leaved poplar tree in the courtyard of Dobry's peasant home was completely hushed with snow. Wool, too, from the autumn shearing was hanging out to dry. The wool grew thicker, the thickest wool imaginable as more and more snow came down. Without making a sound, the sky itself seemed to be coming down bit by bit.

"Nobody has ever seen a happening like this one," Dobry's grandfather said, and followed the little boy to the window. "Snow already, even before the gypsy bear gets here! My back, my legs complain of getting in the grass and the early corn. They wanted a good rubbing before snow set in. Snow? To the devil with gypsies! They should be here with the massaging bear!"

Dobry hung out of the window as far as he could. The rickety outside stairway going down to the ground floor where their two oxen lived had a carpet of snow, immaculate, and the oxen looked up from their stalls each wearing a furry hat of new snow.

Dobry shouted, "Look! Sari and Pernik are surprised too. Look, Grandfather, they wear white fur hats like royalty!"

The grandfather leaned out. "It's true." He shook his head instead of nodding because in Bulgaria you shake your head for "yes" and nod your head for "no." "They do look like royalty," the grandfather said. He drew in his head, shivered, muttered, "You feel the first cold. Anyway, you feel it when one day is like summer and the next day like winter. Come in out of that."

Dobry pulled his head in, turned around. His hair and eyelashes had gone completely white.

"St. Nicholai, the Miracle Maker, bless us all!" The grandfather stared at Dobry. "You look just like me with all that white on you. Snow is blowing in! Close that window tight."

"Wait, wait," Dobry begged and cupping his hands he put them out for snowflakes. "Look, they are beauties," he told the grandfather. "Look at the shapes! Flowers from the sky."

The grandfather shook his head vigorously instead of saying, "Yes, yes." "Each flake is a different one. Perfect! All white flowers—little, new, and no two alike."

Dobry asked him, "And why aren't the snowflakes alike, Grandfather? Different, each one different?"

The grandfather said, "Everything is different, each leaf if you really look. There is no leaf exactly like that one in the whole world. Every stone is different. No other stone exactly like it. That is it, Dobry. God loves variety." Grand-

father found it hard to say exactly what he meant. "God makes better icons than those in the church. He makes a beautiful thing and nothing else in the whole world is exactly like it. That is it, Dobry. Something for you to remember."

"Why?" Dobry asked him.

"Well, it's as good a thing to remember as anything. I never went like you do to the school but I know it. No two things are exactly alike. In odd days like these—snow comes too early, the gypsy bear too late—people study how to be all alike instead of how to be as different as they really are."

Grandfather slid back the window-panel, threw a log on the open fire, pushed it in farther with his foot, and sat himself down on the three-legged stool under the fireplace hood reaching far out into the room.

Dobry, his mother Roda, his grandfather, all of them called their fireplace a "jamal" and a jamal it really was. It stood out from the wall, tiles green, yellow, blue, glimmering in the firelight, and its big yellow chimney was stuccoed to make a picture of quail hiding in ripe grass.

Dobry squatted on the hearth. Above his head under the jamal's hood dangled copper pots, copper kettles, and copper pans, tarnished now because the gypsy cleaner had not yet come to brighten them up for the winter. He looked at the flames, content to watch their colors, their motions, and listen to their chat, but his grandfather interrupted.

"Ours is the most beautiful jamal in the whole village," he said. "No other like it. It knows its work, too. Never smokes. Heats up the whole house instead of trying to change the weather outside. Only Maestro Kolu could have made a jamal like this one."

"Couldn't you make a jamal like this one? You could, couldn't you, Grandfather? And the blacksmith could make one too, couldn't he?"

Grandfather said very loud, "Pff! Pff! Not Pinu, the blacksmith. That fellow! Maestro Kolu is a Macedonian and almost a magician besides. He puts little pipes into a chimney the way God puts blood vessels into our bodies. Perfect! The heat goes around but stays in the house. Maestro Kolu knows the secret and that secret has been growing up for centuries. He knows how to make a jamal as no other man knows it—tiles colored up like our stony earth, the chimney a picture like one of our fields. I tell you, if Maestro Kolu lives to be five hundred years old he'll never have time enough to make the jamals people ask him to make. And——"

Realizing all of a sudden that he was roaring instead of talking, the grandfather stopped to laugh at himself. "Some day you will see Maestro Kolu, maybe, and then you will know for yourself what he is."

The old man got a pipe out from the sash winding seven times around his middle and, his pipe filled, going, he felt around in his sash for a red pepper and gave it to Dobry to nibble. Dobry never could guess at all the things his grandfather tucked away in that broad red sash making a middle for his blue homespun suit. Pipes, coins, red peppers, cheese, bread, garlic, wooden boxes of spices to brighten up his bread in the fields, a painted flute—Dobry often saw these things come out and always asked himself, "What else may be in there?"

Dobry's mother hurried in from the kitchen fetching a bucket of water to heat in the cauldron hanging from big iron chains over the open fire. She added to the brightness the firelight made in this room of plain wooden walls and carved wooden panels—there was so much color to Roda that in the summer field bees often sought her out. Her cheeks and black eyes glowed, her white lace petticoat swirled below a sunflower-colored dress and an apron woven over with roosters just about to crow. A white kerchief topped her head and her hair danced behind her in two long braids.

"What is this?" she asked them. "A boy thinks of everything except going to bed. A big, sleepy boy and long after his supper time! A boy grows big enough to down four bowls of buttermilk at a sitting and he can't tell bedtime yet! We must be up and out before the sun is up and out tomorrow. Peppers to come in and be dried, corn to come in and be husked! When are the roads going to be cleaned up for hauling? There is too much to do now that it snows when it shouldn't. Pop yourself into bed, Dobry!"

Dobry said, "Everybody expects me to go to bed the way bread goes into the oven. Pop! Am I bread? Mother, you should see the way Sari and Pernik go to bed. You should see it! Close one eye, eat a little more, open that eye, close the other, and eat a little more. Very slow. And Grandfather said they were good beasts fit to wear tall fur hats like royalty. Didn't you, Grandfather? You should see their hats, Mother. Snow, very new. Perfect!"

His mother said, "There it is! A boy can think of everything except going to bed. Bread, ovens, fur hats, royalty even. Go to bed!" She stooped and kissed Dobry. "The whole world taken by surprise! All these snowflakes dancing the horo outside—and this boy! Well, I must go and look after the bread. The bread is growing up now."

Dobry said, "Good-night, Grandfather," and kissed him.

The grandfather told him, "Don't forget to pray to St. Triffon about the gypsy bear, will you now? How late those gypsies are and the snow early! Ask St. Triffon to bring the gypsies soon with the massaging bear."

"Do your back and legs complain much tonight?" Dobry asked him.

"Yes, always a little. Ever since I weeded tomatoes when the fields were wet."

"Do we eat the tomatoes now, Grandfather? We always eat tomatoes after the first snow comes."

The grandfather nodded his head emphatically to say, "No, no. It's not winter yet. Tomatoes are for winter. Later snows will cover them just right. Then we'll have tomatoes, a few at a time, and a whole vineful of tomatoes for Christmas Day—the way we always do."

Dobry's grandfather alone of all the villagers knew how to make snow take care of his tomatoes for him. He picked the tomato vines with their ripe fruits, wove them together in a weaving dense enough so that not the smallest chink was left for frost to get through. Snow covered his pyramid of tomatoes on their vines and all winter long he had only to dig down into the snow to bring up tomatoes as fresh but crisper than the morning they first ripened.

"But can't I eat some tomatoes right away?" Dobry begged. "This snow will make them crisp. You said all summer, when I helped you weed the tomatoes, you said to me, 'When snow comes you will be very happy, Dobry, for all this work. When snow comes we will both be warmed to red inside with tomatoes.' Don't you remember,

Grandfather? And snowflakes are dancing a horo dance outside right now."

"Oh, yes, the snowflakes dance but without the music." The Grandfather hummed and made gestures with his hands—he imitated a peasant beating a drum, playing a fiddle, blowing a pair of bagpipes. "I love the music," he cried.

Dobry jumped up, whirled about, dancing the rachanitza. Like every other Bulgarian child, he had learned the national dance when he first learned walking. The grandfather took a flute from his sash, closed his eyes, swayed his body and played the rachanitza music. Dobry danced faster and faster and Grandfather began stamping his feet.

The room was lighted up again with Dobry's mother. She called out, grabbed at them both. The flute stopped, the dance stopped. "Now, good night!" she said crossly and turned back to the kitchen.

Happy from the music, the grandfather said, "Yes, yes, I think we had better have tomatoes now that the snow is here. Bring me in some, Dobry, when there is time. I'll be so busy getting our peppers in out of the snow. Tomatoes—we will both eat a big plateful! Nice and crisp after the snow. The first snow of the year—it is

true we should celebrate. The snow comes too early, the gypsy bear too late—we need them, tomatoes to warm us to red inside. Lots of tomatoes!"

Dobry said, "Perfect!" and kissed his grandfather good-night.

Dobry lay in his bed, but excitement had him awake. The snow was all down, the moon up. A full-grown harvest moon, it stared at Dobry through the window.

"Why do you always follow me around?" Dobry asked the moon. "Everywhere I go there you come looking, looking, looking. Everything happens at once—snow comes when it shouldn't, the gypsy bear doesn't come when it should and you—you say nothing. Just follow me about, staring! How do you expect me to sleep? Nobody could sleep while you stare the way you do and say nothing. I should go for the tomatoes, anyway. Grandfather needs them to warm him to red inside and there will be little time tomorrow. Everything to do."

While he talked, Dobry got out of bed, picked up the homespun breeches he had just taken off and knotted the legs at the bottom, making twin sacks. "One to hold tomatoes enough for my grandfather, the other to hold tomatoes enough for me," he told the moon. He put on goatskin sandals and a long, belted sheepskin coat, slung the breeches like sacks over his shoulder and, calling to the moon, "Well, come on!"—ran out on and down the snow-piled stairway.

Dobry stopped at the floor below to look in on Sari and Pernik. He said to them, "What! No hats? You look just like yourselves. One eye open, one eye closed, eating away. You think of everything, don't you? Everything except going to bed!" He opened the heavy stall door, went in, patted them both and said firmly, "Good night, Sari. Good night, Pernik."

It took Dobry and the moon only a few minutes to go to the small forest of pine and fir trees separating Dobry's home from his mother's fields beyond. He could hear the happy whistle of his own breathing and his feet sounded nice in his ears as he broke through fresh snow. But in a little while the going seemed hard. Dobry stopped to pant freely on a hilltop while the moon rested too, but very far up on a cloud.

Below them the forest was deep in new snow,

immaculate with the heavy snowfall. Trees had gathered to themselves all the snow they could hold; only the points of black fir trees and pines were still uncovered. They branched out like horns and made blue shadows on the freshly covered earth. Dobry could not speak to the moon now. Silence was alive here, he knew, and the moon gave it light. A radiant silence took possession of Dobry as well.

But on a sudden two owls began calling to each other, "Hoot—oo! Hoot—oo!" One of them flew low over the boy's head and he picked up an owl's feather. Then he slid down the hill, loose snow giving way behind him. ("Chasing me," he told himself.) His heart stopped thumping when he saw his mother's fields just ahead. They looked homely, familiar even in the moonlight. Walnut trees and corn-stalks Dobry knew well stood up in the snow. A very fat rabbit out to get carrots instead of tomatoes bounded across the fields, off for his hole, and Dobry noticed how dimly yellow a rabbit can look by moonlight, becoming almost a piece of it.

"Rabbits are always out when you are," Dobry told the moon. "Whenever you are following me around I have only to go outside to see rabbits going places in a big hurry. If you tried to follow a rabbit, first you would have to go very fast—hippetty hop, and besides that you would have to squeeze down a hole. With me you have only to look in through a window."

He stooped over the pyramid of tomatoes, dug down through the snow, filled up both legs of his breeches with tomatoes, slung the pack over his shoulder, called out to the moon, "Come on, moon," and ran for home. The tomatoes felt heavy enough at the start and got heavier as he ran on. But he kept going, running slower and slower down the trail his coming had broken through the new snow. Perspiration squeezed out all over him and he ate handfuls of snow to quench his thirst.

Tired out and hardly able to keep his eyes open, Dobry sat up in bed eating his share of the tomatoes, skin and all just as if they were apples, while the moon stared in at him through the window.

"There is sense to your staring now," Dobry told the moon. "Me—I should hate to just look on while somebody else ate the first tomatoes of the year. Crisp, too, juicy and really cold. Perfect!"

from THE FAMILY UNDER
THE BRIDGE

Natalie Savage Carlson

After the war, there was a time in Paris when there were not enough houses and apartments for people to live in. The poor lived in tents, slept in doorways, or made homes for themselves under bridges. In this selection old Armand, the hobo, first encounters the children. Before the story is finished they have had some funny, some sad, and some exciting adventures together. Get the book and enjoy the wonderful illustrations by Garth Williams along with the heart-warming story.

[A Hobo Adventure]

Once there was an old hobo named Armand who wouldn't have lived anywhere but in Paris. So that is where he lived.

Everything that he owned could be pushed around in an old baby buggy without any hood, so he had no worries about rents or burglars. All the ragged clothing he owned was on his back, so he didn't need to bother with trunks or dry-cleaners.

It was easy for him to move from one hidey-hole to another so that is what he was doing one late morning in December. It was a cold day with the gray sky hanging on the very chimney pots of Paris. But Armand did not mind because he had a tickly feeling that something new and exciting was going to happen to him today.

He hummed a gay tune to himself as he pushed his buggy through the flower market at the side of Notre Dame cathedral. The flowers reminded him that someday it would be spring even though it wasn't bad winter yet.

There were pots of fragile hyacinths and tulips crowded together on planks in front of the stalls.

From *The Family Under the Bridge* by Natalie Savage Carlson, Harper & Brothers. Copyright © 1958 by Natalie Savage Carlson

There were pink carnations and oleanders in great tin pails. Most of all there were bouquets of red-beaded holly, clumps of white-pearled mistletoe and little green fir trees because it would soon be Christmas.

Armand's keen eye caught sight of a pile of broken branches and wilted flowers swept away from one stall. "Anabel" was the name written over the stall, and Armand touched his black beret to the stocky woman whose blue work apron hung below her wooly coat.

"By your leave and in gratitude for your generosity, madame," he said to the woman who was surely Anabel He piled the broken branches on top of his belongings in the baby buggy. Then he fastidiously picked a sprig of dried holly from the litter and pulled it through his torn buttonhole. He wanted to look his best for whatever gay adventure was waiting for him this day.

The woman who must have been Anabel only frowned at Armand as he trundled his buggy toward the Rue de Corse. Past the ancient buildings he shuffled, his buggy headed for the far branch of the Seine River.

But as he entered the square in front of Notre Dame, a hand grasped his arm from behind.

"Your fortune, monsieur," wheedled a musical voice. "You will meet with adventure today."

Armand let go of the handle of the buggy and whirled around to face a gypsy woman in a short fur coat and full, flowered skirt.

He gave her a gap-toothed smile. "You, Mireli," he greeted her. "Your people are back in Paris for the winter?"

The gypsy woman's dark face beamed under the blue scarf. "Doesn't one always spend the winters in Paris?" she asked, as if she were a woman of fashion. "But have you taken to the streets so early?"

Armand shrugged his shoulders under the long overcoat that almost reached to his ankles. "It's back under the bridge for me," he answered. "I've had enough of the crowded corners and tight alleys in the Place Maubert. And I'm tired of sorting rags for that junk dealer. I'm ready for that adventure you're promising me."

Mireli could understand. "That courtyard we rent seems like a cage after the freedom of the long, winding roads," she said, "but the men

have found plenty of work for the winter. A city with as many restaurants as Paris has more than enough pots and pans to be mended. Of course the children can talk of nothing but the fields and woods of spring."

"I can't abide children," grumped Armand. "Starlings they are. Witless, twittering, little pests."

Mireli shook her finger at him. "You think you don't like children," she said, "but it is only that you are afraid of them. You're afraid the sly little things will steal your heart if they find out you have one."

Armand grunted and took the handle of the buggy again. Mireli waved him away, swaying on bare feet squeezed into tarnished silver sandals. "If you change your mind about the bridge, you can come to live with us," she invited. "We're beyond the Halles—where they're tearing down the buildings near the old Court of Miracles."

Armand tramped under the black, leafless trees and around the cathedral by the river side without even giving it a glance.

In the green park behind the flying buttresses, some street urchins were loitering. Two of them played at dueling while a third smaller one watched, munching a red apple. The swordsmen, holding out imaginary swords, circled each other. Closer and closer came the clenched fists, then the boys forgot their imaginary swords and began punching each other.

They stopped their play as Armand went by. "Look at the funny old tramp!" one cried to his playmates.

Armand looked around because he wanted to see the funny old tramp too. It must be that droll Louis with his tall black hat and baggy pants. Then he realized that he was the funny old tramp.

"Keep a civil tongue in your head, starling," he ordered. He fingered the holly in his lapel. "If you don't, I'll tell my friend Father Christmas about your rude manners. Then you'll get nothing but a bunch of sticks like these on my buggy."

The boys looked at him with awe. Father Christmas is the Santa Claus of France. He rides down from the north on his little gray donkey and leaves presents for good children.

The small boy held out his half-eaten apple. "Are you hungry, monsieur?" he asked. "Would you like the rest of this apple?"

But the biggest boy mockingly punched the air with his fist. "Pouf!" he scoffed. "There's no Father Christmas. He's just make-believe."

"If you doubt my word," said Armand with dignity, "just take a look in the Louvre store. You'll find him on the mezzanine floor."

He grinned like one of the roguish gargoyles on the cathedral. There really was a Father Christmas and it was his friend Camille, who felt the urge to work when the weather turned cold.

"I believe you, monsieur," said the boy with the apple. "I saw Father Christmas outside the store yesterday. He was eating hot chestnuts on the street."

Armand hunched his shoulders and quickly walked toward the bridge. Mireli was right. These starlings would steal your heart if you didn't keep it well hidden. And he wanted nothing to do with children. They meant homes and responsibility and regular work—all the things he had turned his back on so long ago. And he was looking for adventure.

Down a few blocks was the bridge under which he lived when the weather wasn't too raw. And plenty of company he had during the summer with all the homeless of Paris staking their claims to this space or that.

"But first I must have dinner," he told himself, looking up at the restaurant across the street. He licked his thumb and held it up. "The wind is just right," he decided.

So he parked his buggy beside the low wall and settled himself in the breeze that came from the restaurant. He pulled all the kitchen smells deep into his lungs. "Ah, steak broiled over charcoal," he gloated. "And the sauce is just right. But they scorched the potatoes."

For two hours Armand sat on the curb enjoying the food smells because that is the length of time a Frenchman allows himself for lunch in the middle of the day.

Then he daintily wiped his whiskered lips with his cuff and rose to his knobby shoes. "And just keep the change, waiter," he said generously, although there wasn't a white-uniformed waiter in sight. "You'll need it for Christmas."

He started down the steps that dropped from the street to the quay beside the Seine. He bounced the back wheels of the buggy down each step. "I am really quite stuffed," he told himself, "but I wish I had taken that apple. It would have been the right dessert after such a rich sauce."

Down the quay he pushed the buggy toward the bridge tunnel that ran along the shore. On the cobbled quay a man was washing his car with the free Seine water. A woman in a fur coat was airing her French poodle. A long barge, sleek as a black seal, slid through the river. It was like coming home after a long absence, thought Armand. And anything exciting could happen under a Paris bridge.

As he neared the tunnel, his eyes widened with surprise and anger. A gray canvas was propped over the niche that had always been his own. And a market pushcart was parked by the pillar.

He raced his buggy across the cobblestones toward the arch. When he arrived there, he reached up and angrily tore down the canvas with one swoop of his arm. Then he jumped back in surprise and horror.

"Oh, là, là!" he cried. "Starlings! A nest full of them!"

Because three startled children snuggled into a worn quilt looked up at him with eyes as surprised as his own. The little girl and the boy cowered deeper into the quilt. But the older girl quickly jumped to her feet. She had direct blue eyes and they matched her determined chin and snubbed nose and bright red hair.

"You can't take us away," she cried, clenching her fists. "We're going to stay together because we're a family, and families have to stick together. That's what mama says."

As Armand glared at the children, a shaggy dog that should have been white came bounding across the quay. It protectively jumped between the tramp and the children, barking fiercely at Armand. The hobo quickly maneuvered his buggy between himself and the dog.

"If that beast bites me," he cried, "I'll sue you for ten thousand francs."

The girl called the dog to her. "Here, Jojo! Come, Jojo! He won't take us away. He's only an old tramp."

The dog stopped barking and sniffed at the wheels of Armand's baby buggy.

The man was insulted. "I'll have you know that I'm not just any old tramp," he said. And he wasn't. "I'm not friendless, and I could be a workingman right now if I wanted. But where are your parents and who are you hiding from? The police?"

He studied the children closely. Redheads they were, all of them, and their clothes had the mismatched, ill-fitting look of poverty.

The older girl's eyes burned a deep blue. "Our landlady put us out because we don't have enough money to pay for the room since papa died," she explained. "So mama brought us here because we haven't any home now. And she told us to hide behind the canvas so nobody could see us, or they'd take us away from her and put us in a home for poor children. But we're a family, so we want to stay together. I'm Suzy and they're Paul and Evelyne."

The boy swaggered a little. "If I was bigger, I'd find a new place for us to live," he boasted.

"It looks to me like you've already found a new place," said Armand, "and it's my old place. You've put me out of my home just like that landlady did to you."

Suzy was apologetic. She moved the pushcart over and measured Armand with one eye closed.

Then she carefully drew a long rectangle on the concrete with a piece of soft coal.

"That's your room," she said. "You can live with us." On second thought, she scrawled a small checkered square at the foot of the rectangle. "There's a window," she said gravely, "so you can look out and see the river."

Armand grumbled to himself and pulled his coat tighter across his chest as if to hide his heart. Oh, this starling was a dangerous one. He'd better move on. Paris was full of bridges, the way the Seine meandered through it. No trouble finding another one. But as he started away, the girl ran over and clutched him by his torn sleeve.

"Please stay," she begged. "We'll pretend you're our grandfather."

Armand snorted. "Little one," he said, "next to a millionaire, a grandfather is the last thing I hope to be." But even as he grumbled, he began unpacking his belongings.

He stacked the branches and twigs, and made a pile of the dead leaves he had gathered. He pulled out a dirty canvas and a rusty iron hook. He set a blackened can with a handle near the leaves. He sorted some bent spoons and knives. Last of all, he pulled out an old shoe with a hole in the sole.

"Might come across its mate one of these days," he explained to the children. "And it fits me just right."

The children wanted to help him. Oh, these starlings were clever. They knew how to get around an old man. Lucky he wasn't their grandfather. But he laid his canvas over the rectangle Suzy had made for him.

He started a fire with the branches and dead leaves. Then he hung a big can over the fire. Into it he dropped scraps of food he unwrapped from pieces of newspaper.

"In the good old days of Paris," he told the children, "they used to ring bells in the market places at the close of day so the tramps would know they were welcome to gather up the leftovers. But no more. Nowadays we have to look after ourselves."

They watched him eating his food. Even the dog that should have been white watched each morsel that went into his mouth and drooled on the concrete. Armand wriggled uneasily. "What's the matter?" he asked gruffly. "Haven't you ever seen anybody eat before?" They said nothing in reply, but four pairs of eyes followed each move of his tin spoon. "I suppose you're hungry," he growled. "Starlings always have to be eating. Get your tinware."

Suzy pulled some stained, cracked bowls and twisted spoons from the pushcart. Armand carefully divided the food, even counting in the dog.

It was dark by the time the children's mother joined them. The lights of Paris were floating in the river, but the only light in the tunnel flickered from a tiny fire Armand had made. He could not see the woman's face well, but he felt the edge of her tongue.

"What are you doing here?" she demanded of the hobo.

Armand was angered. "And I might ask you the same, madame," he retorted. "You have taken my piece of the bridge."

"The bridges don't belong to anybody," said the woman. "They're the only free shelter in Paris."

Suzy tried to make peace. "He's a nice, friendly old tramp, mama," she explained, "and he's going to live with us."

"I'm not a friendly old tramp," said Armand indignantly. "I'm a mean, cranky old tramp, and I hate children and dogs and women."

"Then if you hate us," said Paul, "why did you give us some of your food?"

"Because I'm a stupid old tramp," replied Armand. "Because I'm a stupid, soft-hearted old tramp." Oh, là, là! There it was. He had let slip that he really had a heart. Now this homeless family would surely be after that too.

The mother was displeased to hear that the children had accepted the hobo's food. "We are not beggars," she reminded them. "I have a steady job at the laundry, and that is more than he can say."

She went to work warming a pan of soup and breaking a long loaf of bread that she had brought with her. Armand sat in the rectangle marked by Suzy and thought that this woman's trouble was pride, and that pride and life under the bridge weren't going to work out well together.

By the dying light of the fire, the woman went back and forth to her pushcart, pulling out moth-eaten blankets and making bed-places on the concrete. Just overhead the automobiles roared, lights garlanded the bridge and people walking along the higher quay laughed lightly. But it could have been a million miles away from the little group under the bridge.

"You ought to put the starlings in some charity home until you find a place of your own, madame," suggested Armand, after the children had dropped off to sleep. "This life is not for them. Now, you wouldn't want them to end up like me, would you?"

"Families should stick together through the lean times as well as the fat," replied the woman. "And I have hopes. I'm going to see my sister-in-law soon. She may know of a place for us out in Clichy."

Armand stretched out on his canvas without bothering about any covering. He was used to the cold. He never felt it any more. But he was sure these children would feel it. As he lay on the hard concrete an uneasy thought worried him, like a mouse gnawing at his shoestring. Now that he had befriended these starlings, his life would never again be completely his own.

THE HOUSE IN PARSLEY STREET

Margot Benary–Isbert

The prosperous, busy West Germany of today bears little resemblance to the desolation of the bombed city described in this chapter. The Ark *and its sequel* Rowan Farm *relate the struggles of the Lechow family to rebuild a normal life out of the ruins of the war. They waste no time mourning the past but work and hope to make the present and the future as good and as happy as possible. This book, written originally in German, has been popular with young Germans. The author says that she herself or others she has known have been through and survived just the kind of incidents described in her books. She now lives and writes in this country.*

"The House in Parsley Street." From *The Ark* by Margot Benary–Isbert, copyright 1953 by Harcourt, Brace and Company, Inc

The wind swept around the corners and chased clouds of dust out of the ruins of bombed houses. The cold, clinging darkness of the October evening dropped down upon the strange city from a leaden sky. The streets were deserted. Nobody was out who could possibly help it.

Nevertheless, the little band of people who were walking toward the center of the town was in high spirits. The two girls, Margret and Andrea, walked ahead, chatting gaily with one another. Behind them came their small, dark-haired mother, holding Joey's hand and trying to answer his endless questions. "Will we have a stove, too, Mummy? Will there be other kids there to play with? And if I have to begin school, can I just stay out if I don't like it?"

"You'll like it well enough," his mother said. "It's about time a big boy like you learned to read and write, now you're going on seven. You want to, don't you?"

"I'm not sure," Joey said dubiously. "After all, Tom Thumb never went to school, and he was smarter than the man-eater."

Margret, who was holding the slip of paper from the Housing Office, crossed the street and the others followed her. " 'Down the street by the station,' the man said, 'as far as the square with the trees.' You see, there are the trees. 'Then the first street to the right and the second to the left.' "

"Parsley Street Number 13," Andrea cried, dancing a little jig, as though the address alone contained wonderful and mysterious possibilities.

"Parsley Street sounds nice, doesn't it, Joey," Mother said.

"It sounds green and good to eat. Tell me a story about it."

"Wait a while, we'll be there soon."

Since noon they had stood around in the big, cold gymnasium where the refugees were being assigned quarters. The mothers with little babies had to be taken care of first, of course. But finally their turn had come. After nine months of moving from place to place, from refugee camp to refugee camp, they would now be getting something that could be called a home. Not their own apartment, of course; the cities of West Germany were so crowded that they could not hope for anything like that. But at least they would have their own room. In fact two! Two rooms all to themselves—it was almost too good to be true. Rooms without a crowd of other people, of squabbling women and crying children. How wonderful it will be to be by ourselves, Margret thought, sighing to herself. What would Parsley Street and the house itself be like? The various barracks where they had stayed had always been full of such bad smells. There had been only a small space for each family, and people had to keep potatoes and their supply of firewood under the cots, and hang what few clothes they had on a string above the tattered straw mattress.

"Where are we going now?" the children had asked each time they and their belongings were loaded into a cattle car. No one had known. "Somewhere," had always been the answer.

At home, in Father's book case, there had been a book about the wanderings of Ulysses. Ulysses, too, had wandered about the world for many years after a war before he finally found his way back home. The *Odyssey* had been one of Margret's favorite books. She used to read it over and over with her brother Christian, and they had acted out the parts. Then they had wanted to have wonderful adventures like Ulysses. But now Margret herself had become almost a Ulysses, traveling homeless through the world, and it was not nearly so marvelous as she had imagined. "In fact it has been horrible," she said with a shudder, speaking more to herself than to her sister Andrea who trudged cheerfully along at her side—a slender little girl with her mother's dark hair and her father's blue eyes. She wasn't ten yet—ages younger than Margret, who would soon be all of fourteen.

"Why do you call it horrible?" Andrea asked. "It's been lots of fun—going to so many different places and having so many train rides and so many other children to play with. Joey has always loved it."

Margret nodded. Of course, the younger children had enjoyed it. They hardly remembered what a decent, orderly life was like. They didn't even notice how terribly thin Mother had become, or how much grey there was in her hair. What would Father say about the way Mummy looked when he came back from Russia? "Take good care of your Mummy for me," he had told the three older children when he had had to leave them. That was three years ago now. Margret's thoughts kept returning to this, and she gave her mother a look of deep concern. "You've gotten so terribly thin," she said. "There's hardly anything left of you."

"There's still plenty of me here, don't worry," Mother said, and for a moment little sparks of gold danced in her eyes—the way they used to whenever Father teased her. "I can keep going for quite a while yet, my big girl. I have to, until you learn to sew on the buttons for your brother and sister. Look, there's another one coming off Joey's jacket."

Margret's forehead wrinkled in a frown. "I'd just like to know one time when something isn't coming off Joey," she said. Being a big sister was just about the worst thing that could happen to a person. As if it weren't hard enough already being a girl. Nobody asked Matthias to sew on buttons. On the other hand, of course, he had to split wood and pull the little cart which held the family's baggage—and sometimes even Joey on top of the baggage.

"See if you can read that street sign across the street, Margret," Mother said. "There's just enough light from that window. It can't be much further."

"If it is much further I'm going to cry," Joey threatened. "I'm hungry and I'm cold."

"Cry!" Andrea exclaimed. "What a baby!"

"This is Capuchin Street," Margret called from across the way. "The man at the gym said it's one block after Capuchin Street."

"Look at the slip again."

"Number Thirteen Parsley Street. Mrs. Verduz, the widow of Chief Municipal Secretary Verduz. He must have been something very important, Mother."

"Now you must make a good impression, children," Mother said, and she examined her flock with a worried expression. Her family looked rather wild and ill-kempt, and the wildest looking of them all, big Matthias, was not here yet. It was impossible to take care of clothes that were being worn all the time. During their brief stay with relatives in Hamburg there had been a chance for all of them to rest up and get clean— but all traces of that visit had long since vanished. Hamburg had been full of occupation troops and it had been impossible to get a permit to stay there. Mother had worn out the precious soles of

her shoes going from one official to the next, but in vain. They had been assigned to Hesse and to Hesse they had to go; there was no help for it.

Mother sighed. "It's a good thing Matthias won't be coming with the cart for a while," she said reflectively. "I'm glad I won't have to introduce our whole horde at once to the poor landlady. We'll go down better a spoonful at a time. I feel sorry for her already."

"I don't," Andrea said firmly. "She ought to be glad. We're a very nice family, I think."

"I wish you wouldn't tell her so right off, Andrea," Mother said. "Perhaps she'll notice it herself."

And then they were in it—Parsley Street, a little lane like something out of a picture book. Almost all the houses were undamaged. They were pressed right up against one another as if they had given each other support through the perils of war. Most of them were half-timber houses, with wide flat surfaces of mortar between the dark old beams. In the yellow lamplight from the many windows the family saw that a large number of the beams were carved or painted in bright colors. Beneath the steep gables the attic windows looked out like peering eyes. The doors were painted brown or green, and the hardware on them was shiny brass.

"It must be that one," Margret said. "The skinny little one that looks sort of crooked. Yes, see, there it is: Number Thirteen."

The little house really looked as if it were hunchbacked. It leaned its left shoulder against the house next to it as though it were tottering and feeble from old age. On the great beam that supported the first floor was painted the date 1683, and in intricate lettering was a motto which could not be read in the dim light.

"An historical house," Andrea exclaimed, her eyes sparkling. "Just think of how many things must have happened in it in almost three hundred years. Maybe even a murder," she added hopefully. "Probably there's a ghost. I'd like to see a real ghost."

"I don't like ghosts," Joey said perversely.

"Anyway, Andrea will find out about everything that has ever happened in the house before we've been here three days," Margret said knowingly.

"Let me ring," Joey cried when he saw the gleaming brass bell pull. He pulled it. Inside a little bell tinkled. Then for a while nothing happened. What if nobody were home and they had to stand out in the street and wait? Joey was so overtired he would certainly start to cry. Even the older girls were shivering with cold, and all of them were hungry. The icy wind seemed to reach through their clothes right into their bones.

"Ring again, Joey," Mother said.

Maybe it's an enchanted house and you have to do everything three times, Margret thought. Three was her number, her own secret, magic number; it banished the bad and brought all good things. She had three stars of her own, the stars of Orion's belt. Those stars had stood above the Polish camp where her mother had had to work when she was separated from the children. Matthias had been sent elsewhere, to a men's camp, and for a long time they did not know what was happening to him. Joey and the two girls had been sent to live with a peasant family near the Polish camp. There the girls had had to work hard, but otherwise conditions were pretty decent. And on winter nights the three stars had shone down upon Margret steadfastly. After three months Mother had finally come back to them. Not all those in the camp returned. Many had been buried on the heath. Mother's face was grey and her hair had turned grey, and the gloss had gone out of it. But she was alive, she was back with them, and as if by a miracle Matthias, too, found his way back to them—because the good stars had watched over them.

But where had the stars been before that on the May night when Margret's twin brother Christian was shot, and with him their Great Dane who had leaped at the first of the men who came rushing into the house? Those two, Christian and the dog, Cosi, had been closer to Margret than anyone else, her companions from babyhood. And now she was alone. She never mentioned their names, never spoke of the days when all of them had been together.

"Three times!" she thought, and she rang the bell again.

Immediately they heard a door creaking and footsteps coming downstairs. Margret's heart pounded. If only Mrs. Verduz would be friendly. "Be nice," she murmured as if she were saying a spell. "Please be nice, be nice."

"What's that, Margret?" her mother asked.

"Nothing. You see, someone is opening the door."

The door opened just a tiny crack, hardly big enough for a mouse to slip through. "What do you want?" asked a voice which was just as thin as the crack of the door.

"Good evening," Mother said.

"Good evening," the children's three voices echoed.

"We were sent here, we're to live in your house," Mother explained.

The door opened a few inches more. A tall thin woman stuck her head out and stared at the group. "Is that so?" she said. "You are to live here? Is it possible?"

The light from the hallway fell upon her thin figure. She was wearing a grey dress with a ruche of black lace down the front. She seemed to have stepped right out of great-grandmother's photograph album. An odd-looking pair of glasses hung from a silk ribbon pinned to her dress. These glasses, their mother later explained, were called pince-nez, meaning pinch-the-nose. The lady set them on her nose so that she could see better.

"Good Heavens!" she exclaimed. "Four persons! What are those people at the Housing Office thinking of. I was promised a childless couple. It must be an error."

"No, here it is written down," Margret said, showing her slip of paper. "Here, you see, is the name: Mrs. Verduz. You are Mrs. Verduz, aren't you? And the rooms have been under requisition for a long time."

"No, no, no," the lady cried, raising her hands imploringly. "This is impossible. Four persons! Why, I have only two beds."

"Five persons," Mother said. The grey old lady might as well be told all the dreadful truth at once. "My oldest boy is coming along later on. I'm very sorry we have to invade you at night this way, but there's nothing to be done about it now. The children have been standing around all day; they're tired and frozen, and where else could we go for the night? There's no one left in the gymnasium by this time, and the barracks are already filled up with new people."

"Well, since that's how things stand I suppose you can come in for the night," Mrs. Verduz said unwillingly. "Tomorrow I shall have to go down to the Housing Office right away and explain the mistake."

They climbed the steep staircase. Along the walls hung pictures and devout mottoes in handsome carved frames. On the landing stood two large tubs in which green plants were growing. A big black cat slipped silently between them.

"What a beautiful cat," Margret cried softly. "Andrea, look at the wonderful cat."

She crouched down on a step and coaxed the cat to come to her. Its amber eyes blinked at her; then, with head stretched forward, it cautiously approached and graciously permitted Margret to scratch it behind the ears.

"That's Caliph," the lady said without turning. "He never lets strangers touch him."

"All animals let Margret touch them," Andrea said. Mrs. Verduz turned her head and her eyebrows shot up, half in surprise, half in pleasure. For a moment she looked quite human.

On the ground floor there were two doors, on the second floor three. The third floor was the attic, and here also there were three doors. Mrs. Verduz opened the one opposite the stairs and silently pointed to a spacious room filled with an odd assortment of furniture. It had two windows overlooking Parsley Street, and Andrea rushed over to look out. There was real glass in them, and each had a pair of faded curtains. In one corner stood a drum stove. In the brass lamp, which had once been a kerosene lamp, there was actually an electric bulb! Mrs. Verduz switched

on this lamp as they entered. On both sides of the room the wall sloped sharply down, following the line of the roof.

"How lovely," Andrea said impulsively. Margret glanced reprovingly at her. But what was wrong with saying that the room was attractive, with its big, grey-and-red figured sofa, carved chairs and other old-fashioned things?

Mrs. Verduz raised her glasses to her nose again and studied Andrea with a pleased air. "The bedroom adjoins," she said in an almost kindly tone. "Yes, it is a very fine apartment, but there are only two beds; it won't do for five persons."

The bedroom was narrow. Two beds stood against the long wall, and beneath the small window was a stand which held an enamel washbasin. In one corner were a small table and two chairs.

"We could put one of the beds in the living room," Mother said—and Margret realized that Mother hoped to be able to stay here. "The sofa can be moved in here for Matthias, one bed for the two girls, and the other in the big room for Joey and me. That would do it."

"But I want to sleep with Matthias," Joey said.

"You can later, but this winter I want you sleeping in the warm room so that you won't get any more sore throats."

Downstairs the bell rang. "That's Matthias," Andrea cried, and went clattering down the steps. She could have done it less noisily, because the banisters were perfect for sliding down without a sound. But Andrea had not quite dared to slide because Mother had said they must make a good impression.

"Quiet, Andrea!" Margret called after her— but the warning was already too late. Andrea did not see Mrs. Verduz's face or she would have realized why her sister had called out.

"I'm so sensitive about noise after all the bombings," Mrs. Verduz said. "That is one reason I cannot endure children in the house. I suppose you have your linen with you, Mrs. . . . what was your name again?"

"Lechow," Mother said. "No, no linen, unfortunately . . ."

Mrs. Verduz shook her head in silent disapproval. Not only was her house being filled up with strangers to whom she had to entrust all this good furniture, but on top of it all she would have to let them use her bed linen too.

"We have one wool blanket each," Margret said hastily. "We can get along without sheets. We did in camp."

"Sleep without sheets!" Mrs. Verduz said with a frown. "Not in my house. What would happen to my good mattresses?" With a sigh she went across to the spare attic room. She could be heard rattling keys. Margret winked at her mother and whispered, "Sheets, Mummy! And featherbeds, too—see them all folded up? We won't leave here, no matter how disagreeable she is. And besides the cat is so nice." She bent down and stroked Caliph, who purred and rubbed against her ankles. Obviously it was a case of mutual love at first sight.

Mrs. Verduz returned with a bundle of linen in her arms—snowy white sheets and bright-colored coverlets. The linen smelled rather musty, as though it had not been used for many years.

Matthias was coming up the stairs with Andrea. Between the two of them they were carrying one of the two sacks which contained the family's precious possessions—the wool blankets, some underwear and the one spare set of clothing each owned. Their bread and the rest of their provisions were distributed among their rucksacks. Now they would be getting regular food ration cards, just like the people who belonged here.

Matthias had tucked his precious violin case under his arm and parked the cart in the small courtyard back of the house. Matthias always got the hang of places quickly.

"This is my oldest boy, Matthias," Mother said, and Matthias removed the cap from his blond shock of hair and made a bit of a bow. Margret felt proud of him. Not that she personally placed much importance on fine manners. But if the grey lady didn't let them stay—no, she couldn't bear to think of that! Manners were a small price to pay, if only they could stay.

"Oh, the dirt all these children will track in," Mrs. Verduz wailed, and her face twisted up as though she had a toothache.

"We can always take our shoes off downstairs," Margret suggested.

"And I can sweep the stairs on Saturdays," Andrea said. "I won't mind that a bit."

"Yes," Mrs. Verduz said. "I really cannot be expected to clean up after other people. My maid has just up and left me again. There's no depending on people any more."

"The girls will be glad to help with the work," Mother said.

"That would be fine," Mrs. Verduz replied. The prospect evidently pleased her. (She'll keep us, she'll keep us, Margret rejoiced.) "Yes, I certainly could use a little help in the house. And perhaps the big boy could split some wood now and then and bring it in."

Margret gave Matthias a suggestive poke with her elbow. "I'll do that," he said, nodding. "And me too," Joey promised. "I can split wood and carry it in too—I'm almost seven."

"Well, then, you may as well get settled for the night," the grey lady said, with gracious condescension. "We'll see what tomorrow brings. Good night. Come, Caliph!"

As soon as she had gone Andrea took a hop, skip and jump. "It's fine here, I like it," she exclaimed happily, and dropped down on the sofa to test the springs.

"Be careful of the furniture," Mother warned her. "What do you say, Margret?"

"She's a witch," Margret said darkly.

Mother shook her head. "Just imagine what *we* would have said if an utter stranger with four wild-looking children were suddenly quartered on us and we had to give them our own bed linen besides."

"Why, Mummy!" both girls exclaimed together, and Margret added, "You would probably have said, 'How nice of you to drop in.' And you would at least have offered a good hot drink to people as frozen as we are."

Silently, Matthias unpacked their provisions. He could never see why other people talked so much.

"Eat quickly, children," Mother said. "I'm looking forward so much to sleeping in a real bed again that I can hardly wait. Do you girls still remember how to make a bed?"

"We'll learn again," Andrea said. "I used to do the crib for the Polish woman. But the big beds were never made up as long as we were there, and we slept in the hay, thank Heaven."

"Tomorrow I'll go to the Economic Office about wood and potatoes," Matthias said. "When we have something to run the stove with, it will be nice and comfortable here."

Margret was sure it would be comfortable. Mother would have made a tent in the desert pleasant to live in.

"Then can we stay here?" Joey asked. "And will Father be able to find us?"

"Of course he'll find us," Mother assured him. "We left a trail of pebbles behind us, like Hansel and Gretel."

"Oh, tell me the story, Mummy." While listening, Joey chewed away at a thick slice of bread spread with fake liverwurst.

"You know that we wrote our names down everywhere, wherever we passed. In the camps and in the homes of the relatives in Berlin and Hamburg. And we left our names at the Red Cross and at the railroad stations. All Father has to do is to track us down. And now we'll write letters to all those places again and give our new address, 13 Parsley Street. But go get some water now, children, so we can wash up. I saw the faucet right outside in the hall, to the left of the stairs."

"Wash up?" Andrea and Joey said slowly, and Joey suddenly remembered that he was terribly tired.

"It's really too cold here to wash," Margret said.

Matthias, who was to sleep on the sofa, had already undressed and slipped under the blanket. "Good night," he said.

The others went to the bedroom, and while Mother helped a sleepy Joey to undress, the two girls skillfully made the beds.

"Do you think she'll keep us?" Margret asked as she slipped under the featherbed. "Don't you think she has to? There's nothing she can do about an order from the Housing Office."

"Everything will turn out all right," Mother said. "Isn't it good to be lying in a bed again?"

Andrea pressed close against Margret. The bedding was uncomfortably clammy, but gradually she began to feel warmer. "Being a refugee is very nice after all," she murmured, her teeth chattering.

"Nice?" Margret asked.

"Yes, you know there's something new every day. I've always wanted to live in an old house like this. And at home we were never allowed to

sleep together and I'd freeze to death if I had to sleep alone tonight."

"Joey is asleep already," Mother called out. "Good night. We have a lot to do tomorrow." She shifted about once or twice, as though savoring the pleasure of stretching out in a real bed. Then there was no further sound. Andrea, too, fell asleep instantly. Like a warm little animal, she snuggled up to her sister, breathing softly. Margret alone remained awake, conscious of the calm, healthy, warm little body of her sister. What a happy creature Andrea was, carrying her house on her back like a snail, feeling at home wherever she was. I will never feel at home anywhere again, Margret thought.

Home—that meant the old orchard under the expanse of clear sky in Pomerania, the white house on the outskirts of the town, Father's roses on the edge of the terrace where the family took their breakfast on warm summer days. Cosi would lie in the sun and drink in its warmth. And there was Christian, too. But all this, this strange city with its ruined streets, this old, old house with its steep stairway, this grey old woman who disliked their coming—this could never be home, could it?

Outside came the cries of the owls—many of them had nested in the ruins. Hoo, hoohoohoo, they cried, and it seemed to Margret that the city itself was wailing a complaint against the grey army of refugees who had descended upon it, and who had to be found room for. Suddenly Margret felt afraid. She was tempted to call to her mother as she used to when she was a small child, whenever something frightened her. But no, of course it would not do to wake Mother up. Mother was so tired, and Margret would not even have been able to say what she was afraid of. She listened to the silence of the sleeping house. Outside something rattled. A floorboard creaked. From the times she had spent in her grandparents' farmhouse in Silesia Margret knew that old houses often began to speak at night. Perhaps Caliph the cat was stalking about. What a beautiful animal he was, and how friendly he had been to her right away. Perhaps things were really not so bad. What was it the grey lady had said? He doesn't let strangers touch him! Margret smiled at this, and smiling, she fell asleep.

In adult literature there is a fairly sharp line of demarcation between historical fiction and biography. But in the field of children's books, the distinctions between the two types of writing are so thin as to be almost nonexistent. Historical fiction like *Martin and Abraham Lincoln* (p. 369) comes vividly alive for children, and Martin seems as much an actual person as Lincoln. On the other hand, in many of the biographies for children and youth, the authors have inserted imaginary conversations and episodes which give the books the exciting qualities of fiction. Such books are not pure biography judged by the standards for adult literature, but they are

HISTORICAL FICTION AND BIOGRAPHY

remarkably popular with children, and publishers are turning them out by the score. One father has remarked that the children he knew "steal the volumes from each other, hide them away like pack-rats, and argue intermittently over who has read the most titles in a given series."[1]

Historical fiction, which is currently popular with grownups, is equally popular with children. Over and over again, in every age, children's books parallel adult reading interests. But it is interesting to note that in this generation, when many of the historical novels for grownups have reached an all-time low of eroticism and sensationalism, in the juvenile field they include some of the finest stories available.

Criteria for historical fiction

Since historical fiction is so popular with children and since the books are multiplying to the point where they cannot all be excellent and some may be downright poor or undesirable, it is well to inquire what qualities distinguish the best from the mediocre. Authenticity should be the first requirement. That is, the story should be true to place, period, and people, and that truth should include a fair, unbiased, and objective representation of whatever pivotal historical facts the story turns upon. For example, no one today would consider giving children a story of people involved in the War between the States that presented one side or the other in the role of the villain, wholly wrong or ignoble. Rather the story should show the nobility and suffering of people on both sides of the conflict, devoted conscientiously to what they believed to be right.

Stephen Meader makes a meticulous study of times, places, and customs for each one of his exciting stories. In *River of the Wolves,* as a result of his careful study of the Indians of the period, he portrays the heroic and decent as well as the barbarous and cruel aspects of Indian life and character. The white captives and the Indians learned from each other and even acquired a respect for each other. But there was never any question in the mind of the captive white boy, Dave, about the necessity of getting back to his own people. Esther Forbes' story of the Boston apprentices and the days and deeds that led directly into the American Revolution, *Johnny Tremain,* grew out of her exhaustive research in connection with her biography, *Paul Revere and the World He Lived In.* In *Johnny Tremain* she is careful to show the forbearance of the British soldiers in Boston toward the rebellious colonists, even though the theme of the book is the need of the colonists to throw off the yoke of British oppression. So authentic facts and a fair and tem-

[1] Douglas Adair, "Parson Weems, Streamlined," *New York Times,* Children's Book Section, November 16, 1952, p. 4

pered presentation of both sides of historical situations are as essential to good historical fiction as they are to good biography.

Equally essential are realistic and lively details that re-create the past. For instance, the Indians' astonished interest and delight in Caddie Woodlawn's red hair make them somehow more believable and less stereotyped. The fact that little Benjamin West had no paint brushes but had to make them from the hairs of his cat's tail is not merely funny—it dramatizes for young readers some of the limitations of the past. And the tragic episode of the burned baby in *Calico Bush* is a frightening thing to read about, but it drives home the hard necessities of pioneer life, which is too often presented to young readers as a kind of prolonged picnic.

Historical fiction for children, however, should not be too grim. It should show the triumphant achievement as well as the drudgery, the occasional fun as well as the struggle, and the color and warmth along with the stern austerities. Because after all, except in pathological cases, that is the way life is. Be it ever so drab or even tragic, the human spirit escapes. It soars now and then, like Marguerite Ledoux's in *Calico Bush* with her lonely *"Noël—Noël—Noël!"* sung softly and hopefully in the terrifying wilderness. This is what children should get from historical fiction—the wonder of brave human hearts which dare the impossible, fail or suffer only to rise again and sing.

Criteria for biography

The qualities essential to sound biography for adults are equally important in good biographies for children and young people. For both, biography must be authentic and observe historical truth, but in juvenile biographies conversations may legitimately be manufactured and episodes may be dramatized which are not in the record but are merely based on the implications of the record. It is known that Admiral Penn bitterly opposed his son William's conversion to the Quaker way of life, and so in her biography of Penn, Elizabeth Janet Gray has created a scene of great dramatic intensity between father and son—a scene in which the talk, though imaginary, is true to the spirit of the historical record and to the nature and relationship of father and son. The trial scene which has been chosen for this book is handled in the same way. So, in these fictionalized biographies we are permitted to know the thoughts, motives, and conversations of the heroes, although these are not to be found in the historical record.

The worth of fictionalized biography depends upon the honesty of the author in utilizing verifiable historical facts and in his ability to write his imaginary scenes and dialogue in the spirit of the times and the characters involved. This form of writing is so popular with children today that it is bringing an unprecedented increase of fictionalized biographies for the youngsters to enjoy.

Good adult biography tries to give its readers the whole man, with his faults, weaknesses, and failures and his ability to conquer or rise above them to greatness. This practice is not as true of juvenile biographies as it should be. The biographies of musicians in the series by Opal Wheeler and Sybil Deucher follow a pleasant pattern—the child musician displays the qualities that are to make him notable as a man, there are a few childish pranks or mistakes which are amusing but not serious, and life flows along with a series of successes and never a hint of the grueling struggle and toil or the handicaps and tragedies. It is too neat a pattern; life does not move like that as some of the more recent biographies are beginning to show. To be sure, these biographies are for children of nine or thereabouts, and most of them are as delightful as they are popular. But even at that level, life should not look too easy and too smooth. Carl Sandburg in his *Abe Lincoln Grows Up,* for children of eleven years old and older, gives the sorrows, the privations, and the limitations of Lincoln's early years. His was not a normal, joyous childhood but quite the reverse.

Some authors of juvenile biographies disregard the childhood of their heroes, and boldly present the man. In MacKinley Kantor's *Lee and Grant at Appomattox,* for example, children read about the failures and the drinking which clouded General Grant's early manhood. These, in contrast to Lee's honor and nobility, actually increase the reader's respect for Grant's achievements later and for the generous and noble

heights to which he rose in the hour of the surrender.

George Washington has always seemed a mythical and nebulous figure to most children because biographies have made him a stereotype for honesty and courage. Now, recent lives of Washington present him as a bad speller and a backwoods boy who had to learn both spelling and good manners, but rose to greatness in spite of his limitations. To try to minimize or omit the tragedies of George Washington Carver's early days and to turn him into the figure of a normally happy boy is to falsify the records. Perhaps young children cannot bear all the tragic facts, but the shadows over Carver's childhood point up the brilliance of his achievements later on.

Most juvenile biographies do give rich details of life in other days which help children to relive the past and feel close kinship with their heroes. These lives of great men are unusually well written on the whole, with a sense of pattern and style in the narrative and of unity in the life described. Publishers are selecting eminent writers to produce the new biography, and this has resulted in a decided swing away from the all-sweetness-and-light school of writing to a sensible and truthful realism. Indeed historical facts are so competently and conscientiously handled that the popularity of these juvenile biographies is something to be thankful for and to be encouraged.

Children find qualities in biography that are lacking in other types of literature. It carries the convincing weight of reality and so stirs emulation. The child identifies himself with the hero and begins to think to himself— "If he did that, maybe if I try hard enough, I too can do what needs to be done." Reading about his hero's difficulties and achievements the child gets a clearer picture of his own problems and goals or lack of them. Many distinguished men have testified to the impact of biography on their own lives. Because of its reality it gives courage and helps to clarify or even focus youthful ambitions.

Finally, both historical fiction and biography can re-create a period or a crisis for young readers as factual narratives can rarely do. In the dramatic impact of world events on individual people the conflict takes on meaning and emotional color which historical records lack. If children have discovered the charm of Washington's peaceful, luxurious life at Mt. Vernon, the great parties at the mansions, the pleasant visiting back and forth between the big plantations, they sense at once the sacrifice it must have been to give up this life. For after all, Washington had to turn his back on his best friends, the Tory Fairfaxes, and line up with the ragged colonists in their hazardous rebellion against tyranny. Or the bloody Indian massacres are seen in a new light when a young reader follows Crazy Horse through the hard disciplines of his childhood to his mature decision to save the land for his people. And through an amusing and slight incident, life on the old canals becomes real when children read about two little girls hastily exchanging greetings as the boats pass briefly in opposite directions. It is the concrete episodes and the individual human being that bring the past to life for children. But these juvenile books, good as they are, are not the final word—they are only a beginning. When they make great men and stirring events forever memorable to children they serve as introductions to the wider and richer field of adult history and biography.

HER MAJESTY, THE PHARAOH

Eloise Jarvis McGraw

Mara, an unfortunate slave of the Egyptians, is promised every luxury and eventual freedom if she will spy for the Queen, the feminine Pharaoh, Hatshepsut. But Mara also sells her services to the rival political faction which is trying to put the rightful heir, Thutmose, on the throne. In this chapter Mara, as interpreter for the Syrian princess, visits the court and sees the Pharaoh and her two masters. Her decision to play both ends against the middle, as she puts it, leads to greater peril than she had expected.

A sudden hush fell upon the crowd in the huge, colonnaded guardroom, and all heads turned in one direction. Courtiers, priests, glit-

From *Mara, Daughter of the Nile* by Eloise Jarvis McGraw. Copyright 1953 by Eloise Jarvis McGraw. Published by Coward-McCann, Inc. and used with their permission

tering ladies and grouchy ambassadors fell back silently to make room for the procession which had entered from the courtyard at the far end of the hall.

The chamberlain, tapping his long beribboned wand, paced first. Inanni followed him, with Mara close by her side and the twelve Syrians at her heels. Slowly they moved down the long aisle of watching faces, past all the supercilious, painted eyes and quirking lips, past the arched brows, the murmurs behind hands, the disdainful shrugs—down the whole shining length of the room.

It was the worst ordeal Inanni had had to face, and this one she met like a princess. Mara, close beside her, could feel the plump arm quaking under its gaudy, thick draperies. But Inanni held her chin high and kept her eyes unwaveringly on the back of the chamberlain's neck. Perhaps she was thinking of her brothers.

There was an antechamber to pass through before they stood in front of the tall, bronze doors. Here the chamberlain faced them and rattled off a list of instructions concerning court etiquette of which Mara translated only the least confusing. Then, at last, the doors swung open; the chamberlain stepped forward and flung himself on his face, intoning: "Behold, the majesty of the Black Land! Horus of Gold, Enduring of Kingship, Splendid of Diadems, Ruler of Lower and Upper Egypt, Enduring-of-form-is-Ra, Makere Hatshepsut! May the god live forever!"

Mara, suddenly trembling from head to foot, advanced beside Inanni until they stood inside the room. There, across a stretch of gleaming pavement, stood a raised dais framed by two exquisitely painted columns. Upon the dais rested a great throne fashioned entirely of shimmering electrum—and on the throne sat a woman so coldly beautiful that it took away the breath to gaze on her.

She sat stiffly, her glittering dark eyes fixed, her hands holding emblems shining with gold and enamel. Fluted linen, fine as a cobweb, enveloped her like mist; she was weighted with jewels. Upon her flawlessly modeled chin was tied the narrow ceremonial beard denoting kingship, and upon her head rested the heavy red and white double crown of the Two Kingdoms, with the golden cobra curving out over her brow.

Woman or not, there sat the awesome majesty of Egypt, the sun god incarnate. The entire procession fell to its knees; fourteen foreheads, Mara's among them, touched the cold tiles of the floor.

"Lift up your head, Princess of Syria," said Hatshepsut. "You may approach my majesty."

Her voice was high and metallic. Mara felt the glittering eyes upon her even before she raised her own, with an effort, to meet them. Pharaoh had not relaxed her godlike rigidity, but she had turned her head, and her scrutiny was so thorough, so impersonal, that it made Mara feel like a bird on a spit.

"You may speak, Interpreter," added the queen impatiently.

Mara tried, and failed. In a panic she swallowed, tried again, and this time managed to inform Inanni that she was to rise and walk forward.

"What shall I say, Mara?" came the princess' frightened whisper as she reluctantly obeyed. "Say it for me, please—"

"May Hatshepsut the Glorious—endure forever," stammered Mara. "The princess Inanni presents her respects to your Radiance."

The queen permitted herself a coldly gracious smile. Then to Mara's infinite relief, the probing eyes were withdrawn from her, and Hatshepsut turned her entire attention to Inanni. There followed conventional questions as to her comfort, congratulations on the successful voyage, assurances that she need only speak to have anything she desired.

Mara was breathing more easily now; the nervous sweat had dried on the palms of her hands, and she had regained the use of her tongue. As she translated the stilted phrases she began to be aware of other people in the room. They were standing all about the walls, motionless as shadows, but here and there the twinkle of gold as a head turned, or the flash of jewels from a lifted hand, gave proof that they were people and not painted images.

"And have you had audience with His Highness, your bridegroom?" inquired Hatshepsut.

Scarcely waiting for Inanni's almost inaudible reply, she spoke with a malicious smile to someone standing to her right and slightly behind her, on the dais itself. "What think you, Count Sen-

mut? Is she not all we expected, and even more?"

So that is Count Senmut! thought Mara. Curiously and with awe she studied the most powerful figure in Egypt—a spare, big-shouldered man wearing a twist of amulets about his throat. The queen seemed ageless, but Senmut's darkly handsome face mirrored all the struggle and scheming of her eighteen years upon the throne. His smile, faint though it was, carved harsh furrows from his flaring nostrils to the corners of his mouth; his eyes were rapacious.

He bent to murmur something to the queen, and she laughed. "Aye, it will be a sight. A pity *she* will not enjoy it. Interpreter, inform the princess that she may expect to meet her bridegroom very soon."

As Mara obeyed, Hatshepsut lifted a slim hand loaded with rings, and beckoned lazily to someone who stood half hidden in the shadows beside the throne. Next instant every word of Babylonian she knew fled from Mara's mind. It was Sheftu who stepped forward, with his leopard's grace—but a far, far different Sheftu from the man who had lounged beside her while the sails slapped and the sun sparkled on the river. This one wore royal linen as casually as the other had worn his simple *shenti;* his dark features were arrogant against a headcloth of woven gold. There was gold on his ankles, his arms, and his long, sinewy fingers, and a blaze of emeralds at his throat. Here was the great noble she had tried, and failed to picture—a lord of creation, as remote from her as pharaoh herself. Only the amulet on his left wrist was unchanged, and its curiously knotted flax threads and familiar beads gave her a feeling akin to homesickness, for he who wore it seemed a stranger.

Then, for just an instant, his eyes met hers, and a delicious warmth stole over her. I was wrong, she thought. This is the same who once held me in his arms, though he would not kiss me . . . the very same, by the beard of Ptah, whose grand rich life I hold in the palm of my guttersnipe's hand this minute!

"Send word to Thutmose today," Hatshepsut was murmuring, "that he must receive this Syrian at once. You yourself, Lord Sheftu, arrange for the marriage as soon as may be, and we will have done with her. How stupid and vulgar she is in her tasteless wrappings! A fit consort for my surly half brother, think you not? *Hai!* How I would like to see that meeting—he will grow red in the face, and hurl vases and ornaments to the floor, and pace up and down in his endless pacings, as he always does." Hatshepsut smiled. "Nevertheless, he will obey me—as he always does."

If her venom enraged Sheftu, he gave no hint of it. His expression was as smoothly controlled as his bow. No more than an inclination of the head was required for his exalted rank, and he bent not a hair lower.

"Pharaoh's name is glorious," he remarked amiably—without specifying, Mara noticed, whether it was Hatshepsut or Thutmose to whom he gave the title. "All shall be as pharaoh desires."

"You are ever trustworthy, Lord Sheftu." Hatshepsut smiled on him, and he smiled winsomely back. "And now, my lord, if you will provide our fat princess with refreshment . . ."

He made a careless gesture; at once lackeys bearing sweetmeats and garlanded jars of wine converged on Inanni, then passed through the ranks of the courtiers, who obediently came to life, clinking their wine cups with the rigidly correct, stilted movements which made court etiquette a sort of elegant ballet. Sheftu turned away and walked—almost sauntered—back to his place, arrogant and assured. Not for him the puppetlike movements of these lesser beings.

Mara, still on her knees behind the princess, watched him and admired his daring. Suddenly her eyes riveted on a half-shadowed figure just beyond him. For the second time she felt the shock of a familiar face, but this time the sensation was distinctly unpleasant. For there, grim-faced as the Devourer himself, stood her mysterious new master.

For a moment the man's cold visage held her fascinated. Did he ever change expression? Just so he had looked when he offered her riches and danger back in Menfe. Just so he would still look while he watched the slow death of that gold-decked young renegade beside him. How would they kill Sheftu, once they knew? He could not hope for the mercy of the strangler—not while Hatshepsut and her wily Architect ruled the Black Land. He would more likely meet the torturer's stake. Or perhaps—Mara had

a feeling this would please Count Senmut—perhaps they would bow to Sheftu's ultimate destiny and feed him to the crocodiles; those long, sinister brown-green shapes with their pale mouths wide open, waiting. Just one word from her . . .

I cannot do it! was her first thought. But her second was, Aye, you can do it—since you must.

But was there any need for haste?

The thought calmed her. It would be pleasant to stay at the Golden House a little longer, she told herself. I will not speak quite yet. Later, aye, so be it, but not yet!

At that a new fear struck her. If she delayed, who knew how the cat might jump? It was possible Hatshepsut had met her match in this clever Sheftu. Given a little time, he might bring his plans to maturity and snatch that gleaming throne and give it to his king. *Ai!* Then what would happen to the queen's favorites and their gold—and the dreams of the princess Inanni's interpreter?

Mara knew only too well. Her only sure safety lay in serving her master. But as she looked from him to the indolently lounging Lord Sheftu, it was hard to choose. . . .

The solution that sprang into her mind next instant was so simple, so obvious, that she all but laughed aloud. She would not choose! Why make a choice between these two when each thought her his ally, his bonded slave? Why not play both ends against the middle—serve both, meanwhile serving only herself? Then, when the cat jumped, she would jump with it! Ah, the opportunities that opened for one who knew how to use her wits!

She started at the sound of the queen's voice. "Dismiss the lackeys, Count Senmut. I think this Syrian does not like our wine." The servants withdrew, and Hatshepsut spoke again, this time to Mara. "Bid the princess farewell. May the gods of Egypt and Syria go with her. And offer her my majesty's felicitations on her coming marriage—which will surely be a joyous one."

The voice dripped mockery, and the beautiful lips twisted in a smile remarkably like the one carving furrows on the dark countenance of Count Senmut, behind her. Mara felt her optimism drain away in spite of all she could do, and the sight of the white mask which was Inanni's face lowered her spirits still further. Friendless, homesick, unfortunate princess! Small wonder she had been unable to swallow the wine.

Inanni managed to stammer out her thanks and farewells, and Mara translated with an effort. Hatshepsut nodded, and her smile grew broader; she began to laugh deep in her throat. The sound grew in volume until the chamber was filled with it. Mara found herself remembering the scream of Horus, the royal falcon, as he plummeted down from the sky that morning to seize the lark. Her flesh was creeping as she rose from her knees at last to back slowly toward the door beside the pallid Inanni.

For the queen, still laughing, had raised her gold-and-enameled scepter. The audience was over.

from NIKO: SCULPTOR'S APPRENTICE

Isabelle Lawrence

Isabelle Lawrence can recreate the ancient worlds of Greece and Rome so that they seem as alive as her active young heroes. Niko is an adventure tale, but this excerpt, helpfully prepared by Miss Lawrence, is about a day in school with the young Athenian and his friends.

[School Troubles in Ancient Greece]

They reached the grammar school just as the gong was sounding. Into a small room they dashed. Here the boys' slaves usually waited. Peron gave Niko his book and pen very quickly. "If I don't get to the market soon, the best of everything will be gone. I'll return with your lunch."

Niko started to answer, but someone hit him suddenly in the back. He gasped and spun round, fists up. There stood a fair-haired boy with a wide grin—his best friend, Phocis. Of course Niko fell upon him. And of course the master came roaring out. The boys slunk rapidly into their places on a front bench.

The schoolroom was very bare, but lyres and flutes hung on a wall which had once been white. There were a couple of abacuses, with beads strung on wires, for adding and subtracting. On a low table were some tablets, made of wood, covered with wax. Niko and Phocis had brought their own tablets and pens—sticks tipped with bronze for writing in the wax. These were blunt at the other end for smoothing out mistakes. Not that you were supposed to erase too much.

The master sat on a high stool, holding a rod in his hand. "Niko," he said, rapping, ."you were nearly late."

"Yes, sir."

"Your slave must see that this does not occur again." .

"No, sir. I mean, yes, sir. I mean, it shan't, sir."

"Be sure. Younger boys to the next room for music! Take your flutes and lyres. The rest, write the alphabet—in your best writing."

There were nine boys about Niko's age. They all shouted together, "Alpha! Beta!" on to the last letter—a round O called "Omega"—as they wrote.

"Very good. Now we shall copy. Make lines across your tablets."

Niko's lines were a trifle crooked. He smoothed them out again.

The master pounced. "You are not ready."

"Yes, sir. No, sir." He began drawing them in again.

"Please." Phocis took up the master's attention. "My wax is getting thin."

"You should have had it recoated in the market. Niko! Are you ready?"

"Ready, sir." His lines weren't much straighter than they had been before.

The master pointed to some lines on the wall. They read, "Penelope waited ten weary years for the return of her husband."

"Who knows who Penelope was?"

Up went nine hands—ten, really, for Niko put up two.

"You seem eager, Niko, son of Aristocles. Recite!"

Niko stood up, stammering a trifle, but really sure of his story. Had not his father, ever since he could remember, told him tales of the Trojan

War? Aristo, too, knew much of Homer's long poem about it by heart.

"Once upon a time," Niko began, "there lived in southern Greece, in Sparta, a beautiful queen named Helen. She was loved by all the heroes of Greece. So when she was stolen away by the Trojan prince Paris, the Greek men sailed off gladly to Troy to rescue her—all except two."

The master nodded. The boy was not doing badly. "Continue."

"One of the two men was young Achilles. He knew nothing of the war because his mother had dressed him as a girl and hidden him away with a lot of other girls at some king's court, high up in the mountains. The other"—by now Niko was having a wonderful time—"the other was the wily Odysseus, from the island of Ithaca. Well, Odysseus wouldn't have minded fighting, but he had a baby boy named Telemachus, and a nice wife. Her name was—was Penelope." Niko stopped, well pleased with himself.

"Phocis, pray continue."

Phocis was slower at getting to his feet. His memory was not so good as Niko's, but he began bravely. "Odysseus wanted to stay at home, for he had—"

"Niko has told that," the master interrupted.

"Yes, sir. So he yoked an ox and an ass to his plow. That was quite unusual. Next he sowed his field with salt so the messengers would think him mad and go away. But he—he—"

"The baby—" Niko whispered. Unfortunately the master heard. Down he leaped from his stool and rapped Niko over the knuckles, hard. Niko just managed not to cry out.

Phocis rushed on, hoping his friend would not get into any extra trouble on his account. "The messengers threw Odysseus's baby in front of the plow. His father turned aside. Ha-ha, they saw he was not mad. So he had to fight anyhow."

"Your pace is that of a galley in full career after an enemy ship. The speed of plucking a lyre would be better. Stogis, continue from there."

Stogis, unlike most Athenians, was fat. He rose heavily and spoke very slowly indeed. "The—Trojan—War—lasted ten—years—and Ody—Ody—"

"Sseus!" the others all shouted. The master failed to rebuke them. Probably he could not stand it another second either. "Finish, Stogis, speedily."

"Ody—sseus—lost—his way—coming home. It took him—ten—ten years."

"Your father says it takes you that long to get home every night," the master said with a smile. The boys all laughed. "Why did it take ten years? Antimas?"

Antimas was short and jolly. He shouted very fast, "He was captured by a one-eyed giant, and saved his men from Circe, who had turned them into swine. He was shipwrecked—"

The master stopped him. "What happened when Odysseus got home at last? Very well, Niko, you may finish."

Niko went on proudly. "All the men on the island of Ithaca were trying to marry his wife and eat all his food, so he just took his bow and arrows"—he acted it with dramatic gestures—"and shot them all. One! Two! Three! Four! Five! And he and Penelope and Telemachus and the ox and the ass lived happily together from that time on."

"That will do for now," the master ordered. "Write from my copy."

They all doubled themselves into knots of concentration—all except Stogis. He was so fat that he couldn't tie a knot in himself. The master went from one boy to another. "Sit up straight!" Finally he announced, "Time for recess."

The boys piled out. Stogis was not the last, either—only second from the last. In a small courtyard behind the classroom they stood about, munching nuts and olives. Phocis shared his with Niko, talking all the time.

. . . .

The gong sounded, and they filed back into the classroom and took their places on the rough wooden bench. "Second music class!" the master called. "Niko, you may join the class reading *The Odyssey*."

"And Phocis, sir?"

"Phocis must wait till his lyre-playing is better."

Niko hated to be separated from his friend. But soon he was carried away by the rhythm and sound of the words of Homer's story. They made colorful pictures, racing through his mind.

Penelope, mournful, half-distracted by all her

troublesome suitors. Young Telemachus, feeling he must be the man of the house yet too young to know how to help. Did Aristo sometimes feel like that?

Meanwhile the goddess herself, blue-eyed Athena, binds on her golden sandals. Across the seas she flies, till she reaches rocky Ithaca. She is disguised as a stranger, but of course Telemachus welcomes her to his father's house.

> Enter, oh stranger, in peace.
> Dine first, before telling your errand.

A guest was always sacred. Odysseus's son led the way into his high hall. Athena followed,

> Placing her spear in the spear rack,
> Sitting on linen fine-woven.

Telemachus confides his troubles. The waves beat on the sharp shores. Athena flies off to Olympus to plead for help for Telemachus. Now Father Zeus sends Hermes to free Odysseus from a sea nymph, who is holding him captive on another island.

Niko was far away in days of long ago, his own troubles quite forgotten.

. . . it was noon recess. Peron brought bread and cheese, with some red grapes. Niko ate with Phocis. Then they set out for the athletic field.

Niko's feet began to tingle. In a few minutes he would be running, feeling the beat of mother earth under his feet. They passed older boys wrestling. They were as graceful as statues in motion—gleaming brown bodies covered with olive oil. Others were throwing spears or bending to hurl the heavy bronze weight called the discus.

In no time Niko and Phocis had their tunics off. "I wish I were as fast a runner as you, Niko."

"You are. Let's limber up with the broad jump." His friend was good at this. The joy of the dash, the take-off! The instant when he was airborne! The moment of landing, careful not to overbalance and end up on your nose!

"Excellent, Niko." The sportsmaster measured. "This time you have beaten Phocis."

For a moment Niko was pleased. Then he saw his friend's face. "Just luck. You're really far better than I. Now for the race!"

They were given careful instructions. "Bend forward while waiting for the start. Right foot ahead, right arm outstretched. Swing right arm with left leg. Go!"

They went slowly at first, getting warmed up, then faster, round and round the track. The wind sang in Niko's ears. He noticed Phocis coming up on his heels and took a spurt.

The trainer called, "Head forward!" Niko improved his position. "Enough for today!" the instructor called. "Get clean with your scrapers!"

Niko had a silver scraper which had belonged to his father's family. Perhaps Pheidippides himself had used it, after his two-day run for aid. Peron scraped dust and olive oil from his master's body.

Before his plunge into the pool the boy stood before his teacher. "You—you still think I—may —" In his eagerness he could hardly ask his question. "Phocis was good today too."

"If we practice every day you should represent your class at the games. Later, when you are older, who knows? You may bring back the olive wreath and palm of victory from Olympia."

At Olympia were held the proudest games of them all, with runners from all over Greece. Niko held his breath.

. . . .

from THE VOYAGES OF CHRISTOPHER COLUMBUS

Armstrong Sperry

Here is the first chapter from the first of the Landmark Books, a distinguished series about famous men and events in American history. They may be read in sequence or singly, but every one of the thirty volumes will add to the reader's understanding and appreciation of our national ideals and the men who helped to mold them. Armstrong Sperry, author and artist, won the Newbery Award in 1941 for his exciting adventure tale Call It Courage. *His record of the glories and tragedies of Columbus' life is just as well done.*

Refuge

"Courage, my son. Are you very weary?"

"Yes, Father," the child answered. "Have we a long way still to go?"

The man pointed up the hill. There a massive

building crouched like a watchdog above the seaport of Palos. Its painted walls were flushed with the afterglow of the sun. A sound of vesper bells drifted across the still air.

"We are almost arrived," the man said. "Look! The monastery of Our Lady of La Rabida. For tonight, it is the end of our journey."

The little boy's fingers tightened on the man's. "And we will find rest there?" he demanded hopefully. "And food?"

"For certain," the man reassured him. "The good Franciscans never close the door to one who hungers."

But it was a steep climb up the hill. Long before the two travelers reached the monastery, the man was forced to carry his son. They had covered many miles since dawn. The dust of Spain lay like a powder on their boots and clothing. The day had been unbearably hot, even for that summer of 1491, and the heat had pulled at their muscles, drained their limbs of strength.

With a sigh of relief the man set the boy down upon the doorstep. Then he lifted the silver knocker and let it fall against the ancient worm-bored panel of the door. The noise of the summons echoed through the silence.

As he stood waiting, the man cast a backward glance down the hill whence he and his small son had come. Across the vineyards and beyond the tiled rooftops of Palos, the masts of many ships could be seen on the darkening waters of the Rio Tinto.

Beyond the bar of Saltes, a magnificent galleon was standing out to the open sea. Her sails were dyed blood-red by the Andalusian sun, her flags and pennants whipping on the wind. The man's heart quickened. What would he not have given for such a ship! She was on a westward tack, but her captain would change that soon enough. Men didn't sail into the Sea of Darkness that lay at the western edge of the earth! They sailed south to Guinea, or east to the Golden Horn, or sometimes north as far as Iceland; but never into the unknown West.

"Fools!" the man muttered. "Why won't they listen to me?"

There came a sound of sandals flapping on a

From *The Voyages of Christopher Columbus* by Armstrong Sperry. Reprinted by permission of Random House, Inc. Copyright 1950 by Armstrong Sperry

tiled floor. Then the monastery door swung heavily. A stout little monk, dressed in the humble gown and hood of his order, stared with short-sighted eyes at the two strangers on the doorstep. Though their clothing was shabby, they had not the look of beggars.

"And what might you be seeking?" the monk queried.

"Of your charity, Brother, we seek shelter for the night," the man replied wearily. "A loaf to eat; a cup of milk perhaps——"

The little monk's eyes twinkled. The coming of a stranger, especially one who spoke with a foreign accent, was an event. "There is enough for two and to spare," he said eagerly. "The bread is fresh-baked and the goats have just been milked."

"You are kind to a stranger," the weary traveler said.

"Tsk! It is nothing." The monk smiled. "You have come far?"

"Aye. From Portugal."

"Tsk! Tsk!" The good brother clucked with amazement. "Many days of travel! You must indeed be weary. You are a Portuguese, then?"

"I am an Italian, of Genoa," the stranger replied.

"Indeed!" the brother exclaimed. "And to what name do you answer?"

Unconsciously the man on the doorstep stiffened to full height, and the monk saw that though he was of middle age, he was spare and strongly built. His brow was lofty, his chin squared off, and his nose was as bold as the prow of a ship. Gravely the stranger answered: "Men call me Christopher Columbus. This lad is my son, Diego."

The monk beamed upon them. "I am known as Brother Sebastian," he confided. "Enter, my friends, and be at peace. Our Prior is at the moment engaged but he will receive you shortly."

Now, the Franciscan lay-brother has ever been as noted for his love of talk as for his hospitality. Brother Sebastian proved no exception. Maintaining a running fire of question and comment, he led the two travelers down a dim corridor, then through a courtyard where pomegranates and fig trees stood motionless in the dusk.

It was good to hear news, he said. How stood matters in Portugal? How fared the King? Did

Columbus know that here in Spain, King Ferdinand and Queen Isabella were engaged in a death-struggle to drive the Moors forever from this gracious land?

Quite out of breath, Brother Sebastian flung open a pair of doors. "Take your ease here in the library," he invited, "while I see to the supper. Then I shall inform the Prior that you are here. You will find Father Perez a most wise and learned man. His mind is as full of knowledge as a nut is full of meat. And let me tell you, he is a man of no ordinary connections! Once he was father-confessor to the noble Queen Isabella herself."

With which, the little monk bustled away, leaving a wake of silence. Gratefully the small boy sank into a chair, exhausted; but his father glanced about the library with quickening interest. Row upon row of books, richly bound in fine leathers, lined the walls of the lofty room. A long table was strewn with scrolls and maps. On a work-bench stood an unfinished model of a caravel; and Columbus's practiced eye noted the exact detail with which the little ship was being made. Surely the Prior, or one of the lay-brothers, must have an uncommon interest in ships and the sea.

An astrolabe—an instrument used in astronomy—drew the man's attention. He moved toward it as if drawn by some force within the metal itself. Slowly he reached out and touched it. With that contact it seemed as if the library with its walls of books receded from him, vanishing completely.

Once again his spirit went leaping into the dark toward some star invisible to all but him. How they had laughed at him in Portugal! They called him a dreamer, an addle-pate, an impostor. And the great King John had laughed loudest of all. "I suppose, O most wise Columbus," he had said, "that on the other side of this globe you speak of, men walk upside down and trees grow with their branches hanging downward. And there it rains and snows and hails *upward!* Is this so?" The Court had rocked with laughter.

The man's fists knotted. For a second he shut his eyes to the memory of those hateful faces, closed his ears to the echo of their mocking laughter.

Suddenly he felt a tugging at his sleeve.

"Father," Diego pleaded. "Brother Sebastian brings our supper. Let us eat! I am starved."

The man's hand dropped on the child's head. His eyes were bitter as he thought: "My poor motherless boy. What is to become of you in this world of blind men and fools, where even the most learned see no farther than the end of their noses?" Aloud, he said: "Yes, my son, let us eat."

The tray which Brother Sebastian placed upon the table offered a loaf of bread still warm from the oven; a jug of goat's milk; a plate of cold meats; a bowl of oranges.

"This should fortify you till the morrow," said the little monk, smiling. He lighted tapers at each end of the table, and his eyes danced as he watched the man and the boy address themselves to the food spread before them. They ate in utter silence, as if famished, causing the good brother to restrain his desire to talk. Later, Brother Sebastian would learn all about this stranger with the burning eyes and the lines of bitterness carved about his mouth. Surely this was no ordinary traveler! What misadventures could have brought this man called Christopher Columbus, with a child in his arms, to the doors of Our Lady of La Rabida?

With the last mouthful of food, little Diego's head nodded. Manfully he struggled against the weight of his eyelids; but his thin body slumped forward. One cheek rested on the table.

"He sleeps," murmured Brother Sebastian. "He is small for such a journey, Señor Columbus. I shall carry him to his bed. Father Perez will join you here shortly. He has been told that you are waiting." The monk stooped and gently lifted the sleeping child.

After the good brother's departure, the room seemed filled with shadow. Through the open window drifted the voices of the Franciscans singing the Compline: the last service of the day. The tapers burned steadily in the motionless air.

Columbus sat quite still, lost in brooding. Had he been unwise to flee to Spain? True, there had been no choice in the matter, for only here could he take ship to France. The Portuguese had denied him the right to leave their country. They had stolen his maps and calculations and sent out ships secretly. Yet God had punished them, for their ships had been blown back on their own coasts.

But Columbus had been forced to slink like a thief across the frontier, dragging the child with him. Would he be any more successful in persuading the King of France that the shortest route to the fabled wealth of the Far East lay by sailing *west?*

Suddenly Columbus smote the table with the flat of his hand. He must, he *would* convince the French king! There wasn't so much time any more. The years were slipping away like birds in a mist. Would he live long enough to bring to reality this dream he saw so clearly? Why could he not make others see that dream, too? It seemed that men thought of the oceans only as boundaries beyond which lay destruction. But there were no boundaries to the human spirit.

The man's head sank into his hands. His body stilled. And as he slept, his mind went drifting backward to another place, to a time when he was young again, and the sky was bluer than any sky he remembered since childhood. Whose voice was that calling to him? Ah, now he remembered! It was Bartolomeo, his older brother, crying: "Let's go down to the wharf! There's a ship in from Guinea, with sailors who wear rings of gold in their ears. Come, let's go!"

"Aye!" Christopher shouted back eagerly; for what could be more fun than to see a ship from Guinea, whose sailors wore rings of gold in their ears?

"Aye, Bartolomeo, let's go!"

. . . .

The Prior of La Rabida

Columbus lifted his head. Where was he? What had happened? Where were Bartolomeo and Tonio? All around him was darkness through which he could not see. Suddenly then a light appeared before his eyes as a taper flared. Above the taper a grave elderly face, framed in a monk's cowl, looked steadily into his own.

"You have slept, Señor Columbus," a deep rich voice was saying. "I found you in darkness. The tapers had burned out. You were lost in dreams."

"Who—are you?" Columbus stammered, half rising.

"I am Father Perez," the man answered quietly. "Prior of Our Lady of La Rabida. I bid you welcome, señor."

"Your kindness embarrasses me, Father," the other managed.

"Brother Sebastian has already told me your name and that you come from Portugal. But I do not know your way of life." The Prior remained standing, as if undecided whether to encourage this stranger or put a speedy end to his visit.

"I am a mariner, Father, and a maker of maps," Columbus answered.

At once Father Perez took seat on the opposite side of the table. His interest had been immediately caught; for the learned Prior of La Rabida had long been a student of astronomy and geography. "So!" he echoed, "A maker of maps. I myself have given much thought to the mysteries of the heavens and the earth." As he spoke, he smiled and laid a hand lovingly on the model of the caravel which Columbus previously had noted. "But now and again I play a little," he confessed. "This ship-model is one of my playthings. Tell me—as a mariner you have voyaged far?" There was a hint of eagerness in the grave voice, a glimmer of youthful light in the dark eyes. This elderly man, garbed in the sober habit of Saint Francis, spoke of ships and the sea as only one could who yearned for them.

Columbus warmed to his host. For so long he had been treated with ridicule that now he expanded in the glow of the Prior's interest. "For thirty years, as man and boy, I have followed the sea," he said. "I have crossed the Mediterranean times without number and touched all its coasts. I have been to the English islands, to the Portuguese Azores, to Iceland, and to the Spanish archipelago of the Canaries."

For a second, doubt flickered in the Prior's eyes. "That means you have touched the very boundaries of the whole world, señor."

"Of the known world, yes," Columbus replied. "But not of the whole world. I believe there are still other lands, perhaps continents, to be discovered."

"Indeed! How can you state that so surely, since you have never seen them?"

A sudden smile robbed Columbus's answer of its edge. "How can you state that there is a Heaven, Father, since you have never seen it?"

"Because I believe in it," the Prior answered quietly.

"Exactly! And I share that belief. But to it I add—mathematics."

Father Perez nodded his head thoughtfully. "It is possible," he admitted. "After all, the Canaries were only discovered in my father's time."

From within his shabby doublet, Columbus drew a folded parchment carefully wrapped in waxed silk. He spread it on the table.

"Look you, Father," he explained, eagerly. "The only chart the Portuguese didn't get away from me! It is a map I have drawn of those unknown regions. Although I have not seen them, I know from the facts we already have what those far-off lands must be like."

"Of what facts do you speak?" And Father Perez' tone was cautious. This stranger, he felt uneasily, might be either a lunatic or a genius.

Columbus warmed to his subject. "Gales blowing from the west have washed ashore on Porto Santo timbers of unknown wood, carved without the touch of iron!" he exclaimed. "What hand carved them? And bamboos, too, so thick that one section could hold gallons of wine; and trees, the like of which do not grow in the Azores. Whence did they come? The Governor of Flores himself reported the bodies of two men cast up by the ocean—men with yellow faces and straight black hair, like the people of Asia. What of all this?"

For a second the Prior was silent, touched by a sense of wonder and of awe. Hesitantly, he said: "But who could be found to face such monstrous perils on an unknown ocean? The very thought is terrifying."

A rare smile lighted Columbus's somber face. "He who would make sure of dying in bed should never go to sea," he answered. Suddenly he picked an orange from the bowl on the table. "Consider for a moment, Father, that this is the world," he pleaded. "This point we shall call Lisbon. And here—" he marked another point on the fruit, "is the uttermost region of Cathay: a distance of fourteen thousand miles. Now, instead of voyaging east by land, suppose we sail west by water. What will happen? We shall reach Cathay by traveling only four thousand miles. Think of it! Four thousand miles by sea rather than fourteen thousand by land."

A wry smile twisted the Prior's lips. "You have, it seems, an answer to all objections. But tell me —to what good end do you desire to prove your theory?"

Proudly Columbus's answer came back: "To find the shortest route to the continent of Asia, and to bring to its people a knowledge of the true Faith." There was no mistaking the ringing sincerity of the words. "I believe, good Father, that God has called me to this mission—in giving me, since childhood, a love of far places. He has taught me the secrets of the stars and the sea. He has granted me wisdom for mathematics and skill for making charts. Until I cease to breathe, I must follow His bidding."

The man broke off, made a gesture of helplessness. "And what do I ask for this great venture? Only three ships. Three small ships. Is that so much to ask?"

The Prior sank his chin in thought while the tapers burned low. In his mind the belief was growing that this man called Christopher Columbus, this stranger who had chanced to knock at the doors of La Rabida, had pierced to the heart of the truth.

Conscious now of a great fatigue, Columbus arose and pushed back his chair. That sense of failure which had weighed upon him so heavily and so long had returned. "I have taxed your kindness unduly, Father," he said in a low tone; and folding the chart, replaced it in his doublet. "If you will show me to the chamber where my child sleeps——The hour is late and we must be off at dawn."

"Off?" The Prior roused himself. "To where?"

"I seek a ship to France. To offer this empire of which I speak, this great glory, to the French King."

"But——"

"I have lost too many years already!" the man cried bitterly. "Fourteen of them I gave to Portugal. And for what? They stole my calculations, promising to study them and give me a decision. But secretly they sent out the ships they refused to give me. Now their fleets creep along the coasts of Guinea, getting here a bit of gold and there a Negro slave. But I shall secure for the French Crown a direct route across the western ocean to the vast wealth of Asia."

"But why for the French King?" the Prior objected. "Why not for King Ferdinand and Queen Isabella, when already you stand on the soil of Spain?"

"There is no sovereign I would more gladly

serve than Isabella of Castile," said Columbus heavily. "But how should I ever command the ear of Her Majesty?"

"It is not beyond possibility," the Prior answered slowly, "though this is scarcely the moment to petition Their Majesties for ships and funds. The war with the Moors has drained the Treasury. Still, a thought presents itself to me——"

"And that, good Father?"

"It occurs to me that this port of Palos is under sentence of the Royal Council to furnish two ships for any service the Crown may appoint. With two provided, the cost of a third ship might not seem so formidable to the Queen."

Such a hope surged in Columbus's breast that he could not trust himself to speak; for he remembered that the Prior had once been father-confessor to Queen Isabella herself.

Father Perez was saying: "I shall show you now to your chamber. We will sleep on the notion. Sleep brings wise counsel." And then for a second his thin old body stiffened. He stared into the other's eyes, probing deep. What he discovered must have satisfied him, for he said: "It takes courage to be the first to do a thing which the world needs. The little men turn back and the cowards never start. In me you have found a friend. I believe in you, Christopher Columbus. And remember that the longest day, however hard, has an evening; the longest journey, an end. Go with God, señor."

Columbus bowed his head. Tears stood in his eyes. "God bless and keep you, Father," he whispered.

from THE WONDERFUL WINTER

Marchette Chute

Sir Robert Wakefield, in the year 1596, had run away to London to find work. But when he and his dog Ruff set out, Robin little dreamed that his adventures would include a rescue by Will Shakespeare himself, or that he would find himself a happy part of an actor's family and, eventually, one of the boy actors in Shakespeare's own theater. These chapters provide a vivid picture of the Elizabethan theater and Robin's ordeal in playing the lady.

[Robin Turns Actor]

Robin went to bed that night with his head full of dreams about being an actor. He tried to be grave and sensible about it. Probably he would have only a small part in Mr. Shakespeare's new play, an apprentice in a blue wool cap or a serving boy in a leather apron. But in the back of his mind he could not help feeling that they might wish him to take the part of a knight, with gilded armor and a jeweled sword, bowing his plumed head before some grateful monarch.

He went to sleep with the applause of an excited audience ringing in his ears, knowing quite well he was being a fool but enjoying himself nevertheless.

When Sandy was told the news the next morning he showed a warm interest in the career of his fellow actor. Sandy did not have a part in that afternoon's play, which was about a local murder and required only a small cast, and he offered to bring Robin's costume home with him after the morning rehearsal if Mr. Heminges would lend him the horse.

"It will be a heavy costume," said Sandy, "and it will take you a day or so to get used to the weight."

Perhaps it was armor, after all, and he would be a knight. Robin raced through his work around the house and then lingered by the front door waiting for Sandy to arrive. When he came, the top of his dark head could be seen over the curve of a heavy bundle that was fastened with cord. It was some rich heavy stuff, the color of garnet. Not armor, certainly, but perhaps the costume of a lord.

Sandy settled down to his noon dinner, which had been kept hot for him over the kitchen fire, and Robin swept a place on the floor so that he could roll his costume out and look at it. He unrolled it reverently and found that it was stiff with embroidery and had an intricately brocaded front. But there seemed to be a great deal of it, and Robin stared at it for a full minute before he realized what it was.

"It's a woman's dress!" he said.

Sandy looked up in mild surprise from his slice of hot mutton. "Of course it is," he said, and reached for an extra piece of bread to go with his gravy.

"But I can't wear women's clothes," said Robin, his mind groping with the problem.

"Why not?" inquired Sandy, reaching for a pickle. "Something wrong with them?"

"Of course not," said Robin earnestly. "Not in themselves. But I'm not a woman."

"Everyone else in the company wears them," said Sandy. "And they're not women, either."

Robin thought this over for a moment. He knew quite well that the company was made up of men and boys, but there was surely something wrong somewhere. He thought back to the play about King Henry and was willing to admit that the witch might have been played by a man. And that might be true also of the wicked Duchess of Gloucester. But, he wondered, how about the queen's lady-in-waiting, the one with the narrow hands who moved like music?

"That was Sam Gilburne," said Sandy, loosening his belt and leaning back comfortably. "He is Mr. Phillips's apprentice. And Mr. Pope's boy played the queen."

Robin's mind struggled to adjust itself. "Mr. Heminges," he said cautiously. "Did he ever wear anything like that?" He looked out of the corner of his eye at the garnet velvet, spread in lavish folds along the floor.

"Hundreds of times," said Sandy, "and he still does. There's not a member of the company who hasn't worn skirts over and over again. And if you think there is anything easy about it," he added, "you are quite mistaken. You have to learn a different way of walking and holding your hands, and your skirt will be held out by curved whalebone that is harder to manage than a fisherman's net. I didn't bring your hoops home with me, but you can try them on Friday when we go to the Theatre for rehearsal. Would you like to put the dress on now and see if it fits?"

Robin drew a resolute breath. "Which end do I start from?"

"It can't be expected to fit very well without its underpinnings," said Sandy, leaving the table to come and assist his stricken friend. "You ought to have an under-petticoat, very close fit-

ting and tightly pleated, and then a farthingale with cane or bone hoops. That would take up the extra length in the skirt. In the meanwhile stand up straight, Robin, and don't look so discouraged."

"I feel discouraged," said Robin, his head emerging disconsolately out of the top of the velvet. "There is too much of this thing. If I add hoops and a petticoat I shall never be able to walk at all."

"Walk!" said Sandy. "Your part calls for you to dance."

Robin stood weighted down by the garnet folds and regarded his friend in horror. "No one," he said decisively, "could possibly dance in this."

"It will be shorter when the hoops are attached," Sandy assured him. "Although a little heavier, too, of course. But don't worry. It will come easier with practice."

"Do you mean to tell me," demanded Robin, "that the average girl goes to a dance wearing a thing like this?" His respect for the female sex had always been high, but he could feel it going even higher.

"Well, of course you're playing a Court lady, so the velvet is heavier than it sometimes is and there will be the weight of the jewelry. But Queen Elizabeth wears something like that and she is in her sixties and can dance a galliard with the best of them."

"She is a very remarkable woman," said Robin feelingly. "All women are remarkable."

"They wear corsets, too," said Sandy. "Whalebone, wood, even iron, and then the bodice very tightly laced. We're not expected to do that, especially if we are doing any doubling. It takes too long to get out of the costume."

"I am glad to hear that," said Robin. "Very, very glad." He gave an experimental kick, and the velvet rose up in folds about him. "If I have to do a dance in this thing I hope it will be something slow, like a pavane."

Sandy paused in the work of extricating his friend from his costume. "No, my lad," he said. "It won't be a pavane. The customers don't like those stately old dances. It will be the lavolta."

Robin had heard the name. It was one of those new dances that had come in from Italy. His dancing master had informed his aunts that it was not the kind of dance that a gentleman learned.

"By rights it should be done with a partner," said Sandy. "But I'll show you the basic step as we do it in the Theatre. You know the capriole?"

Robin shook his head.

Sandy suddenly went up into the air in a kind of curved leap, beating his feet together before he came down. "That is the capriole. Then you turn the body with two steps, spring high and pause with the feet coming together again."

He illustrated, and Robin watched with awe. He had never seen anything like it except in the meadows in early spring, when the young lambs leaped into the air and cavorted like acrobats. Robin had never been able to understand how the lambs could do it, and he felt the same thing about Sandy now.

He tried to imagine attempting it himself, encumbered in the folds of garnet velvet on a large stage while thousands of people watched. His heart sank until it seemed to be somewhere in his heels.

"Don't look like that," said Sandy. "You'll have time to practice."

"Are there any lines to say?" asked Robin despairingly.

Sandy looked thoughtful. "I think not. You are one of the nieces of someone named Signior Placentio, and you are going to a ball at the house of someone named Lord Capulet. It's a big social affair, and everyone in the company will be onstage in one part or another. I'm to play a serving boy in that scene, and then later on I am someone named Balthasar. It's one of those Italian stories, full of murders. Your dance comes rather early in the play and you can go home afterward if you like."

Robin stared bleakly at his costume. "I suppose," he said, in tones of foreboding, "that you showed me only the basic step. There is probably more to the dance than that."

"Oh, yes," said Sandy. "Backward and forward and so on. But it is more a matter of memory work than anything else."

"Memorizing I can do," said Robin. "But jumping—" He fell silent.

"I shall take the afternoon off," said Sandy decisively, "and show you how it goes." He went out in the kitchen to lay in a small store of apples for himself and could be heard explaining to Mrs. Knell that they were needed in the cause of a new theatre production. Then he and Robin went up to the third floor, nearly closing the door on Ruff who had followed them anxiously, and Sandy stretched out on the bed while he explained the whole thing with diagrams sketched in the air.

By suppertime there was a neat pile of apple cores on the floor beside the bed and Robin had found a whole series of muscles that he did not know he possessed. But he had managed to solve both the leap and the kick, and although Sandy said frankly that he was not doing them the way a girl would be expected to, it was at least a beginning. Robin then brought in Sandy's share of the wood, to show his gratitude, and his dreams that night were of swordsmen who turned suddenly into goats.

The next morning Robin went out into the garden and practiced among the deserted cabbages and a few wintry flower stalks. He kicked and turned and jumped industriously, all the while counting time under his breath. Mrs. Heminges brought him out a bowl of soup but said nothing, and he kept up his practicing until noon.

Sandy was home for dinner and brought the whalebone hoops with him. He was due back at the Theatre that afternoon and had made the long trip out of pure kindness.

As Robin had feared, it was much worse working with the hoops. He tried to remember Queen Elizabeth, who did difficult dances just for the pleasure of it, and she an old lady and hampered with diamonds.

He then attempted to do the dance with both the dress and the hoops, and at this point Mrs. Heminges interfered.

"Robin," she said gently, "the world will not fall apart if the dance is not perfect by Friday. Calm down, boy."

"I am calm," said Robin. But this was hardly true.

"You will have a partner to help you, you know. He will be a good dancer and you can rely on him, especially on the turns. Do it again now and let me watch you."

Robin, despairing, did it again, and Mrs. Heminges leaned on her broom and watched him.

"That is really very well done," she said. "But don't try to push the hoops as you move. Leave them alone and they will swing with you. And take much shorter steps, Robin."

Gratefully he took her advice, taking shorter steps and feeling calmer already. It was chiefly a matter of rhythm, really, like using a scythe in long grass. An experienced mower knew how to relax and let the scythe do the work, and the same thing was probably true in this case.

Moreover, on Friday he would not have the management of his skirt to worry about. Costumes were too expensive to be worn at rehearsals, and Robin had been allowed to practice in his only because Mr. Heminges had made special arrangements with the man who had charge of the tiring room.

They had all been very kind. The least he could do was to get that last turn right. He wiped his forehead and started counting again under his breath.

[The Play's the Thing]

The Theatre looked deserted in the gray light of early morning, with the trampled grass empty of people and a drift of dirty snow on the north side of the building. If Robin had been alone he would have hesitated about going in. But Sandy pushed the stage door open confidently, and Robin saw that the place was already full of people. They were yawning but they were there.

It was the first time Robin had seen a group of actors offstage, and he watched them with deep interest. They looked, however, just like anyone else. All of them were in street clothes, with heavy quilted doublets to keep out the January cold, and most of the younger ones wore earrings.

Robin looked around for Mr. Shakespeare, because he had worked out a careful speech of gratitude and wanted to deliver it as soon as possible. He finally found him out on the main stage, standing by a post with one foot on the base of the painted column while he talked to Mr. Richard Burbage. He was balancing a manuscript on his knee and waving his hand in a wide sweep that took in the whole of the stage. He and Mr. Burbage were both talking at once.

Robin thought the two men had the liveliest faces he had ever seen, even counting Mrs. Knell's. Mr. Burbage was the handsomer of the two, as magnificent in his gray doublet and breeches as he had been in the silks and velvets of the Duke of Suffolk, but on the other hand Robin loved Mr. Shakespeare better.

He hesitated, not wishing to interrupt what was evidently an important conference, and Mr. Shakespeare saw him. Robin had not expected to be recognized, but Mr. Shakespeare beckoned him over, said he was glad to see him again and introduced him to Mr. Burbage. Mr. Burbage gave him a pleasant nod and Robin bowed deeply. He then drew a long breath and tried to remember the opening sentence of his speech.

A small, elderly man came over, his head thrust forward anxiously like a turtle's. He saw the manuscript on Mr. Shakespeare's knee and reached out a protective hand for it. "Mr. Shakespeare, sir," he said, "that is my script, you know. You all have your individual cue sheets, every one of you. I am the one who holds the book."

"I'm sorry, Simon," said Mr. Shakespeare. "Mr. Burbage and I were just trying to work out the first Capulet entrance. The way it is now, the whole thing is as stiff as a procession."

The bookholder was not to be comforted. "That is a valuable script, sir. It has the licenser's stamp on it. You gentlemen forget and leave things about, and I am the one who would be responsible if it were mislaid. It is a very valuable script, you know." He pried the book out of Mr. Shakespeare's hand and nestled it in his own. "I will read the relevant section to you." He riffled carefully through the bound pages with an expert hand. *"Enter Capulet and Juliet and others of his house, meeting the guests and maskers."* He looked up brightly and waited.

"Thank you," said Mr. Shakespeare. "We may as well start at that point, Dick. It's the most complicated grouping."

The bookholder brought out a little stool for himself. He sat down on it, laid the manuscript open on his knee and clapped his hands three times. The sound echoed back from the walls of the Theatre, and the actors who had been lounging about came forward. Most of them had rolls of paper stuck in their belts and Robin wondered if he ought to have one, too.

Sandy was unrolling his and Robin looked over his shoulder to see the opening lines.

Strike, drum.
Where's Potpan?

"The word *drum* is my cue," Sandy whispered. "When I hear it I come on stage with a napkin over my arm and say, 'Where's Potpan?' I'm supposed to be one of Lord Capulet's serving boys and we're getting dinner ready for the guests at his ball. We don't have our lines memorized until Monday, so we're allowed to carry our cue sheets this morning. Excuse me. I have the first speech."

Robin realized he would not be entrusted with a cue sheet of his own since he had no lines to say. But he would have liked to have some badge of his profession, something that he could stick competently into his belt. He looked around for Mr. Heminges and saw him standing nearby disposing of a group of boys.

"Jackie," said Mr. Heminges, "on my right, as my wife. And Gil, as my daughter, on my left. Robin, you belong on the other side of the stage. You are one of the guests we are advancing to welcome."

"Yes, sir," said Robin, hurrying to obey. He was reluctant to leave the sheltering company of Sandy and Mr. Heminges, and the empty expanse of stage that he had to cross made him feel rather lonely. Then he saw that Mr. Shakespeare was one of the actors on the other side and went and stood behind him, having found a sheltering rock in a rather confusing world.

Sandy had darted out on the stage, with a harassed look and someone's scarf over his arm for a napkin. "Where's Potpan?" he demanded, and his voice, which had seemed all right a moment ago, suddenly sounded hoarse from too much shouting.

Mr. Heminges strode forth, surrounded by his group of boys, and Robin moved forward with the actors on his side of the stage. Mr. Heminges was talking in a rather loud voice, teasing the ladies about having corns on their toes, and Robin was so startled it took him a moment to adjust his thinking. He had forgotten that Mr. Heminges was no longer himself, but someone named Lord Capulet. Mr. Heminges would never have said a thing like that.

The booming, cheerful, rather stupid voice went on, welcoming them all to the Capulet house. Then the two groups split up and began to arrange themselves about the stage, and Robin could see they were following some kind of a pattern. It was probably a familiar one that was often used and he concentrated on staying out of everyone's way. At the same time he tried to look alert and intelligent, like a happy guest at the house of a nobleman.

"Foot it, girls!" shouted Lord Capulet in his big, hearty voice, and Robin realized with a sinking heart that it was time for the dance to begin.

A tall boy in blue took Robin's hand and put his own right foot into the first position for the dance. Robin remembered just in time not to bow, decided not to curtsey either, and put his own foot into the same position. He began counting under his breath, very low so that no one could hear him.

The opening steps were simple ones, and Robin and his partner were able to remain in the same position on the stage. Perhaps everything was going to be all right after all. But then they changed positions with the next couple and Robin had to move backward. He was afraid he might knock into someone and could feel himself getting rigid, which he knew was a mistake.

He tried to relax, as Mrs. Heminges had told him to, and lost track of his counting. He missed his partner's turn on the swing and stumbled, nearly bringing the tall boy down with him. Robin tried to collect himself, but by now he had hopelessly lost the beat of the dance. Then he tried to hurry so as to catch up with the others, gripping his partner with a sweating hand, and they crashed headlong into the couple in front.

The dance came to a standstill and there was a moment's complete silence.

Robin stood in the center of the stage and waited to be ordered out of the building.

"What we probably need," said Mr. Shakespeare, breaking the silence with his pleasant, relaxed voice, "is some music. It is very difficult to keep the rhythm without music." He walked downstage and picked up a treble viol that someone had propped against the corner post. "Suppose we try it again."

A large man with curly brown hair had been sitting next to the bookholder, watching the scene with his chin propped in his hand. He got to his feet and gently removed the bookholder from his stool. Then he reached for a *viol-da-gamba* and sat down on the stool himself with the heavy instrument between his knees.

"What shall it be, Will?" he asked.

"Anything in three-quarters time. Try 'The Lovers in the Rye.'" Mr. Shakespeare struck a note and then stopped. "Henry," he said, "change places with Christopher, please."

Robin's partner stepped back and another young man came forward. He had large, cool hands and took Robin in a firm hold that was very comforting.

The music began. It was a gay tune, very well played, and it seemed to lift the dancers up and carry them along with it. Robin's partner moved lightly but firmly, almost like part of the music, and Robin could feel himself being caught up in the same rhythm. His feet were as sure of themselves as they had been during the final day of his practicing among the cabbages, and they finished on the exact beat as the music ended.

Robin looked devotedly at Mr. Shakespeare and then waited to be scolded. But the actors apparently seemed to feel that the incident was closed, and the scene went on. It consisted of an argument between Lord Capulet and one of his more quarrelsome young relatives, and Robin could not help being pleased when Lord Capulet succeeded in outshouting his kinsman.

Then the mood of the scene changed entirely. Mr. Burbage was bending over the hand of the boy they called Gil and speaking to him in a low, urgent, caressing whisper. Gil answered, and Robin thought he had never heard such a beautiful voice in his life. Mr. Shakespeare must surely enjoy hearing his lines spoken as beautifully as that.

He glanced over at Mr. Shakespeare, who was not smiling. Instead he was chewing the end of his finger and frowning slightly.

"Gil," he interrupted, "just what is Juliet saying at this point?"

"It's a sonnet, sir," said Gil, returning to a more normal tone of voice. "And very beautiful," he added solemnly.

"Thank you," said Mr. Shakespeare. "But Romeo and Juliet are not merely reciting a sonnet. What are they really saying to each other?"

Gil paused to think this out. It took him quite a long time and everyone waited patiently.

"Well," he said finally, "Romeo wants to kiss her. That's what is behind all his talk about pilgrims. And she doesn't want him to. Or at least she says she doesn't." He paused thoughtfully. "But I expect she does, really. She is teasing him a little for being so excited, but she is getting a little excited, too." He paused again. "Very excited. Very stirred up. Juliet is always in a hurry about things."

"Suppose you try the lines again," said Mr. Shakespeare, and even Robin could see a difference this time. The first time he had heard only the sound, but now he heard the meaning.

The big man who had played the *viol-da-gamba* had come up behind Gil and was standing with his hands on his hips. "Don't fall in love with your own voice, Gil," he remarked. "Fall in love with Romeo." Then the tone of his own voice changed suddenly. "Madam, your mother craves a word with you."

"What is her mother?" asked Mr. Burbage rather anxiously.

"Marry, bachelor, her mother is the lady of the house."

Robin perceived that they were going on with the play. He would have liked to stay onstage and see how things were coming out, but Lord Capulet was vigorously saying good night. Robin could hear his big, sleepy voice—"Come on then, let's to bed"—as he himself turned and went offstage with the other guests.

Sandy had to stay in the Theatre until the rehearsal ended because he had another part toward the end of the play, and he and Robin went and sat down on the back stairway. Mrs. Heminges had given them two meat pasties wrapped in a clean napkin in case they should grow hungry during the morning, and they ate them both. Robin had not expected to become hungry in so short a time, and he searched the napkin hopefully for stray crumbs.

"It's the worry," Sandy explained. "Actors eat as much as ditchdiggers."

"I was worried enough," Robin admitted. "And I had good reason to be. But they were very kind."

"Not all actors are kind," said Sandy. "I know a boy in one of the other London companies who was beaten with a strap because he left out one word in a line. But men like Mr. Burbage and Mr. Shakespeare remember their own beginnings. They know you get tense when you're new to the work and that when you fail it's not necessarily for lack of trying. They are always gentle with beginners. But get drunk, or talk back, or be late to rehearsals and you'll wish you had never been born."

Robin abandoned his search for crumbs and licked his fingers thoughtfully. He could hear onstage a squeaky voice saying something, and then in answer a fat, female sort of voice that nevertheless sounded like the large man with the *viol-da-gamba*.

"That would be Thomas Pope," said Sandy, listening, too. "He plays Juliet's nurse, and you won't be able to recognize him when he's dressed for the part. He's talking to Will Kempe, who is playing Peter."

Robin had heard of Will Kempe even in Suffolk. He was the greatest clown in England, the special favorite of Queen Elizabeth, and all the country people knew his name and repeated his jokes.

Robin listened carefully for the squeaky voice again. "Peter must be a very important rôle," he said.

"It's a very small rôle," said Sandy. "He will do well to get half a dozen laughs in all. The Nurse is the big comic part in the play."

"Then I suppose Mr. Pope is much more important than Mr. Kempe," said Robin. "He must be, if he gets bigger parts."

"They are both shareholders, like Mr. Heminges and Mr. Shakespeare, and they all work out the casting together. There is no such thing as anyone getting all the big parts. Gil, for instance, is rehearsing as Juliet this morning, but he will carry a spear in this afternoon's play and not have any lines at all."

"I'll never be good enough even to carry a spear," said Robin despairingly. His sins of the morning had returned full force now that there was no longer any meat pie to distract him.

"You did very well," said Sandy reassuringly. "You were quiet and followed directions, and you didn't run around asking silly questions. Everyone has a little trouble the first time on-stage, and they all knew you were trying."

"But suppose I do something wrong the afternoon the play opens?"

"You won't," said Sandy. "Just keep practicing and get used to the costume. They will let you keep it at home until the last possible minute. Only be careful of it. Those costumes are fearfully expensive and we use them over and over again." He got up and brushed the crumbs from his knee. "Enter Balthasar, Romeo's faithful servant, with a torch and a mattock, whatever a mattock may be."

He sauntered off with a backward wave of the hand, and Robin wondered if he could ever hope to be so splendidly casual about things. Perhaps if he went home at once there might be time to do a little practicing in the garden before dinner. That last step before the turn needed a great deal of attention.

He looked around for Ruff and found him sitting outside on the back stoop, watching the horses and yawning politely. Robin had been a little doubtful about bringing his dog to the Theatre, but Mr. Heminges had said it would be all right and fortunately Ruff had excellent manners.

They walked home together over the frozen brown grass of Finsbury Fields. The sun had come out, warming the back of Robin's neck, and after a little while he began to whistle.

He whistled the whole of "The Lovers in the Rye" and it seemed to him that it was a very fine tune. Perhaps he would not do so badly after all.

THE TRIAL

Elizabeth Janet Gray

Elizabeth Janet Gray (Mrs. Vining) won the Newbery Award in 1923 for her story of medieval life in England, Adam of the Road. *Later, she was chosen to go to Japan to undertake the education of the Japanese crown prince. She has written a fascinating account of her experience in Japan, called* Windows for the Crown Prince. *Mrs. Vining is a Quaker, so her interest in William Penn is understandable. England's illustrious admiral, Penn, was bitterly disappointed when his son William became a convert to the Quaker way of worshipping and living. The admiral had high hopes for his son at court, but this Quaker folly would, he knew, ruin the young man's chances. The two had quarreled bitterly over the issue, although they loved each other dearly. Then, William was cast into prison and brought to trial for conducting a Quaker meeting "to the great disturbance of his [the king's] peace." The trial was to have far-reaching effects on the courts, even in the United States. This episode would make an exciting subject for a dramatization.*

On Thursday the first of September 1670, a sergeant and his yeomen came early in the morning to escort Penn and Mead out of Newgate and down the street called the Old Bailey to the Sessions House, where the court sat at seven. It was a "fair and stately building," with large galleries for spectators.

There were ten justices on the bench. Several of them young William Penn already knew. Sir Samuel Starling was Chief Justice. The Admiral's "buffle-headed" old friend, Sir John Robinson, the Lord Lieutenant of the Tower, was another—and good reason William had for remembering him! A third, Sir Richard Brown, had been particularly brutal in his raids on the Friends' meeting-houses a few years ago, and two more were well known as zealous churchmen and persecutors of Non-Conformists. Altogether they were about as arrogant, puffing, choleric, muddleheaded, prejudiced a lot of judges as one could find anywhere.

The jury was sworn in, twelve slow-witted, plain citizens, with good plain English names, John and James and William and Henry. There was an Edward Bushell, and Thomas Veer was foreman.

The prisoners were brought before the bar, and the indictment read. It was an astonishing piece of writing: a single sentence of two hundred and fifty words looped and bunched together in alternately legal and hysterical phrases. The gist of it was that "William Penn, gent., and William Mead, linen-draper, the fifteenth day of

"The Trial." From *Penn* by Elizabeth Janet Gray. Copyright 1938 by Elizabeth Janet Gray. Reprinted by permission of The Viking Press, Inc., New York

August, with force and arms unlawfully and tumultuously did assemble, and the aforesaid William Penn by agreement between him and William Mead before made, then and there in the open street did take upon himself to preach and speak, by reason whereof a great concourse and tumult of people in the street, a long time did remain and continue in contempt of the Lord the King and of his law, to the great disturbance of his peace and to the great terror of many of his liege subjects."

The Clerk then asked: "What say you, William Penn and William Mead? Are you guilty as you stand indicted, or not guilty?"

They pleaded "Not guilty," and the court was adjourned till afternoon.

While they were waiting, they discussed the errors in the indictment. To begin with, the date was wrong; the day of the meeting was Sunday the fourteenth of August, not the fifteenth. In the second place, they did not meet with force and arms. Nobody had arms except the soldiers. Nobody used force except the soldiers. Then, since they had never seen each other before, they obviously could not have met by agreement before made. And finally, they did not remain and continue in contempt of the King and his law, for the chief officer who came to take them had allowed the meeting to go on after Mead promised that Penn would go with them at the end of it.

In the afternoon they were brought back to the Sessions House, but instead of going on with their trial, the court, "both to affront and to tire them," kept them waiting there for five long hours while trials of felons and murderers were held, and at the end of the time adjourned.

September second they cooled their heels in Newgate.

September third was a Saturday. The sergeant and his yeomen came for them again before seven. Just as they went into the courtroom one of the officers, on a kindly impulse, took off their hats for them. Sir Samuel Starling was quick to see.

"Sirrah," he thundered, "who bid you put their hats off? Put them on again."

So, hats on, they stood before the bar. Ten judges in wigs and robes sat in a portentous row upon the bench and looked down with hostile eyes, while the chief among them proceeded solemnly to fine the prisoners forty marks apiece for wearing their hats in court.

It was childish; it was contemptible. William Penn, who was twenty-five, looked straight into all those hard and prejudiced old eyes, and said calmly: "I desire it may be observed that we came into the court with our hats off (that is, taken off), and if they have been put on since, it was by order from the Bench, and therefore not we, but the Bench, should be fined."

There being no answer to that, the jury was sworn again. Sir John Robinson objected to the way Edward Bushell took the oath. Bushell was known to be a man of tender conscience and tough will, and the judges were a little uneasy about him. They had no good excuse, however, for getting rid of him, and so the trial went forward.

The first witness was called and sworn to tell "the truth, the whole truth, and nothing but the truth, so help me God."

Lieutenant Cook, in command of the soldiers, testified that he saw Mr. Penn speaking to the people but could not hear what he said. Two others said that they saw Penn preaching to some four hundred people and Mead talking to Lieutenant Cook, but could not hear what either Penn or Mead said. There was no further evidence.

Then Penn spoke up and said: "I desire you would let me know by what law it is you prosecute me, and upon what law you ground my indictment."

The Recorder of London, who was the legal expert on the case, answered promptly: "The common law."

At once Penn asked: "What is that common law?" but the legal expert could not produce a definition or an example of it. The other justices on the bench began to shout at Penn, and the Recorder snapped:

"The question is whether you are guilty of this indictment."

Penn corrected him. "The question is not whether I am guilty of this indictment, but whether the indictment be legal." He pointed out that if the common law was so hard to understand it was very far from being common, and he quoted Coke and the Magna Carta.

The Recorder, losing his temper completely, shouted: "Sir, you are an arrogant fellow, and it is not for the honor of the court to suffer you to go on!" To which Penn answered mildly: "I

have asked but one question, and you have not answered me; though the rights and privileges of every Englishman are concerned in it."

"If I should suffer you to ask questions till to-morrow morning," replied the Recorder huffily, "you would never be the wiser."

And young Penn could not resist the temptation to retort: "That is according as the answers are."

That was too much for the judges; they turned purple with rage.

"I desire no affront to the court but to be heard in my just plea. . . ."

The Mayor and the Recorder both broke out in indignant shouts: "Take him away! Take him away! Turn him into the bale-dock."

The bale-dock was a sort of pen at the far end of the courtroom, open at the top but enclosed by high palings so that the prisoners could not see or hear what was going on. Before he was dragged off to this coop, William Penn delivered a ringing challenge:

"Is this justice or true judgment? Must I therefore be taken away because I plead for the fundamental laws of England? However, this I leave upon your consciences, who are of the jury and my sole judges, that if these ancient fundamental laws which relate to liberty and property (and are not limited to particular persuasions in the matter of religion) must not be indispensably maintained and observed, who can say he hath a right to the coat upon his back?"

"Be silent there."

"I am not to be silent in a case wherein I am so much concerned, and not only myself but many ten thousand families besides."

Roughly they pulled him off to the bale-dock. Mead had his turn, stood his ground well, quoted a Latin tag, defined a riot, and was also consigned for his pains to the bale-dock.

There, stuck away in the dimness, they could not hear what was going on in the court, but one of the officers whispered to them that the Recorder was charging the jury. It was absolutely against the law to charge the jury in the absence of the prisoners. Penn flung himself on the palings and pulled himself up so that he could shout over the top of them:

"I appeal to the jury who are my judges!" Loudly as he could, he quoted the law, and he called to the jury to take notice that he had not been heard in his own defense.

"Pull that fellow down, pull him down," bawled the Recorder.

The people in the galleries craned their necks and rustled and buzzed.

"I say these are barbarous and unjust proceedings!" shouted Penn, clinging to the side of the bale-dock.

"Take them away to the hole," commanded the Recorder.

To the hole they went, a sort of dungeon in the Sessions House, a stinking hole, Penn said, and one that the Lord Mayor would not consider a fit sty for his swine. There they stayed while the jury deliberated.

They were a long time at it. After an hour and a half, eight of them returned to the court, and four who disagreed remained in the jury chamber above. The four, of whom Edward Bushell was recognized as the leader, were brought down and scolded and threatened by the court. All twelve of them were then sent back to reach a conclusion, and this time, after more deliberation, they brought the unanimous verdict that William Penn was guilty of speaking in Grace-church Street.

This of course was equal to an acquittal. There was no law against speaking in Grace-church Street. The Mayor tried to make them say "speaking to an unlawful assembly," but they refused. Determined to have a different verdict, he ordered them back to the jury chamber, and they asked for pen, ink, and paper to take with them.

In a little more than half an hour they returned, Penn and Mead were brought back to the bar, and the jury handed in its verdict again, this time written and signed. "We do find William Penn to be guilty of speaking or preaching to an assembly met together in Gracechurch Street, the fourteenth of August last, 1670, and that William Mead is not guilty of the said indictment."

Whereupon the Mayor called Bushell "an impudent, canting fellow," and the Recorder told them all:

"Gentlemen, you shall not be dismissed till we have a verdict the court will accept; and you shall be locked up without meat, drink, fire, and tobacco. You shall not think thus to abuse the court; we will have a verdict, or by the help of God you shall starve for it."

Before the jury departed again, Penn got his word in, and the voice of this young man of twenty-five, whom the Lord Mayor later called "that wild, rambling colt," was the only calm and authoritative voice in the whole amazing, hysterical courtroom.

"My jury, who are my judges, ought not to be thus menaced. Their verdict should be free and not compelled. The bench ought to wait upon them but not forestall them."

But the court was ready to break up for the day and "huddle the prisoners to the jail and the jury to their chamber." As the second day of the trial ended, Penn turned to the jury and said:

"You are Englishmen; mind your privileges, give not away your right."

To which Bushell stanchly made reply: "Nor will we ever do it."

And that night the jury was shut up without "meat, drink, fire, nor any other accommodation."

The next day was Sunday, and it was illegal to hold court. Nevertheless, at seven, the court sat.

The foreman of the jury read the verdict again: "William Penn is guilty of speaking in Gracechurch Street."

The Mayor prompted him: "To an unlawful assembly?" and Edward Bushell answered for him: "No, my lord, we give no other verdict than what we gave last night; we have no other verdict to give."

Another of the justices, Sir Thomas Bludworth, commented gloomily: "I knew Mr. Bushell would not yield," and the Recorder threatened again: "I will have a positive verdict, or you will starve for it." After the night they had just spent, the jury could not look on this as an empty threat.

Penn desired to ask one question: Did the court accept the verdict "Not guilty," given of William Mead?

"It cannot be a verdict," said the Recorder, "because you are indicted for a conspiracy; and one being found guilty and not the other, it could not be a verdict."

Penn's answer was quick. "If not guilty be not a verdict, then you make of the jury and Magna

Carta a mere nose of wax. . . . And if William Mead be not guilty, it consequently follows that I am clear, since you have indicted us of a conspiracy, and I could not possibly conspire alone."

But for the third time the verdict was rejected and the jury sent back to find another. Again it returned with the one answer it had to give.

The court was well-nigh beside itself with rage. It threatened to set a mark on Edward Bushell, to have an eye on him, to cut his nose. And now Penn's voice rings out:

"It is intolerable that my jury should be thus menaced. Is this according to the fundamental law? Are they not my proper judges by the great charter of England? What hope is there of ever having justice done, when juries are threatened and their verdicts rejected? I am concerned to speak and grieved to see such arbitrary proceedings. Did not the Lieutenant of the Tower render one of them worse than a felon? And do you not plainly seem to condemn such for factious fellows who answer not your ends? Unhappy are those juries who are threatened to be fined and starved and ruined if they give not in their verdicts contrary to their consciences."

The Recorder had nothing to say in answer but: "My lord, you must take a course with that fellow."

"Jailer, bring fetters," commanded the Chief Justice, "and stake him to the ground."

"Do your pleasure," replied Penn superbly, "I matter not your fetters."

And now the Recorder's rage did what Penn was later to tell his children anger always does: it threw him into a desperate inconvenience. He made a speech that echoed around London and that he bitterly regretted afterwards.

"Till now," he said, "I never understood the reason of the policy and prudence of the Spaniards in suffering the Inquisition among them. And certainly it will never be well with us till something like the Spanish Inquisition be in England."

It was a dreadful thing to say. The torture and terror of the Spanish Inquisition were fresh in men's minds—Penn's grandfather, Giles Penn, had suffered from it—and in England Popery was more feared and detested than non-conformity.

For the fourth time the jury was ordered to go find another verdict; this time they refused to go, saying there was no other verdict. The Recorder in a passion left the bench, sputtering: "I protest I will sit here no longer to hear these things," but the Mayor called to him to stay while he uttered a few more threats, had the sheriff take the jury up to their room, and adjourned the court.

The prisoners were sent back to Newgate, where at least they had more freedom and comfort than the jury.

At seven o'clock on the morning of Monday, September fifth, the court sat again. The jury staggered in, wan, white, hungry, thirsty, and disheveled.

"Look upon the prisoners," said the Clerk. "What say you, is William Penn guilty or not guilty?"

"Not guilty."

"What say you? Is William Mead guilty, or not guilty?"

"Not guilty."

It was plain and definite this time. There was nothing the Bench could do except to call the roll and make each juror give his verdict separately. Everyone answered firmly: "Not guilty."

The people in the galleries were pleased, so pleased that they "made a kind of hymn about it." All over the courtroom there were little murmurs of satisfaction.

But the affair was not over. The Recorder had his last word. "I am sorry, gentlemen, you have followed your own judgments and opinions rather than the good and wholesome advice which was given you. God keep my life out of your hands: but for this the court fines you forty marks a man, and imprisonment till paid."

They had been threatened with fines and imprisonment, they had faced the ugly temper of the Bench, they must have known this was coming. But forty marks was a lot of money, about twenty-six pounds sterling, in a day when a lieutenant in the Plymouth colony, for instance, got an annual salary of twenty marks, and women worked in the hayfields for a penny a day.

Penn then stepped up toward the Bench and demanded his liberty. He was told that he too was in for fines—the forty mark fine imposed at the beginning of the session for wearing his hat. He began to quote the Magna Carta again, but the Recorder had had all he could stand. "Take

him away," he implored, "take him away, take him out of the court."

But before he went young William Penn had one thing more to say. He said it. "I can never urge the fundamental laws of England but you cry: 'Take him away, take him away.' But it is no wonder, since the Spanish Inquisition hath so great a place in the Recorder's heart. God Almighty, who is just, will judge you for these things."

So the prisoners who had been acquitted, and the jury who had acquitted them, went together to Newgate prison.

That night Penn wrote to his father. "Because I cannot come, I write." He told him the story of the trial, ending: "I am more concerned at thy distemper and the pains that attend it, than at my own mere imprisonment, which works for the best."

The next day he wrote: "I entreat thee not to purchase my liberty. They will repent them of their proceedings. I am now a prisoner notoriously against law."

And the next: "I am persuaded some clearer way will suddenly be found to obtain my liberty, which is no way so desirable to me as on the account of being with thee. . . . My present restraint is so far from being humor that I would rather perish than release myself by so indirect a course as to satiate their revengeful, avaricious appetites. The advantage of such freedom would fall very far short of the trouble of accepting it."

To pay the fine would be to admit its justice. What he wanted was either to be released by the court, or to bring suit against the judges for illegal imprisonment. In this way a principle could be established. This was the course the jury was taking. Every six hours they demanded their freedom, and when at length they were released on bail, they brought suit against the judges—and won their case. The whole body of judges in the King's Bench Court decided that no jury could be fined for its verdict. So it was that as a result of the trial of William Penn the sacredness of trial by jury was established for all time.

But that was nearly a year later.

The Admiral could not wait. He was dying, and he wanted to see his beloved son William again. He secretly paid his fine, and Mead's too, and they were set free.

LONG AFTERNOON

James Daugherty

James Daugherty's biographies Daniel Boone, Poor Richard, *and* Abraham Lincoln *portray the men and the spirit of the times with fidelity and zest. He writes with the same swing and verve to be found in his pictures. But the last part of this last chapter in his life of Daniel Boone is slow moving, suited to the tempo of the old man whose stormy days have run into a quiet twilight. Even so, the reminiscences provide glimpses of the lusty young Daniel, who hunted, pioneered, and gave a droll twist to a story, even as the old Daniel does as he talks to the young artist. You must read the whole book and enjoy the narrative, the poems, and the vigorous pictures. Then, if you like* Daniel Boone, *read Mr. Daugherty's other biographies and John Mason Brown's* Daniel Boone, *one of the finest of the* Landmark Books.

At last the river voyage was ended and the Boones were crossing the Mississippi, the Father of Waters, into the little easy-going town of St. Louis. Boone was treading on the same spot where the great La Salle had built the first fort so long ago. He, too, had been a wilderness explorer of the farthest reaches, with his head full of great visions for a French empire of the Mississippi. And even before La Salle, at a point farther down the river, on a moonless night they had dropped into the dark waters the worn body of another seeker of far horizons, the Spaniard De Soto.

But on that July day in 1800 it was De Lassus, the Spanish Commandant of St. Louis, who welcomed Boone with a graciousness and respect that he had not known among the thankless Kentuckians. Here was an easy grace and gaiety of living that were foreign to the bleak Kentucky cabins. The French and Indians lived together on friendly terms and the Spanish and Americans were drawn together in their common antagonism to the British who had been a constant menace to the territory.

De Lassus knew a man when he saw one. He commissioned Boone as a government official or syndic. Besides the usual grant to a settler of one thousand arpents of land, he gave Boone a tract of ten thousand arpents with his office. The syndic was the government representative who administered law and justice in a lawless land. Boone administered primitive justice according to his own rules of common sense. He knew when a rogue deserved a lashing and he saw to it that he got it well laid on. There was no appeal from his decisions, so everybody had to be satisfied. The Femme Osage country was no place for claim jumpers under the Kentucky syndic. His duties as a judge were light in this simple and honest community. In the whole town there were only two locks, one for the government house and one for the calabozo.

So there was plenty of time for hunting and exploring trips up the Missouri to where the beaver and big game were plentiful. Jesse and Nathan Boone with their families had come to the Missouri country. Daniel Morgan, of course, was there and later came Flanders Calloway and his wife, Boone's beloved Jemima of the Boonesborough siege. They all lived within a half-day's journey of Daniel's cabin. Rebecca was happy amid friends, her children and grandchildren. It was almost another Boonesborough.

Mr. Peck, the traveling preacher, came to the Kentucky colony in Missouri and visited the old hunter. In his fine *Life of Daniel Boone* he describes him. "His high bold forehead was slightly bald and his silvered locks were combed smooth; his countenance was ruddy and fair, and exhibited the simplicity of a child. His voice was soft and melodious. A smile frequently played over his features in conversation. At repeated interviews, an irritable expression was never heard. His clothing was the coarse, plain manufacture of the family; but everything about him denoted that kind of comfort which was congenial to his habits and feelings, and evinced a happy old age."

He was the especial hero of a numerous race of grandchildren for whom he relived with zest his adventurous youth. They swarmed upon his knees and gazed wide-eyed into the fire as he told of the great siege of Boonesborough. These full years of overflowing happiness passed too quickly. History was moving on and dreamy Spanish St. Louis lay directly in her path. The nineteenth century was a husky pioneer baby that had climbed out of its cradle and was wading across the Mississippi. History was always catching up with the Boones.

In 1803 the tall red-headed Virginian, President Thomas Jefferson, bought the Territory of Louisiana for the United States from the little Corsican dictator who ruled Europe with artillery. The price was twelve million dollars; it was a big bargain for a westward-marching democracy.

In the crowd of cheering Americans who watched the stars and stripes raised at St. Louis were two young Americans, Captain Meriwether Lewis and his friend William Clark, younger brother of Clark of Vincennes. They had been personally appointed by the President to head an expedition into the West across the Rockies to the Pacific. On May 14th, 1804, "they proceeded under a gentle breaze up the Missouri," wrote Clark.

The old eagle stood looking into the West at the end of the trail as the young men started on a new enterprise that would blaze the path of empire to the Pacific. Boone had cut a path for history from the Yadkin to the Mississippi and he was ready to roll back the years and ride off into the Far West. But Rebecca and his sons and grandchildren said no, and so he stayed in Missouri. He went on long trapping trips, alone or with a Negro or Indian for a companion.

Now his broad Spanish acres were slipping away. Again he had forgotten under the easy Spanish Commandant to sign the papers. The American commissioners were genuinely sorry but there was the law. The Louisiana Purchase that had doubled the area of the new republic and enriched it with untold wealth left Daniel and Rebecca landless and penniless.

But beaver skins were worth nine dollars apiece and Daniel was planning a big winter's work with the traps. He paddled alone up the Missouri River and made a snug camp well hidden in the bluffs. It was good beaver country and he cunningly set his traps. One morning when he was making the round of his traps he saw smoke rising near his camp. A little cautious scouting showed him the hunting camp of a large body of Indians. It was hostile country for white men; Daniel concealed his tracks as he made for camp and kept out of sight till nightfall when he could safely build a fire and cook food. Next morning there was a blessed blanket of new-laid snow which had covered his traps from the Indians. For a week he lay low and watched the Indian camp, praying that the prowling savages would not stumble on some sign of his presence. One never could tell how luck would break in the wilderness. He had enough dried meat to last a long time. It was twenty days before the snow melted and the Indians packed their camp on the poles of their travois and rode away. He told Mr. Peck he "never felt so much anxiety in his life for so long a period, lest they should discover his traps and search out his camp."

He came back in the spring to the Osage settlement with a big winter catch of fine beaver fur. Saying good-by to his family he packed up the bales on his horses and departed, saying only that he was going to Kentucky on business.

John James Audubon was a young Frenchman who had just come to Kentucky from Philadelphia with his lovely wife, Mary Bakewell, to make his fortune as a merchant. Instead, he was out in the woods studying and drawing birds. He was gaily letting the business go to the dogs. When Daniel Boone came back to Kentucky and sold his furs for a bag of silver dollars to pay his debts, John James Audubon was glad to meet him. They went squirrel barking together and sat up late at night while the old hunter told of Indian escapes and perils, and then lay down on the floor and went to sleep. Audubon thought he had met the rarest bird in all America.

They both had the curious mind to see and to know about America. They shared an enormous zest for living. They wanted to enjoy all of it first-hand, and were not satisfied to settle down and own a few thousand acres with a fence around it. They were a pair of shiftless traipsers, poor as Job's turkey most of the time, walking and riding and flatboating up and down the trails and rivers of America. The rougher and tougher it was the better they liked it. Audubon went everywhere from Labrador to Florida, from Boston to Missouri. He lived with Osage Indians and spoke their language. When he needed money he drew human birds for five dollars a portrait. He drew pen portraits, too, of the strange human birds he met everywhere. His keen eyes missed no detail of the roaring pageant of democracy marching westward.

Here is John James's own story of how he went squirrel barking with Daniel Boone: "Barking off Squirrels is delightful sport, and in my opinion requires a greater degree of accuracy than any other. I first witnessed this manner of procuring Squirrels whilst near the town of Frankfort. The performer was the celebrated Daniel Boone. We walked out together, and followed the rocky margins of the Kentucky River, until we reached a piece of flat land completely covered with black walnuts, oaks, and hickories. As the general mast was a good one that year, Squirrels were seen gambolling on every tree around us. My companion, a stout, hale, and athletic man, dressed in a homespun hunting-shirt, bare-legged and moccasined, carried a long and heavy rifle, which as he was loading it he said had proved efficient in all his former undertakings and which he hoped would not fail on this occasion as he felt proud to show me his skill. The gun was wiped, the powder measured, the ball patched with six-hundred-thread linen, and the charge sent home with a hickory rod. We moved not a step from the place, for the Squirrels were so numerous that it was not necessary to go after them. Boone pointed to one of these animals which had observed us, and was crouched on a branch about fifty paces distant, and bade me mark well the spot where the ball should hit. He raised his piece gradually, until the bead (that being the name given by the Kentuckians for the sight) of the barrel was brought to a line with the spot which he intended to hit. The whip-like report resounded through the woods and along the hills, in repeated echoes. Judge of my surprise when I perceived that the ball had hit the piece of the bark immediately beneath the Squirrel, and shivered it into splinters, the concussion produced by which had killed the animal and sent it whirling through the air, as if it had been blown up by the explosion of a powder magazine. Boone kept up his firing and before many hours had elapsed we had procured as many Squirrels as we wished." It was fun for everybody but the squirrels.

A mid-October afternoon. The oak and the maple were still in full leaf, but the oaks had turned to a crimson that burned in the mellow sunshine. Little yellow leaves were spiraling down from the maples that were blazing in a burnished splendor. Autumn was a parade of blood and gold, proud and splendid.

An old brown hound snuffed among the fallen leaves. The old hunter leaned lightly against a shell-bark hickory. His face under his broad hat-brim was a noble bronze mask fringed with silver hair. Under his arm he carried the long-barreled Kentucky rifle. He was tossing a silver half-dollar in his hand. Through his mind drifted the memories, gold and crimson. Long memories of Rebecca and Squire and Jamie Boone lingered and touched hands and drifted on. Kentucky was a pageant of leaf memories. The figures of Clark of Vincennes and Robertson of Watauga, Nolichucky Jack and Simon Kenton rode down the years, tough-fibered men of action who had been gallant companions. The solemn chieftains—his Shawnee father, Black Fish, and his friend, Logan, Cornstalk and Dragging Canoe, standing by the council fires—rose up out of the past. They had fought it out man to man. They had been great enemies and he, too, was a disinherited son of Kentucky.

He had sold the heavy bales of thick beaver skins for nine dollars apiece and with a fat bag of carefully-guarded silver dollars he had sought out old friends who had lent him money and forgotten, or merchants who had advanced him supplies for which he had never turned in barter or skins. Warm Kentucky hearts glowed to see the old man again. And he paid over the counter every dollar asked on past accounts. He said: "No one can say when I am gone that Boone was a dishonest man."

He was square with Kentucky, Kentucky for which he had given so much and taken so little, and he still had four bits. He felt rather rich. The rambunctious American eagle on the half-dollar gleamed in the late sunlight as he tossed it in the air.

He hummed the old tune that he used to sing in the Kentucky canebrakes.

He whistled to the brown hound and shouldered his long rifle. He would go back to Missouri now. His grandchildren would be waiting for him, waiting to swarm into his lap or to lie on their stomachs on the floor and gaze at the burning hickory logs as he told them the old stories. He would tell them about Black Fish, his Indian father, and how he lived when he was captured by the Shawnees and they made him into an Indian and washed his white blood away in the smoky huts of Chillicothe. They would laugh and say that he was still an Indian.

He had written a memorial to Congress telling them how it had been in the old days and what he had done for Kentucky. He explained how the Spanish Commandant De Lassus had said he wouldn't need the papers signed in New Orleans in order to hold his Spanish lands in Missouri. He should be allowed the lands by the American government. The memorial had got to Washington after a time and the committees had investigated and considered and recommended. So by an Act of Congress the government in Washington put it down on paper that the land which the Spanish government in Missouri had given him was really his after all. They said it was the right thing to do because "it was unjust as it was impolitic that useful enterprise and eminent services should go unrewarded." He didn't understand what that meant about its being "impolitic," but he remembered that his friend Mr. Henderson had been given four hundred thousand acres for his eminent services in getting Daniel Boone to build the Wilderness Road. So he figured that everybody was square.

It didn't much matter anyhow, now that Rebecca had gone on to the Promised Land. But that would be all right, too, for he would be going to get her soon. It would be just as when he had always come back from the wilderness and she would be waiting in the cabin door. They would be moving on together into the happy valleys.

He roused himself and went to the fire where he was roasting a venison steak on the ramrod of his gun. Some friends were coming and he rose to greet them. "Mr. Harding, the painter, has come all the way from St. Louis to take your likeness," they explained. He didn't quite know what it was all about. The next day the young man came and asked him to sit very still while he painted his picture on oil-cloth. So he sat and talked of old memories and answered the young

man's foolish questions. Had he ever been lost? He, Daniel Boone, lost! He thought back a while, shook his head, and said very slowly: "No, but I was right bewildered once for three days."

They were laying the corner-stone of a brand new state in St. Louis in September 1820. The Constitutional Convention was meeting in St. Louis to build a great new state for democracy right in the middle of the continent of America. When the news came that the mighty hunter had gone beyond the borders, beyond the ranges, the Constitutional Convention adjourned that day to remember Boone—of Missouri, of Kentucky, of Carolina, of Virginia and Pennsylvania. Boone—Trail-breaker for destiny for a free people marching on.

So they took a day off for remembrance about humble, great-hearted men whose lives were a strong invisible substance for enduring corner-stones for these United States of America.

from AWAY GOES SALLY

Elizabeth Coatsworth

Elizabeth Coatsworth is a versatile author. Many of her lovely poems, some of which are reprinted in Time for Poetry, *are tucked away between the chapters of* Away Goes Sally *and other books. Her fanciful tale,* The Cat Who Went to Heaven, *won the Newbery award. Whether she writes prose or poetry, she writes with rare distinction.* Away Goes Sally *is the first of a series of historical stories about Sally. Sally's uncles, Joseph and Eben, wanted to move the whole family to Maine, but her Aunt Nannie vowed "I will never leave my own fire nor sleep in any but my own bed." Sally and her young Aunt Esther were as disappointed as the uncles. They gave in, but not Uncle Joseph.*

Aunt Nannie's House

They drove home quickly. When Dorcas stopped at the back door it was still light, but there was no sign of the uncles, or of Jehoshaphat Mountain. Then, as Sally started to take the mare to the barn, she was stopped by several voices coming down the wood-road, men's voices gee-hawing oxen, and the screech of heavy runners on snow. The three aunts paused on the doorstep and Sally jumped from the sleigh to watch, as out of the darkness of the last pine thicket appeared the strangest thing she had ever seen. First came Peacock, Uncle Joseph's big horse, with Uncle Joseph on his back, and then six yoke of oxen, led by the red pair from their own farm, treading through the heavy snow in a slow procession of swaying heads and thick necks. Beside them walked Uncle Eben and Jehoshaphat Mountain with long poles, and behind them—wonder of wonders!—came a little house on runners, a house with windows whose small panes sparkled in the late light, with a doorstep, and a water-barrel under the

drip of the roof, and a chimney pipe from which smoke was actually rising.

Sally jumped up and down, clapping her mittened hands, Aunt Esther uttered a cry of delight, and Uncle Joseph stood up in his stirrups and waved. But Aunt Nannie made no motion, and uttered no sound.

Slowly the line drew to the step and stopped.

"Nannie," said Uncle Joseph in a solemn voice, "here is a house I have built for you and which I give you with all my heart, so that you may travel to the district of Maine and yet never leave your own fire."

He paused and they all waited, Peacock pawing the snow.

But Aunt Nannie's face was still blank with surprise, and did not show her thoughts. She felt behind her for the door to support herself, and once she tried to speak but could not. In the long silence Sally heard her own heart pounding like a colt galloping over a frozen meadow.

"Thank you, Brother Joseph," said Aunt Nannie at last in a small gentle voice, "thank you, my dear, I shall go willingly."

Sally let her breath out in a gasp of joy, and Uncle Joseph jumped from the saddle and kissed Aunt Nannie, who cried a little, mostly from relief because he had made it easy for her to give in and yet keep her word.

"Dorcas will take herself to the barn, Sally," Uncle Joseph called. "Come and see Aunt Nannie's house," and they all crowded in together. It was small, of course, but bright with windows, and warm with the Franklin stove which had a little fire burning in it. Two big beds stood in two corners of the room, covered with the blue eagle woven quilts. There was a smooth wooden sink and several chairs, and china in racks on the walls. Behind the larger room was a small room with two bunks in it for the uncles.

"There will be sleds for the rest of the furniture, Nannie," went on Uncle Joseph. "I have hired some men and their teams from down the road. You will, I imagine, wish to take our own cows, and Dorcas and the sleigh will bring up the rear, so that you may all take an airing when you grow tired of being in the house. And here, Deborah, are your seeds for a new garden, and we will carry some of your bulbs and roots on the sleds."

"And Aunt Esther will be a bride before the leaves turn yellow in Tuggie Noyes' woods!" cried Sally.

"Sally!" protested Aunt Esther laughing a little.

"I may come back and fetch someone to take your place, if it's not too much trouble," said Uncle Eben.

"Eliza is worth a good deal more trouble than that, Brother Sit-by-the-fire!" exclaimed Aunt Esther indignantly.

"How soon do we flit, Brother Joseph?" Aunt Nannie asked as she hung up her cloak on a peg and seated herself in her own chair, taking out her go-abroad sewing which she had brought back with her from Great-aunt Colman's.

"It's a picture to see you," said Uncle Joseph, smiling at her. They looked at each other and made their peace without a word being spoken. "I wanted this to be a surprise for you like the doll's house I made when you were a little girl. That's why I packed you all off to Quincy to have you out of the way while we furnished the house. But you asked when we would leave, Nannie. In a week, if you can be ready, my dear, so that we may have the advantage of the snow. The neighbors will help you."

"It doesn't matter what else you take," said Uncle Eben, "so long as you have plenty of meat-pies and apple-pies, baked beans, doughnuts, chocolate cake, pound cake, roasted chickens, hams——"

"Here, here," said Aunt Deborah, affectionately putting a hand across his lips, "you must not sound so greedy, Brother." She took her hand quickly away, for he had nipped it.

"Only a nibble," he joked her. "I've always said you had a sweet hand, Debby."

Meantime Jehoshaphat Mountain had been unyoking the oxen and taking them yoke by yoke to their quarters in the barn.

"I've been building the house for weeks in the wood lot," went on Uncle Joseph. " 'Twill be a good way to carry our goods and ourselves without having to put up at the ordinaries, which they say are sometimes poor and dirty. And when we reach our land we shall have this to live in until we can build better. A new home, Nannie, on wider acres."

It was Sally who discovered the six little pots steaming in the rack that had been made for them on the stove. Uncle Eben, always ready to help in any matter of food, showed Sally where a pine table let down from the wall. She found the cloth and silver spoons and a jar of cookies, and soon six cups were filled, Uncle Joseph's with coffee, Uncle Eben's with chocolate, Aunt Nannie's with old Hyson, Aunt Deborah's with new Hyson, Aunt Esther's with Souchong, and Sally's with milk and chocolate. And so they shared their first meal in the house that was to carry them to a new land.

The Start

Uncle Joseph rode Peacock to the head of the procession, a dark figure in the early dawn. The men shouted, the oxen strained, and the little house shivered, then jerked forward with a screeching of runners, and the long journey was begun.

"They're off!" shouted Captain Dagget, waving his red muffler.

"They're off!" cried old Mrs. Captain Dagget, her white kerchief thrashing up and down in her mittened hand.

"Hip, hip, hurrah!" piped little John Hale from Sweet Brook Farm, running beside the oxen, waving his stocking cap.

"Good-bye, good-bye! Write me, my dearest Esther!" called Mrs. Caleb, beginning to cry.

All the neighbors were gathered at the doorstep to see them go, although the sun had not yet fully risen, and the snow seemed dark and grave against the pale yellow sky.

Sally stood in the doorway of the little house in her red cloak, with her aunts behind her. She could see the broad strong backs of the twelve oxen straining as they started on their road, and beyond them rose the farmhouse, the only home she had ever known. It looked so low and strong, with its wide chimney and a dark sparkle on the little panes of glass in the windows, and their friends standing on the doorstep! Her cheeks stung with cold and tears, and she felt suddenly a great hollow inside her. Then they came to the road and Uncle Joseph turned in his saddle and waved to her. Peacock was pulling at the bit, prancing, impatient to be off.

"To Maine!" called Uncle Joseph, making a gesture northward. "To Maine!"

The oxen quickened their pace on the beaten highway. Jehoshaphat Mountain shouted cheerfully at them. The sunlight caught the tops of the trees and the church weathervane in the distance. Sally heard a cow low behind her and knew it was old Brindle.

"We're off! We're off!" she thought, her mind turning to the future. "At last, we're off!"

"Come in, child, and shut the door," said Aunt Nannie, and Sally came in. Did ever a little girl go traveling like this before, in a doll's house on runners, seeing everything go by! She hung up her cloak and sat looking out of one of the little windows, watching how astonished people looked at seeing them. Whenever she waved, she did it stiffly, and she pretended she couldn't move her head at all.

"What *is* the matter, Sally?" asked Aunt Deborah, looking up from her sewing. "Have you caught rheumatism, child?"

"No, I'm being a doll," said Sally. "We're all dolls and this is our home."

Aunt Esther jumped up and did a doll's dance. Her eyes were shining, her curls bobbed up and down. Even Aunt Nannie smiled above the stocking she was knitting.

"Now, have we forgotten anything?" asked Aunt Deborah. "Where's Dinah's basket?"

Dinah was the black cat. She was shiny black all over, except for her paws and a star in the hollow of her throat, and a little white chin that always made her look as though she had just been drinking milk.

"Dinah, Dinah," called Sally.

"Mew," said Dinah, answering dismally from under one of the big beds.

Sally got down on her knees and pulled out the covered basket in which Dinah was imprisoned. When she took the cover off, Dinah jumped out, but she paid no attention to any of her mistresses. Round and round the room she went, with her nose extended, smelling everything, her tail stiff, her ears a little flattened. She smelled the pipe from the sink, she went into the corners, she disappeared under the beds, she sniffed at the furniture. She pushed open the door into the little room and investigated that. Then when she had thoroughly looked over every inch of this new home, she exclaimed, "Prrr!," stopped looking wary, and neatly jumped onto one of the beds, in the exact spot where the sunlight from the south window met the warmth of the stove. Kneading the place for a moment with her little white paws to make sure that it was soft, she turned round once, and went to sleep, as though traveling to Maine were something she had done all her life.

"Well, I declare, Dinah," said Aunt Nannie, "you *do* know how to make yourself comfortable! I suppose with all of us cooped up here together you'd best go where you've a mind to, but once in Maine I'll thank you to keep off the beds."

Getting dinner was great fun.

"We can't all be turning round in here like a lot of tops," said Aunt Nannie. "Deborah, you and Esther sit where you are and Sally and I will get things ready."

Sally gave her aunt a grateful look. And Aunt Nannie's ear-drops jingled back at her as Aunt Nannie nodded. They both had to learn to fit their walking to the movement of the house, especially when it jerked over a rut, but soon the potatoes were poked deep into the ashes, and the little table was laid with dishes taken down from the wall. Sally hung onto the doorstep while she dipped water from the barrel outside, breaking the thin skim of ice across it. It felt good outdoors in the cold, sunny air with the oxen pulling solemnly at their yokes and Peacock settled down to a slow walk, and the caw of a crow and the creak of snow for sound. Sally jumped down and ran along beside Jehoshaphat Mountain. An ox rolled his eyes at her, and she put her hand on his spotted white shoulder. It felt warm and muscular to her touch.

At noon they pulled the house to one side of the road, and all the horses and cattle were given feed. The hired men built a fire and ate around it, but Uncle Joseph and Uncle Eben had their dinner in the little house.

"There's no room for me at the table," said Uncle Eben, "but I know where the warmest place in the room is. Scat, Dinah!" And he made himself comfortable where she had been. Dinah blinked her yellow eyes at him, stood up, stretched one leg after another, yawned so that her pink tongue showed stiff and curly, and then lay down again out of his way farther up on the bed.

"Dinah and I understand each other," said

Uncle Eben, scratching her under the chin. "Don't we, Dinah?"

Dinah caught his finger between her two front paws and pretended to bite it, purring in gusts which, with her mouth open, sounded almost like growls.

"Careful, old girl," said Uncle Eben. "You must set an example of good behavior to all the cats in Maine."

That evening they stopped at a farm on the outskirts of Boston where they could find shelter for their animals in the big barn. The teamsters slept in the loft, but Sally and her family made themselves snug in the little house. It was drawn up in a barnyard, across which Sally could see the lighted kitchen windows of the farm, and the dim outlines of its roofs. A man came to see them, holding a lantern, but it was too late for visiting. By candlelight they had their supper of bread and cheese and warm milk just drawn from the cows.

"Twelve miles—a good journey for the first day," said Uncle Joseph, contentedly, after supper. "And now to bed, for we must be up early in the morning."

"Read us first the promise to Joseph, Brother Joseph," said Aunt Deborah, and Sally jumped up and brought the heavy Bible from its box and laid it on Uncle Joseph's knees. He drew the candle near and, after thumbing the pages until he found the place, read in his warm quiet voice:

"'Blessed of the Lord be his land, for the precious things of heaven, for the dew, and for the deep that coucheth beneath, and for the precious fruits brought forth by the sun, and for the precious things put forth by the moon, and for the chief things of the ancient mountains, and for the precious things of the lasting hills, and for the precious things of the earth and the fulness thereof——'"

"That is God's blessing upon farmers," said Aunt Nannie.

"It makes me feel warm inside," whispered Sally to Aunt Esther. And then when the uncles had gone into the back room, they all raced one another to bed. Aunt Nannie and Aunt Deborah shared one bed, Aunt Esther and Sally the other. It was Sally who jumped in first, and she was asleep almost as soon as the blankets were under her chin. But once in the night she woke up to find the room growing cold and Dinah beside her—the cat had jumped up and now, rubbing against her cheek before she slipped in under the clothes, she curled up against Sally's chest, her black head on the pillow beside her mistress's.

WINTER

Rachel Field

A number of Rachel Field's poems from Taxis and Toadstools *are to be found in* Time for Poetry. *They are always favorites, but* Calico Bush, *a historical novel, is one of the finest things she ever wrote. The heroine, Marguerite Ledoux, a French orphan, was bound out to Joel and Dolly Sargent. She traveled with them to a new settlement in Maine and although she loved them and shared all of their hardships without complaint, they never made her feel that she was one of them. This excerpt has about it a poignant loneliness.*

It was a fairly warm day for December and she went out with Debby to watch him split the wood. It was pleasant to see his ax come down so swift and sure each time, and sometimes when he paused to rest he would talk to her for a minute or two. The baby was so well wrapped in a woolen shawl that she looked like a brownish caterpillar with a pink nose and tufts of light hair showing at one end.

"What time of year is it now?" Marguerite asked as Ira stopped to draw his sleeve across his streaming forehead.

"Let's see," he answered going over to the post where he still made his daily notches, dividing the months by means of long horizontal strokes. "Well, I declare, if it ain't got to be the middle o' December! Yes, tomorrow's the seventeenth, time I finished that beaver cap I promised Abby."

"Is it for Christmas?" asked Marguerite.

But he shook his head. "No," he said. "Our folks don't hold with such foolishness. We went to meetin' back in Marblehead on Christmas, I recollect, but there was a Dutch boy I knew told me how they had all kinds o' doin's where he come from."

"You mean, it will be no different from other days?" Marguerite's eyes grew wide with disappointment. "No carols, and no cakes, and no gifts from one to another?"

"I guess that's about right," he told her and went on with the chopping.

If Ira gave her no encouragement in Christmas festivities she knew it would be useless to expect more of Dolly and Joel Sargent. She tried to put the thought from her mind, but as each day came bringing it nearer she found herself remembering more and more the happy preparations for it she had helped to make at home. She dreamed of the Christmas cakes Grand'mère had always baked with such pride, of the seeded raisins and the picked nut-meats stirred ceremoniously in the rich batter. And then there were the carols, with the Sisters in the convent beating time and making sure that not a single "Noël" was left out when all their pupils' voices were lifted together. She tried to tell the children of the tiny carved statues of the Virgin and Joseph and the little Christ Child in the manger, with cattle and sheep and shepherds all painted as perfectly as life, that were brought out on Christmas Eve in the candle-lit chapel. Unfortunately Dolly had overheard part of this recital and had chided her roundly.

"I'll thank you to keep your Popishness to yourself," she had told her. "We may be in too Godforsaken a spot for a meetin' house, but that's no reason to put ideas in the children's heads."

And so it came to be Christmas Eve in the log cabin on Sargents' point with no smell of spice cakes, or incense, or candles, and none to feel the lack of them but Marguerite Ledoux.

She had been out to the post herself that noon, counting the month's notchings to be sure. There could be no doubt—tomorrow would make twenty-five. She would not have missed the holiday preparations so much, she thought, if she might have gone over to see Aunt Hepsa; but she knew there was no chance of this with such a high sea running and snow left in patches from last week's fall. It was rare, Joel had said, to have much fall near the sea. A bad winter ahead, Seth Jordan had predicted, and it looked as if he were right. Frost had covered the little

square panes of glass with such feathery patternings, it required much breathing and scratching to make even a little hole to see out. Marguerite was tired of doing this. The room was almost dark, but she knew that outside there was still half an hour or so left of twilight. She went over to the pegs behind the door and took down the brown cloak and hood.

"What are you doin'?" Dolly asked her as she had her hand on the door.

"I'm—I want to bring more cones," she hazarded, grasping at the first idea that came into her head. "There are not so many left in the basket."

"Well, all right, then," Dolly told her, "only don't fetch in the wet ones that make the fire smoke. Pick 'em from underneath. No, Jacob," she added at a question from the child, "you can't go along—it's too cold."

Marguerite buckled on the shoes Aunt Hepsa had given her, tied on her cloak, and went out basket in hand. Once she shut the door behind her some of the depression which had weighed upon her spirit all day left her. It was impossible to feel so sad out in the snow with the pointed trees and all their shiny dark-green needles. They smelled of Christmas to her. There had been branches of evergreen in the chapel sometimes. Perhaps if she hunted at the edge of the tall woods behind the spring she might find some red partridge berries to bring back to the children. It was bad luck if you gave nothing on Christmas, and they need not know the reason for such a gift.

As she turned into the wood path behind the house she looked across the water to Sunday Island. White places showed on the cleared field round the Jordan house where the snow remained, and the trees above it on the upper pasture where she and Aunt Hepsa had gathered bayberry looked more dark and bristling than ever in the winter twilight. She was glad that a curl of smoke rose from the chimney. Aunt Hepsa must be cooking supper, she told herself, and she paused to send her a Christmas wish across the water.

"I wonder if she's begun her new quilt yet?" she thought as she struck into the wood path. "She had the indigo dye Ethan brought her all ready to make a blue pot."

There were no red berries under the snow in the clearing by the spring where she had hoped to find them, so she went on farther along the blazed trail. It was very still there, with only a light wind stirring the spruce and fir boughs overhead. The light stayed longer there than she had expected, for the snow helped prolong the winter afternoon. Sometimes she stooped to gather cones, taking care to shake off the snow as Dolly Sargent had bidden her. The cold was intense, but her blood was quick and the old homespun cloak and hood enveloped her warmly. There was no sound except her footfalls in the snow. A sudden impulse came upon her to sing one of the carols which she knew the Sisters in the convent must even then be teaching other voices to raise.

She set down the half-filled basket of cones, folded her hands piously under the cloak, and began the first simple little chant that she had ever learned.

"Noël—Noël—Noël!"

Her own voice startled her in the stillness. Then at the sound of the familiar words she grew confident and began the one that had been Grand'mère's favorite because she also had sung it when she was a girl in the little village where she had lived.

> "J'entends le ciel retentir
> Des cantiques des Saints Anges,
> Et la terre tressaillir
> Des transports de leurs louanges.
> C'est l'Oinct qui devoit venir,
> Il est déjà dans ses langes.
> Miracle! prodige nouveau,
> Le fils de Dieu dans le berceau!
> Mais plus grand prodige encore,
> Ce grand Roi, que le ciel adore,
> Doit expirer sur un poteau.
> Noël! Noël! Noël!"[1]

[1] This old carol may be freely rendered as follows:—
> I hear the heavens resound
> To such angelic song
> That trembling stirs the ground,
> While rolls the news along—
> The Heavenly Child is found,
> To Whom all praise belong.
> Oh! wondrous miracle,
> A God in his cradle!
> Yet must we wonder more,
> This King the heavens adore
> Must die upon a cross.

As she sang there in the deepening twilight, she felt strangely comforted. The French words that had lain so long forgotten welled up out of her mind as easily as if she had been with the Sisters in the candle-lit chapel and not alone these thousands of miles away in a snowy wood.

"Noël! Noël!" she cried once more to the ranks of spruces, and then as she turned to retrace her steps something dark and swift moved towards her from behind a tree trunk.

There was not time enough to run away. The words were hardly cool on her lips before he stood beside her—a tall Indian in skins, with a musket that went oddly with his fringes and bright feathers. So silently did he come that not a twig snapped under his foot. He seemed not to dent the snow as he moved over it. His eyes showed bright in the copper of his skin, and a deep scar ran crookedly across one cheek. He came so close that she saw it plainly, and yet she could not move so much as an inch. Her feet seemed rooted in the snow, and if her heart continued to beat, she could not feel it. For what seemed like ages he continued to regard her fixedly with his black, unblinking eyes, while she waited for him to seize the tomahawk from his belt and make an end of her. But he did not move to do so. Instead, his lips parted in a queer smile.

"Noël!" he said, pronouncing the word carefully in a deep, guttural voice. "Noël!"

Marguerite felt her heart begin to beat again, though her knees were still numb and she continued to stare at him incredulously. Surely this must be a miracle, more extraordinary than any bestowed on Saint Catherine or Saint Elizabeth! A savage had come out of the woods to greet her in her own tongue on Christmas Eve! She forced herself to smile back and answer him.

His words were meager and hard to catch, but she made out from them and his signs that he had lived with the French in Quebec. He was bound there now, or so she guessed from his pointing finger. She could not tell how many of her words he understood, but whenever she said "Noël" his eyes would brighten with recognition and he would repeat it after her. "Les Pères Gris," he told her, had cured him. He touched the scar as he spoke and crossed his two lean forefingers to make a cross.

It was almost dark now; only a faint light lingered between the spruces. Pumpkin barked in the distance and Marguerite knew she must hurry back lest they grow alarmed. What would they think, Joel and Dolly Sargent and the rest, if they should come upon her there in the woods holding converse with an Indian? Prompted by an impulse she pulled the cord out from under her dress and jerked off Oncle Pierre's gilt button. It glittered in her hand as she held it out to the tall figure before her.

"Pour un souvenir de Noël," she said as she laid it in his hand before she turned and sped off towards the clearing.

Her heart was still pounding as she came out of the woods and in sight of the log house. Pumpkin bounded to meet her as she paused to put back the cord and its only remaining treasure. She had not thought to make such a Christmas gift, but surely she could not have done less. She could not but feel that somehow it was a fortunate sign, this strange meeting. Perhaps Le Bon Dieu had Himself arranged it that she might be less lonely on Christmas Eve. But she knew there must not be a word of it to the rest. She would never be able to make them understand what she scarcely understood herself. As for Caleb, she could well guess what he would say and that he would think ill of her ever after.

Dolly Sargent scolded her roundly for staying away so long.

"I declare you deserve a beatin'," she told her hotly, "strayin' so far at this time o' night. I vow Debby's got more sense 'n you show sometimes."

There was no mention made of Christmas next day save that Joel asked a lengthier blessing over their breakfast cornmeal than was usual with him. But Marguerite no longer minded. Had she not had her miracle the night before?

from RIVER OF THE WOLVES

Stephen W. Meader

Every book Stephen Meader has written is a thriller, and River of the Wolves *is one of the best. It shows the results of the careful historical research which goes into Mr. Meader's historical stories and accounts for their convincing realism.*

This excerpt begins after Dave has been captured by a band of marauding Indians who massacred his relatives and took their scalps. Yet in the hard days that followed, Dave shared the work of the march in good spirit and began to feel some liking for his captors, especially Nequanis, whose prisoner he was. The results of Dave's behavior are evident in this chapter. You will want to read the book to find out whether or not Dave remains in captivity.

[*Captured by the Abenaki*]

The southwest wind held, and when the tide turned, just before sunset, the canoes put out once more. They paddled until late in the evening and covered another ten or fifteen miles before they camped.

It was not yet dawn when Nequanis shook Dave awake. "We go soon," he told the white boy. "When the sun rises the water will run toward the sea."

Dave built a fire and Nequanis made johnnycakes of corn meal, which he baked on a flat stone, heated in the coals. Matawassie meanwhile had caught several small fish, of a kind unfamiliar to Dave, and they had a more elaborate breakfast than usual.

There was hardly any breeze when they got into the canoes, but the tide was past the flood and they were soon driving along at four or five miles an hour. More wooded islands appeared to the north. Every few miles there was a glimpse of low, white houses on the mainland shore.

From one of these French villages, late in the morning, they saw two big canoes shoot out. There were four men in each, paddling hard and singing lustily as they skimmed along. They passed within a hundred yards, heading northward toward a gap between two islands. Dave could not understand the words of their song, but the rollicking lilt of it and the bright colors of their costumes gave him a feeling of excitement and adventure.

Their blanket-cloth shirts were vivid blue, and they wore red sashes and red knitted caps with tassels that swung rakishly at the side. Their canoes were loaded deep with provisions and duffel.

"They are what the French call 'hivernants,'" Nequanis explained. "Winterers. They go now to a place far up the Saguenay to trap and trade for furs. They will stay there many moons, until the snow melts and the ice goes out of the rivers."

At noon the Indian party went ashore again to wait for a favoring tide. Later, as before, they went on through the evening and put a long stretch of river behind them. Dave thought they must have come eighty or ninety miles in the two days since they left the Chaudière.

The third morning dawned bleak and cloudy, with a northerly wind that made paddling difficult. Even with the tide to help them, they were constantly buffeted by waves that slopped over the port gunwale and threatened to swing the bow off course.

It was grim work, but Dave could sense the same eagerness in the Indians' paddling that he had noticed when they approached the Co-hos intervales. Every mile they gained was bringing them nearer to their home lodges.

That night around the campfire the young braves spent hours daubing their faces with fresh paint, applied with painstaking care. The sober concentration they gave to this task made Dave smile. He was reminded of his older sister Jane, primping for a party. But at the same time he was sure now that they must be close to the River of the Wolves.

When morning came it was fair and still, a perfect early fall day. Reckoning back on his fingers, Dave decided it must be either the last day of August or the first of September, though he could not be sure which.

They got off to an early start and paddled fast with a helping tide. Young Matawassie was humming happily as he swung his blade—a long, tuneless Abenaki chant.

It was just noon when Nequanis gave a whoop of triumph and heaved on the steering paddle, turning the bow toward the wooded shore. In a few minutes they had rounded a point, shaggy with pines and spruces, and were moving up the channel of a narrow, swift-flowing river.

The Indian town was four miles inland from the mouth of the stream. Dave's first glimpse of it came as a surprise, for he had imagined something wilder and more picturesque. Clustered along the bank in a clearing were some thirty houses—not wigwams but square-built huts of logs and poles, chinked with moss and roofed with bark. They stood at various angles instead of lined up along a street, as they would have been in a New England village. At one end of the group of buildings, and a little apart, was a tiny log church with a white cross on top.

As soon as they were within sight of the town, Cochequa lifted his musket and fired it into the air. At the echoing report dogs began to bark and a dozen squaws, a swarm of children and a few old men came running to the bank.

They waded into the water, seizing the gunwales of the canoes in the eagerness of their welcome and chattering like a flock of blackbirds in cherry time.

Dave was dragged bodily out on the bank and hustled up the steep slope. He found himself standing with the other prisoners in a wide cleared space in the middle of the village. It was a kind of town square, irregular in shape and trampled almost as hard as a brick pavement. After the Indians had satisfied their first curiosity as to the white captives, they turned to the warriors and began asking questions.

Dave had a chance to look around him. The houses were less impressive, seen from this level. They looked small and dirty and a smell of rancid grease and wood smoke came from them. There was no glass in the windows. Either they were empty black holes or covered by ragged deerskin, scraped to paper thinness and painted with crude, bright drawings of animals.

On poles in front of several of the cabins bits of hair fluttered in the breeze. They were scalps, Dave realized with a shudder—weather-worn trophies of past expeditions.

At one side of the open space a section of a log, three or four feet in diameter, stood on end, its top covered by a tight-laced piece of rawhide. It looked like a huge drum, and when the boy edged close enough to tap on its head a hollow rumbling sound came forth. He guessed then that the square had been beaten smooth by the feet of braves, doing their tribal dances to the accompaniment of the great drum.

The prisoners had been standing there for nearly half an hour when the jabber of the Indians was suddenly hushed. A figure in a long, flapping black robe was striding toward them from the direction of the chapel.

Cochequa separated himself from the crowd and turned to meet the newcomer.

"Father Pierre," he murmured, and bobbed his head respectfully.

The priest held out a thin, work-worn hand and grasped the hand of the young chief.

"We are glad to welcome you back, my son," he said in good Abenaki. "But not all of you have returned. The others—are they safe?"

"All safe," Cochequa answered. "One, only, has gone to the Happy Hunting Grounds." And he explained that some of the party had stayed in the Co-hos country to wait for the corn harvest.

Father Pierre nodded and a smile of relief passed momentarily over his pale, lined face. He came toward the little group of prisoners. Instinctively Dave felt a kind of sympathy for the gaunt, lonely man. He had never seen a pair of eyes that held such sadness.

With an effort the priest began to speak in slow, queer-sounding English.

"My cheeldren," he said. "Do not be on'appy. You weel be treat' well 'ere. You are not of my Church, but come to me eef you 'ave troubles."

He crossed himself, murmured a few words of Latin and made the sign of benediction over them. Then he turned and strode away toward the little church. The silence was broken as soon as he passed inside the door. The squaws gabbled louder than ever, talking so fast that Dave could understand only a few words here and there.

Half a dozen lean mongrel dogs wandered through the crowd, sniffing curiously at the captives. One of them, a big, tawny-colored animal that had the head and ears of a wolf, came close to Dave and stood looking up at him with intelligent amber eyes.

The boy put out his hand and touched the brute's head. At first he felt a shiver of fear go through the dog, but when his fingers began scratching behind the ears, the animal moved closer, rubbing against his knees, tongue lolling blissfully.

Dave grinned. "I guess we're going to be friends, aren't we, boy?" he said in English. "What's your name, huh? Got to have a name. I'll call you Buck. How's that? Like it, Buck?"

The dog looked pleased and took a quick lick at Dave's hand. But at that moment Matawassie pushed Buck out of the way with a careless swing of his moccasined foot.

"Come," he told the white boy. "We go to the sweat-house. Tonight, when the hunters come back there will be a feast and dancing. We must be clean."

Nequanis joined them and they went through the village to a small wigwam of bark and skins, standing close to the river bank. It was barely large enough to hold the three of them, for a big kettle filled the center of the earth floor. It was half full of water, and sprigs of pennyroyal and other herbs floated on the surface.

The two young braves stripped off their leggins and moccasins and Dave followed their example, tossing his clothes outside as they had done. A moment later he was embarrassed when the flap of the wigwam opened and two giggling squaws shouldered in. They were carrying large stones, heated at the village campfire, holding them on smoking sticks. The stones were dropped with a sizzle and a splash into the kettle and the squaws ducked out again. Dave could hear their voices outside, as they gathered up the clothing and carried it off. They were still chattering about his white skin.

Meanwhile the wigwam had filled quickly with pungent steam. He could feel the sweat starting from every pore in his body. The Indians grunted with pleasure, and in the darkness he heard them rubbing themselves and slapping their wet skin.

The steam bath lasted perhaps a quarter of an hour. Then Nequanis burst out through the entrance flap and sprinted to the top of the bank, taking off in a long, flat dive. Matawassie and Dave were close on his heels. The shock of the cold water made the white boy gasp, but he struck out strongly and felt a tingling glow shoot through his veins. It was as if the cleansing steam had drawn the sluggishness out of him and given him new vigor.

He whooped exuberantly with the Indian lads and when they swam ashore he raced them to the bank. Fresh, clean clothing was waiting for them there. Dave put on a loin-cloth, a pair of deerskin leggins and tough moose-hide moccasins that were better than the ones he had been wearing.

Around his naked upper body he wrapped his blanket, following the example of his companions.

About the time they were dressed, Bemokis and Josh Boles came out of the sweat-house. Josh was stubborn about plunging into the river. When he refused to dive, the bent-backed Indian seized him by the hair, dragged him down the bank and ducked him in the chilly water.

Josh sputtered and struggled but was finally persuaded to swim a few strokes. Nequanis watched him, scowling.

"He is a bad prisoner," the young warrior told Dave. "He will make trouble for himself."

They went up through the village, Dave feeling somewhat conspicuous in his Indian dress. But nobody paid much attention to him. The braves were squatted in the doorways of their cabins renewing their warpaint. The squaws had gone back to their work in the little corn and pumpkin patches that lay between the houses and the edge of the woods.

Nequanis and Matawassie led the way to the smallest and most dilapidated hut in the town. It was at the farther end of the row, only a few yards from the chapel and the priest's house. Dave gathered from the Indians' talk that this was one of several cabins used as bachelor quarters by the younger braves.

"You will live here with us," Nequanis told him. "You will do the squaw work—getting wood, making fires, cooking and washing. That is for now. Afterward, if you prove yourself strong and brave, perhaps the chief will let you become a hunter, as we are."

Dave took the new order of things with good grace. After all, he reflected, the chores he was expected to do were just what any white boy did in the settlements—all but the cooking, which he didn't mind. After the hard, constant labor of the journey northward, his present lot seemed an easy one.

Since he had nothing else to do while the young braves were decorating themselves, he took an ax and followed the path into the forest. In an hour he had cut up half a dozen dead trees and brought back the wood to stack behind the cabin. Then he started to build a fire, but Nequanis told him it was not needed.

"There will be a big campfire tonight," said the Indian, "and much eating. Our chief, Maranoquid, the father of Cochequa, has been on a hunt with the other men of the town. Soon they will come back with meat. If they have made a good kill, some of the meat will be smoked and dried for winter. But there will be enough left over for a feast."

It was about two hours before sunset when a high-pitched Indian war whoop came from the river above the town. The dogs began barking furiously and everybody in the village hurried toward the landing.

Dave saw six canoes coming swiftly downstream. There were four Indians in each one, and they shouted, waved their paddles and pointed to the carcasses of deer and moose that loaded the birch-bark craft deep in the water.

The first man ashore was a stalwart six-foot redskin with mighty shoulders. He wore three eagle feathers in his scalplock, and a long necklace of bears' claws about his neck. Dave did not have to be told that this was Maranoquid, the chief.

Neither the older man nor Cochequa, his son, gave any special sign of joy as they greeted each other. Each had the grave and courteous manner expected of a leader. Maranoquid asked no questions about the war party, nor did Cochequa inquire as to the success of the hunt. Indeed, no one would have needed to ask. The heavily loaded canoes spoke for themselves.

The braves carried the bodies of four deer, a moose, a black bear and some smaller game to the top of the bank, where the squaws immediately set to work with their skinning knives. No rules of behavior governed their tongues and they kept up a running fire of talk and laughter while they ripped the hides off the animals and cut up the meat. The hearts, livers, tongues and other Indian delicacies were put in one pile for immediate cooking. The tougher parts of the carcasses were saved for winter food. But nothing seemed to be wasted. The sinews and intestines—even the hoofs and claws—were carefully removed. Dave knew that they would be used later for stitching clothes, making bowstrings, bags and ornaments.

He went back to the cabin where Nequanis and Matawassie were waiting. They sat cross-legged, wearing such finery as they owned and looking proud and satisfied. The bright new stripes of pigment on their faces made them extra hideous—extra handsome, Dave supposed, to Indian eyes.

"When the feast starts," Nequanis told him soberly, "if you are wise you will not eat too much. You may have to do some running afterwards, and it will be better for you if you can run fast."

The young brave glanced at Matawassie, and Dave thought he caught the flicker of a grin under the streaks of paint.

As darkness crept over the town the great drum began to beat. Dave heard the throb of it and looked out to see what was happening. A dozen squaws were busy around a big cook-fire, stirring kettles and roasting meat on spits. Beyond the immediate circle of light made by the fire, everything looked unreal and shadowy, but an occasional gleam fell on the drum and the strange figure standing behind it. Dave made out the shape of a man, his face painted with weird vertical stripes of yellow. Above his eyes was the grinning head of a wolf, the long white teeth glittering wickedly when the firelight touched them. The wolfskin hung over the man's shoulders but his bare arms moved up and down in rhythm as he struck the taut hide with the flat of his hands.

"That," Nequanis said, from the darkness at Dave's elbow, "is the M'teoulin—the medicine man. He is very old and very wise, and familiar with all the spirits."

The throb of the drum quickened and grew louder. One by one the warriors came out of their houses and went toward the fire. When Maranoquid, the chief, arrived, he dipped his hand in the huge stew kettle, drew out a piece of meat and began eating it. After that they all fell to without further ceremony.

Mindful of Nequanis' advice, Dave did not gorge himself, good as the food tasted. He tried to warn Josh Boles, who was stuffing himself with fat chunks of bear and raccoon meat, but the other boy merely scowled and ate faster.

For nearly an hour the feast went on. At last, when the braves were full almost to bursting, they seated themselves in a circle around the fire and the chief lighted a stone pipe. The pungent

smoke of tobacco and kinnikinnick drifted in a wreath above his eagle crest. When he had taken two or three puffs he passed the pipe to Cochequa and it went on around the circle.

The squaws and the prisoners sat in an outer ring, and still farther from the fire the dogs sniffed and trotted back and forth, scavenging for scraps. Father Pierre was not there. A beam of candlelight, coming from the window of the little church, showed where he knelt at his prayers. The medicine man, on the other hand, was much in evidence. He had left the drum when the feasting began and now he strutted about near the fire, calling on various spirits, gesturing with his skinny arms and doing small feats of magic. He would hold a birch twig in one hand, make a pass over it and cause it to disappear. Dave was not impressed, for he had seen more than one white man who was better at such tricks than the old Indian.

After a while Maranoquid rose and began to speak in the measured sing-song cadence that was typical of the Abenaki ceremonial language. As his deep voice rolled out the sentences, Dave realized it was a kind of poetry.

The chief described the hunt in detail, telling how they had gone up the river; how the first deer had been sighted by such-and-such a warrior; how so-and-so had fired and missed because Lox, the evil one, had turned the bullet in midair. The tale ran on and on till all the game was accounted for and loaded in the canoes.

When Maranoquid finished he turned politely to his son and asked for an account of the war party's experiences.

Cochequa was not the orator his father was, but he spoke well. Dave heard for the first time that the raiding band had attacked two other small settlements near the Connecticut before they reached the Contoocook. As each incident was told, the proper scalp or prisoner was trotted out for inspection. The young chief was fairly modest about his own deeds, but he played up the exploits of Bemokis, making the Indian with the twisted back the principal hero of the expedition.

When Cochequa held up the red scalp and told the story of the looting and burning of the Foster farm, Dave had to hold himself tense to keep from shaking. Then the chief's son turned in his direction and he was seized and led into the circle by his two young captors. He walked stiffly, his back straight and his lips tight. Several of the older warriors grunted their approval of Nequanis and Matawassie for taking him prisoner, and he felt the whole ring of beady eyes centered on him for a long moment. Then he was hustled out again and the narrative continued.

It was now well along toward midnight and there was a chill in the air. The fire had been kept up, but it gave little warmth beyond the inner circle of braves. The squaws and prisoners wrapped their blankets tightly around them and sat shivering while Cochequa was winding up his oration.

The older chief rose, when his son had finished, and complimented all the members of the party on their courage and skill. Then shorter speeches were made by Bemokis and some of the other veteran warriors. And finally the M'teoulin pronounced a few incantations, whirled about in a fantastic dance and appeared to vanish in a puff of smoke.

Dave stared at the place where the sorcerer had stood. Most of the Indians seemed as mystified as he was, but the older braves chuckled and applauded. After a moment the big drum, back in the darkness, began to rumble. Peering behind him, Dave was not surprised to see the wolf mask of the medicine man bobbing above the drumhead.

As the throb of the beat grew faster, the young bucks leaped up and began to prance. Bending from the waist and throwing their knees high, they picked up the rhythm of the drum with their pounding moccasins. One by one other warriors jumped to their feet, until only Chief Maranoquid and a dozen of the more venerable men were left seated.

The booming of the drum quickened in tempo, and the dancing grew wilder as the young braves shouted hoarsely and flung their arms above their heads. Dave caught the fierce excitement. He felt his blood beat faster, in time with the drum's thunder. At the climax, he even wished he could get up there and join in the dance.

At last the warriors had enough. Panting, their copper bodies glistening with sweat, they flung themselves down on their blankets. The pipe went around the circle again. When it reached Bemokis he got to his feet and pointed the reed stem toward the prisoners. Dave could not hear clearly what he said, for his words were drowned out by gleeful whoops and cheers.

All the younger braves sprang up and ran toward their houses. When they came back, each one was carrying a kind of flattened club, three or four feet long.

Dave caught his breath. He understood now what Nequanis had been talking about before the feast. The prisoners—or at least Josh Boles and he—were going to have to run the gantlet!

Ever since he was a child he had heard tales of how the Indians put their male captives to this form of torture. Boys, and even grown men, had been beaten to death in the gantlet, according to stories told in the settlements. The clubs appeared brutal enough, but he could tell by the way the young men swung them that they were lighter than they looked. Probably they were made of spruce.

The braves lined up in a double row, a dozen on a side. Nequanis and Matawassie came toward Dave and another pair of Indians approached Josh Boles. The two boys had their leggins stripped off and were led toward the head of the lane of yelling braves.

Bemokis was the first Indian in line, and he brandished his long club, his cruel face grinning with anticipation. Dave, standing there shivering in his breechclout, set his teeth and waited. Bemokis pointed at him.

"Let that one run first!" he shouted, and the others greeted his words with a cheer.

Dave felt himself pushed forward. A sudden desperate resolve took form in his head. He had been afraid, but now his fear was gone in a surge of bright anger. He started running at top speed. Then, just as he flashed abreast of Bemokis, he swerved straight at him.

The Indian with the twisted back had both arms lifted high, ready to strike a mighty blow. Dave's shoulder caught him squarely in the stomach and doubled him up with his wind knocked out. The boy was lucky then. As the club flew out of Bemokis' fingers he caught it in mid-air. It felt good in his hands—smooth, well-balanced, heavy enough to do damage if it landed in the right places. He whirled the club around his head, parried a glancing blow from the Indian across the way and struck savagely at the next brave in line. Then he raced down the alley, whaling away to right and left as he ran.

He was hit solidly half a dozen times before he reached the other end, but he was still on his feet. Fully expecting the angry mob to follow him, he dashed on another fifty yards before he came to a panting stop. Nobody was near him. He turned and saw the whole crowd roaring and rolling on the ground with laughter.

Nequanis had left the line and was hurrying to meet him. The young Indian had a lump over one eye but he grinned broadly as he slapped Dave on the back.

"You did what I hoped you would do, my Brother," he said. "Even Bemokis must agree now that you have courage."

As they walked back the lines were forming again. The bent-backed Indian had picked up another club and was waiting in his place, crouching a little and wearing a ferocious scowl. Dave felt sorry for Josh Boles.

The stocky white boy was plainly scared. He hung back till a pair of braves caught him by the arms and threw him into the opening between the rows. Stumbling, he put up his arms to protect his head and started to run. The clubs rose and fell like flails—*thwack—thwack—thwack*—landing heavily on his back, shoulders and elbows. The poor lad fell twice but staggered up again and went on. He was blubbering like a baby when he passed the end of the line, and he dropped in a heap, blood oozing from half a dozen bruises on his body.

The Indians turned away from him contemptuously but Dave picked him up, wiped off the blood as best he could and helped him over to his blanket.

"Here," he said, "just lie still and they won't bother you any more. I'll get some water and fix you up the best I can."

Dave brought a kettle from the cabin and ran down to the river. Carrying it back full of cold water he washed Josh's head and body, then wrapped his blanket around him and left him sitting there in the shadows.

It was close to midnight now but the gathering showed no signs of breaking up. Cochequa was standing before the elders of the village, making another harangue. This time he was briefer. Dave paid little attention to what he was saying, but suddenly he saw the young chief stretch out one muscular arm and point directly at him. Nequanis, too, was beckoning. Hesitantly the boy stepped forward and in a moment he was standing inside the circle of warriors, his back to the fire.

"You have seen what this young paleface has done," Cochequa chanted. "He is strong and his heart is brave. On the trail he carried his pack and did not grow weary. In the canoes he worked hard with the paddle. He is of an age when he can be taught to hunt with the skill of an Abenaki.

"Already he speaks a little in our tongue. Our young brother, Nequanis, will vouch for him and teach him. I, Cochequa, ask that you take this white youth into kinship with our tribe."

The faces of the older Indians were as expressionless as blocks of wood. Maranoquid refilled the pipe and it went the rounds while Dave stood uncomfortably in the middle of the ring. The young chief's words had taken him completely by surprise. He felt a thrill of pride when he realized that a real compliment had been paid him, but there was no telling how the warriors would react. He wasn't even sure whether he wanted to become a member of the tribe, for he recalled all too clearly the terrible scene in his uncle's clearing.

Fifteen or twenty minutes dragged by. Then Maranoquid rose slowly and with great dignity.

"Cochequa, my son, has spoken," said he. "Our numbers are few, for many of our men have fallen in battle. If this young paleface is strong and brave, as we have seen and as Cochequa has told us, he may become a true warrior of the Abenakis."

Scattered nods and grunts came from the assembled elders. Finally Bemokis stood up.

"You know me," he said. "I have hated the English since I was a boy. I have killed many and taken many scalps. But I believe this young Bostonnais has courage. I have felt the weight of his blows on my body. I, Bemokis, say he is ready to be taken into the tribe."

Those words seemed to swing the decision. One after another the warriors voiced their approval. As the last one finished speaking, the M'teoulin stalked into the center of the ring. He lifted both thin arms and uttered a scream so sudden and so piercing that Dave leaped back, startled. Then he found Nequanis beside him, steadying him.

"Do not be afraid," the Indian boy whispered. "What comes now will make you a man and an Abenaki."

The medicine man shuffled forward, muttering mysteriously. Out of his robe he whipped a slim, shining knife, and with his other hand he seized Dave's left wrist. The white boy clamped his jaws hard to keep from shivering, for the needle-like point of the knife was poised just above his open hand.

With a quick, careful movement the M'teoulin pricked the end of Dave's middle finger. Then he turned toward Nequanis, took his left hand and went through the same performance.

Mumbling more incantations the old Indian took a drop of Dave's blood on his finger and placed it on Nequanis' tongue. In a moment Dave tasted the Indian lad's blood, warm and salt, in his own mouth.

"Say these words," the medicine man commanded. "He is my brother. I am his brother."

Together the two boys repeated the Indian words.

"At all times and in all places," the M'teoulin continued, "until the squirrel again grows greater than the bear."

"At all times and in all places," they murmured in unison, "until the squirrel again grows greater than the bear."

Dave had a queer feeling, as if he were outside his body and listening to someone else speaking. Then the sorcerer leaped into the air and gave that bloodcurdling scream, and the spell was broken.

"Welcome, Brother," said Nequanis with a grin, and threw his arms around him.

from FLAMING ARROWS

William O. Steele

There is no other writer today who can re-create pioneer life more vividly than William Steele. The particular story from which this chapter is taken is about an Indian raid and the terrifying experiences of the settlers living and fighting inside a stockade. It is also the story of two unusual boys you will not forget. For other exciting stories by this author be sure to read Wilderness Journey, Winter Danger, Tomahawks and Trouble, *and others listed in the bibliography.*

[A Calm Before the Storm]

"I reckon it's suppertime," remarked Chad, letting his ax slip to the ground. He straightened up slowly. He was bone-tired, and his back was one fierce ache. But he was proud of himself. He figured he'd never worked so hard before in all his eleven years, for he'd spent this livelong day chopping trees and had done a man's work.

"I reckon it is," his father answered. "I heared Ambrose bringing the cows up a while ago."

Mr. Rabun turned back to stripping the limbs from a felled tree. His ax rose and fell in swift regular strokes, and the branches dropped neatly away from the trunk. Chad grinned. He admired to see his father work. Things never seemed to get all of a tangle for his pappy the way they did for other folks.

At last Mr. Rabun stood up and wiped his forehead on his sleeve. He looked around at the white-topped stumps and the sprawled logs. "We done a good day's work, Chad," he said slowly. "You was a big help. Two more days and we'll have us enough new ground for a cornfield."

Chad didn't say anything, but he was pleased. He'd worked hard and tried to do everything the right way, the way his pappy had taught him to.

Mr. Rabun slipped his shot pouch and powder horn straps over his shoulder. He shouldered his ax and then picked up his rifle.

Chad too reached for his musket. He hoped his pappy hadn't noticed that he'd almost forgot his gun. He hadn't had it long, and he wasn't yet used to fetching it along every place he went. Nobody in the Cumberland settlements went out in the fields without having his gun handy. At least not more than once.

They took the short cut home, through the woods. It was almost dark among the trees, and Chad wished they'd gone around by the edge of the field instead. The leaves hung dull and dusty, for it was the middle of September, dry and hot. "Injun weather," thought Chad, and he peered into the shadows.

Suddenly Mr. Rabun stopped dead still. Chad halted too, drawing in his breath quick and tightening his hand on his musket. His father stood with his head turned, listening, his rifle half-raised before him.

"I'll shoot the first one with my musket," Chad planned. "And Pappy can get one, and while he's reloading, I can use the ax. That'll take care of three or four of 'em. And if there's more than that, I reckon we'll have to run."

And then he heard what his father was hearing, the little clucking sounds, like water purling over stones, that a flock of turkeys makes calling to each other. It wasn't Injuns after all. Chad let out his breath silently, and his eyes went here and there, trying to make out the birds.

Pretty soon he saw them, walking slowly, stretching their long skinny necks and small heads out of their big bodies to look around suspiciously, and then leaning over to peck at acorns on the ground.

Slowly, carefully, Mr. Rabun raised his rifle to his shoulder. Chad could see his father's finger tighten on the trigger and the flash in the pan when he fired. There was a great noise of gobbling and flapping wings as the flock scattered in every direction. But one turkey lay on the ground, and its wings beat wildly for a minute before it lay still.

Chad ran to pick up the dead bird. It was a gobbler, not a big one, but a young one, tender and delicious.

"Mammy'll like this," he cried as he lifted the turkey by its feet. "I heared her say just this morning she hankered for a turkey."

"Well, it was luck to find 'em," Mr. Rabun answered. "When we first come here, there was turkeys under every bush. Now here it is not but three years later, and a body don't hardly see one 'lessen he goes way off hunting for 'em."

He reloaded his rifle as he talked. "There's just one thing about shooting a turkey," he went on. "When you've shot it, don't forget to put an-other ball in your gun. I've knowed a heap of men got scalped because they got to looking at the game they'd killed and never gave a thought to reloading, and the Injuns heard the shot and sneaked up on 'em."

"You don't reckon there's Injuns around now, do you?" asked Chad.

His father looked at him soberly. "It's the Injuns you don't reckon are around that kill you, most generally," he answered. "But you remember what I say and reload every time you fire."

"Yes, sir," Chad answered solemnly. "I'll carry the turkey," he offered as they set out again. Mr. Rabun took both axes, and Chad slung the bird over his shoulder.

"You know what Amos Thompson said last summer?" Chad went on, keeping his eyes on the shadows ahead. "He said he'd seen a flock of turkeys kill a big old rattlesnake. Said they got around the rattler and took turns running and pecking at it till it was dead. Said the snake would strike at the turkeys, but it never fazed them. Do you reckon all that's really so, Pappy?"

Mr. Rabun pondered. "I've heard that tale," he answered. "I never saw any such thing, but I reckon it must be so. Amos Thompson ain't one to tell he'd seen something when he hadn't. There's some folks I wouldn't believe if'n I heared them tell a thing, for they'd be the kind of folks that might think they'd seen what they hadn't. But Amos ain't like that. If he says he seed it hisself, then he did."

Chad nodded. His pappy was always telling him not to believe everything he heard but to think things through and sift out the truth.

"You wouldn't reckon feathers would do much good when the rattler struck," Chad remarked, rubbing his cheek against the bird's soft feathers.

"You wouldn't, for a fact now," Mr. Rabun agreed. "I've seen a rattler's fangs go through stiff leather. But you study on it and you can see how it works out. Let a turkey ruffle up his feathers, and he's got a power of nothing and feathers between him and the snake. A snake's fangs ain't hardly long enough to get through, no matter how hard he strikes."

They walked on in silence, leaving the woods and stepping out into the red glow of the setting sun. The tall grass at the edge of the field brushed Chad's buckskins with a soft whisper. A bobwhite called three times as they struck out through the cornfield. It was a big field, Chad thought proudly, and there was another one this size near the creek.

Oh, his pappy was a fine farmer. In spite of the many Indian raids and having to rebuild their cabin and make new beds and tables, his father had managed to get the fields cleared and to raise a good crop. Not many in the Cumberland settlements could say as much, Chad reckoned.

They walked on between the rows of dry stalks. Chad's dog Tumbler came running to meet them, and in a few minutes they reached the cabin clearing. Ambrose was standing in the open door. "Here they come, Mammy," he called.

Chad got a whiff of the good smell of stew. He began to run, the turkey flopping on his shoulder. He hadn't known he was so hungry. And wouldn't Mammy be glad to see what he was bringing her?

Sarah met him at the door. She took the turkey and held it up. "Mammy!" she cried. "Look what Pappy shot!"

Chad frowned. She might at least have wondered if Chad hadn't shot it. After all, he'd fetched it in. The trouble with Sarah was she was *too* good at sifting out the truth, even if she was only nine. He couldn't ever fool her the way he could Mammy.

"Oh, Chad, ain't he a fine one?" exclaimed Mammy. "After supper I'll clean him and pluck him."

"Now go wash," ordered Sarah. "Milking's done with and supper's most nigh ready."

Chad yanked her pigtail. A body would think Sarah was a grown-up married lady, the way she acted. She was always bustling about, so busy and important.

After the bowls and spoons were washed, the Rabuns went outside. Chad cleaned the turkey and his mother plucked it, working quickly before the sunlight faded. Mr. Rabun stood in the clearing watching the sky for a change in the weather.

"I reckon he's keeping an eye out for Injuns, too," thought Chad, but he didn't say anything. His mammy didn't like to have them always worrying and fretting about Indians.

She had said, "It's bad enough to have the sav-ages in mind all the time without dinging away at 'em every time you open your mouth. A body can keep a lookout for Injuns and still talk about something else."

When the others had gone in, Chad stayed a few minutes longer enjoying the cool evening air. An owl flew over his head with a soft whish. Stars were coming out, and the night was clear.

"Injun weather, for sure," thought Chad, and went in.

He swung the door shut and barred it with the heavy boards. He hated doing it. It was hot and close in the cabin with the door shut and no window and the fire going. But who would be fool enough to leave a cabin door open at night and the woods full of redskins?

Mammy reached up on the fireboard for the Bible. Every night she made Chad and Sarah read a chapter out of the Book of Kings or Chronicles, for Mr. Rabun wanted all his children to be able to read and cipher well. He himself had gone to school in Pennsylvania and learned Latin and history.

Folks in the Cumberland settlements often traveled a good way to have Henry Rabun read or write a letter. He could survey too and knew some law. Oh, Chad was proud of his pappy. He wanted to be like him, so he struggled with Jehoshaphat and Moab and Elijah the Tishbite. Folks had a mighty hard time in Bible days, it seemed to him.

"I don't reckon I'll let Chad read tonight after all," said Mammy suddenly, laying down the Bible. "I want him to card. I aim to get started spinning tomorrow. Sarah's got to have a new short gown. And I had it in mind to make Pappy a new shirt."

Ambrose frowned darkly. Every year he hoped to have some new clothes, but he'd never yet had them. He got Chad's clothes, cut down from Pappy's.

Chad grinned. He never had any new clothes either, but it never bothered him the way it did Ambrose. It was a funny thing for a five-year-old to worry over.

Mr. Rabun looked up from the ax handle he was carving. "I talked to John Hart the other day about buying a ram from him," he said. "He's leaving here and going back to Virginny. Then in the spring I can get a ewe, and we'll have wool a-plenty—if'n the Injuns don't get 'em," he added in a low voice.

Mammy sighed. They'd had four sheep when they came here in 1781, but the wolves got one and the Indians killed two, and the last one died right after it was sheared. So this wool was the last the Rabuns would have till they got more sheep, unless they used buffalo wool. Chad writhed at the thought. Folks said buffalo wool itched worse than cloth made from nettles.

Chad took the wool carders his mother handed him. He hated to card. But Sarah was knitting winter stockings, and Ambrose, who was stringing shucky beans on a long thong, wasn't handy enough.

He pulled his stool up on the hearth and laid the right-hand card close to the fire to warm. He took a handful of wool and drew it across the left card till it was caught in the teeth. When the right-hand card was hot, he began to stroke the wool with it, tumming it until the wool fibers were all straight.

Mr. Rabun held his wooden handle up and inspected it by the firelight. He turned suddenly to the others and smiled.

"There was a song my pappy used to sing, about a ram from Darby or some such place," he declared. "He was so big a heap of eagles built their nests in his wool or some such foolishness as that."

Mrs. Rabun laughed. "I remember that song," she cried. "His feet was so big they covered an acre. I can recollect the tune a little."

"Sing it, Mammy," begged Chad. He edged his stool back on the hearth. He was about to melt plumb away from the heat.

Mrs. Rabun hummed a little to herself, and then shook her head. "I can call the tune to mind, but I disremember the words. They were so foolish, they wouldn't stick in anybody's head."

"I reckon it would be fine to have a sheep like that," said Sarah. "We could all have new clothes then, even Ambrose."

Ambrose yawned. "I don't reckon we could card that much wool," he spoke up sleepily.

"And it would eat a heap," went on Mr. Rabun. "Clean up a whole savanna of grass in a day, I reckon. Then you'd have to kill it, else all the pasture between here and Kentuck would be used up in a week."

"Think of the mutton pie a ram like that could make," cried Chad. "Wheee, a whole cabin full! Mammy could cook one as big as a flatboat, and we could float it down to New Orleans and sell it for a heap of hard money."

"I can't abide mutton pie," said Sarah, wrinkling her nose. "I'm sick to death of deer meat, but I'd a heap rather eat it than greasy mutton."

"And I don't aim to cook one that big either," laughed Mrs. Rabun. "Ain't no need to talk of eating mutton when we ain't got any. Well, that turkey'll make a nice change from deer," she added. "You was lucky to get it so close to the cabin."

"Change! Why, we had squirrels only last week," Chad pointed out. He had shot the squirrels his very own self.

"Oh, and they was good," Mrs. Rabun cried. "You and Pappy always keep us in meat, and we get more change than most folks. But it's been a long spell since we had turkey."

Ambrose yawned again. He had long since ceased to work. His hands lay still in his lap, and the long string of beans dangled to the floor.

Mrs. Rabun took the beans from him. "Go to bed, Brose," she said gently. "You can finish them tomorrow night."

Ambrose stumbled to his feet and climbed the ladder to the loft. They could hear him moving around for a few minutes, taking off his moccasins and breeches, feeling around in the dark for his quilt, and then he was quiet.

Mr. Rabun ran his hand along the handle to check its smoothness. "Casper Mansker says he aims to build a mill over on his creek," he told them. "Me and Brose won't have to ride clean over to Frederick Stump's for a turn of meal, if'n he does that."

"Remember when we first come here, how we had to grind our corn with a mortar?" Mrs. Rabun asked. "We was lucky to have meal at all, I reckon. But mortar-ground meal ain't nowhere's near as good as stone-ground."

She laid a piece of leather on the floor by Chad. "Put your foot on that, so I can measure," she told him. Then she cut off a portion and sat back down.

Suddenly she dropped the buckskin and half-rose from the stool. "Listen, somebody's outside," she gasped.

Sarah looked up in fear. Mr. Rabun moved quickly toward his rifle.

"Naw," answered Chad. "It's just Tumbler scratching. He hits the wall with his legs."

Mrs. Rabun settled back to her work with a relieved sigh. "I declare I wish I wasn't so nervous about noises," she remarked. She picked up the awl by its horn handle and began to punch holes in the cut leather.

Mr. Rabun checked the powder in his rifle pan, and he too sat back down.

A stillness settled over the cabin. Chad could hear the fire crackle and hiss and the soft sound of the awl in the leather. Sarah put down her knitting and climbed to the loft. Chad watched her with eyes misted with sleep. He reckoned he wasn't going to keep awake much longer. But he kept on working the steel teeth of the card again and again through the wool.

At last Mrs. Rabun folded the deerskin shoes and laid them on a shelf. "Well, you most nigh finished all the wool, Chad," she told him, looking with pleasure at the long slender rolls he had carded. "I'll start spinning in the morning."

She took the two cards and placed them beside the half-finished moccasins. "Ain't it been nice this evening?" she went on. "We ain't talked one single time about Injuns or raids or scalping."

"Maybe not," answered Mr. Rabun gravely. "But I hope you ain't forgot about 'em. They've not bothered us folks north of the Cumberland River very much this summer." He stood the ax helve in the corner. "They're due to give us serious trouble soon, though. And we got to keep our eyes and ears open."

Chad, stooping to put another log on the fire, reckoned that was all Cumberland folks had done since they arrived here, keep their eyes and ears open for Chickamauga Indians. The raids had got so bad a couple of years ago that many of the settlers had been ready to pack up and leave. James Robertson, the leader of the settlement, had talked them out of it, and most had stayed on.

But still the Indians hung around the settlements, and it wasn't a week passed but what somebody was killed and scalped going to the spring or working in the fields. That was bad enough, but the early fall was the time of year the settlers dreaded most. Each year since the white men had come, the savages had made a big attack in September or October. Everybody had gone to the forts; their cabins and cornfields had been burned and their animals killed.

Again this fall a heavy feeling of fear lay over the settlements. Chad could see how his mammy fretted. But he couldn't help thinking things would be better now that he had a gun of his own, a musket he could shoot pretty well. Now he could help his pappy fight the Chickamaugas.

He kicked the logs in place, and Mrs. Rabun banked the fire with ashes. When she stood up, the room was almost dark.

"Maybe there won't be no raids," she said hopefully. "Maybe this fall the Injuns will leave us alone."

Nobody in the shadowy room answered. But when Chad woke later in the night, his mammy's words were the first thing that popped into his head when he heard Tumbler barking outside and the sound of a galloping horse.

from BENJAMIN WEST

AND HIS CAT GRIMALKIN

Marguerite Henry

Benjamin West, America's first distinguished artist, in this entertaining biography is only a little boy with a remarkable friend and ally in his cat Grimalkin. Here we find Benjamin trying to draw for the first time and fearful of his Quaker father's reception of his efforts. The cat plays an important part in father West's decision to let his son draw and the book tells how Grimalkin's tail became even more important to Benjamin than his eloquent "mee-ows." Marguerite Henry writes with rare humor and a tender understanding of both animals and people. No wonder her books are popular with children.

From *Benjamin West and His Cat Grimalkin* by Marguerite Henry, copyright 1947, used by special permission of the publishers, The Bobbs-Merrill Company, Inc.

A Good Fishing Day

There was a kind of magic in the way Grimalkin grew. His fur began to fluff out, soft and black and shining. His tail became thick and uncommonly long. His body waxed strong and very nimble.

And it was like magic the way he took possession of Door-Latch Inn. Almost as soon as Elmira and her kittens were returned to the barn, he began to look after things.

Indoors and out, he set his own tasks. If one of the hound dogs so much as showed his nose in the parlor, Grimalkin cuffed him smartly and sent him yammering out the door. If the chickens got into Mamma's kitchen garden, it was Grimalkin who chased them out. He also took care of the ground hogs and rabbits and snakes. There were the mouse holes to watch too. And the cows to bring in. He not only helped round them up; he also thought it wise to be on hand during the milking. No matter who did the milking—John or Thomas or Samuel or Joseph, or even Papa—he would squirt some of the fresh milk right into Grimalkin's mouth. Grimalkin had to be there to catch it!

Never was a cat so busy. Nor so independent. He slept where he pleased—on the candle shelf, or in a drawer atop Mamma's newly spun cloth, or on Papa's basket-bottom chair. But if the weather was cold, he liked to toast his bones before the fire or crawl into bed with Benjamin. Often, in the dead of night when the moon was full, he would take it into his head to go hunting. And being as clever as he was independent, he asked no one to let him out. With one paw he could lift the door latch as neatly as if he had four fingers and a thumb.

In no time at all Grimalkin was everyone's pet. Papa and Benjamin's four brothers liked him because he was a great ratter and mouser. Mamma and Benjamin's four sisters liked him because, as Mamma so often said, "A more mannerly cat thee would not find anywhere. What other cat in all the Province wipes his paws on the doormat before entering the kitchen? Polite and tidy!" she added with a bright nod.

Even Nanny Luddy, Papa's big mare, liked Grimalkin. She would sleep standing if Grimalkin chose to lie on her bed of straw. Yet Grimalkin treated Nanny Luddy as if he were a king and she his slave. If he leaped upon her back to warm his paws, one would have thought, by the airs he put on, that he was doing her quite a favor.

As for the guests who came and went, Grimalkin openly disapproved them. After investigating them with his nose he left them strictly alone. And when their carts rattled out of the innyard, he helped chase them on their way and then flew back to the inn as if to say, "At last! At last! I have The Family all to myself!"

But if he felt this way toward The Family, he treated Benjamin almost as if he knew that Benjamin had saved his life.

There was nothing he would not do for Benjamin. He would jump through a barrel hoop for him. He would roll over when told. He would box. He would play hide and seek, and a fairly good game of catch and toss. But, more than all this, he was a partner in everything that Benjamin did. And such an understanding grew up between them that strangers would remark on it. "I vow and declare!" they would say. "Grimalkin's tail twitches with excitement and he begins purring at the mere sound of Benjamin's voice."

What these strangers did not know was that Benjamin and Grimalkin could talk to each other almost as person with person. Grimalkin would prick his ears forward and listen gravely to each word of Benjamin's. Then he would make eager little mewing replies, his talk growing louder and louder until he felt certain that Benjamin understood.

There was the day that Benjamin and Grimalkin were left alone to mind Sally. Sally was Benjamin's baby niece.

It was a day made for fishing. Sky overcast. Winds gentle. For a whole hour Benjamin had been sharpening a long pole. He was going to try spearing for trout the way his friends the Indians did.

He had already promised Grimalkin a fishing trip, with all the minnows he could eat.

But just as Benjamin was tucking an apple and some johnnycake into his shirt, he heard the *cloppety-clop* of a horse's hoofs. And then such a hubbub! Rachel, Benjamin's married sister, came flouncing into the house, carrying baby Sally.

"Oh, Mamma!" she cried. "I have been homesick for thee and Benjamin—and everyone."

Benjamin tried hard to look pleased, but in his mind's eye he saw a trout jump out of the water with a silver splash.

Mamma made little cooing noises to the baby. Then she hung Rachel's hood and cloak on a peg as if she were company.

"Benjamin!" she said. "Run up to the front bedchamber and fetch down the cradle we let the little Scotch baby sleep in last night."

With Grimalkin at his heels, Benjamin took the stairs two at a time. He returned breathless with a basket which looked like a great bird's nest on rockers. Grimalkin sat inside it, looking enormously pleased with himself.

"Come, Grimalkin," whispered Benjamin, as he set the cradle down and began edging toward the door.

"Thee, Benjamin!" called Mamma. "Please to fetch thy sisters. They will want to see our dear Sally."

"Where are they, Mamma?" asked Benjamin in despair.

"They are gathering wild mint by the creek!"

"Oh, Benjamin," cried Rachel in her most pleading manner, "I long to be out there with them. If thee were to mind Sally, Mamma and I could have a little outing."

Benjamin bit his lips. He did not mind fetching wood or water. He did not even mind cleaning out the hen house—very much. But minding the baby on a good fishing day!

At a sharp look from Mamma, however, he sat down quickly.

"Oh, thank thee, brother," smiled Rachel. "Here is the flytrap. Please to keep the flies away from Sally's face."

Before Benjamin could say a word, he found himself face to face with the wailing Sally.

"Why, she's mostly mouth!" he said with disgust.

Grimalkin's ears were thrown backward in disapproval. "Can't thee *do* something about this noise?" he seemed to ask.

"Why, of course, I can," replied Benjamin. "I can rock the cradle."

The wailing stopped at once.

The room grew so quiet that Benjamin fancied he could hear the bread rising.

The minutes seemed like hours. The day was going to waste! Benjamin kept tiptoeing to the door to watch for Mamma and Rachel.

"Poor Grimalkin," he sighed, "I promised thee some minnows. And here we are, caught like insects in a web."

He looked about the room. Suddenly his eyes fell on the wells of red ink and black ink on Papa's counter. Beside them lay a goose-quill pen, a sand box for blotting the ink, and a fresh sheet of paper. How smooth and clean the paper looks! thought Benjamin. Then he turned to see if the flies were bothering Sally. And at that precise moment, the baby happened to smile in her sleep.

"Why, Grimalkin!" Benjamin cried. "Sally is less funny-looking when she smiles. She is quite fair." His fingers reached for the goose-quill pen. "I could draw her picture!" he said in amazement. "I believe I could!"

Grimalkin smoothed his whiskers against Benjamin's leg. Then he gazed up with mischievous green eyes. "Well, why doesn't thee do it?" he purred, as plainly as words. "Who is to stop thee?"

Only a Piece of Paper

Benjamin had to work rapidly. Sally's pleasant dream would not last forever. Besides, Mamma and the girls might walk in any minute.

He placed the clean sheet of paper and Papa's ink wells and sand box on a bench beside the cradle. He knelt down on the floor. He dipped the goose-quill pen into the black ink.

Scratch! Scratch! went the pen. With quick strokes he sketched the outline of Sally's head. Then, very lightly, he drew her features. The faint eyebrows. The closed lids. The rounded nose. The smiling lips.

His eyes darted back and forth from Sally's face to his drawing. He forgot about the spear he had made. He forgot about the beautiful red-bellied trout. He forgot everything in the excitement of making his first sketch.

There! He could try the red ink now. He wiped the pen in his hair as he had seen the travelers do. Then he dipped it in the red ink and gave Sally an orange-red mouth. With round-and-round lines he sketched her silken curls. "Why, the color nigh matches her own!" he exclaimed.

Just then Grimalkin leaped on his shoulder and patted his cheek with a gentle forepaw.

"Can thee see any likeness to our Sally?" Benjamin asked of him.

Grimalkin seemed to gaze fixedly at the picture. Then he opened his wide pink mouth. *"Mrr-aow,"* he said, in complete approval.

Benjamin laughed out for joy. But his laughter was cut short. There, in the doorway, stood Mamma and Rachel and Sarah and Hannah and Mary and Elizabeth.

Benjamin sprang to his feet, upsetting the sand

box, and almost upsetting the ink wells. He hid his drawing behind him. He could almost hear Mamma say: "If the world's people wish to draw, well and good. But *thee* is a Quaker, son. Thy grandfather was chief councilor for William Penn himself!"

Mamma stood rigid, holding bunches of bright green mint in her hands. Behind her clustered the girls, their eyes questioning.

At last Mamma came toward Benjamin with slow, measured steps.

"Benjamin!" she said crisply.

"Y-y-yes, Mamma."

"What is thee hiding?"

"Only a piece of paper, Mamma."

"I would see it."

Benjamin winced. He handed her the picture and waited for the shocked, hurt look to cross her face. He watched Rachel and Sarah and Hannah and Mary and Elizabeth gather around the picture. He heard their little gasps of surprise.

Then something happened which Benjamin did not in the least expect. Mamma clapped her hand over her mouth as if to smother an outcry of pleasure. Her eyes grew big with wonder.

"Why, 'tis our Sally!" she exclaimed. "An excellent likeness of our dear Sally." And then she smiled down at Benjamin. "How would thee and Grimalkin like to go fishing now?" she asked. "Papa ever was fond of fresh trout. But what he will say to picture-making, I do not know."

Benjamin's face grew as red as a coxcomb. Why, Mamma had not minded at all!

"What did I tell thee?" Grimalkin seemed to say as he reared up on his hind legs and put his forepaws into Benjamin's hand.

Benjamin's heart danced. He picked up his spear, his apples and his johnnycake, and turned to go.

"We'll be back in time to bring home the cows," he sang out.

Grimalkin lifted the latch, and together the boy and the cat set off across the innyard.

"Oh-ho!" laughed Benjamin. "Thy tail is a weather vane, Grimalkin. It stands straight as a poker whenever thee is happy."

Grimalkin led the way, and the sound of his purring was like the gladness in Benjamin's heart.

Weeks went by before Papa saw the picture of Sally. By day he was busy planting Indian corn and pumpkins. By night the guests hovered around him like bees after honey. They hung on his every word, for while Papa was a man of few words, each one counted.

By the time he had a moment to spare, there was not only the picture of Sally to show him. There was a whole stack of pictures, done on poplar boards, on birch bark—on *anything* that would hold a pen stroke or a smudge of charcoal.

It was midmorning of a bright May day when Papa first heard about the pictures.

"Benjamin!" he called out as he came into the kitchen, bringing the smell of rich black earth with him. "Nanny Luddy has lost a shoe. See if the smith can attend her at once."

"Oh, yes, Papa," replied Benjamin quickly. He grinned at the thought that now Sarah or Hannah or Mary or Elizabeth would have to come down from her bedmaking and take over his job. He was doing a hot and tiresome chore at the time. He was sitting on the hearthstone, turning the crank handle that turned a joint of meat before the fire. And every now and then he had to baste the meat with the brown gravy that dripped into the pan beneath.

Grimalkin sat watchful at Benjamin's feet. Memory told him that sometimes the gravy spattered on the hearthstone, and all of the spatters belonged to him.

"The sun has great power this morning," Papa remarked. "It is pleasant and cool inside."

Cool! thought Benjamin as he wiped the beads of perspiration from his upper lip.

Papa sat down at the table. He began sampling the wild strawberries that Mamma was putting in a pie. Then, looking as sheepish as a boy, he reached over and scooped up on one finger some of the floating island pudding that stood cooling in a bowl. He smiled up at Mamma. "The pudding is exactly to my taste," he observed.

"Benjamin," said Mamma, "this would be the time to show Papa thy pictures."

At the word *picture* Papa coughed and sat bolt upright. His hands tightened on his whip handle until the knuckles stood out white and big. His face went redder than the strawberries. He fixed his hat more firmly on his head.

Oh, oh! thought Benjamin. How quickly Papa can change!

Grimalkin rolled over and over to attract attention, but Papa took less notice of him than if he had been a fly.

"Ho, ho! Look at Grimalkin!" laughed Benjamin nervously.

A heavy silence was the only answer.

Slowly Benjamin got up and walked over to the pine dresser. If only John or Thomas or Samuel or Joseph would come to get Papa! But Door-Latch Inn was as still as a meetinghouse. Only the hens clucked beneath the windows.

With trembling hands, Benjamin took the stack of pictures from the bottom drawer of the dresser. He handed Papa the one of Sally.

It was as if Papa hated even to touch it. Gingerly he laid it on his lap. He reached into his pocket and took out his square-rimmed spectacles. Slowly he adjusted them under his beetling brows. Then he brought the picture up close.

For a long moment he said nothing. Grimalkin lowered his tail at the awful stillness. Mamma's spoon dropped out of her hand with a loud clatter.

Finally Papa placed the drawing on the table. "The image of Sally should be carried in our hearts," he said, as he looked up over the rims of his spectacles. "Not on a piece of paper. Pictures fade; memories remain green forever."

"Green!" shouted Benjamin. "How I long to put green into my pictures! I tried to draw a hummer bird yesterday, as he dipped his beak into a flower. I wanted to paint his shiny green head. But all I had was red and black ink."

Papa shook his head, as he looked at the pictures of redheaded woodpeckers and swamp roses and bushes with scarlet berries.

"It would be better to study cabbages and turnips. Or even gooseberries," he said with a sniff. "These are gay and gaudy. Pride in pictures shows a worldly spirit."

"But, Papa! I am *not* proud of these pictures. I aim to do better. Much better. If only I had more colors!"

At this Papa gave up. "Tell me why it is that thee must draw?" he asked.

Now Benjamin was at a loss. How could he explain the need for putting things on paper? How could he explain that?

"Was it that Sally's smile is fleeting and thee wished to hold it?" asked Mamma.

"That's it, Mamma. That's it! The hummer bird, too, is gone in winter. Yet I could capture him on paper."

Now Grimalkin stretched his muscles and looked up at Papa as if he wished to add a few remarks. First he uttered a little sneeze to attract attention, as people sometimes clear their throats. Then he started talking.

"*Yee-oo, mrr-aow, mee-aw-oo, ye-ah-oo.*" Louder and louder he talked until finally he flung back his head and opened his mouth so wide it showed all the black ridges inside.

Papa sat silent and thoughtful for a moment. Then his eyes twinkled. "Grimalkin is right," he said. "To preserve *good* actions on paper can do no harm. Benjamin is but a lad, Mamma. He will outgrow this." Then turning to Benjamin he said, "Thee may continue with thy drawing —*if* it does not interfere with chores."

Benjamin wanted to scoop Grimalkin up in his arms and dance in circles like a whirl beetle. He wanted to toss Papa's hat to the sky. He wanted to hug Papa until they both gasped for breath. But all he said was, "Thank thee, Papa. Now I shall see about Nanny Luddy's shoe." And he frisked Grimalkin's whiskers for pure joy.

from GEORGE WASHINGTON, LEADER OF THE PEOPLE

Clara Ingram Judson

Washington's boyhood has had a mythlike quality for most children. This selection re-creates the period, the customs, the family, and above all young George Washington and his idolized older brother, Lawrence Washington. Clara Ingram Judson's biographies can be relied upon for their careful historical details. Her many books about American immigrants (They Came From Sweden, They Came From Scotland,

From *George Washington, Leader of the People,* by Clara Ingram Judson. By permission of Wilcox & Follett Company

etc.) and her exciting story about Chicago's Chinatown—The Green Ginger Jar—illustrate her appreciative understanding of widely different people and her profound concern for everything that goes to make our American culture rich and sound.

By the Rappahannock

The farm by the river was the lush green of June in Virginia. The air was warm, fine for growing things. A mocking bird sang in the linden tree and the chatter of wrens mingled with domestic noises of roosters, hens, and ducks in the chicken yard.

A house, high above the Rappahannock, had a comfortable look against a line of tall trees. Nearby, a barn, the kitchen, poultry house, storeroom, smithy and quarters for the slaves made a little settlement such as was usually found on prosperous Virginia farms in that year 1739.

At the horse lot a boy tugged at the heavy gate bar, while his pony, Whitefoot, pawed impatiently, eager to be gone.

"Want help?" Tim, the stableman, called.

"No, I can do it myself," George Washington said quickly. As he tugged again, he noticed that Whitefoot was suddenly still, ears cocked as though he heard a new sound.

"Someone coming, Whitefoot?" George asked, listening. The rhythmic sound of hoofbeats came from far down the lane leading to the main road to Fredericksburg.

George climbed onto the fence for a look. He was sturdy and tall for a boy in his eighth year. Freckles sprinkled his straight nose, and his hands were tanned from long hours out of doors. Now he brushed a lock of sandy-colored hair from his forehead and squinted his gray-blue eyes down the lane.

"It's *Lawrence!*" he cried excitedly. "Whitefoot! Lawrence is coming!"

George jumped down from the fence, pulled out the gate bar, which suddenly seemed lighter, threw himself onto his pony and dashed off down the lane.

A visit from George's twenty-one-year-old half-brother was a thrilling surprise. Lawrence Washington had been home from England only a few months. George admired this tall, handsome brother and saw him far too little.

Lawrence waved as George drew near and grinned with amusement when the boy pulled Whitefoot up short with a flourish that sent pebbles flying.

"Oh, Lawrence! I am so glad to see you!" George cried breathlessly. "I didn't know you were coming today!"

"I started early; I have meant to come for several days," Lawrence said. "Is Father here?"

"No," George told him. "I think he is at the iron works. Maybe you had better ride over and see him?"

"No, my errand is here," Lawrence said. "And I doubt if your mother would let you ride over with me in any case. Where are you bound now?"

"To school," George told him in a bored tone. "That Master Hobby is a tiresome man, Lawrence. He teaches the same thing over and over."

"Perhaps it is a good thing that I came today," Lawrence remarked as they rode along toward the house.

"Did you come about *me?*" George was astonished. But Lawrence merely shook his head and laughed mysteriously.

"I must talk to your mother now," he said. "And you should shut that gate, George. You will be in trouble if a colt gets into the field."

Reluctantly George stopped to close and fasten the gate while Lawrence rode to the hitching post near the house.

George turned Whitefoot into the lot, fastened the gate and called to a stableboy to care for Lawrence's mount. But his manner was absent-minded; his thoughts were on Lawrence. Something was up, that was certain, something that concerned George. But what could be important enough to bring Lawrence on a thirty-mile ride from Hunting Creek farm? In June, too, when a farmer had work to oversee.

Shouts of small children and the bark of a dog guided George to the lawn in front of the house. There, on the high bank Lawrence had joined Mrs. Washington and the younger children, Betty, Sam, and Jack. They had been watching their father's scow as it crossed the river.

"It is a good thing you came today, Lawrence," Mrs. Washington was saying to her stepson as George came near. "While you are in Fredericksburg about George, you can attend to the delivery of my boxes. I saw the ship from England arrive yesterday."

"Am I going to Fredericksburg?" George exclaimed. Many times he had looked toward the white steeple of the church across the river and wondered what was beneath the thick trees. "I have never been to a town," he added.

"That is not surprising," Lawrence said casually. "Virginia has few towns. But you shall see Fredericksburg today, for my errand there is for you. Father thinks it is high time . . ."

"George! Run to the house and put on your best coat," Mrs. Washington interrupted. "Lawrence can explain your father's plan while you are on the ferry. It comes now." The scow had reached the landing at the foot of the ravine.

George glanced down at his shirt and knee-pants. The garments were clean and good enough for Hobby's little school. But he did look shabby compared with Lawrence's elegant coat and breeches, trimmed with shining buttons and buckles. He hurried into the house, brushed his hair and put on his best coat and the shoes with buckles. Lawrence was strolling toward the ravine when he returned and together they hurried to the wharf.

"Lawrence! Tell the captain to have a care for my boxes," Mrs. Washington called after them. "The last time your father ordered goblets, every one was broken on the way."

"I shall see to it," Lawrence promised. "Come, George!"

The children left behind began to fuss.

"I want to ride on the ferry," six-year-old Betty teased.

"I want to go!" Sam planted his feet wide apart and yelled.

Jack was too young to understand but he yelled too.

"Quiet, all of you!" Mrs. Washington commanded. "Better be gone quickly, Lawrence," she called over her shoulder, "or these children will be heard in Fredericksburg."

Laughing, Lawrence and George hurried away. In a few minutes they were aboard the clumsy ferry.

As they pulled away, George looked expectantly at Lawrence.

"So you want to know what this is about?" Lawrence said. "The last time Father came to

Hunting Creek, he told me that he was not pleased with Hobby's teaching. A one-room neighborhood school is good for a time. It is convenient and gives you a start. But Father heard that a better school might be opened in Fredericksburg. He wants to know if the rumor is true. We shall not count on it until we see."

The crossing was brief. Before George had time for many questions, the ferry tied up near the sailing ship from England. Lawrence went at once to attend to Mrs. Washington's boxes.

George marveled that Lawrence knew exactly what to say and do as invoices were checked and boxes marked "Fragile" were moved to the ferry under his watchful eye.

"I am lucky to have a brother as wonderful as Lawrence," George thought humbly. "I wonder if I can ever be as smart and as handsome?" It seemed doubtful.

"Now we can leave," Lawrence said in relief. And the two climbed the steep cobblestone road to the town.

George looked around with keen curiosity. He saw the church with the familiar steeple, many houses, a stone jail with iron-barred windows, shops, and people strolling about.

Lawrence inquired of one of these for the residence of the Reverend James Marye and was directed to the parsonage, by the church. The rector was at home, and Lawrence introduced himself and George and accepted the invitation to come inside.

"My father had hoped to call upon you, sir, about the education of my young brother," he explained as they all sat down. "But because of his many duties at his iron works and the task of managing his three plantations, the matter has been postponed. My father has heard that you may open a school. If this is your intention, we would like to enroll my brother."

The Reverend Marye had looked keenly from one Washington to the other while Lawrence was speaking.

"Where did you receive your education?" he asked.

"At Appleby in England," Lawrence told him. "My father lived in England and attended Appleby. Others of our family went to that school and my brother Augustine, Jr., who is near my age, is there. At the proper time my father plans to take George to England, too. Meanwhile, my brother needs good preparation which my father hopes you can give him."

"Have you had any schooling, George?" Marye asked.

"Yes, sir. Master Hobby teaches me reading and writing and sums," George answered respectfully.

Marye turned to his desk and selected a bit of paper and a quill pen.

"Let me see your writing," he said.

George sat down, took the quill, and wrote his name in his best style. The result was not remarkable. Marye eyed it, frowning.

"Those field schools," he began. Then he paused and rubbed his chin thoughtfully. It was plain he was not favorably impressed with George's instruction. The term "field school" which he used was often applied to a small one-room schoolhouse erected by a group of neighbors. One gave a part of his field, others labor, materials, or tobacco for buying books. The great problem was to find a suitable teacher; the colony of Virginia lacked such men.

"I do better with sums," George ventured to speak up when the silence grew long. "I like arithmetic."

"I hope we are not too late to enter my brother," Lawrence remarked, now a bit anxious at the turn the interview was taking.

"On the contrary, you are too early," Marye answered more cheerfully. "I shall not open my school before autumn, perhaps not until next year. Um-m-m, I wonder if your father has considered the cost of textbooks as well as tuition?"

"My father will not object to any proper charge," Lawrence answered, with due caution about committing his father's purse. "Perhaps you will be good enough to send Father word when your school is about to open?"

"You may count on that," Marye said, now reassured. "Meanwhile, have the boy continue his studies."

The visitors bowed out politely. As they walked down the street, George sighed with relief.

"The Reverend Marye must be a *very* learned man," he said. "He is so very solemn."

"Never mind!" Lawrence answered. "You have to be prepared for Appleby, and Hobby could never do it. Where shall we go now? The ferry can wait."

"I would like to go to the Apothecary's Shop, Lawrence," George said, eagerly. "Our smith has told me about it. The window has two big urns, one red, one green. Candy is for sale," George added hopefully.

Lawrence was willing, and soon they saw the small but enchanting window. Inside, the shop had a luscious fragrance.

"We have some excellent sugar which has just arrived from England," the apothecary told them. He opened a case and took out a shallow wooden bowl in which hunks of a taffylike substance were piled. George's mouth watered as he admired the rich caramel color and watched Lawrence expectantly.

"I shall take two pounds," Lawrence ordered. The apothecary reached for his iron sugar clippers; he used them like tongs to cut off individual portions and place them on the scale.

"Two pounds," he repeated.

"Can you direct us to a baker's shop?" Lawrence asked as he paid for the sugar and handed the sack to George.

"Down the street by the corner there is a good place," the man said.

At the baker's, Lawrence bought caraway comfits. George ate two on the ferry and found them delicious.

"I shall take the rest home for a treat," he decided.

The dining table was set in the wide hall. The stone fireplace was empty this June day, but the hearth was cheerful with bright brasses and an embroidered fire screen. A gold-framed mirror hung on one wall and opposite a handsome floor clock ticked off seconds. Leather-bottomed chairs were set up to a large table covered with a linen tablecloth and set with china and pewter. The children stood by their chairs as their mother entered.

"We saw the ferry coming so we waited dinner," she said. "George has learned to say grace, Lawrence. We are ready, son."

They stood with bowed heads while George recited: "God bless us for what we are about to receive." Then they sat down.

A young serving maid hovered over the children, tying bibs, while an older woman brought food from the kitchen. In Virginia this was often a separate building; the danger of fire was less and flies, drawn by cooking, were kept from the dining room.

The woman set a large platter before Lawrence, who carved the two roast chickens. Then she brought sliced ham, a bowl of greens cooked with bacon, blackberry jam, butter, hot cornbread and handleless cups of hot tea. Later she passed wheat bread and a large bowl piled with fruit picked that morning; early plums, cherries and red currants.

As they were finishing the meal, Lawrence winked at George, who promptly produced the comfits and the sugar.

"I shall persuade Father to take *me* to town soon," Betty announced as she found the last crumb and plunked it into her mouth. George chuckled. They both knew their father had no time for shopping journeys.

The other children drifted out of doors. George sat quietly as Lawrence talked with Mrs. Washington about the school and left messages for his father. Until last winter the Washingtons had all lived at Hunting Creek farm and Mrs. Washington was interested in the place.

"Perhaps your father will come to Hunting Creek soon," she remarked as Lawrence rose to leave.

"I wish he would bring George with him," Lawrence said. "That is, if you can spare him?" George's face brightened and Mrs. Washington half promised.

Striding along by Lawrence, George went to the horse lot where he mounted Whitefoot to ride as far as the main road.

"I wish you could stay longer, Lawrence," George said.

"And who would do my work at Hunting Creek?" scoffed Lawrence. "Lucky for me the day is long so I can get home before dark. But you will be coming to visit me, George. Don't tease Father. Better be surprised when he mentions a visit. Then you may say that I will teach you farming and care of the stock. He will like that, and you will enjoy it more than school." Laughing, Lawrence touched his horse lightly and was on his way.

George rode back to the barn. The Washingtons had slaves to do the work at Ferry farm, but Mr. Washington had told George that a boy old enough to have his own horse must take care of it. That was no hardship; George liked keeping Whitefoot's stall clean, bedding the pony with fresh straw, and measuring out the feed. Usually he talked as he curried and cared for his pony. But today his thoughts were with Lawrence. The prospect of a visit at Hunting Creek farm was far more interesting than a new school.

. . . .

Many Changes

After months without word from the West Indies a letter that Lawrence had written in Jamaica arrived. George was astonished that Lawrence wrote more about smallpox and yellow fever than about glorious battles. After more months word came that the war had turned to Georgia; the fleet was not needed, and Virginians were coming home.

Lawrence arrived late in 1742 and was received with honor by the colony. Later the governor appointed him military adjutant in recognition of his war service, an office that gave him charge of the militia of Virginia.

The returned warrior found changes at Ferry farm. The baby sister had died. Austin, Lawrence's brother who had expected to study law in England, had come home to help his father. He was learning to manage the farm at Pope's Creek.

"I had George visit me for a time," Austin told Lawrence. "He is good company." Lawrence saw that the two got on well.

But George soon showed his family that no one took Lawrence's place in his affections. Now his hero was more fascinating than ever; he had seen foreign places and could tell tales of ships and battles. Lawrence had served on the flagship and was the friend of a real admiral. George followed his brother around and begged to be allowed to go back with him to Hunting Creek.

"And leave school?" Lawrence exclaimed. "Are you failing?"

"Oh, no, Lawrence!" George was shocked. "But I could learn more with you."

Lawrence grinned understandingly. But George stayed in school.

After gay holidays with six sons and daughter Betty crowding the modest house, the older sons went back to work. At Pope's Creek, Austin was trying to set up a business of raising fine horses, much needed in the colony. Lawrence, at Hunting Creek, planned to erect a few needed buildings and clear more fields for growing tobacco. He had told his father that he hoped to marry Anne Fairfax in the spring. As for Gus Washington, he continued his heavy round of duties at his Accokeek Iron Works, Hunting Creek, Pope's Creek, and Ferry farm.

The iron business had first been successful in America in 1717, with a Maryland furnace owned by an English firm. There Gus Washington learned how to take ore from the ground, smelt it, and ship it to England. Colonists were not allowed to make durable goods; that profitable business was reserved for England.

Washington built furnaces, prepared wood for charcoal from his own forest and built ships for transport. All this required scores of laborers who must be housed and fed. Wagons, tools, and all sorts of supplies were needed, and craftsmen, too; wagonwrights, blacksmiths, millers, sawyers, carpenters, and others. Slaves could be trained to work under a skilled manager, but this last was a hard job to fill. Gus Washington had to be his own manager much of the time.

As for George, he did so well in school that his father planned an Easter vacation for him— a visit to his cousins in another county. George was there, in the midst of a day of sports, when a messenger arrived from Ferry farm.

"Your father is ill—very ill!" the man cried as he slid from his exhausted horse. "You are to come home at once."

George dashed for Whitefoot. The messenger was loaned a fresh mount and the two galloped home. George arrived in time to see his strong father stretched flat on his bed, too ill to know his son or to speak. Mrs. Washington let him stand there a few minutes, then she motioned him away.

Soon Lawrence came into the hall. "Father is dead."

"*Dead!*" George exclaimed incredulously. His strong handsome father, the man who had more energy than any person George had ever known —dead? But it was true. This sad loss came a few weeks after George's eleventh birthday.

During those next sad days George thought

often of the ride with his father nearly four years before. He was glad to have had that trip and their talk to remember.

After Augustine Washington had been buried in the family burying ground a mile from Pope's Creek, his will was read. George's father had thought of the future of all his children.

Lawrence, the oldest son, was to have the largest plantation, Hunting Creek farm. That was still the custom in the colony. Austin inherited Pope's Creek farm. George was to have Ferry farm when he was twenty-one and also some other land. Sam and Jack and Charles were each given tracts of several hundred acres and Betty's inheritance was in money. The forty-nine slaves were divided among the heirs, and each child and the mother were given shares in the iron company. Mrs. Washington was to hold and manage her children's property until they became of age.

When this legal business was finally settled, Lawrence and Austin went back to their homes, and life at Ferry farm settled down. George missed Lawrence more than ever because now he had no father.

In July of that year, 1743, Lawrence married Anne Fairfax and the family reassembled for the wedding. The event, so soon after Mr. Washington's death, was not as festive as it might have been, but George thought it very grand. The social life of Virginia was the most elegant of all the colonies.

This marriage brought many changes in George's life. Lawrence's bride invited him for a long visit; she told him to call her Nancy, as Lawrence did. George's mother was willing to have George stay at Hunting Creek now that Lawrence had a bride of distinction.

Nancy's father, Colonel William Fairfax, continued his liking for George. Fairfax was one of the richest and most distinguished men in Virginia; he was a burgess, then a member of the higher body, the Council, and a year after the wedding was made President of the Council. Next to the governor's palace, his home, Belvoir, was the meeting place of the greatest men in the colony.

George was now eleven and a half and naturally quick to observe people and manners. This association with the Fairfax family had taught him fine manners and habits of graciousness; in a measure, it took the place of the training his father had intended him to have in England.

Lawrence and Nancy lived in the story-and-a-half house that was probably built by Gus Washington before he moved there in the seventeen-thirties. It had a center hall and four rooms downstairs and rooms with dormer windows above. They added furniture and hangings, and Nancy had handsome silver and other choice things. George thought the place very elegant, though, of course, it was not large and handsome like Belvoir.

When the pretty things were all in place, Nancy told George they were giving the place a new name.

"This is no longer Hunting Creek farm, George," she said. "We call it Mount Vernon; Mount for the high bank above the river, Vernon for Lawrence's good friend the admiral."

"Mount Vernon," George repeated the words, testing the sound. "That is a good name, Nancy. I like it."

A few days later the Lawrence Washingtons gave a dinner party as a housewarming. The slaves worked early and late with the preparations. They polished silver, washed and ironed linens, and washed the china and every window in the house.

George wondered if a boy going on twelve would be allowed at the table. Nancy soon relieved his mind about that.

"Lawrence thinks this is a good chance for you to learn about grown-up affairs," she said. "Wear that new suit Lawrence ordered from London. Better try it on today, George, and let Lawrence see if it needs any changes. And, George, will you tell Chloe that I shall be out to inspect every duck myself when she has finished cleaning them? Everything is to be perfect at my first party!"

She bustled about happily, keys clicking at her belt like an experienced housewife. George did the errand and then ran upstairs to try on the suit. It had come only that morning.

The guests were very fashionable. The dinner was delicious, George thought, though he was so excited he could not eat as much as usual—well, not quite as much. When the ladies retired to the drawing room to talk of fashions and house-

hold matters, Colonel Fairfax motioned for George to sit by him. The men were talking, at the moment, about war.

"You must feel a satisfaction, Lawrence," a guest across the table remarked, "to know that you could serve the king when he needed you." Lawrence nodded and bowed modestly.

"His majesty needs service in peacetime, too," a man in a green satin coat said. The others looked at him.

"I am thinking of the land west of the mountains," he explained. "Your relative, Lord Fairfax, owns vast acreage. I believe you manage it for him, Fairfax?"

"If you can call it managing," Colonel Fairfax waved his hand casually. "Actually wilderness land has little value. King Charles the Second would not have given it away, years ago, if he had thought well of it."

"You speak of the Fairfax Proprietary, I take it?" a guest in a bright-blue coat and stylish periwig inquired.

"Yes." Fairfax smiled. "An elegant name for a wild, unsurveyed stretch of country. I had a letter from Lord Fairfax the other day—he asks whether there is a demand by settlers for his land. I do not know what to tell him."

"No demand at all, I'd say," some one spoke up. "Not with Indians only a short journey away. Now if the Indians could be persuaded to move west of the Allegheny Range a lively trade in land might open up."

"At great profit to us all," Fairfax laughed and raised his glass. The talk went on until the guests' carriages arrived.

That was only the first of many dinner parties at Mount Vernon. How much of the talk—business, military, and political—a boy of twelve could understand, George himself could hardly have told. But he was a thoughtful lad. He turned men's words over in his mind and began growing up.

Occasionally George rode with Lawrence to see Austin at Pope's Creek. This brother urged George to live with him.

"You like to work with horses, George," he said. "And there are boys your own age nearby —the Lee family, and others." But though George did go for one or two visits, he was always glad to return to Mount Vernon. He loved that place.

When he stayed at Ferry farm he found that life very different from either brother's. There, small children, school, and daily tasks under his mother's supervision kept him busy.

Mrs. Washington had considerable help, both slaves and indentured servants. Still, the mother of five children and manager of a farm had a great deal to do. She must guard the children from daily hazards: poison ivy on the river slope, measles, warts, croup (the terror of those days), and chicken pox. She was also the doctor, and she made her own medicines from herbs grown in her garden or searched out in the forest.

The blacksmith was the dentist, though of course the mother pulled "baby teeth." She tied a string from tooth to doorknob and held the child while some one slammed the door—and pulled the tooth. The blacksmith was called in when a "second tooth" ached. Mother held the patient flat on the table while the smith, with a dramatic flourish of black pincers and sheer strength, yanked out the tooth—and often some bone along with it.

The children all rode horses, too. So the mother must be ready to tie red meat over bruises or set broken bones. It was a busy life, full of surprises.

At school, George studied the classics, writing, algebra, and geometry. Reverend Marye was most particular about writing. He had George copy one hundred and ten rules from an old English volume called *The Rules of Conduct*.

"Write each rule over and over until you have it perfect," the master ordered. "I shall accept no carelessly made letters."

So George wrote in his copybook:

"Mock not, nor jest at anything of importance; break no jests that are sharp biting, and if you deliver anything witty or pleasant, abstain from laughing at it yourself.

"When you see a crime punished, you may be inwardly pleased; but always show pity to the suffering offender.

"Labor to keep alive in your breast that little spark of celestial fire called conscience."

This chore of copying over and over to satisfy his teacher taught George the easy, flowing handwriting that was to be so important to him later.

One Saturday his mother set him at the tedious task of cleaning the storehouse. This was a small building, near the kitchen, where countless articles were put when not in daily use. He moved boxes and bundles. He scrubbed and sorted under her keen eye until someone called her away. While alone, George rummaged in a dark corner. There he found an odd thing made up of iron rods and chains. As his mother returned she heard the sounds he made examining the thing.

"Now what have you there?" she demanded.

"I don't know, Mother," George said. "Do you?"

When she saw what he was holding, she laughed. "Of course I know! That's your father's surveying chain; did you never see it before? His compass is in the desk. Your father always surveyed property he bought to make sure of the boundaries."

"Father knew everything, didn't he?" George said quietly.

Something in the lad's tone caught his mother's attention. She put her hand on his shoulder in a rare gesture of affection.

"Not everything, son," she answered kindly. "But he was a fine man. He had more knowledge than most men in the colony. But a chain is no good to us now. Take it to the smith; he can use the metal." Mary Washington was her practical self again.

"May I keep it because it was Father's?" George asked.

"Oh, yes, if you like. After you have scrubbed the floor, put it in the corner, there. It does not take much room."

She bustled away, the keys at her belt jingling. "He will soon forget," she thought. "Then the smith can have it."

George finished the scrubbing and put the brush and bucket away. As he laid the long chain in the corner he made a promise to himself.

"Monday I shall begin to learn surveying."

from BENJAMIN FRANKLIN

Ingri and Edgar Parin d'Aulaire

This is a selection from one of the D'Aulaires' beautiful picture-biographies for young readers 8 to 10. If the text seems a bit stiff, the bright, powerful pictures give their books a color which the narratives lack. However, even in this selection, the sturdy, intelligent Ben comes to life. All the picture-biographies of this husband and wife team are worth looking up: George Washington, Abraham Lincoln (Caldecott Medal), Leif the Lucky, *and* Pocahontas.

[Boy into Man]

At the time when the King of England ruled over the American colonies there stood a small house on Milk Street in Boston.

In this house there lived a candlemaker whose name was Josiah Franklin. He was a good and pious man, and the Lord had given him a virtuous wife and a blessing of seventeen children, all counted.

Three times each Sunday he led all his children to church and he taught them to be honest and hard-working and satisfied with little.

"He who knows his trade does not have to stand except for kings," said Josiah Franklin. He looked proudly at his ten husky sons and hoped that someday they would all be good tradesmen.

The youngest of his sons was Benjamin. He was born in 1706. He was different from his brothers. He was only knee-high to a grasshopper when he first learned to read and he wondered and asked questions from morning till night. He was a merry little fellow with stocky legs and a bright mind, busy with flights of fancy and practical ideas. He thought it was a pity that his father, who was so busy working to keep them all in food and clothes, should waste so much time saying a long grace every time he ate.

"Father," he said one day as they were sitting down to table, "think of all the time you could save if you would thank the Lord, once and for all, for the whole larder."

His father was pious and serious but he could not help smiling, and when he told his friends what a clever young son he had, they laughed with him and agreed that Benjamin was so bright he might even become a minister. And on the next holiday one of the friends filled Benjamin's little coat pocket with copper pennies. Benjamin had never had a penny of his own before and joyfully he ran to a toy shop, where he offered all his money for a whistle he had set his heart on. He ran home and marched through the house shrilly blowing it while the rest of his family stopped up their ears.

When his sisters and brothers found out that he had spent all of his pennies for the whistle, he was the one who stopped up his ears. They teased him and called him a spendthrift till he wept. He had spent four times as much as the whistle was worth. That was the only time Benjamin ever spent a penny unwisely.

Benjamin lived near the sea, and he early learned to swim and sail. He never grew tired of watching the wind carry the boats over the water, just as it carried his kite up into the sky. One day, while he was swimming, he fastened the kite to himself as if it were a sail and he were a boat. It carried him gently over the water while his friends, who were kicking and splashing, looked on in astonishment. Because he had so many ideas like this, he was usually the leader among his playmates.

Like any boy, he sometimes led them into mischief. Once he got all of his playmates together at the shore where they liked best to fish. The ground was swampy, but near by Benjamin had found a big pile of stones that were to be used for building a house. He and his friends took these stones and built a fine wharf. But when the workmen came and found the stones gone, it helped Benjamin little to plead the usefulness of their work.

After he had been soundly spanked by his father, Benjamin was convinced that nothing is useful that is not honest.

When Benjamin was eight years old, his father sent him to grammar school. He rose to the head of his class in reading and writing, and he read every book he could lay his hands upon. But he was poor in arithmetic. His father began to think that perhaps Benjamin should be a tradesman like his brothers. So, when Benjamin was ten years old, he was taken out of school to learn his father's trade of candlemaking.

Benjamin hated dipping candles and cutting wicks the whole day long. He read and he dreamed. More and more he dreamed about ships and voyages to faraway ports. His father began to fear that his son might become a sailor and be lost at sea. Hoping to find Benjamin a trade that he would really like, he took him to call on joiners and braziers and cutlers and bricklayers in their workshops. Benjamin learned much about these trades but he did not want to follow any of them. At last his worried father persuaded him that, since he was so fond of books, he should become a printer's apprentice. Then he could look at the printed word all day long.

His older brother James had a printing shop and, when Benjamin was twelve, he moved from his father's house and bound himself to be his brother's apprentice for nine years. In return, James was to teach him to print and to give him his board and clothes.

James was a strict master. When his young brother answered back with his quick wit and ready tongue, he boxed his ears severely. Benjamin had to sweep the floor, wash the type, and do all the dirty work while he watched his brother and his helpers print pamphlets and books. By and by James taught him to set type and print.

Benjamin was a hard-working boy and he learned fast. In a few years he was his brother's best worker. He would have liked life in the printing shop very much if he had had more time to read all the books around him. One day he had one of his practical ideas. He asked his brother to give him half of the money he paid for Benjamin's board so he could get his own meals and eat them in the shop when the others went out. James did not mind. He saved money. And Benjamin was happy. Now he had time to read books in peace while he ate his gruel and munched an apple. He did not care much what he ate as long as it was cheap and wholesome. He soon found that he could save half of the money his brother gave him for food. With that he bought books.

Benjamin wanted very much to become a writer himself. When he read something he liked especially well, he rewrote it in his own words. And sometimes he would be hanged if he didn't think that he was better than the author.

One of the things James printed was a newspaper. Benjamin's fingers were itching to write for it, for who does not want to see his own words in print? But he knew that his brother would only laugh and say he was getting too big for his breeches and give him a whack into the bargain. So he kept his writing secret.

One morning his brother found under his door a letter to the newspaper signed Widow Dogood. James did not recognize Benjamin's writing, for he had disguised it. Benjamin chuckled and was very pleased with himself when not only his brother and his friends but also the readers of the paper highly praised the widow's good sense and learning. His brother had many letters from the virtuous lady and printed them all before Benjamin confessed that he was the widow.

James was angry. After that he was stricter than ever with Benjamin. In his eyes Benjamin was a fresh little sprout who believed he could both print and write better than his master.

Benjamin thought he was now too big to be thrashed by his brother. He had been his apprentice for five years and had become a very good printer. Yes, he had even run the printing shop alone while his brother was away. He asked his brother please to let him go so that he could find work for himself elsewhere. But James said no, he must stay till his nine years were up.

Then Benjamin made up his mind to run away. He knew it was wrong but he could no longer stand his brother's harsh treatment. He sold some of his cherished books to get a little money, and late one night he secretly boarded a ship bound for New York. He stood at the rail watching his native town vanish into the night. He felt small and lonesome. His parents would be sad and his brother would be angry. He was only seventeen and he did not know a soul in New York who might help him.

The winds were fair, but even so the trip to New York took three days. During a lull the sailors fished and made a big haul of cod. They invited Benjamin to eat with them, but Benjamin said no, thank you, he ate neither flesh nor fish, for he had read in a book that it was murder to kill and eat creatures that had done him no harm. But he loved codfish and, when the fish was cooking and the good smells reached his nose, he began to hunt about in his mind for a reason to share the sailors' meal. He remembered that when the codfish were cut open he had seen small fish in their stomachs. If big fish ate small fish, why should he not eat big fish? Then he ate heartily and thought to himself how lucky he was to be a thinking creature who could find a good reason for doing what he wanted to do. After that Benjamin always ate what was set before him.

Benjamin liked the sea voyage. When he arrived in New York, he stood at the wharf for a while and thought. He could go to sea if he still wanted to, but he had become a printer, and a printer he would be.

New York was a very small town in 1723 and there was but one printer. He had no work for Benjamin and advised him to go to Philadelphia. Philadelphia was a larger town.

So Benjamin set off for Philadelphia. He had very little money left and could not afford to travel all the way by ship. He stuffed what he could into his pockets and shipped the rest of his belongings. A few pennies paid his passage on a ramshackle old boat that was about to cross to the Jersey shore.

Halfway across, a gale blew up and the rotten sails went to pieces. In the storm a Dutchman fell overboard, Benjamin quickly grabbed him by the hair and pulled him back into the boat. The dripping Dutchman pulled a book out of his pocket and asked Benjamin to dry it for him.

It was the most beautiful book Benjamin had ever seen. It had been printed in Europe with fine type and many pictures. That was the kind of book he would like to print.

He had plenty of time to enjoy the book, for the boat pitched and tossed in the bay of New York for thirty hours. At last the crew managed to bring her to port on the Jersey shore and, cold and wet, Benjamin started to walk. It was a long way on foot, for it is a hundred miles from New York to Philadelphia.

For days he trudged through ruts and mud, in rain and storm, and he began to be sorry he had ever run away. When he reached the Delaware River, he was lucky. A small boat came sailing downstream and the crew took him on board. But soon the wind died down. Benjamin had to help row the boat till his hands were covered with blisters. He looked so bedraggled and forlorn, it was a wonder he was not sent home as a runaway bound boy.

That is the way he arrived in Philadelphia early on a Sunday morning. People in their Sun-day-go-to-meeting clothes were walking through the streets, Benjamin walked along with them, looking this way and that till he came to an open bakeshop. He was very hungry and went in and asked the baker for three pennies' worth of bread. To his surprise, the baker handed him three huge buns, for bread was very cheap in Philadelphia. It was three times more than he could eat! The people turned their heads to hide their smiles when they saw Benjamin walking up Market Street with his pockets stuffed with clothes and his arms full of bread. A pretty girl standing in a doorway snickered and giggled out loud.

He followed the people in the street until he came to a Quaker meetinghouse, which he entered. He was so exhausted that he fell asleep the moment he sat down. He had come to the city of brotherly love, so nobody woke him till the meeting was over. Then a kind Quaker showed him to an inn where he could rest and eat.

Scrubbed and refreshed, Benjamin went out the next morning, and soon he found work as a printer's helper. Nobody laughed at his looks any longer, but everybody laughed at his jokes. It was not long before the people of Philadelphia were telling one another how lucky it was that such a good printer and fine young fellow had settled in their town. Many of them made friends with him. The governor of Pennsylvania came to see if Benjamin was really as clever as people said. He asked him out to dine with him and was much taken by his good sense. He advised Benjamin to go back to Boston and ask his father's forgiveness for running away and his help in setting up a printing shop of his own. Then he, the governor, would help him to get printing to do. That sounded like good advice to Benjamin.

Eight months after he had run away, he sailed back to Boston for a visit. He was dressed in a fine new suit. He had a watch, and silver coins jingled in his pocket. His parents were happy that he had done so well, and readily forgave him. But his father thought he was still too young to have a shop of his own and told him to return to his well-paid work as a printer's helper. His brother would not forgive him and it was not till many years later that the two brothers were friends again.

TOM JEFFERSON
CLIMBS A MOUNTAIN

Frances Cavanah

"Will dinner time never come?"

Tom Jefferson did not dare to say the words aloud; he was in school. It was a very little schoolhouse—built especially for the use of his cousins, his sisters, and himself—on the grounds of Tuckahoe, the beautiful estate in Tidewater, Virginia, where they lived. Though Tom was only five, he was already learning to read and write and cipher. But today he found it very hard to keep his mind upon his sums. Outside the birds sang. Inside there was only the squeak of slate pencils.

Tom was getting hungrier every minute. "I can't stand it any longer," he decided. And, getting up very quietly, he tiptoed from the room.

Once outside, he didn't know just what to do. The air was fragrant with roses and bridal wreath in bloom. In the distance the James River shone like a bright twisted ribbon. On the brow of the wooded hill sprawled the manor house, beyond the avenue of beautiful elms. If the dinner bell would only ring! Perhaps if he said his prayers, it would help the time to pass.

"Our Father, which art in heaven—" Tom knelt beside the schoolhouse on the ground. He finished the Lord's Prayer. Again he said it, and again, and again. He loved the sound of the slow, beautiful words.

Clang-clang! Clang-clang!

"Dinner!" someone shouted, and the little schoolhouse seemed to rustle with excitement. Jane and Mary Jefferson came bursting through the door. Tom's cousins, Judith and Mary Randolph, followed with their little brother, Thomas. Tom jumped up, and the six children raced through the English garden to the manor house. When Tom, his hands carefully washed and his sandy hair smoothed down, took his place at the long dining-room table, he sighed blissfully. There at its head sat his tall father,

carving a big ham. He placed a pink slice on a plate, which a grinning colored servant placed before the hungry boy. Tom took a deep breath, cut a piece of the delicious ham, and sank his fork into a fluffy sweet potato. It was worth waiting for!

Tom's real home was Shadwell, in the wild farm country farther to the west, but he was living at Tuckahoe so that his father could look after the orphaned Randolph children, Tom's cousins. Here the two families of children had wonderful times together. The girls played house at the foot of the big oak tree. The boys flew kites and went swimming. There were orchards where they played tag and "thread the needle." There were horses to ride, stables to visit, and fascinating places to explore. There was the smokehouse where ham was cured, the soaphouse where fat was saved, and then put into big copper kettles to be boiled down and made into soap. In the tobacco houses the leaves of the tobacco plant were stripped and dried, ready to be loaded on the ships that would sail down the river and away to England. Most interesting of all, perhaps, were the slave quarters, where the cousins often played with the little colored boys and girls.

But life at Tuckahoe was not all play. When Tom was six, he began to learn to be a gentleman. On special occasions he wore a dress suit exactly like his father's, with velvet breeches and coat, a flowered waistcoat, and a cocked hat. And sometimes he had to wear a stiff steel-and-canvas corset like his mother's. Tom took dancing lessons, and acted as the host at the children's balls held in the big two-story room that connected the two wings of the house. At such times, the great chandelier, brightly lighted with candles, shone down upon the boys and girls of the neighborhood as they danced the minuet or the Virginia reel.

One day, when Tom was nine, Colonel Jefferson said to him, "I have news for you, my son. I have decided to go back to Shadwell."

Tom's long, freckled face lighted up with pleasure at the thought. At heart he was a pioneer, just as his father was, and he knew that when he returned to Shadwell he would have bears and otters to hunt, buffalo to shoot, rivers to ford, and mountains to climb.

"I have arranged for you to live with Rev. William Douglas a few miles from Shadwell," his father went on. "He will instruct you in Latin, Greek, and French, and many other subjects which I am unprepared to teach you. You are to have the education that I missed. I want you to be a scholar, Son."

"Oh!" Tom sounded disappointed. He had hoped to live at Shadwell. Still, he did want to be a scholar. He had known how to read since he was five, and he had read every book in his father's library. But his mind was still full of questions. Perhaps, under his new teacher, he would find many of the answers.

"I shall like that, Father. But may I spend my vacations at Shadwell?"

"Indeed you shall." Colonel Jefferson smoothed back the sandy hair that grew in bushy masses about his son's temples. "We shall hunt and ride and fish together, and I shall take you on some of my surveying trips. Perhaps you may see the great Cherokee warrior, Ontassete."

Tom learned rapidly under Mr. Douglas. He studied Greek and Latin, and he read the classics. He became very good in mathematics. He was learning new things every day. When he went home to Shadwell, he kept right on learning— only here he learned from the outdoors instead of from books. Vacations at this simple home in the wilderness were everything that his father had promised.

"It is the strong in body who are both strong and free in mind," his father often said, and he taught his son to swim and ride and shoot. Tom liked to explore the high hills near his home. Often he looked across the Rivanna River to his favorite hill, which he called *Monticello,* the Italian word for "little mountain." It was on Colonel Jefferson's land, and Tom knew that some day it would belong to him. Somehow it seemed more beautiful than any of the surrounding mountains. The pine trees looked more majestic, and the dogwood blossoms bloomed with a sweeter fragrance in the spring. Often he rode his horse down to the river's edge, forded the stream, and followed the path that led to the wooded summit. From here he could look down at the town of Charlottesville and out over a great expanse of green valley to other mountains half lost in a blue haze. In all the world

he did not believe that he could find a scene more beautiful.

Another favorite haunt was a deserted Indian town, where Tom sometimes dug for arrows and stone hatchets. The Indians were his father's friends. Several times the chiefs had stopped at Shadwell on their way to Williamsburg, where they had gone to make treaties with the whites. Tom was especially thrilled to see Ontassete, the famous Cherokee warrior, and to listen to his fascinating tales of Indian lore. His English was slow and halting but Colonel Jefferson said that when he spoke in his own language he was a great orator.

One day when Ontassete stopped at Shadwell on his way back from Williamsburg, he had news. "Ontassete go to country across the water to make treaty with white men. Ontassete tell red men farewell when the moon shines in the forest." With a glint of a smile in his dark eyes he glanced at Tom, leaning forward in his chair, his big knuckled hands clasped about his knees.

"Colonel Jefferson good friend to Ontassete. Come to farewell campfire and bring the tall papoose."

Tom's heart was racing with excitement the night that he rode to the Cherokee village with his father. It was almost as light as day when they dismounted and walked under moon-drenched trees to the Indian campfire. There in a solemn circle sat the Cherokee braves, their faces ruddy in the glow, but showing no hint of the grief they felt at saying farewell to the great Ontassete. In the background, among the shadows, hovered the women and children.

Tom and his father walked past them to take their places among the warriors. A huge log, licked by an orange flame, fell apart with a soft crackle, but there was no other sound. The thin gray smoke curled upward and grew thinner in the moonlight, but there was no other movement. To Tom it seemed as though he sat there for a long, long time.

Then, just as he was beginning to wonder if anything was going to happen after all, there was a slight stir in the circle. Ontassete arose and held out his arms to the moon that hung like a great golden ball in the sky. The warriors lifted their faces toward him, waiting, waiting. The chief's words, now that he was speaking in the

Cherokee language, were no longer slow and halting, but came in a full, rushing, golden stream of sound. Tom could not understand a word, but a cold chill ran up his spine. He knew that the Indian warrior was praying that the Great Spirit would grant him a safe voyage and bring him home again to his own people.

Tom remembered that evening all his life. He remembered, too, many happy evenings that he spent at Shadwell. In the summer time the family gathered together under the trees, in the winter around the fire. After the three younger children were tucked in bed, the four older girls —Jane, Mary, Elizabeth, and Martha—helped their mother sew, and Colonel Jefferson read aloud or taught Tom to keep accounts. Then Jane, Tom's favorite sister, would sit at the harpsichord, and Tom would pick up his fiddle. *Squeak—squeak—squeak!* Perhaps the younger children stuffed their fingers in their ears. But Tom did not realize that other people did not always enjoy his playing as much as he did. He practiced three hours every day. When he tucked his violin beneath his chin, he forgot everything else. As he drew the bow across the strings, the dreams in his heart were reflected in his eyes.

Colonel Jefferson died when Tom was fourteen, and Tom went to live and study with Rev. James Maury, who held his classes in a log-cabin schoolhouse. It was rather lonely when he came back to Shadwell for vacations, now that his father was no longer there. But Jane was always ready to play for him on the harpsichord and to listen to his glowing plans for the future. And there was still the little mountain that he loved. Tom shared it with his friend, Dabney Carr, a boy about his own age in the neighborhood. Often they rowed across the river to visit it.

"I have something new for us to read, Dabney —Anson's *Voyage around the World*," Tom said one day, as he stepped into their boat. He placed the book carefully on the seat beside him as though it were a treasure, and picked up the oars.

"Faith, I am glad," Dabney replied, his eyes lighting up with interest. "Let us take it up to our favorite oak tree and read it there." The oak tree stood at the top of the blue-green mountain, and the boys loved it so much that they had made each other a strange promise. Whoever

died first, the other was to bring back his body and bury it beneath the friendly shade. Somehow, beneath the tree's tall branches it was easier to talk of their ambitions, and all things seemed possible.

"That's what I want to do, Dabney," Tom confided eagerly. "I want to travel like Captain Anson. Then I want to come back here and build a beautiful home on top of this mountain."

On and on the boys talked, telling each other of their secret dreams. For hours they sat there, looking down on the bright valley at their feet. It was a valley of pioneers, where every man was free and each had an equal right to carve out for himself the kind of life that he wished to live. It was the way that all Americans should live, thought Tom. Somehow, the freedom and the right to govern himself that the pioneer had found in the wilderness should belong to all men everywhere.

"All men are created equal."

Was that what the wind whispered through the branches of the oak tree? And did the leaves murmur softly, "The right to life, liberty, and the pursuit of happiness"?

Tom stirred restlessly. A shaft of sunlight glinted through the branches and lay across his face. He had no words as yet for the exciting ideas surging through his brain—ideas which later would find expression in the Declaration of Independence. Years of thought and study were to pass before he was to find those ringing phrases that would announce the birth of a new nation and a new way of living to the world.

But already the dream was stirring in his heart.

PATRICK HENRY

Sonia Daugherty

Sonia Daugherty has the knack of making people and scenes from the past as real to young readers as their everyday companions. In this selection, notice how Patrick Henry's actions and his words reveal two different sides of his character.

Reprinted by permission of the publishers, J. B. Lippincott Company, from *Ten Brave Men* by Sonia Daugherty. Copyright, 1951, by Sonia Daugherty

"I know not what course others may take; but as for me, give me liberty, or give me death!"

It was early morning. The sun was shining and birds were singing in the gnarled old oak tree on the bank of the river. The water ran so smoothly and quietly, you could hardly hear it. A man in a coonskin cap was sitting under the oak tree fishing. He listened to the birds and to the river, and watched the silver trout under the water, but his thoughts were far away. His tall shaggy horse nibbled at the grass nearby and waited patiently. He was hungry and the grass was mostly weeds, but he was used to that and he seemed not to mind it.

An old wagon rumbled down the road and slowed up. The man in the wagon looked around and waved his hand. But the fisherman was not looking in his direction and did not see him. The man in the wagon shook his head, and clucked to his horse to go on. He was in a hurry to get to the store, to trade the pelt of the fox he had trapped on his mountain farm, for nails he needed to fix his roof.

"I saw Patrick Henry fishing," he told the storekeeper, later.

"I thought Patrick went to Williamsburg to sit in the House of Burgesses," exclaimed a wiry little man sorting seeds he wanted for his garden.

"So did I," said the farmer. "But there he was sitting on the bank of the South Anna fishing."

"Maybe Louisa County made a mistake to elect Patrick to the House," said the little man.

"Maybe so," said the farmer. "Patrick failed as a storekeeper and he failed as a farmer. He may fail as a politician."

The storekeeper shook his head. Everybody in Hanover came to his store to buy and to trade, and stayed to talk about this one and that one. "Folks think well of Patrick," he said at last. "Patrick is a good lawyer."

"Patrick studied law only six weeks," laughed the little man.

"He is a mighty good lawyer," said the storekeeper again. "He won that 'Parson's Cause' case right over lawyer Lyons' head. People are expecting big things of Patrick."

A rider in buckskin breeches and a coonskin cap over his tousled red hair, pulled up his horse at the door at this moment, and entered the store, carrying a fishing basket over his shoulder. "Good morning," he called out in a friendly voice.

"Good morning, Patrick Henry," said the storekeeper. "We thought maybe you went to Williamsburg."

"I should be on my way there now," admitted Patrick. "But there isn't a better place to think things over than sitting with a fishing rod in your hand and a fish nibbling at the bait."

The men crowded around the newcomer to examine the silvery trout shining against the sides of the basket.

"I'll trade you a new rod for the catch," offered the storekeeper.

"I guess Sally will want half of it," smiled Patrick. "And you take the rest."

The storekeeper went to fetch a basket to transfer his share of the fish while Patrick scanned the shelf. "It isn't a fishing rod I want this morning, but a little present to leave with my wife and the children while I am away to Williamsburg," he said after a while. His eyes fell on a crock of wild honey on the counter, as he spoke. "That's just the thing," he nodded.

"Jim Hastings found a honey tree the other day. It's the best honey I've had in a long while," said the storekeeper, measuring off a generous chunk of golden honey into a container.

Patrick fitted the small crock of honey into the pocket of his hunting jacket, flung the basket of fish to his shoulder and rode away as suddenly as he had come. Humming a tune and weighing in his mind the things he had been thinking about when fishing, he hardly noticed how his horse galloped to get home to breakfast.

"Father is coming, Mother!" Little Martha ran shouting into the house where Sally was preparing her spinning wheel for the day. Sally and her two younger daughters, Ann and Betsy, came out on the porch where Billy, the young terrier was barking a wild welcome at his master. Patrick lifted his little daughters, one after the other, for a swing high above his shoulders. They screamed and laughed, and asked to do it again.

"What?" he cried, pretending to be angry. "Away with you. You are making me work too hard." But they knew he was only pretending and that he would swing them again. They laughed and danced about him and hung on to his hunting jacket.

"I nearly forgot to tell you in this commotion," said Patrick, "I bumped right into a honey tree."

"A honey tree?" shouted little Martha.

"A honey tree, a honey tree," sang the little girls reaching for the crock of honey.

"Help, help," cried Patrick capturing the crock, and handing it to Sally. "The honey tree sent it to you with compliments."

Sally laughed, and took the honey jar. "We were waiting breakfast for you," and she led the family to the belated breakfast.

They gathered around the table and listened wide eyed to Patrick's account of his adventure —"Shandy, the horse, found a four-leaf clover in the weeds. The birds were so pleased they began to sing a dance tune, and would you believe it, the trout in the brook danced to the tune." The little girls shouted with delight. They were used to his stories. But suddenly he stopped talking, got up from the table and began to pack a bundle, to take with him to Williamsburg: a homespun coat and a fresh shirt to wear to the House of Burgesses. "They will be elegant folks there," he said to Sally, pointing with pretended disapproval at the hunting shirt he was wearing.

"They may be dressed in elegant coats, but you'll measure up to the best of them," said Sally with confidence.

"Play us a tune, father," begged little Martha.

"Yes, yes, play us a tune," chimed in Ann and Betsy.

"Who ever heard of it, a tune so early in the morning?" Patrick pretended to look outraged.

"A good-by tune," said little Martha.

"I'll play you a weepy tune then," said Patrick, brushing away imaginary tears.

"A dance tune, father, a merry tune," cried the little girls clapping their hands.

"So? A dance tune? Very well," he said, still pretending to weep. His fiddle in his hands now, he began to play one tune after another. The children danced around him in circles, singing the tunes to keep time. Then his face became stern. He stopped playing, laid the fiddle in its case and tied it into his bundle.

Jack White, his young Negro servant, brought the shaggy horse to the door now.

"There," cried Patrick, "Jack knows I should be on my way."

"Must you go? Do you have to go away?" The little girls clung to his legs and to his arms.

"Be good, be extra good while I am away." He lifted each one for another high swing and a kiss.

Sally walked beside him to where the impatient horse was pawing the ground, eager to be off.

"There will be important questions to decide," said Patrick quietly.

"You will be equal to whatever comes up," Sally assured him.

He leaned over, kissed her good-by, and jumped on his horse. The young terrier ran barking after him as the horse trotted away.

The sun was high in the blue sky, the air was sweet with honeysuckle and wild orange. It was a beautiful morning. Patrick Henry sat on his horse, lost in thought. He had not been in Williamsburg since the day he went there to ask Wythe and Peyton Randolph to sign his license to practice law. He smiled now as he remembered it all—Wythe, the learned scholar, refused even to listen to his arguments.

"You say you studied law alone, and only for six weeks?" asked Wythe with a frown. "Go to college, young man, and study with proper teachers," he told him.

It was a great good fortune for him, mused Patrick, that the venerable Peyton Randolph became interested in his arguments and consented to sign his license to practice law. And two other lawyers did likewise. They believed in him. Why? wondered Patrick, gratefully. He promised them that he would continue to read and to study. But that was not the reason they believed in him; he understood it better now. They were convinced he could be a lawyer by the way he argued his own case with them. "Yes," he cried aloud, and the lean horse under him bounced forward to a quicker pace, raising a cloud of red dust on the bumpy road. "I proved it, I proved I am a good lawyer."

The sun was hot on his shoulders. Patrick took off his cap and mopped his forehead. He felt excited and happy and a little uneasy at the same time. He was going to sit in the House of Burgesses. It was an honor, but more important, he thought soberly, was the opportunity he would now have to help shape events, make changes for the better for the people in the colonies.

It was dusk by the time his horse turned into Duke of Gloucester Street. After Hanover, Williamsburg seemed very elegant to Patrick. Fashionable ladies in silks and velvets passed him by in elegant carriages. Patrick galloped down the entire length of the street from William and Mary College at one end, to the Capitol at the other. He turned about to trot back to the Raleigh Tavern. The uncurtained windows of the tavern sparkled with candlelight. Patrick reined his horse, and watched the parade of gentlemen in powdered wigs, frilled shirts, velvet coats and knee breeches, coming and going in and out of the wide doors of the tavern. It would be a pleasant place to stay the night, but as he jingled his meager purse in his hand, he decided he must find himself a cheaper place. He thought of Sally and his little daughters snug at home. He felt lonely now, wondering where he could find a bed to sleep.

Two men came out of the tavern talking and laughing, and stopped to try a new dance step on the green in front of the tavern. Patrick pulled his violin out of his bundle and started to play a dance tune. A horseman galloped by, and came back presently. A tall slender young man with sandy red hair leaned forward from the saddle—"Patrick Henry," he called out in a surprised voice. "I was wondering who it could be, playing like that."

"Thomas Jefferson," exclaimed Patrick in a delighted voice.

"What are you doing in Williamsburg?" asked Jefferson.

"I guess you haven't heard I've been elected to the House of Burgesses from Louisa County," said Patrick with a slow smile.

"Then you've come to Williamsburg to sit in the House of Burgesses. Stay the night at my house," invited Jefferson.

"Thank you," said Patrick with a wide smile. "I was just wondering where I'd sleep this night."

"I'll hurry and tell Caesar there will be company, and you come along," Jefferson called over his shoulder as he galloped away in the dusk.

Patrick finished playing his tune, and went to find a stable to put his horse away for the night.

Caesar, Jefferson's young slave, was waiting for him at the door when he arrived, the bundle under his arm. "Come right in, sir, come right in." Caesar beamed a wide smile as he led the way into Jefferson's bachelor apartment. It was a pleasant room to come into out of the night. Candles were lit on the fine mahogany table. The white cloth and the silver sparkled in the candlelight. Book shelves crowded with books lined the walls: law books, histories, poetry. Patrick put his bundle on the sofa, took off his coonskin cap, and went to wash the dust from his hands and face.

Jefferson came in from an inner room now, his sandy hair freshly combed, his white face shining with a genial smile. He was seven years younger than Patrick, and he was still a student, studying law at William and Mary College, but already he was a finished gentleman. "You are just in time," he exclaimed gaily. "Caesar is waiting to give us our supper."

The cold meat and hot corn bread tasted good to Patrick after his long ride. There were many things to talk about, pleasant things they both remembered as they sat in the soft candlelight— "Do you remember the first time we met?" asked Jefferson in his slow genial voice. "'Twas a house party at Captain Daindridge's house."

"Ay, at Hanover, at Captain Nathaniel West Daindridge's house. It was Christmas holiday," reminisced Patrick with a wide smile.

"I still remember the dance tunes you played," smiled Jefferson. "But I hear you have become a great lawyer now," he added, shortly.

"I wouldn't claim that." Patrick looked very serious now, and pleased at the same time, that Jefferson had heard a flattering report of him.

"The learned lawyers, here in Williamsburg, talk with much wonder of the way you pleaded that 'Parson's Cause' case," said Jefferson.

"The lawyers are surprised I won the case, because they know I studied by myself, and only for six weeks," grinned Patrick.

"Well, yes," admitted Jefferson. "It's a wonder to us all; and what's more to wonder at is that you win every case you take."

"The 'Parson's Cause' case was my first case," said Patrick. "I was mighty anxious to win that case for my clients. I read and studied in the law books, and prepared my case carefully to make sure my arguments would be correct. But first I made sure I was in the right. When I know a thing is right, I plead from the heart."

"From the heart, I like that," exclaimed Jefferson. "Maybe you didn't need to read law books as long as we all do at college."

"As to that, I promised Peyton Randolph when he signed my license that I would read and study, and I do," said Patrick.

"When you are not fishing and hunting," laughed Jefferson.

"It is true, I'd rather fish and hunt," confessed Patrick with a wide smile. Caesar came in now to clear the table. Jefferson took his violin from the top shelf of his bookcase and began to tune it.

"That 'Parson's Cause' case," said Patrick, "gave me a chance to show the Parliament in England that they can't tell us here in the colonies, what we should pay our clergy. The Parliament in England is running us high handed, what with taxes and trade regulations."

"That's true," Jefferson nodded, his face clouded now. "But we can't deny that England has a right to tax her colonies and that's what we are, a colony to England."

"Nevertheless, they go too far, and now there is that Stamp Act. It's not only a nuisance, but a hardship," cried Patrick, with such heat that Jefferson stopped tuning his violin, and stood waiting to hear what he had on his mind. "We'll have to pay for a stamp every time we use a legal paper, and every time we buy a newspaper or sign a document. Are we going to submit to that?"

Jefferson scratched a few notes on his violin, his face grave and thoughtful. He felt embarrassed that he had not given the question much thought. Patrick seemed to know and to understand things he had hardly thought about. "No one likes the Stamp Act, but what can we do about it?" he asked after a while.

Patrick fumbled in his bundle for his violin and struck up one of the tunes they had played together at the Christmas house party in Hanover. It was a merry tune; they broke out into a song, and began to dance. Another tune came to their minds, and then another. They forgot England, and the tax and law books. Their voices

rang out through the windows into the starlit night. Suddenly there was a loud banging on the door. Jefferson stopped playing and went to the door still holding the fiddle in his hand. A man in a nightshirt and a night cap over his head was shivering in the night air on the doorstep.

"Sir," he cried indignantly. "The whole neighborhood is waiting for you to stop fiddling. It is long past midnight. No one can sleep with such noise going on."

"I am right sorry, sir," apologized Jefferson. "I had no idea it was that late."

"Look at the clock, look at the clock," roared the man, as he turned to go to his house.

Jefferson tiptoed back into his rooms and went to bed. Patrick took off his dusty boots and curled up on the sofa to sleep.

The sun was just rising when Patrick wakened. This was the *day,* he remembered instantly, his first day to sit in the House of Burgesses. He tiptoed noiselessly into the dressing room to wash and dress himself with particular care.

When Jefferson wakened a little later, he saw Patrick sitting at the window dressed in the new homespun coat he had brought with him, his red unruly hair carefully groomed. He was too engrossed, writing on the flyleaf of an old book, to notice Jefferson standing in the doorway.

"I hope you don't mind," he called out when he looked up presently and saw Jefferson watching him with an amused smile.

"Not in the least," Jefferson assured him. "The book is in tatters."

"I didn't want to waken you to ask for paper," explained Patrick, as he tore the leaf from the book, folded it carefully, and put it in his pocket.

Caesar came in with breakfast now, and Jefferson wondered what Patrick had to write down in such a hurry that he couldn't wait to ask for paper. But Patrick Henry didn't offer to tell him.

The Capitol building was crowded to the door for there were many people in Williamsburg who were anxious to hear the debate on the Stamp Act. The law students from William and Mary College were obliged to stand in the doorway to listen to the discourses in the House of Burgesses. Patrick lingered in the entrance for a parting word with Jefferson before he pushed his way through the crowd into the courtroom. Speaker of the House Robinson, was already in his place at the front. The leaders of the House, wealthy plantation owners in powdered wigs and broadcloth coats, were talking in little clusters, laughing at each other's pleasantries.

They didn't seem at all preoccupied with the important question that was to be discussed, marveled Patrick Henry. He was glad to recognize George Johnston, of Fairfax County, standing near by. Here was someone he could sound out—"What will be done about the Stamp Act, sir?" he asked Johnston.

"Nothing more can be done about it," Johnston shrugged his shoulders. "The Stamp Act's been passed. We don't like it, but what can we do about it?" he demanded.

"We can protest," cried Patrick hotly.

"Protest?" Johnston looked surprised.

"If we accept the Stamp Act without a protest it's a sign we've no spirit. That's what they'll think about us in England, and they'll be right. And they'll levy more taxes on us. We'll be taxed and taxed and taxed again and again."

"We have no redress. We can't stop them taxing us. We're subject to the crown," reasoned Johnston.

Patrick pulled out a folded paper from his pocket and handed it to Johnston. "I've written out seven resolutions, sir, if you would care to read them. You might be willing also to second them."

Johnston took the paper and read it slowly. An excited look came into his eyes. "I'm with you, sir, I'll second your resolutions," he cried.

Speaker Robinson was now pounding the table with his silver mace. Patrick slouched into his seat on the long wooden bench with the other burgesses. Two men on the bench beside him were talking in low grumbling voices. "We force the soil so as to grow bigger crops of tobacco so as to pay taxes to England," one of the men was saying.

"Ay, and if we keep on forcing the soil, there'll be no life left in it," said the other man. "It's getting poorer all the time."

"That's it," exclaimed a man in a nearby seat. "Can't raise crops on poor soil."

"I've no glass in my windows, but I must pay taxes to the crown before I spend money on window glass," broke in a third man.

"If we spent some of that tax money on fixing our roads—" mumbled another burgess from the up country.

"The meeting please come to order," cried the clerk.

A gentleman in a powdered wig and a handsome coat, stood up now and began to talk. He looked very imposing as he stood there, talking in a loud voice—"The Stamp Act seems to have caused much talk," he measured every word carefully. "The fact is, this tax is so small it is but a trifle. I see it more as a nuisance rather than a hardship to complain about."

"The cost of the stamp may be small, but it's an extra tax, and it's a tax too much," cried a voice from the back seat in the row of benches.

No one paid attention to the interruption. A stout man with many ruffles of fine lace on his shirt stood up now and began to explain the reason why the colonies should pay the tax with good grace—"The English Parliament deems it necessary to fix the Stamp Act, therefore we, the loyal subjects to the crown, are willing to obey."

"The two gentlemen hold the welfare of the crown before the welfare of the colonies, it seems to me," Patrick whispered to Johnston.

"Governor Fauquier is a Tory as you may have heard, and he has many admirers in the House," Johnston whispered back.

Patrick listened to the speeches of the leaders of the House with a frown, and shifted uneasily in his seat. Suddenly he stood up and began to talk. His voice sounded frightened at the first few words:

"The English Parliament is interfering with the affairs of the colonies," he exclaimed. "The misrule of the English Parliament has brought great hardships to the colonies," Patrick's voice grew louder and firmer.

"Who is this buckskin gentleman, giving his views?" cried an indignant voice from the front.

"An ignorant fellow from the backwoods," said one of the lawyers with a shrug.

Patrick went on talking as if he had not heard them. He was talking about something he understood and treasured. He was talking about liberty, the right of men to govern themselves. His eyes glowed, his voice rang. A spell fell on the assembly as they listened to his arguments— "We submit to taxation without representation," he cried in a challenging voice.

Peyton Randolph frowned. He was a proud Virginia gentleman, and he was also attorney general to the king of England.

"This thing must be stopped," he said to Pendleton. Wythe shook his head. A debate started up now as leaders of the House rose to interrupt Patrick at every word—"Is this new member from Louisa County claiming Virginia has a right to make laws to resist the English Parliament?" demanded an indignant voice.

In answer Patrick unfolded the piece of paper he was holding in his hand and began to read what he had scribbled there early that morning:

"The first adventurers who settled in America brought with them the right of franchise," Patrick pronounced each word in a high fiery voice.

"What's that?" interrupted an angry man at the front. Patrick straightened his shoulders and went on reading from his paper, explaining the rights of the colonies.

"Two royal charters were granted by King James the First that entitled the colonies to all privileges, liberties and immunities . . . as if they were living within the realm of England . . ."

"Patrick Henry may be from the backwoods," called out a burgess from the benches, "but it's Patrick Henry, this man from the backwoods, and not our learned lawyers who is saying what we need to know."

"Yes, that's true," said Wythe to Peyton Randolph. "I now wish I had signed his license to practice law."

Peyton Randolph frowned, his face red and angry.

"Resolved therefore," Patrick went on—"Resolved that the general assembly of this colony have the only sole and exclusive rights and power to lay taxes and impositions upon the inhabitants of this colony."

"This is sedition," cried out a Tidewater gentleman.

"Sedition, sedition," cried out several leaders of the House.

"No person that is not in the general assembly of the colonies has a right to impress taxation on the people of the colonies; such a person should be considered an enemy. Caesar had his Brutus and Charles the Second his Cromwell and George the Third—"

"Shame, shame," interrupted the Speaker of the House, pounding his mace on the table.

"Treason," cried an indignant voice. "Shame, treason, treason," resounded from all sides.

Patrick looked around him slowly, noting the frightened faces. His eyes flashed—"And George the Third may profit by their example." His voice rang and echoed in the ceiling. "If this be treason, make the most of it."

The whole House buzzed with excited voices now. The burgesses crowded around Patrick to congratulate him, clapping him on the shoulder, shaking his hand.

"Who was Caesar?" a farmer was asking.

"Caesar was a dictator in olden times in Rome. He ruled the people of Rome without their consent exactly, and Brutus killed him. And Charles the Second tried to rule England without Parliament; Cromwell and his army beheaded him," explained a more informed burgess with a knowing wink.

At the front of the House, Tidewater gentlemen were talking in troubled voices. Many of them agreed with what Patrick said, but they were not ready to say aloud what might bring on war.

Patrick listened to the buzz of many voices all talking at once. There was to be a vote. They were going to vote on his resolves. The burgesses from the back country were in high spirits, making jokes and laughing. They gave their vote fearlessly; come what might, they were ready for it in their own minds. Patrick listened to the vote as it was taken— Some of the burgesses had gone home to their mountain farms to look after the spring plowing, but there were enough left who would vote for his resolves. "We'll win by a small majority," he whispered to Johnston. He looked very sober now. Virginia must not lose this chance to stand up, and show the English Parliament that the colonies had a spirit in them to resist oppression.

The clerk cleared his throat and announced the vote. The resolves had passed. That meant that the colonies would offer a protest based on what they knew was their right.

The House adjourned. The burgesses could go home now to their plowing. They lingered a while to talk— This was an important day. They all only dimly guessed how important it was. They left the Capitol at last. There was a lot to think about on the way home. This day, May 29, 1765, was a day to remember.

Patrick went now to find his bundle which he had left in a corner of the entry.

"You spoke with courage and with wisdom." Jefferson came up now to press his hand warmly. "From today, I shall take note of the affairs in the colonies."

"You spoke for all Virginia," one of the leaders of the House stopped to say to Patrick as he was leaving the Capitol.

"I hope so, sir," Patrick bowed. He could bow with as much grace as any Tidewater gentleman when he chose. But now he was thinking of going home. He went to get his horse. He could go fishing with an easy mind now, and he might hunt in the woods, and trap a bear, as he once did— But his foremost thought would remain with meetings in Louisa County, and in the Hanover Courthouse, where he would raise his voice to challenge men's minds to think of freedom as a gift already theirs to claim.

His lean horse trotted briskly over the red clay road. Patrick clicked his tongue to spur him on. He was in a hurry to get home to share his happiness with Sally. He had spoken for Virginia. He felt proud of that, but in the back of his thoughts was the hope that all the other colonies might hear of it, and arise to speak for their rights.

from JOHNNY TREMAIN

Esther Forbes

The first episode given here reveals the patience of the British soldiers with the rebellious colonists and the deadly earnestness of the rebels. The second provides a glimpse of the plotters, their ideals, and activities.

["That a Man Can Stand Up"]

Along down Old Country Road, marching through the meager, half-light of the new day, came a company of Minute Men up and out early, drilling for coming battles before it was yet the hour to get to their chores. Left, right, left, right, left . . . they did not march too well. A boy no bigger than Dusty Miller had put a fife to his lips, was trying to blow it. He made awkward little tootles. The men marched on past the defaced gates of the Lytes' country seat, never turning to look at them or Doctor Warren's chaise with Cilla and Johnny under the hood.

Oh, God help them, thought Johnny. They haven't seen those British troops in Boston. I have. They haven't seen the gold lace on the generals, those muskets—all so alike, and everyone has a bayonet. They haven't seen . . .

The chaise overtook and passed the marching farmers.

That musket which Rab did not have bothered Johnny. However, the soldiers never carried them while loitering about alehouses and wharves, or the stables of the Afric Queen. They stood guard with them. They drilled with them. They practiced marksmanship (very badly, Rab said), and now and then over at the foot of the

From *Johnny Tremain* by Esther Forbes. Reprinted by permission of and arrangement with Houghton Mifflin Company, the authorized publishers

Common they executed a deserter with them, but never, not once, as far as Johnny could make out, did they leave them about. Drilling, shooting, marching over, they stacked them at their barracks and there was always at least a sergeant guarding these stacked guns.

Johnny and Rab dropped their voices, even in the privacy of their attic, when they discussed these muskets. The Yankee gunsmiths were working from dawn to dusk preparing guns, making new ones, but as long as Rab had a weapon and was, after all, little more than a boy, he believed he had no chance for a modern gun unless he got it for himself from the British.

"How soon," Johnny whispered, "before they march out . . . and the war begins?"

"God knows," Rab murmured. "God and General Gage. Maybe not until next spring. Armies always move in the spring. But before then I must have a good gun in my hands. A man can stand up to anything with a good weapon in his hands. Without it, he's but a dumb beast."

Johnny had never seen Rab so blocked by anything. Apparently he went through every situation without friction, like a knife going through cheese. Now he was blocked and it made him restless, possibly less canny. One day he told Johnny that he had a contract with a farmer from Medway who was making a business of buying muskets from the British privates and selling them to Minute Men. Rab did not like to ask his aunt for so large a sum. She had little enough to buy food. But she had said, "Weapons before food."

One morning Johnny knew Rab was meeting the farmer at market. He knew that the soldier, returning from guard duty, was going, absent-mindedly, to leave his musket on a pile of straw. It had all been worked out. But when he heard yells and shouts from the market-place and the rattle of British drums calling up reserves, he tore over to Dock Square. He had a feeling that the turmoil was over Rab's gun. He was right.

A solid block of redcoats faced out, presenting their muskets at the market people and inhabitants. The Captain was yelling to the churning hundreds. "Get back, stand back, good people of Boston. This is our own private affair."

"What's happened?" Johnny asked an old hen-wife.

"They've caught one of their own men selling a musket to a farmer."

"Happens he comes from Medway?"

"So 'tis said."

"Happens they caught more than the farmer and the soldier?"

"They caught three in all. They are taking them over to the Province House—for General Gage."

"Gage is in Salem."

"For some colonel, then."

No mob gathered to rescue the two Yankees. All, by now, felt a certain confidence in the British way of doing things. A general, or even a colonel, had the right to punish a soldier caught selling his arms, and also anyone who tempted him.

Johnny tagged the marching soldiers, but it was not until they turned into the Province House that he saw the three prisoners. The British soldier was grinning, and Johnny guessed that he had been put up to this game merely to snare "the yokels."

The farmer was in his market smock. He had long, straight gray hair and a thin, mean mouth. You could tell by looking at him he had gone into this little business for the love of money, not for the love of freedom. Rab had been shaken out of his usual nice balance between quick action and caution by his passionate desire for a good gun. Otherwise he would not have mixed himself up with such a man. Rab himself was looking a little sullen. He was not used to defeat. What would they do to him? They might imprison him. They might flog him. Worst of all, they might turn him over to some tough top sergeant to be taught "a lesson." This informal punishment would doubtless be the worst.

The Province House was a beautiful building and as Johnny hung about the front of it he had a chance to admire it for over an hour. It stood well back from the rattle and bustle of Marlborough Street, with its glassy-eyed copper Indian on top of the cupola and its carved and colored lion and unicorn of Britain over the door. Behind the house he heard orders called and soldiers were hallooing—but worst of all they were laughing. And that was Colonel Nesbit's boy bringing around the Colonel's charger. There was a large group of people still standing in the street. The hilarity of the British soldiers did not ease their fears as to the fate of the prisoners. Johnny could hear the rattle of the men's muskets as they came to attention, and then, all together, four drummers let their sticks fall as one.

Out onto Marlborough Street, with the drummers in black bearskin caps first, and then Colonel Nesbit on horseback, came almost the entire Forty-Seventh Regiment, surrounding a cart. In the cart sat a hideous blackbird, big as a man, shaped like a man, with head hung forward like a moulting crow. It was a naked man, painted with tar and rolled in feathers. Three times already the Whigs had tarred and feathered enemies and carted them through the streets of Boston. Now it was the British turn. The redcoats marched. The Colonel's horse pranced. The cart with its shameful burden bumped over the cobbles. One glance had convinced Johnny this was not Rab. The hideous blackbird had a paunch. Rab had none.

Before the Town House, Colonel Nesbit ordered a halt, and an orderly came forward and read a proclamation. It merely explained what was being done and why, and threatened like treatment to the next buyer of stolen weapons.

Then (Colonel Nesbit was evidently a newspaper reader) the regiment went to Marshall Lane and stopped before the office of the *Spy*. The threat was made that the editor of that paper would soon be treated like the bird in the cart. Then they were heading for Edes and Gill's office. Johnny guessed the *Observer* would come next after the *Boston Gazette,* and ran to Salt Lane to warn Uncle Lorne. He jumped into the shop, slamming the door after him, looking wildly about for the printer. Rab, in his printer's apron, was standing at his bench, quietly setting type.

"Rab! How'd you do it? How'd you get away?"

Rab's eyes glittered. In spite of his great air of calm, he was angry.

"Colonel Nesbit said I was just a child. 'Go buy a popgun, boy,' he said. They flung me out the back door. Told me to go home."

Then Johnny laughed. He couldn't help it. Rab had always, as far as Johnny knew, been treated as a grown man and always looked upon himself as such.

"So all he did was hurt your feelings."

Rab grinned suddenly, but a little thinly.

Johnny told of the tar-and-feathering of the farmer and also that he expected in a short time the Forty-Seventh Regiment would come marching down Salt Lane and stop before the door to read that proclamation about tar-and-feathering seditious newspaper publishers.

"And here they come—those dressed-up red monkeys. But they don't dare do anything but stop, read a proclamation, and move on."

When this was over and the troops moved on down the lane to Union, Johnny and Rab stood in the street and watched them.

"Luckily," said Rab, "I didn't give my money in advance. I'll return it to Aunt Jenifer."

But he still stood in the street watching the stiff rhythm of the marching troops, the glitter of their guns and bayonets, the dazzle of the white and scarlet disappearing at the bottom of the lane.

"They'll make good targets, all right," he said absent-mindedly. "Out in Lexington they are telling us, 'Pick off the officers first, then the sergeants.' Those white crosses on their chests are easy to sight on . . ."

His words frightened Johnny a little. Lieutenant Stranger, Sergeant Gale, Major Pitcairn . . . Johnny could not yet think of them as targets. Rab could.

. . . .

It was fall, and for the last time Sam Adams bade Johnny summon the Observers for eight o'clock that night.

"After this we will not meet again, for I believe Gage knows all about us. He might be moved to arrest Mr. Lorne. He might send soldiers to arrest us all."

"I hardly think they would hang the whole club, sir. Only you and Mr. Hancock."

Johnny had meant this for a compliment, but Sam Adams looked more startled than pleased.

"It has been noticed that every so often many of us are seen going up and down Salt Lane, entering the printing shop. We must, in the future, meet in small groups. But once more, and for the last time . . . And make as good a punch for us as you can."

. . . .

It would be a small meeting, for of the twenty-two original members many had already left town to get away from the threat of arrest by the

British. Josiah Quincy was in England. Of the three revolutionary doctors, only Church and Warren remained. Doctor Young had gone to a safer spot. James Otis was at the moment in Boston. Johnny had not notified him, although he had founded this club in the first place. Ever since he had grown so queer, the other members did not wish him about, even in his lucid periods. He talked and talked. Nobody could get a word in edgewise when James Otis talked.

This, the last meeting, started with the punch bowl on the table instead of ending with it. There was no chairman nor was there any time when the two boys were supposed to withdraw. They were talking about how Gage had at last dared send out a sortie beyond the gate of Boston and, before the Minute Men got word of their plans, they had seized cannon and gunpowder over in Charlestown, got into their boats and back to Boston. Not one shot had been fired and it was all too late when the alarm had been spread and thousands of armed farmers had arrived. By then the British were safe home again. Yet, Sam Adams protested, this rising up of an army of a thousand from the very soil of New England had badly frightened General Gage. Once the alarm spread that the British had left Boston, the system of calling up the Minute Men had worked well indeed. The trouble had been in Boston itself.

"In other words, gentlemen, it was our fault. If we could have known but an hour, two hours, in advance what the British were intending, our men would have been there before the British troops arrived instead of a half-hour after they left."

Johnny had been told off to carry letters for the British officers, to keep on good terms with their grooms and stable boys over at the Afric Queen. Somehow he had failed. He hadn't known. Nobody had known that two hundred and sixty redcoats were getting into boats, slipping off up the Mystic, seizing Yankee gunpowder, and rowing it back to Castle Island for themselves.

Paul Revere was saying, "We must organize a better system of watching their movements—but in such a way that they will not realize they are being watched."

. . . .

There was a heavy footstep across the floor of the shop below. Rab leaped to the ladder's head.

"James Otis," he reported to the men standing about Adams.

"Well," said Sam Adams, a little crossly, "no one needs stay and listen to *him*. He shot his bolt years ago. Still talking about the natural rights of man—and the glories of the British Empire! You and I, John, had as well go home and get a good night's sleep before leaving at dawn to-morrow."

Otis pulled his bulk up the ladder. If no one was glad to see him, at least no one was so discourteous as to leave. Mr. Otis was immediately shown every honor, given a comfortable armchair and a tankard of punch. Seemingly he was not in a talkative mood tonight. The broad, ruddy, good-natured face turned left and right, nodding casually to his friends, taking it for granted that he was still a great man among them, instead of a milestone they all believed they had passed years before.

He sniffed at his punch and sipped a little.

"Sammy," he said to Sam Adams, "my coming interrupted something you were saying . . . 'We will fight,' you had got that far."

"Why, yes. That's no secret."

"For what will we fight?"

"To free Boston from these infernal redcoats and . . ."

"No," said Otis. "Boy, give me more punch. That's not enough reason for going into a war. Did any occupied city ever have better treatment than we've had from the British? Has one rebellious newspaper been stopped—one treasonable speech? Where are the firing squads, the jails jammed with political prisoners? What about the gallows for you, Sam Adams, and you, John Hancock? It has never been set up. I hate those infernal British troops spread all over my town as much as you do. Can't move these days without stepping on a soldier. But we are not going off into a civil war merely to get them out of Boston. Why are we going to fight? Why, why?"

There was an embarrassed silence. Sam Adams was the acknowledged ringleader. It was for him to speak now.

"We will fight for the rights of Americans. England cannot take our money away by taxes."

"No, no. For something more important than the pocketbooks of our American citizens."

Rab said, "For the rights of Englishmen—everywhere."

"Why stop with Englishmen?" Otis was warming up. He had a wide mouth, crooked and generous. He settled back in his chair and then he began to talk. It was such talk as Johnny had never heard before. The words surged up through the big body, flowed out of the broad mouth. He never raised his voice, and he went on and on. Sometimes Johnny felt so intoxicated by the mere sound of the words that he hardly followed the sense. That soft, low voice flowed over him: submerged him.

". . . For men and women and children all over the world," he said. "You were right, you tall, dark boy, for even as we shoot down the British soldiers we are fighting for rights such as they will be enjoying a hundred years from now.

". . . There shall be no more tyranny. A handful of men cannot seize power over thousands. A man shall choose who it is shall rule over him.

". . . The peasants of France, the serfs of Russia. Hardly more than animals now. But because we fight, they shall see freedom like a new sun rising in the west. Those natural rights God has given to every man, no matter how humble . . ." He smiled suddenly and said . . . "or crazy," and took a good pull at his tankard.

". . . The battle we win over the worst in England shall benefit the best in England. How well are they over there represented when it comes to taxes? Not very well. It will be better for them when we have won this war.

"Will French peasants go on forever pulling off their caps and saying 'Oui, Monsieur,' when the gold coaches run down their children? They will not. Italy. And all those German states. Are they nothing but soldiers? Will no one show them the rights of good citizens? So we hold up our torch—and do not forget it was lighted upon the fires of England—and we will set it as a new sun to lighten a world . . ."

Sam Adams, anxious to get that good night's sleep before starting next day for Philadelphia, was smiling slightly, nodding his gray head, seeming to agree. He was bored. It does not matter, he was thinking, what James Otis says these days—sane or crazy.

Joseph Warren's fair, responsive face was aflame. The torch Otis had been talking about seemed reflected in his eyes.

"We are lucky men," he murmured, "for we have a cause worth dying for. This honor is not given to every generation."

"Boy," said Otis to Johnny, "fill my tankard."

It was not until he had drained it and wiped his mouth on the back of his hand that he spoke again. All sat silently waiting for him. He had, and not for the first time, cast a spell upon them.

"They say," he began again, "my wits left me after I got hit on the head by that customs official. That's what you think, eh, Mr. Sam Adams?"

"Oh, no, no, indeed, Mr. Otis."

"Some of us will give our wits," he said, "some of us all our property. Heh, John Hancock, did you hear that? *Property*—that hurts, eh? To give one's silver wine-coolers, one's coach and four, and the gold buttons off one's sprigged satin waistcoats?"

Hancock looked him straight in the face and Johnny had never before liked him so well.

"I am ready," he said. "I can get along without all that."

"You, Paul Revere, you'll give up that silver-craft you love. God made you to make silver, not war."

Revere smiled. "There's a time for the casting of silver and a time for the casting of cannon. If that's not in the Bible, it should be."

"Doctor Warren, you've a young family. You know quite well, if you get killed they may literally starve."

Warren said, "I've thought of all that long ago."

"And you, John Adams. You've built up a very nice little law practice, stealing away my clients, I notice. Ah, well, so it goes. Each shall give according to his own abilities, and some—" he turned directly to Rab—"some will give their lives. All the years of their maturity. All the children they never live to have. The serenity of old age. To die so young is more than merely dying; it is to lose so large a part of life."

Rab was looking straight at Otis. His arms were folded across his chest. His head flung back a little. His lips parted as though he would speak, but he did not.

"Even you, my old friend—my old enemy? How shall I call you, Sam Adams? Even you will give the best you have—a genius for politics. Oh, go to Philadelphia! Pull all the wool, pull all the strings and all the wires. Yes, go, go! And God go with you. We need you, Sam. We must fight this war. You'll play your part—but what it is really about . . . you'll never know."

James Otis was on his feet, his head close against the rafters that cut down into the attic, making it the shape of a tent. Otis put out his arms.

"It is all so much simpler than you think," he said. He lifted his hands and pushed against the rafters.

"We give all we have, lives, property, safety, skills . . . we fight, we die, for a simple thing. Only that a man can stand up."

With a curt nod, he was gone.

Johnny was standing close to Rab. It had frightened him when Mr. Otis had said, "Some will give their lives," and looked straight at Rab. Die so that "a man can stand up."

Once more Sam Adams had the center of attention. He was again buttoning up his coat, preparing to leave, but first he turned to Revere.

"Now *he* is gone, we can talk a moment about that spy system you think you can organize in Boston."

Paul Revere, like his friend, Joseph Warren, was still slightly under the spell of James Otis.

"I had not thought about it that way before," he said, not answering Sam Adams's words. "You know my father had to fly France because of the tyranny over there. He was only a child. But now, in a way, I'm fighting for that child . . . that no frightened lost child ever is sent out a refugee from his own country because of race or religion." Then he pulled himself together and answered Sam Adams's remarks about the spy system.

That night, when the boys were both in bed, Johnny heard Rab, usually a heavy sleeper, turning and turning.

"Johnny," he said at last, "are you awake?"

"Yes."

"What was it he said?"

"That a man can stand up."

Rab sighed and stopped turning. In a few moments he was asleep. As often had happened before, it was the younger boy who lay wide-eyed in the darkness.

"That a man can stand up."

He'd never forget Otis with his hands pushed up against the cramping rafters over his head.

"That a man can stand up"—as simple as that.

And the strange new sun rising in the west. A sun that was to illumine a world to come.

LOST IN THE APPLE CAVE

Carolyn Sherwin Bailey

There are many stories, books, and poems about Johnny Appleseed, but this story gives a long-range picture of the man from the standpoint of one of his beneficiaries. Look up the poem, "Johnny Appleseed," in The Book of Americans *by Rosemary and Stephen Vincent Benét. Carolyn Bailey has written many books for children including her unusual fairy tale* Miss Hickory, *which won the Newbery Award in 1947.*

Swinging her worn shoes from the steps of the covered wagon whose great canvas top had been her only roof for months, Rose looked back along the wilderness road. At its beginning lay the mountains. Where the road ended was a wide river. Rose and her father and mother were on their way from New England to that great unknown place beyond the Ohio River called the West. Everything they owned was packed in the great clumsy wagon, camped now on the banks of the Ohio until a flatboat should come to ferry it across. Rose had loved everything about the trip: the slow movement along strange roads, the tinkle of bells on some peddler's mule, the glimpse of a passing wain full of barrels of maple syrup or of raw hides and raw wool, the evening's camp beside some brook with a supper of cornmeal mush and salt pork cooked over an open fire.

The big wagon was like home to the twelve-year-old girl. In a corner crowded with pewter plates, patchwork quilts, sacks of cornmeal, and gourds of milk, Rose had a family of dolls made of great pine cones she had gathered on the road. She had dressed them in bits of her own calico frock as it had become torn. The little heads of these dolls, made of small wild apples, wore sun-bonnets like Rose's own, or hats made of plaited rushes gathered by the brooks. The pine-cone dolls had a set of dishes made of acorns.

Kicking her heels against the wagon step, feeling the warm harvest sun on her bare legs, Rose wished that she knew what lay within those deep woods at the right of their camp. She was sometimes lonely, for they had not happened to meet any other girl of her age all summer. She watched her mother bending over the knitting she was trying to finish before the sun dipped down into the river in flaming crimson. Her father was trying to catch some fish for supper. Rose stood up at last, swinging a little hand-made basket over her arm.

"I am going for a walk, Mother," she said. "Perhaps I can find some berries in the wood to eat with our porridge tonight."

"Do not go too far, Rose," her mother warned. "Your father saw a big brown bear quite close this morning."

"I will be back by suppertime," Rose said.

In five minutes from the time she left the wagon camp, Rose was out of all sight and sound of it. The faint stir of a passing snake among the fallen leaves in the forest, the rustle of a chipmunk's little feet, the flapping of a crow's wings or an owl's, were the only sounds. Rose hurried, remembering the bear. She never thought that she could lose the trail, but soon it seemed as if she were going round and round, each moment straying deeper into the wilderness. Her arms and legs were scratched by the bushes, each step was less sure. Rose ran. She clung to the little rush basket for comfort. It broke the force of her fall as she stepped down, tumbled, and found herself imprisoned in a cave. The entrance had been carefully screened by leafy boughs and bushes. When she got up and looked about, Rose could not believe her eyes.

The cave smelled deliciously of apples. Eating apples were a new fruit in those days, and rather rare. But here, in a roomy cave that had a little bubbling spring at the back to keep the fruit moist, was shelf upon shelf of wonderful apples such as Rose had never seen, stored away for the winter. There were August apples, the delight of harvesters. There were great golden pippins which made Rose think of the big bell on the church at home that had rung for their courage when the covered wagons started out; hard little russet apples that would keep all winter and be sweeter in March than they were now; and great red spicy apples, grown by grafting a shoot from a wild-apple bough into a bough of a sweet orchard-apple tree. Rose selected one of these apples and sat down in content on the mossy floor to munch it. This might be a bear's cave, she thought, but it was the pleasantest place she had seen in a long time.

Bright skin, delicious juice, crunchy pulp, Rose ate her apple down to its nest of big black seeds. She was just cupping her hands to drink from the spring, when a shadow darkened the door of the cave. Could it be the bear of whom her mother had warned her? Rose was dumb with terror as she saw a dark form closing the cave entrance. But a voice reassured her.

"Don't be afraid, little girl. It's only Appleseed Johnny. Welcome to my orchard!"

The man, strange indeed with his long hair, ragged clothes, and feet bare save for Indian moccasins, held out his hand to Rose.

"Come and see my trees, little girl," he said. "Many of the people of the covered wagons make this orchard of mine their halfway house before they cross the Ohio River. Come and see my house, too, and then I will show you the way to the camp again."

As the man led Rose out of the cave and into a clearing where grew more apple, cherry, peach, and plum trees than she had ever seen before, he talked about himself. He was still a young man, but he said that he had traveled on foot to Pittsburgh all the long way—across mountains, fording streams, and breaking trails through the wilderness—from Springfield in Massachusetts. His name was John Chapman. He was called Appleseed Johnny because he was the only orchard-man of the pioneers. He loved apples, and he knew how much the West needed fruit. The rich soil was fairly aching to nourish the seeds that he had begged from farmers in Pennsylvania and planted there on the banks of the Ohio River.

Appleseed Johnny showed Rose the shed where he sorted and washed apple seeds, started shoots for new trees, and kept his spade and pruning shears. Then they went into the big comfortable cabin he had built for himself of forest wood, lusty logs of oak, chestnut, and pine. An apple bough, gnarled and crooked into the shape of a forest gnome, was perched on the ridge of Appleseed Johnny's cabin for its roof-tree. The nails that held the cedar planks of the door were handmade. So was the star-shaped iron latch that Appleseed Johnny lifted as he opened the heavy door and led Rose inside.

In the light of the big stone fireplace the girl thought that Appleseed Johnny looked like an Indian, as brown, sharp-eyed, and slender. He gave a low call, and down from a shelf near the roof fluttered a fluffy sleepy little owl and nestled on his shoulder.

"I came too far away from our wagon," Rose explained. "Folks say there are bears in these woods."

Appleseed Johnny laughed. He went to the door and made an odd growling sound. Fascinated, Rose saw a shaggy brown animal lumber out of the gathering darkness, sniff at Appleseed Johnny, and then pass by.

"All the wild creatures love this appleman," Rose thought.

Appleseed Johnny came in and filled a big pewter mug with milk for Rose. He put a comb of golden honey and three red apples in her basket. Last, he gave her a little apple tree, no taller than her pine-cone doll, and a small deerskin bag of seeds.

"Now I will guide you to the edge of the woods," he said. "And when you come to your new home in the wilderness, set out this young apple tree in the sunshine, and water it and build a little fence of brush about it to keep off the deer.

"In this bag are precious seeds of other apples, of berries, pears, cherries, grapes, plums, and peaches. Plant them and tend them, for there is no fruit in the wilderness. Your mother will want berries and fruits for her autumn pies, and jellies and preserves for the winter. Your new home in the West will need grapevines growing over it, and a pink cloud of orchard blossoms in the spring."

As Appleseed Johnny talked, he led Rose safely through the darkening forest until she could see her own campfire and smell the fish her mother was cooking.

"Good-by, and thank you," she said.

"Good-by, Little Pioneer," he said. "Remember Appleseed Johnny and plant your trees."

"I will!" she called as she ran over to hide her little tree and the seeds. She ate supper in a dream and in her sleep smelled apples under the canvas top. A flatboat was waiting for them in the morning, and they drifted, wagon and all, over the Ohio River and into the wild lands beyond.

Season after season Appleseed Johnny tended his trees, harvested his fruit, and sorted his seeds. He kept cows and had a row of beehives. Season after season the covered wagons carrying hundreds of pioneers West stopped by his cabin. The travelers were fed apples, honey, and milk and given little bags of Appleseed Johnny's precious seeds.

Rose's covered wagon rolled on into the untilled, wild country of Ohio. Her father told her about Appleseed Johnny. "He was only a boy when he left his home in Massachusetts and tramped out to Pennsylvania," he said. "He took apple seeds in payment for work for the farmers, and he built his house and planted his orchards with his own hands. Hundreds of covered wagons stop at his door, rest, and go on, carrying his bags of seeds."

On, on went the wagon until Rose's father found a farm site. The seasons passed quickly, with so much work to be done. The land was cleared and a cabin built in two years. That was the year that Rose picked berries from the bushes that grew from Appleseed Johnny's seeds. In four years roads were built, the cabin made larger, and Rose's dresses were longer. That was the year that she picked peaches, cherries, and plums from the trees planted from Appleseed Johnny's seeds. In six years Rose was a young lady. It was another October, and the apples from the little tree that Appleseed Johnny had given her were harvested and waiting in the kitchen to be made into apple butter for the winter. Rose would trust no one but herself to do this.

In the sunny kitchen she had set out empty pans, tubs, sharp knives, and a great basket of juicy red apples. On linen thread, hanging from the beams of the kitchen were strips of apples drying. The strong crane in the open fireplace held a brass kettle filled with pared apples, sweet and sour in proportion, the sweet ones at the bottom, with quinces and molasses added for flavor. She had put straw in the bottom of the kettle to keep the cooking apples from burning. Rose would spend days preserving the apples for the winter. Down cellar, tubs of apple sauce would freeze and keep through the winter as sweet as when it was made. The dried apples would be made into pies.

Rose stirred the apple butter, her back to the open door. Suddenly she heard a low call, like that of a little screech owl. She turned and saw a surprising figure.

The man was as tall and straight as an Indian, keen-eyed, and on his back he carried a great sack. He was as ragged as a beggar, his hair had grown to his shoulders and he wore Indian moccasins. He gave his bird call again, and smiled at Rose. "You have grown, my child," he said.

"Appleseed Johnny!" she cried.

"Yes, I am Appleseed Johnny, still planting orchards in the wilderness. I gave away my house, filled this sack with seeds, crossed the Ohio River in a dugout canoe, and have been wandering for many years, scattering seeds, and teaching the pioneers how to plant and tend orchards."

"Come in," Rose begged. "Spend the night with us, and let us feed you as you fed me when I was a covered-wagon girl. These are your apples that I am cooking. Your little tree lived, and every one of your seeds grew and gave us fruit."

An old letter tells us the rest of the story: how Appleseed Johnny, pioneer nurseryman of the early nineteenth century, spent the night in the Rice cabin, made welcome by Roselle Rice and her family who had passed his door many years before. Many covered-wagon children knew Appleseed Johnny, but Rose was the only one who wrote about him. In the morning he started on again. He carried a Bible in the sack with his seeds, and left one leaf of it with Rose. Then he tramped off into the woods farther West and she never saw him again.

But Appleseed Johnny walked for forty years, leaving his little buckskin bags of seeds and his Bible pages at lonely cabins, planting the orchards that now cover acres of the West, sleeping outdoors, making friends with bears, wolves, and foxes, looked upon by the Indians as the Great Spirit. Pioneers went on with his work. Today skilled orchardmen cultivate the vast tracts of fruitland of our West. Following the trail he started, great freight trains return now to the East carrying barrels of Jonathan, Winesap, Spitzenburgh, Northern Spy, Delicious, King, Greening, and Golden Pippin apples for hungry boys and girls. The wild hardy stock poured into the spiced sap of the cultivated growth still gives us new, larger, tastier apples. The sturdy covered-wagon people, going West, gave us our beautiful Western cities, our fertile farms, our fine schools. And every pink apple blossom of the spring is scented with Appleseed Johnny's kindness to little Rose, and every bite of a rosy October apple tastes as sweet as those he laid away in his cave.

THE KITTEN
ON THE CANAL BOAT

Alice Dalgliesh

The period of the old canal boats comes as vividly to life in this story as do the three little girls. Harriet of the quick decisions meets her match in firmness in the unknown child who gets the kitten by sheer force of will. The book from which this story comes is called America Travels, *and its usefulness is proved by the fact that it has gone through twelve printings. The author, Alice Dalgliesh, has written a variety of good books for children. One of the best is* The Bears On Hemlock Mountain, *which is a thriller and a chiller! Miss Dalgliesh is also juvenile editor for Scribner's and so makes a double contribution to good books for boys and girls.*

Harriet lay in her narrow bunk watching pictures move slowly past, framed in the small, square window. Each morning the pictures were different: sometimes a patch of blue sky, white clouds, or green fields, sometimes sheep grazing or cows lying lazily under a tree. Harriet was quite accustomed to moving scenery, for all of her nine summers had been spent on a canal boat. In the winter months Harriet lived in a house, but she much preferred the time spent on the canal where something interesting and different was always happening.

Now the sun was coming in the small, square window and it was time to get up. Harriet jumped out of bed and climbed on a box to look out. The *Red Lion of the West* was nosing slowly along the canal and there was nothing to be seen but fields full of buttercups. Harriet was glad that it was a fine day, for it meant that as the *Red Lion* passed through the next town gay picnic parties might come on board.

Two kinds of people traveled on the sturdy slow-moving canal boats. There were serious people who were really going somewhere. These slept on the boat and either brought their food with them or had their meals cooked by Harriet's mother in the tiny kitchen. These travelers sometimes were moving from one town or village to

another, so they brought with them many bundles and baskets, with a large part of their household belongings. Then there were the gay people who were not really going anywhere but who thought it fun to take a trip on the boat. Harriet loved these picnic parties with laughing ladies who held little parasols over their heads to keep the sun from spoiling their beautiful complexions. They always carried the most interesting lunches put up in dainty baskets.

When Harriet was dressed she went to the kitchen. It was a neat little kitchen with red-checked curtains and a red geranium in the window. These matched the rest of the *Red Lion* which was a trim boat painted red and white with a black stripe. As Harriet entered the kitchen a good smell of crisp bacon came from the frying pan on the small stove. There were other important things to be done, however, so she did not waste much time over breakfast. From a basket in the corner she took two kittens, a gray one and a black one. With a kitten tucked under each arm she went out on the roof of the boat, which was quite flat, like a deck. There she stood and watched her brother, who was walking along the towpath beside Jerry and Jim, the mules that pulled the boat. At the stern stood Harriet's father with his hand on the tiller; it was his job to steer the boat.

Harriet put the kittens down on the deck and sat looking along the canal. This was an exciting day, for on this day the *Red Lion* passed the *Blossoming Bough,* the boat on which lived Harriet's friend, Alice. As the boats passed each other Harriet and Alice waved, and even had time to talk. Now, as Harriet watched, the *Blossoming Bough* turned the corner and came slowly down the canal. She was a pretty boat, as trim as the *Red Lion* but painted green and white with a touch of yellow. As the boats came near each other the *Blossoming Bough* drew off to one side to allow the *Red Lion* to pass. The tow lines were dropped so that the mules pulling the *Red Lion* could step over them.

Harriet stood as close to the edge of the deck as she dared. There was Alice close to the edge of *her* boat. It was well to be careful, for the deck had no railing and canal water was dark and cold.

"Harriet!" called Alice, "I have a new dress."

"What is it like?" asked Harriet.

"Oh, it's white, for Sundays. I'm not allowed to wear it on week days."

"I'm going to have a new dress soon," said Harriet.

"A Sunday dress?"

"Yes, I think it will be white like yours."

The *Red Lion* had slipped past the *Blossoming Bough.*

"Good-by, Harriet!"

"Good-by, Alice!"

There would be no more excitement now until the *Red Lion of the West* reached the next town. Harriet sat on the deck and played with the kittens. Suddenly her father put a horn to his lips and blew a long blast. Harriet ducked her head, for this meant that they were about to pass under a low bridge. It seemed no time at all until they reached the town—and there was a picnic party! It was a particularly interesting picnic party.

There were two pretty ladies with parasols, and two gentlemen, their hats tied to their buttonholes with string to keep them from blowing away. And there was a little girl. Harriet thought, as the little girl stepped daintily onto the deck, that she had never seen anything so beautiful or so exactly like a picture come to life. The little girl had blue eyes, yellow curls, and pink cheeks. Her dress was of the palest pink, and below it showed white lace-trimmed pantalettes. Harriet stood there feeling very dark and solid and different in her calico dress. She could not take her eyes off the little girl. There above the golden curls was a bonnet, a dainty straw bonnet trimmed with pink roses and tied under its owner's chin with a pink bow.

The ladies moved gracefully to a seat, arranged their skirts and sat chatting with the gentlemen. The little girl's mother called her to sit beside her. For five minutes the little girl sat there as prim and as quiet as a china ornament on a shelf. Then she saw the kittens.

"Oh, Mamma!" she said, "look at the darling kittens! A black one and a gray one. The gray one is just the kitten I want!"

"They belong to the little girl who lives on the boat," said her mother.

"Oh, but I *want* one," said the pink child, who had always had what she wanted. "I *want* one, Mamma, I want the gray one. It's my birthday, you know." Two large tears came into the blue eyes.

"Mercy, Florence," said her mother, looking worried, "don't cry! Let's ask the little girl if she will sell us the gray kitten."

"Little girl," said Florence, "will you sell us the gray kitten?"

"No!" said Harriet, her brown eyes very large, her feet planted firmly on the deck.

"But I *want* her," fretted the child.

"He's my favorite kitten," said Harriet.

"She's my favorite *kind* of kitten," said Florence even more fretfully. Then, as suddenly as the sun comes out from behind a cloud, she changed her tone and began to coax. "Won't you let me have her? Please?"

"Well," said Harriet, weakening, "perhaps I will. But *you* must give *me* something that I want very much."

"Oh, I *will!*" smiled Florence. "What is it?"

"Your lovely pink bonnet," answered Harriet.

There was a moment of chatter and fluttering.

"My pink bonnet?"

"Your lovely pink bonnet!"

"Your *new* pink bonnet. Florence, you *can't.*"

But Florence usually had her own way and this was her birthday. Once more two big tears came into her eyes. This time they fell and splashed on the pink dress. Slowly one hand began to untie the strings of the pink bonnet.

"No, Florence."

"Oh, please, Mamma."

"The sun is much too hot."

"Mamma, it's such a lovely day and I can share your parasol." By this time the bonnet was untied. Harriet picked up the gray kitten. With one hand she took the bonnet, with the other she gave up the gray kitten. Then she hurried into the kitchen to find her mother.

Mother shook her head over the queer ways of little girls, but at last she was persuaded that the exchange was a fair one. It was well that she thought so, for by this time wild horses could not have dragged the kitten from Florence's arms.

When the picnic was over a little girl without a bonnet stood on the shore and waved to another little girl on the deck of the canal boat.

"I'll be very kind to your nice gray kitten," called Florence. "And I'm going to call her Velvet."

"*His* name is Tom!" shouted Harriet, but the *Red Lion* was too far along the canal for the pink child to hear. This was just as well, for never in the world could she have owned a kitten with the plain name of Tom.

It was Sunday morning when next the *Red Lion of the West* passed the *Blossoming Bough.* The sound of church bells came faintly across the fields. It was very quiet on the canal. The boats slipped silently along, for on Sundays they were not allowed to blow their horns. Harriet stood as close to the edge of the deck as she dared. Alice stood close to the edge, too. Each little girl was wearing a Sunday dress. Each dress was white, with white pantalettes. Alice's hair was blowing in the breeze, but on Harriet's head there was a bonnet, a dainty straw bonnet with pink roses and pink ribbons tied under the chin.

"Look at my Sunday dress!" screamed Alice.

"Look at mine!"

"Why, Harriet, you have a pink bonnet!"

"Yes, isn't it beautiful?"

There was quite a long silence while Alice took in all the glory of the pink bonnet.

"It's the most beautiful bonnet I ever saw."

Harriet turned around to show the back of the bonnet.

"Did your mother give it to you?"

"No, I got it from a little girl in exchange for a kitten."

"For *what?*" The boats had passed each other.

"For a kitten!"

But the *Red Lion of the West* was now too far away from the *Blossoming Bough.* There was nothing to do but wait until they passed again, then Harriet and Alice could finish their conversation. It was often like that!

THE EARNED NAME

Shannon Garst

This exciting and tragic story of Crazy Horse, who led the Sioux in their last stand against the white invaders of their territory, is one of the few books which tell the story from the Indians' point of view. The early chapters record the rigorous training of an Indian boy, and show Crazy Horse to have been a highly intelligent and resourceful youngster.

As the hunters rode into the Oglala village, laughing and jabbering, the Indian women came out to meet them and ran beside their horses. Has-ka's sister, Laughing One, and his step-mother, Gathers-Her-Berries, ran beside his horse chattering like magpies over his kill.

Reaching camp the women seized the meat and threw the hunks onto beds of leaves while

"The Earned Name" from *Crazy Horse* by Shannon Garst. Reprinted by permission of and arrangement with Houghton Mifflin Company, the authorized publishers

they deftly sliced it into strips which they threw over pole racks to dry, out of reach of the dogs.

That night the campfires sputtered and blazed as the buffalo fat dripped onto them. The air was savory with fine smells of roasting hump and ribs. The Oglalas ate until they were stuffed. Never had food tasted so good to Has-ka. The fact that he had helped in providing meat for the camp made him feel pleasantly important and he was still elated over the fact that Hump had singled him out.

He purposely walked through the camp to see if he would be noticed. He was. Men pointed to him and said, "There goes Has-ka. His arrow brought down a buffalo. He was the youngest one on the hunt."

It was very agreeable to be pointed out and noticed this way. He almost forgot that Hump had to come to his rescue just in time.

When the Oglalas had eaten so much that they could not cram down another mouthful, they danced to the throbbing drums until the food was jounced down enough so that they could eat some more. Has-ka ate and danced with them. He was aware of No Water's glowering, envious glances upon him but this only increased his feeling of triumph. The older boy had gone along on the hunt, but only as one of the boys who led a pack horse on which to bring back the meat. He had had no part in the kill and no one after the hunt had pointed him out as he walked through the village.

Has-ka gorged himself and danced until he grew so sleepy that he crawled off to his sleeping robes. However, he was up at dawn the next morning, eager for more excitement.

Mock buffalo hunts were always a favorite pastime of Sioux youngsters. After one of the real hunts there were often buffalo calves left behind on the plains, which had been unable to keep up with the herd after it had been stampeded. It was the delight of the boys to chase these calves, shooting at them with the blunt arrows they used in their games.

Has-ka, filled with elation over his first buffalo hunt, joined in the noisy horseback chase of one of these young calves. Strongheart was the first to catch up with it. With a yell of triumph the boy shouted, "I, Has-ka the buffalo hunter, will ride this calf!"

Leaning over, he grabbed a handful of the woolly hair of the hump and threw himself onto the calf's back. More frightened than ever by this new terror, the young buffalo increased his speed so that the Indian boys' ponies could scarcely keep up. But what they lacked in speed, they made up for in yelling as they gave chase.

The calf suddenly stopped running and tried by bucking to rid itself of the strange and frightening thing clinging to its back. Has-ka found this change of pace not at all to his liking. His head was rammed down between his shoulders. With each jump that jounced him first to one side, then to the other, he thought he could not stick on, but he righted himself and managed. His companions were not going to be given a chance to laugh at him. He must not lose the importance he had gained. Most of all he dreaded giving No Water another opportunity to ridicule him. Once he was tipped clear over to the side of the calf. It was only the realization of how his comrades would whoop with glee if he were thrown that gave him the determination to right himself and hang grimly on.

Gradually the bucking eased off, then ceased, when the calf became tired.

"I, Has-ka, did ride the buffalo calf," he cried, raising his hand in triumph.

"Has-ka did ride the buffalo calf," his companions chanted.

"I, Has-ka, will ride the buffalo calf into the village," he shouted.

"*Hoka hey! Hoka hey!*" his friends cried, crowding their ponies close to the buffalo calf and driving it toward the Oglala camp. The riderless Strongheart trotted at the rear of the yelling horde.

Drawn by the shouts of the boys the people came from their tepees to see the procession led by young Has-ka riding the buffalo calf.

"Has-ka did ride the buffalo calf!" his friends shouted.

The warrior Hump stood in front of his lodge laughing at the sight. "The buffalo calf seems too tame a mount for you, my friend," he said.

"He was wild enough out there on the hills," young Hump said. "You should have seen Has-ka ride. I thought the calf's bucking would snap his head off as we snap off the head of a grouse."

"It was easy," Has-ka said modestly. A new hope, however, was born within him that his people would now give him a man-like earned name such as Rides the Buffalo Calf instead of the one he so detested.

But the next day he was still called Has-ka.

The incident, though, did reawaken Hump's interest in him and the warrior made him his adopted son, according to the Sioux custom, and taught him the lore of his people, the best way to make weapons and the secrets of warfare, finding in the eager boy an apt pupil.

His own son, young Hump, was restless and had not Has-ka's ambition to become a leader and his father often lost patience with him. The warrior and his pupil, however, were so often together that their tribesmen spoke of them as the "grizzly and his cub."

Was ever another boy so fortunate, Has-ka wondered, as to have so fine a teacher? In every way he strove to make himself like his hero. Yet he never found courage to speak to Hump of his high ambitions for fear of being laughed at. The man, however, at times possessed an uncanny ability to sense what was in the boy's mind.

One day they were returning from a hunt, jogging along in silence. Has-ka had been completely lost in his thoughts, imagining himself leading a band of Oglala warriors against the Crow tribe.

Suddenly Hump said, "To be a leader of your people you must listen often and in silence to the Great Holy Mystery. The day is not too far away when you will go alone to the hills for the Vision Quest."

Has-ka looked startled. He was surprised that Hump knew what was in his mind, and it pleased him that his teacher considered him worthy of the test which would prove whether or not the *Wakan Tanka* would guide him to leadership.

"You think—I may someday be a leader?" Has-ka's tone was hopeful.

Hump gave him a long, strange look, and for a moment did not speak. Finally he said, "The desire for prominence among our people is always in your heart. Why?"

Has-ka met his friend's glance with a questioning look.

"Why?" Hump asked again. "Why is the wish for greatness always with you?"

"Because—" Has-ka floundered for words. "It is a good thing to be great. To be pointed out. To be a leader—"

It was not easy to put into words the reasons for his deepest desire. A shadow of disappointment crossed the warrior's face and Has-ka saw that he was not pleased.

"Your reasons are selfish ones," Hump's tone was harsh. "Leadership is a gift from the *Wakan Tanka*. To be used for the good of the people —not because one would be pointed out."

Has-ka felt humbled. "How does one know if he is singled out for leadership—to serve his people?" he persisted.

"At the time of the Vision Quest," Hump repeated. "It is time you were thinking about getting ready."

As the preliminary step of training for the sterner ordeal ahead, Hump one day ordered him to do without food for an entire day. The warrior blackened Has-ka's face with charred wood as the sign that he was fasting. His comrades pranced about him, tantalizing him by holding juicy chunks of savory buffalo meat close to his mouth, or by offering him *wasna,* dried ground buffalo meat mixed with ground-up plums—a favorite food of the Indians.

He wore a solemn expression on his blackened face as he went about the camp. The holy, set-apart feeling he had today was very pleasant—not like the old set-apart feeling he used to have because of his light complexion and his lack of sureness in himself. In those days the feeling had been so painful and unbearable sometimes that he had wanted to crawl off like a wounded animal.

He kept to himself the entire day, not being in a mood to join the other boys in their rough fun. He wandered along Lodge Pole Creek, then lay on the warm grass with his hands under his head, staring at the lazy clouds floating above him until he drifted off into deep sleep. In his dreams he saw himself single-handed driving off the pony herds of the enemy—slaying enemy chiefs—saving his hero, Hump, from the scalping knife. He saw himself being called upon to stand up beside the campfire to tell of his remarkable coups. Saw his record being painted upon a white buffalo robe. Saw the feathered crown of a chieftain being placed upon his head.

When he awoke he struggled to recapture those pleasant dreams, but now he was wide awake. He got to his feet and strolled along the stream, then wandered to the top of a hill. By now the sun was dipping beyond the western horizon in a blaze of brilliant colors. Light-headed from hunger, Has-ka stretched his hands toward the sinking sun. "A vision, *Wakan Tanka,*" he murmured. "Grant me a vision of greatness. Show me the path I must take."

In his dizzy, elated state he fully expected the golden clouds to part, revealing the *Wakan Tanka.*—Or the Holy Mystery would send one of His animal spirits with a message telling Has-ka that he was truly destined for greatness and that he would be powerful among the Sioux. All of the men who were leaders among Has-ka's people had received such visions or messages at some time or other—usually following a fast.

He stood until his outstretched arms ached—and his soul ached, too, with the waiting. But no vision—no message came. The sun sank. A veil of darkness fell over the world, and Has-ka's spirits sank with the sun. Perhaps he was not destined for greatness after all! His arms fell to his sides and he walked slowly back to the village.

Two sleeps following Has-ka's fast, No Water raced through the village shouting, *"Che-hoo-hoo! Che-hoo-hoo!* All who are brave and strong, line up for *che-hoo-hoo."*

This was a wrestling game in which the Sioux boys chose sides, each boy picking his own opponent. When a wrestler's shoulders were forced to the ground, he was "dead."

Young Hump was one of the leaders; No Water, as usual, was the other. Hump chose Has-ka to be on his side. Has-ka looked over the "enemy" line to pick out someone about his own size and weight to challenge.

He was startled when he heard No Water shout his own name.

"I, No Water," the enemy leader yelled, "do challenge the One Who Cries When the Wasps Sting Him."

The older boy could not have chosen a surer way of arousing Has-ka to anger than with this almost-forgotten taunt. Sudden fury boiled through his veins, yet he was no fool. No Water was larger and heavier—had every chance of winning. But, of course, he had to accept the challenge or be disgraced in the eyes of his comrades.

Soon enemy was upon enemy and the ground was covered with writhing, struggling pairs. Has-ka braced himself as No Water seized him. He fought with every ounce of strength that was in him and when his breath rasped in his throat and he was so exhausted that every muscle felt limp, he gritted his teeth and kept on struggling and straining until unknown reserves of strength came to his help. But grit and determination were not sufficient against superior strength and weight.

At last when many shoulders were pinned to the ground, the victors pretended to take the scalps of those whom they had defeated. It was not until most of the pairs had ended their struggles that No Water managed to throw Has-ka and leap upon him to pin his shoulders to the ground. According to the rules of the game that was supposed to be the end of it, except for the pretended scalping, but No Water knelt on Has-ka's shoulders while his thumbs pressed the beaten boy's windpipe.

Has-ka's breath came out with a gurgling groan—almost a cry. His good friend, He Dog, pulled No Water off.

The *che-hoo-hoo* winners danced the victory dance about the defeated enemy who hunched sullenly in the center of the ring. No Water pointed triumphantly to Has-ka and shouted, "*Hopo!* I, No Water, did beat my enemy He-Who-Cries-When-the-Wasps-Sting. And I did make him cry out again. Has-ka has not the brave heart! Has-ka is a girl!"

The beaten boy's spirits sank to his moccasins. He had thought he was making headway in gaining the respect of his comrades. Now, even though he had done his best, he had disgraced himself again. He had given his rival another chance to gloat over him. Why did the older boy hate him so? Why did he always try to belittle him before his companions?

Disgraced and unhappy Has-ka shunned his comrades until an exciting event made him forget his personal troubles.

An unknown disease had swept through the pony herd the previous winter and there was talk of the need of new horses. Has-ka listened eagerly. He hoped that a pony-stealing expedition was afoot.

The easiest method of acquiring new horses and the one the Sioux liked best because of the excitement it afforded, was to creep at night into some camp of their enemy, the Crows, and drive their tamed horses away. But now the Crows were far beyond the Big Horns, so the Oglalas must round up wild horses to replenish their herds. This method was harder work, for the horses so caught must be broken and the Sioux would be denied the sly pleasure of besting the enemy Crows.

An excited longing swept through Has-ka as he listened to the plans for the wild horse hunt. He made up his mind to go along.

Nearly all of the men, and some of the boys who were old enough, joined the wild horse hunt. Scouts rode out ahead toward the sand hills to see if they could locate a herd of wild horses and after riding for nearly half a sun they gave the blanket signal from a hilltop that they had discovered a herd in the valley below. The Indians scattered, circling the valley, but staying out of sight of the horses. Has-ka was riding Strongheart. He quivered with excitement as his group waited beneath the brow of the hill for the signal to advance.

When the surround was complete, several of the hunters on the south side rode over the hill yelling. The wild horses stampeded in the opposite direction, where Has-ka and his companions were waiting. Some of the hunters strung out across their path. The horses galloped in another direction only to have more hunters block their way. Finding every direction of escape closed to them, the frightened, bewildered animals started circling. When they were milling in a compact bunch, the hunters closed in on them and started thrusting their long sticks with hair rope loops over the heads of the horses they wanted to capture.

Has-ka caught sight of a pony the color of a red autumn leaf. It carried its small, well-shaped head high, nostrils distended. Its eyes were wide open but there was more a look of fight in them than of fear. The instant he saw the red stallion, Has-ka knew that it was a spirited and intelligent animal and he wanted it with all of his heart. So also did Lone Bear and he thrust out his loop trying to get it over the animal's head, but missed. Has-ka thrust out his loop, but he missed, too, for even though the red horse was frightened he was wise and wary.

Finally Lone Bear gave up with a grunt of disgust and concentrated his efforts on a less crafty animal, but no other would satisfy Has-ka. Already some of his comrades were riding toward home trailing their mustangs, which they called crazy horses, tied to the tails of their tame ponies.

At last his loop settled over the neck of the red horse and with a yell of triumph he jerked on the willow pole, drawing the loop tight. The animal reared and snorted, but could not rid itself of the thing around its neck that was fast choking its breath from it.

Has-ka edged Strongheart close to the wild pony and then he did a daring thing. He threw himself onto the red pony's back, with nothing in the world with which to control it but the hair loop around its neck.

With a shrill whinny of rebellion the red horse broke loose from the herd, galloped into the open, bucking, rearing, turning, twisting, omitting none of the tricks a wild horse knows in an effort to dislodge its rider. He sunfished and galloped, but Has-ka clung to his mane, tightening the noose around its neck when necessary, but giving the magnificent animal its head as much as possible. A wild sense of elation swept through the boy. He yelled and his heels pounded the sides of the wild horse. He would ride this horse and finally conquer him.

The hunters stopped trying to capture mustangs to watch the performance that went on all over the hillside between Has-ka and the wild horse, until it was flecked with foam and finally stood with drooping head and heaving sides, too spent to struggle longer. It recognized a master.

Has-ka was spent, too, yet a thrill of triumph swept through him. He had conquered this splendid beast. Loosening his noose he reached forward and grasping an ear he turned the pony's head, his heels pounding its sides. Slowly the red pony obeyed his master's will and stumbled in the direction Has-ka wanted him to go.

When Has-ka, astride the horse he had conquered, rode up to his companions, they shouted, "He has ridden a crazy horse! *Tashunka-Witko! Crazy Horse! Crazy Horse! His name shall be *Tashunka-Witko! Crazy Horse!"

The boy's heart beat faster. At last he had an earned name—and a splendid one. The name of his father, but one which he himself had earned. To the Indians the name meant an untamed, splendid horse of great spirit and courage. He could not have earned a finer name, ever if he had chosen it.

Crazy Horse made his rope into a halter and tied the horse to Strongheart's tail. Neither animal liked being tied to the other, but Strongheart was trained to obey and the wild horse was tired, so they got along well enough.

When the horse hunters reached their village, the first thing they did was to rope and throw the mustangs they had captured. The right fore foot was tied to the left hind foot and the horse allowed to struggle to his feet. Now the ponies could not kick and the process of taming them started at once.

Every day Crazy Horse went to the corral and roped this new horse he named Warrior. He stroked him and talked to him, breaking and training him as he had Strongheart, until finally the spirited pony yielded to the stronger will. Crazy Horse grinned with pleasure, for there

were not two finer ponies in the Oglala camp than Strongheart and Warrior—and well he knew there wasn't a better horseman.

Never was there a day when the boys of Crazy Horse's band were not practicing riding in some form or other. There were races in the early evening, but Crazy Horse's favorite sport and the one he always wanted was the riding contest in which the boys chose sides. When Crazy Horse would gallop his stallion at its utmost speed, past his admiring companions, making it zigzag in its course, with just the tip of his heel showing over its neck, they would cry, "*Tashunka-Witko*—Crazy Horse rides without being seen!" "Crazy Horse was invisible to the enemy!" "Crazy Horse is the finest rider in the Oglala camp!"

"PECULIARSOME" ABE

Carl Sandburg

Carl Sandburg is both a poet and an authority on Lincoln lore. From the first volume of his Lincoln biography he made a cutting for children and young people called Abe Lincoln Grows Up. *It is a remarkable book as this selection shows. Here we meet the young, backwoods Abe, starved for books, starved for an education, and making the little reading he could lay his hands on food for long, long thoughts.* Turn to Time for Fairy Tales *and find some of the fables that caught Abe's young fancy. Turn to* Time for Poetry, *and read in the last section, "Wisdom and Beauty," some of the proverbs he brooded over. In that book also read the moving poem by the Benéts, "Nancy Hanks" and on the same page the answers two children wrote to Nancy's questions about her son.*

The farm boys in their evenings at Jones's store in Gentryville talked about how Abe Lincoln was always reading, digging into books, stretching out flat on his stomach in front of the fireplace, studying till midnight and past midnight, picking a piece of charcoal to write on the fire shovel, shaving off what he wrote, and then writing more—till midnight and past midnight. The next thing Abe would be reading books between the plow handles, it seemed to them. And once trying to speak a last word, Dennis Hanks said, "There's suthin' peculiarsome about Abe."

He wanted to learn, to know, to live, to reach out; he wanted to satisfy hungers and thirsts he couldn't tell about, this big boy of the backwoods. And some of what he wanted so much, so deep down, seemed to be in the books. Maybe in books he would find the answers to dark questions pushing around in the pools of his thoughts and the drifts of his mind. He told Dennis and other people, "The things I want to know are in books; my best friend is the man who'll git me a book I ain't read." And sometimes friends answered, "Well, books ain't as plenty as wildcats in these parts o' Indianny."

This was one thing meant by Dennis when he said there was "suthin' peculiarsome" about Abe. It seemed that Abe made the books tell him more than they told other people. All the other farm boys had gone to school and read "The Kentucky Preceptor," but Abe picked out questions from it, such as "Who has the most right to complain, the Indian or the Negro?" and Abe would talk about it, up one way and down the other, while they were in the cornfield pulling fodder for the winter. When Abe got hold of a storybook and read about a boat that came near a magnetic rock, and how the magnets in the rock pulled all the nails out of the boat so it went to pieces and the people in the boat found themselves floundering in water, Abe thought it was funny and told it to other people. After Abe read poetry, especially Bobby Burns's poems, Abe began writing rhymes himself. When Abe sat with a girl, with their bare feet in the creek water, and she spoke of the moon rising, he explained to her it was the earth moving and not the moon—the moon only seemed to rise.

John Hanks, who worked in the fields barefooted with Abe, grubbing stumps, plowing, mowing, said: "When Abe and I came back to the house from work, he used to go to the cupboard, snatch a piece of corn bread, sit down, take a book, cock his legs up high as his head,

and read. Whenever Abe had a chance in the field while at work, or at the house, he would stop and read." He liked to explain to other people what he was getting from books; explaining an idea to some one else made it clearer to him. The habit was growing on him of reading out loud; words came more real if picked from the silent page of the book and pronounced on the tongue; new balances and values of words stood out if spoken aloud. When writing letters for his father or the neighbors, he read the words out loud as they got written. Before writing a letter he asked questions such as: "What do you want to say in the letter? How do you want to say it? Are you sure that's the best way to say it? Or do you think we can fix up a better way to say it?"

As he studied his books his lower lip stuck out; Josiah Crawford noticed it was a habit and joked Abe about the "stuck-out lip." This habit too stayed with him.

He wrote in his Sum Book or arithmetic that Compound Division was "When several numbers of Divers Denominations are given to be divided by 1 common divisor," and worked on the exercise in multiplication; "If 1 foot contain 12 inches I demand how many there are in 126 feet." Thus the schoolboy.

What he got in the schools didn't satisfy him. He went to three different schools in Indiana, besides two in Kentucky—altogether about four months of school. He learned his A B C, how to spell, read, write. And he had been with the other barefoot boys in butternut jeans learning "manners" under the schoolteacher, Andrew Crawford, who had them open a door, walk in, and say, "Howdy do?" Yet what he tasted of books in school was only a beginning, only made him hungry and thirsty, shook him with a wanting and a wanting of more and more of what was hidden between the covers of books.

He kept on saying, "The things I want to know are in books; my best friend is the man who'll git me a book I ain't read." He said that to Pitcher, the lawyer over at Rockport, nearly twenty miles away, one fall afternoon, when he walked from Pigeon Creek to Rockport and borrowed a book from Pitcher. Then when fodder-pulling time came a few days later, he shucked corn from early daylight till sundown along with his father and Dennis Hanks and John Hanks, but after supper he read the book till midnight, and at noon he hardly knew the taste of his corn bread because he had a book in front of him. It was a hundred little things like these which made Dennis Hanks say there was "suthin' peculiarsome" about Abe.

Besides reading the family Bible and figuring his way all through the old arithmetic they had at home, he got hold of "Aesop's Fables," "Pilgrim's Progress," "Robinson Crusoe," and Weems's "The Life of Francis Marion." The book of fables, written or collected thousands of years ago by the Greek slave, known as Aesop, sank deep in his mind. As he read through the book a second and third time, he had a feeling there were fables all around him, that everything he touched and handled, everything he saw and learned had a fable wrapped in it somewhere. One fable was about a bundle of sticks and a farmer whose sons were quarreling and fighting.

There was a fable in two sentences which read, "A coachman, hearing one of the wheels of his coach make a great noise, and perceiving that it was the worst one of the four, asked how it came to take such a liberty. The wheel answered that from the beginning of time, creaking had always been the privilege of the weak." And there were shrewd, brief incidents of foolery such as this: "A waggish, idle fellow in a country town, being desirous of playing a trick on the simplicity of his neighbors and at the same time putting a little money in his pocket at their cost, advertised that he would on a certain day show a wheel carriage that should be so contrived as to go without horses. By silly curiosity the rustics were taken in, and each succeeding group who came out from the show were ashamed to confess to their neighbors that they had seen nothing but a wheelbarrow."

The style of the Bible, of Aesop's fables, the hearts and minds back of those books, were much in his thoughts. His favorite pages in them he read over and over. Behind such proverbs as, "Muzzle not the ox that treadeth out the corn," and "He that ruleth his own spirit is greater than he that taketh a city," there was a music of simple wisdom and a mystery of common everyday life that touched deep spots in him, while

out of the fables of the ancient Greek slave he came to see that cats, rats, dogs, horses, plows, hammers, fingers, toes, people, all had fables connected with their lives, characters, places. There was, perhaps, an outside for each thing as it stood alone, while inside of it was its fable.

One book came, titled, "The Life of George Washington, with Curious Anecdotes, Equally Honorable to Himself and Exemplary to His Young Countrymen. Embellished with Six Steel Engravings, by M. L. Weems, formerly Rector of Mt. Vernon Parish." It pictured men of passion and proud ignorance in the government of England driving their country into war on the American colonies. It quoted the far-visioned warning of Chatham to the British parliament, "For God's sake, then, my lords, let the way be instantly opened for reconciliation. I say instantly; or it will be too late forever."

The book told of war, as at Saratoga. "Hoarse as a mastiff of true British breed, Lord Balcarras was heard from rank to rank, loud-animating his troops; while on the other hand, fierce as a hungry Bengal tiger, the impetuous Arnold precipitated heroes on the stubborn foe. Shrill and terrible, from rank to rank, resounds the clash of bayonets—frequent and sad the groans of the dying. Pairs on Pairs, Britons and Americans, with each his bayonet at his brother's breast, fall forward together faint-shrieking in death, and mingle their smoking blood." Washington, the man, stood out, as when he wrote, "These things so harassed my heart with grief, that I solemnly declared to God, if I know myself, I would gladly offer myself a sacrifice to the butchering enemy, if I could thereby insure the safety of these my poor distressed countrymen."

The Weems book reached some deep spots in the boy. He asked himself what it meant that men should march, fight, bleed, go cold and hungry for the sake of what they called "freedom."

"Few great men are great in everything," said the book. And there was a cool sap in the passage: "His delight was in that of the manliest sort, which, by stringing the limbs and swelling the muscles, promotes the kindliest flow of blood and spirits. At jumping with a long pole, or heaving heavy weights, for his years he hardly had an equal."

Such book talk was a comfort against the same thing over again, day after day, so many mornings the same kind of water from the same spring, the same fried pork and corn-meal to eat, the same drizzles of rain, spring plowing, summer weeds, fall fodder-pulling, each coming every year, with the same tired feeling at the end of the day, so many days alone in the woods or the fields or else the same people to talk with, people from whom he had learned all they could teach him. Yet there ran through his head the stories and sayings of other people, the stories and sayings of books, the learning his eyes had caught from books; they were a comfort; they were good to have because they were good by themselves; and they were still better because they broke the chill of the lonesome feeling.

He was thankful to the writer of Aesop's fables because that writer stood by him and walked with him, an invisible companion, when he pulled fodder or chopped wood. Books lighted lamps in the dark rooms of his gloomy hours. . . . Well—he would live on; maybe the time would come when he would be free from work for a few weeks, or a few months, with books, and then he would read. . . . God, then he would read. . . . Then he would go and get at the proud secrets of his books.

His father—would he be like his father when he grew up? He hoped not. Why should his father knock him off a fence rail when he was asking a neighbor, passing by, a question? Even if it was a smart question, too pert and too quick, it was no way to handle a boy in front of a neighbor. No, he was going to be a man different from his father. The books—his father hated the books. His father talked about "too much eddication"; after readin', writin', 'rithmetic, that was enough, his father said. He, Abe Lincoln, the boy, wanted to know more than the father, Tom Lincoln, wanted to know. Already Abe knew more than his father; he was writing letters for the neighbors; they hunted out the Lincoln farm to get young Abe to find his bottle of ink with blackberry brier root and copperas in it, and his pen made from a turkey buzzard feather, and write letters. Abe had a suspicion sometimes his father was a little proud to have a boy that could write letters, and tell about things in books, and outrun and outwrestle

and rough-and-tumble any boy or man in Spencer County. Yes, he would be different from his father; he was already so; it couldn't be helped.

In growing up from boyhood to young manhood, he had survived against lonesome, gnawing montony and against floods, forest and prairie fires, snake-bites, horse-kicks, ague, chills, fever, malaria, "milk-sick."

A comic outline against the sky he was, hiking along the roads of Spencer and other counties in southern Indiana in those years when he read all the books within a fifty-mile circuit of his home. Stretching up on the long legs that ran from his moccasins to the body frame with its long, gangling arms, covered with linsey-woolsey, then the lean neck that carried the head with its surmounting coonskin cap or straw hat —it was, again, a comic outline—yet with a portent in its shadow. His laughing "Howdy," his yarns and drollery, opened the doors of men's hearts.

Starting along in his eleventh year came spells of abstraction. When he was spoken to, no answer came from him. "He might be a thousand miles away." The roaming, fathoming, searching, questioning operations of the minds and hearts of poets, inventors, beginners who take facts stark, these were at work in him. This was one sort of abstraction he knew; there was another: the blues took him; coils of multiplied melancholies wrapped their blue frustrations inside him, all that Hamlet, Koheleth, Schopenhauer have uttered, in a mesh of foiled hopes. "There was absolutely nothing to excite ambition for education," he wrote later of that Indiana region. Against these "blues," he found the best warfare was to find people and trade with them his yarns and drolleries. John Baldwin, the blacksmith, with many stories and odd talk and eye-slants, was a help and a light.

Days came when he sank deep in the stream of human life and felt himself kin of all that swam in it, whether the waters were crystal or mud.

He learned how suddenly life can spring a surprise. One day in the woods, as he was sharpening a wedge on a log, the ax glanced, nearly took his thumb off, and left a white scar after healing.

"You never cuss a good ax," was a saying in those timbers.

MARTIN AND
ABRAHAM LINCOLN

Catherine Cate Coblentz

The year before her death, Catherine Coblentz wrote a wonderful fairy tale, The Blue Cat of Castle Town, *which should be read aloud. It embodies her own spirit of service to the "bright enchantment" of "beauty, content and peace." She also wrote many fine historical stories for young readers—*The Falcon of Eric the Red, Blue and Silver Necklace, Sequoya, *and others. But this little story is one of the most touching.* Martin and Abraham Lincoln *is a true incident of the Civil War.*

"Flour and sugar and butter and eggs. Flour and sugar and butter and eggs." Martin Emery kept saying the words over to himself as he went slowly up the lane.

He had heard his mother whispering them again and again these past days. The words reminded him of the songs which his friend, Snowden, sang. Only Martin felt sure Mother's words were not a song but a prayer. For Mother needed so many things for Martin, for Maria, and Amanda, and Anna, the baby.

Martin gulped. When Father was at the Fort near by he had seen to it that Mother had these things. But he was gone. He would be gone for a long time. Somehow or other Martin felt he must take his place and help. After all he wore a new uniform now with shiny buttons. It was just like the one Father was wearing the last time Martin had seen him.

By this time Martin had come to the end of the lane. So he climbed up on the big rock by the roadside. Then he turned about and waved at the little gray house. Maria and Amanda and Anna, the baby, were standing in the doorway. They all waved back. Though Maria had to start Anna's hand going.

Then Martin looked up the road. It was Saturday and time for Snowden and Nellie to appear around the curve. Pretty soon he saw Nellie's long white ears. He heard the bell on Nellie's neck, and the jingle of her harness. He

Martin and Abraham Lincoln by Catherine Cate Coblentz, Childrens Press, Inc., 1947. Used by permission of the publisher

heard the creaking wheels on Nellie's cart. He saw the baskets of fresh vegetables in the back.

He saw Snowden, but Snowden didn't see Martin. Snowden was bent over on the front seat. In his hand was a stub of a pencil; on his knee a piece of paper. He kept frowning and looking at the paper. "I sure got to make a lot of money today," he said loud enough for Martin to hear him. "I sure got to. There's flour to get for Rosebell, and sugar and butter and eggs."

But if Snowden didn't see Martin, Nellie did. As soon as she came to the rock, Nellie stopped still. She looked at Martin. Then she turned her head and looked at Snowden. Then she flicked her ears.

When Nellie flicked her ears it was a sign. As soon as Martin saw it, he began scrambling over the wheel. He climbed up on the seat beside Snowden. Snowden blinked with surprise.

"May I go to Washington with you?" Martin asked.

Snowden started to nod. Then he stopped and asked, "Does your mother know?"

"She knows," said Martin. "That's why she let me wear my new suit." He stood up so Snowden could see the suit better. He stretched his shoulders as high as he could.

Snowden looked him up and down. He didn't miss a quirk of the soldier-like cap or a single shiny button. "Hmm," he said. "Nice, Martin. Just like your father's."

"Father's regiment brought Mother the cloth," said Martin, "and the buttons."

"Snowden," began Martin, as the cart moved on toward Washington, "how do you get flour and sugar and butter and eggs?"

Snowden sighed, "Sometimes I declare I don't know myself, Martin. Rosebell and the children need so many things." He took up the pencil once more. When he put it down again, Martin asked another question.

"When the war is over, will my father come home, Snowden?"

Snowden drew a deep breath. "All the war prisoners will come home then, Martin. All those that the northern army has taken will go back south to their homes. And all those that the southern army has taken will go back to their homes."

"I wish the war was over now," burst out Martin.

Snowden looked at him. "So do I," he said. "Abraham Lincoln does, too, I reckon."

Martin knew who Abraham Lincoln was. His picture was in the little gray house at the end of the lane. He never could decide which picture he liked better, that of his father or of Abraham Lincoln. His mother said they were both very important people. "Mr. Lincoln is the best president this country ever had, Martin," she said. "And your father is the best cobbler."

Best cobbler, best cobbler went Nellie's iron shoes, as they thumped, thumped across the bridge that led from Alexandria into Washington. Martin kicked his feet back to feel whether the empty basket was under the seat. It was. Martin knew why it was there. He knew, too, what would happen to that basket.

At the very first house, Snowden began his morning song. Martin waited to hear what the song was. It was a different one every week. This week it was a good song. Martin joined in after the first time. He sang as loud as he could:

Squash and beans and 'taters,
Garden fresh, garden fresh,
Beans and squash and 'taters.

After every sale, Snowden would put a scoop of beans or 'taters, or maybe a big squash into the basket under the seat.

The faster Snowden sold what he had, the bigger the gifts to the basket. And when everything else was sold that basket would be quite full. When Snowden and Martin and Nellie went home, Snowden would stop at the little gray house at the end of the lane.

"Got some left overs, Mrs. Emery." Snowden would say. "Thought maybe you'd help me out by using them." Then he always added, "Martin was a big help to me today, Mrs. Emery."

Had it not been for Snowden's left overs, Martin knew that he and Maria and Amanda and Anna would be hungry oftener than they were. Now, if they only had flour and sugar and butter and eggs, Mother wouldn't need to worry.

So on this Saturday Martin tried harder than ever to help Snowden as much as he could. He called:

Squash and beans and 'taters,

at the top of his lungs. Earlier in the season it had been:

Rhubarb and radishes, ripe and red.

Later there would be cabbages and parsnips and turnips, and Snowden would make up new songs for them to call.

"You are good at making up songs," said Martin as the cart rattled along the wide streets.

"And you are good at singing them," replied Snowden. "Words said over and over make a good song."

Words said over and over! That made Martin think of his mother, and the words she made into a prayer. He drew a long, quivering sigh.

"Wars, which put fathers in prison when they are needed at home, are a bad thing," Snowden said. He had been watching Martin closely.

Martin nodded. He swallowed the lump in his throat and called:

Squash and beans and 'taters,
Garden fresh, garden fresh,
Beans and squash and 'taters.

However, his voice didn't sound nearly as cheerful as it usually did. Toward the end of the morning it began trailing after Snowden's like a small echo.

Squash and beans and 'taters,

Snowden would sing.

Beans and 'taters,

would come Martin's echo.

Snowden glanced at Martin several times. It was very hot. Martin looked pale. Snowden made up his mind he would take him to a cool spot, while he went off to buy the groceries which Rosebell needed.

So a little before noon, Snowden turned Nellie about. And when they came to a big parklike place filled with shade trees, Snowden pulled the reins.

"Whoa, Nellie," he said.

"Now, Martin," he went on, "you just stay here in the shade and rest until Nellie and I come back. It's a good place for anyone in a uniform like yours. There's been lots of soldiers on this lawn, I can tell you. I've seen them sleeping here at night sometimes. And all over the place in the day. And I've seen them jump up and stand just as proud and straight when Abraham Lincoln came along."

"Came along here, Snowden? Abraham Lincoln?"

"Of course, Martin. See that building there? That's the Capitol, Martin—our Capitol."

Martin stood on the ground and stared. Snowden and Nellie started to leave. Then Nellie stopped and flicked her ears. That made Snowden remember something. He reached in his pocket.

"I most forgot," he said. "Rosebell gave me a sandwich for you, Martin. And an apple."

"I have a sandwich." Martin pointed to his pocket. He did not take it out, for he did not want Snowden to see how small and thin that sandwich was. There was no butter on the bread, only a smear of molasses.

"You'd better take this," urged Snowden. "Rosebell made it special."

"Thank you," said Martin, reaching for the thick sandwich and the apple. He would just take a bite or two out of the sandwich and save the rest for Maria and Amanda and Anna. He would save the apple, too, most of it.

When Snowden and Nellie were gone, and when the last sound of Nellie's bell, the jingle of her harness, and the creaking of the cart wheels faded in the distance, Martin wandered about for a little. Then he climbed on a bench. He ate his thin sandwich. He ate a little of Snowden's thick one. It was so good. Half of it was gone before he knew it. He re-wrapped it in the paper Rosebell had put about it, and laid it on the bench. When Martin wasn't looking a fat squirrel slipped up on the bench and grabbed at it. Martin felt the squirrel touch his hand. He jumped. The squirrel jumped. The sandwich fell and landed in a puddle.

Martin could have cried when he saw that. But he didn't. He would save all the apple, he decided, for Maria and Amanda and Anna. He would not take even a bite.

The sun was hot. Martin went over and sat down on the stone steps of the Capitol. The steps were clean and cool. His eyes closed a little as he leaned back, his head resting against the stone at one side.

Then, as always when he was alone and it was still, Martin began thinking about his father. The lump in his throat began to grow.

He heard someone coming down the steps in back of him. But there was plenty of room so Martin didn't move. He just sat there and watched dreamily as a long shadow moved over the step he was on, and went slither-sliding down the step ahead. And the next. And the next. And the next.

Then the shadow stopped still and stayed in one place. A voice just in back of Martin said, "Well, well! How's my little soldier?"

Soldier! When his father's friends said that, Martin had always done as his father had taught him, jumped to his feet and saluted. So, forgetting how tired and sad he had been, he sprang to his feet, flinging his head back and his hand up at the same time.

As his fingers touched the visor of his little blue cap, Martin's heart began to thud like a drum. For Abraham Lincoln was standing there looking down at him, his sad face losing its look of worry, and breaking slowly into a smile. Abraham Lincoln, himself!

"What is your name, soldier?" the great man asked, gravely returning the salute.

Martin told him.

"Where were you born, Martin?"

"In Vermont. In a log cabin."

The man nodded. "I was born in a log cabin, too."

"I know, Mother told me. She said some day I might get to be President like you."

"All mothers say that, Martin. What does your father say?"

"I don't know." Martin's voice slowed. "You see, he is away. He used to be a cobbler, but now he is your soldier."

"What regiment? And where is he now?"

The lump in Martin's throat was growing worse. It was difficult to make the words come. "The First Vermont—" he managed. And then the sobs had him. "He's in Andersonville Prison," he jerked.

But the great man was bending over. Strong arms were lifting Martin. In another moment the man had taken Martin's place on the steps. Martin was folded into his lap.

The boy's face was hidden now, in Abraham Lincoln's vest.

logs from an old barn that had been torn down. The logs were gnarled and tough. And Ab's ax kept going slower and slower.

" 'What do you get for this job, Ab?' I asked him.

" 'A dollar.'

" 'What do you aim to do with it?'

" 'Buy a pair of shoes,' he said.

" 'You'll never get one shoe at this rate, Ab,' I told him. 'Better go in and warm yourself and you'll work faster.' So he did. Funniest thing, Martin. When Ab came out, that wood was all chopped! Now, what do you think of that?"

Martin sat up and looked straight at Abraham Lincoln. "I think you chopped that wood," he said.

"Maybe you're right," smiled Lincoln. "After all, folks must help each other."

Martin nodded. "I help my mother all I can," he said. "I fix the rough places when they come in the shoes of Maria and Amanda and Anna. I can do it most as well as Father did. Mother says it helps a lot."

"I am sure it does." The President nodded.

"Vermont is a long way off," he went on. "Tell me, how do you happen to be here, Martin?"

Martin wiped the last tear from his cheek with the handkerchief Mr. Lincoln handed him. He could talk now. He wanted to.

"Father went to war," he began. "He was stationed at a fort near Alexandria. So, after a time he found a house near the fort, and sent for Mother and me and Maria and Amanda and Anna. We came on the train. At first we saw Father often. Then one night when some of the soldiers were sent out to take a railroad bridge, Father was captured. He was sent to prison."

"How does your mother manage to take care of you?" asked Abraham Lincoln.

"Well, it's like you said. Folks help. The soldiers—Father's friends—bring their mending to her. They ask her to cook for them. And sometimes they bring their washing for her to do. They pay as much as they can. The soldiers give us cloth for our clothes, too.

"And Snowden helps. Snowden is my friend. He sells vegetables and I help him call. Snowden fills the basket under the seat with vegetables and calls them left overs. He gives the basket to

Abraham Lincoln just sat there, holding the little boy whose sobbing had been so long kept back. A great hand patted him gently and understandingly between the shoulders. When Martin grew quieter the man began to talk.

"So your father is a cobbler. Is he a good cobbler, Martin?"

Martin nodded his head so hard that his nose went up and down against Abraham Lincoln's ribs.

"Good cobblers are mighty important," said the man. "Never made a pair of shoes myself. But I saw a boy once that needed some mighty bad." The President settled his back a little more comfortably into the corner of the step and the wall.

"It happened when I was postmaster back in Illinois," he went on. "People didn't write many letters in those days, so I carried them in my hat. One cold day as I was going along with the letters in my hat, I saw Ab Trout. He was barefoot as the day he was born and chopping a pile of

Mother. But the vegetables aren't left overs. Not really."

Martin didn't tell about his mother's prayer for flour and sugar and butter and eggs. He didn't need to. For Abraham Lincoln seemed to know all about that prayer.

"Hmm!" he began. "It seems to me, Martin, that part of this job of helping belongs to the army—your father's army, and mine. I will speak to somebody, and I'm pretty sure there will be food from the army stores every week for your mother. Things that Snowden and the soldiers can't supply, like butter and bacon and other things."

There wasn't any lump in Martin's throat now. He felt wonderful. But for some reason the tears began to pour down his face.

The man pretended not to see. Instead, he raised himself to his feet, and a sudden frown grew deep between his eyes. "It's my shoe, Martin," he explained. "There's a nail sticking right into my foot. And I keep forgetting to have it fixed."

"Oh, wait," cried Martin. "I can help you." He darted off to a pile of stones by the steps. Luckily he found the kind he wanted right away. When he came back Abraham Lincoln sat on the steps with his shoe off, waiting to be helped.

Martin sat down beside him. He slipped one stone inside the great shoe. With the other he pounded hard on the sole.

"My father showed me how," he boasted between pounds. "He is a good cobbler."

Abraham Lincoln smiled. "I'd like to be a cobbler myself, Martin. A good cobbler."

"That's what I am going to be," nodded Martin.

Down the street he could hear the sound of Nellie's bell, the jingle of her harness and the creaking of the wheels on Nellie's cart. But he finished the shoe and gave it to Abraham Lincoln.

The man put on the shoe. He stood up and set the foot, where the nail had been, down carefully. He pressed harder, while Martin watched his face. There was no frown between Abraham Lincoln's eyes.

"It's a good job, Martin," he praised. "It feels just fine." He paused and looked over Martin's head far into the distance. The worry had gone now from the President's face. "You have helped me, Martin," he said, "more than you know!"

Martin said nothing. He only slipped his hand inside Abraham Lincoln's. They came down the steps together.

They were waiting when Snowden and Nellie arrived.

Snowden's mouth popped wide open. Nellie stopped. She flicked her ears and Snowden swept off his hat.

The man beside Martin lifted his gravely in return. Then he bent and raised Martin high in the air and put him on the seat beside Snowden.

"Good-by, soldier," he said.

Martin saluted. Snowden saluted. Abraham Lincoln saluted. Nellie started toward home.

from AMERICA'S ROBERT E. LEE

Henry Steele Commager

The author of this book is a historian who does not try to add glamour to his hero but lets the facts speak for themselves. Lee does not suffer from this treatment but comes out the noble human being he seemed to all who knew him. Lynd Ward's fine pictures add to the importance of this book.

[Lee at West Point]

Meantime there was the serious business of an education—serious indeed for a boy whose family standards were so high, and whose prospects were so poor. For a time Robert had gone to one of the Carter schools; the family connection was so large that they kept up one school for the Carter girls and one for the boys. When he was thirteen his mother sent him to the Alexandria Academy—General Washington had been one of the trustees—where a genial Irishman named William Leary drilled him in Greek and Latin and mathematics. This would have prepared him for college, but there wasn't enough money for college. Brother Sidney Smith had made himself a career in the Navy; why shouldn't Robert have a career in the Army? Clearly, if he was to be a

From *America's Robert E. Lee* by Henry Steele Commager. Reprinted by permission of and arrangement with Houghton Mifflin Company, the authorized publishers

soldier, the place for him was the Military Academy at West Point. And to West Point he determined to go.

The first problem was to get into the Academy. The requirements for admission were easy enough, ludicrously easy by modern standards. Applicants had to be between the ages of fourteen and twenty, at least four feet nine inches tall, free from physical defects, able to read and write, and competent in arithmetic! Robert could meet these all right. He was seventeen years old, almost six feet tall, in perfect health, and as well educated as almost any boy of his age.

The real difficulty was to get an appointment from the Secretary of War who, at this time, was John C. Calhoun of South Carolina. Competition was sharp, especially in the South, where it was a tradition that the sons of gentlemen go into the Army. Yet Robert's chances were good. It was not only that he was a handsome and likeable young man, well trained in the classics and in mathematics. That helped, of course. Rather it was that he had behind him the powerful Lee connection, and all their friends. And there were many who remembered Light-Horse Harry's services to his country, and who were eager to extend a helping hand to his son. So Robert was able to submit to the Secretary of War not only the usual recommendations from friends and teachers, but letters from no less than five Senators and three Congressmen! Whether it was these letters, or the Lee name, or young Robert himself, we do not know, but in March 1824 Robert E. Lee was informed that he had been appointed to the United States Military Academy at West Point.

On a warm June day in 1825 Lee stepped aboard a gleaming white paddle-wheeler—perhaps it was the *Chancellor Livingston* or the *James Kent*, or even the new *Richmond*—and steamed up the Hudson to West Point. It was only fifty-some miles from New York to the Point, but the trip took half a day, and there was plenty of time to admire the scenery, as lovely as any in the country. It was all new to Robert, yet not wholly strange, not unlike the upper Potomac, which he knew well—the broad blue river, on one side the steep Palisades, on the other trim lawn running down to the water's edge, and handsome mansion houses. The steamer stopped when it came opposite the Point, swinging back and forth in the current. A little skiff put out from the pier, and the lads who were going to the Academy climbed down the rope ladder and into the boat, and were rowed to shore, Robert among them.

Set in a great bend of the Hudson, the Point was as beautiful then as now. It was hemmed in on two sides by the Majestic river; to the south stretched the Highlands, while Storm King Mountain, its summit often hidden in clouds, dominated the north. The magnificence of the natural setting brought out in sharp contrast the shabbiness of the Academy itself. As Lee came up the steep path from the river pier, he saw a group of ugly stucco buildings, squatting on a narrow, treeless plateau. There were the North and South Barracks, which housed the four-hundred-odd cadets, the main Academy building, a long mess hall—also used as a hotel for visitors—and, scattered around the grounds, a group of smaller buildings almost as ugly as the main ones.

Living conditions, Lee quickly learned, were as meager as the buildings. In the summertime Lee and his fellow cadets lived in tents, in what was called—in honor of the President then in the White House—Camp Adams. The rest of the year Lee lived in the old barracks. His room was small, bare, and uncomfortable, heated only by a tiny fireplace, and he had to share it with two or three other lads. Here he studied, in such time as was allowed him, by the flickering light of candles; here he slept, unrolling his mattress on a cold floor. The food, too, as Lee soon learned, was very different from the rich and varied fare he was used to at home. The Academy chef, a thrifty soul, filled his victims up on porridge, bread, soup, and potatoes, with bacon and mutton and beef only on rare occasions. It was, all in all, pretty grim.

Plebe Lee fell quickly into the routine of the Academy. Reveille sounded at sunrise; then came drill and parade for an hour or so; breakfast; five hours of classes and study; an hour for dinner; two more hours of study; two hours for drill; supper, study, and inspection. Taps were sounded at nine-thirty, and lights out at ten. It was all quite strenuous, but once Lee got the hang of it, he managed easily enough. There was not much time for play, and no organized sports at all. Saturday afternoons and Sundays the cadets could swim in the Hudson, or walk to near-by Buttermilk Falls, or find a few hours for reading, and perhaps for visitors.

Life, as Lee soon learned, was hedged around with endless rules and regulations. Woe betide the cadet who forgot them—who was late for classes or forgot to polish his boots or his buttons, who talked out of turn or failed in proper respect to instructors or to upper-classmen, or ventured off ground in search for food or for forbidden entertainment. Colonel Thayer, the Superintendent who had really made the Academy, was a strict disciplinarian, and failure to observe the rules was punished with demerits. Too many of these, and out you went!

The academic requirements, too, were stiff. Colonel Thayer had already established the rule, still an Academy tradition, that every cadet recite in every subject every day. There was no such thing as falling behind in your work, and then boning up for examinations: if you fell behind, you fell out. The course of study was a narrow one. The first year was devoted to mathematics and French. Gradually other subjects were added—drawing, surveying, engineering, a bit of physics and chemistry, a smattering of history, geography, and "moral philosophy." There was also something called "the science of war"—a subject which Lee certainly mastered, whether at the Academy or elsewhere.

This was all theoretical, and you couldn't make a soldier by theory alone. Colonel Thayer knew that well enough: he was an engineer himself. So on top of all the book-study, there was constant drill, and practical training. The cadets learned how to handle artillery, how to build forts, how to lay out roads and build bridges, how to survey and make maps. They were trained in tactics, and in the command of small groups of soldiers. All this was fun for the cadets: it took them out in the open, gave them a chance to ride horses, to use surveying instruments, to fire off guns, gave them a feeling that they were learning things of practical use.

Many a promising career was wrecked on the shoals of rules or grades. Of Lee's class of eighty-seven, almost half failed to graduate. But Lee had no difficulties either with the regulations or with his marks. From the beginning he was up

among the first two or three in his class, and he held this position through the four years he was at the Academy. In his second year Lee was named staff sergeant, and asked to teach mathematics to the Plebes; thereafter he was both instructor and student. In his last year he won the most prized of all Academy distinctions—the position of Adjutant of the Corps. When he graduated he was number two in his class, and what is more, he had come through four years without a single demerit! As a "distinguished cadet" he could choose his own branch of service, and, like so many others, he chose the engineers.

To his classmates Lee was known as the "Marble Model." He may have been a model, but he was far from marble, far from cold and aloof, and there was nothing about him of the prig. Joseph E. Johnston—his classmate and later his ablest general—describes him at this time:

> We had the same intimate associates who thought as I did that no other youth or man so united the qualities that win warm friendship and command high respect. For he was full of sympathy and kindness, genial and fond of gay conversation, and even of fun, while his correctness of demeanor and attention to all duties, personal and official, and a dignity as much a part of himself as the elegance of his person, gave him a superiority that every one acknowledged in his heart.

Here we have the Lee of the future!

A full-fledged officer now, wonderfully handsome in his gray and white uniform, Lee returned to Virginia to visit with family and friends before taking up his professional duties. He came not a moment too soon. For Anne Carter Lee, long an invalid, lay at the point of death. Lee was with her when, a few weeks later, she died. All in all she had not had a very happy life. Her marriage had been a failure, she had been much alone, she had known poverty and sickness. But she had seen all her boys launched in life—Carter in the law, Smith in the Navy, and Robert, now, a lieutenant in the Army. She was proud of them all, as well she might be, and especially proud of Robert, who had been closer to her than any of her other children.

THREE ADVENTURERS

Carol Ryrie Brink

*Caddie Woodlawn, for which "Three Adven-
turers" is the first chapter, won the Newbery
Award the year it appeared, and several library
research studies have placed it at the top in popularity with children throughout the country. Indian John called Caddie Woodlawn "Missee
Red Hair," and their friendship was to stand the
whole community in good stead, when the two
of them were able to avert a bloody war between
the Indians and the white settlers.*

In 1864 Caddie Woodlawn was eleven, and as
wild a little tomboy as ever ran the woods of
western Wisconsin. She was the despair of her
mother and of her elder sister Clara. But her father watched her with a little shine of pride in
his eyes, and her brothers accepted her as one of
themselves without a question. Indeed, Tom,
who was two years older, and Warren, who was
two years younger than Caddie, needed Caddie
to link them together into an inseparable trio.
Together they got in and out of more scrapes
and adventures than any one of them could have
imagined alone. And in those pioneer days Wisconsin offered plenty of opportunities for adventure to three wide-eyed, red-headed youngsters.

On a bright Saturday afternoon in the early
fall Tom and Caddie and Warren Woodlawn sat
on a bank of the Menomonie River, or Red
Cedar as they call it now, taking off their
clothes. Their red heads shone in the sunlight.
Tom's hair was the darkest, Caddie's the nearest
golden, and nine-year-old Warren's was plain
carrot color. Not one of the three knew how to
swim, but they were going across the river, nevertheless. A thin thread of smoke beyond the
bend on the other side of the river told them
that the Indians were at work on a birch-bark
canoe.

"Do you think the Indians around here would
ever get mad and massacre folks like they did up
north?" wondered Warren, tying his shirt up in
a little bundle.

"No, sir!" said Tom, "not these Indians!"

"Not Indian John, anyhow," said Caddie. She
had just unfastened the many troublesome little
buttons on the back of her tight-waisted dress,
and, before taking it off, she paused a moment to
see if she could balance a fresh-water clam shell
on her big toe. She found that she could.

"No, not Indian John!" she repeated decidedly, having got the matter of the clam shell off
her mind, "even if he does have a scalp belt," she
added. The thought of the scalp belt always
made her hair prickle delightfully up where her
scalp lock grew.

"Naw," said Tom, "the fellows who spread
those massacree stories are just big-mouthed
scared-cats who don't know the Indians, I
guess."

"Big-mouthed scared-cats," repeated Warren,
admiring Tom's command of language.

"Big-mouthed scared-cats," echoed a piping
voice from the bank above. Seven-year-old Hetty,
who fluttered wistfully on the outer edge of their
adventures, filed away Tom's remark in her active brain. It would be useful to tell to Mother,
sometime when Mother was complaining about
Tom's language. The three below her paid no
attention to Hetty's intrusion. Their red heads,
shining in the sunlight, did not even turn in her
direction. Hetty's hair was red, too, like Father's,
but somehow, in spite of her hair, she belonged
on the dark-haired side of the family where
Mother and Clara and all the safe and tidy virtues were. She poised irresolutely on the bank
above the three adventurous ones. If they had
only turned around and looked at her! But they
were enough in themselves. She could not make
up her mind what to do. She wanted to go with
them, and yet she wanted just as much to run
home and tell Mother and Clara what they were
about to do. Hetty was the self-appointed news-
bearer of the family. Wild horses could not prevent her from being the first to tell, whatever it
was that happened.

Tom and Caddie and Warren finished un-
dressing, tied their clothes into tight bundles,
and stepped out into the river. The water was
low after a long, hot summer, but still it looked
cold and deep. Hetty shuddered. She had started
to undo one shoe, but now she quickly tied it up
again. She had made up her mind. She turned
around and flew across the fields to tell Mother.

Tom knew from experience that he could just keep his chin above water and touch bottom with his toes across the deep part of the river. It would have been over Caddie's and Warren's heads, but, if they held onto Tom and kept their feet paddling, they could just keep their heads above water. They had done it before. Tom went first with his bundle of clothes balanced on his head. Caddie came next, clutching Tom's shoulder with one hand and holding her bundle of clothes on top of her head with the other. Warren clung to Caddie's shoulder in the same manner, balancing his own clothes with his free hand. They moved slowly and carefully. If Tom lost his footing or fell, they would all go down together and be swept away by the current toward the village below. But the other two had every confidence in Tom, and Tom had not the slightest reason to doubt himself. They looked like three beavers, moving silently across the current—three heads with three bundles and a little wake of ripples trailing out behind them. Last of all came Nero, the farm dog, paddling faithfully behind them. But Hetty was already out of sight.

Presently there was solid river bed beneath their feet again. The three children scrambled out on the other side, shook themselves as Nero did, and pulled on their dry, wrinkled clothing.

"Hurry up, Caddie," called Tom. "You're always the last to dress."

"So would you be, too, Tom, if you had so many buttons!" protested Caddie. She came out of the bushes struggling with the back of her blue denim dress. Relenting, Tom turned his superior intelligence to the mean task of buttoning her up the back.

"I wish Mother'd let me wear boy's clothes," she complained.

"Huh!" said Warren, "she thinks you're tomboy enough already."

"But they're so much quicker," said Caddie regretfully.

Now that they were dressed, they sped along the river bank in the direction of the smoke. Several Indian canoes were drawn up on shore in the shelter of a little cove and beyond them in a clearing the Indians moved to and fro about a fire. Propped on two logs was the crude framework of a canoe which was already partly covered with birch bark. The smell of birch smoke and hot pitch filled the air. Caddie lifted her head and sniffed. It was perfume to her, as sweet as the perfume of the clover fields. Nero sniffed, too, and growled low in his throat.

The three children stopped at the edge of the clearing and watched. Even friendly Indians commanded fear and respect in those days. A lean dog, with a wolfish look, came forward barking.

He and Nero circled about each other, little ridges of bristling hair along their spines, their tails wagging suspiciously. Suddenly the Indian dog left Nero and came toward Caddie.

"Look!" said Caddie. "It's Indian John's dog." The dog's tail began to wag in a friendlier manner, and Caddie reached out and patted his head.

By this time the Indians had noticed the children. They spoke among themselves and pointed. Some of them left their work and came forward.

In all the seven years since the Woodlawns had come from Boston to live in the big house on the prairie, the Indians had never got used to seeing them. White men and their children they had seen often enough, but never such as these, who wore, above their pale faces, hair the color of flame and sunset. During the first year that the children spent in Wisconsin, the Indians had come from all the country around to look at them. They had come in groups, crowding into Mrs. Woodlawn's kitchen in their silent moccasins, touching the children's hair and staring. Poor Mrs. Woodlawn, frightened nearly out of

her wits, had fed them bread or beans or whatever she had on hand, and they had gone away satisfied.

"Johnny, my dear," Mrs. Woodlawn had complained to her husband, "those frightful savages will eat us out of house and home."

"Patience, Harriet," said her husband, "we have enough and to spare."

"But, Johnny, the way they look at the children's hair frightens me. They might want a red scalp to hang to their belts."

Caddie remembered very vividly the day, three years before, when she had gone unsuspecting into the store in the village. As she went in the door, a big Indian had seized her and held her up in the air while he took a leisurely look at her hair. She had been so frightened that she had not even cried out, but hung there, wriggling in the Indian's firm grasp, and gazing desperately about the store for help.

The storekeeper had laughed at her, saying in a reassuring voice: "You needn't be afraid, Caddie. He's a good Indian. It's Indian John."

That was the strange beginning of a friendship, for a kind of friendship it was, that had grown up between Caddie and Indian John. The boys liked Indian John, too, but it was at Caddie and her red-gold curls that the big Indian looked when he came to the farm, and it was for Caddie that he left bits of oddly carved wood and once a doll—such a funny doll with a tiny head made of a pebble covered with calico, black horsehair braids, calico arms and legs, and a buckskin dress! John's dog knew his master's friends. Caddie had been kind to him and he accepted her as a friend.

He rubbed his head against her now as she patted his rough hair. Indian John left his work on the canoe and came forward.

"You like him dog?" he said, grinning. He was flattered when anyone patted his dog.

"Yes," said Caddie, "he's a good dog."

"Will you let us see how you put the canoe together?" asked Tom eagerly.

"You come look," said the Indian.

They followed him to the half-finished canoe. Grunting and grinning, the Indians took up their work. They fastened the pliable sheaths of birch bark into place on the light framework, first sewing them together with buckskin thongs, then cementing them with the hot pitch. The children were fascinated. Their own canoe on the lake was an Indian canoe. But it had been hollowed out of a single log. They had seen the birch-bark canoes on the river, but had never been so close to the making of one. They were so intent on every detail that time slipped by unheeded. Even the squaws, who came up behind them to examine their hair, did not take their attention from the building of the canoe. Caddie shook her head impatiently, flicking her curls out of their curious fingers, and went on watching.

But after awhile Warren said: "Golly! I'm hungry." Perhaps it was the odor of jerked venison, simmering over the fire, which had begun to mingle with the odors of birch and pitch, that made Warren remember he was hungry.

"You're always hungry," said Tom, the lofty one, in a tone of disgust.

"Well, I am, too," said Caddie positively, and that settled it. The sun was beginning to swing low in the sky, and, once they had made up their minds, they were off at once. As quickly as they had come, they returned along the river bank to their crossing place. The Indians stared after them. They did not understand these curious red and white children of the white man, nor how they went and came.

Soon three bundles, three dirty faces, and three fiery heads, shining in the red autumn sun, crossed the river with a little trail of ripples behind them. Safe on the other bank, the three hastily pulled on their clothes and started to take a short cut through the woods, Nero trotting at their heels.

from A SOUNDING TRUMPET

Louise Hall Tharp

The following excerpt gives two chapters from the biography of Julia Ward Howe. The spirited little redhead of the first chapter grew into a beautiful young woman as her father foresaw. She married a distinguished doctor and had a lively family of children, among them Laura Richards, many of whose nonsense verses you will find in Time for Poetry. *In the second chap-*

ter given here the mature Julia Ward Howe is in Washington with her husband during the Civil War. This chapter tells how she happened to write "The Battle Hymn of the Republic."

Independence Day

The brisk notes of a French clock chimed the quarter hour as Julia ran downstairs. To her delight, she found the door of the front parlor wide open. At the windows, the heavy silk draperies had been looped to one side, while lace glass-curtains fluttered in the breeze. Sunshine flooded this formal room which was usually kept closed and dim. Julia tiptoed inside.

A long mirror reached from floor to ceiling between the two windows. Julia inspected herself carefully. Yes—her rebellious red hair was as flat and smooth as a dampened hairbrush could make it. Her ears and neck were still pink from a hard scrubbing. She looked like a little girl who meant to be very good indeed on this holiday morning. Then her gray eyes began to twinkle. The laughter spread, and suddenly Julia Ward was a very imp of mischief!

A muffled footfall on the carpeted floor made Julia spin around. Here came William, the Negro butler, with a huge feather duster under his arm. "My, my, Miss Julia, aren't you up pretty early?" exclaimed William, reproachfully. "'Pears to me like you couldn't wait for nurse to come and dress you."

"Oh, who could sleep on a morning like this!" cried Julia, pirouetting gaily before the mirror. "Do you realize what day it is?"

"Shore do," sighed William. "The old gentleman goin' to come here today. Got to get my parlor all shined up for the Colonel. So don't you go dancin' the roses right off that carpet—even if it is the Fourth of July!"

Julia laughed and managed to stand still for perhaps half a minute. "Grandfather calls this 'Independence Day,' William. I thought I'd show my independence by getting up when I pleased. Are Sam and Henry back yet?"

William's solemn black face relaxed into a grin. "No, ma'am! Those boys goin' to show up missin' if they don't watch out. Hate to think what their father will say." With an expert twist of the wrist, William flecked the dust out of the deep carving on the mahogany sofa. "Don' know

as I blame the boys," he confided. "Most run off to have a look myself."

"I was going," announced Julia, "but the boys just wouldn't take me."

Now William was really shocked. It was one thing for the Ward boys to see the sights of New York town on the Fourth of July, but the Ward sisters never stirred abroad save in their father's carriage, or with a nurse or governess. "Miss Julia," warned William solemnly, "there's limits to independence!"

Julia tossed her red head. "When I grow up, I'm going to do things and see things—even if I *am* a girl. If they ever again have anything as wonderful as a balloon ascension at Battery Park, I'll be there to see the balloon!"

But Julia knew perfectly well that this small declaration of independence of hers would do her no earthly good at the present time. If she saw anything at all now, it would have to be from the parlor window. Impatiently, she shoved aside the lace curtain and leaned out.

Directly across the way was a park, surrounded by a neat iron railing. This was Bowling Green. Long ago, in old New York, British settlers in white periwigs and knee breeches loved to roll the heavy bowling balls here on the grass, in sight of the broad Hudson. A gilded statue of King George the Third of England had looked down upon his loyal subjects from astride a gilded horse.

But now there was no statue to be seen from Julia's window. One night in 1776 an angry mob had surged over Bowling Green. "Give us Liberty," they shouted, as they tore down the gilded king. The statue proved to be made of lead, so men melted it down into bullets for the battle for freedom.

Grandfather had been a lieutenant-colonel under General Washington, and Julia had heard many stories of the Revolution. But even today, on the Fourth of July, it is likely that Julia Ward was not thinking about history. She was a very-up-to-date little girl, and this was 1828. Today Julia wanted nothing in the world so much as to see a gas balloon! She climbed on a chair in the hope of seeing past Bowling Green into Battery Park, but it was no use.

With a sigh, Julia resigned herself to watching the holiday crowd as it surged past her door.

An omnibus, drawn by four white horses, pulled up at the curb. It was already crowded. A huge barrel on wheels came lumbering along. It was a street sprinkler, and Julia laughed to see the pedestrians scatter out of the road. Now they scattered again for something else, and Julia craned her neck to see what commanded so much respect. A huge black and white sow came around the corner, followed by four little pigs.

The omnibus had started, but the pigs, serenely certain that they owned the right of way, continued across the street to a fine wilted cabbage which lay waiting for them in the gutter. The bus driver swore, but prudently pulled up. With a contemptuous flip of her left ear, Mrs. Pig acknowledged the courtesy while the babies marched in her wake, looking neither to the right nor to the left. "Mother will manage everything," they seemed to say. And the pig family settled down to its business of garbage collecting right in front of the town house of Samuel Ward, Esquire.

Julia giggled. Father had already written letters to the *Evening Post* suggesting that pigs be kept off the streets of New York. But of course they never would be.

Behind her, the mantel clock chimed seven quick strokes, as if hurrying to catch up with time. Julia began to feel anxious. She craned her neck, trying to see all the way down the street, but there was no sign of Sam or Henry. In the back parlor, William was arranging eight chairs. Each one faced Father's big armchair with the little table beside it. William reverently dusted the family Bible and placed it upon the table. With it went a small Episcopal prayer book.

Overhead, sounds of activity increased. A warning voice cried, "No, Francis Marion Ward, how many times do I have to tell you!" Aunt Eliza had been just in time to prevent Julia's younger brother from sliding down the banister.

The rustle of starched petticoats announced Julia's little sisters. They ran into the front parlor with cries of delight. But Aunt Eliza was close behind.

"Go to your seats, girls," she said. "There isn't time to look out of the window now." Dark-haired Louisa and five-year-old Ann Eliza obeyed. Their brother, Francis Marion, climbed into a haircloth-covered chair which pricked his legs.

Reluctantly, Julia started for the back parlor. Then she gave one last glance over her shoulder and stopped dead in her tracks. Over in Battery Park, a great golden sphere rose slowly among the trees. At about tree-level, it halted and swayed gently in the breeze. "The balloon!" cried Julia her eyes bright with excitement. The younger children screwed around in their seats and would have dashed to the window but for Aunt Eliza's restraining hand.

The door from the hall opened, and an ominous sound brought Julia to herself with a start. Father was clearing his throat. She looked around quickly, and there he was, settling himself in the big chair and reaching in his pocket for his gold-rimmed glasses. Julia scuttled for the back parlor and slid into her seat. In summer, Father began family prayers at seven-fifteen sharp; in winter, at seven-forty-five. Sad was the fate of any child whose chair was empty at that moment. The parlor clock chimed its hurried notes.

For a moment Julia thought of nothing but her glimpse of the beautiful balloon. Then, with a sudden sinking of heart, she saw that there were still two empty places. Sam and Henry were late! Faithful William was hovering near the front door to let in the boys as quickly and silently as possible, but he could not help them now. The hour had struck.

Father reached for his Bible. He took a good look at the empty chairs, and Julia's throat hurt as she imagined how sad it would be for Sam and Henry to be punished on a holiday. Then Father paused and took a huge gold watch out of his pocket. "Those newfangled mantel clocks are unreliable," he exclaimed, getting up and going into the front parlor. "Give me a good tall clock, every time." He scowled at the clock's pretty enameled face and set the filigree gold hands back two and a half minutes.

While Father looked reprovingly at the frivolous little clock, the front door opened softly, and closed more softly still. Sam and Henry tiptoed to their seats.

"Did you see them put the gas in the balloon?" Julia whispered.

"Oh, yes," they gasped, badly out of breath. "Julia, you must get Father to let you go!"

Julia nodded as Father walked majestically to his seat. If he noticed that two previously empty chairs were now occupied by two very red-faced and breathless small boys, he made no sign. Father read aloud from the Bible, then he turned to the prayer book. The children bowed their heads.

After family prayers, the Wards trooped down another flight of stairs to breakfast. The dining room was below the street level and none too well lighted by barred windows looking out upon a stone areaway. Aunt Eliza took her place behind a massive silver coffeepot at one end of the table. Father barricaded himself behind his newspaper at the other. Among themselves the young Wards talked in low tones, taking pains not to disturb their elders. Children were supposed to be seen and not heard, Aunt Eliza would say.

"Did you get into the park?" asked Julia cautiously.

The boys nodded. "We paid our fee at the gate. At first we couldn't see any balloon, though, and we thought we'd been cheated," Sam replied.

"Where was it?" Julia demanded.

"Why, it was flat on the ground—just a huge piece of yellow silk all sewed together in squares," Henry explained. "On top was a mass of rope like a great fish net."

"And then the silk began to heave gently," added Sam. "You would swear the balloon was coming alive!" Sam had a poetic imagination.

"That was because the men from the gas company began filling the balloon with gas," said practical Henry.

Father cleared his throat and the children fell silent immediately. "It says in the paper that the gas company has agreed to install street lamps all the way up Broadway beyond Grand Street," he announced. "Now, that will be a fine thing. We'll have over a mile of well-lighted streets. New York is getting to be quite a city."

Seeing that Father was in a good mood, Julia boldly put a question. "Doesn't it tell in the paper about the Fourth of July celebration, Father? I wish we could go to see the balloon."

"Eh? Oh—that." Father rattled the pages. " 'Parade of military and firemen. Balloon ascension at Battery Park.' Well, I expect the proprietors of Castle Garden will make a mint of money out of the crowd."

"Please, Father, may we go?" Julia asked eagerly.

Named for her mother, who had died some years before, Julia was her father's favorite child. But Samuel Ward was so overcome with grief at the loss of his beautiful young wife that he had become stern and strictly religious. He expected Julia to be painfully good. Now, as he read further in the paper, he gave a snort of indignation. "Why, it says here that a woman is going up in that balloon! What are we coming to? No, indeed, Julia, you may not go to see such a shocking, vulgar sight."

"But Father," cried Julia, "what's wrong about it? I think she must be very brave, and I'd like to see her."

Father promptly began a lecture to the effect that all girls should stay at home and just be sweet and obedient. Julia listened in silence, thinking her own thoughts. That red hair of hers came from her mother's side of the family, and with it she inherited her warmhearted, independent nature.

One of Julia's ancestors on her mother's side was General Francis Marion, the "Swamp Fox" of revolutionary fame, who outwitted the British in South Carolina. Her little brother, Francis Marion Ward, was named for this hero, but Julia was the one who could outflank her opponents every time. When Father had finished, Julia quietly continued her campaign. "There will be patriotic speeches by some of the old soldiers at Battery Park, Father," she remarked. "Grandfather Ward told me so."

Mr. Ward smiled indulgently. "Father will be there, resplendent in his uniform, I expect. Probably he'll get to telling some of those old stories of his."

"Well, there aren't many Revolutionary heroes like your father left," remarked Aunt Eliza, stirring her coffee in a casual sort of way. "I expect he would like to have the older children come to hear him speak."

Samuel Ward glanced at Julia's pleading gray eyes. "Send for the carriage if you've a mind, Eliza," he said. "The older children may go, I suppose. Julia, pay close attention and try to learn something about your country. But mind you behave all morning, or you shan't go after all."

The look of forlorn hope on Julia's face changed instantly to joy. Her eyes shone with the glory of anticipation. "Oh, Father, I'll be good as gold!" she cried.

She'll grow up to be very beautiful, thought Samuel Ward, pride mingling with anxiety. "All right, all right," he said gruffly, as he left the room. "Mind you behave."

. . . .

"Mine Eyes Have Seen the Glory"

The city of Washington was seething with excitement by the time Julia got back to Willard's Hotel. Dispatch riders galloped through the streets. From time to time a detachment of infantry marched past the hotel with no sound save the rhythmic crunch of heavy boots and an occasional shouted command. Inside the hotel lobby, groups of half-hysterical people were trying in vain to make arrangements to get out of town.

Julia was not the kind of person to try to escape to the North while every road and railroad was needed to move troops. She could keep calm and, if need be, help her husband with the wounded. Meanwhile she was tired, so she went to bed and slept soundly.

About dawn, Julia awoke. Once more men were marching in the street below. As she lay listening, she thought about the men and boys on the road from Upton's Hill. The song she sang to them came back to her—but with new words. Julia lay perfectly still, while stanza after stanza sang itself over in her mind. Then she got up, and in the gray light of dawn she wrote down the words.

In the morning, Julia wondered if the whole thing had been a dream. She went to the desk and found a sheet of paper with her husband's Sanitary Commission heading. Her writing was hard to read because the light had been so poor. But here were the words which had come to her in the night:

"Mine eyes have seen the glory of the coming of the Lord;
He is trampling out the vintage where the grapes of wrath are stored;
He hath loosed the fateful lightning of his terrible swift sword;
    His truth is marching on.

"I have seen Him in the watchfires of a hundred circling camps;
They have builded Him an altar in the evening dews and damps;
I can read His righteous sentence by the dim and flaring lamps;
    His day is marching on.

"I have read a fiery gospel writ in burnished rows of steel:
'As ye deal with my contemners, so with you my grace shall deal;
Let the hero born of woman crush the serpent with his heel;
    Since God is marching on.'

"He has sounded forth the trumpet that shall never call retreat;
He is sifting out the hearts of men before His judgment-seat;
Oh, be swift, my soul to answer Him! Be jubilant, my feet!
    Our God is marching on.

"In the beauty of the lilies Christ was born across the sea,
With a glory in His bosom that transfigures you and me:
As He died to make men holy, let us die to make men free,
    While God is marching on."

There was one more stanza, but Julia decided not to use it. She made one or two slight changes and showed the poem to Dr. Clarke and the other friends who had been with her the day before. "This is the song!" exclaimed Dr. Clarke. "I can just hear our boys singing these inspired words."

One of the ladies asked Julia for the original copy of the poem.

"Willard's Hotel
Julia W. Howe
to
Charlotte B. Whipple"

That is what Julia wrote on the other side of the sheet. Then she handed her friend what was, in time, to become a priceless historical manuscript.

After Julia got home to Boston she sent her

poem to the *Atlantic Monthly*. "What title would you like?" she asked the editor, and "The Battle Hymn of the Republic" was suggested. They paid her ten dollars, and she was pleased to see her "Battle Hymn" on the front page of the next number of the magazine. As far as Julia Ward Howe knew, she had merely written another poem. It was a good one, to be sure, but no one seemed to pay much attention to it.

However, the Rev. Charles Cardwell McCabe, who was known as the "singing chaplain" of the 122nd Ohio Regiment of Volunteers, read the *Atlantic Monthly*. When he saw the "Battle Hymn" he was so struck with it that he learned it by heart before he got up from his chair. He went right out among the soldiers and began to teach them the new song. It took, and it spread like wildfire.

In 1863, Chaplain McCabe was taken prisoner and sent to Libby Prison. The gaunt old building on the bank of the James River had once been Libby's ship chandlery. Now it was packed with prisoners of war who slept on the floor at night and took turns watching at the window by day, hoping that the armies of the North would soon come marching to their rescue.

Down in the cellar of the building, some men had recently tunneled their way to freedom. Now the dirt floor had been covered in with masonry, a bloodhound patrolled the prison along with the guards and discipline was very strict. Chaplain McCabe found the prisoners in a mood of desperate discouragement. They asked him eagerly for news of the war, but there was little he could tell them that afforded any comfort. The fortunes of the North were still at a low ebb. But he had a new song to sing—and Chaplain McCabe cheered his fellow prisoners with "The Battle Hymn of the Republic."

"Two of your officers are to be executed because of the escape of the men in the cellar," the prisoners were told. "Draw lots and see which of you are to die." There was nothing to do but obey. Chaplain McCabe's fine voice was heard singing, and the prisoners joined in:

"In the beauty of the lilies, Christ was born across the sea,
As He died to make men holy, let us die to make men free."

The officers chosen for execution marched away.

Next day, the two officers were brought back again, to everybody's surprise and joy. The order of execution had been countermanded. They were not to die after all.

The prisoners were given food only once a day. For a while they got bean soup and corn bread. They complained, for the soup was terrible. Soon they longed for some of that soup again, for now they got only the corn bread and not very much of that. Corn husks were ground up and added to the meal to make it go farther. Sometimes a cockroach was found, firmly baked into a prisoner's small square of bread. "He's probably very nourishing," joked Chaplain McCabe. "Cheer up, men. The reason we have so little food is plain to see. Our army must have cut off Confederate supplies. We are winning the war at last."

It was an up-hill job for the chaplain to encourage the prisoners. General McClellan, the little Napoleon, was discredited now. He had organizing ability, but in the field he was a hopeless procrastinator. General succeeded general, but the results were always the same—disaster for the North.

News came to Libby Prison that the North had been defeated once and for all—at Gettysburg! Then a Negro servant, old Ben, slipped in with the news that a flood on the Potomac had swept away Lee's pontoon bridge, and Gettysburg was a Northern victory. Chaplain McCabe led the prisoners as they sang:

"Mine eyes have seen the glory of the coming of the Lord."

Before the Civil War was over, Chaplain McCabe was released from Libby Prison. He was asked to speak to a large audience in Washington and tell about his experiences. He told what "The Battle Hymn of the Republic" meant, both to the Ohio Volunteers and to the prisoners of war.

"Who wrote this hymn, anyway?" people began asking each other.

Julia Ward Howe was still blissfully unconscious that she was famous. She went right on raising money for the war, taking care of the children and making her home a happy place for family, friends and neighbors. Then one day came a letter from the Hon. George Bancroft, famous historian. Would Mrs. Howe attend a celebration at the Century Club in New York in honor of the poet Bryant's seventieth birthday? Would she read a poem?

"Good gracious, the whole thing must be a mistake!" cried Julie. "Why, the best poets in this country will be there!" But she sat right down, anyway, and wrote some lines for Bryant's birthday. Julia really admired Bryant, and had no trouble thinking of pleasant things to say about him.

When she got on the train for New York, there was Oliver Wendell Holmes, bound for the same celebration. "Mrs. Howe, I will sit beside you, but you must not expect me to talk," he said. "I must spare my voice for the evening, when I am to read a poem at the Bryant celebration."

Julia's eyes twinkled. "Let's both keep quiet," she suggested. "I have a poem to read at the Bryant celebration, as well." Holmes, who had a good opinion of himself, stared at Julia in astonishment. He had supposed she was just a pretty woman he happened to know who was bound for New York on a shopping tour. In a few minutes he had forgotten all about saving his voice, for Julia was immensely clever in a battle of wits. The great Dr. Holmes couldn't help showing off a bit for such an attractive woman.

The celebration was a brilliant affair. Emerson spoke and Holmes read his poem, of course. But it was Julia Ward Howe who sat on the platform between Mr. Bancroft and Mr. Bryant.

"This is the poet who has written the most stirring lyric of the war," said Mr. Bryant. The people clapped and cheered. They also stared at Julia, for somehow they had imagined that the writer of "The Battle Hymn of the Republic" would be an elderly lady in a lace cap, or else a very strong-minded-looking female in spectacles.

A photograph, taken at this time, shows that Julia was an unusually beautiful woman. Her hair was parted and drawn smoothly down to accent the delicate oval of her face. Her mouth was sensitive and sweet, while her shadowy gray eyes were full of sympathy and imagination. She loved fashionable clothes but chose them with taste, so that now they seem quaint but not grotesque. Most Civil-War-time photographs were far from flattering. If Julia looked so lovely in

her picture, it was no wonder that her New York audience sat up and applauded.

When she got home, Julia wrote all about how wonderful people had been to her. "I want to leave a record for my grandchildren," she said, laughing. "Such a thing could never happen again." But she was wrong, for this was only the beginning—the first recognition of the author of the "Battle Hymn." From now on, Julia Ward Howe was a famous woman and she led more and more of a public life.

. . . .

INDEPENDENCE DAY

Laura Ingalls Wilder

Farmer Boy is the one book in the Wilder series devoted to the Wilder family. The other seven, beginning with Little House in the Big Woods, are concerned with the adventures of the Ingalls family as it pioneers westward into new country. In the last three books, beginning with The Long Winter, the Ingalls family and Almanzo Wilder meet and share the same vicissitudes and adventures. Laura marries Almanzo, and later writes this wonderful series of books, a saga of pioneering in this country. The Fourth of July described in the following episode must have been about 1867. One of the important things Almanzo Wilder's father did for his son was to give him a sense of values. Children will be interested perhaps in a comparison of prices then and now.

Almanzo was eating breakfast before he remembered that this was the Fourth of July. He felt more cheerful.

It was like Sunday morning. After breakfast he scrubbed his face with soft soap till it shone, and he parted his wet hair and combed it sleekly down. He put on his sheep's-gray trousers and his shirt of French calico, and his vest and his short round coat.

Mother had made his new suit in the new style. The coat fastened at the throat with a little flap of the cloth, then the two sides slanted back to

"Independence Day." From *Farmer Boy* by Laura Ingalls Wilder. Copyright 1933 by Harper & Brothers. Reprinted by permission of Rose Wilder Lane

show his vest, and they rounded off over his trousers' pockets.

He put on his round straw hat, which Mother had made of braided oat-straws, and he was all dressed up for Independence Day. He felt very fine.

Father's shining horses were hitched to the shining, red-wheeled buggy, and they all drove away in the cool sunshine. All the country had a holiday air. Nobody was working in the fields, and along the road the people in their Sunday clothes were driving to town.

Father's swift horses passed them all. They passed by wagons and carts and buggies. They passed gray horses and black horses and dappled-gray horses. Almanzo waved his hat whenever he sailed past anyone he knew, and he would have been perfectly happy if only he had been driving that swift, beautiful team.

At the church sheds in Malone he helped Father unhitch. Mother and the girls and Royal hurried away. But Almanzo would rather help with the horses than do anything else. He couldn't drive them, but he could tie their halters and buckle on their blankets, and stroke their soft noses and give them hay.

Then he went out with Father and they walked on the crowded sidewalks. All the stores were closed, but ladies and gentlemen were walking up and down and talking. Ruffled little girls carried parasols, and all the boys were dressed up, like Almanzo. Flags were everywhere, and in the Square the band was playing "Yankee Doodle." The fifes tooted and the flutes shrilled and the drums came in with rub-a-dub-dub.

"Yankee Doodle went to town,
Riding on a pony,
He stuck a feather in his hat,
And called it macaroni!"

Even grown-ups had to keep time to it. And there, in the corner of the Square, were the two brass cannons!

The Square was not really square. The railroad made it three-cornered. But everybody called it the Square, anyway. It was fenced, and grass grew there. Benches stood in rows on the grass, and people were filing between the benches and sitting down as they did in church.

Almanzo went with Father to one of the best front seats. All the important men stopped to shake hands with Father. The crowd kept coming till all the seats were full, and still there were people outside the fence.

The band stopped playing, and the minister prayed. Then the band tuned up again and everybody rose. Men and boys took off their hats. The band played, and everybody sang.

"Oh, say, can you see by the dawn's early light,
What so proudly we hailed at the twilight's last gleaming,
Whose broad stripes and bright stars through the perilous night,
O'er the ramparts we watched were so gallantly streaming?"

From the top of the flagpole, up against the blue sky, the Stars and Stripes were fluttering. Everybody looked at the American flag, and Almanzo sang with all his might.

Then everyone sat down, and a Congressman stood up on the platform. Slowly and solemnly he read the Declaration of Independence.

"When in the course of human events it becomes necessary for one people . . . to assume among the powers of the earth the separate and equal station. . . . We hold these truths to be self-evident, that all men are created equal. . . ."

Almanzo felt solemn and very proud.

Then two men made long political speeches. One believed in high tariffs, and one believed in free trade. All the grown-ups listened hard, but Almanzo did not understand the speeches very well and he began to be hungry. He was glad when the band played again.

The music was so gay; the bandsmen in their blue and red and their brass buttons tootled merrily, and the fat drummer beat rat-a-tat-tat on the drum. All the flags were fluttering and everybody was happy, because they were free and independent and this was Independence Day. And it was time to eat dinner.

Almanzo helped Father feed the horses while Mother and the girls spread the picnic lunch on the grass in the churchyard. Many others were picnicking there, too, and after he had eaten all he could Almanzo went back to the Square.

There was a lemonade-stand by the hitching-posts. A man sold pink lemonade, a nickel a glass, and a crowd of the town boys were standing around him. Cousin Frank was there. Almanzo had a drink at the town pump, but Frank said he was going to buy lemonade. He had a nickel. He walked up to the stand and bought a glass of the pink lemonade and drank it slowly. He smacked his lips and rubbed his stomach and said:

"Mmmm! Why don't you buy some?"

"Where'd you get the nickel?" Almanzo asked. He had never had a nickel. Father gave him a penny every Sunday to put in the collection-box in church; he had never had any other money.

"My father gave it to me," Frank bragged. "My father gives me a nickel every time I ask him."

"Well, so would my father if I asked him," said Almanzo.

"Well, why don't you ask him?" Frank did not believe that Father would give Almanzo a nickel. Almanzo did not know whether Father would, or not.

"Because I don't want to," he said.

"He wouldn't give you a nickel," Frank said.

"He would, too."

"I dare you to ask him," Frank said. The other boys were listening. Almanzo put his hands in his pockets and said:

"I'd just as lief ask him if I wanted to."

"Yah, you're scared!" Frank jeered. "Double dare! Double dare!"

Father was a little way down the street, talking to Mr. Paddock, the wagon-maker. Almanzo walked slowly toward them. He was faint-hearted, but he had to go. The nearer he got to Father, the more he dreaded asking for a nickel. He had never before thought of doing such a thing. He was sure Father would not give it to him.

He waited till Father stopped talking and looked at him.

"What is it, son?" Father asked.

Almanzo was scared. "Father," he said.

"Well, son?"

"Father," Almanzo said, "would you—would you give me—a nickel?"

He stood there while Father and Mr. Paddock looked at him, and he wished he could get away. Finally Father asked:

"What for?"

Almanzo looked down at his moccasins and muttered:

"Frank had a nickel. He bought pink lemonade."

"Well," Father said, slowly, "if Frank treated you, it's only right you should treat him." Father put his hand in his pocket. Then he stopped and asked:

"Did Frank treat you to lemonade?"

Almanzo wanted so badly to get the nickel that he nodded. Then he squirmed and said:

"No, Father."

Father looked at him a long time. Then he took out his wallet and opened it, and slowly he took out a round, big silver half-dollar. He asked:

"Almanzo, do you know what this is?"

"Half a dollar," Almanzo answered.

"Yes. But do you know what half a dollar is?"

Almanzo didn't know it was anything but half a dollar.

"It's work, son," Father said. "That's what money is; it's hard work."

Mr. Paddock chuckled. "The boy's too young, Wilder," he said. "You can't make a youngster understand that."

"Almanzo's smarter than you think," said Father.

Almanzo didn't understand at all. He wished he could get away. But Mr. Paddock was looking at Father just as Frank looked at Almanzo when he double-dared him, and Father had said Almanzo was smart, so Almanzo tried to look like a smart boy. Father asked:

"You know how to raise potatoes, Almanzo?"

"Yes," Almanzo said.

"Say you have a seed potato in the spring, what do you do with it?"

"You cut it up," Almanzo said.

"Go on, son."

"Then you harrow—first you manure the field, and plow it. Then you harrow, and mark the ground. And plant the potatoes, and plow them, and hoe them. You plow and hoe them twice."

"That's right, son. And then?"

"Then you dig them and put them down cellar."

"Yes. Then you pick them over all winter; you throw out all the little ones and the rotten ones. Come spring, you load them up and haul them here to Malone, and you sell them. And if you get a good price, son, how much do you get to show for all that work? How much do you get for half a bushel of potatoes?"

"Half a dollar," Almanzo said.

"Yes," said Father. "That's what's in this half-dollar, Almanzo. The work that raised half a bushel of potatoes is in it."

Almanzo looked at the round piece of money that Father held up. It looked small, compared with all that work.

"You can have it, Almanzo," Father said. Almanzo could hardly believe his ears. Father gave him the heavy half-dollar.

"It's yours," said Father. "You could buy a sucking pig with it, if you want to. You could raise it, and it would raise a litter of pigs, worth four, five dollars apiece. Or you can trade that half-dollar for lemonade, and drink it up. You do as you want, it's your money."

Almanzo forgot to say thank you. He held the half-dollar a minute, then he put his hand in his pocket and went back to the boys by the lemonade-stand. The man was calling out,

"Step this way, step this way! Ice-cold lemonade, pink lemonade, only five cents a glass! Only

half a dime, ice-cold pink lemonade! The twentieth part of a dollar!"

Frank asked Almanzo:

"Where's the nickel?"

"He didn't give me a nickel," said Almanzo, and Frank yelled:

"Yah, yah! I told you he wouldn't! I told you so!"

"He gave me half a dollar," said Almanzo.

The boys wouldn't believe it till he showed them. Then they crowded around, waiting for him to spend it. He showed it to them all, and put it back in his pocket.

"I'm going to look around," he said, "and buy me a good little sucking pig."

The band came marching down the street, and they all ran along beside it. The flag was gloriously waving in front, then came the buglers blowing and the fifers tootling and the drummer rattling the drumsticks on the drum. Up the street and down the street went the band, with all the boys following it, and then it stopped in the Square by the brass cannons.

Hundreds of people were there, crowding to watch.

The cannons sat on their haunches, pointing their long barrels upward. The band kept on playing. Two men kept shouting, "Stand back! Stand back!" and other men were pouring black powder into the cannons' muzzles and pushing it down with wads of cloth on long rods.

The iron rods had two handles, and two men pushed and pulled on them, driving the black powder down the brass barrels. Then all the boys ran to pull grass and weeds along the railroad tracks. They carried them by armfuls to the cannons, and the men crowded the weeds into the cannons' muzzles and drove them down with the long rods.

A bonfire was burning by the railroad tracks, and long iron rods were heating in it.

When all the weeds and grass had been packed tight against the powder in the cannons, a man took a little more powder in his hand and carefully filled the two little touchholes in the barrels. Now everybody was shouting,

"Stand back! Stand back!"

Mother took hold of Almanzo's arm and made him come away with her. He told her:

"Aw, Mother, they're only loaded with powder

and weeds. I won't get hurt, Mother. I'll be careful, honest." But she made him come away from the cannons.

Two men took the long iron rods from the fire. Everybody was still, watching. Standing as far behind the cannons as they could, the two men stretched out the rods and touched their red-hot tips to the touchholes. A little flame like a candle-flame flickered up from the powder. The little flames stood there burning; nobody breathed. Then—BOOM!

The cannons leaped backward, the air was full of flying grass and weeds. Almanzo ran with all the other boys to feel the warm muzzles of the cannons. Everybody was exclaiming about what a loud noise they had made.

"That's the noise that made the Redcoats run!" Mr. Paddock said to Father.

"Maybe," Father said, tugging his beard. "But it was muskets that won the Revolution. And don't forget it was axes and plows that made this country."

"That's so, come to think of it," Mr. Paddock said.

Independence Day was over. The cannons had been fired, and there was nothing more to do but hitch up the horses and drive home to do the chores.

That night when they were going to the house with the milk, Almanzo asked Father,

"Father, how was it axes and plows that made this country? Didn't we fight England for it?"

"We fought for Independence, son," Father said. "But all the land our forefathers had was a little strip of country, here between the mountains and the ocean. All the way from here west was Indian country, and Spanish and French and English country. It was farmers that took all that country and made it America."

"How?" Almanzo asked.

"Well, son, the Spaniards were soldiers, and high-and-mighty gentlemen that only wanted gold. And the French were fur-traders, wanting to make quick money. And England was busy fighting wars. But we were farmers, son; we wanted the land. It was farmers that went over the mountains, and cleared the land, and settled it, and farmed it, and hung on to their farms.

"This country goes three thousand miles west, now. It goes 'way out beyond Kansas, and beyond the Great American Desert, over mountains bigger than these mountains, and down to the Pacific Ocean. It's the biggest country in the world, and it was farmers who took all that country and made it America, son. Don't you ever forget that."

A STRANGE GAME
OF HIDE-AND-SEEK

Olive W. Burt

This story tells of a lifelong interest beginning in childhood. The modest little book from which this chapter comes gives many examples of Burbank's keen observations and ingenious experiments when he was still only a boy. The book is easy to read as this episode shows and is one of a long series of popular biographies, Childhood of Famous Americans. *They are especially valuable for children who find reading difficult.*

"All who're out may come in free!" The children playing in the big shady yard took up the cry, but no one came in to the hide-and-seek "home."

"Luther!" Lizzie shouted as loud as she could. "Luther! Don't you hear? You can come in free!"

"Oh, he's gone off somewhere," said Henry crossly. "He's always forgetting that he's playing a game. Come on! I'll race you to the brook. Last one there's a Red Man!"

Away ran Henry, as fast as his bare feet could carry him across the grass, with Sarah and Lizzie close behind.

Alfred hung back. He couldn't beat the others to the brook and he didn't want to be a Red Man. He would go look for Luther.

It was a summer afternoon in the year 1856. The yard where the children were playing was around the old Burbank house. It was a lovely yard. Tall elm trees gave shade, and old apple trees spread their limbs to make good climbing easy.

Bright flower beds here and there made pretty

patterns against the grass. Some were round, some were diamond-shaped, and some beds were in the form of hearts. Farther down the lot were the vegetable garden and the orchard.

The house itself was of red brick. The front windows looked out on the country road that wound past, wide and dusty, to the town of Lancaster, Massachusetts, three miles away. It was a big, squarish house, with a white frame wing snuggled up against one end. In this wing Luther, the oldest of the "three little Burbanks," had been born seven years before.

Now Alfred, the "middle-between" little Burbank, ran across the yard toward the rock wall. It separated his mother's garden from the meadow. He was pretty sure he knew where to find his brother.

Alfred made no noise as he climbed over the wall and went searching among the deep grass and daisies and clover blossoms. It wasn't long before he came upon Luther, half-hidden in the grass. Alfred stood and watched him, wondering what his brother could be doing.

Luther was still playing hide-and-seek, but his playmates were not boys and girls. They were honeybees!

He had hidden from the other children in the deep clover of the meadow behind the rock wall. As he sat there waiting for a good chance to come in free, his bright blue eyes were alert. He looked at the clover blossoms and the bees that droned above them. As he watched, he saw something he had never noticed before.

A big, fat honeybee came zooming over the wall. It stopped on a blossom. Then it pushed its hairy body deep into the pink cup of the flower. It buried its head among the curled petals as if it wanted to get every drop of nectar.

Luther smiled as he watched the greedy bee. He was still smiling when the bee backed out of the flower, spread its wings and flew away. Luther watched it fly a little distance and light on another pink blossom.

As the boy watched, he forgot the game and his playmates in the yard. He was interested in the flight of this fat, greedy bee. It flew right over daisies and buttercups. It paid no attention to the beautiful red roses that spilled over the garden wall.

Luther didn't blame the bee for passing over the daisies and buttercups. They were not nearly so fragrant as the clover. But to fly right past the roses as if he couldn't see them! Luther couldn't believe it. He got to his feet and followed the bee.

Luther was not afraid of losing this bee and following another. To his clear blue eyes each bee was different from every other bee. Long ago he had noticed that every daisy in the field was different from its neighbors. Each rose, too, had its own special form and color, so that anyone who looked closely enough could tell it from all others.

He was still watching the bee when Alfred found him. "What are you doing?" Alfred asked.

Luther told him about the bee, but Alfred didn't care what the bee did. "You spoiled our game," he reminded Luther. "Henry and the girls have gone home."

Luther was sorry. "I forgot," he said.

Just then their mother's voice came across the meadow. "Luther!" she called. "Alfred!"

It was suppertime already! The two little boys started up through the meadow toward the house.

They looked a great deal alike as they ran along together, though Luther was seven and Alfred was not yet five years old. They were dressed alike too. Both wore jeans—long trousers made of heavy gray cloth—and cotton shirts. They wore neither shoes nor stockings. Mr. Burbank was a well-to-do farmer, and there was good lumber in his woods and fine red clay for bricks in the hollow. The lumber and bricks brought him extra money. But Mrs. Burbank knit all the family stockings by hand, and it took a long time. The boys wore them only when they dressed up on Sundays.

Luther was rather small for his age, with light yellow hair that curled up in front. His eyes were blue and merry, and he was fond of jokes and tricks. Alfred was large for his age and more sturdily built than his brother.

When the boys reached the house, they found that their mother had already set the table. Two-year-old Emmy was in her high chair, pounding her spoon against her mug.

Luther went to the table and started to count the plates. His mother smiled at him.

"It is only Cousin Levi," she said. "Better get washed, Luther."

Luther hurried to the wash bench near the pump in the big kitchen. He was glad it was Cousin Levi, for now he could find out about the bee. And he was hungry and wanted his supper. Luther was shy with strangers. Whenever he found an extra place set for someone he didn't know, he would slip away and stay in the meadow while the family ate. Sometimes he would sit under the open kitchen window so that he could hear the talk. Many of his father's visitors were preachers or teachers or students who knew the things Luther himself wanted to know.

But Cousin Levi was different. Luther was never shy with this tall, good-natured teacher who explained things to him.

As soon as he had a chance, after grace was said, Luther asked Cousin Levi about the bee.

"He spoiled our hide-and-seek game!" Alfred said crossly.

"Luther was playing hide-and-seek with the bee!" Cousin Levi laughed. "And I think I can explain why the bee's goal was always clover blossoms."

Luther stopped eating to listen.

"It seems that some instinct causes a bee to go to only one kind of flower in a day," Cousin Levi went on. "If he starts on clover blossoms, he goes to clover blossoms all day long. If he starts with roses, he goes only to roses. In that way, he fills his pouch with only one kind of nectar. His fuzzy back gets covered with only one kind of pollen—"

"What's pollen?" asked Alfred.

"It's a sort of flower dust that makes plants grow," Cousin Levi answered. "Roses must have pollen from other roses, and daisies must have pollen from other daisies if they are to form seeds so that we can have new plants next year."

"I thought the bees' job was just to make honey," Luther said. "I didn't know that they had two jobs to do."

"And maybe the pollen-carrying job is the more important," Mr. Burbank suggested.

"I don't think so," Alfred said. He spread a big spoonful of honey on his brown bread. "I think making honey is more important."

"Me, too! Me, too!" shouted Emmy, and everyone laughed.

But Luther was thinking, "I'm glad I played hide-and-seek with that bee!"

from DR. GEORGE WASHINGTON CARVER

Shirley Graham and George D. Lipscomb

One of the most original scientists this country has ever produced was the mild-mannered, dedicated Negro, Dr. George Washington Carver. These two chapters show the tragic beginning and provide just a glimpse of the wonderful fruition of a life of service. Every young American should read the whole biography with gratitude for and pride in the achievements of this great and humble man.

Was the Tiny Boy Worth a Horse?

"Heraus! Heraus mit sie! I say—get up!"

It was still dark outside, but down in the kitchen the German farmer was shaking the wooden ladder that led to the boy's place under the eaves.

"Get up—you! *Raus mit!* Or—must I come up?" Now the voice was threatening and the tiny black boy shivered as he tumbled off his pallet. They said he was six or seven years old, plenty old enough to milk the cow, tend the hog and chickens and do something about keeping weeds from choking the already sparse garden. But the rusty little legs and arms were like pipe-stems, his hands bony, with long, curling fingers, his face was pinched. In that little dark face, his eyes burned like coals of fire. And, even though he could not speak, Frau Carver had noted that he saw everything.

Yesterday, he had hoed in the garden for many hours. His back still ached with fatigue. Now, spindly legs still trembling with sleep, he clumsily crawled down the ladder and there in the kitchen was Frau Carver, still swathed in yards and yards of sleeping clothes, on her head a nightcap. But how glad he was to see her!

"No! No, *mein Mann,*" she was saying to her husband. "He is too small. After yesterday, he is too tired. I have work for him to do in the house this morning. He cannot go."

"And who will help me in the fields?" the farmer asked angrily. "Have we money? Our

Reprinted by permission of Julian Messner, Inc., from *Dr. George Washington Carver* by Shirley Graham and George D. Lipscomb; copyright date, June 3, 1944 by Julian Messner, Inc.

crops, poor as they are, will rot. We will starve and he also!"

"God is good," the woman's voice was soothing. "Not a sparrow falls that he does not know. Let be the little fellow. Soon he will be big and strong." The little boy's eyes were fast upon her, drinking in every word.

"*O weh!*" exploded Farmer Carver. "I had a *horse*—" he paused significantly, "and now," his eyes fell on the shrinking little boy—"*this!*"

There was a twinkle in his wife's eyes, as she replied, "He was not so much of a horse—that one!"

"Stupid!" And the man went out slamming the door behind him.

Frau Carver laid her large hand on the little boy's head. His eyes were slowly filling with tears. It was true. He couldn't talk.

"Bah," she laughed. "He does not mean that. Quick now, make the fire. Once he has something in that stomach, all will be well."

And the clean, starched smell of her wide skirts filled his being with comfort.

The distant Ozark hills showed black against a faintly colored sky as Farmer Carver crossed the yard with its numerous outhouses and approached the huge barn. He sighed as he thought how empty it now was. He stamped his feet partly to keep them warm and partly because of the helpless rage. Of course, that child could help him very little, but what was he to do? Once he would have looked out over blue grass pasture land and a checkerboard of wheat and corn prairie. Once the large frame house of his nearest neighbor could not be seen for the thick orchard of fruit trees. But, now, the land itself seemed starved and beaten and only the smoked blackened ruins of his neighbor's house remained.

More than any other border state, Missouri had been torn and devastated by the War between the States. Since 1854 when an Act of Congress left the issue of slavery to be decided by the individual states, Kansas and Missouri had been caught in the struggle between free and slave states. Pro-Union and Pro-Southern groups made the war a peculiar horror. And the prosperous German farmers on the Ozark plateau suffered most. Hard-working, industrious immigrants, they had come to settle new homes in this land of plenty. The idea of slavery was abhorrent

to them. When they needed extra help, they sometimes bought a few slaves and treated them as they were accustomed to treating hired help in Europe—as dependent members of their household. This attitude did not endear the German farmers to their slave-owning neighbors and when difficulties arose, it was upon the immigrants that their fury was lashed.

Moses Carver saw his land and ownings dwindle before the storm. He could not hire men to work his farm and he would not encourage the traffic of poor human beings, most of whom he suspected had been kidnapped.

At that time, Carver's wife had Mary, a soft-spoken, gentle slave girl, to help about the house. Mary's husband was owned on a huge plantation not many miles away. Often she had begged the German farmer to buy him, but George was a valuable slave, and his owner was a hard master. Sometimes weeks passed before George could get away to see his wife and three children. So it was a long time before they knew he was killed—falling from an ox team, they said. After that Mary was very silent, except at night when she sang her baby to sleep.

Farmer Carver's face softened as he looked across the field at the tumbled log cabin where Mary and her children had lived. Of course his wife was right. How could he expect that poor sick baby to work? He'd never be strong.

He struggled with the heavy barn door, finally getting it back upon its rusty hinges. His eyes fell upon the dust-covered harness hanging high above an empty stall. His anger stirred faintly again. But she had no right to say the horse was worthless! That he would not forgive!

Five years had passed since that bitter cold night when he had hurried home from the village, disturbed by that ominous notice: "Keep a careful watch on your slaves! Nightriders have crossed the border!" The settlers in Diamond Grove were bolting their doors and locking their gates with caution. Snatching slaves was more profitable than horse-thieving or rustling cattle. Though the War between the States was nearing an end, slaves still brought good prices in the markets of Arkansas and Texas.

When he reached home, Mary had already gone to her cabin. He heard her softly singing to her babies as he examined the latch. He had put his horse up, carefully bolting the door. Nightriders would take anything.

Susan had already heard the news and was worried. He spoke lightly of the whole matter.

"But I hear they crossed the river with some slaves," his wife said.

"Probably headed back the other way then."

"You can't be sure," Susan replied.

"Well, they'll not bother us. They can see I've got no slaves such as they want."

"Perhaps we'd better bring Mary and the children into the house to live," Frau Carver suggested.

"Oh, they'll be all right. The slavers are looking for men to work."

But he had been wrong. Late in the night he heard the scream. It was Mary. He grabbed his gun and ran out into the yard. But in the blackness he could see nothing. Only the galloping of horses and the slave woman's muffled cries came back to him out of the night. He rushed to the cabin. On the ground outside, her head bleeding, lay Mary's little girl. The little boy stood over his sister, whimpering. Inside, the cabin was empty. Mother and baby were gone!

By this time Frau Carver was calling.

There were no telephones in those days. It was several hours later that Farmer Carver reached the village of Diamond Grove and rounded up help. He was not alone in his trouble. Several slaves had been stolen that night and soon a posse was formed. Farmer Carver could not go with them. The little slave girl had died before he left the house, and Frau Carver was almost hysterical. One of the women offered to return with him to her.

"Could we go back in your cart?" Farmer Carver asked. "My horse is faster than anything the nightriders have. I'd like to let one of the men ride fast on horseback to follow the raiders."

This was agreed upon.

"What shall we do if we catch up with them," asked one of the men. "They won't give up your slaves easily."

"Bargain with them," answered Farmer Carver. "My wife says we must get Mary back. I'm not a rich man, but I'll pay anything in reason."

"Did you bring money with you?" asked a second man.

Farmer Carver frowned. "No, and you'll need money. I'll tell you," he thought a moment, "give them the horse if necessary, but," he added quickly, "only if necessary. If they'll return, let them do so, and I'll pay them."

The men rode off. Days passed with no word. But nearly a week later they appeared at Farmer Carver's farm and told what had happened.

The nightriders had evaded them, thrown them off the trail and appeared gone. But the posse had waited at the border and finally they had come upon them trying to slip across. No shots were fired for fear of killing the slaves, and finally the thieves agreed to take the horse in exchange for the mother and baby.

"Tie him to a tree, retire out of sight. We'll examine the horse, and, when you hear us blow a horn, come and get your slave and her baby."

The men did not trust them, but a storm had come up and they realized they were at the mercy of the nightriders. So they had tied the horse to a tree and gone six hundred paces around the bend of the river. When they heard the horn it was far away and they knew that the nightriders had already put a mile or so between them. They dashed forward, found the baby soaking wet and shaking with cold on the ground by the tree, but the mother was nowhere about. The nightriders had tricked them and had taken her off with them.

When Frau Carver heard this story, tears had run down her cheeks. She had taken the dirty, soggy bundle in which lay the still form of the child. At first, they thought it was dead, but after a long time her tender ministrations brought some warmth back into the chilled frame. For days and weeks a racking cough choked the feeble breath until it seemed the baby could not live and even when life seemed promised, the baby's growth and development seemed stunted. But Frau Carver would not be discouraged.

"Mary's child must live—he will live!" She said it over and over again.

And at last, Mary's child did take a grip on life. He stood, he walked. He grew a little, but he could not speak. The violent cough, it seemed, had torn his vocal chords. Try as he might, he could not form words. Sometimes he uttered little squeaking noises.

Of Mary they had never heard again. So all that they had gotten for their valuable horse was this poor, weakened, speechless child. Farmer Carver shook his head dismally. What was he to do? He moved from one morning chore to another, hardly noticing that the sun was shining. Then he felt a gentle tug on his coat.

There beside him stood the little boy. He was smiling and pointing towards the house. Farmer Carver understood.

"So," he said heartily, "breakfast is ready. Well, I am ready for it. *Raus mit!*"

And taking the little brown hand in his, the big farmer strode across the yard. The little boy smiled happily. Frau Carver was right, as usual. The big man didn't mean it!

. . . .

"Gentlemen, I Give You the Peanut!"

For three days now the Ways and Means Committee of the House of Representatives had been listening to reasons why they should or should not pass a certain tariff bill which had come up before the house. The bill had been introduced as an emergency bill and was designed to protect the producers of this country from infringement of their rights by putting a high tariff on the same products as they came into the country. Rice, for instance, could be raised in China for a few cents a bushel. In 1921 China was not at war and coolies worked for next to nothing. It cost so little to raise the rice that even after shipping it over here, it could sell for much less than the rice raised in our own country. Our growers did not want such competition.

The Congressman from South Dakota quite agreed—about rice and wheat and corn. But, as the Congressman from Pennsylvania said, and not too softly, the hearings were becoming tedious. Before the Committee had come spokesmen for meat packers, poultry farmers, dairymen, manufacturers, date growers, walnut growers. All of them brought statistics which they presented in a highly efficient manner. Now, to cap the climax somebody from the Virginia-Carolina Co-operative Peanut Exchange was complaining because they could not sell their peanuts! This was carrying the matter too far. Peanuts! Monkey-food, boys called them. Fine to munch at a circus, but surely nobody was seriously thinking of including *peanuts* in a tariff bill!

The Congressman from Michigan got up and wandered out. Another man representing the New York Peanut Association was pointing out that "whereas the present tariff imposes duty of three-eighths of one cent per pound on unshelled peanuts and three-fourths of one cent on shelled peanuts it affords no protection to American producers. We are asking that—" The voice went on. Sheets were being rustled. Somebody dropped a book.

One of the officials of the United Peanut Growers Association groaned audibly and whispered to the man beside him, "It's no use, Bill. We're sunk!"

"Steady," whispered back the other man, "it's two-thirty. This room's so crowded, we can't see who's in the back. Maybe he's here."

The speaker had finished and the chairman fitted his glasses and peered at the sheet before him. "Thank you, Mr. Smith. Now," he looked closely, "Mr. Carver—is Mr. Carver in the room?"

The two officials held their breath. There was a movement near the door where several men were standing. No one had come forward, and the chairman said, "We'll go on. I guess Mr. Carver is not here. Will Mr.—"

"Pardon me, sir," a high, shrill voice was heard in the back of the room, "this case is heavy and awkward. It's difficult to get through."

Heads were turned and a way cleared in the aisle. Then the Congressmen saw the slender, slightly stooped Negro, in his green-black alpaca, carrying a large wooden case. Under his arm was the old golf cap. Having reached the front of the room, he eased the case to the floor, stuffed the cap in his pocket and stood waiting. The chairman stared at him.

"What—what—?"

"I am George Washington Carver."

"Oh—oh, yes. You've come to speak on the tariff."

Several gentlemen in the room could not help laughing. One man asked bluntly, "What do you know about the Hawley-Smoot bill?" There was laughter.

But the old man turned and with a twinkle in his eye said, "Not a thing. Do you?" When the laughter had died down he added, smiling, "I've come to talk about peanuts!"

The chairman had to rap for order. He said

rather sternly, "Very well, Mr. Carver, will you please come to the stand? You have ten minutes."

They leaned forward to see as the unusual figure stepped up, opened his case and began talking.

"I've been asked by the United Peanut Growers Association to tell you something about the possibility of the peanut and its possible extension," he began. "I come from Tuskegee, Alabama, where I am engaged in agricultural research work. I have given some attention to the peanut and can tell you that it is one of the very richest of all the products of the soil—rich in food value, rich in properties of its chemical constituents, and wonderfully rich in possibilities for utilization."

The Congressmen were leaning forward, their eyes eager. Now the Negro opened his case and was removing the contents: bottles of every size, description and color, little boxes, several small plaques.

"If I may have a little space to put these things down," he suggested. And the clerk quickly cleared the table for him.

"Thank you," said Mr. Carver. "Now I should like to exhibit them to you. I am just going to touch a few high places here and there, because in ten minutes you will tell me to stop. These are a few of the products which we have developed from the peanut." He held up a tube. "This is breakfast food containing peanut and sweet potato—twin brothers. It is wholesome, easily digested and delicious in flavor. A perfectly balanced diet with all the nutriments in it could be made from the sweet potato and peanut."

One of the Congressmen took the tube in his hand and examined it.

"Here is ice cream powder made from the peanut," continued Mr. Carver. "Simply mixed with water, it produces an unusually rich and delicious ice cream, not to be distinguished from ice cream made with pure cream." He held up several small bottles of different color. "In these bottles are dyes extracted from the skin of peanuts. I have found thirty different dyes. They have been tested in the laboratory and found to hold their colors and to be harmless to the skin. Here is a substitute for quinine. We can hardly overestimate the medicinal properties of the peanut. They are many and varied. These are vari-

ous kinds of food for live stock. You will find that cattle thrive on them and the increase in milk is pronounced."

He looked up at the wall clock and remarked.

"I see my time is about up. I should like to say that the soil and climate of the South is particularly suited to the cultivation of peanuts and that they could be produced in much greater quantities if a larger market for them were developed."

He stopped and began gathering up his bottles. The Congressmen looked at each other with amazement. Mr. Garner, from the back of the room, called out, "Mr. Chairman, all this is very interesting. I think his time should be extended."

"Very well, gentlemen," answered the chairman, "do you all agree?"

"Yes! Yes!" they answered in one voice.

"Will you continue, Mr. Carver," asked the chairman, smiling.

"I shall be happy to do so, sir."

From the front row Mr. Rainey asked, "Is the varied use of the peanut increasing?"

"Oh, yes," came the quick reply, "we are just beginning to know its value."

"In that case, is it not going to be such a valuable product that the more we have of them here the better we are off?"

"Well, now that depends. It depends upon the problems that these other gentlemen have brought before you," declared Mr. Carver, with a smile.

"Could we get too much of them—they being so valuable for stock food and everything else?" asked a man at the back of the room.

"Well, of course, we would have to have protection for them." There was laughter. "That is, we could not allow other countries to come in and take over our rights."

"I thought you said you didn't know anything about tariff," called out a voice.

"Well, I know it's what keeps the other fellow out of our business!" replied the old man. When the laughter had died down he went on, "I wish to say here in all sincerity that America produces better peanuts than any other part of the world, so far as I have been able to find out."

"Then," said Mr. Rainey, "we need not fear these inferior peanuts from abroad at all. They would not compete with our better peanuts."

"Well, you know that's like everything else. You know some people like oleomargarine just as well as they do butter. So sometimes you have to protect a good thing."

"The dairy people did not ask for a tax on oleomargarine," Mr. Oldfield spoke up, "but they did put a tax on butter."

"And," said Mr. Garner, "they did use the taxing power to put it out of business."

"Oh, yes, yes, sir. That is all the tariff means—to put the other fellow out." There was much laughter again. The twinkling eyes turned to the chairman, "Maybe—maybe—I'd better stop!"

But the chairman leaned forward, wiping his eyes, "Go ahead, brother. Your time is unlimited."

"Well," picking up a small bottle, "here is milk from peanuts."

Mr. Oldfield laughed. "Don't you think we ought to put a tax on that peanut milk so as to keep it from competing with the dairy products?"

"No, sir. It is not going to affect the dairy product. It has a distinct value all its own."

"Why won't it replace the dairy product?" someone asked.

"We do not now have as much milk and butter as we need in the United States."

"How does it go in punch?" asked a teasing voice.

"Well," came the grave answer, "I'll show some punches."

"Attaboy!"

"Here is one with orange, here one with lemon, and this one with cherry!" Each time holding up a bottle with different colored liquids. "Here is instant coffee which already has in it cream and sugar, here is the preparation for making regular coffee. Here is buttermilk, Worchestershire sauce, pickles—all made from the peanut!"

There was a moment of breathless silence. Then someone asked, "Did you make all those products yourself?"

"Yes, sir, they are made in the research laboratory. That's what a research laboratory is for. The sweet potato products number one hundred and seven up to date."

Mr. Garner leaned forward, "What? I didn't catch that last statement."

"From sweet potatoes we have made ink, rel-ishes, pomade, mucilage, to mention only a few things. But I must stick to peanuts." There was laughter. "Here are mock oysters which would fool most of you. I have developed recipes for mock meat dishes from peanuts. They are delicious. We are going to use less and less meat as science develops the products of nature."

"So, you're going to ruin the live stock business!" came a voice.

"Oh, no, but peanuts can be eaten when meat can't. Peanuts are the perfect food. They are always safe. God has given them to us for our use. He has revealed to me some of the wonders of this fruit of His earth. In the first chapter of Genesis we are told, 'Behold, I have given you every herb that bears seed upon the face of the earth, and every tree bearing seed. To you it shall be meat.' That's what He means about it—meat. There is everything there to strengthen, nourish and keep the body alive and healthy."

The chairman cut in here to ask, "Mr. Carver, where did you go to school?"

"The last school I attended was Agricultural College of Iowa. You doubtless remember Mr. Wilson, who served in the Cabinet here so long, Secretary James Wilson. He was my teacher for six years."

Several Congressmen nodded their heads. "What research laboratory do you work in now?" asked one.

"I am at Tuskegee Institute, Tuskegee, Alabama."

Mr. Carew rose, "You have rendered this committee a great service."

"I think," said Mr. Garner, "he is entitled to the thanks of the committee."

Every member stood up, clapping heartily.

"Did the Institute send you here or did you come of your own volition?"

"I was asked to come by the United Peanut Growers Association to talk about," he paused and his eyes twinkled again,—"peanuts!"

There was more warm, hearty laughter. One Congressman called out, "Come again soon, and bring the rest of your products with you."

The bottles had been carefully replaced in the case. The chairman leaned forward and said sincerely, "We want to compliment you, sir, on the way you have handled your subject."

Dr. Carver bowed with gracious dignity, presented his brief to the clerk and walked quietly from the room.

"Well, I'll be blowed!" The official of the United Peanut Growers Association wiped the perspiration from his brow.

"And you were going to tell him what to say!" commented his companion.

"Aw, shut up!" grinned the official.

The committee moved that the hearings were finished. Its members rose, adjourned to another room and voted to include the peanut in the Emergency H.R. 2435 Tariff Bill.

In the late afternoon sunshine an insignificant black man paused one moment under the sleeping arch, then descended the Capitol steps.

It was over. Now, he could go back to his laboratory!

from THE WRIGHT BROTHERS

Quentin Reynolds

The Wright Brothers, *one of the fine books in the Landmark Series, carries the two brothers through their successful flight at Kitty Hawk, but the foundation for that triumph is to be found in the second chapter given here "Get It Right on Paper." The book is fascinating and easy reading.*

Learning from Mother

Susan Wright wasn't like other mothers.

She was younger and prettier than most other mothers, and she liked to laugh and she liked to play games with her three youngest children; Wilbur, who was eleven; Orville, who was seven; and Katharine, who was four.

The other mothers would shake their heads and say, "Susan Wright spoils those children; lets 'em do anything they want. No good will come of it."

But Susan Wright only laughed. In the summer she'd pack a picnic lunch and she, the two boys and little Kate (no one ever called her Katharine) would go and spend a day in the woods. Mrs. Wright knew the name of every bird and she could tell a bird by his song. Wilbur and Orville learned to tell birds too.

From *The Wright Brothers* by Quentin Reynolds. Reprinted by permission of Random House, Inc. Copyright 1950 by Random House, Inc.

One day they sat on the banks of a river near Dayton, where they lived. Wilbur and Orville were fishing. Everyone called Wilbur "Will," and of course Orville was "Orv." The fish weren't biting very well. Suddenly a big bird swooped down, stuck his long bill into the river, came out with a tiny fish, and then swooped right up into the sky again.

"What makes a bird fly, Mother?" Wilbur asked.

"Their wings, Will," she said. "You notice they move their wings and that makes them go faster."

"But Mother," Will said, not quite satisfied, "that bird that just swooped down didn't even move his wings. He swooped down, grabbed a fish, and then went right up again. He never moved his wings at all."

"The wind doesn't just blow *toward* you or *away* from you," she said. "It blows *up* and *down,* too. When a current of air blows up, it takes the bird up. His wings support him in the air."

"If we had wings, then we could fly too, couldn't we, Mother?" Wilbur asked.

"But God didn't give us wings." She laughed.

"Maybe we could make wings," Wilbur insisted.

"Maybe," his mother said thoughtfully. "But I don't know. No one ever did make wings that would allow a boy to fly."

"I will some day," Wilbur said, and Orville nodded and said, "I will, too."

"Well, when you're a little older maybe you can try," their mother said.

That was another thing about Susan Wright. Most other mothers would have thought this to be foolish talk. Most other mothers would have said, "Oh, don't be silly, who ever heard of such nonsense!" But not Susan Wright. She knew that even an eleven-year-old boy can have ideas of his own, and just because they happened to come from an eleven-year-old head—well, that didn't make them foolish. She never treated her children as if they were babies, and perhaps that's why they liked to go fishing with her or on picnics with her. And that's why they kept asking her questions. She always gave them sensible answers.

They asked their father questions too, but he

was a traveling minister and he was away a lot.

"It's getting chilly," Mrs. Wright said suddenly. "Look at those gray clouds, Will."

Wilbur looked up. "It's going to snow, I bet," he said happily.

"No more picnics until next Spring," his mother said. "Yes, it looks like snow. We'd better be getting home."

As they reached home, the first big white snowflakes started to fall. They kept falling all that night and all the next day. It was the first real snowstorm of the year.

In the morning the wind was blowing so fiercely that Wilbur found it hard to walk to the barn where the wood was stored. The wind was so strong it almost knocked him down. He burst through the kitchen door with an armful of wood for the stove, and he told his mother about the wind.

"The thing to do is to lean forward into the wind," she said. "Bend over, and that way you get closer to the ground and you get under the wind."

That night when Wilbur had to make the trip for more wood, he tried his mother's idea. To his surprise it worked! When he was bent over, the wind didn't seem nearly so strong.

After a few days the wind stopped, and now the whole countryside was covered with snow. Wilbur and Orville, with little Kate trailing behind, hurried to the Big Hill not far from the house.

Orville's schoolmates were all there with their sleds. It was a good hill to coast down because no roads came anywhere near it, and even if they had, it wouldn't have mattered. This was 1878 and there were no automobiles. Horse-drawn sleighs traveled the roads in winter. The horses had bells fastened to their collars, and as they jogged along the bells rang and you could hear them a mile away.

Most of the boys had their own sleds; not the flexible fliers boys have now, but old-fashioned sleds with two wooden runners. No one ever thought of owning a "bought" sled. In those days a boy's father made a sled for him.

The boys who had sleds of their own let Wilbur and Orville ride down the hill with them. Ed Sines and Chauncey Smith and Johnny Morrow and Al Johnston all owned sleds, but they liked to race one another down the long hill.

When this happened Wilbur and Orville just had to stand there and watch. Late that afternoon the boys came home, with little Kate trailing behind, and their mother noticed that they were very quiet. She was wise as well as very pretty, and she soon found out why they were unhappy.

"Why doesn't Father build us a sled?" Wilbur blurted out.

"But Father is away, Will," his mother said gently. "And you know how busy he is when he is at home. He has to write stories for the church paper and he has to write sermons. Now suppose we build a sled together."

Wilbur laughed. "Whoever heard of anyone's mother building a sled?"

"You just wait," his mother said. "We'll build a better sled than Ed Sines has. Now get me a pencil and a piece of paper."

"You goin' to build a sled out of paper?" Orville asked in amazement.

"Just wait," she repeated.

Get It Right on Paper

Will and Orv brought their mother a pencil and paper, and she went to the minister's desk and found a ruler. Then she sat down at the kitchen table. "First we'll draw a picture of the sled," she said.

"What good is a picture of a sled?" Orville asked.

"Now Orville, watch Mother." She picked up the ruler in one hand and the pencil in the other.

"We want one like Ed Sines has," Orville said.

"When you go coasting, how many boys will Ed Sines's sled hold?" she asked.

"Two," Wilbur said.

"We'll make this one big enough to hold three," she said. "Maybe you can take Kate along sometimes." The outline of a sled began to appear on the paper. As she drew it she talked. "You see, Ed's sled is about four feet long. I've seen it often enough. We'll make this one five feet long. Now, Ed's sled is about a foot off the ground, isn't it?"

Orville nodded, his eyes never leaving the drawing that was taking shape. It was beginning to look like a sled now, but not like the sleds the other boys had.

"You've made it too low," Will said.

"You want a sled that's faster than Ed's sled, don't you?" His mother smiled. "Well, Ed's sled is at least a foot high. Our sled will be lower—closer to the ground. It won't meet so much wind resistance."

"Wind resistance?" It was the first time Wilbur had ever heard the expression. He looked blankly at his mother.

"Remember the blizzard last week?" she asked. "Remember when you went out to the woodshed and the wind was so strong you could hardly walk to the shed? I told you to lean over, and on the next trip to the woodshed you did. When you came back with an armful of wood you laughed and said, 'Mother, I leaned 'way forward and got under the wind.' You were closer to the ground and you were able to lessen the wind resistance. Now, the closer to the ground our sled is the less wind resistance there will be, and the faster it will go."

"Wind resistance . . . wind resistance," Wilbur repeated, and maybe the airplane was born in that moment. Certainly neither Will nor Orville Wright ever forgot that first lesson in speed.

"How do you know about these things, Mother?" Wilbur asked.

"You'd be surprised how much mothers know, Will." She laughed. She didn't tell the boys that when she was a little girl at school her best subject had been arithmetic. It just came naturally to her. It was the same when she went to high school. And when she went to college, algebra and geometry were her best subjects. That was why she knew all about things like "wind resistance."

Finally she finished the drawing. The boys leaned over the table to look at it. This sled was going to be longer than Ed's sled and much narrower. Ed's sled was about three feet wide. This one looked as if it would be only half that wide.

"You made it narrow," Wilbur said shrewdly, "to make it faster. The narrower it is, the less wind resistance."

"That's right." His mother nodded. "Now let's put down the exact length of the runners and the exact width of the sled."

"But that's only a paper sled," Orville protested.

"If you get it right on paper," she said calmly, "it'll be right when you build it. Always remember that."

" 'If you get it right on paper, it'll be right when you build it,' " Wilbur repeated, and his mother looked at him sharply. Sometimes Will seemed older than his eleven years. Little Orville was quick to give you an answer to anything, but as often as not he'd forget the answer right away. When Will learned something he never forgot it.

"Mother, you make all your clothes," Wilbur said thoughtfully. "You always make a drawing first."

"We call that the pattern," his mother said. "I draw and then cut out a pattern that's exactly the size of the dress I am going to make. And . . ."

"If the pattern is right, it'll be right when you make the dress," he finished. She nodded.

"Now you two boys get started on your sled." She smiled. "There are plenty of planks out in the barn. Find the very lightest ones. Don't use planks with knots in them. You saw the planks to the right size, Will—don't let Orville touch the saw."

"May we use Father's tools?" Wilbur asked breathlessly.

His mother nodded. "I don't think your father will mind. I know you'll be careful with them. Just follow the drawing exactly," she warned once more.

The two boys, followed by little Kate, hurried out to the barn. Both realized that this was an important occasion. Wilbur always chopped the wood for the stove when his father was away, but he had never been allowed to use the gleaming tools that lay in his father's tool chest.

Three days later their sled was finished. They pulled it out of the barn and asked their mother to inspect it. She had her tape measure with her and she measured it. The runners were exactly the length she had put down in her drawing. In fact, the boys had followed every direction she had given them. The runners gleamed. Orville had polished them with sandpaper until they were as smooth as silk.

"We thought of one other thing, Mother," Will said. "We found some old candles in the woodshed. We rubbed the runners with the candles. See how smooth they are?"

Mrs. Wright nodded. She had forgotten to tell the boys that, but they'd thought it out for themselves. "Now try your sled," she told them.

Followed by Kate, the boys dragged their new sled to the hill only half a mile away where their pals were coasting. They looked at the new sled in amazement. It was long and very narrow. It looked as though it wouldn't hold anyone. The runners were thin compared to those on their own sleds.

"Who made that for you?" Ed Sines asked.

"Mother showed us how," Wilbur said proudly. Some of the boys laughed. Whoever heard of a boy's mother knowing how to make a sled?

"It looks as if it would fall apart if you sat on it," Al Johnston said, and he laughed too.

"Come on, we'll race you down the hill," another cried out.

"All right, two on each sled," Wilbur said. He wasn't a bit afraid. He was sure the drawing had been right, and because he and Orv had followed the drawing, he knew that the sled was right.

They lined the four sleds up. Will and Orv sat on their sled, but it didn't "fall apart." Suddenly Wilbur got an idea.

"Get up, Orv," he said. "Now lie down on the sled . . . that's it . . . spread your legs a bit." Will then flopped down on top of his brother. "Less wind resistance this way," he whispered.

"Give us all a push," Ed Sines yelled.

And then they were off. It was an even start.

The four sleds gathered speed, for at the top the slope was steep. Will looked to the right. Then to the left. He brushed the stinging snow out of his eyes but he couldn't see the other sleds. He looked behind. They were straggling along, twenty and now thirty feet in back of him. The new sled skimmed along, the runners singing happily. Both Will and Orv felt a strange thrill of excitement. They approached the bottom of the long hill. The other sleds were far, far behind now.

Usually when the sleds reached the bottom of the hill they slowed down abruptly and stopped. But not this sled. It kept on; its momentum carried it on and on a hundred yards farther than any of the other sleds had ever reached. Finally it stopped.

Shaking with excitement, Will and Orv stood up.

"We flew down the hill, Orv," Will said breathlessly.

"We flew," Orv repeated.

Now Ed and Al and Johnnie ran up, excited at what had happened. No sled had gone so far or so fast as the one Will and Orv had built.

"You *flew* down the hill," Ed Sines gasped. "Let me try it?"

Wilbur looked at Orv, and some secret message seemed to pass between them. They had built this sled together, and it was the best sled there was. They'd always work together building things.

"Orv," Will said, "I've got an idea. This sled can do everything but steer. Maybe we can make a rudder for it. Then we can make it go to the right or to the left."

"We'll get Mother to draw one," Orv said.

"We'll draw one, you and I," Wilbur said. "We can't run to Mother every time we want to make something."

By now little Kate had come running down the hill.

"You promised," she panted. "You said you'd take me for a ride."

"Come on, Kate." Will laughed. "The three of us will coast down once. And then you can try it, Ed."

They trudged up the hill, pulling the sled. Two words kept singing in Wilbur's ears. "We flew . . . we flew . . . we flew. . . ."

The Old Testament presents a galaxy of hero tales unsurpassed in variety and interest. But whether the story is about David and Goliath or Joseph and his brothers or Samuel or Samson or Solomon, these Old Testament heroes have one characteristic which differentiates them from the heroes of most other tales. They carry with them a sense of their responsibility and close relationship to their God. When they sin, they defy God's commands—what God tells them is right. When they undertake impossible tasks, it is because they

OLD TESTAMENT STORIES

are strong in the strength of the Lord. When they are discouraged, confused, or defeated, they seek God's guidance and help, and obtain it. These are religious concepts to be built into children's lives and our own. Children like these old stories because the heroes are men of action. There is violence, but there are also fortitude and faith. Whether the story is about David the giant killer or Joseph the dreamer, who became a practical man of affairs, or Samson, who was betrayed by his own weakness and redeemed himself only by his death, there are moral and spiritual implications in the story. It is true that children may sense the deeper significance of these stories only vaguely, but a dramatization or even a discussion of the tale will clarify and reinforce the meaning. Great characters, dramatic conflicts, suspense, and terrifying action may make these stories memorable, but it is the reiterated emphasis upon man's relationship to God that makes them significant.

DAVID AND GOLIATH

A shepherd boy against a giant, a sling shot against armor of brass! But the boy knows that the Lord "saves not with sword and spear," and so, strong in the strength of the Lord, he is unafraid and conquers. Here is a drama made to be played and spoken by children and its implications never to be forgotten.

When Saul was king over Israel, the Philistines called together their armies for war against the Israelites. The Philistines were gathered at Shochoh, and King Saul and the men of Israel were gathered by the valley of Elah and they drew up in battle line facing the Philistines. And the Philistines stood on a mountain on one side, and Israel stood on a mountain on the other side, and there was a valley between them.

Then there came out a champion from the camp of the Philistines named Goliath of Gath. He was six cubits and a span high.[1] He had a helmet of brass on his head, and he was armed with a coat of mail that weighed five thousand shekels of brass. He had greaves of brass upon his legs and a javelin of brass between his shoulders. The staff of his spear was as big as a weaver's beam and the spear's head weighed six hundred shekels of iron. A shield bearer walked before the champion.

Goliath shouted across the valley to the armies of Israel and said to them, "Why have you come out in battle array? Am not I a Philistine and you are the servants of Saul? Choose a man from among you and let him come down to meet me. If he can fight me and kill me then will we be your servants, but if I overcome him and kill him, then shall you be our servants and serve us." And Goliath shouted again, "I defy the

"David and Goliath." From I Samuel 17:1–54, as adapted by May Hill Arbuthnot
[1] Over nine feet tall.

armies of Israel this day. Send me a man from among you that we may fight together."

When Saul and the Israelites heard the words of the champion, they were greatly frightened and knew not what to do. And Goliath the Philistine drew near, morning and evening for forty days, and shouted his challenge to the Israelites.

Now in Bethlehem, there was an old man named Jesse, who had eight sons, and the youngest was called David. The three oldest sons were Eliab, Abinadab, and Shammah, and they had followed King Saul to battle. David went with them, but later he returned to Bethlehem to care for his father's sheep. One day, Jesse said to David, "Take a measure of parched corn and these ten loaves and run quickly to the camp where your brothers are. And carry these ten cheeses to the captain of their thousand and find out how your brothers fare."

So David rose up early in the morning and left the sheep with a keeper and set off for the camp of the Israelites as his father had commanded him to do. He came to the camp just as the Israelites were making ready to go into battle. For the Israelites and the Philistines were both drawn up in battle line, army against army. For no man had accepted the challenge of Goliath the champion.

David left his supplies with a man who looked after such things and ran quickly into the battle lines looking for his brothers. Just as he found them and was talking to them, Goliath of Gath, champion of the Philistines, came out of the ranks and shouted his same words again, and David heard them: "Give me a man from among you that we may fight together."

Again the men of Israel fled from the champion and were sore afraid. They said to David, "Did you see this man who has come out to defy Israel? Surely the man who is able to kill this Philistine, King Saul will reward with great riches and give him his daughter in marriage and make his father's house free in Israel."

Then David said to the men standing by him, "What did you say shall be done for the man who overcomes yonder Philistine and takes away the shame of Israel? For who is this Philistine that he should dare to defy the armies of the living God?"

And the people told him again what King Saul would surely do for the man who could kill the Philistine.

But when Eliab, the oldest brother, heard what David said, he was angry with his young brother and said to him, "Why have you come here and with whom did you leave those few sheep in the desert? I know your arrogance and the wickedness in your heart. You have come here because you want to watch this battle."

And David said, "What have I done now? And what cause have you to speak to me like that?" And he turned away from his brothers, and talked again with the men who answered him as before. And some of the words David spoke the men repeated to King Saul, and the king sent for David.

When David came before the king, the boy said, "Let no man's heart be afraid because of that Philistine. Your servant will go and fight with him."

But Saul looked at David and replied, "How can you expect to go against this Philistine to fight with him? You are only a boy, and Goliath has been a man of war from his youth."

Then David told the king this story. "Sometimes, when your servant was a shepherd with his father's sheep, a lion or a bear would come and take a lamb out of the flock. Then I would go after him and attack him and take the lamb out of his mouth. And when the beast rose against me, I would catch him by the beard, smite him, and kill him. Your servant killed both the lion and the bear, and this Philistine shall fare the same, for he has defied the armies of the living God. Moreover, the Lord who delivered me out of the paw of the lion and out of the paw of the bear, He will deliver me out of the hand of this Philistine."

So Saul said to David, "Go and may the Lord be with you."

Then, the king put his own armor on David. He put a helmet of brass on his head and armed him with a coat of mail. He also girded him with a sword over his armor. And David struggled to go, for he wanted to try the armor. But he said to Saul, "I cannot wear these, for I have not proved them."

And he took off the king's armor. Then David took his staff in his hand and he chose five smooth stones out of the brook and put them in a shepherd's bag which he had with him and, with his sling in his hand, he went out to meet the Philistine.

The Philistine came near to David, keeping his shield bearer directly in front of him. But when he came near enough to see David, he scorned him, for he saw that he was only a youth, ruddy and fair of face. And Goliath called out, "Am I a dog that you come against me with sticks?" And he cursed David and said, "Come on, and I'll give your flesh to the birds of the air and the beasts of the field."

David replied to the Philistine, "You come to me with a sword, a spear, and a shield, but I come to you in the name of the Lord of Hosts, the God of the armies of Israel, whom you have defied. This very day the Lord will deliver you into my hands, and I will smite you and take your head from your body and this day I will give your dead body and the dead of the camp of the Philistines to the birds of the air and the wild beasts of the earth. This will I do that all the earth may know there is a God in Israel. And all this assembly shall know that the Lord saves not with sword and spear. For the battle is the Lord's, and He will give you into our hands."

And when David had finished speaking, Go-

liath drew near to meet him, and David ran towards the Philistine. And as he ran, he put his hand in his bag and chose a smooth stone. This he put in his sling and took aim. The stone struck the Philistine in his forehead, and he fell upon his face on the ground.

So David prevailed over the Philistine with a sling and with a stone and smote the Philistine and killed him. But there was no sword in David's hand.

Therefore, David ran and stood over the Philistine and took the champion's own sword out of its sheath and slew him and cut off his head. When the Philistines saw that Goliath, their champion, was dead, they fled. Then, the men of Israel arose and shouted and pursued the Philistines and plundered their tents.

David took the head of Goliath to Jerusalem, but he put Goliath's armor in the Philistine's tent.

SAMSON

Samson is the tragic story of a great and godly man who stubbornly insisted upon having his own way and upon his right to get even with his enemies, forgetting that " 'Justice is mine,' saith the Lord." Yet in the days before Israel had kings, Samson was their judge and ruled them well for twenty years. Then, again, he used his great strength for vengeance and paid dearly for his folly. The end of his story leaves the reader with feelings of admiration and pity for this remarkable man.

Now there was a certain man of Zorah whose name was Manoah, and he and his wife were childless. But one day, an angel of the Lord appeared to the woman and said to her, "You are going to bear a son. See that you drink no wine or liquor nor eat anything that is unclean. When your son is born, no razor is ever to be used on his head; for the boy is to be a Nazarite, given to God from the day of his birth. And he shall deliver Israel from the hand of the Philistines."

In time, it came to pass as the angel had told the woman. She bore a son and called his name Samson. The Lord blessed the child and he grew

"Samson." From Judges 13–16, as adapted by May Hill Arbuthnot

up and the spirit of the Lord began to work within him.

Samson went down to Timnath and saw a woman there who pleased him, so he returned to his father and mother and said, "I have seen a woman in Timnath, a daughter of the Philistines; she pleases me and I want her for my wife."

Then his father and his mother said to him, "Is there no girl among all your own people that you must take a wife from the Philistines, our enemies?"

But Samson said, "She pleases me well. Get her for me in marriage."

So Samson and his mother and father went down to Timnath, and when they came to the vineyards of Timnath, behold a young lion came roaring out against Samson. And the spirit of the Lord came upon him mightily, and he tore the lion apart with his hands as if it were no bigger than a kid. But he told not his father or his mother what he had done.

Samson talked with the woman of Timnath, and she pleased him well, so the marriage arrangements were made. After a time, he returned to take her for his wife and on the way, he turned aside to see the carcass of the lion he had slain. Behold there was a swarm of bees and honey in the carcass, which he took out with his hands and began to eat. When he came to his father and mother, he gave them the honey to eat also, but he did not tell them that he had taken it out of the carcass of the lion.

When they came to the woman of Timnath, Samson made a great feast, as was customary for the bridegroom to do. And the Philistines sent thirty young men to be with him. Samson said to them, "I will now tell you a riddle. If you can solve it within the seven days of this feast, I will give you thirty sheets and thirty changes of garments. But if you cannot solve the riddle, then you shall give me thirty sheets and thirty changes of garments."

Then he told them his riddle. "Out of the eater came forth meat and out of the strong came forth sweetness."

The young men of the Philistines thought about the riddle for three days, but they could not solve it. On the seventh day they said to Samson's wife, "Coax your husband to tell you the answer to this riddle. If you don't find out for us, we'll burn you and your father's house. Have you brought us here to take away from us everything that we have?"

So Samson's wife wept before him and said, "You hate me. You don't really love me at all. You have put forth a riddle to my countrymen and have not told it to me."

"I have not told the answer to my father nor my mother," Samson said, "so why should I tell it to you?"

Then his wife wept and begged Samson so hard to tell her the answer to the riddle that he finally told her, and she told the Philistines. Then the Philistines said to Samson, "What is sweeter than honey and what is stronger than a lion?"

And Samson said to them, "If you had not plowed with my heifer, you would not have found out my riddle."

And Samson slew thirty men of Ashkelon and took their spoils and gave them to the thirty Philistines who had solved the riddle. Then he was so angry that he returned to his father's house, and his wife was given to a man who had been his companion and friend.

But it came to pass in the time of the wheat harvest, that Samson decided he wanted his wife. When he went to the house, her father would not let him in, saying, "I thought, of course, that you utterly hated her, so I gave her as a wife to your companion. But is not her younger sister fairer than she? Why not take the younger sister instead of her?"

Then Samson turned away without answering, but he said to himself, "Though I do the Philistines an injury, I shall be blameless because of what they have done to me."

And he went out and caught three hundred foxes and, turning the foxes tail to tail, he put a torch between each pair of tails and set the brands on fire. He turned the foxes loose in the standing grain of the Philistines, and so burnt up all the standing grain of the Philistines and the shocks and also their vineyards and their olive groves.

"Who has done this?" said the Philistines, and the people answered, "Samson, the son-in-law of the Timnite, because his wife was given to his companion."

The Philistines then burned the wife and her father. And Samson said to them, "Because you have done this, I shall take my revenge on you, and after that I will cease."

And Samson smote the Philistines hip and thigh, with great slaughter. Afterwards he went away and dwelt in a cleft of the rock Etam. But the Philistines followed him there, and the Judeans, where they camped at Lehi, cried out, "Why are you come against us?"

The Philistines answered, "To bind Samson are we come up, to do to him as he has done to us."

Then three thousand of the men of Judah went to the top of the rock Etam and said to Samson, "Know you not that the Philistines are our rulers? What have you done to us?"

And Samson answered, "As they did to me so I have done to them."

"But we must turn you over to our rulers," they said. "We have come to bind you and deliver you into the hand of the Philistines."

"Then swear to me that you will not fall upon me yourselves," Samson said.

And they answered him saying, "No, that we will not do. We will bind you fast and deliver you into their hands, but we ourselves will surely not kill you."

So they bound him with two new cords and brought him from the rock to Lehi where the Philistines were and they shouted against him. But the spirit of the Lord came mightily upon Samson, and the ropes on his arms became as flax that had been burned with fire and his bonds melted from his hands. Then he found the jawbone of an ass and, taking it in his hand, he slew a thousand men with it and he cried aloud,

"With the jawbone of an ass
Heaps upon heaps of men have I slain.
With the jawbone of an ass
I have slain a thousand men."

Then when he had finished speaking, he cast away the jawbone and he was sore athirst and he called on the Lord and said, "Thou hast given thy servant great deliverance. Shall I now die of thirst?"

And the Lord smote a hollow place, and water gushed out. After Samson had drunk of this water, his spirits revived. He went forth from there and became a great judge in Israel and he governed Israel for twenty years in the time of the Philistines.

After a time, Samson loved a woman in the valley of Sorek, whose name was Delilah. The lords of the Philistines came to the woman and said to her, "See if you can entice him to tell you wherein his great strength lies. And find out how we can overpower him so that we can take him prisoner and punish him for what he has done to us. If you will do this, we will everyone of us give you eleven hundred pieces of silver."

So Delilah said to Samson, "Tell me, I pray you, what is the source of your strength and what will overpower you?"

And Samson answered her, "If I were bound fast with seven green withes that were never dried, then I should be as weak as any other man."

Then the lords of the Philistines brought Delilah the seven green withes that had never been dried, and she bound him with them. Now there were men lying in wait in an inner room, and she said to Samson, "The Philistines are upon you, Samson."

But Samson broke the withes as a thread of tow would break when it comes near the fire. So the source of his strength was not known.

And Delilah said to Samson, "Behold you have mocked me and told me lies. Tell me now, I pray you, what would overcome your strength?"

And Samson replied, "If I were bound fast with new ropes that had never been used, then should I be weak as other men."

So Delilah took new ropes and bound him with them. Then she cried, "The Philistines are upon you, Samson."

And the men who were lying in wait fell upon him but he broke the ropes off his arms like thread.

And again Delilah said, "Again you have mocked me and told me lies. Tell me what there is that will hold you?"

And Samson said, "If you weave seven locks of my hair into your web."

So Delilah did this while Samson slept and she fastened his hair with a pin and cried out, "Samson, the Philistines are upon you."

And Samson waked from his sleep and pulled out both the loom and the web.

And Delilah said to Samson, "How can you say, 'I love you' when your heart is not with me? You have mocked me three times and you have never told me wherein your great strength lies."

This she said to him over and over until his soul was vexed unto death, and he told her his whole heart.

He said, "No razor has ever been used on my head, for I have been a Nazarite, dedicated to God from my birth. If I were to be shaved, then my strength would go from me, and I would become weak like any other man."

Delilah knew then that he had told her his secret. So she sent for the lords of the Philistines and said, "This time he has told me his whole heart." Then they brought her the money they had promised, and Delilah put Samson to sleep on her knees. While he was sleeping, she sent for a man to shave off the seven locks of Samson's hair, and he became helpless and his strength left him.

So she said, "The Philistines are upon you, Samson."

And Samson woke from his sleep and thought, "I will escape as I have before. I will shake off my bonds." But he did not know that his strength had left him and the spirit of the Lord had departed from him.

Then the Philistines seized him, put out his eyes, and brought him down to Gaza bound with fetters of brass. They put him in a prison where he had to grind the grain. But his hair began to grow as soon as it was shaved off, and this the Philistines did not notice.

After a time, the lords of the Philistines gathered together to offer a great sacrifice to their god Dagon and to rejoice together because, they said, "Our god has delivered into our hands, Samson, our enemy."

And when the people saw the blind Samson, they praised their god that he had delivered to them their enemy, the destroyer who slew many of them.

Now it came to pass, when they were merry that they said, "Bring Samson to us that he may make sport for us." And the blind Samson was led out of the prison and he made sport for the Philistines, between the pillars of the hall.

And Samson said to the boy who led him by the hand, "Suffer me to feel the pillars that support the building, that I may lean against them."

The building was full of men and women and the lords of the Philistines were all there and on the roof there were about three thousand men and women, all watching Samson make sport for them.

And Samson cried to the Lord and said, "O Lord God, remember me I pray you, and strengthen me, I pray you, only this once, O God, that I may be avenged upon the Philistines for my two eyes."

Then Samson took hold of the two middle pillars upon which the building stood, one with his right hand and the other in his left. And Samson said, "Let me die with the Philistines." And he bowed himself with all his might, and the house fell upon the lords of the Philistines and upon all the people that were therein. So that the dead which Samson slew at his death were more than they which he slew in his life.

THE STORY OF JOSEPH

The story of Joseph and his brothers is one of the greatest epics in literature. It is the drama of the brothers' hate of a favored younger brother and their crime against the boy. They paid dearly for their ill deed to the lad, but years later, Joseph showed them how God had turned their evil to good. It is also the story of a pampered younger son, a dreamer of dreams, who dared to dream greatness for himself when he was only a stripling. Perhaps because of this, Joseph, too, had to suffer many ills before his dreams came true. But what saved Joseph from his own youthful arrogance, his brothers' jealousy, the wrath of his employer, and the misery and inaction of a long prison term were his complete innocence and his reliance on God's guidance in all he said and did. That guidance changed Joseph the dreamer into Joseph the practical man of affairs and active ruler of a great land. His reliance on God kept him free, too, from every taint of bitterness and resentment against those who had ill used him. When the brothers came before him at last, they found only compassion, generosity, and deep affection.

The Coat of Many Colors

Now Jacob, who was sometimes called Israel, had twelve sons, but he loved the youngest boy, Joseph, best of all. When Joseph was seventeen years old, Jacob made him a coat of many colors.

Then the brothers saw that their father loved this boy more than he loved them and they hated Joseph and could not speak peaceably to him.

They hated him still more when he told them about a dream he had dreamed. He said, "Hear, I pray you, my brothers, this dream which I have dreamed. We were binding sheaves in the field and, lo, my sheaf arose and stood upright, and behold, your sheaves stood round about and bowed down to my sheaf."

His brothers said, "Shall you indeed rule over us?" And they hated him more and more for his dream and his words.

But Joseph dreamed still another dream which he told to his brothers. "Behold, I have dreamed again," he said. "And in this dream the sun and the moon and eleven stars all bowed down to me."

When Joseph told this dream to his father, Jacob rebuked him saying, "What is this dream that you have dreamed? Do you mean that your mother and I and your eleven brothers shall indeed bow down to you?"

The brothers hated Joseph still more, but Jacob, although he reproved the boy, remembered his saying.

After this, Jacob's eleven sons went to Shechem to feed their father's flocks, and Jacob said to Joseph, "Your brothers are feeding my flocks in Shechem. Go, I pray you, and see whether all is well with them and bring me word."

So Joseph set off for Shechem, but when he came there he could not find his brothers. He was wandering in the field when a man saw him and asked him what he was seeking. Joseph replied, "I am looking for my brothers. Tell me, I pray you, where are they feeding their flocks?"

And the man answered, "They have left this place, but I heard them say, 'Let us go to Dothan.'"

So Joseph set off for Dothan, and he found his brothers there. But they, when they saw him coming, plotted together to kill him. They said, one to another, "Behold, the dreamer comes! Let us kill him and throw his body into the pit. We can say some evil beast has killed and eaten him. Then we'll see what becomes of his dreams."

"The Story of Joseph." From Genesis 37, 39, 40, 41, and 43 as adapted by May Hill Arbuthnot

But Reuben, the oldest brother, wished to save the boy; so he said, "No, we must not kill him. We must shed no blood. Lay no hand upon him, but rather cast him into this pit, here, in the wilderness." This he said in order that he might get the boy out of their hands and deliver him safely to their father once more. The brothers agreed.

So, when Joseph was come to them, they stripped him of his coat of many colors and threw him into an empty pit where there was no water. Then they sat down to eat and as they were eating, they saw coming towards them a great company of Ishmaelites with their camels, bearing spices and balm and myrrh from Gilead to Egypt. When Judah, one of the brothers, saw the caravan, he said, "What good will it do us if we slay our brother and hide his blood? Come, let us sell him to these Ishmaelites. Then our hand will not be upon him, for he is our brother."

The others agreed to this plan. So, they lifted Joseph out of the pit and sold him to the Ishmaelites for twenty pieces of silver, and the Ishmaelites went away with Joseph to Egypt.

After they were gone, the brothers took Joseph's coat of many colors and dipped it in the blood of a goat. Then they took the coat to Jacob and said, "This we have found. Do you know whether or not it is your son's coat?"

And Jacob knew the coat and he cried out, "It is my son's coat. An evil beast has killed Joseph and devoured him." And Jacob wept and mourned for his son for many days. All his sons and daughters rose up to comfort him, but he refused to be comforted and said, "I will go down to my grave mourning for my son Joseph." And he wept the more.

Joseph In Egypt

The Ishmaelites took Joseph to Egypt where they sold him to Potiphar, one of King Pharaoh's officers, a Captain of the Guard. The Lord was with Joseph. He prospered in the house of his Egyptian master and found favor in his eyes. For when Potiphar saw that all Joseph did in his house was a success, because the Lord was with him, he made him overseer of his household and put him in charge of all his property. And because of Joseph, the Lord blessed the Egyptian's house and his fields and Potiphar had no more worry about his possessions.

Joseph grew to be a handsome and a goodly young man. Potiphar's wife liked him and wanted him to do her will instead of his master's. But when she urged Joseph to do something dishonorable he refused, saying, "Behold my master has given everything he has into my hand. He trusts me, and I will do no wickedness against him and in the eyes of my God."

This made the woman angry, so she turned against Joseph and told her husband lies about his overseer. Potiphar believed her, and his wrath was kindled and he had Joseph thrown into the prison where the king kept his prisoners bound. But the Lord was with Joseph and he found favor in the sight of the jailer. This man turned over to Joseph's hand all the prisoners in his charge and again Joseph's work was a success. He looked after everything that needed to be done, and the jailer did not have to oversee anything. Whatever Joseph did, the Lord prospered him.

It came to pass that Pharaoh, King of Egypt, was angry with his butler and his baker, and he sent them to the same prison where Joseph was, and they were put in Joseph's charge. One morning, Joseph came to them and found them looking sad, so he asked them, "Why are you looking so gloomy?"

"Because we have each of us dreamed a dream," they said. "And there is no one here to tell us what our dreams mean."

"Interpretations belong to God," Joseph said. "But tell me your dreams, I pray you."

So the chief butler told his dream first. He said, "In my dream a vine was before me, and on the vine there were three branches, and these budded, and the blossoms shot forth and clusters of grapes grew on them. And Pharaoh's cup was in my hand, so I squeezed the grapes into the cup and gave it to Pharaoh."

Joseph answered, "This is the meaning of your dream. The three branches are three days. Within three days Pharaoh will summon you and restore you to your place, so that you shall place Pharaoh's cup in his hand as you used to do when you were his butler. When this happens, and it is well with you, I pray you show kindness to me. Mention me to Pharaoh that he may release me from this prison. For indeed I was stolen away out of the land of the Hebrews, and here I have done nothing wrong that I should be put into this dungeon."

Now when the baker saw that the interpretation of the butler's dream was good, he also told his dream to Joseph. He said, "In my dream I had three white baskets upon my head. And in the uppermost basket there were all manner of baked foods for Pharaoh. But the birds did eat them out of the basket on my head."

And Joseph said, "This is the meaning of your dream. The three baskets are three days. Within three days Pharaoh shall summon you and hang you on a tree, and the birds shall eat your flesh."

On the third day, which was Pharaoh's birthday, he held a feast for all his servants. He sent for the chief butler and the chief baker. The chief butler he restored to his duties again and he gave the cup into Pharaoh's hand as before. But the chief baker Pharaoh hanged, as Joseph said he would do. But when the chief butler was restored to his place, he did not keep Joseph in mind but forgot him.

So Joseph remained in prison for two more years. Then, King Pharaoh himself dreamed, and in his dream he stood by a river. Seven fat and beautiful cattle came up out of the river and fed in the meadow. Then seven lean, ugly cattle also came up out of the river and devoured the seven fat cattle. So Pharaoh woke, but he slept again and dreamed the second time. In his dream seven ears of corn came up on one stalk, thick and good, and behold seven thin ears, blasted by the east wind, sprang up after them and devoured the seven thick, good ears.

When morning came, Pharaoh's spirit was troubled and he called for all the magicians and wise men of Egypt to tell him what his dreams meant. But not one of them could interpret Pharaoh's dream for him.

Then Pharaoh's butler said to the king, "This day I remember my faults. For when you were angry with your servants and put both me and the baker in prison, we dreamed a dream one night, he and I. And there was a young man in the prison, a Hebrew, who had been a servant to the Captain of the Guard, and we told our dreams to him. He interpreted our dreams for us, and everything happened just as he told us

it would. I was restored to my office, and the baker was hanged, as the young Hebrew told us."

When King Pharaoh heard this, he sent for Joseph at once. They brought him hastily out of his dungeon, and he shaved himself and changed his raiment and was brought at once to Pharaoh.

The King said, "I have dreamed two dreams and none can say what they mean. But I have heard that you can understand dreams and can interpret their meaning."

Joseph replied, "It is not in me but it is God, who shall give Pharaoh an answer of peace."

Then Pharaoh told Joseph his two dreams, and when Joseph had heard them he said, "Pharaoh's dreams are one. God has shown Pharaoh what he is about to do. The seven good cattle and the seven good ears of corn are seven years, and the dream is one. The seven thin cattle and the seven empty, blasted ears of corn, which came after them, are seven years of famine. This which I have spoken is what God is about to do to Pharaoh. There shall be seven years of plenty throughout all the land of Egypt. Then there shall arise seven years of famine, and all the plenty shall be forgotten in the land of Egypt and famine shall consume the land, and it shall be very grievous. Because the dream was doubled, it means that God will shortly bring it to pass. Pharaoh, therefore, should look for a man who is discreet and wise and set him over the land of Egypt. And let him appoint officers to take up a fifth part of all the corn and other foods that are gathered in the plenteous years and let them store the food in the cities. And that food shall be a store against the seven years of famine that are to come to the land of Egypt, that the land shall not perish from the famine."

This plan was good in the eyes of Pharaoh, and he said to his courtiers, "Can we find such a man as this, a man filled with the spirit of God?"

Then Pharaoh said to Joseph, "Since God has showed you all this, there is surely no man so wise and discreet as you are. I will set you over my house, and my people shall be ruled according to your word. Only on the throne will I be greater than you. Behold, I have set you over all the land of Egypt."

King Pharaoh took the ring off his finger and put it on Joseph's finger and arrayed him in vestures of fine linen and put a gold chain around his neck. And Pharaoh made Joseph ride in the second chariot which he had, and the people cried before him, "Bow the knee!" And Joseph was ruler over all the land of Egypt.

Later, Pharaoh gave Joseph as his wife, Asenath, and before the years of famine set in, two sons were born to them. The firstborn he called Manasseh, and the second he called Ephraim. And Joseph traveled everywhere throughout all the land. In the plenteous years the land produced great crops, and Joseph gathered the food and stored it in the cities. And the corn he stored was like the sands of the sea. There was so much he could no longer count it.

But at last, the seven years of plenty came to an end and the seven years of want began. The lack of food was over all the lands, only in Egypt was there food. And when the Egyptians began to be hungry, they cried to Pharaoh for food, and Pharaoh said to them, "Go to Joseph and do what he tells you."

So Joseph opened the storehouses to the Egyptians, and all the other countries also came to Joseph to buy corn, for the famine was sore throughout the lands.

"And your sheaves . . . bowed down to my sheaf."

Now, in Canaan, when Jacob, the father of Joseph, heard that there was corn in Egypt, he said to his sons, "Why do you sit staring at each other and do nothing? Behold I have heard there is corn in Egypt. Go there and buy food for us that we may live and not die."

So, ten sons of Jacob traveled to Egypt with other people from the land of Canaan. But their father Jacob would not let Benjamin, the youngest boy, go with them lest something happen to him. Benjamin and Joseph were the children of the same mother, and Jacob loved them more than he loved his other sons.

Now Joseph was, of course, the governor over all the land of Egypt, and the people who wished to buy corn had to go to him. So, his ten brothers bowed low before him with their faces to the earth. They did not know him, but he knew them at once, and he remembered his dreams about them. He spoke harshly to them as if they were strangers, for he did not want them to recognize him.

"Where do you come from?" he asked, and they told him they came from the land of Canaan. "You are spies," Joseph said roughly. "You have come to see the nakedness of this land."

"No, my Lord," the brothers replied. "We have only come to buy food. We are honest men, the sons of one father, and no spies."

And again he accused them of being spies and they replied, "There are twelve of us, the sons of one father. The youngest son has remained at home with our father, and one son is no more. But we have come, not to spy, but to buy food."

Joseph said, "If this is true, you will have to prove it to me. Let one of you return home and bring your youngest brother to me. The rest of you shall stay in prison until the two return. Then we shall see whether there is any truth in what you say, for by Pharaoh's life, I believe you are spies."

Then Joseph put them all in prison for three days. After that, he said. "If you be true men, prove it to me and live, for I do fear God. One of you shall remain here in prison, and all the others shall return to Canaan with corn for the famine in your houses. But you must bring your youngest brother to me so that the truth of your words shall be proved. Do this and live."

When the brothers heard this, they said to one another, "This has happened to us because we are guilty concerning our brother, Joseph."

And Reuben said to his brothers, "You remember I begged you not to sin against the child Joseph, but you would not listen to me. Now, perhaps Benjamin's blood will be required of us."

All this they said because Joseph had been speaking to them through an interpreter so they did not think he could understand their words. But, of course, he did understand them, and when he heard what Reuben said, he turned away and wept. Then he returned to the brothers and bound Simeon before their eyes. And Joseph secretly commanded his steward that their sacks should be filled with corn and every man's money restored to his sack. Besides this, he gave them enough provisions to last them for the journey home.

The nine brothers loaded their asses with the corn and set off for home. But on the way, they stopped at an inn and one of them opened his sack to give his ass some corn, and in the sack he found his money. The brothers were frightened when they discovered what had happened. Their hearts failed them, and they said, "What is this that God has done to us?"

When they reached home, they told Jacob about the governor of all Egypt who had spoken roughly to them and accused them of being spies. And they told Jacob everything that had happened, and when they emptied their sacks, every man found his money inside.

When he had heard their story and seen all the money, Jacob said, "You have bereaved me of my sons. Joseph is no more. Now, Simeon is gone, and you would take Benjamin from me. Everything is against me."

And Reuben spoke to his father, "If I do not bring Benjamin and Simeon back to you, you may kill my own two sons."

But Jacob was not satisfied. "No," he said, "Benjamin shall not go down to Egypt. His own brother Joseph is dead, and if something happens to Benjamin, it will bring my gray hairs with sorrow to the grave."

A Feast in the Land of the Egyptians

The famine was sore in the lands. After awhile Jacob and his sons and their families had eaten all the corn which they had brought out of the land of Egypt. So Jacob said to his sons, "Go again to Egypt and buy food."

But Judah protested, "The Egyptian did solemnly swear to us, 'You shall not see my face if you do not return with your youngest brother.'"

"But why did you tell the Egyptian that you had another brother?" Jacob asked. "It was an ill thing to do to me."

"The man asked us all sorts of questions, and we had to answer him truly," the brothers replied. "He asked, 'Is your father yet alive? Have you another brother?' We answered his questions for we could not know that he would say, 'Bring your brother to me.'"

Then Judah said to his father, "Send the lad Benjamin with me, and we will go at once. I will be responsible for him. For we must have food that we may live and not die, both we and thou and also our little ones."

At last Jacob said, "If this must be, go now, and take with you a present for the man—a little balm and a little honey, spices, myrrh, nuts, and almonds. And be sure to take double money in your hands to pay back the money that you found in your sacks which, perhaps, was an oversight. Take your brother Benjamin also and may

God Almighty have mercy on you and on your brother that the man may send him back to me, lest I again be bereaved."

So the nine brothers took Benjamin with them, a present for the Egyptian, and double money in their hands and set off for Egypt. They came at last before Joseph and bowed low before him. And Joseph, when he saw his brother Benjamin, commanded his stewards to prepare a great feast and to bring all these brothers to eat with him. And the steward did so, and he brought the brothers to Joseph's house. The brothers were frightened. They thought that perhaps because of the money that was returned to them, the Egyptian might now fall upon them and make them his slaves. So they talked to the steward at the door of Joseph's house and said, "Oh sir, we came down the first time to buy food. But when we came to the inn on our way home, every man's money was in his sack. We do not know who put it there, but this time we have brought double that money to pay for food."

And the steward replied, "Peace be with you. Fear not. Your God and the God of your fathers has given you treasure in your sacks. I had your money. It is well with you." And he brought Simeon to them, and led them into Joseph's house, where they could wash themselves and make ready for the feast. And the steward saw that their asses were also fed.

When Joseph came home, the brothers brought him their presents and they bowed themselves to the earth before him, and he asked them how they fared and said, "Is your father well, the old man of whom you spoke? Is he yet alive?"

And they answered, "Thy servant, our father, is alive and well," and again they bowed themselves to the earth.

Joseph lifted up his eyes and saw his own brother, Benjamin, and said, "And is this your younger brother, of whom you spoke? God be gracious to you, my son." And then, Joseph was so moved at the sight of his brother that he had to leave the room in haste to find a place where he could weep unseen. In his own room he wept; then he washed his face and returned to the feast where he restrained himself and bade the steward set out the food.

The servants set Joseph's food before him and he ate by himself. The brothers also had their food set before them by themselves, for the Egyptians who were there might not, according to their laws, eat with any Hebrews. But Joseph kept sending special dishes from his table to Benjamin's place until the lad had five times as much as anyone else. Everyone ate and drank and made merry with Joseph.

After the feast, Joseph commanded his steward, "Fill the men's sacks with food, as much as they can carry, and put every man's money in the mouth of his sack. But put my own silver cup in the sack of the youngest brother together with his corn money."

So the steward did as Joseph commanded him, and as soon as the morning was come, the men were sent on their way with their asses laden with the sacks of food. Before they had gone very far, Joseph called his steward and said to him, "Up, follow these men and when you overtake them, ask them why they have rewarded good with evil. Say to them, 'One of you has my lord's silver cup from which he drinks.'"

The steward did this, and when he spoke these words to the brothers, they cried out, "Why would my lord speak to us like this? God forbid that we should do any such thing. Don't you remember how we brought back the money we found in our sacks? How then could my lord think we would steal gold or silver out of his house? But search us, and if the cup is found on anyone of us, that one shall die and the others shall be slaves to your master."

Then they speedily opened up their sacks, and the steward searched them, from the sack of the oldest brother to the youngest. And the cup was found in Benjamin's sack. The brothers cried out and tore their clothes, and after they had reloaded their asses, they returned to the city.

The brothers came again before Joseph and fell down before him and Joseph spoke. "What is this that you have done? You might know that I would find you out."

And Judah said, "What can we say, my lord, to prove our innocence? God is punishing us for our sins, and now we are here, the slaves of my lord, both we and he in whose possession the cup was found."

"No," said Joseph, "I could not think of doing

such a thing, God forbid. Only the man in whose hand the cup was found shall stay here to be my servant. The rest of you shall go in peace to your old father."

Then Judah came close to Joseph. "My lord, I pray, let me speak a word in your ear and do not let your anger blaze against me, for I know right well that you are as powerful as Pharaoh. You asked about our father and brother, and we told you that our father was old and the boy a child of his old age, a little one, the only one left of the mother whom Jacob loved. The other child Joseph is no more, so this boy my father loves more than any of us. When we told our father that you would not see us again to sell us corn unless we brought this lad with us, he said to us, 'You know the wife I loved had but two sons. One is gone from me, and if any mischief should befall this boy, it would bring my gray hairs in sorrow to the grave.' So, then, I became surety for my brother Benjamin. Now therefore, I pray you, let me become your servant instead of the lad and let him go in peace to my father."

When Joseph heard Judah plead for the boy, he could restrain himself no longer and he said to his attendants, "Have everyone withdraw from this room except these brothers." And Joseph was left alone with his brothers, and he made himself known to them. "I am Joseph," he cried. "Does my father yet live?" And he wept as he spoke, and his brothers were so overcome with fear that they could not answer him.

"Come nearer to me," Joseph said, and when they came nearer, he continued, "I am your brother Joseph, whom you sold into slavery in Egypt. But do not be grieved nor angry with yourselves for what you did. God sent me ahead of you to this land to save life. For two years now, famine has prevailed over all the land, and there are still five years to come when there will be no ploughing and no reaping. God sent me ahead of you to save a remnant of the earth and so to preserve you and your posterity. So now it was not you who sent me here but God. And it is God who has made me a father to Pharaoh, a ruler over all the land of Egypt and the cause of this great deliverance. Go now in haste to my father Jacob and tell him what I have said. And tell him not to tarry there in the land of Canaan,

but come to me and you shall all dwell in the land of Goshen and be near me with all your children and your children's children and your flocks and your herds and all that you possess. And here will I nourish you for the five remaining years of the famine lest any of you fall into poverty. And say to my father that your own eyes and the eyes of Benjamin have seen me and you have heard my words. And tell my father of my glory in Egypt and all the things you have seen. Make haste now, and bring my father to me."

Then Joseph wept and embraced his brother Benjamin and Benjamin wept too on Joseph's neck. And Joseph kissed all his brothers and they talked together.

Then the news was heard in Pharaoh's palace, and everyone began to speak of it and to say, "Joseph's brothers are come."

Pharaoh was pleased with the news and said to Joseph, "Tell your brothers to load their asses and go into the land of Canaan to fetch your father and your household. Come to me and I will give you some of the best land in Egypt for you and your family and you shall eat the fat of the land. Tell your brothers to take wagons from Egypt to bring back their wives and little ones and your father too. Never mind your goods, for the best of all Egypt will be yours."

So Joseph gave his brothers wagons, as Pharaoh had commanded, and he gave them provisions for the journey. He also gave each man a rich garment, and to Benjamin he gave three hundred pieces of silver and five changes of raiment. And to his father, Joseph sent ten asses laden with the good things of Egypt and ten she asses laden with corn, bread, and meat. And Joseph warned his brothers not to quarrel with each other on the journey.

When the brothers came to the land of Canaan and their father Jacob, they told him, "Joseph, your son, is still alive and he is governor over all of the land of Egypt!"

But Jacob was stunned by the news and did not believe them. Then the brothers told him all the words Joseph had spoken to them and all the splendor of his life in Egypt. But still Jacob could not believe their stories until he saw the wagons Joseph had sent to bring his father to

Egypt. Then Jacob believed the stories and his spirits rose. "It is enough," he said. "I believe you. My son is still alive and I shall see him again before I die."

So Jacob set off for Egypt with all of his sons and their wives and their little ones in the wagons which Pharaoh had sent. And Judah went ahead to tell Joseph that his father was coming.

So Joseph went out in his chariot and drove to meet his father. And they embraced each other and wept for joy, and Jacob said, "Now, my son, I can die in peace for I have seen your face and know that you are still alive."

And Joseph preserved his father and his brothers and all their households in the land of Egypt.

BIBLIOGRAPHY

GENERAL REFERENCES

ARBUTHNOT, MAY HILL, *Children and Books*, Scott, Foresman, 1957. Folk tales, myths, fables, and modern fanciful tales are discussed fully in Chapters 11–14.

ARBUTHNOT, BRIGGS, CLARK, LONG, and WHITE, *Children's Books Too Good to Miss*, Press of Western Reserve University, Cleveland, 1948. 75c. Here is a list of books, old and new, which children should have a chance to know. The books are grouped in four age levels—under 6; 6, 7, and 8; 9, 10, 11; 12 and 13. Careful and readable annotations and price lists make this bibliography useful for ordering, either for an individual child or for a school library.

HAZARD, PAUL, *Books, Children and Men*, tr. by Marguerite Mitchell, Horn Book, 1944. A member of the French Academy and professor of comparative literature both in France and in the United States writes engagingly of the great children's books of many countries.

JORDAN, ALICE M., *From Rollo to Tom Sawyer and Other Papers*, decorated by Nora S. Unwin, Boston, Horn Book, 1949.

KIEFER, MONICA, *American Children Through Their Books, 1700–1835*, University of Pennsylvania Press, 1948. This book will be of special value to students interested in the history of American books for children. Miss Kiefer's book is carefully documented and indexed.

MONTGOMERY, ELIZABETH RIDER, *The Story Behind Modern Books*, Dodd, Mead, 1949. Every elementary school will wish to add to its library Mrs. Montgomery's book about the modern authors and illustrators of children's books.

SAWYER, RUTH, *The Way of the Storyteller*, Viking, 1942. Informally written in Ruth Sawyer's fine style, this is a contribution both to the art of storytelling and the history of the old tales. It also contains eleven unusual stories.

BIOGRAPHICAL REFERENCES

BARNES, WALTER, *The Children's Poets*, World Book Company, 1924. Interesting notes about the older poets of childhood.

KUNITZ, STANLEY J., *British Authors of the 19th Century*, Wilson, 1936.

KUNITZ, STANLEY J. and HAYCRAFT, HOWARD, *American Authors, 1600–1900*, Wilson, 1938. A biographical dictionary of American literature, complete in one volume.

KUNITZ, STANLEY J. and HAYCRAFT, HOWARD, *The Junior Book of Authors*, 2nd ed. revised, Wilson, 1951. Includes biographical or autobiographical sketches of authors of both classic and contemporary juvenile literature.

KUNITZ, STANLEY J. and HAYCRAFT, HOWARD, *Twentieth Century Authors*, Wilson, 1942; First Supplement, 1955. A biographical dictionary of modern literature. Gives information about writers of this century of all nations.

POETS CHILDREN ENJOY

ALDIS, DOROTHY, *All Together: A Child's Treasury of Verse*, Putnam, 1952.

ALLEN, MARIE LOUISE, *A Pocketful of Poems*, Harper, 1957.

BARUCH, DOROTHY, *I Like Machinery*, Harper, 1933.

BEHN, HARRY, *The Little Hill*, Harcourt, Brace, 1949.
Windy Morning, Harcourt, Brace, 1953.
The Wizard in the Well, Harcourt, Brace, 1956.

BENÉT, ROSEMARY and STEPHEN VINCENT, *A Book of Americans*, Rinehart, 1933.

BROOKS, GWENDOLYN, *Bronzeville Boys and Girls*, Harper, 1956.

CHUTE, MARCHETTE, *Rhymes About the City*, Macmillan, 1946.

CIARDI, JOHN, *The Reason for the Pelican*, Lippincott, 1959.
CONKLING, HILDA, *Poems by a Little Girl*, Stokes, 1920.
DE LA MARE, WALTER, *Rhymes and Verses; Collected Poems for Children*, Holt, 1947.
FARJEON, ELEANOR, *Poems for Children*, Lippincott, 1951. *The Children's Bells*, Walck, 1960.
FIELD, EUGENE, *Poems of Childhood*, Scribner's, 1904, 1925. A Scribner's Illustrated Classic, n.d. The last is the one now in print.
FIELD, RACHEL, *Taxis and Toadstools*, Doubleday, 1926. *Poems*, Macmillan, 1957.
FROST, FRANCES M., *The Little Whistler*, Whittlesey House, 1949.
The Little Naturalist, Whittlesey House, 1959.
FROST, ROBERT, *You Come Too; Favorite Poems for Young Readers*, Holt, 1959.
FYLEMAN, ROSE, *Fairies and Chimneys*, Doubleday, 1920.
GREENAWAY, KATE, *Under the Window*, Warne, n.d.
LEAR, EDWARD, *The Complete Nonsense Book*, Dodd, Mead, 1942.
LINDSAY, VACHEL, *Johnny Appleseed and Other Poems*, Macmillan, 1928.
MC CORD, DAVID, *Far and Few: Rhymes of the Never Was and Always Is*, Little, Brown, 1952.
MC GINLEY, PHYLLIS, *All Around the Town* (a city alphabet), Lippincott, 1948.
MILNE, A. A., *The World of Christopher Robin*, Dutton, 1958. (*When We Were Very Young* and *Now We Are Six* combined in one volume.)
RICHARDS, LAURA E., *Tirra Lirra; Rhymes Old and New*, Little, Brown, 1955.
RILEY, JAMES WHITCOMB, *Rhymes of Childhood*, Bobbs-Merrill, 1891.
ROBERTS, ELIZABETH MADOX, *Under the Tree*, Viking, 1922.
ROSSETTI, CHRISTINA, *Sing-Song*, Macmillan, 1924.
SANDBURG, CARL, *Early Moon*, Harcourt, Brace, 1930.
SMITH, WILLIAM JAY, *Laughing Time*, Little, Brown, 1955. *Boy Blue's Book of Beasts*, Little, Brown, 1957.
STARBIRD, KAYE, *Speaking of Cows*, Lippincott, 1960.
STEARNS, MONROE, *Ring-A-Ling*, Lippincott, 1959.
STEVENSON, ROBERT LOUIS, *A Child's Garden of Verses*, Oxford, 1947.
TEASDALE, SARA, *Stars To-Night*, Macmillan, 1930.
TIPPETT, JAMES, *I Live in a City*, Harper, 1927.
WYNNE, ANNETTE, *For Days and Days*, Stokes, 1919.

MOTHER GOOSE EDITIONS OF SPECIAL INTEREST

Marguerite de Angeli's Book of Nursery and Mother Goose Rhymes, ill. by Marguerite de Angeli, Doubleday, 1954.
Ring o' Roses; A Nursery Rhyme Picture Book, ill. by L. Leslie Brooke, Warne, n.d.
LANGSTAFF, JOHN, *Frog Went A'Courtin'*, ill. by Feodor Rojankovsky, Harcourt, Brace, 1955.
LANGSTAFF, JOHN, ed., *Over in the Meadow*, ill. by Feodor Rojankovsky, Harcourt, Brace, 1957. Single nursery rhymes with music.
LINES, KATHLEEN, ed., *Lavender's Blue*, ill. by Harold Jones, Watts, 1954.
OPIE, IONA and PETER, eds., *The Oxford Nursery Rhyme Book*, ill. from old chapbooks with additional pictures by Joan Hassal, Oxford, 1955.
The Tall Book of Mother Goose, ill. by Feodor Rojankovsky, Harper, 1942.
Mother Goose, ill. by Tasha Tudor, Oxford, 1944.
The Real Mother Goose, ill. by Blanche Fisher Wright, Rand McNally, 1916, with later editions.

A FEW SUPPLEMENTARY ANTHOLOGIES OF POETRY

ADSHEAD, GLADYS L. and DUFF, ANNIS, *An Inheritance of Poetry*, Houghton, Mifflin, 1948. Chiefly for adolescents.
ASSOCIATION FOR CHILDHOOD EDUCATION, *Sung Under the Silver Umbrella*, Macmillan, 1935. For children 4 to 9.
BREWTON, JOHN E., *Under the Tent of the Sky*, Macmillan, 1937. The best of the author's many anthologies.
COLE, WILLIAM, ed., *Humorous Poetry for Children*, ill. by Ervine Metzl, World, 1955.
Story Poems New and Old, ill. by Walter Buehr, World, 1957. Fresh material in both these areas.
Poems of Magic and Spells, ill. by Peggy Bacon, World, 1960. A collection of ninety poems of mystery about strange people or things. Ages 9 and up.
DE LA MARE, WALTER, ed., *Come Hither*, ill. by Warren Chappell, Knopf, 1957. An entrancing collection.
FERRIS, HELEN, *Favorite Poems Old and New*, ill. by Leonard Weisgard, Doubleday, 1957. A varied selection of over 700 poems for children of all ages.
HUFFARD, GRACE T. and others, *My Poetry Book*, Winston, rev. ed., 1956. A large collection, well selected.
MC DONALD, GERALD D., *A Way of Knowing*, A Collection of Poems for Boys, ill. by Clare and John Ross, Crowell, 1959. In spite of the subtitle, girls will like this collection of vigorous poetry as well as the boys do.
PLOTZ, HELEN, ed., *Imagination's Other Place; Poems of Science and Mathematics*, ill. by Clare Leighton, Crowell, 1955. For older children, youth, and adults, this is a superb collection of poems.
READ, HERBERT, ed., *This Way Delight*, ill. by Juliet Kepes, Pantheon, 1956. A small, choice collection of authentic poetry from the Elizabethans to Dylan Thomas.
THOMPSON, BLANCHE, *Silver Pennies*, Macmillan, 1925.
More Silver Pennies, Macmillan, 1938. Small collections of choice modern poetry for children and youth.
UNTERMEYER, LOUIS, *The Golden Treasury of Poetry*, ill. by Joan Walsh Anglund, Golden Press, 1959. A large, attractively illustrated collection of poetry, chiefly from the older poets. The comments add much to the text.

ADULT POETRY REFERENCES

ABERCROMBIE, LASCELLES, *Poetry; Its Music and Meaning*, Oxford, 1932. A detailed analysis of the elements involved in the music of poetry and the relation of music to meaning. Difficult reading but rewarding.
ARBUTHNOT, MAY HILL, *Children and Books*, 1957. Chapters 4–10 are about poets and poetry, including a discussion of verse choirs and various helps in using poetry with children.
ARNSTEIN, FLORA, *Adventure into Poetry*, Stanford University Press, 1951. A teacher's careful record of her step-by-step procedures in conducting an experiment in creative writing with a group of elementary-school children. Sound literary taste, endless patience and tact make this an invaluable study.
AUSLANDER, JOSEPH and HILL, FRANK ERNEST, *The Winged Horse; The Story of the Poets and Their Poetry*, Doubleday, 1927. Written for young people, this book is good reading for adults.
DUFF, ANNIS, *"Bequest of Wings"; A Family's Pleasures with Books*, Viking, 1944. Charming account of introducing two children to books, especially poetry. Good!
EASTMAN, MAX, *The Enjoyment of Poetry*, Scribner's, new ed., 1951. Good reading; note especially the chapters on "Poetic People," which includes children, and "Practical Values of Poetry."

ERSKINE, JOHN, *The Kinds of Poetry and Other Essays,* Bobbs-Merrill, 1920. Read the fine chapter on "The Teaching of Poetry."

HIGHET, GILBERT, *The Powers of Poetry,* Oxford, 1960. A brief introduction to the oral-aural aspects of poetry, with delightful chapters on poets and types of poetry.

ISAACS, J., *The Background of Modern Poetry,* Dutton, 1952. Scholarly first aid to adults who find modern poetry hard to take.

OPIE, IONA and PETER, *The Oxford Dictionary of Nursery Rhymes,* Oxford, 1951. An exhaustive study of the origins and variants of nursery rhymes. A treasure of sources for students of this field.

BOOKS ON VERSE CHOIRS

ABNEY, LOUISE, *Choral Speaking Arrangements for the Upper Grades,* Expression, 1952.

ADAMS, HILDA and CROASDELL, ANNE, eds., *A Poetry Speaking Anthology,* Books I, II, III, Methuen, 1938. This single volume contains three small books on Infant Work, Junior Work, and Senior Work, corresponding to the middle grades, upper grades, and high school.

ARBUTHNOT, MAY HILL, *Children and Books,* Scott, Foresman, 1957. Chapter 10, "Verse Choirs."

BROWN, HELEN A. and HELTMAN, HARRY J., eds., *Choral Readings for Fun and Recreation,* Westminster Press, 1956.

DE WITT, MARGUERITE E., ed., *Practical Methods in Choral Speaking,* Expression, 1936. A compilation of papers by American teachers covering methods from the primary grades through the university.

GULLAN, MARJORIE, *The Speech Choir,* Harper, 1937. This is one of the most useful of Miss Gullan's books, because it is both an anthology and a methods text. It contains American poetry as well as English ballads, with detailed descriptions of the presentations.

HAMM, AGNES C., *Choral Speaking Technique,* 3rd ed., Tower Press, 1951.

HICKS, HELEN GERTRUDE, *The Reading Chorus,* Noble & Noble, 1939.

KEPPIE, ELIZABETH, *The Teaching of Choric Speech,* Expression, 1932. Beginners like this small book because of its detailed directions for a step-by-step development. The methods follow the much too formal procedures of the earliest books in the field.

KEPPIE, ELIZABETH E. and others, *Speech Improvement Through Choral Speaking,* Expression Co., 1942.

PUPPETS

FICKLEN, BESSIE, *Handbook of Fist Puppets,* Stokes, 1935. Detailed instructions for making hand puppets and their theater are given along with three plays.   12–adult

HOBEN, ALICE M., *The Beginner's Puppet Book,* Noble, 1938. Covers the simplest kind of puppets, with diagrams and photographs to amplify the text. Contains also a few plays which may be studied by the teacher for suggestions; but children should make their own plays.   10–13

JAGENDORF, MORITZ ADOLF, *Penny Puppets, Penny Theater and Penny Plays,* ill. by Fletcher Clark, Bobbs, 1941. Nine short and humorous plays are given along with directions for making inexpensive puppets, marionettes, and theaters.   10–14

MILLS, WINIFRED H., and DUNN, LOUISE M. *Marionettes, Masks and Shadows,* ill. by Corydon Bell, Doubleday, 1927. A standard book on the history of puppets, their construc-

tion, the setting, scenery, lighting, and training of the puppeteers.   12–14

PELS, GERTRUDE. *Easy Puppets,* ill. by Albert Pels, Crowell, 1951. A unique handbook on how to make puppets from almost anything from potatoes to papier mâché. The book also includes directions for making stages, scenery, curtains, and props. Even young children could follow her step-by-step directions.   7–14

Puppetry, a yearly publication from 1930 to 1940, Paul McPharlin, Puppetry Imprints, Birmingham, Michigan. These copiously illustrated, inexpensive little imprints are invaluable. Photographs, text, and diagrams make every detail clear and are richly suggestive of puppet possibilities.

COLLECTIONS OF FOLK TALES [1]

African and Ethiopian

AARDEMA, VERNA, *Tales from the Story Hat: African Folk Tales,* ill. by Elton Fax, Coward, 1960. In West Africa the storyteller wears a broad-brimmed hat from which dangle tiny objects representing tales of magic and wonder and fun.   7–11

COURLANDER, HAROLD, and HERZOG, GEORGE, *The Cow-Tail Switch, and Other West African Stories,* ill. by Madge Lee Chastain, Holt, 1947. Seventeen tales of West Africa, told in lively style and revealing much of the customs and life of the people.   10–12

COURLANDER, HAROLD, and LESLAU, WOLF, *The Fire on the Mountain and Other Ethiopian Stories,* ill. by Robert W. Kane, Holt, 1950. Ethiopian folk tales, outstanding in style, illustrations, and content.   10–14

DAVIS, RUSSELL, and ASHABRANNER, BRENT, *The Lion's Whiskers: Tales of High Africa,* ill. by James Teason, Little, 1959. Woven into these forty-one tales from Ethiopia and its borderlands are "a little history, a bit of geography, some personal adventure, and a liberal sprinkling of anthropology."   11–15

RICKERT, EDITH, *The Bojabi Tree,* ill. by Anna Braune, Doubleday, 1958. An old African folk tale about the hungry, forgetful jungle animals who finally earn their dinner.   5–8

SHERLOCK, PHILIP MANDERSON, *Anansi, the Spider Man,* ill. by Marcia Brown, Crowell, 1954. These stories, told by Jamaicans, had their roots in African folklore.   9–12

Arabian

BROWN, MARCIA, *The Flying Carpet,* ill. by author, Scribner's, 1956.   6–10

COLUM, PADRAIC, ed., *The Arabian Nights: Tales of Wonder and Magnificence,* ill. by Lynd Ward, Macmillan, 1953. This new and attractive edition of an outstanding collection will appeal to younger readers.   10–14

WILLIAMS-ELLIS, AMABEL, ed., *The Arabian Nights,* ill. by Pauline Diana Baynes, Criterion, 1957. Jewel-like pictures illustrate these vivid retellings of thirty favorites.   10–14

Chinese

HSI YU CHI, *The Adventures of Monkey,* ill. by Kurt Wiese, adapted from the Chinese by Arthur Waley, Day, 1944.

[1] All 1959–1960 titles for folk tales, fables, epic, myth, and fanciful tales, together with their annotations, are added by the kindness of Miss Ruth Hadlow, Assistant Supervisor of Work with Children, Cleveland Public Library.

Monkey is the traditional Chinese Mickey Mouse—adventurous, impudent, and curious. His antics and magic are good fun but decidedly intellectual. 12–16

RITCHIE, ALICE, *The Treasure of Li-Po*, ill. by T. Ritchie, Harcourt, 1949. These six Chinese fairy tales have dignity and distinction, wit and wisdom. They are delightful to tell or to read aloud or to be read by imaginative children. 10–14

English, Scottish, and Welsh

JACOBS, JOSEPH, ed., *English Fairy Tales*, Putnam's, n.d. *More English Fairy Tales*, Putnam's, n.d.
These are not only reliable sources for the favorite English tales but are also appealing to children in format and illustrations. 9–12
Favorite Fairy Tales Told in England, retold by Virginia Haviland, ill. by Bettina, Little, 1959. An easy-to-read, attractive edition of six familiar English folk tales. Miss Haviland has done a similar piece of work for the tales of Germany and France. 6–11

JONES, GWYN, *Welsh Legends and Folk Tales*, ill. by Joan Kiddell-Monroe, Oxford, 1955. Retellings of ancient sagas as well as folk and fairy tales are included. 11–14

REEVES, JAMES, *English Fables and Fairy Stories*, ill. by Joan Kiddell-Monroe, Oxford, 1954. 10–14

TREGARTHEN, ENYS, *The White Ring*, ed. by Elizabeth Yates, ill. by Nora S. Unwin, Harcourt, 1949. An exquisite Celtic fairy tale about the Cornish fairies. To be read aloud. 7–12

WILSON, BARBARA KER, *Scottish Folk Tales and Legends*, ill. by Joan Kiddell-Monroe, Oxford, 1954. 11–14

YOUNG, BLANCHE C., ed., *How the Manx Cat Lost Its Tail, and Other Manx Folk Stories*, ill. by Nora S. Unwin, McKay, 1959. 7–12

Eskimo

GILLHAM, CHARLES EDWARD, *Beyond the Clapping Mountains: Eskimo Stories from Alaska*, ill. by Chanimum, Macmillan, 1943. Illustrated by an Eskimo girl, these are unusual and highly imaginative tales. 10–12

Finnish

BOWMAN, JAMES CLOYD, and BIANCO, MARGERY, *Tales from a Finnish Tupa*, from a tr. by Aili Kolehmainen, ill. by Laura Bannon, Whitman, 1936. Here are the everyday folk tales of the Finnish people, not the epic stories. 10–14

French

DOUGLAS, BARBARA, comp., *Favorite French Fairy Tales; Retold from the French of Perrault, Madame D'Aulnoy, and Madame Le Prince de Beaumont*, ill. by R. Cramer, Dodd, 1952. "Beauty and the Beast" and "Prince Darling" by Mme. de Beaumont and "The White Cat" and "Goldenlocks" by Mme. D'Aulnoy are included with the Perrault tales. 9–12

PERRAULT, CHARLES, *Favorite Fairy Tales Told in France*, retold by Virginia Haviland, ill. by Roger Duvoisin, Little, 1959. 7–11
Gustave Doré Album: All the French Fairy Tales, retold by Louis Untermeyer, ill. by Gustave Dore, Didier, 1946. The reproduction of the superb Dore illustrations makes this edition a notable one. 9–12

PICARD, BARBARA, *French Legends, Tales and Fairy Stories: Retold*, ill. by Joan Kiddell-Monroe, Oxford, 1955. A rich source of folklore ranging from epic literature to medieval tales; from legends to fairy tales. 10–14

German

GRIMM, JACOB and WILHELM, *Favorite Fairy Tales Told in Germany*, retold by Virginia Haviland, ill. by Susanne Suba, Little, 1959. 7–11
Grimm's Fairy Tales, tr. by Margaret Hunt, rev. by James Stern, Pantheon, 1944. This is the edition teachers should examine or own, and by which other editions should be checked.
Grimm's Fairy Tales, tr. by Mrs. E. V. Lucas, Lucy Crane, and Marian Edwards, ill. by Fritz Kredel, Grosset, 1945. A recent edition that is thoroughly satisfying to children. 9–12
Grimm's Tales, ill. by Helen Sewell and Madeleine Gekiere, Oxford, 1954. A collection of sixteen tales. 10–12
Household Stories, tr. by Lucy Crane, ill. by Walter Crane, Macmillan, 1923. 10–12
Gone Is Gone, retold and ill. by Wanda Gag, Coward, 1935. 6–8
Tales from Grimm, freely tr. and ill. by Wanda Gag, Coward, 1936. 8–12
Three Gay Tales from Grimm, tr. and ill. by Wanda Gág, Coward, 1943. 8–12
Popular Stories, tr. by Edgar Taylor, ill. by George Cruikshank, a reprint of the first English edition, Clowes, London, 1913. This edition is interesting to adults as a reproduction of the first English translation of the Grimm tales.

Indian

BABBITT, ELLEN C., *The Jataka Tales*, ill. by Ellsworth Young, Appleton, 1912.
More Jataka Tales, ill. by Ellsworth Young, Appleton, 1912.
These fables have more elaborate plots and characterization than Aesop's fables, and are often rather humorous. Large libraries should have these even if they are still out of print. 6–10

TURNBULL, LUCIA, *Fairy Tales of India*, retold and ill. by Hazel Cook, Criterion, 1960. Sixteen tales, many unfamiliar to American children, that are full of Oriental color and wisdom. Published in England under the title *Indian Fairy Tales*. 8–13

Irish

BENNETT, RICHARD, *Little Dermot and the Thirsty Stones, and Other Irish Folk Tales*, ill. by Richard Bennett, Coward, 1953. Eight lively tales for younger readers. 9–12

COLUM, PADRAIC, *The Big Tree of Bunlahy*, ill. by Jack Yeats, Macmillan, 1933. This collection from one of our most successful adapters of myths gives the storytelling background of each tale. 8–12

JACOBS, JOSEPH, ed., *Celtic Fairy Tales*, ill. by John D. Batten, Putnam's, 1893.
More Celtic Fairy Tales, ill. by John D. Batten, Putnam's, n.d.
Jacobs includes Welsh, Scotch, Cornish, and Irish in his two Celtic collections. 9–12

O'FAOLAIN, EILEEN, *Irish Sagas and Folk-Tales*, ill. by Joan Kiddell-Monroe, Oxford, 1954. 10–14

Italian

BOTSFORD, MRS. FLORENCE H., *Picture Tales from the Italian*, ill. by Grace Gilkison, Stokes, 1929. These nineteen tales are amusing and are interspersed with short rhymed riddles.   7–10

VITTORINO, DOMENICO, *Old Italian Tales*, ill. by Kathryn L. Fligg, McKay, 1958. Twenty short tales alive with humor and wisdom.   7–12

Japanese

MCALPINE, HELEN and WILLIAM, *Japanese Tales and Legends*, ill. by Joan Kiddell-Monroe, Walck, 1959. Traditional tales of Japan's legendary past, folk tales, and the epic of the Heike. A volume in the distinguished Oxford series of myths and legends.   10–15

STAMM, CLAUS, *The Very Special Badgers, A Tale of Magic from Japan*, ill. by Kazue Mizumura, Viking, 1960. An old Japanese tale about two tribes of wily badgers, bitter rivals, that set out to prove which is stronger by pitting their best "cheater and changer" against the other. Amusing ink sketches.   6–10

UCHIDA, YOSHIKO, *The Dancing Kettle and Other Japanese Folk Tales;* retold; ill. by Richard C. Jones, Harcourt, 1949. Fourteen Japanese folk tales, well told, moralistic, and full of magic.   9–12
The Magic Listening Cap, More Folk Tales from Japan, ill. by author, Harcourt, 1955.   9–12

Mexican and South American

BRENNER, ANITA, *The Boy Who Could Do Anything, and Other Mexican Folk Tales*, ill. by Jean Charlot, W. R. Scott, 1942. These curious tales have the ring of authenticity.   8–12

HENIUS, FRANK, comp., *Stories from the Americas*, ill. by Leo Politi, Scribner's, 1944. Twenty folk tales or legends which are favorites of the peoples in Mexico, Central and South America.   9–11

STORM, DAN, *Picture Tales from Mexico*, ill. by Mark Storm, Stokes, 1941. Nineteen stories, many of them animal tales involving the lion as well as the native coyotes and rabbits.   8–10

Norwegian

ASBJÖRNSEN, PETER CHRISTIAN, and MOE, JÖRGEN, *East of the Sun and West of the Moon*, ill. by Hedvig Collin, Macmillan, 1953. A new and attractive edition of a title published twenty-five years ago. Based on the Dasent translation.   10–14

JONES, GWYN, *Scandinavian Legends and Folk Tales*, ill. by Joan Kiddell-Monroe, Oxford, 1956.   8–12

Russian

AFANASIEV, ALEXANDER N., *Russian Fairy Tales,* tr. by Norbert Guterman, Pantheon, 1945. Here, at last, is a reliable English source of the Russian tales collected by Afanasiev in the nineteenth century. The fables, talking beast tales, adventure stories, and romances are developed with a prodigal use of magic and much that is gory and terrifying. An adult source.

CARRICK, VALERY, *Picture Tales from the Russian*, tr. by Nevill Forbes, Stokes, 1913. Eleven little animal stories for the five- and six-year-olds.   5–6

RANSOME, ARTHUR, *Old Peter's Russian Tales*, ill. by Dimitri Mitrokhin, Nelson, 1917. This is the teacher's most practical source for the Russian tales.   8–12

Spanish

BOGGS, RALPH STEELE, and DAVIS, MARY GOULD, *The Three Golden Oranges*, ill. by Emma Brock, Longmans, 1936. Romantic and exciting stories for older children. One remarkable ghost story.   10–12

DAVIS, ROBERT, *Padre Porko*, ill. by Fritz Eichenberg, Holiday, 1939.   8–12

SAWYER, RUTH, *Picture Tales from Spain*, ill. by Carlos Sanchez, Stokes, 1936. Eleven little stories for children 7 to 10 years old, with rhymed riddles in between. Miss Sawyer has the ideal storytelling style.   7–10

United States: North American Indian

BELL, CORYDON, *John Rattling-Gourd of Big Cave: A Collection of Cherokee Indian Legends*, ill. by author, Macmillan, 1955. An outstanding collection of twenty-four legends.   10–14

BROUN, EMILY, *A Ball for Little Bear*, ill. by Dick Mackay, Aladdin, 1955. How the world was rescued from darkness after Big Bear took the sun from the sky for Little Bear to play with.
How Rabbit Stole Fire, ill. by Jack Ferguson, Aladdin, 1954. How Rabbit stole sacred fire and gave it to the people.   7–10

MAC FARLAN, ALLAN A., *Indian Adventure Trails; Tales of Trails and Tipis, Ponies and Paddles, Warpaths and Warriors*, ill. by Paulette Jumeau and Bob Hofsinde (Gray Wolf), Dodd, 1953. These stories offer more plot and action than many Indian folk tales.   11–14

MACMILLAN, CYRUS, *Glooskap's Country, and Other Indian Tales*, ill. by John A. Hall, Oxford, 1956. First published in 1918, this is one of the finest collections of Indian stories.   8–12

PENNEY, GRACE, *Tales of the Cheyennes*, ill. by Walter Richard West, Houghton, 1953. Long-ago legends explaining nature and customs, and a group of humorous tales.   10–14

United States: North American Negro

HARRIS, JOEL CHANDLER, *Complete Tales of Uncle Remus*, ed. by Richard Chase, Houghton, 1955.
Uncle Remus, His Songs and Sayings, rev. ed., ill. by A. B. Frost, Appleton, 1947.   8–adult

United States: Tall Tales

BLAIR, WALTER, *Tall Tale America*, ill. by Glen Rounds, Coward, 1944. A legendary history of our humorous heroes.   10–14

BONTEMPS, ARNA, and CONROY, JACK, *Sam Patch, the High, Wide and Handsome Jumper*, ill. by Paul Brown, Houghton, 1951. This tall tale is enhanced with wonderful action pictures of the jumpingest boy in the world.   10–12

BOWMAN, JAMES CLOYD, *Pecos Bill*, ill. by Laura Bannon, Whitman, 1937.   11–14

FELTON, HAROLD, *John Henry and His Hammer*, ill. by Aldren A. Watson, Knopf, 1950. The author has compiled a dramatic and effective account of the Negro superman's whole life, which is a part of our railroad epic.   10–13

MALCOMSON, ANNE, *Yankee Doodle's Cousins*, ill. by Robert McCloskey, Houghton, 1941. This is one of the finest and most satisfying collections of real and mythical heroes from all sections of the United States.   10–14

PECK, LEIGH, *Pecos Bill and Lightning*, ill. by Kurt Wiese, Houghton, 1940. A brief edition with copious illustrations to aid and comfort the slow reader. 8–12

ROUNDS, GLEN, *Ol' Paul the Mighty Logger*, ill. by author, Holiday, 1949. Glen Rounds has retold some of the Paul Bunyan stories with an earthy, exuberant zest that is delightful. 10–adult

SHAPIRO, IRWIN, *How Old Stormalong Captured Mocha Dick*, ill. by Donald McKay, Messner, 1942. Not only Stormalong, but the legendary superwhale, Moby (or Mocha) Dick. A good yarn. 10–14

Yankee Thunder, the Legendary Life of Davy Crockett, ill. by James Daugherty, Messner, 1944. 10–14

SHEPHARD, ESTHER, *Paul Bunyan*, ill. by Rockwell Kent, Harcourt, 1941. This is a good version of the Paul Bunyan epic. 10–14

TURNEY, IDA VIRGINIA, *Paul Bunyan, the Work Giant*, ill. by Norma Madge Lyon and Harold Price, Binfords & Mort, 1941. For slow readers who could never complete the whole epic, this brief text with its enormously funny pictures should make a satisfying substitute. 8–12

Variants of European folk tales in the United States

CHASE, RICHARD, ed., *Grandfather Tales*, ill. by Berkeley Williams, Jr., Houghton, 1948. 9–12

Jack and the Three Sillies, ill. by Joshua Tolford, Houghton, 1950. 7–10

The Jack Tales, ill. by Berkeley Williams, Jr., Houghton, 1943. 9–12

Wicked John and the Devil, ill. by Joshua Tolford, Houghton, 1951. 9–12

The American versions of the old world tales are as vigorous and fresh as the mountain people of the Cumberlands and the Smokies from whom they came.

JAGENDORF, MORITZ ADOLF, *The Marvelous Adventures of Johnny Caesar Cicero Darling*, ill. by Howard Simon, Vanguard, 1949. Johnny Darling is a spinner of superlative yarns. His tall tales are compiled by a notable folklorist and make a welcome addition to American frontier humor. 10–adult

New England Bean-Pot, ill. by Donald McKay, Vanguard, 1948. The dry humor characteristic of the New England people is found in these folk tales from the six states. 10–13

SAWYER, RUTH, *Journey Cake, Ho!*, ill. by Robert McCloskey, Viking, 1953. Mountain folk-tale version of *The Pancake*. Attractive picture book. 6–10

Other Countries

ĆURĆIJA-PRODANOVIĆ, NADA, *Yugoslav Folk-Tales*, ill. by Joan Kiddell-Monroe, Walck, 1957. 10–14

DEUTSCH, BABETTE, and YARMOLINSKY, AVRAHM, *Tales of Faraway Folk*, ill. by Irena Lorentowicz, Harper, 1952. A unique collection of tales from Baltic, Russian, and Asiatic lands. Told with simplicity that will have special appeal for young readers. 9–12

FILLMORE, PARKER, *The Shepherd's Nosegay, Stories From Finland and Czechoslovakia*, ed. by Katherine Love, ill. by Enrico Arno, Harcourt, 1958. Eighteen old favorites selected by a children's librarian from three out-of-print books of folk tales retold by Mr. Fillmore. 9–13

JEWETT, ELEANORE MYERS, *Which Was Witch? Tales of Ghosts and Magic from Korea*, ill. by Taro Yashima (pseud. for Jun Iwamatsu), Viking, 1953. Fourteen stories with sparkle and suspense, excellent for storytelling. 9–13

KELSEY, ALICE GEER, *Once the Mullah*, ill. by Kurt Werth, Longmans, 1954. Stories told by the Mullah give insight into Persian life and folklore and are often exceedingly funny. 9–12

MERRILL, JEAN, *Shan's Lucky Knife; A Burmese Folk Tale Retold*, ill. by Ronni Solbert, W. R. Scott, 1960. A Burmese folk tale telling how Shan, a country boy, tricks Ko Tin, a crafty boat-master from Rangoon. Illustrated with black, brown, and orange pictures of life along the Irrawaddy River and of the Burmese street bazaars. 7–11

MÜLLER-GUGGENBÜHL, FRITZ, *Swiss-Alpine Folk-Tales*, tr. by Katharine Potts, ill. by Joan Kiddell-Monroe, Walck, 1958. These tales and *Yugoslav Folk-Tales* are distinguished collections of national folklore in the Oxford series of myths and legends. 10–14

Anthologies of folk tales

BELTING, NATALIA M., *Cat Tales*, ill. by Leo Summers, Holt, 1959. Why does a dog chase a cat? Why does a cat catch mice? Here are sixteen fun-filled cat stories from many lands that answer such wonderings. 8–11

COURLANDER, HAROLD, *The Tiger's Whisker, and Other Tales and Legends from Asia and the Pacific*, ill. by Enrico Arno, Harcourt, 1959. Simple concepts and brevity make these suitable storytelling material for a wide range of children. 7–14

LINES, KATHLEEN, comp. *A Ring of Tales*, ill. by Harold Jones, Watts, 1959. A distinguished treasure trove of stories, old and new, familiar and not-so-familiar. 7–11

MACNEILL, JAMES, *The Sunken City, and Other Tales from Round the World*, ill. by Theo Dimsson, Walck, 1959. A direct, vigorous style marks these twenty folk tales that are just right for the storyteller. 8–12

ROSS, EULALIE S., comp. *The Buried Treasure, and Other Picture Tales*, ill. by Josef Cellini, Lippincott, 1958. Twenty-two favorite fables and folk tales selected from the Picture Tales series. 7–10

Single folk tales in picture book form

CHAUCER, GEOFFREY, *Chanticleer and the Fox*, adapted and ill. by Barbara Cooney, Crowell, 1958. 6–9

GRIMM, JACOB and WILHELM, *Hansel and Gretel*, ill. by Warren Chappell, music by Humperdinck, Knopf, 1944. 8–12

The Shoemaker and the Elves, ill. by Adrienne Adams, Scribner's, 1960. 5–9

The Sleeping Beauty, ill. by Felix Hoffmann, Harcourt, 1960. 6–11

Snow White and the Seven Dwarfs, ill. by Wanda Gág, Coward, 1938.

The Traveling Musicians, ill. by Hans Fischer, Harcourt, 1955. 4–8

The Wolf and the Seven Little Kids, ill. by Felix Hoffmann, Harcourt, 1959. 5–9

PERRAULT, CHARLES, *Cinderella; or The Little Glass Slipper*, ill. by Marcia Brown, Scribner's, 1954. 5–9

Puss in Boots, ill. by Marcia Brown, Scribner's, 1952. 6–9

Puss in Boots, ill. by Hans Fischer, Harcourt, 1959. 5–8

Dick Whittington and His Cat, adapted and ill. by Marcia Brown, Scribner's, 1950. 4–8

The Fast Sooner Hound, adapted from American folklore by Arna Bontemps and Jack Conroy, ill. by Virginia Burton, Houghton, 1942. 8–12

The Five Chinese Brothers, an old tale retold by Claire Huchet Bishop, ill. by Kurt Wiese, Coward, 1938. 5–10
The Old Woman and Her Pig, ill. by Paul Galdone, McGraw (Whittlesey), 1960. 3–6
Stone Soup, an old tale retold and ill. by Marcia Brown, Scribner's, 1947. 7–10

COLLECTIONS OF FABLES

Aesop's fables

JACOBS, JOSEPH, ed., *The Fables of Aesop,* ill. by Kurt Wiese, Macmillan, 1950. This classic edition of the fables includes Jacobs' short history of the fables and is delightfully illustrated by Kurt Wiese. 10–12
TOWNSEND, GEORGE TYLER and JAMES, THOMAS, trs., *Aesop's Fables,* ill. by Glen Rounds, Lippincott, 1950. This translation is simpler than Jacobs' and the humorous illustrations appeal strongly to children. 10–12

French fables

The Fables of La Fontaine, tr. by Margaret Wise Brown, ill. by André Hellé, Harper, 1940. This large picture book with bright colors is designed for children. 8–10

Indian Fables

GAER, JOSEPH, *The Fables of India,* ill. by Randy Monk, Little, 1955. Beast tales from three outstanding collections of Indian fables: the Panchatantra, the Hitopadesa, and the Jatakas. 12–16
The Panchatantra, tr. by Arthur W. Ryder, Univ. of Chicago, 1925. Adult students of the fables will be interested in discovering here the sources of many Aesop and La Fontaine fables.

Modern fables

BRENNER, ANITA, *A Hero by Mistake,* ill. by Jean Charlot, W. R. Scott, 1953. Afraid of his own shadow, this little man accidentally captures some bandits, is hailed as a hero, and learns to behave like one. 6–8

COLLECTIONS OF MYTHS AND EPICS

English epics

LANIER, SIDNEY, *The Boy's King Arthur,* ill. by N. C. Wyeth, ed. from Sir Thomas Malory's *History of King Arthur and His Knights of the Round Table,* Scribner's, 1942. An authoritative and popular version of this hero cycle; the best one to use for reading or telling. 10–14
MC SPADDEN, J. WALKER, *Robin Hood and His Merry Outlaws,* ill. by Louis Slobodkin, World Pub., 1946. 9–12
PYLE, HOWARD, *The Merry Adventures of Robin Hood of Great Renown in Nottinghamshire,* ill. by author, Scribner's, 1933. This is the great prose edition of the Robin Hood tales, the best source both for reading and telling. This earlier edition is better than the streamlined 1946 edition. 12–14
Some Merry Adventures of Robin Hood, rev. ed., ill. by author, Scribner's, 1954. This book contains a dozen stories adapted from the longer book, and would serve as an introduction for younger readers. 10–13
The Story of King Arthur and His Knights, ill. by author, Scribner's, 1933. 12–14

SANDYS, E. V., *Beowulf,* ill. by Rolf Klep, Crowell, 1941. A recent and satisfying version of *Beowulf,* dramatically illustrated. 12–16

Greek and Roman myths and epics

CHURCH, ALFRED JOHN, *The Odyssey for Boys and Girls,* Macmillan, 1906. An excellent source for children to read or adults to tell. Stories are arranged in chronological order. 10–14
COLUM, PADRAIC, *The Adventures of Odysseus and the Tale of Troy, or The Children's Homer,* ill. by Willy Pogany, Macmillan, 1918. A distinguished version, in cadenced prose. 10–14
The Golden Fleece; and the Heroes Who Lived Before Achilles, ill. by Willy Pogany, Macmillan, 1921. A companion volume to *The Children's Homer.* 10–14
COOLIDGE, OLIVIA E., *Greek Myths,* ill. by Edouard Sandoz, Houghton, 1949. Mrs. Coolidge has retold twenty-seven of the most widely known Greek myths. Here the gods are not idealized—indeed the book opens with an unappealing tale of trickery—but the stories have authenticity. They will appeal to youth. 10–16
DE SÉLINCOURT, AUBREY, *Odysseus the Wanderer,* ill. by Norman Meredith, Criterion, 1956. A lusty, modern retelling of the Odyssey. 11–adult
HAWTHORNE, NATHANIEL, *A Wonder Book for Girls and Boys,* ill. by Walter Crane, Houghton, 1851.
Tanglewood Tales for Girls and Boys, Houghton, 1853. 10–14
The Golden Touch, ill. by Paul Galdone, McGraw (Whittlesey), 1959. 10–14
HOMER, *The Odyssey,* abridged and tr. by George Kerr, ill. by John Verney, rev. ed. Warne, 1958. 10–14
KINGSLEY, CHARLES, *The Heroes,* ill. by Vera Bock, Macmillan, 1954. Thirty of the tales are beautifully retold and make a fine cycle for the storyteller. 10–14
SEWELL, HELEN, *A Book of Myths,* selections from Bulfinch's *Age of Fable,* ill. by Helen Sewell, Macmillan, 1942. Striking illustrations suggestive of ballet postures and movement distinguish this collection. 10–14

Norse myths and epics

COLUM, PADRAIC, *Children of Odin.* ill. by Willy Pogany, Macmillan, 1920. Norse myths and hero tales retold in a continuous narrative ending with the death of Sigurd. 10–14
SELLEW, CATHARINE, *Adventures with the Heroes,* ill. by Steele Savage, Little, 1954. Retold in simple language are the stories of the Volsungs and Niblungs. 9–12

Other national epics

BALDWIN, JAMES, *The Sampo: A Wonder Tale of the Old North,* ill. in color by N. C. Wyeth, Scribner's, 1912. Hero Tales from the Finnish *Kalevala.* 9–12
DEUTSCH, BABETTE, *Heroes of the Kalevala,* ill. by Fritz Eichenberg, Messner, 1940. This version has not only literary distinction but continuity. Text and illustrations bring out the lusty humor of the tales. 10–14
GAER, JOSEPH, *The Adventures of Rama,* ill. by Randy Monk, Little, 1954. One of the best-loved epics of India. 12–14

MODERN FANCIFUL TALES

ANDERSEN, HANS CHRISTIAN, *Fairy Tales,* 1835.
Ill. by George and Doris Hauman, Macmillan, 1953. 10–14

Ill. by Rex Whistler, Macmillan, 1950.   10–12

The Emperor and the Nightingale, retold and ill. by Bill Sokol, Pantheon, 1959. Retold with sensitive feeling and strikingly illustrated in a modern manner.   9–12

The Emperor's New Clothes, tr. and ill. by Erik Blegvad, Harcourt, 1959. A charming companion to the translator-illustrator's *The Swineherd*.   7–10

The Emperor's New Clothes, ill. by Virginia Lee Burton, Houghton, 1949. An enchanting edition of Andersen's funniest story. Children and adults will find Virginia Burton's pictures as irresistible as the story.   7–10

Seven Tales, tr. and adapted by Eva Le Gallienne, ill. by Maurice Sendak, Harper, 1959. Pleasant, appreciative renderings of some of Andersen's simpler tales with the illustrations done in a medieval manner. Large, clear print and wide margins add to the appeal of this volume.   8–12

The Steadfast Tin Soldier, ill. by Marcia Brown, Scribner's, 1953. Beautiful pastel illustrations.   6–10

The Swineherd, tr. and ill. by Erik Blegvad, Harcourt, 1958.   5–9

AYMÉ, MARCEL, *The Wonderful Farm*, tr. by Norman Denny, ill. by Maurice Sendak, Harper, 1951. The wonderful farm is quite an ordinary French farm except that the animals happen to talk. This is a book both children and adults will enjoy.   7–10

BAILEY, CAROLYN, *Miss Hickory*, ill. by Ruth Gannett, Viking, 1946. (Newbery Medal)

BANNERMAN, HELEN, *Little Black Sambo*, ill. by author, Stokes, 1900.   3–6

BARRIE, SIR JAMES, *Peter Pan*, ill. by Nora Unwin, Scribner's, 1950. Peter Pan, the boy who never grew up, and all his delightful companions are beautifully visualized for the children by Nora Unwin's illustrations for this new edition.   9–12

BATE, NORMAN, *Who Built the Highway? A Picture Story*, ill. by author, Scribner's, 1953. This is the first of several picture books by this author about machines and the workers who use them.   6–9

BECKER, EDNA, *900 Buckets of Paint*, ill. by Margaret Bradfield, Abingdon, 1949. Appealing pictures in full color accompany this amusing story of an old woman moving from house to house trying to satisfy her four fussy pets. The conclusion will bring anticipatory chuckles from astute small fry.   4–7

BELL, THELMA HARRINGTON, *Pawnee*, ill. by Corydon Bell, Viking, 1950. "Pawnee was a buckskin brave. But everyone thought Pawnee was just a doll." This distinction was a source of confusion both to Pawnee and Bobby Spencer's family. Amusing fantasy of a boy's doll.   5–8

BIANCO, MARGERY, *The Little Wooden Doll*, ill. by Pamela Bianco, Macmillan, 1925. A wistful, appealing tale reminiscent of Hans Christian Andersen.   6–10

BOSTON, L. M., *Treasure of Green Knowe*, ill. by Peter Boston, Harcourt, 1958.   11–15

BROOKS, WALTER, *Freddy and the Man from Mars*, Knopf, 1954.

Freddy Goes to Florida, Knopf, 1949.

Between these two books lies a long series of Freddy stories that enjoy enormous popularity. Freddy the pig, Charles the rooster, Jinx the cat, and their friends can be counted on for fun and excitement.   9–12

BROWN, MARGARET WISE, *The Runaway Bunny*, ill. by Clement Hurd, Harper, 1942. A small bunny discovers that he can never run away from his mother's love.   4–7

BRUNOFF, JEAN DE, *The Story of Babar, the Little Elephant*, Random, 1933. A series of these books follows.   5–8

BULLA, CLYDE, *The Poppy Seeds*, ill. by Jean Charlot, Crowell, 1955. A suspicious old man who in an arid land kept his clear spring to himself learns that to share is to be rich.   7–10

BURTON, VIRGINIA, *Choo Choo*, ill. by author, Houghton, 1937.

The Little House, ill. by author, Houghton, 1942.

Katy and the Big Snow, ill. by author, Houghton, 1943.   4–9

CARROLL, LEWIS, *Alice's Adventures in Wonderland* and *Through the Looking Glass* in 1 vol., ill. by John Tenniel, Heritage, 1944. (1865 and 1871)   10–adult

CAMERON, ELEANOR, *The Wonderful Flight to the Mushroom Planet*, ill. by Robert Henneberger, Little, 1954. Two small boys and their inventive neighbor build a space ship and take off to aid the people of a dying planet.   9–11

COBLENTZ, CATHERINE CATE, *The Blue Cat of Castle Town*, ill. by Janice Holland, Longmans, 1949. The blue kitten, born under a blue moon, learned the river's song, "Enchantment is made of three things—of beauty, peace and content."   12–14

CROWLEY, MAUDE, *Azor*, Oxford, 1948.

Azor and the Haddock, ill. by Helen Sewell, Oxford, 1949.

Azor and the Blue-Eyed Cow, ill. by Helen Sewell, Oxford, 1941.

Azor is a small, everyday sort of boy who happens to understand animals when they talk to him. Their confidences sometimes get him into trouble but his complete honesty and good will invariably save the day. 5–8

DAUGHTERTY, JAMES, *Andy and the Lion*, ill. by author, Viking, 1938. Young Andy has read about lions but never expected to meet one. The encounter ends in high adventure for both of them, and for the young reader. 6–8

DAVIS, ALICE, *Timothy Turtle*, ill. by G. B. Wiser, Harcourt, 1940.   4–7

DE LA MARE, WALTER, *The Three Mulla-Mulgars*, ill. by Dorothy Lathrop, Knopf, 1919.   12–16

DE LEEUW, ADELE, *Nobody's Doll*, ill. by Anne Vaughan, Little, 1946. The story of a lost doll and a kindly Scottie, both of whom finally come to the little boy and girl they yearn for. Each adventure is a complete episode. Good to read aloud.   7–10

DOLBIER, MAURICE, *Torten's Christmas Secret*, ill. by Robert Henneberger, Little, 1951. The freshest, gayest, Christmas story in years involves Santa's toy factory, hard-working gnomes, lists of good and bad children and lovely glimpses of Santa's frosty, sparkling Arctic world.   4–8

DRUON, MAURICE, *Tistou of the Green Thumbs*, tr. by Humphrey Hare, ill. by Jacqueline Duhéme, Scribner's, 1958. A unique fantasy, beautifully told, of a small French boy who used his strange gift with flowers to bring happiness and peace to others.   9–13

DU BOIS, WILLIAM PÈNE, *Peter Graves*, ill. by author, Viking, 1950. "The Horrible House of Horton" or "The House of the Horrible Houghton" was known far and wide. Houghton was an inventor who was always having to be rescued by the fire department. A boy, Peter Graves, went to see him with hair-raising results.   10–14

DUVOISIN, ROGER, *Petunia, Beware!* ill. by author, Knopf, 1958. This is one of several amusing books about Petunia, a silly and adventurous goose.   4–8

ELKIN, BENJAMIN, *Six Foolish Fishermen*, ill. by Katherine Evans, Childrens Press, 1957. At the end of their day each of the six fishermen forgot to count himself and was sure one had drowned. A small boy points out their foolish mistake. A perfect read-aloud.   4–7

ETS, MARIE HALL, *Mister Penny*, ill. by author, Viking, 1935. Poor Mr. Penny's good-for-nothing animals did nothing to help themselves or him. But after they ate up old Thunderstorm's garden, they redeemed themselves and saved Mr. Penny from a life of toil. Amusing pictures! 6–8

Mr. T. W. Anthony Woo, ill. by author, Viking, 1951. Mr. Woo, the cobbler, his cat, dog, and mouse live together, but not too happily. When Mr. Woo's meddling sister moves in with the idea of reforming them, they unite against the common enemy and learn to live peacefully. Humorous pictures add to the fun. 4–8

FAIRSTAR, MRS., pseud. for Richard Horne, *Memoirs of a London Doll,* ill. by Emma L. Brock, Macmillan, 1922. A classic doll story of another age. 9–12

FATIO, LOUISE, *The Happy Lion,* ill. by Roger Duvoisin, McGraw (Whittlesey), 1954. An unlocked gate inspires the amiable lion in a little French zoo to return the calls of the villagers with wild results. Roger Duvoisin's drawings in color are humorous and full of atmosphere. This first story about the Happy Lion has been followed by others equally hilarious and popular. 5–8

FIELD, RACHEL, *Hitty, Her First Hundred Years,* ill. by Dorothy P. Lathrop, Macmillan, 1929. Hitty's adventures in her hundred years are varied and satisfying to little girls. 10–13

FRISKEY, MARGARET, *Seven Diving Ducks,* ill. by Lucia Patton, McKay, 1940. One little duck was afraid to dive but finally made it. 4–7

GÁG, WANDA, *Millions of Cats,* ill. by author, Coward, 1928.
Snippy and Snappy, ill. by author, Coward, 1931.
The Funny Thing, ill. by author, Coward, 1929. 4–9

GANNETT, RUTH STILES, *My Father's Dragon,* Random, 1948.
The Dragons of Blueland, ill. by Ruth Chrisman Gannett, Random, 1951. 6–10

GEISEL, THEODORE SEUSS (pseud. Dr. Seuss), *Bartholomew and the Oobleck,* ill. by author, Random, 1949.
And to Think That I Saw It on Mulberry Street, Vanguard, 1937.
Horton Hatches the Egg, Random, 1940.
The King's Stilts, Random, 1939.
McElligot's Pool, Random, 1947. 6–12

GODDEN, RUMER, *Impunity Jane,* ill. by Adrienne Adams, Viking, 1954. An excellent doll story. 8–10
The Mousewife, ill. by William Pène du Bois, Viking, 1951. Expanded into a story from a note in Dorothy Wordsworth's Journal, this is an exquisitely written little fable of the friendship of a mouse and a caged dove. 6–9

GRAHAME, KENNETH, *The Wind in the Willows,* ill. by Ernest Shepard, Scribner's, 1960. The Golden Anniversary Edition of this beloved classic has, in addition to Mr. Shepard's familiar black and white drawings, eight new full-page drawings in color. 10–adult
Ill. by Arthur Rackham, Heritage, 1944. 10–adult

GRAMATKY, HARDIE, *Little Toot,* ill. by author. Putnam's, 1939.
Hercules, ill. by author, Putnam's, 1940.
Loopy, ill. by author, Putnam's, 1941.
A tug boat, an ancient fire engine, and an airplane are amusingly personified in these popular picture-stories. 4–9

HALE, LUCRETIA P., *The Peterkin Papers,* ill. by Harold Brett, Houghton, 1924. (1880) 9–12

HEINLEIN, ROBERT, *Red Planet,* Scribner's, 1949.
Rocket Ship Galileo, Scribner's, 1947.
Space Cadet, Scribner's, 1948. 12–adult

HOLT, ISABELLA, *The Adventures of Rinaldo,* ill. by Erik Blegvad, Little, 1959. How a rather old and worn albeit courageous knight seeks and wins a wife and castle makes a jaunty, whimsical tale in the manner of Don Quixote. 10–13

HOPP, ZINKEN, *The Magic Chalk,* tr. from the Norwegian by Susanne H. Bergendahl, ill. by Malvin Neset, McKay, 1959. Translated into more than eight languages, this delightful tale of fun and fantasy tells of John Albert Brown Sunnyside who found a piece of witch's chalk by which he could draw himself in and out of fabulous adventures. 7–10

JANICE (pseud.), *Little Bear's Sunday Breakfast,* ill. by Mariana, Lothrop, 1958. Little Bear steps right out of the old folk tale and hurries to Goldilocks' house, he is so hungry. 3–6

JOHNSON, CROCKETT (pseud. of David J. Leisk), *Ellen's Lion,* ill. by author, Harper, 1959. Twelve whimsical stories about Ellen's conversations with her stuffed toy lion—talk, though seemingly absurd, carries bits of wisdom. 6–9

JONES, ELIZABETH ORTON, *Twig,* ill. by author, Macmillan, 1942. Twig was lonely, so she made a tomato can house for a fairy, and sure enough, an elf came to visit her. When Twig finally discovered that everyday life can be magical too, she did not need her elf any more. 9–11

JOSLIN, SESYLE, *What Do You Say, Dear?* ill. by Maurice Sendak, W. R. Scott, 1958. Manners for the youngest in a delightful read-aloud. Simple phrases of courtesy become memorable through the nonsense situations which inspire them. 4–7

KAHL, VIRGINIA, *Away Went Wolfgang!* ill. by author, Scribner's, 1954. Wolfgang was the least useful dog in an Austrian village, until the housewives discovered that when Wolfgang ran, he could churn a whole cartful of milk into butter! 5–8
The Duchess Bakes a Cake, ill. by author, Scribner's, 1955. A humorous, rhymed story of the duchess who was carried skyward atop the light fluffy cake she had baked. 6–10
The Perfect Pancake, ill. by author, Scribner's, 1960. A light-hearted rhymed story about the good wife who limited her "feathery, fluffy, and flavory" pancakes one to a person. 6–10

KENDALL, CAROL, *The Gammage Cup,* ill. by Erik Blegvad, Harcourt, 1959. The self-satisfied, unimaginative Minnipins exile four of their members who are nonconformists. How the exiles warn the villagers of attack by their ancient enemies makes an enthralling fantasy that has originality and charm. 9–12

KIPLING, RUDYARD, *The Jungle Book,* ill. by Kurt Wiese, Doubleday, 1932. 12–14
Just So Stories, Doubleday, 1902. Each story published in a separate volume, ill. by Feodor Rojankovsky, Harper. 8–12

LEWIS, CLIVE STAPLES, *The Lion, the Witch and the Wardrobe,* Macmillan, 1950. The first of a series of books about the imaginary land of Narnia. 10–14

LIPKIND, WILLIAM, and MORDVINOFF, NICOLAS, *Chaga,* Harcourt, 1955. Chaga the elephant was none too kind to creatures smaller than himself. He learns his lesson when he swallows some grass that makes him shrink to a very small size. 5–8
The Two Reds, Harcourt, 1950.
Finders Keepers, Harcourt, 1951. (Caldecott Award) The two Reds are a boy and a cat, who mistrust each other for good reasons. After they escape together from a common peril, they are fast friends ever after. *Finders Keepers,* written in folk-tale style, is the rollicking fable of two dogs who solve the problem of who shall keep the bone, with admirable common sense. 4–8

LOFTING, HUGH, *The Story of Dr. Dolittle,* ill. by author, Stokes, 1920.
The Voyages of Dr. Dolittle, ill. by author, Stokes, 1922.

There are seven more books in the Dolittle series, but the first two remain the favorites. 9–12

LORENZINI, CARLO (pseud. Collodi), *The Adventures of Pinocchio,* tr. by Carol Della Chiesa, ill. after Attilio Mussino, Macmillan, 1951. The rascally puppet is at his best in these lively illustrations, which are the nearest to the original Mussino pictures now available. 9–11

MACDONALD, GEORGE, *At the Back of the North Wind,* ill. by George and Doris Hauman, Macmillan, 1950.
The Princess and the Goblin, ill. by Nora S. Unwin, Macmillan, 1951.
Here are new editions of two old favorites, beautifully written but moralistic and limited in their appeal. 9–12

MASON, ARTHUR, *The Wee Men of Ballywooden,* ill. by Robert Lawson, Garden City, 1937. 10–14

MC GINLEY, PHYLLIS, *The Horse Who Lived Upstairs,* Lippincott, 1944.
The Horse Who Had His Picture in the Paper, ill. by Helen Stone, Lippincott, 1951.
In the first book, it takes a trip to the country to teach discontented Joey that he is a true city dweller at heart. The second book finds Joey again restless. This time he yearns for publicity that will silence the policeman's boastful horse. The climax is utterly satisfying. 4–8

MCLEOD, EMILIE, *Clancy's Witch,* ill. by Lisl Weil, Little, 1959. How nine-year-old Clancy helps a witch with seven black pots, seven black cats, and thirteen brooms unhaunt an empty house. 7–10

MILNE, A. A., *The World of Pooh,* ill. by E. H. Shepard, Dutton, 1957. Distinctive color illustrations give a festive air to this new large-print volume, containing *Winnie-the-Pooh* and *The House at Pooh Corner.* 5–10

MINARIK, ELSE H., *Father Bear Comes Home,* ill. by Maurice Sendak, Harper, 1959.
Little Bear, ill. by Maurice Sendak, Harper, 1957. Easy-to-read books for the primary. 4–8

NORTON, MARY, *The Borrowers Afield,* ill. by Beth and Joe Krush, Harcourt, 1955. 9–12
The Borrowers Afloat, ill. by Beth and Joe Krush, Harcourt, 1959. 9–12

PEARCE, A. PHILIPPA, *Tom's Midnight Garden,* ill. by Susan Einzig, Lippincott, 1959. When the ancient grandfather clock struck thirteen, Tom entered into charming and suspenseful adventures in time and eternity. (Winner of the Carnegie Medal as the outstanding English children's book of 1958.) 10–13

PEET, BILL, *Hubert's Hair-Raising Adventure,* ill. by author, Houghton, 1959. Haughty and vain, Hubert the lion learns a lesson in humility when he loses his elegant mane. Clever rhythmic verse makes this just right for reading aloud, and the brightly colored cartoon-like art work makes it fun for looking, too. 6–9

POTTER, BEATRIX, *The Tale of Peter Rabbit,* ill. by author, Warne, 1903. A favorite nursery classic followed by *The Tale of Benjamin Bunny, Jemima Puddleduck,* and many others, all illustrated by the author and published by Warne. 3–8

PROKOFIEFF, SERGE, *Peter and the Wolf,* ill. by Warren Chappell, with a foreword by Serge Koussevitzky, Knopf, 1940. This is a delightful version of the story of how Peter outwits the wolf. It is especially valuable as an introduction to the orchestral recording of the story. 7–12

PYLE, HOWARD, *Wonder Clock,* ill. by author, Harper, 1887.

REY, H. A. *Curious George Gets a Medal,* ill. by author, Houghton, 1957. Curious George, the little monkey hero of many popular tales, daringly rockets into space and wins a medal for his courage. 5–8

RUSKIN, JOHN, *King of the Golden River,* ill. by Fritz Kredel, World Pub., 1946. (1840) 10–14

SAUER, JULIA L., *Fog Magic,* Viking, 1943. Girls enjoy this sensitive and beautifully written story of a little girl who goes back in time to a people and a village which no longer exist. The day comes when she knows that her "fog magic" must end. 10–12

SCHLEIN, MIRIAM, *The Raggle-Taggle Fellow,* ill. by Harvey Weiss, Abelard, 1959. Written in a folk-tale manner, this engaging story of Dick, a wandering musician, holds wisdom and entertainment for the story hour. 7–10

SEUSS, DR. *See* Theodore Seuss Geisel.

SHARP, MARGERY, *The Rescuers,* ill. by Garth Williams, Little, 1959. A clever fantasy concerning the adventures of three mice who attempt to rescue a Norwegian poet from the dungeon of the Black Castle. Adults will catch the satire. Charming mousey drawings. 9–adult

SHURA, MARY FRANCIS, *Simple Spigott,* ill. by Jacqueline Tomes, Knopf, 1960. A friendly Scottish spook proves a wonderful guide and companion to three American children who visit Scotland. A first-person narrative that happily blends fantasy and realism. 7–10

SLEIGH, BARBARA, *Carbonel: The King of the Cats,* ill. by V. H. Drummond, Bobbs, 1957. Humorous magical tale of two children who rescue the king of cats from the spell of an old witch.
The Kingdom of Carbonel, ill. by D. M. Leonard, Bobbs, 1960. 9–12

SMITH, AGNES, *The Edge of the Forest,* ill. by Roberta Moynihan, Viking, 1959. Poetic, mystical, sensitive, yet starkly realistic at times, this presents the power of love and of death in the relationship of a young black leopardess and an orphaned lamb. 11–15

STEELE, WILLIAM O., *Andy Jackson's Water Well,* ill. by Michael Ramus, Harcourt, 1959. When a terrible drought hit frontier Nashville, Andrew Jackson, attorney-at-law, and his friend, Chief Ticklepitcher, went east to get water. Their hilarious and exaggerated experiences are told with a lively dry humor and perfectly illustrated by Michael Ramus' line drawings. 9–14

SWAYNE, SAMUEL F. and ZOA, *Great-grandfather in the Honey Tree,* ill. by authors, Viking, 1949. Pioneer days in Indiana are the background of this amusing tall tale of Great-grandfather's hunting trip. His fantastic adventures land him up to his neck in honey. The hilarious absurdity of this tale tickles children. 5–12

THURBER, JAMES, *Many Moons,* ill. by Louis Slobodkin, Harcourt, 1943. Told in fairy-tale style, this is the appealing story of a little princess who yearned for the moon but learned to be satisfied with less. 7–10

TITUS, EVE, *Anatole and the Cat,* ill. by Paul Galdone, McGraw (Whittlesey), 1957. An alert little French mouse outwits the cat who interferes with his duties as Cheese Taster in M'sieu Duval's cheese factory. 5–7
Anatole and the Robot, ill. by Paul Galdone, McGraw (Whittlesey), 1960. That French mouse *magnifique,* First Vice-President in Charge of Cheese Tasting, meets the challenge of a cheese-testing machine. 5–7

TRAVERS, P. L. *Mary Poppins,* ill. by Mary Shepard, Harcourt, 1934.
Mary Poppins Comes Back, ill. by Mary Shepard, Harcourt, 1935.
Mary Poppins Opens the Door, ill. by Mary Shepard and Agnes Sims, Harcourt, 1943.
This wind-borne nurse sternly ignores the magic which charms her charges and keeps them hoping for Mary's return. 8–12

UNGERER, TOMI, *Emile,* ill. by author, Harper, 1960. The originator of Crictor and the Mellops now introduces another uncommon picture-book character—an engaging octopus. 5–8

WALDEN, DANIEL, *The Nutcracker*, ill. by Harold Berson, Lippincott, 1959. In contrast to the vigorous Chappell version (Knopf, 1958), this retelling of the familiar Nutcracker ballet is marked by grace and delicacy in both text and pictures. Both versions are welcome. 8–12

WATKINS-PITCHFORD, DENYS J., *The Little Grey Men*, ill. by the author, Scribner, 1949. Rich in woodland atmosphere is this story of the adventures of four little gnomes. First published in England, this book won a Carnegie Medal award (British equivalent of the Newbery Medal). 10–13
Forest of the Railway, ill. by the author, Dodd, 1957.

WHITE, ANNE H., *The Story of Serapina*, ill. by Tony Palazzo, Viking, 1951. Serapina, the cat who could carry in milk bottles with her tail and both discipline and entertain the children, is a modern tall tale or fantasy of great originality. It is also very funny. 8–12

WINTERFELD, HENRY, *Castaways in Lilliput*, tr. from the German by Kyrill Schabert, ill. by William Hutchinson, Harcourt, 1960. Adrift on a rubber raft, three Australian children are cast ashore on a fully modernized Lilliput. A good introduction to the Swift story. 9–13

YOUNG, ELLA, *The Unicorn with the Silver Shoes*, ill. by Robert Lawson, Longmans, 1932. This exquisite Irish fairy lore about Ballor's son and his adventures with a Pooka should be read aloud for its beauty and subtle humor. 10–14

ANIMAL STORIES[1]

ALDRICH, MARY M., *Too Many Pets*, ill. by Barbara Cooney, Macmillan, 1952. The arrival of each new pet in the Gay family is a cause of rejoicing among the children and for a few groans from the parents. 6–10

ANDERSON, C. W., *Billy and Blaze*, ill. by author, Macmillan, 1936. 6–10
Blaze and the Gypsies, ill. by author, Macmillan, 1937. 6–10
Blaze Finds the Trail, ill. by author, Macmillan, 1950. 5–8
Deep Through the Heart, ill. by author, Macmillan, 1940. 10–14
High Courage, ill. by author, Macmillan, 1941. 10–14
Salute, ill. by author, Macmillan, 1940. 7–12

BALCH, GLENN, *Horse in Danger*, ill. by Lee J. Ames, Crowell, 1960. A vigorous, well-told tale of modern horse rustling on Tack Ranch in Idaho. 10–12

BAUDOUY, MICHEL-AIMÉ, *Old One-Toe*, tr. by Marie Ponshot, ill. by Johannes Troyer, Harcourt, 1959. A French version of the hunted and the hunters with both fox and human characters warmly portrayed. Old One-Toe is a chicken killer and the farmers are justified in hunt-

ing him. But after Piet has stalked and studied the rogue he finds himself siding with the fox. 10–12

BEATTY, HETTY BURLINGAME, *Little Wild Horse*, ill. by author, Houghton, 1949. A small boy's dream comes true—a real ranch in the West and the taming of a little wild horse to be his very own. 3–7

BELL, THELMA HARRINGTON, *Yaller-Eye*, ill. by Corydon Bell, Viking, 1951. When Randy forgets to feed old Yaller-Eye, the cat wanders away to find food and loses her foot in a trap. Randy, full of remorse, has to contend with his daddy who thinks the cat should die. Fine story of a boy's love for his pet. 6–9

BIALK, ELISA, *Jill's Victory*, ill. by Edward Shenton, World Pub. Co., 1952. City-bred Jill has much to learn from her farm cousins. This is a story of adjustment to new standards of achievement. When Jill wins her 4-H membership, she is as proud as her cousins are when, after failing, she wins in the horse show. 10–14
Taffy's Foal, ill. by William Moyers, Houghton, 1949. A little girl meets two major problems in one year—her father's second marriage and the death of her adored horse. 7–12
Wild Horse Island, ill. by Paul Brown, Houghton, 1951. Horses, mystery, and good family relationships make this story of life in northwestern Montana unusually interesting. Good character development and lively plot. 9–12

BORG, INGA, *Parrak, the White Reindeer*, ill. by author, Warne, 1959. A white reindeer calf grows up to become leader of the herd. Brilliantly colored pictures of Lapland. 5–9

BUFF, MARY and CONRAD, *Dash and Dart*, ill. by authors, Viking, 1942. The first year in the life of twin fawns is beautifully told and illustrated. The cadenced prose of the text reads aloud well and the pictures in sepia or full color are exquisite. 5–8
Hurry, Skurry, and Flurry, ill. by Conrad Buff, Viking, 1954. Another beautifully illustrated book by the Buffs, this one about frolicking squirrels. 5–8

BULLA, CLYDE, *Star of Wild Horse Canyon*, ill. by Grace Paull, Crowell, 1953. An easy-to-read western story. 7–9

BURT, OLIVE, *Prince of the Ranch*, ill. by Bob Myers, Bobbs-Merrill, 1949. Prince, a city-bred collie, learning to herd sheep, is suspected of being a killer. His master defends the dog and both eventually prove themselves first-rate workers. A good dog story and a good western. 10–14

CALHOUN, MARY, *Houn' Dog*, ill. by Roger Duvoisin, Morrow, 1959. A warm and humorous tale that will be enjoyed by many young readers. 7–9

CHIPPERFIELD, JOSEPH E., *Wolf of Badenoch, Dog of the Grampian Hills*, ill. by C. Gifford Ambler, Longmans, 1959. Magnificent descriptions of nature highlight this perceptive story of shepherding in Scotland. 12–15

CLARK, DENIS, *Black Lightning*, ill. by C. Gifford Ambler, Viking, 1954. Black Lightning, a black leopard, regains his jungle freedom after harsh captivity in a circus. 12–16
Boomer, ill. by C. Gifford Ambler, Viking, 1955. An Australian kangaroo, adopted as a household pet, later returns to the wild and becomes a leader of his kind. 12–16

COGGINS, HERBERT, *Busby & Co.*, ill. by Roger Duvoisin, Whittlesey, 1952. Keeping a beaver as a pet is not easy, as Jerry Gardner soon realized. Plenty of adventures, excitement, and a delightful style make this a good story to read aloud. 6–10

COOPER, PAGE, *Pat's Harmony*, ill. by Olive Grimley, World, 1952. This is a heart-warming story of affection between

---

[1] For her help in revising the bibliography for Animal Stories, Today in the United States, Today in Other Lands, Historical Fiction, Biography, and Biblical Times, Mrs. Arbuthnot is grateful to Miss Adeline Corrigan, Supervisor of Work with Children, Cleveland Public Library.

a great horse and a girl who believed in him. Minor characters are also well drawn. 10–14

DE JONG, MEINDERT, *Along Came a Dog,* ill. by Maurice Sendak, Harper, 1958. A sensitive story of a crippled red hen and the stray dog who protects her. 10–13

The Little Cow and the Turtle, ill. by Maurice Sendak, Harper, 1955. 8–12

CREDLE, ELLIS, *The Flop-Eared Hound.* (See Bibliography, Today in the United States: Negro Stories.)

DELAFIELD, CLELIA, *Mrs. Mallard's Ducklings,* ill. by Leonard Weisgard, Lothrop, 1946. A beautiful picture-book with interesting text of the seasonal cycle of ducks from egg to winter flight. 6–8

DENNIS, MORGAN, *Burlap,* ill. by author, Viking, 1945. A worthless old farm dog suddenly proves himself by helping to capture an escaped circus bear. 6–9

DOWNEY, FAIRFAX, *Free and Easy, the Story of a Narragansett Pacer,* ill. by Frederick Chapman, Scribner's, 1951. This semihistorical story of a unique breed of horses is also an adventure tale and a romance. 10–14

DUDLEY, RUTH, *Hank and the Kitten,* ill. by Louis Darling, Morrow, 1949. An easy-to-read story about a small dog and its efforts to escape a stray kitten. 4–8

EARLE, OLIVE L., *Thunder Wings,* ill. by author, Morrow, 1951. This authentic record of the development of the ruffed grouse from the egg to maturity is well told and illustrated. 6–10

FALLADA, HANS, *That Rascal, Fridolin,* tr. from the German by Ruth Michaelis-Jena and Arthur Ratcliff, ill. by Imre Hofbauer, Pantheon, 1959. Appealing story of the life of a pet badger. 10–12

FLACK, MARJORIE, *Story about Ping,* ill. by Kurt Wiese, Viking, 1933. 6–9

Tim Tadpole and the Great Bullfrog, ill. by author, Doubleday, 1934. 7–9

Wag-Tail Bess, ill. by author, Doubleday, 1933. 6–9

FROST, FRANCES, *Maple Sugar for Windy Foot,* ill. by Lee Townsend, Whittlesey, 1950.

Sleighbells for Windy Foot, ill. by Lee Townsend, Whittlesey, 1948.

Windy Foot at the County Fair, ill. by Lee Townsend, Whittlesey, 1947.

The same delightful people and the same little pony lend adventure, warmth, and fun to these choice stories of American family life. 9–14

GATES, DORIS, *Little Vic,* ill. by Kate Seredy, Viking, 1951. When Pony River, a Negro boy, sees Little Vic, he believes that the colt will be as great a horse as his sire Man O'War. The boy endures every hardship willingly in his devotion to the colt. A moving, well-told story. 9–12

GEORGE, JOHN AND JEAN, *Meph, the Story of a Pet Skunk,* ill. by Jean George, Dutton, 1952. This is not only the story of a tame skunk but also the story of the reclamation of an eroded farm and its effect on an embittered farmer and his unhappy son. 11–16

Vison, the Mink, ill. by Jean George, Dutton, 1949. The vicious mink is not an appealing hero, but this book is a fine record of its life. 11–15

Vulpes, the Red Fox, ill. by Jean George, Dutton, 1948. This story of a red fox and his hunters is superbly told and illustrated. It will delight readers from ten to any age. The hunters win but Vulpes has lived a good fox life. 10–14

HADER, BERTA and ELMER, *The Big Snow,* ill. by authors, Macmillan, 1948. Beautiful pictures of small animals preparing for a winter that was worse than they dreamed. They struggled through with the help of human friends. Caldecott Award. 5–10

HENDERSON, LUIS, *Amik, the Life Story of a Beaver,* ill. by author, Morrow, 1948. Fascinating account of the wisdom and skills of the beavers. 10–14

HENRY, MARGUERITE, *Album of Horses,* ill. by Wesley Dennis, Rand McNally, 1951. 8–14

Brighty of the Grand Canyon, ill. by Wesley Dennis, Rand McNally, 1953.

Justin Morgan Had a Horse, ill. by Wesley Dennis, Rand McNally, 1954. 10–16

King of the Wind, ill. by Wesley Dennis, Rand McNally, 1948. 8–14

Little-or-Nothing from Nottingham, ill. by Wesley Dennis, Whittlesey, 1949. 7–12

Misty of Chincoteague, ill. by Wesley Dennis, Rand McNally, 1947. 8–12

Sea Star, Orphan of Chincoteague, ill. by Wesley Dennis, Rand McNally, 1949. 8–12

Animal stories by this author are invariably dramatic and exciting but never sensational and they are written with fidelity to horse or dog nature. Moreover, her human characters are never stereotypes but well-drawn, unique individuals. *Album of Horses* gives brief accounts of all the different breeds of horses. King of the Wind was the great Arabian horse which sired the ancestors of our modern race horses. This sometimes tragic but always exciting tale won the Newbery Medal. Little-or-Nothing from Nottingham is a circus dog which has temper tantrums because he can never find the bones he buried the night before. Misty is a little wild horse, caught and tamed by two island children. This little horse was in Mrs. Henry's stable, is now back with the wild horses. Sea Star is an orphaned colt, also from Chincoteague Island, rescued by the same children. Wesley Dennis' superb illustrations are forever associated with the books.

HOFF, SYD, *Julius,* ill. by author, Harper, 1959. The humorous account of a gorilla who makes friends with a small boy. A beginning-reading book. 6–7

JOHNSON, MARGARET, *Snowshoe Paws,* ill. by author, Morrow, 1949. 6–8

JOHNSON, MARGARET and HELEN, *Barney of the North,* Harcourt, 1939. 7–10

The Runaway Puppy, Harcourt, 1942. 5–7

Stablemates, Harcourt, 1942. 7–10

The Story of Rickey, Harcourt, 1939. 5–7

KALNAY, FRANCIS, *Chúcaro, Wild Pony of the Pampa,* ill. by Julian de Miskey, Harcourt, 1958. A moving story of a boy and his training of a wild horse. 9–11

KJELGAARD, JIM, *Big Red,* ill. by Bob Kuhn, Holiday, 1956. 12–16

Kalak of the Ice, ill. by Bob Kuhn, Holiday, 1949. 10–14

Swamp Cat, Dodd, 1957. 12–16

Snow Dog, ill. by Jacob Landau, Holiday, 1948. 12–16

These stories are justly popular. They are well written, with plenty of action and both human characters and animals are well drawn. Big Red is an Irish setter, the constant companion of Danny Pickett. Their adventures together climax in tracking down a huge outlaw bear. Kalak, known to the Eskimos as the "mist bear," is a heroic figure in her struggle to protect her cubs and survive. Snow Dog, part Husky and part Staghound, is an orphan struggling for survival in the north woods until he is befriended by a lone trapper. In *Swamp Cat* young Andy Gates plants muskrat colonies on his worthless Louisiana swampland heritage only to have them endangered by human and animal enemies.

KNIGHT, ERIC, *Lassie Come Home,* ill. by Marguerite Kirmse, Winston, 1940. A popular story of a collie's faithfulness to her master 10–16

KNIGHT, RUTH ADAMS, *Halfway to Heaven*, ill. by Wesley Dennis, Whittlesey, 1952. This is a great story for family reading. It is the story of the dedicated life of one young monk of the St. Bernard Hospice, high in the Alps, and of his love for the magnificent dogs with which he works. 10–14

LATHROP, DOROTHY, *Hide and Go Seek*, ill. by author, Macmillan, 1938. 7–10
Who Goes There? ill. by author, Macmillan, 1935. 7–9
Who Goes There? tells about a winter picnic for birds and animals in the forest. *Hide and Go Seek* is about flying squirrels. Both are exquisitely illustrated.

LIPKIND, WILLIAM and MORDVINOFF, NICOLAS, *The Two Reds*, Harcourt, 1950. The two Reds, boy and cat, both city dwellers, were enemies because they both yearned for the same goldfish but for different reasons. 4–8

LIPPINCOTT, JOSEPH WHARTON, *Grey Squirrel*, ill. by George F. Mason, Lippincott, 1954.
Little Red, the Fox, ill. by George F. Mason, Lippincott, 1953.
Long Horn, Leader of the Deer, ill. by George F. Mason, Lippincott, 1955.
Persimmon Jim, the Possum, ill. by George F. Mason, Lippincott, 1955.
Striped Coat, the Skunk, ill. by George F. Mason, Lippincott, 1954. 9–11

MC CLOSKEY, ROBERT, *Make Way for Ducklings*, ill. by author, Viking, 1941. Since this episode really happens in Boston each year, it is largely realistic with a few thoughts and words permitted the sagacious Mrs. Duck. Caldecott winner. 4–8

MC CLUNG, ROBERT M., *Spike, the Story of a Whitetail Deer*, ill. by author, Morrow, 1952. A clear, factual story of the first year in the life of a whitetail deer. 5–10
Stripe, the Story of a Chipmunk, ill. by author, Morrow, 1951. These easy-to-read animal stories by a scientist and artist are well told, interesting to read to five-year-olds, and good reading for slow readers of nine and ten. 5–10

MC MEEKIN, ISABEL MC LENNAN, *Ban-Joe and Grey Eagle*, ill. by Corinne B. Dillon, Watts, 1951. An excellent race horse story with well-drawn children and grownups and an absorbing plot.
Kentucky Derby Winner, ill. by Corinne B. Dillon, McKay, 1949. A boy-centered horse story of unusual value. It concerns young Jackie Spratt and his passion for "Risty" (Aristides), the horse which eventually won the first Kentucky Derby. Fine people, good horse lore, and considerable humor make this a memorable story. 9–14

MEADER, STEPHEN, *Red Horse Hill*, ill. by Lee Townsend, Harcourt, 1930. Bud Martin is happy when he wins a chance to work with horses in a New Hampshire village. In the process, he discovers a great racer. 11–16

MINARIK, ELSE H., *Father Bear Comes Home*, ill. by Maurice Sendak, Harper, 1959. Attractive beginning reader. 6–7

NEWBERRY, CLARE, *April's Kittens*, ill. by author, Harper, 1940.
Babette, ill. by author, Harper, 1937.
Barkis, ill. by author, Harper, 1938.
Marshmallow, ill. by author, Harper, 1942.
Mittens, ill. by author, Harper, 1936.
Percy, Polly and Pete, ill. by author, Harper, 1952.
Clare Newberry's drawings of cats are so entrancing the slight stories do not matter. *Percy, Polly and Pete* is the best story, and the lesson to small cat lovers who hug their kitties too hard is pleasantly administered. 5–8

O'HARA, MARY, *Green Grass of Wyoming*, Lippincott, 1946. 12–adult
My Friend Flicka, Lippincott, 1941. 10–14
Thunderhead, Lippincott, 1943. 10–14
These books are a trilogy about the McLaughlin's horse ranch, where the problems are complicated by a bad wild-horse strain. Exciting reading.

RAWLINGS, MARJORIE KINNAN, *The Yearling*, ill. by N. C. Wyeth, Scribner's, 1939. This is a poignant story of growing up, when the boy Jody learns to face and accept the tragic necessity of disposing of his pet deer, which has become a menace to the family's livelihood. 10–adult

REYNOLDS, BARBARA, *Pepper*, ill. by Barbara Cooney, Scribner's, 1952. This amusing story of a boy's attempt to domesticate a baby raccoon and the complications that developed as Pepper matured is especially popular with boys. 8–12

ROBINSON, TOM, *Buttons*, ill. by Peggy Bacon, Viking, 1938. Wonderful picture-story of an alley cat who became a gentleman. 6–10

ROUNDS, GLEN, *Stolen Pony*, ill. by author, Holiday, 1948. A moving story of a pony stolen by horse thieves and abandoned when it was found he was blind. A faithful dog guides the pony home. 8–12

SCOTT, SALLY, *Binky's Fire*, ill. by Beth Krush, Harcourt, 1952. A frightened puppy becomes—to his own surprise—the hero of the evening.

SEREDY, KATE, *Gypsy*, ill. by author, Viking, 1951. Children of any age and all cat-loving adults will enjoy Miss Seredy's magnificent pictures and simple account of a growing kitten. 4–

SMITH, E. BOYD, *Chicken World*, ill. by author, Putnam's, 1910. Beautiful picture-book of domestic fowls. 4–10

SOJO, TOBA, *The Animal Frolic*, ill. with reproductions from the drawings of Kakuyu, Putnam, 1954. Reproduction of a twelfth-century scroll by a famous Japanese artist. 6–8

STEARNS, DAVID M., *Chuckle*, ill. by Sharon Stearns, Farrar, 1939. The story of a puppy who weathered a flood in company with a woodchuck.
Sniffy, ill. by Sharon Stearns, Farrar, 1940. Appealing story of a skunk.

STOLZ, MARY, *Emmett's Pig*, ill. by Garth Williams, Harper, 1959. A small boy is delighted with the gift of a real pig for a pet. 4–8

STONG, PHIL, *Honk: the Moose*, ill. by Kurt Wiese, Dodd, 1935. This is undoubtedly one of the most amusing animal tales we have. A hard winter drives a hungry moose into the cozy confines of a livery stable and the problem is to get rid of him. 9–12

VANDIVERT, RITA, *The Porcupine Known as J. R.*, photos by Will Vandivert, Dodd, 1959. Engaging story with photographs of a young porcupine. 5–7

WALDECK, THEODORE J., *Jamba the Elephant*, ill. by Kurt Wiese, Viking, 1942.
Lions on the Hunt, ill. by Kurt Wiese, Viking, 1942.
The White Panther, ill. by Kurt Wiese, Viking, 1941. Authentic and exciting stories of wild animals. 10–14

WARD, LYND, *The Biggest Bear*, ill. by author, Houghton, 1952. The Orchard family said, "Better a bear in the orchard than an Orchard in a bear." But Johnny was bound to get a bear and he did. A prize tale with wonderful pictures. 4–8

WEISGARD, LEONARD, *Pelican Here, Pelican There*, ill. by author, Scribner's, 1948. Gorgeous modernistic pictures of a Florida pelican blown by a hurricane to Alaska. What he sees on his return trip is good geography, good art, and real fun. 5–10

WRISTON, HILDRETH T., *Show Lamb*, ill. by Peter Burchard, Abingdon-Cokesbury, 1953. A fine story of life on a Vermont sheep farm over a century ago. 10–13

TODAY IN THE UNITED STATES

ASSOCIATION FOR CHILDHOOD EDUCATION, *Told under the Blue Umbrella*, ill. by Marguerite Davis, Macmillan, 1933. A collection of realistic stories. 4–10

AUSTIN, MARGOT, *Barney's Adventure*, ill. by author, Dutton, 1941. Good circus story for the kindergarten. 4–9

BALET, JAN B., *Amos and the Moon*, ill. by author, Oxford, 1948. A distinguished picture-book telling about Amos' struggles to capture the moon. 4–7

The Five Rollatinis, ill. by author, Lippincott, 1959. Gay circus tale in which Bambino, youngest of the Rollatinis, wins his way into a daring horseback act. 4–7

BELL, THELMA HARRINGTON, *Mountain Boy*, ill. by Corydon Bell, Viking, 1947. Randy, a mountain boy, was good at reading wood lore but determined not to read reading. How his mother broke down his resistance makes a delightful story in homespun style. His next adventure is with Yaller-Eye, his cat. (See Bibliography, Animal Stories.)

BENARY-ISBERT, MARGOT, *The Long Way Home*, tr. from the German by Richard and Clara Winston, Harcourt, 1959. Orphaned during World War II, thirteen-year-old Chris leaves his native village in Eastern Germany to find a new home in the United States. 12–16

BIALK, ELISA, *Taffy's Foal*. (See Bibliography, Animal Stories.)

BRINK, CAROL RYRIE, *Family Grandstand*, ill. by Jean M. Porter, Viking, 1952.

Family Sabbatical, ill. by Susan Foster, Viking, 1956. These delightful stories tell of the activities of a professor's family in a Midwestern college town and during a year's trip to France. 9–12

BULLA, CLYDE, *A Ranch for Danny*, ill. by Grace Paull. Crowell, 1951. This sequel to *Surprise for a Cowboy* continues the experiences of Danny in the West. Two cowboy songs with music are included. 7–10

CHASTAIN, MADYE LEE, *Bright Days*, ill. by author, Harcourt, 1952.

Fripsey Fun, ill. by author, Harcourt, 1955.

Fripsey Summer, ill. by author, Harcourt, 1953. 9–12

CLEARY, BEVERLY, *Ellen Tebbits*, ill. by Louis Darling, Morrow, 1951.

Henry Huggins, ill. by Louis Darling, Morrow, 1950. These and the many other stories about Ellen and Henry are fun to read aloud to almost any age group and most nine- or ten-year-olds can read them for themselves. Whether Henry is trying to take a stray dog home, or standing by while Beezus buys a bicycle of the wrong sex, these stories are hilarious Americana. 8–12

CREDLE, ELLIS, *The Flop-Eared Hound*. (See Bibliography, Today in the United States: Negro Stories.)

DALGLIESH, ALICE, *American Travels*, ill. by Hildegard Woodward. Macmillan, 1933. 8–9

Blue Teapot, ill. by Hildegard Woodward, Macmillan, 1931. 9–10

Book for Jennifer, ill. by Katherine Milhous, Scribner's, 1940. 9–12

Relief's Rocker, ill. by Hildegard Woodward, Macmillan, 1932. 9–10

The Smiths and Rusty, ill. by Berta and Elmer Hader, Scribner's, 1936. 8–10

Miss Dalgliesh's nice stories of the everyday activities of children are climaxed by *The Bears on Hemlock Mountain*, which is a thriller. (See Bibliography, Historical Fiction: American.)

DAVIS, LAVINIA R., *The Wild Birthday Cake*, ill. by Hildegard Woodward, Doubleday, 1949. This is a full-bodied story of a little boy living intensely in his outdoor environment, with minor adventures appropriate to his age. Enchanting pictures add to the beauty and interest of this fine book. 5–9

DE REGNIERS, BEATRICE, *A Little House of Your Own*, ill. by Irene Haas, Harcourt, 1955. Even a child needs privacy that is respected, and many an odd place becomes a house of your own. 5–7

The Giant Story, ill. by Maurice Sendak, Harper, 1953. A little boy plays giant all day long until . . . 4–6

The Snow Party, ill. by Reiner Zimnek, Pantheon, 1959. Amusing picture story book of a Dakota family who entertain a houseful of guests one night during a snowstorm. 5–7

Was It a Good Trade? ill. by Irene Haas, Harcourt, 1956. Sheer hilarity in words and pictures. 4–7

DU SOE, ROBERT C., *Three Without Fear*, ill. by Ralph Ray, Jr., Longmans, 1947. Dave Rogers, shipwrecked off the coast of California, is rescued by two Indian children. The three children lead a Robinson Crusoe existence of incredible hardship and survive only through the fortitude and ingenuity of the two Indians. 10–14

ENRIGHT, ELIZABETH, *The Four-Story Mistake*, ill. by author, Rinehart, 1942.

The Saturdays, ill. by author, Rinehart, 1941.

Then There Were Five, ill. by author, Rinehart, 1944.

Thimble Summer, ill. by author, Rinehart, 1938.

The Saturdays, The Four-Story Mistake, and *Then There Were Five* tell the story of the Melendy children, first in New York City, where they evolve a scheme for taking turns on successive Saturdays in spending their allowances, and in the second two books in the country. *Thimble Summer* is a delightful story of the adventures of a little girl on a Wisconsin farm today. 8–12

ESTES, ELEANOR, *Ginger Pye*, ill. by author, Harcourt, 1951. Newbery Award, 1952.

The Middle Moffat, ill. by Louis Slobodkin, Harcourt, 1942.

The Moffats, ill. by Louis Slobodkin, Harcourt, 1941.

Rufus M., ill. by Louis Slobodkin, Harcourt, 1943.

Ginger Pye, like *The Moffats*, is a lively family story. The children make and solve their own problems often with hilarious results. Louis Slobodkin's pen-and-ink sketches illustrate the Moffat books with humor. 9–12

ETS, MARIE HALL, *Play with Me*, ill. by author, Viking, 1955. Charming picture story of a little girl and all the little wild things she meets on a walk through the meadow. 2–5

GARST, SHANNON, *Cowboy Boots*, ill. by Charles Hargens, Abingdon-Cokesbury, 1946. On his uncle's ranch, Bob learns cowboy skills with many discouragements and great persistence. He finally wins his boots. 9–12

GATES, DORIS, *Blue Willow*, ill. by Paul Lantz, Viking, 1940. The story of Janey Larkin, the daughter of migrant workers, who longed for a real home. 9–12

Sarah's Idea, ill. by Marjorie Torrey, Viking, 1938. A girl's story of California ranch life and a coveted burro. 8–10

GEORGE, JEAN, *My Side of the Mountain*, ill. by author, Dutton, 1959. Living a year alone in a tree house in the Catskill Mountains, the hero-narrator of the story meets the outdoor challenges of nature with courage and competence. 10–16

GRAY, ELIZABETH JANET, *The Fair Adventure*, ill. by A. K. Reischer, Viking, 1940. Generally rated as one of our best girl stories, this is an effective picture of a lovable, modern family. 12–14

GUILFOILE, ELIZABETH, *Nobody Listens to Andrew*, ill. by Mary Stevens, Follett, 1957. A humorous sustained story for beginning readers. The title describes the grownups' reactions when Andrew tells them there's a bear in his bed. 6–7

HARRIS, ISOBEL, *Little Boy Brown*, ill. by André François, Lippincott, 1949. This story concerns a city boy's day in the country and his return to his confined skyscraper life. 5–8

HAYWOOD, CAROLYN, *"B" Is for Betsy*, ill. by author, Harcourt, 1939.
Little Eddie, ill. by author, Morrow, 1947.
Between *"B" Is for Betsy* and the Eddie books, there are many titles. Each relates the mild adventures of suburban children at home, at school, or in the community. Eddie has more humor than most of them. 5–10

HENDERSON, LE GRAND, *Augustus and the River*, ill. by author, Bobbs-Merrill, 1939. This is the first of innumerable Augustus books about a happy-go-lucky migrant family, who have fun anywhere. 7–12

HOLBERG, RUTH, *Rowena Carey*, ill. by Grace Paull, Doubleday, 1949. A delightful story of a fat, horse-loving little girl who never gets a horse but does achieve jodhpurs and an occasional ride. 9–12

JONES, ALLETTA, *Peggy's Wish*, ill. by Mary Stevens, Abingdon-Cokesbury, 1949. A strenuous, redheaded orphan yearns in vain to be adopted. Her summer on the Meredith farm is a heaven-sent opportunity except for the presence of two members of the family who seem to dislike her. The happy ending comes after considerable excitement. 8–12

KINGMAN, LEE, *Peter's Long Walk*, ill. by Barbara Cooney, Doubleday, 1953. There is childlike spontaneity in this story of a five-year-old boy who goes in search of a new playmate, and returns to his old animal friends. 5–7
The Quarry Adventure, ill. by Barbara Cooney, Doubleday, 1951. The story of the reformation of a bookworm thrown suddenly into the midst of a family of seven children, an emergency, and a mystery. 10–12

KRASILOVSKY, PHYLLIS, *Benny's Flag*, ill. by W. T. Mars, World, 1960. The true story of how an Indian boy's entry in a flag contest came to be chosen as the official flag of Alaska. Striking illustrations of Alaska. 7–9

KRUMGOLD, JOSEPH, *Onion John*, ill. by Symeon Shimmin, Crowell, 1959. Andy Rusch, Jr., is a typical American boy growing up in a small town, devoted to his father who is his hero, but fascinated with Onion John, an eccentric town character. There is a father-son conflict which is more happily resolved than Onion John's problems. Amusing and skilfully told. Newbery Medal, 1960. 10–16

LANSING, E. H., *Deer Mountain Hideaway*, ill. by Marc Simont. Crowell, 1953. 9–12
Deer River Raft, ill. by Marc Simont, Crowell, 1955. 9–12
Liza of the Hundredfold, Crowell, 1959. An absorbing story rich in the background of the Kentucky mountain country. 11–14
The Pony That Kept a Secret, ill. by Barbara Cooney, Crowell, 1952. This is a welcome sequel to *The Pony That Ran Away*. Both books center on the activities of the twins, Ted and Sue, and their pony Twinkle.

LAWRENCE, MILDRED, *Peachtree Island*, ill. by Mary Stevens, Harcourt, 1948.
Sand in Her Shoes, ill. by Madye L. Chastain, Harcourt, 1949.

Tallie, ill. by Paul Galdone, Harcourt, 1951.
Miss Lawrence writes warmly and understandingly of little girls in the process of making difficult adjustments. The locale of each story is different and so are the lively heroines. Sharing work and responsibility with grownups is stressed, but so are adventures, play, and gaiety. These and other books by Miss Lawrence are deservedly popular with girls. 9–12

LENSKI, LOIS, *Cowboy Small*, ill. by author, Oxford, 1949. This should be one of the most popular of all the "Small" books, for every detail of cowboy gear and work is described and illustrated. 4–8
The Little Airplane, ill. by author, Oxford, 1938. 3–7
The Little Auto, ill. by author, Oxford, 1934. 3–7
The Little Sail Boat, ill. by author, Oxford, 1937. 3–7
The Little Train, ill. by author, Oxford, 1940. 6–8
Papa Small, ill. by author, Oxford, 1951. 4–8
(See also Bibliography, Today in the United States: Other Minority Groups.)

LIPKIND, WILLIAM and MORDVINOFF, NICHOLAS, *Even Steven*, Harcourt, 1952. If this is not down to rock bottom realism, it is the kind of ranch, cowboy, crooks, and heroism that children dream about. 4–6

MC CLOSKEY, ROBERT, *Blueberries for Sal*, ill. by author, Viking, 1948. A picture-story about Sal and her mother, who tangle with a bear and her cub. Eventually, each mother—human and animal—gets her own child and blueberries, too. 3–7
Lentil, ill. by author, Viking, 1940. Amusing story of a boy living in a small middle-western town who saves the day with his harmonica. 8–12
One Morning in Maine, ill. by author, Viking, 1952. Another Sal story with glorious pictures of Maine woods and water. This time Sal has lost her first tooth, but after the first shock, life goes on serenely and there is "Clam chowder for lunch!" 3–7
Time of Wonder, ill. by author, Viking, 1957. The fun of vacationing on the Maine seashore. Caldecott Award, 1958. 6–9

MC GINLEY, PHYLLIS, *The Most Wonderful Doll in the World*, ill. by Helen Stone, Lippincott, 1950. A small girl cannot distinguish between things as they are and as she dreams they might be. A lost doll becomes more and more remarkable until the real doll is a shock when it is found. Gentle, humorous treatment of a common ailment!

PETERSHAM, MAUD and MISKA, *The Box with Red Wheels*, ill. by authors, Macmillan, 1949. This entrancing picture book is the Petershams at their colorful best. The mysterious "box" which so attracts the animals contains a delightful baby, who is as charmed with the barnyard animals as they are with her. 4–8

RENICK, MARION, *Pete's Home Run*, ill. by Pru Herric, Scribner's, 1952.
Nicky's Football Team, ill. by Marian Honigman, Scribner's, 1951.
These stories have no literary qualities but they do introduce children successfully to football, baseball, and good sportsmanship. 7–10

ROBERTSON, KEITH, *Henry Reed, Inc.*, ill. by Robert McCloskey, Viking, 1958. Entertaining story of how Henry Reed and his dog Agony upset an entire neighborhood but enjoyed a splendid summer. 10–12
The Mystery of Burnt Hill, ill. by Rafaello Busoni, Viking, 1952. 12–14
Three Stuffed Owls, ill. by Jack Weaver, Viking, 1954. 10–14

ROBINSON, THOMAS PENDLETON, *Trigger John's Son*, ill. by Robert McCloskey, Viking, 1949. Trigger is an orphan in the process of being adopted when he decides to inspect his future parents. He gets off the train prematurely, falls in with a boys' gang and a blind hermit, and action begins. Boys delight in Trigger's scrapes and good intentions, and Robert McCloskey's sensitive drawings add to the fun. 10–14

SAUER, JULIA, *The Light at Tern Rock*, ill. by Georges Schreiber, Viking, 1951. A Christmas story set against the wild beauty and isolation of a lonely sea-girt lighthouse. The story is beautifully told and illustrated, and the moral problem involved makes it unusual. 9–12

SCHAEFER, JACK, *Old Ramon*, ill. by Harold West, Houghton, 1960. A convincing character study of an old shepherd who is wise not only in the ways of sheep but also in the ways of young boys. An effective read-aloud story. 10–14

SCHNEIDER, NINA, *While Susie Sleeps*, ill. by Dagmar Wilson, W. R. Scott, 1948. Pleasantly cadenced text tells about the creatures that sleep the darkness through and those that wake and work at night. 4–7

SORENSON, VIRGINIA, *Miracles on Maple Hill*, illus. by Beth and Joe Krush, Harcourt, 1956 (Newbery 1957). A warm story of a family's experiencing the wonder of woods and fields at all seasons. 9–12

SPYKMAN, E. C., *A Lemon and a Star*, Harcourt, 1955. The amusing adventures of the four motherless Cares youngsters. For superior readers. 11–14

TORREY, MARJORIE (pseud. for T. Chanslor), *The Merriweathers*, ill. by author, Viking, 1949. Strong family affection, an energetic attack on problems, and a genuine friendliness make the seven Merriweathers a delightful family to read about. 12–16

TRESSELT, ALVIN, *Follow the Wind*, ill. by Roger Duvoisin, Lothrop, 1950.
Hi, Mister Robin! ill. by Roger Duvoisin, Lothrop, 1950.
I Saw the Sea Come In, ill. by Roger Duvoisin, Lothrop, 1954.
Rain Drop Splash, ill. by Leonard Weisgard, Lothrop, 1946.
Sun Up, ill. by Roger Duvoisin, Lothrop, 1949.
White Snow, Bright Snow, ill. by Roger Duvoisin, Lothrop, 1947. Caldecott Award.
These picture-stories and others by the same author-artist team are little dramas of weather and seasonal changes. 4–6

TUDOR, TASHA, *Pumpkin Moonshine*, ill. by author, Oxford, 1938. This Halloween story makes a good introduction to the small, beautifully illustrated books of Tasha Tudor. 4–7

TUNIS, JOHN R., *The Duke Decides*, ill. by James MacDonald, Harcourt, 1939.
The Iron Duke, ill. by Johan Bull, Harcourt, 1938.
The best college stories we have for the pre-college boy. *The Iron Duke* is about an Iowa boy's adjustments to Harvard. *The Duke Decides* finds him a member of the Olympic track team. 12–16
The Kid Comes Back, Morrow, 1946. The readjustment of a boy back from the service. A baseball story. 12–14
Kid from Tomkinsville, ill. by J. H. Barnum, Harcourt, 1940. Roy Tucker, a small-town boy, makes a big-league baseball team. Fine story of his training, mistakes, and triumphs. All the Tunis books are popular sports stories with a strong emphasis on community ideals. 11–15

UDRY, JANICE MAY, *The Moon Jumpers*, pictures by Maurice Sendak, Harper, 1959. The delight of playing in the moonlight out-of-doors is caught in the artist's luminous drawings. A rare picture-story. 4–7

WILSON, HAZEL, *Herbert*, ill. by John Barron, Knopf, 1950.
Herbert Again, ill. by John Barron, Knopf, 1951.

Island Summer, ill. by Richard Floethe, Abingdon-Cokesbury, 1949.
More Fun with Herbert, ill. by John N. Barron, Knopf, 1954.
The Owen Boys, ill. by William Sharp, Abingdon-Cokesbury, 1947.
Herbert is a younger Homer Price and his adventures and vicissitudes are equally funny. *The Owen Boys* and *Island Summer* are family stories with amusing ups and downs but with the boys as the center of interest. These are decidedly boy stories and extremely popular. 8–12

WOOLLEY, CATHERINE, *David's Railroad*, ill. by Iris Beatty Johnson, Morrow, 1949. For six-year-olds, this is a significant story of a small boy's obsession with his electric railroad. David neglects his chores, grows genuinely naughty, but is finally transformed into a "solid citizen."
Railroad Cowboy, ill. by Iris Beatty Johnson, Morrow, 1951. David's interest in his electric train is now broadening to an intense concern with real trains. His club of train fans really sees trains and travels. 6–8

YASHIMA, TARO, *Umbrella*, ill. by author, Viking, 1958. Day after day small Momo waited and hoped for rain so that she might use her bright red birthday boots and new umbrella. Charming picture book. 5–8

YATES, ELIZABETH, *Mountain Born*, ill. by Nora Unwin, Coward, 1943.
A Place for Peter, ill. by Nora Unwin, Coward, 1952. Peter is a little boy in the first book, growing into farm activities and enjoying the companionship of a pet lamb. Through his pet, Peter comes to know birth, death, and the continuity of life. In the second book, Peter is a sturdy thirteen-year-old but in unhappy conflict with his father. Again, farm animals and activities help both Peter and his father. 10–14

Negro Stories

BEIM, LORRAINE and JERROLD, *Two Is a Team*, ill. by Ernest Crichlow, Harcourt, 1945. Two little boys find that they get more done as a team than singly. That they are of two different races makes no difference; it's the team that is important. 6–9

BIANCO, MARGERY, *Forward, Commandos!* ill. by Rafaello Busoni, Viking, 1944. Amusing story of a happy gang which includes one Negro child. Good relationships and good play. 7–9

BURGWYN, MEBANE HOLOMAN, *Lucky Mischief*, ill. by Gertrude Howe, Oxford, 1949. This book combines the virtues of being a good mystery, a story about 4-H activities, and a picture of a substantial, rural Negro community. The feud between two boys is finally dissolved in their devotion to their pet steers. 10–14

CREDLE, ELLIS, *The Flop-Eared Hound*, ill. with photographs by Charles Townsend, Oxford, 1938. Boot-jack's dog is always misbehaving and being given away, until finally, the dog proves his worth and becomes a permanent member of the family. 6–9

EVANS, EVA KNOX, *Araminta*, ill. by Erick Berry, Putnam, 1935.
Jerome Anthony, ill. by Erick Berry, Putnam, 1936.
Favorites with all children, these stories are unexcelled for mild humorous realism. 7–10

FAULKNER, GEORGENE, and BECKER, JOHN, *Melindy's Medal*, ill. by C. E. Fox, Messner, 1945. A humorous and tender story of a little Negro girl's achievement. 8–12

HUNT, MABEL LEIGH, *Ladycake Farm*, ill. by Clotilde Embree Funk, Lippincott, 1952. This joyous story of a Negro family beginning a new life on a farm has its tragic moments, too. A delightful family group by any standard, and a first-rate story—with social values.   9–12

JACKSON, JESSE, *Call Me Charley*, ill. by Doris Spiegel, Harper, 1945. The story of the ups and downs in a young Negro's friendship with a white boy in a white community.   9–12

LANG, DON, *On the Dark of the Moon*, ill. by Nedda Walker, Oxford, 1943. A moving story of a little Negro boy's love for his pet raccoons and possum.   9–14

LATTIMORE, ELEANOR FRANCES, *Junior, a Colored Boy of Charleston*, ill. by author, Harcourt, 1938. An understanding story of a little Negro boy's efforts to earn money for his family.   8–10

MEANS, FLORENCE CRANNELL, *Great Day in the Morning*, Houghton, 1946. In this book a lovable Negro girl experiences the bitterness of racial prejudice but has the courage to go on. At Tuskegee she comes to know Dr. Carver and decides to become a nurse.   12–14

NEWELL, HOPE, *A Cap for Mary Ellis*, Harper, 1953. Two young nursing students enter as the first Negro trainees in a New York State hospital. Their story is told with warmth and humor.   12–16

STERLING, DOROTHY, *Mary Jane*, ill. by Ernest Crichlow, Doubleday, 1959. A young Negro girl enrolls in a newly integrated junior high school where she is lonely and has problems to solve in winning friendship and understanding.   12–14

North American Indian Stories

ABEITA, LOUISE, *I Am a Pueblo Indian Girl*, told by E-Yeh-Shure', Morrow, 1939. A young Pueblo Indian girl describes with simplicity and beauty the things that are familiar and important to her.   8–12

ARMER, LAURA, *Dark Circle of Branches*, ill. by Sidney Armer, Longmans, 1933.
Waterless Mountain, ill. by author and Sidney Armer, Longmans, 1931.
Two fine stories of Navaho Indian life, although they are difficult for children because of their mysticism and lack of action.   12–14

BAILEY, FLORA, *Summer at Yellow Singer's*, ill. by Ralph Ray, Macmillan, 1948. Two children spend a summer with the Navaho Indians and enter completely into the Indian way of life. A good story and authentic description of modern Navaho life.   8–12

BLEEKER, SONIA, *American Indian Tribes*, ill. by Althea Karr, Morrow, 1950—
Indians of the Longhouse, the Story of the Iroquois.
The Apache Indians, Raiders of the Southwest.
The Sea Hunters, Indians of the Northwest.
The Cherokee, Indians of the Mountains.
The Crow Indians, Hunters of the Northern Plains.
Factual narratives with good story interest, these books written by an anthropologist give children authentic information about the family life, work and play, customs, and history of each tribe.

BRONSON, WILFRID S., *Pinto's Journey*, Messner, 1948. A fine adventure story about a Navaho Indian boy of modern times. Brilliant pictures in color.   8–10

BUFF, MARY, *Dancing Cloud*, rev. ed., ill. by Conrad Buff, Viking, 1957.   8–10
Hah-Nee, ill. by Conrad Buff, Houghton, 1956.   8–10
Magic Maize, ill. by Conrad Buff, Houghton, 1953.   9–12

BULLA, CLYDE, *Eagle Feather*, ill. by Tom Two Arrows, Crowell, 1953.   7–10

CLARK, ANN NOLAN, *Blue Canyon Horse*, ill. by Allan Houser, Viking, 1954. A beautiful story of a young Indian boy and his horse.   8–10
In My Mother's House, ill. by Velino Herrera, Viking, 1941. This is a fine story written with simplicity and beauty about the Tewa Indian children.   8–12
Little Navajo Bluebird, ill. by Velino Herrera, Viking, 1943. This is the story of a little Navaho girl who loves her home and the old ways of life, but who learns to accept going to the white man's school.   8–12

COBLENTZ, CATHERINE CATE, *Sequoya*, Longmans, 1946. The story of a great Cherokee who developed the Cherokee alphabet and taught his people to read.   12–14

HAYES, FLORENCE, *Hosh-Ki, the Navajo*, ill. by Charlotte Anna Chase, Random, 1943. An Indian boy adjusts to new ways.   10–12

LAURITZEN, JONREED, *The Ordeal of the Young Hunter*, ill. by Hoke Denetsosie, Little, 1954. A distinguished story of a twelve-year-old Navaho boy who grows to appreciate what is good in the cultures of the white man and the Indian.   11–14

MC GRAW, ELOISE JARVIS, *Moccasin Trail*, Coward, 1952. Although this story centers on a white boy's decision to leave the Crow Indians, who rescued and raised him, and return to his own people, it tells much about the Indians, their ideals, customs, and limitations.   12–adult

MC NICKLE, D'ARCY, *Runner in the Sun*, ill. by Allan Houser, Winston, 1954. Before the coming of the white men to the Southwest, a young Indian lad makes a hazardous journey to find a hardier maize.   12–14

PHELPS, MARGARET, *Chia and the Lambs*, ill. by Ann Eshner, Macrae Smith, 1944. A graceful story of a little Indian girl and her lamb.   8–10

Other Minority Groups

ANGELO, VALENTI, *The Bells of Bleecker Street*, ill. by author, Viking, 1949.   10–14
The Golden Gate, ill. by author, Viking, 1939.   10–12
Hill of Little Miracles, ill. by author, Viking, 1942.   10–14
Nino, ill. by author, Viking, 1938.   10–12
Paradise Valley, ill. by author, Viking, 1940.   8–12
In *The Bells of Bleecker Street* twelve-year-old Joey finds himself the accidental possessor of a toe from the statue of St. John. His struggles to return the toe, his adventures with his gang, and his father's return from the war make an amusing story and bring this Italian neighborhood vividly to life. *Nino* is the story of the author's own childhood in Tuscany. *The Golden Gate* tells of Nino's first years in America and his family's adjustment to their new home and country. *Hill of Little Miracles* shows Rieco, who was born with one leg too short, starting on the road to normalcy. This book abounds with the good nature and gaiety of the Italians on Telegraph Hill. *Paradise Valley* is the sensitive story of a little Mexican boy who lived in an old railroad caboose in Nevada.

ASSOCIATION FOR CHILDHOOD EDUCATION, *Told Under Spacious Skies*, ill. by William Moyers, Macmillan, 1952.
Told Under the Stars and Stripes, ill. by Nedda Walker, Macmillan, 1945.   8–12
The first book is made up of regional stories. The second book is an anthology of short stories about various minority groups in our cities and throughout the country.

BAKER, CHARLOTTE, *Necessary Nellie*, ill. by author, Coward, 1945. Some little California-Mexican children prove to the judge that their stray dog Nellie is really "necessary."   5–9

CARROLL, RUTH and LATROBE, *Beanie*, ill. by authors, Oxford, 1953. This story is followed by several others about Beanie and his family, the Tatums. Magnificent sketches of the Smoky Mountains. 7–9

DE ANGELI, MARGUERITE, *Henner's Lydia*, ill. by author, Doubleday, 1936. 7–10
Skippack School, ill. by author, Doubleday, 1939. 8–12
Thee, Hannah! ill. by author, Doubleday, 1940. 8–12
Up the Hill, ill. by author, Doubleday, 1942. 8–12

JUSTUS, MAY, *Here Comes Mary Ellen*, ill. by Helen Finger, Lippincott, 1940.
Lucky Penny, ill. by Frederick T. Chapman, Aladdin 1951.
Mountain people come vigorously alive in these and other stories by this author. Mary Ellen is an appealing little girl and the two boys with their dogs and mules make a lively tale. 8–12

KRUMGOLD, JOSEPH, *. . . and now Miguel*, ill. by Jean Charlot, Crowell, 1953. The story of twelve-year-old Miguel, who wishes to be accepted as a man, is told with humor and tenderness. Fine picture of sheepherding in New Mexico. Newbery Award. 9–12

LANSING, E. H., *Shoot for a Mule*, ill. by Susanne Suba, Crowell, 1951. This Kentucky mountaineer story has feuds and a shooting match into the bargain. Our hero is bound to get a mule of his own and he succeeds. Humorous, exciting, and fun to read. 8–12

LENSKI, LOIS, *Bayou Suzette*, ill. by author, Lippincott, 1948.
Blue Ridge Billy, ill. by author, Lippincott, 1946.
Boom Town Boy, ill. by author, Lippincott, 1948.
Judy's Journey, ill. by author, Lippincott, 1947.
Prairie School, ill. by author, Lippincott, 1951.
Strawberry Girl, ill. by author, Lippincott, 1945.
These regional stories are a remarkable contribution to the child's understanding of the people, work, and conditions in different sections of this country. The titles indicate locale or work. *Prairie School* is the story of courage and resourcefulness with which a teacher and children met the Dakota blizzard of 1949, which marooned them in their schoolhouse. Every book is a good story with lively characters. 8–12

LINDQUIST, JENNIE D., *The Golden Name Day*, ill. by Garth Williams, Harper, 1955. The delightful quest of a Swedish name day for a little American girl in the midst of her loving Swedish relatives. 8–10
The Little Silver House (sequel to *The Golden Name Day*), ill. by Garth Williams, Harper, 1959. The mystery of a little silver house and a festive Swedish Christmas will please young readers. 8–10

LOWNSBERY, ELOISE, *Marta the Doll*, ill. by Marya Werten, Longmans, 1946. Hanka, a little Polish girl, longs for a soft, cuddly doll such as her American cousins have. Her sister Marysia gives up a new skirt to buy the doll. Hanka and her doll Marta are inseparable and share the pleasant adventures of everyday living. 7–10

MILHOUS, KATHERINE, *The Egg Tree*, ill. by author, Scribner's, 1950. This beautifully illustrated picture-book of an Easter egg tree in rural Pennsylvania has started egg trees blooming all over this country. Authentic folk art and bright colors made it the Caldecott winner. 6–8

OAKES, VANYA, *Willy Wong, American*, ill. by Weda Yap, Messner, 1951. Here is the old struggle of a little Chinese boy to be accepted as a hundred per cent American. A good family story.

POLITI, LEO, *A Boat for Peppe*, ill. by author, Scribner's, 1950.
Juanita, ill. by author, Scribner's, 1948.
Little Leo, ill. by author, Scribner's, 1951.
Moy Moy, ill. by author, Scribner's, 1960.

Pedro, the Angel of Olvera Street, ill. by author, Scribner's, 1946.
Song of the Swallows, ill. by author, Scribner's, 1949. Caldecott Award.
These appealing picture-stories have slight plots but a tender beauty that is unique. Pedro and Juanita show the Christmas and Easter customs of the Mexican colony at Olvera Street in Los Angeles. The swallows are the famous birds of San Capistrano Mission. Peppe takes part in the blessing of the fishing boats at Monterey, but Little Leo journeys to Italy and converts a whole village of children to the charms of playing Indian. And Moy Moy, the little sister of three brothers in Chinatown, finds the New Year's festivities wonderful. 5–8

SEREDY, KATE, *A Tree for Peter*, ill. by author, Viking, 1941. A story of shanty town, complicated by a rather confusing symbolism, but a beautiful story with some of Kate Seredy's finest pictures. 8–12

TAYLOR, SYDNEY, *More All-of-a-kind Family*, ill. by Mary Stevens, Follett, 1954. Further heart-warming adventures of an affectionate Jewish family. 9–12

TUNIS, JOHN R., *Keystone Kids*, Harcourt, 1943. A fine sports story for the teen-ager. The happy solution to anti-Semitic feeling is achieved by the children. 12–16

UCHIDA, YASHIKO, *The Promised Year*, ill. by William M. Hutchinson, Harcourt, 1959. A little Japanese girl and her black cat learn to adjust to their new home and friends in California. 8–12

WARNER, GERTRUDE, *Children of the Harvest*, ill. by Janet Smalley, Friendship Press, 1940. Another story of migrant workers, their troubles, and triumphs. 12–16

WILSON, LEON, *This Boy Cody*, ill. by Ursula Koering, Watts, 1950.
This Boy Cody and His Friends, ill. by Ursula Koering, Watts, 1952.
Joyous stories of Cody Capshaw, his family, friends, and neighbors in the Cumberland Mountain region. House building, fiddle making, berrying, riddles, tall tales, livestock, pets, and a tag-along small sister add interest, complications, and fun to Cody's adventures. 9–12

TODAY IN OTHER LANDS

China

HANDFORTH, THOMAS, *Mei Li*, ill. by author, Doubleday, 1938. The pleasant adventures of a little Chinese girl at the Fair. A picture-book which won the Caldecott Medal for 1939. 5–8

LATTIMORE, ELEANOR FRANCES, *Little Pear and His Friends*, ill. by author, Harcourt, 1934. 6–10
Little Pear and the Rabbits, ill. by author, Morrow, 1956. 6–10
Three Little Chinese Girls, ill. by author, Morrow, 1948. 7–10

LEWIS, ELIZABETH, *Ho-Ming, Girl of New China*, ill. by Kurt Wiese, Winston, 1934. 12–16
To Beat a Tiger, ill. by John Heuhnergarth, Winston, 1956. 12–16
When the Typhoon Blows, ill. by Kurt Wiese, Winston, 1942. 12–16

LIANG, YEN, *Dee Dee's Birthday*, ill. by author, Oxford, 1952. Dee Dee is Chinese, but any child of any country would like to have a birthday celebration such as Dee Dee has in Pekin. 3–7

MARTIN, PATRICIA MILES, *The Pointed Brush*, ill. by Roger Duvoisin, Lothrop, 1959. Story of Chung Wee, small sixth son of the House of Chung, who goes to school only because he is least needed in the rice fields, and who convinces his family that "the man who knows the written word has strength." 7-9

LIDE, ALICE, *Yinka-Tu the Yak*, ill. by Kurt Wiese, Viking, 1938. A curious story of a Mongol boy and his adventures with his pet yak. Wonderful pictures by Kurt Wiese add to the interest of the book. 9-12

MUHLENWEG, FRITZ, *Big Tiger and Christian*, ill. by Rafaello Busoni, Pantheon, 1952. Here are nearly six hundred pages packed with adventure, people, and strange places in a story so unusual no one who reads the first chapter will want to put it down. An English and a Chinese boy carry through a dangerous mission for General Woo in wartime China. They travel by truck, ponies, and camel, encounter kindly people and villains, but come through it all competently and with their sense of humor intact. 12-adult

TREFFINGER, CAROLYN, *Li Lun, Lad of Courage*, ill. by Kurt Wiese, Abingdon-Cokesbury, 1947. Story of a Chinese boy who compensates for his fear of the sea by a four months' vigil on a barren mountaintop, alone. He learns a way of life for himself and his people. 9-12

WIESE, KURT, *Fish in the Air*, ill. by author, Viking, 1948. An amusing account of what happened to a small boy who would buy the largest kite in the market. Lovely, bright pictures. 6-8

WOOD, ESTHER, *Silk and Satin Lane*, ill. by Kurt Wiese, Longmans, 1939. 9-12

YOUNG, EVELYN, *Wu and Lu and Li*, ill. by author, Oxford, 1939. Picture book of Chinese toddlers, appealing and beautiful. Older boys and girls can study the costumes for dramatizations. 5-6

England, Scotland, and Ireland

ARDIZZONE, EDWARD, *Little Tim and the Brave Sea Captain*, ill. by author, Oxford, 1936. A picture-book of life at sea with five-year-old Tim as the hero. This first story has been succeeded by numerous books about Tim, all with fine pictures and very popular. 4-9

MC LEAN, ALLAN CAMPBELL, *Master of Morgana*, Harcourt, 1959. A boy's great determination helps to solve a mystery on the Isle of Skye. 14-16
Storm over Skye, ill. by Shirley Hughes, Harcourt, 1957. 13-16

RANSOME, ARTHUR, *Coot Club*, ill. by author and Helene Carter, Lippincott, 1935.
Peter Duck, ill. by Helene Carter, Lippincott, 1933.
Pigeon Post, ill. by Mary E. Shepard, Lippincott, 1937.
Swallowdale, ill. by Helene Carter, Lippincott, 1932.
Swallows and Amazons, ill. by Helene Carter, Lippincott, 1931.
We Didn't Mean to Go to Sea, ill. by author, Lippincott, 1938.
Winter Holiday, ill. by Helene Carter, Lippincott, 1934. This is a series of books about English children living in the Lake district of England. The children spend most of their time outdoors, and meet emergencies with resourcefulness and intelligence. 12-14

STREATFEILD, NOEL, *Ballet Shoes*, ill. by Richard Floethe, Random, 1937.
Circus Shoes, ill. by Richard Floethe, Random, 1939.
Theater Shoes, ill. by Richard Floethe, Random, 1945. The "Shoes" books are a series of gay tales with vocational themes. 10-14

VAN STOCKUM, HILDA, *The Cottage at Bantry Bay*, ill. by author, Viking, 1938. The story of the escapades of the lively O'Sullivan children—Michael, Brigid, and the twins Francie and Liam. 10-14

Pegeen, ill. by author, Viking, 1941. This tells of the scrapes and misdeeds of Pegeen, a mischievous orphan, who has come to live with the O'Sullivans. 10-14

France

CARLSON, NATALIE SAVAGE, *The Happy Orpheline*, ill. by Garth Williams, Harper, 1957. Imaginative and amusing story of 20 orphans, happy in their home outside of Paris, afraid only of being adopted. 8-10
A Brother for the Orphelines, ill. by Garth Williams, Harper, 1959. A delightful sequel to *The Happy Orpheline*, this tells of the efforts of the orphans to keep a baby boy foundling left on their doorstep. 7-11

BISHOP, CLAIRE HUCHET, *Pancakes Paris*, ill. by Georges Schreiber, Viking, 1947. A half-starved postwar French child receives a miraculous package of American pancake mix. How he meets two American soldiers and gets the directions for the pancakes translated makes a heartwarming tale. 8-12
Twenty and Ten, ill. by William Pene du Bois, Viking, 1952. During the Nazi occupation of France, nineteen French children with their teacher were asked to feed and hide ten Jewish children. How these fifth-graders shared their food and managed with their teacher held in jail is a moving and satisfying story. 9-12

COATSWORTH, ELIZABETH JANE, *The House of the Swan*, ill. by Kathleen Voute, Macmillan, 1948. Exciting, modern mystery tale about two U.S. orphans in France. 9-14

FRANÇOISE, pseud. (Francoise Seignebosc), *Jeanne-Marie at the Fair*, Scribner's, 1959.
Jeanne-Marie Counts Her Sheep, Scribner's, 1951.
Jeanne-Marie in Gay Paris, Scribner's, 1956
Noël for Jeanne-Marie, Scribner's, 1953.
Springtime for Jeanne-Marie, Scribner's, 1955.
Popular picture-story book series about a sunny little French girl and her adventures. 5-7

Holland

DE JONG, MEINDERT, *Dirk's Dog Bello*, ill. by Kurt Wiese, Harper, 1939. The story of a boy's love for his much too large and hungry dog. A fine picture of present-day Dutch life. Hard reading. 10-12
The Wheel on the School, ill. by Maurice Sendak, Harper, 1954. A tenderly told story of how a Dutch fishing village brings back the storks to settle there again. Newbery Award. 9-12

DODGE, MARY MAPES, *Hans Brinker; or the Silver Skates*, ill. by Hilda Van Stockum, World Publishing, 1946. 10-12

SEYMOUR, ALTA HALVERSON, *Kaatje and the Christmas Compass*, ill. By W. T. Mars, Wilcox & Follett, 1954. A good description of holiday customs and modern life. 8-11

Italy

ANGELO, VALENTI, *The Honey Boat*, ill. by author, Viking, 1959. Friendly picture of an Italian family at work and at play. 10-12

BETTINA, pseud. (Bettina Errlich), *Pantaloni*, ill. by author, Harper, 1957. This author-artist has never made more beautiful pictures than she has for this appealing picture-story of an Italian boy's search for his dog. 5-9

VAN STOCKUM, HILDA, *A Day on Skates*, ill. by author, Harper, 1934. A Dutch schoolmaster takes his flock on a day's skating tour. 8-10

Mexico and South America

BANNON, LAURA, *Manuela's Birthday*, ill. by author, Whitman, 1939. A popular and lively story with brilliant pictures. 6–9

BEIM, LORRAINE and JERROLD, *The Burro That Had a Name*, ill. by Howard Simon, Harcourt, 1939. An amusing story of a boy's attachment for a burro. 6–9

CLARK, ANN NOLAN, *A Santo for Pasqualita*, ill. by Mary Villarejo, Viking, 1959. Orphaned Pasqualita, adopted by a kind elderly couple, achieves her dream of having a patron saint of her very own. 6–9
Secret of the Andes, ill. by Jean Charlot, Viking, 1952. In this story, Cusi lives among the great peaks of the Andes mountains, guarding a hidden herd of royal llamas and learning from old Chuto the sacred traditions of his Incan ancestors. Even after his journey to the world of men, Cusi knows that his destiny lies in the remote heights cherishing the flock. 10–14

CREDLE, ELLIS, *My Pet Peepelo*, photographs by Charles Townsend, Oxford, 1948. Delightful story of a little Mexican boy who finds he just can't bear to sell his pet turkey, because something you love is better than money. 7–12

DESMOND, ALICE CURTIS, *The Lucky Llama*, ill. by Wilfrid Bronson, Macmillan, 1939. A charming picture of boy and llamas. 10–12

ETS, MARIE and LA BASTIDA, AURORA, *Nine Days to Christmas*, Viking, 1959. (Caldecott Medal 1960) Small Ceci enjoys her first posada in this brightly illustrated book of present-day Mexico. 5–8

GARRETT, HELEN, *Angelo the Naughty One*, ill. by Leo Politi, Viking, 1944. The amusing reform of a small Mexican boy who did not like to take baths. 6–9

HADER, BERTA and ELMER, *Story of Pancho and the Bull with the Crooked Tail*, ill. by authors, Macmillan, 1942. A very funny story of a little Mexican boy's accidental capture of a ferocious bull. 5–9

HALL, ESTHER GREENACRE, *Mario and the Chuna*, ill. by J. M. de Aragon, Random, 1940. A chuna is an Argentine bird that can spit a pebble out of its beak with unerring aim. A really funny story with a good picture of primitive rural life. 9–12

LONG, EULA, *Far Away Holiday*, ill. by author, Morrow, 1947. The struggles of a little Mexican girl to make a proper flower wand for the church procession almost fail. A pleasant picture of family life.

PARISH, HELEN RAND, *At the Palace Gates*, ill. by Leo Politi, Viking, 1949. Appealing adventure story of a small Peruvian hillbilly living on his own in Lima. 9–12

RITCHIE, BARBARA, *Ramón Makes a Trade* (Los Cambios de Remón), ill. by Earl Thollander, Parnassus, 1959. A picture story with English and Spanish text which tells of an enterprising Mexican boy who succeeds in trading his pottery jar for a much-desired green parakeet. 8–10

SAWYER, RUTH, *The Least One*, ill. by Leo Politi, Viking, 1941. A touching little tale of a boy's love for his donkey and his deep religious faith that the little burro will come back to him. 8–10

TARSHIS, ELIZABETH K., *The Village That Learned to Read*, ill. by Harold Haydon, Houghton, 1941. A robust story with humor and an amusing moral. Important in its focus on the national drive for literacy. 10–12

Pacific Islands

CROCKETT, LUCY HERNDON, *Lucio and His Nuong*, ill. by author, Holt, 1939. An amusing picture-book and a story popular from second grade to high school. Six-year-old Lucio and a huge water buffalo are the principal characters in a story of the Philippines. 8–12

SPERRY, ARMSTRONG, *Call It Courage*, ill. by author, Macmillan, 1940. This Newbery Award book is an exciting adventure story and also the tale of one boy's conquest of fear. 10–12

Scandinavian Countries

ANCKARSVARD, KARIN, *The Mysterious Schoolmaster*, tr. from the Swedish by Annabelle Macmillan, ill. by Paul Galdone, Harcourt, 1959. A coastal village in Sweden provides the background for this captivating tale of two children who outwit an international spy. 10–12

BESKOW, ELSA, *Pelle's New Suit*, ill. by author, Harper, 1929. 3–8

BURGLON, NORA, *Children of the Soil*, ill. by Edgar Parin d'Aulaire, Doubleday, 1932. (Sweden)
The Gate Swings In, ill. by Richard Floethe, Little, 1937. (Sweden)
Sticks Across the Chimney, ill. by Fritz Eichenberg, Holiday, 1938. (Denmark)
Good stories with wholesome ideals and rousing plots centered around mysteries. 10–14

LINDGREN, ASTRID, *Rasmus and the Vagabond*, tr. from the Swedish by Gerry Bothmer, ill. by Eric Palmquist, Viking, 1960. Nine-year-old Rasmus runs away from a Swedish orphanage and meets Paradise Oscar, a lovable tramp, with whom he has many adventures. How he finds home and happiness is well told in this touching tale. 10–12

Switzerland

CHONZ, SELINA, *A Bell for Ursli*, ill. by Alois Carigiet, Oxford, 1950. One of the most beautiful picture-stories to come out of Europe, this is also an exciting adventure story of a small Swiss boy determined to have the largest bell to ring in the spring processional. 6–9

ULLMAN, JAMES RAMSEY, *Banner in the Sky*, Lippincott, 1954. A dramatic and exciting story of young Rudi's determination to become a mountain climber and one day conquer the Citadel. 12–16

VAN DER LOEFF, A. RUTGERS, *Avalanche!* ill. by Gustav Schrotter, Morrow, 1958. The dramatic story of an avalanche that struck the tiny Swiss village of Urteli and how it affected three young boys. 11–13

Eskimo Stories

DOONE, RADKO, *Nuvat the Brave*, ill. by Hans Wallen, Macrae Smith, 1934. An Eskimo boy overcomes his cowardice. 10–12

FREUCHEN, PIPALUK, *Eskimo Boy*, ill. by Ingrid Vang Nyman, Lothrop, 1951. This epic tale, translated from the Danish, is the grimmest, most terrifying picture of Eskimo life we have had. It is the story of a boy's fight to save his family from starvation. The realistic details make it unsuitable for young children, but the heroism of the boy and his deeds are good for older children to read about. 10–12

LIPKIND, WILLIAM, *Boy with a Harpoon*, ill. by Nicolas Mordvinoff, Harcourt, 1952. Here are "Will and Nick" in serious vein and Will Lipkind turns out to be an anthropologist of parts. This is a substantial story of Eskimo life for younger children than Freuchen's book, but it too should banish forever the igloo stereotype of

Arctic life. An absorbing story ot a boy's attempts to rid himself of a derogatory nickname and win a respected place in the community of men.   7–10

Other Countries

AYER, JACQUELINE, *Nu Dang and His Kite,* ill. by author, Harcourt, 1959.
A Wish for Little Sister, ill. by author, Harcourt, 1960. Colorful picture stories of Siam.   5–8

BENARY-ISBERT, MARGOT, *Castle on the Border,* tr. by Richard and Clara Winston, Harcourt, 1956.   14–16
Rowan Farm, tr. by Richard and Clara Winston, Harcourt, 1954.   12–15

BOTHWELL, JEAN, *The Little Flute Player,* ill. by Margaret Ayer, Morrow, 1949. Minor disasters stalk Teka, the little flute player of the village, and grow into tragedy when the famine comes. This ten-year-old boy takes his father's place as his family faces starvation.   8–12

BROWN, MARCIA, *Henry—Fisherman,* ill. by author, Scribner's, 1949. Small Henry of the Virgin Islands yearns for the day when he can go fishing with his father. When that day comes, he dodges a baby shark and comes home in triumph, "a fisherman for true." Lithe, brown bodies against the clear, brilliant colors of island and sea add to the beauty and grace of this brief tale.
                                                        7–10

BUCK, PEARL, *The Big Wave,* prints by Hiroshige and Hokusai, Day, 1948. Significant story built around the theme that "life is stronger than death." Two Japanese boys adventure together, survive a terrible catastrophe, and begin life anew.   9–14

DAVIS, NORMAN, *Picken's Exciting Summer,* ill. by Winslade, Oxford, 1950.
Picken's Great Adventure, ill. by Winslade, Oxford, 1949. Picken is an African boy, the son of a chief, but he is a typical eight-year-old of any land. He rescues a small monkey that becomes his constant companion and their adventures make two exciting stories.   7–10

JONES, ELIZABETH ORTON, *Maminka's Children,* ill. by author, Macmillan, 1940. The story is not important, but is written with great charm and tenderness. This tale of Czechoslovakia has lovely pictures, humor.   10–12

LINDGREN, ASTRID, *Sia Lives on Kilimanjaro,* photographs by Anna Riwkin-Brick, Macmillan, 1959. Slight story of Sia, lovely native girl. Beautiful photography of a little known area.   6–8

LINDQUIST, WILLIS, *Burma Boy,* ill. by Nicholas Mordvinoff, McGraw, 1953. An absorbing story of a boy's search for a lost elephant.   9–11

PRISHVIN, MIKHAIL, *The Treasure Trove of the Sun,* trans. from the Russian by Tatian Balkoff-Drowne, ill. by Feodor Rojankovsky, Viking, 1952. This Russian story is beautiful in format, pictures, and content. An orphaned brother and sister nearly lose their lives in a cranberry bog, but are saved by an orphaned dog.   8–12

RANKIN, LOUISE, *Daughter of the Mountains,* ill. by Kurt Wiese, Viking, 1948. A little Tibetan girl undertakes a long and perilous journey alone to retrieve her beloved dog. She is sustained by a deep religious faith.   9–12

SEREDY, KATE, *Chestry Oak,* ill. by author, Viking, 1948. An involved and difficult story with a deeply significant theme—the fall of an ancient house and its rebirth in a new land. The boy Michael and his great horse Midnight are the central figures of the tale.   10–14
The Singing Tree, ill. by author, Viking, 1939.   10–14

SERRAILLIER, IAN, *The Silver Sword,* ill. by C. Walter Hodges, Criterion, 1959. An inspiring narrative of four

courageous children of Warsaw after World War II. The three who have been separated from their parents set off to find them and are joined by a fourth child. Their journey covers three hard years but their spirit never falters.   10–14

STINETORF, LOUISE A., *Musa, the Shoemaker,* ill. by Harper Johnson, Lippincott, 1959. A lame Algerian boy, apprenticed to a shoemaker, grows up in a village of acrobats but achieves success in another skill.   9–11

VON GEBHARDT, HERTHA, *The Girl from Nowhere,* tr. by James Kirkup, ill. by Helen Brun, Criterion, 1959. Absorbing story of Magdalene, nine-year-old girl from nowhere who arouses wonder and suspicion among the children of a small German town. When she finally leaves them they find they are strangely lost without her.   10–12

WEIL, ANN, *Red Sails to Capri,* ill. by C. B. Falls, Viking, 1952. An unusual story about the discovery of the Blue Grotto at Capri, told entirely in dialogue. Considerable suspense and delightful people.   9–12

YASHIMA, TARO, (pseud. for Jun Iwanatsu), *Crow Boy,* ill. by author, Viking, 1955. This story of a small outcast Japanese boy has unusual social values as well as great pictorial beauty.

HISTORICAL FICTION[1]

American

ALCOTT, LOUISA MAY, *Little Women,* ill. by Jessie Willcox Smith, Little, 1934 (1868). Although this forerunner of modern realism for children and young people is chiefly a story of family life, it is also a story of life in Civil War times. Recent editions by World Publishing Company and Grosset & Dunlap have added to its attractions, but it still remains a girl's book.   12–16

BAILEY, JEAN, *Cherokee Bill, Oklahoma Pacer,* ill. by Pers Crowell, Abingdon-Cokesbury, 1952. A fine story of a boy and his horse. The setting is on the Kansas-Oklahoma border at the time of the opening of the Cherokee Strip.   12–14

BERRY, ERICK, (pseud. for Allena Best), *Hay-Foot, Straw-Foot,* ill. by author, Viking, 1954. Tale of a little drummer boy in the French and Indian wars who inspired the tune of "Yankee Doodle."   9–12

BLEEKER, SONIA, *American Indian Tribes.* (See Bibliography, Today in the United States: North American Indian.)

BULLA, CLYDE ROBERT, *Down the Mississippi,* ill. by Peter Burchard, Crowell, 1954.   8–10
Riding the Pony Express, ill. by Grace Paull, Crowell, 1948. An easy-to-read story of a boy who carried the mail in an emergency.   8–10
John Billington, Friend of Squanto, ill. by Peter Burchard, Crowell, 1956.   7–10
Squanto, Friend of the White Men, ill. by Peter Burchard, Crowell, 1954.   8–10
The Secret Valley, ill. by Grace Paull, Crowell, 1949. A Missouri family go to California in search of gold, but find other treasures instead.   8–10

CARR, MARY JANE, *Children of the Covered Wagon: a Story of the Old Oregon Trail,* ill. by Bob Kuhn, Crowell, 1943. An excellent story of a pioneer family on a journey

[1] Bibliography for historical fiction and biography compiled largely by Miss Mildred Phipps, supervisor of work with children, Pasadena Public Library, and Miss Gladys English, formerly supervisor of work with children, Los Angeles Public Library.

from Missouri to the Willamette Valley, Oregon, in 1844. 9–12

Young Mac of Fort Vancouver, ill. by Richard Holberg, Crowell, 1940. Outstanding for fine characterizations and authentic historical background. This is a story of a thirteen-year-old Scotch-Indian boy who accompanies a group of French fur traders on a trip down the Columbia River to Fort Vancouver, Washington. 12–14

CAUDILL, REBECCA, *Tree of Freedom*, ill. by Dorothy B. Morse, Viking, 1949. An outstanding pioneer story, which gives a detailed picture of life in 1770, near Louisville, Kentucky. The story involves some growing family relationships and appealing characters. 12–14

CHILDHOOD OF FAMOUS AMERICANS SERIES, Bobbs-Merrill. These fictionalized, easy-to-read biographies of over sixty famous Americans—national heroes, scientists, baseball players, writers, musicians, etc., are extremely popular with children. They should be used chiefly with slow readers but even good readers like them and they serve as introductions to more substantial biographies. 8–10

CLUFF, TOM, *Minutemen of the Sea*, ill. by Tom O'Sullivan, Wilcox & Follett, 1955. In the first naval battle of the Revolutionary War the people of Machias Township in Maine fought off the King's Navy rather than surrender their lumber for enemy use. 10–14

COATSWORTH, ELIZABETH, *Away Goes Sally*, ill. by Helen Sewell, Macmillan, 1934. 10–12

Boston Bells, ill. by Manning de V. Lee, Macmillan, 1952. 6–10

Five Bushel Farm, ill. by Helen Sewell, Macmillan, 1939. 10–12

The Fair American, ill. by Helen Sewell, Macmillan, 1940. 10–12

Sword of the Wilderness, ill. by Harve Stein, Macmillan, 1936. 10–14

The White Horse, ill. by Helen Sewell, Macmillan, 1942. 10–12

First Adventure, ill. by Ralph Ray, Macmillan, 1950. 6–10

Away Goes Sally, Five Bushel Farm, The Fair American, and *The White Horse* deal with the adventures of Sally and her cousin Andrew. The last one is the most exciting. The cousins are captured by pirates and sold as slaves to the sultan of Morocco. In *Boston Bells* John Singleton Copley, the artist, lived on Boston's Long Wharf during the time of the press gangs. In *Sword of the Wilderness* young Seth Hubbard is captured by In**dians during the French and Indian Wars. *First Adventure* is based on a true incident about a little boy of** the Plymouth colony who was lost in the woods and taken to an Indian village in 1621.

COBLENTZ, CATHERINE CATE, *The Falcon of Eric the Red*, ill. by Henry C. Pitz, Longmans, 1942. In the New World settlement of Vineland, Jon and his falcon play a gallant part. Falconry and a fine historical story of Greenland make this an unusually good book. 10–12

CONSTANT, ALBERTA W., *Miss Charity Comes to Stay*, ill. by Louise Darling, Crowell, 1959. Lively imaginative young Betsy "authors" this appealing story of life in the Oklahoma Territory in 1893. 10–12

CRAWFORD, PHYLLIS, *"Hello, the Boat!"* ill. by Edward Laning, Holt, 1938. A resourceful family journey from Pittsburgh to Cincinnati in 1816 aboard a steamboat fitted out as a store. 9–11

DALGLIESH, ALICE, *Adam and the Golden Cock*, ill. by Leonard Weisgard, Scribner's, 1959. A small boy faces a personal problem of divided loyalty when General Rochambeau's army comes to his Connecticut town during the Revolution. 7–9

The Bears on Hemlock Mountain, ill. by Helen Sewell, Scribner's, 1952. This adventure story is based on an historical episode. There weren't supposed to be any bears on Hemlock Mountain, but there *were*, as poor Jonathan proved. This is not only a thriller, it is a chiller, this good author's very best! 5–10

DALGLIESH, ALICE, *The Courage of Sarah Noble*, ill. by Leonard Weisgard, Scribner, 1954.

The 4th of July Story, ill. by Marie Nonnast, Scribners, 1956.

The Thanksgiving Story, ill. by Helen Sewell, Scribners, 1954. 7–10

DE ANGELI, MARGUERITE, *Thee, Hannah!* ill. by author, Doubleday, 1940. A vivid picture of Quaker life in old Philadelphia is given in this story of lively Quaker Hannah. Beautiful illustrations in color and black and white. 8–10

DOUGLAS, EMILY, *Appleseed Farm*, ill. by Anne Vaughan, Abingdon-Cokesbury, 1948. Ten-year-old Penny hears about a visit Johnny Appleseed once made to her family's Indiana farm. 8–10

EDMONDS, WALTER D., *Cadmus Henry*, ill. by Manning de V. Lee, Dodd, 1949. The Civil War from the Confederate side is the scene of this humorous and appealing tale of a young soldier's misadventures. 12–14

The Matchlock Gun, ill. by Paul Lantz, Dodd, 1941.

Tom Whipple, ill. by Paul Lantz, Dodd, 1942.

These books, written by a successful novelist, are vigorous and unusual. *The Matchlock Gun* (Newbery Award) relates the heroism of a small boy and his mother during an Indian raid. *Tom Whipple* is the incredible story of a farm boy who set off to see the Czar of all the Russians and did. 10–12

FOLLETT, HELEN, *House Afire!* ill. by Armstrong Sperry, Scribner's, 1941. An amusing story of Peter Stuyvesant's efforts to reduce the fire hazards of New Amsterdam and clean it up besides. 9–11

GENDRON, VAL, *The Fork in the Trail*, ill. by Sidney Quinn, Longmans, 1952. A young boy sets up a trading post on the route to the West during the Gold Rush Days. A good picture of the period. 12–14

GRAY, ELIZABETH JANET, *Beppy Marlowe of Charlestown,* (1715), ill. by Loren Barton, Viking, 1936.

The Fair Adventure (modern), ill. by Alice K. Reischer, Viking, 1940.

Jane Hope (1860), Viking, 1933.

Meggy MacIntosh (1775), ill. by Marguerite de Angeli, Viking, 1930.

This is Elizabeth Gray's fine series about North Carolina. The period of each book is indicated. The series shows the changes in manners, customs, and problems of one region. 12–16

GREY, KATHERINE, *Hills of Gold*, ill. by Tom Lea, Little, 1941. 9–11

Rolling Wheels, ill. by Frank Schoonover, Little, 1937. 12–14

Rolling Wheels tells of the long heroic journey from Indiana to California by pioneers seeking their fortune in the West. *Hills of Gold* is a sequel to *Rolling Wheels* in which the Lambert family join the California gold rush.

HINTERNHOFF, JOHN, *Barry's Boys*, ill. by Clifford N. Geary, Holt, 1952. The adventures of a young midshipman on board the first ship in our Colonial navy. 12–14

HODGES, C. WALTER, *Columbus Sails*, ill. by author, Coward, 1939. Fiction but based on facts, and tremendously moving. This is a popular book. 12–14

HOLLING, HOLLING C., *Paddle-to-the-Sea*, ill. by author, Houghton, 1941.

Seabird, ill. by author, Houghton, 1948.

Tree in the Trail, ill. by author, Houghton, 1942. Perhaps the first book is more geography than history for it is the account of an Indian boy's toy canoe which follows our Great Lakes to the sea and back. *Seabird* is a story of American ships in terms of one family of shipbuilders. In *Tree in the Trail* a cottonwood tree on the Santa Fe trail to California was a landmark for Indians and white men. All three books are superbly illustrated.   10–12

JOHNSON, ANNABEL and EDGAR, *Torrie*, Harper, 1960. Fourteen-year-old Torrie Auders travels by covered wagon from St. Louis to California in 1846. In the excitement of the adventure, she gains a new understanding of and admiration for her family.   12–16

KEITH, HAROLD, *Rifles for Watie*, Crowell, 1957. Jeff Bussey, Union volunteer at sixteen, gains insight and sympathy for the problems and ideals of both the North and the South in this powerful Civil War story. Newbery Award, 1958.   12–16

KOHLER, JULILLY H., *Harmony Ahead*, ill. by Peter Burchard, Aladdin, 1952. Fifteen-year-old Allan Ward is the hero of this well-documented story of Robert Owen's group which travels down the Ohio River to New Harmony, Indiana, in 1825.   12–14

LAMPMAN, EVELYN, *Tree Wagon*, ill. by Robert Frankenberg, Doubleday, 1953.   10–13

LATHAM, JEAN LEE, *Carry On, Mr. Bowditch*, ill. by John O'Hara Cosgrove II, Houghton, 1955. Although he never had a day's schooling after he was ten years old, Nathaniel Bowditch became an outstanding astronomer and mathematician, and in 1802 published a book still considered the bible of modern navigation. Newbery Award, 1956.   11–15

This Dear-Bought Land, ill. by Jacob Landau, Harper, 1957. An outstanding story of Captain John Smith and the settlement of Jamestown.   11–14

LENSKI, LOIS, *Puritan Adventure*, ill. by author, Lippincott, 1944. Massachusetts is the scene of this vivid tale of Colonial times when a gay young aunt from England visits a strict Puritan family bringing gaiety and laughter with her.   12–14

MALKUS, ALIDA, *Colt of Destiny*, ill. by Manning de V. Lee, Winston, 1950. A vivid picture of the California mission days.   12–16

Little Giant of the North, ill. by Jay Hyde Barnum, Winston, 1952. This rousing adventure story helps to answer the question of why the French got on with the Indians and the English failed. This tells of Henry Kelsey's success in 1688 in getting the Indians to work with him.   10–14

MASON, MIRIAM, *The Middle Sister*, ill. by Grace Paull, Macmillan, 1947.

Susannah, the Pioneer Cow, ill. by Maud and Miska Petersham, Macmillan, 1941. Easy-to-read, entertaining stories of pioneering. The first one is about a timid little girl trying to keep her small apple tree safe. The second one centers on a home-loving cow which went pioneering with great reluctance.   8–10

Caroline and Her Kettle Named Maude, ill. by Kathleen Voute, Macmillan, 1951. An amusing story of a little pioneer girl who asked for a gun but was given a kettle. How she uses this kettle as a weapon will delight young readers.   8–10

MC GRAW, ELOISE JARVIS, *Moccasin Trail*. (See Bibliography, Today in the United States: North American Indian.)

MC MEEKIN, ISABEL, *Journey Cake*, Messner, 1942. Six motherless children, in the care of an intrepid old free Negro woman, journey through the wilderness to join their father in Boone's Kentucky. Followed by *Juba's New Moon*. Both books have good historical details. 10–12

MEADER, STEPHEN W., *Jonathan Goes West*, ill. by Edward Shenton, Harcourt, 1946.

Red Horse Hill, Harcourt, ill. by Lee Townsend, 1930.

River of the Wolves, ill. by Lee Townsend, Harcourt, 1948.

The Buckboard Stranger, ill. by Paul Caile, Harcourt, 1954.

The Fish Hawk's Nest, ill. by Edward Shenton, Harcourt, 1952.

Who Rides in the Dark? ill. by James MacDonald, Harcourt, 1937.

Exciting stories, with historical background and usually an element of mystery, these and other books by this author are well written and exceedingly popular. 10–14

MEADOWCROFT, ENID, *By Secret Railway*, ill. by Henry C. Pitz, Crowell, 1948. A story of a white boy's rescue of a freed Negro who had been carried South again, illegally.   11–14

By Wagon and Flatboat, ill. by Ninon MacKnight, Crowell, 1938. In the post-Revolutionary period a family travels from Gray's Ferry to Ohio in a Conestoga wagon and a flatboat.   10–12

On Indian Trails with Daniel Boone, ill. by Lloyd Coe, Crowell, 1947. Thrilling adventures of the Boone family as they move West into the Indian country.   8–10

MEANS, FLORENCE CRANNELL, *A Candle in the Mist*, ill. by Marguerite de Angeli, Houghton, 1931. Pioneer life in a Minnesota settlement in the 1870's is difficult, but fifteen-year-old Janey faces it with high courage.   12–14

MEIGS, CORNELIA, *Covered Bridge*, ill. by Marguerite de Angeli, Macmillan, 1936.

Master Simon's Garden, ill. by John Rae, Macmillan, 1929.

Willow Whistle, ill. by E. B. Smith, Macmillan, 1931. These well-written stories of other days and ways are not easy reading but they are rewarding books for the able child. Action and theme carry the interest. 10–14

MIERS, EARL SCHENK, *Billy Yank and Johnny Reb: How They Fought and Made Up*, ill. by Leonard Vosburgh, Rand, 1959. A challenging account of the men, battles, and causes of the Civil War, North and South.   12–16

O'DELL, SCOTT, *Island of the Blue Dolphins*, Houghton, 1960. An Indian girl shows remarkable courage and resourcefulness in living alone on an island off the coast of Southern California for eighteen years. An outstanding historical episode.   12–16

RIETVELD, JANE, *Nicky's Bugle*, ill. by author, Viking, 1947. Nicky was a Wisconsin pioneer on the side. His main business in life was earning enough money to buy a glorious bugle. His adventures were astonishing and often hilarious.   9–12

STEELE, WILLIAM O., *The Buffalo Knife*, ill. by Paul Galdone, Harcourt, 1952.

The Far Frontier, ill. by Paul Galdone, Harcourt, 1959.

Tomahawks and Trouble, ill. by Paul Galdone, Harcourt, 1955.

Wilderness Journey, ill. by Paul Galdone, Harcourt, 1953.

Winter Danger, ill. by Paul Galdone, Harcourt, 1954.   9–12

SWIFT, HILDEGARDE R., *The Railroad to Freedom*, ill. by James Daugherty, Harcourt, 1932. A true story of a Negro slave who helped her people to freedom during the Civil War.   10–14

WIBBERLEY, LEONARD, *Peter Treegate's War*, Farrar, 1960. American Revolutionary days are vividly re-created as the background for the hero, a high-spirited sixteen-year-old boy, who attempts to resolve conflicting loyalties between his real and foster fathers. (Sequel to *John Treegate's Musket*, Farrar, 1959) .   12–16

WILDER, LAURA INGALLS, *By the Shores of Silver Lake*, ill. by Garth Williams, Harper, 1953.

Farmer Boy, ill. by Garth Williams, Harper, 1953.

Little House in the Big Woods, ill. by Garth Williams, Harper, 1953.

Little House on the Prairie, ill. by Garth Williams, Harper, 1953.

Little Town on the Prairie, ill. by Garth Williams, Harper, 1953.

The Long Winter, ill. by Garth Williams, Harper, 1953.

On the Banks of Plum Creek, ill. by Garth Williams, Harper, 1953.

These Happy Golden Years, ill. by Garth Williams, Harper, 1953.

These eight books cover the saga of a pioneer family and the childhood of the author to the time of her marriage. This is the family invincible, able to stand up to misfortunes and tragedies because they are strong in love and loyalty. No American child should miss these books.   9–14

ZIEGLER, ELSIE R., *The Face in the Stone*, ill. by Ray Abel, Longmans, 1959.

How a young master carver of Siberia finds life in a new land, and helps with the building of the Chicago skyscrapers.   12–16

European

BUFF, MARY, *Apple and the Arrow*, ill. by Conrad Buff, Houghton, 1951. This is the stirring story of William Tell and his son Walter, with many dramatic illustrations by Swiss-born Conrad Buff.   10–12

COBLENTZ, CATHERINE CATE, *Beggar's Penny*, ill. by Hilda Van Stockum, Longmans, 1943. A fine historical story of the siege of Leyden by the Spanish.   11–12

The Bells of Leyden Sing, ill. by Hilda Van Stockum, Longmans, 1944. A story about the English exiles' last year in Leyden before sailing for America. Contains some new historical information, exciting and long secret.   11–13

CHUTE, MARCHETTE, *The Innocent Wayfaring*, ill. by author, Dutton, 1955. Fourteenth-century England brought vividly and authentically to life.   11–14

DE ANGELI, MARGUERITE, *Black Fox of Lorne*, ill. by author, Doubleday, 1956. Adventures of twins, Jan and Brus, in tenth-century Scotland.   8–12

The Door in the Wall, ill. by author, Doubleday, 1949. When Robin, son of Sir John de Bureford, is stricken with an illness that leaves his legs paralyzed and his back bent, it is Brother Luke who helps him to find a "door in the wall" and nurses him back to strength and courage. This tender and beautiful book is not only a valuable addition to children's literature of the medieval period, but it should bring courage to any child crippled with polio. Newbery Award.   8–10

DIX, BEULAH M., *Merrylips*, ill. by Frank T. Merrill, Macmillan, 1925. About a little lass who longed to be a boy when England was in the midst of civil war.   10–12

EATON, JEANETTE, *Betsy's Napoleon*, ill. by Pierre Brissaud, Morrow, 1952, New ed. When Napoleon first went to St. Helena he stayed at Betsy's home. This story faithfully follows her memoirs.   10–12

EVERNDEN, MARGERY, *Knight of Florence*, ill. by Rafaello Busoni, Random, 1950. The art of Florence in the Middle Ages as it affects the life of a noble family whose eldest son aspires to be an artist.   10–12

GIBSON, KATHARINE, *Oak Tree House*, ill. by Vera Bock, Longmans, 1936. Almost fairy tales, these whimsical stories of medieval times are charmingly written. An oak tree house is what every child would like, a complete house in a tree with cat and dog and finally the young king himself.   8–9

GRAY, ELIZABETH JANET, *Adam of the Road*, ill. by Robert Lawson, Viking, 1942. When Adam, by mischance, loses both his father and dog, he seeks them on the highways and byways of thirteenth-century England.   6–9

HEWES, AGNES, *Boy of the Lost Crusade*, ill. by Gustaf Tenggren, Houghton, 1923. A French boy joins the Children's Crusade in the hope of finding his father.   12–14

KENT, LOUISE, *He Went with Christopher Columbus*, ill. by Paul Quinn, Houghton, 1940.   12–14

He Went with Marco Polo, ill. by C. LeRoy Baldridge, Houghton, 1935.   12–14

He Went with Vasco da Gama, ill. by Paul Quinn, Houghton, 1938.   12–15

The adventures of boys who accompanied the three great explorers of the Middle Ages.

KNIGHT, RUTH ADAMS, *Halfway to Heaven*, ill. by Wesley Dennis, Whittlesey, 1952. An inspiring story of a young priest of the St. Bernard Hospice and the dogs which were trained to rescue travelers from the storms and avalanches of the dangerous pass from Italy to Switzerland.   12–14

LEIGHTON, MARGARET, *Judith of France*, ill. by Henry C. Pitz, Houghton, 1948. Teen-age girls or superior readers of twelve will enjoy this romantic historical novel about Charlemagne's spirited granddaughter. The pathetic pawn of kings, she comes into her own at last.   12–16

MAGOON, MARIAN AUSTIN, *Little Dusty Foot*, ill. by Christine Price, Longmans, 1948. Absorbing story of the far-traveled merchants of medieval days. The young "dusty-foot" and his talking magpie are a delightful pair, and their adventures have proved exceedingly popular. 10–14

PARKER, RICHARD, *The Sword of Ganelon*, ill. by William Ferguson, McKay, 1958. A remarkable and stirring tale of ninth-century England invaded by the Danes.   11–16

PYLE, HOWARD, *Men of Iron*, ill. by author, Harper, 1891. The training of knights, the clash of battle and all the glamor of feudal England under Henry IV.   12–14

Otto of the Silver Hand, ill. by author, Scribner's, 1888. The appealing story of a boy whose father, a German robber baron, places him in a medieval monastery to assure his safety.   10–12

SUTCLIFF, ROSEMARY, *The Armourer's House*, ill. by C. Walter Hodges, Oxford, 1951. Tamsyn moves to live with her uncle's family in London in the time of Henry VIII. Delightful characters and vivid details make this a rewarding story.   10–14

The Lantern Bearers, ill. by Charles Keeping, Walck, 1959. Dramatic story of fifth-century Britain, beautifully and vividly told.   12–adult

Queen Elizabeth Story, ill. by C. Walter Hodges, Oxford, 1950. Perdita's dearest wish is realized when she sees the great Queen Elizabeth.   10–12

TREECE, HENRY, *Perilous Pilgrimage*, ill. by Christine Price, Criterion, 1959. The Children's Crusade portrayed in exciting incident and vivid prose.   11–14

Ancient Times

BRUCKNER, KARL, *The Golden Pharaoh*, tr. from the German by Frances Lobb, ill. by Hans Thomas, Pantheon,

1959. An excellent introduction to one of the most sensational archaeological discoveries of our time, tomb of Tutankhamen, Egyptian Pharaoh. 11–14

COE, FREDERICK L. *Graven with Flint,* ill. by Robert Hallock, Crowell, 1950. The adventures of two Cro-Magnon boys. 12–14

GERE, FRANCES, *Boy of Babylon,* ill. by author, Longmans, 1941. This lively story with many pictures gives a good idea of life in ancient Babylon. 10–12

JONES, RUTH FOSDICK, *Boy of the Pyramids; a Mystery of Ancient Egypt,* ill by Dorothy Bayley Morse, Random, 1952. Kaffe, a ten-year-old Egyptian boy whose home is near the ancient city of Memphis, watches the building of a pyramid on the desert and sees the Nile in flood. 10–12

KJELGAARD, JIM, *Fire-Hunter,* ill. by Ralph Ray, Holiday, 1951. The adventures of a prehistoric boy with saber-toothed tigers, mammoths, and cave bears. 12–14

LAWRENCE, ISABELLE, *The Gift of the Golden Cup,* ill. by Charles V. John, Bobbs, 1946.
The Theft of the Golden Ring, ill. by Charles V. John, Bobbs, 1948. The adventures of twelve-year-old Atia and her seven-year-old brother Gaius, whose uncle is Julius Caesar. Vivid pictures of Roman life. 11–14

LOWNSBERRY, ELOISE, *A Camel for a Throne,* ill. by Elizabeth T. Wolcott, Houghton, 1941. A daughter of the pharaoh is brought up as a commoner. How her identity is finally made known is an exciting story, rich with historical details. 10–14

MEADOWCROFT, ENID, *The Gift of the River, a History of Ancient Egypt,* illustrations adapted from Egyptian sources by Katharine Dewey, Crowell, 1937. Adapted from source material in both text and pictures. A useful book for children studying ancient history. 9–12

MORRISON, LUCILE, *The Lost Queen of Egypt,* ill. by Franz Geritz, Lippincott, 1937. This story of ancient Egypt solves the mystery of the disappearance of the young queen, when her husband Tutankhamen, king of Egypt, dies. 12–14

RIENOW, LEONA, *The Bewitched Caverns,* ill. by Allen Pope, Scribner's, 1948. The life and times of Cro-Magnon man are portrayed in an exciting way, through two primitive children who solve a hair-raising mystery. 9–14
The Dark Pool, ill. by Allen Pope, Scribner's, 1949. A continuation of the adventures of the Cro-Magnon brother and sister. Reveals even more of the brutality and violence of primitive man's existence. It shows also a developing moral code. 9–14

SHORE, MAXINE, *The Captive Princess,* ill. by Kreigh Collins, Longmans, 1952. Story of the Roman conquest of Britain in which a Druid princess falls in love with a Roman soldier. 12–14

SNEDEKER, CAROLINE DALE, *A Triumph for Flavius,* ill. by Cedric Rogers, Lothrop, 1955. The story of a young Roman boy who, in compassion for his Greek slave and teacher, works to secure his freedom. Interesting background of ancient Rome and early Christian days. 8–11
The Forgotten Daughter, ill. by Dorothy Lathrop, Doubleday, 1933. When Chloe's Greek mother died, she suffered many hardships until her Roman father remembered her and made a home for her in Rome. An interesting picture of ancient Greece and Rome. 12–14

BIOGRAPHY

Collections of Biographies

BARTLETT, ROBERT, *They Stand Invincible; Men Who Are Reshaping Our World,* Crowell, 1959. Thoughtful profiles of 12 men who dedicated themselves to the pursuit of world peace and understanding. 12–15

BEARD, ANNIE E. S., *Our Foreign-Born Citizens; What They Have Done for America,* Crowell, 1946. Short biographies of famous American men and women and their contributions in art, science, business, and politics.

BOYNICK, DAVID K., *Pioneers in Petticoats,* Crowell, 1959. Biographies of women who pioneered in aviation, law, medicine, and merchandising. 12–19

COTTLER, JOSEPH, *Heroes of Civilization,* ill. by Forrest W. Orr, Little, 1931. Among the thirty-five famous people living in different countries and at different periods are: Marco Polo, Madame Curie, Louis Pasteur, Edward Jenner, and Albert Einstein. 10–14

DAUGHERTY, SONIA, *Ten Brave Men,* ill. by James Daugherty, Lippincott, 1951. Good accounts of such national heroes as Roger Williams, Patrick Henry, Thomas Jefferson, and Andrew Jackson. 11–14
Ten Brave Women, ill. by James Daugherty, Lippincott, 1953. 11–15

FARJEON, ELEANOR, *Ten Saints,* ill. by Helen Sewell, Oxford, 1936. Stories of St. Francis, St. Christopher, and other less well-known saints, beautifully told. 8–12

FENNER, PHYLLIS, compiler, *Yankee Doodle; Stories of the Brave and the Free,* ill. by John Alan Maxwell, Knopf, 1951. Excerpts from books of American historical fiction by such outstanding authors as Elizabeth Coatsworth, Constance Skinner, Esther Forbes. 9–12

FISHER, DOROTHY CANFIELD, *And Long Remember; Some Great Americans Who Have Helped Me,* ill. by E. J. Keats, McGraw (Whittlesey), 1959. Incidents in the lives of great Americans which had special meaning for the author, such as Thomas Jefferson, Dorothea Dix, Robert E. Lee. 10–14

FOSTER, GENEVIEVE, *Abraham Lincoln's World,* ill. by author, Scribner's, 1944. This pageant of world happenings during the lifetime of Lincoln makes history real for children and illumines the character and achievements of Lincoln himself. 12–14
Augustus Caesar's World; A Story of Ideas and Events from 44 B.C. to 14 A.D., ill. by author, Scribner's, 1947. The relationship of people and happenings in the Roman Empire which, at the time, included most of the known world. 12–14
Birthdays of Freedom, ill. by author, Scribner's, 1952. This book, sponsored by the American Library Association, records the growth of freedom in the world. It begins with the Declaration of Independence, and then goes back in time to ancient Egyptians, the Hindus, Chinese, Greeks, and so on over the centuries. 10–14
George Washington's World, ill. by author, Scribner's 1941. The life of Washington is related against a background of events and of people living in other parts of the world at that time. 12–14

KAUFMAN, HELEN L., *History's 100 Greatest Composers,* ill. by Samuel Nisenson, Grosset, 1957. Excellent portraits accompany each biography. 11–adult

KUNITZ, STANLEY J. and HAYCROFT, HOWARD, *The Junior Book of Authors,* 2nd ed. revised, Wilson, 1951. Brief biographies of more than 280 authors and illustrators of children's books.

LIFE INTERNATIONAL—EDITORS OF, comps. *Nine Who Chose America,* photographic illustrations, Dutton, 1959. Brief life stories of men and women who came to America and achieved success. 12–adult

MCCONNELL, JANE and BURT, MORTON, *Presidents of the United States,* portraits by Constance Joan Narr, Crowell, 1951. Sketches of their lives are closely interwoven with political and economic changes. 12–14

MEYER, EDITH PATTERSON, *Champions of Peace,* ill. by Eric von Schmidt, Little, 1959. Carefully documented stories of Nobel Peace Prize winners. 12–16

MONTGOMERY, ELIZABETH RIDER, *The Story Behind Great Books,* ill. by Friedebald Dzubas, Dodd, 1946.

The Story Behind Great Stories, ill. by Elinore Blaisdell, Dodd, 1947.

The Story Behind Modern Books, Dodd, 1949. Short sketches about authors and illustrators of children's books, with notes about the books they have written.

MORGAN, JAMES, *Our Presidents,* Macmillan, 1949. Brief biographies of our presidents from Washington to Truman, with short accounts of each presidency. 12–14

REINFELD, FRED, *The Great Dissenters: Guardians of Their Country's Laws and Liberties,* Crowell, 1959. Inspiring stories of men important in the history of our country through political, social, and judicial means. Included are Ralph Waldo Emerson, Henry David Thoreau, and Oliver Wendell Holmes. 12–15

RICHARDSON, BEN ALBERT, *Great American Negroes,* rev. by William A. Fahey, ill. by Robert Hallock, Crowell, 1956. Vivid accounts of twenty-one Negroes who have overcome prejudice and who have contributed to American culture in many fields. 12–16

SICKELS, ELEANOR M., *In Calico and Crinoline, True Stories of American Women, 1608–1865,* ill. by Ilse Bischoff, Viking, 1935. Their role in the settlement of the country and in its multi-faceted development. 12–16

SIMON, CHARLIE MAY, *Art in the New Land,* ill. by James McDonald, Dutton, 1945. Stories of famous American artists from Benjamin West to Grant Wood, with illustrations and descriptions of their work. 12–14

Figures in American History

AULAIRE, INGRID and EDGAR PARIN D', *Abraham Lincoln,* ill. by authors, Doubleday, 1939. 6–10

Benjamin Franklin, ill. by authors, Doubleday, 1950. 6–10

Buffalo Bill, ill. by authors, Doubleday, 1952. 6–10

Columbus, ill. by authors, Doubleday, 1955. 6–10

George Washington, ill. by authors, Doubleday, 1936. 6–10

Leif the Lucky, ill. by authors, Doubleday, 1951. 6–10

Pocahontas, ill. by authors, Doubleday, 1946. 6–10

AVERILL, ESTHER, *Cartier Sails the St. Lawrence,* ill. by Feodor Rojankovsky, Harper, 1956. A factual account of the three voyages. Distinctive illustrations. 10–14

King Philip, the Indian Chief, ill. by Vera Belsky, Harper, 1950. This is the story of the chief of the Wampanoag Indians of New England, who led his tribe and others in fighting against the colonists in 1675. 12–14

BELL, MARGARET E., *Kit Carson, Mountain Man,* ill. by Harry Daugherty, Morrow, 1952. A short, dramatic biography with large print and many illustrations. 8–10

BONTEMPS, ARNA, *Frederick Douglass: Slave-Fighter-Freeman,* ill. by Harper Johnson, Knopf, 1959. Sympathetic biography of a distinguished Negro leader. 11–14

DALGLIESH, ALICE, *The Columbus Story,* ill. by Leo Politi, Scribner's, 1955. 8–11

DAUGHERTY, JAMES, *Abraham Lincoln,* ill. by author, Viking, 1943. A substantial biography that compares favorably with Carl Sandburg's. 12–16

Daniel Boone, original lithographs in color by the author, Viking, 1939. Awarded the Newbery Medal in 1940, *Daniel Boone* is a vigorously written and illustrated biography of a rugged American. 12–16

Of Courage Undaunted, Across the Continent with Lewis and Clark, ill. by author, Viking, 1951. This stirring account of the Lewis and Clark expedition gives young readers a clear understanding of the courage and resourcefulness of the explorers. 12–16

Poor Richard, ill. by author, Viking, 1941. A beautifully written and illustrated book which emphasizes Franklin's patriotic achievements. 12–16

DAVIS, JULIA, *No Other White Men,* maps by Caroline Gray, Dutton, 1937. An unforgettable account of the Lewis and Clark expedition, not only of the explorations but of the friendship which existed between the two great leaders. 12–14

EATON, JEANETTE, *Leader by Destiny: George Washington, Man and Patriot,* ill. by Jack Manley Rosé, Harcourt, 1938. A definitive biography which shows Washington as a very human, often bewildered man with a gift of inspiring confidence in other men. 12–16

Narcissa Whitman; Pioneer of Oregon, ill. by Woodi Ishmael, Harcourt, 1941. This inspiring story of the great pioneer woman is based on early letters and memoirs. 12–16

That Lively Man, Ben Franklin, ill. by Henry C. Pitz, Morrow, 1948. Franklin's many-sided career from printer to colonial ambassador to France and England is well portrayed. 10–14

Washington, the Nation's First Hero, ill. by Ralph Ray, Morrow, 1951. A short dramatic biography with many attractive illustrations. 9–12

FAST, HOWARD, *Haym Salomon; Son of Liberty,* ill. by Eric M. Simon, Messner, 1941. A moving story of the great Polish Jew who helped finance the American Revolution. Difficult reading at elementary level. 12–16

FISHER, GEORGE CLYDE, *The Life of Audubon,* ill. with paintings and drawings by John James Audubon, Harper, 1949. This biography of the famous naturalist by a former staff member of the American Museum of Natural History is glorified by superb reproductions of Audubon's own paintings both in black and white and full color. 10–14

FORBES, ESTHER, *America's Paul Revere,* ill. by Lynd Ward, Houghton, 1946. Vigorous prose and superb illustrations make this book a treasure for children to own. It is not easy reading but will do much to illumine the history of that day. 12–16

FOSTER, GENEVIEVE, *Abraham Lincoln,* ill. by author, Scribner's, 1950.

Andrew Jackson, ill. by author, Scribner's, 1951.

George Washington, ill. by author, Scribner's, 1949.

Theodore Roosevelt, ill. by author, Scribner's, 1954.

These books are simply written and cover outstanding achievements of the hero from birth to death. 9–12

The World of Captain John Smith, 1580–1631, ill. by author, Scribner's, 1959. Striking picture of the British adventurer and colonist, set against seventeenth-century England and America. 11–14

FREEMAN, DOUGLAS SOUTHALL, *Lee of Virginia,* Scribner's, 1958. 12–adult

GARST, DORIS SHANNON, *Jim Bridger, Greatest of the Mountain Men,* ill. by William Moyers, Houghton, 1952. An exciting story of a farm boy who went into the West when it was a wilderness and became the most famous of the mountain men. 12–16

GARST, DORIS SHANNON and WARREN, *Ernest Thompson Seton, Naturalist,* Messner, 1959. An inspiring account of the artist-naturalist, based on Seton's autobiography. 12–14

GOTTSCHALK, FRUMA, *The Youngest General, a Story of Lafayette,* ill. by Rafaello Busoni, Knopf, 1949. The author had access to unusual original sources in writing this well-documented life of Lafayette. The lively, fascinating text will bring both Lafayette and Washington vividly to life for young readers. 10–14

GOWDY, GEORGE, *Young Buffalo Bill*, ill. by Howard Simon, Lothrop, 1955. Emphasis is on the young boy forced to assume responsibility for the family at his father's death. A well-told story. 11–14

GOULD, JEAN, *That Dunbar Boy: The Story of America's Famous Negro Poet*, Dodd, 1958. 12–16

GRAHAM, SHIRLEY, *The Story of Phillis Wheatley*, ill. by Robert Burns, Messner, 1949. This book tells the story of a remarkable woman, a young Negro poet who lived in Boston in Revolutionary days. 12–14

GURKO, MIRIAM, *The Lives and Times of Peter Cooper*, ill. by Jerome Snyder, Crowell, 1959. Well-written account of a versatile American inventor, businessman, and philanthropist. 12–16

HAVILAND, VIRGINIA, *William Penn: Founder and Friend*, ill. by Peter Burchard, Abingdon-Cokesbury, 1952. (Makers of America Series.) An easy-to-read biography of the great Quaker who founded Pennsylvania. 9–12

HAWTHORNE, HILDEGARDE, *Give Me Liberty*, ill. by Woodi Ishmael, Appleton-Century, 1945. An exciting biography of one of our most colorful colonials, Patrick Henry. 12–14

HOGEBOOM, AMY, *Christopher Columbus and His Brothers*, ill. by author, Lothrop, 1951. Unlike other biographies of Columbus in that the author presents him as one of four brothers all working together on plans for exploration and discovery. 9–12

HOLBROOK, STEWART H., *America's Ethan Allen*, ill. by Lynd Ward, Houghton, 1949. Spirited illustrations in color add to the dramatic story of the "Green Mountain Boys" and their fighting leader. 10–16

HUNT, MABEL LEIGH, *Better Known as Johnny Appleseed*, ill. by James Daugherty, Lippincott, 1950. The life of John Chapman, "American pioneer, missionary, and apple lover," based on old legends and reminiscences, gathered by the author during many years of research. 12–16

JUDSON, CLARA INGRAM, *Abraham Lincoln, Friend of the People*, ill. by Robert Frankenberg; Kodachromes of the Chicago Historical Society Lincoln dioramas, Wilcox & Follett, 1950. An excellent biography of Lincoln which shows much research. 10–14

Andrew Jackson, Frontier Statesman, ill. by Lorence F. Bjorklund, Wilcox & Follett, 1954. 11–15

City Neighbor; the Story of Jane Addams, ill. by Ralph Ray, Scribner's, 1951. The life of the great woman who founded Hull House in Chicago. 10–14

George Washington, Leader of the People, ill. by Robert Frankenberg, Wilcox & Follett, 1951. Beautiful illustrations and well-written text make this an outstanding book. 10–14

Thomas Jefferson, Champion of the People, ill. by Robert Frankenberg, Wilcox & Follett, 1952. A well-documented biography of one of the great figures in American history. 12–16

LANDMARK BOOKS, Random, 1951. This series is a distinguished addition to children's knowledge of their country. Written by notable authors, the books are sometimes biographies (*Daniel Boone, Ben Franklin of Old Philadelphia*, etc.) and sometimes they enlarge upon great moments in history (*The Landing of the Pilgrims, Our Independence and the Constitution*, etc.) or great movements (*The California Gold Rush, Trappers and Traders of the Far West*). They are freshly and vigorously written, and although many of them lend themselves to use in social studies, they are equally valuable for the child's private library. So far, this series

has had many imitators but no rivals. More recently a World Landmark Series has been published which gives the same fine treatment to world figures and events.

LAWSON, ROBERT, *They Were Strong and Good*, ill. by author, Viking, 1940. These stories of the author's four grandparents and his mother and father are told with humor and affection and illustrated with large black and white drawings. 9–12

LE SUEUR, MERIDEL, *Chanticleer of Wilderness Road*, ill. by Aldren A. Watson, Knopf, 1951. Young readers not ready for the more difficult Rourke biography of David Crockett will find this one completely satisfying. Legends, tall tales, and facts are humorously woven together. 10–14

LISITZKY, GENEVIEVE, *Thomas Jefferson*, ill. by Harrie Wood, Viking, 1933. A well-written book about a brilliant and great American for mature readers. 12–16

MEADOWCROFT, ENID, *Abraham Lincoln*, ill. by Kurt Wiese, Crowell, 1942. A good biography of Lincoln for younger readers, giving them the usual anecdotes of his childhood, and carrying him through the war years to his death. 10–12

MEANS, FLORENCE CRANNELL, *Carvers' George*, ill. by Harve Stein, Houghton, 1952. A well-written and moving account of the great Negro scientist from his tragic infancy to his triumphant old age, honored and beloved by his own people and the world. 8–12

NOLAN, JEANNETTE COVERT, *Andrew Jackson*, ill. by Leej Ames, Messner, 1949. This fictionalized biography of Jackson with its simplification of political issues and amplification of the man's romance and achievements will appeal to young readers. 12–16

The Story of Clara Barton of the Red Cross, ill. by W. C. Nims, Messner, 1941. An outstanding account of the great nurse who organized service to the wounded during the Civil War. 12–16

NORTH, STERLING, *Young Thomas Edison*, ill. by William Barsse, Houghton, 1958. Warm biography of the scientific wizard for younger readers. 10–12

PEARE, CATHERINE OWENS, *Mary McLeod Bethune*, Vanguard, 1951. The story of a great Negro woman who has dedicated her life to the education of her people. 12–19

The Helen Keller Story, Crowell, 1959. 10–12

PETRY, ANN, *Harriet Tubman: Conductor on the Underground Railroad*, Crowell, 1955. 12–16

ROGERS, FRANCES and BEARD, ALICE, *Paul Revere, Patriot on Horseback*, ill. by author, Lippincott, 1943. A readable account of Revere, easier to read than Miss Forbes' book. 12–15

ROURKE, CONSTANCE MAYFIELD, *Audubon*, with twelve colored plates from original Audubon prints, Harcourt, 1936. This is a fascinating account of Audubon's life and travels from Florida and the Louisiana bayou to the Ohio and Mississippi rivers, drawing and painting as he went. It does perpetuate the now exploded myth of Audubon as the lost dauphin of France. 12–16

Davy Crockett, ill. by James MacDonald, Harcourt, 1934. One of the liveliest accounts we have of the legendary Davy. 12–16

SANDBURG, CARL, *Abe Lincoln Grows Up*, ill. by James Daugherty, Harcourt, 1928. The finest account we have of Lincoln's childhood and youth from the author's famous adult book, *Abraham Lincoln, the Prairie Years*. 12–16

SHIPPEN, KATHERINE, *Leif Eriksson, First Voyager to America*, Harper, 1951. Well-written, exciting biography of the explorer of Vineland. 11–13

STEFFENS, LINCOLN, *Boy on Horseback*, ill. by Sanford

Tousey, Harcourt, 1935. The boyhood of Lincoln Steffens, taken from his autobiography.   12–16

SYME, RONALD, *Champlain of the St. Lawrence*, ill. by William Stobbs, Morrow, 1952.   12–14
Columbus: Finder of the New World, ill. by William Stobbs, Morrow, 1953.   10–14
Henry Hudson, ill. by William Stobbs, Morrow, 1955.   10–12
John Smith of Virginia, ill. by William Stobbs, Morrow, 1954.   10–12
La Salle of the Mississippi, ill. by William Stobbs, Morrow, 1953.   12–14

VANCE, MARGUERITE, *The Lees of Arlington; the Story of Mary and Robert E. Lee*, ill. by Nedda Walker, Dutton, 1949. The childhood romance and happy home life of Robert and Mary Lee will interest older girls.   12–14
Martha, Daughter of Virginia; the Story of Martha Washington, ill. by Nedda Walker, Dutton, 1947. History, romance, and biography are combined in this story of Martha Dandridge, the belle of Colonial Virginia, who became the First Lady of the United States.   12–14
Patsy Jefferson of Monticello, ill. by Nedda Walker, Dutton, 1948. A delightful biography of a beguiling young heroine with pleasant glimpses of her father, Thomas Jefferson.   10–14

VINTON, IRIS, *The Story of John Paul Jones*, ill. by Edward A. Wilson, Grosset, 1953.   10–13

WYATT, EDGAR, *Cochise: Apache Warrior and Statesman*, ill. by Allan Houser, Whittlesey, 1953.   11–14

YATES, ELIZABETH, *Amos Fortune, Free Man*, ill. by Nora S. Unwin, Aladdin, 1950. The moving account of a Negro slave who purchased his own freedom and became a benefactor of his race. Newbery Award.   12–16

Other Historical Figures

BAKER, NINA BROWN, *Sir Walter Raleigh*, Harcourt, 1950. The many-sided aspects of Raleigh's character are well portrayed and the Elizabethan background is fully drawn.   12–14

BENZ, FRANCIS E., *Pasteur, Knight of the Laboratory*, ill. by James MacDonald, Dodd, 1938. A good account of the crusader for the health of humanity.   12–14

BLACKSTOCK, JOSEPHINE, *Songs for Sixpence; A Story About John Newbery*, ill. by Maurice Bower, Wilcox & Follett, 1955. The story of John Newbery, one of the earliest publishers of children's books, for whom the Newbery Award is named.   9–12

BOUTET DE MONVEL, MAURICE, *Joan of Arc*, ill. by author, Century, 1907. This superbly illustrated picture-biography is also available in French. It is a book to own both in schools and homes.   10–14

BRAYMER, MARJORIE, *The Walls of Windy Troy: A Biography of Heinrich Schliemann*, ill. with photographs, Harcourt, 1960. A strong portrayal of Heinrich Schliemann, the man who proved that Troy was more than just a legendary city.   12–16

BULLA, CLYDE, *Song of St. Francis*, ill. by Valenti Angelo, Crowell, 1952. The appealing story of St. Francis of Assisi presented in simple fashion for the youngest readers.   7–10

DALGLIESH, ALICE, *Ride on the Wind*, ill. by Georges Schreiber, Scribners, 1956. The boyhood and famous flight of Charles Lindbergh.   6–10

DE LEEUW, ADÈLE, *The Story of Amelia Earhart*, ill. by Harry Beckhoff, Grosset, 1955. A beautifully told story of a warm, brave-hearted woman.   10–12

DESMOND, ALICE CURTIS, *Bewitching Betsy Bonaparte*, ill. with photographs, Dodd, 1958. A romantic historical biography of Baltimore belle Betsy Patterson and her ill-fated marriage to Napoleon's younger brother Jerome.   14–adult

HUNT, MABEL LEIGH, *"Have You Seen Tom Thumb?"* ill. by Fritz Eichenberg, Lippincott, 1942. An entertaining biography of Charles Sherwood Stratton, midget in P. T. Barnum's circus.   11–14

IVES, MABEL LORENZ, *He Conquered the Andes, the Story of San Martin, the Liberator*, ill. by Forrest Orr, Little, 1943. Unusually appealing account of a great patriot. Popular with boys.   10–14

JEWETT, SOPHIE, *God's Troubadour, the Story of Saint Francis of Assisi*, ill. by Elinore Blaisdell, Crowell, 1940. Beautiful illustrations add to the appeal of this story of a favorite saint.   10–14

JUDSON, CLARA INGRAM, *Soldier Doctor; the Story of William Gorgas*, ill. by Robert Doremus, Scribner's, 1942. A lively account of the man whose work against yellow fever made possible the building of the Panama Canal.   10–12

KING, MARIAN, *Elizabeth, the Tudor Princess*, ill. by Elinore Blaisdell, Stokes, 1940. Girls like this well-written biography of a great queen in the making.   12–14
Young Mary Stuart, Queen of Scots, Lippincott, 1954. A moving biography of the young queen which places emphasis on her childhood and the years in France.   11–14

KOMROFF, MANUEL, *Julius Caesar*, Messner, 1955. Vivid introduction to a great leader and his achievements and an excellent picture of the Roman Empire.   10–12

LAVINE, SIGMUND, *Steinmetz: Maker of Lightning*, ill. with photographs, Dodd, 1955. A happy combination of good characterization and scientific information.   13–adult

MALVERN, GLADYS, *Dancing Star, the Story of Anna Pavlova*, ill. by Susanne Suba, Messner, 1942. Girls like especially the details of the dancer's early training and the glamor of her triumphs.   10–14

MANTON, JO, *The Story of Albert Schweitzer*, ill. by Astrid Walford, Abelard-Schuman, 1955. Beautifully written biography of the famous musician and missionary to Africa.   12–16

MCNEER, MAY YONGE, *John Wesley*, ill. by May McNeer and Lynd Ward, Abingdon-Cokesbury, 1951. The rather somber story of the founder of the Methodist church with large illustrations in rich colors, which make this gallant man more than ordinarily appealing.   10–14
Martin Luther, ill. by Lynd Ward, Abingdon-Cokesbury, 1953. The fighting spirit of Martin Luther makes his life both difficult and thrilling.   12–14

NOLAN, JEANNETTE COVERT, *Florence Nightingale*, ill. by George Avison, Messner, 1946. This warm, readable biography of Florence Nightingale stresses her work rather than her personal life.   12–14

ROOS, ANN, *Man of Molokai, the Life of Father Damien*, ill. by Raymond Lufkin, Lippincott, 1943. This book tells of his work for the lepers on the island of Molokai for whom he gave his life.   12–16

ROSEN, SIDNEY, *Doctor Paracelsus*, ill. by Rafaello Busoni, Little, 1959. Excellent biography of the sixteenth century Swiss-German physician and alchemist, who challenged the medical superstitions of his time.   12–16
Galileo and the Magic Numbers, ill. by Harve Stein, Little, 1958. A distinguished biography, rich in background.   12–adult

SOOTIN, HARRY, *Gregor Mendel: Father of the Science of Genetics*, Vanguard, 1959. A straightforward biography of the scientist who explained the laws of heredity.

SYME, RONALD, *Balboa, Finder of the Pacific,* ill. by William Stobbs, Morrow, 1956. 10–12
Cortes of Mexico, ill. by William Stobbs, Morrow, 1951. The tremendous adventure of the conqueror of Mexico makes an exciting story. 12–14
Magellan, First Around the World, ill. by William Stobbs, Morrow, 1953. 10–12

TANNENBAUM, BEULAH and STILLMAN, MYRA, *Isaac Newton: Pioneer of Space Mathematics,* ill. by Gustav Schrotter, McGraw (Whittlesey), 1959. A good account of the British mathematician and philosopher who formulated and proved the law of gravity. 12–16

TREASE, GEOFFREY, *Sir Walter Raleigh, Captain and Adventurer,* Vanguard, 1950. Raleigh's adventures on land and sea are set against the romantic background of Elizabethan England. Vivid details. 12–14

VANCE, MARGUERITE, *Marie Antoinette, Daughter of an Empress,* ill. by Nedda Walker, Dutton, 1950. A sympathetic portrait of the lonely young queen is presented against the background of the rising tide of revolution in France. 12–14
Song for a Lute, ill. by J. L. Pellicer, Dutton, 1958. Attractive narrative of Anne Neville, queen of Richard III. 12–14
The Empress Josephine from Martinique to Malmaison, ill. by Nedda Walker, Dutton, 1956. An excellent selection of detail makes this a vivid biography. 13–16

WELLS, HELEN, *Barnum, Showman of America,* ill. by Leonard Vosburgh, McKay, 1957. An outstanding and highly entertaining picture of the man and his times. 12–adult

WIBBERLEY, LEONARD, *The Life of Winston Churchill,* Farrar, 1956. 12–16

WOOD, LAURA NEWBOLD, *Louis Pasteur,* ill. with photographs, Messner, 1948. The story of one of the world's great scientists, whose experiments and research made a great contribution to modern medicine and surgery. 12–14
Raymond L. Ditmars, ill. with photographs, Messner, 1944. The early struggles of a young scientist to obtain and study the snakes that became his lifework. 10–14

WOODHAM-SMITH, CECIL, *Lonely Crusader; the Life of Florence Nightingale, 1820–1910,* McGraw, 1951. Special emphasis on her early life 14–16

Musicians

BENET, LAURA, *Enchanting Jenny Lind,* ill. by George G. Whitney, Dodd, 1939. The romantic and appealing story of the "Swedish Nightingale." 12–14

EWEN, DAVID, *Story of George Gershwin,* ill. by Graham Bernbach, Holt, 1943. Memories of an American composer of popular music by a personal friend. 12–16
Tales from the Vienna Woods: The Story of Johann Strauss, ill. by Edgard Cirlin, Holt, 1944. The composer of some of the world's greatest and best-loved dance music is presented against the background of romantic nineteenth-century Vienna. 12–14

GOSS, MADELEINE, *Beethoven, Master Musician,* ill. by Carl Schultheiss, Holt, 1946. A sensitive and thwarted genius portrayed with rare sympathy. 12–16
Unfinished Symphony; The Story of Franz Schubert, ill. by Carl M. Schultheiss, Holt, 1941. His creative genius, the simplicity of his nature, and a feeling for his music are all blended in this portrait of a great composer. 12–16

KELLOGG, CHARLOTTE, *Paderewski,* Viking, 1956. An unforgettable picture of the great Polish musician and statesman. 13–adult

KOMROFF, MANUEL, *Mozart,* ill. by Warren Chappell and with photographs, Knopf, 1956. Written to commemorate the two-hundredth anniversary of Mozart's birth, this is an outstanding biography. 11–15

PURDY, CLAIRE LEE, *He Heard America Sing; The Story of Stephen Foster,* ill. by Dorothea Cooke, Messner, 1940. A sympathetic picture of Foster. 12–14

Artists

DEUCHER, SYBIL, *Millet Tilled the Soil,* ill. by Dorothy Bayley, Dutton, 1939. Millet is a difficult hero to reduce to child size, but this is a popular book and introduces the most frequently used pictures of the artist. 8–12

DEUCHER, SYBIL and WHEELER, OPAL, *Giotto Tended the Sheep,* ill. by Dorothy Bayley, Dutton, 1938. A picture of fourteenth-century Italy and of the shepherd boy who became an artist. 8–10

RIPLEY, ELIZABETH, *Dürer,* ill. by Dürer, Lippincott, 1958.
Goya, ill. by Goya, Oxford, 1956.
Leonardo da Vinci, ill. by Leonardo, Oxford, 1952.
Michelangelo, ill. by Michelangelo, Oxford, 1953.
Picasso, ill. by Picasso, Lippincott, 1959.
Rembrandt, ill. by Rembrandt, Oxford, 1955.
Vincent Van Gogh, ill. by Van Gogh, Oxford, 1954.

Writers

BECKER, MAY L., *Presenting Miss Jane Austen,* ill. by Edward Price, Dodd, 1952. This picture of the life and times of Jane Austen will interest older girls. 14–16

COLLIN, HEDVIG, *Young Hans Christian Andersen,* ill. by author, Viking, 1955. Sensitively told story of the Danish writer from his childhood years to his first literary recognition. 11–14

GRAY, ELIZABETH JANET, *Young Walter Scott,* end papers by Kate Seredy, Viking, 1935. One of the fine biographies written for young people. 12–14

MASON, MIRIAM E., *Yours with Love, Kate,* ill. by Barbara Cooney, Houghton, 1952. One of the first kindergarten teachers in America, Kate Douglas Wiggin also became a well-loved author of children's books. 12–16

MEIGS, CORNELIA, *Invincible Louisa,* ill. with photographs, Little, 1933. An absorbing life of Louisa May Alcott, the beloved author of *Little Women.* 12–16

PROUDFIT, ISABEL, *River Boy, the Story of Mark Twain,* ill. by W. C. Nims, Messner, 1940. An excellent life of the author of Tom Sawyer, for older boys and girls. 10–14
Treasure Hunter, the Story of Robert Louis Stevenson, ill. by Hardie Gramatky, Messner, 1939. A full-length biography of a favorite children's author. 10–14

WAITE, HELEN, *How Do I Love Thee? The Story of Elizabeth Barrett Browning,* Macrae Smith, 1953. An absorbing story of the Victorian poetess, climaxed by her romance with Robert Browning. 12–16

BIBLICAL TIMES

BARNHART, NANCY, *The Lord Is My Shepherd,* ill. by author, Scribner's, 1949. A beautiful book in text and format which tells the Bible stories briefly but with considerable use of Biblical language. 9–14

BOWIE, WALTER RUSSELL, *The Bible Story for Boys and Girls,* ill. by Edward and Stephani Godwin, Abingdon-Cokesbury, 1951. Here is a continuous story of the New Testament from the birth of Christ, through the Pauline journeys to John's vision of the Holy City. Good to read aloud. 6–10

CEDER, GEORGIANA D., *Ann of Bethany*, ill. by Helen Torrey, Abingdon-Cokesbury, 1951. A little Jewish girl warns Joseph and Mary of King Herod's search for the Christ Child. 9–11

Ethan, the Shepherd Boy, ill. by Helen Torrey, Abingdon-Cokesbury, 1948. Ethan is working with his uncle in the hills near Bethlehem at the time of the Nativity. Told with sincerity and beauty. 9–11

DE JONG, MEINDERT, *The Mighty Ones; Great Men and Women of Early Bible Days*, ill. by Harvey Schmidt, Harper, 1959. Many great men and women of early Bible days come alive in these colorful, imaginative stories based on Old Testament accounts. 12–16

JONES, MARY ALICE, *Bible Stories*, ill. by Manning de V. Lee, Rand McNally, 1952. Sixteen stories from the Old Testament and four from the New Testament are simply told and gorgeously illustrated with twenty-six pictures in full color. For parents to use with children as an introduction to Bible stories. 5–9

LILLIE, AMY MORRIS, *Nathan, Boy of Capernaum*, ill. by Nedda Walker, Dutton, 1945. How the presence of Jesus in his village changed the life of a ten-year-old boy. 10–12

LONG, LAURA, *The Chosen Boy*, ill. by Clotilde Funk, Bobbs-Merrill, 1952. The story of Moses who led his people from slavery to the promised land. 9–12

MALVERN, GLADYS, *Behold Your Queen!* ill. by Corinne Malvern, Longmans, 1951. There is romance, drama, and suspense in this story of Esther, Queen of Persia. 12–14

Tamar, ill. by Corinne Malvern, Longmans, 1952. How the teachings of Jesus changed the lives of the people of Capernaum. 12–16

MENOTTI, GIAN CARLO, *Amahl and the Night Visitors*, narrative adaptation by Frances Frost, ill. by Roger Duvoisin, Whittlesey, 1952. This beautifully told and illustrated book of the Christmas opera tells how the Three Kings stopped to rest at a poor shepherd's house and the wonderful results of their visit. A book to treasure and reread each Christmas. 7–adult

VANCE, MARGUERITE, *While Shepherds Watched*, ill. by Nedda Walker, Dutton, 1946. A beautiful retelling of the Nativity story. 7–9

SHIPPEN, KATHERINE B., *Moses*, Harper, 1949. The story of a great leader's sense of dedication to his people and to God. 12–14

INDEX OF AUTHORS AND TITLES

In the Index of Authors and Titles, Book One: Time
for Poetry is designated by P; *Book Two:* Time for Fairy Tales
by FT; *and Book Three:* Time for True Tales *by* TT